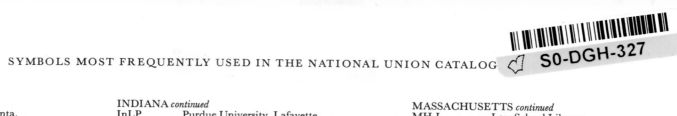

GEORGIA continued

GAU	Atlanta University, Atlanta.
GAuA	Augusta College, Augusta.
GColuC	Columbus College, Columbus.
GCuA	Andrews College, Cuthbert.
GDC	Columbia Theological Seminary, Decatur.
GDS	Agnes Scott College, Decatur.
GDecA*	Agnes Scott College, Decatur.
GDecCT*	Columbia Theological Seminary, Decatur.
GDoS	South Georgia College, Douglas.
GEU	Emory University, Atlanta.
GHi	Georgia Historical Society, Savannah.
GMM	Mercer University, Macon.
GMW	Wesleyan College, Macon.
GMiW	Woman's College of Georgia, Milledgeville.
GMilvC*	Woman's College of Georgia, Milledgeville.
GOgU	Oglethorpe University, Oglethorpe University.
GSDe*	University of Georgia, DeRenne Library.
GU ·	University of Georgia, Athens.
GU-De	— DeRenne Georgia Library.
GU-Ex	— Georgia State College of Business Administration Library, Atlanta.

HAWAII

HU	University of Hawaii, Honolulu.
HU-EWC	Center for Cultural and Technical Interchange between East and West, Honolulu.

ILLINOIS

I	Illinois State Library, Springfield.
IC	Chicago Public Library.
ICA	Art Institute of Chicago, Chicago.
ICF	Chicago Natural History Museum, Chicago.
ICF-A	— Edward E. Ayer Ornithological Library.
ICHi	Chicago Historical Society, Chicago.
ICIP	Institute for Psychoanalysis, Chicago.
ICJ	John Crerar Library, Chicago.
ICMILC*	Center for Research Libraries, Chicago.
ICMcC	McCormick Theological Seminary, Chicago.
ICN	Newberry Library, Chicago.
ICRL	Center for Research Libraries, Chicago.
ICU	University of Chicago, Chicago.
ICarbS	Southern Illinois University, Carbondale.
IEG	Garrett Theological Seminary, Evanston.
IEN	Northwestern University, Evanston.
IEdS	Southern Illinois University, Edwardsville.
IGK	Knox College, Galesburg.
IHi	Illinois State Historical Library, Springfield.
ILS	St. Procopius College, Lisle.
IMunS	Saint Mary of the Lake Seminary, Mundelein.
INS	Illinois State University, Normal.
IRA	Augustana College Library, Rock Island.
IRivfR	Rosary College, River Forest.
IU	University of Illinois, Urbana.
IU-M	— Medical Sciences Library, Chicago.
IU-U	— Chicago Undergraduate Division, Chicago.

IOWA

IaAS	Iowa State University of Science and Technology, Ames.
IaDL	Luther College, Decorah.
IaDuC	Loras College, Dubuque.
IaDuU	University of Dubuque, Dubuque.
IaDuU-S	— Theological Seminary Library.
IaDuW	Wartburg Theological Seminary, Dubuque.
IaU	University of Iowa, Iowa City.

IDAHO

IdB	Boise Public Library.
IdPI	Idaho State University, Pocatello.
IdPS*	Idaho State University, Pocatello.
IdU	University of Idaho, Moscow.

INDIANA

In	Indiana State Library, Indianapolis.
InAndC	Anderson College, Anderson.
InCollS*	St. Joseph's College, Rensselaer.
InGo	Goshen College Biblical Seminary Library, Goshen.
InHi	Indiana Historical Society, Indianapolis.
InIB	Butler University, Indianapolis.

INDIANA continued

InLP	Purdue University, Lafayette.
InNd	University of Notre Dame, Notre Dame.
InOlH*	St. Leonard College Library, Dayton, Ohio.
InRE	Earlham College, Richmond.
InRenS	St. Joseph's College, Rensselaer.
InStme	St. Meinrad's College & Seminary, St. Meinrad.
InU	Indiana University, Bloomington.

KANSAS

K	Kansas State Library, Topeka.
KAS	St. Benedict's College, Atchison.
KAStB*	St. Benedict's College, Atchison.
KHi	Kansas State Historical Society, Topeka.
KKcB	Central Baptist Theological Seminary, Kansas City.
KMK	Kansas State University, Manhattan.
KStMC*	St. Louis University, School of Divinity Library, St. Louis, Mo.
KU	University of Kansas, Lawrence.
KU-M	— Medical Center Library, Kansas City.
KWiU	Wichita State University, Wichita.

KENTUCKY

Ky-LE	Library Extension Division, Frankfort.
KyBgW	Western Kentucky State College, Bowling Green
KyHi	Kentucky Historical Society, Frankfort.
KyLo	Louisville Free Public Library.
KyLoS	Southern Baptist Theological Seminary, Louisville.
KyLoU	University of Louisville, Louisville.
KyLx	Lexington Public Library.
KyLxCB	Lexington Theological Seminary, Lexington. (Formerly College of the Bible)
KyLxT	Transylvania College, Lexington.
KyMoreT	Morehead State College, Morehead.
KyU	University of Kentucky, Lexington.
KyWA	Asbury College Library, Wilmore.
KyWAT	Asbury Theological Seminary, Wilmore.

LOUISIANA

L	Louisiana State Library, Baton Rouge.
L-M	Louisiana State Museum Library, New Orleans.
LCA	Not a library symbol.
LCS	Not a library symbol.
LHi	Louisiana History Society, New Orleans.
LNHT	Tulane University Library, New Orleans.
LNT-MA	Tulane University, Latin American Library, New Orleans.
LU	Louisiana State University, Baton Rouge.
LU-M	— Medical Center Library, New Orleans.
LU-NO	— Louisiana State University in New Orleans.

MASSACHUSETTS

M	Massachusetts State Library, Boston.
MA	Amherst College, Amherst.
MB	Boston Public Library.
MBAt	Boston Athenaeum, Boston.
MBBC*	Boston College, Chestnut Hill.
MBCo	Countway Library of Medicine. (Harvard-Boston Medical Libraries)
MBH	Massachusetts Horticultural Society, Boston.
MBHo*	Massachusetts Horticultural Society, Boston.
MBM*	Countway Library of Medicine (Harvard-Boston Medical Libraries).
MBMu	Museum of Fine Arts, Boston.
MBU	Boston University.
MBdAF	U.S. Air Force Cambridge Research Center, Bedford.
MBrZ	Zion Research Library, Brookline.
MBrigStJ*	St. John's Seminary, Brighton.
MBtS	St. John's Seminary Library, Brighton.
MCM	Massachusetts Institute of Technology, Cambridge.
MCR	Radcliffe College, Cambridge.
MCSA	Smithsonian Institution, Astrophysical Observatory, Cambridge.
MChB	Boston College, Chestnut Hill.
MH	Harvard University, Cambridge.
MH-A	— Arnold Arboretum.
MH-AH	— Andover-Harvard Theological Library.
MH-BA	— Graduate School of Business Administration Library.
MH-FA	— Fine Arts Library. (Formerly Fogg Art Museum)
MH-G	— Gray Herbarium Library.
MH-HY	— Harvard-Yenching Institute. (Chinese-Japanese Library)

MASSACHUSETTS continued

MH-L	— Law School Library.
MH-P	— Peabody Museum Library.
MH-PR	— Physics Research Library.
MHi	Massachusetts Historical Society, Boston.
MMeT	Tufts University, Medford.
MNF	Forbes Library, Northampton.
MNS	Smith College, Northampton.
MNoeS	Stonehill College Library, North Easton.
MNtcA	Andover Newton Theological School, Newton Center.
MSaE	Essex Institute, Salem.
MShM	Mount Holyoke College, South Hadley.
MU	University of Massachusetts, Amherst.
MWA	American Antiquarian Society, Worcester.
MWAC	Assumption College, Worcester.
MWC	Clark University, Worcester.
MWH	College of the Holy Cross, Worcester.
MWalB	Brandeis University, Waltham.
MWelC	Wellesley College, Wellesley.
MWhB	Marine Biological Laboratory, Woods Hole.
MWiW	Williams College, Williamstown.
MWiW-C	— Chapin Library.

MARYLAND

MdAN	U.S. Naval Academy, Annapolis.
MdBE	Enoch Pratt Free Library, Baltimore.
MdBG	Goucher College, Baltimore.
MdBJ	Johns Hopkins University, Baltimore.
MdBJ-G	— John Work Garrett Library.
MdBP	Peabody Institute, Baltimore.
MdBWA	Walters Art Gallery, Baltimore.
MdU	University of Maryland, College Park.
MdW	Woodstock College, Woodstock.

MAINE

MeB	Bowdoin College, Brunswick.
MeBa	Bangor Public Library.
MeU	University of Maine, Orono.
MeWC	Colby College, Waterville.
MeWaC*	Colby College, Waterville.

MICHIGAN

Mi	Michigan State Library, Lansing.
MiAC	Alma College, Alma.
MiD	Detroit Public Library.
MiD-B	— Burton Historical Collection.
MiDA	Detroit Institute of Arts, Detroit.
MiDU	University of Detroit, Detroit.
MiDW	Wayne State University, Detroit.
MiEM	Michigan State University, East Lansing.
MiEalC*	Michigan State University, East Lansing.
MiGr	Grand Rapids Public Library.
MiH*	Michigan College of Mining and Technology, Houghton.
MiHM	Michigan College of Mining and Technology, Houghton.
MiU	University of Michigan, Ann Arbor.
MiU-C	— William L. Clements Library.

MINNESOTA

MnCS	St. John's University, Collegeville.
MnH*	Minnesota Historical Society, St. Paul.
MnHi	Minnesota Historical Society, St. Paul.
MnRM	Mayo Clinic and Foundation Library, Rochester.
MnSJ	James Jerome Hill Reference Library, St. Paul.
MnSSC	College of St. Catherine, St. Paul.
MnU	University of Minnesota, Minneapolis.

MISSOURI

MoHi	Missouri State Historical Society, Columbia
MoK	Kansas City Public Library.
MoKL	Linda Hall Library, Kansas City
MoKU	University of Missouri at Kansas City, Kansas City.
MoS	St. Louis Public Library.
MoSB	Missouri Botanical Garden, St. Louis.
MoSC*	Concordia Seminary Library, St. Louis.
MoSCS	Concordia Seminary Library, St. Louis.
MoSM	Mercantile Library Association, St. Louis.
MoSU	St. Louis University, St. Louis.
MoSU-D	— School of Divinity Library, St. Louis.
MoSW	Washington University, St. Louis.
MoU	University of Missouri, Columbia.

The National Union Catalog

Pre-1956 Imprints

The National Union Catalog

Pre-1956 Imprints

A cumulative author list representing Library of Congress printed cards and titles reported by other American libraries. Compiled and edited with the cooperation of the Library of Congress and the National Union Catalog Subcommittee of the Resources Committee of the Resources and Technical Services Division, American Library Association

Volume 583

TAOKA, SAYOJI - TAUBER, RICHARD

Mansell 1978

© 1978 Mansell Information/Publishing Limited

© 1978 The American Library Association

All rights reserved under Berne and Universal Copyright Conventions and Pan American Union.

Mansell Information/Publishing Limited
3 Bloomsbury Place, London WC1

The American Library Association
50 East Huron Street, Chicago, Illinois 60611

The paper on which this catalog has been printed is supplied by
P. F. Bingham Limited and has been specially manufactured by the
Guard Bridge Paper Company Limited of Fife, Scotland.
Based on requirements established by the late William J. Barrow
for a permanent/durable book paper it is laboratory certified
to meet or exceed the following values:

Substance 85 gsm
pH cold extract 8·6
Fold endurance (MIT $\frac{1}{2}$kg. tension) 1200
Tear resistance (Elmendorf) 73 (or 67 × 3)
Opacity 89%

Library of Congress Card Number: 67–30001
ISBN: 0 7201 0774 1

Printed by Balding & Mansell Limited, London and Wisbech, England
Bound by Bemrose & Sons Limited, Derby, England

American Library Association

Resources and Technical Services Division

Publisher's Note

Because of the large number of sources from which the information in the National Union Catalog has been collected over a long period of time an understanding of its scope and an acquaintance with its methods is necessary for the best use to be made of it. Users are therefore earnestly advised to make themselves familiar with the introductory matter in Volume 1. This fully defines the scope of the Catalog and sets out the basis on which the material reported to the National Union Catalog has been edited for publication in book form.

National Union Catalog Designation

Each main entry in the Catalog has been ascribed a unique identifying designation. This alphanumeric combination appears uniformly after the last line of the entry itself and consists of:

1   The letter N, signifying National Union Catalog.
2   The initial letter under which the entry is filed.
3   A number representing the position of the entry within the sequence under its initial letter.

This National Union Catalog designator is sufficient both to identify any main entry in the Catalog and to establish its position within the sequence of volumes. It is, however, recommended that when referring to titles by the National Union Catalog designation a checking element, such as the key word or initials of the title, be added.

Reported Locations

Alphabetic symbols which represent libraries in the United States and Canada follow the National Union Catalog designation. These groups of letters signify which libraries have reported holding copies of the work. The first library so represented usually is the one that provided the catalog information.

Printed on the end sheets of each volume is a list of most frequently used symbols, each followed by the full name of the library. *List of Symbols*, containing a comprehensive list of symbols used, is published as a separate volume with the Catalog. The Library of Congress has also issued *Symbols Used in the National Union Catalog of the Library of Congress*. In cases where a symbol is not identified in these lists the National Union Catalog Division of the Library of Congress will, on enquiry, attempt to identify the library concerned.

Other Developments

Under the terms of their agreement with the American Library Association, the publishers have undertaken to apply, as far as is practicable, new developments in library science and techniques which may have the effect of further enhancing the value of the Catalog. To this end, the publishers will be pleased to receive suggestions and enquiries relating to technical and production aspects of the Catalog and will be glad to consider proposals calculated to improve its utility and amenity. Mansell Information/Publishing Limited will be pleased also to advise libraries on possible applications of the methods and techniques developed for this and similar projects to their own requirements.

J.C.
London, *August 1968*

Taoka, Sayoji
see
Taoka, Reiun, 1870-1912.

Taopi and his friends, or, The Indians' wrongs
and rights
see under   [Welsh, William] 1807-1878,
comp.

Taormina, Giuseppe.
Il marchese di Torre Arsa e la Sicilia nel
MDCCCXLVIII.   Palermo, Tip. dello Statuto,
1889.
21 p.   port.   f°.
Cover serves as title-page.
"Estratto dal giornale La Sicilia artistica ed
archeologica, anno III, fasc. III, 1889".

NT   0035208   MH

PQ4710   Taormina, Giuseppe.
T36   Ranieri e Leopardi; considerazioni e ricerche, con documenti inediti.   Milano, R.
Sandron, 1899.
116 p.   (Biblioteca "Sandron" di scienze
e lettere, n.2)
Bibliographical references in notes: p.
[103]-116.

1. Leopardi, Giacomo, conte, 1798-1837.
2. Ranieri, Anto-   nio, 1806-1888.

NT   0035209   CU MH IU

Taormina, Lorenzo. Sant' Ambrogio e
Plotino. (In: Miscellanea di studi di
letteratura cristiana antica, [v. 4]
(1954) p. [41]-85)

Microfilm. Bibliographical footnotes.

1. Ambrosius, Saint, Ep. of Milan.
2. Plotinus.

NT   0035210   NN

Taormina.   Festival internazionale di musica contemporanea.   *23d, 1949*
see International Society for Contemporary Music. *23d
festival, Palermo and Taormina, 1949.*

Taormina. Mostra di arti decorative, 1928.
...La Mostra di arti decorative di Taormina, 1928; catalogo,
notizie, rilievi.   Messina: V. Ferrara[, 1928].   62 p. incl. plates.
illus.   12°.

At head of title: Associazione messinese, sport e turismo.

489348A. 1. Decorative art—Exhibi-   tions—Italy—Taormina. I. Associazione messinese, sport e turismo.
N. Y. P. L.   August 19, 1930

NT   0035212   NN

Taormina, and other poems
see under   [Lowe, Helen]

Taos, Fernandez de, pseud.
see   Fernandez de Taos, pseud.

Taos, a romance of the massacre
see under   [Field, Joseph M   ]
1810-1856.

Taos County, New Mexico.   Fernandez de
Taos, 1881.

NT   0035216   PPL

Taos county project.
Annual report. 1st-
1940/41-
Albuquerque, N. M., University of New Mexico press, 1941-
v.   23cm.
Issued as the University of New Mexico bulletin.   Catalog series.
Report year for 1941 ends June 30; for 1942-   Aug. 31.

1. Taos co., N. M.
Library of Congress   F802.T2T3   44-53708
                                    [2]   978.9

NT   0035217   DLC OU TxU

Taosug exercises.   [n.p., 195-?]
62 l.   28 cm.

1. Sulu language—Dialects—Taosug.

NT   0035218   NIC

Taou, Pao-chün.
A regional study of Shantung and its significance in the
life of North China.   Chungking, 1943.
Microfilm copy (negative) of typescript.
Collation of the original, as determined from the film: 244 l., diagrs.,
maps, tables.
Includes bibliographies.

1. Shantung, China—Econ. condit.   I. Title.

Microfilm 1876 HC   Mic 58-6707

NT   0035219   DLC

Taoufik Khiari, Mohamed
see   Khiari, Mohamed Taoufik, 1912-

Taoussi, Athanase, ed. and tr.
Le Cantique des Cantiques de Salomon.   Texte
et traduction de la Vulgate...   Abbeville [1919]
see under   Bible. O. T. Song of
Solomon. French. 1919. Taoussi.

Taoussi, Athanase.
Le Ve centenaire du concile oecuménique de
Florence et l'unité dans l'eglise du Christ...
Istanbul, imp. Rizzo, 1938.

511, [3] p.   illus. fronts.

NT   0035222   DDO

Taoutel, *Ferdinand.*
Beirut, Syria.   Université Saint-Joseph. *Bibliothèque orientale.*
Catalogue raisonné des manuscrits de la Bibliothèque orientale de l'Université St Joseph, par le p. L. Cheikho, s. J.
1-VI.
(*In* Beirut, Syria.   Université Saint-Joseph. *Mélanges.* Beyrouth
etc., 1913-29.   24½-26½cm.   [t.] 6, p. [213]-304; [t.] 7, p. [245]-304;
[t.] 10, p. [105]-179; [t.] 11, p. [191]-306; [t.] 14, p. [41]-171. (Tables
générales, dressées par le p. F. Taoutel, s. J., p. [107]-171))

Taoutel, Ferdinand, *ed.*
وثائق تاريخية عن حلب [تأليف] فردينان توتل. بيروت،
المطبعة الكاثوليكية، ١٩٤٠-[1940-
v. plates, port., facsims. 25 cm.
Added t. p.: Contribution à l'histoire d'Alep [par] Ferdinand
Taoutel.
At head of title, v.   نصوص ودروس
Vol. 1-   نشرت بها في «المشرق» :
CONTENTS.— [١] الحوادث والأخبار اغتلا عن يومية نعوم البخاش ١٨٥٥—
١٨٦٥ وفيها من المخطوطات —

[٢] اخبار الموارنة وما اليهم من ١٦٠٦ الى يومنا: (١) ١٦٠٦-١٦٢٧-١٨٢٧.

1. Aleppo—Hist.   I. Title. II. Title: Contribution à l'histoire
d'Alep.   (Series: Nuṣūṣ wa-durūs, 2 [etc.])
Title transliterated: Wathā'iq ta'rīkhīyah 'an Ḥalab.

DS51.A3T3   N E 63-1199

NT   0035225   DLC MU WU

Taoyuan hsien, *Formosa*
see
T'ao-yüan, *Formosa.*

Tap, E
Les atrocités allemandes en France et en
Belgique, stigmatisées par l'image, d'apres
documents, par E. Tap.   Paris, Librairie de
l'estampe, c1915.
1 v. (unpaged) 14 plates. 28 x 39 cm.
1. European War, 1914-1918. Atrocities.
2. European War, 1914-1918. Pictorial works.
I. Title.

NT   0035227   OrU NBuG MH PHi

Tap, H   J
Herziening Lager-Onderwijswet 1920, een toelichting op
de Wijzigingswet van 25 Juni 1948, Staatsblad I 254.   Alphen aan den Rijn, N. Samsom, 1948.
72 p.   25 cm.

1. Educational law and legislation—Netherlands.   I. Title.

                                                 50-21487

NT   0035228   DLC

Tap, H   J
Herziening Lager-Onderwijswet 1920, een toelichting op
de Wijzigingswet van 19 Januari 1950, Staatsblad K 14.
Alphen aan den Rijn, N. Samsom, 1950.
51 p.   25 cm.

1. Educational law and legislation—Netherlands.   I. Title.

                                                 53-32541

NT   0035229   DLC NNC-T

Tap, Jacob Meindert Pieter.
De intraveneuze chloralhydraat-narcosse bij het paard; een experimenteel en klinisch onderzoek naar hare waarde in de operatieve chirurgie ... Utrecht, N. V. drukkerij Schilt, 1923.

4 p. l., 145 p., 1 l. 23^{cm}.

Proefschrift—Veeartsenijk. hoogeschool, Utrecht.
"Literatuur" : p. [143]–145.
"Stellingen" : leaf laid in.

1. Chloral. 2. Injections, Intravenous.

Agr 27—337

U. S. Dept. of agr. Library   41T162
for Library of Congress   [a40b1]

NT 0035230   DNAL

Tap, John
    see Tapp, John, fl. 1596-1615.

Tap Núñez de Rendón, Nicolás
    see Tapia y Núñez de Rendón, Nicolás, 1770–(ca.) 1823.

Tap & tavern.   Philadelphia, Penn., 1935–

NT 0035233   PP

Tập-chí hoạt động khoa học.
[Hanoi] Ủy Ban Khoa Học và Kỉ Thuật Nhà nu-ớ-c.
v. 27 cm. monthly.
In Vietnamese.

1. Science—Periodicals. 2. Technology—Periodicals. I. Vietnam (Democratic Republic, 1946–) Ủy Ban Khoa Học và Kỉ Thuật Nhà Nước.

Q4.T29   72-211108

NT 0035234   DLC

Tap dancing for everyone. 15 graded tap routines with costume sketches ...
    see under The Del-Wrights.

Tập san nghiên cứu văn sủ địa.
[Hà-nội] Ban nghiên cứu văn sủ địa Việt Nam.
no. in v. 24 cm. monthly.
Superseded by: Nghiên cứu lịch sủ.
Other title : Revue des études littéraires, historiques et géographiques.

1. Vietnam—Periodicals. I. Ban Nghiên cứu văn sủ địa Việt Nam. II. Title: Revue des études littéraires, historiques et géographiques.

DS556.T36   75-648392
    (MARC-S)

NT 0035236   DLC

Tập san Quốc-phòng.
Saigon, Vĩnh Lộc.
v. 24 cm. monthly.
"Nguyệt-san nghiên-cứu quân-sự chính-trị kinh-tế xã-hội."

1. Vietnam—Periodicals. 2. Asia—Politics—Periodicals.
I. Vĩnh Lộc.

DS557.A5A35   73-642898
    MARC-S

NT 0035237   DLC

Tập văn họa ký niệm Nguyễn Du. — [Hà-nội : Hội Quảng Tri, 1942]
56 p., [11] leaves of plates : ill. : 29 cm.

1. Nguyễn Du, 1765-1820—Addresses, essays, lectures.

PL4378.9.N5Z89   75-986979

NT 0035238   DLC

El tapa-boca, o, Residenciador residenciado
    see under [Isla, José Francisco de] 1703-1781.

Pamphlet Tapa boca o sea Coleccion de articulos en
Peru pro y en contra de la nacionalidad del jeneral
1850 Echenique. [Lima? 185-]
T16   T.-p. missing. Title supplied from Biblioteca
    peruana(3393)

1. Echenique, José Rufino, Pres.Peru,1808-1879.

NT 0035240   CtY

Tapaboca a los sacrilegos detractores del ciudadano doctor José Maria Aguirre, cura de la Santa Veracruz. [México : Impr. del C. A. Valdés, á cargo de J. M. Gallegos, 1828] 7 p. 19½cm.

Caption-title.
Signed: El amigo del dr. Aguirre.
In answer to the pamphlet "Gracias singulares del C. coronel José Maria Tornel," in the controversy between Tornel and Aguirre.

1. Aguirre, José María, 1778-Maria, d. 1853. 3. Gracias singulares I, El amigo del dr. Aguirre.
N. Y. P. L.
1852. 2. Tornel y Mendivil, José del C. coronel José Maria Tornel.
July 24, 1941.

NT 0035241   NN CtY

Pamphlet Tapaboca al ciudadano Paz. No es mi ánimo
Mexico hacer la defensa del informe dirigido al Rey
1820 por el Illmo.Sr.D.Manuel de la Bodega y
T16   Mollinedo, ya porque la verdad y la justicia n
    necesitan de apología, como porque Vd. no se
    propone tampoco atacarlo, sin embargo de que
    el título de su papel promete una formal y
    vigorosa impugnacion ... [Méjico,1820]
    Caption and part of text used as title.
    Signed: El Ciudadano Franco.

1. Bodega y Mollinedo, Manuel de la

NT 0035242   CtY

Tapaboca; ó sea Contestacion documentada al insulso y desaliñado folleto que, con el nombre impropio de memoria, ha publicado en Paris el reo prófugo D. José Ildefonso Suarez (alias) el Mulon, ex-asesor general primero interino del gobierno de la Habana y de su comision militar ejecutiva permanente... Matanzas, Impr. de J. Miguel de Oro, 1839.

97 p. 19½^{cm}.
A refutation of "Breve memoria escrita por el oidor honorario de la audiencia de Cuba, D. José Ildefonso Suarez, para satisfacer á la nacion y á su gobierno supremo de las calumniosas acusaciones que le han hecho algunos enemigos." [Paris, 1838]
Subject entries: 1. Suárez, José Ildefonso. Breve memoria. 2. Cuba—Pol. & govt.

3-33183

Library of Congress, no.   F1783.T17

NT 0035243   DLC InU MH

Lilly TAPACARÍ,BOLIVIA(City) Junta municipal
HJ 9385 Informes que presentan el administrador
.T17 I 4 y la comision especial de la Junta municipal
Mendel de la 2a. seccion de la provincia de Tapacari,
    encargada de revisar los libros de su tesoro
    desde su creacion en 1872, hasta el presente
    año. -- Cochabamba : Imprenta del siglo, 1878.
    19 p. ; 4to(22 cm.)

    Cover title.
    In wrappers, stitched as issued.

NT 0035244   InU

Lilly Tapacarí,Bolivia(City). Junta Municipal
HJ 9385 Memoria del presidente de la Junta Muni-
.T17 I 39 cipal de la primera sección de la provincia de
Mendel Tapacarí. -- Cochabamba : Imprenta de El he-
    raldo, 1892-1895.
    [2] no. ; 21.5 cm.

    Cover title.
    Not in René-Moreno,Bibl.boliviana.
    No.2 title varies, different publisher.
    Reports for the fiscal years 1892 and 1894.
    In original   wrappers. no. 2 in green.

NT 0035245   InU

Tapada, Portugal. Real observatorio
astronomico de Lisboa
    see Lisbon. Observatorio astronomico.

Tapaghian, Harowt'iwn.
Մատեեն-Դաւիթ. Վաստուբովանեքի զատստուսբորբպատով
Փակիզ, Ղեզարունստմեան Ձպ·, 1954:
76 p. illus. 21 cm.
Cover title: Մատեեն-Դաւիթ.
An abridged poetical adaptation, in the Van dialect, of the Armenian epic Sasownts'i Dawit'.

I. Sasownts'i Dawit'. II. Title.   *Title romanized: Sasonts'i-Dawit'.*

PK8548.T28S2   78-247897

NT 0035247   DLC

T'apagian, Mihran Kh
(Handès hay ew ёndhanowr grakanowt'ean)
Հայոց եւ ёնդհանուր գրականութեան պրբ[Մինան
Խ· Թապագեան: [4· Պոլիս] Տպագր· Ձ· Հ· Վերակբեան
[i. e. Պէրպէրեան, cover 1909]
12, 270 p. port. 19 cm.
On cover: Գրական սեղմ· ստոստաւ, սրտակ:
Includes bibliographical references.

1. Literary form. I. Title.

PN45.5.T34   75-587031

NT 0035248   DLC

G961 TAPAJOS, MANUEL PEDRO MONTEIRO, 1857-
T15f   Fronteira sul do Amazonas; questão de limites,
    por Manoel Tapajós ... Rio de Janeiro, Typo-
    graphia L'Etoile du sud, 1898.
    147,[1]p. fold. maps. 19½cm.
    Caption title: Questão de limites entre os
    estados do Amazonas e Matto-Grosso.
    A series of articles previously published in
    Jornal do commercio.--cf. Sacramento Blake,
    v.6, p.179.
    1. Amazonas, Brazil - Bound. - Matto Grosso.
    2. Matto Grosso, Brazil (State) - Bound. -
    Amazonas. I. Title.

NT 0035249   TxU CSt NNC

Tapajós, Torquato Xavier Monteiro, 1853-1897.
Apontamentos para a climatologia do valle do Amazonas, por Torquato Tapajós... Rio de Janeiro: Imprensa nacional, 1889.
xx, 148 p. tables. 8°.

Preface and concluding tables by Barão do Ladário.

249009A. 1. Meteorology—Brazil.   2. Climate—Brazil.
N. Y. P. L.   November 1, 1926

NT 0035250   NN RPB IU

G614.0981
T16e
   TAPAJOS, TORQUATO XAVIER MONTEIRO, 1853-1897.
    ... Estudos de hygiene. A cidade do Rio de
Janeiro. Primeira parte: Terras, aguas e ares:
idéas finaes. 1º volume. Rio de Janeiro,
Imprensa nacional, 1895.
    xv, 288p.,2l. 24½cm.
    At head of title: Torquato Tapajós.
    The two other proposed volumes of this work
were not published.—cf. Sacramento Blake,
Dic. Bibliog. brazileiro, v.7, p.317.
    "Obras consultadas": p.287-288.
    1. Rio de Janeiro - Sanit. affaire. I.
Title.

NT   0035251   TxU

Tapajós, Torquato Xavier Monteiro, 1853–1897.
   Estudos sobre o Amazonas; limites do estado,
por Torquato Tapajós ... Rio de Janeiro, Typ. do Jornal
do commercio, Rodrigues & comp.,
   v. 21ᵐ.
    Caption title (1. ptc., 2. sér., p i5i) : Os estados do Amazonas e de Matto-
Grosso e seus limites.
    Imprint of i1. ptc, 1. sér.i : Rio de Janeiro, Typ. Lenzinger, 1895.

    1. Amazonas, Brazil—Bound.—Matto Grosso. 2. Matto Grosso, Brazil
(State)—Bound.—Amazonas.

   Library of Congress   F2546.T17   7—34822

NT   0035252   DLC TxU MH-L DPU DCU-IA WU MH CSt

TAPAJÓS,Torquato,1853-1897.
   Nuvens medrosas. Rio de Janeiro,Imperial
Instituto artistico,1874.

   Port.
   At head of titleVersos de T.Tapajoz.

NT   0035253   MH

Tapajós, Torquato, 1853–1897.
   ...Provincia do Amazonas, navegação directa, cartas ao Exm.º
Sr. dr. Antonio dos Passos Miranda... ser. 1— Rio de Janeiro:
Typ. da-Escola de-S. J. Alves, 1886   v.   22½cm.

   1. Shipping. Inland—Brazil—   Amazonas. 2. Passos Miranda,
Antonio dos.   September 30, 1938
N.Y.P.L.

NT   0035254   NN

Tapajos, Torquato Xavier Monteiro, 1853–1897.
   ... O valle do Amazonas e os Apontamentos para o Diccionario geographico do Brazil. Rio de Janeiro, Typ. da Escola de
S. J. Alves, 1888.
   118, il p. 18½ᵐ.

   1. Amazon valley. 2. Amazon river. 3. Moreira Pinto, Alfredo, d.
1903. Apontamentos para o Diccionario geographico do Brazil. I.
Title.
                                35—36378

   Library of Congress   F2504.M88   918.1

NT   0035255   DLC TxU RPB WU CtY

981
T172B
   Tapajos, Vicente.
    Breve história do Brasil. ¿Porto,
Porto Editora, 195-¿
    199 p. maps (1 fold.) 19 cm.
(Colecção luso-brasileira, 2)

    Errata slip inserted.

    1. Brazil. History.

NT   0035256   NcD

Tapajos, Vicente.
   Historia da América. São Paulo, Companhia Editora
Nacional ¡1954¿
   454 p. illus. 22 cm. (Biblioteca do espírito moderno. Sér. 3:
História e biografia, v. 57)
   Includes bibliography.

   1. America—Hist.

   E18.T3   56–34512 ‡

NT   0035257   DLC OU

F2521
T35
1944
   Tapajós, Vicente
    História do Brasil.   3. ed.   São Paulo, Companhia Editora
Nacional [1944?]
    494 p. illus., fold. maps. (Biblioteca do espírito moderno.
Ser. 3: História e biografia [i. e. biografia] v. 41)

    1. Brazil - Hist.

NT   0035258   CU PU NBuU

   Tapajós, Vicente.
    Historia do Brasil adaptada ao curso de
colégio. São Paulo, Companhia editora nacional,
1944.
    [4] l., [11]-48] p.   illus., maps (part fold.)
22 cm.
    1. Brazil - Hist.

NT   0035259   CU

Ayer
1300
B8
T17
1946
   TAPAJÓS. VICENTE.
    História do Brasil. 2. edição. São
Paulo, Companhia Editora Nacional,1946.
    491p. illus.,maps. 23cm. (Biblioteca
do espírito moderno. Ser.3. História e biografia. v.41)

NT   0035260   ICN DPU LNT TxU CSt

G981
T17h
1953
   Tapajós, Vicente.
    ... História do Brasil. 5. ed. São Paulo,
Companhia editora nacional [1953]
    2p.l.,[3]-516p.,1l. illus.(incl. ports.)
maps (1 fold.) 22cm. (Biblioteca do espírito moderno; serie 3.ª: História e biografia, vol. 41)

    1. Brazil - Hist. I. Series.

NT   0035261   TxU

   Tapajos Gomes,
    ... Francisco Braga. Desenhos de J. Carlos. Rio de Janeiro,
Irmãos Pongetti, 1937.
    1 p. l., ¡7¿–41 p., 1 l. front. (mounted port.) 19¼ᵐ.
    "Composições mais vulgarisadas de Francisco Braga": p. ¡33¿–41.

    1. *Braga, Francisco, 1868–
                           41–40884
   Library of Congress   ML410.B78G6
                         ¡2¿   927.8

NT   0035262   DLC PP

B
67
T3
   Tapajóz, Estellita
    Ensaios de philosophia e sciencia. S¡ão¿
Paulo, Typ. Paulista, 1898.
    175p. 21cm.

      1. Science - Philosophy - Addresses, essays,
lectures 2. Philosophy - Addresses, essays,
lectures¡ I. Title

NT   0035263   WU

TAPAJOZ (Roleiro da capitania de Matto Gross**
navegação do rio). 1861.

   pp. 1–54.
   This is the captain's log-book.
   Imperfect:- all after p. 54 torn out.

NT   0035264   MH

   Tapales, Ramon.
    Singing and growing; for the primary grades. Illus-
trated by Pedro T. Paguia. Manila, Bookman ¡ᶜ1952¿
    252 p. illus. (part col.) 21 cm.
    Unacc. melodies; part of the words in English, part in Tagalog, and
part in Tagalog with English translation.

    1. School song-books, Philippine.   I. Title.

   M1994.T17S5   M 57–1675

NT   0035265   DLC

   Tapalpa, Mexico (Jalisco)
    Cuadro general estadístico de la villa de
Tapalpa
    see under   [González, Camilo]

   T'ap'alts'yan, K'ristap'or, 1911–
    (Oske bovit)
    Ոսկէ հովիտ ¡զրեց¿ Քր. Թափալցյան։ Երեւան, Հայպետ-
հրատ, 1955:
    809 p. 23 cm.
    A novel.

    I. Title.

   PK8548.T3O8   74–222923

NT   0035267   DLC

   T'ap'alts'yan, K'ristap'or, 1911–
    (Paterazm)
    Պատերազմ ։ վէպ ¡զրեց¿ Քր. Թափալցյան։ ¡Երեւան,
Հայպետհրատ, 1946–
    v. 21 cm.

    I. Title.

   PK8548.T29P3   73–222447

NT   0035268   DLC

   Tapanakumāra Bandyopādhyāya
    see
    Bandyopadhyay, Tapankumar.

   Tapanamohana Caṭṭopādhyāya, 1896–
    see
    Caṭṭopādhyāya, Tapanamohana, 1896–

   Tapanamohana Chaṭṭopādhyāya
    see
    Chatterji, Tapanmohan.

Tápanes, Pedro S., ed.

Almanaque y guía social matancera ... 1.– edición; 1933– Matanzas, "Estrada", 1933–

NT 0035273   MH

Tapani. Porvoo
1922
Toimittaneet Eva Hirn ja Anna Inkeri Relander

Tapankumar Bandyopadhyay
see
Bandyopadhyay, Tapankumar.

Tapankumar Raychaudhuri
see
Raychaudhuri, Tapankumar.

Tapanmohan Chatterji
see
Chatterji, Tapanmohan.

Tapanmohan Chattopadhyay
see
Caṭṭopādhyāya, Tapanamohana, 1896–

Wason   Tapanuli (Residency) Ordinances, etc.
JS7025   Verzameling gewestelijke keuren, ver-
T17/A2   ordeningen en reglementen voor de residentie
     Tapanoeli. Bijgewerkt tot ultimo Februari
     1931. ₍Medan, Varekamp, 1931₎
     323 p. 25cm.

     1. Local government--Indonesia. I. Title.

NT 0035278   NIC

Wason   Tapanuli-Sumatera Timur (Propinsi) Djabatan
DS646.1   Penerangan.
A4   Perdjuangan rakjat; 5 x 17 Agustus.
     ₍Sibolga, 1950₎
     168 p. illus. 25cm.

     Cover title.

     1. Sumatra--Hist. 2. Indonesia--Hist.--
Revolution, 1945-1949. I. Title.

NT 0035279   NIC

Taparelli, Aloys
     see Tapparelli d' Azeglio, Luigi, 1793–
1862.

Taparelli, Costanza (Alfieri di Sostegno) *marchesa d'Azeglio*
     see Azeglio, Costanza (Alfieri di Sostegno) Tapparelli,
marchesa d', d. 1862.

Taparelli, Luigi, *marchese d'Azeglio*
see
Tapparelli d'Azeglio, Luigi, 1793–1862.

Taparelli, Luis
     see Tapparelli d'Azeglio, Luigi,
1793–1862.

Taparelli, Massimo, *marchese d' Azeglio*
     see **Azeglio, Massimo Tapparelli,** *marchese* **d',** 1798–1866.

Taparelli d'Azeglio, Luigi
see
Tapparelli d'Azeglio, Luigi, 1793–1862.

Taparelli d'Azeglio, Massimo
marchese, 1798-1866
     See
Azeglio, Massimo Taparelli, marchese d',
1798-1866

Taparelli d'Azeglio, Prospero Aloysius
see
Tapparelli d'Azeglio, Luigi, 1793–1862.

Taparelli d'Azeglio, Vittorio Emanuele
     see Azeglio, Vittorio Emanuele
Tapparelli, marchese d', 1816–1890.

T'ap'arhakan.
     (Dēpi kakhaghan)
     Վէպ կախաղան / Թափառական. — Դութըն : Տպարան
Հայրենիքը, 1932.
     877 p. : ill. ; 24 cm.

     1. T'ap'arhakan. I. Title.
     DS195.3.T36A33   75-972808

NT 0035289   DLC

WZ   TAPARO, Ottavio
250   Compendio delli casi di chirurgia ... Di nuovo ristampato ...
T172c   Roma, Fabio di Falco, 1663.
1663   47 p. 15 cm.

NT 0035290   DNLM

Tapasyānanda, swami.
Herbert, Jean, *ed. and tr.*
     ... Études sur Rāmana maharshi ... Introduction et traduc-
tion de Jean Herbert. Paris, A. Maisonneuve; ₍etc., etc.₎
1940–

Tapatío, El Pensador, pseud.
     Carta primera de el Pensador tapatío...
     see under title

Tapaturmantorjunta. Liikennejaosto.
     Suomen tieliikenneonnettomuudet
     see under title

Tapaturmantorjuntayhdistys.
     Luottamusmies ja työturvallisuus
     see under Suomen ammattiyhdistysten
keskusliitto.

Tapay-Szabo, Gabriella
     see Szabo, Gabriella.

4PN   **Tápay-Szabó, László,** 1877– *1941.*
1047   Az amerikai sajtó szabadsága. Budapest,
     1929.
     80 p.

NT 0035296   DLC-P4

Tápay-Szabó, László, 1877–
     A bolsevizmus Magyarországon a proletár-
diktatura okirataiból. Irta Dʳ Szabó
László. Budapest, Az Athenaeum irodalmi
és nyomdai r.-t. kiadása, 1919.
     240 p. 15½cm.

NT 0035297   MH-L

Tápay-Szabó, László, 1877-1941.
     Csokanai; regényes életrajz. Budapest,
Dante Könyvkiadó ₍c1941₎
     335 p. plates, ports.

     1. Csokanai Vitéz, Mihály, 1773-1805 -
Fiction. I. Title.

NT 0035298   NNC

Tápay-Szabó, László, 1877-1941.
     Documents secrets de la propagande bolchéviste, publiés par
Dʳ Ladislas Szabó. Berne: F. Wyss, 1920. 54 p. 8°.

     1. Hungary.—History, 1918-19.   2. Bolshevism, Hungary.
N. Y. P. L.   November 1, 1921.

NT 0035299   NN CSt-H CU

Tápay-Szabó, László, 1877–1941.
     Irredenták; drámai költemény két felvonásban. Buda-
pest, Budapesti Hirlap, 1923.
     148 p. 18 cm.
     L. C. copy replaced by microfilm.
               Microfilm 28775 PH

     I. Title.
     [PH3351.T34 I 7]   77-255208

NT 0035300   DLC

Tápay-SZABÓ, LÁSZLÓ, 1877–
    Jókai élete és müvei [Budapest] Rákosi
J., 1904.
    367 p. illus., ports., facsims.

1. Jókai, Mór, 1825-1904.

NT 0035301 InU NNC MH

Tápay-Szabó, László, 1877- 1941.
V15
M213   Magyar Balázs hadjárata Veglia szigetén, irt
v.4   dr. Szabó László. Budapest, a Magyar Adria
    egyesület kiadása, 1915.

    47 p. 17°. (On cover: Magyar Adria könyv-
tár, szerkeszti Gonda Béla, 1. szorozat, 4)
    "Jegyzetek": p.[45]-47.

1.Veglia (island). I.Title.

NT 0035302 CSt-H

PH
3351
.T34   Tápay-Szabó, László, 1877-1941.
M3   Magyar hibák - magyar gondok. Budapest,
    Athenaeum [pref. 1927]
    204 p.

    At head of title: Szabó László.

NT 0035303 NNC

Tápay-Szabó, László, 1877–
    ... Meraviglie nel corso dei secoli, con 41 tavole in nero e a
colori. [Milano] Genio [1943]
    2 p. l., 9–118 p. illus., plates (part col., part double) diagrs. 32ᶜᵐ.
    "Traduzione dall' ungherese di Filippo Faber."

    1. Architecture, Ancient. 2. Wonders.   ɪ. Faber, Filippo, tr.
    ɪɪ. Title.
    NA210.T35   **47–33694**

NT 0035304 DLC

Tápay-Szabó, László, 1877-1941.
    Mi okozta az összeomlást és a forradalmakat?
Hadvezérek, államférfiak és diplomaták emlék-
iratai nyomán. Budapest, Athenaeum, 1922.
    158 p. 23 cm.

NT 0035305 NNC DLC-P4 MH

Tápay-Szabó, László, 1877-1941.
    A modern ujságirás. Budapest, Dick
Manó, [1916]
    221 p. 20 cm.
    1. Journalism. I. Title.

NT 0035306 NNC OC1 MH

Tápay-Szabó, László, 1877-1941. Aus 88036.5
    [Szeged halála és feltamadása; az 1879. évi árviz
és a város ujjáépitésének története. Szeged, A
Délmagyararország Hirlap, 1929

    3 v. illus.

1. Floods - Szeged, 1879

NT 0035307 MH

PH
3351
.T34   Tápay-Szabó, László, 1877-1941.
S9   Szegény ember gazdag élete; Szabó László emlé-
    kezései. Budapest, Athenaeum, 1928.
    2 v. plates, ports.

    Autobiographical.

NT 0035308 NNC InU

Tape, Gerald Frederick, 1915–
    Beta-spectra of iodine, by Gerald F. Tape ... [Lancaster,
Pa., Lancaster press, inc., 1939]
    1 p. l., 965–971 p. diagrs. 26½ x 20ᶜᵐ.
    Thesis (ᴘʜ. ᴅ.)—University of Michigan, 1940.
    "Reprinted from the Physical review, vol. 56, no. 10, November 15,
1939."

    1. Spectrum analysis. 2. Iodine.   ɪ. Title.

    Michigan. Univ. Library   A 42–4534
    for Library of Congress   QC462.I 6T3

NT 0035309 MiU MH DLC

Tape, Gerald Frederick, 1915–
    University of Illinois cyclotron oscillator. Office of Naval
Research. Task contract N6ori–71 T. O. 1. Urbana [1950]
    27 l. illus., diagrs. 28 cm. (Illinois. University. Dept. of Phy-
sics. Technical report no. 1)

    1. Oscillators. 2. Cyclotron.   (Series)

                               A 52–9524
    Illinois. Univ. Library
    for Library of Congress   [1]

NT 0035310 IU

Tape, Henry Aaron, 1889–
    Factors affecting turnover of teachers of the one-room rural
schools of Michigan, by Henry Aaron Tape, ᴘʜ. ᴅ. ... New
York, Teachers college, Columbia university, 1939.
    vii, 85 p. incl. illus. (map) tables, forms. 23ᶜᵐ. (Teachers college,
Columbia university. Contributions to education, no. 773)
    Issued also as thesis (ᴘʜ. ᴅ.) Columbia university.
    Bibliography : p. 73.

    1. Teachers—Michigan. 2. Rural schools—Michigan.   ɪ. Title.
    ɪɪ. Title : Turnover of teachers of the one-room rural schools of Michigan.

    Library of Congress   LB1567.T17 1939 a   39–22268
    ———— Copy 2.   LB5.C8   no. 773
    Copyright A 131307   [8]   371.140977

    PSt OCU OU ViU NNC NcU
NT 0035311   DLC WaTU MtU PU-Penn OrU PBm PPT KEmT

Tape, Rollo, pseud.
    see   Wyckoff, Richard Demille, 1873–
1935.

Tape and wire recording
    see under   Radio Constructor.

---

*8010A
.305   Tape recording. v. 2, no. 2-
    Jan./Feb. 1955-
    [Washington, etc., Mechanization, Inc., etc.,
    1955-
        v. illus. 29cm.
    Bimonthly, Jan./Feb. 1955-Sept./Oct. 1956;
    monthly, Dec. 1956-
    Title varies: 1955-Sept./Oct. 1956, Magnetic
    film & tape recording. Dec. 1956-Mar. 1960,
    Hi-fi tape recording.
    1. Magnetic recorders and recording—Period.
    2. Periodicals, English. I. Title: Magnetic
    film & tape   recording. II.Title:
    Hi-fi tape   recording.

NT 0035314 MB

Tape recording in the classroom
    see under   [Minnesota Mining and
    Manufacturing Company]

789.9   Tape topics. v.1-   1951-   Dallas,
T16   Tex., World Tapes for Education, inc., 1951-
        v. illus. 28 cm.
    Some issues include Roster of World Tapes
    for Education members
    Earlier volumes issued by World Tapes under
    earlier name: World Tape Pals
    1.Phonotapes in education—Period
    2.Phonotapes—Period I.World Tapes for
    Education, inc

NT 0035316 LU

Tapella, Omar.
    Extraviadas en su luz. [Novela] Montevideo, Fonta-
nillas y González, Impresores [1947]
    277 p. 20 cm.

    ɪ. Title.
                               A 52–3649
    New York. Public Libr.
    for Library of Congress   [1]

NT 0035317 NN TxU DPU IU

Tapella, Omar.
    ... Humanismo!! El nuevo orden de un ingenuo soñador
reflejos de algunas inquietudes y angustias de esta época
Montevideo, Talleres gráficos "33" s. l., 1943.
    146 p., 1 l. 21ᶜᵐ.
    "Esta trabajo fué premiado en el Concurso de remuneración a la
labor literaria de 1942 por el jurado del Ministerio de instrucción pública
y previsión social."

    ɪ. Title.
                               A 45–4755
    New York. Public library
    for Library of Congress   [2]

NT 0035318 NN MoU

G868.83
T1615n   Tapella, Omar.
    Nuestro vivir torturado; esbozo de una patología
    de la personalidad. [Narración novelada] Monte-
    video, Imp. Fontanillas, 1945.
    175p. illus. 20cm.

NT 0035319 TxU MoU

W
1045   Tapella, Pedro A
T175a   Antecedentes, títulos y trabajos.
1944   Buenos Aires, López, 1944.
    14 p. 23 cm.

NT 0035320 DNLM

Tapella, Pedro A
    ... Introducción al estudio de la alergia. B[ueno]s A[ire]s,
A. López, 1941.
    265, [1] p. illus. (incl. map) diagrs. 23½ᶜᵐ.
    "Bibliografía" at end of each chapter.

    1. Allergia.
                              43–43429
    Library of Congress   RC48.T3
                      [2]   615.37

NT 0035321 DLC DNLM

Tapella, Pedro A
... Tratado de cardioangiología. Buenos Aires, Lopez & Etchegoyen, 1946.
xiii, 946 p. illus. 26½ᵐ.
Contains author's signature.

1. Heart—Diseases. 2. Vascular system—Diseases. ₍2. Cardiovascular system—Diseases₎

Med 47–543

U. S. Army medical library   [WG140qT172t 1946]
for Library of Congress   ₍4₎

NT 0035322   DNLM PPC

Tapenius (Carl Nils Anders). *Historiskt-nosographiska anmärkningar om elephantiasis nodosa.* 60 pp. 8°. *Helsingfors, J. C. Frenckell & Son.* 1840.

NT 0035323   DNLM

Taper, *pseud.*
see
Noskowski, Witold.

Taper sleeve pulley works.
Catalogue. The Taper-sleeve pulley works, manufacturers of patent wood pulleys, and shafting, hangers, pillow blocks, journal boxes, shaft couplings. Erie, Penn'a, U. S. A. ₍Erie, Pa., Dispatch printing co.,ⁿ 1889₎
32 p. illus. 23ᵐ.

1. Pulleys. 2. Machinery—Catalogs.

Library of Congress   TJ1103.T17   6–34159†

NT 0035325   DLC

Taperell, H. J., joint author.

HD8858
.R7
Roydhouse, Thomas Richard, 1862–
The Labour party in New South Wales; a history of its formation and legislative career ... with biographies of the members, and the complete text of the Trade disputes conciliation and arbitration act, 1892, by Thomas R. Roydhouse and H. J. Taperell. London, S. Sonnenschein & co.; ₍etc., etc.₎ 1892.

Taperell, John, 1710–
A new miscellany: containing The art of conversation, and several other subjects. By John Taperell... London, Printed for the author, 1731.
40 p.   22 cm.

NT 0035327   CtY

Taperell, John, 1710–
A new miscellany. Containing several subjects in verse, and the same in prose, in imitation of sermons. On swearing... divine love,... the prodigal son... ₍etc.₎ By John Taperell, gent. ... London, Printed for the author, 1763.
iv, 92 p.   22.5 cm.

NT 0035328   CtY

Taperell, John, 1710–
Poems on several occasions... Together with some short rules for conversation. The second ed. Vol. 1, ... By John Taperell, Gent. Sometime student of the University of Oxford. London, Printed for E. Withers, 1750.

NT 0035329   DFo MH

Taperell, John, 1710–
Swearing: A satire... London, 1751.
23 p. 8°. (In "Poems," 3)

NT 0035330   CtY

Map
G
5744
L6
ca. 1560
Taperell, Nicholas.
The ancient cities of London and Westminster in the early part of the reign of Queen Elizabeth. London, 1849.
map 75 x 188 cm.
No scale given.
"This map, after a lengthened and careful investigation of historical works, ancient records, &c. was redrawn and published in the year 1849..."

1. Lond on--Maps.

NT 0035331   NIC

RA427
.R55
Tapernoux, Armand, ₍joint author.
1899–
Rochaix, Anthelme, 1881–
Hygiène des milieux ruraux; hygiène publique et sociale, par mm. les professeurs A. Rochaix ... ₍et₎ A. Tapernoux ... avec 38 figures et 3 planches hors texte. Paris, Vigot frères; ₍etc., etc.₎ 1943.

SF251
.R6
Tapernoux, Armand, ₍joint author.
1899–
Rochaix, Anthelme, 1881–
Le lait et ses dérivés: chimie, bactériologie, hygiène, par mm. les professeurs A. Rochaix ... ₍et₎ A. Tapernoux ... Avec 56 figures. Paris, Vigot frères; Lyon, Librairie médicale, 1942.

Tapernoux, Armand, 1899–
... Les relations entre l'acidité potentielle et l'acidité actuelle du lait... Ambilly-Annemasse [1928]
Thèse - Univ. de Lyon.
"Bibliographie": p. [79]–81.
Pamphlet.

NT 0035334   CtY

Tapernoux, Benjamin.
...Les cartels... St. Maurice: Imprimerie de l'Œuvre St. Augustin, 1929.   277 p.   8°.
Dissertation, Lausanne, 1929.
Bibliography, p. ₍270-₎273.

483812A. 1. Cartels—Jurisp.
N. Y. P. L.   September 24, 1930

NT 0035335   NN CU-L KU PU MH

Tapernoux, Marc.
Le chèque barré. St-Maurice, 1930.
108 p.   24 cm.
Thèse—Lausanne.
Bibliography: p. ₍194₎–108.

1. Checks.   I. Title.

66–50414

NT 0035336   DLC NN CtY PU

TAPERNOUX, Ph.
La neutralité de la Suisse et la guerre en Italie. Bruxelles, impr. de A. Labroue et comp., 1859.

Pamphlet.

NT 0035337   MH

Tapernoux, Pierre Marc.
The food-situation of the world. Zürich, IUL, 1947.
135 p.   32 cm.
At head of title: International Union of Federation of Workers in the Food and Drink Trades.
In English, Swedish, French, and German.

1. Food supply.   I. International Union of Food and Drink Workers' Associations.   II. Title.

HD9000.5.T27   56–37262

NT 0035338   DLC MH

NK
3042
.T17
The TAPESTRIES of the Vienna imperial court. Vienna, Krystallverlag ges. m. b. h., 1922.
20p., 2ℓ., XLIV plates (part col.)   30ᶜm.
Each colored plate accompanied by guard sheet with descriptive letterpress.
The Vienna collection of tapestries by H. Schmitz: p.[3]–13.
The Boucher gobelins and the meuble rose in the Viennese imperial palace, by Edmund Wilhelm Braun: p.[15]–20.
The plates, with brief descriptions, were selected from Ludwig Baldass, Die Wiener Gobelinsammlung. Wien, 1920.
1. Tapestry – Vienna. I. Schmitz, Hermann, 1882– II. Braun, Edmund Wilhelm, 1870–

CSt NBuG DI–GS
NT 0035339   TxU MiU MH MiD GU OClW InU NjP NcD CU DI

Tapestry; a magazine of verse.
Flint, Mich., Flint poetry forum
v. in   28½ᵐ.   quarterly.
Reproduced from type-written copy.

1. Poetry—Period.   I. Flint poetry forum, Flint, Mich.
45–50260

Library of Congress   PS301.T3
₍2₎   811.005

NT 0035340   DLC NN

The tapestry hangings of the House of lords: representing the several engagements between the English and Spanish fleets, in the ever memorable year MDLXXXVIII, with the portraits of the Lord High-Admiral, and the other noble commanders, taken from the life
see under   [Morant, Philip] 1700–1770.

Tapestry monographs.
no.
London: Oxford Univ. Press, 193   23cm.
v.   plates.

NT 0035342   NN

746.3
T16
v
over-
size
The tapestry of Bayeux. New York, Pageant Book Co. ₍n.d.₎
cover-title, ₍32₎ col plates.   66 x 49cm.
Loose leaf.

1. Bayeux   tapestry

NT 0035343   ViW DeU

Z
1746
B341
195-

The Tapestry of Bayeux. New York, Pageant
Book Co. [195-]
17 col. plates (in portfolio) 67cm.

Cover title.

1. Bayeux tapestry.

NT 0035344   TxU MiU NN

Tapestry or dye painting. 12 pp. Plates.   *5002.45.1
(In Art work manuals. Vol. 1, no. 2. New York. 1882.)
The title is on the cover.

K8443 — Tapestry. — Dyeing and dyestuffs.

NT 0035345   MB

The tapestry weavers [1883]
     see under [Chester, Anson Gleason]

The tapestry weavers [and other poems] New York,
J. Pott and company, 1900.
32 p. col. front. 19½ᶜᵐ.
     3-13557

NT 0035347   DLC RPB ViU

Tapetes de punto. Madrid, Publicaciones "Knitted" [1935]
cover-title, 32 p. illus. 27 x 21½ᶜᵐ.

1. Knitting.
     36-30481
Library of Congress   TT825.T3
   [2]   646.26

NT 0035348   DLC

Die tapezierkunst. Vorlagen fuer decoration und moeblirung moderner herren- und damenzimmer, salons, schlafzimmer, arbeitszimmer, erker u. s. f. in allen stilen. Berlin, E. Wasmuth, 1895.
[9] p. 80 (i. e. 77) col. pl. (part fold.) 49½ᶜᵐ.
Issued in 10 parts, 1887-95.
In 3 portfolios.

1. House decoration. 2. Upholstery. 3. Furniture. 4. Wall-paper.
Library of Congress   NK2130.T2
     10-4107

NT 0035349   DLC PP IEN MiGr OCl PPPM ICJ

Tapfer, Francesch Antoni.
Ina fideivla memoria dil Antoni Tapfer;
translatada ord' il Tudestg. Cuera, 1835.
24 p. 24°.
Contains a biographical notice of Tapfer, and
his "Devotiun della messa".

NT 0035350   NIC

Business
HB
87
.T16

Tapfer, Friederike, 1927-
Der wirtschaftspolitische Beitrag der
Klassik; Versuch einer neuen Würdigung.
1954.
157 p.

Thesis, Erlangen.
Published also without thesis note.
Bibliography: p. [153]-157.

NT 0035351   NNC

Tapfer, Friedrich Wilhelm
     see Tapfer, Wilhelm.

Tapfer (Renée) [1903-]. *Contribution à
l'étude du syndrome de Van der Hoeve. 36
pp. 8°. Paris. 1927. No. 440.

NT 0035353   DNLM CtY

Tapfer, Siegfried, 1900-
Die hormonale steuerung der geburt, von prof. dr. Siegfried Tapfer ... Mit 65 abbildungen im text. Berlin und Wien, Urban & Schwarzenberg, 1944.

viii, 108 p. illus., diagrs. 24½ cm. (Added t.-p.: Einzelschriften zur frauenheilkunde, hrsg. von prof. dr. A. I. Amreich ... Bd. 1)
"Schrifttum": p. 98-108.

1. Labor (Obstetrics) 2. Hormones.
RG669.T3   A F 47-6102
Minnesota. Univ. Libr.
for Library of Congress   [1]†

IaU NbU MiU DLC
NT 0035354   MnU InLP MdBJ CtY DNLM NNC IU ViU CoU

Tapfer, Siegfried, 1900-
Typische gynäkologische Operationen unter besonderer Berücksichtigung technischer Vorteile. München, Urban & Schwarzenberg, 1952.
57 p. illus. 32 cm.

1. Gynecology, Operative.   I. Title.
RG104.T3   618.1   53-15448 ‡

NT 0035355   DLC ICU DNLM

TAPFER, W(ilhelm)
Die deutschen Privat-Stadtposten. o. O. (1906
Königsberg, Phil. Diss.

NT 0035356   MH PU CtY NN ICRL

Das tapfere Schneiderlein
     see under [Grimm, Jakob Ludwig Karl]
1785-1863.

Lilly
DL 703
.T172
1698

DER TAPFERE UND VERLIEBTE GUSTAV VON VASA :
oder, Die Wunderwerck der Liebe an den nordischen Höfen ... : aus den [sic] Französischen übersetzt. -- Franckfurt und Leipzig : R. J. Helmers, 1698.
317 p., [1] leaf of plates : front. (port.)
; 8vo (16 cm)

In yellow boards, all edges sprinkled.

1. Gustaf I Vasa, King of Sweden, 1496-1560.
I. Title: Die   Wunderwerck der Liebe an
den Nordischen   Höfen.

NT 0035358   InU NjP

Tapfers Herze; alte und neue Kriegslieder für
Schulen
     see under Dresdner Gesanglehrer-Verein.

Tapfort, pseud.
Le succès... par Tapfort. [Paris: Éditions Gulliver, 1935]
280 p. nar. 8°.
Cover-title.

NT 0035360   NN

DC
135
.L12
T17

Taphanel, Achille.
La Beaumelle et Saint-Cyr d'après des
correspondances inédites et des documents
nouveaux. Paris, Plon, Nourrit, 1898.
viii, 425 p. front.

1. La Beaumelle, Laurent Angliviel de, 1726-1773. 2. Saint-Cyr, France (Seine-et-Oise)
Maison royale de Saint Louis.

NT 0035361   MiU LU CSt NcD TNJ CU

Taphanel, Achille, ed.
Mémoires de Manseau, intendant de la Maison
royale de Saint-Cyr
     see under Manseau,

Taphanel, Achille.
Le théâtre de Saint-Cyr (1689-1792) d'après des documents inédits ... Avec une eau-forte de Ch. Waltner. Versailles, Cerf et fils; Paris, J. Baudry, 1876.
xi, 288 p. front. (port.) plan. 8°.

     1-F-3808
NjP
NT 0035363   DLC GU FU PU NmU CtY OU CU NcU NN MH MB

PN
2636
S3
T3
1882

Taphanel, Achille
Le théâtre de Saint-Cyr (1689-1792) d'après
des documents inédits. Avec une eau-forte de
Ch. Waltner. Paris, L. Cerf, 1882.
288p. port. 22cm.
Bibliographical footnotes.

1. Saint Cyr, France (Seine-et-Oise) Théâtre de Saint-Cyr 2. Saint Cyr, France (Seine-et-Oise) Maison royale de Saint Louis I. Title

NT 0035364   WU MiU

Taphanel, Benoit Robin
     see Robin-Taphanel, Benoit.

Taphanel (Édouard) [1884-]. *Les cas
de fièvre de Malte contractés à Paris et dans la
région parisienne. 72 pp. 8°. Paris, 1910.
No. 455.

NT 0035366   DNLM

Taphanel (Henri Dominique) [1886-]. *Syphilis et eczéma. 61 pp. 8°. Paris, 1913.
No. 321.

NT 0035367   DNLM CtY

Taphoureau-Launay, *Mme. L.*
Coupe et confection, par Mᵐᵉ L. Taphoureau-Launay ...
311 gravures dont 160 modèles de patrons. Paris, Larousse [*1913]
256 p. illus. 20½ᶜᵐ. fr. 3
"La mode féminine à travers les ages": p. [234]-253.

1. Garment cutting. 2. Dressmaking. 3. Costume.
     14-596
Library of Congress   TT515.T3

NT 0035368   DLC ICJ

Taphouse, Thomas William, 1838–1905.
    Catalogue of the valuable and interesting musical library, consisting of ancient and modern printed music, musical manuscripts, and collections of the late T. W. Taphouse...(late mayor of Oxford). /Which will be sold by auction...by Messrs. Sotheby, Wilkinson & Hodge...on Monday, the 3rd of July, 1905 and following day...   London: J. Davy & Sons [1905].   1 p.l., 87 p.   8°.

1. Music.—Bibliography.
N. Y. P. L.   January 8, 1916.

NT   0035369   NN ViU IaU CtY CU CSmH

Taphouse, Thomas William, 1838–1905.
    ... The musical library of Mr. T. W. Taphouse
        see under title

Tapi en turapa
        see under   [Gulick, Louisa (Lewis)]

ML
423   **Tapia, A   G**
G17   Manuel Garcia; su influencia en el laringologia y en el arte del canto. Madrid, Imprenta y Librería de Nicolas Moya, 1905.
1905   225 p.   illus..facsims..music.ports.
        Bibliography: [p.229-230]

    1.Garcia,Manuel,1805-1906.   2.Singing.

NT   0035372   NSyU

Tapia, Alejandro
        see
    Tapia y Rivera, Alejandro, 1826–1882.

Tapia, Ambrosio
        see
    Tapia y Gil, Ambrosio.

Tapia, Andrés de.
    Relacion sobre la conquista de México.
    41 p.   (Icazbalceta, J.G., Col. de documentos para hist. de México, v. 2, p. 554)

NT   0035375   MdBP

Tapia (Antonio A.) * Reflexiones sobre algunos articulos del titulo ii del Código penal. 40 pp., port. 8°. *México, F. R. Blanco.* 1877.

NT   0035376   DNLM

Tapia, Antonio García
        see   **García Tapia, Antonio.**

4HF-   **Tápi, Antonio M**
196   Nociones de teneduria de libros por partida doble. 3. edicion corregida y aumentada. Mexico, Antigua Impr. de E. Murgia, 1896.
        2 v. in 1.

NT   0035378   DLC-P4

Tapia, Atilio Sivirichi
        see   **Sivirichi Tapia, Atilio.**

Tapia, Atols
He96A   Tres cruces; cuentos. Buenos Aires, Seijas
T162   y Gaynnarte [1954]
T6   97 p.   20 cm. (Autores hispano americanos, 3)

NT   0035380   CtY

Tapia, Augusto.
    ... Las cavernas de Ojo de Agua y Las Hachas; historia geológica de la región de La Brava en relación con la existencia del hombre prehistórico, por Augusto Tapia. Buenos Aires, 1937.
    122, [4] p. illus., xxvi pl., maps, tables, profiles. 27ᶜᵐ. (Argentine republic. Dirección de minas y geología. Boletín nᵒ 43)
    At head of title: República argentina. Ministerio de agricultura de la nación. Dirección de minas y geología.
    Part of the illustrative matter is folded, part in pocket. Each plate accompanied by leaf with descriptive letterpress.
    "Obras citadas": p. [123]-[124]

    1. Caves—Argentine republic. 2. Geology—Argentine republic—La Brava. 3. Man, Prehistoric—Argentine republic.
    QE231.A3 no. 43   G S 38–272 †
    U. S. Geol. survey. Library
    for Library of Congress   [a47d1]†

NT   0035381   DI-GS CU ViU DLC MtBuM

QE231   **Tapia, Augusto.**
.A35
no. 25-26   **Gröber, Paul, 1885-**
    ... Condiciones geológicas de la quebrada de Ullún en relación con un proyectado dique de embalse (provincia de San Juan) Por Pablo Groeber y Augusto Tapia ... Buenos Aires, Talleres gráficos del Ministerio de agricultura de la nación, 1926.

Tapia, Augusto.
    ... Condiciones hidrogeológicas de los campos de la "S. A. Estancias y colonias Trenel" territorio nacional de la Pampa, por Augusto Tapia. Buenos Aires, Talleres gráficos del Ministerio de agricultura de la nación, 1930.
    27 p. incl. tables. iv fold. pl. (3 plans, profile) 26½ᶜᵐ. ([Argentine republic] Dirección general de minas, geología e hidrología. Publicación no. 91)
    At head of title: República argentina. Ministerio de agricultura de la nación.

    1. Water-supply—Argentine republic.   I. Title.
                                        G S 31–147
    Library, U. S. Geological   Survey (420) P no. 91
    Library of Congress   [QE231.A35 no. 91]

NT   0035383   DI-GS MtBuM TxU MB ICU

Tapia, Augusto.
    ... Geología del Paso de las Carretas y sus alrededores relacionada con la construcción de un dique de embalse. Parte general por Augusto Tapia. Parte especial por Remigio Rigal. Con 3 figuras y 16 láminas ... Buenos Aires, 1933.
    56 p. illus., xvi pl. (part fold.: incl. maps) 26½ cm. (Argentine republic. Direccion de minas y geología. Boletín nᵒ 37)
    At head of title: Republica argentina. Ministerio de agricultura de la nación. Dirección de minas y geología.
    Each plate accompanied by leaf with outline drawing.
    "Bibliografía": p. 55–56.

    1. Geology—Argentine republic. 2. Dams. 3. Quinto river.
    I. Rigal, Remigio.
    QE231.A3 no. 37   G S 34–77 rev
    U. S. Geol. Survey. Libr.
    for Library of Congress   [r48d1]†

NT   0035384   DI-GS CU DLC MtBuM

Tapia, Augusto.
    ... Lugar favorable para el empotramiento de un dique de embalse en el curso superior del río San Juan, "Las Juntas," por Augusto Tapia y Remigio Rigal ... Con 12 láminas ... Buenos Aires, Talleres gráficos del Ministerio de agricultura de la nación, 1933.
    15 p. xiii pl. (incl. fold. map, fold. profile) 26ᶜᵐ. (Argentine republic. Dirección de minas y geología. Boletín nᵒ 35)
    At head of title: República argentina. Ministerio de agricultura de la nación. Dirección de minas y geología ...
    "Bibliografía": p. 15.

    • 1. Dams. 2. San Juan river, Argentine republic. I. Rigal, Remigio, joint author.
    QE231.A3 no. 35   G S 34–78
    U. S. Geol. survey. Library
    for Library of Congress   [a47c1]†

NT   0035385   DI-GS MtBuM CU MB DLC

Tapia, Augusto.
    ... Pilcomayo, contribución al conocimiento de las llanuras argentinas, por Augusto Tapia. Con 13 láminas, 3 planos, 7 croquis y 26 perfiles. Buenos Aires, 1935.
    124 p. illus., xiii pl., maps, profiles. 27 cm. (Argentine republic. Dirección de minas y geología. Boletín nᵒ 40)
    At head of title: República argentina. Ministerio de agricultura de la nación. Dirección de minas y geología ...
    Part of the illustrative matter is folded.
    "Obras citadas": p. [119]-124.

    1. Physical geography—Argentine republic. 2. Pilcomayo river.
    3. Geology—Argentine republic. 4. Pampas.
    QE231.A3 no. 40   G S 36–56 rev
                        (558.2) 551.0982
    ——— Copy 2.   GB151.T3
    U. S. Geol. survey. Library
    for Library of Congress   [r47d1]†

NT   0035386   DI-GS MtBuM CU DLC

Tapia, Augusto.
    ... Sobre los rasgos principales de la glaciacion actual en la Isla Laurie (Archipiélago de las Orcadas del Sur), por Augusto Tapia ... Buenos Aires, Talleres gráficos del Ministerio de agricultura de la nación, 1925.
    36 p. 7 pl. (incl. fold. map) 26ᶜᵐ. ([Argentine Republic] Dirección general de minas, geología e hidrología. (Sección: Geología) Publicación no. 7)
    At head of title: República Argentina. Ministerio de agricultura de la nación.
    "Bibliografía": p. 35–36.
    1. Glaciers—Laurie Islands, South Orkneys. I. Title.
                                        G S 25–461
    Library, U. S. Geological'   Survey (420) P no. 7

NT   0035387   DI-GS MtBuM TxU OU

Tapia, Bartolomé de
    Breve reflexión jurídica por don Pedro Phelipe de Padilla Pacheco ... en el pleyto, que en el grado segundo de suplicación, tiene pendiente en el consejo, con Don Luis Gabriel Lopez Hogazon ... [s.l. : s.n., ca. 1710?].
    14 [leaves ; fol.(28.8 cm.)

    Typesigned at end: Lic. D. Bartolomé de Tapia.
    Approximate imprint date implied from first instance case of Nava Noroña, Nicolás Félix de. Por don Pedro   Phelipe de Padilla Pacheco ... Lilly/
    Disbound.

NT   0035388   InU

Tapia, Carlo de, marquis de Bellomonte
    Caroli Tapiae jureconsulti [de religiosis rebus tractatus in authan. ingressi, c.de sacros. eccles... Neapoli, ex Typographia Stelliolae, 1594.
    4p.l.,539,[49]p.incl.port. 20.5cm.

NT   0035389   NNUT

Tapia, Carlo de, marquis de Bellomonte.
    Decisiones sacri neapolitani concilii. Neapoli, 1629.

NT   0035390   MH-L

Tapia, Carlos, appellee.

    U. S. *Dept. of justice.*
    ... The People of Porto Rico, Epifanio Mesa, and Alvaro Padial, appellants, v. Carlos Tapia. Appeal from the District court of the United States for the district of Porto Rico. The People of Porto Rico and Charles E. Foote, judge of the District court of Mayaguez, plaintiffs in error, v. Jose Muratti. In error and on writ of certiorari to the Supreme court of Porto Rico. Brief for the People of Porto Rico. Washington, Govt. print. off., 1918.

Tapia, Carlos.
    Tablas de logaritmos y naturales. La Paz, Bolivia, Editorial U. M. S. A. [1952]
    56, [158] p. 19 cm.

    1. Logarithms. 2. Mathematics—Tables, etc.   I. Title.
    QA55.T2   54–29991 ‡

NT   0035392   DLC

Tapia, Daniel
see Tapia Bolívar, Daniel.

Tapia, Diego de.
Confessonario en lengua cumanagota, y de otras Naciones de Indios de la Provincia de Cumaná, con vnas Advertencias previas al Confessonario para los Confessores. Por fray Diego de Tapia, indigno Frayle Menor, Hijo de la Santa Recoleccion de la Provincia de Sevilla, y Missionario Apostolico en las vivas Conversiones de Piritu ... Madrid, P. Fernandez, 1723.
19 p. l., 732 (i. e. 728) p. 15cm.
Signatures ¶-¶¶¶, A-Z, Aa-Zz in eights, except ¶¶¶ and Zz, which are in fours (nos. 582-585 omitted in paging)

The second preliminary leaf, an engraving of the "Virgen de los milagros," is wanting in this copy.
"Advertencias previas": p. 1-238.
p. 239-456: "Platica, en que se enseña a los Indios el modo de confessarse, y se les amonesta, que no callen pecado alguno en la Confession, y para esto se pone vn exemplo" (in Spanish and Cumana) Reprinted in facsimile in 1888 by Dr. Julius Platzmann, as v. 4 of "Algunas obras raras sobre la lengua cumanagota," under title: Confessonario mas lato en lengua cumanagota ...
p. 457-696: "Confessonario mas breve. Introduccion a la Confession" (in Spanish and Cumana) Reprinted in facsimile in 1885, by Dr. Julius Platzmann, as v. 5 of "Algunas obras raras sobre la lengua cumanagota."

4-8654†

NT 0035395   DLC RPJCB

Tapia, Diego de.
Confessonario mas breve en lengua cumanagota por fr. Diego de Tapia, publicado de nuevo por Julio Platzmann. Edicion facsimilar. Leipzig, B. G. Teubner, 1888.
4 p. l., 236 p. 23cm. (Added t.-p.: Algunas obras raras sobre la lengua cumanatoga, publicadas de nuevo por Julio Platzmann. Vol. v)
"Este Confessonario mas breve ocupa las páginas 457 hasta 696 del original (i. e. the author's Confessonario en lengua cumanagota, y de otras naciones de Indios de la provincia de Cumaná, con vnas advertencias previas al Confessonario para los confessores ... Por fray Diego de Tapia ... Madrid, P. Fernandez, 1723; Véase Ch. Leclerc, Bibliotheca americana, Paris, 1878, no. 2201. La reproduccion del texto es rigorosamente facsimilar fuera de la foliatura y de las signaturas de los pliegos, que comienzan de nuevo, conservándose la pagination (!) antigua abajo en paréntesis."—Advertencia.
The "Confessonario mas lato" (p. 239-456 of the original) forms v. 4 of this series.
1. Cumana language—Texts.   I. *Platzmann, Julius, 1832-1902, ed.
II. Catholic church. Liturgy and ritual. Cumana.   III. Title.

3-30413 Revised

Library of Congress   PM5876.T25

NT 0035397   DLC PU-Mu TxU NN

Tapia, Diego de.
Confessonario mas lato en lengua cumanagota por fr. Diego de Tapia, pub. de nuevo por Julio Platzmann. Edicion facsimilar. Leipzig, B. G. Teubner, 1888.
4 p. l., 218 p. 23cm. (Added t.-p.: Algunas obras raras sobre la lengua cumanagota, publicadas de nuevo por Julio Platzmann. vol. IV)
Caption title: Platica, en que se enseña a los Indios el modo de confessarse, y se les amonesta, que no callen pecado alguno en la confession, y para esto se pone vn exemplo.

"Este Confessonario mas lato ocupa las páginas 239 hasta 456 del original (i. e. Confessonario en lengua cumanagota, y de otras naciones de Indios de la provincia de Cumaná, con vnas advertencias previas al Confessonario para los confessores ... Por fray Diego de Tapia ... Madrid, P. Fernandez, 1723; Véase Ch. Leclerc, Bibliotheca americana, Paris, 1878, no. 2201. La reproducción del texto es rigorosamente facsimilar fuera de la foliatura y de las signaturas de los pliegos, que comienzan de nuevo, conservándose la pagination (!) antigua abajo en paréntesis."—Advertencia.
The "Confessonario mas breve" (p. 457-696 of the original) forms v. 5 of this series.
1. Cumana language—Texts.   I. *Platzmann, Julius, 1832-1902, ed.
II. Catholic church. Liturgy and ritual. Cumana.   III. Title.

3—30414

Library of Congress   PM5876.T27

NT 0035399   DLC PU-Mu NN NNH

Tapia, Donato Guevara
see Guevara Tapia, Donato.

Tapia, Eduardo Mendoza
see Mendoza Tapia, Eduardo.

Tapia, Ernesto Ochoa y
see Ochoa y Tapia, Ernesto.

Tapia, Esteban de
see
Tapia y Paredes, Esteban, 1560 (ca.)-1604.

Tapia, Esteban Pichardo y
see Pichardo y Tapia, Esteban, 1799-1879.

PQ
6226
.T4
v.52

Tapia, Eugenio de, 1776-1860.
La Acelina; en tres actos por D. E. T. Madrid, B. García, 1800.
255-334 p. (In Teatro español. ¡Madrid, etc., 1787-1935¡ v. 52, ¡2¡)
Detached from a collection.

NT 0035405   MiEM OO

834H36
OrFr

Tapia, Eugenio de, 1776-1860.
La bruja, el duende y la inquisición; poema romántico-burlesco, y otras composiciones satíricas. 2.ed. Madrid, Impr. de Yenes, 1841.
58p. illus. 16cm.
Bound with Heine, Henrich. Intermezzo. Paris, 1857.

NT 0035406   IU

Tapia, Eugenio de , 1776-1860
La bruja; the witch; or, A picture of the court of Rome; found among the manuscripts of a respectable theologian... tr. from the Spanish by Markophrates, ¡pseud.¡ Lond. 1840.
188 p.

NT 0035407   OCl

Tapi, Eugenio de, 1776-1860.
Discurso histórico-crítico, sobre la decadencia del imperio musulman en España, y las causas que retardaron en la monarquia castellana los progresos de la restauracion y de las letras hasta el siglo XIII ... Madrid, Impr. de Yenes, 1838.
62 p.
Cover-title: La decadencia musulman en España.

NT 0035408   WaPS

Tapia, Eugenio de, 1776-1860.
Dupont rendido. Romance heroico, por Don Eugenio Tapia... ¡Madrid? 1808?¡ 6 p. 18½cm.
Caption-title.

1. Poetry, Spanish. 2. Bailen, de l'Etang, Pierre Antoine, comte, N. Y. P. L.   Battle of, 1808—Poetry. 3. Dupont 1765-1840—Poetry.   May 21, 1940

NT 0035409   NN InU CU-BANC

Tapia, Eugenio de, 1776-1860.
Elementos de jurisprudencia mercantil, por d. Eugenio de Tapia ... Nueva edicion, considerablemente aum., y refundida con arreglo al nuevo Código de comercio, decretado por S. M. en real cédula de 30 de mayo de 1829 ... Valencia, I. Mompie de Montagudo ¡1838¡
2 v. in 1. 21½cm.
Half-title: Adiciones al Febrero novisimo.
Vol. 2 has imprint: Madrid, Librería de d. J. García.
1. Commercial law—Spain.   I. Febrero, José, 1733?-1790.   Febrero novisimo. II. Title.

33-12944

NT 0035410   DLC MH

Tapia, Eugenio de, 1776-1860.
Elementos de jurisprudencia mercantil, por d. Eugenio de Tapia ... Nueva edicion, considerablemente aum., y refundida con arreglo al nuevo Código de comercio, decretado por S. M. en real cédula de 30 de mayo de 1829 ... Valencia, I. Mompié de Montagudo ¡1838¡
2 v. in 1. 21½cm.
Half-title: Adiciones al Febrero novisimo.
Vol. 2 of another issue of the same year has imprint: Madrid, Librería de d. José García.
1. Commercial law—Spain.   I. Febrero, José, 1733?-1790.   Febrero novisimo. II. Title.

33-12945

NT 0035411   DLC

TAPIA, Eugenio de, 1776-1860.
Elementos de jurisprudencia mercantil. Paris, 1845.
8°.

NT 0035412   MH-L

Tapia, Eugenio de, 1776-1860.
Elementos de jurisprudencia mercantil, por d. Eugenio de Tapia ... autor del Febrero novisimo ... Nueva ed., considerablemente aumentada, y refundida con arreglo al nuevo Código de comercio, decretado por S. M. en real cédula de 30 de mayo de 1829. Paris, Rosa, Bouret y cia., 1850.
2 p. l., ii, 259 p. 21½cm.
Half-title: Adiciones al Febrero novisimo.
1. Commercial law—Spain. 2. Commercial law.   I. Febrero, José, 1733?-1790. Febrero novisimo. II. Title.

27—6799

NT 0035413   DLC RPB

¡Tapia, Eugenio de¡ 1776-1860.
Ensayos satíricos en verso y prosa, por el licenciado machuca; inquilino que fue de la casa negra. ¡Madrid¡ Imprenta nacional, 1820¡
143 p. 14½ cm.

NT 0035414   NjP NNH

Tapia, Eugenio de, 1776-1860, supposed author.
... La enterrada en vida, comedia en cinco actos
see under title

Tapia, Eugenio de, 1776-1860, ed.

Febrero, José, 1733?-1790.
Febrero mejicano, ó sea La libreria de jueces, abogados y escribanos que refundida, ordenada bajo nuevo metodo, adicionada con varios tratados y con el título de Febrero novísimo dió á luz d. Eugenio de Tapia, nuevamente adicionada con otros diversos tratados, y las disposiciones del derecho de Indias y del patrio, por el lic. Anastasio de la Pascua ... Méjico, Impr. de Galvan á cargo de M. Arévalo, 1834-35.

Tapia, Eugenio de, 1776–1860, ed.

Febrero, José, 1733?–1790.
Febrero novísimamente redactado, con las variaciones y mejoras espresadas en el prospecto, que sirve de prólogo á la obra. Por d. Eugenio de Tapia ... Madrid, Viuda de Calleja e hijos. 1845–46.

Tapia, Eugenio de, 1776–1860, ed.

Febrero, José, 1733?–1790.   FOR OTHER EDITIONS SEE MAIN ENTRY
Febrero novisimo; ó, Librería de jueces, abogados, escribanos, y médicos legistas refundida, ordenada bajo nuevo metodo, y adicionada con un tratado del juicio criminal, y algunos otros; por don Eugenio de Tapia ... Nueva ed., notablemente enmendada, mejorada, y aumentada con el nuevo Codigo de comercio y Ley de enjuiciamiento, un diccionario judicial, las adiciones al Febrero novisimo, ó Elementos de jurisprudencia mercantil, por el mismo autor y las Ordenanzas de Bilbao ... Paris, Rosa, Bouret y cia., 1850.

Tapia, Eugenio de, 1776–1860.
El hijo predilecto, ó La parcialidad de una madre comedia en cuatros actos y en verso, por Don Eugenio de Tapia. Madrid, Impr. de Yenes, 1839.

70 p. 19½ᶜᵐ. (*On cover:* Galeria dramatica)

1. Title.

22–4312

Library of Congress   PQ6570.T2H5

NT   0035419   DLC PU OO NN

Tapia, Eugenio de, 1776–1860.
El hijo predilecto; ó, La parcialidad de una madre. Comedia en cuatro actos y en verso. Madrid, Impr. de Yenes, 1839.
70p.
Microcard edition.

NT   0035420   ICRL MoU OrU

Tapia, Eugenio de, 1776–1860.
Historia de la civilizacion española desde la invasion de los Árabes hasta la época presente. Por Don Eugenio de Tapia ... Madrid, Impr. de Yenes, 1840.

4 v in 2. 18½ᶜᵐ.

1. Spain.—Civilization.

4–26787

Library of Congress   DP48.T17

NT   0035421   DLC NNH CU MB IaU PU OO OClU WU TNJ MiU

Tapia, Eugenio de, 1776–1860.
Juguetes satíricos en prosa y verso... Madrid, Yenes, 1839.
121 p. 15 ᶜᵐ.

NT   0035422   NjP IEN NcD

Tapia, Eugenio de, 1776–1860.
Manual de practica forense en forma de dialogo, con el correspondiente formulario de pedimentos: por Don Eugenio de Tapia ... 4. ed. considerablemente aumentada. Madrid, Perez ₁1832₎

3 p. l., 500 p., 1 l. 15ᶜᵐ.

1. Civil procedure—Spain. 2. Courts—Spain. 3. Law—Spain. 1. Title.

27–10378

NT   0035423   DLC CU

TAPIA, Eugenio de, 1776–1860.
Manual teorico–practico de los juicios de inventario y particion de herencias. 3a ed. Paris, 1833.

NT   0035424   MH-L

Tapia, Eugenio de, 1776–1860.
Manual teórico–práctico de los juicios de inventario y partición de herencias. Por el excmo sr. d. Eugenio de Tapia. 5. ed., reformada con arreglo á las disposiciones publicadas hasta el dia, y adicionada con gran número de formularios. Madrid, L. P. Villaverde, 1872.

3 p. l., 375, ₁3₎ p. 15½ᵗᵐ.

1. Inventories of estates—Spain. 2. Partition—Spain.

42–41448

NT   0035425   DLC

Tapia, Eugenio de, 1776–1860   FOR OTHER EDITIONS SEE MAIN ENTRY

Febrero, José, 1733?–1790.
Nuevo Febrero mexicano. Obra completa de jurisprudencia teórico-práctica, dividida en cuatro tomos: en el primero y segundo se trata de la parte teórica; en el tercero de las sustanciaciones de todos los juicios y de todos los tribunales establecidos en la república; y en el cuarto del derecho administrativo. Publicada por Mariano Galvan Rivera ... México ₁Impreso por S. Pérez, 1851–52₎

Tápia, Eugenio de, 1776–1860.
Poesias.
24 p. (Cueto, L. A. de, Poet. lir. del siglo 18, v. 3, p. 677: Bibliot. de autor. españ.)

NT   0035427   MdBP

Tapia, Eugenio de, 1776–1860.
Poesias de Don Eugenio de Tapia ... ₁Madrid₎ imprenta nacional, 1821.
222 p., 1 l. 15ᶜᵐ.

21–3396

Library of Congress   PQ6570.T2A17

NT   0035428   DLC CoU NNH

Tapia, Eugenio de, 1776–1860.
Poesias de Don Eugenio de Tapia. Madrid, Perez, 1832.
2 v. in 1. 15 cm.
Error in binding: v. 1, p. 225–263 bound after v. 2, p. 224; v. 2, p. 225–262 and "Indice" bound after v. 1, p. 224.

NT   0035429   NcD IEN NNH WaU

Tapia, Eugenio de, 1776–1860.
Practica criminal, con un prontuario alfabetico de delitos y penas. Por el licenciado Don Eugenio de Tapia ... Valencia, Impr. de I. Mompié, 1830.
2 v. 21ᶜᵐ.
Title vignettes

1. Criminal procedure—Spain. 2. Criminal law—Spain. 3. Punishment. 1. Title.

28–28928

NT   0035430   DLC

Tapia, Eugenio de, 1776–1860, tr.
El Preso, ó El parecido
see under title

Tapia, Eugenio de, 1776–1860.
Prontuario de contratos y sucesiones hereditarias, con un discurso preliminar, en que se indican las principales reformas que necesita nuestra legislacion en estas materias. Por D. Eugenio de Tapia ... Megico, A. Gadea, 1840.

2 v. 15½ᵗᵐ.

1. Contracts. 2. Inheritance and succession—Mexico. ₍2. Succession and descent—Mexico₎ 1. Title.

24–15830

NT   0035432   DLC

Tapia, Eugenio de, 1776–1860.
Prontuario de contratos y sucesiones hereditarias, con un discurso preliminar en que se indican las principales reformas que necesita nuestra legislacion en estas materias. Por D. Eugenio de Tapia ... Valencia, Impr. de D. I. Mompié de Montagudo, 1840.

2 v. 15ᶜᵐ.

1. Contracts. 2. Inheritance and succession—Spain. ₍3. Succession and descent—Spain₎ 1. Title.

28–28356

NT   0035433   DLC TxU

Tapia, Eugenio de, 1776–1860.
Tratado de jurisprudencia mercantil: por don Eugenio de Tapia ... Valencia. Impr. de I. Mompié. 1828.

4 p. l., 262 p. 22ᶜᵐ.

"El favor dispensado por el público á los dos manuales de **práctica forense** y de particion de herencias que dió á luz el autor del presente tratado, le estimuló á dedicarse á otra tarea mas penosa, cual es una refundicion de la Librería de escribanos de don José Febrero ... Este tratado forma parte de la nueva obra."—Advertencia.

1. Commercial law—Spain. 1. Febrero, José. 1733?–1790. Febrero novísimo. II. Title.

33–12943

NT   0035434   DLC NjP

Tapia, Eugenio de, 1776–1860.
Tratado de jurisprudencia mercantil: segun las leyes de España é Indias... Perpiñan, reprinted, 1828.
21.5 cm.
Este tratado forma parte de una nueva obra, cual es una refundicion de la Librería de escribanos de José Febrero. Cf. Advertencia.

NT   0035435   CtY

Tapia, F   **Prado y**
   see
Prado y Tapia, F

Tapia, Francisco.
... El origen de la tierra, por Francisco Tapia; editado por El Paraguay ilustrado. Asunción, Talleres nacionales de H. Kraus, 1896.
12 p. 18 cm.
At head of title: Poema.
I. El Paraguay ilustrado. II. Title.

NT   0035437   TxU

Gz
989
L861Yt   TAPIA, FRANCISCO
El tirano Francisco Solano López arrojado de las escuelas; esplicación que da el señor Francisco Tapia, director de la Escuela normal nacional de maestros, de las razones que ha tenido en vista para prohibir el uso de unos cuadernos que llevan un atentado de biografía del tirano López al lado de un retrato del mismo; narración de algunas de las inauditas crueldades del tirano, matronas y virgenes martires, ofensas a la sociedad paraguaya, declaraciones de los fiscales del tirano.

Asunción, Escuela tipográfica salesiana, 1896.
61p. 22cm.

1. López, Francisco Solano, 1827–1870. 2. Asunción. Escuela normal nacional de maestros.

NT   0035439   TxU AzU ICarbS MH

Tapia, Francisco de, father.
Representacion qve haze el R. P. lector fray Francisco de Tapia, pro-ministro de la provincia de San Antonio de los Charcas en el reyno del Perù, para el capitulo general que se celebrò en Roma el año passado de mil y setecientos, al rey nuestro señor, y à su Real Consejo de las Indias, sobre la conversion de los infieles de la provincia de Apolovanua, y sus confines, en el distrito del obispado de la ciudad de la Paz, y nuevo camino que abriò para su mejor consecucion. ₍Madrid? 1701₎   12 f.   29cm. (f°.)

Sabin 94347. Medina BHA 7601.
Caption-title.
With bookplate of José M. Rodriguez.

593826B. 1. Indians, S. A.—Reg.   areas—Bolivia—Missions. 2. Indians,
S. A.—Reg. areas—Bolivia. 3. Fran-   ciscans—Bolivia.
N. Y. P. L.   October 10. 1951

NT 0035440   NN

Tapia, Franklin Fernández
    see Fernández Tapia, Franklin.

TAPIA, Fructos de León, 1588-1626

    See LEÓN TAPIA, Fructos de, 1588-1626.

Tapia, German Ochoa y
    see Ochoa y Tapia, German.

Tapia, Girolamo Calà de
    see Calà de Tapia, Girolamo, 1632-1700.

Tapia, Guillermo López
    see
    López Tapia, Guillermo.

Tapia, Honorio, ed.
F2661
.A6   Anuario "Cosmos" de la república del Paraguay. 1943–

    Asunción ₍1943?–

Tapia, Irma Elena Villalobos
    see Villalobos Tapia, Irma Elena.

Tapia, Jaime Villalobos
    see Villalobos Tapia, Jaime.

Tapia, Jesús García
    see
    García Tapia, Jesús.

TAPIA, José Agustín.
Exposicion rectificando los errores que ha consignado Romualdo Villamil en su folleto . . contra Manuel H. Guerra. Pas, 1859.

(2) ≠ 15 p.

NT 0035450   MH-L

Tapia, José Félix, 1910-
    . . . Los 2.000 bombardeos de Malta.   Madrid, 1945.   62 p.
illus. 18cm. (Hechos y hombres de la guerra. 18.)

1. World war, 1939-1945—Malta.
N. Y. P. L.   2. Malta—Hist., 20th cent.
                                        April 28, 1949

NT 0035451   NN

Tapia, José Félix, 1910-
    Ensayos sobre organización de la educación nacional. ₍n.p. Biblioteca Tierra y Libertad₎ 1945.
    47 p. 16cm. (Colección pedagógica, no. 8)
    Signed: José de Tapia, Entrains-sur-Nohan (Nièvre) 8 de febrero de 1945.
    "Printed in France" stamped on t.-p.

    1. Education and state. 2. Education and state - Spain.   I. Title.

NT 0035452   CSt-H

4HD
1997   Tapia, Jose Felix, 1910-
        Londres, ganado y perdido por Hitler.
        Madrid [   ] 1944
        62 p.   (Hechos y hombres la guerra, 9)

NT 0035453   DLC-P4

868
T172lu Tapia, José Félix, 1910-
        La luna ha entrado en casa; novela en 4 fases y una sonrisa. ₍1.ed.₎ Barcelona, Ediciones Destino ₍1946₎
        271 p. 19 cm. (Ancora y delffn ₍32₎)
        "Premio Eugenio Nadal 1945."

NT 0035454   MiU InU IU CU OOxM TxU

He88
T162   Tapia, José Felix, 1910-
L7   La luna ha entrado en casa; novela en 4
1954   fases y una sonrisa. [2. ed.] Barcelona, Ediciones Destino[1954]
        267p. 20cm. (Ancora y delfín, 32)
        "Premio Eugenio Nadal 1945."

        OCU CSt IEN MoSU PPT NCH ICU TU IEdS
NT 0035455   CtY MiDW MtU ICN OCU OO WaU CtY CLSU MH

Tapia, José Luis.
    Vida, obra y muerte de Verdi; biografía novelada. México ₍Comité Nacional Verdi₎ 1951.
    179 p. illus. 20 cm.

    1. Verdi, Giuseppe, 1813-1901—Fiction. 2. Musical fiction.

ML3925.V38T3   52-34640 ‡

NT 0035456   DLC NN OU

Tapia, José María Ortiz y
    See
    Ortiz y Tapia, José María.

Tapia, José Peláez y
    see Peláez y Tapia, José.

Tapia, José Ramón Moreno Sotomayor y
see
Moreno Sotomayor y Tapia, José Ramón.

Western
Americana
Zc50   Tapia, Joseph de, 1645-1698.
692ta   La mina rica de Dios en vn sermon, que predicò el p. Ioseph de Tapia ... a las siestas de la Concepcion purissima de Maria Sanctissima Señora N. Que celebran en el Real de Minas de la Concepcion de los Alamos, entre la provincia de Cinaloa, y Sonora el año de 1691 ... En Mexico, por Doña Maria de Benavides, viuda de Juan de Ribera en el Empedradillo, 1692.
        4 p. ℓ., 14 numb. ℓ. illus. 20 cm.
        Signatures: a4..-4)2

NT 0035460   CtY

Tapia, Juan Antonio de.

Law   Puebla, Mexico (Archdiocese), defendant.
        Alegacion de los derechos que por parte del promotor fiscal del Obispado de la Puebla de Los Angeles se hace a esta Real Audiencia, para que en conformidad de lo determinado, en diez y seis de mayo de mil setecientos y setenta, se sirva declarar que en conocer y proceder el provisor de dicha ciudad no hace fuerza en la causa que expresa. ₍Puebla₎ Impr. del Real Seminario Palafoxiano. 1771.

Tapia, Juan Antonio de.
        Exhortacion del sr. dr. d. Juan Antonio de Tapia, dean de la santa iglesia de Valladolid, y gobernador en sedevacante de aquel obispado, à fin de que sus diocesanos contribuyan conforme à sus facultades para las actuales necesidades de la peninsula. ₍n. p.₎ 1808₎
F1203   4 p. 21cm. ₍Papeles varios. v. 18, no. 19₎
P16
v.18:19   Caption title.
x   "Dada en Valladolid de Michoacán à 29 de octubre de 1808."

NT 0035462   CU-BANC InU

Tapia, Juan Cristobal Romea y
    see Romea y Tapia, Juan Cristobal, 1732-1766.

Tapia, L. G.
    Ecos del Pisuerga. Versos. Tomo I.
    Valladolid, Imprenta de Garrido, 1879.
    vol. 1.

NT 0035464   NNH

Tapia, Lucas Mendoza de la
    see Mendoza de la Tapia, Lucas.

Tapia, Lucio.
    Programas de educación primaria, correspondientes al primer año de educacion primaria superior detallados por meses, semanas y días... México, Libreria de la viuda de Ch. Bouret, 1913.
    63 p.   23 cm.

NT 0035466   LNT

pF1225   Tapia, Lucio
.32   Programas de educación primaria, correspondientes al primer
T3   año elemental, detallados por meses, semanas y días, escritos
1911   para servir de guía metodológica, basada en la ley relativa, á
     los maestros de las escuelas nacionales primarias del Distrito Federal
     y territorios. México, Librería de la Vda. de Ch. Bouret, 1911.
     78 p. 23cm.

     1. Education, Primary - Mexico - Curricula. I. Title.

NT   0035467   CU-BANC

Tapia, Lucio.
     Programas de educación primaria, correspondientes al se-
gundo año superior, desarrollados por meses y semanas y desti-
nados para servir de guía metodológica a los maestros de las
escuelas N. primarias del distrito federal y territorios, por el
profesor Lucio Tapia... México: Vda. de C. Bouret, 1914.
76 p. 2. ed. 8°.

     With autograph of author.

1. Education, Elementary--Courses   of study--Mexico.
N.Y.P.L.   July 10, 1925

NT   0035468   NN

Tapia, Lucio, and A. Krumm-Heller.
     Trilogía heroica; historia condensada del último movimiento
libertario en México. México: A. Botas. 1916. 50 p. 12°.

     Authors' names at head of title.

1. Mexico—History, 1910-16. 2.   Krumm-Heller, Arnold, jt. au.
N.Y.P.L.   July 6, 1917.

     LNT
NT   0035469   NN PPT AzU NcU DLC-P4 InU CoU PPiU NBuU

TAPIA, LUCIO.
     Trilogía heroica; historia condensada del último
movimiento libertario en México, [por] Lucio Tapia [y]
Krumm-Heller. México, A. Botas, 1916. 50 p.
20cm.

     Microfiche (neg.) 1 sheet. 11 x 15cm. (NYPL FSN 12,643)

1. Mexico--Hist.--Revolution-   ary period, 1910-1920.
I. Krumm-Heller, Arnold, joint   author.

NT   0035470   NN

Tapia, Lucio.
     Viaje a través de México por dos niños huérfanos;
escenas y pasajes del México antiguo y del México moderno. Libro de lectura corriente para uso de los alumnos de las escuelas primarias de la república, escrito por
el profesor Lucio Tapia ... 4. ed. reformada cuidadosa-
mente por el autor e ilustrada con doce mapas de opor-
tunidad. México, Herrero hermanos, sucesores, 1913.
     2 p. l., [7]-333 p. illus. (incl. maps) 18½ᶜᵐ.

1. Mexico.   I. Title.

Library of Congress   F1208.T17   26-2507

NT   0035471   DLC

865T16   Tapia, Luis de, 1871- 1937
Oa1916   Así vivimos.   Madrid, 1916.
         318p.

NT   0035472   IU

3177   Tapia, Luis de, 1871- 1937.
.355   Bombones y caramelos. Prólogo de D. Benito
.319   Pérez Galdós. Madrid, Estab. Tipográfico de el
     Liberal, 1911.
        230[i.e.122.] p. illus. 19 cm.

NT   0035473   NjP IU PU MoU

861.6
T172   Tapia, Luis de, 1871-1937.
     50 [i.e. cincuenta] coplas de Luis de Tapia.
     [Madrid, Edición de los admiradores de Luis
     Tapia] 1932.
     78 p. port. 20 cm.

     Palabras de Benito Pérez Galdós y de Ramón
Pérez de Ayala: p. [5]

NT   0035474   ICarbS PPiU IU

865T16   Tapia, Luis de, 1871-1937
K1914   Coplas. Madrid, Biblioteca Hispania, 1914.
     297p. 19cm.

NT   0035475   IU ICU

865T16   Tapia, Luis de, 1871-1937.
K1917   Coplas del año. Serie III.   Madrid,
     1917-20.
     3v.

NT   0035476   IU OC1 PU CaBVaU CU NIC WaPS

861.6
T172e   Tapia, Luis de, 1871-1937.
     En la casa y en la calle.   Madrid, Renacimien-
to, 1917.
     268 p. 20 cm.

     Short stories.

NT   0035477   ICarbS CaBVaU

4PQ
Span.
1012   Tapia, Luis de, 1871-1937.
     Luis de Tapia, sus mejores versos.
     Prólogo de Antonio Zozaya. Portada
     e ilustraciones de Ibáñez. Retrato
     por L. de Oroz. Madrid [Iriarte,
     1930]
     79 p.

     (Los Poetas, año 3, no. 80)

NT   0035478   DLC-P4

DC736   Tapia, Luis de, 1871-1937.
T172   ...Un mes en París, un día en Reims, una hora
     en Madrid. Madrid, Talleres tipográficos de
     El Imparcial, 1919.
     157 p., 1 l. illus. (plans) 19½ᶜᵐ.

     Mainly the author's impressions of Paris
during April 1918 as war correspondent for El
Imparcial, Madrid.

     1. European war, 1914-1918 - France - Paris.
2. European war,   1914-1918 - France - Reims.
3. European war,   1914-1918 - Press correspondents. I. El Im-   parcial, Madrid. II. Title.

NT   0035479   CSt-H

3177   Tapia, Luis de, 1871-1937.
.353   Salmos. Madrid, Fé, 1904.
.381   76 p. 19 cm.

NT   0035480   NjP

Tapia, Luis Gómez de
    see   Gómez de Tapia, Luis, 16th cent.

Tapia, Luis T. Molina de la
    see   Molina de la Tapia, Luis T.

Tapia, Manuel.
     ... Concepto y clínica de los procesos epituberculosos infan-
tiles y su relación con las infiltraciones y la atelectasia, por el
doctor Manuel Tapia. Pôrto, Edições Lopes da Silva, 1943.
     2 p. l., [vii]-viii, 103 p., 1 l. plates. 25½ᶜᵐ. (Trabajos de la Estancia
sanatorial del Caramulo (colección monográfica) Director: dr. Jerónimo
Lacerda)
     "Bibliografía": p. [99]-103.

     1. Children—Diseases. 2. Lungs—Collapse. 3. Tuberculosis.
     I. Title.
Library of Congress   RC311.1.T3   44-21847
                                    [2]   616.246

NT   0035483   DLC

Tapia, Manuel.
     ... Contribución al estudio del valor de la tomografía en la
tuberculosis pulmonar, por el dr. Manuel Tapia. Pôrto, Edições Lopes da Silva, 1942.
     80 p., 1 l. plates. 25½ᶜᵐ. (Trabajos de la Estancia sanatorial del
Caramulo (colección monográfica) Director: dr. Jerónimo Lacerda)
     "Bibliografía": p. [77]-80.

     1. Tuberculosis—Diagnosis. 2. Diagnosis, Radioscopic.
     RC311.1.T32   616.246075   Med 47-617

NT   0035484   DLC

WF   Tapia, Manuel
651.T8   Contribución al estudio del valor de
T172c   la tomografía en la tuberculosis pul-
1944   monar. Madrid, Aguado, 1944.
     80 p. illus. (Trabajos de la
     Estancia Sanatorial del Caramulo (Colec-
     ción monográfica))

     Bibliography: p. [77]-80.

     1. Tuberculosis - Diagnosis. 2. Lungs -
     Radiography. I. Series: Estancia Sanatorial
     de Caramulo   (Portugal) Trabajos.

NT   0035485   DNLM

Tapia, Manuel.
     ... Formas anatomoclínicas de la tuberculosis pulmonar
(diagnóstico y tratamiento) ... Madrid, Ediciones Afrodisio Aguado, 1941-
     v. illus., diagrs. 27½ cm.

     1. Tuberculosis.   I. Title.

     RC311.T2   616.246   45-51273 rev

NT   0035486   DLC

WF   TAPIA, Manuel
200   Las formas anatomoclínicas de la
T172f   tuberculosis tráqueobronquial en sus
.950   relaciones con la tuberculosis pulmonar
     del niño y del adulto, por Manuel Tapia
     con la colaboración de José Manuel
     Soares de Oliveira y Luis Cerezo.
     [1. ed.] Madrid, Editorial Alhambra
     [1950]
     718 p. illus.
     1. Tuberculosis

NT   0035487   DNLM

WF   TAPIA, Manuel
300   Formas anatomoclínicas, diagnóstico
qT172f   y tratamiento de la tuberculosis pulmonar.
1939   Pôrto, Artes Gráficas [etc.], 1939-42.
     3 v. in 4. illus.
     At head of title, t. 1-2: Trabajos del
     Sanatoria del Caramulo.
     Title of t. 3 varies slightly.
     1. Tuberculosis   Series: Guardão,
     Portugal. Estancia Sanatorial do
     Caramulo. Trabalhos

NT   0035488   DNLM

WF
651.T8
qT172f
1945

Tapia, Manuel
Formas anatomoclínicas, diagnóstico
y tratamiento de la tuberculosis pulmonar.
(2. ed. corr. y considerablemente aumentada) Lisboa, Livraria Lusó Espanhola,
1945-46.
2 v. illus. (Trabajos del Sanatorio
del Caramulo)

1. Tuberculosis

NT   0035489   DNLM NNC

Tapia, Manuel.
... Neumonias atípicas, infiltrados fugaces sucedáneos (síndrome de Löffler) e infiltrados hiperérgicos (síndrome de Leitner) por los dres. Manuel Tapia y Celso Horta Vale. Pôrto, Ediçôes Lopes da Silva, 1942.
84 p., 1 l. plates. 25ᶜᵐ. (Trabajos de la Estancia sanatorial del Caramulo (colección monográfica) Director: dr. Jerónimo Lacerda)
"Bibliografía": p. ₁81₁–84.

1. Pneumonia. I. Horta Vale, Celso, joint author. II. Title.
44–900

Library of Congress   RC771.T3
₃₁   616.241

NT   0035490   DLC

Tapia, Manuel.
El neumotorax extrapleural, por Manuel Tapia, Luís Quintella ₁y₁ Anselmo Ferraz Carvalho. Lisboa ₁etc.₁ Livraria Luso-Espanhola, 1947.
246 p. illus. 25 cm.
"Bibliografía consultada": p. ₁239₁–244.

1. Pneumothorax. ₁1. Pneumothorax, Artificial₁ I. Ferraz Carvalho, Anselmo, joint author. II. Quintella, Luís, joint author.
Med 48–893

U. S. Army Medical Libr.   [WF668T172n 1947]
for Library of Congress   ₁1₁

NT   0035491   DNLM

WF
300
qT172p
1932

TAPIA, Manuel
Patogenia y evolución de la tuberculosis
pulmonar ₁por₁ Manuel Tapia ₁et al.₁
Madrid, Ruiz, 1932.
viii, 62 p., 97 plates.
1. Tuberculosis - Etiology &
pathogenesis

NT   0035492   DNLM

Tapia, Manuel.
... Los procesos epituberculosos infantiles; concepto, clínica y relaciones con las infiltraciones y la atelectasia ... 2. ed. Madrid, Morata, 1945.
197 p. illus. 25ᶜᵐ.

1. Tuberculosis ₁in children₁ I. Title.
Med 46–254

U. S. Army medical library   ₁WS280T172p 1945₁
for Library of Congress   ₁4₁

NT   0035493   DNLM

Tapia, Manuel.
... Profilaxis de la difteria (con 8 figures)
Madrid, Editorial Paracelos, 1925.
iii [1] 128 p., 1 l. 6 pl. on 4 l. (2 col.)
22 cm.
"Bibliografía": p. 125-[129]
1. Diphtheria.

NT   0035494   CU

Tapia (Manuel) & Blanco (Julio). Tifus exantemático, prólogo por Gregorio Marañón.
xiv, 175 pp., 1 pl. 10 chs. 12ᵐ. Madrid, 1921.

NT   0035495   DNLM

WF
551.T8
T172t
1947

Tapia, Manuel
La tuberculosis traqueobronquial (estudio
anatomoclínico) Lisboa, Livraria Luso-
Espanhola, 1947.
232 p. illus.

Bibliography: p. 225-229.

1. Bronchi - Tuberculosis 2. Trachea -
Tuberculosis

NT   0035496   DNLM

Tapia, Manuel Luengo
see   Luengo Tapia, Manuel.

Tapia, Manuel Muñoz
see   Muñoz Tapia, Manuel.

HJ6846
.A5
1915

Tapia, Mariano E.
Bolivia. *Laws, statutes, etc.*
Leyes orgánicas y reglamento general de aduanas de la república de Bolivia, con un apéndice que contiene: las leyes, decretos supremos y demás disposiciones vigente en el ramo. Reimpresión autorizada al dr. Mariano E. Tapia ... ₁La Paz₁ Imp. Velarde, 1915.

Tapia, Martín de, *b. ca.* 1540.
Vergel de música. Madrid, 1954–
v. col. facsim. 27 cm. (Colección Joyas bibliográficas, 11
"Tirado unicamente doscientos cincuenta ejemplares en papel verjurado de La Gelldense, S. A., nominados y numerados del 1 al 250." No. 44.

1. Music. (Series)

ML171.T173   57–47525

NT   0035500   MnU GU PSt MH NcD MoU NIC FMU CtU
DLC NjP TNJ MiU KyU MB IaU NN ViU MiU

Tapia, Martín de, *b. ca.* 1540.
... Vergel de mvsica || spiritual speculatiua y actiua. del || qual, muchas, diuersas y suaues flores se puedé coger. Dirigi- || do al yllustrissimo y Reuerédissimo Señor dō Frácisco Tello || de San Doual Obispo de Osmay del Cōsejo de su Magestad || ¶ Autor el Bachiller Tapia Numantino. || ¶ Tratase lo primero con grāde artificio y profundidad, las || alabanças, las gracias, la dignidad, Las virtudes y prerrogati-⁸ || uas dela musica y despues, Las artes de Cantollano, Organo y Contrapūto, en suma y en Theorica. ¶ Esta tassado cada volume en papel A tres Reales. ₁Colophon: ... Se || acabo de imprimir el presēte libro ... el q̄l fue impresso

ēla Incly || ta vniuersidad dela Villa del Burgo de Osma por Diego || Fernandez de Cordoua impressor. Acabose a veynte y ocho || dins del mes de Mayo, Año de nuestra redemp || cion de mil y quiniētos y setenta años₁
4 p. l. cxx numb. l. diagrs. 19ᶜᵐ.
Includes three approbations, the first undated, the others dated 1559.
At head of title the arms of the bishops of Osmay, surrounded by quotations from the Psalms (32, 149, 95, 67) within line borders. Printer's mark following colophon on recto of last leaf. Leaves liv and lxxi numbered lv and lxxxvij respectively.

1. Music.
Library of Congress   ML171.T17   8–17868 Revised

NT   0035502   DLC CU NNH MH ICN NRU-Mus

Ayer
3A
196
no.2

TAPIA, MATHIAS DE, 1657-1717.
Treurig verhael van de reyze en martel-
dood van ... Ignatius Toebast, en eenige
andere Jesuiten en missionarissen in d'Indien, als ook kortbondige beschryvinge van
verscheyde onbekende landen, woeste natien,
en goddeloos heydendom in de Indien. Voor-
gedragen in een brief ... door ... Mathias
de Tapia, van de Societeyt Jesu ... uyt
het spaensch in 't nederduytsch overgezet

Continued in next column

Continued from preceding column

door eenen priester der zelve Societeyt
₁i.e. Nicolas Valckenborg₁ ... Te Gend,
By J. F. Vander Schueren ₁ca.1786?₁
16p. 18cm.
Possibly issued with: Wonderbaere
reyze, by Ignatius Toebast.

NT   0035504   ICN RPJCB

Tapia, Oscar Flores
see   Flores Tapia, Oscar.

Tapia, Pedro A   Ceballos
see   Ceballos Tapia, Pedro A

PQ 6341
.P16 T17

TAPIA, PELAYO DE   ,comp.
El libro de los juegos florales cervantistas
y otras fiestas, organizadas por la Colonia
Española de Valparaíso en los días 22 y 23 de
abril de 1916, en homenaje al autor del inmortal
libro "El ingenioso hidalgo Don Quijote de la
Mancha." Compilación y reseñas por Pelayo de
Tapia. Valparaiso, Chile, Soc. Impr. y Lit.
Universo ₁1916₁
242 p. illus., music, ports.
At head of title: El tricentenario de
Cervantes en Chile.

NT   0035507   InU ICarbS

Tapia, Pelayo de.
... El primer viaje alrededor de la tierra
(1519- Magallanes y Elcano - 1522) Valparaiso,
Imp. "Revista económica", 1920.
40 p. 23 cm.
1. Voyages arount the world. 2. Cano, Juan
Sebastián del, d. 1526. 3. Magalhães, Fernão de,
d. 1521.

NT   0035508   CU

Tapia, Raphael J
El texto "I ad Corintios c. XV, vv. 21-22";
estudio crítico-histórico sobre la interpreta-
ción de dicho texto en los principales Padres
y autores eclesiásticos. México, Editorial
Jus, 1955.
64 p. 24 cm.

Part of thesis--Pontificia Università
Gregoriana, Rome.
"Indice bibliografico": p. 9-12.

1. Bible.   N.T. 1 Corinthians XV,
21-22.

NT   0035509   DCU

Tapia, Renato Carrasco
see   Carrasco Tapia, Renato.

Tapia, Ricardo Márquez
see   Márquez Tapia, Ricardo, 1887-

Tapia, Roberto A   Capestany
see   Capestany Tapia, Roberto A

Tapia, Rosendo Ochoa

see

Ochoa Tapia, Rosendo.

Tapia, Santiago
　　Detall de la accion, 20 de Oct. de 1861.
En la sierra intermedia de Pachuca al
mineral del Monte, 1861.
　　see under　Mexico. Ministerio de
guerra y marina.

Tapia, Santiago.
　　Exposicion que eleva al soberano congreso de
la union estefana longoria...　Mexico, 1868.
　　12 p.　(Political pamphlets, 149:1)

NT 0035515   DLC

Tapia, Susana González
　　see　González Tapia, Susana.

Tapia, Tomás
　　La religión en la conciencia y en la vida.　Madrid,
Impr. y Estereotipia de M.Rivadeneyra, 1869

　　41 p.　(Madrid. Universidad. Conferencias
dominicales sobre la educación de la mujer. 12.con-
ferencia, 9 de mayo de 1869)

　　1. Women and religion

NT 0035517   MH

Tapia, Virgilio Cabanellas y
　　see　Cabanellas, Virgilio.

Tapia, Willebaldo Bahena

see

Bahena Tapia, Willebaldo.

4RA　Tapía Alarcón, Luis
253　　Salubridad pública y legislación
sanitaria. Valparaiso, 1927.
　　160 p.

NT 0035520   DLC-P4

Case
B　　**TAPIA ALDANA, JACOBUS.**
67　　　_Dialogus de triplici bono et vera hominis
.862　nobilitate, qui Philemon inscribitur._　Sala-
manticæ,Excudebat C.Bonardus,1588.
　　｢16｣,436,｢15｣p.　28cm.

　　Title vignette (coat of arms)　Initials;
printer's device at end.

NT 0035521   ICN

Tapia Aranda, Enrique.
　　... Del contagio venereo y del nutricio; tesis que para obtener
el título de licenciado en derecho presenta Enrique Tapia
Aranda.　Mxeico ｢!｣ ｢Ocampo hnos.｣ 1937.
　　31 p.　23½ᵐ.
　　At head of title: Universidad nacional autónoma de México. Facultad
de derecho y ciencias sociales.

　　1. Venereal diseases—Prevention.　ɪ. Title.
　　　　　　　　　　　　　　　　　38–20049

NT 0035522   DLC

Tapia Arqueros, Hugo.
　　... Las obligaciones naturales, por Hugo Tapia Arqueros.
Santiago, Chile, Editorial Nascimento, 1941.
　　vii, 236 p.　27½ᵐ.　(Colección de estudios jurídicos, publicada bajo la
dirección de Luis Barriga Errázuriz ...　ɪɪɪ)
　　"Bibliografía": p. ｢217｣–224.

　　1. Natural obligations.　2. Natural obligations—Chile.
　　　　　　　　　　　　　　　　　44–17975

NT 0035523   DLC

Tapia Bolívar, Daniel.
　　Breve historia del toreo.　｢México｣ Editorial México, 1947.
　　487 p.　17 cm.
　　On cover: De Francisco Romero a Silverio Pérez y Luis Procuna.

　　1. Bull-fights.
　　GV1107.T27　　　　791.8　　　　A 48–1134*
New York.　Public Libr.
for Library of Congress　　｢1｣†

NT 0035524   NN NjP TxU CtY FU DLC

Tapia Bolívar, Daniel.
　　... Ha llovido un dedito.　Madrid ｢Talleres Espasa-Calpe,
s. a.｣ 1935.
　　3 p. l., ｢9｣–166 p.　19ᵐ.
　　CONTENTS.—Ha llovido un dedito.—Un viajecito a Rusia.—Diez o doce
crónicas.

　　ɪ. Title.
　　　　　　　　　　　　　　　　　35–35028
Library of Congress　　　　PQ6637.A7H2 1935
　　　　　　　　　　　　　　　｢2｣　　　　　864.6

NT 0035525   DLC

Tapia Bolívar, Daniel.
　　... Teoría de Pepe-Hillo, biografía y tauromaquia ...　México
｢Talleres de la Editorial intercontinental｣ 1945.
　　2 p. l., 7–248, ｢1｣ p., 3 l.　19ᵐ.　(Colección Málaga.　Serie Gibralfaro)

　　1. Delgado y Gálvez, José, 1754–1801.　2. Bull-fights.　ɪ. Title.
　　GV1107.T3　　　　927.918　　　　47–3340

NT 0035526   DLC TxU IU

W 4　TAPIA BRAVO, Norberto
M61　　Informe médico sanitario del municipio
1952　de Temascalcingo, estado de México;
algunos casos de artritis reumatoide
tratados con la cortisona.　México,
Ortega, 1952.
　　45 p.
　　Tesis - Univ. de Mexico.
　　1. Public health - Mexico - Mexico
(State)

NT 0035527   DNLM

F1938
.5　　**Tapia Brea, Manuel.**
.T7T3　　Reseña de un viaje triunfal.　Ciudad Trujillo, Editora del
Caribe, 1954.
　　207 p.　illus., ports.　16 x 24 cm.

　　1. Trujillo Molina, Rafael Leónidas, Pres. Dominican Republic,
1891–　ɪ. Title.
　　　　　　　　　　　　　　　　　A 55–10373
Florida.　Univ.　Librar｣
for Library of Congress　　｢3｣

NT 0035528   FU DLC NN ViU

Tapia Cañas, Rubén.
　　El delito.　León, Nicaragua ｢cover 1950｣
　　52 p.　27 cm.
　　Tesis—Universidad Nacional de Nicaragua.

　　1. Criminal law.　2. Criminal law—Nicaragua.　3. Punishment.
ɪ. Title.
　　　　　　　　　　　　　　　　　52–43262

NT 0035529   DLC

4HD　Tapia Carvajal, Juan
1584　　Legislación del trabajo en Chile,
algunos antecendentes historicos.
｢Santiago de Chile｣ 1937.
　　160 p.

NT 0035530   DLC-P4

Tapia Centeno, Carlos de.
　　Arte novissima de lengua mexicana, que dictò D. Carlos
de Tapia Zenteno ...　En Mexico, por la viuda de D. Joseph Bernardo de Hogal. año de 1753.
　　11 p. l., 58 p.　1 illus. (coat of arms)　20ᵐ.
　　The 10th preliminary leaf contains a wheel-shaped acrostic on the author's name.

　　1. Aztec language—Grammar.
　　　　　　　　　　　　　　　　　11–12582
Library of Congress　　　　PM4063.T2

CU MH NNH
NT 0035531   DLC PU-Mu NjP InU PPAmP OCl ICN RPJCB

Tapia Centeno, Carlos de
　　Arte novissima de lengua mexicana, que dictò
D. Carlos de Tapia Zenteno. En Mexico, por la vi-
uda de D. Joseph Bernardo de Hogal. año de 1753.
　　Microfilm copy, made in 1954, of the original
in the Colección Cuevas, Asociación Histórica
Americanista.　Positive.
　　Negative film in St. Louis University Library.
　　Collation of the original: 11 p. l., 58 p.
1 illus. (coat of arms)
　　The 10th preliminary leaf contains a wheel-
shaped acrostic on the author's name.
　　1. Aztec lang-　　　uage--Grammar.

NT 0035532   MoSU

Tapia Centeno, Carlos de.
　　Arte novísima de lengua mexicana, que dictó D. Cárlos
de Tapia Zenteno ...　Quien lo saca a luz debajo de la
proteccion del Illmo. Sr. Dr. D. Manuel Rubio Salinas ...
Con licencia de los superiores.　En Mexico, por la viuda
de D. José Bernardo de Hogal, año de 1753.　Reimpreso
en 1885.　México, Impr. de I. Escalante, 1885.
　　42 p.　33½ᵐ.　(｢Colección de gramáticas de la lengua mexicana. t. 3｣
p. ｢1｣–42)
　　Half-title: Apéndice al t. ɪɪɪ de los Anales del Museo nacional de
México. Documentos para la lingüística de la República Mexicana.
　　1. Aztec language—Grammar.　ɪ. Title.　ɪɪ. Title: Documentos para la
lingüística de la República Mexicana.
　　　　　　　　　　　　　　　　　22–3378
Library of Congress　　　　PM4063.A1 1885
———　Copy 2.　　　　　　　PM4063.T3

NT 0035533   DLC RPJCB LNT WaU PPAmP TxU NN

Tapia Centeno, Carlos de.
Noticia de la lengua huasteca, que en beneficio de sus nacionales, de orden del illmô. sr. arzopispo ¡¹¡ de esta santa Iglesia metropolitana, y a sus expensas, da Carlos de Tapia Zenteno ... Con cathecismo, y doctrina christiana para su instruccion, segun lo que ordena el santo concilio mexicano, enchiridion sacramental para su administracion, con todo lo que parece necessario hablar en ella los neoministros, y copioso diccionario para facilitar su inteligencia. Mexico, En la impr. de la Bibliotheca mexicana, 1767.
5 p. l., 128 p. 29¼ᶜᵐ.
Title within ornamental-border.

"Diccionario ¡castellano-¡huasteco": p. 46–88.
"Doctrina christiana fielmente traducida de la que escribió el R. P. Bartholomé Castaño de la Compañía de Jesus": p. 96–128.
Licenses dated 1746.
The edition of 1746 with title "Arte de la lengua huasteca," as quoted by Ludwig, Lit. of Amer. aborig. lang., p. 83, and by Viñaza, Bibl. español. de lenguas indíg. de Amér. no. 323, cannot have existed, since the author in his dedicatory letter to the archbishop and in his preface states that although the book had to be delayed until the archbishop ordered it printed at his expense.
1. Huasteca language—Grammar. 2. Huasteca language—Glossaries, vocabularies, etc. I. Catholic church. Liturgy and ritual. Huasteca. II. Castaño, Bartolomé, 1601–1672.
Library of Congress   PM3831.T3   5–41113

NT 0035535   DLC InU PU–Mu TxU CU–BANC WU NIC PPL ICN
OCU OCl MWA RPJCB NNH NN NNC NjP MB CSmH NHi ViU

TAPIA CENTENO, Carlos de.
Pradigma apologetico arte, vocabulario y doctrina en lengua Huasteca.
145 p. 8vo.
Reproduced by W. E. Gates.

NT 0035536   MH–P

TAPIA CENTENO, CARLOS DE
Paradigma apologetico, Que desea Persuadir ingenuo, escribiendo desapassionado la notia de la Huasteca a los VV. Sacerdotes, q pueden cultivarla. Descripcion de su paiz, Y demonstracion evidente de la vanidad de el horror, que se le tiene; Noticia De la Lengua Huasteca.
177pp. 21.2cm. Latter section printed in Mexico, 1767. Pilling 3802.

NT 0035537   ICN

Tapia Ch   , Marco Aurelio.
... El cultivo del trigo. 2. ed. Pasto, Impr. del departamento, 1940.
160 p. illus. 18¼ᶜᵐ.
"Bibliografía": p. 155.

1. Wheat—Colombia. 2. Wheat—Diseases and pests. 3. Fertilizers and manures.
Library of Congress   SB191.W5T25   42–33617
¡2¡   633.11

NT 0035538   DLC

Tapia Colman, Simón, 1909–
Leyenda gitana; suite para orquesta. México, Ediciones Mexicanas de Música ¡¹1955¡
score (124 p.) 33 cm.
CONTENTS.—La gitana y el caballero.—Rito nupcial, zambra, bacanal.—Nocturno.—Danzas de la buena ventura.

1. Suites (Orchestra)—Scores.   I. Title.
M1003.T19L5   63–31312/M

NT 0035539   DLC CSt

Tapia Colman, Simón, 1909–
¡Danzas, violin & orchestra; arr.¡
Suite española. ¡Reducción¡ para violín y piano. México, D. F., Ediciones Mexicanas de Música ¡1955¡
score (58 p.) and part. 33 cm.
Caption title: Seis danzas, suite española para violín y orquesta.

1. Suites (Violin with orchestra)—Solo with piano.   I. Title.
M1013.T175D4   63–26168/M

NT 0035540   DLC MiU

Tapia Cruzat, Enrique
4K Chile 94
Los hijos ilejítimos en nuestra lejislación. Concepción, 1920.
61 p.

NT 0035541   DLC–P4

Tapia de Castellanos, Esther, 1842–189
Los canticos de los niños, por la inspirada poetisa Esther Tapia de Castellanos, presentados en la 2.ª exposición de "Las clases productoras" y dedicados a esta sociedad. Guadalajara,Ant.imp. de D.Rodriguez, 1881.
2 p.l., ii,¡5¡-89 p. 19¼ cm.
With this are bound: Composiciones literarias leidas en la solemne distribución de premios entre los alumnos del Liceo de varones del estado... Guadalajara,1873 and Contestación

que da el lic. Juan S.Castro, a la "Breve exposición jurídica presentada... por el lic.·d. Manuel Briseño Ortega... Guadalajara, 1891.

NT 0035543   CSt

Tapia de Castellanos, Esther, 1842–1897.
869.1 T16f
Flores sisvestres ¡i.e. silvestres¡ composiciones poeticas. Publicadas por J. M. Vigil. Mexico, Impr. de I. Cumplido, 1871.
xxviii, 368p. port. 19cm.

I. Title: Flores silvestres.

NT 0035544   IU CU–BANC CSt TxU

Tapia de Castellanos, Esther, 1842–1897.
869.1 T16
Obras poéticas. Guadalajara ¡México¡ Tall. de Impr., Litografía, Encuadernación y Rayados L. G. González, 1905.
2v. port. 20cm.

NT 0035545   IU

Tapia de Castellanos, Esther, 1842–1897.
Rasgos biográficos i algunas de las poesias inéditas de Esther Tapia de Castellanos
see under   Rivera y Sanroman, Agustín, 1824–1916.

Tapia de Lesquerre, Lola.
PQ7797 .T233P5
Pinceladas de gloria (estampas históricas); poesías. Buenos Aires, Editorial Tor ¡1936¡
138 p. 19 cm.

1. Argentine republic--Hist.---Poetry.
I. Title.

NT 0035547   MB

Tapia de Maytorena, Santos.
Law
Díaz González, Prisciliano María.
Informe a la vista pronunciado ante la 1ª sala de la Suprema corte de justicia, por el lic. Prisciliano Maria Diaz Gonzalez combatiendo como patrono de don Felipe Arellano, apoderado de doña Santos Tapia de Maytorena y el recurso de denegada suplica interpuesto por la parte de los sres. Encinas en los autos de oposicion al denuncio de denuncias del rancho de Mapobampo. México, mayo 19 de¡l¡ 1882. Mexico, Impr. de G. Horcasitas, 1882.

Tapia Depassier, Carlos
RK 51 .T17
Tratamiento odontológico de la primera dentición y algunos conceptos sobre alimentación en el infante. Santiago [Chile] Imp. y Lito., Leblanc, 1939.
80 p. illus. tables.
Tesis- Universidad de Chile. Facultad de Biología y Ciencias Médicas. Escuela Dental.

1. Dentistry- Children. 2. Teeth-diseases. 3. Infants- Nutrition. I. Title.

NT 0035549   DPAHO

Tapia Falik, Julio.
Estudios de algunos problemas que plantea la aplicación de la Ley de impuestos a la renta a las sociedades. ¡Santiago de Chile¡ 1952.
84 p. 27 cm.
Tesis (licenciatura en ciencias jurídicas y sociales)—Universidad de Chile.
Includes bibliography.

1. Corporations—Chile—Taxation.
59–38139 ‡

NT 0035550   DLC MH–L DPU

Tapia Farfan de Morales, Francisca.
Flores de Ortiga, poesías. Buenos Aires, [n. p.] 1934]
59 p., 2 l. 19 cm.

NT 0035551   NcU

Tapia Fernández, Carlos.
... A propósito del método de Blair Bell en el tratamiento del cáncer por las salas de plomo, por el Dr. Carlos Tapia Fernández. Santiago de Chile ¡Imp. Chile¡ 1928.
11 p. 22¼ᶜᵐ.
At head of title: Revista médica de Chile, año LVI, n.º 8, octubre 1928 (Apartado)

1. Cancer.   I. Bell, William Blair, 1871–
29–16201
Library of Congress   RC261.T25

NT 0035552   DLC

Tapia Freses, Alejandro.
Curso de química inorgánica (para 4o. año de instrucción secundaria) desarrollo y ampliación del programa oficial, por Alejandro Tapia Freses ... Lima, Perú, D. Miranda, 1936.
2 p. l., ii, v p., 1 l., 151 (i. e. 351) p. illus. (incl. ports.) diagrs. 21½ x 16¼ᶜᵐ.
Error in paging: p. 351 incorrectly numbered 151.
Bibliography: p. v.

1. Chemistry, Inorganic.
40–16220
Library of Congress   QD33.T3
¡2¡   546

NT 0035553   DLC

Tapia Freses, Alejandro.
Química orgánica, con prácticas de laboratorio para el 5° año de instrucción secundaria, desarrollo y ampliación del programa oficial, por Alejandro Tapia Freses ... Lima, Perú ¡Imprenta peruana de E. Z. Casanova¡ 1936.
4 p. l., 240 p. illus. (incl. ports.) diagrs. 21½ᶜᵐ.

1. Chemistry, Organic.
40–16221
Library of Congress   QD253.T3
¡2¡   547

NT 0035554   DLC

Tapia Freses, Alejandro.
Química orgánica, con prácticas de laboratorio, para el 5°
año de instrucción secundaria; desarrollo y ampliación del
programa oficial, por el doctor Alejandro Tapia Freses ...
3. ed. Lima, Perú, Lib. e imp. de D. Miranda, 1942.
229, ₍2₎ p. illus. (incl. ports.) diagrs. 20½ᵐ.

1. Chemistry, Organic.   44–16372

Library of Congress   QD253.T3 1942
₍2₎   547

NT 0035555   DLC

Tapia Freses, Alejandro
Las vitaminas ... Lima, D. Miranda, 1941.
3 p. l., 104 p. illus.

"Bibliografía": p. ₍103₎-104.

1. Vitamins.

NT 0035556   NNC

Tapia Garzón, Sixto P.
Conferencia sustentada por el señor Sixto P. Tapia G. en el
salón de lectura popular Maria Piedad Castillo Levi de la Academia Medardo Angel Silva (el 12 de octubre de 1938) en la IX
exposición de obras, folletos, revistas y periódicos nacionales.
Prólogo del dr. Victor Manuel Rendón, prefacio del sr. Juan
Antonio Alminate. Guayaquil ₍1939₎ 16 p. illus. 20cm.

1. Books—Exhibitions—Ecuador   —Guayaquil, 1938.
N. Y. P. L.   June 21, 1944

NT 0035557   NN CU

Tapia H., Miguel.
Eritrofleina.
Inaug. diss. Chile, 1928 (Santiago)
Bibl.

NT 0035558   ICRL

RF28
.I48   Tapia Hernando, Rafael G., ed.

International Congress of Otolaryngology. *2d, Madrid,*
1932.
Catalogue des portraits. Rédigé par Rafael G. Tapia
Hernando. Madrid, Helios, 1932.

Tapia Labardini, Héctor.
Necesidad de un registro especial para muebles. ₍México₎
1950.
80, ₍1₎ p. 24 cm.
Tesis (licenciatura en derecho)—Universidad Nacional Autónoma
de México.
Bibliography : p. ₍81₎

1. Personal property—Mexico. 2. Recording and registration—
Mexico. I. Title.
52–21325

NT 0035560   DLC

DS107.4
.T73   Tapia Moore, Astolfo.
Así crece Israel, conferencia dictada ...
el 19 de octubre de 1950. Santiago de
Chile, 1950.
27 p. illus. 19cm.
At head of title: Instituto Chileno-Israelí
de Cultura; Comisión Chilena de Cooperación
Intelectual, Universidad de Chile.

1. Israel - Descr. I. Instituto Chileno-
Israelí de Cultura. II. Title.

NT 0035561   CSt-H OCH

Tapia Moore, Violeta.
Estudio sobre el desarrollo de las finanzas y la deuda
pública. Santiago de Chile, 1951.
226, ₍8₎ p. 27 cm.
Tesis (licenciatura en ciencias jurídicas y sociales)—Universidad
de Chile.
Bibliography: p. ₍227₎

1. Finance, Public—Chile. 2. Debts, Public—Chile.

HJ930.T3   60–25415

NT 0035562   DLC DPU

Tapia Muñoz, Salvador.
... Arrendamiento de predios rústicos y
aparcería... Santiago de Chile [Stanley] 1946.
124 p. 26 cm.
Thesis - Universidad de Concepción, 1946.
"Bibliografía": p. 123-124.

NT 0035563   DPU

Tapia Olarte, Eulogio, 1908–
"5 grandes escritores cuzqueños en la literatura peruana."
Cuzco, D. Miranda, 1946.
54 p. 22 cm. (Ediciones conmemorativas del 250 aniversario de
la Univ. Nacional del Cuzco, no. 3)
CONTENTS.—El Inca Garcilaso de la Vega.—Juan Espinoza Medrano
(Lunarejo)—Narciso Aréstegui.—Clorinda Matto de Turner.—Angel
Vega Enriquez.

1. Peruvian literature—Cuzco. 2. Garcilaso de la Vega, el Inca,
1539–1616. 3. Espinosa Medrano, Juan, fl. 1660. 4. Matto de Turner,
Clorinda, 1854–1909? 5. Aréstegui, Narciso, 1805–1869. 6. Vega
Enriquez, Angel. I. Title. II. Series: Cuzco, Perú. Universidad.
Ediciones conmemorativas del 250 aniversario, no. 3.

PQ8492.C8T3   860.9   48–1957*

NT 0035564   DLC NcD DPU CU TxU NcU

Tapia Quijada, César.
El derecho de propiedad en el espacio atmosférico. México, 1951.
77 p. 23 cm.
Tesis (licenciatura en derecho)—Universidad Nacional Autónoma
de México.
Bibliography : p. 73–74.

1. Airspace (Law) 2. Airspace (Law)—Mexico. I. Title.
56–26950

NT 0035565   DLC NNC MH-L

Tapia Robson, Santiago Wealands, 1898–
The national Spanish fiesta; or, The art of bullfighting.
With the collaboration of F. Velasco Gil. Madrid ₍Velasco
Gil₎ 1953.
135 p. illus. 19 cm.

1. Bull-fights. I. Title.
A 53–6537

Indiana. Univ. Libr.   GV1107.T17
for Library of Congress   ₍2₎

NT 0035566   InU TxU WaS NN LU

791.8
T162n   Tapia Robson, Santiago Wealands, 1898–
The national Spanish fiesta; or, The art
of bullfighting, by Santiago Wealands Tapia
Robson with the collaboration of F. Velasco
Gil. 2d ed. Madrid ₍F. Velasco Gil, °1953₎
135 p. illus.

1. Bull-fights I. Title

NT 0035567   MiD

W 4
C53
1946   **TAPIA ROMERO,** Alfredo
Enfermedad reumática y glomérulo-
nefritis difusa. Santiago, Senda, 1946.
40, ₍3₎ p.
Tesis - Univ. de Chile.
1. Glomerulonephritis 2. Rheumatic
fever

NT 0035568   DNLM

W 4
M61
1949   **TAPIA ROSETE,** José Gabriel
Informe del servicio social en la
población de Chipilo (Francisco Javier
Mina), Puebla. México, Ortega, 1949.
51 p.
Tesis - Univ. de México.
1. Public health - Mexico - Francisco
Javier Mina 2. Social conditions - Mexico - Francisco Javier Mina

NT 0035569   DNLM

TL504
.C65   Tapia Salinas, Luis, ed.

Comisariado Español Marítimo, s. a.
Anuario aeronáutico español. 1951–
Madrid, Editorial Católica.

Tapia Salinas, Luis.
Aportación española al desarrollo del tráfico y derecho
aéreo internacional. Madrid ₍195–₎
18 p. illus. 25 cm. (Consejo Superior de Investigaciones Científicas. Instituto "Francisco de Vitoria." Sección de Derecho Aeronáutico. ₍Serie roja₎ 3₎)
"Este trabajo tiene como base el artículo del mismo autor titulado
'España, la O. A. C. I. y la política aérea internacional' ... publicado en
la Revista de aeronáutica, número 116, convenientemente rectificado y
ampliado a la vista del tiempo transcurrido y circunstancias actuales."

1. Aeronautics—Spain. 2. International Civil Aviation Organiza-
tion. 3. Aeronautics—Laws and regulations. I. Title. (Series:
Spain. Consejo Superior de Investigaciones Científicas. Instituto
Francisco de Vitoria. Sección de Derecho Aeronáutico. Serie roja, 3)

TL526.S7T3   58–28378

NT 0035571   DLC MH-L

Tapia Salinas, Luis
Creación y actividades de la Sección de
derecho aéreo en el Instituto Francisco de
Vitoria de derecho internacional. Madrid, 1950.
JX3   11 p. 24ᵐ. (Spain. Consejo Superior de
S7341   Investigaciones Cientificas. Instituto Francisco
C75   de Vitoria. Sección de Derecho Aeronautico. Pub-
I5dpr   licaciones. Serie Roja. 1)
"Separata de la "Revista española de derecho
internacional" vol. III, núm. 1, 1950."
1. Aeronautics - Laws and regulations -
Societies. Series.

NT 0035572   MiU-L CtY-L

Tapia Salinas, Luis.
La duración del transporte aéreo a efectos de la responsabilidad. Madrid, Instituto Francisco de Vitoria₎ 1952.
23 p. 25 cm. (Consejo Superior de Investigaciones Científicas.
Instituto "Francisco de Vitoria." Sección de Derecho Aeronáutico.
Serie roja, 7)
"El presente trabajo ha sido extractado y seleccionado de algunos
capítulos de la obra Regulación jurídica del transporte aéreo, del
mismo autor."

1. Liability for aircraft accidents. 2. International Conference on
Private Law Affecting Air Questions. 2d, Warsaw, 1929. I. Title.
(Series: Spain. Consejo Superior de Investigaciones Científicas. Instituto Francisco de Vitoria. Sección de Derecho Aeronáutico. Serie
roja, 7)
58–22850

NT 0035573   DLC MH-L CtY-L

Tapia Salinas, Luis.
Manual de derecho aeronáutico, por Luis Tapia Salinas ...
prólogo por el excmo. sr. d. Felipe Acedo Colunga ... Barcelona, Bosch ₍1944₎
2 p. l., 264 p. 22ᵐ.

"Bibliografía": p. ₍245₎

1. Aeronautics—Spain—Laws and regulations. 2. Air warfare.
45–20279

Library of Congress   HE9025.S75T3
₍3₎   387.7

NT 0035574   DLC MH-BA CtY NNC

Tapia Salinas, Luis.
La regulación jurídica del transporte aéreo. ¡Madrid¡
Ministerio del Aire ¡1953¡
605 p. 22 cm. (Consejo Superior de Investigaciones Científicas.
Instituto "Francisco de Vitoria." Sección de Derecho Aeronáutico.
Serie verde, 1)
PARTIAL CONTENTS.—Apéndices: Convenio de Varsovia. Proyecto
de Convenio para unificación de las disposiciones relativas a la responsabilidad del transportista en el transporte aéreo internacional
(Comité Jurídico de O. A. C. I.) Ley de bases de la navegación
aérea española. Bibliografía (p. ¡535¡-551) Otros trabajos de
derecho aeronáutico del autor (p. 553-554) Publicaciones periódicas
y documentos (p. 555-557)
1. Aeronautics—Laws and regulations.   I. Title.   (Series:
Spain. Consejo Superior   de Investigaciones Científicas. Instituto Francisco de Vi-   toria. Sección de Derecho Aeronáutico. Serie verde, 1)
54–41501

NT 0035575   DLC CtY-L NNC

TAPIA SANZ, Gregorio.
Juzgados de paz.   Arequipa, Tipografía,
Franklin, 1917.

pp. 20.   12º.
Tésis --- Arequipa.

NT 0035576   MH-L

Tapia Suárez, Orlando.
... De la responsabilidad civil en general y de la responsabilidad delictual entre los contratantes. Memoria de prueba para
optar al grado de licenciado en la Facultad de ciencias jurídicas
y sociales de la Universidad de Chile. Concepción ¡Escuela
tipográfica salesiana¡ 1941.
3 p. L, ¡9¡–524 p. 26ᶜᵐ.   (Universidad de Concepción. Publicaciones
del Seminario de derecho privado de la Facultad de ciencias jurídicas y
sociales)
On cover: Obra premiada por la Universidad de Concepción.
"Bibliografía": p. ¡483¡–496.
1. Legal responsibility—Chile. 2. Contracts—Chile.
42–20759

NT 0035577   DLC CtY DPU

Tapia Tortoriello, Ramón.
... Legislación forestal, sus antecedentes históricos. Texto
de la Ley forestal recientemente aprobada por el h. Congreso
de la unión. Observaciones a dicha ley y contraproyecto de
ley. Tesis que para obtener el título de licenciado en derecho,
presenta el alumno Ramón Tapia Tortoriello. México, D. F.,
1943.
106 l. 27ᶜᵐ.
At head of title: Universidad nacional autónoma de México. Facultad de derecho.
Reproduced from type-written copy.
"Bibliografía": 106th leaf.
1. Forestry law and legislation—Mexico.
45–20758
Library of Congress   SD569.T3
¡2¡   634.90972

NT 0035578   DLC CU

Tapia Villarroel, Noel Guillermo.
... El movimiento cooperativo en Inglaterra y en Chile;
memoria de prueba para optar al grado de licenciado en la
Facultad de ciencias jurídicas y sociales de la Universidad de
Chile. Santiago de Chile, Imprenta "Cultura," 1943.
107. ¡5¡ p. 26½ᵐᵐ.
At head of title: Noel Gmo. Tapia Villarroel.
"Bibliografía": p. ¡108¡
1. Cooperation—Gt. Brit. 2. Cooperation—Chile.
44–30012
Library of Congress   HD3486.T3

NT 0035579   DLC CU DPU

Tapia y Acuña, Eugenio.
Proyecto de organización administrativa y contable de un
centro deportivo. México, 1949.
112 p. forms (part fold.) 24 cm.
Tesis (contador público y auditor) — Universidad Nacional de
México.
Errata slip inserted.
1. Recreation centers—Accounting.   I. Title.
GV182.T3
50–36449

NT 0035580   DLC

Tapia y Ballesteros, Juan de, 17th cent.
...Fuerza de amor, y venganza. De Juan de
Tapia y Ballesteros...¡Sevilla, ...17—¡

32 p.

NT 0035581   00

PQ7439
.T3C8   **Tapia y Rivera, Alejandro,** 1826–1882.
1944   La cuarterona; drama original en tres actos, por Alejandro
Tapia y Rivera ... ¡San Juan, P. R., Imprenta Venezuela, 1944¡

PQ7439   **Tapia y Díaz, Alejandro,** 1882–   ed.
.T3Z5   FOR OTHER EDITIONS
1946   SEE MAIN ENTRY
Tapia y Rivera, Alejandro, 1826–1882.
Mis memorias; o, Puerto Rico como lo encontre y como lo
dejo, por Alejandro Tapia y Rivera. San Juan, P. R., Imprenta Venezuela ¡1946¡

Tapia y Fernandez (Ricardo). * Apuntes
para el pronóstico en los derrames de pecho, y
algunas consideraciones acerca de su marcha.
82 pp., 1 l. 8°. *México, J. J. Terrazas,* 1894.

NT 0035584   DNLM

Tapia y Gil, Ambrosio.
Aragon ante la codificacion general civil de España. Folleto jurídico, dedicado al excelentísimo señor don Luis
Franco y Lopez y á la Comision organizadora de los trabajos preparatorios para la convocatoria de un Congreso
de jurisconsultos aragoneses, publicado por d. Ambrosio
Tapia ... Zaragoza, Tip. de J. Sanz, 1880.
115, ¡1¡ p. 21½ cm.
1. Civil law—Aragon. 2. Civil law—Spain. 3. Law—Spain—Codifi-
cation. 4. Congreso de Jurisconsultos Aragoneses, Saragossa.   I.
Title.
41–41579

NT 0035585   DLC

Tapia y Gil, Ambrosio.
La responsabilidad médica ante los tribunales de justicia.
3 ed. Teruel ¡España¡ Imp. de la Casa Provincial de Beneficencia, 1908.
185, xiv p. 22 cm.
Includes bibliographical references.
1. Medical law and legislation—Spain.   I. Title.
70–454448

NT 0035586   DLC MiU MH-L

Tapia y Gil, Ambrosio.
Los suicidios en España.   Madrid, Librería
de V. Suárez, 1900.
253 p. 20cm.

1. Suicide - Spain I. Title

NT 0035587   WU MoU CU MH

Tapia y Moreno, Evaristo, plaintiff.
Informe en derecho que hace el licenciado...
see under   Barreda, José Francisco de.

¡Tapia y Núñez de Rendón, Nicolas¡ 1770–
ca. 1823.
Diálogo entre don Justo Claro y don
Prudencio Bueno sobre el estado en que
se halla la nación, por Mirtilo Sicuritano ¡pseud.¡   Madrid, Aguado, 1823.
8 p. 19½ ᶜᵐ.

NT 0035589   NjP MiU NNH

Tapia y Núñez de Rendón, Nicolás,
1770–1823.
Proclama mis avisos lira por Mirtilo
Sicuritano. Badajoz, en la Imprenta del
Gobierno, año de, 1810.

NT 0035590   NNH

DP402   **Tapia y Paredes, Esteban,** 1560 (ca.)–1604.
.T9C3   **Canilleros, Miguel Muñoz de San Pedro,** *conde de, ed.*
Crónicas trujillanas del siglo XVI (manuscritos de Diego
y Alonso de Hinojosa, Juan de Chaves y Esteban de Tapia)
¡1. ed. Cáceres¡ Publicaciones de la Biblioteca Pública y
Archivo Histórico de Cáceres, 1952.

Tapia y Rivera, Alejandro, 1826–1882.
La antigua sirena; leyenda, por Alejandro Tapia y Rivera.
2. ed. San Juan, P. R., Imprenta Venezuela, 1944.
303 p., 2 l. 23ᶜᵐ.
"La primera edición de esta obra aparece en 'El bardo de Guamaní' ...
que publicó el autor en la Habana en 1862."
"Fe de erratas": slip inserted.

I. Title.
44–46931
Library of Congress   PQ7439.T3A7 1944
¡2¡   863.5

NT 0035592   DLC WaU NBuU CtY WU NcU

Tapia y Rivera, Alejandro, 1826–1882.
El bardo de Guamaní. Ensayos literarios de Alejandro
Tapia y Rivera ... Habana, Impr. del Tiempo, 1862.
616 p. port. 23ᶜᵐ.
CONTENTS.—Roberto d'Evreux.—Bernardo de Palissy.—La palma del
cacique.—La antigua sirena.—Vida del pintor puerto-riqueño José Campeche.—Un alma en pena.—"Adios al buen tiempo." Poesías y menesíla-
nos.—El aprecio á la muger es barómetro de civilizacion.—La Satanlada.
I. Title.
15–21065
Library of Congress   PQ7439.T3B3

NT 0035593   DLC NN CtY CU

Tapia y Rivera, Alejandro, 1826–1882.
Bernardo de Palissy; o, El heroismo del trabajo; biodrama
original en dos partes y cuatro actos, por Alejandro Tapia y
Rivera. ¡San Juan, P. R., Imprenta Venezuela, 1944¡
147 p., 2 l. incl. port. 22½ᶜᵐ.
"Representada por primera vez en la ciudad de San Juan, Puerto
Rico, la noche del 12 de abril de 1857. Segunda edición. La primera
está incluida en El bardo de Guamaní, publicado en la Habana en 1862."
"Bibliografía ¡juicio crítico publicado en 'El Mercurio' de Puerto
Rico al recibirse allí la edición de la pieza hecha en la Habana¡" (p.
¡139¡–147) signed: Román Baldorioty de Castro.
1. Palissy, Bernard, 1510?–1590—Drama.   I. Title.
A 45–1955
New York. Public library
for Library of Congress   PQ7439.T3B4 1944
¡2¡†   862.5

NT 0035594   NN CaBVaU FU WaU CtY DLC

Tapia y Rivera, Alejandro, 1826–1882.
Bernardo de Palissy, o El heroismo del
trabajo, biodrama original en dos partes y
cuatro cuadros. Segunda edición. San Juan,
P. R., Imprenta Venezuela, 1944. 147 p.

[Velázquez, Gonzalo. Biblioteca de obras
puertorriqueñas (Microfilm) no. 903]

NT 0035595   NN

Tapia y Rivera, Alejandro, 1826–1882, *ed.*
Biblioteca historica de Puerto-Rico, que contiene varios documentos de los siglos xv, xvi, xvii y xviii, coordinados y anotados por D. Alejandro Tapia y Rivera. Puerto-Rico, Imprenta de Marquez, 1854.
587, 14 p. 2 fold. tab. 20½cm.
Contents.—Fragmentos de la Historia general y natural de las Indias, por Gonzalo Fernandez de Oviedo.—Cronica general de las Indias, por Antonio de Herrera. Lo referente á la isla de Puerto-Rico.—Historia del Nuevo mundo ... por el Sr. Juan de Laët.—Documentos inéditos, siglos xv y xvi, referentes á la isla de San Juan, recopilados por J. B. Muñoz.—Estracto de varias cedulas y cartas del rey, de 1509 á 1543.—Estracto de varias cartas dirigidas al soberano, de 1515 á 1555.—Copia íntegra de algunos documentos que se hallan en la propia coleccion de Muñoz.—Varias reales cedulas de 1538 á 1561.—Corsario Drake.—Siglo 17 [documentos]—Descripcion de la isla y ciudad de Puerto-Rico, y de su vecinidad ... Enviada por ... Diego de Torres Vargas ... 1647.—Siglo 18 [documentos]—Indice.
1. Puerto Rico — Hist. — Sources. 2. Drake, Sir Francis, 1540?–1596. I. Oviedo y Valdéz, Gonzalo Fernández de, 1478–1557. II. Herrera y Tordesillas, Antonio de, 1559–1625. III. Laet, Joannes de, 1593–1649. IV. Muñoz, Juan Bautista, 1745–1799. V. Torres Vargas, Diego de.
7—41355
Library of Congress F1973.T17

NT 0035597 DLC NNC NN NNH DPU MB CU-BANC

Tapia y Rivera, Alejandro, 1826–1882, *ed.*
Biblioteca histórica de Puerto-Rico, que contiene varios documentos de los siglos xv, xvi, xvii y xviii coordinados y anotados por Alejandro Tapia y Rivera. 2. ed. San Juan de Puerto Rico, 1945.
612 p., 1 l. incl. tables (2 fold.) 20cm. (Publicaciones del Instituto de literatura puertorriqueña)
Contents.—Fragmentos de la Historia general y natural de las Indias, por Gonzalo Fernández de Oviedo.—Crónica general de las Indias, por Antonio de Herrera. Lo referente a la isla de Puerto Rico.—Historia del nuevo mundo ... por el sr. Juan de Laet.—Documentos inéditos, siglos xv y xvi. los que referentes a la isla de San Juan, se encuentran recopilados por J. B. Muñoz.—Estracto de varias cédulas y cartas del rey, de 1509 a 1543.—Estracto de varias cartas dirigidas al soberano, de 1515 a 1555.—Copia integra de algunos documentos que se hallan en la propia colección de Muñoz.—Varias reales cédulas de 1538 a 1561.—Corsario Drake.—Siglo 17 [documentos]—Descripción de la isla y ciudad de Puerto Rico, y de su vecindad. Enviada por Diego de Torres Vargas 1647.—Siglo 18 [documentos]
1. Puerto Rico—Hist.—Sources. 2. Drake, Sir Francis, 1540?–1596. I. Oviedo y Valdez, Gonzalo Fernández de, 1478–1557. II. Herrera y Tordesillas, Antonio de, 1559–1625. III. Laet, Johannes de, 1593–1649. IV. Munoz, Juan Bautista, 1745–1799. V. Torres Vargas, Diego de.
46–2220
Library of Congress F1973.T17 1945
[4] 972.95

PSt KU CU-BANC
NT 0035599 DLC MH NN WaU PU OCl TxU NcD FU ICU NBC

Tapia y Rivera, Alejandro, 1826–1882.
Camoens, drama original en cuatro actos por Alejandro Tapia y Rivera. Madrid, Estab. tip. de T. Fortanet, 1868.
74 p., 1 l. 19½cm.
I. Title.
21–19644
Library of Congress PQ7439.T3C2 1868

NT 0035600 DLC CtY

Tapia y Rivera, Alejandro, 1826–1882.
Camoens. Drama original en tres actos, por Alejandro Tapia y Rivera. Refundido y corr. por el autor, para esta segunda ed.: la primera fué hecha en Madrid en 1868. Puerto-Rico, Estab. tip. de Acosta, 1878.
75, [1] p. 18cm.
1. Camões, Luiz de, 1524?–1580—Drama. I. Title.
22–2567
Library of Congress PQ7439.T3C2 1878

NT 0035601 DLC

Tapia y Rivera, Alejandro, 1826–1882.
Camoens; drama original en tres actos, por Alejandro Tapia y Rivera. 3. ed. Refundido y corregido por el autor para la segunda edición en 1878, Establecimiento tipográfico de Acosta, calle de La Fortaleza no. 21, San Juan, Puerto Rico. La primera fué hecha en Madrid en 1868. [San Juan, P. R., Imprenta Venezuela, 1944]
120 p., 2 l. incl. port. 23cm.
"Este drama fué representado por primera vez en esta isla, en el teatro de la capital, 2 de agosto de 1868."
"Hero, monólogo trágico por Alejandro Tapia y Rivera; la música, de d. Mateo Sabatés. 2. ed." (without the music): p. [107]–120.
"Camoens ... Algunas erratas": leaf laid in.
1. Camões, Luiz de, 1524?–1580—Drama. I. Sabatés, Mateo, 1838–1920. II. Title. III. Title: Hero.
New York. Public library for Library of Congress A 45–2544
PQ7439.T3C2 1945
[3]† 862.5

NT 0035602 NN CaBVaU WaU FU PrU DLC CtY

TAPIA Y RIVERA, Alejandro, 1826–1882.
Cofresi; novela. Puerto-Rico, Tip. de Gonzalez, 1876.

NT 0035603 MH

Tapia y Rivera, Alejandro, 1826–1882.
Cofresí; novela, por Alejandro Tapia y Rivera. 2. ed. San Juan, Puerto Rico, Imprenta Venezuela, 1943.
2 p. l., [7]–268 p., 2 l. 21½cm.
"La primera edición de esta obra fué publicada en 1876."
1. Cofresí y Ramírez de Arellano, Roberto, 1791–1825—Fiction.
A 44–1117
Harvard univ. Library for Library of Congress [2]

NT 0035604 MH PSt WaU CtY

Tapia y Rivera, Alejandro, 1826–1882.
Cofresí; novela, por Alejandro Tapia y Rivera. 3. ed. San Juan, P. R., Imprenta Venezuela, 1944.
268 p., 2 l. 23cm.
"La primera edición de esta obra fué publicada en 1876."
1. Cofresí y Ramírez de Arellano, Roberto, 1791–1825—Fiction.
A 45–3311
Iowa. Univ. Library for Library of Congress [PQ7439.T3C]
[2] 863.5

NT 0035605 IaU FU

Tapia y Rivera, Alejandro, 1826–1882.
Conferencias sobre estética y literatura, pronunciadas en el Ateneo puerto-riqueño, por D. Alejandro Tapia y Rivera. Puerto-Rico, Tip. de Gonzalez & co.. 1881.
311 p. 19cm.
1. Literature—Addresses, essays, lectures. 2. Esthetics.
11–14965
Library of Congress PN45.T3

NT 0035606 DLC

Tapia y Rivera, Alejandro, 1826–1882.
Conferencias sobre estética y literatura, por Alejandro Tapi: y Rivera. San Juan, P. R. [Imprenta Venezuela] 1945.
4 p. l., [9]–295, [1] p. illus. (port.) 22½cm.
"Segunda edición."
1. Literature—Esthetics.
45–22213
Library of Congress PN45.T3 1945
[2] 801

MH NNC
NT 0035607 DLC CaBVaU WaU NcU NcD FU NBuU NN CtY

Tapia y Rivera, Alejandro, 1826–1882.
La cuarterona, drama original en tres actos, por Alejandro Tapia y Rivera. Madrid, Estab. tip. de T. Fortanet, 1867.
72 p. 20cm.
I. Title.
22–2566
Library of Congress PQ7439.T3C8

NT 0035608 DLC NN OCl

Tapia y Rivera, Alejandro, 1826–1882.
La cuarterona; drama original en tres actos, por Alejandro Tapia y Rivera ... [San Juan, P. R., Imprenta Venezuela, 1944]
104, [2] p., 1 l. incl. port. 23cm.
"La primera edición fué impresa en Madrid, España, en 1867. Esta segunda edición lleva algunas correcciones que dejó manuscritas el autor. (A. T. hijo.)"
"Estreñado en San Juan, Puerto Rico en la noche del sábado 17 de agosto de 1878 en el teatro 'Moratín'."
I. Tapia y Díaz, Alejandro, 1882– II. Title.
A 45–2547
New York. Public library for Library of Congress PQ7439.T3C8 1944
[2]† 862.5

NT 0035609 NN WaU FU CaBVaU NcU ICU CtY MH NNC DLC

Tapia y Rivera, Alejandro, 1826–1882.
Cuentos y artículos varios, por Alejandro Tapia y Rivera. San Juan, Puerto Rico [Imprenta Venezuela] 1938.
84 p., 2 l. 22cm.
Contents.—El hambre de progreso.—El loco de Sanjuanópolis.—Don Asino.—Universidad para Puerto Rico.—El aprecio a la mujer es barómetro de civilización.—Puerto Rico visto sin espejuelos por un cegato.—Trabajar es orar.—Recuerdos del San Juan.—Recuerdos del Santiago.
I. Title.
39–18846
Library of Congress PQ7439.T3C85
—— Copy 2. [2] 868.5

NT 0035610 DLC PU CtY FU CLSU CU WaU OCl NjP NN

Tapia y Rivera, Alejandro, 1826–1882.
Discurso pronunciado... en honor de don Alejandro Tapia y Rivera... 1883
see under
Acosta y Calvo, José Julían, 1825–1892.

Tapia y Rivera, Alejandro, 1826–1882.
Enardo and Rosael, an allegorical novella. [Translated from the Spanish by Alejandro Tapia, Jr., and others] New York, Philosophical Library [1952]
56 p. illus. 23 cm.
I. Title.
PZ3.T1633En 863.5 52–14466 ‡

OU FU ViU IEN TxCM
NT 0035612 DLC AzU NmLcU NNC WU INS NN NcU PU PSt

Tapia y Rivera, Alejandro, 1826–1882.
Enardo y Rosael; o, El amor a través de los siglos; novela original por Alejandro Tapia y Rivera. San Juan, P. R., Imprenta Venezuela, 1944.
52 p., 2 l. 19½ cm.
"Tercera edición. Esta obra fué publicada por primera vez en la revista del autor 'La Azuncena' en el año 1872. La segunda vez fué en 1880 en su libro 'Miscelánea.'"
Contents.—Enardo y Rosael.—El 30 de junio.—A mi verdadera Eva.
I. Title.
A 45—1922
New York. Public Libr., for Library of Congress PQ7439.T3E5 1944
[a50c½]† 863.5

NT 0035613 NN CtY NNC MB TxU CaBVaU WaU NcU DLC

Tapia y Rivera, Alejandro, 1826–1882.
Ensayos literarios. Habana, 1862.
port. 8°

NT 0035614 NN

Tapia y Rivera, Alejandro, 1826–1882.
La leyenda de los veinte años, por Alejandro Tapia y Rivera. 2. ed. San Juan, Puerto Rico [Imprenta Venezuela] 1938.
84 p., 2 l. 22cm.
"Consta de 1,000 ejemplares."
"La primera [edición] fué editada en 1874."
I. Title.
39–19871
Library of Congress PQ7439.T3L4 1938
—— Copy 2. [2] 863.5

NT 0035615 DLC CtY PU CLSU CU OCl NN DPU NjP

Tapia y Rivera, Alejandro, 1826–1882.
La leyenda de los veinte años; novela original de Alejandro Tapia y Rivera. San Juan, P. R., Imprenta Venezuela, 1944.
84 p., 2 l. 23ᶜᵐ.

"Tercera edición. La primera fué editada en 1874."

ɪ. Title.

Iowa. Univ. Library   A 45–3308
for Library of Congress   [PQ7439.T3L   ]
                          ₍2₎   863.5

NT 0035616   IaU KU NcU TU

Pr863.2
T172l4

Tapia y Rivera, Alejandro, 1826–1882.
La leyenda de los veinte años y A orillas del Rhin. 4. ed. San Juan, Puerto Rico [Imprenta Venezuela] 1952.
123 p. port. 23cm.

"La primera [edicion] fue editada en 1874."

I. Title. II. Title: A orillas del Rhin.

NT 0035617   FU NN

TAPIA Y RIVERA, Alejandro, 1826–1882.
Mis memorias o Puerto Rico como lo encontré y como lo dejo. New York, N.Y., De Laisne Y Rossboro, Ind., [1927].

Port.

NT 0035618   MH

Tapia y Rivera, Alejandro, 1826–1882.
Mis memorias; o, Puerto Rico como lo encontre y como lo dejo, por Alejandro Tapia y Rivera. New York, N. Y., De Laisne & Rossboro, inc. ₍1928₎
226 p., 1 l. port. 23½ᶜᵐ.

Edited by Alejandro Tapia y Díaz.

ɪ. Tapia y Díaz, Alejandro, 1882– ed. ɪɪ. Title: Puerto Rico como lo encontre y como lo dejo.
                                          29–2014
Library of Congress   PQ7439.T3Z5 1928

NT 0035619   DLC PU KU TxU CU PBL MWA WaU NN MB

Tapia y Rivera, Alejandro, 1826–1882.
Mis memorias; o, Puerto Rico como lo encontre y como lo dejo, por Alejandro Tapia y Rivera. San Juan, P. R., Imprenta Venezuela ₍1946₎
278, ₍2₎ p. illus. (incl. ports.) 22½ᶜᵐ.

Edited by Alejandro Tapia y Díaz. cf. Dos palabras.
"Segunda edición."

ɪ. Tapia y Díaz, Alejandro, 1882– ed. ɪɪ. Title: Puerto Rico como lo encontre y como lo dejo.
                                          46–18391
Library of Congress   PQ7439.T3Z5 1946
                      ₍2₎   860.81

NT 0035620   DLC PSt WU MnU FU NN TxU CaBVaU

Tapia y Rivera, Alejandro, 1826–1882.
... Miscelanea. Novelas, cuentos, bocetos y otros opúsculos. Puerto-Rico, Gonzalez & co., 1880.
260, ₍2₎ p. 18½ᶜᵐ.

ɪ. Title.

                          21–19617 Revised
Library of Congress   PQ7439.T3A16 1880

NT 0035621   DLC IU

Tapia y Rivera, Alejandro, 1826–1882.
Noticia historica de Don Ramon Power, primer diputado de Puerto-Rico, con un apéndice que contiene algunos de sus escritos y discursos, por Alejandro Tapia y Rivera. Puerto Rico, Est. tip. de Gonzalez, 1873.
49 p. 19ᶜᵐ.

1. Power y Giral, Ramón, 1775–1813. 2. Porto-Rico—Hist.

                          12–26134
Library of Congress   F1971.P88

NT 0035622   DLC

Pr863.2
T172p
1952

Tapia y Rivera, Alejandro, 1826–1882.
La palma del cacique. La leyenda de los veinte años. A orillas del Rhin. Prólogo de Manuel García Díaz. 2. ed. México, D. F., Editorial Orion, 1952.
236 p. 19cm. (Colección literaria Cervantes)

"La primera edición fué publicada en 1874.'

I. Title. II. Title: La leyenda de los veinte años. III. Title: A orillas del Rhin.

NT 0035623   FU RPB NN

Tapia y Rivera, Alejandro, 1826–1882.
La palma del cacique. La leyenda de los veinte años. A orillas del khin. Segunda edición México, Editorial Orión, 1953. 92, 104, 40 p.

Colección Literatia Cervantes. [Velázquez, Gonzalo. Biblioteca de obras puertorriqueñas (Microfilm) no. 1048]

NT 0035624   NN

Tapia y Rivera, Alejandro, 1826–1882.
La palma del cacique, leyenda histórica de Puerto Rico, y poesías, por Alejandro Tapia y Rivera. ₍San Juan, P. R., Imprenta Venezuela, 1939₎
59 p., 2 l. 22ᶜᵐ.
"Tercera edición."

ɪ. Title.

                          43–27121
Library of Congress   PQ7439.T3P27
                      ₍2₎   863.5

NT 0035625   DLC

Tapia y Rivera, Alejandro, 1826–1882.
La palma del cacique, leyenda histórica de Puerto Rico, y poesías, por Alejandro Tapia y Rivera. ₍San Juan de Puerto Rico, Imprenta Venezuela, E. Franklin & co., 1943₎
60 p., 2 l. 23ᶜᵐ.
"Cuarta edición ... La primera edición fué publicada en 1852."

ɪ. Title.

Iowa. Univ. Library   A 45–3309
for Library of Congress   [PQ7439.T3P   ]
                          ₍2₎   863.5

NT 0035626   IaU KU TU NcU ICU MB CtY MH NN

Tapia y Rivera, Alejandro, 1826–1882.
La palma del cacique, leyenda primitiva de Puerto-Rico... Madrid, S. Martinez Ael., 1852.
85 p. 16 cm.

NT 0035627   CtY

Tapia y Rivera, Alejandro, 1826–1882.
... La parte del leon. Drama en tres actos y en prosa. Puerto-Rico, Tip. de Gonzalez & co., 1880.
1 p. l., 56 p., 1 l. 20ᶜᵐ.

ɪ. Title.

                          30–15067
Library of Congress   PQ7439.T3P3

NT 0035628   DLC

Tapia y Rivera, Alejandro, 1826–1882.
La parte del león, drama en tres actos y en prosa. Original de Alejandro Tapia y Rivera. San Juan, P. R., Imprenta Venezuela, 1944.
111 p., 2 l. incl. pl., port. 22½ᶜᵐ.

"Segunda edición. La primera fué editada en 1880."
"Carta a don Alejandro Tapia y Rivera" signed Carlos Peñaranda: p. ₍99₎–111.

ɪ. Title.

New York. Public library   A 45–2189
for Library of Congress   PQ7439.T3P3 1944
                          ₍3₎†   862.5

NT 0035629   NN WaU CaBVaU NcU ICU CtY DLC

Tapia y Rivera, Alejandro, 1826–1882.
Postumo el transmigrado. Historia de un hombre que resucitó en el cuerpo de su enemigo, por Alejandro Tapia y Rivera. Puerto-Rico, Impr. de J. Gonzalez Font, 1882.
2 v. in 1. 18ᶜᵐ.

Vol. 2 has title: Postumo envirginiado; ó, Historia de un hombre que se coló en el cuerpo de una mujer, por Alejandro Tapia y Rivera. Segunda parte de Póstumo el transmigrado.

ɪ. Title. ɪɪ. Title: Postumo envirginiado.
                          21–19633 Revised
Library of Congress   PQ7439.T3P7

NT 0035630   DLC

Tapia y Rivera, Alejandro, 1826–1882.
Póstumo el transmigrado; historia de un hombre que resucitó en el cuerpo de su enemigo, por Alejandro Tapia y Rivera. San Juan, P. R., Imprenta Venezuela, 1945.
2 v. in 1. illus. (port.) 23ᶜᵐ.

Paged continuously.
Vol. 2 has title: Póstumo envirginiado; ó, Historia de un hombre que se coló en el cuerpo de una mujer, por Alejandro Tapia y Rivera. Segunda parte do Póstumo el transmigrado.
"Segunda edición."

ɪ. Title. ɪɪ. Title: Póstumo envirginiado.
                          46–696
Library of Congress   PQ7439.T3l7 1945
                      ₍3₎   863.5

NT 0035631   DLC WaU FU PSt CaBVaU NNC CtY

Tapia y Rivera, Alejandro, 1826–1882.
Póstumo el transmigrado, historia de un hombre que resucitó en el cuerpo de su enemigo. Segunda edición San Juan, P. R., Imprenta Venezuela, 1945. 340 p.

[Velázquez, Gonzalo. Biblioteca de obras puertorriqueñas (Microfilm) no. 1049]

NT 0035632   NN CLSU

Tapia y Rivera, Alejandro, 1826–1882.
Roberto d'Evreux, drama histórico en cuatro actos. Original de Alejandro Tapia y Rivera ... ₍San Juan, P. R., Imprenta Venezuela, 1944₎
118, ₍2₎ p. incl. port. 23ᶜᵐ.

"Tercera edición. La primera fué editada en 1857. La segunda aparece en 'El bardo de Guamaní' publicado en la Habana en 1862."
"Representado por primera ves en el teatro de San Juan, Puerto Rico, por varios señores aficionados, en la noche del 19 de setiembre ₍sic₎ de 1856."
"Juicio crítico publicado en 'El Boletín mercantil de Puerto Rico' antes de la impresión del drama" signed J. J. de Acosta: p. ₍93₎–110.

1. Essex, Robert Devereux, earl of, 1566–1601—Drama. ɪ. Title.

New York. Public library   A 45–2190
for Library of Congress   PQ7439.T3R6 1944
                          ₍3₎†   862.5

NT 0035633   NN WaU CaBVaU NcU CtY DLC MiD

Tapia y Rivera, Alejandro, 1826–1882.
La Sataniada; grandiosa epopeya dedicada al príncipe de las tinieblas, por Crisófilo Sardanápalo [pseud.]
Madrid, Impr. de A. J. Alaria, 1878.

5 p. l., xxi, 404 p., 1 l. 19½ᶜᵐ.

I. Title.

22-7075

Library of Congress   PQ7439.T3S2

NT 0035634   DLC PU

Tapia y Rivera, Alejandro, 1826–1882.
La sataniada; grandiosa epopeya dedicada al príncipe de las tinieblas por Crisófilo Sardanápalo (Alejandro Tapia y Rivera) [San Juan, P. R., Imprenta Venezuela, 1945]

340 p., 4 l. illus. (incl. port.) 23ᶜᵐ.

"Segunda edición."—p. [6]

I. Title.

46–15968

Library of Congress   PQ7439.T3S2 1945
       [2]   861.5

NT 0035635   DLC NN WaU NcU FU NNC CtY CaBVaU

Tapia y Rivera, Alejandro, 1826–1882.
Vasco Nuñez de Balboa, drama historico en tres actos por Alejandro Tapia y Rivera. Puerto-Rico, Estab. tip. de González, 1873.

80 p., 1 l. 18½ᶜᵐ.

1. Balboa, Vasco Núñez de, 1475–1519—Drama.   I. Title.

21–21817

Library of Congress   PQ7439.T3V2

NT 0035636   DLC

Tapia y Rivera, Alejandro, 1826–1882.
Vasco Nuñez de Balboa; drama histórico en tres actos por Alejandro Tapia y Rivera. (2. ed.) La primera fué editada en 1873, Establecimiento tipográfico de González, Fortaleza 15, San Juan, Puerto Rico. [San Juan, P. R., Imprenta Venezuela, 1944]

114, [2] p. incl. port. 22½ᶜᵐ.

"Estrenado por la Compañía Robreño y Irigoyen en la capital de Puerto Rico el 11 de noviembre de 1872."

1. Balboa, Vasco Núñez de, 1475–1519—Drama.   I. Title.

A 45–1900

New York. Public Library
for Library of Congress   PQ7439.T3V2 1944
       [3]   862.5

NT 0035637   NN FU CaBVaU MiD CtY DLC

Tapia y Rivera, Alejandro, 1826–1882.
Vida del pintor puertorriqueño José Campeche, por Alejandro Tapia y Rivera. San Juan, P. R. [Imprenta Venezuela] 1946.

106 p., 1 l. incl. port. 22ᶜᵐ.

"Segunda edición."
Bibliographical foot-notes.
The author's Noticia histórica de don Ramón Power, primer diputado de Puerto Rico, con un apéndice que contiene algunos de sus escritos y discursos (p. [49]–106) has special t.-p.
Vida del pintor puertorriqueño José Campeche first published in El Bardo de Guamaní in Havana in 1882. The first edition of Noticia histórica de don Ramón Power was published in San Juan, Puerto Rico, in 1873.

1. Campeche, José, 1751–1809.   2. Power y Giral, Ramón, 1775–1813.

ND314.C3T3 1946   927.5   47–23913

NT 0035639   DLC NN PBL

Tapia y Robles, Juan Antonio de. Ilvstracion del renombre de Grande. Principio, grandeza y etimologia. Pontifices, santos, emperadores, reyes, i varones ilvstres qve le merecieron en la voz pvblica de los hombres ... Madrid, F. Martinez, 1638. 6 p. l., 100 numb. l. ports. 20cm.

NT 0035640   CU NNH

Tapia y Salcedo, Gregorio, d. 1671.

Solórzano Pereira, Juan de, 1575–1655.
D. Philippo. IV. Hispaniarvm, et Indiarvm, regi. opt. max. d. d. Joannes de Solorzano Pereira ... Emblemata regio politica in centvriam vnam redacta, et laboriosis at que vtilibus commentarijs illustrata D. E. C. Cum priuilegio in typographia Domin. Garciæ Morras, Matriti, 1653.

Tapia y Salcedo, Gregorio,   d. 1671.
Exercicios de la gineta ... Por Don Gregorio de Tapia y Salzedo ... En Madrid: Por Diego Diaz, Año 1643.
13 p. l., 116, [4] p. 28 pl., port. 14x20cm.
Described in C.F.G.R.Schwerdt, Hunting, hawking, shooting, London, 1928, vol.2, p.247.

[call number: Roor Uzfe45 643t]

NT 0035642   CtY

Tapia Zenteno, Carlos de
see
Tapia Centeno, Carlos de.

Tapias, Santiago López
see
López Tapias, Santiago.

Tapias Martín, José.
El trabajador y sus derechos. Madrid, 1952.
118 p. 20 cm.

1. Labor laws and legislation—Spain.   I. Title.

55–16094 ‡

NT 0035645   DLC MH-L

Tapias Pilonieta, Arturo D.
... Del protesto de las letras de cambio. Estudio presentado en la Facultad de Jurisprudencia del Colegio mayor de nuestra señora del Rosario para obtener el título de doctor en derecho y ciencias políticas. Bogota, Casa editorial de "La Republica", 1917.
3 p. l., [9]–62 p. 23ᶜᵐ.

NT 0035646   MiU-L

TAPIE, ————, abbé.
Notes et souvenirs sur l'abbé Petit, chanoine, vicaire général, chancelier de l'archevêché de Paris, mort à Jérusalem le 11 octobre 1888.
2e éd. Paris, Bureaux de la Semaine religieuse 1889.

Port.

NT 0035647   MH

Tapie, Alice
Étude d'une réaction de déviation du complément à système hemolytique anti-humain (Musso).
Tarbes, 1940
Thèse - Toulouse

NT 0035648   CtY-M

Tapie, Auguste.
Du delit de revelation de secrets. Toulouse, 1899.
Inaug.-diss. - Toulouse.
Bibl.

NT 0035649   ICRL

Tapie, Auguste.
Du secret professionnel envisage au point de vue de la loi penale. Toulouse, 1899.
Inaug.-diss. - Toulouse.
Bibl..

NT 0035650   DLC

Tapie (J.) [1860–]. *De la polydactylie 54 pp., 1 pl., 4°. Paris, 1885, No. 139.

NT 0035651   DNLM

Tapie, J., 1860–
—— Travail et chaleur musculaires. 88 pp. 8°. Paris, Asselin & Houzeau, 1886.

NT 0035652   DNLM

Tapie, Jean.
... Les hématomes leucémiques (contribution à l'étude pathogénique des hémorragies leucémiques) ... Toulouse, 1921.
24.5 cm.
Thèse - Univ. de Toulouse.

NT 0035653   CtY

Tapie, Jean, ed.

Herrmann, Gustav, 1854–
... Précis d'anatomie pathologique. 3. éd., rev. et cor., par J. Tapie ... et L. Morel ... Avec 378 figures dans le texte. Paris, G. Doin & cⁱᵉ, 1937.

Tapie (Jean-Dosithée). *Chorée, ses divers modes de traitement. 40 pp. 4°. Paris, 1874, No. 461.

NT 0035655   DNLM

Tapié, L. [call number: VK555 .T2]
Guide pratique du navigateur, contenant les modèles de tous les calculs astronomiques usités à la mer... suivi de tables pour faciliter les calculs les plus usuels, de tables pour faire le point, etc. par L. Tapié... Havre, T. Cochard, 1856.
[8], xix, 94, 8, [1], 16 p. 3 fold. pl. 26cm.

1. Navigation. 2. Nautical astronomy.

NT 0035656   ICU MB DN

Tapie (Lucien) [1872–]. *Contribution à l'étude de la lipomatose symétrique à prédominance cervicale. 70 pp. 8°. Paris, 1899, No. 143.

NT 0035657   DNLM

Tapie, Marie Hilaire, *père,* 1855–
... A través de las selvas brasileñas; segunda parte de En las selvas vírgenes del Brasil; versión española de Germán Gómez de la Mata. Obra ilustrada con 32 fotografías. Barcelona, Ediciones y publicaciones Iberia ₁1930₎

2 p. l., 7–275 p. plates, port. 21½ᵐ.

At head of title: R. p. Marie H. Tapie.
"Primera edición; diciembre 1930."

1. Indians of South America—Brazil. 2. Indians of South America—Missions. 3. Missions—Brazil. I. Gómez de la Mata, Germán, 1887– tr. II. Title. *Translation of* Chevauchées à travers déserts et forêts vierges du Brésil inconnu.

Library of Congress   F2520.T1752   32–2615 Revised
    ₁r40c2₎   980.4

NT 0035658   DLC TxU

Tapie, Marie Hilaire, *père,* 1855–
... Chevauchées à travers déserts et forêts vierges du Brésil inconnu; avec vingt photographies et une carte. Paris, Plon ₁1928₎

2 p. l., v, 252 p. plates, ports., double map. 19ᵐ.

At head of title: Père Marie H. Tapie, a. o. p.

1. Indians of South America—Brazil. 2. Indians of South America—Missions. 3. Missions—Brazil. I. Title.

Library of Congress   F2520.T165   36–4081
    ₁s40c1₎   980.4

NT 0035659   DLC ICU NN

Tapie, Marie Hilaire, *père,* 1855–
... Chez les Peaux-Rouges, feuilles de route d'un missionnaire dans le Brésil inconnu; avec dix-huit photographies hors texte et une carte. Paris, Plon ₁1926₎

2 p. l., iii, 291 p. plates, ports., map. 20ᵐ.

1. Indians of South America—Brazil. 2. Indians of South America—Missions. 3. Missions—Brazil. I. Title.

Library of Congress   F2520.T17   27–18954
Copyright A—Foreign   33101

NT 0035660   DLC ICU CtY NN

Tapie, Marie Hilaire, *père,* 1855–
... En las selvas vírgenes del Brasil; traducción de José Bouso García ... Obra ilustrada con 26 fotografías. Barcelona, Ediciones y publicaciones Iberia ₁1929₎

2 p. l., 7–358 p., 1 l. plates, ports., fold. map. 21½ᵐ.

At head of title: R. p. Marie H. Tapie.
"Primera edición, febrero 1929."

1. Indians of South America—Brazil. 2. Indians of South America—Missions. 3. Missions—Brazil. I. Bouso García, José, tr. II. Title. *Translation of* Chez les Peaux-Rouges.

Library of Congress   F2520.T175   32–2614 Revised
    ₁r40c2₎   980.4

NT 0035661   DLC TxU

Tapie (Maurice) [1881–]. *De l'emploi de l'indigo-carmin dans l'exploration fonctionnelle des reins. 50 pp., 2 pl. 8°. Montpellier, 1910. No. 75.

NT 0035662   DNLM CtY

N   Tapié, Michel.
6490   Un art autre où il s'agit de nouveaux
T3   dévidages du réel.   Paris, G. Giraud et
Art   fils, 1952.
Coll.   1 v. (unpaged)   illus.   25 cm.

1. Art, Modern - 20th century. 2. Aesthetics. I. Title: Un art autre.

NT 0035663   NBuU FU NN IaU IEN

Tapié, Michel.
Impressionisti; venti tavole a colori. Bergamo, Istituto italiano d'arti grafiche ₁1952₎

4 p., 20 col. plates (in portfolio) 31 cm.

Cover title.

1. Impressionism (Art) 2. Paintings, French.   A 53–5326

Harvard Univ. Library
for Library of Congress   ₁1₎

NT 0035664   MH OOxM LU WaSpG

759.1
F776Zt   **Tapié, Michel.**
    Jackson Pollock [par] Michel Tapié [et]
    Alfonso Ossorio.   Paris, P. Facchetti, 1952.
    [8]p.   illus.   25cm.

Cover title.

1. Pollock, Jackson, 1912–

NT 0035665   IEN

Tapié, Michel.
Karel Appel

see under

Amsterdam. Stedelijk Museum.

Tapié, Michel.
Mathieu.   [New York, 1952]
   see under   Alexander Iolas gallery,
New York [supplement]

Tapié, Michel
Matta. [Exposé] mai 1949
   see under title

ND588
.E75B6   **Tapié, Michel.**
    Bousquet, Joë.
    Max Ernst. Textes de Joe Bousquet et Michel Tapié.
    ₁Paris₎ R. Drouin, 1950.

Tapié, Michel.
Mirobolus Macadam & cⁱᵉ; hautespates de J. Dubuffet. ₁Paris₎ R. Drouin, 1946.

56 p. illus. 25 cm.

1. Dubuffet, Jean, 1901–   I. Title.
        A 48–4571*

Harvard Univ. Library
for Library of Congress   ₁1₎

NT 0035670   MH CtY ICU NN IEN

DB80
.T26   Tapié, Michel
    Les nationalités slaves d'Autriche-Hongrie
    de 1850 à 1914. Paris, Centre de Documentation
    Universitaire ₁1947₎
    107p. 27cm. (Les cours de Sorbonne)

Cover-title.

1. Slavs in Austria - Hist. 2. Slavs in Hungary - Hist. I. Title.

NT 0035671   PSt

Tapié, Pierre Louis Roger Victor, 1893–
... De la valeur diagnostique de l'écoulement de sang par le mamelon... Bordeaux, 1923.
25.5 cm.
Thèse - Univ. de Bordeaux.

NT 0035672   CtY

Tapie, Victor Lucien, 1900–

Atlas historique ... Paris, Les Presses universitaires de France, 1936–

327.44   Tapié, Victor Lucien, 1900–
T16pCZk   Bílá Hora a francouzská politika. Úvod napsal
    Josef Šusta. Přeložil Zdeněk Kalista.   V
    Praze, Melantrich c1936.
    499p.   22cm.   (Historica, knihovna postav a
    charakterů, sv. 15)
    Translation of La politique étrangère de la
    France et la début de la guerre de Trente ans.
    Bibliographical footnotes.

NT 0035674   IU CSt ICU InU

D246
.P7   **Tapié, Victor Lucien,** 1900–
    Préclin, Edmond.
    Le XVIIᵉ ₁i. e. dix-septième₎ siècle, monarchies centralisées
    (1610–1715) par Edmond Préclin et Victor-L. Tapié. ₁1.
    éd.₎ Paris, Presses universitaires de France, 1943.

D286
.P7   **Tapié, Victor Lucien,** 1900–
    Préclin, Edmond.
    Le XVIIIᵉ ₁i. e. dix-huitième₎ siècle. ₁1. éd.₎ Paris, Presses
    universitaires de France, 1952.

Tapié, Victor Lucien, 1900–
Une église tchèque au xvᵉ siècle: l'Unité des frères, par Victor-L. Tapié ... Paris, E. Leroux, 1934.

3 p. l., ₁ix₎–xi, 125, ₁2₎ p. 22½ᵐ.

"Cette étude est le développement d'un article paru dans la Revue des sciences religieuses, de l'Université de Strasbourg, en avril 1931."—Avant-propos.
"Bibliographie": p. ₁ix₎–xi.

1. Bohemian brethren. 2. Bohemia—Church history. I. Title.
    ₁Full name: Victor Lucien Marie Joseph Tapié₎
        35–10709 Revised

Library of Congress   BX4021.T35
    ₁r46b2₎   284.6

NT 0035677   DLC CtY MiU MH-AH DDO ICU

Tapié, Victor Lucien, 1900–
L'Europe centrale de 1598 à 1660. Paris, Centre de documentation universitaire [1955]

NT 0035678   MH

D 209
T3   Tapié, Victor Lucien, 1900–
    L'Europe centrale et orientale de 1689 à
    1796.   Paris, Centre de documentation
    universitaire ₁1952-53₎
    v. 27 cm. (Les Cours de Sorbonne)

At head of title: Certificat d'études supérieures d'histoire moderne et contemporaine. Includes bibliography.
Contents. –

    v. 4. La Pologne jusqu'au troisième partage.

NT 0035679   OU MH CaBVaU NjR

Tapié, Victor Lucien, 1900–
La France de Louis XIII et de Richelieu. ¡Paris¡ Flammarion ¡1952¡

561 p. 20 cm. (Collection "L'Histoire")

1. France—Hist.—Louis XIII, 1610–1643. I. Title.
Full name: Victor Lucien Marie Joseph Tapié.

DC123.T3   944.032   52–4981 ‡

NNC NN CtY OU ViU OCU InStme MoSU CoU CaBVaU MtU
NT 0035680   DLC NcU LNT NSyU WaU TU PSt MB NcD ICU

Tapié, Victor Lucien, 1900–
Histoire de l'Amérique latine au xixᵉ siècle. Paris, Aubier ¡1945¡

298 p. map. 23 cm.
Bibliography: p. ¡275¡–282.

1. Spanish America—Hist.—1830–
Full name: Victor Lucien Marie Joseph Tapié.

F1413.T3   980   A 50–7686
Texas. Univ. Librar¡
for Library of Congress   ¡2¡†

NcU DLC OrU
NT 0035681   TxU CtY MH CLU NNC NNU ICN NcD MsU CU OU

Tapié, Victor Lucien, 1900–
Joaquim Nabuco, 1849–1910. Translated by Jacob Bean. ¡Paris¡ UNESCO ¡1949¡

39 p. 19 cm. (Great anniversaries)
United Nations Educational, Scientific and Cultural Organization. Publication no. 449.
Bibliography: p. 39.

1. Nabuco, Joaquim, 1849–1910. (Series: United Nations Educational, Scientific and Cultural Organization. UNESCO publication no. 449)
Full name: Victor Lucien Marie Joseph Tapié.

F2536.N179   923.281   50–13370

OrU OCl NIC NN ViU NcD CSt ICU
NT 0035682   DLC CU TxU OU CaBVa CaBViPR ICarbS FU MH

1630   Tapié, Victor Lucien, 1900–
.891   Le monde slave de 1790 à 1850. Paris, Centre
      de Documentation Universitaire ¡1950–
      pt. 28 cm. (Les cours de Sorbonne)

      Cover title.
      Includes bibliographies.

      1.Civilization, Slavic. 2.Russia - Hist.-
      19th cent. I.Title.

NT 0035683   NjP NIC IU MH CaBVaU

DC121   Tapié, Victor Lucien, 1900–
.P32
      Pagès, Georges, 1867–1939.
      Naissance du grand siècle; la France de Henri IV à Louis
      XIV, 1598–1661. Avec la collaboration de Victor-L. Tapié.
      ¡Paris¡ Hachette ¡1948¡

Tapié, Victor Lucien, 1900–
... Le pays de Teschen et les rapports entre la Pologne et
la Tchécoslovaquie ... Paris, Paul Hartmann, éditeur, 1936.

82 p., 2 l. incl. map. 21ᶜᵐ. (Centre d'études de politique étrangère.
Section d'information. Publication no. 3—1936)

1. Teschen. 2. Poles in the Czechoslovak republic. 3. Poland—Foreign relations—Czechoslovak republic. 4. Czechoslovak republic—Foreign relations—Poland. I. Title.
¡Full name: Victor Lucien Marie Joseph Tapié¡
A 38–597

Carnegie endow. int. peace.   Library JX32.C42 no. 3
for Library of Congress   ¡2¡

NT 0035685   NNCE GU MH NcGU NN NNC CtY NNUN

Tapié, Victor Lucien, 1900–
La politique étrangère de la France et le début de la guerre
de trente ans (1616–1621) par Victor-L. Tapié ... Paris, E.
Leroux, 1934.

viii, 672 p. 22½ᶜᵐ.
"Bibliographie": p. ¡631¡–651.
1. France—For. rel.—Austria. 2. Austria—For. rel.—France.

3. Thirty years' war, 1618–1648. 4. Bohemia—Hist. I. Title.
¡Full name: Victor Lucien Marie Joseph Tapié¡
34–31956 Revised
Library of Congress   DC123.5.T3
       ¡r46c2¡   944.032

NT 0035686   DLC CaBVaU NNC CtY NcD CU ViU CoU KU WaU

DB83   Tapié, Victor Lucien, 1900–
.T26   La révolution de 1848 dans l'empire
      d'Autriche (1848–1851) Paris, Centre de Documentation Universitaire [1954]
      79p. 27cm. (Les Cours de Sorbonne)

      Cover title.
      Bibliography: p.i-iii.

      1. Austria - Hist. - Revolution, 1848–1849.
      I. Title.

NT 0035687   PSt WaU OU CaBVaU

Tapié, Victor Lucien, 1900–
La Russie de 1598 à 1660. Paris, Centre de documentation universitaire ¡1954¡

2 v. 27 cm. (Les Cours de Sorbonne)
At head of title: Certificat d'études supérieures d'histoire moderne
et contemporaine.
CONTENTS.—1. Le temps des troubles (1598–1613)—2. Le relève-
ment de l'état russe (1613–1660)

1. Russia—Hist.—1533–1613. 2. Russia—Hist.—1613–1689.
I. Title.

DK114.T3   61–34162 ‡

NT 0035688   DLC WaU OU CaBVaU

Tapié, Victor Lucien, 1900–

La Russie de 1855 à 1894. Paris, Centre
de Documentation Universitaire [1949]

100 p.

NT 0035689   CaBVaU

Tapié, Victor Lucien, 1900–
La Russie de 1855 à 1894. Paris, Centre de documentation universitaire [1952]

106 p.

NT 0035690   MH

Tapié de Céleyran (Gabriel) [1869–].
* Sur un cas d'élytrocèle postérieure (hernie
déshabitée du cul-de-sac de Douglas). 43 pp.,
2 l. 8°. *Paris,* 1899, No. 250.
——— The same. 43 pp., 2 l. 8°. *Paris, G.
Steinheil,* 1899.

NT 0035691   DNLM

ND553
.T7T3
      Tapié de Céleyran, Mary.
      Notre oncle Lautrec. Genève, P. Cailler, 1953.

      94 p. illus., ports. 18 cm. (Collection Écrits et documents de
      peintres, 9)

      1. Toulouse-Lautrec Monfa, Henri Marie Raymond de, 1864–1901.
      (Series)
                    A 54–3777

      Harvard Univ. Library
      for Library of Congress   ¡2¡

NT 0035692   MH NN DLC

Tapié de Céleyran, Michel
see
Tapié, Michel.

Tapiès, F   de.
La France et l'Angleterre, ou Statistique morale et
physique de la France, comparée à celle de l'Angleterre,
sur tous les points analogues; par le Chᵉʳ F. de Tapiès ...
Versailles, Chez l'auteur; ¡etc., etc.¡ 1845.

2 p. l., v, 501 p. tables. 25ᶜᵐ.

1. France—Economic conditions. 2. France—Pol. & govt. 3. Gt. Brit.—
Economic conditions. 4. Gt. Brit.—Pol. & govt.

Library of Congress   HC275.T17   5–21440†

NT 0035694   DLC PU ICU MH NN

Tapies, Joaquín
see
Tapies Riu, Joaquín.

Tapies, Ramón Bertrán
see **Bertrán Tapies, Ramón,** 1905–

43X   Tapies Riu, Joaquin.
Cath   La Biblia entera. Barcelona,
540   Deposito: Rambla de Cataluña [1953]
      265 p.

NT 0035697   DLC-P4

Tapio, pseud.
Suunnestamisopas. Toimittaneet Tapio [pseud.]
ja Esaias [pseud. Helsinki] Kustannusosakeyhtiö
Kivi [1948]

125 p. illus.

NT 0035698   MH

4PH Tapio, Marko
Fin   Lasinen pyykkilauta; romaani
336   äidistä ja pojasta. [4. painos]
     Porvoo, W. Söderström [1952]
     202 p.

NT 0035699   DLC-P4 OC1 NN

TAPIO, MARKO.
Novelleja. Porvoo, Helsinki, W. Söderström [1954] 127 p.
19cm.

1. Fiction, Finnish.

NT 0035700   NN InU NNC

Tapio, Paavo Kustaa, 1898–
... Immunisierungsversuche durch subkutane und per-
kutane einverleibung abgetöteter abortusbazillen bei
kleinen versuchstieren ... Lucka i. Thür., Druck von R.
Berger, 1925.

24, ¡2¡ p. 22½ᶜᵐ.
Inaug.-diss.—Leipzig.
Lebenslauf.
"Literaturverzeichnis": page after p. 24.

1. Abortion.

Agr 26–55

Library, U. S. Dept. of   Agriculture 41T163

NT 0035701   DNAL DNLM DLC CtY ICRL

Tapiola, Arvi
Arra matkustaa. Rauma, O.Y. Länsi-Suomen
kirjapaino, 1953

128 p. illus.

NT 0035702   MH

TAPION VUOSIKIRJA ... TAPIO'S YEARBOOK,

no. 25 (1953) -   1954 -

Helsinki, Keskusment salautakunta Tapio,
1954-

Continues Keskusmetsaseura Tapio.
Metsanhoitolautakuntien toiminta (99.9 K48M)
and Keskusmetsaseura Tapio. Toiminta (99.9
K48T). Beginning with v. 30 (51) 1958,
includes Metsanhoitoyhdistys toiminta. Drops

numbering with 1969.
(35) 1. Forests and forestry. Finland.
I. Keskusmetsalautakunta Tapio. II. Tapio's
yearbook.

NT 0035704   DNAL

Tapionlinna, Tellervo.
Järvikoulun runotar; Dorothy Wordsworth ja hänen vai-
kutuksensa William Wordsworthiin ja S. T. Coleridgeen.
[Porvoossa, 1946]

430 p. illus., ports. 20 cm.

Yliopistollinen väitöskirja—Helsinki.
Errata slip inserted.
Bibliography: p. [391]-392; [422]-428.

1. Wordsworth, Dorothy, 1771-1855. 2. Wordsworth, William, 1770-
1850. 3. Coleridge, Samuel Taylor, 1772-1834. I. Title.

PR5849.T3   53-25260

NT 0035705   DLC NN PU NjP NIC CtY NNC

Tapis anciens de la Chine. Paris, E. Henri [1932]
[4] p. illus., 20 col. mounted pl. 39ᶜᵐ.
Issued in portfolio.

1. Rugs, Chinese.   39-12834

Library of Congress   NK2809.C8T3
[2]   745

WaSp
NT 0035706   DLC CtY PU CSt NIC OCl OO OU NN OrCS Wa

NK2808   Le tapis d'Orient; provenance, fabrication,
.T22   particularités, entretien. Ouvrage documentaire
(Or)   pour spécialistes et amateurs. [Genève, 1947?]
139 p. illus., 16 col. plates.
"Edité par les maisons suisses d'importation de
tapis d'Orient authentiques: Forster, Hettinger,
Hassler, Geelhaar, Schuster, Vidal."
Maps on lining-papers.
Preface signed: W. Deonna.

1. Rugs, Oriental.

NT 0035707   ICU NN MH MiU

Tapis de Finlande, Nouvège, Suède
see under   Stornsen, R

[745   Tapis de la Chine (Collections particu-
T172   lières) Soieries et velours orient-
aux (Collections du Musée des arts
décoratifs)... Paris, A. Guérinet
n.d.
n.p., plates. 40½cm.

In portfolio.

NT 0035709   NcD PP OCl

... Tapis de Pologne, Lithuanie, Yougoslavie. Paris, H.
Ernst [1930?]

3 p. l., 30 col. mounted pl. 39ᶜᵐ. (Éditions Arts & couleurs)

"Presque tous ces spécimens ont été exposés en 1927 à Paris, au
Musée des arts décoratifs, pavillon de Marsan, palais du Louvre."
Issued in portfolio.

1. Rugs. 2. Carpets.

Library of Congress   NK2842.T3   32-25550
[2]   745

NcGU CtY OOxM OCl OU OO MiD OClMA
NT 0035710   DLC CLSU CaOTP WaS PPMoI NBuG NN IU TxU

745.52   Tapis de quelques peuples russes. Paris,
T172r   E. Henri [1926?]
[2] l., 44 plates (part col., in portfolio)
39 cm.

"Les tapis ... etaient exposés au Pavillon
Russe, lors de l' Exposition des arts décoratifs [Paris] en 1925".

1. Rugs. Russian.

NT 0035711   N OCl

Les tapis polonais au pavillon de Marsan, Palais
du Louvre
see under   Paris. Musée des arts
décoratifs.

... Tapis roumains. Paris, H. Ernst [1928]

3 p. l., 34 col. mounted pl. 38½ x 28½ᶜᵐ. (Éditions Art & couleurs)

"Les tapis reproduits dans cet album figuraient presque tous à l'expo-
sition de tapis organisée à Paris au Musée des arts décoratifs de juin à
septembre 1927; les autres étaient aux expositions d'art roumain de
Genève 1925, et de Paris 1925, aux Tuileries, Musée du jeu de paume."
Introduction signed: D'après M. Tzigara-Samurcas.
Issued in portfolio.

1. Rugs. Rumanian. 2. Textile industry and fabrics—Rumania.
I. Tzigara-Samurcas, Alexandru.

Library of Congress   NK2869.T3   32-25549
[2]   745

KU OU NcD TxU WaS WaT OrCS
NT 0035713   DLC CLSU OO NcGU MB PP IU OClMA LU FTaSU

La Tapisserie. Paris, Éditions du Chêne, 1947.

104 p. illus., 9 col. plates. 31 cm. (La Tradition française)

Pref. signed: P. V.
Articles by Pierre Verlet, Guillaume Janneau, Roger-Armand
Weigert and others.
"Bibliographie": p. 103.

1. Tapestry—France. I. Verlet, Pierre. (Series)

NK3049.A1T3   746.3   A 48-7078*

Yale Univ. Library
for Library of Congress   [a52b1]†

NT 0035714   CtY InStme AAP Or NNC NNU NcU NN DLC

La Tapisserie. [Paris, Visages du monde, 1951?]

23 p. illus. 28 cm. (Visages du monde, no 108 des cahiers tri-
mestriels d'art et de littérature)

1. Tapestry—France—Hist.

NK3049.A1T33   56-30425 ‡

NT 0035715   DLC

Tapisserie broderie de la reine Mathilde (XIe.
siècle)
see under   Tostain, Charles

... Tapisserie de la reine Mathilde... retraçant
en 57 scènes les principales peripeties du
"conquest d'Engleterre"... Edition absolument
complète exécutée au moyen de photographies
directes de l'original; traduction... du texte
brodé dans la tapisserie et notes historiques en
[français et en anglais]... Bayeux,
R. Deslandes [1909]
59 p. incl. illus. 38 x 28.5 cm.
At head of title: Bibliotheque de Bayeux
library.
T.-p. and text in French and English.
1. Bayeux tapestry.

NT 0035717   CtY MH IEN

Tapisserie de la reine Mathilde retraçant en 57 scènes les
principales peripeties du "conquest d'Engleterre." Edition
absolument complète exécutée au moyen de
photographies 24/30 directes de l'original; traduction
du texte brodé dans la tapisserie et notes historiques
en français et en anglais ... Bayeux, R. Deslandes
[1910]

plate (10 x 1008ᵐᵐ) fold. to 10 x 28½ᶜᵐ.   fr. 2.50

1. Bayeux tapestry.
Library of Congress   NK3049.B3T3   10-12549

NT 0035718   DLC

La Tapisserie française, muraille et laine, textes de Germain
Bazin [et al.] Résumé chronologique par Denise Majorel et
Gislaine Yver. Paris, P. Tisné, 1946 [i. e. 1947]

24 p. illus., 69 plates (part col.) 34 cm.

1. Tapestry, French. I. Bazin, Germain. II. Majorel, Denise.

NK3049.A1T35   746.3   49-17344*

IEN NjP DSI CLSU WU OrCS WaS
NIC MiD OCl OKentU NcD CSt MiDA CU MH TxDaM KU INS
NT 0035719   DLC PU-FA OClMA MdBWA NcGU OOxM OU NN MB

La tapisserie gothique, premiere serie
see under   Demotte, G J

Tapisserie-, Spitzen- und Posamenten-Zeitung. Zentral-Organ
für die Fabrikanten und Verkäufer von Tapisseriewaren, Stickereien, Spitzen...
Jahrg. 7 (Oct. 1906 – Sept. 15, 1907)
Darmstadt: A. Koch. 1906-07.   f°.

1 v. illus., pl.
Semi-monthly.
Editor: Oct. 1906 – Sept. 15, 1907, A. Koch.
Preceded by Der Tapisserist.
Continued as Tapisserie- und Stickerei-Zeitung.

1. Embroidery.—Per. and soc. publ.   2. Lace.—Per. and soc. publ.
N. Y. P. L.   May 15, 1916.

NT 0035721   NN

Tapisserie- und Stickerei-Zeitung; Zentral-Organ für die Fabri-
kation und den Handel von Tapisseriewaren, Stickereien, Spitzen...
Jahrg. 8-9 (Oct. 1907 – Sept. 15, 1909)
Darmstadt: A. Koch, 1907-09.

2 v. illus., pl.
Semi-monthly.
Editor: Oct. 1907 – Sept. 15, 1909, A. Koch.
Preceded by Tapisserie-, Spitzen- und Posamenten-Zeitung.
Continued as Stickerei-Zeitung.

1. Embroidery.—Per. and soc. publ.   2. Lace.—Per. and soc. publ.
N. Y. P. L.   May 15, 1916.

NT 0035722   NN

Tapisseries de Dijon et du chevalier Bayard,
représentant l'une du siège de Dijon par les
Suisses, en 1513
see under   [Jubinal, Achille i. e. Michel
Louis Achille] 1810-1875.

Les tapisseries de Jean Lurçat
    see under   [Courthion, Pierre]

Les tapisseries de l'abbaye de Saint-Robert de la
   Chaise-Dieu
    see under   [Bonnefoy, Géraud]

Les tapisseries de l'Apocalypse de la
  Cathédral d'Angers accompagnees du texte de
  l'Apocalypse ...   Paris [1942] c319 p.
    see under Bible. N. T. Revelation.
  French. 1942. Le Maistre.
    For same title with collation 72 p., 72 plates
  see under Lejard, [André, 1889-   ed.

---

                               *Cab.40.10.1
Tapisseries, Les, de la cathédrale d'Angers, dites tapisseries du roi
  René. Représentations de l'Apocalypse. Die Wandstickereien
  des Königs René in der Cathedrale zu Angers.
  Leipzig. Hiersemann. [1882.] 72 photographs on 38 sheets.
  47 cm.

K6330 — Tapestry. — Angers Cathedral.

NT 0035727   MB MH

N1678 Les tapisseries de la cour impériale
T3   de Vienne.   Vienne, Krystallverlag,
1922 F   1922.
      20 p. 44 plates (20 col.)   31cm.

    Translation of Die Gobelins des
  Wiener kaiserlichen Hofes.
    Each col. plate preceded by guard
  sheet with descriptive letterpress.
    Contents.-La collection de tapisse-
  ries viennoise, von H. Schmitz.-Les
  tapisseries d'après Boucher,et le
  "Meuble rose" du palais impérial à
  Vienne, von   E.W. Braun.

NT 0035728   MWiCA MoU CLSU NBuG MH

Tapisseries de notre temps
    see under [Janneau, Guillaume] 1887-

Tapisseries de Valenciennes, du chateau d'Haroué,
  et de la collection Dusommerard.
  6 plates.

NT 0035730   RP

     Tapisseries des Gobelins, de Beauvais & des
  Flandres: broderies & scieries de diverses
fNK3000 époques. Paris, A. Guérinet [1913]
T3
    2 v. plates. 40cm. In 1|2 brown cloth
  portfolios.

    No text; each vol. contains 1 leaf with title,
  imprint and table des planches.

    1. Beauvais tapestries. 2. Gobelin tapestry.
  3. Tapestry--Netherlands. 4. Embroidery.

NT 0035731   CSmH RP MdBWA

    Tapisseries des Gobelins, de Beauvais & des Flandres; bro-
  deries & soieries de diverses époques...   Paris: A. Guérinet
  [1926?]. 2 v. plates. f°. (Matériaux et documents d'art
  décoratif.)

    Caption-title.
    v. 2 called 2ᵉ sér.

                           J. S. BILLINGS MEM. COLL.
  1. Tapestry, French. 2. Title. 3. Ser.
  N. Y. P. L.   July 14, 1927

NT 0035732   NN OC1MA

Les Tapisseries du Cardinal de Clugny
  (1480-1483) Mémoire du XVIIIe siècle...
    see under Varax, L. de, vicomte, ed.

... Les Tapisseries du Musée de l'ancien
  archeveché à Aix-en-Provence...
    see under Aix, France. Musée de
  l'ancien archeveché.

    **TAPISSERIES du quinzième siècle conservées à
  la cathédrale de Tournay. Leur fabrication à
  Arras en 1402. Histoire,description précédées
  d'une notice sur la fabrication des tapisseries
  en Flandre et particulièrement à Arras. Tournay,etc.,1883.**

    f°. pp.(2),394. 14 plates,and wdcts.

NT 0035735   MH

Tapisseries et étoffes coptes. [Paris, H. Ernst, 19—]
  cover-title, 2 p. l., 48 mounted pl. (part col.) 38½ᶜᵐ.
  In portfolio.

  1. Textile industry and fabrics—Egypt. 2. Tapestry. 3. Art, Coptic.

  Library of Congress   NK8988.T3   21—4515

            TxU CSt OrP MtU WaS Wa OrCS OrU
         PPT OU MiU OCU OC1ND NBB MB IU OKentU FU NcGU DSI
NT 0035736   DLC PPPM DDO PPMoI CtY NB NN PP PU-Mu

Tapisseries françaises d'aujourd'hui. Französische
  Wandteppiche der Gegenwart. Augustiner-
  Museum Freiburg
    see under Freiburg i. B. Vereinigte Samm-
  lungen der Stadt. Augustinermuseum.

Case
F   Les **TAPISSERIES** royales. Representans au
39   naïf les plus rares affaires de ce temps.
.326 [n.p.]1624.
        23p. 16cm.
1623re2
       Binder's title: Refo[rmation] de Fra[nce]

NT 0035738   ICN WU

Der **Tapisserist**; Zeitschrift für die Interessen der Tapisserie und
  verwandten Branchen.
  Jahrg.

  Berlin: C. M. A. Müller & Co., 190 –06.   f°.

    v. illus.

    Semi-monthly.
    Editor :   – Sept. 15, 1906, W. Plessner.
    Continued as Tapisserie-, Spitzen- und Posamenten-Zeitung.

  1. Embroidery.—Per. and soc. publ.   2. Lace.—Per. and soc. publ.
  N. Y. P. L.   May 15, 1916.

NT 0035739   NN

Der Tapizierer und Sattler
    see Der Sattler und Tapizierer

S21   Tapke, Victor Ferdinand, 1890-   joint author.
.A6
no. 2089 Leukel, Robert Whilmer, 1888-
        Barley diseases and their control [by R. W. Leukel and
    V. F. Tapke. Washington, U. S. Govt. Print. Off., 1955]

          Tapke, Victor Ferdinand, 1890-   joint
    author.
  Leukel, Robert Whilmer, 1888-
        Barley diseases controlled by seed treatment. [By R. W.
    Leukel ... and V. F. Tapke ...] Washington, U. S. Govt. print.
    off., 1934.

S21   Tapke, Victor Ferdinand, 1890-   joint author.
.A6
no. 2069 Leukel, Robert Whitmer, 1888-
        Cereal smuts and their control [by R. W. Leukel and V. F.
    Tapke. Washington, U. S. Govt. Print. Off., 1954]

Tapke, Victor Ferdinand, 1890-
    Effects of the modified hot-water treatment on germi-
  nation, growth, and yield of wheat.

  (*In* U. S. Dept. of agriculture. Journal of agricultural research. vol.
  XXVIII, no. 1, Apr. 5, 1924, p. 79-98. 5 pl. on 3 L 25ᶜᵐ. Washington, 1924)
    Contribution from Bureau of plant industry (G—362)
    "Literature cited": p. 97.

    1. [Hot-water treatment] 2. Wheat. 3. Germination. [2, 3. Wheat—
  Germination]
                                       Agr 24-673
    Library, U. S. Dept. of   Agriculture 1Ag84J vol. 28

NT 0035744   DNAL OO OU OC1MN

          Tapke, Victor Ferdinand, 1890-   joint
    author.
  Stanton, Thomas Ray, 1885-
       ... Field studies on resistance of hybrid selections of oats
    to covered and loose smuts. By T. R. Stanton ... F. A. Coff-
    man ... and V. F. Tapke ... Washington [U. S. Govt. print.
    off.] 1934.

Tapke, Victor Ferdinand, 1890-
    Formaldehyde seed treatment for oat smuts. [By V. F.
  Tapke] Washington, U. S. Govt. print. off., 1928.

    4 p. illus. 20½ x 9½ᶜᵐ. (U. S. Dept. of agriculture. Miscellaneous
  publication no. 21)
    Contribution from Bureau of plant industry.

    1. Formaldehyde. 2. Ustilaginene. 2. Oat smut. 3. Seeds. 4. Dis-
  infection and disinfectants. [3, 4. Seeds—Disinfection]
                                       Agr 28-378
    Library, U. S. Dept. of   Agriculture 1Ag84M no. 21

NT 0035746   DNAL PPT WaWW OC1 OU

          Tapke, Victor Ferdinand, 1890-   joint author.
  Tisdale, Wendell Holmes, 1892-
       Infection of barley by *Ustilago nuda* through seed in-
    oculation. By W. H. Tisdale ... and V. F. Tapke ...
    (*In* U. S. Dept. of agriculture. Journal of agricultural research. vol.
    XXIX, no. 6, September 15, 1924, p. 263-284. illus. 25ᶜᵐ. Washington,
    1925)

Tapke, Victor Ferdinand, 1890– joint author

Stanton, Thomas Ray, 1885–
Influence of hulling the caryopsis on covered-smut infection and related phenomena in oats. By T. R. Stanton ... F. A. Coffman ... V. F. Tapke ... G. A. Wiebe ... R. W. Smith ... and B. B. Bayles ...
(*In* U. S. Dept. of agriculture. Journal of agricultural research. v. 41, no. 8, Oct. 15, 1930, p. 621–633. 23½ᶜᵐ. Washington, 1930)

Tapke, Victor Ferdinand, 1890–
Influence of humidity on floral infection of wheat and barley by loose smut ...
(*In* U. S. Dept. of agriculture. Journal of agricultural research. v. 43, no. 6, Sept. 15, 1931, p. 503–516. illus., maps. 23½ᶜᵐ. Washington, 1931)
Contribution from Bureau of plant industry (G-784)
Published October 13, 1931.
"Literature cited": p. 515–516.

1. Loose smut of barley. 2. Loose smut of wheat.
Agr 31-1284

Library, U. S. Dept. of   Agriculture 1Ag84J   vol. 43, no. 6
Library of Congress   [S21.A75   vol. 43, no. 6]

NT   0035749   DNAL OU DLC

Tapke, Victor Ferdinand, 1890–
Influence of varietal resistance, sap acidity, and certain environmental factors on the occurrence of loose smut in wheat.
(*In* U. S. Dept. of agriculture. Journal of agricultural research. v 39, no. 5, Sept. 1, 1929, p. 313–339. illus., map. 23½ᶜᵐ. Washington, 1929)
Contribution from Bureau of plant industry (G-688)
Published September 13, 1929.
Thesis (PH. D)—Cornell university, 1927.
"Literature cited": p. 337–339.
1. Loose smut of wheat. 2. Wheat—Diseases and pests.
Agr 29-1520

[S21.A75 vol. 39, no. 5]
Library, U. S. Dept. of   Agriculture 1Ag84J   vol. 39

NT   0035750   DNAL DLC OU OC1MN

Tapke, Victor Ferdinand, 1890– joint author.

Coffman, Franklin Arthur, 1892–
Inheritance of resistance in oats to *Ustilago levis*. By F. A. Coffman ... T. R. Stanton ... B. B. Bayles ... G. A. Wiebe ... R. W. Smith ... and V. F. Tapke ...
(*In* U. S. Dept. of agriculture. Journal of agricultural research. v. 43, no. 12, Dec. 15, 1931, p. 1085–1099. 23½ᶜᵐ. Washington, 1932)

Tapke, Victor Ferdinand, 1890–
Physiologic races of *Ustilago hordei* ...
(*In* U. S. Dept. of agriculture. Journal of agricultural research. v. 55, no. 9, Nov. 1, 1937, p. 683–692. 23½ᶜᵐ. Washington, 1937)
Contribution from Bureau of plant industry (G-1069)
Published Dec. 29, 1937.
"Literature cited": p. 691–692.

1. Barley—Diseases and pests. 1. Barley smut.
Agr 38-60

U. S. Dept. of agr. Library   1Ag84J vol. 55, no. 9
for Library of Congress   [S21.A75 vol. 55, no. 9]

NT   0035752   DNAL DLC

Tapke, Victor Ferdinand, 1890–
... Single-bath hot-water and steam treatments of seed wheat for the control of loose smut (*Ustilago tritici* (Pers.) Jens.) By V. F. Tapke ... Washington (Govt. print. off.) 1926.
29 p. illus., diagr. 23ᶜᵐ. (U. S. Dept. of agriculture. Department bulletin no. 1383)
Contribution from Bureau of plant industry.
"Literature cited": p. 28.
1. Hot-water treatment. 2. Loose smut. 3. Wheat—Diseases and pests. I. Title.
Agr 26-405

Library, U. S. Dept. of   Agriculture 1Ag84B no. 1383

NT   0035753   DNAL OC1MN OU OO WaWW OC1

Tapke, Victor Ferdinand, 1890– joint author.

Tisdale, Wendell Holmes, 1892–
... Smuts of wheat and rye and their control. (By W. H. Tisdale and V. F. Tapke) (Washington, U. S. Govt. print. off., 1927)

Tapke, Victor Ferdinand, 1890–
... Studies on the natural inoculation of seed barley (*Hordeum vulgare* L.) with covered smut (*Ustilago hordei*) ...
(*In* U. S. Dept. of agriculture. Journal of agricultural research. v. 60, no. 12, June 15, 1940, p. 787–810. illus., pl. 23½ᶜᵐ. Washington, 1940)
Contribution from Bureau of plant industry (G-1168)
In cooperation with the New York (Cornell) Agricultural experiment station.
Published Aug. 22, 1940.
"Literature cited": p. 808–810.
1. Barley—Diseases and pests. 1. Barley smut—Control. 2. Barley—Seed.
Agr 40-646

U. S. Dept. of agr. Library   1Ag84J vol. 60, no. 12
for Library of Congress   [S21.A75 vol. 60, no. 12]
(030-72)

NT   0035755   DNAL OU

Tapke, Victor Ferdinand, 1890–
A study of the cause of variability in response of barley (*Hordeum vulgare* L.) loose smut (*Ustilago nuda* (Jens.) Kell. and Sw.), to control through seed treatment with surface disinfectants ...
(*In* U. S. Dept. of agriculture. Journal of agricultural research. v. 51, no. 6, Sept. 15, 1935, p. 491–508. illus., pl. 23ᶜᵐ. Washington, 1935)
Contribution from Bureau of plant industry (G-976)
Published Jan. 3, 1936.
"Literature cited": p. 506–508.
1. Barley—Diseases and pests. 2. Loose smut of barley. 3. Seeds—Disinfection.
Agr 36-202

Library, U. S. Dept. of   Agriculture 1Ag84J vol. 51, no. 6
Library of Congress   [S21.A75 vol. 51, no. 6]
(5*)

NT   0035756   DNAL OC1 OU DLC

Tapke, Victor Ferdinand, 1890–   joint author.

Faris, James Abraham, 1890–1933.
... Wheat smuts and their control. (By J. A. Faris, V. F. Tapke, and H. A. Rodenhiser. Washington, U. S. Govt. print. off., 1933)

Tapken, Anton.
Geburtshilfe, für Landwirte bearbeitet von A. Tapken ... Dritte, verbesserte und vermehrte Auflage ... Berlin, P. Parey, 1908.
viii, 167, (1) p. illus. 19ᶜᵐ.   (On cover: Thaer-Bibliothek. Bd. 99)

NT   0035758   ICJ

Tapken, Anton.   619.02 R400
Die Praxis der Tierarztes. Ein Leitfaden nach den Erfahrungen aus 35 jähriger Praxis, von Veterinärrat A. Tapken, ... Mit 16 Abbildungen. Berlin, R. Schoetz, 1914.
xi, 397, (1) p. 16 illus. 24½ᶜᵐ.

NT   0035759   ICJ

Tapken, Anton.
UeberGeburtshilfe beim Schwein.
31 pp. 8°.   Leipzig, A. Felix, 1893.
Forms 3. Hft. v. 3, of Thiermed. Vortr.

NT   0035760   DNLM DNAL

Tapken (Friedrich) [1883–   ]. *Ueber einen Fall von Hydrops vaceiniforme (Bazin). 47 pp. 8°. München, Kastner & Callwey, 1911.

NT   0035761   DNLM

Tapken, Hildegard
Jeunesse allemande. Bruxelles, Éditions "Steenlandt" (1943?)
24, (59) p. of photographs. 24ᶜᵐ.

1. Nationalsozialistische deutsche Arbeiter-Partei. Hitler-Jugend. 2. Youth. I. Title.

NT   0035762   ViU

Tapken, Johannes, pr. Tierarzt: Beitrag zur Kenntnis der Eitererreger des Pferdes. Hannover: Schaper 1909. 86 S. 8°
Gießen, Veterinär-Med. Diss. v. 12. Okt. 1909, Ref. Olt
[Geb. 13. Jan. 83 Varel; Wohnort: Varel; Staatsangeh.: Oldenburg; Vorbildung: Realgymn. Osnabrück Reife O. 01; Studium: Gießen 3, Berlin Tierärztl. Hochsch. 1, Münster 2, Berlin Tierärztl. Hochsch. 3 S.; Rig. 9. Juli 09.]
[U 10. 1260

NT   0035763   ICRL NjP MBCo

Tapla, Theodor Johann Georg, 1853–
Geodätische constructionen und berechnungen. Directiven für die herstellung kleinerer geodätischer elaborate aus feld-daten und für die berechnung einfacher dreiecks-syteme, von Theodor Tapla ... Leipzig und Wien, F. Deuticke, 1895.
3 p. l., 87 p. diagrs. on 14 fold. pl. 24ᶜᵐ.

1. Triangulation.
7-31471

Library of Congress   QB321.T3

NT   0035764   DLC DI-GS

Tapla, Theodor Johann Georg, 1853–   526.9 Q102
Grundzüge der niederen Geodäsie, ... , von Theodor Tapla, ...
1–[IV]. ... Leipzig und Wien, F. Deuticke, 1901–1911.
4 vol. in 2. 24ᶜᵐ.
"Der III. Teil ... stellt nämlich eine neue Auflage der Geodätischen Konstruktionen und Berechnungen darallerdings in wesentlich verändelter und erweiterter Form."—Pref.
Contents.—1. Methoden und Dispositionen (Dispositiomslehre.) 1901. [6], 58 p. 55 diagrs. on 9 fold. pl.—2. Instrumentenkunde. 1908. vii, [1], 279 p. incl. tables. 248 illus. on 25 fold. pl.—3. Kartierung. 1906. vii, 107 p. 14 fold. diagr.—4. Verwertung von geodätischen Aufnahmen. 1911. vi, 62 p. 92 diagr. on 10 fold. pl.

NT   0035765   ICJ NN

---

515   **Tapla, Theodor Johann Georg, 1853–**
T16v2   Vademekum der darstellenden geometrie. Für schüler gewerblicher lehranstalten, für schüler und absolventen des gymnasiums sowie für praktiker. 2.durchgesehene aufl. Wien, 1909.
182p. fold.plates.

NT   0035766   IU MH

Taplamacioğlu, Mehmet
... Un estudio comparativo sobre el Consejo de estado en Turquia. Ankara, 1955.
62 p. 23½cm.
"Publicada en annales de l'Université d'Ankara, 1955."
"Bibliografía": p. (61)–62.

NT   0035767   MH-L

DR741   **Taplamacioğlu, Mehmet.**
B7T176   Regimenes de los estrechos del Bosforo y de los Dardanelos. (Istanbul) Imp. Universitaria (1954)
31 p. 25cm.
"Bibliografía (!)": p. 31.
"Tirada aparte de Annales de l'Université d'Ankara."

1. Straits. 2. Bosporus. 3. Dardanelles. I. Title.

NT   0035768   CSt-H

Taplex Corporation, New York.
The Taplex budget and record for personal or family expenses; a simple, yet efficient expense record...establishing the possibility of saving a specific sum each month. New York: Taplex Corporation (cop. 1918).   1 p.l., 159 p.   illus. sq. 4°.

1. Bookkeeping for personal and   domestic affairs. 2. Title.
N. Y. P. L.   October 2, 1918.

NT   0035769   NN CU

Taplex Corporation, New York.
The Taplex household record of expenses; designed for use in conjunction with the Taplex budget for personal and family expenses. New York, Taplex corporation [1922?]
[32] p. incl. forms. 17 x 12 cm .
Text runs parallel with back of cover.
1. Domestic economy – Accounting.

NT 0035770   CU

Tapley, Charles Sutherland, 1899–
From Muddy Boo to Blind Hole, by Charles Sutherland Tapley. Danvers, Mass., Priv. print., 1940.
24 p. front. 23½ᶜᵐ.

1. Danvers, Mass.—Descr.   I. Title.   42–15273
Library of Congress   F74.D2T16
                           (2)   917.445

NT 0035771   DLC

Tapley, Charles Sutherland, 1899–
Rebecca Nurse, saint but witch victim, by Charles Sutherland Tapley. Boston, Mass., Marshall Jones company (ᶜ1930)
xiii, 105 p. front. (port.) plates. 20ᶜᵐ.

1. Nurse, Mrs. Rebecca (Towne) 1621–1692. 2. Witchcraft—Salem, Mass.
                                                   30–33553
Library of Congress   BF1576.T23
    copyright A 31429   (3)   272.8

        MH-L
NT 0035772   DLC TU NIC PU MU ViU TxU WaT MB MWA MH

Tapley, Daniel J.
The new recreation. Amateur photography: a practical instructor, by D. J. Tapley ... New York, S. W. Green's son, 1884.
140, (2) p. front., illus., diagrs. 19ᶜᵐ.

1. Photography—Handbooks, manuals, etc.
                                                    9–5413
Library of Congress   TR146.T17

NT 0035773   DLC PPGi OC1 PPF OU OOxM MB NN

Tapley, Earl Mays.
Preparation for teaching general education courses in junior colleges. 1955.
200 l.
Thesis – Univ. of Chicago.
1. Teachers, Training of – U.S. 2. Education – Study and teaching.

NT 0035774   ICU

Tapley, Earl Mays.
Preparation for teaching general education courses in junior colleges. Chicago (Library, Dept. of Photographic Reproduction, University of Chicago) 1955.
Microfilm copy (positive) of typescript.
Collation of the original, as determined from the film: xi, 200 l. tables.
Thesis—University of Chicago.
Bibliography: leaves 193–200.

1. Education—Study and teaching.   I. Title: Teaching general education courses in junior colleges.

Microfilm 4549 LB   Mic 57–5456

NT 0035775   DLC OrU

Tapley, Harriet Silvester, 1870–
Chronicles of Danvers (old Salem village) Massachusetts, 1632–1923, by Harriet Silvester Tapley ... Danvers, Mass., The Danvers historical society, 1923.
xii p., 1 l., 283 p. front., plates, ports., facsims. 25ᶜᵐ.

1. Danvers, Mass.—Hist.   I. Title.
                                                   23–9783
        F74.D2T17

NT 0035776   DLC PHi OC1WHi NIC MB MWA

Tapley, Harriet Silvester, 1870–   *2358.20.64.No.1
Dr. William Stearns, merchant and apothecary, with some account of the Sprague family.
(*In* Essex Institute, Salem, Mass. Historical collections. Vol. 64, No. 1, pp. 1–19. Portraits. Salem, Mass. 1928.)

D6638 — Stearns, William, 1754–1819. —Sprague family.

NT 0035777   MB

Tapley, Harriet Silvester, 1870–   ed.
Essex institute, *Salem, Mass.*
Early coastwise and foreign shipping of Salem; a record of the entrances and clearances of the port of Salem, 1750–1769. Salem, Mass., The Essex institute, 1934.

Tapley, Harriet Silvester, *1870–*   *2358.20.64.No.3
Francis Boardman Crowninshield Bradlee.
(*In* Essex Institute, Salem, Mass. Historical collections. Vol. 64, no. 3, pp. 193–198. Portraits. Autograph facsimile. Salem, Mass. 1928.)

D6204 — Bradlee, Francis Boardman Crowninshield, 1881–1928.

NT 0035779   MB

Tapley, Harriet Silvester, 1870–
Genealogy of the Tapley family ... Comp. by Harriet Silvester Tapley. Danvers, Mass. (Printed by the Endecott press) 1900.
1 p. l., xix, 256 p. front., plates, ports., maps. 24ᶜᵐ.
"Gilbert Tapley of Salem, Massachusetts, 1634–1714, and his descendants": p. (77)–225.

1. Tapley family (John Tapley, b. 1638) 2. Tapley family (Gilbert Tapley, 1634–1714) 3. Tapley family.
                                                   1–16041
Library of Congress   CS71.T173 1900

NT 0035780   DLC PHi MB MWA Nh

Tapley, Harriet Silvester, 1870–   ed.
Danvers historical society, *Danvers, Mass.*
The historical collections
v. 1–
Danvers, Mass., The Society, 1913–

Tapley, Harriet Silvester, 1875–   joint comp.
Putnam, Elizabeth Cabot.
The Hon. Samuel Putnam and Sarah (Gooll) Putnam, with a genealogical record of their descendants. Comp. by Elizabeth Cabot Putnam and Harriet Silvester Tapley. (Reprinted from the Danvers historical collections, volume x) Danvers, Mass., 1922.

Tapley, Harriet Silvester, 1870–   ed.
Danvers historical society, *Danvers, Mass.* The historical collections. (*Indexes*)
... Index to vols. vi–xx: under direction of the Committee on publication. Danvers, Mass., The Society, 1933.

Tapley, Harriet Silvester, 1870–
Essex institute, *Salem, Mass. Oak Knoll collection.*
John Greenleaf Whittier manuscripts. The Oak Knoll collection. (Salem, Mass., 1931)

Tapley, Harriet Silvester, 1870–
The Province galley of Massachusetts Bay, 1694–1716; a chapter of early American naval history, by Harriet Silvester Tapley. Salem, Mass., 1922.
1 p. l., 39 p. incl. tables. front., facsims. 25ᶜᵐ.
Illustrated t.-p.
"Reprinted from the Historical collections of the Essex institute, vol. LVIII."

1. Province galley (Ship)

NT 0035785   MiU DN MiD NN CtN1CG

Tapley, Harriet Silvester, 1870–
St. Peter's church in Salem, Massachusetts, before the revolution, by Harriet Silvester Tapley. Salem, Mass., The Essex institute, 1944.
iv, 92 p. front., illus. (incl. plan) ports., facsims. 23½ᶜᵐ.
"Reprinted from the Essex institute historical collections, volume LXXX."
Bibliographical foot-notes.

1. Salem, Mass. St. Peter's church.   I. Essex institute, Salem, Mass.
Harvard univ. Library   A 45–1242
    for Library of Congress °   (1)

NT 0035786   MH PHi WaS NcD ICU

Tapley, Harriet Silvester, 1870–
Salem imprints, 1768–1825; a history of the first fifty years of printing in Salem, Massachusetts, with some account of the bookshops, booksellers, bookbinders and the private libraries, by Harriet Silvester Tapley. Salem, Mass., The Essex institute, 1927.
x, 512 p. front., illus., plates, ports., facsims. 24½ᶜᵐ.
"Material ... obtained almost entirely from the Archives of the Essex institute."—Pref.
"Salem imprints, 1768–1825": p. (301)–486.
1. Printing—Hist.—Salem, Mass. 2. American newspapers—Salem, Mass. 3. American literature—Massachusetts—Salem—Bibl. 4. Book industries and trade—Salem, Mass. 5. Salem, Mass.—Libraries. I. Essex institute, Salem, Mass. II. Title.
Library of Congress   Z209.S16T2   27–14554

        NcU RPB KMK ViU
        OrU RPJCB MWA NBu NIC PP PU MiU MH OO LU MB MWA NcD
NT 0035787   DLC CU-A MB CaBVaU WaSp CBGTU IdPI WaS

Tapley, Harriet Silvester, 1870–   *4558.133.10
Some personal characteristics of Doctor Samuel Holten. As revealed by his letters and journals and the testimony of contemporaries.
(*In* Danvers Historical Society. Historical Collections. Vol. 10, pp. 49–68. Portrait. Facsimile. Danvers. 1922.)

M4667 — Holten, Samuel, 1738–1816.

NT 0035788   MB

Tapley, J. F., Co., New York, plaintiff.
... J. F. Tapley co., plaintiff, against Emil Newman, et als., defendants, summons, complaint, affidavits and order. Austin, McLanahan & Merritt, attorneys for plaintiff... New York, City, New York [1917?]

NT 0035789   MdBJ

Tapley, J. F., co., *New York.*
Useful information concerning book impositions, including all the modern layouts & practical advice to the publisher and printer; comp. and pub. by J. F. Tapley co. ... New York 1914

23 p. illus. 21½ᶜᵐ.

1. Printing, Practical—Imposition, etc. I. Title.

Library of Congress   Z255.T26   14-20678

NT 0035790   DLC

Tapley, J. F., co., *New York.*
Useful information concerning book impositions, including all the modern and many special layouts hitherto not generally known. 2d ed., rev. and enl. Comp. and pub. by J. F. Tapley co. New York 1920.

59, [1] p., 1 l. illus. 21½ᶜᵐ.

Blank for "memoranda" (1 leaf at end)

1. Printing, Practical—Imposition, etc. I. Title.

Library of Congress   Z255.T26 1920   21-1213

NT 0035791   DLC ICJ PV MiU OCl OU

Tapley, J. F., Co., *New York.*
Useful information concerning book impositions. 3d ed., rev. and enl. New York 1932.
70 p. illus. 21cm.

Blank for "Memoranda": p. 70.

NT 0035792   NNC

R655.27   **Tapley, J. F., Co.,** New York
T163u   Useful information concerning book
      impositions. 4th ed., rev. and enl. New
      York 1955.
      52 p. illus.

1. Printing - Imposition, etc. I. T.

NT 0035793   MiD

Tapley, J. F., co., *New York.*
Why the present high costs in bookbinding? A few pertinent facts that will interest the publisher, the manufacturer and the public. New York, J. F. Tapley company, 1920.

21 p. incl. tables. 22ᶜᵐ.

1. Bookbinding.

Library of Congress   Z266.T17   20-11904

NT 0035794   DLC PV

    Tapley, John H
      Pioneering in security for employees; a
    statement by J.H. Tapley, managing director,
    Swift Canadian Co., limited. [n.p.] 1937.
    folder ([4] p.)

1. Swift Canadian Company Ltd.
2. Non-wage payments - Canada I. Title

NT 0035795   CaOTU

QD1099 **Tapley, Mark Watkins, 1897–**
.T22   ...The absorption spectra of the halogenoplati-
      nates. A method of preparation of the double flu-
      orides of the platinum group metals... by Mark
      Watkins Tapley. Chicago,1923.
        1 l.,18 numb.l. diagrs. 29ᶜᵐ.
        Typewritten.
        Thesis(Ph.D.)-University of Chicago,1923.
        Bibliographical foot-notes.

      1.Absorption spectra   2.Platinum group.
      3.Halogenoplatinates   4.Complex fluorides.

NT 0035796   ICU

Tapley, Mark Watkins, 1897–
... A method for the preparation of the double fluorides of the metals of the platinum group and the adsorption spectra of the halogeno platinates ... by Mark W. Tapley ... [Easton, Pa., 1924]

14 p. diagrs. 26ᶜᵐ.

Thesis (PH. D.)—University of Chicago, 1923.
"Private edition—distributed by the University of Chicago libraries, Chicago, Illinois."
"Reprinted from the Journal of the American chemical society, vol. XLVI, no. 2, February, 1924."

1. Fluorides. 2. Platinum. 3. Absorption spectra.

                       24-31021

Library of Congress   QD181.F1T3 1923
Univ. of Chicago Libr.   [2]

NT 0035797   ICU DLC MH-C OU

Tapley, Philip C.   2397.188
Author's biography.
(In Brook's William Grant. Stories in song and other poems ... Pp. 15–16. Lewiston, Me. 1900.)

NT 0035798   MB

Tapley, Roberts, 1896–   tr.

    Reuter, Gabriele, 1859–
      Daughters, the story of two generations, by Gabriele Reuter, translated from the German by Roberts Tapley. New York, The Macmillan company, 1930.

    Tapley, Roberts, 1896–
      Harm's way, by Roberts Tapley. New York, A. A. Knopf, 1930.

6 p. l., 3–353 p., 1 l. 19½ᶜᵐ.

1. Title.

Library of Congress   PZ3.T1634Har   30-7792

NT 0035800   DLC

    Tapley, Roberts, 1896–   tr.

    Febvre, Lucien Paul Victor, 1878–
      Martin Luther: a destiny, by Lucien Febvre ... translated by Roberts Tapley. New York, E. P. Dutton & co., inc. [1929]

    Tapley, Roberts, 1896– tr.

    Gunnarsson, Gunnar, 1889–
      Seven days' darkness, by Gunnar Gunnarsson; translated by Roberts Tapley. New York, The Macmillan company, 1930.

    Tapley, Roberts, 1896–   tr.

    Romieu, Emilie.
      Three virgins of Haworth, being an account of the Brontë sisters, by Emilie and Georges Romieu; translated from the French by Roberts Tapley ... New York, E. P. Dutton & co., inc. [1930]

Tapley, Rufus Preston, 1823–1893.
Eulogy of Abraham Lincoln, sixteenth president of the United States, pronounced by Rufus P. Tapley, esq., April 19, 1865, at Saco, Maine, including the report of the proceedings of the town of Saco consequent upon his death. Biddeford, Printed at the Union and journal office, 1865.

27 p. 22½ᶜᵐ.

1. Lincoln, Abraham, pres. U. S.—Addresses, sermons, etc. I. Saco, Me. Citizens.

Library of Congress   E457.8.T19   12—7431

NT 0035804   DLC PHi PPL NIC MWA OClWHi MiU-C

385.74 **Tapley, Rufus Preston, 1823–1893.**
T163s   Speech delivered in the House of repre-
    sentatives, Feb. 17th and 19th, 1865, on
    the repeal of the law prohibiting the ex-
    tension of the "broad" or "mixed" gauge
    within the limits of this state.
    [Portland, Me. 1865?]
    20p.

NT 0035805   IU MB

    Tapley, William T & others
      Sweet corn.   Geneva, 1934.
      111 p.

NT 0035806   PP

Tapley-Soper, Harry, 1876– ed.

    Topsham, *Eng. (Parish)*
      ... Parish of Topsham, co. Devon. Marriages, baptisms & burials, A. D. 1600 to 1837. From the parochial register, the register of the independent meeting, the register of the Presbyterians, the register of the Quakers, together with copies of memorial inscriptions ... Transcribed and edited by H. Tapley-Soper ... Exeter, The Devon and Cornwall record society, 1938.

Tapley-Soper, Harry, 1876– ed.

    Exeter, *Eng. (Diocese)*
      ... The registers of baptisms, marriages & burials of the city of Exeter ...
      Exeter, The Devon and Cornwall record society, 1910–

Tapley-Soper, Harry, 1876– ed.

    Branscombe, *Eng. (Parish)*
      ... The register of baptisms, marriages & burials of the parish of Branscombe, Devon, 1539–1812. Transcribed and ed. by H. Tapley-Soper ... and Elijah Chick. Exeter, The Devon and Cornwall record society, 1913.

Tapley-Soper, Harry, 1876– joint ed.

    Lustleigh, *Eng. (Parish)*
      ... The register of baptisms, marriages & burials of the parish of Lustleigh, Devon, 1631–1837. And extracts from the bishops' transcripts. 1608–1811. Transcribed and edited by the Rev. Herbert Johnson, M. A., and H. Tapley-Soper. Exeter, The Devon and Cornwall record society, 1927–30.

Tapley-Soper, Harry, 1876– ed.

    Ottery St. Mary, *Eng. (Parish)*
      ... The register of baptisms, marriages & burials of the parish of Ottery St. Mary, Devon, 1601–1837 ... Transcribed and edited by H. Tapley-Soper ... Exeter, The Devon and Cornwall record society, 1908–29.

DA670   **Tapley-Soper, Harry, 1876–** ed.
.D49D6
vol. 21   **Camborne,** *Eng. (Parish)*
      The register of marriages, baptisms & burials of the Parish of Camborne, Co. Cornwall, A. D. 1538 to 1837. Ed. by H. Tapley-Soper. Exeter, 1945.

Tapley-Soper, Harry, 1876–   joint ed.

Truro, Eng. St. Mary (*Parish*)
... The register of marriages, baptisms & burials of the parish of St. Mary, Truro, co. Cornwall, A. D. 1597 to 1837 ... transcribed and edited by Miss Susan E. Gay, Mrs. Howard Fox, Miss Stella Fox ₍and₎ H. Tapley-Soper. Exeter, The Devon and Cornwall record society, 1940.

DA670
.D49D6
vol. 19

Tapley-Soper, Harry, 1876–   joint ed.

Widecombe in the Moor, Eng. (*Parish*)
... The register of marriages, baptisms & burials of the parish of Widecombe-in-the-Moor, Devon. Transcribed and edited by the Rev. E. C. Wood ... and H. Tapley-Soper ... Exeter, The Devon and Cornwall record society, 1938.

The Tapleys of Folkstone, England
    see under   ₍Cotton, Lillian (Tapley)₎ 1873–

Taplin, Alfred Betts, 1857–
Hypnotic suggestion and psychotherapeutics, by A. Betts Taplin ... Liverpool, Littlebury bros.; London, Simpkin, Marshall, Hamilton, Kent & co., ltd., 1918.
168 p. 19ᶜᵐ.
Bibliography : p. 167.

1. Hypnotism—Therapeutic use. 2. Mental suggestion. 3. Therapeutics, Suggestive.

Library, U. S. Surgeon-   General's Office   S G 19–158

NT   0035816   DNLM WU-M PPC

Taplin, Alfred Betts, 1857–   134 R201
Hypnotism, by A. Betts Taplin, ... Liverpool, Littlebury Bros., ltd.; ₍etc., etc.₎, 1912.
[8], 133, [3] p. 16×12½ᶜᵐ.
"Bibliography," 1 p. at end.

NT   0035817   ICJ DLC-P4

WM
415
T173h
1928

TAPLIN, Alfred Betts, 1857–
Hypnotism and treatment by suggestion. 4th ed. Liverpool, Littlebury, 1928.
135 p.

NT   0035818   DNLM

Taplin, Edith Smith
Phi Kappa zeta; history of the fraternity, 1896–1921, told by its members. Compilation by Edith Smith Taplin, illustrations by Louise Norris. Cleveland, O. 1921.
14 p. illus.

NT   0035819   OClWHi

TAPLIN, Gardner Blake.
The life, works, and literary reputation of John Byrne Leicester Warren, Lord de Tabley.
Typewritten. 29 x 21 cm.
Thesis, Ph.D. – Harvard University, 1942.

NT   0035820   MH

Taplin, George.
Threlkeld, Lancelot Edward, 1788–1859.
An Australian language as spoken by the Awabakal, the people of Awaba, or lake Macquarie (near Newcastle, New South Wales) being an account of their language, traditions, and customs: by L. E. Threlkeld. Re-arranged, condensed, and ed., with an appendix, by John Fraser ... Sydney, C. Potter, govt. printer, 1892.

Taplin, George   ed.
The folklore, manners, customs, and languages of the South Australian aborigines: gathered from inquiries made by authority of South Australian government. 1st series. Adelaide, E. Spiller, government printer, 1879.
Microfilm copy (negative) of the original. Collation of the original: viii, 174 p., 1 ℓ., 28, xii p. plates, mounted photos. (incl. front.)
"Vocabulary of the 'Narrinyeri' language": p. 125–141.
"Comparative table of words selected from 43 aboriginal languages": p. 142–155.

"Degrees of kinship" (tables): p. 156–174.
"Addendum" (1 ℓ., 28, xii p. at end) has title: Grammar of the Narrinyeri tribe of Australian aborigines. By G. Tauplin. Adelaide, E. C. Cox, government printer, 1878.
"Facsimiles of letters written by aborigines educated at the mission schools" on pages i-xii and filmed between pages 24 and 25 of the Addendum.

1. Ethnology – South Australia. 2. Australian languages. 3. Narrinyeri language.   I. Title.

NT   0035823   WU

Taplin, George, *ed.*
The folklore, manners, customs, and languages of the South Australian aborigines: gathered from inquiries made by authority of South Australian government. Edited by the late Rev. G. Taplin ... 1st series. Adelaide, E. Spiller, government printer, 1879₍–80₎
viii, 174 p., 1 l., 28, p. plates, mounted photos. (incl. front.) 21½ᶜᵐ.
"Vocabulary of the 'Narrinyeri' language": p. 125–141.
"Comparative table of words selected from 43 aboriginal languages": p. 142–155.
"Degrees of kinship" (tables) : p. 156–174

"Addendum" (1 l., 28 p. at end) has title: Grammar of the Narrinyeri tribe of Australian aborigines. By the late Rev. G. Taplin ... Adelaide, E. Spiller, government printer, 1880.
"Facsimiles of letters written by aborigines educated at the mission schools", listed in Table of contents and in Index as p. 29 of the Addendum, are not found in this copy; page 28 ends with the word "Finis," followed by printer's address at foot of page.

1. Ethnology—South Australia. 2. Australian languages. 3. Narrinyeri language.   I. Title.

Library of Congress   DU325.T3   1–10972 Revised

NT   0035825   DLC PPAmP PU CU MH OCl PPAN MiU DAU

Taplin, George.
Grammar of the Narrinyeri tribe of Australian aborigines. Adelaide, E. Spiller, 1880.
28 p. 8°. ₍With his Folklore, manners and customs of the South Australian aborigines ... Adelaide, 1879₎

1–10973

NT   0035826   DLC CtY WaU IEN ICU CaBVaU MH

Taplin, *Rev.* George. The Narrinyeri. 156 pp. 2 pl. (Woods, J. D., *Native tribes of South Australia*, p. 1.)

NT   0035827   MdBP OCl

Taplin, George.
The Narrinyeri: an account of the tribes of South Australian aborigines, inhabiting the country around the lakes Alexandrina, Albert and Coorong, and the lower part of the river Murray: their manners and customs. Also, an account of the mission at Point Macleay. By the Rev. George Taplin ... Adelaide: J. T. Shawyer, 1874. iv, 107 p. incl. tables. front. 8°.

4459A. 1. Australian tribes.   2. Title.
N. Y. P. L.   May 24, 1921.

NT   0035828   NN UU CoU CtY CSt

Taplin, George.
The Narrinyeri: an account of the tribes of South Australian aborigines inhabiting the country around the Lakes Alexandrina, Albert and Coorong, and the lower part of the River Murray: their manners and customs. Also, an account of the mission at Point Macleay. Second edition, revised. By the Rev. Georg Taplin... Adelaide, E. S. Wigg & Son, 1878.
iv p., 1 l. [2] –156 p. col. plates. 23 cm.

NT   0035829   CU-A MnU

Taplin, George.
The native tribes of South Australia comprising the Narrinyeri by the Rev. Geo. Taplin; the Adelaide tribe by Dr. Wyatt, the Encounter Bay tribe by the Rev. C. W. Schurmann... with an introductory chapter by J. D. Woods. Adelaide, 1879.

NT   0035830   PPAN MH-Z

Taplin,   George.
Notes on a comparative table of Australian languages.   n. p. ₍188–?₎   84–88 p., 1 table.   8°.
Excerpt.

1. Australian languages.
N. Y. P. L.   June 9, 1913.

NT   0035831   NN

Taplin, Henry.
Short-hand adapted to the meanest capacity, wherein the rules are few, plain, and easy; the characters not burthensome to memory: and the hand shorter & more intelligible than any other extant. Together with the principles on which it is founded; also an alphabetical praxis, &c. By Henry Taplin ... London, Printed for the author ₍etc.₎, 1760₎
1 p. l., xi, 40 p. 16 pl. on 8 l. 17ᶜᵐ.
Engr. t.-p.
1. Shorthand.

Library of Congress   Z56.T17   11–12981

NT   0035832   DLC CtY

₍Taplin, Henry₎
Stenography, or, Short hand, with the principles on which it is founded according to grammar and true philosophy. By R. Tailor ₍pseud?₎ Edinburgh, Printed for the author, 1791.
1 p. l., ix, [1], 11–47 p. 16 pl. on 9 l. 17½ cm.
Apparently a surreptitious issue of the 2d authorized edition, London, 1791.

41
T16
1791b

NT   0035833   CtY NN ICN

TA165
.A63

Taplin, John Ferguson, 1913–   joint author.
Ahrendt, William Robert, 1919–
Automatic feedback control ₍by₎ William R. Ahrendt ₍and₎ John F. Taplin. 1st ed. New York, McGraw-Hill, 1951.

TA165
.A65

Taplin, John Ferguson, 1913–   joint author.
Ahrendt, William Robert, 1919–
Automatic regulation, by William R. Ahrendt and John F. Taplin. Prelim. ed. Washington ₍1947–

Taplin, R   B.
A discussion of the problem "How much to zone for business" prepared for the City Planning Section of the League of California Municipalities, by R. B. Taplin... September 21, 1931. ₍Long Beach, Cal., 1931.₎   6 l.   28cm.

Caption-title.
Reproduced from typewritten copy.

730809A.   1. ₍Zoning.   I. League of
Francisco.   California Municipalities, San
N. Y. P. L.   October 4, 1934

NT   0035836   NN

Taplin, Walter.
Britain's new economy. ₍Toronto₎ Canadian Institute of International Affairs, 1955.
13 p.   21 cm.   (Behind the headlines, v. 15, no. 4)

1. Gt. Brit.—Econ. condit.—1945—   ɪ. Title.
F1034.B4   vol. 15, no. 4   55–12623 ‡

NT   0035837   DLC CaBViP NN ViU CaOTU

Taplin, Walter.
James Joyce wrote English.   Mistley, Essex, England, The Critic press, 1947.
p.₍11₎-16.   25cm.

In The Critic; a quarterly review of criticism, v.1, no.1, Spring, 1947, p.₍11₎-16.

1. Joyce, James, 1882-1941. I. The Critic, v.1, no.   1.

NT   0035838   KU IEN CSt

Taplin, William, *d.* 1807.
Works by this author printed in America before 1801 are available in this library in the Readex Microprint edition of Early American Imprints published by the American Antiquarian Society.
This collection is arranged according to the numbers in Charles Evans' American Bibliography.

NT   0035839   DLC

610.88   ₍TAPLIN, William₎ d.1807.
T164a   The Aesculapian labyrinth explored; or, Medical mystery illustrated;/in a series of instructions to young physicians, surgeons, accouchers, apothecaries, druggists, and practitioners of every denomination, in town and country; interspersed with a variety of risible anecdotes affecting the faculty; inscribed to the college of wigs,- by Gregory Glyster, an old practitioner ₍pseud.₎ Dublin, printed by Z. Jackson for P. Wogan, P. Byrne, W. M'Kenzie,

J. Jones and Grueber and M'Allister, 1789.
70, ii p.

1. Medicine - Anecdotes, facetiae, satire, etc. I. Title. II. Title: Medical mystery illustrated.

NT   0035841   WaU CtY NjR

₍Taplin, William₎ d.1807.
An appeal to the representatives on the part of the people respecting the present destructive state of the game, and the operative spirit of laws, erroneously said to be framed for its increase and preservation; but experimentally tending to a speedy annihilation in every part of the kingdom. With a prefatory address to the Right Hon. William Pitt, by the author of The Gentleman's stable directory ... London, G. G. J. and J. Robinson, 1792.
2 p.l., lvi, 119 p.   front.   23.5 cm.

NT   0035842   MH-BA MiU InU

SF
955
.T28
1796

Taplin, William, d. 1807.
A compendium of practical and experimental farriery, originally suggested by reason and confirmed by practice, equally adapted to the convenience of the gentleman, the farmer, the groom, and the smith ... Brentford, printed by P. Norbury, for G. G. and J. Robinson, 1796.
xi, [1], 274, [2] p.   illus.   22 cm.

Spine title: Taplin's Farriery.
Index to v. 1 of The gentleman's stable directory ([8] p.) bound in at end of copy 1.
Copy 2 lacks half-title leaf with advertisement on verso.
Bookplates of former owners.

1. Horses - Diseases.   ɪ. Title.

NT   0035843   MiEM CtY CSt

Taplin, William, *d.* 1807.
A compendium of practical and experimental farriery, originally suggested by reason and confirmed by practice. Equally adapted for the convenience of the gentleman, the farmer, the groom, and the smith. Interspersed with such remarks, and elucidated with such cases, as evidently tend to insure the prevention, as well as to ascertain the cure of disease. By William Taplin ... Wilmington ₍Del.₎ Printed by Bonsal & Niles, for Robert Campbell, bookseller, Philadelphia. M,DCC,XCVII.
viii, 290, ₍6₎ p.   17¼ᵐ.
1. Horses—Diseases.   ɪ. Title.

A 34-2452

Title from H. E. Hunt-   ington Libr. Printed by L. C.

PU ViWC OU DLC DeWI NN RPJCB MWA
NT   0035844   CSmH PU-V PMA MiU DNLM PPT PPL DeU CU-A

Taplin, William, *d.* 1807.
A compendium of practical and experimental farriery, originally suggested by reason and confirmed by practice. Equally adapted for the convenience of the gentleman, the farmer, the groom, and the smith. Interspersed with such remarks, and elucidated with such cases, as evidently tend to insure the prevention, as well as to ascertain the cure of disease. By William Taplin ... Richmond, Printed by H. Pace, 1803.
vi, ₍7₎-185, ₍5₎ p.   14cm.
P. ₍5-5₎ at end of book bound after p. 185.

NT   0035845   ViU CSmH DNLM MiU

---

*fEC75   [Taplin, William, d.1807, ascribed author]
G5745T   ... A dose for the doctors; or, The
1770   Aesculapian labyrinth explored./In a series of instructions to young physicians, surgeons, accouchers, apothecaries, druggists, and chymists. Interspersed with a variety of risible anecdotes affecting the faculty. Inscribed to the College of wigs, by Gregory Glyster [pseud.] ...
London:Printed for G.Kearsley,no.46,Fleet-street.MDCCLXXXIX.

2p.l.,75p.   28cm.,in case 29.5cm.
At head of title: Third edition.
Ascribed to Taplin, with reservations, by the BM and U.S. Surgeon-General's catalogues.
Bound with Goldsmith's The traveller ... 1770, and The deserted village ... The sixth edition ... 1770.

NT   0035847   MH CtY

RBS.131.   Taplin, William.
For the draft, road, field, or turf. The gentleman's stable...
Lond., printed and Dublin, reprinted, W. Wilson, 1791.

NT   0035848   NNNAM

RBS.131.   Taplin, William.
For the draft, road, field, or turf. The Gentleman's stable...
Lond, printed and Dublin, reprinted, W. Wilson, 1792.

NT   0035849   NNNAM

SF
955
.T3
1700

Taplin, William, d. 1807.
The gentleman's stable directory; or, Modern system of farriery ... To which is now added a supplement, containing practical observations upon thorn wounds, punctured tendons, and ligamentary lameness ... With a successful method of treating the canine species in that destructive disease called the distemper ... 10th ed., considerably enlarged, and carefully corrected. London, printed for G. G. J. and J. Robinsons [sic, 17--]
xxiv, 519 p.   illus.   21 1/2 cm.

Caption title: The modern system of farriery.
Spine title: Taplin's Farriery.
"Genuine ... horse medicines, prepared at the medical dispensary of the author ...": p. [503]-504.
Bookplate of G. A.   and V. M. Dimoc.
Mark of Kalamazoo   Public Library.

1. Horses.   2. Horses - Diseases.   3. Veterinary medicine - Early works to 1800.   I. Title.

NT   0035851   MiEM KMK MeB OU

Taplin, William, d. 1807.
The gentleman's stable directory; or, Modern system of farriery... With an appendix containing experimental observations upon the management of draft horses, their blemishes and defects... [6th ed., corr., improved, and considerably enl.] London printed; and Dublin reprinted by W. Wilson ... and sold by T. White, Cork; Watson & co., Limerick; and J. and W. Magee, Belfast, 1789.
xx, 364 p.   19 cm.
At head of title: For the draft, road, field, or turf.

NT   0035852   PU NNNAM PU-V

---

x636.1   Taplin, William, d.1807.
T16g   The gentleman's stable directory; or, Modern
1789   system of farriery. Comprehending the present entire improved mode of practice: likewise all the most valuable prescriptions and approved remedies, accurately proportioned and properly adapted to every known disease to which the horse is incident. Interspersed with occasional remarks upon the dangerous and almost obsolete practice of Gieson, Bracken, Bartlet, Osmer,

and others. Also directions for feeding, bleeding, purging and getting into condition for the chase. To which are now added, useful instructions for buying and selling; with an appendix, containing experimental observations upon the management of draft horses, their blemishes and defects. 7th ed., considerably enl., and carefully corr. London, Printed for G. Kearsley, 1789.
v. port.   22cm.

NT   0035854   IU

SF
955
T3
1789

Taplin, William, d. 1807.
The gentleman's stable directory : or modern system of farriery... / by William Taplin. - 8th ed., considerably enl. and carefully corrected. - London : G. Kearsley, 1789.
434 p.

1. Horses.   2. Horses—Diseases.   I. Title.

NT   0035855   KMK

WZ
260
T173g
1791

TAPLIN, William, d. 1807
... The gentleman's stable directory; or, Modern system of farriery. Comprehending all the most valuable prescriptions and approved remedies, accurately proportioned and properly adapted to every known disease to which the horse is incident ... To which is now added, a supplement, containing practical observations upon thorn wounds, punctured tendons, and ligamentary lameness ... With a successful method of

treating the canine species, in that destructive disease called the distemper ... London, G. G. J. & J. Robinson ₍etc.₎ 1791.
xxiv, 519 p.   port.   21 cm.
At head of title: The eleventh edition, considerably enlarged, and carefully corrected.

Continued in next column

Continued from preceding column

First published in London in 1778.
There is no evidence that the present copy
was accompanied by the second volume,
which was first published in 1791.
"Horse medicines prepared at the medical dispensary of the author" (advertisement): p. ₍503₎-504.

NT 0035858   DNLM CLU-M CtY PPL MH

Taplin, William, d. 1807.
636.1   The gentleman's stable directory; or,
T173G   Modern system of farriery ... London, Robinson,
1793-96.
2 v. port. 22 cm.
Vol. 1: 12th ed.; v. 2: 4th ed.

1. Horses. 2. Horses. Diseases. I. Title.

N Vi KMK PU-V PU CSt CtY
NT 0035859   NcD CSmH DNLM DSI MiEM IU NBuG OU CU-A

Taplin, William, d. 1807.
The gentleman's stable directory: or, Modern system of farriery ... To which is added, a supplement, containing practical
observations upon thorn wounds, punctured tendons, and ligamentary lameness. With ample instructions for their treatment and cure; illustrated by a recital of cases ... With a
successful method of treating the canine species, in that destructive disease called the distemper. Two volumes in one.
12th ed. By William Taplin ... Philadelphia: Printed by
T. Dobson, at the Stone house, n° 41, South Second street.
M,DCC,XCIV.
xvi, ₍4₎, 295 p., 2 l., ₍iii₎-iv, 299-540 p. 21½ᶜᵐ.

Numerous errors in pagination.
Vol. 2 (2 L., ₍iii₎-iv, 299-540 p.) has special t.-p.: The gentleman's
stable directory: or, Modern system of farriery ... Containing experimental remarks upon breeding, breaking, shoeing, stabling, exercise,
and rowelling. To which are added, particular instructions for the
general management of hunters and road horses: with concluding observations upon the present state of the turf.

1. Horses. 2. Horses—Diseases. I. Title.
35-36583
Library of Congress   SF955.T3 1794

CSmH MBCo MBAt MWA MeU IEN-M PPL RPJCB PPGenH TKL
NT 0035861   DLC NjP KyLx GU PSt NN NjP ScCMu PHatU

TAPLIN, WILLIAM, D. 1807.

The gentleman's stable directory ; or,
modern system of farriery ; comprehending of
the most valuable prescriptions and approved
remedies ... / by William Taplin. -- 15th
ed. rev. -- London : Printed for G. G. and
J. Robinson, and G. Kearsley by J. Crowder
and E. Hemfted, 1803.
xvi, 502, [10] p. : ill., port.
Earlier ed. cataloged as R 41 T164, in
1805 work reissued as 2 Volumes of which

Vol. 1 is out-of-print. Vol. 2 is cataloged
as R SF955.T3 1805. Includes index.
(25) 1. Veterinary surgery. 2. Veterinary
medicine. 3. Horses. I. Farriery.
II. Title.

NT 0035863   DNAL

TAPLIN, WILLIAM, D. 1807.

The gentleman's stable directory ; or
modern system of farriery ... Vol. II / by
William Taplin. -- 6th ed. -- London
Printed for John Stockdale, 1805.
viii, 416 p.
Vol. 1 is unavailable, complete. 1803 ed.
cataloged as R SF955.T3 1803 Includes
index.
(25) 1. Veterinary medicine. 2. Horses.
I. Farriery. II. Title.

NT 0035864   DNAL

Taplin, William, d. 1807.
The gentleman's stable directory ; or, Modern
system of farriery. Comprehending all the
most valuable prescriptions and approved remedies, accurately proportioned and properly
adapted to every known disease to which the
horse is incident ... To which is now added, a
supplement, containing practical observations
upon thorn wounds, punctured tendons, and ligamentary lameness, with ample instructions for
their treatment and cure; with a successful

method of treating the canine species, in that
destructive disease, the distemper. By William
Taplin, surgeon. The sixteenth edition. London; Printed for John Stockdale, Piccadilly;
and George Robinson, Paternoster row, 1810.
2 v. 22ᶜᵐ.

Vol. II has title: The gentleman's stable
directory; or, Modern system of farriery. Con-

taining experimental remarks upon breeding,
breaking, shoeing, stabling, exercise, and
rowelling. To which are added, particular instructions for the general management of hunters and road horses: with concluding observations upon the present state of the turf.

1. Horse. 2. Horse - Diseases. I. Title.

NT 0035867   NNC MiEM

WZ   TAPLIN, William, d. 1807
270   The gentleman's stable directory: or,
T173g   Modern system of farriery ... A new ed.
1812   ... Philadelphia, James Webster, 1812.
2 v. in 1 (xvi, ₍4₎, 540 p.) 21 cm.
Vol. 2 has special half title only: The
modern system of farriery.
An edition called the 12th with the same
paging was published in Philadelphia in
1794 (Evans 27771)
The contents are the same as in the
1796 London edition.

NT 0035868   DNLM PPT-M NN CtY

TAPLIN, William, d. 1807.
A guide to purchasers of horses; with a
postscript on equestrian equipment,written for
this edition. Glasgow, Robertson & Atkinson,
Oliver & Boyd, etc.,etc.,1829.

48°. pp.32.
"Much of what follows is fromthe writings
of Taplin,the celebrated Newmarket jockey,
as modernized by the author of 'Hints'"

NT 0035869   MH

Taplin, William, d. 1807.
The modern system of Farriery.   about 1800.
540 p.

NT 0035870   UPB

Spec.
SF   Taplin, William, d. 1807.
301   Multum in parvo; or, Sportsman's eques-
T3   trian monitor. London, Printed for the
author, 1796.
A1309   104 p. 2 plates (incl. front.) 15.1 cm.
Engraved t.-p., with vignette.

1. Horses. I. Title.

NT 0035871   CtU

Taplin, William, d.1807.
Observations on the present state of the
game in England, in which the late methods
of preservation are clearly refuted and condemned: the real cause, or causes of the deficiency demonstrated; and proposals offered
for its more sure and effectual preservation.
By William Taplin. London: Printed for T.
Davies, in Russel-street, Covent-Garden, 1772.
2 p.l., 39 p. 21 cm.

NT 0035872   CtY MoU

Taplin, William, d. 1807.
The sporting dictionary and rural repository of general information upon every subject appertaining to the
sports of the field ... By William Taplin ... London,
Vernor ₍and₎ Hood ₍etc.₎ 1803.
2 v. fronts. plates. 21½ᶜᵐ.

1. Sports—Dictionaries. 2. Hunting—Dictionaries.
12-23590
Library of Congress   SK11.T17

MWA
NT 0035873   DLC CtY PU-V PP CU MU ScU ViW MiEM NN

Taplin, William, d. 1807.
Taplin improved; or, A compendium of
farriery, wherein is fully explained the nature and
structure of that useful creature a horse
see under title

Taplin, Winifred Maitland (Shaw)
see   Shaw, Winifred Maitland, 1906-

Taplin, Winn Lowell, 1925-
The Vermont problem in the Continental
Congress and in interstate relations, 1776-
1787, by Winn L. Taplin. ₍Ann Arbor, Mich.₎
1955.
322ℓ. illus.,map.
Thesis--University of Michigan.
Bibliography: ℓ.310-321.
Microfilm (positive) (University Microfilms, Ann Arbor, Mich. Doctoral dissertation series. Publication no.19,720)

NT 0035876   UU NNC TxU

TAPLIN improved; or, A compendium of
farriery. Wherein is fully explained the
nature and structure of that useful creature, a horse; with the diseases and
accidents he is liable to; and the methods
of cure. Exemplified by ten elegant cuts,
each the full figure of a horse ... Likewise rules for breeding and training of
colts: practical receipts for the cure of
common distempers incident to oxen,
cows, calves, sheep, lambs, hogs, &c.

By an experienced farrier. London,
Printed by H. Harrison for N. Frobisher,
York, 1790.

Microfilm copy (negative) made in 1959,
of the original in the British Museum.
Collation of the original, as determined
from the film: 144 p. 8 plates.

Imperfect: 1 plate wanting.
"The work ... had nothing whatever to
do with Taplin; his name was introduced
in order to help the sale."—Smith, The
early hist. of veterinary lit., v. 2, p. 173.
A York 1792 edition of apparently the
same work (also 144 p.) is listed in the
Brit. Mus. Cat. as "A new edition" of

Henry Bracken's Farriery improv'd; and
American editions appeared in Baltimore
in 1794 and in Philadelphia in 1796 and
1798 under Bracken's name and with title:
Farriery improved. It is not, however,
the same work as Bracken's Farriery
improv'd, first published in London in
2 v., 1737-43.

"Taplin improved; or, Advice to the
purchasers of horses": p. ₍5₎-30. This
was published anonymously in London in
1766 under title: Ten minutes advice to
every gentleman going to purchase a horse.
"Observations and receipts for the cure
of most common distempers incident to
horses": p. ₍31₎-74. The "Observations"

Continued in next column

Continued from preceding column

(p. ₍31₎-53) are abridged from Burdon's
The gentleman's pocket-farrier (London,
1730)
"Methods for destroying moles":
p. 133-137.
"Additions": p. 137-138.
Bracken, Henry, 1697-1764

II. Burdon, William. The gentleman's
pocket-farrier III. An experienced farrier
IV. Taplin, William, d. 1807 V. Ten
minutes advice to every gentleman going
to purchase a horse Title: Farriery
improved

NT 0035883   DNLM

Taplin improved; or, A compendium of
farriery, wherein is fully explained the
nature and structure of that useful creature a horse; with the diseases and accidents he is liable to; and the methods of
cure... Likewise rules for breeding and
training of colts... to which is prefixed
... advice to the purchasers of horses.

By an experienced farrier. [Lane's ed.]
London, Printed for W. Lane at the
Minerva press, 1796.   144 p.   illus.
18cm.

1. Horse—Diseases. 2. Veterinary medicine.
I. Taplin, William, d. 1807. II. An experienced farrier.

NT 0035885   NN

WZ   TAPLIN improved; or A complete treatise on
270   the art of farriery, wherein are fully ex-
T1736   plained the nature and structure of that
1815   useful creature, a horse; with the diseases
          and accidents he is liable to; and the
          methods of cure. Exemplified by ten
          elegant cuts, each the full figure of a
          horse ... Likewise, rules for breeding
          and training of colts: practical receipts
          for the cure of common distempers in-
          cident to oxen, cows, calves, sheep,

lambs, hogs, &c. To which is prefixed
Ten minutes advice to the purchasers of
horses. By Henry Bracken, M. D. Troy
₍N. Y.₎ Printed and sold by Francis
Adancourt, and also sold by Whiting &
Powers, ₍etc., etc.₎ 1815.
204 p. 10 plates. 17 cm.

First plate has caption: Fronticepiece
₍sic₎ to Adancourt's edition of Taplin's
farriery.
Published in York in 1790 under title:
Taplin improved; or, A compendium of
farriery. William Taplin had nothing to
do with the work; his name was used to
help the sale.

A York 1792 edition of apparently the
same work is listed in the Brit. Mus. Cat.
as "A new edition" of Henry Bracken's
Farriery improv'd; and American editions
appeared in Baltimore in 1794 and in
Philadelphia in 1796 and 1798 under
Bracken's name and with title: Farriery
improved. It is not, however, the same

work as Bracken's Farriery improv'd,
published in London in 2 v., 1737-43.
Published anonymously in New Haven in
1816 under title: A complete treatise on
the art of farriery. Published in Troy,
N. Y., in 1826 under title: The American
farrier, or New-York horse doctor; being
a further improvement upon Adancourt's

"Taplin improved."
"Additional information ... relative to
the cure of horses": p. ₍111₎-119.
"On shoeing horses" (extracted from a
treatise lately published in England by
James White): p. 119-128.
"Addenda": p. ₍200
I. Adancourt, Francis, ed.

Continued in next column

Continued from preceding column

II. Bracken, Henry, 1697-1764
III. Burdon, William. The gentleman's
pocket-farrier IV. Taplin, William, d.
1807 V. Ten minutes advice to every
gentleman going to purchase a horse
VI. White, James, d. 1825

NT 0035892   DNLM NIC MU GU

Tapling, Thomas Keay.
The Tapling collection of stamps and postal
stationery at the British Museum. A descriptive
guide and index by F. J. Melville.   London,
Lawn & Barlow [1905]
viii, 55 p.   12°.

NT 0035893   NN

SF613   Taplinger, Richard J.
.H4A3   FOR OTHER EDITIONS
1952   SEE MAIN ENTRY
         Henderson, J. Y.
         Circus doctor; as told to Richard Taplinger. London,
         Davies ₍1952₎

[Taplow, William P   ] supposed
author.
The private opinions of a British blue
jacket
see under   Maclaren, Hamish.

Tapman, Lillian Smith.
Our lesser brethren, by a wayfarer (Lillian Smith-Tapman)
Richmond Hill, L. I., N. Y., L. S. Tapman ₍°1937₎
181 p. 20ᵐᵐ.

ɪ. Title.
                                              38-463
Library of Congress   BR125.T27

NT 0035896   DLC

₍Tapman, Lillian Smith₎
The success of failure, by a wayfarer. New York, Tapman
publishing company ₍°1913₎
299 p. 19ᵐᵐ.

ɪ. Title.
                                              13—24400
Library of Congress   PZ3.T1635S

Wa OrU
NT 0035897   DLC PPPrHi OCU ViU PHi NcD CtY ICJ OU

Tapman, Lillian Smith.
Two poems: The plaint of labor, The world of penance,
by a wayfarer (Lillian Smith-Tapman) Richmond Hill, L. I.,
N. Y., L. S. Tapman ₍°1936₎
42 p. 20ᵐᵐ.

ɪ. Title: The plaint of labor. ɪɪ. Title: The world of penance.
                                                   37—221
Library of Congress   PS3539.A52T8 1936
——— Copy 2.
Copyright A 102044   ₍2₎   811.5

NT 0035898   DLC

Tapman, Lillian Smith.
The unprodigal son, by a wayfarer (Lillian Smith-Tapman)
Richmond Hill, N. Y., L. S. Tapman ₍°1935₎
81 p. 20ᵐᵐ.

1. Prodigal son. ɪ. Title.
                                              36-4048
Library of Congress   BT378.P8T3
——— Copy 2.
Copyright A 90073   ₍3₎   226.8

NT 0035899   DLC

Tapner, Benjamin.
The whole proceedings ...
see under   Gt. Brit. Courts of oyer and
terminer and general gaol delivery.

Tapner, John.
The school-master's repository; or, Youth's
moral preceptor. Containing a select store of
curious sentences and maxims, in prose and
verse... Designed more particularly for the use
of schools... London [1761?]
17 cm.

NT 0035901   CtY

Tapola, Selim
Vaaranlento; Hopeasiiven mukana maailman ympäri.
Helsinki, Kansankirja [1945]
134 p. (Poikien sininen sarja, 1)

NT 0035902   MH

Tapolski, William, 1866–
Der Kaffeeterminhandel... von William Tapolski...   Ham-
burg: L. Gräfe & Sillem, 1896.   56 p. incl. tables.   21½cm.
Inaugural-Dissertation — Heidelberg, 1896.
Vita.

1. Coffee—Trade and stat.
N. Y. P. L.   October 31, 1939

NT 0035903   NN PU CtY ICRL MH

Tapon (Emile). *Contribution à l'étude des
points d'ossification du squelette par la radio-
graphie. 54 pp. 8°. Paris, 1914. No. 251.

NT 0035904   DNLM CtY

Tapon-Chollet, ———.

Bonaparte, Jérôme Napoléon, 1805-1870.
Cour impériale de Paris. Première chambre. Appel du
jugement de la première chambre du Tribunal de première
instance de la Seine, du 15 février 1861. M. Jérôme-Napoléon
Bonaparte et mᵐᵉ Élisabeth Patterson contre S. A. I. le prince
Napoléon. ₍Baltimore, J. S. Waters, 1861?₎

PQ   Tapon Fougas, Francisque.
2286   Les antimisérables. Petite galerie
T17   des Misérables. Poème héroi-comique.
           Bruxelles, Tous les libraires, 1862.
           4 pts. (256 p.) 19cm.

Cover titles.
Parody on Victor Hugo's Les misérables.

1. Hugo, Victor Marie, comte. Les
misérables.   I. Title.

NT 0035906   NIC

PQ
2449   Tapon-Fougas, F[rancisque]
T173p   ... La princesse Delhi-la; ou, Des
lilas; petite parodie en cinq actes et
en vers burlesques, de Dalila, grand
drame en trois actes et en prose ...
Bruxelles [Typ.de J.Vanbuggenhoudt]
1857.
47p. 15cm.
At head of title: Dixième drame réformateur.

I. Feuillet, Octave. Dalila. II. Title.

NT   0035907   NRU

Taponier, Edmond.
*Etude de l'action des bromures alcalins sur
le carbonate de báryum.   Genève, W. Kündig et
Fils, 1905.
48 p.   8°.

NT   0035908   NN ICRL

Tapowewina
see under   [Guéguen, Jean Pierre] 1838-

Tapp, David.
Fünffzehen Jährige curiöse und denckwürdige auch sehr gefährliche ost-
indianische Reise-Beschreibung, so sich
im Jahr Christi 1667. angefangen, und...
im 1628ten Jahre geendet hat...
Hannover und Wolffenbüttel, G. Freytag,
1704.

201, 102-220 p.   20cm.

NT   0035910   MnU

Tapp, Edwin J
A miscellany of verse, by Edwin J. Tapp.
Dunedin, N.Z., A.H. and A.W. Reed [1937]
69 p.   18 cm.

NT   0035911   NBuU MH TxU

[Tapp, Frank] 1883-
Thames castles, suite by Graeme Stuart [pseud.] Full
orch. London, Bosworth [1947]
piano-conductor score (16 p.) and   parts. 31 cm.
Cover title.
"Duration 4 minutes."
CONTENTS.— The Tower Beefeaters.—Hampton Court.—Windsor
Castle.

1. Suites (Orchestra)—Scores (reduced) and parts. I. Title.

M1350.T   48-27834*

NT   0035912   DLC

Tapp, George Hambleton
see
Tapp, Hambleton.

UF
545   Tapp, George M
.G7T3   Personal [a scrapbook of letters and copies
of letters pertaining to Mr. Tapp's career
mainly as chief clerk to the director general
of ordnance factories, also newspaper clippings
about the Royal Arsenal, etc., from 1857-1900.
n.p., n.d.]
1 v. (unpaged) 23 cm.

Cover title.

1. Woolwich, Eng. Royal Arsenal.

NT   0035914   OkU

Tapp, Hambleton.
George Rogers Clark, 1752-1818; a brief biographical
sketch. Louisville, 1955.
11 p. 24 cm. (Bulletin of the George Rogers Clark Memorial
Foundation)

1. Clark, George Rogers, 1752-1818.

E207.C5T3   923.973   56-41040 ‡

NT   0035915   DLC

E
5   TAPP, HAMBLETON.
.R 742   Otto A.Rothert, 1871-   , secretary of the
Filson club, 1917-1945... [Louisville,Ky.,1945]
p.[67]-96. ports. 25cm.

"Reprinted from the Filson club history
quarterly, Louisville, Kentucky, April 1946."

NT   0035916   ICN MB KyHi

Tapp, Hambleton.
A physical education program for the Kentucky high
school together with guides for organizing and teaching
physical education. Based upon researches and writings of
Rome Rankin, under direction of the College of Education,
University of Kentucky. [Frankfort, 1948]
[823]-904 p. 23 cm. (Educational bulletin, v. 15, no. 11)

1. Physical education [and training,—Kentucky. [2. Physical education—Teaching. I. Rankin, Rome.   (Series: Kentucky. Dept.
of Education. Educational bulletin, v. 15, no. 11)

L152.B35 vol. 15, no. 11   371.7323   E 48-27 rev*

U. S. Office of Education   Library
for Library of Congress   [r51c1†]

NT   0035917   DHEW DLC

F451
.W3   Tapp, Hambleton, ed.

Wallis, Frederick A   ed.
A sesqui-centennial history of Kentucky; a narrative historical edition ... preserving the record of the growth and
development of the commonwealth, and chronicling the genealogical and memorial records of its prominent families and
personages. Frederick A. Wallis, supervising editor, genealogical and biographical. Hambleton Tapp, author and
editor, historical. Hopkinsville, Ky., Historical Record
Assn. [1945]

Tapp, Harold Astley, 1892-
... United services college, 1874-1911; a short account of
Rudyard Kipling's old school at Westward Ho! by Major
H. A. Tapp ... with a preface by Major-General L. C. Dunster-
ville ... ("Stalky") Aldershot, Printed by Gale & Polden,
ltd. [1934]
iv, 59 p. illus. (incl. ports., facsim.) pl. 25½cm.
At head of title: For private circulation only.

1. Windsor, Eng. Imperial service college. 2. Kipling, Rudyard,
1865-   Stalky & co. I. Title.

Library of Congress   LF795.W756T3   34-40889
[3]   [373.4229] 373.223004229

NT   0035919   DLC DeU CtY NjP

Tapp, Harry F., ed.
American oil burner association.
Handbook of domestic oil heating, edited by Harry F. Tapp
... 1st ed., 1st printing. New York city, American oil burner
association, inc. [*1928]

Tapp, Harry F.

American oil burner association.
Handbook of oil burning, by Harry F. Tapp ... New York,
American oil burner association [*1931]

Film   Tapp, Henry Lee
D215   An investigation of the use of imagery in
4   the works of Wolfram von Eschenbach. [New
Haven] 1953
281 l. 29 cm.

Thesis - Yale, 1953.
Bibliography: l. 264-281.
Microfilm of typescript. Ann Arbor, Mich.,
University Microfilms, 1965. 1 reel. 35 mm.

1. Wolfram von Eschenbach, 12th cent.

NT   0035922   CtY

QD319   Tapp, Hermann.
.T67   Ueber die oxydationsproducte der schwefel-
kohlensaeureaether. Braunschweig, 1874.
Diss. - Rostock.

NT   0035923   DLC

Tapp, Jean.
"Les merveilles de la nature" par les plantes. L'usage des
plantes médicinales les plus actives et les plus usuelles et
leurs applications thérapeutiques; conseils pratiques, etc.
4. éd. [Montréal] 1948.
622 p. illus. 24 cm.

1. Medicine, Popular. 2. Botany, Medical. I. Title.

RC82.T3 1948   55-58906 ‡

NT   0035924   DLC

Tapp, Jesse Washington, 1898-
... Farm practices under corn-borer conditions. [By Jesse
W. Tapp, and George W. Collier, and C. R. Arnold] [Wash-
ington, U. S. Govt. print. off., 1928]
ii, 21 p. illus., maps, diagr. 23½cm. (U. S. Dept. of agriculture.
Farmers' bulletin no. 1562)
Joint contribution from Bureau of agricultural economics, Bureau of
entomology, Ohio state university Dept. of rural economics, Michigan
agricultural experiment station, Michigan agricultural extension service.

1. European corn borer. 2. Farms. [2. Farm management] I. Arnold, Carl R., 1891-   joint author. II. Collier, George Warner, 1897-
joint author.
Agr 28-15

Library, U. S. Dept. of   Agriculture 1Ag84F no. 1562

NT   0035925   DNAL WaWW CaBVaU PBa OC1 OO OU

Tapp, Jesse Washington, 1898-
... More profit for the wheat farmers of central Kansas. [By Jesse W. Tapp and W. E. Grimes] [Washing-
ton, Govt. print. off., 1924]
ii, 14 p. illus., diagrs. 23cm. (U. S. Dept. of agriculture. Farmers'
bulletin no. 1440)
Contribution from Bureau of agricultural economics.

1. Agriculture—Kansas. 2. Farms. [2. Farm management] 3. Wheat.
I. Grimes, Waldo Ernest, 1891-   joint author. II. Title.
Agr 25-193

Library, U. S. Dept. of   Agriculture 1Ag84F no. 1440

NT   0035926   DNAL WaWW CaBVaU PBa OC1 OO OU

Tapp, Jesse Washington, 1898-   joint author.

Taylor, Henry Charles, 1873-
... Practical farm economics, by Henry C. Taylor ... H. R.
Tolley ... and J. W. Tapp ... Washington, Govt. print. off.,
1924.

Tapp, Jesse Washington, 1898-   joint author.

Grimes, Waldo Ernest, 1891-
... A study of farm organization in central Kansas. By
W. E. Grimes, J. A. Hodges, and R. D. Nichols ... and
Jesse W. Tapp ... Washington, Govt. print. off., 1925.

S561
.P62

Tapp, Jesse Washington, 1898–   joint author.

Pond, George Augustus, 1889–
    ... A study of farm organization in southwestern Minnesota. By George A. Pond ... and Jesse W. Tapp ... Washington, Govt. print. off., 1924.

Tapp, Jesse Washington, 1898–   joint author.

Elliott, Foster Floyd, 1895–
    ... Types of farming in North Dakota. By F. F. Elliott and Jesse W. Tapp ... and Rex E. Willard ... Washington, U. S. Govt. print. off., 1928.

Tapp, John, fl. 1596–1615.
    The arte of navigation
      see under   Cortés, Martin, fl. 1551.

Tapp, John, fl. 1596–1615.
    The path-way to knowvledge; containing the whole art of arithmeticke, both in whole numbers and fractions; with the extraction of roots; as also a briefe introduction or entrance into the art of cossicke numbers, with many pleasant questions wvought ... thereby. Digested into a plaine and easie methode by way of dialogue, for the better vnderstanding of the learners thereof. Wherewith is also adioyned a briefe order for the keep-   ing of marchants bookes

of accompts, by way of debitor and creditor. London, Printed by T. Purfoot, for T. Pauier, 1613.
    Includes also "A briefe introduction or entrance into the art of cossicke number, drawne out of M.Valentine Menher his Arithmeticke", "An.Dom.1612. The iovrnall or dayes booke marked with the letter A", and "An.Dom.1612. The leager or booke of debitor and creditor, marked with this letter A".

    Short-title catalogue no.23677 (carton 861)

    1.Arithmetic--Before 1846.   2.Bookkeeping. I.Mennher, Valentin.

NT 0035934   MiU

Tapp, John, fl. 1596–1615.
    The path-way to knowledge; contayning the whole art of arithmeticke ... Digested into a plaine and easie method by way of dialogue ... London, Printed by T. Purfoot, for T. Pauier, 1621.
    4 p.l., 374, [47] p.

    Microfilm of the original in the Henry E. Huntington Library. Ann Arbor, Mich., University Microfilms. 35 mm. (English books, 1475-1640, reel 1118)

    Filmed with Jack Straw. The life and death of Iacke Straw ... London, 1593 [i.e. 1594]

    1. Arithmetic.   I. Title.

NT 0035936   CtY-D MiU NNC

[Tapp, John] fl. 1596–1615.
    The Seamans Kalender, Or An Ephemerides [sic] of the Sun, Moone, and certaine of the most notable fixed Starres. Together with many most needfull and necessary matters, to the behoofe and furtherance principally of Marriners and Seamen: but generally profitable to all Trauailers, or such as delight in the Mathematicall studies. The Tables being for the most part Calculated from the yeere 1601. to the yeare 1624. By I. T. Lon-

[Tapp, John] fl. 1596–1615. "The Seamans Kalender... (Card 2)
don. Printed by E. Allde for Iohn Tapp. 1602.   50 l. incl. tables. chart, illus.   4°.
    Film reproduction (35 mm.) of the original in the British museum. Position III. Negative.
    STC 23679.
    Title vignette.

F488.   1. Nautical almanacs–   Gt. Br., 1602. I. T., J. II. Title. N.Y.P.L.   January 24, 1940

NT 0035938   NN CtY

[Tapp, John]
    The seamans kalender, or An ephemerides of the sun, moone, and certain of the most notable fixed stars ... By I.T. London, Printed by E. Allde for J. Tapp, 1602.
    [102] p. diagrs.

    Microfilm of the original in British Museum. Ann Arbor, Mich., University Microfilms. 35 mm. (English books, 1475-1640, reel 1157)
    Filmed with Smith, Henry, 1550?-1591. Gods

arrowes against atheists. London, 1593.

NT 0035940   CtY-D MiU NNC

Tapp, John, fl.1596–1615.
    The seamans kalendar, or An ephemerides of the sunne, moon, and certaine of the most notable fixed starres. The fifth edition, newly corrected and enlarged, with an abridged table of signes, and some propositions thereupon, concerning arithmeticall nauigation. London, Printed by E.Allde, for I.Tappe, 1615.
    Short-title catalogue no.23680 (carton 1085)

    1.Navigation--Early works to 1800. I.Title.

NT 0035941   MiU NNC

Tapp, John, fl. 1596–1615.
    The Seamans kalender, or, An ephemerides of the Sunne, moone, and certaine of the most notable fixed Starres. The ninth edition. Newly corrected and enlarged; with an abridge Table of sines, and some propositions thereupon, concerning arithmeticall nauigation. London, by Edvv, All-de, for Iohn Tap, ... 1625.
    sm. 4to. 1/2 calf.

NT 0035942   CSmH

Tapp, John, fl.1596–1615.
    The seamans kalender. Or An ephemerides of the sunne, moone, and certaine of the most notable fixed starres. The ninth edition. Newly corrected and enlarged; with an abridged table of sines, and some propositions thereupon, concerning arithmeticall nauigation. London, Printed by E.All-de for I.Tap, 1625.
    Short-title catalogue no.23681 (carton 1036)

    1.Navigation--Early works to 1800.

NT 0035943   MiU

Tapp, John, fl.1596–1615.
    The sea-mans kalender: or, An ephemerides of the sun, moon, and certain of the most notable fixed stars. As also a table of the longitude and latitude of all the most eminent places of the world: first calculated by John Tap. Since corr. and inlarged, with many additions. viz. new exact tables of the north-star ... with the discovery of a way to finde the long hidden secret of longitude, by Henry Bond ... All which are now newly calculated and corrected, and many new

rules and tables added, by Henry Phillippes, philo-nauticus. London, Printed by Will. Leybourn, fo[r] George Hurlock, and are to be sould at his shop at Magnus Church-corner in Thames street, 1664.
    3 p.l., 179, [1] p. illus. 19 cm.
    Title within ornamental border.
    Signatures: A-Z⁴.
    Errata leaf inserted between prelim.l. and text.

    Imperfect: p.11-12 wanting; diagr. on p.9 with movable part (detached in pocket at end)

    I. Bond, Henry, 17th century. II. Phillippes, Henry.

NT 0035946   CtY

Tapp, John, fl. 1596–1615.
    Tap's arithmetick, or, The path-way to the knowledge of the ground of arts. Containing the whole art of arithmetick ... The second edition, corrected, revised, amended, & amplyfied ... by P. Ray. Whereunto is added, A brief way for keeping marchants books of accounts, by way of debitor and creditor. London, Printed by J. Streater for J. Wright, 1658.
    448, [47] p. 17cm.

NT 0035947   NNC

Tapp, M. Virginia, joint author.

Dorris, Fern E.
    Learning to look at our world [by] Fern E. Dorris ... [and] M. Virginia Tapp ... Illustrations by Kurt Werth. New York, Chicago [etc.] Silver Burdett company [1942]

Tapp, Robert B.
    The place of the non-Christian religions in American Protestant seminary education; a critical survey and suggested curriculum with emphasis on the underlying educational philosophy. August 1952.
    vii,322f. illus. 29cm.

    Thesis - Univ. of Southern California. Typewritten.
    1.Religions. 2.Theology - Study and teaching.
    FILM 300
    no.1 r.176b

NT 0035949   CLSU

Tapp, Sidney Calhoun, 1870–
    The answer to evolution and its fallacy (from the Bible and science) by Sidney C. Tapp ... Kansas City, Mo., S. C. Tapp [1925]
    24 p. 22½ᶜᵐ.

    1. Evolution. 2. Bible and science. I. Title.   25-16003

    Library of Congress   BL263.T3

NT 0035950   DLC

Tapp, Sidney Calhoun, 1872–
    Argument of Sidney C. Tapp in the matter of application for the pardon of Hon. Caleb Powers. Denver, Colo., Twentieth Century Printing and Publishing Co. [n.d.]
    31 p. 20 cm.
    1. Powers, Caleb, 1869-1932. 2. Kentucky - Pol. & govt. 1865–

NT 0035951   CoU

Tapp, Sidney Calhoun, 1870–
    Christian instruction and devotion ...Kansas city, Mo. Sidney C. Tapp [19—]
    140 p.

NT 0035952   OU MH

Tapp, Sidney Calhoun, 1870–
    The divine mystery of the holy faith, by Sidney C. Tapp ... Kansas City, Mo., S. C. Tapp [1925]
    1 p. l., 33 p. 22ᶜᵐ.

    I. Title.

    Library of Congress   BS680.S5T28   25-5631

NT 0035953   DLC NRCR

Tapp, Sidney Calhoun, 1870–
The duality of the Bible; or, The scriptural church and Christianity, by Sidney C. Tapp ... Kansas City, Mo., The author [1917]
3 p. l., 328 p. illus. (incl. port.) 20ᶜᵐ. $2.00

1. Title.

Library of Congress   17–4991

NT 0035954 DLC

Tapp, Sidney Calhoun, 1870–.
The glory of North Carolina. [poem] [San Antonio, n. p., 1929]
3 p. D.

NT 0035955 NcD NcU

Tapp, Sidney Calhouns, 1870–
The light and the Christ within... c1923.

NT 0035956 NRCR

Tapp, Sidney Calhoun, 1870–
Mr. Tapp's sex interpretation of the Bible as a means of peace and prevention of crime, insanity and disease...1916.

NT 0035957 OC1

Tapp, Sidney Calhouns, 1870–
Mother nature's way to health through the law of the seed and her seven healing forces, by Sidney C. Tapp... Harry Lee Green... Kansas City, Mo., The Christian purity and health league [c1930]
118 p. 17.5 cm.

NT 0035958 DLC

Tapp, Sidney Calhoun, 1870–
Poems. San Antonio, Texas, Pub. by the author, 1932.
16 p.

NT 0035959 NcC

Tapp, Sidney Calhoun, 1870–   3445.168
Prayer and devotion.
— Kansas City, Mo. Tapp. [1926.] 37 pp. 22.5 cm.
Selections from the Bible.
The title is on the cover.

D6511 — T.r. — Prayer. — Devotion, Books of

NT 0035960 MB

BS680 Tapp, Sidney Calhoun, 1870–
S5T32 Prayer and praise... Kansas City, Mo.
  [c1925]

NT 0035961 DLC OC1

Tapp, Sidney Calhoun, 1870–
Purity and regeneration. This book reads from right to left. Kansas City, The scriptural church college [c1922]
6 p. l. 23 cm.

NT 0035962 MH–AH

Tapp, Sidney Calhoun, 1870–
The Scriptural church college (Incorporated)... Kansas City, Mo. U.S.A. ... Sidney C. Tapp... President ... n.d.

NT 0035963 NRCR

TAPP, SIDNEY CALHOUN, 1870–
The secret sins of the Bible. Kansas City, Mo., The Author, 1918. 40 p., port. 19cm.

Microfiche (neg.) 1 sheet. 11 x 15cm. (NYPL FSN 11,382)

1. Sex and religion.

NT 0035964 NN

Tapp, Sidney Calhoun, 1870–
The sex force of the Bible, by Sidney C. Tapp... Kansas City, Mo.: Published by the author, cop. 1920. 48 p. port. 12°.

1. Sex.—Ethics. 2. Bible.—Ethics.
N. Y. P. L.   July 12, 1920.

NT 0035965 NN

Tapp, Sidney Calhoun, 1870–
Sex, the key to the Bible, by Sidney C. Tapp ... Kansas City, Mo., The author [1918]
1 p. l., 5–172 p., 1 l. incl. plates, ports. 18½ᶜᵐ.

1. Title.
Library of Congress HQ61.T25 18–10603

NT 0035966 DLC

Tapp, Sidney Calhoun, 1870–
Sex, the key to the Bible, by Sidney C. Tapp ... [2d and rev. ed.] Kansas City, Mo., The author [1918]
3 p. l., [9]–172 p., 1 l. incl. plates, ports. 18½ᶜᵐ.

1. Title.
Library of Congress HQ61.T25 1918 a 18–19594

NT 0035967 DLC

Tapp, Sidney Calhoun, 1870–
Sexology of the Bible; the fall and redemption of man a matter of sex, by Sidney C. Tapp ... Kansas City, Mo., The Burton publishing company [1913]
181 p. incl. front. (port.) 18½ᶜᵐ. $2.00

1. Title.
      13–25356

NT 0035968 DLC

Tapp, Sidney Calhoun, 1870–
Sexology of the Bible; the fall and redemption of man a matter of sex. 2d and rev. ed., by Sidney C. Tapp ... Kansas City, Mo., Pub. by the author, under auspices of the Sidney C. Tapp international Biblical society [1915]
179 p. incl. port. 18½ᶜᵐ. $2.00

1. Title.
      15–14676

NT 0035969 DLC NRCR OO

Tapp, Sidney Calhoun, 1870–
The story of Anglo-Saxon institutions; or, The development of constitutional government by Sidney C. Tapp, PH. B. New York and London, G. P. Putnam's sons, 1904.
ix, 245 p. 20ᶜᵐ.

1. Gt. Brit.—Constitutional history. 1. Title.
Library of Congress JN121.T2 4–16795 Revised

  CU–AL NjP OKentU OrU MtU
NT 0035970 DLC ICJ MB NN PP NcU FU CoU FMU NcD OC1

Tapp, Sidney Calhoun, 1870–
The struggle, by Sidney C. Tapp ... New York, A. Wessels company, 1906.
324 p. 19½ᶜᵐ.
"The author has not attempted to conform to the plot of the conventional novelist, but to tell the story of the real burden under which the American people are staggering."—Pref.

1. Title.
      6—3126
Library of Congress PZ3.T164S

NT 0035971 DLC NcU CaBVaU

Tapp, Sidney Calhoun, 1870–
The truth about the Bible (the scriptural church) by Sidney C. Tapp ... Published by the author. Kansas City, Mo., Burton publishing company, 1912.
289 p. front. (port.) 22½ᶜᵐ. $3.00

      12–28365.

NT 0035972 DLC

Tapp, Sidney Calhoun, 1870–
The truth about the Bible (the scriptural church) by Sidney C. Tapp ... Kansas City, Mo., The author, under the auspices of the Sidney C. Tapp international Biblical society [1915]
417 p. ports. 20½ᶜᵐ. $3.00

1. Title.
      15–18739

NT 0035973 DLC

Tapp, Sidney Calhoun, 1870–
The truth about the Bible (the scriptural church) by Sidney C. Tapp ... 3d and rev. ed. Kansas City, Mo., The author, under the auspices of the Sidney C. Tapp international Biblical society [1916]
535 p. ports. 20½ᶜᵐ. $3.00

1. Title.
      16–4401

NT 0035974 DLC

Tapp, Sidney Calhoun, 1870–
What every man and woman should know about the Bible, by Sidney C. Tapp ... Kansas City, Mo., The author [1917]
303 p. illus. (incl. port.) 19ᶜᵐ. $2.00

1. Sex. 1. Title.
Library of Congress HQ61.T3 17–20850

NT 0035975 DLC

Tapp, Sidney Calhoun, 1870–
Why Jesus was a man and not a woman, by Sidney C. Tapp ... Kansas City, Mo., The author [1914]
vi, 7–311 p. 20½ᶜᵐ. $2.00

I. Title.

14-19304

NT 0035976 DLC

Tapp, Sidney Calhoun, 1870–
Why we die, by Sidney C. Tapp ... Kansas City, Mo., Schooley stationery and printing co. [1920]
2 p. l., 9–299 p. front. (port.) 19ᶜᵐ.

1. Sexual ethics. I. Title.

Library of Congress HQ31.T3

20-14206

NT 0035977 DLC MiU

Tapp, William Henry
Anne Boleyn & Elizabeth at the royal manor of Hanworth. London, Bailey bros. & Swinfen [1953?]
vi, 23 p. illus., plates, ports., facsims.

Bibliographical footnotes.

1. Elizabeth, queen of England, 1533–1603.
2. Ann Boleyn, queen consort of Henry VIII, 1507–1536.

NT 0035978 NNC NcGU CaBVaU CtY MB MH NN OC1 MnU

Tapp, William Henry.
Jefferyes Hamett O'Neale, red anchor fable painter, and some contemporaries, by William H. Tapp, M. C. London, University of London press, ltd. [1938]
xvi, 66, [6] p. col. front., 34 pl. (incl. ports., facsims.) on 17 l. 25½ x 19¼ᶜᵐ.

"First published ... 1938."
Blank pages for "Notes" ([6] at end)

1. O'Neale, Jefferyes Hamett, 1734 (ca.)–1801. 2. Pottery—England.

Library of Congress NK4485.T3

39-16224

[2] 927.38

NT 0035979 DLC PP CtY NcGU WaU CaBVaU

Law

Tapp, William Henry.

Sunbury-on-Thames, *Eng. Charter.*
The Sunbury charter. [By] W. H. Tapp. [Sunbury-on-Thames, W. H. Tapp, 1952]

Tapp, William John.
An inquiry into the present state of the law of maintenance and champerty, principally as affecting contracts. By William John Tapp ... London, V. & R. Stevens and sons, 1861.
xx, 128 p. 18½ᶜᵐ.

1. Maintenance and champerty.

16-4552

NT 0035981 DLC PU-L

Tappaan, Beth.
Children's books around the year; a handbook of practical suggestions for teachers, librarians and booksellers, compiled by Beth Tappaan. [New York] Children's book council [1945]
128 p. 21ᶜᵐ.
Bibliography: p. 124–128.

1. Children's literature. 2. Books and reading. I. Children's book council, New York.

Library of Congress ° Z1037.A1T3

45-10453

[5] 028.5

NT 0035982 DLC PPPL PPD TU NcGU IaU

Tappahannock, Va. Essex county woman's club
see
Essex county woman's club, *Tappahànnock, Va.*

Tappahannock, Va. Rappahannock Institute
see Rappahannock Institute, Tappahannock, Va.

Tappahannock, Va. St. Margaret's School
see St. Margaret's School, Tappahannock, Va.

Ov30 **Tappahannock, Va. Town manager.**
+T33c Annual report ...
[Tappahannock]
28cm.

Mimeographed.

NT 0035986 CtY

Tappan, Anna Helen, 1888–
Plane sextic curves invariant under birational transformations, by Anna Helen Tappan ... [Baltimore, 1915]
1 p. l., p. [309]–336. 31ᶜᵐ.
Thesis (PH. D.)—Cornell university, 1914.
"Reprinted from American journal of mathematics, vol. XXXVII, no. 3, July, 1915."

I. Transformations (Mathematics)

16-2633

Library of Congress QA601.T3
Cornell Univ. Libr.

NT 0035987 NIC DLC MiU

Tappan, Benjamin, 1773–1857.

Ohio. *Courts of common pleas.*
Cases decided in the courts of common pleas in the fifth circuit of the state of Ohio, commencing with May term, 1816. To which is added the opinion of Judge McLean in the case of Landerback vs. Moore. By Benjamin Tappan ... Rev. ed. Norwalk, O., The Laning printing company, 1899.

Tappan, Benjamin, 1773–1857.
A discourse delivered before the Historical and philosophical society of Ohio, at the annual meeting of said society in Columbus, December 22, 1832. By Benjamin Tappan, president of said society ... Columbus [O.] J. R. Emrie, printer, 1833.
16 p. 20½ᶜᵐ.

1. Ohio. I. Historical and philosophical society of Ohio.

Library of Congress F491.T17

1-22587

NT 0035989 DLC NcD OOxM OC1WHi

Tappan, Benjamin, 1773–1857.
Discourse delivered before the Historical & philosophical Society of Ohio... Columbus, 1838.
16 p. 8°. [In v. 28, Silliman Scientific miscellany]

NT 0035990 CtY

Tappan, Benjamin 1773–1857
Modern "Democracy," the ally of slavery. Speech of Hon. M. W. Tappan, of N. Hampshire, in the House of Representatives, July 29, 1856. [Wash. D. C. 1856?]
15 p.

NT 0035991 OC1WHi

815.3
T17s **Tappan, Benjamin,** 1773–1857.
Remarks on abolition petitions, delivered in Senate, February 4, 1840. [Washington? 1840?]
4 p. 26cm. [Bound with Tappan, B. Speech on the permanent prospective pre-emption law. Washinton, 1841]

1. Slavery in the U.S. - Law.

NT 0035992 TNJ PU OC1WHi ICU PHi NN NIC NRU MiU-C

Tappan, Benjamin, 1773–1857.
Report [of] the Joint committee on the Library...
see under U.S. Congress. Joint Committee on the Library.

[**Tappan, Benjamin**] 1773–1857.
A review of the question whether the common law of England...1817

see under

[Goodenow, John Milton]

Tappan, Benjamin, 1773–1857.
Speech of Mr. B. Tappan of Ohio on the permanent prospective pre-emption law delivered in the Senate of the United States January 29, 1841. Washington, Blair and Rives, 1841.
7 p. 23cm.

Volume of pamphlets.

NT 0035995 NNC TNJ

Tappan, Benjamin 1773–1857
Speech of Mr. Tappan of Ohio in Senate. Feb. 23, 1841––the bill to incorporate the banks of the District of Columbia being under consideration...
n. p. n. d.
8 p.

NT 0035996 OC1WHi

Tappan, Benjamin, 1773–1857.
Speech of Mr. Tappan, of Ohio, on the joint resolution proposing an amendment to the constitution of the United States, so as to limit the term of office of the judges of the supreme and inferior courts; delivered in the Senate of the United States, January 16, 1843. Steubenville [O.] Morris & Frazer, printers, 1843.
11 p. 19 1/2 cm. Grey boards.
In double columns.
1. Judges--U. S. 2. U. S.—Officials and employees--Appointment, qualifications, tenure, etc.

NT 0035997 CSmH OC1WHi

Tappan, Benjamin, 1773-1857.
Speech of the Hon. Benjamin Tappan of Ohio
on the United States fiscal bank bill, delivered in the Senate of the United States,
July 14, 1841. Washington, Blair and Rives,
1841. Washington, Blair and Rives, 1841.
15 p. 22cm.

NT 0035998   NNC DLC

[TAPPAN, Benjamin, 1773-1857].
Suggestions respecting the debt of the late
republic of Texas. [Steubenville, Ohio, 1852.

pp. 7.
Half-title serves as title-page.
Signed: Benj. Tappan. Steubenville, Ohio,
Mar. 25, 1852.

NT 0035999   MH

TAPPAN. (Benjamin) 1788 - 1863. An Address, delivered
at the request of the Washington Benevolent Society of Kennebec,
at their Celebration of Peace, March 2d, 1815. By Benjamin Tappan, A.M. Minister of Augusta. *Hallowell: Printed by Goodale &
Burton.* 1815. 8vo, pp. 15.

NT 0036001   MB NNHi MBAt CSmH MH MeHi MHi

Tappan, Benjamin, 1788-1863.
The believer's last enemy destroyed. A sermon delivered
November 17, 1830, at the funeral of Rev. Fifield Holt, late
pastor of the Congregational church in Bloomfield. By Benjamin Tappan ... Augusta, Printed by W. Hastings, 1831.
20 p. 22cm.

1. Holt, Fifield, 1784-1830.   I. Title.
                                                27-10754
Library of Congress   BX7260.H56T3

NT 0036002   DLC

Tappan, Benjamin, 1788-1863.

Paine, Elijah, 1757-1842.
A collection of facts in regard to Liberia, by Judge Paine,
of Vermont: to which is added the correspondence of the Rev.
Benjamin Tappan, of Maine, and Francis S. Key, esquire, of
the District of Columbia. Woodstock, Vt., Printed by A.
Palmer, 1839.

Tappan, Benjamin, 1788-1863
Life and writings of President Appleton ...

Detached from Literary and theological
review, v. 4, no. 15, Sept. 1837, p. 351-372.

1. Appleton, Jesse, 1772-1819.

NT 0036004   MeB

Special
Coll.   Tappan, Benjamin, 1788-1863
A sermon, delivered at the interment of the
Reverend Jesse Appleton, D.D. A.A.S., presi-
dent of Bowdoin College, in Brunswick, Maine,
who died Nov. 12th, 1819; aet. 47. Hallowell
[Me.] Printed by E. Goodale, 1819.
39 p. 24 cm.

Author's autograph presentation copy.

1. Appleton, Jesse, 1772-1819.

          PPPrHi
          MeBa CSmH DLC MB CtY ICN MeP DLC InU CSt MnU PHi
NT 0036005   MeB RPB NN MWA MHi NNHi MBAt NNUT MH

BX7260
.T16   Tappan, Benjamin, 1788-1863.
Ad17   A sermon delivered at Vassalboro, June
20, 1821, at the interment of Mrs. Sarah
B. Adams, consort of Rev. Thomas Adams,
who died 18th June, Aet. 25. Hallowell
[Me.] Goodale, Glazier & Son, 1821.
14 p.

1. Adams, Sarah Barnard, d. 1821. 2.
Memorial service. I. Title.

NT 0036006   CtHC MH

Tappan, Benjamin, 1788-1863.
A sermon, delivered in Hallowell, October 23, 1848, at the
interment of the Rev. Eliphalet Gillett, D. D. By Benjamin
Tappan ... Hallowell, Masters, Smith & co., printers, 1848.
16 p. 23cm.

1. Gillett, Eliphalet, 1768-1848.
                                                27-7894
Library of Congress   BX7260.G425T3

NT 0036007   DLC MWA

Tappan, Benjamin, 1788-1863.
A sermon delivered in Wells, June 27, 1821;
before the Maine missionary society, at their
fourteenth anniversary. By Benjamin Tappan ...
Hallowell [Me.] Printed by S. K. Gilman, 1821.

36 p. 21 cm.

Presentation inscription on title-page.
Report of the trustees of the Maine missionary
society, p. [25]-36.
1. Missions—Addresses, essays, lectures. I.
Maine Missionary   society.

NT 0036008   CSmH ICN MeB MiU-C MH ICN MNtcA

Tappan, Benjamin, 1788-1863.
A sermon in Winthrop, September 25, 1822,
before the Kennebec missionary society [with
appendix] Hallowell, 1822.
20 p. O.

NT 0036009   RPB

TAPPAN, Benjamin, 1788-1863
Song of angels at the birth of Christ. A sermon.
Augusta, 1828. 23 pp. 8 .

NT 0036010   MB

Tappan, Benjamin, 1788-1863.
Why is my liberty judged of another man's
conscience? A sermon, delivered in Augusta, on
March 12, 1837. By Benjamin Tappan ...
Augusta [Me.] Smith & Robinson, printers, 1837.
16 p. 22 cm. Orig. blue paper covers.

NT 0036011   CSmH RPB

TAPPAN, BENJAMIN, 1815-
A discourse commemorative of Deacon E.P.
Mackintire. Preached Feb. 14, 1864, to the
Winthrop church, Charlestown, Mass.— Boston,
Printed for the church, 1864.
22p.

Binder's title: Individual biography.

NT 0036012   ICN RPB MH

TAPPAN, BENJAMIN, 1815-
Our help in God when the godly cease. A discourse occasioned by the death of Dea. Chester
Adams: preached June 3, 1855, in the Winthrop
church, Charleston, Mass., by the pastor, Benjamin Tappan, jr. Boston, Crocker, 1855.
24p.

Binder's title: Individual biography.

NT 0036013   ICN RPB

PS1631
.A35T3   Tappan, Caroline (Sturgis) 1819-1888.

Emerson, Ralph Waldo, 1803-1882.
Thoreau's pencils; an unpublished letter from Ralph
Waldo Emerson to Caroline Sturgis, 19 May, 1844. [Cam-
bridge, Mass., 1944.

Tappan, Mrs. Cora L. V.
          see Richmond, Mrs. Cora Linn Victoria
(Scott) 1840-1923 .

Tappan, Daniel D
Hymn for the hundredth anniversary of the
Congregational church in Winthrop, Me.,
Sept. 4, 1876.
In, Winthrop, Me. - Congregational church, ...
Centennial... 1876. 23 cm. 24 p. p. 6.

NT 0036016   RPB

Tappan, Daniel Langdon, 1855-
Tappan—Toppan genealogy; ancestors and descendants of Abraham Toppan of Newbury, Massachusetts,
1606-1672, by Daniel Langdon Tappan. Arlington,
Mass., Priv. print. by the compiler, 1915.
4 p. l., 164 p. front. (coat of arms) 2 pl., port. 24½cm.
"Two hundred copies printed."

1. Tappan family (Abraham Toppan, b. 1606?)
Library of Congress   CS71.E175 1915   15-18653

NT 0036017   DLC ICN WaS MB MWA OClWHi NN

Tappan, David, 1752-1803.
Works by this author printed in America before 1801 are available
in this library in the Readex Microprint edition of Early American
Imprints published by the American Antiquarian Society.
This collection is arranged according to the numbers in Charles
Evans' American Bibliography.

NT 0036018   DLC

Tappan, David, 1752-1803.
[The works] Boston, 1807.
2 v. 22 cm.

NT 0036019   RPB

AC901
.W3   Tappan, David, 1752-1803.
An address delivered to the students of
Phillips Academy in Andover, immediately after
the yearly examination and exhibition...
Exeter, pr. by Stearns & Winslow, 1794.
11 p. (Waterman pamphlets, 167:7)

NT 0036020   DLC

Tappan, David, 1752-1803.

Willard, Joseph, 1738-1804.
An address in Latin, by Joseph Willard ... and a discourse in English, by David Tappan ... delivered before
the university in Cambridge, Feb. 21, 1800, in solemn
commemoration of Gen. George Washington. [Charles-
town, Mass.] E. typis Samuel Etheridge, 1800.

BX7233
.T2B4
1800

TAPPAN, DAVID, 1752-1803.
The beauty and benefits of the Christian church, illustrated in two sermons, delivered to the first religious society in Plymouth, on January 5, 1800, being the Lord's-day immediately following the ordination of the Reverend Mr. Kendall to the work of the Gospel ministry in that society. By David Tappan ... Boston, Printed by S. Hall, 1800.
46 p. 22½cm.
1. Kendall, James, 1769-1859. 2. Sermons, English.

CSt MH-AH MMeT MH MhI MHa InU MP1 MDeep MiD-B NN MWA DLC MSaE N MiD RPJCB MBC MBAt MB ICMe
NT 0036022 ICU CSt MiU-C NHi NCH CtY NAuT NNC NNUT

Tappan, David, 1752-1803.
The character and best exercises of unregenerate sinners set in a scriptural light, in a discourse delivered by David Tappan, A. M., pastor of the Third church in Newbury. Published at the desire of many who heard it. Newburyport [Mass.]: Printed and sold by John Mycall. 1782.
60 p. 20½cm.

1. Sermons, American. I. Title.

A 35-1735
Title from H. E. Huntington Libr. Printed by L. C.

NT 0036023 CSmH CtY MoU NcD N NN ICU MH MWA RPJCB

Tappan, David, 1752-1803.
The character and death of the servant of God considered... in a sermon delivered at Byfield: January 18th, 1784. Occasioned by the decease of the Rev. Moses Parsons, A.M., pastor of the church of Christ in that place, who departed this life Dec. 14 1783. By David Tappan, A.M ... Newbury-port: Printed by John Mycall, 1784. 50, 19 p. 8°.
Appended, with independent paging but continuous registration: An oration delivered at the interment of the Rev. Moses Parsons...by Levi Frisby. Title-page within mourning borders. Edges untrimmed.

1. Parsons, Moses, 1716-83. 2. By-
N. Y. P. L. field, Mass. May 11, 1915.

NT 0036024 NN InU N MiU-C MWA MH MeB RPJCB CtY

Tappan, David, 1752-1803.
Christian thankfulness explained and enforced. A sermon, delivered at Charlestown, in the afternoon of February 19, 1795. The day of general thanksgiving through the United States. By David Tappan ... Printed by Samuel Hall, no. 53, Cornhill, Boston, 1795.
40 p. 21½cm.
[Hazard pamphlets, v. 63, no. 7]

1. U. S.—Pol. & govt. 1789-1797.
Library of Congress AC901.H3 vol. 63
20-12737

NNUT WHi MoU MHi MBAt MH CtY OO PHi MnHi
NT 0036025 DLC MiU-C CtW MB CtHi RPJCB MBC MA MWA

Case
C
52
.863

TAPPAN, DAVID, 1752-1803.
The connexion between faith in God, or in the principles of natural religion, and a suitable regard to Jesus Christ and his gospel; illustrated in a discourse, delivered at Portsmouth, N. Hampshire, before the reverend association of Congregational ministers of that town and vicinity... Portsmouth, J. Melcher, 1792.
29p.

NT 0036026 ICN CtY RPJCB MH-AH NHi MWA MBAt DLC

Tappan, David, 1752-1803.
Copy of an address delivered to the students of Phillips academy in Andover, immediately after the yearly examination and exhibition, before the Board of trustees, on the seventh of July, 1794. By David Tappan ... Exeter, Printed by Stearns & Winslow, M,DCC,XCIV.
11 p. 16½cm.

I. Phillips academy, Andover, Mass.
A 32-291
Title from Phillips Academy. Printed by L. C.

NT 0036027 MAnP NNUT MWA MH MB

[Tappan, David] 1752-1803.
. Copy of the address delivered to the students of Phillips' academy, in Andover, immediately after the examination and exhibition, on July 18, 1791. Exeter, Printed by H. Ranlet, for the trustees of said academy, 1791.
8p. 20cm.
Attributed to Rev. David Tappan in Sabin's Dictionary of books relating to America.

NT 0036028 CtY MH NN MHi

Tappan, David, 1752-1803.
A discourse delivered at the Third parish in Newbury, on the first of May, 1783, occasioned by the ratification of a treaty of peace, between Great-Britain, and the United States of America. By David Tappan, A. M., pastor of the church in said parish. Salem: Printed by Samuel Hall, near the Court-house. 1783.
19 p. 18½cm.
Imperfect: half-title wanting.

. U. S.—Hist.—Revolution—Addresses, sermons, etc.
Library of Congress E297.T17 8-25612 Revised

MiU-C CtY RPJCB
NT 0036029 DLC N NN MWA MiU-C CSmH MH NNUT NHi MBAt

Tappan, David. 1752-1803.
Discourse delivered before the University in Cambridge, Feb. 21, 1800, in commemoration of Gen. Washington. [Cambridge] 1800.
44p 8°

NT 0036030 MeB MWA MH

Tappan, David, 1752-1803.
A discourse delivered in the chapel of Harvard college, June 17, 1794, at the request of the senior class of students, on occasion of their approaching departure from the university, preparatory to their receiving its public honors. By David Tappan, A. M., Hollis professor of divinity in said college. Published by desire of the hearers. Boston, Printed by E. W. Weld and W. Greenough, at the Magazine office, no. 49, State street. MDCCXCIV.
16 p. 20½cm.

A 32-1046
H. E. Huntington library for Library of Congress [a40b1]

ViU RPJCB MBAt MWA NHi NNUT
NT 0036031 CSmH CSt CtY ICU MH InU MoU NcD ICN NN

Case
E
5
.9156

TAPPAN, DAVID, 1752-1803.
A discourse delivered in the chapel of Harvard college, November 17, 1795. occasioned by the death of Mr. John Russell, a member of the senior class in that university; who expired... October 29... Boston, Printed by J. W. Folsom, for the author, 1795.
16p.

MWA MBAt NN MeWC DLC CtY
NT 0036032 ICN MA CSt NHi NNUT MiU-C RPJCB MH MB

BX7233
.T2B4
1800

TAPPAN, DAVID, 1752-1803.
A discourse delivered in the chapel of Harvard college, June 19. 1798. occasioned by the approaching departure of the senior class from the university. By David Tappan... Boston, Printed by Manning & Loring, 1798.
28 p. 20½cm. [With his The beauty and benefits of the Christian church. Boston, 1800]

RPJCB 1. Baccalaureate addresses.

ICN InU NcD CtY CSt DLC MoU
NT 0036033 ICU NN MH MWA NNUT NHi MBAt NjR RPJCB

Tappan, David, 1752-1803.
A discourse, delivered in the South meeting-house in Andover, before His Excellency the governor, the honorable Council, the president of the Senate, and speaker of the House of representatives of the commonwealth of Massachusetts, at the funeral of His Honor Samuel Phillips, esq., late lt. gov. of said commonwealth, Feb. 15, 1802. By David Tappan ... Boston: Printed by Young and Minns, state printers. 1802.
27 p. 20cm.

1. Phillips, Samuel, 1752-1802.
18—12648
Library of Congress F69.P63
——Copy 2. [Mis- cellaneous pamphlets, v. 223, no. 11]
AC901.M5 vol. 223

PPHi MHi CSmH NIC MnU
MH OClWHi ODW PHi OO CtY CSt InU MiEM MiU-C WHi
NT 0036034 DLC NNG NNUT MB MBAt NNHi ICN NN MeB MWA

BX7233
.T2B4
1800

TAPPAN, DAVID, 1752-1803.
A discourse, delivered to the Religious society in Brattle-street, Boston, and to the Christian congregation in Charlestown, on April 5. 1798. being the day of the annual fast in the commonwealth of Massachusetts. By David Tappan... Boston, Printed by S. Hall, 1798.
31 p. 20cm. [With his The beauty and benefits of the Christian church. Boston, 1800]
Imperfect: half-title wanting.
1. Fast day sermons

MBAt NIC MBU ICN DLC MWA
NT 0036035 ICU RPJCB NNUT NN MH MA NHi MHi CtY CSt

Tappan, David, 1752-1803.
A discourse, delivered to the Religious Society in Brattle-Street, Boston, and to the Christian congregation in Charlestown, on April 5, 1798, being the day of the annual fast in the Commonwealth of Massachusetts ... 2d ed. Boston, Printed by S. Hall, 1798.
31 p. 23cm.

NT 0036036 NIC NN RPJCB MWA DLC NcD

Tappan, David, 1752-1803.
A discourse delivered to the students of Harvard college, September 6, 1796. Designed for the special benefit of the new class, which lately joined the society; by David Tappan ... Boston, Printed by Manning & Loring, 1796.
20 p. 21½cm.

E 13-251
Library, U. S. Bur. of Education

RPJCB NN MBAt MH NHi NNUT
NT 0036037 DHEW CtY DLC NcD MoU CSt MiU-C MeB MWA

Tappan, David, 1752-1803.
A discourse, in English.
(In Willard, Joseph, D.D., President of Harvard College. 1738-1804. An address, in Latin ... Feb. 21, 1800, in solemn commemoration of General George Washington. Pp. 11-44. [Charlestown.] 1800.)

This card was printed at the Boston Public Library, July 30, 1912.
H7954 — Washington, George

NT 0036038 MB MWA NHi DLC

Tappan, David, 1752-1803.
The duty of private Christians to pray for their ministers; shewn in two sermons delivered at the Third parish in Newbury, April 24th, 1777. By David Toppan, A. M. Being the Sabbath after his ordination to the pastoral office in that place. Newbury-Port: Printed by John Mycall. MDCCLXXVIII.
viii, 56 p. 18½cm.
Half-title: Mr. Toppan's sermons on the duty of Christians to pray for their ministers.

1. Congregational churches—Sermons. 2. Sermons, American.

Library of Congress BX7233.T25D8 5-20520
[a36b1] 252.058

NT 0036039 DLC NN MoU MH-AH MB RPJCB

Tappan, David, 1752-1803.
A friendly dialogue, in three parts between Philalethes and Toletus
see under Spring, Samuel, 1736-1819.

---

*AC7
T1656
803f

Tappan, David, 1752-1803.
A funeral discourse, delivered to the Benevolent congregational society in Providence in the state of Rhode Island, on the Lord's day after the interment of Enos Hitchcock D.D. who died February 27, 1803, in the 59th year of his age. By David Tappan, D.D. professor of divinity in Harvard college.
Cambridge, Printed at the University press by W. Hilliard. 1803.
24p. 21cm., in folder 22.5cm.
Stitched, un- bound; in cloth folder.
Inscribed: Rev. Tristram Gilman - from the Author.

ICN RHi MiD
NT 0036041 MH PMA CtY InU CSt NcD RPB PHi MH OO

Tappan, David, 1752–1803.
Lectures on Jewish antiquities; delivered at Harvard university in Cambridge, A. D. 1802 & 1803. By David Tappan ... Cambridge [etc.] W. Hilliard and E. Lincoln, 1807.
1 p. l., [vii], [8]–364 p. 22½ᶜᵐ.

1. Jews—Antiq. 2. Bible—Antiq.

Library of Congress   DS111.T17   5—7828

KyU PMA MB MBrZ MeB NN MH MWA PU MWA MeAu OClWHi
NT 0036042   DLC NcD PU PPDrop PPL CtY PP OCH OO DeU

Tappan, David, 1752–1803.
A minister's solemn farewel to his people. A discourse delivered to the Third Church and congregation in Newbury, by David Tappan ... on occasion of his intended removal from them to the University of Cambridge ... Portsmouth: Printed and sold by John Melcher, 1793. 35 p. 16°.

The half-title and p. 33–35 wanting.

                                        FORD COLLECTION.
1. Conduct of life.   May 13, 1916.
N. Y. P. L.

MnU CtY
NT 0036043   NN MB MBAt MWA NNUT MH RPJCB DLC MiU-C

Tappan, David, 1752–1803.
The question answered, "Watchman, what of the night?" A discourse delivered at Newbury, May 15, 1783, being the day appointed by authority for the annual fast in the Commonwealth of Massachusetts. Salem, Printed by S. Hall, 1783.
19 p. 16 cm.

1. Fast-day sermons.   I. Title.
BX7233.T25Q4 1783   65–58546

ICN
NT 0036044   DLC MiU-C MBAt MH-AH MWA CtHi NNUT RPJCB

Tappan, David, 1752–1803.
A sermon delivered April 18, 1803, at the funeral of Mrs. Mary Dana, consort of Rev. Joseph Dana, D. D., pastor of the South Church in Ipswich, who died April 13, in the 53d year of her age. Cambridge, Printed at the University Press by W. Hilliard, 1803.
21 p. 21 cm.
1. Dana, Mary, d. 1803. 2. Funeral sermons.

MH ICN NN RPB
NT 0036045   NcD RPB MWA OClWHi NNUT MiD PHi InU CSt

Tappan, David, 1752–1803.
A sermon delivered at Kennebunk, September 3, 1800. At the ordination of Rev. Nathaniel Fletcher, colleague pastor with Rev. Daniel Little. By David Tappan, D.D., Hollis professor of divinity in Harvard College. Cambridge: Printed by William Hilliard. 1800. 34 p. 8°.

                                        FORD COLLECTION
1. Fletcher, Nathaniel Hill, d. 1834. 2. Kennebunk, Me.
N. Y. P. L.   March 16, 1915.

MAnP
       NNUT RHi NHi MiD-B MHi MH-AH MBC C-S CSmH CSt MBAt
NT 0036046   NN MH MWA MB RPJCB PHi CSt MH DLC CtY NNC

BX7233   TAPPAN, DAVID, 1752–1803.
.T2B4   A sermon delivered at the ordination of the Rev.
1800   John Thornton Kirkland to the pastoral care of the
          New South church and congregation in Boston, February
          5th, 1794. By David Tappan ... Boston, Printed at the
          Apollo press, by Belknap and Hall, 1794.
              43 p. 19½cm. [With his The beauty and benefits of
          the Christian church. Boston, 1800]
              Imperfect: half-title wanting.
              1. Kirkland, John Thornton, 1770–1840. 2. Ordination
          sermons.

         NHi NNUT CSt MB CtY PPL
NT 0036047   ICU RPJCB NN MeB MWA MH DLC ICN MBAt MHi

BX7233   TAPPAN, DAVID, 1752–1803.
.T2B4   A sermon, delivered at the ordination of the Rev.
1800   Timothy Dickinson, to the pastoral care of the church
          in Holliston, February 18, MDCCLXXXIX. By David
          Tappan ... To which are added, the charge, by the Rev.
          Amariah Frost ... and the right hand of fellowship, by
          the Rev. David Kellogg ... Boston, Printed by I. Thomas
          and company, 1789.
              44 p. 20½cm. [With his The beauty and benefits
          of the Christian church. Boston, 1800]
              1. Dickinson, Timothy, 1761–1813. 2. Ordination sermons.

       NN DLC NcD NIC
NT 0036048   ICU MH-AH MWA MBAt RPJCB ICN CtY MiU-C

Tappan, David, 1752–1803.
A sermon delivered at the Third Parish in Newbury, July 24, 1794; occasioned by the sudden death of eight persons belonging to the society, who were drowned in the river Merrimack on the nineteenth of the same month. Newburyport [Mass.] Printed by Blunt & March, 1794.
vi, 25 p. 21 cm.
L. C. copy imperfect: cover wanting.

1. Disasters—Religious interpretations. 2. Sermons, American.

BX7233.T252S38   58–53577

       NNUT PMA RPJCB PHi CtY MnU InU
NT 0036049   DLC MH-AH MBAt MWA MB PHi MHi MnHi NHi

BX7233
.T25S3   Tappan, David, 1752–1803.
1802   A sermon delivered at Wiscasset in the
          district of Maine, September 8, 1802, at
          the installation of the Rev. Hezekiah
          Packard to the pastoral office in that
          place. Cambridge, Printed at the University Press by William Hilliard, 1802.
              36 p. 24 cm.
              1. Ordination sermons. 2. Packard, Hezekiah, 1761–1849.

       NNUT
NT 0036050   ViU CtY PHi DLC RPB CSt MH CSmH MWA

BX7233   TAPPAN, DAVID, 1752–1803.
.T2B4   A sermon, delivered before the annual convention
1800   of the Congregational ministers of Massachusetts,
          in Boston, June 1, 1797. By David Tappan ... Boston, Printed by S. Hall, 1797.
              34 p. 20½cm. [With his The beauty and benefits
          of the Christian church. Boston, 1800]
              Imperfect: half-title wanting.

              1. Theology, Pastoral. 2. Sermons, English.

       RPJCB MWA NN MA MBAt MBU CSt DLC InU CtY MnU NcD NIC
NT 0036051   ICU   NNUT NNC MB MH ICN NHi MHi M

BX7233   TAPPAN, DAVID, 1752–1803.
.T2B4   A sermon, delivered to the first congregation in
1800   Cambridge, and the Religious society in Charlestown
          April 11, 1793, on occasion of the annual fast in the
          commonwealth of Massachusetts. By David Tappan ...
          Boston, Printed by S. Hall, 1793.
              31 p. 21cm. [With his The beauty and benefits
          of the Christian church. Boston, 1800]

              1. Fast day sermons.

       PHi CtY DLC MBU CtY
NT 0036052   ICU NN MB MH MWA MeB MiU-C MBAt NIC NcU

BX7233   Tappan, David, 1752–1803.
.J46S4   A sermon, preached at Newbury, Third parish, April 18th,
Rare Bk. 1774. At the ordination of the Reverend Mr. David Toppan,
Coll.   to the work of the ministry, and pastoral care of the church
          and congregation in that place. By the Reverend Mr. Jedidiah Jewett, M. A. ... Newbury-port: Printed by E. Lunt and
          W. H. Tinges. MDCCLXXIV.

Jewett, Jedidiah, 1705?–1774.

Tappan, David, 1752–1803.
A sermon preached before His Excellency John Hancock, esq., governour; His Honor Samuel Adams, esq., lieutenant-governour; the honourable the Council, Senate, and House of representatives, of the commonwealth of Massachusetts, May 30, 1792. Being the day of general election. By David Tappan, A. M., pastor of a church in Newbury. Printed in Boston, Massachusetts: at the State press, by Thomas Adams, printer to the honourable, the General court. 1792.
39 p. 21ᶜᵐ.
Half-title: Mr. Tappan's election sermon. May 30, 1792.
1. Election sermons—Massachusetts.
Library of Congress   BV4260.M5 1792   31–25310
——— Copy 2.   [Waterman pamphlets, v. 127, no. 12]
Imperfect: last page   wanting; supplied in manuscript.
                             AC901.W3 vol. 127

       NNUT MoU MnU TU NIC InU NN
       MB MWA MBAt CSmH MeB ICU CtY M NBuG MH MA NNHi NcU
NT 0036054   DLC MH NcD CU-A MiU-C ViU MiU MHi RPJCB

Tappan, David, 1752–1803.
Sermons on important subjects. By the late Rev. David Tappan ... To which are prefixed a biographical sketch of the author; and a sermon preached at his funeral by Dr. Holmes. Cambridge, W. Hilliard; Boston, Lincoln & Edmands, 1807.
viii, [9]–23, [1], 22, 334 p. 24ᶜᵐ.
                                                    3–29256

       OO MH-AH MWiW PPPrHi
NT 0036055   DLC NN MeB CSt PMA NcD DeU ViU MSohG OC

Tappan, David, D.D. 1752–1803.   No. 11 in 4419.11
The treaty of peace. A discourse delivered in the Third Parish in Newbury, Massachusetts, on the 1st of May, 1783, occasioned by the ratification of the treaty of peace between Great Britain and the United States of America.
(In Moore, Frank, editor. The patriot preachers of the American Revolution. Pp. 289–309. [New York.] 1860.)

NT 0036056   MB

Tappan, David, 1752–1803.
Two friendly letters from Toletus to Philalethes, or from the Rev. David Tappan to the Rev. Samuel Spring, containing remarks on the sentiments and reasonings of the latter, in his Dialogue on the nature of duty. Newbury-port: Printed by John Mycall, M,DCCLXXXV.
136 p. 18½*.
"Appendix, (number I.) By the author of 'The sacrifice of the wicked explained and distinguished'" (i. e. Joseph Dana) : p. [115]–119.
"Appendix, (number II.) A letter from Toletus to Amartolos, containing brief remarks on the 'Private conference' between him and Philalethes" : p. [120]–136.
1. Spring, Samuel, 1746–1819. A friendly dialogue ... upon the nature of duty. 2. Man (Theology)—Early works to 1800. I. Dana, Joseph, 1742–1827. II. Title.
Library of Congress   BT700.S7T3   40–38598
——— Copy 2.   [Waterman pamphlets, v. 133, no. 7]
                             AC901.W3 vol. 133, no. 7

       NjP MWA MBAt RPJCB NN NIC MB MHi CSmH PHi NHi NjP NN
NT 0036057   DLC MiU-C N PMA MoU PHi CtY MH RPB MiU-C

Tappan, David, 1752–1803.
Washington, George, pres. U. S., 1732–1799.
Washington's political legacies. To which is annexed, an appendix, containing an account of his illness, death, and the national tributes of respect paid to his memory, with a biographical sketch, of his life and character. His will, and Dr. Tappan's discourse, before the University of Cambridge. New-York: Printed by George Forman, no. 64, for C. Davis, no. 167, Water-street. 1800.

Tappan, David Stanton, 1845–1922.
Inauguration of Rev. David Stanton Tappan ... see under Miami University, Oxford, Ohio.

Tappan, Mrs. Edith Haskell, ed.

New Hampshire federation of women's clubs.
An anthology of New Hampshire poetry ... [sponsored by] New Hampshire federation of women's clubs. [Manchester, N. H., The Clarke press, °1938]

Tappan, Edith Haskell.
Stray rhythms, verses of my leisure hours, by Edith Haskell Tappan. North Montpelier, Vt., The Driftwind press, 1931.

2 p. l., 3–48 p. 18½ᶜᵐ.

ɪ. Title.

CA 31–281 Unrev'd
Library of Congress   PS3539.A53S7 1931
——— Copy 2.
Copyright A 36019   811.5

NT 0036061   DLC

Tappan, Edmund March, 1824–1860, joint comp.

M2117   ₍Day, George Tiffany₎ 1822–1875, comp.
.D29C5   The choralist : a collection of hymns and tunes, for public, social, and family worship ... Dover, N. H., Freewill Baptist printing establishment ₍ᶜ1859₎

BR1725   **Tappan, Edmund March, 1824–1860.**
T36A3   The words of a man. Selected and arranged by Eva March Tappan. Cambridge, printed at the Riverside Press ᶜ1914₎
              xix,115p. ports. 18cm.

I. Tappan, Eva March, 1854–1930, comp.
II. Title.

NT 0036063   IaU MWA

Tappan, Edward Arthur, joint author.

Stafford, George Thomas.
Practical corrective exercises ₍by₎ G. T. Stafford ₍and₎ E. A. Tappan ... Champaign, Ill., Bailey and Himes, ᶜ1927.

Tappan, Eli Todd, 1824–1888.
Elements of geometry. By Eli T. Tappan ... New York, D. Appleton & company, 1885.

v, ₍2₎, 253 p. diagr. 20½ᶜᵐ.

1. Geometry.

Library of Congress   QA453.T17   3—19807

NT 0036065   DLC CU MiHM KyU

Tappan, Eli Todd, 1824–1888.

Ohio teachers' association. *Centennial committee.*
A history of education in the state of Ohio. A centennial volume. Pub. by authority of the General assembly. Columbus, O. ₍The₎ Gazette printing house₎ 1876.

M326.080   **Tappan, Eli Todd, 1824–1888.**
P19   Inaugural address of Eli T. Tappan, president of the Ohio Teachers' association, delivered at Zanesville, O., July 3, 1866.
v.12
no.15   8p. 22cm.

NT 0036067   DHU OO

Tappan, Eli T₍odd₎ 1824–1888.
Notes and exercises on surveying: for the use of students in Kenyon college. By Eli T. Tappan ... Gambier, O., Edmonds & Hunt, printers, 1878.

17, ₍1₎ p. 21½ᶜᵐ.

1. Surveying.

Library of Congress   TA549.T19   5–38944†

NT 0036068   DLC

Tappan, Eli T₍odd₎ 1824–1888.
Notes and exercises on surveying, for the use of students in Kenyon college; by Eli T. Tappan ... Mt. Vernon, O., Republican steam printing house, 1881.

14 p. tab. 23ᶜᵐ.

1. Surveying.

Library of Congress   TA549.T2   5–38943†

NT 0036069   DLC

Tappan, Eli Todd, 1824–1888.
... Treatise on geometry and trigonometry; for colleges, schools and private students. Written for the mathematical course of Joseph Ray, ᴍ. ᴅ., by Eli T. Tappan ... Cincinnati, Sargent, Wilson & Hinkle; Chicago, Cobb, Pritchard & co.; ₍etc., etc., ᶜ1868₎

viii, 9–420 p. tab., diagr. 21ᶜᵐ. (Eclectic educational series)

1. Geometry. 2. Trigonometry.

Library of Congress   QA529.T17   3—20980

NIC ViU CU
NT 0036070   DLC KyU DN ODW WaU OO PSC NcD   OCl OCU

Tappan, Eli T₍odd₎ 1824–1888.
... Treatise on plane and solid geometry ... Written for the mathematical course of Joseph Ray, ᴍ. ᴅ., by Eli T. Tappan ... Cincinnati, Sargent, Wilson & Hinkle; New York, Clark & Maynard; ₍etc., etc., 1864₎

viii, 9–276 p. diagr. 19½ᶜᵐ. (Eclectic educational series)
On cover: Ray's series.

Subject entries: Geometry.

Library of Congress, no.   QA453.T18.   3–19808†

NIC
NT 0036071   DLC OC CU DAU PHi PPF MH OO OCl MiU ICJ

---

ar V   **Tappan, Eli Todd, 1824–1888.**
19505   Treatise on plane and solid geometry ...
              Written for the mathematical course of Joseph
              Ray, M. D., by Eli T. Tappan ... Cincinnati,
              Van Antwerp, Bragg ₍c1868₎
                 viii, 9–276 p. diagr. 20cm. (Eclectic
              educational series)

              On cover: Ray's series.

              I. Ray, Jose   ph, 1807–1855.

NT 0036072   NIC

RA513   **Tappan, Eli Todd, 1824–1888.**
1892   Treatise on plane and solid geometry: for
              colleges, schools, and private students.
              Written for the mathematical course of Joseph
              Ray, M. D., by Eli T. Tappan ... New-York,
              Cincinnati, Chicago, American Book Co. ₍c1892₎
                 276p.19cm. (Eclectic educational series)

              At head of title: Eclectic educational
              series.
              Original cloth binding.

NT 0036073   OC

TAPPAN, Eli Todd, 1824–1888.
Treatise on plane and solid geometry for colleges, schools, and private students. Written for the mathematical course of Joseph Ray. Cincinnati,etc., Van Antwerp, Bragg & Co., ₍1877?₎

"Eclectic educational series."

NT 0036074   MH

Tappan, Eugene.

Gannett, *Mrs.* **Deborah (Sampson) 1760–1827.**
An address delivered in 1802 in various towns in Massachusetts, Rhode Island and New York, by Mrs. Deborah Sampson Gannett, of Sharon, Massachusetts, a soldier of the American revolution. Reprinted by the Sharon historical society, with an introduction by Eugene Tappan, corresponding secretary of the society. Boston, Press of H. M. Hight, 1905.

F74   **Tappan, Eugene, 1840–1908.**
S4S4   **Gannett, Deborah (Sampson) 1760–1827.**
no. 2   An addr₍e₎ss, delivered with applause, at the Federal-Street Theatre, Boston, four successive nights ... beginning March 22, 1802; and after, at other principal towns ... by Deborah Gannet. Dedham, Printed and sold by H. Mann, for Mrs. Gannet, at the Minerva Office, 1802.

Tappan, Eugene.
A memorial of Eugene Tappan, esq. Sharon, 1910.
70 p. (Sharon Historical Society of Sharon, Publications, No. 6)

NT 0036077   PHi

Tappan, Eva March, 1854–1930, comp.
... Adventures & achievements, selected & arranged by Eva March Tappan. ₍1st ed.₎ ₍Boston, New York, etc.₎ Houghton, Mifflin & company, 1907.

xii p., 2 l., 3–494, ₍2₎ p. front., 10 pl., 2 port. 22ᶜᵐ. (Half-title: The children's hour ... vol. viii)

Series title also at head of t.-p.
Title within ornamental border.
"The first edition of The children's hour is limited to 1000 numbered copies." This copy not numbered.

ɪ. Title.

Library of Congress   PZ5.C437 vol. 8   7—31221

NN MB NIC PPT OLak OCl Vi NcD OKentU
NT 0036078   DLC WaS WaSp OCl KMK ViU NcD OClh OClW

₍**Tappan, Eva March₎ 1854–1930, comp.**
... Adventures & achievements. Boston, Houghton Mifflin company ₍ᶜ1929₎

xii, ₍1₎, 380, ₍1₎ p. col. front., illus., col. plates. 22ᶜᵐ. (Half-title: The children's hour ... vol. VIII)

Series title also at head of t-p.
Title within ornamental border; illustrated lining-papers in colors.

ɪ. Title.

Library of Congress   PZ5.C437.2 vol. VIII   30–8363

NT 0036079   DLC PPT OClh OO OU

Tappan, Eva March, 1854–1930.
American hero stories, by Eva March Tappan ... Boston, New York ₍etc.₎ Houghton, Mifflin and company, 1906.

vi, 265, ₍1₎ p. front., illus. 20ᶜᵐ.

1. U. S.—Biog. ɪ. Title.

Library of Congress   E176.T17   6—13065

MH OCl OLak OClW NN MB Or
NT 0036080   DLC NcD PPT PBa PP MB DHEW NN WaSp NN MB

Tappan, Eva March, 1854–
... American hero stories, by Eva March Tappan ... Boston, New York [etc.] Houghton Mifflin company [*1920]
vi, 279 p. front., illus., ports. 20ᶜᵐ. (The Tappan-Kendall histories)
$0.92

1. U. S.—Biog.   ɪ. Title.

Library of Congress   E176.T172   20—10628

NT   0036081   DLC WaT Or OEac OU OC1h OCU ViU

Tappan, Eva March, 1854–1930
American hero stories, new and enlarged
ed. with illus. Bost. 1925.

NT   0036082   OC1

Tappan, Eva March, 1854–1930.
American hero stories; prepared for Sight-
saving class use by Robert B. Irwin.   Clear
type pub. committee, 1926 [c20]
2 v.   (Clear type series)

NT   0036083   OrP

Tappan, Eva March, 1854–
... American hero stories, by Eva March Tappan, ᴘʜ. ᴅ.
New and enl. ed., with illustrations by Frank E. Schoonover.
Boston and New York, Houghton Mifflin company, 1926.
viii p., 1 l., 301 p. col. front., col. plates. 22ᶜᵐ. (Riverside book-shelf)

1. U. S.—Biog.   ɪ. Title.

Library of Congress   E176.T17 1926   26—15589

   WaSp WaS
NT   0036084   DLC MB PP OO TU OLak PPL PWcS PP OrP

E
176   Tappan, Eva March, 1854–1930.
T17   American hero stories / by Eva March Tappan.
1934   - Rev. ed. – Boston : Houghton, Mifflin, c1934.
      279 p. : ill. – (The Tappan-Kendall
      histories)

      1. United States—Biography. II. Title.

NT   0036085   KMK PP OrP

Tappan, Eva March, 1854–1930.
American history stories for very young readers, by
Eva March Tappan ... Boston and New York, Houghton
Mifflin company, 1924.
vi p., 1 l., 144 p. front., illus. 20½ᶜᵐ.
"These stories first appeared in the Junior home magazine."

1. U. S.—History, Juvenile.   ɪ. Title.

Library of Congress   E178.3.T17   24—21928

   OO MB NN MH
NT   0036086   DLC PU PP GU Or OrP WaSp OC1 OEac OLak

Tappan, Eva March, 1854–1930.

Carnegie, Andrew, 1835–1919.
... Andrew Carnegie's own story for boys and girls. New
ed. with teaching equipment by Anna Brochhausen. Boston,
New York [etc.] Houghton Mifflin company [*1930]

Tappan, Eva March, 1854–   *comp.*
... The book of humor, selected & arranged by Eva
March Tappan. [Boston] Houghton Mifflin company,
1916.
xiii, [1], 527, [1] p., 1 l. col. front., plates. 19½ᶜᵐ. (The children's hour. [vol. xɪɪɪ]) $1.75
Title within ornamental border.

Library of Congress   ᴰZ5.C437 vol. 13   17—877

   MB NN
NT   0036088   DLC KMK OC1 OrU WaSp OC1h ViU OC1 OEac

[**Tappan, Eva March**] 1854–1930, *comp.*
... The book of humor. Boston, Houghton Mifflin company
[*1929]
xiii, [1], 507, [1] p. col. front., illus., col. plates. 22ᶜᵐ. (Half-title: The children's hour ... vol. vɪ)
Series title also at head of t-p.
Title within ornamental border; illustrated lining-papers in colors.

ɪ. Title.

Library of Congress   PZ5.C437.2 vol. vɪ   30–8362

NT   0036089   DLC PPT OC1h OU OO

Tappan, Eva March, 1854–1930.
Chaucer, Geoffrey, *d.* 1400.
The Chaucer story book, by Eva March Tappan ...
Boston and New York, Houghton Mifflin company, 1908.

Tappan, Eva March, 1854–1930, comp.
The children's hour ... Selected & arranged by
Eva March Tappan. [Boston, New York, etc.]
Houghton Mifflin company [*1907]
10 v. col. fronts., 2 illus., plates, ports.,
2 fold. facsims., diagr. 19.5 cm.

Title within ornamental border.
Error in binding, v. 9: p. 73–86 and plate
following repeated.
Bookplate of Louise F. Cadot, v. 1 and 2.
Contents. – v. 1. Folk stories & fables. – v. 2

Myths from many lands. – v. 3. Stories from the
classics. – v. 4. Stories of legendary heroes. –
v. 5. Stories from seven old favorites. – v. 6.
Old fashioned stories & poems. – v. 7. The out-
of-door book. – v. 8. Adventures & achievements.
– v. 9. Poems & rhymes. – v. 10. Modern stories.

     1. Children's stories. I. Title.

NT   0036092   Vi NcD MWelC PP PPFr

Tappan, Eva March, compiler, 1854– *1930*.
The children's hour. Selected & arranged by Eva March Tappan.
[Boston.] Houghton Mifflin Co. [1907–]16. 15 v. Portraits.
Plates, some colored. Facsimile. Decorated title-pages. 19 cm.
Contents. — 1. Folk stories & fables. 2. Myths from many lands. 3.
Stories from the classics. 4. Stories of legendary heroes. 5. Stories
from seven old favorites: The Pilgrim's progress; Robinson Crusoe;
Gulliver's travels; Don Quixote; Arabian nights; The travels of Baron
Munchausen; Tales from Shakespeare. 6. Old-fashioned stories & poems.

L88ɪ — T.r. — Literature. Colls.

7. The out-of-door book. 8. Adventures and achievements. 9. Poems
and rhymes. 10. Modern stories. 11. Stories of nature. 12. Sports
and pastimes. 13. The book of humor. 14. Modern triumphs. 15.
Wonders of science.   ᴅʟᴄ: PZ5. C437
Vol. 15 contains an index to the whole series.
Some of the plates are missing.

L88ɪ

NT   0036094   MB OO PRosC OU PG1S OU ODW NN NNUW DLC

Tappan, Eva March, 1854–1930, *ed.*
The children's hour, Eva March Tappan, editor. School ed.
Teacher's manual. [Boston] Houghton Mifflin company [*1925]
46 p. 19½ᶜᵐ.
"Prepared especially for the use of the schools of Indiana, based on the
eight preliminary readers adopted by the state text book committee."

ɪ. Title.   cᴀ 25—519 Unrev'd

Library of Congress   .B1573.T3

NT   0036095   DLC

Tappan, Eva March, 1854–1930.
Children's stories and poems   Houghton,

NT   0036096   OrU

Tappan, Eva March, 1854–
The Christ story, by Eva March Tappan ... Boston
and New York, Houghton, Mifflin and company, 1903.
x, 416 p., 1 l. incl. 25 pl. front., 42 pl. 19½ᶜᵐ.
"The decorative designs on the chapter titles are from drawings by E.
Pollak."

1. Jesus Christ.   ɪ. Title.

Library of Congress   BT302.T3   3—25611

   NN MBrZ
NT   0036097   DLC NRU PP WaSp OrP Or OC1 OLak OC1h MB

Tappan, Eva March, 1854 –1930.
The colonial period, 1607–1765.
(In Short history of America's literature)

NT   0036098   MC

Tappan, Eva March, 1854–
... Diggers in the earth, by Eva March Tappan ... Boston, New York [etc.] Houghton Mifflin company [*1916]
iv p., 1 l., 108 p. illus. 19ᶜᵐ. (Her The Industrial readers, book ɪɪ)
$0.45

1. Mines and mineral resources. 2. Readers and speakers—1870–
ɪ. Title.

Library of Congress   PE1127.G4T3   16—21068

NT   0036099   DLC PWcS PPT PPPL OC1 OO OEac OCU MB NN

Tappan, Eva March, 1854–1930.
Diggers in the earth. Boston, etc., Houghton
Mifflin co. [1919]

"The industrial readers, 2."

NT   0036100   MH

Tappan, Eva March, 1854–
... Diggers in the earth, by Eva March Tappan ... Rev.
ed. ... Boston, New York [etc.] Houghton Mifflin company
[*1929]
iv p., 1 l., 110 p. illus. 19½ᶜᵐ. (Her The industrial readers, book ɪɪ)

1. Mines and mineral resources. 2. Readers and speakers—1870–
ɪ. Title.

Library of Congress   PE1127.G4T3 1929 book ɪɪ   29–21680

NT   0036101   DLC

Tappan, Eva March, 1854–1930.
Dixie Kitten, by Eva March Tappan ...   Boston and New York, Houghton Mifflin company, 1910.
4 p. l., 86 p., 1 l.   front., illus.   20ᶜᵐ.
Illustrated end-papers.

Not in LC   10—36092

Library of Congress

NT   0036102   NN Or PPFr

Tappan, Eva March.   1854–
Dixie kitten.
— Boston.   Houghton Mifflin Co.   1911.   (8), 86 pp.   Illus.   Plate.   19 cm.

K5279 — T.r. — Cats.

NT   0036103   MB

Tappan, Eva March, 1854–1930.
Dixie kitten.
Boston.   Houghton Mifflin Co.   1917.   Illus.   Plate.   19 cm.

L4036 — T.r. — Cats.

NT   0036104   MB

Tappan, Eva March, 1854–1930.
Early customs of New England.
(In her Our country's story)

NT   0036105   MC

E178
.1
.T17
1902a
Tappan, Eva March, 1854–
... An elementary history of our country, by Eva March Tappan ...   Boston, New York ₍etc.₎ Houghton Mifflin company ₍°1902₎.
5 p. l., 267 p.   front., illus., maps.   19½ᶜᵐ.
On cover: Our country's story.

Earlier editions have title: Our country's story; an elementary history of the United States.

NT   0036106   ViU NN PU OrP

Tappan, Eva March, 1854–1930.
An elementary history of our country, by Eva March Tappan ...   Boston, New York ₍etc.₎ Houghton Mifflin company ₍°1914₎.
6 p. l., 254, xv p.   front., illus., maps.   19½ᶜᵐ.
"Twentieth impression, rev. and printed from new electrotyped plates, November, 1914."
Earlier editions have title: Our country's story; an elementary history of the United States.

1. U. S.—Hist.   I. Title.

Library of Congress   E178.1.T18   15—1493

NT   0036107   DLC MH PPT PWcS OCl OEac OO OClh

Tappan, Eva March, 1854–1930.
... An elementary history of our country, by Eva March Tappan ...   Boston, New York ₍etc.₎ Houghton Mifflin company ₍ 1920₎
6 p. l., 256, xv p.   front., illus., maps.   19½ᶜᵐ.   (The Tappan-Kendall histories) $1.08
"Twenty-sixth impression, January, 1920."
Earlier editions have title: Our country's story; an elementary history of the United States.

NT   0036108   ViU MH

Tappan, Eva March, 1854–
... An elementary history of our country, by Eva March Tappan ...   Boston, New York ₍etc.₎ Houghton Mifflin company ₍°1922₎
6 p. l., 257, xv p.   col. front., illus., maps.   19½ᶜᵐ.   (The Tappan-Kendall histories) $1.08
"Twenty-eighth impression, January, 1922."
Earlier editions have title: Our country's story; an elementary history of the United States.

1. U. S.—Hist.   I. Title.

Library of Congress   E178.T18   1922   22—15057

NT   0036109   DLC DHEW MB

Tappan, Eva March, 1854–1930.
... An elementary history of our country, by Eva March Tappan ...   Boston, New York ₍etc.₎ Houghton Mifflin company ₍°1928₎
6 p l., 263, xvi p.   col. front., illus., maps.   19½ᶜᵐ.   (The Tappan-Kendall histories)

1. U. S.—Hist.   I. Title.

Library of Congress   E178.1.T18   1928   28—16216

NT   0036110   DLC PBa WaSp DHEW

Tappan, Eva March, 1854–1930.
... An elementary history of our country, by Eva March Tappan ...   Boston, New York ₍etc.₎ Houghton Mifflin company ₍°1932₎
6 p. l., 268, xvi p.   col. front., illus., maps.   19½ᶜᵐ.   (The Tappan-Kendall histories)

1. U. S.—Hist.   I. Title.

Library of Congress   E178.1.T18   1932   32—18012
Copyright A 53080   ₍3₎   973

NT   0036111   DLC OrP DHEW

Tappan, Eva March, 1854–1930.
... An elementary history of our country, by Eva March Tappan ...   Boston, New York ₍etc.₎ Houghton Mifflin company ₍°1937₎
6 p. l., 274, xvi p.   col. front., illus., maps.   19½ᶜᵐ.   (The Tappan-Kendall histories)
On cover: Our country's story.

1. U. S.—Hist.   I. Title.

Library of Congress   E178.1.T18   1937   37—4979
———— Copy 2.
Copyright A 105252   ₍5₎   973

NT   0036112   DLC NN

Tappan, Eva March, 1854–1930.
Ella, a little schoolgirl of the sixties; a book for children and for grown-ups who remember, by Eva March Tappan, with illustrations by Ruth J. Best.   Boston and New York, Houghton Mifflin company, 1923.
4 p. l., 174 p.   col. front., plates.   19½ᶜᵐ.

I. Title.   23—17272

Library of Congress   PZ7.T165El

Or WaSp MB NN

NT   0036113   DLC PP CoU CU PPFr PWcS OCl OO OEac OrP

Tappan, Eva March, 1854–1930.
England's story; a history for grammar and high schools, by Eva March Tappan ...   Boston, New York ₍etc.₎ Houghton, Mifflin and company ₍1901₎.
xx p., 1 l., 370 p., 1 l.   front., illus., maps (part double)   19½ᶜᵐ.

1. Gt. Brit.—Hist.—Compends.   I. Title.   1—24419

Library of Congress   DA32.T175

Or OrP WaS

NT   0036114   DLC PV PPLas PBa MB OCU ViU NN MB WaSp

Tappan, Eva March, 1854–
England's story; a history for grammar and high schools, by Eva March Tappan ...   Boston, New York ₍etc.₎ Houghton Mifflin company ₍°1922₎.
xx p., 1 l., 374, xii p.   illus. (incl. ports.) maps (part double)   19½ᶜᵐ.
"Revised edition."
"Twenty-seventh impression, January, 1922."

1. Gt. Brit.—Hist.—Compends.   I. Title.

Library of Congress   DA32.T175   1922   22—14997

NT   0036115   DLC PPT KMK MtU OrP DHEW OCl OEac

Tappan, Eva March, 1854–
England's story; a history for grammar and high schools, by Eva March Tappan ...   Boston, New York ₍etc.₎ Houghton Mifflin company ₍°1928₎
xii p., 1 l., 378, xix p.   front., illus. (incl. ports.) maps (part double)   19½ᶜᵐ.
"Revised edition."

1. Gt. Brit.—Hist.—Compends.   I. Title.

Library of Congress   DA32.T175   1928   28—25853

NT   0036116   DLC

Tappan, Eva March, 1854–1930.
England's story; a history for grammar and high schools, by Eva March Tappan ...   Boston, New York ₍etc.₎ Houghton Mifflin company ₍°1929₎
xii p., 1 l., 378, xix p.   front., illus. (incl. ports.) maps (part double)   19½ᶜᵐ.
"Revised edition."

NT   0036117   ViU MH OO OClh

Tappan, Eva March, 1854–1930, ed.

Emerson, Ralph Waldo, 1803–1882.
... Essays and poems, edited by Eva March Tappan.   Boston, New York ₍etc.₎ Allyn and Bacon ₍°1926₎

Tappan, Eva March, 1854–
European hero stories, by Eva March Tappan ...   Boston, New York ₍etc.₎ Houghton Mifflin company ₍°1909₎
xi, 249, ₍1₎ p.   front., illus., maps.   19½ᶜᵐ. $0.65

1. Europe—Hist.   2. Heroes.

Library of Congress   PZ9.T165E   10—2318

NT   0036119   DLC PP WaSp OrP Or OCl OLak MB NN OO

Tappan, Eva March, 1854–1930

Longfellow, Henry Wadsworth, 1807–1882.
... Evangeline, a tale of Acadie, by Henry Wadsworth Longfellow.   New ed., with a biographical sketch by Eva March Tappan, and introductions and study helps by Margaret Ashmun.   Boston, New York ₍etc.₎ Houghton Mifflin company ₍°1916₎

Tappan, Eva March, 1854–1930.
... The farmer and his friends, by Eva March Tappan ...   Boston, New York ₍etc.₎ Houghton Mifflin company ₍°1916₎
iv p., 1 l., 106 p.   illus.   19ᶜᵐ.   (Her The Industrial readers, book 1)

1. Agriculture—Juvenile literature.   2. Readers and speakers—Agriculture.   I. Title.   16—15525

Library of Congress   PE1127.G4T3

OCl ViU NN

NT   0036121   DLC OrP MB PPT PWcS DHEW OO OClW OEac

Tappan, Eva March, 1854-1930.
The farmer and his friends. Boston, etc.,
Houghton Mifflin co. [1919]

"The industrial readers, 1."

NT 0036122   MH

Tappan, Eva March, 1854-
... The farmer and his friends, by Eva March Tappan ...
Rev. ed. Boston, New York [etc.] Houghton Mifflin company
[*1929]
iv p., 1 l., 115 p. illus. 19ᶜᵐ. (*Her* The industrial readers, book 1)

1. Agriculture—Juvenile literature. 2. Readers and speakers—Agriculture. I. Title.
                                                          29-12642
Library of Congress   PE1127.G4T8 1929

NT 0036123   DLC OClh

Tappan, Eva March, 1854-   *comp.*
... Folk stories & fables, selected & arranged by Eva March
Tappan. [1st ed.] [Boston, New York, etc.] Houghton, Mif-
flin & company, 1907.
xxix, [1], 529, [1] p., 1 l. front., 14 pl., fold. facsim. 22ᶜᵐ. (*Half-title:*
The Children's hour ... vol. 1)
Series title also at head of t.-p.
Title within ornamental border.
"The first edition of The children's hour is limited to 1,000 numbered
copies." This copy not numbered.

I. Title.
Library of Congress   PZ5.C437 vol. 1
                                                          7-31223

     NcD KyLoU OEac OClW NcD OCl
NT 0036124   DLC WaSp WaS OKentU KMK NN OClh Vi ViU

[Tappan, Eva March] 1854-1930, *comp.*
... Folk stories and fables. Boston, Houghton Mifflin com-
pany [*1929]
xxvii, [1], 399, [1] p. col. front., illus. col. plates, fold. facsim. 22ᶜᵐ.
(*Half-title:* The children's hour ... vol. 1)
Series title also at head of t.-p.
Title within ornamental border; illustrated lining-papers in colors.
Introduction signed: Eva March Tappan.

I. Title.
                                                          30-9138
Library of Congress   PZ5.C437.2 vol. 1

NT 0036125   DLC PPT OClh OU

Tappan, Eva March, 1854-1930.

U. S. Food administration.
Food saving and sharing, telling how the older children of
America may help save from famine their comrades in allied
lands across the sea, prepared under the direction of the United
States Food administration in coöperation with the United
States Department of agriculture and the Bureau of educa-
tion. Garden City, New York, Doubleday, Page & company,
1918.

Tappan, Eva March, 1854-
A friend in the library ... By Eva March Tappan.
Boston and New York, Houghton Mifflin company [*1909]
12 v. 20½ᶜᵐ.

Half-title: A friend in the library; a practical guide to the writings of
Ralph Waldo Emerson, Nathaniel Hawthorne, Henry Wadsworth Longfellow, James Russell Lowell, John Greenleaf Whittier, Oliver Wendell
Holmes.
CONTENTS.—[v. 1] Living and thinking.—[v. 2] Travel.—[v. 3] Home
life.—[v. 4-5] History and biography.—[v. 6] Humor.—[v. 7] Juvenile literature.—[v. 8] Religion.—[v. 9] Nature.—[v. 10] Fiction.—[v. 11] Literature.—
[v. 12] Autobiography.
Library of Congress
                                                          9-32659 Additions

NT 0036127   DLC ViU WaSp

Tappan, Eva March, 1854-1930.
George Washington, Father of his country,
1732-1799.
(In American History stories for very young
readers, Boston, Houghton, Mifflin Co., 1924)

NT 0036128   MB

Tappan, Eva March, 1854-   *tr.*
The golden goose, and other fairy tales, tr. from the Swedish
by Eva March Tappan ... Boston and New York, Houghton,
Mifflin and company, 1905.
4 p. l., [3]-240 p., 1 l. illus. 19½ᶜᵐ.
CONTENTS.—The golden goose.—The giant's house with the roof of
sausages.—The simple-minded giant.—The stolen princess.—The black
box and the red.—The little wild man.

I. Title.
Library of Congress   PZ8.T17G
                                                          5-35790

        OrAshS Or OrP MB
NT 0036129   DLC OCl OClh NN NNC CU OEac OLak OO WaSp

Tappan, Eva March, 1854-1930, *tr.*
The golden goose, and other fairy tales, tr. from the Swedish
by Eva March Tappan ... Boston and New York, Houghton,
Mifflin company, [*1933]
4 p. l., [3]-240 p., 1 l. illus. 19½ᶜᵐ.
CONTENTS.—The golden goose.—The giant's house with the roof of
sausages.—The simple-minded giant.—The stolen princess.—The black
box and the red.—The little wild man.

NT 0036130   PWcS Or OrP

Tappan, Eva March, 1854-
Hero stories of France, by Eva March Tappan ... Boston and New York, Houghton Mifflin company, 1920.
4 p. l., 204 p., 1 l. col. front. (port.) plates. 21ᶜᵐ. $1.75

1. France—Biog. 2. France—History, Juvenile. I. Title.
Library of Congress   DC39.T2
                                                          20-7446

        OCl MH GU NN WaSp WaS FMU
NT 0036131   DLC OOxM AAP PPFr PP PBa OEac OClh OLak

Tappan, Eva March, 1854-
Heroes of progress; stories of successful Americans, by
Eva March Tappan ... Boston, New York [etc.] Houghton
Mifflin company [*1921]
iv p., 1 l., 263 p. illus. (incl. ports.) 19½ᶜᵐ. $1.25

1. U. S.—Biog. I. Title.
Library of Congress   CT217.T3
                                                          22-2485

        MH MB NN Or WaSp WaS
NT 0036132   DLC OCl PPT PPPL OLak OU OCU OEac ViU

Tappan, Eva March, 1854-1930.
Heroes of progress; stories of successful Americans, by Eva
March Tappan ... Boston, New York [etc.] Houghton Mifflin
company [*1928]
iv p., 1 l., 273 p. illus. (incl. ports.) 19½ᶜᵐ.

1. U. S.—Biog. I. Title.
                                                          28-18014
Library of Congress   CT217.T3 1928

NT 0036133   DLC OClh

Tappan, Eva March, 1854-
Heroes of the middle ages (Alaric to Joan of Arc) by
Eva March Tappan ... London, G. G. Harrap & company, 1911.
252 p. front., illus., plates, maps. 21½ᶜᵐ.
Paging irregular.
CONTENTS.—The first period: The barbarian invasion. — The second
period: The forming of the Germanic nations.—The third period: The
Teutonic invasions.—The fourth period: The rise of nationalities.—The
fifth period: The crusades.—The sixth period: The time of progress and
discovery.—The seventh period: The struggles of the nations.
1. Europe—Hist.—476-1492. 2. Middle ages—Hist. I. Title.
                                                          A 12-862
Title from Enoch Pratt   Free Libr. Printed by L. C.

NT 0036134   MdBE Or OClh NN

Tappan, Eva March, 1854-
Heroes of the middle ages (Alaric to Columbus) by Eva
March Tappan ... London, G. G. Harrap & company,
1912.
252 p. incl. front., illus., plates, maps. 21½ᶜᵐ. ("Told to the ages")
CONTENTS.—The first period: The barbarian invasion.—The second
period: The forming of the Germanic nations.—The third period: The
Teutonic invasions.—The fourth period: The rise of nationalities.—The
fifth period: The crusades.—The sixth period: The time of progress and
discovery.—The seventh period: The struggles of the nations.
1. Europe—Hist.—476-1492. 2. Middle ages—Hist. I. Title.
                                                          A 13-2105
Title from Queens   Borough Pub. Libr. Printed by L. C.

NT 0036135   NJQ WaS PWcS OEac

Tappan, Eva March, 1854-1930
Heroes of the middle ages....London,
1919.

NT 0036136   OCl

Tappan, Eva March, 1854-1930.
Heroes of the middle ages; Alaric to
Columbus. Lond. Harrap, 1924.
252 p. (Told through the ages.)

NT 0036137   PP

Tappan, Eva March, 1854-
The house with the silver door, by Eva March Tappan ...
Boston and New York, Houghton Mifflin company, 1913.
5 p. l., 3-184, [2] p. col. front., col. plates. 20ᶜᵐ. $1.00

I. Title.
Library of Congress   PZ8.T17H
                                                          13-19120

NT 0036138   DLC PPFr OrP OEac NN

Tappan, Eva March, 1854-
In feudal times; social life in the middle ages, by E. M.
Tappan ... London, G. G. Harrap & company, 1913.
361 p. incl. front., illus. 21½ᶜᵐ.
Published Boston and New York. 1911. under title: When knights
were bold.

1. Civilization. Medieval. I. Title.
Library of Congress   D127.T3
                                                          14-2033

NT 0036139   DLC KU Or OrU PPPL WaS OrP ICJ NN

Tappan, Eva March, 1854-1930.
In feudal times; social life in the middle ages.
London, Harrap, 1921.
359 p. (Told through the ages)

NT 0036140   PP

Tappan, Eva March, 1854-1930.
In feudal times; social life in the middle ages, by E. M.
Tappan ... London, G. G. Harrap & company, [1934]
359 p. incl. front., illus. 21½ᶜᵐ.
Published Boston and New York, 1911, under title: When knights
were bold.

NT 0036141   ViU

Tappan, Eva March, 1854–
In the days of Alfred the Great, by Eva March Tappan
... Illustrated by J. W. Kennedy. Boston, Lee and
Shepard, 1900.
vii p., 1 l., 296 p. front., plates. 19ᶜᵐ.

1. Alfred the Great, king of England, 849–901—Fiction. ɪ. Title.
0—5164
Library of Congress   PZ3.T166 T

Or OrP
NT 0036142   DLC NN PP PBa WU ICU MoU OEac OO PU MB

Tappan, Eva March.
In the days of Alfred the Great.
Boston.
ᵀ othrop, Lee & Shepard Co. [191–?]

H₀₁₉₂ — T.r. — England. Hist. Fict. Anglo-Saxon Period. 828–1066.

NT 0036143   MB

Tappan, Eva March, 1854–1930.
... In the days of Queen Elizabeth, by Eva March Tappan ...
illustrated from famous paintings. Boston, Lee and Shepard,
1902.
vi p., 2 l., 294 p. front., plates, ports. 19ᶜᵐ. (Makers of England
series)

1. Elizabeth, queen of England. 1533–1603—Fiction. ɪ. Title.
2—20825
Library of Congress   PZ3.T166 In

PBa Or OrP WaSp
NT 0036144   DLC NcD PPPH-I PU PPT PPD OEac OO NN

Tappan, Eva March, 1854–1930.
... In the days of Queen Victoria, by Eva March Tappan ..
illustrated from famous paintings and engravings and from
photographs. Boston, Lee and Shepard, 1903.
vii p., 1 l., 354 p. front., plates, ports. 19ᶜᵐ. (Makers of England
series)

1. Victoria, queen of Great Britain and Ireland, 1819–1901—Fiction.
ɪ. Title.
3—14845
Library of Congress   PZ3.T166 Inq

NT 0036145   DLC PP TxU MB PWcS OO Or OrP WaSp

Tappan, Eva March, 1854–1930.
In the days of Queen Victoria, illustrated from famous paint-
ings and engravings and from photographs. Boston: Lothrop,
Lee & Shepard Co. [cop. 1903] vii p., 1 l., 354 p., 12 pl. 12°.

1. Victoria, queen of England.   2. Title.
N. Y. P. L.   June 7, 1911.

NT 0036146   NN MH MB

Tappan, Eva March, 1854–
In the days of William the Conqueror, by Eva March Tappan ... illustrated by J. W. Kennedy. Boston, Lee and Shepard, 1901.
ix, 298 p. front., plates. 19ᶜᵐ.

1. William, the Conqueror, king of England, 1027–1087—Fiction.
ɪ. Title.
1—16502
Library of Congress   PZ3.T166 Inw

OO PSt MB FMU ICU Or WaSp
NT 0036147   DLC OKentU OOxM PPPH-I NN PBa ViU OEac

PE1127   Tappan, Eva March, 1854–1930.
.G4T3   The industrial readers.   Boston, New York,
c1916.

NT 0036148   DLC OCU PU-Penn

Tappan, Eva March, 1854–1930.
A letter written at Plymouth by John Billington
to his grandmother in England.   (In her Letters
from colonial children)
"These letters reflect admirably conditions and
life in colonial times from the child's point of view
and are both good history and delightful literature"

NT 0036149   MC

Tappan, Eva March, 1854–1930
Letters from colonial children, by Eva
March Tappan. Bost. N.Y. 1907.

318.

NT 0036150   OC1h PPFr

Tappan, Eva March, 1854–1930.
Letters from colonial children, by Eva March Tappan.
Boston and New York, Houghton Mifflin company, 1908.
xii p., 1 l., 318, [2] p. front., illus. 22 x 17½ cm.

1. U. S.—Soc. life & cust.—Colonial period—Fiction. 2. U. S.—
Hist.—Colonial period—Fiction. ɪ. Title.
8—23916
Library of Congress   PZ7.T165L

WaSp Or
NT 0036151   DLC OCU OC1 OEac OLak NN OKentU OrP WaS

Tappan, Eva March, 1854–1930
Letters from colonial children.
— Boston. Houghton Mifflin Co. 1911. xiii, 319, (1) pp. Illus.
Portraits. Plates. Autograph facsimiles. 21 cm.

K₄₉₈₉ — T.r. — Children. — American Colonies. Manners. — Letters. Colls.

NT 0036152   MB WaSp PP

Tappan, Eva March, 1854–1930.
The little book of our country, by Eva March Tappan.
New York, Pub. for the Educational bureau, National war
work council of Young men's Christian associations by Association press, 1919.
86 p. 14ᶜᵐ.

1. U. S.—Hist.   ɪ. Title.
19—3171
Library of Congress   E178.T17

NT 0036153   DLC OO OU

Tappan, Eva March, 1854–1930
The little book of the flag, ...
Bost. N.Y. 1916.

NT 0036154   OC1

Tappan, Eva March, 1854–
The little book of the flag, by Eva March Tappan. Boston,
New York [etc.] Houghton Mifflin company [c1917]
v, 122 p. col. front. 18ᶜᵐ. $0.40

1. Flags—U. S.
17—25612
Library of Congress   CR113.T3

NcD NN Or OrP WaSp
NT 0036155   DLC AAP PPT MB ICRL DHEW OLak OEac OC1h

Tappan, Eva March, 1854–1930.
The little book of the flag, by Eva March Tappan. Enl. ed.
Boston, New York [etc.] Houghton Mifflin company [c1937]
v, [1], 130 p. col. front., illus. 18ᶜᵐ.

1. Flags—U. S.
37–15577
Library of Congress   CR113.T3 1937
———— Copy 2.
Copyright A 108079   [3]   929.90973

NT 0036156   DLC GU OrP OC1

Tappan, Eva March, 1854–1930.
The little book of the war, by Eva March Tappan ...
Boston, New York [etc.] Houghton Mifflin company [c1918]
v, [1], 138 p. pl., maps. 19ᶜᵐ. $0.60

1. European war, 1914—   —Juvenile literature.   ɪ. Title.
18—22888
Library of Congress   D522.7.T3

Or OrP WaSp MB MH NN
NT 0036157   DLC PPT PWcS PPPL MnHi NRU DHEW OLak OCU

Tappan, Eva March, 1854–1930.
The little lady in green, and other tales, by Eva March Tappan ... Boston and New York, Houghton Mifflin company,
1925.
6 p. l., 226 p. incl. front., plates. 20½ᶜᵐ.
"The basis of this book is Ur folksagans rosengårdar, a collection of
stories from different countries, made by Richard Bergstrom and published in Sweden some years ago."
CONTENTS.—The little lady in green.—The man who meant what he
said.—The Rose Queen.—The brothers who went out into the world.—
The woman who had what she wanted.—The wishing ring.—The stones
in the kettle.—Snowwhite.—The enchanted feather.—The frog princess.—
The bee, the mouse, the muskrat, and the boy.—The country of the stupid
folk.
ɪ. Bergström, Richard, 1828–1893. Ur folksagans rosengårdar.
ɪɪ. Title.
25—19645
Library of Congress   PZ8.T17L1

NT 0036158   DLC WaSp WaS

Tappan, Eva March 1854–1930
Makers of England. Bost, 19—

v.

NT 0036159   OO

Tappan, Eva March, 1854–1930.
... Makers of many things, by Eva March Tappan ... Boston, New York [etc.] Houghton Mifflin company [c1916]
iv p., 1 l., 101 p. illus. 19ᶜᵐ. (Her The Industrial readers, book ɪɪɪ)
CONTENTS. — The little friction match. — About india rubber.—"Kid"
gloves. — How rags and trees become paper. — How books are made.—
From goose quill to fountain pens and lead pencils.—The dishes on our
tables.—How the wheels of a watch go around.—The making of shoes.—
In the cotton mill.—Silkworms and their work.

1. Manufactures. 2. Readers and speakers—1870–   ɪ. Title.
16—26936
Library of Congress   PE1127.G4T3 book 3

ViU MB NN
NT 0036160   DLC PPT PPPL PWcS OrP OEac OO OCU OC1

Tappan, Eva March, 1854–1930.
Makers of many things. Boston, etc., Houghton
Mifflin co. [1918]

"The industrial readers, 3."

NT 0036161   MH

Tappan, Eva March, 1854–
... Makers of many things, by Eva March Tappan ... Rev.
ed. Boston, New York [etc.] Houghton Mifflin company
[c1929]
iv p., 1 l., 119 p. illus. 19½ᶜᵐ. (Her The industrial readers, bk. ɪɪɪ)

1. Manufacturers. 2. Readers and speakers—1870–   ɪ. Title.
29–16413
Library of Congress   PE1127.G4T3 1929

NT 0036162   DLC OC1h PP GU WaSp

Tappan, Eva March, 1854-1930.
   Miles Standish, commander-in-chief of the
Pilgrims.   [In her American hero stories]

NT 0036163   NC

Tappan, Eva March, 1854-1930, *comp.*
   ... Modern stories, selected & arranged by Eva March Tappan. [1st ed.] [Boston, New York, etc.] Houghton, Mifflin & company, 1907.
   xi, [1], 485, [1] p., 1 l. front., 12 pl. 22ᶜᵐ. *(Half-title: The children's hour ... vol. x)*

   Series title also at head of t.-p.
   Title within ornamental border.
   "The first edition of the Children's hour is limited to 1000 numbered copies." This copy not numbered.

      ɪ. Title.   7—31216
   Library of Congress   PZ5.C437 vol. 10

      ViU NN Vi MB NcD WaSp
NT 0036164   DLC OC1h OEac OC1 NN OC1W PPT NIC OC1

Tappan, Eva March, 1854–   *comp.*
   ... Modern triumphs, selected & arranged by Eva March Tappan. [Boston] Houghton Mifflin company, 1916.
   xiii, [1], 528 p., 1 l. col. front., plates. 19½ᶜᵐ. *(The Children's hour. [vol. xɪvɪ)* $1.75
   Title within ornamental border.

      ɪ. Industrial arts—Hist.   ɪ. Title.
   Library of Congress   PZ5.C437 vol. 14   17—878

NT 0036165   DLC OC1h OC1 ViU MB NN

[Tappan, Eva March] 1854–1930, *comp.*
   ... Modern stories. Boston, Houghton Mifflin company [ᶜ1929]
   xi, [1], 417, [1] p. col. front., illus., col. plates. 22ᶜᵐ. *(Half-title: The children's hour ... vol. x)*
   Series title also at head of t.-p.
   Title within ornamental border; illustrated lining-papers in colors.

      ɪ. Title.   30—10345
   Library of Congress   PZ5.C437.2 vol. x

NT 0036166   DLC PPT OU OO OC1h

Tappan, Eva March, 1854–   *comp.*
   ... Myths from many lands, selected & arranged by Eva March Tappan. [1st ed.] [Boston, New York, etc.] Houghton, Mifflin & company, 1907.
   xiii, [1], 509, [1] p., 1 l. front., 12 pl. 22ᶜᵐ. *(Half-title: The children's hour ... vol. ɪɪ)*
   Series title also at head of t.-p.
   Title within ornamental border.
   "The first edition of The children's hour is limited to 1000 numbered copies." This copy not numbered.

      ɪ. Title.   7—31218
   Library of Congress   PZ5.C437 vol. 2

      OC1 OLak OC1W NN MB Vi
NT 0036167   DLC WaSp OC1W OKentU NcD OC1 KMK ViU OO

[Tappan, Eva March] 1854–1930, *comp.*
   ... Myths from many lands. Boston, Houghton Mifflin company [ᶜ1929]
   xiii, [1], 334, [1] p. col. front., illus.. col. plates. 22ᶜᵐ. *(Half-title: The children's hour ... vol. ɪɪ)*
   Series title also at head of t.-p.
   Title within ornamental border; illustrated lining-papers in colors.

      ɪ. Title.   30—9139
   Library of Congress   PZ5.C437.2 vol. ɪɪ

NT 0036168   DLC PG1B PPT OC1h OU

Tappan, Eva March, 1854-1930.
   Nicholas Poreton the Poet.
   Un. of Pa. Thesis, 1896.

NT 0036169   PU

Tappan, Eva March, 1854- 1930.
   Old ballads in prose, by Eva March Tappan; illustrated by Fanny Y. Cory. Boston and New York, Houghton, Mifflin and co., 1901.
   7 p. l., 228 p., 1 l. front., plates. 18½ᶜᵐ.

      ɪ. Title.
                                               1—22018
   Library of Congress   PZ3.T166O

      PPFr NN CoU MB WaSp OrP WaS
NT 0036170   DLC OEac PP PWcS CoU OC1 OLak OC1h PU

Tappan, Eva March, 1854-1930.
   Old ballads in prose. School ed. Houghton, c1901.
   164 p.

NT 0036171   Or

J
PZ7
T174
O 4   Tappan, Eva March, 1854-1930.
            Old ballads in prose. Illustrated by Fanny
         Y. Cory. School ed. Boston, Houghton,
         Mifflin [1929]
            164 p. illus. 19cm.

NT 0036172   GU

Tappan, Eva March, 1854-1930, *comp.*
   ... Old fashioned stories & poems, selected & arranged by Eva March Tappan. [1st ed.] [Boston, New York, etc.] Houghton, Mifflin & company, 1907.
   xvi p., 1 l., 477, [1] p., 1 l. front., 15 pl. 22ᶜᵐ. *(Half-title: The children's hour ... vol. vɪ)*
   Series title also at head of t.-p.
   Title within ornamental border.
   "The first edition of The children's hour is limited to 1000 numbered copies." This copy not numbered.

      ɪ. Title.   7—31214
   Library of Congress   PZ5.C437 vol. 6

      OC1 OEac OLak OKentU ViU
NT 0036173   DLC WaS WaSp NcD OO OC1W NN Vi OC1 PPT

Tappan, Eva March, 1854-1930, comp.
   An old, old story book, comp. from the Old Testament
      see under   Bible. O.T. English.
   Selections. 1910.   (also: 1938?)

Tappan, Eva March, 1854-1930
   Old world hero stories, ...Bost. N. Y.
1901.

NT 0036175   OC1

Tappan, Eva March, 1854-1930.
   Old world hero stories.   Boston, Houghton, c1909-
      2v. in 1.

NT 0036176   PP

Tappan, Eva March, 1854-1930.
   Old world hero stories, by Eva March Tappan ... Boston, New York [etc.] Houghton, Mifflin company [ᶜ1911]
   ix, [2], 130, [2], 261, [1] p. front., illus. (incl. maps) 20 cm.

      ɪ. Title.

   (✱) (PZ7)   11—24093

      OrAshS OrMonO OrLgE MtBC Or OrP
NT 0036177   PPPL PBa PWcS OLak OC1h OEac OO MB NN

Tappan, Eva March, 1854-1930.
   On the need of a Free Public Library in Philadelphia. Paper presented to the Philadelphia branch of the Association of Collegiate Alumnae: Jan. 30, 1892.
   Phila., 1892.
      9 p.

NT 0036178   PHi PPFr PPAmP

Tappan, Eva March, 1854- 1930.
   Our country's story; an elementary history of the United States, by Eva March Tappan ... Boston, New York [etc.] Houghton, Mifflin and company [1902]
   vii, 267, [1] p. front., illus., maps. 19½ᶜᵐ.

      ɪ ɪɪ S.—Hist.   ɪ. Title.
   Library of Congress   E178.1.T17   2—14118
   Copyright A 32774

      NBuU MB NN Or OrU OrMonO OrLgE WaSp
NT 0036179   DLC PBa PU PWcS OC1 OU DHEW OLak OCU ViU

Tappan, Eva March, 1854–
   Our country's story; an elementary history of the United States, by Eva March Tappan ... Boston, New York [etc.] Houghton, Mifflin and company [ᶜ1908]
   1 p. l., 254 p. illus., maps. 19½ᶜᵐ.
   Supplementary chapter: Texas (p. 249-254)
   First published 1902.

      ɪ. U. S.—Hist.   ɪ. Title.
   Library of Congress   E178.1.T178   8—2968

NT 0036180   DLC

Tappan, Eva March, 1854–
   Our country's story; an elementary history of the United States, by Eva March Tappan ... Boston, New York [etc.] Houghton, Mifflin and company [ᶜ1908]
   vii, 267 (i. e. 271) p. incl. front., illus. maps. 19½ᶜᵐ.
   Supplementary chapter: Virginia (p. [249]-252d)
   First published 1902.

      ɪ. U. S.—Hist.   8-2967
   Library of Congress   E178.1.T179 Copyright

NT 0036181   DLC DHEW

Tappan, Eva March, 1854-1930.
   ... Our European ancestors; an introduction to United States history, by Eva March Tappan ... Boston, New York [etc.] Houghton Mifflin company [ᶜ1918]
   vi p., 1 l., 263 p. illus. 19½ᶜᵐ. (The Tappan-Kendall histories)
   $0.76

      1. Europe—Hist. 2. America—Disc. & explor.   ɪ. Title.
   Library of Congress   E189.T17   18—19818

      MB NN OrP Or WaSp WaS
NT 0036182   DLC PPL PPCI PU OLak OEac OC1 OC1W ViU

Tappan, Eva March, 1854-1930, *comp.*
   ... The out-of-door book, selected & arranged by Eva March Tappan. [1st ed.] [Boston, New York, etc.] Houghton Mifflin & company, 1907.
   xiii, [1], 516, [2] p. front., 11 pl. 22ᶜᵐ. *(Half-title: The children's hour ... vol. vɪɪ)*
   Series title also at head of t.-p.
   Title within ornamental border.
   "The first edition of The children's hour is limited to 1000 numbered copies." This copy not numbered.

      ɪ. Title.   7—31219
   Library of Congress   PZ5.C437 vol. 7

      OEac OC1 Vi OKentU WaSp
NT 0036183   DLC OC1 NcD OC1W ViU NN KMK PPT OLak

[Tappan, Eva March] 1854–1930, *comp.*
... The out-of-door book. Boston, Houghton Mifflin company [1929]

xiii, [1], 516, [1] p. col. front., illus., col. plates. 22ᶜᵐ. (*Half-title:* The children's hour ... vol. VII)

Series title also at head of t.-p.
Title within ornamental border; Illustrated lining-papers in colors.

I. Title.

Library of Congress   PZ5.C437.2 vol. VII   30–9137

NT 0036184   DLC PPT OC1h OU MiU–C

[Tappan, Eva March] 1854–1930, *comp.*
... The out-of-door book; with illustrations by Mark Robinson. Boston and New York, Houghton Mifflin company, 1935.

1 p. l., v–xiii, [1], 516, [1] p. col. front., illus., col. plates. 22ᶜᵐ. (Riverside bookshelf)

Illustrated lining-papers in colors.

1. Children's stories.   I. Title.

Library of Congress   PZ5.T283Ou   36–35622

NT 0036185   DLC PPT

Tappan, Eva March, 1854–1930.
Plymouth, the first colony in New England.
(In her Elementary history of our country)

NT 0036186   MC

Tappan, Eva March, 1854–   *comp.*
... Poems & rhymes, selected & arranged by Eva March Tappan. [1st ed.] [Boston, New York, etc.] Houghton, Mifflin & company, 1907.

xxii, 2 l., 3–514, [2] p. front., 14 pl. 22ᶜᵐ. (*Half-title:* The Children's hour ... vol. IX)

Series title also at head of t.-p.
Title within ornamental border.
"The first edition of The children's hour is limited to 1000 numbered copies." This copy not numbered.

I. Title.

Library of Congress   PZ5.C437 vol. 9   7–31222

NT 0036187   PPT OEac OLak OC1 Vi
DLC WaS WaSp MB OC1 NIC KMK OC1h NN ViU

[Tappan, Eva March] 1854–1930, *comp.*
... Poems & rhymes. Boston, Houghton Mifflin company [1929]

xx, [1], 407, [1] p. col. front., illus., col. plates. 22ᶜᵐ. (*Half-title:* The children's hour ... vol. IX)

Series title also at head of t.-p.
Title within ornamental border; Illustrated lining-papers in colors.

I. Title.

Library of Congress   PZ5.C437.2 vol. IX   30–8364

NT 0036188   DLC PPT OC1h OU OO

Tappan, Eva March, 1854–

... Poems for the study of language prescribed in the course of study for the common schools of Illinois ... Rev. ed., 1919. Boston, New York [etc.] Houghton Mifflin company [ᶜ1919]

NT 0036190   MB

TAPPAN, Eva March, 1854–1930.
The poetry of Nicholas Breton.
(In Modern language association of America. Publications. Vol 13, pp. 297–332. Baltimore, 1898.)

NT 0036190   MB

Tappan, Eva March, 1854–
The Prince from Nowhere, and other tales, by Eva March Tappan ... Boston and New York, Houghton Mifflin company, 1928.

5 p. l., 206, [1] p. col. front., col. plates. 20½ᶜᵐ.

"Stories ... from the Swedish of Richard Bergstrom. Some of them are translated with a degree of literalness; in others I have enlarged somewhat freely; and in a few I have sometimes taken a hint or suggestion from the northern folklore and used the myth less as a story than as material for a story."

1. Tales, Swedish.   I. Bergström, Richard, 1828–1893.   II. Title
NN

Library of Congress   PZ8.T17Pr   28–21214

NT 0036191   DLC OC1h NN

Tappan, Eva March, 1854– 1930.
Robin Hood, his book, by Eva March Tappan ... illustrated by Charlotte Harding. Boston, Little, Brown company, 1903.

xiv, 267 p. col. front., illus., 5 col. pl. 21ᶜᵐ.

I. Title.

Library of Congress   PZ8.1.R55T   3–26880

OrP WaSp WaS
NT 0036192   DLC OO PP PBa PWcS ViU OC1 OO OLak Or

Tappan, Eva March, 1854–
Robin Hood, his book; illustrated by Charlotte Harding. Boston: Little, Brown, & Co., 1905. ix, xiv, 267 p., 6 col'd pl. illus. 8°.

1. Robin Hood.
N. Y. P. L.   May 29, 1911.

NT 0036193   NN OC1 OLak MB

Tappan, Eva March, 1854–
Robin Hood: his book.
— Boston. Little, Brown & Co. 1912. Illus. Colored plates. 19½ cm., in 8s.

H86ᵣ — T.r. — Hood, Robin

NT 0036194   MB

DK4
T3
Tappan, Eva March, 1854–1930.
Russia, Austria-Hungary, the Balkan states, and Turkey. Boston, Houghton Mifflin [1914]
xiii, 582 p. illus. 21ᶜᵐ. (The World's story, v.6)

1. Russia. 2. Austria. 3. Hungary. 4. Czechoslovak Republic. 5. Balkan Peninsula. 6. Turkey

NT 0036195   CSt

Tappan, Eva March, 1854–1930, *ed.*

Emerson, Ralph Waldo, 1803–1882.
... Select essays and poems; ed. by Eva March Tappan ... Boston, Allyn and Bacon [1898]

Tappan, Eva March, 1854–1930.
Short history of America's literature with selections from colonial and revolutionary writers. Bost., Houghton, 1906–07.

255 p.

NT 0036197   PPPL ViU

Tappan, Eva March, 1854–1930.
A short history of America's literature, with selections from colonial and revolutionary writers, by Eva March Tappan ... Boston, New York [etc.] Houghton, Mifflin and company [ᶜ1907]

xii p., 1 l., 255 p. front., illus., ports. 19½ᶜᵐ.

"References": p. [241]–246.

1. American literature—Hist. & crit. 2. American literature—Colonial period. 3. American literature—Revolutionary period.

Library of Congress   PS92.T3   7–31175

NT 0036198   DLC MtBC MB UU MtU Wa WaSpG MiU OC1 ODW

Tappan, Eva March, 1854–1930.
A short history of America's literature, with selections from colonial and revolutionary writers, by Eva March Tappan ... [Rev. ed.] Boston, New York [etc.] Houghton Mifflin company [ᶜ1920]

xii p., 1 l., 255 p. front., illus. (incl. ports.) 19½ᶜᵐ.

"References": p. [241]–246.

NT 0036199   ViU

Tappan, Eva March, 1854–
A short history of America's literature, with selections from colonial and revolutionary writers, by Eva March Tappan ... Rev. ed. Boston, New York [etc.] Houghton Mifflin company [ᶜ1929]

xiv p., 1 l., 255 p. front., illus. (incl. ports.) 19½ᶜᵐ.

"References": p. [241]–246.

1. American literature—Hist. & crit. 2. American literature—Colonial period. 3. American literature—Revolutionary period.

Library of Congress   PS92.T3 1929   29–6256

NT 0036200   DLC

Tappan, Eva March, 1854–1930.
A short history of America's literature, by Eva March Tappan ... with additional chapters by Rose Adelaide Witham ... Boston, New York [etc.] Houghton Mifflin company [ᶜ1932]

vi p., 1 l., 211, xxiii p. illus., ports. 19½ᶜᵐ.

"References": p. [i]–vi at end.

1. American literature—Hist. & crit. 2. American literature—Colonial period. 3. American literature—Revolutionary period.   I. Witham, Rose Adelaide, 1873–

Library of Congress   PS92.T3 1932   33–1205
Copyright A 57807   710.9

NT 0036201   DLC

Tappan, Eva March, 1854–1930.
A short history of America's literature, by Eva March Tappan; with additional chapters by Rose Adelaide Witham. Boston, etc., Houghton Mifflin co. [c.1935]

NT 0036202   MH

Tappan, Eva March, 1854–1930.
A short history of England's and America's literature, by Eva March Tappan ... Boston, New York [etc.] Houghton, Mifflin and company [ᶜ1906]

xix, 420 p., 1 l. front. (port.) illus., map. 19½ᶜᵐ.

"References": p. [388]–399.

1. English literature—Hist. & crit. 2. American literature—Hist. & crit.

Library of Congress   PR85.T32   6–13320

MB MWA NIC
NT 0036203   DLC MtU OrP WaSp OEac OLak MiU PPFr DAU

Tappan, Eva March, 1854–1930.
A short history of England's and America's literature, by Eva March Tappan ... Boston, New York [etc.] Houghton, Mifflin and company [191–?]

xix, 420 p., 1 l. front. (port.) illus., map. 19½ᶜᵐ.

"References": p. [388]–399.

NT 0036204   ViU

Tappan, Eva March, 1854–

A short history of England's and America's literature, by Eva March Tappan ... ₍Rev. ed.₎ Boston, New York ₍etc.₎ Houghton Mifflin company ₍ᶜ1920₎

xix, 421 p. front., illus., ports., double map. 19½ᶜᵐ. $1.68

"References": p. ₍391₎–402.

1. English literature—Hist. & crit. 2. American literature—Hist. & crit.

Library of Congress   PR85.T32 1920   20–10289

NT   0036205   DLC

Tappan, Eva March, 1854–

A short history of England's and America's literature. by Eva March Tappan ... ₍Rev. ed.₎ Boston, New York ₍etc.₎ Houghton Mifflin company ₍ᶜ1921₎

xix, 434 p. front., illus. (incl. ports.) double map. 19½ᶜᵐ. $1.84

"References": p. ₍403₎–414.

1. English literature—Hist. & crit. 2. American literature—Hist. & crit.

Library of Congress   PR85.T32 1921   21–15492

NT   0036206   DLC PCW

Tappan, Eva March, 1854–1930.

A short history of England's and America's literature, by Eva March Tappan ... Rev. ed. Boston, New York ₍etc.₎ Houghton Mifflin company ₍ᶜ1930₎

5 p. l., 434 p. front., illus. (incl. ports.) double map. 19½ᶜᵐ.

"References": p. ₍403₎–414.

1. English literature—Hist. & crit. 2. American literature—Hist. & crit.

Library of Congress · PR85.T32 1930   30–18767

Copyright A 26240   ₍5₎   ‡20.9

NT   0036207   DLC

Tappan, Eva March, 1854–1930.

A short history of England's literature, by Eva March Tappan ... Boston, New York ₍etc.₎ Houghton, Mifflin and company ₍ᶜ1905₎

xv, 276 p., 1 l. front. (port.) illus., double map. 19½ᶜᵐ.

"References": p. ₍256₎–263.

1 English literature—Hist. & crit.

Library of Congress   PR85.T3   5–8088

OO MH MB NN

NT   0036208   DLC IdU PPFr KEmT PP PWcS PPT PPPL ViU

Tappan, Eva March, 1854–1930.

A short story of America's literature, with selections from colonial and revolutionary writers, by Eva March Tappan ... Boston, New York ₍etc.₎ Houghton, Mifflin and company ₍ᶜ1907₎

xii p., 1 l., 255 p. front., illus., ports. 19½ᶜᵐ.

"References": p. ₍241₎–246.

1. American literature—Hist. & crit. 2. American literature—Colonial period. 3. American literature—Revolutionary period.

Library of Congress   PS92.T3   7–31175

NT   0036209   DLC

Tappan, Eva March, *1854–*

A sketch of Longfellow's life.
(*In* Longfellow, Henry Wadsworth. Evangeline. Pp. *1–18*. Plates. Boston. [*1916*.])

M5343 — Longfellow, Henry Wadsworth, *1807–1882.*

NT   0036210   MB

Tappan, Eva March, 1854–1930, *comp.*

... Sports & pastimes, selected & arranged by Eva March Tappan. ₍Boston₎ Houghton Mifflin company, 1916.

xv, ₍1₎, 578, ₍2₎ p. col. front., plates. 19½ᶜᵐ. (The Children's hour. ₍vol. xii₎)

Title within ornamental border.

1. Sports. 2. Games. I. Title.

    17—876

Library of Congress   PZ5.S437 vol. 12

NT   0036211   DLC PU KMK OCl ViU NN MB

Tappan, Eva March, 1854–   *comp.*

... Stories from seven old favorites, selected & arranged by Eva March Tappan. ₍1st ed.₎ Boston, New York, etc.₎ Houghton, Mifflin & company, 1907.

xiii, ₍1₎, 441, ₍1₎ p., 1 l. front. 13 pl. 22ᶜᵐ. (Half-title: The Children's hour ... vol. v)

Series title also at head of t.-p.
Title within ornamental border.
"The first edition of The children's hour is limited to 1000 numbered copies." This copy not numbered.

CONTENTS.—The pilgrim's progress.— Robinson Crusoe.— Gulliver's travels.—Don Quixote.—The Arabian nights.—The travels of Baron Munchausen.—Tales from Shakespeare.

I. Title.

Library of Congress   PZ5.C437 vol. 5   7—31217

NcD OKentU KMK

NT   0036212   DLC WaSp OCl OEac OLak MB PPT MB Vi NN

₍**Tappan, Eva March**₎ 1854–1930, *comp.*

... Stories from seven old favorites. Boston, Houghton Mifflin company ₍ᶜ1929₎

xiii, ₍1₎, 441, ₍1₎ p. col. front., illus., col. plates. 22ᶜᵐ. (Half-title: The children's hour ... vol. v)

Series title also at head of t.-p.
Title within ornamental border; illustrated lining-papers in colors.

I. Title.

Library of Congress   PZ5.C437.2 vol. v   30–8361

NT   0036213   DLC PPT OU OClh

Tappan, Eva March, 1854–1930, *comp.*

... Stories from the classics, selected & arranged by Eva March Tappan. ₍Boston, New York, etc.₎ Houghton, Mifflin & company, 1907.

xvii, ₍1₎, 495, ₍1₎ p., 1 l. front., 12 pl. 22ᶜᵐ. (The children's hour. ₍vol. iii₎)

Title within ornamental border.
"The first edition of The children's hour is limited to 1000 numbered copies." This copy not numbered.

I. Title.

    7—31215

Library of Congress   PZ5.C437 vol. 3

PPT OCl MB Vi NcD ViU

NT   0036214   DLC WaSp OCl KMK OLak OClW OEac OClh NN

₍**Tappan, Eva March**₎ 1854–1930, *comp.*

... Stories from the classics. Boston, Houghton Mifflin company ₍ᶜ1929₎

xiii, ₍1₎, 328, ₍1₎ p. col. front., illus., col. plates. 22ᶜᵐ. (Half-title: The children's hour ... vol. iii)

Series title also at head of t.-p.
Title within ornamental border; illustrated lining-papers in colors.

I. Title.

Library of Congress   PZ5.C437.2 vol. iii   30–10343

NT   0036215   DLC PPT OClh OU

Tappan, Eva March, 1854–1930.

Stories of America for very young readers, by Eva March Tappan ... Boston and New York, Houghton Mifflin company, 1926.

vi p., 1 l., 141 p. front., illus. 21ᶜᵐ.

"All but four of these stories first appeared in the Junior home magazine."

1. U. S.—History, Juvenile. I. Title.

    26—15066

Library of Congress   E178.3.T18

NT   0036216   DLC WaSp Or NN OCl OClh PPFr PP

Tappan, Eva March, 1854–1930, *comp.*

... Stories of legendary heroes, selected & arranged by Eva March Tappan. ₍1st ed.₎ ₍Boston, New York, etc.₎ Houghton, Mifflin & company, 1907.

xii p., 1 l. 474, ₍2₎ p. front., 12 pl. 22ᶜᵐ. (Half-title: The children's hour ... vol. iv)

Series title also at head of t.-p.
Title within ornamental border.
"The first edition of The children's hour is limited to 1000 numbered copies." This copy not numbered.

I. Title.

Library of Congress   PZ5.C437 vol. 4   7—31220

OEac NcD

NT   0036217   DLC OCl WaSp NN Vi OClh MB PPT OCl OLak

₍**Tappan, Eva March**₎ 1854–1930, *comp.*

... Stories of legendary heroes. Boston, Houghton Mifflin company ₍ᶜ1929₎

xii, ₍1₎, 370, ₍1₎ p. col. front., illus., col. plates. 22ᶜᵐ. (Half-title: The children's hour ... vol. iv)

Series title also at head of t.-p.
Title within ornamental border; illustrated lining-papers in colors.

I. Title.

Library of Congress   PZ5.C437.2 vol. iv   30–10344

NT   0036218   DLC OU OClW PPT

Tappan, Eva March, 1854–1930, *comp.*

... Stories of nature, selected & arranged by Eva March Tappan. ₍Boston₎ Houghton Mifflin company, 1916.

xiii, ₍1₎, 553, ₍1₎ p., 1 l. col. front., plates. 19½ᶜᵐ. (The children's hour. ₍vol. xi₎)

Title within ornamental border.

1. Natural history—Juvenile literature. I. Title.

    17—875

Library of Congress   PZ5.C437 vol. 11

NT   0036219   DLC OCl KMK OCl OClh NN MB

Tappan, Eva March, 1854–

The story of our Constitution, by Eva March Tappan ... Boston, Lothrop, Lee & Shepard co. ₍1922₎

199 p. front., plates, ports. 19½ᶜᵐ.

1. U. S. Constitution.

Library of Congress   JK37.T3   22—17629

IdU-SB Or OrP

NT   0036220   DLC PP PPFr PWcS OClh OCl OU MB NN WaSp

Tappan, Eva March, 1854–1930.

The story of our Constitution, by Eva March Tappan ... 1940 ed. brought up to date by William F. Schuyler. ₍New York₎ Lothrop, Lee & Shepard co. ₍1940₎

7, 11–203 p. front. 19½ᶜᵐ.

1. U. S. Constitution. I. Schuyler, William F.

    40–34937

Library of Congress   JK37.T3 1940

Copyright   ₍2₎   342.739

NT   0036221   DLC WaSp Or OrStbM

Tappan, Eva March, 1854–1930.

The story of the Greek people; an elementary history of Greece, by Eva March Tappan ... Boston, New York ₍etc.₎ Houghton Mifflin company ₍ᶜ1908₎

vi p., 2 l., 257, ₍1₎ p. front., illus., maps. 20ᶜᵐ.

1. Greece—Hist. I. Title.

    8—30942

Library of Congress   DF215.T3

OO PG1B

NT   0036222   DLC Or PBa PPT PP WaSp OrP MB NN OCl OU

DF215 .T2 Tappan, Eva March, 1854-1930.
The story of the Greek people. «New ed.» London, George G. Harrap «1929»
248 p. illus.

1. Greece--Hist. I. Title.

NT 0036223 ICU

Tappan, Eva March, 1854–1930.
The story of the Greek people; an elementary history of Greece, by Eva March Tappan ... Boston, New York [etc.] Houghton Mifflin company [c1936]
vi p., 2 l., 257, [1] p. front., illus., maps. 20cm.

NT 0036224 GU MH

Tappan, Eva March, 1854–
The story of the Roman people; an elementary history of Rome, by Eva March Tappan ... Boston, New York [etc.] Houghton Mifflin company [c1910]
4 p. l., 251, [1] p. front., illus., maps. 19½cm. $0.65

1. Rome—Hist.

Library of Congress DG210.T2 11—1045

NN MtBC WaSp WaS IdU OrP Or OrU
NT 0036225 DLC TxU PBa PU PP OCl OEac OU OLak OClh

Tappan, Eva March, 1854-1930.
The story of the Roman people; an elementary history of Rome. Boston, Houghton Mifflin, 1911.

NT 0036226 MH PPFr

Tappan, Eva March, 1854–
... Travelers and traveling, by Eva March Tappan ... Boston, New York [etc.] Houghton Mifflin company [c1916]
iv p., 1 l., 120 p. illus. 19cm. (Her The Industrial readers, book IV) $0.45

CONTENTS.—How railroads are built and trains are run.—How the railroads carry mail and people.—How refrigeration brings us food.—How freight and express are managed.—About compressed air.—How the trolley car runs.—How elevated roads and subways are built.—What the motor car is doing.—Transportation by rivers and canals.—The great highway of the ocean.—About roads and bridges.

1. Transportation. 2. Readers and speakers—1870– I. Title.

Library of Congress E1127.G4T3 book 4 16—26937

NN MB WaSp WvFS
NT 0036227 DLC PPT PWcS PPCI OLak OCU OClW OCl ViU

Tappan, Eva March, 1854-1930.
Travelers and traveling. Boston, etc., Houghton Mifflin co. [1919]

"The industrial readers, 4."

NT 0036228 MH

Tappan, Eva March, 1854–1930.
... Travelers and traveling, by Eva March Tappan ... Rev. ed. Boston, New York [etc.] Houghton Mifflin company [c1930]
iv p., 1 l., 130 p. illus. 19cm. (Her The industrial readers, book IV)

1. Transportation. 2. Readers and speakers—1870– I. Title.

Library of Congress PE1127.G4T3 bk. IV 30-5925
——— Copy 2. HE152.T3

NT 0036229 DLC OrP

Tappan, Eva March, 1854-1930.
Washington and the children.
(In American History stories for very young Readers, Boston, Houghton, Mifflin Co., 1924)

NT 0036230 MB

Tappan, Eva March, 1854–
When knights were bold, by Eva March Tappan. Boston and New York, Houghton Mifflin company, 1911.
xii p., 1 l., [2], 365, [1] p., 1 l. front., illus. 24½cm. $2.00

1. Civilization, Medieval. I. Title.

Library of Congress D127.T2 11—28668

IdU IdB OrLgE OrP WaSp
IaU OClMA OCl ODW MiU MB NN MtBC Or OrU OrStbM WaElC
NT 0036231 DLC MsSM NBuU PCW PBa PSt PWcS PP OClh

Tappan, Eva March, 1854-1930
When knights were bold,....Bost. N. Y. 1915.

381 p.

NT 0036232 OU

D 127 .T2 1939 Tappan, Eva March, 1854-1930.
When knights were bold. Boston, Houghton Mifflin [1939]
xii, 381 p. illus. 21 cm.

1. Civilization, Medieval I. Title

NT 0036233 NmLcU OEac Vi WaU

Tappan, Eva March, 1854–1930, comp.
... Wonders of science, selected & arranged by Eva March Tappan. [Boston] Houghton Mifflin company, 1916.
xiv, [1], 523, [1] p. col. front., plates. 19½cm. (The Children's hour. [vol. XV])
Title within ornamental border.

1. Science—Juvenile literature. I. Title.

Library of Congress PZ5.437 vol. 15 17—879

NT 0036234 DLC OCl OKentU OEac OClh OCl ViU NN MB

Tappan, Eva March, 1854– comp.
Wonders of science. School ed. Selected and arranged by Eva March Tappan. Boston, New York [etc.] Houghton Mifflin company [c1927]
xiii, 257 p. front., plates. 19½cm.

1. Science—Juvenile literature. I. Title.

Library of Congress Q163.T25 27-24690

NT 0036235 DLC PU PWcS PPT DHEW OU ViU

Tappan, Eva March, 1854-1930, comp.
The words of a man
see under Tappan, Edmund March, 1824-1860.

Tappan, Eva March, editor.
The world's story. A history of the world in story, song and art. Boston. Houghton Mifflin Co. 1914. 14 v. Plates. 20½ cm.
Contents. — 1. China, Japan, and the islands of the Pacific. 2. India, Persia, Mesopotamia and Palestine. 3. Egypt, Africa and Arabia. 4. Greece and Rome. 5. Italy, France, Spain and Portugal. 6. Russia, Austria-Hungary, the Balkan States and Turkey. 7. Grmany, the Netherlands and Switzerland. 8. Norway, Sweden, Denmark, Iceland, Greenland and the search for the Poles. 9. England. 10. England, Scotland, Ireland and Wales. 11. Canada, South America, Central America, Mexico and the West Indies. 12, 13. The United States. 14. An outline of universal history, by Carl Ploetz, translated and enlarged by William H. Tillinghast, with additions covering recent events [1904-1914].
Vol. 14 is catalogued separately.

K3978 — T.r. — History. Universal.

NT 0036237 MB NN

Tappan, Eva March, 1854–1930, ed.
... The world's story; a history of the world in story, song and art, ed. by Eva March Tappan. Boston and New York, Houghton Mifflin company, 1914–1918.
15 v. fronts. (v. 1–13, 15) plates (part double) 22 cm.
Subtitles of each volume at head of title.
Each plate accompanied by guard sheet with descriptive letterpress.
"The first edition of The world's story is limited to seven hundred and fifty numbered copies."
Vol. XIV has title: An outline of universal history, by Carl Ploetz; tr. and enl. by William H. Tillinghast, with additions covering recent events.

CONTENTS.—I. China, Japan and the islands of the Pacific.—II. India, Persia, Mesopotamia and Palestine.—III. Egypt, Africa and Arabia.—IV. Greece and Rome.—V. Italy, France, Spain and Portugal.—VI. Russia, Austria-Hungary, the Balkan states and Turkey.—VII. Germany, the Netherlands and Switzerland.—VIII. Norway, Sweden, Denmark, Iceland, Greenland and the search for the poles.—IX. England.—X. England, Scotland, Ireland and Wales.—XI. Canada, South America, Central America, Mexico and the West Indies.—XII–XIII. The United States.—XIV. An outline of universal history.—XV. The world war, ed. by H. W. Dresser.

1. World history. I. Ploetz, Karl Julius, 1819–1881. II. Tillinghast, William Hopkins, 1854–1913, tr. III. Dresser, Horatio Willis, 1866– IV. Title.

D24.T3 14—17942

PPT IdPI IdB OrStbM
NT 0036239 DLC MB WaWW NIC OCl PPF PPFr OClND OClW

Tappan, Frank Lee, 1857–
Aquaria fish, management and care of the aquarium and its inhabitants, by Frank L. Tappan. [Minneapolis? Minn., 1911]
94 p., 2 l. incl. front., illus. 23cm. $1.00
CONTENTS.—pt. 1. The propagation and care of the Paradise fish.—pt. 2. Arrangement and care of the aquarium.

1. Aquariums. 2. Fish-of-Paradise. 11-15342

Library of Congress QL78.T3

NT 0036240 DLC MB CU ICJ

Tappan, Frank Lee, 1857–
The way to health, by Dr. Frank L. Tappan. New York, Harbinger house [1942]
104 p. 21cm.

I. Title. 42-16904

Library of Congress BF1999.T27
[2] [159.9132] 131.3:

NT 0036241 DLC

TT520 .T17 [Tappan, Frank O]
[The new century garment cutter. Toledo, O., c1896]

NT 0036242 DLC

Tappan, Franklin D.
The passing of the Grand army of the republic [by] Franklin D. Tappan. Worcester, Mass. [Commonwealth press] 1939.
xi, 273 p. front., plates, 3 port. on 1 pl., 4 plans on 1 pl. 26½cm.
"This volume is no. 111 of the limited memorial edition."
Bibliography: p. 265–266.

1. Grand army of the republic. Dept. of Massachusetts. George H. Ward post, no. 10. I. Title.

Library of Congress E462.1.M38W3 39-17751
——— Copy 2.
Copyright A 131273 [3] 369.151

NT 0036243 DLC MH TxU

Tappan, G[eorge] Arthur, ed.
Our State house, illustrated, historical, and biographical ... Boston, Tappan pub. co., 1900.
130 p. illus. obl. 16°.

Subject entries: 1. Massachusetts—Biog. 2. Massachusetts—Capital and capitol.
Mar. 14, 1901-22

Library of Congress, no. F73.8.S8T2. Copyright.

NT 0036244 DLC MB

Tappan, George Arthur, editor.
A twentieth century souvenir. The officers and the men, the stations without and within, of the Boston Police.
— Boston. Twentieth Century Biography Co. [1901.] 234 pp. Portraits. Plates. L. 8°.

G2731 — T.r. — Boston, Mass. Police. — Boston, Mass. Biog.

NT   0036245   MB

[Tappan, George H   ]
Ex-Chief Justice Hall, of Colorado Territory. [Denver? 1864?]
11 p. 19ᶜᵐ.
Caption title.
A letter, with testimonials, addressed to the President of the United States, asking for the appointment of Benjamin F. Hall to the office of governor of Colorado Territory.

1. Hall, Benjamin Franklin, 1814-1891. 2. Colorado—Pol. & govt.

11–26678

Library of Congress   F780.H17

NT   0036246   DLC

Tappan, George L
Andrew Johnson—not guilty. New York, Comet Press Books [1954]
139 p. 22 cm.

1. Johnson, Andrew, Pres. U. S., 1808-1875.

E667.T3   923.173   54–7722 ‡

NT   0036247   DLC NN IdPI TU PP PSt

Tappan, George L
What Protestants believe.
Pamphlet.
Article from Monday morning. Nov. 11, 1946.

NT   0036248   PPPrHi

Tappan, Gladys
Louisiana basketry.   Baton Rouge, 1930.
27 p. (Louisiana. Agricultural & mechanical college, Extension division, Extension circular no. 136)

NT   0036249   PP

Tappan, Harvey.
Pioneer history of St. Clair County, taken from public records. Address by Judge Harvey Tappan, St. Clair County pioneer society, Algonac, June 28, 1910. [Algonac, Mich.,1910]
1 p. l., 8 numb. l. 25½ᶜᵐ.
Printed on one side of leaf only.
Text runs parallel with back of cover.

1. St. Clair Co., Mich.—Hist.

17–12311

Library of Congress   F572.S3T17

NT   0036250   DLC

Tappan, Harvey.
School law and a history and description of the educational system of Michigan. By Harvey Tappan, LL. B. Port Huron, Mich., The Sherman company, printers, 1889.
8 p., 1 l., [9]–155, xii p. 18ᶜᵐ.

1. Educational law and legislation—Michigan. 2. Education—Michigan.

8–12754

Library of Congress   LA307.T3

NT   0036251   DLC DHEW MiU

Tappan, Helen Niña, 1917–
Foraminifera from the Arctic slope of Alaska, by Helen Tappan. Washington, U. S. Govt. Print. Off., 1951–
v. illus., maps. 29 cm. (Geological Survey professional paper 236)
Includes bibliographies.
CONTENTS.—A. General introduction and Part 1: Triassic Foraminifera.—B. Part 2: Jurassic Foraminifera.—C. Part 3: Cretaceous Foraminifera.

1. Foraminifera, Fossil. 2. Paleontology—Triassic. 3. Paleontology—Alaska. I. Title. (Series: U. S. Geological Survey. Professional paper 236)

QE75.P9   no. 236–A, etc.   550'.8 s   74–604840
                        MARC

NT   0036252   DLC WU MiU KU DI-GS

Tappan. Helen Niña, 1917–
Foraminifera from the Duck Creek formation of Oklahoma and Texas. Chicago, 1942.
iv, 94 l. 7 plates. 32 cm.
Typescript (carbon copy)
Thesis—University of Chicago.
Bibliography: leaves 90–94.

1. Foraminifera, Fossil—Oklahoma. 2. Foraminifera, Fossil—Texas. 3. Paleontology—Cretaceous. I. Title: Duck Creek formation of Oklahoma and Texas.

QE772.T28   62–56218

NT   0036253   DLC

Tappan, Helen Niña, 1917–
Foraminifera from the Duck Creek formation of Oklahoma and Texas. [n. p., 1943]
476–517 p. 7 plates. 24 cm.
Thesis—University of Chicago.
"Reprinted from the Journal of paleontology, vol. 17, no. 5, September, 1943."
Bibliography: p. 515–517.

1. Foraminifera, Fossil—Oklahoma. 2. Foraminifera, Fossil—Texas. 3. Paleontology—Cretaceous. I. Title: Duck Creek formation of Oklahoma and Texas.

QE772.T3   563.12   A 44–1353 rev*
Chicago. Univ. Libr.
for Library of Congress   [r62d½]†

NT   0036254   ICU DLC TxU

Tappan, Helen Niña, 1917– joint author.
Q11
.S7
vol. 117,
no. 15   Loeblich, Alfred Richard, 1914–
The foraminiferal genus *Triplasia* Reuss, 1854, by Alfred R. Loeblich, Jr. and Helen Tappan. Washington, Smithsonian Institution, 1952.

Tappan, Helen Niña, 1917– joint author.
Q11
.S7
vol. 126,
no. 3   Loeblich, Alfred Richard, 1914–
A revision of some glanduline Nodosariidae (Foraminifera) by Alfred R. Loeblich, Jr., and Helen Tappan. Washington, Smithsonian Institution, 1955.

Tappan, Helen Niña, 1917– joint author.
Q11
.S7
vol. 128,
no. 5   Loeblich, Alfred Richard, 1914–
Revision of some recent foraminiferal genera, by Alfred R. Loeblich, Jr., and Helen Tappan. Washington, Smithsonian Institution, 1955.

Tappan, Helen Niña, 1917– joint author.
Q11
.S7
vol. 121,
no. 7   Loeblich, Alfred Richard, 1914–
Studies of Arctic foraminifera, by Alfred R. Loeblich, Jr. and Helen Tappan. Washington, Smithsonian Institution, 1953.

Tappan, Henry Philip, 1805–1881.
Abraham Lincoln. Rede bei der gedächtnissfeier in der Dorotheenkirche zu Berlin, 2. mai 1865, gehalten von dr. H. P. Tappan, corresp. mitglied der Französischen academie. Autorisirte uebersetzung. Frankfurt am Main, H. Keller, 1865.
iv, 36 p. 23ᶜᵐ.
A translation by Wilhelm Jordan of the author's A discourse on the death of Abraham Lincoln ...

1. Lincoln, Abraham, pres. U. S.—Addresses, sermons, etc. I. Jordan, Wilhelm, 1819-1904, tr.

Library of Congress   E457.8.T175   12—7712

NjP
NT   0036259   DLC PHi PU NIC N CtY MiU OC1WHi MiU-C

Tappan, Henry Philip, 1805–1881
Addresses, 1846–58.
6 pts, in 1 v.

NT   0036260   MiU

25.3   Tappan, Henry Philip, 1805–1881.
Baccalaureate address, delivered at the commencement of the university, June 27, 1855. Ann Arbor, E. B. Pond, 1855.
11 p. 8°. [With his. The progress of educational development]

NT   0036261   DLC PPL MiU-C

Tappan, Henry Philip, 1805–1881.
Brief memorials of an only daughter. By Rev. Henry P. Tappan ... New York, Wiley and Putnam, 1844.
285 p. 18ᶜᵐ.
"Printed for private distribution."
An account of the life of Mary C——, daughter of friends of the author, who was born at Fishkill Landing, N. Y. in 1825 and died in 1842.

21–14609 Revised

Library of Congress   CT275.C12T3

NT   0036262   DLC CtY

Tappan, Henry Philip, 1805–1881.
A discourse, delivered by Henry P. Tappan, D. D. at Ann Arbor, Mich., on the occasion of his inauguration as chancellor of the University of Michigan, December 21st, 1852. Detroit, Advertiser power presses, 1852.
52 p. 23ᶜᵐ.

1. Michigan. University.

Library of Congress   LD3295 1852   7–11090†

NT   0036263   DLC NRU PPPrHi MiU OC1WHi OO NjP NN

Tappan, Henry Philip, 1805–1881.
A discourse on education, delivered at the anniversary of the Young ladies' institute, Pittsfield, Mass., October 2, 1846. By Henry P. Tappan ... New-York, R. Lockwood & son, 1846.
43 p. 21½ᶜᵐ.
Published by request.

1. Education—Addresses, [essays], lectures, [etc.]

E 15–2095

Library, U. S. Bur. of   Education LB41.T2

NT   0036264   DHEW PHi MiU-C OC1WHi OO MiU NjP MH NN

Tappan, Henry Philip, 1805–1881.
Discourse on mental development...
Ann Arbor, 1855.

NT   0036265   PPL

Tappan, Henry Philip, 1805–1881.
A discourse on the death of Abraham Lincoln ... delivered Tuesday, May 2, 1865, in the Dorotheen-church, Berlin, by Henry P. Tappan ... Berlin, Printed by G. Lange [1865]
46 p. 21ᶜᵐ.

1. Lincoln, Abraham, pres. U. S.—Addresses, sermons, etc.

Library of Congress   E457.8.T17   12—4320

NT 0036266   DLC NIC PPL N MB OClWHi CSmH

Tappan, Henry Philip, 1805–1881.
A discourse on the life and character of the Rev. Herman Morton ... delivered in the Dutch Reformed Church in Lafayette Place. (In: Norton (Rev. Herman) The life of the Rev. H. Norton ... New York, 1853. 16°. p. 11–79)

NT 0036267   NN

TAPPAN, HENRY PHILIP, 1805–1881.
The doctrine of the will, applied to moral agency and responsibility. By Henry P. Tappan ... New-York, Wiley and Putnam, 1841.
ix, [1]p., 1 l., 348p. 19cm.

1. Free will and determinism.

Printed by Wesleyan   University Library

NjNbS NjP MH NN IU OO
NT 0036268   CtW PPWe IEG ScU MiU CtY MiU NNUT NNR

E173
Am33
Reel
371

Tappan, Henry Philip, 1805–1881.
The doctrine of the will applied to moral agency and responsibility. New York, Wiley and Putnam, 1841.
(American culture series, 371:2)
Microfilm copy made by University Microfilms, Ann Arbor, Mich.
Collation of original: 348 p.

NT 0036269   IaAS

Tappan, Henry Philip, 1805–1881.
The doctrine of the will, determined by an appeal to consciousness. New York, Wiley & Putnam, 1840.
ix, 318 p.
Microfilm. Ann Arbor, Mich., University Microfilms, 1964. 1 reel. 35 mm. (American culture series, 255:7)

1. Will.   i. Title.
Microfilm 01291 reel 255, no. 7 E   Mic 67–64

PPStCh ICRL PPWe MeB NjNbS NN NNR CtY NjR NNUT KEmT
NT 0036270   DLC MiU NcD OCl ViU RPB NjP ICN MH ICU

Tappan, Henry Philip, 1805–1881.
Elements of logic, together with an introductory view of philosophy in general, and a preliminary view of the reason. By Henry P. Tappan. New York, & London, Wiley and Putnam, 1844.
xi, [1], 461 p. 18½ᶜᵐ.

1. Logic. 2. Philosophy.
    9—32923
Library of Congress   BC108.T3

NT 0036271   DLC DCU ViU CtY OO NjP NN NNUT

BC108
.T2

Tappan, Henry Philip, 1805–1881.
Elements of logic; together with an introductory view of philosophy in general, and a preliminary view of the reason. By Henry P. Tappan. New York, D. Appleton and company, 1856.
467 p. 20ᵐᵐ.

1. Logic. 2. Philosophy.
    15—13982
Library of Congress   BC108.T3 1856

MeB MB ICJ ICU
NT 0036272   DLC PPL ViU CtHT-W OOxM OCX ScU NjP

Film
79
reel
306
no.5

Tappan, Henry Philip, 1805–1881.
Elements of logic: together with an introductory view of philosophy in general, and a preliminary view of the reason. New York D. Appleton and company, 1856.
(American culture series, 306:5)

Microfilm copy (positive) made by University Films, Ann Arbor, Mich.
Collation of the original: 467p.
1. Logic.   2. Philosophy.

NT 0036273   FTaSU PSt KEmT IaAS

Tappan, Henry Philip, 1805–1881
Elements of logic; together with an introductory view of philosophy in general, and a preliminary view of the reason....N.Y. 1860.

467 p.

NT 0036274   MiU PU

Tappan, Henry Philip, 1805–1881.
Elements of logic together with an introductory view of philosophy in general and a preliminary view of reason,
New York, 1862.

NT 0036275   NNUT

Tappan, Henry Philip, 1805–1881.
Elements of logic; together with an introductory view of philosophy in general, and a preliminary view of the reason. By Henry P. Tappan ... New York, D. Appleton and company, 1870.
467 p. 20ᶜᵐ.

NT 0036276   ViU MH NjNbS

Tappan, Henry Philip, 1805–1881.
Elements of logic; together with an introductory view of philosophy in general, and a preliminary view of the reason. By Henry P. Tappan ... New York, D. Appleton and company, 1871.
467 p. 20ᶜᵐ.

1. Logic. 2. Philosophy.
    15—16184
Library of Congress   BC108.T3 1871

NT 0036277   DLC

TAPPAN, HENRY PHILIP, 1805–1881.
An essay on the expression of passion in oratory. By Henry P. Tappan ... New York: Printed by C.W.Benedict, 1848. 18 p. 22½cm.

1. Oratory.

NT 0036278   NN CtY NjP MiU

Tappan, Henry Philip, 1805–
A friendly letter from Dr. Tappen, dated Berlin, Nov. 8th, 1865. (Bay City, 1933)
(3) p., facsim: (4) p. 31 cm.
"Introductory note" signed: William L. Clements.
"This is one of thirty copies made for distribution at a dinner given in Bay City, Michigan, Dec. 1st, 1933, for the Board of Regents of the University of Michigan. This copy number 21."
Letter written to Dr. Corydon L. Ford.
Portrait of Dr. Tappan as title-vignette.

NT 0036279   MiU-C

Tappan, Henry Philip, 1805–1881.
The growth of cities: a discourse delivered before the New York geographical society, on the evening of March 15th, 1855. By Henry P. Tappan ... New York, R. Craighead, printer, 1855.
50 p. 22ᶜᵐ.

1. Cities and towns—Growth.

Library of Congress   HB2161.T17   5—17730

NN
NT 0036280   DLC NNUT PPL NIC NBuU-L PHi MiU NjP MWA

Micro
Film
D50
reel
236
no.5

Tappan, Henry Philip, 1805–1881
The growth of cities: a discourse delivered before the New York geographical society, on the evening of March 15th, 1855. By Henry P. Tappan ... New York, R. Craighead, 1855.
1 reel. 35mm. (American culture series, reel 236, no.5)
Microfilm (positive) made in 1963 by University Microfilms, Ann Arbor, Mich.
Collation of the original: 50p.

1. Cities and   towns - Growth.   I. Title.
II. Series.

NT 0036281   PSt KEmT ICRL IaAS FTaSU

Tappan, Henry Philip, 1805–1881.
Illustrious personages of the nineteenth century. With an introduction by Henry P. Tappan ... New York, Stringer & Townsend, 1853.
1 p. l., vi, [1], 317 p. front., ports. 25ᶜᵐ.
Added t.-p., engr.
The plates are engraved by John Sartain.
CONTENTS.—The royal family of England.—Thomas Chalmers.—Sir Robert Peel.—Alfred Tennyson.—Miss Pardoe.—The Emperor Nicholas.—Thomas Babington Macaulay.—Walter Savage Landor.—Lord Jeffrey.—Mrs. Norton.—Douglas Jerrold.—Thomas Noon Talfourd.—William Wordsworth.—Victor Hugo.—Joanna Baillie.—Thomas Campbell.—Viscount de Chateaubriand.—Alphonse de Lamartine.—Louis Kossuth.
1. Biography.   i. Sartain, John, 1808–1897, engr.   ii. Title.
    24–16873
Library of Congress   CT119.T3

NT 0036282   DLC ICN TU NjP MiU OCl

CT
211
A52
v.4
no.6

Tappan, Henry Philip, 1805–1881.
A letter to Rev. Joel Hawes, D. D., on Dr. Taylor's theological views [by the author of Views in theology] New York, J. P. Haven, 1832.
49 p. 23cm.
"From Views in theology, no. X, for May, 1832."

1. Taylor, Nathaniel William, 1786–1858. I. Hawes, Joel, 1789–1867.

NT 0036283   NIC NNC

[Tappan, Henry Philip] 1805–1881.
A letter to the Rev. Noah Porter, D.D. pastor of the Cong. church, Farmington, Con. on the statements of the Christian spectator. In reference to Dr. Bellamy's doctrines. From no. XV. of Views in theology, for Nov. 1834. New-York: John P. Haven, 148 Nassau-Street, American tract society's house. 1834.
50 p. 21cm.

Signed on p.50: The author of Views in theology.

NT 0036284   MiU-C CtY-D MH NN ICN NNC

Tappan, Henry Philip, 1805–1881.
The mutual responsibilities of physicians and the community, being an address to the graduating class of the medical college of the University of Michigan. Delivered March 27th, 1856. By Henry P. Tappan, D.D., LL.D. chancellor of the University of Michigan. Detroit, Mich.: Issued from the office of Peninsular Journal of Medicine. Free Press Print. 1856.
25 p. 23cm.
YA9192
1. Physicians. I. t. II. Suppl.

PBL
NT 0036285   MiU-C NjP NN NNC DNLM OClh MiU MiD DLC

E
465
P18
.6
Tappan, Henry Philip, 1805-1881.
President Tappan's annual message to the second moot congress of the Law department of the University of Michigan. Delivered 6th December, 1862. Ann Arbor, C.G. Clark, jr., 1862.
12 p. 22 cm.
No.29 in volume lettered: Pamphlets. Civil war. 6.

NT 0036286   MiU MiU-L MH-L PPL PHi

Tappan, Henry Philip, 1805-1881.
President Tappan's message to the Law congress of the University of Michigan. Delivered January 18th, 1862 ... Ann Arbor, Clark, Wiltsie & co., printers, 1862.
12 p. 21½ cm.
"Chancellor Tappan ... acting as president of the United States for the Moot congress of the University of Michigan, delivered his annual message ... January 18th, 1862, the two Houses convening in joint session to receive it."—p. [3]

1. U. S.—Pol. & govt.—Civil war.   I. Michigan. University. Law congress.
16-9915
Library of Congress   E458.2.T17

NT 0036287   DLC MB

Tappan, Henry Philip, 1805-1881.
The progress of Christianity, the history of the world. A sermon, delivered at Pittsfield, Mass. In the Congregational Church, January 2, 1831 ... Pittsfield, Printed by Phinehas Allen and Son [1831]
Unbound. 8vo.

NT 0036288   CSmH RPB NjP

Tappan, Henry P[hilip], 1805-1881.
The progress of educational development: a discourse delivered before the literary societies of the University of Michigan ... June 25, 1855, by Henry P. Tappan ... Ann Arbor [Mich.] E. B. Pond, printer, 1855.
51, 11 p. 21½ cm.
Cover-title: Dr. Tappan's discourse and baccalaureate.
"Baccalaureate address, delivered at the commencement of the university, June 27, 1855": 11 p. at end.

1. Education—Hist.
6-39628†
Library of Congress   LA25.T2

NT 0036289   DLC Mi CtY MiU-C MiU NN

LA
25
.T2
1971
Tappan, Henry P[hilip], 1805-1881.
The progress of educational development: a discourse delivered before the literary societies of the University of Michigan ... June 25, 1855, by Henry P. Tappan ... Ann Arbor [Mich.] E. B. Pond, printer, 1855.
51, 11 p. 21½ cm.
Photocopy. Ann Arbor, Mich., University Microfilms, 1971.

NT 0036290   IaAS

[**Tappan, Henry Philip**] 1805-1881.
Proofs that the common theories and modes of reasoning respecting the depravity of mankind exhibit it as a physical attribute, with a view of the scriptural doctrine relative to the nature and character of man as a moral agent. New-York, F. & R. Lockwood, 1824.
vi, [7]-104 p. 22½ cm.

1. Good and evil. 2. Liberty of the will.
9-33446†
Library of Congress   BJ1406.T3

NT 0036291   DLC OO MiU-C CtY PPPrHi MH-AH

Tappan, Henry Philip, 1805-1881.
Public education: an address; delivered in the hall of the House of representatives, in the Capitol at Lansing, on the evening of January 28th, 1857, by Henry P. Tappan ... Detroit, Printed by H. Barns, 1857.
40 p. 22 cm.

1. Michigan. University. 2. Education—Addresses, [essays], lectures, [etc.] I. Title.
E 15-2096
Library, U. S. Bur. of   Education LD3256.5.T2

NT 0036292   DHEW Mi MiU MiU-C NjP NN

Tappan, Henry Philip, 1805-1881.
Public education: an address, delivered in the hall of the House of Representatives, in the Capitol at Lansing, on the evening of January 28th, 1857. Detroit, Printed by M. Barns, 1857.
(American culture series, 64 : 7)
Microfilm copy (positive) made in 1956 by University Microfilms, Ann Arbor, Mich.
Collation of the original: 40 p.
1. Michigan. University. 2. Education—Addresses, lectures, etc. I. Title.
Microfilm 01291 reel 64, no. 7 E   Mic 59-7933

NT 0036293   DLC ICRL NRU KEmT IaAS

Tappan, Henry Philip, 1805-1881.
Review by Rev. Dr. H. P. Tappan of his connection with the University of Michigan. Detroit, The Detroit free press steam book and job printing establishment, 1864.
52 p. 22½ cm.

1. Michigan. University.
7-11093†
Library of Congress   LD3275.1852.A2

NT 0036294   DLC DHEW MiU NjP MB

Tappan, Henry Philip, 1805-1881.
A review of Edwards's "Inquiry into the freedom of the will." Containing I. Statement of Edwards's system. II. The legitimate consequences of this system. III. An examination of the arguments against a self-determining will. By Henry Philip Tappan ... New York, J. S. Taylor, 1839.
xiv p., 1 l., [15]-300 p. 19½ cm.

1. Free will and determination. 2. Edwards, Jonathan, 1703-1758. Inquiry concerning the freedom of the will.
10-20982
Library of Congress   BF621.T2

OCX NjP MeB OU NN MB NcD TNJ-R MCE PPPrHi
NT 0036295   DLC PU PPWe PPA IEG DeU NjNbS MiU OO OU

Tappan, Henry Philip, 1805-1881.
A review of Edwards's "Inquiry into the freedom of the will." New York, John S. Taylor, 1839.
300p. (American culture series, reel 287)
Microfilm edition
Positive copy

NT 0036296   ICRL PSt KEmT IaAS FTaSU

Tappan, Henry Philip, 1805-
A serious letter from Dr. Tappan dated December 9th, 1863. (Bay City [1833])
(5) p.m. facsim: (4) p. 31 cm.
"Introductory note" signed: William L. Clements.
"This is one of twenty-five copies made for distribution at a dinner given in Bay City, Michigan, Dec. 1st, 1933 for the Board of Regents of the University of Michigan; This is copy number 21.
Letter written from Berlin to James C. Clements, Ann Arbor
Portrait of Dr. Tappen as Title-vignett[e]

NT 0036297   MiU-C

30085
.895
Tappan, Henry Philip, 1805-1881.
The spirit of literature and art; an oration delivered at the first semi-centennial anniversary of the Philomathean society, Union College, on the 25th day of July, 1848... Albany, Weed, 1849.
53 p. 22 cm.

NT 0036298   NjP RPB MH

Tappan, Henry Philip, 1805-1881.
A step from the New world to the Old, and back again; with thoughts on the good and evil in both. By Henry P. Tappan ... New York, D. Appleton and company, 1852.
2 v. 19 cm.
CONTENTS.—I. England, Scotland, and Holland.—II. The Rhine, Switzerland, Belgium, and France.

1. Europe—Descr. & trav.   I. Title.
3-16784
Library of Congress   D919.T17

NT 0036299   DLC PPA PPL MiU OOxM NN MB NWM

Tappan, Henry Philip, 1805-1881.
A treatise on the will: containing I. A review of Edwards' Inquiry into the freedom of the will. II. The doctrine of the will determined by an appeal to consciousness. III. The doctrine of the will applied to moral agency and responsibility. Appendix on Edwards and the necessitarian school. By Henry P. Tappan ... A new ed., revised and corrected by the author. Glasgow, Lang, Adamson, & co.; London, Ward & co.; [etc., etc.] 1857.
xv, [1] p., 1 l., [3]-611 p. 23½ cm.
1. Free will and determinism. 2. Edwards, Jonathan, 1703-1758. Inquiry concerning the freedom of the will.

NT 0036300   MiU MdBP

6570
.895
.2
Tappan, Henry Philip, 1805-1881.
The university; its constitution, and its relations, political and religious. A discourse delivered June 22d, 1858, at the request of the Christian library association... Ann Arbor, McCracken, 1858.
36 p. 21½ cm.

1. Universities and colleges.

NT 0036301   NjP MH NN Nh MiD CU MiU

Tappan, Henry Philip, 1805-1881.
The university: its constitution and its relations, political and religious; a discourse delivered June 22d, 1858, at the request of the Christian Library Association. Ann Arbor, Printed by S. B. McCracken, 1858.
36 p.
"Published by the Regents at the request of the alumni."
Microfilm. Ann Arbor, Mich., University Microfilms, 1963. 1 reel. 35 mm. (American culture series, 236:7)
1. Education, Higher. I. Title.
Microfilm 01291 reel 236, no. 7 E   Mic 67-61

NT 0036302   DLC FMU IaAS KEmT PSt FTaSU ICRL

Tappan, Henry Philip, 1805-1881.
University education. By Henry P. Tappan, D. D. New York, G. P. Putnam, 1851.
120 p. 19½ cm.

1. Universities and colleges. 2. Education, Higher.
6-29833
Library of Congress   LB2321.T21

NT 0036303   DLC PU CU OrCS DHEW MiU OCl OU NjP NN

M-film
370
Am3
236-6

Tappan, Henry Philip, 1805-1881.
    University education.   New York, G. P.
Putnam, 1851.
    120 p.

    Microfilm (positive) Ann Arbor, Mich.,
University Microfilms, 1963. 6th title of 13.
35 mm. (American culture series, reel 236.6)

    1. Universities and colleges. 2. Education,
Higher.

NT   0036304   KEmT IaAS IU PSt FTaSU ICRL

Tappan, J., ed.
    The intemperate
        see under   [Sigourney, Lydia Howard
(Huntley)] 1791-1865.

Ga
HE2791
W527T3

Tappan, J   Nelson, appellant.
    J. Nelson Tappan, trustee of H. Clews & Co.,
appellant, vs. the State of Georgia et al.
Appeal from Chancery Court of Hamilton County,
Tennessee. By N.J. Hammond. [n.p.] 1878.
    14 p.   23cm.

    At head of title: Statement of facts and
argument for the State of Georgia. No. 1934,
Supreme Court of Tennessee, September term,
1878.

    Caption title lists defendants as the
Western & Atlantic Railroad, the Western &
Atlantic Railroad Company, and the State of
Georgia.

    I. Clews (Henry) & Company, appellant. II.
Western and Atlantic Railroad, defendant. III.
Western and Atlantic Railroad Company, defendant
IV. Tennessee. Supreme Court.

NT   0036307   GU

Tappan, J. Nelson, appellant.
    Statement of facts and argument for the state of
Georgia. No. 1934. Supreme Court of Tennessee,
September term, 1878. J. Nelson Tappan, trustee
of H. Clews & Co., appellant, vs. the state of
Georgia et al. Appeal from Chancery Court of
Hamilton County, Tennessee. By Vandyke, Cooke &
Vandyke, Chattanooga, Tennessee. [n.p., 1878?]
    13 p.   8vo.

NT   0036308   GU-De

[Tappan, James]
    Memorial ... For an act to render Masonic and extra-
judicial oaths penal, and in aid of the Memorial for a
full investigation into Freemasonry, and the repeal of the
charter granted to the Grand lodge. [Boston, 1834]
    9 p. 24¹ᵐ. [Massachusetts. General court, 1834] House. [Doc.] 7)
    To the honorable the Senate and House of representatives, in General
court assembled.
    Signed: James Tappan [and 63 others]

    1. Freemasons. Massachusetts.   I. Title.
                              CA 26-565 Unrev'd

    Library of Congress   HS527.T3

NT   0036309   DLC PHi MWA

Tappan, Julia.

Perkins, *Mrs.* Ina J   N.
    Growing healthy children. A study made for the Child
health organization of America, now a part of the American
child health association, by Mrs. Ina J. N. Perkins, revised by
Julia Tappan. Washington, Govt. print. off., 1923.

Tappan, Lee Roy J[ohn] 1880–
    The meditations of Ali Ben Háfiz, by Lee Roy J. Tap-
pan. 938 A. D. [Newark Valley? N. Y., 1902]
    3 p. l., 35 p. 23ᵐᵐ.
    "Of this work there have been privately printed on antique laid, deckle
edge paper, one hundred and fifty copies, this being number 1-0."
                              2-28859

NT   0036311   DLC

Tappan, Lewis, 1788-1873.
    Address to the churches of Jesus Christ
        see under   Evangelical Union Anti-
Slavery Society of New York.

Tappan, Lewis, 1788-1873   FOR OTHER EDITIONS
                                      SEE MAIN ENTRY
American and foreign anti-slavery society.
    Address to the non-slaveholders of the South, on the
social and political evils of slavery. New York, Am. &
for. anti-slavery society [1849]

Slavery
E
441
M46
v.31
no.2

    [Tappan, Lewis] 1788-1873.
        The African captives. Trial of the pris
oners of the Amistad on the writ of Habeas
Corpus, before the Circuit Court of the
United States, for the District of Connecti
cut, at Hartford; Judges Thompson and Judson
Sept. term, 1839.   New York, 1839.
        vi, 47 p. 23cm.

        No. 2 in a vol. lettered: A. S. pam-
phlets, 3.
        May anti-   slavery pamphlets, v.
31.
        1. Amistad   (Schooner) I. Title.

NT   0036314   NIC

Tappan, Lewis 1788-1873
American slavery, N.Y. 185-

    8 p.

NT   0036315   OClWHi

Slavery
E
441
M46
v.188
no.8

    [Tappan, Lewis] 1788-1873.
        American slavery [a letter] to the editor
of the British Banner. [New York, J.A.
Gray, printer, 1852?]
        28 p. 20cm.

        May anti-slavery pamphlets, v. 188.
        DLC: YA/6954

        1. Slavery in the U.S.--Controversial lit-
erature--1852.   2. Slavery and the
church. I. Title

NT   0036316   NNC DLC CtY

---

*
E185
.61
.T216
1866

    Tappan, Lewis, 1788-1873.
        Caste: a letter to a teacher among the
freedmen. [Boston, The American Tract
Society, 1866?]
        24 p. 19cm. (American Tract Society
publication, no. 180)
        Caption title.
        DLC: YA25262
        1. U. S.--Race question. 2. Caste--India.
I. Title.

NT   0036317   ViU DLC DHU

Tappan, Lewis, 1788-1873.
    Caste: a letter to a teacher among the freedmen. By Lewis
Tappan ... New-York, W. E. Whiting [1867?]
    24 p. 19ᵐ.
    Caption title.

    1. Negroes. 2. U. S.—Race question.
                                 43-43184

    Library of Congress   E185.61.T216

NT   0036318   DLC OClWHi OO

TAPPAN, Lewis, 1788-1873.
    [Circular issued about 1846 & sent to the
governors of the West Indian Islands.] n.p.,
[1846?].

    1 sheet.

NT   0036319   MH

Tappan, Lewis, 1788-1873.

    [American and foreign anti-slavery society]
    The Fugitive slave bill: its history and unconstitutionality;
with an account of the seizure and enslavement of James Ham-
let, and his subsequent restoration to liberty. 3d ed. New-
York, W. Harned, 1850.

Tappan, Lewis, 1788-1873.
    Human rights—extra
        see under   American anti-slavery society.

Tappan, Lewis, 1788-1873.
    History of the American missionary association
        see under   American missionary association.

SPECIAL COLLECTIONS
B326.973
T165

    [Tappan, Lewis] 1788-1873.
        Immediate emancipation, the only wise and
safe mode. [New York, 1861]
        16 p. 13cm.

        1. Slavery in U. S. - Emancipation.

NT   0036323   NNC PPL NjP NBuG TxU

Tappan, Lewis, 1788-1873.
    Is it right to be rich? By Lewis Tappan. New York
A. D. F. Randolph & co., 1869.
    cover-title, 24 p. 19ᵐᵐ.

    1. Wealth, Ethics of.   I. Title.
                                 21-13285

    Library of Congress   BR115.W4T3

NT   0036324   DLC ICRL LU OO NBLihi MB NN

Tappan, Lewis
    Is it right to be rich? 3d. ed.
New York, Randolph, 1869.

    23 p.

NT   0036325   PPPrHi

[Tappan, Lewis] 1788-1873.
Letter from a gentleman in Boston to a Unitarian clergyman of that city. Boston, T. R. Marvin, printer, 1828.
20 p. 19½cm.

1. Unitarianism. I. Title.

Library of Congress BX9847.T3 6-26351

NT 0036326 DLC MH CtY MB MiU OO NcD OClWHi Nh NjR

BX9847 .T3 1828 a
[Tappan, Lewis] 1788-1873.
Letter from a gentleman in Boston to a Unitarian clergyman of that city. 2d ed. Boston, T. R. Marvin, printer, 1828.
20 p. 19cm.

1. Unitarianism I. Title.

Library of Congress BX9847.T3 1828 a 46-40093

NT 0036327 DLC

[Tappan, Lewis] 1788-1873.
Letter from a gentleman in Boston to a Unitarian clergyman of that city. 3d ed. Boston, T. R. Marvin, printer, 1828.
20 p. 18cm.
[Miscellaneous pamphlets, v. 356, no. 4]

I. Title.

Library of Congress AC901.M5 vol. 356 6-26352

NT 0036328 DLC

[Tappan, Lewis] 1788-1873.
Letter from a gentleman in Boston to a Unitarian clergyman of that city. 4th ed. Boston, T. R. Marvin, printer, 1828.
20 p. 17½cm. [Theological pamphlets, v. 43, no. 5]

1. Unitarianism. I. Title.

6-26353

NT 0036329 DLC

Tappan, Lewis, 1788-1873.
A letter to a teacher among the freedmen,
see his Caste: a letter to a teacher among the freedmen.

Tappan, Lewis, 1788-1873.
Letter to Eleazer Lord, esq. in defense of measures for promoting the observance of the Christian sabbath. By Lewis Tappan. New York: Sold by John P. Haven, 142 Nassau Street; H.C. Sleight, Clinton Hall; Jonathan Leavitt, 182 Broadway. Sleight and Robinson, printers. [1831?] Ten cents single. Four dollars per hundred.
cover-title, 24 p. 18.5cm.
Includes printed matter inside front wrapper, and on back wrapper.
Letter is dated July 20th, 1831.

NT 0036331 MiU-C PPPrHi NjP MH-AH

[Tappan, Lewis,] 1788-1873.
Letter to the Convention of Ministers and Representatives of the Evangelical Branches in the Church in Brooklyn. New York: J. A. Gray & Green, 1866. 24 p. 8°.
Appendix: History of the Free Churches in the city of New-York, p. [13]-[24].

746637. 1. Brooklyn, N. Y.—Churches. 2. New York (city)—Churches. 3. Convention of Ministers and Representatives of the Evangelical Branches in the Church in Brooklyn, 1866. 4. Title.
N. Y. P. L. February 27, 1930

NT 0036332 NN NBB

[Tappan, Lewis] 1788-1873.
Letters respecting a book "dropped from the catalogue" of the American Sunday school union in compliance with the dictation of the slave power. New York, American and foreign anti-slavery society, 1848.
36 p. 18cm.
YA:25058

1. Jacob and his sons, or The second part of a conversation between Mary and her mother. 2. American Sunday-school union. 3. Slavery and the church. 4. Slavery in the U. S.—Controversial literature—1848.

11-12654

Library of Congress E449.T17

NT 0036333 DLC NIC PHi OO MH CtY MeWC

Micro-fiche
Tappan, Lewis, 1788-1873.
Letters respecting a book "dropped from the catalogue" of the American Sunday school union in compliance with the dictation of the slave power. New York, American and foreign anti-slavery society, 1848.
2 sheets. 10.5 x 14.8 cm. ([Slavery, source material and critical literature])
Microfiche (negative) of typescript.
Collation of the original: 36 p. 18 cm.
1. American Sunday School Union. 2. Slavery and the church. 3. Slavery in the United States--Controversial literature--1 48. I. Title

NT 0036334 OOxM PSt

[Tappan, Lewis] 1788-1873.
The life of Arthur Tappan ... New York, Hurd and Houghton, 1870.
432 p. front. (port.) 19½cm.
Introduction signed: Lewis Tappan.

1. Tappan, Arthur, 1786-1865. 2. Slavery in the U. S.—Anti-slavery movements. I. Title.

Library of Congress E449.T16 20-7567

UU
OU OOxM MiU OO TU ICU IU MWA OClWHi PLF MeB CU NIC
NT 0036335 DLC DAU MsSM PPPrHi PPFr PPL ViHaI NcD

FILM B T174t
Tappan, Lewis, 1788-1873.
The life of Arthur Tappan. New York, Hurd and Houghton, 1870.
432p. port.
Microfilm (negative) Urbana, University of Illinois Library Photographic Reproduction Div., 1964. 1 reel. 35mm.
1. Tappan, Arthur, 1786-1865. 2. Slavery in the U.S.--Anti-slavery movements.

NT 0036336 IU KEmT PSt

[Tappan, Lewis] 1788-1873.
The life of Arthur Tappan ... New York, Hurd and Houghton, 1871.
432 p. front. (port.) 19½cm.
Introduction signed: Lewis Tappan.

NT 0036337 ViU PHi PHC MWA MdBP NjP NN NIC

E 449 .T16 T17 1871a
[Tappan, Lewis] 1788-1873.
The life of Arthur Tappan ... New York, Hurd and Houghton, 1871.
432 p. front. (port.) 19½cm.
Introduction signed: Lewis Tappan.
Photocopy. Ann Arbor, University Microfilms, 1969. 432 p.(on double leaves)

NT 0036338 MiU

Tappan, Lewis, 1788-1873, ed.
Memoir of Mrs. Sarah Tappan
see under Tappan, Mrs. Sarah (Homes) 1748-1826.

Tappan, Lewis.
New York, 1846. Dear Sir, A year since, the executive committee of the American and foriegn anti-slavery society, decided to revive and enlarge their operations
see under American and Foreign Anti-Salvery Society.

Tappan, Lewis, 1788-1873.
Proceedings of the session of Broadway tabernacle against Lewis Tappan, with the action of the presbytery and General assembly. New York: For sale at no.143 Nassau Street. 1839.
64 p. 23cm.
"Published by Tappan."-Sabin.Bibl.americana, no.94370.
1. Slavery in the U.S.-Controversial literature-1839. I.t. II. Assn. III. Broadway Tabernacle Anti-Slavery Society, New York.

NNU-W
NT 0036341 MiU-C NBuG MBAt NIC OO DHU MoU NNUT CtY

[Tappan, Lewis] 1788-1873.
Remarks on prisons and prison discipline. Boston, Printed by I. R. Butts and co., 1826.
36 p. 21½cm.
From the Christian examiner, vol. III, no. III.

1. Prisons—U. S. 2. Prisons—Gt. Brit.

9-19953

Library of Congress HV9469.T2

NT 0036342 DLC MB

Slavery E 441 M46 v.153 no.16
Tappan, Lewis, 1788-1873.
Reply to charges brought against the American and Foreign Anti-Slavery Society, &c, &c, &c. By Lewis Tappan...with an introduction by John Scoble. London, R. Barrett, printer, 1852.
24 p. 23cm.
May anti-slavery pamphlets, v. 153.
1. American and Foreign Anti-Slavery Society. I. Ti le.

NT 0036343 NIC DHU MWA OClWHi NNC

Tappan, Lewis, 1788-1873.
A side-light on Anglo-American relations, 1839-1858, furnished by the correspondence of Lewis Tappan and others with the British and foreign anti-slavery society, edited, with introduction and notes, by Annie Heloise Abel ... and Frank J. Klingberg ... [Lancaster, Pa.] The Association for the study of negro life and history, incorporated, 1927.
vii, 407 p. 24cm.
Running title: The Tappan papers.

1. Slavery in the U. S.—Anti-slavery movements. 2. Slavery in Great Britain—Anti-slavery movements. 3. British and foreign anti-slavery society, London. 4. American and foreign anti-slavery society. 5. Gt. Brit.—Relations (general) with U. S. 6. U. S.—Relations (general) with Gt. Brit. I. Abel, Annie Heloise, 1873- ed. II. Klingberg, Frank Joseph, 1883- joint ed. III. Association for the study of negro life and history, inc. IV. Title. V. Title: The Tappan papers.

28-12379

Library of Congress E449.T175

OU OO ViU WaU ViHaI OCl
NT 0036345 DLC OrP DHU WaS OrPS MoSW PP PU NcD MH-L

E458.1 T28
[Tappan, Lewis,] 1788-1873.
The war: its cause and remedy. [New York, 1861]
4p. 13cm. in 15cm.
DLC: YA24462
With this is bound his: Immediate emancipation ... [New York, 1861]
1. U. S.-Hist.-Civil war.-Causes.
2. Slavery in the U. S.-Emancipation.
a.a. Tappan, Lewis, 1788-1873.

NT 0036346 NBuG OClWHi DLC NN

Tappan, Lucy.
Topical notes on American authors, by Lucy Tappan ... New York, Boston [etc.] Silver, Burdett, and company, 1896.
334 p. 19ᶜᵐ.
"General reference books": p. 9-11.

1. Authors, American.

Library of Congress   PS94.T3   12-39219

NT 0036347   DLC NN NcD MtU PPT OClUr OCl MB MiU

Tappan, Lucy
Topical notes on American authors.
N.Y., Silver Burdett, 1898.

NT 0036348   PPCCH MB

TAPPAN, Mary S.
The maid of Monmouth ; or, restitution.
N. Y. Nesbitt & co. 1851. 53 pp. 8°.
A story of 1774.

NT 0036349   MB ICU

Tappan, Mason Weare, 1817-1886.
Concord railroad corporation v. George Clough. Closing argument of Hon. Mason W. Tappan, counsel for defendant, delivered before the board of referees, at Concord, N. H., January 1, 1869. Concord, The People steam press, 1869.
112 p. 22½ᶜᵐ.

I. Concord railroad corporation. II. Clough, George.   A 15-2304

Title from Bureau of   Railway Economics. Printed by L. C.

NT 0036350   DBRE MH-L

973.66   Tappan, Mason Weare, 1817-1886.
T16m   Modern "democracy", the ally of slavery.
Speech of Hon. M. W. Tappan, of New Hampshire, in the House of representatives, July 29, 1856.
[New York, Greeley & McElrath, 1856]
15p. 22cm.

Caption title.

1. Campaign literature, 1856--Republican. 2. Slavery in the U.S.--Controversial literature--1856.

NT 0036351   IU PPL PHi TNF NNC

E   Tappan, Mason Weare, 1817-1886.
449   Modern "democracy," the ally of slavery.
T175   Speech of Hon. M. W. Tappan, of New Hampshire, in the House of Representatives, July 29, 1856. [Washington, Buell and Blanchard, printers, 1856.]
15 p. 23cm.
DLC: YA5000J17

1. Slavery in the U. S.--Controversial literature--1856.   I. Title.

NT 0036352   NIC MoKU PHi PU DLC MWA Nh OClWHi NN

Tappan, Mason Weare, 1817-1886.
Slavery agitation-nullification-the Lecompton constitution, speech delivered in the House of Representatives. March 31, 1858. n. p., n. d.

NT 0036353   Nh MBAt

TAPPAN Mason W[eare], 1817-1886.
Speech of Hon. Mason W. Tappan, president of the Republican State Convention, held at Concord September 14, 1866. Concord, Republican Press Association, 1886.

pp. 7.

NT 0036354   MH

Tappan, Mason Weare, 1817-1886.
Speech of Mr. M. W. Tappan in the House of Representatives July 29, 1806
see his   Modern Democracy, the alley of Slavery.

Tappan, Mason Weare, 1817-1886.
The union as it is, and the constitution as our fathers made it: speech of Hon. Mason W. Tappan, of N.H., delivered in the House of Representatives, U. S., February 5, 1861. [Washington, D. C., National Republican Office, 1861.]
7 p.
DLC: YA5000J17

NT 0036356   GEU NIC MH OClWHi DLC

JX1977   Tappen, Paul Wilbur, 1911-
.A2
ST/SOA/
SD/1,etc.   **United Nations.** *Dept. of Social Affairs.*
Comparative survey on juvenile delinquency. New York, United Nations Dept. of Social Affairs, Division of Social Welfare, 1952-53.

Tappan, Paul Wilbur, 1911-   *ed.*
Contemporary correction. 1st ed. New York, McGraw-Hill, 1951.
xvii, 434 p. illus. 24 cm. (McGraw-Hill series in sociology and anthropology)
Includes bibliographies.

1. Prisons.   I. Title.

HV8751.T3   365.6   51-7319 ‡

MiU TU DNLM
NT 0036358   DLC FMU MsU CU-I IEN CaOTP MB NN CU TxU

Tappan, Paul Wilbur, 1911-
Delinquent girls in court, a study of the Wayward minor court of New York [by] Paul Wilbur Tappan ... New York, Columbia university press, 1947.
xvi, 265 p., 1 l. 22ᶜᵐ.
Thesis (J. Sc. D.)--Columbia university, 1945.
Published also without thesis note.
Vita.
Bibliography : p. [243]-251.

1. New York (City) Girl's term. 2. Juvenile delinquency—New York (City) 3. Prostitution—New York (City)   I. Title.
HV9094.N5T3   364.52   A 47-2370
Columbia univ. Libraries
for Library of Congress   [3]†

NT 0036359   NNC NIC DLC

Tappan, Paul Wilbur, 1911-
Delinquent girls in court, a study of the Wayward minor court of New York [by] Paul W. Tappan. New York, Columbia university press, 1947.
xvi, 265 p. 22ᶜᵐ.
Issued also as thesis (J. Sc. D.) Columbia university.
Bibliography : p. [243]-251.
1. New York (City) Girl's term. 2. Juvenile delinquency—New York (City) 3. Prostitution—New York (City)   I. Title.
HV9094.N5T3 1947a   364.52   47-3254

ICU TxU ViU-L TxU NcD NcGU ScU PLF
NT 0036360   DLC ICarbS PU-PSW PSt OrU-L CU MB ICJ

Law   Tappan, Paul Wilbur, 1911-

New Jersey. *Commission on the Habitual Sex Offender.*
The habitual sex offender; report and recommendations of the Commission on the Habitual Sex Offender as formulated by Paul W. Tappan, technical consultant. [Trenton, 1950]

Tappan, Paul Wilbur, 1911-
Juvenile delinquency. 1st ed. New York, McGraw-Hill Book Co., 1949.
x, 613 p. illus. 24 cm. (McGraw-Hill publications in sociology)
Bibliography : p. 581-602.

1. Juvenile delinquency.

HV9069.T3   364.36   49-1986*

PBm PPT CU ICU TxU MB OO OU ViU NcRS IdPI
KyU OWorP KEmT CaBVaU WaU-L CaBVa InAndC-T KU PBL
OrCS Or MtU MtBC AU NIC KyU-A MiU OrPS NBuC NBuU
NT 0036362   DLC WaWW WaSpG WaSp WaS Wa OrU MU OrP

BX8641
.T17   Tappan, Paul Wilbur, 1911-
Mormon-Gentile conflict; a study of the influence of public opinion on in-group versus out-group interaction with special reference to polygamy. [n.p.] 1939.
[8], 613 l. 29 cm.
Thesis (Ph.D)--University of Wisconsin, 1939.
Bibliographic notes.
Appendix of primary sources.

1. Mormon and Mormonism--Hist. 2. Polygamy. 3. Social interaction.   I. Title.

NT 0036363   IEG

Tappan, Rodolfo Navarrete
see Navarrete Tappan, Rodolfo.

Tappan, Samuel F
Colorado Territory. [Washington, 1866]
13 p. 23½ᶜᵐ.

1. Colorado—Economic conditions.

Library of Congress   F780.T17   4-27745†

NT 0036365   DLC MH LNT

Tappan, *Mrs.* Sarah (Homes) 1748-1826.
Memoir of Mrs. Sarah Tappan: taken in part from the Home missionary magazine, of November, 1828, and printed for distribution among her descendants ... New-York, West & Trow, printers, 1834.
150 p. front. (port.) 19½ᶜᵐ.
Preface signed : L. T. [i. e. Lewis Tappan]
"Family record" : p. 119-150.

1. Tappan family.   I. Tappan, Lewis, 1788-1873, ed.   II. Title.

Library of Congress   BR1725.T25.A4   10-12537 Revised
        [r30c2]   920.7

MB
NT 0036366   DLC CtY OKentU MWA PBL NN WHi NHi NNUT

BV4520
.L65   [Tappan, Sarah (Jackson) Davis]
Letters to a young Christian. By a lady. Boston, American tract society [18—]
174 p. 15cm.
"First pub. in the 'Advocate and guardian'."—Pub. note.

1. Christian life.

NT 0036367   ICU

BV   [Tappan, Sarah (Jackson) Davis]
1551   Letters to a young Christian. By S.J. New-
.L65   York, American female guardian society, 1852.
115 p.

NT 0036368   MiU

[TAPPAN, Mrs. Sarah (JACKSON) DAVIS.]
Letters to a young Christian. By S.J. 4th
ed. N.Y. 1858.

NT 0036369   MH-AH

352.043
T18   Tappan, Th.
Handbuch für die provinzialständische ver
waltung der provinz Hannover Hrsg. von Th.
Tappan...Hannover, Hahn, 1880.
xiv,537 p.   23 cm.

NT 0036370   MiU

Tappan, William, ed.

Homerus.
Pope's translation of Homer's Iliad, books I, VI, XXII, XXIV,
ed. with introduction and notes by William Tappan. Boston,
Ginn & company, 1898.

Tappan, William Bingham, 1794-1849.
All night in prayer [and] Hymns for the closet.
In Newcomb, Harvey. The closet. Boston,
1838. 12 cm. p. 1-2 and p. [151]-160.

NT 0036372   RPB

Tappan, William Bingham, 1794-1849.
*XH   Celebration hymn, on the introduction of the
.80   Cochituate water in Boston, October, 25, 1848.
.225   [Boston, 1848.]
no.38   broadside. 23.5 x 20cm.
Verse by Tappan and George Russell.
On yellow paper.

NT 0036373   MB

TAPPAN, WILLIAM BINGHAM, 1794-1849.
The daughter of the isles, and other poems. By William
B. Tappan. Boston: W.D. Ticknor and Co., 1844. 256 p.
11½cm.

Added engraved t.-p.

775309A. 1. Poetry, American. I. Title.

NT 0036374   NN MH NNC RPB OO CtY CCamarSJ

F865   Tappan, William Bingham, 1794-1849.
T2   For California! [Poem. Boston? Jenks, Printer, 1849?]
x   broadside. 25x20cm.

"Presented in Boston just as I was starting for California":
ms. inscription of J.C. Chambers with his signature.
"Note" by P. Stow.

NT 0036375   CU-BANC

Tappan, William Bingham, 1794-1849.
Gems of sacred poetry. New-York, H. Dayton, 1860.
ix, 332 p. 19 cm.

I. Title.

PS2969.T6G4   49-30018*

NT 0036376   DLC NNUT NNU-W RPB

Tappan, William Bingham, 1794-1849

Gift of love. [Poems] Boston, J.
Buffum [1849]
128p. col. front. 12 cm.

NT 0036377   RPB NjP NNC NN NNUT MBU-T

TAPPAN, WILLIAM BINGHAM, 1794-1849.
Gift of love.   Boston, G. W. Cottrell [185-?] 128 p.
13cm.

Poems.
Another edition included in the annual publication cataloged under the
same title.

I. Gift books. I. Title.

NT 0036378   NN NNC IaU

Tappan, William Bingham, 1794-1849.
Gift of remembrance, a present for all seasons.
By William B. Tappan.   Boston, Published by J.
Buffum [184-?]
124 p. incl. front. (col.) 11 1|2 cm.

1. Gift-books (annuals, etc.) I. Title.

NT 0036379   CSmH NNC MH RPB Nh CtW OU RPB NNC

Tappan, William Bingham, 1794-1849.
Hymn, to be sung with Rev. Mr. Wood's half-
century sermon.
With-Wood, Benj. Sermon at Upton, June 1,
1846.

NT 0036380   RPB

Tappan, William Bingham, 1794-1849.
*XH   Hymn, written for the opening of the New
.80   Sailor's Home, Nov. 3, 1845.
.225   [Boston, 1845.]
no.33   broadside. 20 x 25cm.
Printed as two facing pages.

Tappan, William Bingham, 1794-1849.
... La Fayette's welcome. A new patriotic
song
see under   Fest, Frederick.

Tappan, William Bingham, 1794-1849.
Late and early poems, by William B. Tappan. Worcester
[Mass.] E. N. Tucker [1849]
256 p. 13¼cm.

I. Title.

                                              31-12876
Library of Congress   PS2969.T6L3

NT 0036383   DLC MWA NN MH PU CSmH CtY IaU NcU

283.42   Tappan, William Bingham, 1794-1849.
Zn5t17   The life of Rev. John Newton. Compiled by William B.
Tappan. Revised by the Committee of Publication. Philadelphia,
American Sunday-School Union, 1829 [c1828]
124 p. port. 14 cm.

1. Newton, John, 1725-1807. I. Title.

NT 0036384   N

Tappan, William Bingham, 1794-1849.
Lyric poems. Philadelphia, Ash & Mason,
1826.
140p. 20cm.

Added engraved t.-p.

PPL

NT 0036385   IEN PHi PPPrHi RPB ViU CtW NjP MH ICN

Tappan, William Bingham, 1794-1849.
Lyrics. By William B. Tappan ... Philadelphia, H. C.
Carey and I. Lea; New York, H. C. Carey & co., 1822.
132 p. 19½cm.

Engr. t.-p., with vignette.
"Consists, in part, of pieces written since the publication of my poems
the last spring; the remainder are selected from a volume of my early
metricals published two years since, of which the edition is now exhausted."

Library of Congress   PS2969.T6L8   15-11601

NNC MH PHi NNHist P
NT 0036386   DLC ViU OU WaWW PHC PHi NNUT CtY MWA MB

SPECIAL COLLECTIONS
B612T165
T
1849   Tappan, William Bingham, 1794-1849.
The memento. Boston, G. W. Cottrell [1849]
128 p. 12cm.

Added title-page in colors.
Poems.

NT 0036387   NNC RPB CtY NcU

B   Tappan, William Bingham, 1794-1849.
W7492t   Memoirs of Captain James Wilson. Compiled for
the American Sunday school union, by W. B. Tappan.
Philadelphia, American Sunday school union [1829?]
142p. incl. front., illus. 14½cm.

1. Wilson, James, 1795-1856. I. American Sunday
school union.

NT 0036388   IU ViU PP MWA ViLxW TxU

Tappan, William B[ingham] 1794-1849.
Missions: a poem, delivered at the anniversary of the
Porter rhetorical society in the Theological seminary,
Andover, Sept. 4, 1838. By William B. Tappan. Boston,
Whipple & Damrell, 1838.
32 p. 12cm.

                                              6-18377

NT 0036389   DLC PU MB NNHist

Case
Y   TAPPAN, WILLIAM BINGHAM, 1794-1849.
285   New England, and other poems.   Phila-
.T 161   delphia, Printed for the author, 1819.
108p. front. 15cm.

ICU MH MB PPL NNUT NNHist NNC CSmH MWA DLC
NT 0036390   ICN PPL CtY KyU NNUT IaU RPB CU NN ViU

Tappan, William Bingham, 1794-1849.
Ode.
In- Barnes, Albert. Oration 1835.
Philadelphia.

NT 0036391   RPB

Tappan, William Bingham, 1794-1849.
Original hymn [written for the half-century
celebration of Rev. Isaac Braman
With- Braman, I. Semi-cent. discourse 1847.

NT 0036392   RPB

Tappan, William Bingham, 1794-1849.
Poems, by William B. Tappan ... Philadelphia, J. Crissy, 1822.
3 p. l., ₍v₎-x, ₍11₎-252 p. 18ᶜᵐ.

31-12877

Library of Congress   PS2969.T6 1822

NN NNUT
NT 0036393   DLC MdBP PU ViU DeU MWA MnU CSmH IU MH

SPECIAL COLLECTIONS
B812T165
L33
1834   Tappan, William Bingham, 1794-1849.
The poems of William B. Tappan. Philadelphia, H. Perkins, 1834.
360 p. port. 16cm.

CSmH IU MWA NN RPB ODW MH MiU CtY
NT 0036394   NNC NcD TU NIC PPPrHi PPL ViU ICN PHi

Tappan, William Bingham, 1794-1849.
The poems of William B. Tappan, not contained in a former volume. Philadelphia, H. Perkins; Boston, Perkins and Marvin, 1836.
1 p. l., ₍v₎-xvi, ₍17₎-324 p. 15½ᶜᵐ.
Companion volume to the author's Poems (1834) cf. Publisher's note.
Imperfect? half-title wanting?

31-12879

Library of Congress   PS2969.T6 1836

PU NNHist NNUT MWA NNC NjR
NT 0036395   DLC NNUT OC1 OC1W CoU CU-A MsU PHi ViU

Tappan, William Bingham, 1794-1849.
Poems and lyricks, by William B. Tappan. Boston, Crocker and Ruggles, 1842.
viii, 264 p. 18ᶜᵐ.

31-12878

Library of Congress   PS2969.T6P6

NT 0036396   DLC PU NNUT OU ViU NcU NjR MB ICU

4PS
451   Tappan, William Bingham, 1794-1849.
Poetry of life. Boston, C. H. Peirce, 1848.
304 p.

ViU CtY
NT 0036397   DLC-P4 NjP RPB NNU-W NNUT NN ICN OU MH

811
T175po   Tappan, William Bingham, 1794-1849.
Poetry of life. Hartford, S. Andrus, 1850 ₍c1847₎.
304 p. illus. 17 cm.

NT 0036398   NcU CtY RPB

Tappan, William Bingham, 1794-1849.
Poetry of the heart, by William B. Tappan. Boston, J. Buffum ₍*1845₎.
128 p. incl. col. front. 12ᶜᵐ.

I. Title.

10-23263

Library of Congress   PS2969.T6P7

NT 0036399   DLC TU NcD MWA

Za
T165
845p   Tappan, William Bingham, 1794-1849
Poetry of the heart, by William B. Tappan.
Worcester, E. N. Tucker ₍c1845₎
256p. 11½cm.
Added col. t.-p.

NT 0036400   CtY MB RPB

BARRETT Tappan, William Bingham, 1794-1849.
Poetry of the heart. Troy [N.Y.] Merriam, 1846.

NT 0036401   ViU RPB NcD

Tappan, William Bingham, 1794-1849.
The poet's tribute. Poems of William B. Tappan. Boston, D. S. King and Crocker & Brewster, 1840.
3 p. l., ₍5₎-325 p. front. (port.) 18ᶜᵐ.
Added t.-p., engraved, with vignette.

I. Title.

31-12880

Library of Congress   PS2969.T6 1840

MiU OO NcD CSmH IU MH
NT 0036402   DLC OKentU ViU NBuG CtY OU MWA PU OCH

PS2969
T6S2   Tappan, William Bingham, 1794-1849.
Sacred and miscellaneous poems: by William B. Tappan. Boston, Benjamin B. Mussey; London, Chapman, brothers, 1847₍c1846₎
ix₍1₎p., 14₍, ₎332p. 18½cm.
Added t.-p., illum.
"This volume is the second of a series, comprising my revised poems; of which, 'Poetry of the heart,' published a year since, is the first"; p. ₍X₎

ICN
NT 0036403   NBuG RPB PU NcA-S ViU CSmH NBuG CtY TU

Tappan, William Bingham, 1794-1849.
Sacred and miscellaneous poems: by William B. Tappan. Boston, B. B. Mussey and co., 1848.
ix [2] 332 p. 18 cm.
Added colored t.-p.

NT 0036404   NNU-W OU NN

Tappan, William Bingham, 1794-1849.
Songs of Judah, and other melodies. By William B. Tappan ... Philadelphia: Published by S. Potter & co. 87 Chesnut street. 1820. ₍Wm. Brown, printer₎
3 p. l., ₍v₎-xi, 204 p. 15ᶜᵐ.
Added t.-p., engraved, with vignette.
With this are bound: Hymns, selected from various authors, for the use of the Unitarian church in Washington. Washington, 1821; and Mengwe; a tale of the frontier. A poem ₍by Samuel J. Bayard₎ Philadelphia, 1825.

I. Title.

31-12881

Library of Congress   PS2969.T6S6

PPL PPHi
NT 0036405   DLC PHi PPL ViU ICN MeB NcU MWA MH NNUT

Tappan, William Bingham, 1794-1849.
The Sunday school and other poems. By William B. Tappan. Boston and Cambridge, J. Munroe and company, 1848.
3 p. l., ₍v₎-x p., 1 l., ₍13₎-251 p. 18ᶜᵐ.
Added t.-p. in colors.
Libby catalogue lists this as the 1st ed.

Title.

1-10784

Library of Congress   PS2969.T6S8

NT 0036406   DLC CtY MH NN

Tappan, N.Y. Protestant Dutch Reformed church

see

Tappan, N.Y. Reformed church

Tappan, N.Y. Reformed church
The marriage records of the Reformed Dutch churches of Tappan & Clarkstown, Rockland co., N.Y. 1694-1831. Copied, and slightly re-arranged, from the translation made by the Rev. David Cole, D. D., with notes by Walter Kenneth Griffin... ₍New York, 1909₎ 195 p. front. 36cm. ₍Griffin manuscripts. v. 1₎
In manuscript.
Several pages blank.

475142. 1. Tappan, N.Y.—Geneal.   2. Rockland county, N.Y.—Geneal.
I. Cole, David, 1822-1903, tr.   II. Griffin, Walter Kenneth, d. 1912.
III. Clarkstown Reformed church,   West Nyack, N.Y.   *Card revised*
N.Y.P.L.   January 31, 1945

NT 0036408   NN

Tappan, N. Y. Reformed church.
Record of marriages ₍1699-1824₎ from the Protestant Reformed Dutch church at Tappan, Rockland Co., New York. Translated from the Dutch by Dr. D. S. Cole. Copied from his original translation Sept. 1909. ₍n. p., 1924?₎
2 p. l., 55 numb. l. 28 x 21½ᶜᵐ.
Autographed from type-written copy.
Copied under the direction of, and verified by Florence E. Youngs.
1. Registers of births, etc.—Tappan, N. Y.   I. Cole, David, 1822-1903,
tr. II. Youngs, Mrs. Florence Evelyn (Pratt) 1868-   III. Title.
25-25166

Library of Congress   F129.T17T2

NT 0036409   DLC

Tappan, N. Y. Reformed church.
Two hundred and fifty years of service, 1694-1944 ... Tappan, N. Y., Tappan Reformed church ₍1944₎
2 p. l., 57, ₍1₎ p., 1 l. illus. (incl. ports.) 26ᶜᵐ.
"Four hundred copies ... Number 18."
By Howard C. Schade.

45-18215

Library of Congress   BX9531.T3A5
                        ₍2₎   285.7747

NT 0036410   DLC MH-AH

Tappan & Bradfords, publisher.
Map of Watertown, Mass. Surveyed by order of the town, 1850. Surveyors S. D. Eaton, Ellridge Whiting. Boston, Tappan & Bradfords Lith., 1850.
27.5 x [   ] in.

NT 0036411   MH MB

TAPPAN & McKILLOP.
The commercial agency annual for 1857. New York, 1857.

NT 0036412   MH

Tappan Junior High School, Ann Arbor, Mich.
see Ann Arbor, Mich. Tappan Junior High School.

Ndy98
S9
+T165b   Tappan stove company.
Annual report ...
₍Mansfield, Ohio₎
18-28cm.

1942 has title: Balance sheet.

NT 0036414   CtY

Tapparelli, Costanza (Alfieri di Sostegno) *marchesa d'Azeglio*
   see Azeglio, Costanza (Alfieri di Sostegno) Tapparelli, *marchesa d', d.* 1862.

Tapparelli, Luigi, 1793-1862.
   see   Tapparelli d'Azeglio, Luigi, 1793-1867.

Tapparelli, Massimo, *marchese d'Azeglio*
   see Azeglio, Massimo Tapparelli, *marchese d'*, 1798-1866.

Tapparelli, Roberto, *marchese d'Azeglio*
   see
Azeglio, Roberto Tapparelli, *marchese* d', 1790-1862.

Tapparelli, Vittorio Emanuele, *marchese d'Azeglio*.
   See
Azeglio, Vittorio Emanuele Tapparelli, marchese d', 1816-1890.

271.83
T161   **Tapparelli d'Azeglio, Luigi,** 1793-1862
   Carteggi del p. Luigi Tapparelli d'Azeglio della Compagnia de Gesù, pubblicati per cura di Pietro Pirri. ¡Torino, Fratelli Bocca, 1932;
   802 p. front. (port.) illus. 27ᶜᵐ. (*Added t.-p.:* R. Deputazione sovra gli studi di storia patria per le antiche provincie e la Lombardia. Biblioteca di storia italiana recente (1800-1870) vol. xiv)
   "Bibliografia": p. ¡25;-56.

   1. Tapparelli d'Azeglio, Luigi, 1793-1862—Bibliography. I. Pirri, Pietro, ed.
   Title from Univ. of Minn.   A C 36-2458
   Library of Congress   [DG551.D5 vol. 14]
    ¡2¡   (945.08)

NT 0036420   MnU MoSU

TAPPARELLI D'AZEGLIO, Luigi, *1793-1862.*
Corso elementare di natural diritto ad uso scuole. 2a ed. Napoli, 1850.

NT 0036421   MH-L

BJ
1133   *Tapparelli d'Azeglio, Luigi, 1793-1862.*
.T17   Corso elementare di natural diritto ad uso
1851 delle scuole. Prima edizione libornese. Livorno, V. Mansi, 1851.
   376 p. 16 cm.

   First published 1843.

   1. Ethics.

NT 0036422   DCU

Tapparelli d'Azeglio, Luigi, 1793-1862.
   Curso de direito natural, primeira edição
brasileira do Pe. Nicolau P. Rossetti, S.J.
São Paulo, Brasil, Editora Anchieta, s.a., 1945,
   549 p. 21 cm. ([Anchietana, estante vii ... v. 1])
   Translation from Italian Saggio di Diritto naturale appoggiato sul fatto.

NT 0036423   DPU

BV
107   Tapparelli d'Azeglio, Luigi, S.J., 1793-1862.
.T171   Cours élémentaire de droit naturel à l'usage
F8   des écoles. 5. éd., considérablement augmenté
   par l'auteur, traduite de l'italien par M.
   l'abbé C.-A. Ozanam. Paris, Leipzig, Tournai,
   H. Casterman, 1863.
   xvi, 416 p. 19cm.

   1. Natural law.

NT 0036424   DCU CtY

4K   Tapparelli d'Azeglio, Luigi, 1793-1862.
1332   Curso elemental de derecho natural
   para uso de las escuelas. Traducido
   de la 6. ed., enriquecida por el autor
   con nuevas notas. Paris, Libraria de
   A. Bouret, 1875.
   431 p.

NT 0036425   DLC-P4 MH-L

Tapparelli d'Azeglio, Luigi, 1793-1862.
   ... De l'origine du pouvoir; traduit de l'italien
par le R. P. Pichot ... Paris, P. Lethielleux
[1896]
   viii, 356 p. 20 cm.
   1. Natural law. 2. Law-philosophy. I. Title.

NT 0036426   MBtS

4JC   Tapparelli d'Azeglio, Luigi, 1793-1862.
355   Della nazionalità; breve scrittura.
   Genova, Tip. de' Fratelli Ponthenier,
   1847.
   38 p.

NT 0036427   DLC-P4

4JC-   Tapparelli d'Azeglio, Luigi, 1793-1862.
287   Della nazionalità, breve. Rivista ed accresciuta notabilmente dall'autore con una risposta del
   medesimo, alle osservazioni di Vicenzo Gioberti.
   Edizione 2., con note aggiunte dall'editore.
   Firenze, P. Ducci, 1849.
   87 p.

NT 0036428   DLC-P4 MH

Div.S. Tapparelli d'Azeglio, Luigi, 1793-1862.
Rom
Coll   Discorso in onore dell'apostolo San Paolo
   recitato nella pia unione del clero romano sotto
   l'invocazione di esso apostolo delle genti il
   di 27 gennaio 1851 ... Torino, Tipografia
   nazionale di G. Biancardi compagni, 1851.
   23 p. 21cm.

NT 0036429   NcD

TAPPARELLI D'AZEGLIO, Luigi, *1793-1862.*
Ensayo teórico de derecho natural apoyado en los hechos. Traducido . . . por Juan Manuel Orti y Lara. Madrid, 1866-68.

   4 v.

NT 0036430   MH-L NcU

Tapparelli d'Azeglio, Luigi, 1793-1862.
   Ensayo teorico de derecho natural, apoyado en
los hechos, por el R. P. Luis Taparelli ... tr.
directamente de la última ed. Italiana hecha en Roma,
y corr. y aum. por su autor, por D. Juan Manuel
Orti Y Lara ... 2 ed. Madrid, Nueva Librería é
Impr. de San José, 1884.
   3 v. 21.5 cm.
   "Epilogo razonado del ensayo de derecho natural"
t. 2., p. 475-549.

NT 0036431   CtY-L

JF   Tapparelli d'Azeglio, Luigi, S.J., 1793-1862.
54   Esame critico degli ordini rappresentativi
.T17   nella società moderna, per Luigi Taparelli.
   Roma, Tip. della Civiltà Cattolica, 1854.
   2 v. 23 cm.
   Bibliographical footnotes.

   1. Representative government and representation. 2. Political science. 3. Politics,
practical. I. Title.

NT 0036432   DCU

Tapparelli d'Azeglio, Luigi, 1793-1862.
   Essai sur les principes philosophiques de l'économie politique; recueil d'articles pub. par le P. Taparelli d'Azeglio
dans la Civiltà cattolica, de 1856 à 1862. Traduction française inédite, avec introd., bibliographie et notes par Robert
Jacquin. Paris, P. Lethielleux, 1943.
   127 p. 22 cm.
   Robert Jacquin's thèse complémentaire—Univ. de Paris.
   "Bibliographie": p. ¡11¡-15.

   1. Economics. I. Jacquin, Robert.

   HB177.T3   49-44877*

NT 0036433   DLC MH ICN IMunS CtY MoSU-D

Tapparelli d'Azeglio, Luigi, 1793-1862.
   Essai sur les principes philosophiques de l'économie poli-
tique; recueil d'articles pub. par le P. Taparelli d'Azeglio
dans la Civiltà cattolica, de 1856 à 1862. Traduction fran-
çaise inédite, avec introd., bibliographie et notes par Robert
Jacquin. Paris, P. Lethielleux, 1943. 127 p. 22cm.
   Film reproduction. Negative.
   Robert Jacquin's thèse complémentaire—Univ. de Paris.
   "Bibliographie": p. ¡11¡-15.

   1. Economics, 1858-1889—Italian authors. I. Jacquin R.

NT 0036434   NN

BV
107   Tapparelli d'Azeglio, Luigi, S.J., 1793-1862.
.T17   Essai théorique de droit naturel. Traduit
F8   de L'italien d'après la dernière édition avec
   approbation de l'auteur. Paris, Tournai, H.
   Casterman, 1857.
   4 v. 24cm.

   1. Natural law.

NT 0036435   DCU OCX PV

Tapparelli, d' Azeglio, Luigi, 1793-1862.
   Essai théorique de droit naturel, basé sur les
faits, par le R. P. Taparelli d'Azeglio ... Tr. de
l'italien d'après la dernière éd. avec approbation
de l'auteur. 2. éd. Tournai, Vve H. Casterman
[etc., etc.] 1875.
   2 v. 27 cm.
   "Le P. Onclair eut une part à cette traduction
faite par plusieurs Jesuites de la province de
Belgique" Backer, Bibl. de la Comp. de Jésus,
éd. Sommervogel. t. v. col. 1918.

NT 0036436   CtY

Tapparelli d'Azeglio, Luigi, 1793-1862.
   Essai théorique de droit naturel, basé sur les faits, par le
R. P. Taparelli d'Azeglio ... Tr. de l'italien d'après la der-
nière éd. avec approbation de l'auteur. 3. éd. Tournai, Vᵛᵉ H.
Casterman; ¡etc., etc.¡ 1883.
   2 v. 27ᶜᵐ.
   "Le P. Onclair eut une part à cette traduction faite par plusiers
Jesuites de la province de Belgique."—Backer, Bibl. de la Comp. de
Jésus, éd. Sommervogel. t. v. col. 1918.

   1. Natural law. 2. Social sciences. 3. International law and relations.
   I. Onclair, Auguste, 1822— tr.

                                     9—32823
   Library of Congress   JC236.T35 1883

NT 0036437   DLC CU-L ViU

Tapparelli d'Azeglio, Luigi, 1793–1862.
Exámen crítico del gobierno representativo en la sociedad moderna, por el R. P. Luis Taparelli...traducido del italiano por el Pensamiento español... Madrid: Imprenta de el Pensamiento español, 1866–67. 2 v. 20cm.

60765–6. 1. Government, Representa-   tive.   *Revised*
N. Y. P. L.   *December 22, 1936*

NT 0036438   NN MH WaPS NjP

Tapparelli d'Azeglio, Luigi, 1793–1862.
... Examen critique des gouvernements représentatifs dans la société moderne, tr. de l'italien par le P. Pichot, s. J. ... Paris, P. Lethielleux [1905]
4 v. 21½ᶜᵐ.

Vol. 1 has caption title: De l'origine du pouvoir; v. 2 has caption and running title: Principes théoriques des gouvernements modernes; v. 3 and 4 have caption title and v. 3 has also running title: Principes des gouvernements modernes. Application.
Pichot first published v. 1 under title: De l'origine du pouvoir. Tr. de l'italien par le R. P. Pichot. Paris, Lethielleux, 1896.

CONTENTS.—t. I. Unité social. Suffrage universel. Origine du pouvoir. Émancipation des peuples adultes.—t. II. Liberté. Liberté de la presse. De l'enseignement. Naturalisme. Félicité sociale. Division des pouvoirs.—t. III. Application des principes. La nation modernisée. La législature. Le pouvoir exécutif. La patrie. L'état.—t. IV. Administration ou Économie pratique. Force armée. Pouvoir judiciaire. Épilogue. Appendice: Examen de l'opuscule de M. de Montalembert: Des intérêts catholiques au XIXᵉ siècle.

1. Montalembert, Charles Forbes René de Tryon, comte de, 1810–1870. Des intérêts catholiques au XIXᵉ siècle. 2. Representative government and representation. I. Pichot, ——, s. J., tr.

Library of Congress   JF54.T2   6—15738

NT 0036440   DLC ICJ

Tapparelli d'Azeglio, Luigi, 1793–1862.
Influence of Catholic prayer on civilization, tr. by Jeremiah Cummings. Boston, 1848.
36 p. O.
From Brownson's quarterly review.

NT 0036441   RPB

Tapparelli d'Azeglio, Luigi, S.J., 1793–1862.
La preghiera cattolica considerata in ordine alla civiltà de' popoli; ragionamento ... letto nell'Accademia di religione cattolica il giorno 9 luglio 1846. Roma, Tipografia della belle arti, 1846.
46 p. 23 cm. ([Pamphlets, v. 40])
"Estratto dagli Annali delle scienze religiose, serie II, fasc. VIII."

NT 0036442   PLatS

Tapparelli d'Azeglio, Luigi, 1793–1862.
Saggio teoretico di diritto naturale, appoggiato sul fatto. Opera del P. Luigi Taparelli... Livorno, V. Mansi, 1845.
704 p. 23.5 cm.

NT 0036443   CtY

Tapparelli d'Azeglio, Luigi, 1793–1862.
Saggio teoretico di diritto naturale, appoggiato sul fatto, opera del p. Luigi Taparelli ... corretta ed accresciuta dall' autore ... Napoli, Tipografia Tramater, 1844–45.
5 v. in 2. 19½ᶜᵐ.
"Una seconda edizione."—A chi legge.
"Catalogo delle edizioni di autori citati": v. 5, p. [210]–212.

1. Natural law. 2. Social sciences. 3. International law and relations. I. Title.
                                 36–21765

Library of Congress   JC236.T3 1844   320.1

NT 0036444   DLC MH-L PV OC1JC

Tapparelli d'Azeglio, Luigi, S.J., 1793–1862.
Saggio teoretico di dritto naturale, appoggiato sul fatto. Corretta ed accresciuta dall' autore. Napoli, All'Uffizio della Civiltà Cattolica, 1850.
2 v. 24 cm.

BV 107 .T17 1850

1. Natural law.

NT 0036445   DCU MoSU

Tapparelli d'Azeglio, Luigi, 1793–1862
Saggio teoretico di dritto naturale appoggiato sul fatto; opera corretta ed accresciuta dall' autore. Roma, Civiltà cattolica, 1855.
2 v. 25 cm.

JC 236 .T3

1. Natural law. 2. Social sciences. 3. International law.

NT 0036446   WU DLC-P4

Tapparelli d'Azeglio, Luigi, 1793–1862.
Saggio teoretico di dritto naturale appoggiato sul fatto, opera del p. Luigi Taparelli, D. C. D. G., con molte e considerevoli aggiunzioni fatte dall' autore nell' ultima edizione di Roma del 1856 sulla quale è stata fedelmente eseguita la presente sesta edizione ... Palermo, A spese degli editori, 1857.
2 v. 24ᵐ.

1. Natural law. 2. Social sciences. 3. International law.
                                   35–17874

Library of Congress   JC236.T3 1857
                 [a45b1]   320.1

NT 0036447   DLC MiDU CLg DCU

Tapparelli d'Azeglio, Luigi, 1793–1862.
Saggio teoretico di dritto naturale appoggiato sul fatto; opera. Corretta ed accresciuta dall' autore. 2. edizione con un'appendice. Prato, Tip. Giachetti, figlio, 1883.
2 v.

4JC- 284

NT 0036448   DLC-P4 PLatS MBtS MH-L

Tapparelli d'Azeglio, Luigi, 1793–1862.
Saggio teoretico di dritto naturale appoggiato sul fatto; opera del P. Luigi Taparelli ... cor. ed accresciuta dall' autore. 3. ed. Roma, Civiltà cattolica, 1900.
2 v. 24ᶜᵐ.
"Della vita e degli scritti dell' autore": vol. 1, p. [v]–xii.

1. Natural law. 2. Social sciences. 3. International law and relations. I. Title.
                                   13—16251

Library of Congress   JC236.T4

NT 0036449   DLC

Tapparelli d'Azeglio, Luigi, 1793–1862.
Saggio teoretico di dritto naturale, appoggiato sul fatto. Quarta edizione. Roma, Civiltà Cattolica, 1928.
v. 24 cm.

JC 236 T4 1928

1. Natural law. 2. Social sciences. 3. International law and relations.

NT 0036450   IMunS DLC-P4

Tapparelli d'Azeglio, Luigi, 1793–1862
Saggio teoretico di dritto naturale appoggiato sul fatto; opera del P. Luigi Taparelli. 8. edizione riveduta quinta dell' ultima corretta e accresciuta dall' autore. [Roma] "La Civiltà Cattolica" [1949]
2 v. front. (port.) 25 cm. (I Trattati Cattolici filosofia, 1)

JC236 T4 1949

NT 0036451   RPB MiDW MoSU-D IMunS MBtS

Tapparelli d'Azeglio, Luigi, 1793 –1862.
Sintesi di diritto naturale. Bologna, N. Zanichelli, 1940.
74 p.

4K 2267

NT 0036452   DLC-P4 MH-L MBtS

Tapparelli d'Azeglio, Luigi, 1793–1862.
Versuch eines auf Erfahrung begründeten Naturrechts, von Aloys Taparelli. Aus dem Italienischen übersetzt von Fridolin Schöttl und Carl Rinecker. Regensburg, G.J. Manz, 1845.
2 v.

JC236 T2314

Translation of Saggio teoretico di dritto naturale appoggiato sul fatto.
Bibliographical footnotes.

1. Natural law. 2. Law – Philosophy. 3. Sociological jurisprudence. 4. Individuality. 5. International law.

NT 0036453   CU

Tapparelli d'Azeglio, Luis
     see   Tapparelli d'Azeglio, Luigi, 1793–1862.

TAPPARELLI D'AZEGLIO, Massimo, marchese,1798– 1866.

     See AZEGLIO, Massimo Tapparelli, marchese d'.

Tapparelli d'Azeglio, Vittorio Emanuele, *marchese*
     see
Azeglio, Vittorio Emanuele Tapparelli, *marchese* d', 1816–1890.

TAPPARI, Giovanni
Ricordi al candidato pel grado di oculistica. Padova, Tip. Penada, 1841.
75 p.

WW T175r 1841

NT 0036457   DNLM

Tappari, Pietro, joint ed.

Italy. *Laws, statutes, etc.*
Codice finanziario del regno d'Italia. Raccolta sistematica di tutte le leggi, regolamenti, decreti e circolari sulle imposte dirette e indirette e sulle tasse (diritti) con notizie illustrative dei singoli istituti finanziari sotto l'aspetto storico, economico e giuridico e con un' appendice sui tributi locali, per cura degli avvocati prof. Sebastiano Gianzana, Francesco Bo e Pietro Tappari ... Torino, Unione tipografico-editrice, 1896–98.

Tappari, Pietro, joint author.

Bo, Francesco.
La legislazione mineraria dell' Italia, ordinata ed annotata dagli avvocati Francesco Bo e Pietro Tappari ... Roma [etc.] Unione tipografico-editrice, 1890.

Tappari, Pietro, *dramatist.*
Non è tutto oro quel che luce; commedia di un atto solo del dottore Pietro Tappari di Badia. [Venezia, Rizzi, 1821]
48 p. 16cm. (Giornale teatrale. fasc. XXVII [pt. 3])

PG 1231 .A8 G5 fasc.27

NT 0036460   MdBJ

Tappari, Pietro, dramatist.
La pittura, ode... pubbl. per le nozze
Crescini-Meneghini.   Padova, 1826.
2 p.l., vii-xix p., 1 l.   18 cm.
1. Crescini, Jacopo. 2. Meneghini, Adelaide.

NT   0036461   CtY

Tapparone Canefri, Cesare, 1838-1891.
Analisi della dichiarazione...   Genova,
n. d.

NT   0036462   DNLM

QL428   Tapparone Canefri, Cesare, 1838-1891.
.5   Contribuzioni per una fauna malacologica
.N5T2   delle isole Papuane; ...   [Genova, 1874-]

NT   0036463   DLC

Canefri, Cesare, 1838-1891.
Esame della lettera del Sigr.   Genova, n. d.
8 p.

NT   0036464   DNLM

Tapparone Canefri, Cesare, 1838-1891.
Études Malacologiques, par C. T. Canefri.
1879.
(Museum Pauluccianum)
C. T. v. 15.

NT   0036465   PPAN

QL   Tapparone Canefri, Cesare, 1838-1891.
426   Fauna malacologica della Nuova Guinea e delle
.D9   isole adiacenti, per C. Tapparone Canefri. Pte. I.
T18   Molluschi estramarini ... Genova, Tipografia
del R. Istituto Sordo-Muti, 1883.

1 p.l., [5]-313 p.   illus., XI pl., fold. table.   25^{cm}.

1. Mollusca--New Guinea. I. Title.

NT   0036466   MiU DSI

Tapparone Canefri, Cesare, 1838-
Intorno ad una nuova specie di *Nephrops*, genere di
crostacei decapodi macruri; nota di Cesare Tapparone
Canefri. Torino, Stamperia reale, 1873.
7 p.   pl.   31^{cm}.
"Estr. dalle Memorie della Reale accademia delle scienze di Torino,
serie II., tom. XVII."

1. Nephrops.

Library of Congress   QL444.D3T2   6-37019†

NT   0036467   DLC

Tapparone Canefri, Cesare, joint author.

Lessona, Michele, 1823-1894.
Nota sulla *Macrocheira kaempferi* Sieb. e sopra una
nuova specie del genere *Dichelapsis*; di M. Lessona e
C. Tapparone-Canefri. [Torino] Stamperia reale di G. B.
Paravia e c.. 1874.

Tapparone Canefri, Cesare, 1838-1891.
Storia della malattia del pittore.   Genova,
n. d.
7 p.

NT   0036469   DNLM

Tapparone Canefri, Cesare, 1838-1891.
Viaggio dei signori O. Antinori, O. Beccari ed A. Issel
nel mar Rosso, nel territorio dei Bogos, e regioni circo-
stanti durante gli anni 1870-71. Studio monografico sopra i muricidi del mar Rosso di C. Tapparone Canefri.
Genova, Tip. del R. Istituto sordo-muti, 1875.
76 p.   pl.   25^{cm}.
"Estratto dagli Annali del Mus. civ. di st. nat. di Genova, vol. VII, 1875."

1. Muricidae. 2. Mollusks—Red Sea.

Library of Congress   QL430.5.M9T2   11-3736

NT   0036470   DLC PPULC PPAN

Tapparone Canefri, Cesare, 1838-1891.
Zoologia del viaggio intorno al globo della regia fregata
Magenta durante gli anni 1865-68. Malacologia (gas-
teropodi, acefali e brachiopodi)   Torino, G. B. Paravia
e comp., 1874.
1 p. l., [5]-161, [9] p.   IV pl.   31^{cm}.
"Estr. dalle Memorie della Reale accademia delle scienze di Torino,
serie II. tom. XXVIII."

1. Mollusks. 2. Brachiopoda. 3. Magenta (Corvette)

Library of Congress   QL406.T17   6-25137†

NT   0036471   DLC PPAN

Tappart, Ruardus
   see
     Tapper, Ruard, 1487-1559.

Tappe, Dr.
Gerbert oder Papst Sylvester II und seine
zeit...   Berlin, 1869.
p. 20-50.   26 cm.
Programm: Die Königstädtische realschule
[Berlin]

NT   0036473   RPB

Tappe, Albrecht, 1914-
Die Eignung der Steinzemente als zahnärzt-
liches Füllungsmaterial. Vergleichende Betrach-
tungen und Versuche über die Eigenschaften der
Phosphat- Silikat- und Steinzemente...
Lengerich i. W. [1938]
Inaug. -diss. - Bonn.
Lebenslauf.
"Literatur": p. 37.

NT   0036474   CtY

Tappe, Alfred
   see   Tappe, Hermann Alfred, 1874-

PG2109   Tappe, August Wilhelm, 1778-1830.
.T2   Erstes russisches grammatisches lesebuch über
die formenlehre; oder: Russische uebersetzungen der
deutschen aufgaben nach den hauptlehren der grammatik in der sprachlehre, von August Wilhelm Tappe
... Zur 5.aufl.der russischen sprachlehre für
Deutsche gehörig.   St.Petersburg[etc.]Beim verfasser,1819.
32 p.   20½^{cm}.   [With his Neue theoretisch-praktische russische sprachlehre für Deutsche.   St.
Petersburg,1819]

NT   0036476   ICU

Tappe,   August Wilhelm, 1778-1830.
Erstes russisches grammatisches Lesebuch über die Formenlehre,
oder: russische Übersetzungen der deutschen Aufgaben nach
den Hauptlehren der Grammatik in der Sprachlehre. Zur 6.
Auflage der russischen Sprachlehre für Deutsche gehörig.
St. Petersburg.   Kray.   1826.   32 pp.   20 cm., in 8s.
No. 2 in 3035.15

M 3809 — Russia. Lang. Grammar. For Germans.

NT   0036477   MB

Tappe, August Wilhelm, 1778-1830.
Karamzin, Nikolai Mikhailovich, 1766-1826.
Geschichte Russlands, nach Karamsin. Aus der urschrift
deutsch bearbeitet, und mit vielen anmerkungen, als erläute-
rungen und zusätzen, begleitet, von August Wilhelm Tappe ...
Dresden und Leipzig, Arnold. 1828-31.

Tappe, August Wilhelm, 1778-1830, ed.
Neue theoretisch-praktische russische sprachlehre für deutsche mit beispielen, als aufgaben
zum uebersetzen aus den deutschen in das Russisc[he]
nach den hauptlehren der grammatik, nebst einem
abrisse der geschichte Russlands, von Dr. August
Wilhelm Tappe.   St. Petersburg, beim verfasser,
in der deutschen hauptschule zu St. Petri; Riga,
bei J. C. G. Hartmann, 1810.
2 v.   plate.
v. 2 has t.-p.: Neues russisches elementar-
lesebuch, für deutsche... 1810.

NT   0036479   PMA

PG2129   Tappe, August Wilhelm, 1778-1830.
.G4   Neue theoretisch-praktische Russische Sprach-
T36   lehre für Deutsche. Zweite verb. und verm. Aufl.
1812   St. Petersburg, beim Verfasser; Riga, bei Hartmann, 1812.
312p.   22cm.

1. Russian language - Text-books for foreigners
- German.

NT   0036480   PSt MH NN

Tappe, August Wilhelm, 1778-1830.
Neue theoretisch-praktische russische
Sprachlehre... 5. verb. u. verm. Aufl.
St. Petersburg, 1819.

NT   0036481   NjP

Tappe,   August Wilhelm   1778-1830.
Neue theoretisch-praktische russische Sprachlehre für Deutsche
mit vielen Beispielen, als Aufgaben zum Uebersetzen aus dem
Deutschen in das Russische und aus dem Russischen in das
Deutsche, nach den Hauptlehren der Grammatik, nebst einem
Abrisse der Geschichte Russlands bis 1826. 6. verbesserte und
vermehrte Auflage.
St. Petersburg. Kray. 1826. xii, 337 pp. 20 cm., in 8s.

M 3809 — Russia. Lang. Grammar. For Germans.

NT   0036482   MB

PG2111   Tappe, August Wilhelm, 1778-1830.
T3   Neue theoretisch-praktische russische Sprachlehre für Deutsche, mit vielen Beispielen, als
Aufgaben zum Uebersetzen aus dem Deutschen in
das Russische und aus dem Russischen in das
Deutsche, nach den Hauptlehren der Grammatik,
nebst einem Abrisse der Geschichte Russlands
bis 1835. 7. verb. und verm. Aufl. St. Petersburg, gedruckt bei K. Kray [etc.], 1835.
352 p. 21^{cm}
Erstes russisches grammatisches Lesebuch

Continued in next column

Continued from preceding column

über die Formenlehre, oder: russische Uebersetzungen der deutschen Aufgaben nach den
Hauptlehren der Grammatik in der Sprachlehre.
Zur 7. Aufl. der russischen Sprachlehre für
Deutsche gehörig.   St. Petersburg, gedruckt
bei K. Kray ⸢etc.⸣ 1835.
32 p. 21ᶜᵐ
Bound with his Neue theoretisch-praktische
russische Sprach-   lehre für Deutsche ...

___Neues russisches Elementar-Lesebuch, für
Deutsche, enthaltend: Sentenzen und Maximen,
Fabeln, Anekdoten, eine geographisch-statis-
tische Uebersicht Russlands, eine Komödie im
Auszuge, Bruchstücke aus Karamsins Schriften
und Aufgaben aus dem Slawonischen. Durchaus
accentuirt, nebst Uebersetzungen, Wörtern und

Phraseologien, als zweiter Theil der theoretisch-praktischen russischen Sprachlehre. 8.
unveränderte Aufl.   St. Petersburg, gedruckt
bei K. Kray ⸢etc.⸣ 1835.
119 p. 21ᶜᵐ
Bound with his Neue theoretisch-praktische
russische Sprachlehre für Deutsche ...
1. Russian lan-   guage - Grammar. 2.
Russian language -✓   Text-books for foreigners - German. 3.   Russian language - Readers. I. Title.]

NT 0036486   CSt MB ICN

Tappe, August Wilhelm, 1778-1830.
Neues Russisches elementar-lesebuch.
St. Petersburg, 1811.
8vo.

NT 0036487   NN

Tappe, ___ August Wilhelm, 1778-1830.
Neues russisches Elementar-Lesebuch, für Deutsche . . . als Theil
der theoretisch-praktischen russischen Sprachlehre. 6. unveran-
derte Auflage.
St. Petersburg. Simonsen & Comp. 1823. 119, (4) pp. 20 cm.,
in 8s.

M3809 — Russia. Lang. Reading-books. For Germans.

NT 0036488   MB

Bonaparte
Collection   Tappe, August Wilhelm, 1778-1830.
No. 12,790
            Neues russisches elementar-lesebuch,
        für Deutsche, enthaltend: sentenzen und
        maximen, fabeln. anekdoten, eine geogra-
        phisch-statistisch uebersicht Russ-
        lands, eine komödie im auszuge, bruch-
        stücke aus Karamsins schriften und auf-
        gaben aus dem slawonischen. Durchaus
        accentuirt, nebst uebersetzungen, wörten
        und phraseologien, als zweiter theil

        der theoretisch-praktischen russischen
        sprachlehre… 8.unveränderte aufl.
        St.Petersburg,1835.   (with his Neue
        theoretisch-praktische russische
        sprachlehre… 1835)

NT 0036489   ICN MH MB

Tappe, David T   b.1649.
    David Tappens Funffzehen jährige curiöse
und denckwürdige auch sehr gefährliche ost-
indianische Reise-Beschreibung / So sich im
Jahr Christi 1667 angefangen / und durch
göttlichen Beystand im 1682ten Jahre
geendet hat / auf vielfältiges Verlangen guter
Freunde zum Druck übergeben./ Hannover und
Wolffenbüttel Zu finden bey G.Freytag,1704.
3p.ℓ.,220[i.e.320]p. 20½cm.
Pages 202-320 wrongly numbered 102-220.

NT 0036490   CtY CU

Tappe, Dietrich August Wilhelm
    see   Tappe, August Wilhelm, 1778-1830.

Tappe, Donald T
    ... The status of beavers in California, by Donald T. Tappe
... ⸢Sacramento, California state printing office⸣ 1942.
59 p. illus. (incl. maps) 23ᶜᵐ.   (California.   Dept. of natural resources.   Division of fish and game.   Game bulletin no. 3)
"Literature cited" : p. 58-59.

1. Beavers.   2. Mammals—California.
                                    43-52661
Library of Congress   SK373.A33 no. 3
                                    ⸤4⸥   (639.1061794) 639.1

NT 0036492   DLC

Tappe, Eberhard, 16th cent.
    see   Tappius, Eberhard, 16th cent.

ar W   Tappe, Erich, 1875-
53492   Die s.g. irregulären Personal-Servituten
no.9   nach Gemeinem Recht, unter besonderer Berück-
          sichtigung des Bürgerlichen Gesetzbuches für
          das Deutsche Reich.   Berlin, Nauck, 1899.
          42 p.   24cm.

          Inaug.-Diss.--Erlangen.

NT 0036494   NIC MH-L ICRL

Tappe, Franz August Wilhelm
                    see
Tappe, Wilhelm, 1842-

Tappe, Friedrich.
    Soziologie der japanischen Familie; Grundanschauungen,
Ethik und Recht des japanischen Familiensystems.   Münster, Westf., Aschendorff ⸢1955⸣
    154 p. 24 cm.   (Schriften des Instituts für Christliche Sozialwis-
senschaften, Bd. 2)
    "Literaturverzeichnis" : p. 148-154.

    1. Family—Japan.   2. Japan—Soc. condit.   I. Title.   (Series:
Münster. Universität.   Institut für Christliche Sozialwissenschaften.
Schriften, Bd. 2)
Duke Univ. Library   A 56-5713
for Library of Congress   ⸤2⸥

         CaBVaU OrU WaU
NT 0036496   NcD NNC DS NN ICU LU RPB CU MiU DLC NBC

Tappe, Georg.
    Deutschlands Entwicklung im Laufe seiner
Geschichte, von Waldtraut Bohm und Gerhard
Strodtkötter.   Bückeburg, E. Fusbahn [c1938]
124 p.

NT 0036497   DLC

Tappe, Georg.
    Kleiner Geschichtsatlas über Deutschlands
Entwicklung für Haus and Schule
    see under   Fusbahn (Ernst) Verlag,
Bückeburg, Ger.

AC   Tappe, Herbert, 1910-
831   Die schwangerschaftunterbrechung aus eugenischer
        und ethischer indikation im geltenden und künftigen
        recht. ... Emsdetten, 1935.   72 p.
            Inaug. Diss. - Göttingen, 1935.
            Lebenslauf.
            Literatur.

NT 0036499   ICRL CtY InU

1889-
Tappe, Georgius. De Philonis libro qui inscribitur Ἀλέξανδρος
ἢ περὶ τοῦ λόγον ἔχειν τὰ ἄλογα ζῷα quaestiones selectae.
Gottingae 1912: Dieterich. 8o S. 8°
Göttingen, Phil. Diss. v. 28. Sept. 1912, Ref. Wendland, Poblenz
[Geb. 7. März 89 Alfeld a. L.; Wöhnort: Hannover: Staatsangeh.: Preußen;
Vorbildung: Gymn. Northeim Reife O. 07; Studium: Freiburg i. B. 1, Bonn 2,
München 1, Göttingen 5 S.; Rig. 14. Febr. 12.]   [U 12. 5461

NT 0036500   ICRL MiU NN MH IU CtY PU

Tappe, Herbert, 1910-
    Die Schwangerschaftsunterbrechung aus
eugenischer und ethischer Indiaktion im geltenden
und künftigen Recht.   Emsdetten, H. & J. Lechte,
1936.
72 p.

NT 0036501   DLC

Tappe, Hermann Alfred, 1874-
    *Zur pharmakologischen Kenntniss einiger
Kondenstationsprodukte des Chlorals.
Lüdenscheid, H. Crone jr., 1904.
52 p. 8°.
Inaug.-diss. - Bonn.

NT 0036502   DNLM MBCo

W 4   TAPPE, Jacob, 1603-1680, praeses
H47   Disputatio inauguralis medica de ileo ... Helmaestadii,
1664   Typis Henningi Mulleri, 1664.
T.1   [44] p. 19 cm.
              Diss. - Helmstedt (B. Horne, respondent)

              L. Horne, Barthold, fl. 1664, respondent

NT 0036503   DNLM

W 4   TAPPE, Jacob, 1603-1680, praeses
H47   Disputatio medica de amore insano ... Helmestadii, Ty-
1661   pis Henning Mulleri, 1661.
T.1   [20] p. 18 cm.
              Diss. - Helmstedt (J. Wollin, respondent)

              L. Wollin, Johann, fl. 1661, respondent

NT 0036504   DNLM

W 4   TAPPE, Jacob, 1603-1680, praeses
H47   Disputatio medica de apoplexia ... Helmestadi, Typis
1663   Henningi Mulleri, 1663.
T.1   [32] p. 20 cm.
              Diss. - Helmstedt (B. Lembken, respondent)

              L. Lembken, Burchard, fl. 1663, respondent

NT 0036505   DNLM

Tappe, Jacob, 1603-1680, praeses.
Disputatio medica de febri ephemera
    see under Heye, Friedrich, respondent.

W 4   TAPPE, Jacob, 1603-1680, praeses
H47   Disputatio medica de hydrophobia ... Helmaestadii, Ty-
1659   pis Henningi Mulleri, 1659.
T.1   [32] p. 18 cm.
              Diss. - Helmstedt (H. Meibom, respondent)

              L. Meibom, Heinrich, 1638-1700, respondent

NT 0036507   DNLM

Tappe, Jacob, 1603-1680, praeses.
Disputatio medica de mania
    see under Huhn, Georg, respondent.

W 4　TAPPE, Jacob, 1603-1680, praeses
H47　　Disputatio medica de melancholica desipientia ...
1652　Helmaestadii, Typis Henningi Mulleri, 1652.
T. 1　　[28] p.　19 cm.
　　　　Diss. — Helmstedt (S. Scheffer, respondent)

　　　I. Scheffer, Sebastian, 1631-1686, respondent

NT　0036509　　DNLM

Tappe, Jacob, 1603-1680, praeses.
　Disputatio medica de phrenitide
　　　see under　Müller, Johann Paul,
resp ondent.

W 4　TAPPE, Jacob, 1603-1680, praeses
H47　　Disputatio medica inauguralis de arthritide ...　Helmestadii,
1664　Typis Henningi Mulleri, 1664.
T. 3　　[35] p.　19 cm.
　　　　Diss. - Helmstedt (J. J. Müller, respondent)

　　　I. Müller, Johann Julius, fl. 1664, respondent

NT　0036511　　DNLM

W 4　TAPPE, Jacob, 1603-1680, praeses
H47　　Disputatio medica pathologica de comate et caro ...
1668　Helmestadii, Typis Henningi Mülleri, 1668.
T. 1　　[24] p.　20 cm.
　　　　Diss. - Helmstedt (E. Barnstorff, respondent)

　　　I. Barnstorff, Ernst, fl. 1668-1672, respondent

NT　0036512　　DNLM

Tappe, Jacob, 1603-1680, praeses.
　Disputatio medica pathologica de sensus
tactus depravatione...
　　　see under　Stisser, Statius Fridericus,
respondent.

Tappe, Jacob, 1603-1680, praeses.
　Disputatio physiologica de somno naturali
eiusque causis
　　　see under　Stisser, Henricus, respondent.

WZ　TAPPE, Jacob, 1603-1680
250　　Oratio de tabaco ejusque hodierno abusu ... Helmestadii,
T175o　Typis Henningi Mulleri, 1653.
1653　　[32] p.　20 cm.

NT　0036515　　DNLM

WZ　TAPPE. Jacob, 1603-1680
250　　Oratio de tabaco ejusque hodierno abusu ...　2. ed. auctior.
P3651t　Helmestadii, Typis & sumptibus Henningi Mulleri, 1660.
1684　　[36] p.　19 cm.
　　　　Imperfect: sig. E2-3 wanting.
　　　　Bound with Pechlin, J. N. Theophilus Bibaculus. Kilonii, 1684.

NT　0036516　　DNLM MH OC1

WZ　TAPPE, Jacob, 1603-1680
250　　Oratio de tabaco ejusque hodierno abusu ... 3. ed. auctior.
T175o　Helmestadii, Typis & sumtibus Henrici Davidis Mülleri, 1673.
1673　　[43] p.　20 cm.

NT　0036517　　DNLM CU NNNAM

Tappe, L　　B　　de
　Curiosa naturae arcana inclyti regni Boemiae
et appertinentium provinciarum Moraviae et
Silesiae dissertationibus et quaestionibus
philosophicis indagata.　Vetero-Pragae, 1724.

　(10), 185 p.　f°.

NT　0036518　　MH

Tappe, Oscarus L.
　Analectorum Horatianorum specimen. Ber., 1865.

NT　0036519　　NjP

Tappe, Josef, 1911-
　... Besteht eine Abhängigkeit der Schwanger-
schaftsdauer von der Jahrezeit?...　Lengerich
i. W. [1938]
　Inaug.-diss. - Köln.
　Lebenslauf.
　"Literatur": p. 27.

NT　0036520　　CtY

Tappe, Peter Heinz, 1903-
　... Anzeigestellung und Arten zur Extraktion
der unteren Weisheitszähne...　Würzburg,
1935.
　Inaug.-diss. - München.
　Lebenslauf.

NT　0036521　　CtY

Berk　Tappe, Sylvester, d. 1747
　　Geographische und historische Beschreibung
des Jüdischen Landes. Hildesheim, Ludolph
Schröder, 1711. 87 pp. Pp. 1-6 badly mutilated.

NT　0036522　　OSW

Berk　Tappe, Sylvester, d. 1747
　　Kurtze Anweisung wie die vier chronologische
General-Tabellen über die Universal-Historie.
Braunschweig und Hildesheim, Ludolph Schröder,
1721. 272, 38 pp.

NT　0036523　　OSW

Berk　Tappe, Sylvester, d. 1747
　　Das Licht im Schatten. Hildesheim, Ludolph
Schröder, 1721. 152 רp.

NT　0036524　　OSW

Tappe, Walter, ed.
　Jean Paul [pseud.] Eine Auswahl aus seinen
Schriften
　　　see under　[Richter, Johann Paul
Friedrich] 1763-1825.

Tappe, Walter.
　... Das kultproblem in der deutschen dramatik vom
sturm und drang bis Hebbel, von dr. Walter Tappe.
Berlin, E. Ebering, 1925.

　5 p. l., [3]-96 p. 24cm. (Germanische studien ... hft. 37)
　"Literatur": 4th prelim. leaf.

　　1. German drama—18th cent.—Hist. & crit. 2. Religion in literature.
I. Title.

　Library of Congress　　PT619.T3　　25-14507

　　　　　　　　　OU CaBVaU
NT　0036526　　DLC CoU PU NcD CLSU CtY TxU KU CU MU NcU

[Tappe, Walter J.]
　"White paper" on Spain.　San Francisco, The
Monitor, 1946.

　12 p.　15 cm.
　Cover-title.
　"From the Monitor, official organ of The
Archdiocese of San Francisco... March 9, 1946."
Signed at end: Rev. Walter J. Tappe.

NT　0036527　　MH NN

AC　Tappe, Werner, 1906-
831　　Stereoisomere Camphenilole. ...　Breslau, 1937.
　　17 p.
　　Inaug. Diss. - Breslau, 1937.
　　Lebenslauf.

NT　0036528　　ICRL CtY

Tappe, Wilhelm.
　Nachtrag zu der wahren Gegend und Linie
der dreitägigen Hermannsschlacht...　Essen,
G. D. Bädeker, 1822.
　vi, 7-36 p.　illus.　22 cm.
　　1. Teutoburger Wald, Battle of, A. D. 9.

NT　0036529　　NN

Tappe, Wilhelm i. e. Franz August Wilhelm, 1842-
　Die einheimischen eidechsen ...　Oberhausen, Druck
von A. Spaarmann, 1868.
　40 p.　19½cm.
　Inaug.-diss.—Bonn.
　Vita.

　　1. Reptiles—Germany. 2. Lizards.

　Library of Congress　　QL666.L2T2　　6-24416†

NT　0036530　　DLC

Tappehorn, Anton, 1823-1907.
　Anleitung zur verwaltung des heiligen bussssacramentes.
Von Ant. Tappehorn ... 2., verb. und verm. aufl. Dülmen, A.
Laumann (F. Schnell) 1880.
　2 p. l., iv, 494, [2] p. 20cm.

　　1. Penance.　　42-29155

　Library of Congress　　BX2260.T3

NT　0036531　　DLC

BQV　Tappehorn, Anton, 1823-1907.
230　　Anleitung zur Verwaltung des heil. Busssakra-
S2　mentes / von Anton Tappehorn -- 6. Aufl. neube-
T3　arb. von Joseph Genius. -- Dülmen : A. Laumann,
　　1927.
　　[ix], 368 p. ; 23 cm.

　　1. Penance. 2. Penance (Canon law).
I. Genius, Joseph. II. Title.

NT　0036532　　CU-L

BS2851　Tappehorn, Anton, 1823-1907.
4.T17　　Ausserbiblische Nachrichten; oder,
　　Die Apokryphen über die Geburt, Kind-
heit und das Lebensende Jesu und Mariä.
Paderborn, Druck und Verlag von F.
Schöningh, 1885.
　88 p.　21cm.

NT　0036533　　NjPT OC1JC CtY

Spec.
Coll.
BX
2169
T363

Tappehorn, Anton, 1823-1907.
Brod der Engel: vollständiges Andachtsbuch
für die Verehrer des allerh. Altarssakraments.
Mit Genehmigung der geistlichen Obrigkeit.
6. Aufl. Dülmen, A. Laumann, Katholische
Verlags-Buchhandlung [n. d.]
xxix, 607 p. illus. 13 cm.
The Angels' bread: complete prayers for
the devoted admirers of the Holy of Holies
altar sacrament. With the approbation of

spiritual authority.

1. Catholic Church—Prayer-books and devotions—German. 2. Lord's Supper—Prayer-
books and devotions—German. I. Title. rw

NT 0036535 IEdS

Tappehorn, Anton, 1823-1907.
Erklärung und Predigtenwürfe zu den sonn-
und festtäglichen Evangelien des katnolischen
Kirchenjahres. 2. verb. u. bedeutend vermehrte Aufl. Dülmen i.W., A. Laumann; Louisville, Ky., Joseph Stuecker ‹1895›
2v. 23cm.

NT 0036536 PLatS

Tappehorn, Anton, Father, 1823-1907.
Leben des heiligen Ansgar, Apostels von Dänemar
und Schweden und die geschichte der verbreitung
des christenthums im skandinavischen Norden.
Münster, Theissing, 1863.

xii, 290 p. 22 cm.

1. Ansgar, O.S.B., Saint, Bp., of Hamburg & Bremen
2. Denmark - Church history - 801-865. 3. Sweden -
Church history.
4. Benedictines in   the Scandinavian countries

NT 0036537 PLatS NjPT NRCR IaU DLC

Tappehorn, Anton.
Das leben des heiligen Willehad, ersten
bischofs von Bremen. Dülmen i.W.,
A. Laumann, 1901.
49 p.

NT 0036538 MH

BQV
396
T36

[Tappehorn, Anton]
Organon, oder kurze Andeutungen über kirch-
liches Verfassungswesen der Katholiken, mit
vorzugweiser hinsicht auf Staaten gemischter
Confession. Augsburg, C. Kollman & J.P. Himmer,
1829.
xii, [2], 242 p.

1. Catholic Church in Germany. 2. Church
and state in Germany. I. Title.

NT 0036539 CU-L

Tappehorn, Anton, 1823-1907
Der priester am kranken und sterbebette.
Paderborn...1872.

247 p.

NT 0036540 OClJC

Tappehorn, Anton 1823-1907
Der priester am kranken und sterbebette.
Dritte vermehrte auflage. Paderborn...1893.

276 p.

NT 0036541 OClJC

Tappehorn, Anton, 1823-1907.
Der Priester am Kranken- und Sterbebette. An-
leitung zur geistlichen Krankenpflege. 2 verm.
Aufl. Paderborn und Münster, Ferdinand
Schöningh, 1896.

x, 264p. 15cm.

1. Sick-calls. 2. Sick--Prayerbooks and devotions. 3. Prayers for the sick. 4. Blessings.
I. Title.

NT 0036542 PLatS

Tappehorn, F
Die vollkommene Association, als Vermitt-
lerin der Einheit des Vernunftstaates und der
Lehre Jesu. Ein Beitrag zur ruhigen Lösung
aller grossen Fragen dieser Zeit. Augsburg,
1834.
vi, 82 p. 22 cm.

NT 0036543 CtY

Tappehorn (Theod.) "De emphysemate pul-
monum. vi, 7-42 pp. 8°. Wirceburgi, F. E.
Thein, 1848.

NT 0036544 DNW

Tappeiner, Anton Josef Franz Xaver Hermann,
edler von Tappein
see
Tappeiner, Hermann, edler von Tappein, 1847- 1927.

APPEINER, Franz, edler von Tappein, 1816-1902.   2233.(
Die Abstammung der Tiroler und Raeter.
(In Beiträge zur Anthropologie ... von Tirol. Pp. 1-37.]
nnsbruch, 1894.)

NT 0036546 MB

Tappeiner, Franz, edler von Tappein, 1816-1902.
Studien zur anthropologie Tirols und der Sette Comuni,
von dr. Franz Tappeiner. Innsbruck, Wagner, 1883.

2 p. l., 64 p. xxxix (i. e. 40) fold. tab. 27cm.

"Ich glaube, dass dieses material von zusammen 8120 schädeln und
köpfen eine hinreichend breite grundlage bietet, um darauf eine statistische
uebersicht der schädel- und kopfformen Tirols und der Sette Comuni auf-
zubauen."—Vorwort.

1. Anthropometry—Tyrol. 2. Anthropometry—Sette Comuni. 3. Craniology—Tyrol. 4. Craniology—Sette Comuni.

(Full name: Franz Xaver Hermann Anton Josef Tappeiner,
edler von Tappein)

Library of Congress   GN585.I8T3   19-8464

NT 0036547 DLC IEN

TAPPEINER, Franz, edler von Tappein, 1816-1902.
Zum schluss der majafrage. Meran, S. Pötzel-
berger, 1897.

4°. pp. 26.

NT 0036548 MH

von Tappeiner (Franz Hugo) [1883-   ].
* Untersuchungen über den Angriffsort der
fluoreszierenden Substanzen auf rote Blutkör-
perchen. [Munich.] 25 pp., 1 l. 8°. Berlin,
J. Springer, 1908.

NT 0036549 DNLM

Tappeiner, Franz Xaver Hermann Anton Josef,
edler von Tappein, 1816-1902
see Tappeiner, Franz, edler von
Tappein, 1816-1902.

QY
T175a

TAPPEINER, Hermann, Edler von Tappein,
1847-1927
Anleitung zu chemisch-diagnostichen
Untersuchungen am Krankenbette. [1.]-9
Aufl. München, Univ. Buchhandlung,
1885-1908.
v. illus.

NT 0036551 DNLM MiU PPC CtY-M NN

Tappeiner, Hermann, edler von Tappein,
1847-1927.
Anleitung zu chemisch-diagnostischen
Untersuchungen am Krankenbette. 11 Aufl.
München, Rieger, 1920.
154 p.

NT 0036552 PPC

Tappeiner, Hermann, Edler von Tappein, 1847-1927.
Anleitung zu chemisch-diagnostischen Untersuchungen am
Krankenbette, von Dr. H. v. Tappeiner ... Mit 12 Figuren im
Text. 9. umgearbeitete Auflage. München, M. Rieger'sche
Universitäts-Buchhandlung, 1908.

vii, 136 p. illus. 17½cm.

NT 0036553 ICJ ICU

Tappeiner, Hermann, edler von Tappein,
1847-1927.
Anleitung zu chemisch-diagnostischen
untersuchungen am krankenbette, von dr.
H. v. Tappeiner ... Mit 12 figuren im text.
8. umbearb. aufl. München, M. Rieger, 1903.
iv, 126 p. illus. 18 cm.
1. Diagnosis. I. Title.

NT 0036554 MoSU

Tappeiner, Hermann, edler von Tappein, 1847-
Introduction to chemical methods of clinical diagnosis, by
Dr H. Tappeiner ... Tr. from the 6th German ed., with an
appendix on micro-biological methods of diagnosis, by Edmond J. McWeeney ... London, New York [etc.] Longmans,
Green, and co., 1898.
xvi, 152 p. illus. 18½cm.

1. Diagnosis.   i. McWeeney, Edmond Joseph, 1864-   tr.
(Full name: Anton Josef Franz Xaver Hermann Tappeiner,
edler von Tappein)
6-38751 Revised

Library of Congress   RB37.T22
r51e½

NT 0036555 DLC MH MB

QV
T175L

TAPPEINER, Hermann, Edler von Tappein,
1847-1927
Lehrbuch der Arzneimittellehre und
Arzneiverordnungslehre unter besonderer
Berücksichtigung der deutschen und
österreichischen Pharmakopoe. [1.]-
10. Aufl. Leipzig, Vogel, 1890-1913.
v.
3d ed. on microfilm.

NT 0036556 DNLM

Tappeiner, Hermann, edler von Tappein,
1847-1927.
Lehrbuch der Arzeimittellehre und
Arzneiverordnungslehre unter besonderer
Berücksichtigung der deutschen und österreichischen Pharmakopoe. 2. Aufl. Leipzig, Vogel,
1895.
302 p.

NT 0036557 PPC MoSU OClW-H

Tappeiner, Hermann, edler von Tappein
1847–1927.
Lehrbuch der Arzneimittellehre und
Arzneiverordnungslehre unter besonderer
Berücksichtigung der deutschen und österreichischen Pharmakope. 3. Auf. Leipzig, Vogel,
1899.
326 p.

NT 0036558   PPC

Tappeiner, Hermann von, edler von Tappein,
1847–1927.
Lehrbuch der Arzneimittellehre und
Arzneiverordnungslehre unter besonderer
Berücksichtigung der deutschen und österreichischen Pharmakope, von Dr. H. v. Tappeiner...
5. neu bearb. Aufl. Leipzig, F.C.W. Vogel,
1904.
vii [1] 347 [1] p. table. 22.5 cm.

NT 0036559   CtY-K PPC OU

Tappeiner, Hermann von, *edler von Tappein,* 1847–
Lehrbuch der arzneimittellehre und arzneiverordnungslehre
unter besonderer berücksichtigung der deutschen und österreichischen pharmakopoe, von dr. H. v. Tappeiner ... 6. neu
bearb. aufl. Leipzig, F. C. W. Vogel, 1907.
vii, ₍1₎, 378 p. tables. 22½ᶜᵐ.

1. Pharmacy.
₍Full name: Anton Josef Franz Xaver Hermann
Tappeiner, edler von Tappein₎

Agr 8–943 Revised

[RM121.T]

Library. U. S. Dept. of   Agriculture 396T16

NT 0036560   DNAL CtY-M

Tappeiner, Herman, edler von Tappein, 1847–1927.
Lehrbuch der arzneimittellehre und arzneiverordnungslehre unter besonderer berücksichtigung der deutschen und österreichischen
pharmakope. 7 neu bearb. aufl. Leipzig, F.
C.W. Vogel, 1908.
384p.

NT 0036561   ICRL CtY PPC

Tappeiner, Hermann, *edler von Tappein,* 1847–
Lehrbuch der arzneimittellehre und arzneiverordnungslehre unter besonderer berücksichtigung der deutschen und österreichischen pharmakope, von dr. H. v.
Tappeiner ... 8. neu bearb. aufl. Leipzig, F. C. W.
Vogel, 1910.
vii, ₍1₎, 394 p. 23½ᶜᵐ.   M. 20
1. Materia medica. 2. Therapeutics.
₍Full name: Anton Josef Franz Xaver Hermann Tappeiner,
edler von Tappein₎

Library of Congress   RM121.T3   ˚⁾–9934 Revised

NT 0036562   DLC ICJ

Tappeiner, Hermann von, edler von Tappein, 1847–
1927
Lenrbuch der Arzneimittellehre und Arzneiverordnungslehre unter besonderer Berücksichtigung der deutschen und österreichischen Pharmakopoe. 9e. neu bearbeitete Auflage. Leipzig.
Vogel. 1912.

vii, 429 pp. 23 cm.

NT 0036563   MH DNLM

Tappeiner, Hermann, Edler von Tappein, 1847–
Lehrbuch der Arzneimittellehre und Arzneiverordnungslehre unter besonderer Berücksichtigung der
deutschen und österreichischen Pharmakopie. 10.
Aufl. Leipzig, F.C.W.Vogel, 1913.
439 p.
Original t.p. missing.

NT 0036564   ICJ

Tappeiner, Hermann, *Edler von Tappein,* 1847–1927.
Lehrbuch der Arzneimittellehre und Arzneiverordnungslehre, unter besonderer Berücksichtigung der deutschen und
österreichischen Pharmakope. 13. z. T. neu bearb. Aufl.
Leipzig, F. C. W. Vogel, 1919.

viii, 499 p. 23 cm.

1. Materia medica. 2. Therapeutics.
*Full name: Anton Josef Franz Xaver Hermann
Tappeiner, Edler von Tappein.*

RM121.T3 1919   50–51502

NT 0036565   DLC

Tappeiner, Hermann, edler von Tappein, 1847–1927.
Lehrbuch der Arzneimittellehre und Arzneiverordnungslehre; unter besonderer Berücksichtigung der deutschen und österreichischen Pharmakopoe. 14. neu bearb.Aufl. Leipzig, F.C.W.
Vogel, 1920.
508 p.

NT 0036566   ICJ PPC

QV
55
T175L
1922

TAPPEINER, Hermann, Edler von Tappein,
1847–1927
Lehrbuch der Arzneimittellehre und
Arzneiverordnungslehre unter besonderer
Berücksichtigung der deutschen und
österreichischen Pharmakope. 15. neu
bearb. Aufl. Leipzig, Vogel, 1922.
vii, 516 p.

NT 0036567   DNLM PPC CtY

QY
T175a
1888

TAPPEINER, Hermann, Edler von Tappein,
1847–1927
Manuel de diagnostic chimique au lit
du malade. Traduction faite sur la 2.
éd. allemande par M. Nicolle, et mise
au courant des dernières connaissances
par l'auteur. Paris, Lecrosnier et
Babé, 1888.
xiv, 115 p. illus.
Translation of Anleitung zu chemisch-
diagnostischen Untersuchungen am
Krankenbette

NT 0036568   DNLM

Tappeiner, Hermann, *edler von Tappein,* 1847–1927.
Methoden beim arbeiten mit sensibilisierenden fluoreszierenden stoffen. Von H. v. Tappeiner.

(*In* Abderhalden, Emil, ed. Handbuch der biologischen arbeits-
methoden ... Berlin, 1920–   25ᶜᵐ. abt. IV, Angewandte chemische und physikalische methoden. t. 7ʙ ₍1935₎ p. ₍1071₎–1082. illus.)
Bibliographical foot-notes.

1. Fluorescence.
₍Full name: Anton Josef Franz Xaver Hermann
Tappeiner, edler von Tappein₎

A C 36–2711

Title from Ohio State   Univ.
Library of Congress   [QH324.A3 1920 abt. 4, t. 7ʙ]
    ₍2₎   (574.072)

NT 0036569   OU

Tappeiner, Hermann, *Edler von Tappein,* 1847–
... Die photodynamische Erscheinung (Sensibilisierung durch
fluoreszierende Stoffe) von H. v. Tappeiner

(*In* Ergebnisse der Physiologie. Wiesbaden, 1909. 26ᵐᵐ. 8. Jahrg.,
p. ₍698₎–741)
"Literatur": p. ₍698₎–702.

NT 0036570   ICJ OC1W-H

QC
T124s
1907

TAPPEINER, Hermann, Edler von Tappein,
1847–1927
Die sensibilisierende Wirkung
fluorescierender Substanzen; gesammelte
Untersuchungen über die photodynamische
Erscheinung, hrsg. von H. v. Tappeiner
und A. Jodlbauer. Leipzig, Vogel,
1907.
viii, 210 p. illus., ports.

I. Jodlbauer, A

NT 0036571   DNLM ICJ NNC PPC CU

---

von Tappeiner, Hermann, 1847–1927.
—— Ueber die Entwicklung und die Aufgaben
der Pharmakologie. Rede gehalten bei der
Eröffnungsfeier des pharmakologischen Instituts
in München. 13 pp., 1 diag., 1 pl. 8°. München, J. F. Lehmann, 1893.
Repr. from: München. med. Wchnschr., 1893, xl.

NT 0036572   DNLM MiU

Tappeiner, Josef, joint author.
Atlas der Haut- und Geschlechtskrankheiten
see under Arzt, Leopold.

Tappelet, Ernst.
Über den stand der mundarten in der deutschen
französischen Schweiz. Zurich, 1901.
40 p.

NT 0036574   PBm

Tappen, Abraham B
A decision of Judge Tappen's which saved the
city of Newburgh one million of dollars
see under New York (State) Supreme Court.

Tappen, Abraham B.
... Max Maretzek, respondent, against William
Cauldwell, and Horace P. Whitney, appellants
see under New York (City) Superior Court.

D545
.M3D6

Tappen, Adolf.
... **Documents** allemands sur la bataille de la Marne: Mon
rapport sur la bataille de la Marne, par le général feldmaré-
chal von Bulow.—Jusqu'à la Marne en 1914, par le général
Tappen ...—La mission du lieutenant-colonel Hentsch, par
le lieutenant-colonel en retraite W. Muller-Loebnitz. Avec
3 croquis. Traduction française et préface par le lieutenant-
colonel L. Kœltz ... Paris, Payot, 1930.

Tappen, Adolf.
Geschichte des Hannoverschen Pionier-
Bataillons Nr. 10 von seiner formation bis zum
jahre 1885; nach offiziellen quellen zusammengestellt und bearbeitet., Minden
i. W., J.C.C. Bruns, 1885.
26 folded plans in pocket at end.

NT 0036578   MH

Tappen, Adolf.
Namur vor und im weltkrieg, herausgegeben von der kaiserlichen fortifikation Namur; mit 180 abbildungen, karten
und plänen nach alten ansichten und neuaufnahmen. 1.
bis 4. tausend. München, R. Piper & co., 1918.

Tappen, Christopher, jr. Sketches of the weather and
progress of vegetation at Kingston in Ulster County. [Al-
bany. 1819.] 8°.
Transactions of the Society for the promotion of useful arts, 1819, iv,
pt. 2, pp. 7–9.

NT 0036580   MH-A

Tappen, Edith M.
Mother-in-law. A play in one act.
Franklin, O., c1933.
19 p. 19 cm.
On cover: Eldridge popular one-act plays.

NT 0036581 RPB OCl DLC

Tappen, Frederick D., 1839-1902.
A banker's will
see under title

Tappen, Frederick D., 1839-1902.
Proceedings of a meeting of the Association
held in memory of Frederick D. Tappen
see under New York Clearing House
Association.

Tappen, George.
Professional observations on the architecture of the
principal ancient and modern buildings in France and
Italy: with remarks on the painting and sculpture, and
a concise local description of those countries. Written
from sketches and memoranda made during a visit in the
years 1802 and 1803. By George Tappen ... London,
Printed for the author by W. Ballintine, 1806.

4 p. l., 316 p. pl. 22ᶜᵐ.

1. Architecture—France. 2. Architecture—Italy.

11–28651

Library of Congress NA950.T3

NT 0036584 DLC PPD NcR

Tappen, George.
A short description of a tour through France and Italy,
for the purpose of viewing the painting, sculpture, &
architecture, of those countries. By George Tappen ...
London, Printed for the author, by S. Hamilton, 1804.

2 p. l., 80 p. 21ᶜᵐ.

At end: The tour through Italy to be continued.

1. France—Descr. & trav. 2. Architecture—France.

20–14275

Library of Congress DC26.T3

NT 0036585 DLC

Tappen, Gerhard.
Bis zur Marne, 1914; Beiträge zur Beurteilung der Krieg-
führung bis zum Abschluss der Marne-Schlacht, von Tappen...
Oldenburg i. O.: G. Stalling. 1920. 32 p. 2. ed. 8°.

1. European war, 1914– — Cam-   paigns.
N. Y. P. L.   Sept 11, 1922.

NT 0036586 NN MH CSt-H DLC-P4 MiU

WG
25092
Tappen, Hans, 1879–
Synthesen in der Phenanthren-Reihe.
[Berlin]. 1904.
46 p.

Inaug.-Diss. - Berlin

NT 0036587 CtY ICRL PU

Tappen, J. S., respondent.
... De remediis emendandae laesionis ex dote
see under Reinharth, Tobias Jacob,
1684-1743, praeses.

Tappen, Johann.
... De jure retentionis ...
see under Struve, Georg Adam,
1619-1692, praeses.

Tappen, Johann, respondent.
... De praescriptione mendaciorvm rescriptis
et mandatis opponi solita ...
see under Hahn, Heinrich, 1605-1668,
praeses.

Tappen, Johann Peter, respondent.
...De eo qvod justum est circa renitentem
complexa...
see under Brunnemann, Jacob, d.
1735, praeses.

Tappen, John, 1766?-1831.
The county and town officer, or, A concise view of the duties
and offices of county and town officers in the state of New-
York, with appropriate precedents. In two parts. By John
Tappen ... Kingston: Printed and published by J. Tappen.
1816.

4 p. l., [5]-363, [1], viii p. 22ᶜᵐ.

1. Local government — New York (State) 2. Forms (Law) — New
York (State) I. Title.

32–20595

NT 0036592 DLC CtY N NNC DeU MH MWA MnU-L

CT3290
.U5
1944
Tappen, Kathleen B.
U. S. *Office of inter-American affairs. Research division.*
... Prominent women in Latin America, by Kathleen Tappen
and Berenice T. Morris. [Washington] Research division, So-
cial and geographic section, 1944.

HQ1532
.U5
1944
Tappen, Kathleen B.
U. S. *Office of inter-American affairs. Research division.*
... The status of the women in Argentina, by Kathleen B.
Tappen. [Washington] Research division, Social and geo-
graphic section, 1944.

HQ1542
.A3U5
1944
Tappen, Kathleen B.
U. S. *Office of inter-American affairs. Research division.*
... The status of women in Brazil, by Kathleen B. Tappen.
[Washington] Research division, Social and geographic section,
1944.

HQ1547
.U5
1944
Tappen, Kathleen B.
U. S. *Office of inter-American affairs. Research division.*
... The status of women in Chile, by Kathleen B. Tappen.
[Washington] Research division, Social and geographic section,
1944.

GN999
Tappen, Neil Campbell, 1920–
A functional analysis of the face with
split-line technique. 1952.
81 l.

Thesis—Univ. of Chicago.

1. Face. I. Title.

NT 0036597 ICU

TAPPEN, Otto.
Die internationale schiedsgerichtsbarkeit, ihr
wesen, und ihre heutige bedeutung. Dortmund,
1936.

pp.9+(1)+91+(2).
Inaug.-diss. --- Köln.

NT 0036598 MH CtY

Tappen, Rudolf, *ed.*
Rechtsprechungsbrevier; ein Wegweiser durch die neuere
Rechtsprechung und Literatur. 2. Aufl. Berlin, J. M.
Weiss [1939]

198 p. 21 cm.

"Die erste Ausgabe ist vor einigen Jahren unter dem Titel 'Aus
der Praxis–für die Praxis' erschienen."

1. Law reports, digests, etc.—Germany. 2. Law—Germany—Bibl.
I. Title.

48–43137*

NT 0036599 DLC MH-L

Tappen, Theda.
Goslar. Marktkirche. *Bibliothek.*
Katalog der Marktkirchen-bibliothek zu Goslar. Hrsg.
von pastor prim. K. Bormann und Theda Tappen. Hannover, E. Geibel, 1911.

Tappen, Wilhelm, 1883–   Die Regelung der Gesamt-
hypothek nach geltendem deutschen Rechte. Cöln a. Rh.:
Neubner 1911. 79 S. 8°
Heidelberg, Jur. Diss. v. 6. Juni 1911, Ref. Endemann
[Geb. 8. Okt. 83 Soest; Wohnort: Cöln; Staatsangeh.: Preußen; Vorbildung:
Gymn. Soest Reife O. 03; Studium: Göttingen 2, Bonn 4, Heidelberg 1 S.;
Rig. 27. April 11.] [U 11. 2152

NT 0036601 ICJ ICRL MH-L

Tappenbeck, Dietrich.
Geologie des Mollogebirges und einiger benachbarter gebiete
(Niederländisch Timor) ... door Dietrich Tappenbeck ...
Amsterdam, N. v. Noord-Hollandsche uitgevers maatschappij,
[1939]

4 p. l., [xi]-xvi, 105 p. incl. illus., tables. viii pl. on 4 l. 24ᶜᵐ.
Proefschrift—Amsterdam.
Each plate accompanied by descriptive letterpress except pl. viii.
Stamped on cover: Geologisch instituut. Mededeeling no. 84. Univer-
siteit van Amsterdam.
"Schriftenverzeichnis": p. [104]-105.

1. Geology—Timor. I. Title: Mollogebirges und einiger benachbarter
gebiete, Geologie des.

G S 40–151

U. S. Geol. survey. Library   G (501) AmSum no. 84
for Library of Congress   [QE349.T58]
                                 [2]

NT 0036602 DI-GS IU CU CtY NSyU

Tappenbeck, Ernst.
Deutsch-Neuguinea, von Ernst Tappenbeck. Berlin, W.
Süsserott, 1901.

1 p. l., 178 p. illus., pl., fold. map. 21½ᶜᵐ. (Süsserotts kolonialbibliothek, bd. 1)

1. New Guinea (German)

2—11108

Library of Congress DU742.T2

NT 0036603 DLC CU CtY NcD NN MB

Tappenbeck, Ernst.
Ein wirtschaftliche studie über den
zusammenschluss des Brennereigewerbes
see his 1908 [i. e. Neunzehnhundertacht]

Tappenbeck, Ernst.
... 1908. Eine wirtschaftliche Studie über den Zusammenschluss des Brennereigewerbes und seine Aussicht für die Zukunft. Ein Mahnruf an die deutschen Brenner! von E. Tappenbeck ... 2. Auflage. Berlin, W. Süsserott, 1906.
107 p. 20½ᶜᵐ.

NT 0036605   ICJ

Tappenbeck, Ernst.
Wie rüste ich mich für die Tropenkolonien aus? Von Ernst Tappenbeck... Berlin: W. Süsserott, 1905. 69 p. 8°. (Süsserott's Kolonialbibliothek. Bd. 10.)

79990A.   1. Food, Tropics.   2. Tropics.—Hygiene. 3. Series.
N. Y. P. L.   April 25, 1943.

NT 0036606   NN MH

Tappenden, Henry John.
... Reversions and life interests, by H. J. Tappenden, F. I. A. Cambridge ₍Eng.₎ Pub. for the Institute of actuaries Students' society, at the University press, 1934.
xii, 57 p., 1 l. fold. forms. 22ᶜᵐ. (Institute of actuaries Students' society's Consolidation of reading series)

1. Reversion—Gt. Brit. 2. Estates (Law)—Gt. Brit.
39–11791

NT 0036607   DLC WaU-L NN CU RPB NNC

F863
.6
T3
x

Tappendorf, Frederick, plaintiff and respondent.
(J. H. Dungan and James Monroe, defendants and appellants)

Assault and battery.
J. G. Swinnerton, attorney for respondent and Chamberlin & De Haven, of counsel; S. M. Buck, attorney for appellant₎. Before the California Supreme Court.
Conte₋₋₋
₍1₎ Respondent's points and authorities. 1877. (8 p.)

NT 0036608   CU-BANC

Tapper, Emil.
Auf dem Gauturnfest. Schwank mit Gesang in zwei Aufzügen, von Emil Tapper. Berlin: E. Bloch ₍1901₎ 27 p. 18½cm. (Ludwig Blochs Herren-Bühne. Nr. 57.)
Without music.

883424A.   1. Drama, German.   I. Title.
N. Y. P. L.   June 8, 1937

NT 0036609   NN

LC6999   **Tapper, Ethel Winifred, 1915–**
The potential objectives of general humanities courses. 1950.
124 l.

Typewritten.
Thesis--Univ. of Chicago.

1. Education, Humanistic.

NT 0036610   ICU

Tapper, G
Förgätmigej; nya dikter, dialoger och högtidssänger. Chicago, Ill. ₍Tryckt hos J. V. Martenson₎ 1903.

300 p. illus., port. 20cm.

NT 0036611   MnU

830.9   **Tapper, Pater Heinrich, 1907–**
T16g   Die gestalt des Petrus in der literatur des ausgehenden mittelalters und des 16. jahrhunderts ... Limburg a.d. Lahn, Limburger vereinsdruckerei g.m.b.h., 1935.
103p.

Inaug.-diss.--Frankfurt a.M.
"Literaturangaben": p. ₍3-5₎

1. Peter, Saint, apostle. 2. German literature--Early modern (to 1700)--Hist. & crit.

NT 0036612   IU

Tapper, Edward William.
A physics note-book; heat, light and sound, by E.W. Tapper ... London, Methuen & co., ltd. ₍1933₎
vii, 100 p., 1 l. incl. diagrs. 18 cm.

1. Heat. 2. Light. 3. Sound.

NT 0036613   OU

Tapper, Ruard, 1487-1559.
Explicationis articvlorvm venerandae Facvltatis Sacrae Theologiae Generalis Studij Louanieñ. circa dogmata ecclesiastica ab annis triginta quatuor controuersa, vnà cum responsione ad argumenta aduersariorum, tomvs primus ₍-secvndvs₎ Lovanii, Apud M. Verhasselt, 1555-57.
2 v. in 1. port. 31 cm.
Commentary, with text, on the first 20 of the 32 articles of Dec. 6, 1544. No more published.
Text of articles 21-32 is included in plan of work at end of v. 1.
1. Catholic Church—Doctrinal and controversial works—Catholic authors. 2. Sacraments—Catholic Church. I. Louvain. Université. Facultas Theologica. Articuli orthodoxam religionem sanctamque fidem nostram respicientes. 1555. II. Title: Explicationis articulorum venerandae   Facultatis Sacrae Theologiae ...
Lovaniensis... tomus.
BX1750.T3   75–410099

NT 0036614   DLC PU DCU

BT 70
.T 36
1582 QC   **Tapper, Ruard, 1487-1559.**
Rvardi Tapperi ... Omnia, qvae haberi potvervnt opera ... Coloniae Agrippinae, In officina Birckmannica, 1582.
2 v. in 1. 32cm.

1. Theology, Doctrinal. 2. Early printed books - 1500-1600.

NT 0036615   MdBJ

Tapper, Ruard, 1487-1559.
Spiritvs vertiginis vtrivsqv Germaniae in religionis dissidio, vnde cunctae calamitates vera origo, progressus, ac indubitatus curandi modus
see under   Loos, Cornelis, 1546-1595.

Tapper, Ruth M
The full years; the life story of Helen I. Root. Winona Lake, Ind., Young People's Missionary Society, 1948.
96 p. illus., ports. 20 cm.

1. Root, Helen Isabel, 1873-1945. I. Title.
BV3705.R6T3   922.754   48–22834*

NT 0036617   DLC

Tapper, Thomas, 1864-1958.
... The ABC of keyboard harmony, by Thomas Tapper ... Boston, The Arthur P. Schmidt co. ₍1943₎
27 p. illus. (music) 31 x 23½ᶜᵐ. (*His* First year series)
Schmidt's educational series, no. 448.
Publisher's plate no.: A. P. S. 15153.

1. Harmony, Keyboard. I. Title.
44–36604
Library of Congress   MT224.T37
₍3₎   781.3

NT 0036618   DLC NN Or WaS

Tapper, Thomas, 1864-1958.
The boy as a citizen, by Thomas Tapper ... New York, The Platt & Peck co. ₍1913₎
3 p. l., 9-93 p. 16ᶜᵐ. ₍The inspiration books, ed. by T. Tapper₎ $0.35

1. Boys. I. Title.

Library of Congress   HQ797.T3   14–345

NT 0036619   DLC ICRL DHEW OClW ICJ

Tapper, Thomas, 1864-1958.
Boy as a citizen. N.Y., Platt, c1915.
93 p. (Inspiration books.)

NT 0036620   PU

Tapper, Thomas, 1864-
Building an executive personality, organizing character for success...N. Y. 1936.

128 p.

NT 0036621   OCl

Tapper, Thomas, 1864-
The business of living; making an art of life, ...N.Y. 1936.

125 p.

NT 0036622   OCl

Tapper, Thomas, 1864-1958.
Chats with music students; or, Talks about music and music life. By Thomas Tapper ... Philadelphia, T. Presser, 1890.
xii, 9-340 p. 18 x 14ᶜᵐ.

1. Music—Instruction and study.
4—498
Library of Congress   ML3795.T14

NT 0036623   DLC PWcS PPCPh OClMN MB KEmT OU

ML
3795
T14   **Tapper, Thomas, 1864-**
Chats with music students; or, Talks about music and music life. ₍3d ed.₎ Philadelphia, T. Presser, 1891.
xii, 340 p. 18cm.

1. Music - Instruction and study

NT 0036624   WU MtBC OrU CLSU

Tapper, Thomas, 1864-
Chats with music students; or, Talks about music and music life, by Thomas Tapper. Rev. ed. ... Philadelphia, T. Presser, 1901.
xii, 9-340 p. 18 x 14ᶜᵐ.

1. Music—Instruction and study. I. Title.
3—32177
Library of Congress   ML3795.T15

WaSp Or OrU
NT 0036625   DLC PPLas PP PPCI OClMN FMU NIC OCl MtBC

Tapper, Thomas, *1864-1958.*
 Chats with music students; or,
Talks about music & music life.   Phil.
Presser, 1906.

  340 p.

NT 0036626   PU

Tapper, Thomas, 1864-   ed.
Stevenson, Robert Louis, 1850-1894.
 ... A child's garden of verses, by Robert Louis Stevenson, with introduction and notes by Thomas Tapper ... illustrated by Etheldred B. Barry. Boston, The Page company, 1918.

Tapper, Thomas, 1864-*1958.*
 The child's music world; being some chapters in the story of music made for young readers by Thomas Tapper. Philadelphia, The Hatch music company, 1897.

  212 p. 18ᶜᵐ.
 "Bibliography": p. 211-212.

  1. Music—Hist. & crit.   I. Title.
                                                  6-11564

  Library of Congress   ML3930.T17

NT 0036628   DLC MB NN WU

Tapper, Thomas, 1864-
 ... Child's own book of great musicians, by Thomas Tapper. ₍A series₎ ... Philadelphia, Theodore Presser co.

  v. fold. pl. 24ᶜᵐ.
 Cover-title.

  1. Musicians.   I. Title.

  Library of Congress   ML3930.T172   15-26940

NT 0036629   DLC

Tapper, Thomas, 1864-   ed.
 Choir and choral magazine
  see under title

Tapper, Thomas, 1864-   *ed.*
 ... Classics from the 17th and 18th centuries, compiled and edited by Dr. Thomas Tapper ... New York, Schroeder & Gunther, inc., ᶜ1938.

  31 p. 30½ᶜᵐ.
 At head of title: No. 123.
 Publisher's plate no.: S. & G. inc. 1761.
 For piano solo.
 "Annotations": p. ₍2₎-₍3₎

  1. Piano music—To 1800. 2. Harpsichord music—To 1800.   I. Title.
                                                  45-41413

  Library of Congress   M20.T3C5

NT 0036631   DLC

Tapper, Thomas, 1864-
 Developing mental power; mind training for efficiency....A project in the Franklin system of personal advancement. N.Y. 1936.

  118 p.

NT 0036632   OC1

Tapper, Thomas, 1864-*1958.*
 The education of the music teacher, by Thomas Tapper ... Philadelphia, Theodore Presser co., 1914.

  223 p. illus. 20½ cm.
 Reprinted in part from the Outlook, the Ætude and the Evening Journal.

  1. Music — Instruction and study. 2. Music — Instruction and study—U. S. 3. Music teachers.   I. Title.

  MT1.T15   14—19702

NT 0036633   DLC DHEW OC1 OU OO ODW NN IaU MU

Tapper, Thomas, 1864-
 The education of the music teacher, by Thomas Tapper ... Philadelphia, Theodore Presser co., 1915.
  223 p. illus. 20½ᶜᵐ. $1.50
 Reprinted in part from the Outlook, the Ætude and the Evening Journal.

NT 0036634   ViU WaTU WaSp PP

Tapper, Thomas, 1864-
 Efficiency; its spiritual source, by Thomas Tapper ... New York, The Platt & Peck co. ₍ᶜ1911₎
  3 p. l., 5-107 p. 19ᶜᵐ. $1.00

  I. Title.

  Library of Congress   14-6189

NT 0036635   DLC ICRL TU DHEW OC1W ICJ

Tapper, Thomas, 1864-
 Essentials in music history, by Thomas Tapper ... and Percy Goetschius ... New York, C. Scribner's sons, 1914.
  xviii p., 1 l., 365 p. front., illus. (incl. ports., facsims.) 20½ᶜᵐ. $2.00
 "The essentials of a music library ₍contributed by Frank M. Marling₎": p. 329-352.

  1. Music—Hist. & crit.   I. Goetschius, Percy, 1853-   joint author.
  Library of Congress   ML161.T28   14—18081

                NN OC1W OrP Or WaS CU
                CoU NIC PPLas PP PPCI PWcS OO OC1 OC1h MiU OCU MB
NT 0036636   DLC NBuC WU CLSU MiEM WaTU WaSp OKentU

Tapper, Thomas, 1864-
 Essentials in music history, by Thomas Tapper ... and Percy Goetschius ... New York, C. Scribner's sons, 1917.
  xviii p., 1 l., 365 p. front., illus. (incl. ports., facsims.) 20½ᶜᵐ. $2.00
 "The essentials of a music library ₍contributed by Frank H. Marling₎": p. 329-352.

R669
T175

NT 0036637   CU

Tapper, Thomas, 1864-
 Essentials in music history, by
Thomas Tapper & Percy Goetschius...
N. Y., Scribner, 1925.

  365 p.

NT 0036638   PPCI

ML
161
T28
1927
 Tapper, Thomas, 1864-
 Essentials in music history, by Thomas Tapper ... and Percy Goetschius ... New York, C. Scribner's sons, 1927.
  xviii p., 1 l., 365 p. front., illus. (incl. ports., facsims.) 20½ᶜᵐ.
 "The essentials of a music library ₍contributed by Frank H. Marling₎": p. 329-352.

NT 0036639   WU WaTU PHi

Tapper, Thomas
 Essentials in music history...Scribner 1929.

  365 p.
 By Thomas Tapper and Percy Goetschius.

NT 0036640   OU OC1W OrP

Tapper, Thomas, 1864-
 Everyone an executive; personality through organized effort, by Thomas Tapper, LITT. D.; prepared under the supervision of the Editorial board of the University society ... New York, The University society, incorporated ₍ᶜ1936₎
  vi, 128 p., 1 l. 20½ᶜᵐ. (Personal engineering series. ₍vol. IV₎)

  1. Personality. 2. Success.   I. University society, New York.   II. Title.
                                                  36—15900
  Library of Congress   HF5386.T17
  —— —— Copy 2.
  Copyright A 96052   ₍5₎   170

NT 0036641   DLC OC1U

Tapper, Thomas, 1864-*1958,* ed.
 The first piano book.
 = Boston. Oliver Ditson Co. 1911. (3), 39 pp. [Tapper's Graded piano course.] 31½ cm.

  H6806 — Pianoforte. Instruction books. — S.r.

NT 0036642   MB

Tapper, Thomas, *1864-*
 The first piano book. Rev. and enl.
Bost. 1915.

  63 p;

NT 0036643   OC1

ML
390
T17
 Tapper, Thomas, 1864-1958.
 First studies in music biography.
 Philadelphia, T. Presser ₍1900₎
  316 p. illus., facsims., music. 18cm.

  Contents.--Bach.--Handel.--Haydn.--Mozart--Beethoven.--Schubert.--Mendelssohn.--Schumann.--Chopin.--Wagner.

  1. Musicians.

                OO ODW OOxM MB OrP WaSp WaS
NT 0036644   NIC OrAshS OC1 OCX PP PU PSt MSohG Vi

Tapper, Thomas, 1864-
 First studies in music biography. ₍By₎ Thomas Tapper. Philadelphia, T. Presser ₍1901₎
  316 p. illus. (incl. facsims., music) plates, ports. 17½ x 13ᶜᵐ.
  CONTENTS. — Bach. — Handel.—Haydn.—Mozart.—Beethoven.—Schubert.—Mendelssohn.—Schumann.—Chopin.—Wagner.

  1. Musicians.
  Library of Congress   ML390.T17   1—30401

NT 0036645   DLC OrP WaS Or OrAshS OC1MN OEac

Tapper, Thomas, 1864-*1958.*
 First year analysis (musical form) by Thomas Tapper ... Boston, New York ₍etc.₎, A. P. Schmidt, ᶜ1914.
  iv p., 1 l., 113 p. 17ᶜᵐ.
 The material for analysis is provided in a separate volume, entitled: Musical form and analysis. cf. Pref.

  1. Musical form.   I. Title.
                                                  14-11204
  Library of Congress   MT58.T3 1914

NT 0036646   DLC NcC PWcS OrP WaSp WaS OC1 MB

Tapper, Thomas, 1864–
… First year analysis (musical form) by Thomas Tapper … Boston, New York, The Arthur P. Schmidt co. [*1935]

iv p., 1 l., 117 p. illus. (incl. music) 17½ᶜᵐ. (First year series)

"Augmented edition."
"Material for analysis … is provided in a separate volume, entitled: Musical form and analysis. (Schmidt's educational series, no. 122.)"—Pref.

1. Musical form. ɪ. Title.

Library of Congress MT75.T28 1935 35–20134

——— Copy 2.

Copyright A 86527   ⟨2⟩   781.508

NT 0036647 DLC NcD MtBC OC1JC OC1ND

Tapper, Thomas, 1864–
… First year analysis (musical form) by Thomas Tapper … [Augm. ed.] Boston, New York, The Arthur P. Schmidt co. [1944]

iv p., 1 l., 118 p. illus. (incl. music) 17ᶜᵐ. (First year series)

"Material for analysis … is provided in a separate volume, entitled: Musical form and analysis (Schmidt's educational series, no. 122.)"—Pref.

1. Musical form. ɪ. Title.

            45–13323

Library of Congress MT58.T3 1944

        ⟨2⟩   781.508

NT 0036648 DLC NcD NcU IEN OrU

Tapper, Thomas, 1864–
First year counterpoint (two and three voices) by Thomas Tapper … Boston, New York [etc.] A. P. Schmidt, ©1913.

2 p. l., iii–iv p., 1 l., 102 p. 17½ᶜᵐ. $1.00

1. Counterpoint.

            14—1959

Library of Congress MT55.T29

NT 0036649 DLC PWcS PP PSt OC1 NN

Tapper, Thomas, 1864–
… First year counterpoint (two and three voices) by Thomas Tapper … Boston, New York, The Arthur P. Schmidt co., ©1935.

iv p., 1 l., 106 p. illus. (music) 17½ᶜᵐ. (First year series)

"Augmented and revised edition."

1. Counterpoint.

Library of Congress MT55.T29 1935 35–6556

——— Copy 2.

Copyright A 81577 ⟨2⟩   781.4

NT 0036650 DLC IEN OrU MtBC OC1JC

MT
55
.T29
1935a **Tapper, Thomas,** 1864–
… First year counterpoint (two and three voices) by Thomas Tapper … Boston, New York, The Arthur P. Schmidt co., ©1935.

iv p. 1 l. 106 p. illus. (music) 17½ᶜᵐ. (First year series)

"Augmented and revised edition."

Photocopy. Ann Arbor, Mich., University Microfilms, n.d.

NT 0036651 INS

Tapper, Thomas, 1864–1958.
First year harmony, by Thomas Tapper … Boston, New York [etc.] A. P. Schmidt, ©1908.

vii, 156 p. 17½ᶜᵐ.

1. Harmony.

Library of Congress MT50.T11   8—5145

OO OC1 CU NN OrP Or

NT 0036652 DLC IEN NcGU MB NcC PP MoSW WU ViU OC1ND

Tapper, Thomas, 1864–
… First year harmony, by Thomas Tapper … Boston, New York, The Arthur P. Schmidt co., ©1930.

vii, 177 p. illus. (music) 17½ᶜᵐ.

At head of title: Augmented and revised edition.

1. Harmony.

Library of Congress MT50.T11 1930 30–9341

NT 0036653 DLC Vi PPCCH WaDp OC1 OC1JC

Tapper, Thomas, 1864–
… First year harmony, by Thomas Tapper … Boston, New York, The Arthur P. Schmidt co. [©1938]

vii, 177 p. illus. (music) 17½ᶜᵐ.

At head of title: Augmented and newly revised edition.

1. Harmony.

            38–9487

Library of Congress MT50.T11 1938

——— Copy 2.

Copyright A 115503 ⟨3⟩   781.3

NT 0036654 DLC WaU OrU ViU IEN MtU OrP WaSp OrStbM

Tapper, Thomas, 1864–
First year melody writing, by Thomas Tapper … Boston, New York [etc.] A. P. Schmidt, 1911.

iv, 135 p. 17ᶜᵐ. $1.00

1. Melody.

            11–21189

Library of Congress MT47.T2

     WaSp

NT 0036655 DLC NcC PWcS WU AzU NN OC1 OC1ND OrP WaS

Tapper, Thomas, 1864–
… First year melody writing, by Thomas Tapper … [Rev. and augm. ed.] Boston, New York, The Arthur P. Schmidt co., ©1946.

iv, 138 p. illus. (music) 17ᶜᵐ. (His First year series)

1. Melody.

            46–20770

Library of Congress MT47.T2 1946

        ⟨2⟩   781.4

NT 0036656 DLC IEN FU FMU WaS

Tapper, Thomas, 1864–
First year music history, by Thomas Tapper, ʟɪᴛᴛ. ᴅ. Boston, New York, The Arthur P. Schmidt co. [©1926]

v, 269 p. illus. (music) 19ᶜᵐ.

1. Music—Hist. & crit. 2. Music—Manuals, text-books, etc. ɪ. Title.

            28–682

Library of Congress MT160.T17

NT 0036657 DLC N OC1 ODW MB

Tapper, Thomas, 1864–1958.
First year musical theory (rudiments of music) by Thomas Tapper … Boston, New York [etc.] A. P. Schmidt, ©1912.

iii, 115 p. 17½ᶜᵐ. $1.00

1. Music—Manuals, text-books, etc.

            12–4469

Library of Congress MT7.T27

OOxM NN

NT 0036658 DLC WaS PWcS AzU OrP MtBC PPT OC1 OCU

Tapper, Thomas, 1864–
From Palestrina to Grieg; first year music biography, by Thomas Tapper … Boston, New York, The Arthur P. Schmidt co. [©1929]

v, 247 p. illus. (music) 20½ᶜᵐ.

Companion volume to the author's "First year music history".
cf. Pref.
"At the conclusion of each biography [except the first] the companion chapter of First year music history is recorded."—Pref.

1. Musicians. 2. Music—Manuals, text-books, etc. ɪ. Title.

            30–1785

Library of Congress ML390.T17F8

NT 0036659 DLC PRosC KEmT OKentU OrP OC1 MB NN

Tapper, Thomas, 1864–
… From Palestrina to Grieg; first year music biography, by Thomas Tapper, ʟɪᴛᴛ. ᴅ. [Rev. ed.] … Boston, New York, The Arthur P. Schmidt co., ©1946.

v, 247 p. illus. (music) 20½ᶜᵐ.

Companion volume to the author's First year music history. *cf.* Pref.
"At the conclusion of each biography [except the first] the companion chapter of First year music history is recorded."—Pref.

1. Composers. ɪ. Title.

ML390.T18 1946 927.8 47–617

NT 0036660 DLC ScU NcD IEN WaS

Tapper, Thomas, 1864–
Getting on in life, by Thomas Tapper … New York, The Platt & Peck co. [©1913]

89 p. 16ᶜᵐ. [The inspiration books, ed. by T. Tapper] $0.35

1. Success. ɪ. Title.

Library of Congress BJ1611.T3 13–15628

NT 0036661 DLC OC1W

Tapper, Thomas, 1864–1958, ed.
Graded pieces for four hands. Book 2.
= Boston. Oliver Ditson Co. 1911. v. Autograph facsimile. [Tapper's Graded piano course.] 31½ cm.

r18667 — S.r. — Pianoforte. Instruction book*

NT 0036662 MB

Tapper, Thomas, 1864– joint author.

Ripley, Frederic Herbert, 1854–
… Harmonic first reader, by Frederic H. Ripley … and Thomas Tapper … New York, Cincinnati [etc.] American book company [1903]

Tapper, Thomas, 1864– joint author.

Ripley, Frederic Herbert, 1854–
… Harmonic fifth reader (with bass) by Frederic H. Ripley … and Thomas Tapper … New York, Cincinnati [etc.] American book company [1904]

Tapper, Thomas, 1864– joint author.

Ripley, Frederic Herbert, 1854–
… Harmonic fourth reader, by Frederic H. Ripley … and Thomas Tapper … New York, Cincinnati [etc.] American book company [1903]

Tapper, Thomas, 1864– joint author.

         FOR OTHER EDITIONS
         SEE MAIN ENTRY

Ripley, Frederic Herbert, 1854–
… Harmonic primer, by Frederic H. Ripley … and Thomas Tapper … New York, Cincinnati [etc.] American book company [1903]

Tapper, Thomas, 1864–   joint author.

Ripley, Frederic Herbert, 1854–
... Harmonic second reader, by Frederic H. Ripley ... and Thomas Tapper ... New York, Cincinnati [etc.] American book company [1903]

Tapper, Thomas, 1864–   joint author.

Ripley, Frederic Herbert, 1854–
... Harmonic third reader, by Frederic H. Ripley ... and Thomas Tapper ... New York, Cincinnati [etc.] American book company [1903]

Tapper, Thomas, 1864– 1958
How to build a fortune, by Thomas Tapper ... New York, The Platt & Peck co. [ᶜ1913]

6 p., 2 l., 9–230 p. 18½ᵐ.

1. Saving and thrift.   I. Title.
Library of Congress   HG7931.T2

14—423

NT 0036669   DLC ICJ MB NN OC1

Tapper, Thomas, 1864–   joint author.

Azulay, Gertrude.
The illustrated book of great composers ... by Gertrude Azulay and Thomas Tapper ... London [etc.] Boosey & co., ltd. [1937]

Tapper, Thomas, 1864–1958
An illustrated history of music.   London: John Murray. 1915. xviii(i), 365 p., 1 pl. illus., port. 8°.
Music in text.
By Thomas Tapper and Percy Goetschius.

1. Goetschius, Percy, jt. au. 2.   Music.—History and criticism.
V. P. I.   December 20, 1915.

NT 0036671   NN MiD

Tapper, Thomas, 1864–
Key to "First year harmony," with additional exercises, by Thomas Tapper ... Boston, Leipzig [etc.] A. P. Schmidt, ᶜ1915.

66 p. 23ᵐ.

1. Harmony.
15–22994
Library of Congress   MT50.T111

NT 0036672   DLC NcGU IU OU NN

Tapper, Thomas, 1864–
Let's take an inventory, by Thomas Tapper, LITT. D.; prepared under the supervision of the Editorial board of the University society ... New York, The University society, incorporated [ᶜ1936]

vi, 130 (i. e. 131) p. incl. plates, diagr. 20½ᵐ. (Personal engineering series. [vol. I])
Extra numbered page inserted.

1. Conduct of life.   I. University society, New York.   II. Title.
36–15668
Library of Congress   BJ1581.T25
————— Copy 2.
Copyright A 96055   [5]   170

NT 0036673   DLC

Tapper, Thomas, 1864–
Little stories of inspiration, by Thomas Tapper ... New York, The Platt & Peck co. [ᶜ1913]

92 p. 16ᵐ. [The inspiration books, ed. by T. Tapper] $0.35

1. Success.   I. Title.
Library of Congress   HF5386.T18

14–328

NT 0036674   DLC ICRL OC1W ICJ

Tapper, Thomas, 1864–   ed.

Hale, Edward Everett, 1822–1909.
... The man without a country, by Edward Everett Hale; with introduction and notes by Thomas Tapper ... illustrated by L. J. Bridgman. Boston, The Page company, 1917.

Tapper, Thomas, 1864– 1958
Mastering your job, by Thomas Tapper, LITT. D. Prepared under the supervision of the editorial board of the University society ... New York, The University society, incorporated [ᶜ1936]

viii, 95 p. 20½ᵐ. (Personal engineering series. [vol. V])

1. Applications for position. 2. Success.   I. University society, New York.   II. Title.
36–13814
Library of Congress   HF5386.T185
————— Copy 2.
Copyright A 95403

NT 0036676   DLC OC1 OC1U

Tapper, Thomas, 1864–   joint author.

Ripley, Frederic Herbert, 1854–
... Melodic first reader, by Frederic H. Ripley ... and Thomas Tapper ... New York, Cincinnati [etc.] American book company [ᶜ1906]

Tapper, Thomas, 1864–   joint author.

Ripley, Frederic Herbert, 1854–
... Melodic fourth reader, by Frederic H. Ripley ... and Thomas Tapper ... New York, Cincinnati [etc.] American book company [ᶜ1906]

Tapper, Thomas, 1864–   joint author.

Ripley, Frederic Herbert, 1854–
... Melodic second reader, by Frederic H. Ripley ... and Thomas Tapper ... New York, Cincinnati [etc.] American book company [ᶜ1906]

Tapper, Thomas, 1864–   joint author.

Ripley, Frederic Herbert, 1854–
... Melodic third reader, by Frederic H. Ripley ... and Thomas Tapper ... New York, Cincinnati [etc.] American book company [ᶜ1906]

Tapper, Thomas, 1864–
Melody writing, first year. The Arthur P. Schmidt Co., 1911.

NT 0036681   OCX

Tapper, Thomas, 1864–
Mind training for efficiency, by Thomas Tapper, LITT. D. Prepared under the supervision of the editorial board of the University society ... New York, The University society, incorporated [ᶜ1936]

vi, 118 p., 1 l. 20½ᵐ. (Personal engineering series. [vol. II])
Bibliography : p. 116–118.

1. Mental discipline.   I. University society, New York.   II. Title.
36–13848
Library of Congress   BF636.T25
————— Copy 2.
Copyright A 95402   [5]   [159.98] 150.13

NT 0036682   DLC OC1U NN

Tapper, Thomas, 1854–   joint author.

Ripley, Frederic Herbert, 1854–
Music in the grades; a manual to accompany the Melodic music readers, by Frederic H. Ripley ... and Thomas Tapper ... New York, Cincinnati [etc.] American book company [ᶜ1906]

Tapper, Thomas, 1864–
The music life and how to succeed in it. By Thomas Tapper ... Philadelphia, T. Presser, 1891.

x, 9–346 p. 18ᵐ.

1. Music—Instruction and study.   I. Title.
6—12635
Library of Congress   ML3795.T17

MB WaSp WaS Or
NT 0036684   DLC PPC PP CoU IEN NIC KEmT OC1 OO OOxM

TAPPER, Thomas, 1864–
The music life and how to succeed in it.
=   Phila. Presser. 1892. x, 9–346 pp. 16°.

NT 0036685   MB WU PPCCH OU ODW MB

MT3   Tapper, Thomas, 1864–
U5T17   The music supervisor; his training, influence, and opportunity.   Boston, O. Ditson [ᶜ1906]
208 p. 19ᵐ.

1. School music supervision.   I. Title.   NUC

NT 0036686   CSt PU PP

Tapper, Thomas, 1864–
The music supervisor; his training, influence and opportunity, by Thomas Tapper, LITT. D. Boston, Oliver Ditson company; New York, C. H. Ditson & co.; [etc., etc., ᶜ1916]

208 p. illus. (plan, music) diagrs. 18½ᵐ.
Reprinted in part from various sources.
Bibliography : p. 203–208.

1. Music—Instruction and study.   I. Title.
16—18769
Library of Congress   MT10.T28

MB TNJ-P NN WU WaTU MtU IdU MtBC WaSp Or OrU
NT 0036687   DLC MoSW ODW OU OO OC1 CoU PWcS DHEW

Tapper, Thomas, 1864–1953
Music talks with children, by Thomas Tapper ... Philadelphia, T. Presser, 1897.

xii, 13–174 p. 18ᵐ.
"Works ... referred to": p. 173–174.

1. Music—Instruction and study.   I. Title.
6—32322
Library of Congress   ML3930.T174

Or WaSp WaS
NT 0036688   DLC IEdS PP PPT PWcS PPCPh OC1 OEac MB

Tapper, Thomas, *1864-*
    Music talks with children.   Philadelphia: Theodore Presser, 1901.   xii, 13-174 p.   16°.

    Bibliography, p. 173-174.

1. Music.
N. Y. P. L.   July 2, 1913.

NT   0036689   NN WaS ViU NcC

780.7
T167m
1925   TAPPER, THOMAS, 1864-
    Music talks with children, by Thomas Tapper ... Philadelphia, T. Presser co. [c1925]   xii, 13-174p.   18cm.

    "Works ... referred to": p.173-174.

    1. Music - Instruction and study.   I. Title.

NT   0036690   TxU

781.5
T16f   Tapper, Thomas, 1864-   ed.
sup.   ... Musical form and analysis, supplementary material to "First year analysis"; annotated, fingered and edited ...   Boston [etc.] The Arthur P. Schmidt co., c1914.
    55p.   (Schmidt's educational series, no.122)

    Plate no.: A.P.S. 10268²,

    1. Musical form.   I. Tapper, Thomas 1864-
First year analysis (musical form)

NT   0036691   IU OC1

Tapper, Thomas, 1864-   ed.
Musical record and review.
    Boston, O. Ditson & co.; [etc., etc.] 18

Tapper, Thomas, *1864-1958, ed.*
    One hundred rhythmic studies for the piano.
= Boston. Oliver Ditson Co. 1903. (4), 48 pp. F°.

F3940 — Pianoforte. Instruction books.

NT   0036693   MB

Tapper, Thomas, 1864-
    Pictures from the lives of the great composers for children [by] Thomas Tapper.   Philadelphia, T. Presser, 1899.
    v p., 2 l., 11-185 p.   18½ cm.

    1. Composers—Juvenile literature.   2. Music—Juvenile literature.

    ML3930.A2T33   0—75

NT   0036694   DLC PU PP OC1MN OC1 MB

JGN
ML
3930   Tapper, Thomas, 1864-
.T176   Pictures from the lives of the great composers for children [by] Thomas Tapper.   Philadelphia, T. Presser, 1903.
    185 p.

    #Musicians.

NT   0036695   MoU

---

q786.3   Tapper, Thomas, *1864-*
T16r   Relaxation. 10 studies in rhythm and expression for the pianoforte.   Boston, Arthur P. Schmidt, c1915.
    15p.   (Edition Schmidt, no.173)

NT   0036696   IU

Tapper, Thomas, 1864-   joint author.
Ripley, Frederic Herbert, 1854-
    ... Rote song book; first steps in music, by Frederic H. Ripley ... and Thomas Tapper ... New York, Cincinnati [etc.] American book company [c1902]

Tapper, Thomas, 1864-
    A score of famous men, by Thomas Tapper ... New York, The Platt & Peck co. [c1913]
    3 p. l., 9-112 p.   16ᵐᵐ.   [The inspiration books, ed. by T. Tapper] $0.35

    1. Biography.   I. Title.

    Library of Congress   CT107.T3   14-426

NT   0036698   DLC OC1W

Film
3143
Item 1   Tapper, Thomas, *1864-1958*
Music   Second year harmony.   Boston, A.P. Schmidt
Lib'y   [1911]
    141p.   17cm.

    Microfilm (negative)   1 reel (various items) 35mm.

    1. Harmony.

NT   0036699   TxU

Tapper, Thomas, 1864-
    Second year harmony (a sequel to "First year harmony") by Thomas Tapper ... Boston, New York [etc.] A. P. Schmidt, c1912.
    iii, 134 p.   17ᵐᵐ.

    1. Harmony.

    Library of Congress   MT50.T121   12—25173

    OC1ND NN
NT   0036700   DLC PWcS PSt MtBC WaSp WaS ViU OC1 OO

Tapper, Thomas, 1864-
    ... Second year harmony (a sequel to "First year harmony") by Thomas Tapper ... Boston, New York, The Arthur P. Schmidt co., c1932.
    1 p. l., 142 p.   illus. (music)   17½ᵐ.
    At head of title: Augmented and revised edition.

    1. Harmony.
    Library of Congress   MT50.T12 1932   32—30665
    ———— Copy 2.
    Copyright   A 56528   [2]   781.3

NT   0036701   DLC Or OrP WaSP MtU OrU

781.3
T175s   Tapper, Thomas, 1864-
1940   Second year harmony (A sequel to "First year harmony") Augm. and rev. ed.   Boston, A.P. Schmidt, 1940.
    142p.   illus.(music)   17cm.

    1. Harmony.   I. Title.

NT   0036702   IEN OrU

Tapper, Thomas, 1864—   ed.
    The seven keys to success; based on the Franklin system of personal advancement; Thomas Tapper, LITT. D., editor-in-chief.   New York, The University society, incorporated [c1939, ©1971] p.   22ᵐ.
    Each of the seven "keys" was originally published separately in the Personal engineering series. The first was published under title: Body training for service; the second: Mind training for efficiency; the third: Everyone an executive; the fourth: Mastering your job; the fifth: Business technic; the sixth: Applying salesmanship in business and personal life; the seventh: Financial independence. Each is preceded by a page of explanatory letterpress and has special t.-p. and separate paging.

    CONTENTS.—Preface.—key I. Maintaining health and energy, by H. J. Johnson.—key II. Developing mental power, by Thomas Tapper.—key III. Building an executive personality, by Thomas Tapper.—key IV. Mastering a job, by Thomas Tapper.—key V. Learning a business, by D. S. Beasley.—key VI. Applying salesmanship, by D. S. Beasley.—key VII. Gaining financial security, by L. F. Smith.

    1. Success.   I. Title.
    Library of Congress   HF5386.T187 1939   39-20229
    ———— Copy 2.
    Copyright   A 130662   [2]   174

NT   0036704   DLC PP CoU

Tapper, Thomas, 1864-   **joint author.**
Ripley, Frederic Herbert, 1854-
    ... A short course in music ... by Frederic H. Ripley ... and Thomas Tapper ... New York, Cincinnati [etc.] American book company [1898]

---

q786.3   Tapper, Thomas, *1864-1958*
T16s   Sight reading and memory lessons for the pianoforte.   Boston, Arthur P. Schmidt, c1906.
    48p.   (Schmidt's educational series, no.12)

NT   0036706   IU OO OrP

Thóroddsen, Jón Þórðarson, 1819-1868.
    Sigrid, an Icelandic love story. By Jon Thordsson Thoroddsen. Translated from the Danish by C. Chrest. Edited by Thomas Tapper, jun. New York, T. Y. Crowell & co. [1887]

780.7   Tapper, Thomas, *1864-*
T16ma   Study plan and questionnaire on the chapters of The music supervisor. Designed for individual and for class room use.   [New York, c1916]
    11p.

NT   0036708   IU

M786.3
T175   Tapper, Thomas, 1864-   ed.
Music   Tapper's graded piano course.   Boston,
lib.   O. Ditson, c1906.
    38p.   33cm.   (Graded studies, Book III)

    1. Piano - Studies and exercises.   I. Title.

NT   0036709   NcU OC1

Tapper, Thomas, 1864-
    Tapper's graded piano course. Manual for teacher and pupil. Boston, O. Ditson, c1906.
    3 v.   33 cm.

    Vol. 1-3. Imperfect: cover and t. p. of v. 1 wanting. Title from v. 2. Vol. 1 may have been published by A. P. Schmidt, Boston. CONTENTS. - Grade 1. Lessons in form, melody and dictation. - Grade 2. Lessons in form and melody. - Grade 3. Lessons in form

Continued in next column

Continued from preceding column

and harmonic analysis.

 1. Piano music, Juvenile - Collections.
2. Music - Theory, Elementary.
(1) TITLE: Graded piano course.

NT 0036711 NN MB

Tapper, Thomas, 1864–
 ...Graded piano course....Graded studies
Bost. 1926.

 v. 1.

NT 0036712 OCl

Tapper, Thomas, 1864-1958, ed.
Browning, Robert, 1812–1889.
 ... The young folks Browning; selected from the poems of
Robert Browning, with introduction and notes by Thomas
Tapper ... illustrated by Louis Meynell. Boston, The Page
company, 1919.

Tapper, Thomas, 1864-1958.
 Youth and opportunity; being chapters on the factors
of success, by Thomas Tapper ... New York, The Platt
& Peck co. [1912]
 301 p. 18½ᶜᵐ. $1.00

 1. Success. I. Title.

— —Library of Congress HF5386.T2 12—9676

NT 0036714 DLC PU PPT NcC IaU NcD OrP OClW OCl OO NN

R629.126 Tapper, Thomas Pitt Cholmondeley.
T167a Amateur racing driver. London, G. T.
 Foulis [1954?]
 172 p. illus.

 1. Automobile racing I. T.

NT 0036715 MiD

TAPPER, Walther.
 Die haftung für tierschäden nach §§833,
834 B.G.B. Inaug.-dis. Münster i.W. Berlin,
sw.13. 1904.

NT 0036716 MH-L ICRL

Tappermann, Franz, 1906–
 Synthese von Verbindungen der a-Phenoxy-
a'-phenyl-aceton-reihe. (Vorstufen zur
Hämatoxylinsynthese)... Bonn, 1931.
 Inaug.-diss. - Bonn.
 Lebenslauf.
 [Full name: Franz Wilhelm Theodor
Tappermann]

NT 0036717 CtY

Tappert, C **Reinhold**
 Der artikel über die höllenfahrt
Christi. n.p., n.p., [pref. 1901]

 36 p.

NT 0036718 PPLT NcD

Tappert (Carol. Ludov. Franciac.) [1800–].
*De ossium regeneratae nonnulla, adjecto casu
singulari regeneratae mandibulae. 26 pp., 2 l.
8°. Berolini, F. Nietack, [1831]. [Also, in: P.,
v. 1508.]

NT 0036719 DNLM

Tappert, Edwin Carl
 A Greek hagiologic manuscript in Phila-
delphia.
 [Ph. 1937.] Pamp. 13 pp.

 (Reprinted from Transactions of the American Philological Association. Vol.
LXVIII. 1937.)

NT 0036720 PPL PPLT

Tappert, Dionys Maria, O. Carth.
 Der heilige Bruno, Stifter des Karthäuser-
Ordens, in seinem leben und wirken. Luxemburg,
Peter Brück, 1872.

 8-526 p. front. 21 cm.

 1. Bruno, Saint, 1039 (ca.) - 1101.
2. Carthusians.

NT 0036721 PLatS NjPT

Microfilm Tappert, Esther Elizabeth
Hum. International intellectual and cultural
64–8 cooperation between two wars. New Haven, Conn.,
 Yale University Photographic Services [1945]

 Microfilm copy (negative) of typescript.
 Collation of the original: 316l.
 Thesis - Yale University.
 Bibliography: leaves [301]-316.

 1. Intellectual cooperation 2. League of Nations.
Intellectual Co-operation Organization I. Title.

NT 0036722 NBC

Tappert, Georg Wilhelm, 1880–
 ...Acht unveröffentlichte schnitte und
ein titelschnitt vom stock gedruckt,
mit einem text von Dietrich. Kiel,
November-verlag 1918 [c1919]
 [6] p. 8 pl.(1 col.) (Der schwarze
turm. heft.3)

 Limited ed.

NT 0036723 NjP

Tappert, Gustave Heinrich.
 Gedenkbuch zum 25- jährigen jubilaeum der
St. Paulus gemeinde
  see under Highland, Ill. Sankt Paulus
Katholische Gemeinde. [supplement]

Tappert, Hermann, 1887– Die Entwicklung des Brandversicherungs-
 wesens in Thüringen. Hannover: Rechts-, staats- u. sozialwiss.
 Verl. 1914. 37 S. 8° ¶ Vollst. als: Abhandlungen d.
 Gesellsch. f. feuerversicherungsgeschichtl. Forschung. Bd 2,
 u. als: Abhandlungen aus d. Gebiet d. Feuerversicherungs-
 wissensch. Bd 23.
 Jena, Phil. Diss. v. 18. Jan. 1914, Ref. Pierstorff
 [Geb. 5. Okt. 87 Eisenach; Wohnort: Jena; Staatsangeh.: Sachsen-Weimar;
 Vorbildung: RG. Eisenach Reife 07; Studium: Jena 2, München 1, Berlin 1,
 Jena 3 S.; Rig. 19. Juli 13.] [U 14. 4019]

NT 0036725 ICRL MH CtY

Tappert, John George, 1906–
 An experimental investigation of de Broglie's equation ...
[by] John George Tappert ... Philadelphia, 1938.
 1 p. l., p. 1085–1088. 2 diagr. 26½ x 20ᶜᵐ.
 Thesis (PH. D.)—University of Pennsylvania, 1938.
 "Reprint from the Physical review, vol. 54, no. 12, December 15, 1938."

 1. Wave mechanics. 2. *Broglie, Louis, prince de, 1892–
I. Title: De Broglie's equation.

 Library of Congress QC174.2.T3 1938 39–11919
 Univ. of Pennsylvania Libr.
 ——— ———Copy 2. [3] 530.1

NT 0036726 PU NcD PSC PPD OCU DLC MH

016.92 **Tappert, Katherine.**
T26v ... Viewpoints in biography, an arrangement of books
 according to their essential interest, by Katherine Tappert ... Chicago, American library association publishing board, 1921.
 69 p. 23½ᶜᵐ. (The Viewpoint series, Josephine Adams Rathbone, editor)
 Arranged under subjects, with author and subject indexes.
 Annotated.

 1. Biography—Bibl. I. American library association. II. Title.

 Library of Congress Z5301.T17 21—26897

 CaBVaU KEmT WaWW WaS
NT 0036727 DLC WaTU OrP IdU MH PSt Wa IdU-SB ICJ

Tappert, Theodore Gerhardt, 1904–
 Die anpassung der Lutherischen Kirche
Europas an die amerikanische umgebung.
 [34] p. O.
 n. t. p.
 Vorlesung auf der 8. Hochschultagung der
Luther-Akademie in Sondershausen, August, 1939.
 Zeitschrift für systematische theologie,
 17. jahrgang, 1. vierteljahrsheft, p. [51] 184.

NT 0036728 PPRETS

Tappert, Theodore Gerhardt, 1904–
 The church in the changing world. Philadelphia, Muhlenberg Press [1949]
 144 p. illus., maps. 20 cm.
 "Based upon ... [the author's] The church through the ages [pub-
lished in 1941]"
 Bibliography: p. 141–144.

 1. Church history. I. Tappert, Theodore Gerhardt, 1904– The
church through the ages. II. Title.

 BR146.T29 270 50–4616

NT 0036729 DLC PPLT

Tappert, Theodore Gerhardt, 1904–
 ... The church through the ages; a study of the history of the
Christian church [by] Theodore G. Tappert. Philadelphia
Pa., The United Lutheran publication house [1941]
 144 p. 19½ᶜᵐ. (The Lutheran leadership course)
 "Prepared under the auspices of the Parish and church school board
of the United Lutheran church in America."
 Includes bibliographies.

 1. Church history. I. United Lutheran church in America. Parish
and church school board. II. Title.
   41–23373
 Library of Congress BR146.T3
  [3] 270

NT 0036730 DLC NcD

BR146 Tappert, Theodore Gerhardt, 1904– The church
.T29 through the ages.

 Tappert, Theodore Gerhardt, 1904–
 The church in the changing world. Philadelphia, Muhlenberg Press [1949]

Tappert, Theodore Gerhardt, 1904–
Henry Melchior Muhlenberg and the American Revolution, by Theodore G. Tappert... ₍Scottdale, Pa., 1942₎ 19 p. 25cm.

"Reprinted from Church history, vol. xi, no. 4, December, 1942."

1. Muhlenberg, Henry Melchior,   1711–1787.
N. Y. P. L.   December 30, 1943

NT 0036732   NN PPLT

Tappert, Theodore Gerhardt, 1904–
FOR OTHER EDITIONS
SEE MAIN ENTRY
Sasse, Hermann, 1895–
Here we stand; nature and character of the Lutheran faith, by Hermann Sasse ... translated, with revisions and additions, from the second German edition, by Theodore G. Tappert. New York and London, Harper & brothers ₍°1938₎

Tappert, Theodore Gerhardt, 1904–   tr.

Muhlenberg, Henry Melchior, 1711–1787.
The journals of Henry Melchior Muhlenberg ... translated by Theodore G. Tappert and John W. Doberstein ... Philadelphia, The Evangelical Lutheran ministerium of Pennsylvania and adjacent states and the Muhlenberg press, 1942–

BR331
.E5T3
Tappert, Theodore Gerhardt, 1904–   ed. and tr.

Luther, Martin, 1483–1546.
Letters of spiritual counsel. Edited and translated by Theodore G. Tappert. Philadelphia, Westminster Press ₍1955₎

Tappert, Theodore Gerhardt, 1904–
Our neighbors' churches. ₍Philadelphia, Muhlenberg Press ₍1954₎
96 p. illus. 18 cm. (Faith and action series)

1. Sects—U. S.   I. Title.
BR516.T35   280.973   54–4810 ‡

NT 0036736   DLC WaSp PPLT

Tappert, T₍heodore₎ G₍erhardt₎, 1904–
The prospects of the Lutheran Church in America.   Phil.n.p.1945.
16p.O.

Pub.under the auspices of the German Conference of the Evangelical Lutheran Ministerium of Pa.

NT 0036737   PPLT

BR325
.B57
Tappert, Theodore Gerhardt, 1904–   joint tr.

Boehmer, Heinrich, 1869–1927.
Road to reformation ₍by₎ Heinrich Boehmer; Martin Luther to the year 1521, translated from the German by John W. Doberstein and Theodore G. Tappert ... Philadelphia, Pa., Muhlenberg press, 1946.

Tappert, T₍heodore₎ G₍erhardt₎, 1904–
The symbols of the Church.   (see Fendt, E₍C₎   ed.   What Lutherans are thinking.   ₍c1947₎   p.345–367).

Tappert, Walter, 1900–
Die geschaeftsfaehigkeit bei einem fall von seniler Demenz.
Inaug. diss.   Bonn, 1926.
Bibl.

NT 0036740   ICRL DNLM CtY

Tappert, Wilfried Carl Heinrich
Angels' Christmas; a pageant for the Christmastide.   Phil., U.L.P.H., ₍1929₎
21 p.

NT 0036741   PPLT

Tappert, Wilfried Carl Heinrich.
The cross of glory, an Easter pageant, by Wilfried Tappert. Philadelphia, Pa., The United Lutheran publication house ₍1931₎
26 p. 18¼ᵐ.

1. Easter—Drama.   I. Title.
CA 31–174 Unrev'd
Library of Congress   PN6120.E2T3
Copyright A 33652   792

NT 0036742   DLC PPLT RPB

Tappert, Wilfried Carl Heinrich.
The Holy Night; a Christmas pageant, by Wilfried Tappert. Philadelphia, Pa.: The United Lutheran Publ. House₍, 1925₎.
26 p. illus. (music.)   12°.

In 4 parts.
Incidental music given or indicated.

1. Christmas—Drama. 2. Pageants.   3. Title.
N. Y. P. L.   September 3, 1926

NT 0036743   NN PPLT

Tappert, Wilfried Carl Heinrich.
Immanuel, a Christmas mystery, by Wilfried Tappert. Philadelphia, Pa., The United Lutheran publication house ₍°1931₎
29 p. 19ᵐ.

1. Christmas plays.   I. Title.
CA 32–5 Unrev'd
Library of Congress   PN6120.C5T25
——— Copy 2.
Copyright A 42984   [394.268] 812.5

NT 0036744   DLC PPLT

TAPPERT, WILFRIED Carl Heinrich.
The light of the world; a Christmas pageant, by Wilfried Tappert.   New York [etc.] E.Kaufmann, Inc. [1935]
23 p.   18½cm.

Cover-title.

836195A. 1. Pageants—U.S. 2. Christmas—Drama. I. Title.

NT 0036745   NN

Tappert, Wilfried Carl Heinrich.
The Resurrection story; a pantomime, by Wilfried C. H. Tappert.   Philadelphia: United Lutheran Publ. House₍, cop. 1927₎.
20 p.   12°.

1. Pantomime. 2. Title.
N. Y. P. L.   September 20, 1927

NT 0036746   NN PPLT

Tappert, Wilhelm, 1830–1907, ed.
Allgemeine musik-zeitung
see under title

Tappert, Wilhelm, 1830–1907, ed.
Conversations-lexikon der tonkunst. Hrsg. als beilage der Neuen musikzeitung. Köln, P. J. Tonger ₍1881–85₎

Tappert, Wilhelm, 1830–1907.
Deutsche Lieder aus dem 15. 16. und 17. Jahrhundert für ein Singstimme mit Begleitung des Pianoforte frei bearbeitet.   Berlin, C. A. Challier and Co. [18–]
1 p. l., 50 p.   4°.

NT 0036749   NN MH

Tappert, Wilhelm, 1830–
... Die entwicklung der musik-notenschrift vom 8. jahrhundert bis zur gegenwart. Katalog der special-ausstellung von Wilh. Tappert. Berlin, mai 1898 ... ₍Berlin, W. Büxenstein, 1898₎
22 p. 17½ᵐ.

At head of title: Allgemeine musik-ausstellung zur errichtung eines Wagner-denkmals in Berlin ...

1. Music—Bibl.—Catalogs. 2. Musical notation.
Library of Congress   MT 141 N8T2   6–23626

NT 0036750   DLC

Tappert, Wilhelm, 1830–1907.
Fifty studies for the left hand alone. Book 1–2.   New York: G. Schirmer ₍cop. 1892₎.   Publ. pl. nos. 10213–10214.   2 v. in 1. f°.   (G. Schirmer's edition of pianoforte studies.)

Cover-title.
Revised and fingered by Wilhelm Scharfenberg.

1. Piano.—Studies (left hand).   2. Scharfenberg, Wilhelm, 1819–95, editor.
N. Y. P. L.   June 9, 1916.

NT 0036751   NN

Tappert, Wilhelm, 1830–1907.
Für und wider. Eine blumenlese aus den berichten über die aufführungen des bühnenweihfestspieles Parsifal. Hrsg. von Wilhelm Tappert. Berlin, T. Barth, 1882.
50 p. 22½ᵐ.

1. Wagner, Richard—Performances—Baireuth.
13–33552
Library of Congress   ML410.W17T2

NT 0036752   DLC NIC MB

Tappert, Wilhelm, 1830–1907.
Leitfaden für die besucher des Richard Wagner'schen bühnenfestspiels: "Der ring des Nibelungen." Geschichtliche und erläuternde mittheilungen, von Wilhelm Tappert. Berlin, H. Weinholtz (P. Heyder) 1881.
58 p., 1 l.   20ᵐ.

1. Wagner, Richard. Der ring des Nibelungen.
10–24338
Library of Congress   MT100.W25T3

NT 0036753   DLC

Tappert, Wilhelm, 1830–
Musik und musikalische erziehung. Von Wilhelm Tappert ... Berlin, J. Guttentag, 1867.
72 p. 22ᶜᵐ.

1. Music—Instruction and study.

Library of Congress   MT1.T17
6–4739

NT 0036754   DLC CU

Tappert, Wilhelm, 1830–1907.
Musikalische studien. Von Wilhelm Tappert ... Berlin, I. Guttentag, 1868.
3 p. l., ₍3₎–252 p. 21½ᶜᵐ.
CONTENTS.—Wandernde melodien.—Ein umbildungs-process.—Der übermässige dreiklang.— Die alterirten akkorde. — Ein dogma. — Zooplastik in tönen.

1. Music—Addresses, essays, lectures.
15–576

Library of Congress   ML60.T29

NT 0036755   DLC OCH CtY CU NN MB

Tappert, Wilhelm, 1830–1907.
Richard Wagner im spiegel der kritik; wörterbuch der unhöflichkeit, enthaltend grobe, höhnende, gehässige und verleumderische ausdrücke, die gegen den meister Richard Wagner, seine werke und seine anhänger von den feinden und spöttern gebraucht wurden; zur gemütsergötzung in müssigen stunden gesammelt von Wilhelm Tappert. 2., bedeutend verm. und umgearb. aufl. des "Wagnerlexikons." Leipzig, C. F. W. Siegel's musikalienhandlung (R. Linnemann) 1903.
vii, ₍1₎, 106 p. 22½ᶜᵐ.
1. Wagner, Richard, 1813–1883.
5–4941

Library of Congress   ML410.W19T17

NT 0036756   DLC MH NcD NN

ML
410
W19
T17
1915
Tappert, Wilhelm, 1830–1907.
Richard Wagner im spiegel der kritik; wörterbuch der unhöflichkeit, enthaltend grobe, höhnende, gehässige und verleumderische ausdrücke, die gegen den meister Richard Wagner, seine werke und seine anhänger, von den feinden und spöttern gebraucht wurden; zur gemütsergötzung in müssigen stunden gesammelt von Wilhelm Tappert. 3. Aufl. des Wagnerlexikons. Leipzig, C.F.W. Siegel's Musikalienhandlung (R. Linnemann) 1915.

vii, 106 p. 22 cm.

1. Wagner, Richard, 1813–1883. I. Title.

NT 0036758   CaBVaU CU NIC MH IEN TxU MiU

Tappert, Wilhelm, 1830–1907.
Richard Wagner, sein leben und seine werke; von Wilhelm Tappert. Elberfeld, S. Lucas, 1883.
viii, 100, ₍3₎ p. incl. double facsim. front. (port.) 22½ᶜᵐ.
"Chronologisches verzeichniss der musikalisch-dramatischen werke Richard Wagner's": p. ₍98₎–100.

1. Wagner, Richard, 1813–1883.
9–7880

Library of Congress   ML410.W1T1

NT 0036759   DLC MB

M
40
'17s
TAPPERT, WILHELM, 1830–1907, comp.
Sang und klang aus alter zeit. Hundert musikstücke aus tabulaturen des XVI. bis XVIII. jahrhunderts. Gesammelt und übersetzt von Wilhelm Tappert. Mit dem portrait des letzten lautenisten Christian Gottlieb Scheidler... Berlin, L. Liepmannssohn ₍pref.1906₎
129p. 23x27cm.

Contains pieces of tablature in facsimile of old notation with transcription in modern notation as well as   compositions in modern notation only.

IaU CaBVaU
NT 0036760   ICN NcD NIC TxU CtY MiU NcU MH NN ICU

Tappert, Wilhelm, 1830–
Sebastian Bachs compositionen für die laute, von Wilhelm Tappert. ₍Berlin, 1901₎
16 p. 27ᶜᵐ.
p. 12–16, advertising matter.
Sonderdruck aus den "Redenden künsten," VI. jahrgang, heft 36–40.

1. Bach, Johann Sebastian, 1685–1750.
6–39977

Library of Congress   ML410.B13T2

NT 0036761   DLC ICN

TAPPERT, WILHELM, 1830–1907.
Sebastian Bachs Compositionen für die Laute, von Wilhelm Tappert. [Berlin, 1901] 16 p. 27cm.

Microfiche (neg.) 1 sheet. 11 x 15cm. (NYPL FSN 10, 567)
P.12–16, advertising matter.
"Sonderabdruck aus den Redenden Künsten,' VI. Jahrgang, Heft 36–40."

1. Bach, Johann Sebastian—— Lute music. 2. Bach, Johann Sebastian. Lute music.

NT 0036762   NN

Tappert, Wilhelm, 1830–1907.
70 Erlkönig-kompositionen. Gesammelt von Wilhelm Tappert. Katalog. Neue und verm. ausg. ... Berlin, A. Stahl, 1906.
16 p. illus. (facsims., music) 18ᶜᵐ.
"Die erste ausgabe dieses katalogs, betitelt: '54 Erlkönig-kompositionen', erschien 1898. Im nächsten jahre liess ich die Nachträge A–E drucken. Mit einem Nachtrag F ist diese neue ausgabe vermehrt."
Slip bearing additional title (71, "erhalten mai 1907") mounted on p. 16.
1. Goethe, Johann Wolfgang von. Erlkönig—Bibl. 2. Goethe, Johann Wolfgang von—Music. I. Title: Erlkönig kompositionen.
8–314 Revised

Library of Congress   ML2862.T17
₍r33h2₎   781.97

NT 0036763   DLC CtY

---

qMT
226
.T37S8
Tappert, Wilhelm, 1830–1907.
Studies for the left hand alone ₍by₎ W. Tappert. Rev. and fingered by Wm. Scharfenberg. ₍New York₎ G. Schirmer, c1892.
2 v. in 1. 35 cm. (G. Schirmer's standard edition of pianoforte studies)

1. Piano—Studies and exercises. I. Title.

NT 0036764   OkU

Tappert, Wilhelm, 1830
Das verbot der quinten-parallelen. Eine monographische studie, von Wilhelm Tappert. Leipzig, H. Matthes, 1869.
1 p. l., 98 p. 15 x 11ᶜᵐ.

1. Harmony.
8–6400†

Library of Congress   MT50.T17

NT 0036765   DLC CtY

Tappert, Wilhelm, 1830–1907, compiler.
54 Erlkönig-Kompositionen. Gesammelt von Wilh. Tappert. Berlin: L. Liepmannssohn, 1898. 14 p. illus. (music.) 12°.
With this is bound his: Nachträge zum Erlkönig Kataloge. Berlin, 1899. 12 p. illus. (music.) 12°.

1. Goethe, Johann Wolfgang von: Erlkönig.
N. Y. P. L.   January 14, 1920.

NT 0036766   NN MH MB CtY CU

Tappert, Wilhelm, 1830–1907.
Ein Wagner-lexicon. Wörterbuch der unhöflichkeit enthaltend grobe, höhnende, gehässige und verläumderische ausdrücke welche gegen den meister Richard Wagner, seine werke und seine anhänger von den feinden und spöttern gebraucht worden sind. Zur gemüths-ergötzung in müssigen stunden gesammelt von Wilhelm Tappert. Leipzig, E. W. Fritzsch, 1877.
iv p., 1 l., 48 p., 1 l. 22¾ᶜᵐ.

1. Wagner, Richard, 1813–1883. I. Title.
5—20183

Library of Congress   ML410.W19T16

NT 0036767   DLC IEN ViU MH

Tappert, Wilhelm, 1830–
Wandernde melodien. Eine musikalische studie, von Wilhelm Tappert. 2. verm. und verb. aufl. Berlin, Brachvogel & Ranft, 1889.
2 p. l., 95, ₍1₎ p. 22½ᶜᵐ.
With music.

Subject entries: 1. Melody. 2. Folk-songs.
8–81829

Library of Congress, no.   ML2950.T175.

NT 0036768   DLC MH CtY NcU ViU NjP CU NN

Tappert, Wilhelm, 1830–1907.
₍Gesänge. Op. 12, no. 1–2₎
Zwei Gesänge für eine tiefere Stimme mit obligatem Cello und Begleitung des Claviers, componirt von W. Tappert. Op. 12... Berlin: T. Barth ₍ca. 1875₎ Publ. pl. no. B. 72. 2 parts in 1 v. 23½cm.
Songs for 1 voice with violoncello obligato and piano accompaniment in score.
Violoncello part.
CONTENTS.—Im Frühlinge.—Wiegenlied.

1. Songs, with various instruments.   2. Songs, German.
N. Y. P. L.   June 8, 1936.

NT 0036769   NN

TAPPERT, Wilhelm, 1830–1907.
12 alte deutsche lieder für eine singstimme mit begleitung des pianoforte frei bearbeitet. Berlin, ₍18..₎.
4°. pp.21.

NT 0036770   MH

Tappert, Wilhelm, 1860–
Bilder und vergleiche aus dem Orlando innamorato Bojardo's und dem Orlando furioso Ariosto's. Nach form und inhalt untersucht ... Marburg, Univ.-buchdr. (R. Friedrich) 1885.
2 p. l., 50 p. 21ᶜᵐ.
Inaug.-diss.—Marburg.
Lebenslauf.
Published in full as Ausgaben und abhandlungen aus dem gebiete der romanischen philologie ₍hft.₎ 56 (2 p. l., 129 p.)

1. Bojardo, Matteo Maria, conte di Scandiano, 1434–1494. Orlando innamorato. 2. Ariosto, Lodovico. Orlando furioso. 3. Simile.
26–3546

Library of Congress   PQ4570.T3

NT 0036771   DLC NcD NjP MH

Tappert, Wilhelm, 1860–

... Bilder und vergleiche aus dem Orlando innamorato Bojardo's und dem Orlando furioso Ariosto's. Nach form und inhalt untersucht, von Wilhelm Tappert. Marburg, N. G. Elwert, 1886.

2 p. l., 129 p. 23ᶜᵐ. (Ausgaben und abhandlungen aus dem gebiete der romanischen philologie ... 56)

Published in part (2 p. l., 50 p.) as the author's inaugural dissertation, Marburg, 1885.

1. Bojardo, Matteo Maria, conte di Scandiano, 1434–1494. Orlando innamorato. 2. Ariosto, Lodovico. Orlando furioso. 3. Simile.

                       22—18499

Library of Congress   PC13.A87 hft. 56

     WaU
NT 0036772   DLC PBm CaBVaU OU MiU OClW IU MB MdBP CU

Tappert, William, ed.

Verhandlungen der zweiten allgemeiner deutsch-amerikanischen Katholiken-versammlung
see under   Congress of German Speaking Catholics of the United States of America. [supplement]

Tapperts, Eduardus, 1864–

De coniunctionum usu apud manilium quaestiones selectae.
Inaug. diss.   Munster, 1892.

NT 0036774   ICRL NjP

Tappertz, Paul, 1901–

Die Haftpflicht des Kraftfahrzeughalters bei unbefugter Benutzung des Fahrzeuges, unter Berücksichtigung des bisherigen österreichischen Rechts. Köln, Dissertationsdruckerei Orthen, 1940.

50 p. 22 cm.

Inaug.-Diss.—Cologne.
Lebenslauf.
"Verzeichnis der benutzten Schriften": p. 5–6.

1. Automobiles—Laws and regulations—Germany. 2. Torts—Germany. I. Title.

                       49–43892*

NT 0036775   DLC

Tappeser (Johann) [1878–]. *Beitrag zur Casuistik der Gliome des Gross und Kleinhirnes, des Rückenmarks und der Retina. [Würtzburg.] 28 pp., 2 l. 8°. *Altenessen, W Lehmann, 1902.

NT 0036776   DNLM ICRL

Tappeser (Leonhard) [1904–]. *Ueber Frühfälle von Tabes dorsalis. 34 pp. 8°. Bonn, P. Kubens, 1928.

NT 0036777   DNLM ICRL CtY

Tappeser, Wilhelm.

Versuche über die Verdunstung des Wassers. München, R. Oldenbourg, 1944.

14 p. illus. 30 cm. (Beihefte zum Gesundheits-Ingenieur, Reihe 1, Heft 40)

"Schrifttum": p. 14.

1. Evaporation.   (Series: Der Gesundheits-Ingenieur. Beihefte, Reihe 1, Heft 40)

QC304.T25   536.44   50–49194

NT 0036778   DLC

Il Tappeto nero, racconto originale ... Firenze, Dalla tipografia e calcografia Goldoniana, 1823.

40 p. 2 plates 14 cm.

Bound with: Bertolotti, Davide. Il sasso rancio. Firenze, 1823.

NT 0036779   CtY

Tappey (Ernest T[aylor]) [1853–]. Intraperitoneal adhesions. 4 pp. 8°. [New York, 1895.]
Repr. from: Am. Gynec. & Obst. J., N. Y., 1895, vii.

NT 0036780   DNLM

La tappezzeria di Bayeux
see under   Lejard, André, 1899– [supplement]

Tappi, G   Joint author.

Esercitazioni di chimica farmaceutica analisi qualitativa
see under   Angeletti, Antonio.

4HD-888   **Tappi, Manlio.**

Considerazioni sulle transformazioni fondiarie in Tripolitania. Firenze, Istituto agricolo coloniale italiano, 1927.

62 p. (Relazioni e monografie agrario-coloniali, n. 13)

NT 0036783   DLC-P4

Tappi. v. [1]– 1918–

[Easton, Pa., etc., Technical Association of the Pulp and Paper Industry]

v. in illus. 31 cm.

Annual? 1918– (semiannual? 1926–27); monthly, Jan. 1949–

Vol. numbers irregular: v. 1– (1918–) called ser. 1–
Title varies: 1918, Papers and addresses presented at the annual meeting of the Technical Association of the Pulp and Paper Industry (cover title: Technical Association papers)—1919, Technical papers and addresses ... (cover title: Technical Association papers)—1920—Technical Association papers.

INDEXES:
     Author index:
       Vols. 1–25, 1918–42, in v. 26.

1. Paper making and trade—Period. I. Technical Association of the Pulp and Paper Industry.

TS1080.T3   676.06273   19–5316 rev*

Library of Congress   [r52p3]

    CU-SB NcRS NNC PP OU MiU
    CL CaBVaU ICJ CaBVa WaS WaT OrP NN TxU LU PU PSC
NT 0036785   DLC OrCS MtBC MB Wa Or IU DNAL NhU CaOTP

Tappi Committee on Abstracts and Bibliography
see   Technical Association of the Pulp and Paper Industry. Committee on Abstracts and Bibliography.

Tappi standards
see under   [Technical Association of the Pulp and Paper Industry]

Tappie,

... De la réforme des Justices de paix; discours prononcé à l'audience solennelle de rentrée, le 4 novembre 1879, par m. Tappie, avocat général. Bordeaux, G. Gounouilhou, 1879.

29 p. 21ᶜᵐ.

At head of title: Cour d'appel de Bordeaux.
No. 17 in a volume of pamphlets lettered: Magistrats bordelais.

1. Justices of the peace—France. 2. France. Justices de paix. I. France. Cour d'appel (Bordeaux) II. Title.

                       32–23621

NT 0036788   DLC

Tappin, Clarence Leon, 1892–

French culture, by Clarence L. Tappin ... and Dorothy M. Crawford ... New York, N. Y., Globe book company [*1939]

viii, 88 p. illus. 19½ᶜᵐ.

Discussion of each topic in English, followed by questions and answers in French.

1. French language—Chrestomathies and readers. 2. France—Civilization. I. Crawford, Dorothy M., joint author. II. Title.

Library of Congress   PC2127.C5T3   39–25475
——— Copy 2.
Copyright A 132631   [2]   448.6

NT 0036789   DLC OCl

Tappin, Harold.

[Wytche Hazelle. Piano-vocal score. English]

Wytche Hazelle; Hasty Pudding play, 1900. Libretto and lyrics by J. H. Holliday and E. L. Dudley. Boston, O. Ditson [*1900]

85 p. 28 cm.

1. College operas, revues, etc.—Harvard. I. Holliday, John Hodgman, d. 1947. Wytche Hazelle. II. Dudley, Edward Lawrence, 1879– Wytche Hazelle. III. Title.

M1504.T174WF   M 54–1063

NT 0036790   DLC RPB MB

Tapping, Amy Pryor.

American child health association.

Porto Rico; an inquiry into the health, nutritional and social conditions in Porto Rico as they may affect children. [By] Committee of American child health association staff, Samuel J. Crumbine ... Harold H. Mitchell ... Amy Pryor Tapping ... New York city, American child health association [1930?]

Tapping (T[homas]) 1817–1886.

Derbyshire lead-mining terms; with a reprint of Manlove's 'Rhymed chronicle.' (In: Eng. Dialect Soc. [Pub.] *London*, 1874. 8°. v. 5, pp. 1–41.)

NT 0036792   NN MdBP

Tapping, Thomas, 1817–1886.

An exposition of the statutes (5 & 6 Vict. cap. 99, and 23 & 24 Vict. cap. 151), passed for the regulation of ore-mines, collieries, and ironstone mines, designed as a practical guide for official inspectors, owners, viewers, captains, managers, and agents, with reference to governmental inspection and the employment of mine labour under the above statutes; also, a notice of the Truck act, (1 & 2 W. 4, cap. 37), and a carefully prepared form of pit bond, with notes, an appendix of the abov [1] statutes, and a copious index. By Thomas Tapping ... London, V. & R. Stevens and sons, 1861.

xxiv, 82, 11, 14 p. 18ᶜᵐ.

1. Mining law—Gt. Bri'   I. Gt. Brit. Laws, statutes, etc.

                       38–15425

NT 0036793   DLC

TAPPING, Thomas, 1817–1886.

[Glossary of] terms relating to the leadmines at Wirksworth, Derbyshire.

(In See [MANLOVE Edward. The liberties and customes of the leadmines within the wapentake of Wirksworth.] 1874. 8°.)

NT 0036794   MH

Tapping, Thomas, 1817–1886.

The law and practice of the high prerogative writ of mandamus, as it obtains both in England, and in Ireland. By Thomas Tapping ... London, W. Benning and co., 1848.

2 p. l., [vii]–iii, 501 p. 25ᶜᵐ.

1. Mandamus—Gt. Brit. 2. Mandamus—Ireland.

                       16–1349

NT 0036795   DLC GU-L PU-L

Tapping, Thomas, 1817–1886.

The law and practice of the high prerogative writ of mandamus, as it obtains both in England, and in Ireland. By Thomas Tapping ... Philadelphia, T. & J. W. Johnson, 1853.

4 p. l., (v)–lv (i. e. liv), (55)–539 p. 23ᶜᵐ. (*Added t.-p.*: The Law library. (v. 76), April, May, and June, 1852))

Error in paging: p. liv erroneously numbered lv.

1. Mandamus—Gt. Brit. 2. Mandamus—Ireland.

40–20473

      MtU CaBVa ViU-L
NT   0036796   DLC PPB PU-L PU NIC-L MH-L NNU-W WaU-L

Tapping, Thomas, 1817–1886.

The principles of the cost-book system practically considered; embracing suggestions for the formation of a cost-book mining company, by Thomas Tapping ... London: Mining Jour., Railway and Commercial Gazette, 1867. 12 p. 12°.

419211A.   1. Accounting and book-   keeping for mines.
N. Y. P. L.   July 13, 1931

NT   0036797   NN

Tapping, Thomas, 1817–1886.

The Readwin prize essay on the cost book, its principles and practice as applicable to mining, embracing a code of rules and conditions, and also one of bye-laws, for the perfect constitution and regulation of a cost book mining association; also, suggestions for the improvement of the present anomalous state of the law in reference to mining; and a consideration of the alterations necessary in the law for the limitation of liabilities in mining partnerships. The 2d ed., much enl. and considerably augm., with numerous notes and additions. An appendix, containing full and authentic reports of leading cases on mining law, and a copious index. By Thomas Tapping ... London, Shaw and sons, 1854.

xvii, 197 p. 22ᶜᵐ.

With this is bound: Childs, R. W. A letter to R. B. Crowder, esq., m. p., on mining partnerships, upon the cost-book system ... London, 1854.

1. Mining industry and finance—Gt. Brit. 2. Mining law—Gt. Brit. 3. Mining law—Gt. Brit.—Cases. 4. Limited liability—Gt. Brit. I. Title. II. Title: The cost book.

43–21418

NT   0036799   DLC CaBVaU IU MH

Tapping, Thomas, 1817–1886.

Manlove, Edward, *fl.* 1667.

The Rhymed chronicle of Edward Manlove concerning the liberties and customs of the lead mines within the wapentake of Wirksworth, Derbyshire. The 2d ed., reprinted from the text of the original edition of 1653, and collated with the several manuscripts preserved among the additional mss. 1872–1835, Brit. mus.: with notes, etc., etc. to which is affixed a glossary of the principal mining and other obsolete terms ... and a list extracted from the "Ducatus Lancastriæ," of all the causes relative to the

---

Tapping, Thomas, 1817–1886.

A treatise on the Derbyshire mining customs and mineral court act, 1852, (15 & 16 Vict. c. cLXIII.), analytically and practically arranged: embracing firstly, the mining customs articles, duties and officers of the wapentake of Wirksworth, and of the manors or liberties of Crich, Ashford, Stoney Middleton and Eyam, Hartington, Litton, Peak Forest, Tideswell, and Youlgreave, in the county of Derby; and secondly, the practice and proceedings of the several great and small barmote courts of the above-mentioned places. With notes, cases, references, and a copious index. By Thomas Tapping ... London, Shaw and sons, 1854.

xi, 166 p. 18ᶜᵐ.

1. Mining law—Derbyshire, Eng. 2. Customary law—Derbyshire, Eng. 3. Courts—Derbyshire, Eng. I. Gt. Brit. Laws, statutes, etc. II. Title: Derbyshire mining customs and mineral court act, 1852. III. Title: Barmote courts, Practice and proceedings of the ...

38–15424

NT   0036802   DLC PPAN

Tapping, Thomas, 1817–1886.

A treatise on the High Peak Mineral Customs and Mineral Courts Act, 1851. London, 1851. 10–128 p. 8°.

NT   0036803   PBL

Tapping fixtures for small parts
     see under   Machinery publishing co.,
London.

Tapping Pot.   **Niagara Falls, N.Y.**

NT   0036805   PP

Tappio, Jacob, 1603–1680
     see   Tappe, Jacob, 1603–1680.

PN6410
.E83
1666

Tappius, Eberhardus, 16th cent.

Erasmus, Desiderius, *d.* 1536.

Adagiorum epitome. Ed. novissima; ab infinitis fere mendis, quibus cæteræ scatebant, repurgata; nonnullisque in locis adaucta. Cum triplici indice. Oxoniæ, Typis W. Hall, & venales prostant apud T. Bowman, 1666.

Tappius, Eberhardus, 16th cent.

Epitome adagiorum post nouissimam D. Erasmi Roterodami ... recognitionem
     see under   Erasmus, Desiderius, *d.* 1536.
Adagiorum epitome. 1542.

Rare Book
Collection
PN6404
.T3
1539

Tappius, Eberhardus, 16th cent.

Germani/corum adagiorum/ cum Latinis ac Grae-/cis collatorum, centu-/riæ septen./ Per Eberhardum Tappium Lunenser./ Συγγραμη ποωπτελεαι Εἰς δ' ἀνήρ ὃ πανθ'ὁρᾷ/ Cum gratia priuilegio imperiali/ ad Septennium./ Ex libera Argentina, in aedibus/ Wuendelini Rihelij, Anno/ M. D. XXXIX. (1539)/ (1)–244 (19) l. 17cm.

Ms. notes inside front cover and throughout text.

NT   0036809   NcU ICN OCl MH

Case
Y
0595
863

TAPPIUS, EBERHARD, 16th cent.

Germanicorvm adagiorvm cvm latinis ac graecis collatorvm, centuriæ septem. Iam denuo recognita et locupletatæ per ipsum authorem. Cum indice. Argentorati, Per W.Rihelium,1545.

244 numb.leaves,(37)p.,1 leaf. 17cm.

Printer's device on verso of last leaf.
In stamped pigskin binding, with clasps.

NT   0036810   ICN NcU MiU MH

Tappius, Eberhardus, 16th cent.

Franck, Sebastian, 1499–1542.

Sprichwörter / schöne / weise / herrliche clůgreden / vnnd hoffsprüch / darinnen der alten vnd nachkommen / aller nationen vnnd sprachen gröste vernunfft vnnd klůgheyt. Was auch zů ewiger vnnd zeitlicher weissheyt / tugent / zucht / kunst / haußhaltung vnnd wesen dienet / gespürt vnnd begriffen würt. Zusamentragen in ettlich tausent / inn lustig höflich teutsch bekürzt / beschriben vnnd aussgeleget / durch Sebastian Francken ... Franckenfurt am Meyn, Getruckt bey Christian Egenolffen (1541)

Rare Book
Room
Uzn73
542t

Tappius, Eberhard, 16th cent.

Waidwerck vnd Federspiel. Von der Häbichen vnnd Falcken Natur / Art / vnnd Eygenthumb / wie mann sie berichten / gewehnen / ätzen / vnnd von allen jren Kranckheyten soll erledigen ... Durch Eberhardum Tappium ... zů Strassburgk Bey M. Jacob CammerLander. (1542) (80)p. illus. 21cm.

Described in C.F.G.R.Schwerdt, Hunting, hawking, shooting, London, 1928, vol.2, p.249.

NT   0036812   CtY

SK321
T3
1542a
Case
B

Tappius, Eberhardus, 16th cent.

Waidwerck und Federspiel. Von der Häbichen vnnd Falcken natur, art vnnd eygenthumb, wie mann sie berichten, gewehnen, ätzen, vnnd von allen Häbich, vnnd Falcken tregern vast nötig vnnd zu wissen nützlich ... Zu Strassburgk bey M. Jacob Cammer Lander (anno M.D.XLij) Stuttgart, J. Scheible, 1888) (74) p. illus.

"Dieses Werk wurde in 250 nummerierten Exemplaren auf Handpapier nach holländischer Art hergestellt.   No.198."

NT   0036813   CU ICU CtY

Tappius, Jacobus, 1603–1680.
     see   Tappe, Jacob, 1603–1680.

Tapply, Horace G., 1910–

The fly tyer's handbook, by H. G. Tapply; photos by the author. Boston, Mass., National sportsman inc., 1940.

2 p. l., 3–72 p. illus. 18 x 14ᶜᵐ.

1. Flies, Artificial. I. Title.

Library of Congress   SH451.T3   40–9922
—— Copy 2.
Copyright AA 328498   (2)   799.12

NT   0036815   DLC Or OCl

Tapply, Horace G   1910–

The fly tyer's handbook. Illustrated by Lu Henderson. New York, O. Durrell (1949)

69 p. illus. 23 cm.

1. Flies, Artificial. I. Title.

SH451.T3 1949   799.12   Agr 49–473*
U. S. Dept. of Agr. Libr.   414T16F
for Library of Congress   (7)†

NT   0036816   DNAL PP NIC DLC MB OCl WaT WaS

Tapply, Horace G   1910–

... Tackle tinkering; drawings by Jack Murray, photographs by the author. (New York) A. S. Barnes & company (1946)

ix, 214 p. illus., plates. 23½ᶜᵐ.

At head of title: H. G. Tapply.

1. Fishing—Implements and appliances. I. Title.

                             Agr 46–9
U. S. Dept. of agr. Library   414T16
for Library of Congress   SH451.T33
                 (15)†   799.1078

     CaBVa CaBViP Or NcC
NT   0036817   DNAL OrP PP PSt OCl TxU TU DLC WaS WaT

PS635
.Z9T18

Tappmeyer, Stella Hamblen.

"The babe that nobody wants"... Warrenton, Mo., 1930. 1 pam   12°

NT   0036818   DLC RPB

Tappmeyer, *Mrs.* **Stella Hamblen.**
The battle, by Stella Hamblen Tappmeyer. Boston, Mass., Meador publishing company [°1929]
186 p. front. (port.) 21^{cm}.
A story of Christian devotions.

 I. Title.

Library of Congress   PZ3.T1665Bat   29-16828

NT 0036819   DLC

Tappolet, Agnes Michaelis
see under   Michaelis-Tappolet, Agnes.

Tappolet, Ernst, 1870- 1939.
Die alemannischen lehnwörter in den mundarten der französischen Schweiz. Kulturhistorisch-linguistische untersuchung von Ernst Tappolet ... Basel, Universitäts-buchdruckerei F. Reinhardt, 1913-16.
2 v. fold. map. 24$\frac{1}{2}$^{cm}.
Rektorats programm (1913, 1915, 1916) Univ. Basel.
"Erscheint auch im verlag von Karl J. Trübner, Strassburg."
"Literaturangaben": [v. 1] p. [100]-101; v. 2, p. [206]-207.
Contents.—[1. teil] Kulturhistorischer teil. Linguistischer teil.—2. teil. Etymologisches wörterbuch.
1. French language—Dialects—Switzerland. 2. German language—Dialects—Alemannic. 3. French language—Foreign words and phrases—German.
Library of Congress   AS322.B22 1913, 1915/16   26-18964 Revised
———— Copy 2.   PC3146.T3

      CtY MH
NT 0036821   DLC ICN NjP OU MB CU WaU TxU PU NN GU

Tappolet, Ernst, 1870-
Die alemannischen lehnwörter in den mundarten der französischen Schweiz. Kultur-historisch-linguistische untersuchung von Ernst Tappolet. Strassburg, K. J. Trübner, 1914-
  v.   fold. map. 25^{cm}.
Issued also as Rektoratsprogramm, Univ. Basel.
"Literaturangaben" v. 1, p. [100]-101.

1. French language—Dialects—Switzerland. 2. German language—Dialects—Alemannic. 3. French language—Foreign words and phrases—German.
Library of Congress   PC3146.T32   40-22802

NT 0036822   DLC OC1W IU NIC MiU MH NcU

Tappolet, Ernst, 1870-1939.
Aus romanischen sprachen und literaturen. Festschrift Heinrich Morf zur feier seiner fünfundzwanzigjährigen lehrtätigkeit von seinen schülern dargebracht. Halle a. d. S., M. Niemeyer, 1905.

Tappolet, Ernst, 1870-   *ed.*
... Dialectes suisses, enregistrés en collaboration avec les Archives phonographiques de l'Université de Zurich. Patois de la Suisse romande, canton du Valais ... Berlin, Preussische staatsbibliothek, 1929-
pts. 23^{cm}. (Lautbibliothek; phonetische platten und umschriften, hrag. von der Lautabteilung der Preussischen staatsbibliothek. Nr. 50-54, 56-60, 62, 65-69, 71-72   Berlin, Institut für lautforschung an der Universität Berlin; in kommission bei O. Harrassowitz, Leipzig, 1934-
Imprint varies: no. 51, 54, 57, 62, 67, 68.
"Textes transcrits et traduits par [E. Tappolet et] J. Jeanjaquet."
1. French language—Dialects—Valais—Phonetic transcriptions.   I. Jeanjaquet, Jules Edouard,   1867-   ed. II. Zürich. Universität. Phonogrammarchiv.   III. Title.
Library of Congress   P215.L35 no. 50-54,   45-42131
[2]   (414.082)   447.9

NT 0036824   DLC

PC   Tappolet, Ernst, 1870-
3171   Les données fondamentales des conditions lin-
.V3   guistiques du Valais (Suisse); Conférence
T3   faite au deuxième congrès international de
       linguistique romane, à Sion, le 9 juin 1930.
       Sion, 1931.
       [9]-22, 7 p. fold. map.

         "Extrait de la Revue de linguistique romane,
       t. 7"
         Bibliographical footnotes.

NT 0036825   DGU

Tappolet, Ernst, 1870-1939.
Die e-Prothese in den französischen Mundarten. (Festschrift zum 14. Neuphilologentage. Zürich, 1910. 8°. p. 158-183.)

1. French language.—Dialects.
N. Y. P. L.   March 17, 1911.

NT 0036826   NN MB

Tappolet, Ernst, 1870-1939.
Festschrift für Ernst Tappolet ...
see under title

Tappolet, Ernst, 1870-1939.

Glossaire des patois de la Suisse romande, élaboré avec le concours de nombreux auxiliaires et rédigé par L. Gauchat ... J. Jeanjaquet ... [et] E. Tappolet ... avec la collaboration de E. Muret ... Neuchâtel & Paris, V. Attinger, 1924-

---

447   **Tappolet, Ernst,** 1870- 1939.
T16r   Die romanischen verwandtschaftsnamen, mit besonderer berücksichtigung der französischen und italienischen mundarten ... Strassburg, 1895.
       178 p.   maps.

1. French language—Dialects. 2. Italian language—Dialects.

NT 0036829   IU CU LU ICU MB MH CtY ICRL

Tappolet, Ernst, 1870-1939.
Eine soziale Reform; ein Wort zur Alkoholfrage. Zürich & Leipzig, T. Schröter, 1899.
35 p.   8°.

NT 0036830   DNLM

TAPPOLET, Ernst, 1870-
Die sprache des kindes. [Basel, 1907.]

1. 8°. pp. (16).
Sep.-abzug aus dem nicht erschienen heft 2 der Mittel-europäischen monatsschrift.

NT 0036831   MH

Tappolet, Ernst, 1870-
La synonymie patoise dans la Suisse romande (sommeil, jour et nuit, lait et fromage) Lausanne, Imprimeries réunies (s.a.) 1915.

21 cm.
"Extrait du Bulletin du Glossaire des patois de la Suisse romande, 13.année, 1914," p. [41]-61.

NT 0036832   MH

Tappolet, E[rnst], 1870-1939.
Ueber den Stand der Mundarten in der deutschen und französischen Schweiz. Zürich : Zürcher & Furrer, 1901. 40 p. 8°. (Gesellschaft für deutsche Sprache in Zürich. Mitteilungen. Heft 6.)
   Title from cover.

1. Swiss dialects.
N. Y. P. L.   November 17, 1911.

NT 0036833   NN CU PU

Tappolet, Ernst, 1870-1939.
Ueber die Bedeutung der Sprachgeographie, mit besonderer Berücksichtigung französischer Mundarten. (In: Aus romanischer Sprachen und Literaturen Festschrift. Meinrich Morf ... Halle a. d. S., 1905. p. 385-416)

NT 0036834   NN CtY

Tappolet, Ernst, 1870- 1939.
... Wustmann und die Sprachwissenschaft. Von Dr. E. Tappolet. Zürich, E. Speidel, 1898. 28 p. 22cm. (Gesellschaft für deutsche Sprache und Literatur, Zürich. Mitteilungen. Heft 3.)

1. Wustmann, Gustav, 1844-1910.   2. German language—Study and teaching. I. Ser.
N. Y. P. L.   July 15, 1940

NT 0036835   NN PU

Tappolet, Ernst, 1870-1939.
Zur Agglutination in den französischen Mundarten... [Basel, 1907]
1 p. l. [324]-340 p.   24.5 cm.
Aus der Festschrift zur 49. Versammlung deutscher Philologen und Schulmänner".
1. French language - Dialects.

NT 0036836   CtY

Tappolet, Walter.
Regina Ullmann; eine Einführung in ihre Erzählungen. St. Gallen, Tschudy, 1955.
69 p. plate, port. 21 cm.

1. Ullmann, Regina, 1884-

                                       A 55-10320
Harvard Univ. Library
for Library of Congress

NT 0036837   MH FTaSU CU NN CtY NIC

830.119
T168   TAPPOLET, Walter
       Vom neuen kirchenlied.   Basel,
       F. Reinhardt [1941]

       32 p.   20cm.

         1. Hymns, German. History and criticism.
       I. Title.

NT 0036838   MnU MH

Tappolet, Werner, 1892-
Arthur Honegger
see under   Tappolet, Willy, 1890-

Tappolet, Werner, 1892-
Beiträge zur kenntnis der lokalvergletscherung des Säntisgebirges ... von Werner Tappolet ... St. Gallen, Druck der buchdruckerei Zollikofer & cie., 1922.
1 p. l., 66 p., 1 l. fold. map. 23^{cm}.
Inaug.-diss.—Zürich.
Separatabdruck aus dem 58. bd., t. 2, 1922 des Jahrbuches der St. Gallischen naturwissenschaftlichen gesellschaft.
Literatur und kartenverzeichnis: p. 62-66.
Lebenslauf: p. [67]

1. Glaciers—Switzerland. I. Title.

                                       G S 25-297
Library. U. S. Geological   Survey 250(535) T16

NT 0036840   DI-GS ICRL ICU

Tappolet, Werner, 1914–
Die formelle richterliche prozessleitung im zürcherischen zivilprozess ... von Werner Tappolet ... Lachen, Buchdruckerei A. Kessler, "Gutenberg," 1941.

73, [1] p. 22½ᵐ.

Diss.—Zürich.
Lebenslauf.
"Literatur-verzeichnis": p. 7–8.

1. Civil procedure—Zürich (Canton) 2. Judges—Zürich (Canton)
I. Title.

43–33947

NT 0036841   DLC ICRL

Tappolet, Willy, 1890–
Arthur Honegger, von Willy Tappolet. Zürich und Leipzig, Gebrüder Hug & co., 1933.

iv, 272 p. incl. illus. (music) plates, ports., facsim. (music) diagrs. 22ᵐ.

"1. auflage, 2000 exemplare."
"Literaturverzeichnis": p. 243–251.
"Verzeichnis der werke (seit 1914)": p. 252–266.

1. Honegger, Arthur, 1892–

Library of Congress   ML410.H79T3   34–17275
Copyright A—Foreign   24542
[2]   927.8

NT 0036842   DLC OClW ICN WU CtY OClW ICU

Tappolet, Willy, 1890–
... Arthur Honegger; adaptation française de Hélène Breuleux. Neuchâtel, Éditions de la Baconnière [1938].

3 p. l., [9]–311 p., 1 l. front., illus. (music) ports., facsim. (music) diagrs. 19ᵐ.

"Il ne s'agit pas d'une simple traduction [de l'édition originale allemande] Le texte a été remanié, corrigé et complété."—Introd.
"Bibliographie": p. [263]–276. "Catalogue des oeuvres (de 1910 à décembre 1938)": p. [277]–[299]. "Musique enregistrée: liste des disques": p. [300]–301.

1. Honegger, Arthur, 1892–   I. Breuleux, Hélène, tr.

Library of Congress   ML410.H79T5   40–21194
   927.8

NT 0036843   DLC PU-FA CaBVaU PU CLU

ML410
.H79
T5
1939
Tappolet, Willy, 1890–
Arthur Honegger; adaptation française de Hélène Breuleux. [2. éd.] Neuchâtel, Editions de la Baconnière [1939].
315p. illus. 20cm.

"Il ne s'agit pas d'une simple traduction [de l'édition originale allemande, Le texte a été remanié, corrigé et complété."
Bibliography: p. [263]–276. Catalog of works, 1910–1938 p. [277]–[300]. Discography: p. [301]–303.

NT 0036844   PSt CaBVaU MH PP

Tappolet, Willy, 1890–
Arthur Honegger. Zürich, Atlantis Verlag [1954].

253 p. illus., ports., diagrs., facsim., music. 23 cm.

"Verzeichnis der Werke": p. 234–244.
Bibliography: p. 245–247.

1. Honegger, Arthur, 1892–

ML410.H79T3 1954   A 55–2712

Oregon. Univ. Libr.
for Library of Congress   [1]†

MiU DLC
NT 0036845   OrU NIC OU WaU NN InU ICN TxU ICarbS

PT2553 **Tappolet, Willy,** 1890–
.W25Z8T2 Heinrich Weber ... Zürich, Diss.-druckerei Gebr. Leemann & co., 1917.

103. [1] p. 22ᵐ.

Inaug.-diss.—Zürich.
Curriculum vitae.
"Quellen": p. [3]–4; "Bibliographie": p. [94]–103.

1. Weber, Heinrich, 1821–1900.

NT 0036846   ICU ICRL ICN NNU-W

ML410
.R23T3
Tappolet, Willy, 1890–
Maurice Ravel, Leben und Werk. Olten, O. Walter [1950]

190 p. ports. 19 cm. (Musikerreihe, 8)

"Die Werke von Maurice Ravel": p. 176–182.
"Literaturangabe": p. 182–185.

1. Ravel, Maurice, 1875–1937.   (Series)

A 51–4816

Oregon. Univ. Libr.
for Library of Congress   [2]

NT 0036847   OrU CU ICN NN MH OU WU

Tappolet, Willy, 1890–
La notation musicale et son influence sur la pratique de la musique du moyen âge à nos jours. [Neuchâtel] La Baconnière [1947].

112 p. illus., facsims., music. 19 cm.

"Liste des ouvrages cités": p. [108]–105.

1. Musical notation. I. Title.

ML431.T3   781.24   47–29129*

ICU CaBVaU
NT 0036848   DLC NcD TU IU PBm OO WU PU CtY MB NN

Tapponnier, Paul.
...Dans le Proche Orient. Paris, 1921. 24 p. 8°.

1. European war, 1914–18, Bulgaria.   2. Neuilly (Treaty of), 1919.
N.Y.P.L.   January 9, 1924.

NT 0036849   NN MH

Den tappra Miss Meeker's egen berättelse om hennes fångenskap och lidanden bland Ute-Indianerne. Den sköna Miss Annie Colesons berättelse om hennes fångenskap och äfventyr bland Sioux-Indianerne i Minnesota. Chicago, Chas. Heck [1887?] 52, 42 p. illus. 23cm.

Cover-title.
[Part 1] has title: Ute-blodbadet. Den tappra Miss Meekers fångenskap! Berättadt af henne sjelf, samt hennes mors och Fru Prices berättelser om deras samt deras barns förfärliga lidanden. Öfversättning från Engelskan af —r——n— På utgifvarens förlag.

[Part 2] has title: Miss Annie Colesons berättelse om sin fångenskap bland Sioux-Indianerne... Forfattad af henne sjelf.
Illustrated with wood engravings by Van Ingen & Snyder, Pictorial Printing Co., Chicago, and Baker & Co., Chicago.
[Part 1] includes "Studentens berättelse. Ett slädparti i de dödas sällskap, eller universitetets skelett," p. 37–50, and "Ett nytt indianskt knep," p. 51–52.

266414B. 1. Indians, N.A.— [Captivities. 2. Indians, N.A.—Ute.
II. Price, Flora Ellen. III. Title: I. Meeker, Arvilla Delight (Smith).
Meekers fångenskap! Ute-blodbadet. Den tappra Miss
N.Y.P.L.   June 5, 1944.

NT 0036851   NN

Tapray, Jean François, ca.1738–ca.1819
Quartets, op. 18
Deux quatuor pour le clavecin ou le pianoforte avec accompagnement de clarinette ou violon alto et basson qui pour être exécuté par un violoncelle, oeuvre XVIIIᵐᵉ Paris, Le Duc [18—]

4 pts. (cimbalo ò pianoforte, clarinetto ò violino, viola, fagotto ò basso)
Microfilm (negative)
Original in British Museum, London

NT 0036852   MH-Mu

Tapray, Jean François, ca.1738–ca.1819
Symphonies, op. 21
Deux symphonies pour le clavecin avec accompagnement de deux violons, alto, et basse, les cors et l'alto ad libitum, oeuvre XXIᵉ. Paris, Le Duc [18—]

7 pts. (piano, violino primo, violino secondo, viola, basso, corno primo, corno secondo)
Microfilm (negative)
Original in British Museum, London

NT 0036853   MH-Mu

Tapray, Jean François, ca.1738–ca.1819
Duo de Silvain dans le sein d'un pere, trio de Zemire et Azor veillons mes soeurs, ariette de la derniere piece en sonate pour le forte piano ou le clavecin avec un accompagnement de violon. Paris, Chez l'Auteur [17—]

1 pt. (clavecin)
Microfilm (negative)
Original in Conservatoire Bibliothèque, Paris
Clavecin part is incomplete

NT 0036854   MH-Mu

Tapray, Jean François, ca.1738–ca.1819.
Ouvertures de Rose et Colas, du Deserteur ...
see under [Monsigny, Pierre Alexandre de], 1729–1817.

Tapray, Jean François, ca.1738–ca.1819
Quatuor concertans, op. 19
Quatuor concertans pour le clavecin ou le forte-piano, flûte, alto et basson, oeuvre XIX. La flûte et le basson peuvent être remplacés par un violon et une violoncelle. Paris, Boyer [17—]

4 pts. (cembalo, flûte ou violon, alto, basson ou violoncelle) (Journal de pieces de clavein, 6)
Microfilm (negative)
Original in Conservatoire Bibliothèque, Paris

NT 0036856   MH-Mu

Tapray, Jean François, ca.1738–ca.1819
Quatuor et ariettes de Lucile et du Tableau parlant pour le clavecin ou le forte piano. Paris, Desjardin [17—]

Score (8 p.)
Microfilm (negative)
Original in British Museum, London

NT 0036857   MH-Mu

Film
10714
Tapray, Jean François, ca.1738–ca 1819.
[Simphonie concertante, harpsichord, piano & orchestra, op.8, D major.
Simphonie concertante pour le clavecin et le piano avec orchestre [de] deux violons, alto, basse et cors...par M.Tapraÿ...oeuvre 8.
A Paris, Chez M. de Roullede [ca.1785?]
8 pts.
Microfilm (negative) London, British Museum (e.14), 1967. 1 reel. 35mm.
On reel with the composer's Simphonie concertante, harpsichord, piano & string orchestra, op.15, G major. Paris, ca.1785.

NT 0036858   IaU MH-Mu

Tapray, Jean François, ca.1738–ca.1819
Sonatas, violin & keyboard, op. 1
Six sonates pour le clavecin avec accompagnement de violon ad libitum, oeuvre Iᵉ. Paris, Chez l'Auteur [17—]

2 pts. (violino, clavecin)
Microfilm (negative)
Original in Conservatoire Bibliothèque, Paris

NT 0036859   MH-Mu

---

sVM
219
T 175s
op.10
TAPRAY, JEAN FRANÇOIS, 1738–ca.1819.
[Sonatas, violin & harpsichord, op.10]
Six sonates pour le clavecin ou le piano avec accompagnement de violon ad libitum. Oeuvre X ... A Paris,[Chez l'auteur,ca.1779]
2 parts. 26x36cm.

"Gravées par Richomme."
Imperfect: violin part wanting.
Contents.—C major.—G major.—D major.—A major.— F major.—D major.

NT 0036860   ICN

sVM
219
T 175s
TAPRAY, JEAN FRANÇOIS, 1738-ca.1819.
Six sonates très faciles pour le clavecin, avec accompagnement de violon ad libitum ... A Paris, Chez M. Tapray [ca.1781]
2 parts. 26x35cm.

"Gravées par M.elle Desjardin."
Imperfect: violin part wanting.
Contents.—C major.—G major.—D major.
—F major.—A major.—D major.

NT 0036861   ICN CU

Tapray, Jean François, ca.1738-ca.1819
Sonatas, violin & keyboard. Selections
Six sonates très faciles pour le clavecin avec un
accompagnement de violon ad libitum. Paris, Tapray [17—]

1 pt. (clavecin)
Microfilm (negative)
Original in Conservatoire Bibliothèque, Paris

NT 0036862   MH-Mu

Tapray, Jean François, ca.1738-ca.1819
Works, keyboard. Selections
[Six sonnattes pour le clavecin (et morceaux d'orgue
avec un violon ad libitum. 1776] Manuscript

Score (26 p.)
Microfilm (negative)
Original in Bibliothèque Nationale, Paris

NT 0036863   MH-Mu

Tapray, Jean François, ca.1738-ca.1819
Trios, keyboard & strings, op. 6
Sonates en trio pour le clavecin ou le piano, un violon
et un alto, oeuvre VI. Paris, Chez l'Auteur [17—]

Score (17 p.)
Microfilm (negative)
Original in Bibliothèque Nationale, Paris

NT 0036864   MH-Mu

M23
T317
op.11
Case
X
Tapray, Jean François, 1738-1819.
[Sonatas, piano, op. 11]
Trois sonates pour le clavecin ou le piano ... Oeuvre XI.
Paris, Chez l'Auteur [ca.1780?]
12 p. (in portfolio)

"Catalogue des oeuvres de M. Tapray pour le clavecin": p. [1]

NT 0036865   CU ICN

Tapray, Jean François, ca.1738-ca.1819
Sonatas, keyboard, op. 11
Trois sonates pour le clavecin ou le piano, oeuvre XI.
Paris, Chez l'Auteur [17—]

Score (24 p.)
Microfilm (negative)
Original in Conservatoire Bibliothèque, Paris

NT 0036866   MH-Mu

WI
T175e
1878
TAPRET, O
Étude clinique sur la péritonite
chronique d'emblée. Paris, Delahaye,
1878.
203 p.

NT 0036867   DNLM

Taprobane
see
Ceylon.

The Taprobanian; a Dravidian journal of oriental
studies in and around Ceylon, in natural history, archaeology, philology, history...
v.1-   Oct. 1885-
Bombay, Education Society's press; London,
Trübner & co., 1887-

NT 0036869   OCl CU NIC

YA
23945
The Taproot.   [n.p., n.d.]
4 p.   (American tract society, no. 261)

NT 0036870   DLC OClWHi

Taproots; from the Trailside Museum, Forest Preserve District
of Cook County, Illinois ... [Riverside, Ill., 1940-   ]
Library has v. 1, Feb. 1940, *to date*. illus. 29cm. irregular.
Cover-title; no index.

NT 0036871   ICJ

Taps, published by the Class of 1902, Gloucester
high school.   Gloucester, Mass., 1902.
unp. ports. illus. music.   21 cm.

NT 0036872   RPB

Taps ... published by the senior class of Clemson A. & M.
college of South Carolina
[Clinton, S. C., '19
v. illus. (incl. ports.) plates. 27½cm.

1. Clemson agricultural college of South Carolina.

Library of Congress   S537.C65   25-15357

NT 0036873   DLC

Taps. New York, A. D. F. Randolph [1869?]
5 l. illus. 27½cm.
Illustrated t.-p.
In verse.

Library of Congress   PS991.A1T34   30-19463

NT 0036874   DLC

"Taps": published in memory of the Students'
army training corps at William and Mary
college, Williamsburg, Virginia ...
Published December the sixth, 1918.
56 p.   ports., illus.   28 cm.
1. U.S. Army. Students' training corps.
William and Mary college, Williamsburg, Va.
I. William and Mary college, Williamsburg, Va.

NT 0036875   ViW

Taps and dies catalogues.   1918.
8 pph. bd. in 1 v.

NT 0036876   PPF

... Taps and threading dies ...   New York City,
The Industrial press, c1910.
34 p.   illus., tables.   22 cm.
(Machinery's data sheet series ... no. 3)
1. Taps and dies.

NT 0036877   CU PP OCl MiD

"Taps for the old West's army posts.
clipping from N.Y. Times Magazine, June 21,
1931. ill.

NT 0036878   DNW

76
-TA6544
Taps ["Put it out! Put it out! Put it
out!". n.p., Torrey brothers, printers,
1869?]
5 l. illus. (music) 30 cm.

Title vignette in colors.
An anonymous poem.

1. U.S.—History—Civil war—Poetry.
I. Title: "Put it   out! Put it out!
"ut it out"

NT 0036879   RPB

Tapscott, Fred T.
British-Israel axioms. Prospectus of a series
of tractates in rebuttal of British-Israelism.
Vancouver, Lumberman print. co., n.d.
cover-title, 40 p.   23 cm.

NT 0036880   CaBViPA

Tapscott, Jacob.
Tentamen medicum inaugurale, de chlorosi: quod ... ex
auctoritate ... Gulielmi Robertson ... Academiae edinburgenae
praefecti ... pro gradu doctoratus ... eruditorum examini
subjicit, Jacobus Tapscott, Anglo-Americanus. Ad diem 7
decembris [1765] ... Edinburgi, A. Donaldson. MDCCLXV.
5 p. l., 35 p. 19½cm.
"Corrigenda": slip mounted on verso of p. 35.

1. Chlorosis.

Library of Congress   RC641.T3   37-18805

NT 0036881   DLC PPL DNLM ICJ PPC NNNAM

TL521
.A33
no. 1207
Tapscott, Robert J., joint author.
Amer, Kenneth B
Studies of the lateral-directional flying qualities of a tan-
dem helicopter in forward flight, by Kenneth B. Amer and
Robert J. Tapscott. Washington, U. S. Govt. Print. Off.,
1954 [i. e. 1955]

Tapscott, Robert L., ed.
Liverpool engineering society.
Transactions of the Liverpool engineering society.
v. 1-
Liverpool, The Society. 1881-1904.

Tapscott, Samuel Wallace, 1877–
Backward glances, a viv'd picture of rural life as we lived it in and around Bigby fork in Itawamba county in the 1880's and 1890's. By Sam W. Tapscott ... ⌐Booneville, Miss.₁ Booneville printing company₁ 1943.
218 p. incl. front. (port.) illus. 20ᵐ.

ɪ. Title.

44–27696

Library of Congress   CT275.T284A3
⌐2₁   920

NT 0036884   DLC

Zc10
850tad
...Tapscott's emigrants' guide to the United States, Canada & California₁ containing a brief description of the United States, their government, climate, soil, and production ... and a general description of Canada, California, and the Oregon territory ... Liverpool, W. Tapscott and co., 1851.
45p., 1ℓ. 18cm.
At head of title: Fourth edition.
Original wrappers.

NT 0036885   CtY

Case
G
833
864
...TAPSCOTT'S emigrants' guide to the United States, Canada, and California: containing a brief description of the United States, their government, climate, soil, and productions, with particular notice of Ohio, Indiana, Illinois, and Missouri... also, instructions to emigrants concerning the voyage, tables of travelling routes, distances, railroad and steamboat fares, etc. Liverpool, W. Tapscott and co., 1853.
38p. 19½cm.

At head of title: Fifth edition.

NT 0036886   ICN

Tapsell, Enid.
Historic Maketu. Hui hui mai! By Enid Tapsell. Illustrations by H. Dansey, jnr. ⌐Rotorua₁ Rotorua morning post printing house, 1940.
2 p. l., 74, ⌐1₁ p. illus. 24½ᵐ.

1. Maketu, N. Z.—Hist.   ɪ. Title.

41–9554

Library of Congress   DU430.M3T3
⌐2₁   993.1

NT 0036887   DLC

Tapsell, Enid.
Historic Maketu. Hui hui mai! By Enid Tapsell; illustrations by H. Dansey, jnr. Special limited 1st ed. ... ⌐Rotorua₁ Rotorua morning post printing house, 1940.
2 p. l., 74, ⌐1₁ p. illus. 25ᵐ.

1. Maketu, N. Z.—Hist.   ɪ. Title.

43–44819

Library of Congress   DU430.M3T3 1940 a
⌐2₁   993.1

NT 0036888   DLC CtY

Tapsell, Florence A
... Fairy stories from Italy; retold by Florence A. Tapsell. Leeds [etc.] E. J. Arnold [1915]
48 p. illus. (The "A. L." bright story readers, no. 127)
Cover-title.
Grade II.

NT 0036889   OCl

Tapsell, Florence A
... Fairy stories from Persia, retold by Florence A. Tapsell. Leeds [etc.] E. J. Arnold [1915]
48 p. illus. (The "A. L." bright story readers, no. 126)
Cover-title.
"Grade II".

NT 0036890   OCl

Tapsell, Florence A
... 'Mid forest shadows (Nigeria and the Gold Coast) ... Leeds [etc., 1916?]
cover-title, 32 p. illus. 18 cm. (Little people in far-off lands. F16)

NT 0036891   CtY

Tapsell, Herbert James.
Creep of metals, by H. J. Tapsell ... London, H. Milford, Oxford university press, 1931.
xiv, 285, ⌐1₁ p. illus., pl., diagrs. 25ᵐ.
Bibliography: p. ⌐264₁–273.

1. Metals—Testing.   ɪ. Title.

32—16022

Library of Congress   TA460.T3
⌐n45e1₁   620.17

NcD NcRS CtY CU PPF
NT 0036892   DLC OrCS MiU OCU OCl OU IU NN MB PPT

Tapsell, Herbert James.

Gt. Brit. *Dept. of scientific and industrial research. Engineering research board.*
... Properties of materials at high temperatures ... London, H. M. Stationery off., 1927–32.

629.06236
Tapsell, Herbert James.   1   v.1011
... Some mechanical tests of cast bars of alpax. By H. J. Tapsell, A.C.G.I. Work performed for the Engineering Research Board of the Department of Scientific and Industrial Research. December, 1925. London, H. M. Stationery Off., 1926.
cover-title, 9 p. incl. tables. diagrs. 25ᵐᵐ. (⌐Great Britain₁ Aeronautical Research Committee. Reports and memoranda, no. 1011 (M. 34))
At head of title: L. A. 48.

NT 0036894   ICJ

Tapsell, Herbert James.
... The strength at high temperatures of a cast and a forged steel as used for turbine construction, by H. J. Tapsell ... and A. E. Johnson ... London, H. M. Stationery off., 1931.
iv, 33 p. incl. illus., tables, diagrs. 24½ᵐ. (⌐Gt. Brit.₁ Dept. of scientific and industrial research. Engineering research board. Special report no. 17)
At head of title: Dept. of scientific and industrial research. Engineering research ...

1. Steel—Testing. 2. Turbines.   ɪ. Johnson, A. E., joint author.
ɪɪ. Title.   32–14104 Revised

Library of Congress   TA473.T3
⌐r41142₁   620.17

NT 0036895

Tapsell, Herbert James.
The strength of materials at high temperatures
(Métaux et machines, v. 18(245), p. 168–74(1934))

NT 0036896   OU NN IU OCl

Tapsico, Lewis

An address delivered before the different African benevolent societies, on the first of January, 1819, and published at their particular request ... Philadelphia, Printed for the author, 1819.
8 p. 21 cm.

1. Negroes. Philadelphia

NT 0036897   NcD

F2926.
T35
Tapson, Alfred Joseph, 1909–
The Indian problem on the Argentine pampa, 1735-1852. ⌐Berkeley, 1952₁
iv, 209 l. maps.

Thesis (Ph.D. in History) – Univ. of California, June 1952.
Bibliography: p. 178-206.

NT 0036898   CU

Ayer
5A
970
TAPSON, ALFRED JOSEPH, 1909–
The Indian problem on the Argentine Pampa, 1735-1852. [Los Angeles] Univ. of California 1952.
iv, 206ℓ. maps(fold.) 28cm.

Dissertation – Univ. of California, 1952.
Bibliography: ℓ. 178-206.
Xerox copy.

NT 0036899   ICN

Tapson, Susanna.
The genii of the lamp shade, by Susanna Tapson. New York, 1923. 49 p. sq. 24°.

267064A. 1. Lamp shades. 2. Lighting   of dwellings.   January 8, 1927
N. Y. P. L.

NT 0036900   NN

Nvrk30
641T
The tapsters downfall and the drunkards joy, or, A dialogue between Leather-beard the tapster of the Sheaves, and Ruby-nose, one of his ancient acquaintance ...
⌐London₁ Printed in the yeare, 1641.
1p. ℓ., 6p. 18cm.
Signature: A⁴.
Title-woodcut.

NT 0036901   CtY ICN

WL
200
T175a
1949
TAPTAS, Jean N
Arachnoïdites opto-chiasmatiques et maladie neurovasculaire, par J. N. Taptas et Th. Dimopoulos. Paris, Masson, 1949.
110 p.
1. Arachnoid - Inflammation
2. Optic chiasm I. Dimopoulos, Théodore

NT 0036902   DNLM

WL
342
T175m
1953
TAPTAS, Jean N
Maux de tête et névralgies; douleurs cranio-faciales. Paris, Masson, 1953.
230 p.
1. Headache   2. Neuralgia

NT 0036903   DNLM ICJ

QU   TAPTAS, Nicolas
120   Nutrition tissulaire; respiration
T175n diaphragmatique et circulation. ₍Paris₎
1954   L'Expansion scientifique française ₍1954₎
     157 p. illus.
     1. Blood - Circulation 2. Respiration
     Title

NT 0036904   DNLM ICJ

Taptas, Nicolas.
    Respiration et machine humaine; contribution à la physio-
pathologie nasale avec applications cliniques dans les affections nasales et auriculaires et cardio-pulmonaires. Préf. du
professeur F. Lemaître. Paris, Le François, 1947.
    xvi, 221 p. illus. (part col.) 25 cm.

    1. Respiratory organs—Diseases.

    RC711.T3   616.2   49–52084*

NT 0036905   DLC

Taptoe; geïllustreerde weekrevue van "Het Volk." 1.-
jaar; 1 Apr. 1945–
Gent.
    v. illus., ports. 31–38 cm.
    "Geïllustreerde Zondagsbijlage van het Volk," Apr. 1–Oct. 21, 1945;
"Geïllustreerde Zondagsuitgave van het Volk," Oct. 28, 1945–
Includes an introductory issue unnumbered and undated.

    L. C. set incomplete: v. 1, no. 1, 7–8 wanting.
    I. Het Volk (Ghent)
    AP15.T3   053.931   49–52352*

NT 0036906   DLC

Taptun, A   S
    Нарезание орудийных стволов. Москва, Оборонгиз
НКАП, Глав. ред. вооружения и боеприпасов, 1945.
    178, ₍2₎ p. illus., diagrs. 21 cm.
    Errata slip mounted on t.-p.
    "Литература": p. ₍180₎

    1. Ordnance—Manuf.   I. Title.
                     Title transliterated: Narezanie orudiĭnykh stvolov.
    UF530.T3   49–55429*

NT 0036907   DLC

Tapuach, Max
    Zur Kenntnis der Hydratisomerie...
    Inaug. Diss.   Zurich, 1907

NT 0036908   ICRL

    Oo tapwatumoowin mena oo tipetotumoowin ootayu-
mehaw
        see under [Hunter, James] 1817–1881.

Tapwell, Thomas.
    Friendly address to the poor of Great Britain
on the present scarcity of wheat & dearness of
wheaten bread.   London, Rivington, 1796.
    12 p.

NT 0036910   PU

Tapy, George Henry, 1869–1932.
    Outline of psychology. [Crawfordsville, Ind. ?
19 –?]
    58 p.   25 cm.
    Pub. by the Department of psychology and
education, Wabash college.
    Recto of each leaf blank.

NT 0036911   CtY MH

---

al-Taqi, Kamāl.
    (Murāfaʿat al-muḥāmī Kamāl al-Taqī)
مرافعة المحامي كمال التقي بدعوى القوميين الاجتماعيين في
المحكمة العسكرية بدمشق. ₍دمشق₎ 1955.
    45 p. 25 cm.

    1. al-Ḥizb al-Sūrī al-Qawmī al-Ijtimāʿī. 2. Trials (Political crimes
and offenses)—Syria. I. al-Ḥizb al-Sūrī al-Qawmī al-Ijtimāʿī. II.
Title.
                    76–971425

NT 0036912   DLC

Taqi, Mir
    see
Muḥammad Taḳī, called Mīr, d. 1810.

BD331   Taqi, Muhammad
T36   To happiness: a condensed rational
     discussion.   Delhi, Jayyed Press, 1948.
     10p. 25cm.

     Cover title.

     1. Reality. 2. Happiness.

NT 0036914   IaU OrU NIC

Taqi al-Dīn, Aḥmad.
    (Aḥmad Ḥasanayn Bāshā, faqīd Miṣr al-ʿaẓīm)
احمد حسنين باشا، فقيـد مصر العظيم / احمـد تقي
الدين. — دمشق : المكتبة الكبرى للتأليف والنشر، 1947.
    117 p. ; 20 cm.
    A novel.

    1. Ḥasanayn, Aḥmad Muḥammad, 1889–1946—Fiction. I. Title.
    PJ7864.A43A75   75–587490

NT 0036915   DLC

Taqi al-Dīn, Khalīl.
الإعدام، مجموعة قصص ₍تأليف₎ خليل تقي الدين. بيروت،
دار المكشوف، 1940.
    158 p. 20 cm.

    I. Title.
               Title romanized: al-Iʿdām.
    PJ7864.A435 I 3   N E 68–1454

NT 0036916   DLC

Taqi al-Dīn, Saʿīd.
غابة الكافور، مجموعة قصص عاشها سعيد تقي الدين. بيروت،
دار العلم للملايين، 1951.
    132 p. illus. 21 cm.

    I. Title.
               Title romanized: Ghābat al-kāfūr.
    PJ7864.A44G5   N E 68–1410

NT 0036917   DLC NjP NNC

Taqi al-Dīn, Saʿīd.
حفنة ريح، مهزلة في فصل واحد. موجة نار، مجموعة قصص.
مراسلات ₍تأليف₎ سعيد تقي الدين. ₍بيروت، دار العلم للملايين
1948₎
    280 p. illus., port. 21 cm.

    I. Title.
               Title romanized: Ḥafnat rīḥ.
    PJ7864.A44H3   N E 68–1422

NT 0036918   DLC

Taqī al-Dīn, Saʿīd.
سيداتي سادتي ₍تأليف₎ سعيـد تقي الدين. ₍الطبعة 1₎
بيروت، دار الشرق الجديد ₍1955₎
    160 p. 21 cm.

    I. Title.
               Title romanized: Sayyidātī sādatī.
    PJ7864.A44S2   N E 68–1411

NT 0036919   DLC

Taqī al-Dīn al-Nabhānī
    see
al-Nabhānī, Taqī al-Dīn.

Taqī al-Dīn al-Subkī
    see
al-Subkī, Taqī al-Dīn ʿAlī ibn ʿAbd al-Kāfī, 1284–1355.

Taqī al-Dīn ibn Ḥijjah al-Ḥamawī
    see
**Ibn Ḥijjah al-Ḥamawī, Taqī al-Dīn Abū Bakr ibn ʿAlī,
d. 1434.**

Taqīʾzādah, Hasan
    see
    Taqizadeh, Hasan.

Taqizadeh, Hasan.
بيست مقاله تقيزاده، محتوى بر ترجمه سيزده مقاله از
انگليسي و فرانسه بوسيله احمد آرام، ترجمه يك مقاله از
آلماني بوسيله كاووس جهانداري، پنج مقاله فارسي، و تعليقات
بر كتاب «گاه شماري در ايران قديم». تهران، 1341 ₍1963₎
    20, 371 p. 25 cm. (مجموعه ايرانشناسي، 23)
    انتشارات بنگاه ترجمه و نشر كتاب، 150
    Added t. p.: Twenty Iranian studies, by Seyyed Hassan Taqizadeh.
    1. Iran—Hist.—Addresses, essays, lectures. I. Title. (Series:
Majmūʿah-i Īrānshināsī, 23. Series: Bungāh-i Tarjumah va Nashr-i
Kitāb. Intishārāt, 150)
               Title transliterated: Bīst maqālah-i Taqīzādah.
    DS252.5.T3   N E 67–1875

NT 0036924   DLC

Taqizadeh, Hasan.
    Essai sur l'ancien calendrier iranien, par S. H. Taqizadeh.
Teheran, Librairie Teheran, 1938.
    cover-title, 2 p. l., 12, 389 p. 23½ cm.
    In Persian.
    European sources included in text and foot-notes.
    Errata (slip and 12 p.) inserted.

    1. Calendar, Persian.
    CE34.T275   48–34042

NT 0036925   DLC

Taqizadeh, Hasan.
    (Maqālāt-i Taqīʾzādah)
مقالات تقيزاده، زير نظر ايرج افشـار. ₍تهران؟ شركت
سهامي افست   13 i. e. 19
    v. illus. 25 cm.

    AC127.T36   74–216822

NT 0036926   DLC

Taqizadeh, Hasan.
Old Iranian calendars. London, Royal Asiatic Society, 1938.
57 p. 22 cm. (Prize publication fund, v. 16)
Abridgment of Essai sur l'ancien calendrier iranien (Teheran, 1938)

1. Calendar, Persian. I. Title. (Series: Royal Asiatic Society of Great Britain and Ireland. Prize Publication Fund. ₍Publications₎ v. 16)

CE34.T3   529.3   40–1582 rev*

NT   0036927   DLC NcD OrU OC1 TxU UU MH NcU NN MiU

TAQIZADEH, Hasan.
The old Iranian calendars again.
Reprinted from the BSOAS., 1952, xiv/3. pp. 604–611.

NT   0036928   DDO

PN5463
.T36B5
Orien
Arab
Taqlā, Bishārah, 1852–1901.
₍Bishārah Taqlā Bāshā₎
بشاره تقلا باشا ١٨٥٢–١٩٠١، اقوال الجرائد، مرائي الشعراء، مختارات من اقوال الفقيد المنشورة في الاهرام. مصر، مطبعة الاهرام، ١٩٠٢.

Taqt al-dtn al-Maqrtzt
see Maqarizi, Ahmad ibn Ali, 1364–1492.

Taquechel, Eugenio.
La Alhambra romántica, leyenda morisca, por Eugenio Taquechel. Madrid ₍Talleres Espasa-Calpe, s. a.₎ 1928.
235 p. 19ᶜᵐ.

1. Alhambra. I. Title.   38–18656

Library of Congress   DP402.A4T3
    946.8

NT   0036931   DLC TU NN

Taquechel, Jorge Castellanos
see
Castellanos Taquechel, Jorge.

Taques de Almeida Paes Leme, Pedro, 1714–1777.
... Historia da capitania de S. Vicente, com um escorço biographico do autor, por Affonso de E. Taunay. S. Paulo ₍etc.₎ Comp. melhoramentos de São Paulo (Weiszflog irmãos incorporada) ₍19–₎
176 p., 1 l. 19¼ᶜᵐ.
"Copiado do manuscripto original existente no archivo do Instituto historico e geographico brasileiro."—p. ₍5₎

1. São Paulo, Brazil (State)—Hist. I. Escragnolle Taunay, Affonso de, 1876– ed.
    42–29513

Library of Congress   F2631.T168

NT   0036933   DLC LNT CtY PPT CU TxU ICN WU NjP

Taques de Almeida Paes Leme, Pedro, 1714–1777.
... Informação sobre as minas de S. Paulo. A expulsão dos jesuitas do Collegio de S. Paulo. Com um estudo sobre a obra de Pedro Taques, por Affonso de E. Taunay. S. Paulo ₍etc.₎ Comp. melhoramentos de S. Paulo (Weiszflog irmãos incorporada) ₍19–
215, ₍1₎ p. 19¼ᶜᵐ.

1. São Paulo, Brazil (State)—Hist. 2. Mines and mineral resources—Brazil—São Paulo (State) 3. Jesuits in Brazil. I. Escragnolle Taunay, Affonso de, 1876– ed. II. Title. III. Title: A expulsão dos jesuitas do Collegio de S. Paulo.
    42–11702

Library of Congress   F2631.T17
.9.   981

NjP
NT   0036934   DLC KU TxU NcD LNT CU PPT NIC ICU WU ICN

Ayer
1300.5
B8
T18
1946
TAQUES DE ALMEIDA PAES LEME, PEDRO, 1714–1777.
Informação sobre as minas de S. Paulo. A expulsão dos Jesuitas do Collegio de S. Paulo. Com um estudo acerca da obra de Pedro Taques por Affonso de E. Taunay. S. Paulo, Editora Comp. Melhoramentos de S. Paulo₍1946₎
215p. 20cm.

NT   0036935   ICN

Taques de Almeida Paes Leme, Pedro, 1714–1777.
Informação sobre as minas de S. Paulo e dos certoens da sua capitania desde o anno de 1597 até o prezente de 1772 com relação chronologica dos administradores dellas regimentos, e jurisdicção a elles conferida, á qual ficou residindo nos governadores, e capitaens generaes da mesma capitania. ₍1772.₎
Manuscript. sm. 4°.

Sao Paulo, Brazil

NT   0036936   MH NNC

₍**Taques de Almeida Paes Leme, Pedro**₎ **1714–1777.**
... Nobiliarchia paulistana, historica e genealogica ... Rio de Janeiro, Imprensa nacional, 1926–
v. ports., facsims. 23ᶜᵐ. (Revista do Instituto historico e geographico brasileiro ... Tomo especial)
"Segunda edição accrescida de uma parte inedita. Com uma biographia de Pedro Taques e estudo critico de sua obra, por Affonso d'Escragnolle Taunay ... e uma concordancia com a obra do dr. Luiz Gonzaga da Silva Leme e a propria nobiliarchia, por Augusto de Siqueira Cardoso."

1. São Paulo, Brazil (State)—Geneal. 2. Taques de Almeida Paes Leme, Pedro, 1714–1777. I. Escragnolle Taunay, Affonso de, 1876– II. Instituto historico e geographico brasileiro, Rio de Janeiro. Revista ... Tomo especial. III. Title.
    28–15359

Library of Congress   F2631.T18

NT   0036937   DLC ICarbS LNT IaU TxU NcD NcU MH WaU

Taques de Almeida Paes Leme, Pedro, 1714–1777.
Nobiliarchia paulistana historica e genealogica. 3. ed. acrescida da parte inédita, com uma biografia do autor e estudo crítico de sua obra por Afonso de E. Taunay. São Paulo, Livraria Martins Editôra ₍1953₎
3 v. plates, ports., facsim. 26 cm. (Biblioteca histórica paulista, 4)

1. São Paulo, Brazil (State)—Geneal. 2. Taques de Almeida Paes Leme, Pedro, 1714–1777. I. Escragnolle Taunay, Affonso de, 1876– II. Title. (Series)

F2631.T185   *981.6   54–19232 rev

ICU WU CU
NT   0036938   DLC CtY PPT CaOTP LNT ViU WU NN ICN TxU

FN42
S3T3
Taques de Almeida Paes Leme, Pedro, 1714–1777.
Noticias das minas de São Paulo e dos sertões de mesma capitania. Introdução e notas de Afonso de E. Taunay. S. Paulo, Vivraria Martins ₍1954₎
226 p. plates. (Biblioteca histórica Paulista, 10)
"Dêste volume, o décimo da Biblioteca histórica Paulista, comemorativa do IV centenário da fundação de São Paulo, fizeram-se à parte em papel 'vergé', 50 exemplares numerados de 1 a 50. 127. "

1. Mineral industries - São Paulo, Brazil (State)

NT   0036939   CU NcD NN IU NjP ICU MH InU KU ViU

G981.6
T169i
1954
Taques de Almeida Paes Leme, Pedro, 1714–1777.
Noticias das minas de São Paulo e dos sertões da mesma capitania. Introd. e notas de Afonso de E. Taunay. ₍3. ed.₎ S₍ão₎ Paulo, Livraria Martins ₍1954₎
226p. illus. 26cm. (Biblioteca histórica paulista, 10)

Previous eds. published under title: Informação sôbre as minas de S. Paulo.

NT   0036940   TxU MH CaOTP

Taquet, Andre, 1889–
*Spondyhtes post-infectieuses et associations de troubles névropathiques. Lille, 1919.
45 p. 8°.
No. 29.

NT   0036941   DNLM CtY

QA33
T175
1688
Taquet, Andrew.
The elements of arithmetick in three books, the seventh, eighth and ninth of Euclid. London, printed for William and Joseph Marshal ₍169–?₎

NT   0036942   DAU

Taquet (Gustave-Alexandre). *Quelques mots sur le tubercule pulmonaire à propos de phthisie et de prophilaxie. 32 pp. 4°. Paris, 1869, No. 213.

NT   0036943   DNLM

Taquet (Jean) ₍1898– ₎. *La race bleue du nord. 119 pp. 8°. Paris, 1930.
Ecole nat. vét. d'Alfort.

NT   0036944   DNLM CtY MH

Taquet, Léon, 1903–
... Contribution à l'étude du traitement prophylactique de la syphilis ... Paris, 1930.
Thèse - Univ. de Paris.
"Bibliographie": p. ₍77₎–85.

NT   0036945   CtY

Taquet, Paul, *1852 —*   L663.5 Q102
** La distillerie dans le monde entier. (Souvenir de l'Exposition universelle de 1900.) Par Paul Taquet, Raymond Berthault, Louis Bourne, Alfred Bert-Taquet. Préface de M. Monis. viii,[2], 602 p. il. F. Paris : La Revue vinicole, pref. 1901.

NT   0036946   ICJ

HD9350
.7
.F82T2
TAQUET, PAUL, 1852-
...Un impôt de 500 millions. Réforme de l'impôt des boissons. Paris, Hourdequin-Deschaux₍1888₎
xix,544 p. diagr. 18½cm.

1. Liquor traffic--France--Taxation.

NT   0036947   ICU

₍**Taquet, Paul** ₎ *1852 —*   336.19 Q400
** Le monopole de l'alcool. Les monopoles en général. — Le monopole de l'alcool sous ses différentes formes et modalités (étude générale). — Le monopole sur l'alcool à l'étranger. — Les divers monopoles en France. — Les projets de monopole sur l'alcool. Paris, Guillaumin et cie, 1904.
₍4₎, 334 p. 18ᶜᵐ.
Author's name on cover.

NT   0036948   ICJ ICU

[Taquet, Paul] 1852–
Les raisins secs; leur rôle et leur importance dans l'alimentation. Étude économique et sociale par Paul de Sorgues [pseud.] et Raymond Berthault ... Paris, L. Carpentier, 1890.
3 p. l., [v]–xii, [13]–290 p. 25½ᵐ.

1. Raisins. [1. Raisin] I. Berthault, Raymond, joint author. II. Title.

Agr 16—303

U. S. Dept. of agr. Library   95T16
for Library of Congress   [a41b1]

NT 0036949   DNAL

Taquet, Paul, 1852–   614.34 Q900
.... La répression des fraudes sur les boissons. La définition et l'étiquetage des boissons d'après la loi du 1ᵉʳ août 1905 sur la répression des fraudes et falsifications et les règlements rendus pour son exécution. Interprétation et documentation complète de toutes les prescriptions réglementaires concernant la composition, la définition, l'étiquetage des vins, vins mousseux, eaux-de-vie, spiritueux, liqueurs, sirops, cidres, vinaigres, bières, et la procedure en matière de prélèvements, de poursuites, d'analyses, d'expertises, etc. Préface de M. E. Roux, ... Paris, Pichot, 1909.
vi, 318, [2] p. 22ᵐ.
At head of title: Paul Taquet, ...
Cover-title: La loi sur la répression des fraudes et des falsifications.

NT 0036950   ICJ ICRL

Taquet, Paul, 1852–
... Universel-vinicole; les boissons dans le monde entier; la vigne, le vin, l'alcohol, les boissons, l'agriculture dans les principales contrées du globe. Production—consommation—exportation—importation. [Par] Paul Taquet ... Paris, L. Carpentier [1889]
1 p. l., vi, 485 p. 18¼ᵐ.
At head of title: Exposition universelle de 1889. Production—commerce—industrie des boissons.
1, 2. Wine and wine making. [1. Wine making] [2. Wines] 3. Paris. Exposition universelle, 1889.

Agr 16—90

U. S. Dept. of agr. Library   390.1T16
for Library of Congress   [a41b1]

NT 0036951   DNAL CU-A CU

Taquey, Charles.
... Richard Cobden; un révolutionnaire pacifique; préface de Jacques Rueff. Paris, Gallimard [1939]
2 p. l., [7]–242 p., 1 l. 21ᵐ.
"Index bibliographique": p. [236]–239.

1. Cobden, Richard, 1804–1865.

40—25187

Library of Congress   HB103.C6T3
Copyright A—Foreign   43987
     [2]   330.942

NT 0036952   DLC KU CtY ICU

La Taquigrafía.
Año

Barcelona: Academia de taquigrafía, 19   4°.
v.
Monthly.
Numbering continuous.
Año   also called epoca.

1. Shorthand—Per. and soc. publ.
N. Y. P. L.   March 19, 1925

NT 0036953   NN

Taquigrafía, ó arte de escribir tan de prisa como se habla
see under   Mármol, Manuel María del, 1776–1840.

La taquigrafía al alcance de todos los que quieran aprenderla
see under   [Paluzíe y Cantalozella, Estéban] 1808–1873.

Taquigrafía española: correspondencia comercial
see under   Pitman, Sir Isaac, 1813–1897.

Taquigrafía española de Isaac Pitman. Adaptación á la lengua española
see under   Pitman, Sir Isaac, 1813–1897.

Taquigrafía española facilitada, sistema Martí, para aprender a escribir 150 palabras por minuto, sin maestro. Bogotá, Talleres de ediciones Colombia, 1928.
20 p. 6 pl. 23½ᵐ.

1. Shorthand, Spanish. I. Martí, Francisco de Paula, 1762–1827.

Library of Congress   Z94.T17   33–37981
     [2]   653.46

NT 0036958   DLC

Taquigrafía y mecanografía por y para el arte.
v. 1

Habana, 1930–   22½ – 27½ cm.
v. illus. (ports.)
Monthly.
Published by the Comision organizadora del primer congreso cubano de taquigrafía.
Title varies: July   Revista cubana de taquigrafía;
Taquigrafía y mecanografía por y para el arte.

1. Shorthand—Per. and soc. publ.   I. Comision organizadora del primer congreso cubano de taquigrafía.   II. Revista cubana de taquigrafía.
N. Y. P. L.   September 6, 1934

NT 0036959   NN

El Taquígrafo Gregg. año 1– enero 1924–
New York, The Gregg publishing company [1924–
v. illus. 18¼ᵐ. quarterly.
Director: J. R. Gregg.
Editor: Jan. 1924–   A. Herrera B.

1. Shorthand, Spanish—Period. I. Gregg, John Robert, 1867–
     28–13033

Library of Congress   Z94P.T17

NT 0036960   DLC NN

Taquinet le Bossu
see under   Kock, [Charles] Paul de, 1793–1871.

WG   TAQUINI, Alberto C
420   El corazón pulmonar. Buenos Aires,
T175c   El Ateneo [1954]
1954   xi, 285 p. illus.
     1. Embolism - Pulmonary

NT 0036962   DNLM

RC683
T16   Taquini, Alberto C
... Exploración del corazón por vía esofágica; tesis de doctorado por ... Alberto C. Taquini. Buenos Aires, "El Ateneo", 1936.
7 p. l., [xiii]–xvi, 231 p., 2 l. illus. (part col.) diagrs. 23cm.

At head of title: Universidad nacional de Buenos Aires. Facultad de ciencias médicas ...
"Bibliografía": p. [207]–219.

1. Heart - Diseases - Diagnosis. 2. Diagnosis Radioscopic.

NT 0036963   NNC PU-Med OEac DNLM CtY-M

Taquoy (Léon). * De la coxalgie. 46 pp. 4°.
Paris, 1860, No. 14.

NT 0036964   DNLM

PK6723   Taqwīm al-Ḥaqq Kākākhel, joint author.
T3
Orien   **Tasnīm al-Ḥaqq Kākākhel.**
Push   د پښتو قواعد [تاليف د تسنيم الحق كاكاخيل [او] تقويم الحق كاكاخيل. [پشاور، اداره اشاعت سرحد [گذارش] 1953]

تقويم تونس العام، الاداري والتجاري، الصناعي والفلاحي.
النشرة   لسنة
[Éditions franco-arabes,   تونس
v. illus. 27 cm.
Issues for   have added t. p.: Indicateur général tunisien
bilingue: administratif, agricole, industriel, commercial.

1. Tunisia—Indus.—Direct. 2. Tunisia—Pol. & govt.—Period. I. Title: Indicateur général tunisien.
     Title transliterated: Taqwīm Tūnis al-'āmm.

HC547.T8T3   N E 62–1115

NT 0036966   DLC

Tar, Béla.
Ipartörvény mai érvényében
see under   Hungary. Laws, statutes, etc.

Za   Tar, Jack, pseud.
Za1   To the President of the United States.
C1   Jack Tar's ahoi! to Major Jack Downing, or the Hartford-Convention-man. [n.p., n.d.] broadside. 27 x 15 cm.
     Poem.

NT 0036968   CtY

Tar, Jacques, pseud.
... Noëls étranges sur mer et dans le ciel. Paris, Les Éditions Denoël [1941]
99 p., 1 l. 19ᵐ.

1. Christmas stories. I. Title.

PQ2639.A68N6   A F 47–702
Newberry Library
for Library of Congress   [4]†

NT 0036969   ICN MH DLC

A Tar.
An impartial account of the late proceedings of the seamen of the port of Tyne
see under title

Tar an' feathers, v. 1-   Fall, 1940-
     Chapel Hill, Carolina publications union, 1940-
          illus. Q.
     Library has: v. 1-
          Published eight times during the college year
     from October to May inclusive.

NT 0036971   NcU

... Tar and oil for road improvement; report of
     progress of experiments at Jackson, Tenn.
          see under U.S. Bureau of Public Roads.

Tar baby.   Chapel Hill,1919-
     Library has:
     v.1-date.
     Discontinued after v.4,no.1.

NT 0036973   NcU

Tar-Bo-Rah; being the annual of the senior
     class, Tarboro High School. ₍Raleigh₎,1916-
     Library has:
     1916,

NT 0036974   NcU

Tar heel ...
          see also Tarheel ...

FCp784.71
T17w   Tar Heel ₍pseud.₎
          Wearin' of the grey, written by Tar Heel;
     arranged for the piano forte. Baltimore,
     Wm. C. Miller, ᶜ1866.
          5 p. 32cm.

          1. N.C.--Songs I. Title.

NT 0036976   NcU

Tar heel.   Chapel Hill, 1893-
     Library has:
     v.1-date.

NT 0036977   NcU

FCp378
UE   Tar Heel, Chapel Hill, N.C.
          News release to preparatory and high school
     papers from The Daily Tar Heel, v.1, no.1-4,
     April 29-May 20, 1935. ₍Chapel Hill₎
          1 v. 36cm. weekly.
          No more published?

          1. N.C. University--Periodicals

NT 0036978   NcU

Tar heel.   Elizabeth City, 19 -
     Library has:
     Nov.23,1906,May 3,1907,May 10,1907,May 24,1907
     Je.14,1907,July 12,1907,July 26,1907,Oct.25,
     1907,Nov.15,1907,Jan.17,1908,May 29,1908,Je.12
     1908,Oct.9,1908,Oct.15,1908,Oct.23,1908,Nov.6,
     Dec.11,1908,Dec.23,1908,Jan.15,1909,Apr.9,1909
     July 9,1909, July 23,1909,

     Weekly.

NT 0036979   NcU

W 1   TAR HEEL cancer news.
NO376   Mount Airy, A. C. S., North Carolina.
          Division ₍1951?₎-
               v.
          Continues North Carolina cancer news.
          I. American Cancer Society. North
          Carolina Division

NT 0036980   DNLM

Tar heel club news....
     Raleigh, N.C. Agricultural extension service.

NT 0036981   OC1

TX715   Tar Heel cook book, compiled by the
T3   Business and Professional Women's
          Club, Washington, N. C. ₍Wash-
          ington, N. C., n. d.₎
               60, ₍2₎ p. 22 cm.

          Cover title.

          1. Cookery, American - North Caro-
     lina. I. Business and Professional
     Women's Club.   Washington, N. C.

NT 0036982   NcRS

Tar heel economist.
     ₍Raleigh, N. C., Agricultural Extension Service₎
          v. in ill. 29 cm. monthly.
     Continues: Tarheel farm economist.
     Key title: Tar heel economist, ISSN 0039-9612

          1. North Carolina—Economic conditions—Periodicals. I. North
     Carolina. State University, Raleigh. Agricultural Extension Serv-
     ice.
     HD1401.T34   330.9'756'04   76-648398
                                                    MARC-S

NT 0036983   DLC NcRS

Tar Heel Educational Society, Southern Pines, N. C.
     An economic primer: our nation's biggest
     racket
          see under Plainspeaker, Simon ₍pseud.₎

L11   The Tar heel elementary school bulletin; a bulle-
.T2   tin devoted to the problems of the North Caro-
          lina elementary principals and teachers. v.1-
               Nov.1942-   Greensboro, N.C.,
          Department of Education, Woman's College, Uni-
          versity of North Carolina.
               v. illus. quarterly

          1. Education--Period. 2. Public schools--North
     Carolina.

NT 0036985   ICU

MED   Tar Heel nurse.
RT
1   Raleigh, N. C.
.T3   v. illus. quarterly.
          Began publication in 1939. Cf. Union
     list of serials.
          Official publication of the North Caro-
     lina State Nurses' Association.

     #Nurses and nursing--Societies, etc.

NT 0036986   MoU MiU NcU

C371.716
S37   Tar Heel school food service. 1946-
          Raleigh, State Dept. of Public Instruction.
               v. illus. 22-28cm. monthly, Sept.-May.
          Title varies: -Sept. 1964, School lunch
     in the Tar Heel State.
          Cover title, Sept. 1969-   North Caro-
     lina school food service.

NT 0036987   NcU

The Tar Heel state. A leaflet of interesting
     information about North Carolina
          see under North Carolina. Dept. of
     Public Instruction.

Tar heel topics.   Chapel Hill, Student survey
     department of the University of N. C., 1928-
     1932.
          illus. D.
          Library has: v. 1, no. 1-v. 5, no. 4,
     January, 1928-August, 1932.
          Discontinued after August, 1932, when the
     title and volume sequence was taken by another
     periodical issued by the Dean of students.
     Monthly.
          Not issued: Sept. Oct. 1928; Sept. Oct.
     1929; Oct. 1930; Feb. 1931, July-Dec. 1931;
     Jan.-May, 1932.

NT 0036989   NcU

A Tar Heel traveler.
     Letters from a Tar Heel traveler in Mediter-
     ranean countries
          see under title

Tar heel underwriter
     see   The Dixie underwriter.

The tar man; or, The fox and the hare, a Virginia nursery
     tale written and illustrated by Mrs. A. H. P. ... ₍n. p., 18—₎
          cover-title, ₍8₎ p. plates. 22ᶜᵐ.

     I. P., Mrs. A. H. II. A. H. P., Mrs.
                                                    43-39049
     Library of Congress   PZ8.3.T146

NT 0036992   DLC

...The Tar of all weathers; or, A British
     seaman's chest of conviviality...
     ₍Devonport, Printed and sold by S. and
     J. Keys, 18--?₎
          cover-title,16 p.

     Without music.

NT 0036993   NjP

... Tar oils as possible Diesel fuels
    see under   Institution of mining engineers.
Utilization of coal committee.

Tar River Baptist Association
  see **Baptists.** *North Carolina. Tar River Baptist Association.*

Tar water, a ballad, inscribed to the Right
Honourable Philip, earl of Chesterfield
  see under   [Williams, Sir Charles
Hanbury] 1708–1759.

Tara Ali Baig
  see
  Baig, Tara Ali.

Tara Basu
  see
Basu, Tarapada.

... Tārā-Bhakti-Sudhārnava ...
  see under   [Narasimha, disciple of
Gadādhara] 17th cent.

Tara Chand, 1888–
  see
Chand, Tara, 1888–

Tara Chand Rajdhan
  see   Rajdhan, Tara Chand, 1897–

Tārā-dāsa Datta
  see **Dutt, Taradas.**

Tara Devi.
  Zoleikha and the enchanted jungle. Illus. by C. H. G.
Moorhouse. Bombay, Thacker [1947]
   43 p. 25 cm.

   I. Title.

PZ8.T173Zo   S A 63–1584 ‡

NT 0037003   DLC

Tara Dutt Gairola
  see
Gairola, Tara Dutt.

Tārā Nāth Tarkabāchaspati
  see
  Tarkavachaspati, Taranatha, 1812–1885.

Tārā Pāṇḍē
  see
  Pande, Tara, 1914–

Tārā Pāṇḍēya
  see
  Pande, Tara, 1914–

Ṭara Românească
  see
  Wallachia.

Tara Singh
    see   Singh, Tara.

Tara Singh, 1885–1967
  see
Singh, Tara, 1885–1967.

Tara Sirkar
    see   Sirkar, Tara.

Tara (Andrea). *Dell' amianto. 35 pp. 8°.
Pavia, Fusi & Co., 1848. [P.. v. 2226.]

NT 0037012   DNLM

TARA, Desmond O. , pseud.

  See PIFFARD, Nina H.

Tara, Hollis B
  The political, economic, and psychological warfare conducted by Serbia against Austria-Hungary, 1903–1914.
[Washington] 1947.
   151 l. 29 cm.
   Thesis (M. sc.)—Georgetown University.

   1. Serbia—For. rel.—Austria. 2. Austria—For. rel.—Serbia.
3. Panslavism. I. Title.

DR360.T3   52–33903 ‡

NT 0037014   DLC

Tārā, Javād.

خداشناسی علمی، یا رشد حکمت در اسلام، مشکلات فلسفه
و حل آنها. نگارش جواد تارا. [تهران، کتابفروشی
زوار ـ ادب [؟ـ195]

   7, 440 p. 22 cm.

   1. Islamic theology.   I. Title. II. Title: Rushd-i ḥikmat dar
Islām.
                    Title transliterated: Khudāshināsī-i 'Ilmī.

BP166.T37   N E 67–315

NT 0037015   DLC

Tara, John Theodore Cuthbert Moore-Brabazon, *baron Brabazon of*
  see **Brabazon, John Theodore Cuthbert Moore-Brabazon,**
baron, 1884–

    Tara (Stéphan-Vincent-Marie) [1887–].
    *De l'anasarque chez le nourrisson. 84 pp.
    8°. Paris, 1912. No. 372.

NT 0037017   DNLM MH

055.9   Țara noastră; revistă literară, politică și
TA   socială. an.1-   1907–
       Cluj.
         v. illus. 23cm.

    Publication suspended, Dec.1909–Sept.1922.
    Vols. for 1907–09 published in Sibiu.

NT 0037018   IU

4TK   Taraba, István
278   Távbeszélő és távjelző berende-
       zések. [Budapest] Népszava [1952]
       169 p.

   (Népszava műszaki könyvtára)

NT 0037019   DLC-P4

FILM
3099   Taraba, Wolfgang Friedrich Wilhelm

     Verganenheit und Gegenwart bei Eduard
Mörike. Münster, 1953.
    Microfilm copy (negative) of typescript.
    Collation of the original: vii, 200 l.
    Thesis (Ph.D.)—Westfälischen Willhelms-
Universität zu Münster, 1953.
    Bibliography: leaves 195–199.

   1. Mörike, Eduard Friedrich, 1804–1895.

NT 0037020   ViU

Tarabay, Antonio Murad
    see   Murad Tarabay, Antonio.

PG8715   Tarabildienė, Domicelė (Tarabildaitė) 1912–   illus.
.B3
     Balys, Jonas, 1909–   comp.
       Šimtas liaudies baladžiu. Parengė J. Balys. Iliustravo
       D. Tarabildienė. Kaunas, LTSR valstybinė leidykla, 1941.

Tarabini, Ferdinando Castellani
see   Castellani Tarabini, Ferdinando.

Tarabini, Luigi.   L616.12 R206
.... Cardiopatie da lavoro (lavoro del cuore ed attività musco-
lare). Tesi di libera docenza, del dott. Luigi Tarabini, ...
Modena, G. Ferraguti e c., tipografi, 1912.
vi, [2], 181 p. illus., 3 fold. pl., IV fold. tables. 26ᶜᵐ.
At head of title: Istituto di clinica medica generale di Modena.
"Bibliografia," p. [159]–181.

NT 0037024   ICJ

BR65   Tarabla, Maria Lina, 1915– ed.
.I3 I85
   Ignatius, *Saint, bp. of Antioch, 1st cent.*
      ... Lettere. Lettera e Martirio di san Policarpo. A cura di
   Maria Lina Tarabla. Torino [etc.] G. B. Paravia e c. [1945]

Tarabla, Maria Lina, 1915–
   Santo Ignazio d'Antiochia lettere ...
      see under Ignatius, saint, bp. of
   Antioch, 1st cent.
         Le Lettere ...

BX   Taraborelli, Giuseppe, S.P.
2509   Luce di cielo nella valle santa. Trevi nel
.P47   Lazio, Comitato Feste IX Centenario S. Pietro
T3   Er. [1952]
        133 p. illus., plates. 22cm.

        1. Peter, Saint, of Trevi, 1027(ca.)–1052.

NT 0037027   DCU NN

Tarabori, Augusto Ugo.   2779a.154
Gian Pietro Lucini. Con introduzione di Carlo Linati e versi in-
editi del Lucini.
Milano. Caddeo & c. 1922. xv, 272 pp. 19 cm., in 8s.
Nota bibliografica, pp. 269–272.

M6862 — Lucini, Gian Pietro, 1867–1914. — Linati, Carlo, pref.

NT 0037028   MB IEN

Tarabotti, Angelica
   see Tarabotti, Arcangela.

TARABOSHI.
   I delitti del "Taraboshi", ovvero La civiltà
europea a Scutari d'Albania. Scutari, Tip.
Taraboshi di C.T.R., 1914.

   16 cm.
   At head of title: Terenzio Tocci.

NT 0037030   MH

[Tarabotti, Arcangela]
   Che le donne siano della spetie degli hvomini. Difesa
delle donne, di Galerana Barcitotti [pseud.], contra Horatio Plata, il traduttore di quei fogli, che dicono: Le donne
non essere della spetie degli huomini. Norimbergh, Par
I. Cherchenbergher, 1651.

   5 p. l., clxxx [i. e. clxxxii] p. 14¾ᶜᵐ.

   1. Woman. 2. Plata, Orazio. Discorso piacevole, che le donné non sieno
della specie degli uomini.

                                                    9–1556†
   Library of Congress   HQ1201.T2

NT 0037031   DLC ICN

BX4215 [Tarabotti, Arcangela]
.T2   La semplicita ingannata, di Galerana Bara-
Rare Bk totti [pseud.]. Leida, G. Sambix, 1654.
        [24], 307, [3] p. (blank) 13cm.
        Elsevier device (sphere) on t. p.
        Imperfect; imprint out off.
        Willems 740.
        Book-plate of Edward V. Utterson.

        1. Convents and nunneries. I. Title.

NT 0037032   ICU PU MdBP

El-Taraboulsi, Mohamed Ahmed, 1926–
   Directed substitution in cellulose.   1952.
   163 l.
   Thesis - Ohio State University.

NT 0037033   OU

4K Ger. -   Tarabrin, Eugen.
563   Grundsätzliche Entscheidungen der Vollver-
        sammlungen und des Ausschusses der Advokaten-
        kammer in Böhmen.   Reichenberg, Im Selbst-
        verlage des Deutschen Anwaltsverbandes, 1936.
        51 p.

NT 0037034   DLC-P4

Tarabrin, Evžen.
   Nástin vývoje advokacie v zemích koruny české,
(XIII–XVIII. stol.) Praha, Jednoty Advokátu
Ceskoslovenských, 1936.
   48 p.
   Bohemian.

NT 0037035   OC1

K   Tarabrin, Evžen.
T176   Zásadní usnesení a rozhodnutí valných hromad a
Z37   výboru Advokátní komory v Čechách. Sebral a
1935   systematicky upravil Evžen Tarabrin. Praha,
       Nakl. Jednoty advokátů československých, 1935.
       52 p.

       1. Lawyers--Czechoslovak Republic. I. Title.

NT 0037036   NSyU

Tarabukin, Nikolaĭ Mikhaĭlovich, 1899–1956.
   (Opyt teorii zhivopisi)
   Опыт теории живописи. Москва, Всерос. пролет-
культ, 1923.
   69 p. 22 cm.

   1. Painting. 2. Composition (Art) I. Title.

   ND1475.T37   75–564387

NT 0037037   DLC MH

Ṭarābulus al-Gharb (*City*)
   see
   Tripoli.

(Ṭarābulus al-Gharb wa-Barqah fī barāthin al-istiʿmār al
-Iṭālī)
طرابلس الغرب وبرقه فى براثن الاستعمار الايطالى ، صحائف سود.
[n.p.] دار المستقبل للطبع والنشر والاعلان [194–؟]
160 p. illus. 20 cm.
الشافعى ، محمد على . صفحات مدونة من نظائع الطليان ؛ :CONTENTS
طرابلس الغرب وبرقه ، ١٩١١ ـ ١٩٣١ . احوال طرابلس وبرقه الاجتماعية
فى ظل الاستعباد الفاشيستى ، متقولة عن كتاب لجميعة العرب فى طرابلس الغرب
وضع المهاجرين الطرابلسيين فى القطر المصرى . ـ محمود ، احمد . السيد عمر
المختار ، طرائف من نشانه وجهاده من اعدامه واقوال العرب فيه .

Continued in next column

Continued from preceding column

   1. Tripoli—History. 2. Barca—History. 3. Italians in Libya. 4.
al-Mukhtār, ʿUmar, 1860?–1931.   I. al-Shāfiʿī, Muḥammad ʿAlī.
Ṣafaḥāt mudawwanah min fazāʾiʿ al-Ṭulyān fī Ṭarābulus al-Gharb
wa-Barqah, 1911–1931. 194–? II. Fajīʿat al-ʿArab fī Ṭarābulus al
-Gharb. Aḥwāl Ṭarābulus wa-Barqah al-ijtimāʿīyah fī ẓill al-istiʿbād
al-Fāshistī. 194–? III. Maḥmūd, Aḥmad, al-Ustādh. al-Sayyid
ʿUmar al-Mukhtār. 194–?

   DT239.T7T37   75–587592

NT 0037040   DLC

al-Ṭarābulusī, ʿAlī, ed.

DT324   Lyautey, Louis Hubert Gonzalve, 1854–1934.
.L894   سقط المتاع فى سياسة المشير ليوطى نحو الاهالى ، كتاب
Orien   سياسى ، اجتماعى ، تاريخى ، ادبى . جامع شوارده : على
Arab   الطرابلسى . [الرباط المطبعة الرسمية المغربية [1925]

al-ṬARĀBULUSĪ, AMJAD, 1918—
   La critique poétique des Arabes jusqu'au
Ve siècle de l'Hégire (XIe siècle de J.C.)
Damas, Institut Français de Damas, 1955.
301 p.

   Cover date 1956.
   Appendice des Textes Arabes, pp. 259–
298.

   1. Arabic poetry--Hist. & crit. I. Title.

NT 0037042   InU

al-Ṭarābulusī, Amjad, 1918–
النقد واللغة فى رسالة الغفران . [تاليف: احمد الطرابلسى .
[دمشق مطبعة الجامعة السورية 1951.
(دروس ومحاضرات بكلية الآداب ، His 1) .216 p. 25 cm
Bibliography : p. [211]–214.

   1. Abū al-ʿAlāʾ, al-Maʿarrī, 973–1057. Risālat al-ghufrān.
   I. Title.
                        Title romanized: al-Naqd wa-al-
                        lughah fī Risālat al-ghufrān.

   PJ7750.A25R537   N E 68–1663

NT 0037043   DLC UU

al-Ṭarābulusī, Amjad, 1918–
نظرة تاريخية فى حركة التاليف عند العرب فى اللغة والأدب
والتاريخ والجغرافيا [تاليف: امجد الطرابلسى . [دمشق مطبعة
الجامعة السورية ،
.1955–
(دروس ومحاضرات بكلية الآداب ، His 2) .v. 25 cm
Bibliography: v. 1, p. [184]–[189]
CONTENTS.—   جزء [1] اللغة والأدب —.
   1. Arabic literature--Hist. & crit. I. Title.
                  Title romanized: Naẓrah tārīkhīyah
                  fī ḥarakat al-taʾlīf ʿinda al-ʿArab.

   PJ7510.T35   N E 68–1865

NT 0037044   DLC

al-Ṭarābulusī, Ibrāhīm ibn Ismāʿīl
   see
   Ibn al-Ajdābī, Ibrāhīm ibn Ismāʿīl.

al-Ṭarābulsī, Muḥammad Nabīh.
المجرمون الاحداث فى القانون المصرى والتشريع المقارن ، تاليف
محمد نبيه الطرابلسى . مصر، مطبعة الاعتماد [1948؟]
320 p. 24 cm.
رسالة الدكتوراه ـ جامعة فواد الأول
Errata slip inserted.
Bibliography: p. [312]–315.

   1. Juvenile delinquency--Egypt. I. Title.
                  Title transliterated: al-Mujrimūn al-abdāth.

                                          N E 65–404

NT 0037046   DLC

Taracad Subramania Ramakrishnan
see
Ramakrishnan, Taracad Subramania, 1899–

Tārācanda
see
Chand, Tara, 1888–

Taracena, Alfonso, 1897?–
... Los abrasados, novela tropical. México, Ediciones Botas, 1937.
264 p., 2 l. 19½ᵐ.

ɪ. Title.
37-19400

Library of Congress   PQ7297.T35A63

₍2₎   863.6

NT   0037049   DLC CoU CU CtY NcD NcU OC1 OU MtU ViU
TU KU

Taracena, Alfonso, 1897–
... Autobiografía, cuentos. México, Ediciones Botas, 1933.
187 p., 1 l. 19ᵐ.
Contents.—Autobiografía.—El discurso oficial.—Idilio roto.—La expiación de la serpiente.—La cruz de Tindú.—Abuelito.—El regalo de Navidad.— Una mujer sin corazón.—Mi trágica amistad.—Medio hermano.—Forasteros.—En pro del casticismo.—El poder del pensamiento.— El caballero de la triste figura.

ɪ. Title.
35-11545

Library of Congress   PQ7297.T35A3   928.6

NT   0037050   DLC MH MiU IU OU

Taracena, Alfonso, 1897?–
... Bajo el fuego de helios, novela con detalles de historia y de leyenda. Mexico, Editorial "Bolívar", 1928.
121, ₍1₎ p. 14ᵐ. (Biblioteca hispano-americana)
"Para la Ilustre Library of Congress, Washington, D. C. El autor" in manuscript on half-title.

ɪ. Title.
28-11502

Library of Congress   PQ7297.T35B3   1928

NT   0037051   DLC NN

Taracena, Alfonso, 1897?–
... Carranza contra Madero. ₍México, D. F., Editorial "Bolívar", 1934.
26 p., 1 l. 22ᵐ. (Biblioteca de los Andes)

1. Carranza, Venustiano, pres. Mexico, 1859–1920. 2. Madero, Francisco Indalecio, pres. Mexico, 1873–1913. 3. Mexico—Hist.—Revolution, 1910–   ɪ. Title.
38-15214

Library of Congress   F1234.C38
₍3₎   972.08

NT   0037052   DLC TU IU NN

Taracena, Alfonso, 1897–
... Cuentos frente al mar. Mexico, Editorial "Bolívar", 1928.
90, ₍4₎ p., 1 l. 13½ᵐ. (Biblioteca hispanoamericana)
Contents.—El discurso oficial.—Idilio roto.—La expiación de la serpiente. — La cruz de Tindú. — Abuelito.—El regalo de Navidad.—Una mujer sin corazón.—Mi trágica amistad.—Medio-hermano.—Forasteros.

ɪ. Title.
29-18628

Library of Congress   PQ7297.T35C8

NT   0037053   DLC NN

Taracena, Alfonso, 1897–
... 10 personajes extravagantes. México, D. F., Editorial "Bolívar", 1930.
86 p., 5 l. 13½ᵐ. (Biblioteca hispanoamericana)
Contents.—En pro del casticismo.—La mujer original.—Los pellejos del gato. — Reporter profesional. — El señorito 1930. — Las siete vacas flacas.—El poder del pensamiento.—El jefe de sección.—El duende del volcán.—El caballero de la triste figura.

ɪ. Title.
30-24665

Library of Congress   PQ7297.T35D5

NT   0037054   DLC NN

Taracena, Alfonso, 1897–
... En el vertigo de la revolucion mexicana ... Mexico, D. F., Editorial "Bolívar", 1930–
v. 21ᵐ. (Biblioteca de los Andes)

1. Mexico—Hist.—Revolution, 1910–   2. Mexico—Hist.—Revolution, 1910–   —Chronology. ɪ. Title.
30-1651

Library of Congress   F1234.T17

NT   0037055   DLC CtY TxU CoU OC1 NN

Taracena, Alfonso, 1897?–
En el vertigo de la revolución. ₍Translated by E. B. Newman. n. p.₎ 1931₎
262 l. 27 cm.
Typescript (carbon copy)
English translation of En el vertigo de la revolución mexicana.

1. Mexico — Hist. — 1910–1946.   2. Mexico — Hist. — 1910–1946— Chronology.   ɪ. Title.
F1234.T1713   972.081   59–59486 ‡

NT   0037056   DLC

Taracena, Alfonso, 1897–
... Francisco I. Madero y la verdad. ₍México, D. F., Editorial "Bolívar"₎ 1933.
46 p., 1 l. 21ᵐ. (Biblioteca de los Andes)
At head of title: ... Taracena.
"Artículos ... en defensa de Madero, respondiendo a los ataques de eminentes escritores del antiguo régimen."—Leaf at end.

1. Madero, Francisco Indalecio, pres. Mexico, 1873–1913.
33–2912

Library of Congress   F1234.M246
₍2₎   923.172

NT   0037057   DLC NcD WaU NN

Taracena, Alfonso, 1897?–
... Lecciones de historia hispano-americana, arregladas para las escuelas del continente. México, Ediciones Botas, 1938.
4 p. L., ₍11₎–27 (i. e. 277) p., 5 l. illus. (incl. ports., maps) 22ᵐ.

1. Spanish America—Hist.   ɪ. Title.
41–22093

Library of Congress   F1410.T3
₍2₎   980

NT   0037058   DLC TxU DPU

Taracena, Alfonso, 1897?–
Madero, el héroe cívico; prólogo de José Vasconcelos. México, Ediciones Xochitl, 1946.
186 p. illus., port. 20 cm. (Vidas mexicanas, 29)

1. Madero, Francisco Indalecio, Pres. Mexico, 1873–1913.
(Series)
A 50–2449

Yale Univ. Library
for Library of Congress   ₍2₎

NT   0037059   CtY OU CU NcU NN TxU NNC MH IaU TU CU-BANC
CoU OKentU NIC

F7389

Taracena, Alfonso, 1897?–
Madero, el héroe cívico; prólogo de José Vasconcelos. México, Ediciones Xochitl, 1946.
186 p. illus., port. 20 cm. (Vidas mexicanas, 29)

Microfilm (positive) New York, Columbia University Library, 1971. 1 reel.
Master negative no. 0010.

NT   0037060   NNC

Taracena, Alfonso, 1897?–
... Madero, vida del hombre y del político; prólogo de José Vasconcelos. México, Ediciones Botas, 1937.
xvi, 604 p., 4 l. 19ᵐ. (Hombres de México. 1)

1. Madero, Francisco Indalecio, pres. Mexico, 1873–1913. 2. Mexico—Pol. & govt.—1910–
38–21316

Library of Congress   F1234.M248
₍2₎   923.172

NT   0037061   DLC NBuU TU DAU OC1 OU DPU

F1234
.M248
1938

Taracena, Alfonso, 1897?–
Madero, vida del hombre y del político. Prólogo de José Vasconcelos. 2. ed. México, Ediciones Botas, 1938.
604p. (Hombres de México, 1)

1. Madero, Francisco Indalecio, Pres. Mexico, 1873–1913. 2. Mexico - Pol. & govt. - 1910-

NT   0037062   NcU NcD NmLcU CaBVaU

Taracena, Alfonso, 1897–
... Mexicanas modernas. ₍México, D. F., Editorial "Bolívar"₎ 1932.
80 p. 20½ᵐ. (On cover: Biblioteca de los Andes)
At head of title: Taracena.
A novel.

ɪ. Title.
32–31643

Library of Congress   PQ7297.T35M4
₍2₎   863.6

NT   0037063   DLC TU OU NN

Taracena, Alfonso, 1897?–
... Mi vida en el vértigo de la revolución mexicana (anales sintéticos.—1900–1930) México, D. F., Ediciones Botas, 1936.
715 p. 19½ᵐ.
"Primera serie" published 1930 with title "En el vértigo de la revolución mexicana."

1. Mexico—Hist.—Revolution, 1910–   2. Mexico—Hist.—Revolution, 1910–   —Chronology. ɪ. Title.
37–32488

Library of Congress   F1234.T173
———— Copy 2.   ₍3₎   972.08

NT   0037064   DLC MiEM WaSpG GU FTaSU DAU CtY NBuU MU
IaU AU OU NN InU MH NIC ICarbS TxU NcU

972
T176r

Taracena, Alfonso, 1897?–
La revolución desvirtuada; continuación de La verdadera revolución mexicana. Mexico, B. Costa-Amic
v. 20cm.

1. Mexico. Hist. 1910-1946. 2. Mexico. Hist. 1946-   3. Mexico. Hist. Chronology. I.   Title.

NT   0037065   IEN

Taracena, Alfonso, 1897–
... La tragedia zapatista. México, D. F., Editorial "Bolívar", 1931.

89, [4] p. 20ᶜᵐ. (Biblioteca de los Andes)

Colophon dated: 1932.

1. Zapata, Emiliano, 1869 (ca.)–1919. 2. Mexico—Hist.—Revolution, 1910—. I. Title.

Library of Congress   F1234.T19   33–1929

[2]   [972.08] 923.272

NT   0037066   DLC NN MShM

TARACENA, ALFONSO, 1897–
La verdadera revolución mexicana. [1. ed.]
México, Editorial Jus.   v.   24cm.
(Colección México heroico, no. 2, 9, 34, 37, etc.)

1. Mexico—Hist.—Revolutionary period, 1910–1920. 2. Mexico—Hist. 1920—. 3. Mexico—Hist.—Chronology. I. Series. no. 2. II. Series. no. 9. III. Series. no. 34. IV. Series. no. 37.

NT   0037067   NN DAU

F1234   **Taracena, Alfonso,** 1897?–
T22   La verdadera revolucion mexicana. 2. ed., correigida y aumentada. Mexico, Editorial Jus
     v.

     Contents.—

           4. etapa, 1915–1916.—

NT   0037068   WaU

F1321   Taracena, Angel
T25   Apuntes históricos de Oaxaca. Oaxaca, México, 1941.
     224 p. 23cm.

     "Síntesis de las obras inéditas del mismo autor tituladas: 'Historia precortesiana de Oaxaca,' 'Los conquistadores de Oaxaca,' 'Oaxaca colonial' y 'Oaxaca independiente.'"

     1. Oaxaca, Mexico (State) - History. I. Title.

NT   0037069   CU-BANC InU CtW

Taracena, Angel.
... Efemérides oaxaqueñas. Oaxaca, México, 1941.

5 p. l., 9–147 p. 23ᶜᵐ.

"Erratas más notables": leaf inserted.

CONTENTS.—Efemérides. Indice onomástico y de sucesos de las efemérides.—Las calles de Oaxaca.—Apuntes biográficos.—Bibliografía (p. [139]–147)

1. Oaxaca, Mexico (State)—Hist.—Chronology. 2. Oaxaca, Mexico (City)—Streets. 3. Oaxaca, Mexico (State)—Biog. I. Title.

                         42–25048

Library of Congress   F1321.T26

[3]   972.7

NT   0037070   DLC GU FU NIC CU-BANC IU

F1321   Taracena, Angel
T27   Episodios históricos oaxaqueños.   Oaxaca, México,
193_   v. 23cm.

     1. Oaxaca, Mexico (State) - History. I. Title.

NT   0037071   CU-BANC

Taracena, Angel.
Juárez, católico apostólico romano. México, 1948.

134, [6] p. 20 cm.

"Bibliografía": 4 p. at end.

1. Juárez, Benito Pablo, Pres. Mexico, 1806–1872.

F1233.J9546   923.172   49–1529*

NT   0037072   DLC OClW TxU IU

F1226   Taracena, Angel
F5   Porfirio Díaz. [1. ed.] México, Editorial Jus, 1960.
no. 88   212 p. illus., ports. 24cm. (Figuras y episodios de la historia de México, no. 88)

     Bibliographical footnotes.

NT   0037073   CU-BANC

Taracena, Angel.
... Santa Anna en Oaxaca. Oaxaca de Juárez [Ramírez Belmar, impresor] 1935.

57, [1] p., 1 l. 22½ᶜᵐ. (*His* Episodios históricos oaxaqueños. II)

"Bibliografía": p. [4] of cover.

1. Santa Anna, Antonio López de, pres. Mexico, 1795–1876.

                         41–11744

Library of Congress   F1321.T27 t. 2

[2]   (972.7) 923.172

NT   0037074   DLC LNT CU-BANC IU NNC

Taracena, Blas
     see
Taracena Aguirre, Blas.

Taracena, Eduardo Estrada
     see   Estrada Taracena, Eduardo.

Taracena, Emilio Sosa
     see
Sosa Taracena, Emilio.

Taracena, José Ernesto Calderon
     see   Calderon Taracena, José Ernesto.

Taracena, Julio Sosa
   see   Sosa Taracena, Julio.

Taracena, Rosendo.
... Apuntes históricos de Tabasco; arreglados para uso de las escuelas con la aprobación de la Dirección general de educación pública del estado. México, Ediciones Botas, 1937.

6 p. l., [19]–126 p. illus., ports. 19ᶜᵐ.

"Bibliografía": p. [117]–119.

1. Tabasco, Mexico—Hist. 2. Tabasco, Mexico—Biog. I. Title.

                         38–3338

Library of Congress   F1351.T37

[3]   972.6

NT   0037080   DLC NN

Taracena, Salomé, 1854–1903.
Ortigas y jazmines, poesías [por] Salomé Taracena (El Negro Melenudo) Juicio literario de Francisco J. Santamaría. Villahermosa, 1948.

118 p. 20 cm. (Publicaciones del Gobierno del Estado (escritores tabasqueños) 30)

I. Title.

PQ7297.T357O7   53–21366 ‡

NT   0037081   DLC MH CtY NN

N   **Taracena Aguirre, Blas.**
7101   Arte romano, por Blas Taracena. Arte paleo-
.A8   cristiano, por Pedro Batlle Huguet. Arte visi-
v.2   godo. Arte asturiano, por Helmut Schlunk.
     Madrid, Plus-Ultra [1947]
     441 p. (Ars Hispaniae; historia universal
     del arte hispánico, v.2)

     Bibliography: p. 417–427.

     1. Art, Roman-Spain. 2. Christian art and symbolism-Spain. 3. Art, Early Christian-Spain. 4. Art, Visigothic- Spain. 5. Art, Asturian. I. Batlle Huguet, Pedro. Arte paleocristiano. II. Schlunk, Helmut. Arte visigodo. III. Schlunk, Helmut. Arte asturiano. IV. T. V.Ser

NT   0037082   DAU MH INS NCornIC

Taracena Aguirre, Blas.
Carta arqueológica de España: Soria
     see his   Soria.

Taracena Aguirre, Blas.
...La cerámica antigua española, por B. Taracena Aguirre. [Madrid] 1942. 32 p. illus. 20cm. (Escuela de artes y oficios artísticos, Madrid. Publicaciones. no. 7.)

"Bibliografía," p. [33]

1. Pottery, Spanish. I. Ser.

N. Y. P. L.   April 23, 1945

NT   0037084   NN MH-FA

Taracena Aguirre, Blas.
La cerámica ibérica de Numancia, por el dr. B. Taracena Aguirre; memoria doctoral premiada por la Universidad de Madrid el año 1923. Madrid, Samarán y compañía, 1924.

2 p. l., 80 p. illus., 2 fold. pl. 27ᶜᵐ.

"Principales publicaciones referentes a la cerámica ibérica de Numancia": p. 79.

1. Pottery—Spain. 2. Spain—Antiq. I. Title.

Library of Congress   NK4123.T3   33–30229

[2]   738

NT   0037085   DLC CtY

Taracena Aguirre, Blas.
Excavaciones en Navarra [por] Blas Taracena Aguirre y Luis Vázquez de Parga. Pamplona, Institución Príncipe de Viana, Consejo de Cultura de Navarra, 1947–

v. illus., maps (part fold.) 28 cm.

CONTENTS.—v. 1. 1942–1946.

1. Navarre (Province)—Antiq. 2. Excavations (Archaeology)—Spain—Navarre (Province). I. Vázquez de Parga, Luis, joint author. II. Title.

DP302.N265T3   913.465   49–27069*

NT   0037086   DLC NN MH-P IU ICarbS MH

Fine Arts
DP402
.N9T3   Taracena Aguirre, Blas.
    ...Guía del Museo numantino.   Madrid,
Tip. de la "Rev. de arch., bibl. y
museos", 1923.
    43p.   illus.,8 plates.   25cm.
    Bibliography: p.42-43.

    1.Numantia.   2.Excavations (Archaeology
- Numantia.   3.Soria, Spain.   Museo
numantino.

NT   0037087   NNU-W CU

Taracena Aguirre, Blas.
    Las invasiones germánicas en España durante la segunda
mitad del siglo III de J. C. Primer Congreso Internacional
de Pirenaístas. Zaragoza, 1950.
    13 p.   25 cm.   (Instituto de Estudios Pirenaicos. ¡Monografías¡
Historia, 5; no. general, 22)
    "Haneditado 500 ejemplares en separata."
    Issued also as part of Actas del Primer Congreso Internacional de
Pirenaístas, Sept. 1950.
    Bibliographical footnotes.
    1. Spain—Hist.—Roman period, 218 B. c.–414 A. D.   2. Migrations of
nations.   I. Congreso Internacional de Pirenaístas.   1st, San Sebastián, Spain, 1950.   II. Title.   (Series: Spain. Consejo Superior de
Investigaciones Científicas. Instituto de Estudios Pirenaicos. Monografías. Historia, 5. Series: Spain. Consejo Superior de Investigaciones Científicas.   Instituto de Estudios Pirenaicos.
Monografías, 22)
    DP94.T3   55–32662

NT   0037088   DLC NN CSt

Taracena Aguirre, Blas.
    Memoria sobre las excavaciones en el castro de Navárniz
(Vizcaya)   Por B. Taracena Aguirre y A. Fernández de
Avilés. ¡Madrid¡ Junta de Cultura de la Excelentísima
Diputación de Vizcaya, 1945.
    45 p.   illus., fold. map.   25 cm.

    1. Navárniz, Spain—Antiq.   I. Fernández de Avilés, A. de, joint
author.
    DP402.N39T3   55–22295

NT   0037089   DLC IaU IdU

Taracena Aguirre, Blas.
    ... Numance.   Exposition internationale de
Barcelone, 1929.
    27 p.   illus. , 1 folded plan.
    At head of title: "IV congrès international
d'archéologie".

NT   0037090   DDO

Taracena Aguirre, Blas.
    ... Soria, por B. Taracena Aguirre. Madrid, 1941.
    180 p., 6 l.   illus., plates, fold. map, plans (part fold.)   27ᶜᵐ.   (Carta
arqueológica de España)
    At head of title: Consejo superior de investigaciones científicas. Insti-
tuto Diego Velázquez.
    Includes bibliographies.

    1. Soria, Spain (Province)—Antiq.   I. Spain. Consejo superior de
investigaciones científicas. Instituto Diego Velázquez.
                                       44–12452
    Library of Congress   DP302.S735T3
                        ¡2¡   913.463

NT   0037091   DLC FU PU OU CaBVaU TxU

Taracena Aguirre, Blas.
    Soria, guía artística de la ciudad y su provincia, por B.
Taracena y J. Tudela. Soria, Imp. E. las Heras, 1928.
    244, ¡7¡ p.   illus. (incl. plans) plates, 2 fold. maps.   17ᶜᵐ.

    1. Soria, Spain—Descr. & trav.   I. Tudela, J   joint author.
                                    32–24939 Revised
    Library of Congress   DP302.S73T3
                        ¡33b2¡   914.63

NT   0037092   DLC MH

Taracena Campos, Manuel Antonio.
    El delito de infanticidio.   México, 1952.
    xv, 91 p.   19 cm.
    Tesis (licenciatura en derecho)—Universidad Nacional Autónoma
de México.
    Bibliography: p. 91.

    1. Infanticide—Mexico.   I. Title.

                                        57–27063

NT   0037093   DLC MH-L

G383.2297281
T17e   Taracena Flores, Arturo.
    The eighth issue of the postage stamps of
Guatemala, by Arturo Taracena Florex. [Trans-
lated for the International Society of Guatemala Collectors by Richard Cone.   Guatemala?
1952?]
    4p.   22cm.
    Caption title.
    Cover title: Official decrees and related
correspondence concerning the "Central American
Exposition" issue of 1897.

    Taken from "Guatemala filatelica, Apr.–Sept.
1952, no.65-66."

    1. Postage-stamps – Guatemala.   I. Title.
II. Title: Official decrees and related cor-
respondence concerning the "Central American
Exposition" is-   sue of 1897.

NT   0037095   TxU

Taracena y Aguirre Blas
    see
    Taracena Aguirre, Blas.

Tarachand, Dr.
    see   Chand, Tara, 1888–

Tarachand Chukruburtee
    see   Tarachanda Chakravarti.

Tarachand Deumal Gajra
    see   Gajra, Tarachand Deumal.
[supplement]

Tarachand Karnani, Bhawan
    see   Karnani, Bhawan Tarachand, 1924–

Fqc59   Tarachanda Chakravarti
T17   A dictionary in Bengalee and English. By
Tarachand Chukruburtee.   Calcutta:Baptist
mission press,1827.
    xvi,250p.   20cm.

NT   0037101   CtY MH NN

Tarachia, Angelo, tr.
    Relazione della morte del christianissimo
Lvigi XIII
    see under title

4DG   Tarachia, Angiolo
882   Feste celebrate in Mantova alla
venvta de serenissimi arcidvchi
Ferdinando Carlo, e Sigismondo
Francesco d'Avstria, et arcidvchessa
Anna Medici, il carnevale dell'anno
1652; breve narrazione.   Mantova,
Osanna, stampatori ducali [1652]
    52 p.

NT   0037103   DLC-P4

Tarachus, Saint, martyr.
    Atti dei tre santi martiri Taraco, Probo e
Andronico
    see under title [in supplement]

Taraçona, Pere Hieroni
    see   Tarazona, Pedro Jerónimo, 16th c.

Taracous-Taracouzio, Timothy Andrew

    see

Taracouzio, Timothy Andrew, 1896–

Taracous-Tarakuzio, Timofei Andre-
    evich

    see

Taracouzio, Timothy Andrew, 1896–

Taracouzio, Timothy Andrew, 1896– 1958.
    International coöperation of the U. S. S. R. in legal matters,
by T. A. Taracouzio ...
    (*In* American journal of international law. Concord, N. H., 1937.
v. 31, p. 55–65)

    1. Extradition—Russia.   2. Letters rogatory—Russia.   3. Judgments,
Foreign.   I. Title.
                                         A 37–88
    Carnegie endow. int. peace.   Library
       for Library of Congress   [JX1.A6   vol. 31]
                         ¡2¡   (341.05)

NT   0037108   NNCE CaBVaU

Taracuzio, Timothy Andrew.
    The law in the Union of Socialist Soviet
Republics.   1. Marxian interpretation of the law.
2. The Soviet laws in theory and practice.
In Harvard University, Law School, Lectures
on comparative private law, 1930-31.

NT   0037109   MH-L

Z6458 Taracouzio, Timothy Andrew, 1896- 1958.
R9T17 The Russian collection of the Harvard Law
school library, by T.A. Taracouzio.
(In Harvard alumni bulletin. Boston, 1935.
23½ᶜᵐ. v.37, p. ₍750₎-756. illus.)

1.Harvard university. Law school. Library.
Russian collection. 2.Law - Russia - Bibl.

NT 0037110 CSt-H

Taracouzio, Timothy Andrew, 1896- 1958.
The Soviet union and international law; a study based on
the legislation, treaties and foreign relations of the Union of
socialist soviet republics, by T. A. Taracouzio. New York,
The Macmillan company, 1935.
xvi, 1 l., 530 p. 24ᶜᵐ.
Half-title: Bureau of international research, Harvard university and
Radcliffe college.
Bibliography: p. ₍481₎-510.
1. International law and relations. 2. Russia—For. rel.—1917-
ɪ. Russia (1923– U. S. S. R.) ɪɪ. Bureau of international research
of Harvard university and Radcliffe college. ɪɪɪ. Title.
Library of Congress JX1555.Z5 1935 35-6168
——— Copy 2.
Copyright A 82206 ₍5₎ 341.0947

OU OO OCU NcU CaBVaU ViU MtU WaU OrU OrPR NNC MB
NT 0037111 DLC PBm PU-L PU OClW NBuU-L NN NcD MiU

Taracouzio, Timothy Andrew, 1896- 1958.
Soviets in the Arctic; an historical, economic and political
study of the Soviet advance into the Arctic, by T. A. Taracouzio, PH. D. New York, The Macmillan company, 1938.
xiv p., 1 l., 563, ₍2₎ p. incl. tables. 7 maps (1 fold., in pocket) 24ᶜᵐ.
Half-title: Bureau of international research, Harvard university and
Radcliffe college.
Appendices (p. ₍371₎-499) include official documents.
Bibliography: p. ₍501₎-546.
1. Arctic regions. ɪ. Russia (1923– U. S. S. R.) ɪɪ. Bureau of
international research of Harvard university and Radcliffe college.
ɪɪɪ. Title.
39—1252
Library of Congress G630.R8T3
₍a45q1₎ 919.8

CaBVaU IU WU PU PSt NcD ViU OCl OU OEac DAS Wa
NT 0037112 DLC DSI OrP OrCS OrPR MtBC WaS OrU NIC

Taracouzio, Timothy Andrew, 1896- 1958.
War and peace in Soviet diplomacy, by T. A. Taracouzio.
New York, The Macmillan company, 1940.
x, 354 p. 24 cm.
Half-title: Bureau of international research, Harvard university
and Radcliffe college.
Bibliography: p. ₍299₎-311. "Appendix: Subject index of the Soviet
treaties, agreements and conventions in force": p. ₍313₎-342.
1. Russia—Pol. & govt.—1917- 2. Russia—For. rel.—1917-
ɪ. Bureau of international research of Harvard university and Radcliffe college. ɪɪ. Title.
DK266.T25 327.47 40—29989

IdPI OrP OrPR
PSC NcD CU OCU OU OCl NcD KU WaTU OrCS CaBVaU UU
NT 0037113 DLC ViU KMK MeB GU KyU ScU PU PBm PPT OO

Undergraduate
Library Taracouzio, Timothy Andrew, 1896- 1958.
DK War and peace in Soviet diplomacy, by T. A. Taracouzio.
266 New York, The Macmillan company, 1940. ₍Ann Arbor, Mich.,
.T18 1960₎
1940a x, 354 p. 24ᶜᵐ.
Half-title: Bureau of international research, Harvard university and
Radcliffe college.
Bibliography: p. ₍299₎-311. "Appendix: Subject index of the Soviet
treaties, agreements and conventions in force": p. ₍313₎-342.
Photocopy (positive) made by University Micro-
films.
Printed on double leaves.

NT 0037114 MiU NBuC

Taracus, Saint
see Tarachus, Saint, martyr.

Taradash, Daniel.
From here to eternity (Motion picture script)
see under title [supplement]

TARADASH, DANIEL.
The silver hut; a play [in three acts] [New York,
D. Evans] c1938. 50, 44, 41 l. 30cm.

Typescript.

1. Drama, American. I. Title.

NT 0037117 NN

Taradash, Daniel.
Storm center; screenplay

see under

Storm center (Motion picture script)

PS3539 Taradash, Daniel
.A5775 Thy mercy, a play, by Daniel Taradash.
1937 [New York?, c1937]
p.l., 2-50 numb. l., 1 l., 52-76 numb.l.,
1 l., 77-94 numb. l., 1 l., 96-136 numb.l.
28½x23½ cm.

NT 0037119 DLC

Taradatta Panta
see Panta, Taradatta.

Tarade, Alfred de. Culture des rosiers écussonnés sur églantiers. 8°. pp. 31. Paris. 1828.

NT 0037121 MBH

Tarade, Alfred de. Culture des rosiers écussonnés sur
églantiers. 2ᵉ éd. Paris. 1831. sm. 8°. pp. 31.

NT 0037122 MH-A

Tarade, Emile de
see Tarade, Gilbert Philippe Emile de.

Tarade, *Gilbert Philippe Émile de.*
Éducation du chien, ou traité complet des
moyens de cultiver l'intelligence de ce
précieux animal, d'obtenir de lui toutes
sortes de services, de l'amener au point de
pouvoir jouer aux dominos, etc., etc., par
Émile de Tarade. Paris, Librairie Scientifique, Industrielle & Agricole, 1866.
363 p. 19cm.

1. Dogs. I. Title.

NT 0037124 ViW

QS TARADE, Gilbert Philippe Emile de
T176e Élémens d'anatomie et de physiologie
1841 comparées, dédiés aux gens du monde;
ou, Étude succincte des ressorts et des
phénomènes de la vie chez l'homme et
chez les animaux, avec des observations
philosophiques et morales. Paris, 1841.
xv, 549 p. illus.

NT 0037125 DNLM

Tarade, G₍ilbert₎ P₍hilippe₎ Émile de. Fr 8100.1
Notice généalogique et biographique sur la famille de Tarade et
sur ses alliances. Tours, E. Mazereau, 1870.
pp. 236. Ports., coats-of-arms and facsimile-plates.
Presentation copy with author's autograph "Émile de Tarade" on title-page.

Tarade Family

NT 0037126 MH

Tarade, *Gilbert Philippe Émile de.*
... Traité de l'élevage et de l'éducation
du chien; moyens de cultiver l'intelligence
de ce précieux animal d'obtenir de lui toutes
sortes de services utiles de l'amener au point
de pouvoir jouer aux dominos, etc., etc. Par
Émile de Tarade. Paris, Librairie Scientifique,
Industrielle et Agricole Eugène Lacroix ₍1871₎
363 p. 19½ cm. (Bibliothèque des Professions
Industrielles et Agricoles, Série H, No. 22)

1. Dogs. I. Title.

NT 0037127 ViW

Tarade, *Gilbert Philippe Émile de.*
Traité de l'élevage et de l'éducation du Chien. Paris.
16mo. 363 p. 1763-

NT 0037128 ViW

Tarade, Jacques, fl. 1659.
Desseins de toutes les parties de l'église de
Saint Pierre de Rome, levés sur les lieux en
1659 & présentés au roy. Avec le parallele de
cette église de celle de Nᵗʳᵉ-Dame de Paris et de
la catedrale de Strasbourg. Paris, Jombert, n.d.
1 v. plates, plans.

NT 0037129 MH

Avory
AA Tarade, Jacques, fl. 1659.
523 Desseins de toutes les parties de l'église
P6 de Saint Pierre de Rome, la première et la
T17 plus grande de toutes les églises du monde
chrestien. Levé exactement sur les lieux par
Jacques Tarade ... Tous les desseins ₍gravés₎
par le Sᵗ Marot ... ₍Paris?₎ 16—.
15 plates (part fold., incl. port.) 44 cm.

Engraved t.p.

First ed. as described in A. Mauban's Jean
Marot, p. 62-64, 216.
Imperfect copy: portrait and plate 9 wanting.
Last plate is a later addition, described by
Mauban as plate 22 of the enlarged 2nd ed.

NT 0037131 NNC

Tarade, Théodore Jean, 1731-1788.
Le triomphe de l'amour, premier cantatille à
voix seule avec accompagnement, mise en musique
par Mr. Tarade, ordinaire de l'Academie royale
de musique. ... Les paroles sont de Mr. de La
Hogue. Paris, La Chevardiere [etc., ca. 1760]
1 p. l., 8 p. 33.5 cm.
Compressed orchestra score.
"Catalogue de musique vocale et instrumentale

gue M. de Lachevardiere ... a fait graver
... " on verse of t.-p.
[With Lescot, F. Iris, cantatilles a voix scule...]

NT 0037133 DLC

Tārādevi.
गृह-शिल्प. नेविका नारादेवी. ।1. संस्करण. काठमाडौं।नेपाली भाषा प्रकाशिनी समिति, संवत् 1997 ।1940 or 1।
4. 193 p. illus. 18 cm.
In Nepali.

1. Needlework. 2. Cookery, Indic. I. Title.
Title romanized: Gṛha-śilpa.

TT751.T37   S A 68–14116

NT   0037134   DLC

Tarafa, Francisco, *fl.* 1550.
Crònica de cavallers catalans. Transcripció i estudi crític per Alexandre d'Armengol i de Pereyra. ।Barcelona। Asociación de Bibliófilos de Barcelona, 1952–54.
2 v. col. coats of arms, col. facsim. 33 cm.
Issued in portfolios.
111 copies printed. "Consta de cent exemplars ... numerats de 1 a 100 ... Exemplar núm. 26. Destinat a la Library of Congress, Washington."
Includes bibliographical notes.

1. Catalonia—Geneal. 2. Catalonia—Nobility. 3. Heraldry—Catalonia. I. Armengol y de Pereyra, Alejandro de. II. Title.

CR2149.T3   53–19998 rev

NT   0037135   DLC WU

Tarafa, Francisco, *fl.* 1550.
De origine, ac rebus gestis regum Hispaniæ liber, multarum rerum cognitione refertus. Antverpiæ, In ædibus I. Steelsij, 1553.
201 p. 16 cm.
Title vignette (port.)

1. Spain—Hist. I. Title.

DP64.T19   4–30729 rev*

NT   0037136   DLC RPJCB NNH CLU MH MnU NN

Tarafa Francisco, fl. 1550. it. auth.
Vasaeus, Joannes, *d.* 1550.
Rervm Hispaniae memorabilivm annales, a Ioanne Vasaeo Brvgensi, et Francisco Tarapha Barcinonensi, non minvs docte qvam breuiter, ad hæc vsq. tempora deducti. Quibus accessit succincta rerum à Philippo Secūdo catholico rege gestarum descriptio: omniumq. regum Hispaniæ genealogia, recens ex italico translata. Omnia partim noua, partim ad primam æditionem accuratè recusa: cum indice locupletissimo. Coloniae, apud L. Alectorium, & hæredes I. Soteris. 1577.

Tarafa ibn al-Abd al-Bakri
see
Ṭarafah ibn al-'Abd.

Tarafa y Govin, Josefina, *ed.*

SB231
.R43
1954

FOR OTHER EDITIONS
SEE MAIN ENTRY

Reynoso, Alvaro, 1829–1889.
Ensayo sobre el cultivo de la caña de azúcar. Explicación por Pelayo García. ।Reedita por Josefina Tarafa y Govin। 5. ed. Habana, 1954.
606 p. 22 cm.

Microfilm
12281
PJ

Tarafah ibn al-'Abd.
Ahlwardt, Wilhelm, 1828–1909, *ed.*
The divans of the six ancient Arabic poets Ennabiga, 'Antara, Tharafa, Zuhair, 'Alqama and Imruulqais; chiefly according to the mss. of Paris, Gotha, and Leyden; and the collection of their fragments with a list of the various readings of the text. London, Trübner, 1870.

Ṭarafah ibn al-'Abd.
Dīwân de Ṭarafa ibn al-'Abd al-Bakrī, accompagné du commentaire de Yoûsouf Al-A'lam de Santa-Maria, d'après les manuscrits de Paris et de Londres, suivi d'un appendice renfermant de nombreuses poésies inédites tirées des manuscrits d'Alger, de Berlin, de Londres et de Vienne, publié, traduit et annoté, par Max Seligsohn ... Paris, É. Bouillon, 1901.
xvi, 171, ।1। p., 1 l., 160 p. 25½ᶜᵐ. (*Added t.-p.:* Bibliothèque de l'École des hautes études ... Sciences historiques et philologiques, 128. fasc.)
Issued in 3 parts, 1899–1901.
"Ouvrages consultés": p. xiv–xvi.

I. Seligsohn, Max. II. Yûsuf ibn Sulaimân, al-Shantamarî, called al-A'lam.

4—17960

Library of Congress   AS162.B6 fasc. 128

NT   0037141   DLC OU NBuU CtY OCU MoU CU MiU OCl NjP

PJ7633
.I6
Orien
Arab

Ṭarafah ibn al-'Abd.
العقد الثمين في دواوين الشعراء الثلاثة الجاهليين. بيروت، طبع بنفقة لطف الله الزهار بالطبعة اللبنانية، ١٨٨٦ ।1886।

PJ7741
.T2M9
1742

Ṭarafah ibn al-'Abd.
Moallakah, cum scholiis Nahas. e mss. Leidensibus Arabice edidit, vertit, illustravit Joann. Jacob. Reiske. Lugduni Batavorum, Apud Joannem Luzac, 1742.
liv, 130 p. table.

I. al-Nahhas, d.950. II. Reiske, Johann Jacob, 1716–1774, ed. III. Mu'allaḳat.

NT   0037143   ICU MH

492.7
L954
Theol.

Ṭarafah ibn al-'Abd.
Tarafae Moallaca cum Zuzenii scholiis. Textum ad fidem Codicum Parisiensium diligenter emendatum Latine vertit, vitam Poetae accurate exposuit, selectas Reiskii annotationes suis subiunxit indicem Arabicum addidit Ioannes Vullers. Bonnae ad Rhenum, typis regiis Arabicis, ex officina Fr. Baadeni, 1829.
viii, 90, ।31। p. 23cm.
Arabic and Latin text.
Bound with other pamphlets of similar nature.

I. Vullers, Johann August, 1803–1880, ed.

NT   0037144   TxDaM MH CU PU OCl ICU NIC

Ṭarafa ibn al-'Abd.
Tarafa's Mo'allaqa. Mit dem Kommentar des abû Bekr Mohammed b. el-Qâsim el-Anbâri. Hrsg. von O. Rescher. Stambul: Imprimerie "Nefaset," 1329/1911. 2 p.l., iii, 7, 140 p. 12°.

1. Arabic literature—Poetry.   2. Anbâri (Abû Bakr Muhammad ibn al-Kâsimal.). 3. Rescher, O., editor.
N. Y. P. L.   December 24, 1912.

NT   0037145   NN CtY OCl ICU

TARAFAH ibn al-'Abd.
Mu'allaqa des Tarafa. Übersetzt und erklärt von Bernhard Geiger.

(In Wiener Ztsch.f.d.Kunde d.Morgenlandes, 1905,v.19,p.323–370).

NT   0037146   MH

PJ7797
.L39T3

TARAFAH IBN AL-'ABD.
Nonnulla Tarafae poëtae Carmina ex arabico in latinum sermonem versa notisque adumbrata...quam... scripsit unaque cum thesibus adiectis...Bernhard Vandenhoff... Berolini,1895.
।1।,81,।2।p. ।21cm.
Inaug.-diss.--Berlin.
Vita.
"Index librorum et compendiorum":p.।11।-15.

NT   0037147   ICU CU NjP OCl PPDrop ICRL

Ṭarafah ibn al-Abd

3423.176

i narafa.
(In Lagarde, P. A. de. Symmicta. Vol. I, pp. 198–202. Göttingen. 1877.)
German translation, by Friedrich Rückert, of portions of the Moallakāh of Tarafah.

G8129 — Arabia. Lit. Poetry.

NT   0037148   MB

Tarahiko Kori
see Kori, Tarahiko, 1890–1924.

HQ1742
T37

Tarafdar, Radhika Lal
Womanhood in Hindu society, ancient and modern. [Dacca, published by the author] 1936.
50 p.

1. Women in India. 2. India - Social life and customs. I. Title.

NT   0037150   CU

Taragan, Bension.
Les communautés israélites d'Alexandrie; aperçu historique depuis les temps des Ptolémées jusqu'à nos jours, par Bension Taragan. Alexandrie, Les Éditions juives d'Égypte, 1932.
150 p. illus. (incl. ports.) 21½ᶜᵐ.

1. Jews in Alexandria.

45–43115

Library of Congress   DS135.E4T3

NT   0037151   DLC CU PPDrop OCH

Tarai and Bhabar Development Committee
see **United Provinces of Agra and Oudh.** *Tarai and Bhabar Development Committee.*

PS
3539
A525

Tarail, Mark
Poems of the people. ।New York, Author, c1933।
31p. 22cm.
Cover title.

NT   0037153   WU

Tarain, Jehan, 1905–
.. Contribution à l'étude du diagnostic différentiel entre certaines formes de maux de Pott et les tumeurs intrarachidiennes ... Lyon, 1930.
Thèse - Univ. de Lyon.
"Bibliographie": p. [55]–56.

NT   0037154   CtY

F
1783
.M38T3x

Tarajano, Juan José.
Perennidad del apóstol. [La Habana] Comité de Divulgación Fraternal Gran Logia Occidental de la Orden Caballero de la Luz [1954]
33 p. 18 cm.

1. Martí, José, 1853–1895-- Addresses, essays, lectures. I. Title

NT   0037155   OKentU

Tarajano González, Juan J., joint author.

Alvarez Noval, Miguel.
... Manual para el agente de la autoridad, de acuerdo con el vigente Código de defensa social. 2. ed. La Habana, Editorial "Alfa", 1940.

Tarajanz, Sedrak.
Das gewerbe bei den Armeniern ... Leipzig, C. Grumbach, 1897.

1 p. L, 63, ₁1₁ p. 22ᶜᵐ.
Inaug.-diss.—Leipzig.
Vita.

1. Armenia—Indus. 2. Agriculture—Armenia.

1–G–2822

Library of Congress   HC495.T17

NT   0037157   DLC CtY

---

al-Tarājim wa-al-siyar
    see under   Hasan, Muhammad 'Abd al-Ghanī.

Tarak Chandra Das
    see   Das, Tarak Chandra.

Tarakad Vythinatha Ramakrishna Aiyar
    see
Ramakrishna Aiyar, Tarakad Vythinatha, 1880–

M
780.81 Tarakan, Sheldon.
S319W1   Johann Hermann Schein: Complete works, edited by Arthur Prufer. Alphabetical index, with incipits. ₁n.p., n.d.₂
1v.(unpaged)

Thematic incipits of the instrumental music, text incipits of the vocal music.
Photocopy of typescript.

1. Schein, Johann Hermann, 1586-1630 – Dictionaries, indexes, etc. 2. Schein, Johann Hermann, 1586-1630 – Thematic catalogs

NT   0037161   NBC

Tārakanātha Bālī
    see
    Bālī, Tārakanātha.

Tarakanatha Dasa
    see   Das, Taraknath, 1884-1958.

Tārakanātha Gaṅgopādhyāya
    see
    Ganguli, Taraknath, 1844-1891.

[Tarakanof, Timothy]
Narrative of the adventures of the crew of the Russian-American Company's ship St. Nicolai, wrecked on the northwest coast of America. By The Supercargo of the ship.   n.p. [1808?]
2 l. 36 cm.
Excerpt from Newspaper, signed by Y. Z.

NT   0037165   CaBViPA

272.9 Tarakanoff, Vassili Petrovitch.
T176   Statement of my captivity among the Californians. Written down by Ivan Shishkin, & tr. from the Russian by Ivan Petroff, with notes by Arthur Woodward. Los Angeles, G. Dawson, 1953.
47 p. illus. 19 cm. (Early American travels series, 16)
"200 copies printed by Saul & Lillian Marks at the Plantin Press, Los Angeles, Engravings by Morton Dimondstein."
1. Persecution   2. California. Hist. 3. Rossiisko-amer. Ikanskaia kompaniia, Leningrad. I. Title. Series.

CU–S NIC NjP CU–BANC NN WaS IEN CoD CSt PP NBuG
NT   0037166   N CLSU TxU OrU CaBVaU CaBViPA ICN NNC Or

Tarakanov, K. N., ed.
Естествознание в школе; научно-популярный и методический журнал. ₁г. 1₁–
1946–
Москва, Гос. учебно-педагог. изд-во.

Tarakanov, K. N., ed.
QH302
.S5
Shibanov, Aleksei Aleksandrovich, *comp.*
Сборник статей по вопросам мичуринской биологии; в помощь учителю биологии средней школы. Под ред. К. Н. Тараканова. Москва, Гос. учебно-педагог. изд-во, 1950.

Tarakanova, E   I
Петрографическое изучение бурых углей Кушмурунского месторождения. Москва, Гос. научно-техн. изд-во лит-ры по геологии и охране недр, 1954.
50, ₁2₁ p. illus. 22 cm. (Труды лабораторий геологических управлений, трестов, экспедиций и партий, вып. 4)
Bibliography: p. ₁51₁

1. Lignite—Kazakhstan.   I. Title.
               Title transliterated: Petrograficheskoe izuchenie burykh uglei.

TN834.R9T3   56–28238

NT   0037169   DLC

Tarakanova, S   A
(Boiarskoe i monastyrskoe zemlevladenie v novgorodskikh piatinakh v domoskovskoe vremia)
Боярское и монастырское землевладение в новгородских пятинах в домосковское время / С. А. Тараканова-Белкина. — Москва : Изд. Гос. исторического музея, 1939.
117, ₁3₁ p. ; 22 cm.
Bibliography: p. 114–₁118₁

1. Land tenure—Novgorod, Russia (Duchy)   I. Title.

HD719.N63T37   74–237037

NT   0037170   DLC CSt

Tarakanova, S   A
Древний Псков. ₁Ответственный редактор А. В. Арциховский₁ Москва, Изд-во Академии наук СССР, 1946.
53 p. illus. 22 cm.

1. Pskov, Russia (City)—Hist.   I. Title.
            Title transliterated: Drevnii Pskov.

DK651.P8T3   52–66539 ‡

NT   0037171   DLC NBC ICU CSt MiU

Tarakanova-Belkina, S   A
    see
    Tarakanova, S   A

Tarakchandra Das
    see   Das, Tarakchandra.

Tarakçioğlu, Nurettin C
Le contrôle de la puissance paternelle. Neuchâtel, 1955.
154 p. 24 cm.
Thèse—Neuchâtel.
Bibliography: p. ₁145₁–150.

1. Parent and child (Law)—Switzerland.   i. Title.

56–56155

NT   0037174   DLC CU–L ICU CtY–L MH–L

Tarakdji, A.
... L'avortement criminel; étude médico-légale, juridique et psycho-sociale ... par A. Tarakdji ... Toulouse, Imprimerie moderne, Paillès et Chataigner, 1937.
xii, ₁3₁–185, ₁1₁ p. 24ᶜᵐ.
Thèse—Univ. de Toulouse.
"Bibliographie": p. ₁183₁–185.

1. Abortion—France. 2. Abortion.   i. Title.

42–10235

NT   0037175   DLC CtY NN MH

Tarakhovskaia, Elizaveta IAkovlevna.
At Black sea.   Moscow State Pr. Dept., 1928.
10 p.

NT   0037176   PU

Tarakhovskaia, Elizaveta IAkovlevna.
Метро. Изд. 3. Москва, Изд-во детской лит-ры, 1938.
₁16₁ p. illus. 22 cm.
"Для школьного возраста."

1. Metrostroi, Moscow—Poetry.   *Title transliterated:* Metro.

PZ64.T3 1938   50–41533

NT   0037177   DLC

PZ64
.3
.O55
1932
Tarakhovskaia, Elizaveta IAkovlevna.
(Oktiabr')
Октябрь / Е. Тараховская ... ₁et al.₁ ; художник К. Кузнецов ... ₁et al.₁ — Москва : ОГИЗ, Молодая гвардия, 1932.

Tarakhovskaia, Elizaveta IAkovlevna.
Стихи и сказки. Москва, Гос. изд-во детской лит-ры, 1954.
190 p. illus. 23 cm.

Title transliterated: Stikhi i skazki.

PZ64.3. T3   57–42756 †

NT   0037179   DLC

Taraknath Das
    see Das, Taraknath, 1884-1958.

Tāraknāth Gaṅgopādhyāy
  see
Ganguli, Taraknath, 1918- 1970.

Taraknath Ganguli
    see Ganguli, Taraknath, 1844-1891.

Taraknath Ganguli
  see
Ganguli, Taraknath, 1918-1970.

Tarakus-Tarakuzio, Timofeĭ Andreevich
  see
Taracouzio, Timothy Andrew, 1896-1958.

Tarakuzio, Timofeĭ Andreevich
  see
Taracouzio, Timothy Andrew, 1896-1958.

Taraldlien, Bendik.
    Fyresdal. Kristiania, A.
Cammermeyers forlag, 1910.

      129 p. illus., ports., map.
32cm.

NT 0037186   MnU

Taraldlien, Bendik.
    Fyresdal, med bilaete. 2. utg. Oslo, Cammermeyer ₁1949₎
  94 p. illus., ports., map. 30 cm.

    1. Fyresdal, Norway.

                    A 51-1195
  Minnesota. Univ. Lib.
  for Library of Congress   ₁2₎

NT 0037187   MnU NN

GR220   TARALDLIEN,BENDIK
.T17   Telemark; gamal og ny tid, v.
  Skien, Varden,
      v. illus. ports.

    1. Folk-lore--Norway--Telemarken. Folklore cd.

NT 0037188   InU

Taraldsen, Arne.
    A/s Lys & luft; en profitørs saga og litt av hvert fra
hjemmefronten. Oslo, Norsk forlag Ny dag, 1946.
  unpaged (chiefly illus.) 21 x 30 cm.

    1. World War, 1989-1945—Humor, caricatures, etc. 2. Profiteer-
ing—Norway. I. Title: Lys & luft.

  D745.7.N6T3   63-34628 ‡

NT 0037189   DLC

325.34
T176b   Taralletto, Giuseppe.
      Le basi dell' economia coloniale e la colon
izzazione. Napoli, Libreria del Goliardo,
1928.
    52p. 22cm.

      1. Colonization. 2. Agriculture. Europe.
Colonies.

NT 0037190   IEN

HD7090   Taralletto de Falco, Giuseppe, ed.
L3
    Lavoro e previdenza. ott./nov. 1949-
  ₁Roma₎

Tarallo, Giulio.
    Le temps civil suivant la science, ou bien Le cadran sphéri-
que rotatif d'après le Conférence internationale de Washington pour le choix d'un premier méridien commun, par Jules
Tarallo ... Naples, Stabilimento Industrie editoriali meridionali, 1930.
  49 p. incl. illus., ports. 24½ᶜᵐ.

    1. Time. 2. Horology. I. Title.

                              31-4992
  Library of Congress   QB209.T3   529.75

NT 0037192   DLC

Tarallo, Roberto.
    ... La fede di credito ed il quarto centenario del Banco di
Napoli. Napoli, R. Pironti, 1940.
  4 p. l., ₁7₎-138 p., 1 l. 25ᶜᵐ.
  "Bibliografia": p. ₁135₎-138.

    1. Banco di Napoli, Naples. 2. Bank-notes.
                           42-32382
  Library of Congress   HG3000.N4B28

NT 0037193   DLC

Taraloka Siṅgha
  see
Singh, Tarlok, 1913-

Taralon, Jean,
    Chateaudun. Paris, Vincent, Fréal & cie
₁1948₎
    31 p. illus., plan. 20cm. (Les plus
excellents bâtiments de France)

    Cover-title.
    "Bibliographie sommaire": p. ₁32₎
      1. Chȃteaudun, Chȃteau de. I. Les plus
excellents bȃtiments de France.

NT 0037195   NNC NN

Taralon, Jean.
  Gauguin

  see under

  Gauguin, Paul, 1848-1903.

759.011
T176g
    Taralon, Jean.
      The grotto of Lascaux. Paris, Caisse
nationale des monuments historiques, n.d.

      1 v. illus. 18cm.

      1. Lascaux Cave, France. 2. Cave -
drawings. I. Title.

NT 0037197   FU

    Taralon, Jean
      Jumièges. ₁Paris₎ Éditions du Cerf ₁1955₎
38 p. illus., plans. 18cm. (Nefs et
clochers)

      Bibliography: p. ₁40₎

NT 0037198   NNC IU NcD PLatS

ND553   Taralon, Jean.
.G27T34
folio   Gauguin, Paul, 1848-1903.
      Paintings. Introd. by Jean Taralon. ₁Translated from
the French by Denys Sutton₎ London, L. Drummond ₁1949₎

ND553   Taralon, Jean.
.G27T3
folio   Gauguin, Paul, 1848-1903.
      Peintures. Introd. de Jean Taralon. Paris, Éditions du
Chêne, 1949.

    Taralrud, Marius, 1894-
      Ueber nebenwirkungen des wismuts bei der
Syphilisbehandlung mit besonderer Berucksichtigun
der Mundschleimhautschadigungen 1930.
      Inaug.- diss.- Univ. zu Berlin.

NT 0037201   OU DNLM CtY

Taramasso (Plinio). *Étude toxicologique de
l'adrénaline.* 31 pp. 8°. *Genève, 1907.*

NT 0037202   DNLM

Taramasso, Giacomo.
    ... S. E. l'On. Facta. Chieri: G. Bori, 1924. 63 p. 12°.

  I. Facta, Luigi, 1861- . 2. Italy—   Politics, 1924.
  N.Y.P.L.   December 13, 1924

NT 0037203   NN

Taramati Gupte
see
Gupte, Taramati.

Taramelli, Antonio, 1868–
... Bibliografia romano-sarda, a cura di Antonio Taramelli;
nota introduttiva di C. Galassi Paluzzi. Roma, Istituto di
studi romani, 1939.

1 p. l., ₅₎–86 p., 1 l. 24ᶜᵐ. (... Bibliografie ragionate dell' Italia
romana. I)

At head of title: Istituto di studi romani.

1. Sardinia—Bibl. I. Rome (City) Istituto di studi romani.
II. Title.

Library of Congress   Z2364.S2T3   42–28587

NT   0037205   DLC NIC NNC

943.01   Taramelli, Antonio, 1868–
T17c   Le campagne di Germanico nella Germania.
Pavia, Premiato stabilimento tipografico successori Bizzoni, 1891.
xxvi, 188p.

"Le fonti a cui noi attingiamo il racconto delle campagne di Germanico": p.xx.

NT   0037206   IU

Taramelli, Antonio, 1868–
Di un frammento di bassorilievo romano con rappresentanza
militare scoperto in Torino. Memoria del dott. A. Taramelli.

(*In* Atti della R. Accademia dei Lincei. Classe di scienze morali,
storiche e filologiche. Memorie. Roma, 1903. 29ᶜᵐ. ser. 5, vol. VIII,
pte. 1ª, p. ₃₃₎–48 incl. illus., plan, diagr.)

Bibliographical foot-notes.

1. Sculpture, Roman. 2. Bas-relief.
    A C 38–2791

Illinois. Univ. Library
for Library of Congress   [AS222.R645 ser. 5, vol. 8]
    ₍2₎   (065)

NT   0037207   IU NcU MoU

Taramelli, Antonio, 1868–
Guida del Museo Nazionale di Cagliari
see under   Cagliari. Museo Nazionale.

Taramelli, Antonio, 1868–
... Il R. Museo G. A. Sanna di Sassari. (67 illustrazioni)
Roma, La Libreria dello stato, a. XII E. F. ₍1933₎

62 p., 1 l. incl. plates. 18½ᶜᵐ. (Itinerari dei musei e monumenti
d'Italia. ₍n. 29₎)

At head of title: Ministero della educazione nazionale. **Direzione
generale delle antichità e belle arti** ... Antonio Taramelli ₍e₎ **Emilio
Lavagnino.**
Plans on p. ₍2₎–₍4₎ of cover.

1. Sassari, Sardinia. Museo G. A. Sanna. I. Lavagnino, Emilio,
1898–
    45–46656

Library of Congress   N2963.T3
    ₍2₎   708.5

NT   0037209   DLC NcU NIC OU CtY NcD DDO

Taramelli, Antonio, 1868–
... Il R. Museo nazionale e la Pinacoteca di Cagliari. (78
illustrazioni) Roma, La Libreria dello stato, a XIV E. F. ₍1936₎

82 p. incl. plates, plans. 18½ᶜᵐ. (Itinerari dei musei e monumenti
d'Italia. ₍n. 54₎)

At head of title: Ministero della educazione nazionale. Direzione
generale delle antichità e belle arti ... Antonio Taramelli ₍e₎ Raffaello
Delogu.
Plans on p. ₍2₎ and ₍4₎ of cover.

1. Cagliari. Museo nazionale. I. Delogu, Raffaello.
    45–46344

Library of Congress   N2526.T3

NT   0037210   DLC NIC CU NN WaS NNC

709.45   Taramelli, Antonio, 1868–
Ar76   ... I nuraghi ed i loro abitatori.   Roma, Is-
v.16   tituto nazionale "L.U.C.E." ₍1930₎
    ₍15₎p. 24 pl.   (On cover: L'Arte per tut-
ti. 16)

Illustration on cover.
"Bibliografia": p.₍14₎

1. Sardinia—Antiq. 2. Sepulchral monuments—
Sardinia. I. Title.

NT   0037211   IU NcD OU NNC

Taramelli, Torquato, 1845–1922.
Die alcuni Echinide eocenici dell' Istria.
1874.
Geol. T. v. 23ᵇ.

NT   0037212   PPAN

Taramelli, Torquato, 1845–1922.
Il canton Ticino meridionale ed i paesi finitimi. Spie-
gazione del foglio XXIV. duf. colorito geologicamente da
Spreafico, Negri e Stoppani, per Torquato Taramelli ...
Berna, In commissione presso J. Dalp, 1880.
231, ₍1₎ p. 2 fold. col. pl., map, fold. profile. 30½ᶜᵐ. and map. 51 x 73ᶜᵐ.
(*Added t.-p.:* Materiali per la carta geologica della Svizzera pub. dalla Commissione geologica della Società elvetica di scienze naturali a spese della
Confederazione. vol. XVII)
————— Appendice ed indice. Berna, In commissione presso J. Dalp, 1880.
30 p., 1 l., ₍10₎ p. 30½ᶜᵐ.
1. Geology—Switzerland—Ticino.
    G S 13–603

Library, U. S. Geol.   survey (535) qB   fg. 17

NT   0037213   DI-GS NIC MdBP PPAN ICJ CU

Taramelli, Torquato, 1845–1922.
La carta geologica d'Italia.   1881.
G. T. v. 28a.

NT   0037214   PPAN

TARAMELLI, Torquato, 1845–1922.
Carta geologica della Lombardia del prof.
Torquato Taramelli. Scala 1/250,000 Pubblicata
con concorso del reale instituto, lombardo di
scenze ₍sic.₎ e lettere. Milano, 1890.
33 x 31 in.
Spiegazione della carta geologica. [By T.
Taramelli.] Milano, [1890].
pp.58.
"Bibliografia geologica paeleontologica
della Lombardia" pp.1–29

NT   0037215   MH

Taramelli, Torquato, 1845–1922.
Catalogo ragionato delle Rocce dei Friuli.
Roma, 1877.
G. T. v. 52ª, v. 73

NT   0037216   PPAN

Taramelli, Torquato, 1845–1922.
Dei terreni Morenici ed alluvionali del Friuli.
1875.
(Monografica geologica)
Geol. T. v. 23ᵇ.

NT   0037217   PPAN

Taramelli, Torquato, 1845–1922.
... Della geologia del Trentino.
(In Società geografica italiana, Rome. Pagine
geografiche della nostra guerra.   Roma, 1917.
p. [39]–68)
1. Trentine Alps.

NT   0037218   CU

Taramelli, Torquato, 1845–1922.
Della Salsa di Querzola, nella provincia di
Reggio.   21 Luglio, 1881.
Geol. T. v.

NT   0037219   PPAN

Taramelli, Torquato, 1845–1922.
Delle posizioni stratigrafica delle Rocce
Ofiolitiche nell' Appennino. Nata di Torquato
Taramelli.   Roma, 1884.
G. T. v. 72.

NT   0037220   PPAN

554.5   Taramelli, Torquato, 1845–1922.
T17d   ... Descrizione geologica della provincia di
Pavia, con annessa carta geologica.   Milano,
G. Civelli, 1882.
163p. fold.map.

At head of title: T. Taramelli.
Bibliographical foot-notes.

1. Geology—Pavia (Province)

NT   0037221   IU

---

*QE   Taramelli, Torquato, 1845–
272   Descrizione geologica della Provincia di Pavia, con annessa
P28T17   carta geologica / T. Taramelli. – 2. ed., notevolmente aum.
1916   Novara : Istituto Geografico de Agostini, 1916.
139 p. : ill., map (1 fold. col. in pocket) ; 31 cm.

Bibliography: p. [137]–139.

1. Geology – Italy – Pavia (Province). 2. Geology, Stratigraphic – Cenozoic. 3. Geology, Stratigraphic – Italy.
I. Title.   geol

NT   0037222   CLU

Taramelli, Torquato, 1845–1922.
Di alcuni scoscendimenti posglaciali sulle
Alpi meridionale ...   1881.
G. T. v. 28ª.

NT   0037223   PPAN

DT   Taramelli, Torquato, 1845–1922.
11   Geografia e geologia dell' Africa di
E90   T. Taramelli e V. Bellio.   Milano, Hoepli,
1890.
334p. maps.

I. Bellio, Vittore, joint author.
II. Title.   (QE320)

NT   0037224   MBU

[Taramelli, Torquato,] 1845–1922.
... Idrografia del bacino dell' Isonzo. Parte 1–   Venezia: C. Ferrari, 1918–   v.   chart.   4°.   (Italy. Ufficio idrografico, Venice. Pubbl. no. 81

Contents: Parte 1. [TARAMELLI, T.] Cenni geologici e struttura tettonica.

1. Isonzo river, Italy.   2. Ser.
N. Y. P. L.   May 7, 1925

NT   0037225   NN

[Taramelli, Torquato,] 1845–1922.
... Idrografia del bacino del Tagliamento. Parte 1–
Venezia: C. Ferrari, 1921–   v.   4°.   (Italy. Ufficio idrografico, Venice. Pubbl. no. 72

Contents: Parte 1. [TARAMELLI, T.] Struttura geologica.

1. Tagliamento river, Italy.   2. Ser.
N. Y. P. L.   May 7, 1925

NT   0037226   NN

Taramelli, Torquato, 1845–1922.
... Il massiccio del Grappa...   Novara: Istituto geografico de Agostini, 1918.   40 p.   map, plates.   8°.   ("Quaderni geografici." Anno 1, no. 6.)

Plates printed on both sides.

1. Geology—Italy—Treviso   (province).   2. Ser.
N. Y. P. L.   December 30, 1926

NT   0037227   NN

Taramelli, Torquato, 1845–1922.
Monografia stratigrafica e paleontologica del Lias delle Provincie Venete.
(Appentix T. V. Ser. V. degli atti dell'Isl. Venete.)
G. T. v.

NT   0037228   PPAN

Taramelli, Torquato, 1845–1922.   L551.76 N900
Monografia stratigrafica e paleontologica dei lias nelle provincie Venete. Premiata dal R. istituto veneto di scienze, lettere ed arti nel concorso dell' anno 1879....   xi,89,[2] p.   10 pl. F. Venezia 1880.
Published as supplement to and reprinted from *Atti dell' Istituto*, Series 5, vol. 5.

NT   0037229   ICJ PPAN

Taramelli, Torquato, 1845–1922.
Note illustrative alla Carta geologica della provincia di Belluno rilevata negli anni 1877–81, dal professore Tamamelli Torquato.   Pavia, Premiata tipografia fratelli Fusi, 1883.
1 p.l., [5]–215,11 p., 1 l.   III fold.pl.   20cm.
Cover-title: ... Con tre tavole di spaccati e la Carta geologica staccata; pubblicazione fatta col concorso del Ministero della pubblica istruzione e del R.Istituto veneto di scienze,lettere ed arti.
"Nota bibliografica": p.14–36.

1.Geology—Italy—Belluno.

NT   0037230   MiU IU

Taramelli, Torquato, 1845–1922.
Osservazioni geologiche fatte dal Prof. Torquato Taramelli nel raccogliere alcuni campioni di Serpentini.   Roma, 1882.
G. T. v. 28a.

NT   0037231   PPAN

551.4   Taramelli, Torquato, 1845–1922.
T171p   ... Il paesaggio lombardo e la geologia ...
Pavia, Premiato stabilimento tipografico successori Bizzoni, 1909.
34p.

"Discorso per l'inaugurazione degli studii."

1. Geology—Lombardy.

NT   0037232   IU

Taramelli, T[orquato] 1845–1922.
Parole dette in occasione della morte di Quintino Sella nell' adunanza del R. Istituto lombardo di scienze e lettere del giorno 20 marzo 1884 dal m. e. Prof. T. Taramelli. [Milano, Tip. Bernardoni, 1884]
12 p.   24cm.
"Estratto dai Rendiconti del R. Istituto lombardo, serie II, vol. XVII, fasc. VI."

1. Sella, Quintino, 1827–1884.   I. R. Istituto lombardo di scienze e lettere, Milan.

Library of Congress   QE361.S46T   4–28797†

NT   0037233   DLC

Taramelli, Antonio, 1868–
Sardegna Romana, by A. Taramelli,
S. Vardabasso, R. Binaghi, and others
see under   Rome (City) Istituto di studi romano. Sezione sarda.

Taramelli, Torquato, 1845–1922.   554.5 0100
Spiegazione della carta geologica del Friuli (provincia di Udine), del professore Taramelli Torquato, ...   Pavia, Tip. Fusi, 1881.
187, [4] p. incl. tables.   19cm.
"Nota delle pubblicazioni risguardanti la geologia friulana." p. 16–23.

NT   0037235   ICJ NN

Taramelli, Torquato, 1845–1922.   *5340.10.18
Stratigrafia della serie paleozoica nelle Alpi carniche. Plate.
(In Reale istituto veneto di scienze, lettere ed arti. Memorie. Vol. 18, pp. 203–218. Venezia, 1874.)

E2163 — Alps, Carinthian. Geol. — Paleozoic rocks.

NT   0037236   MB NIC PPAN

---

q551.48   Taramelli, Torquato, 1845–1922.
T17s   ... Studio geo-idrologico del bacino della Turrite di Gallicano ...   Lucca, Tipografia A. Marchi, 1903.
75p.   fold.map.

At head of title: Comitato permanente per la difesa delle acque del Serchio.

1. Serchio river.   I. Comitato permanente per la difesa delle acque del Serchio.

NT   0037237   IU

Taramelli, Torquato, 1845–1922.
Sul deposito di salgemma di Lungro nella Calabria Citeriore.   7 Marzo 1880.
Geol. T. v. 73.

NT   0037238   PPAN

Taramelli, Torquato, 1845–1922.
Sulla formazione serpentinossa dell'Appenino Pavese.   Roma, 1878.
G. T. v. 52a & 73.

NT   0037239   PPAN

Taramelli, Torquato, 1845–1922.
Sulla posizione stratigrafica della zona fillitica di Rotzo e dei calcari marini che la comprendono.   1881.
G. T. v. 28a.

NT   0037240   PPAN

---

q551.22   Taramelli, Torquato, 1845–1922.
T17t   ... I terremonti andalusi cominiciati il 25 dicembre 1884; memoria di T. Taramelli e G. Mercalli.   Roma, Tipografia della R. Accademia dei Lincei, 1886.
110p. incl.tables.   2 double pl., 2 fold.maps.
At head of title: Reale accademia dei Lincei (Anno CCLXXXIII 1885–86)
"Serie 4a.- Memorie della Classe di scienze fisiche, matematiche e naturali. Vol.III.- Seduta del 12 giugno 1885."
Bibliographical foot-notes.

NT   0037241   IU NjP

Taramelli, T[orquato] 1845–1922.
... I tre laghi. Studio geologico orografico con carta geologica.   Milano, F. Sacchi e figli, 1903.
1 p. l., [5]–124 p., 1 l.   3 fold. maps.   24½cm.
"Nota delle pubblicazioni risguardanti la geologia della regione dei tre laghi e che furono stampate dopo il 1890": p. [11]–21.

1. Geology—Italy, Northern.

Library, U. S. Geol.   survey   G S 6–468

NT   0037242   DI-GS ICJ

---

al-Ṭārami, Jawād, 1847–1907.
(Ḥāshiyah 'alá Qawānīn al-uṣūl)
حاشية على قوانين الأصول ، من تأليفات جواد الطارمي .
قم ، المصطفوى المحمدي [1953]، 1372.
307 p.   25 cm.
Reproduced from ms. copy.

1. al-Qummī, Abū al-Qāsim ibn Muḥammad, d. 1815 or 16. Qawānīn al-uṣūl.   2. Islamic law — Interpretation and construction. 3. Shiites.   I. Title.

74–226012

NT   0037243   DLC

Taran, Konstantin Aleksandrovich.
Сливщик-наливщик нефтебаз. Допущено в качестве учеб. пособия. Москва, Гос. научно-техн. изд-во нефтяной и горно-топливной лит-ры, 1951.
160 p. illus. 22 cm. (В помощь новым кадрам нефтяной промышленности)
At head of title: К. А. Таран и Л. А. Мацкин.

1. Petroleum—Storage.   I. Matskin, Leonid Arkad'evich, joint author.   II. Title.
Title transliterated: Slivshchik-nalivshchik neftebaz.

TP692.5.T3 1951   60–22747 ‡

NT   0037244   DLC

Taran, Mikhail Ivanovich.
Буро-взрывные работы на открытых разработках. Свердловск, Гос. научно-техн. изд-во лит-ры по черной и цветной металлургии, 1951.
193, [3] p. diagrs., tables. 23 cm.
Bibliography: p. [194]

1. Boring. 2.Blasting. I Title.
Title transliterated: Buro-vzryvnye raboty na otkrytykh razrabotkakh.

TN279.T3 1951   60–29184

NT   0037245   DLC

Taran, Mikhail Ivanovich.
Буро-взрывные работы на открытых разработках.
Учеб. пособие для производственно-техн. обучения рабочих. Изд. 2, испр. и доп. Свердловск, Гос. научно-техн. изд-во лит-ры по черной и цветной металлургии, 1954.
255 p. illus. 22 cm.
Errata slip inserted.
Bibliography: p. [252]

1. Boring. 2. Blasting.   I. Title.
Title transliterated: Buro-vzryvnye raboty na otkrytykh razrabotkakh.

TN279.T3 1954   55-28520

NT 0037246   DLC

---

q621.398 Taran, V   D
T17eEb   Electric welding with series-fed arcs. <Translated from Avtogennoe delo, v.17, #3-4, pp.16-18 1946> [Altadena, Calif., H. Brutcher Technical Translation Service, 1947?]
9ℓ.   30cm.

At head of title: no.1905.

1. Electric welding.   I. Brutcher, Henry Eric, 1897-   tr.

NT 0037247   IU

TARANAKI, N.Z. (Provincial District) Provincial council.
Minutes.
New Plymouth.   v.

Film reproduction. Positive.

NT 0037248   NN

MW74   Taranaki daily news.
N42   A poem in stone. Commemorating 100 years of
Xtl7p endeavour in St. Mary's Parish, New Plymouth.
       [2d ed. New Plymouth? N.Z., 1943?]
       38 p. illus., ports. 22 cm.

Cover title.
Foreword signed: G.H. Gavin, Vicar.
"Compiled, printed and published by the Taranaki daily news company limited as a tribute to a beautiful and historic church."
"Mr. H.E. Carey, of the staff of the Daily news ... is the author of the letterpress."

1. New Plymouth, N.Z. St. Mary's Church.
2. New Zealand - Church history.   I. Title (2)

NT 0037250   CtY-D

Taranaki provincial trades directory
see **Universal** business directory for Taranaki Province.

Taranatha, kunsnjing, b. 1573
   see   Taranatha, Jo-nań-pa, b. 1575.

Tārānātha, Jo-nań-pa, b. 1575.
   Tārānāthae de doctrinae Buddhicae in India propagatione narratio. Contextum Tibeticum e codicibus Petropolitanis edidit Antonius Schiefner.   Petropoli: Eggers et socii, 1868.   x, 220 p.   8°.

Added t.-p. in Russian.

1. Tibetan literature. 2. Buddhism   —India. 3. Schiefner,   Anton
N. Y. P. L.   von, 1817-1879, editor.
                                                January 27, 1925

NT 0037253   NN PU CtY MH

Taranatha, Jo-nań-pa, b. 1575.
   Taranathae De doctrinae buddhicae in India propagatione narratio; contextum tibeticum e codicibus petropolitanis edidit Antonius Schiefner. Petropoli, Eggers...... Issakof.1898.

220 p.

NT 0037254   OCl

Tārānātha, Jo-nań-pa, b. 1575.
   Tārānātha's Edelsteinmine, das buch von den vermittlern der sieben inspirationen; aus dem tibetischen übers. von Albert Grünwedel. [4],212,[1]p.   Petrograd, Imprimerie de l'Académie impériale des sciences, 1914.   (Bibliotheca buddhica, v. 18)

Thibetan title at head of title-page. Added title-page in Russian.

NT 0037255   OCl TxU NIC WaU

TĀRĀNĀTHA, Jo-nań-pa, b.1575.
   Tārānāthās Edelsteinmine, das Buch von den Vermittlern der Sieben Inspirationen. Aus dem Tibetischen übersetzt von Albert Grünwedel. Petrograd, 1914. 2 p.l., 212 p. 8°. (Bibliotheca Buddhica. v. 18)

Film reproduction. Master negative.

NT 0037256   NN

Tārānātha, Jo-nań-pa, b. 1575.
   Tārānātha's Geschichte des Buddhismus in Indien; aus dem tibetischen uebersetzt von Anton Schiefner. St. Petersburg, Commissionäre der Kaiserlichen akademie der wissenschaften, Eggers et co.; [etc., etc.], 1869.
   xii, 346 p. 24½ cm.
Verso of t.-p.: Gedruckt auf verfügung der Kaiserlichen akademie der wissenschaften.
Translation of Rgya gar chos 'byuń.

1. Buddha and Buddhism—India—History. 2. Mahayana Buddhism—History.   I. Schiefner, Anton, 1817-1879, tr. II. Title: Geschichte des Buddhismus in Indien.

BQ286.T3715   6-23685

NT 0037257   DLC WU MiU NIC WaU CtY OCl NIC NN CtY

BL   Taranatha, Jo-nań-pa, b. 1575.
420   Mystic tales of Lāmā Tāranātha; a religio-sociological history
T33   of Mahayana Buddhism. Translated into English by Bhupendranath Datta. Calcutta, Ramakrishna Vedanta Math [1944]
       98 p. plates., port. 23 cm.

"For the first time this book is now translated into ... English from German. Originally ... written in Tibetan ... and translated into German by ... A. Gruenwedel." - Publisher's note.
An abstract in English of Edelsteinmine, A. Grünwedel's translation into German of Lāmā Tāranātha's first book on India.

1. Buddha and   Buddhism - Hist. I. Title.

NPurMC
NT 0037258   CU-S NNC CtY RPB MH NIC WU NN HU IU

Tārānātha Tarkavāchaspati Bhaṭṭāchārya
see
Tarkavachaspati, Taranatha, 1812-1885.

Tārānātha Vidyāratna
see
Vidyāratna, Tārānātha.

Taranchuk, M   V
   Постоянно действующие факторы, решающие судьбу войны. 2., доп. изд. Москва, Воен. изд-во, 1954.
   133 p. 20 cm.
——— Microfilm copy (positive)
Made by the Library of Congress.
Negative film in the Library of Congress.
Microfilm Slavic 782 AC

1. Military art and science.   I. Title.
Title transliterated: Postoánno deĭstvuiùshchie faktory, reshaiùshchie sud'bu voĭny

U43.R9T3 1954   64-32878

NT 0037261   DLC

PL248
.T27
D8   **Tarancı, Cahit Sıtkı,** 1910-1956.
          Düşten güzel / Cahit Sıtkı Tarancı. -- Istanbul : Varlık Yayınevi, 1952.
          59 p. ; 17 cm. -- (Yeni Türk şiiri serisi ; 14) (Varlık yayınları ; sayı 145)

NT 0037262   OrPS

Tarancı, Cahit Sıtkı, 1910-1956.
   ...Otuz beş yaş. [Istanbul] Varlık yayınları [1946]   133 p.   18cm. (Yeni türk şiiri serisi. 1)

1. Turkish literature—Poetry.

NT 0037263   NN

895.4T171
U
          Tarancı, Cahit Sıtkı, 1910-1956.
          Otuz beş yaş. 3. basılış. İstanbul, Varlık yayınevi [1952]
          127 p. (Yeni türk şiiri serisi: 1)

Poems.

NT 0037264   NNC

PL
248   **Tarancı, Cahit Sıtkı,** 1910-1956.
.S13   Peyami Safa; hayatı ve eserleri [yazan]
Z5   Cahit Sıtkı. Istanbul, Semih Lûtfi Kitabevi,
T18   1940.
          69 p.   20 cm. (Son devrin meşhur şair ve edipleri serisi,11)

1. Safa, Peyami, 1899-1961.

NT 0037265   MiU

Tarancı, Halit.
   Milletçe kalkınmanın esasları ve şartları; refah yolu. İstanbul, Cumhuriyet Mat[b]aası, 1952.
   271 p. tables. 25 cm.
Bibliography: p. [263]

1. Turkey—Economic policy.   I. Title.

HC405.T3   61-28403

NT 0037266   DLC DLC-P4

Tarancı, Hüseyin Cahit Sıtkı
see
Tarancı, Cahit Sıtkı, 1910-1956.

Taranco, Felipe María Garín Ortiz de
   see   **Garín Ortiz de Taranco, Felipe María.**

Tarancón, José Esteban
   see   **Esteban Tarancón, José.**

Tarancón, Vicente Enrique
  see
  Enrique Tarancón, Vicente, *Bp.*, 1907–

Tarancón de Valencia, José.
  Apuntes de un estudio sobre el pueblo ibero, por José Tarancón de Valencia. Madrid, Ruiz hermanos, 1931–
    v. diagr. 25ᶜᵐ.

  1. Iberians.   ɪ. Title.

Library of Congress   ᵣP53.1.2T3   33–8351
                  ᵣ2ᵢ   572.9466

NT 0037271   DLC

---

*FC5
T1713
561a
  Tarander, pseud.?
  Les actes de Poissy, mis en ryme francoyse par Tarander. Plvs trois cantiques, dont le premier est au nom des fidelles de la France, les deux derniers, sont faitz au nom d'vn prince chrestien, estant en affliction.
  [Paris? ca.₁1561]
    8°. [23]p. 17.5cm.
    Signatures: A⁸,B⁴.
    The last two cantiques are satires on Condé.

NT 0037272   MH

  Taránek, Karl J.
    Monographie der Nebeliden Böhmen's.
    Prag, 1882.
      55 p.   pl.   sq. Q.

NT 0037273   RPB

Taránek, Karl J
  Rozsivky (Diatomaceae). Praze, v komisi knihkupectvi dra Grégra & Ferd. Dattla, 1879.

    73 [4] p. illus. 1pl. 21 cm.

NT 0037274   MH–F

SH211
E8
no.320
  Taranetz, A   J
    Pacific salmon. Oncorhynchus. Extract: Handbook for identification of fishes of Soviet Far East and adjacent waters. [n.p.,n.d.]
    [1], 3 1.   plates (mounted illus.) 19 cm. (English translations of fishery literature, no. 320)
    "U.S.S.R. Pacific Scientific Institute of Fisheries and Oceanography. 'Bulletin, volume 11. Pp. 58–63. Vladivostok, 1937. Translated by Dimitri Khrenov."

    1. Salmon. ɪ.   Khrenov, Dimitri, tr.
    ɪɪ. Title.   (Series)

NT 0037275   DI

Taranez, A
  Absorption de la lumière par la chlorophylle et rétention d'eau par les tissus en rapport avec la réaction photopériodique des plantes.
    (*In* Annales des sciences naturelles. Botanique et biologie végétale. Paris. 26 cm. 11. sér., t. 11 (1950) p. ₁21ᵢ–₁28ᵢ diagrs., tables)
    Bibliography: p. ₁28ᵢ

  1. Photosynthesis. 2. Photoperiodism.
    [QH3.A61   11. sér., t. 11]   A 52–6545

Illinois. Univ. Library
for Library of Congress   ᵣ1ᵢ

NT 0037276   IU

Taranger, Absalon, 1858–1930.
Abu∂ jar∂ar heimilar tekju
  Sproglig-historiske studier tilegnede professor C. R. Unger. Kristiania, H. Aschehoug & co., 1896.

NT 0037277

Taranger, Absalon, 1858–1930.
  ... Den angelsaksiske kirkes indflydelse paa den norske; udgivet af den Norske historiske forening. Kristiania, Grøndahl & søns bogtrykkeri, 1890.
    xii p., 1 l., 459 p. 20ᶜᵐ. ₁Historisk tidsskrift. Tillægsskrift 12ᵢ
    Published in 3 parts, 1890–91.

  1. Norway—Church history. 2. Gt. Brit.—Church history. ɪ. Norske historiske forening, Christiania. ɪɪ. Historisk tidsskrift.
                          5–8259
Library of Congress   DL401.H63

NT 0037278   DLC PU NIC NdU

Taranger, Absalon, 1858–1930.
  Bergens kommunes forhold til St. Jørgens hospital. En retshistorisk undersøgelse af dr. juris Absalon Taranger ... Bergen, Griegs bogtrykkeri, 1900.
    39 p. 22 x 18ᶜᵐ.

  1. Bergen, Norway. Sankt Jørgens hospital.
                        13–33504
Library of Congress   RA989.N8B5

NT 0037279   DLC

Taranger, Absalon, 1858–1930.
  Bondens sædvaneret i Telemarken og Nedenæs. Af Absalon Taranger ... Kristiania, C. Schibsteds bogtrykkeri, 1901.
    24 p. 24ᶜᵐ.
    Separataftryk af "Aftenposten."

                        13–20937

NT 0037280   DLC

₁Taranger, Absalon₁ 1858–1930.
  ... Brødrene Niels og Christopher Josten. (Et bidrag til vor handelsstands historie i forrige aarhundrede.) For "Aftenposten" af T. ₁Kristiania, Trykt hos C. Schibsted, 1889₁
    ₁45₁ p. 17ᶜᵐ.
    Caption title.
    At head of title: Eftertryk forbydes.
    From Aftenposten.

  1. Josten, Niels, d. 1729. 2. Josten, Christopher, fl. 1695–1732. 3. Norway—Comm.—Hist. ɪ. Title.
                        19–18582
Library of Congress   HF3665.T3

NT 0037281   DLC

Taranger, Absalon, 1858–1930.
  Fremstilling af de haalogalandske almenningers retslige stilling. Bodø, 1892.
    56 p.

NT 0037282   MH–L

Taranger, Absalon. Frostatingstedet. På gammel-historiske tomter. [Steinkjer, 1926.] 8°. pp. 33–45.   IcG2T182
  "Særtryk av Nordtröndelags Historielags årbok 1926."

NT 0037283   NIC

  Taranger, Absalon, 1858–1930.
    En Hexeproces fra Østerdalen i det 17de Aarhundrede. Ved A. Taranger.
    (In Vidar; Tidsskrift for Videnskab, Literatur og Politik. Christiania, 24cm. 7. Hefte (1887), p. ₁553ᵢ–560)

    1. Trials (Witchcraft)—Sweden. ɪ. Title. ɪɪ. Vidar; Tidsskrift for Videnskab, Literatur og Politik.

NT 0037284   NIC

Taranger, Absalon, 1858–1930.
  Inntrykk fra America, av Absalon Taranger. Oslo: Lutherstiftelsens bokhandel a s, 1927. 110 p. 8°.

  1. United States—Descr. and trav.,   1910–   2. Norwegians in U. S.
N. Y. P. L.   October 26, 1928

NT 0037285   NN

Taranger, Absalon, 1858–1930.
  Kirkegodsets retsforhold. Kritiske anmærkninger til Ebbe Hertzberg: Om eiendomsretten til det norske kirkegods. En retshistorisk betænkning. Kristiania 1898. Af Absalon Taranger ... Kristiania, "Norges sjøfartstidende"s ₁!₁ trykkeri, 1902.
    82 p. 23½ᶜᵐ.
    Særtryk af Norsk retstidende.

                            15–18564

NT 0037286   DLC

Taranger, Absalon, 1858–1930.
  —— Konrad Maurer. *Extr. fr.* Tidsskrift for Retsvidenskab. XVI. Aarg. Christiania, 1903. 8°. pp. 1–17.   IcA29M452
  The article is followed by Dr. Max v. Vleuten's list of Maurer's writings (pp. 17–29).

NT 0037287   NIC

Taranger, Absalon, 1858–1930.
  Lærebok i norsk familieret, av Absalon Taranger. Kristiania, Cammermeyer, 1911.
    4 p. l., 123 p. 21ᶜᵐ.

  1. Domestic relations—Norway.   ɪ. Title.
                          13–5844 Revised

NT 0037288   DLC

₁Taranger, Absalon,₁ 1858–1930.
  Magnus Erlingssons Kroningsår; Foredrag i Oslo Videnskapsakademi den 22. september 1922. (In: Festskrift til Finnur Jónsson, 29. Maj 1928. København, 1928. 4°. p. ₁181–₁198.)
    Signed: Absalon Taranger.

  1. Magnus Erlingsson, king of   Norway, 1156–1184.
N. Y. P. L.   January 16, 1929

NT 0037289   NN

Taranger, Absalon, 1858–1930, ed.
  Magnus Lagabøters bylov
    see under   Norway. Laws, statutes, etc.

Taranger, Absalon, 1858-1930, ed. & tr.
   Magnus Lagabøters landslov ...
      see under   Norway. Laws, statutes, etc.

Taranger, Absalon. The meaning of
the words *óðal* and *skeyting* in the old
laws of Norway. *In* Essays in legal
history. Read before the International
Congress of historical studies held in
London in 1913. Ed. by Paul Vino-
gradoff. Oxford, 1913. pp. 159-173.

NT   0037292   NIC

Taranger, Absalon, 1858-1930, ed.

Norway. *Laws, statutes, etc.* FOR OTHER EDITIONS
SEE MAIN ENTRY
  Norges gamle love, 2. række, 1388-1604; ifølge offentlig
foranstaltning udg. ved Absalon Taranger ... Christiania, I commission hos Grøndahl & søn. 1912

Taranger, Absalon, 1858-1930.

Norges historie, fremstillet for det norske folk af professor dr.
A. Bugge, rigsarkivar E. Hertzberg, dr. Osc. Alb. Johnsen,
professor dr. Yngvar Nielsen, professor dr. J. E. Sars, professor A. Taranger. Kristiania, H. Aschehoug & co. (W.
Nygaard) 1909-17.

Taranger, Absalon, 1858-1930.
  Norsk familierett, av Absalon Taranger. 2. omarb. utg
Oslo, Cammermeyer, 1926.
  6 p. l., 295 p. 21ᶜᵐ.
  First edition has title: Lærebok i norsk familieret.
  "Forkortelser" (bibliography) : 5th-6th prelim. leaves.

  1. Domestic relations—Norway.   I. Title.
                                  36-5711

Library of Congress   (2)   [347.809481]   349.481076

NT   0037295   DLC

Taranger, Absalon, 1858-1930.

—— Norsk Kirkeret. Forelæsninger ved
det praktisk-teologiske Seminar. I. Kir-
kerettens og Kirkeforfatningens Historie.
Kristiania, Cammermeyer, 1910. 8°. pp.
(4) + 63.   IcG2T181

NT   0037296   NIC

Taranger, Absalon, 1858-1930.
  Den norske besiddelsesret indtil Christian V's norske lov.
Halvdel 1–   ...   Kristiania: Aktiebogtrykkeriet, 1897–
  v.   8°.
  Bibliographical footnotes.
  Tillæg til "Tidsskrift for retsvidenskab" 1897.

1. Possession (in law)—Norway.   2. Tidsskrift for retsvidenskab.
3. Title.
N. Y. P. L.   December 18, 1924

NT   0037297   NN NIC MiU-L MH-L

Taranger, Absalon, 1858-1930.
  De norske perlefiskerier i ældre tid af A. Taranger.
Kristiania, Grøndahl og søns bogtrykkeri, 1889.
  54 p. 21½ᶜᵐ.
  Reprint from Historisk tidsskrift udg. af den Norske historiske fore-
ning, 3. række, 1. bd., p. (185)-237.

  1. Pearl-fisheries—Norway.
                               13-22049

Library of Congress   SH377.N6T3

NT   0037298   DLC

Taranger, Absalon, 1858-1930.
  Norwegische bürgerkunde (verfassung und verwaltung) von
Absalon Taranger ... Vom verfasser durchgesehene überset-
zung nach der 7. aufl. (1923) von dr. H. v. Spesshardt, hrsg.
mit unterstützung des Nordischen institutes der Universität
Greifswald ... Greifswald, L. Bamberg, 1925.
  80 p. 24½ᶜᵐ.
  "Grundgesetz des königreichs Norwegen": p. (60)-77.

  1. Norway—Constitutional law. 2. Administrative law—Norway.
  I. Spesshardt, Hugo Victor, freiherr von, 1860–   tr. II. Title.
                                   28-23995

NT   0037299   DLC

Taranger, Absalon, 1858-1930.
  Om betydningen af herað og heraðskirkja i de ældre kristen-
retter. Af A. Taranger ... Kristiania, Grøndahl & søns bogtrykkeri, 1887.
  67 p. 21ᶜᵐ.
  "Særskilt aftryk af Historisk tidsskrift, 2. række, 6. bind."

  1. Ecclesiastical law—Norway.   2. Local government—Norway.
  I. Title: Herað og heraðs-kirkja.
                                 19—19197

Library of Congress   BR1008.T3

NT   0037300   DLC NIC

Taranger, Absalon, 1858-1930.
  Om eiendomsretten til de norske præstegaarde. Af
Absalon Taranger ... Kristiania, "Norges sjøfartsti-
dende"'s trykkeri, 1896.
  2 p. l., 102 p. 23½ᶜᵐ.
  Særtryk af "Norsk retstidende."

                                   15-18563

NT   0037301   DLC

Div.S.   Taranger, Absalon, 1858-1930.
265.62
T176P   Prestenes bekjennelsesplikt i den norske
        kirke. Betenkning avgitt til det kgl. Kirke-
        og undervisnings-departement. Oslo, Steen-
        ske (1928)
        84 p. 25 cm.

        "Særtrykk av Norvegia sacra, 1927."
        Bibliographical footnotes.
        1. Confession. Norske Kirke. I. Title.

NT   0037302   NcD

Taranger, Absalon, 1858-1930.
  Religiøse lægmandsbetragtninger, av Absalon Taranger. Kristiania, Cammermeyers boghandel, 1912.
  4 p. l., 196 p. 20ᶜᵐ.

  I. Title.
                                    13-3849

NT   0037303   DLC

BV764   Taranger, Absalon, 1858-1930.
.N6T3   Tillegg til norsk kirkerett; forelesninger
        ved de praktiskteologiske seminarer, av
        Absalon Taranger.
        Oslo, Cammermeyers boghandel 1928.
        3 p.l., 116 p. 23cm.

NT   0037304   DLC

Taranger, Absalon, 1858-1930.

—— Trondheimens forfatningshistorie.
Trondhjem. 1929. 8°. pp. 59, (1).
                    IcG2T183
  "Det kgl. norske Videnskabers Selskabs Skrif-
ter 1929. Nr. 5."

NT   0037305   NIC

Taranger, Absalon, 1858-1930.
  Tyske og engelske missionærer i Norge. En kort replik
til professor Konrad Maurer. (Kristiania, Trykt hos
Grøndahl & søn, 1893)
  21 p. 21½ᶜᵐ.
  Caption title.
  Reprint from Historisk tidsskrift udg. af den Norske historiske fore-
ning, 3. række, 3. bd., p. (191)-211.
  Reply to Prof. Maurer's Nogle bemærkninger til Norges kirkehistorie.

  1. Maurer, Konrad von, 1823-1902. Nogle bemærkninger til Norges
kirkehistorie. 2. Norway—Church history.
                               18-1784

Library of Congress   BR1004.M5

NT   0037306   DLC

Taranger, Absalon, 1858-1930.

—— Udsigt over den norske Rets Historie.
Forelæsninger, 1ste Semester, 1907. IV.
Privatrettens Historie. Kristiania. Kart- &
Litograferingskontoret, n. d. 4°. pp. (2) +
ix + 399. *Autographed.*   IcG2T179

NT   0037307   NIC

Taranger, Absalon, 1858-1930.
  Udsigt over den norske rets historie; forelæsninger af dr.
jur. Absalon Taranger ... Christiania, Cammermeyer, 1898–
19
  v. 18ᶜᵐ.

  1. Law—Norway—Hist. & crit.   I. Title.
                                  32-13027

NT   0037308   DLC NIC MH PU-L CtY

Taranger, Absalon, 1858-1930.
  ... Utsikt over den norske retts historie ... 2. utg., utgitt
ved Knut Robberstad. Oslo, Nationaltrykkeriet, 1935–
  v. 23½ᶜᵐ.
  CONTENTS.—I. Innledning. Rettskildenes historie.

  1. Law—Norway—Hist. & crit.   I. *Robberstad, Knut, 1899–   ed.
                                  43-31392

NT   0037309   DLC IU

Taranger, Absalon, 1858-1930
  ... Vort retsmaals historie 1388-1604.
Et bidrag til vort skriftmaals historie.
Kristiania, Cammermeyer, 1900.
  35 p. 22½cm.

NT   0037310   MH-L IU IaU

W 6   TARANGET, André Louis Étienne, praeses
P3   Dissertatio botano-medica. De viribus plantarum ... Duaci,
v.1640   Derbaix [1783]
no. 9   18 p. 23 cm.
         Diss. - Douai (F. J. Lestiboudois, respondent)

        I. Lestiboudois, François Joseph, respondent

NT   0037311   DNLM

W 6
P3
v.1640
no.3

TARANGET, André Louis Étienne, *praeses*
Dissertatio physiologica. De alimentorum in chylum, chyli
in lac, lactis in sanguinem conversione ... Duaci, Derbaix
[1783]
[4] p. 23 cm.
Diss. - Douai (P. J. F. Gelez, respondent)

L. Gelez, Pierre Joseph Félix, respondent

NT 0037312   DNLM

RC
183
F8 T17

TARANGET, André Etienne Louis
Réflexions sur la vaccine, suivies d'un
rapport sur les vaccinations practiquées
dans la ville de Douai, Département du Nord,
depuis fructidor, an 10 jusqu'en frimaire,
an 12. Par André Taranget, docteur en médecine ... Douai, De l'imprimerie de Marlier
[an 12, 1804]
8vo 77, [9] p. tables 19 cm.
In late marbled wrappers.
1. Vaccination.   2. Vaccination--France--
Douai.

NT 0037313   MBCo

Tarango, Belina Escobedo
see   Escobedo Tarango, Belina.

Tarango, Fernando Figueroa
see
Figueroa Tarango, Fernando, 1921-

Taranguera, Nicolás Mora de la
    see   Mora de la Taranguera, Nicolás.

NA5621
F514T3

Tarani, Fedele, 1858-1933.
La Badia di S. Pancrazio in Firenze.
Pescia, Tip. E. Cipriani [1923?]
84 p. 20 cm.
Bibliographical footnotes.

1. Florence. Badia di San Pancrazio.

NT 0037317   CSt

NA1121
F632.25
M65
T37

Tarani, *Fedele,* 1858-1933.
La Basilica di S. Miniato al Monte;
guida storico-artistica, dell'Abate
D.F. Tarani...   Firenze, Tip.
Arcivescovile, 1909.
111 p. 11 plates. 17 cm.

Author's autograph inscription.
From the library of Ugo Ojetti.-cf.
Holstein, J., firm, Frankfurt am
Main. Katalog 37, no. 1552.

NT 0037318   MWiCA CSt

BX3050
.V3xT3

Tarani, Fedele, 1858-1933.
L'ordine Vallomrosano [i.e.
Vallombrosano] : note storico-
cronologiche / D. F. Tarani. Firenze :
Scuola Tipografica Calasanziana, 1920
[i.e. 1921]
215 p. : ill. ; 19 cm.

1. Benedictines. Congregatio Vallis
Umbrosae. I. Title

NT 0037319   NjP

Tarani, Fedele, 1858-1933.
... Visioni franco spagnole. Firenze, Scuola tipografica
dell'Istituto Gualandi per sordomuti e sordomute [1929?]
2 p. l., 193 p., 1 l. 20 cm.
At head of title: D. F. Tarani.

1. Spain—Descr. & trav.   2. Lourdes.   3. Churches—Spain.   4. Pilgrims and pilgrimages.   I. Title.

                                34–12467

Library of Congress   BX2323.T3   [914.6] 231.73

NT 0037320   DLC NN

PQ4843
A64
P4

Tarani, Umberto
Petali al vento. [Versi.] Rieti [Tip.
Belisari, 1954.]
57 p. 22 cm.

NT 0037321   RPB

Tarani a Spalannis, Andrea.
Manuale theoretico-practicum pro minoribus
poenitentiariis apostolicis, nec non pro aliis
privilegiatis confessariis, pagellam S. Poeniten-
tiariae praesertim habentibus confectum ...
Romae, F. Pustet, 1906.
679, 1 p.   19 cm.
1. Penance (Sacrament) - Handbooks for
confessors. I. Catholic Church. Poenitentiaria
Apostolica. II. Title.

NT 0037322   KAS

Taranikoff (Eugénie) [1871–]. *Du traitement de la scoliose chez les adultes. 41 pp., 3
l., 2 pl. 8°. *Paris,* 1901, No. 366.
——. The same. 41 pp., 2 l., 2 pl. 8°. *Paris,*
G. Steinheil, 1901.

NT 0037323   DNLM

TN871
.3
.M4

Tarankov, V. V., *joint author.*
Metaksa, P I
Строительство нефтяных скважин в море. Москва, Гос.
научно-техн. изд-во нефтяной и горно-топливной лит-ры,
1954.

Taranne, Nicolas Rodolphe, 1795-1857, ed.
Éloge de Paris
    see under   Joannes de Janduno, d. 1328.

Taranne, Nicolas Rodolphe, 1795-1857, ed.
Du Cange, Charles Du Fresne, *sieur,* 1610-1688.
Les familles d'outre-mer, de Du Cange, pub. par M. E.-G.
Rey ... Paris, Imprimerie impériale, 1869.

Taranne, *Nicolas Rodolphe, 1795-1857, ed.*
Manuscrits de la bibliothèque d'Avranches
    see under   Avranches, France. Biblio-
thèque.

Taranne, Nicolas Rodolphe, 1795-1857.
Gregorius, *Saint, bp. of Tours,* 538-594.
Sancti Georgii Florentii Gregorii, episcopi turonensis,
Historiæ ecclesiasticæ Francorum libri decem, ex duobus
codd. mss. nunc primum, cura Leglay et Teulet, collatis.
Emendaverunt et animadversionibus Theod. Ruinart,
d. Bouquet-aliorumque doctorum virorum, et suis illu-
straverunt J. Guadet et N. R. Taranne ... Parisiis, apud
J. Renouard, 1836–38.

Taranov, Anatoliĭ Pavlovych.
Культурно-освітня робота сільських рад. Київ, Держ.
вид-во політ. літ-ри УРСР, 1955.
42 p. 20 cm. (На допомогу працівникам сільських рад депутатів
трудящих, 5)
At head of title: Академія наук Української РСР. Сектор дер-
жави і права.

1. Local government—Russia.   I. Title.
                      Title transliterated: Kul'turno-
                      osvitnia robota sil'skykh rad.

JS6058.T3   56–37816 rev ‡

NT 0037329   DLC

Taranov, G   F
Работа на колхозной пасеке. Изд. 6., перер. Под ред.
Е. Ф. Лискуна. Москва, Гос. изд-во сельхоз. лит-ры, 1950.
127 p. illus., port. 20 cm. (Библиотечка колхозного животно-
вода)

1. Bee culture—Russia.   I. Title.
               Title transliterated: Rabota na kolkhoznoĭ paseke.

SF531.T25 1950   57–18752

NT 0037330   DLC

Taranov, G   F
Догляд бджіл протягом року. Вид. 2. Київ, Держ. вид-
во колгоспної і радгоспної літ-ри УСРР, 1935.
133 p. illus. 22 cm.

1. Bee culture.   I. Title.
               Title transliterated: Dohliad bdzhil protiahom roku.

SF531.T3 1935   55–45553

NT 0037331   DLC

Taranov, G   F
Выращивание и использование сильных пчелиных се-
мей. Москва, Гос. изд-во сельхоз. лит-ры, 1953.
126 p. illus. 20 cm.

1. Bee culture.   I. Title.
               Title transliterated: Vyrashchivanie i ispol'-
               zovanie sil'nykh pchelinykh semeĭ.

SF531.T27   54–43481

NT 0037332   DLC

Taranov, Gleb.
... Курс чтения партитур; под редакцией Дм. Рогаль-Ле-
вицкого. Москва, Ленинград, Государственное издательство "Искусство," 1939.
358, [2] p. illus. (music) fold. pl. (music) fold. tab. 23 cm.
At head of title: Глеб Таранов.
Errata slip mounted on t.-p.

1. Score reading and playing.   I. Rogal'-Levitskiĭ, Dmitriĭ Romanovich, ed.   *Title transliterated:* Kurs chteniia partitur.

                                  43–44292

Library of Congress   MT85.T3

NT 0037333   DLC

Taranov, Gleb.
₁Suite, piano, op. 4₎

Сюита для фортепиано, соч. 4. Москва, Гос. музыкальное изд-во, 1935.

26 p. 30 cm.

Contents.—Рассвет.—Сказка.—Старинный танец.—Романеска.—Марш.

1. Suites (Piano)   *Title transliterated:* Siuita dlia fortepiano.

M24.T177 op. 4   M 56–422

NT 0037334   DLC

Taranov, H   **F**
see
Taranov, G   **F**

LB1028
.5
.M65
1964

Taranov, Vladimir Mikhaĭlovich, ed.

Moskovskaiā konferentsiiā po primenenīiū tekhnicheskikh sredstv i programmirovannogo obucheniiā v srednei i vysshei shkole. *1st, 1964.*

Применение технических средств и программированного обучения в средней специальной и высшей школе; вопросы теории, организации, методики использования в преподавании естественных, гуманитарных наук, музыкальных дисциплин и спорта. Обучающая аппаратура и средства наглядности. Под общей ред. В. М. Таранова. Москва, Советское радио, 19

Taranovski, Feodor

see

Taranovskiĭ, Fedor Vasilévich, 1875–*1936*.

Taranovski, Kiril.

Руски дводелни ритмови I–II. Уредник Петар Колендих. Београд ₁Научна књига₎ 1953.

376 p. diagrs., 16 fold. tables (in pocket) 25 cm. (Српска академија наука. Посебна издања, кн.. 217. Одељење литературе и језика, кн. 5)

Summary in Russian.

1. Russian language—Versification.   I. Title.   (Series: Srpska akademija nauka, Belgrad. Posebna izdanja, knj. 217)
₍i umetnosti₎   *Title transliterated:* Ruski dvodelni ritmovi.

AS346.B53 vol. 217   55–18562

NT 0037338   DLC MCM TxU MH CSt

Taranovskiĭ, Fedor Vasil'evich, 1875–1936.

Догматика положительнаго государственнаго права во Франціи при старомъ порядкѣ. Юрьевъ, Тип. К. Маттисена, 1911.

633 p. 25 cm.

1. France—Constitutional history.   I. Title.
Title transliterated: Dogmatika polozhitel'nago gosudarstvennago prava

JN2341.T3   54–48628 ‡

NT 0037339   DLC ICJ NjP

Taranovskiĭ, Fedor Vasil'evich, 1875–1936.

... Енциклопедија права. Београд, Издавачка књижарница Г. Кона, 1923.

xix, 534 p. 23 cm.

At head of title: Dr. Феодор Тарановски ...
Includes bibliographies.

1. Law—Hist. & crit.   2. Jurisprudence.   3. Political science.   I. Title.

       41–37037

NT 0037340   DLC

Taranovskiĭ, Fedor Vasil'evich, 1875–1936.
₁Elementy osnovnykh zakonov v Ulozhenii TSaria Alekseia Mikhailovicha₎

Элементы основных законов в Уложении Царя Алексея Михайловича. К истории политического строя удельной Руси. Харбин, Типо-лит. Л. М. Абрамовича, 1928.

68 p. 20 cm.

Includes bibliographical references.

1. Land tenure—Russia—Law. 2. Political crimes and offenses—Russia. I. Taranovskiĭ, Fedor Vasil'evich, 1875–1936. K istorii politicheskogo strofa udel'nof Rusi. II. Title. III. Title: K istorii politicheskogo strofa udel'nof Rusi.

       72–220706

NT 0037341   DLC

Taranovskiĭ, Fedor Vasil'evich, 1875–1936.

Historja prawa południowo-słowiańskiego; najnowsze publikacje. Lwów, 1927.

88 p. 24 cm. (Pamiętnik historyczno-prawny, t. 3, zesz. 5)

1. Law—Yugoslavia—Hist. & crit.   I. Title.

       58–51440

NT 0037342   DLC

JN6511   **Taranovskiĭ, Fedor Vasil'evich, 1875–1936.**
.T19   Historja prawa rosyjskiego. Lwów, Nakł. Red. «Pamiętnika historyczno-prawnego» 1928–
     v. (Pamiętnik historyczno-prawny, t. 6, zesz. 1)
     Includes bibliography.

     1. Russia—Constitutional history.

NT 0037343   ICU

Taranovskiĭ, Fedor Vasil'evich, 1875– *1936*.

... Историја српског права у Немањинкој држави ... Београд, Издавачка књижарница Г. Кона, 1931.

3 v. 23 cm.

At head of title: Dr. Теодор Тарановски ...
Includes bibliographies.

Contents.—I део. Историја државног права.—II део. Историја кривичног права.—III део. Историја грађанског права.—IV део. Историја судског уређења и поступка.

1. Law—Serbia—Hist. & crit. 2. Serbia—Constitutional history. 3. Criminal law—Serbia—Hist. 4. Civil law—Serbia—Hist. 5. Courts—Serbia. I. Title.

       R7–31061

NT 0037344   DLC

Taranovskiĭ, Fedor Vasil'evich, 1875–1936.

Учебникъ энциклопедіи права. Юрьевъ, Тип. К. Маттисена, 1917.

534 p. 26 cm.

"Отдѣльный оттискъ изъ 'Ученыхъ записокъ Императорскаго Юрьевскаго университета.'"

1. Jurisprudence.   2. Political science.   I. Title.
Title transliterated: Uchebnik ėntsiklopedii prava.

       63–56100 rev

NT 0037345   DLC

Taranovskiĭ, Fedor Vasil'evich, 1875–1936.

Увод у историју словенских права. Београд, Издавачка књижарница Г. Кона, 1922.

208 p. 23 cm.

At head of title: Проф. др. Ф. Тарановски.
"Књижевност": p. 208.

1. Law, Slavic—Hist. & crit.   I. Title.

       41–37039

₍2₎   Second Official

NT 0037346   DLC

Taranovskiĭ, Fedor Vasil'evich, 1875–1936.
... Увод у историју словенских права. 2. прерађено и допуњено изд. Београд, Издавачка књижарница Г. Кона, 1933.

ix, 260 p. 24 cm.

At head of title: Dr. Теодор Тарановски ...
Includes bibliographies.

1 Law, Slavic – Hist. & crit.   I. Title

       41–37038

NT 0037347   DLC

Taranovskiĭ, Fedor Vasil'evich, 1875–1936.
Замѣтки о Монтескьѣ. Ярославль, 1913.

38 p. 26 cm.

"Отдѣльный оттискъ изъ № 1, 1913 г. 'Юридическихъ записокъ,' издаваемыхъ Демидовскимъ юридическимъ лицеемъ."

1. Montesquieu, Charles Louis de Secondat, baron de La Brède et de, 1689–1755. De l'esprit de lois.
Title transliterated: Zamĕtki o Montesk'e.

JC179.M8T3   43–35511 rev*

NT 0037348   DLC

Taranovskiĭ, Kirill
see
Taranovski, Kiril.

Taranovskiĭ, N   **G**
₍Lev Sirenin₎
Левъ Сиренинъ; повѣсть. Харьковъ, Тип. Губ. правленія, 1898.

160 p. 25 cm.

At head of title: Н. Г. Тарановскій.

I. Title.

PG3470.T3L4 1898   74–214713

NT 0037350   DLC

Taranovskiĭ, N   **G**
₍Povĕsti i razskazy₎
Повѣсти и разсказы. Харьковъ, Тип. Губ. правленія, 1898.

176 p. 26 cm.

At head of title: Н. Г. Тарановскій.
CONTENTS: Вѣщій сонъ.—Якодомъ.—Потухшія свѣчи.—Убійца-художникъ.

PG3470.T3P6 1898   74–214742

NT 0037351   DLC

Taranovskiĭ, N   **G**
₍Sochinenīia₎
Сочиненія Н. Г. Тарановскаго. Харьковъ, Тип. Губ. правленія, 1887.

411 p. 26 cm.

CONTENTS: Ландыши съ дѣтской могилки; святочный разсказъ.—Петръ Петровичъ Чижовъ; повѣсть.—Борисъ Танинъ; романъ.—Странная исторія; разсказъ.

PG3470.T3S6 1887   74–214177

NT 0037352   DLC

Taranowicz, John, d. 1938.

Skarga, Piotr, 1536–1612.
... The eucharist, translated by Edward J. Dworaczyk. Milwaukee, The Bruce publishing company ₁°1939₎

Taranowicz, John, d. 1938.
... Katechizm większy religji chrześcijańsko-katolickiej z krótkiemi objaśnieniami. Przeznaczony do użytku szkoł i rodzin polskich ... Ramsey, N. J., Don Bosco Polish institute; Warszawa, Lipowa, 14, 1925.

252, [4] p. 18^{cm}.

At head of title: Ks. Jan Taranowicz.
Based on Joseph Deharbe's Catechism.

1. Catholic church—Catechisms and creeds. I. Deharbe, Joseph, 1800-1871. II. Title.

Library of Congress   BX1966.P7T25

25-7961

NT 0037354   DLC IEdS

Taranowicz, John, d. 1938.
Mniejszy katechizm z dodatkiem zawierającym przygotowanie do spowiedzi i komunji św. ułożył i do użytku młodzieży szkół parafjalnych w Ameryce zastosował ks. Jan Taranowicz ... W New Britain, Conn., Drukiem "Przewodnika katolickiego", 1921.

126 p. 17¼^{cm}.

Library of Congress   BX1966.P7T3

21-14578

NT 0037355   DLC

Taranowicz, John, d. 1938.
Ofiara Nowego Zakonu; rozważania o Mszy św. i powszechne nabożeństwa polskie ułożył Ks. Jan Taranowicz. Nakładem autora ... New York, Wydawnictwo im. S. Konarskiego, *1927.

1 p. l., x p., 1 l., 434 p. illus. 14^{cm}.

"Kalendarz całego roku": p. v-x.

1. Prayer-books. 2. Mass. 3. Catholic church—Prayer-books and devotions. I. Title.
Library of Congress   BX2125.P6T3

28-8537

NT 0037356   DLC

Taranowicz, John, d. 1938.
Ofiara Nowego Zakonu; rozważania o Mszy św. i powszechne nabożeństwa polskie. New Britain, Conn., Wydanictwo [sic] im. S. Koharskiego; skł. gł.: Introligatornia Progress Book Bindery, *1929.

iv, 247 p. illus. 14 cm.

1. Mass—Prayer-books and devotions—Polish. I. Title.
BX2125.P6T3 1929

52-54848

NT 0037357   DLC

BX1968   **Taranowicz, John,** d. 1938.
.T3   ... Pictorial catechism; explanation to the catechetical pictures (in colors) of Deveraux view co., inc. in accordance with the Baltimore catechism. Brooklyn, New York, c1923.

NT 0037358   DLC

Taranowski, Teodor
see
Taranovskiĭ, Fedor Vasil'evich, 1875-1936.

Tarant, Deborah.
מיַן יידיש בוך, איַנס. געצײַכנט פֿון מאַריס פֿאַס. מיט
יאָרק, פֿאַרלאַג פֿון דעם יידישן פֿראָטערנאַלן פֿאָלקס־
[New York] 1944, אָרדן

155 p. illus. 24 cm.

1. Primers, Yiddish   *Title transliterated:* Mayn yidish bukh.

PJ5116.T35

49-32586

NT 0037360   DLC

Tarant, Hans Georg.   *Map 47.13.1.Plate 14
De waare Grond Teeckening vande Hooft Stadt Cocthien geleegen in der Custe Malabar . . . Cochin, inserted in the manuscript-atlas of Johannes Vingboons, c. 1665. [Map facsimile. 1696?] Scale, 16.6 Rynland rods to 1 inch. (.04126 miles to 1 inch.) Size, 17¾ × 28 inches.
(*In* Wieder, F. C., editor. Monumenta cartographica. Vol. 1, plate 14. The Hague. 1925.)
Critical text, vol. 1, p. 16.
The original is a pen-drawing.

N3220 — Cochin, City, India. Descr. Maps.

NT 0037361   MB

Taranta, Valesco de
    see   **Balescon de Tarente,** fl. 1380-1418.

Taranta, Valescus de
    see   **Balescon de Tarente,** fl. 1380-1418.

Taranta, Vasco de
    see   **Balescon de Tarente,** fl. 1380-1418.

TARANTEL; satirische Monatsschrift der Sowjetzone. 1-124; [Okt.] 1950-Apr. 1962. Berlin-Charlottenburg [etc.]   3 v.   illus.(part col.)   23-25cm.

Lacking: no. 1, Oct. 1950.
Monthly, Nov. 1950-1959; bimonthly (slightly irregular), 1960-Apr. 1962.
Subtitle varies slightly.
Edited by H. Bär.
Includes occasional supplements.

1. Satire, Political--Germany-- humor, German--Per. and soc.   Per. and soc. publ. 2. Wit and publ. I. Bär, Heinrich, ed.

NT 0037365   NN OrU

Bonaparte Collection No.5558   TARANTELLA in ter parlá romanesco detta delli massiccioni, ossia Alissandro er grevetto delli monti, che aricconta alla sua rigazza le su bravure cha ha fatto pè cagione d'amore. Lucca [n.d.]

11p. 17½cm.

NT 0037366   ICN

[Tarantelli, Cesidio.]
Democrazia cristiana; ovvero, Un reformista cristiano che distrugge le teorie sbalorditorie dell'On. Ferri!! Sulmona: Angeletti, 1904. 8 p. 8°.

1. Socialism and Christianity. 2. Ferri, Enrico. 3. Title.   May 3, 1913.
N. Y. P. L.

NT 0037367   NN

WE   **Tarantelli, Eugenio**
840   Malattie cutanee e infezioni sessuali.
T176m   Roma, Edizioni italiane [1946]
1946   694 p. illus.

1. Skin diseases 2. Venereal diseases

NT 0037368   DNLM

WI   **TARANTELLI, Eugenio**
200   Malattie dermato-veneree della
T176m   bocca e gengivo-stomatiti. Roma,
1948   Edizioni italiane [1948]
     75 p. illus.
     1. Mouth - Diseases

NT 0037369   DNLM ICJ

Tarantini, Gaetano.
... Sul furto di frutti pendenti. Trani, V. Vecchi, 1895.

20 p. 25½cm.

Bibliographical footnotes.

NT 0037370   MH-L

TARANTINI, Giovanni.
Di alcune cripte nell'agro di Brindisi. Napoli, 1878.

NT 0037371   MH

Tarantini, Leopoldo, 1811-1882.
Arringhe dell'avvocato Leopoldo Tarantini, con una prefazione del prof. Enrico Pessina e un cenno biografico dell'avv. Michele Mirenghi. 2. ed. Trani, Vecchi & c., 1928.

xiii, 360 p. 25^{cm}.

First edition 1889.

1. Tarantini, Leopoldo, 1811-1882. [1. Biography—Italy] 2. Trials—Italy. I. Pessina, Enrico, 1828- ed. II. Mirenghi, Michele. III. Title.

30-29096

NT 0037372   DLC

TARANTINI, Leopoldo, 1811-1882.
Don Carlos; a lyric tragedy, in three acts. The music by M. Costa. Written by Leopoldo Tarantini. [London, 1844].

pp.79.
Italian text and English translation. Words only.

NT 0037373   MH-Mu

4K-   Tarantini, Leopoldo, 1811-1882.
691   In difesa di Giovanni Passannante, accusato di tentato regicidio, discorso pronunziato nel di 7 marzo 1879, innanzi alla Corte di assise di Napoli (dal resoconto stenografico) Napoli, Stab. tip. C. F. Giannini, 1879.
     32 p.

NT 0037374   DLC-P4

Tarantini, Leopoldo, 1811-1882.
Luisella
    see under   Pacini, Giovanni, 1796-1867.

Tarantini, Leopoldo, 1811-1882.
L'osteria di Andujar
    see under   Lillo, Giuseppe, 1814-1863.

Tarantini, Leopoldo, 1811-1882.
Per Salvatore Daniele condannato alla
pena di morte e ricorrente presso la
Corte di cassazione di Napoli. ₍Napoli,
N. Jovene, 1877₎

75 p. 23cm.

NT 0037377   MH-L

Tarantino, Anjelo.
Lado i kare acon, ame ocoyo Father A.
Tarantino. London, Macmillan, 1952. 50 p.
illus., map. (Treasury of East African
history series.)

"History of the Lango people of Uganda."

1. Lango (African tribe) 2. Dyur language
- Texts. (TITLE)

NT 0037378   NN CU

Tarantino, F. R.
Phthalocyanine blue
see under   American cyanamid company.
Calco chemical division.

Adelmann
R   Tarantino, Francesco Saverio.
128   Dissertazione fisiologica intorno alla
.6   generazione dell'uomo.   Napoli, Nella
S227   stamperia Raimondiana, 1779.
116 p. 21cm.

Bound with: Santilli, Eustachio. Manuale medico per uso della gente di Campagna
del regno di Napoli. 1791.
Some pages misbound between p. 97 and p.
114.

1. Reproduc   tion. 2. Embryology—
Early works to   1800.

NT 0037380   NIC

TARANTINO, Giuseppe.
Giovanni Locke; studio storico. Milano-Torino,
Fratelli Dumolard, 1886.

pp.19.
"Estratto dalla Rivista di filosofia scien-
tifica, serie 2, anno v, vol. v, settembre, 1886."

NT 0037381   MH OC1W

TARANTINO, Giuseppe.
Il principio dell'Etica e la crisi morale contemporanea; memoria. Napoli, A. Tessitore & figlio
1904.

pp.48.
"Estratta dal vol. XXXV degli Atti della R.
Accademia di Scienze Morali e Politiche di
Napoli."

NT 0037382   MH

Tarantino, Giuseppe.   171 Q102
27497 ... Il problema della morale di fronte al positivismo ed alla metafisica. Prolusione al corso di filosofia morale, letta nella R.
Università di Pisa il di 31 gennaio 1901.   Pisa, tipografia A. Val-
enti, 1901.
43 p. 24½cm.
At head of title: Giuseppe Tarantino.

NT 0037383   ICJ ICRL

Tarantino, Giuseppe
Saggi filosofici. Napoli, Stab. tipografico
del prof. V. Morano, 1885.
xii, 353 p.

Bibliographical footnotes.

1. Philosophy - Addresses, essays, lectures.
2. Psychology - Addresses, essays, lectures.

NT 0037384   NNC

---

arW   Tarantino, Giuseppe.
35682   Saggio sul criticismo e sull'associa-
zionismo di Davide Hume.   Napoli, V.
Morano, 1887.
75 p. 24cm.

1. Hume, David, 1711-1776.

NT 0037385   NIC

Tarantino, Giuseppe.
Saggio sulle idee morali e politiche di Tommaso Hobbes
per Giuseppe Tarantino ...   Napoli, F. Giannini & figli,
1900.
3 p. l., 144 p. front. 24½cm.

1. Hobbes, Thomas, 1588-1679.
1-I-117

Library of Congress   B1247.T2

NT 0037386   DLC NIC

Tarantino, Jacinto Roque.
Impuesto: ganancias eventuales; comentarios, críticas,
casos prácticos, texto de la Ley 12.922 y reglamentaciones.
₍Córdoba, República Argentina, Editorial Assandri₎ 1947.
106 p. 24 cm.

1. Capital gains tax—Argentine Republic.   I. Argentine Republic.
Laws, statutes, etc.

54-33944

NT 0037387   DLC TxU

Tarantino, Jacinto Roque.
... Impuestos a los "beneficios extraordinarios" y "réditos."
Decretos nacionales nros. 18.230 y 18.229. El articulado,
antecedentes y comentario. Apéndice: sobre fundamentos y
aspectos críticos a las leyes de impuesto a los réditos. Regla-
mentación general del Decreto nº 18.229. ₍Córdoba, Talleres
gráficos de E. Litvack₎ 1944.
1 p. l., ₍5₎-136 p., 1 l. 23½ cm.

1. Excess profits tax—Argentine Republic.   I. Argentine Republic. Laws, statutes, etc.

HJ4685.A6T3   336.243   45-16025

NT 0037388   DLC

Tarantino, Mario
La congiura catilinaria (Studio storico)
Catania, Tip. sicula di Monaco & Mollica, 1898.
93 p. 26 cm.
Bibliographical footnotes.
1. Rome - Hist. - Conspiracy of Cataline,
65-62 B. C. I. Title.

NT 0037389   OCU MH

TARANTINO, Mario.
Questioni cronologiche intorno alla congiura
catilinaria. Catania, Monaco & Mollica, ₍1898₎.

pp.9.
"Estratto dalla memoria La congiura
catilinaria."

NT 0037390   MH

TARANTINO, Mario.
Tito Livio e la guerra annibalica in Italia;
note storiche. Giarre, 1901.

NT 0037391   MH

Tarantino, Nicola.
...Orazio; studio critico. Milano,
Albrighi, 1935₎
101 p. 19½ cm.

1. Horatius Flaccus, Quintus. I. Main
cd. (SC)

NT 0037392   NjP

Tarantino, P. Conti.
See
Conti Tarantino, P.

Tarantino, Pellegrino.
Disoccupazione agricola e cantieri di
lavoro.   Avelino, Tip. Pergola, 1955.

NT 0037394   NNU

Tarantino, Salvatore J
Awareness: an introduction to a theory of consciousness, by
Salvatore J. Tarantino. ₍New York₎ c1945. 20 f. 29cm.

377581B. 1. Consciousness.
N. Y. P. L.   January 20, 1947

NT 0037395   NN

TARANTO, Bonaventura da.

See MORONE, Bonaventura, *1557 - 1621.*

DG975   Taranto, Consalvo di
F65T3   La Capitanata nell' ano 1848.   Deliceto,
Tip. Balestrieri, 1910.
85 p.

1. Foggia, Italy - Hist.

NT 0037397   CU MH

923.146   Taranto, Consalvo di
C284
III-D   L'infante di Spagna, Carlo III Borbone
in Italia prima della conquista del regno.
Napoli, Stab.-tip. N. Jovene, 1905.
109 p.   26 cm.

      Bibliography: p. [7-8]

        1. Carlos III, King of Spain, 1716-1788.
I. Title.

NT   0037398   NcD

PC   Taranto, Francesco.
1619   Vocabolario domestico italiano ad uso
.D6   de' giovani, ordinato per categorie da F.
T3   Taranto e C. Guacci. 2. ed.   Napoli,
1851   Stamperia del Vaglio, 1851.
       xxiii, [x], 568 [111] p.

       Bibliography: p. i-x[j].
       1. Italian language - Glossaries, vocabular-
ies, etc. 2. Italian language - Dictionaries.
I. Guacci, Carlo.   II. Title.

NT   0037399   DGU

---

457   Taranto, Francesco.
T17v   Vocabolario domestico italiano ad uso
de Giovani ...   Napoli, 1856.
     568p.
    By F. Taranto and Carlo Guacci.

NT   0037400   IU

Bonaparte
Collection TARANTO, FRANCESCO.
No.4872   Vocabolario domestico italiano ad uso de'gio-
vani, ordinato per categorie da F.Taranto e C.
Guacci. 3. edizione.   Napoli,Stamperia del
Vaglio,1856.
     xxxii,678p.   22½cm.

     "Libri da'quali si è tratto solamente quello
ch'è paruto acconcio a questo vocabolario":
p.[xxv]-xxix.

NT   0037401   ICN NcU IU DGU MH

     Taranto, Giuseppe
     Analisi degli indizi e della qualità
dei testimoni in materia criminale, per
l'avv. Giuseppe Taranto ... Palermo,
Lao, 1880.
     88, [1] p.   22½cm.
     Bibliographical footnotes.

NT   0037402   MH-L

TARANTO,Giuseppe.
     Del grado del delitto nella sua forza morale.
Palermo,Lao,1882.
     8°.

NT   0037403   MH-L

     Taranto, Giuseppe.
     Del tentativo punibile e sue relazioni colla
complicità nei reati.   Palermo, 1878.
     194 p.

NT   0037404   PU-L MH-L

TARANTO,Giuseppe.
     Delle persone necessarie nel giudizio penale.
Palermo,Stabilimento tipografico Lao,1882.

     pp.69+(1).   8°.

NT   0037405   MH-L

617.78   TARANTO, Isaac M   de
T171o   Les ostéomes de l'orbite.   Paris,
L. Boyer, 1901.
     275 p.

     Thèse - Paris. Faculté de medecine.
     Bibliography: p.[271]-275.

     1. Eye-sockets - Tumors.   I. Title.

NT   0037406   WaU DNLM

Taranto, Italy (City)   Associazione sportiva
       see
   Associazione sportiva Taranto.

Taranto, Italy (City)   Biblioteca comunale
     "Pietro Acclavio."
       Bibliografia: Su alcuni manoscritti ...
nella ... biblioteca
       see under   Drago, Ciro.

Z240   Taranto, Italy (City)   Biblioteca comunale
.R3412   "Pietro Acclavio."
   Reggio Emilia. Scuola di bibliografia italiana.
     Notazione bibliografica degli incunabuli conservati nelle
biblioteche comunali di Barletta, Corato, Foggia, Taranto.
Reggio d'Emilia, 1932.

Taranto, Italy (City)   Camera di commercio, industria e
     agricoltura
       see
   Taranto, Italy (Province)   Camera di commercio, in-
     dustria e agricoltura.

    Taranto, Italy (City)   Circolo di cultura
     see   Circolo di cultura, *Taranto.*

Taranto, Italy (City)   Comitato per le
     onoranze a Mario Costa.
   Portaci, Niccolò Tommaso, 1872-   *comp.*
     ... Mario Costa, note di vita e d'arte a cura di Nicc. Tomm.
Portaci. Taranto, A. Cressati, 1934.

Taranto, Italy (City)   Galleria dell'ente provinciale
     del turismo.
     Cinquanta pittori contemporanei, con pref.
di R. Carrieri.   [Taranto, 1936]
     1 v.   illus.
     At head of cover-title: Galleria d'arte Taras.

NT   0037413   MH-FA

NK4640   Taranto, Italy (City)   Museo nazionale.
.C6 I 7
fasc. 15,   **Drago, Ciro.**
etc.   R. Museo nazionale di Taranto.   Roma, Libreria dello
fol.   Stato, 1940-

     Taranto, Italy (City)   Museo nazionale

       I Museo nazionale di Taranto ...
        see under   Quagliati, Quintino.

     Taranto, Italy.   Museo nationale

     Taranto museo nazionale.   [Taranto?] Ente provinciale per
il turismo [19—]   43 p.   illus.   23cm.
    Cover title.
    Signed: Ciro Drago.

     — I. Art, Ancient—Collections—   Italy—Taranto. I. Drago, Ciro.

NT   0037416   NN

   Taranto, *Italy (Province)*
     ... Deliberazioni coi poteri del Consiglio provinciale adottate
dalla Commissione reale ... 1924–
Taranto [19
       v.   26-30[+cm].
     At head of title: Amministrazione provinciale di Taranto.
     The Commissione reale per l'amministrazione straordinaria della
"Provincia jonica", Nicola Mattei president, was installed in office on
Jan. 19, 1924.
     1. Taranto (Province)—Pol. & govt.   I. Taranto, Italy (Province)
Consiglio.   II. Italy.   Commissione reale per l'amministrazione della
provincia jonica.   III. Mattei, Nicola.   IV. Title.

                             CA 31-695 Unrev'd

     Library of Congress   J389.T3R1
                     [2]   352.045758

NT   0037417   DLC

   Taranto, Italy (Province)

   Faustini-Fasini, Eugenio, 1874-
     ... Nicola Fago "il Tarantino" e la sua famiglia (nuovi con-
tributi) Taranto, Fratelli Filippi, 1931.

   **Taranto, Italy (Province)   Camera di commercio, industria
     e agricoltura.**
     Indici delle produzioni agricole della provincia di Ta-
ranto.   [Taranto? 1948]
     36 p.   illus., maps.   31 cm.

       1. Agriculture—Italy—Taranto (Province)

     HD1975.T3T3   50-38327 rev

NT   0037419   DLC

     Taranto, Italy (Province)   Camera di commercio,
       industria e agricoltura.
       Rassegna economica.
         Title varies: 1949-   Bollettino
     mensile.

NT   0037420   DNAL

   Taranto, Italy (Province) Consiglio.

   Taranto, *Italy (Province)*
     ... Deliberazioni coi poteri del Consiglio provinciale adottate
dalla Commissione reale ... 1924–
Taranto [19

TARANTO, ITALY (PROVINCE). *Ente provinciale per il turismo.*
Martina Franca. [Taranto, 1953?] [18] p. illus. 22cm.

1. Martina Franca, Italy.   t. 1953.

NT 0037422   NN

Taranto, Italy (Province).   Ente provinciale
per il turismo.
Taranto, la città dei due mari. [Bari, 1953?]
39 p. illus. 23cm.

Cover-title: Taranto antica.
Additional illus. and map inserted.

1. Taranto, Italy—Descr.   t. 1953.

NT 0037423   NN

Taranto; bollettino mensile
see   Taranto, Camera di commercio,
industria e agricoltura.
Rassegna economica.

Tarantola, Clemente.
Industrie agrarie, con 183 figure nel testo.
Introduzione del Ettore Garino-Canina. [Torino
Unione Tipografico-Editrice Torinese [1954]
972 p.

At head of title: C.Tarantola, C.Campisi, E.
Bottini, F.Emanuele.
CONTENTS—pt.1. Enologia (C.Tarantola) – pt.2
Industira olearia (C.Campisi) – pt.3. Industria
casearia (E.Bottini) – pt.4. Conserve alimentari
di origine vegetale (F.Emanuele)

NT 0037425   InLP DNAL

Tarantola, Gaetano
Praktische darstellung der mailandischen
steuerregulirung im achtzehnten jahrhundert
begrundet...Aus dem italienischen. Jena.
Croker, 1821.

32 p.

NT 0037426   MiU

---

q630.945 Tarantola, Gaetano.
T17s   Il sistema pratico del censimento prediale
milanese instituito nel secolo XVIII …   Milano
Tipografia di G. G. Destefanis, 1816.
[127?]p. incl.tables(part double) 2 fold.maps,
fold.plan.

1. Agriculture--Stat.   2. Agriculture--Milan
(Province)

NT 0037427   IU

La Tarantola
see under   Albergati-Capacelli, Francesco,
Marchese, 1728-1804.

Tarantous, Henry A., 1889—

Swingle, Calvin Franklin, 1846—   FOR OTHER EDITIONS
SEE MAIN ENTRY
Automobile catechism and repair manual; a series of
questions and answers covering the construction, care,
and operation of automobiles, also complete instructions
for locating troubles and making adjustments and re-
pairs of all kinds. Prepared expressly for owners, chauf-
feurs, garage men and automobile machinists, by Calvin
F. Swingle … and H. A. Tarantous … Chicago, F. J.
Drake & co. [*1916]

TL151   Tarantous, Henry A., 1889—
.B65
Bonilla, Antonio.
Guía del automovilista hondureño. Abarca el cuidado y
operación del automóvil. También da las instrucciones para
localizar las molestias y hacer las correspondientes repara-
ciones. Por el ingeniero mecánico Antonio Bonilla … [Te-
gucigalpa, Talleres tipográficos nacionales, 1941]

Tarantous, Henry A. 1889-
A handy manual for the motorist. N.Y.

127 p.

NT 0037431   OC1

Tarantov, S   N
Влияние методов прессования на структуру и механи-
ческие свойства прутков дуралюмина. Под ред. И. С.
Виштынецкого и С. М. Воронова. Москва, Гос. изд-во
обор. лит-ры, 1940.
Microfilm copy. Negative.
Collation of the original as determined from the film: 99, [5] p.
illus.
Bibliography: p. [102]

1. Duralumin   I. Title

Title transliterated: Vliйanie metodov presso-
van[i]a na strukturu … duralиumina.

Microfilm TS-9   Mic 53-294

NT 0037432   DLC

Tarantová, Lydie.
Zrada sídlí v Bělehradě. Praha, Mladá fronta, 1952.
77 p. illus. 22 cm. (Otázky dneška, sv. 32)

1. Yugoslavia—Pol. & govt.—1945—   2. Tito, Josip Broz, Pres.
Yugoslavia, 1892—   I. Title.

DR370.T3   54-28982

NT 0037433   DLC

TARANTOVÁ, MARIE.
V. J. Tomášek… Praha, Orbis, 1946. 54 p. 18cm. (Kdo je.
14-15)

1. vyd.

1. Tomášek, Václav Jan, 1774-1850.

NT 0037434   NN ICN

TF650   Tarantowicz, Donat, joint author.
.K7
Krzemieniecki, Aleksander.
Mierniki eksploatacyjne w kolejnictwie. [Wyd. 1.] War-
szawa, Wydawn. Komunikacyjne, 1953.

Rare
book
coll.   The tarantula; or, The dance of fools.
PR4069   A satirical work. By the author of the
.B5   Rising sun. London, Printed by M. Allen
T3   for Holmes and Whitteron, 1809.
2v. fold. front. 18cm.

I. Title. II. Title: The dance of fools.

NT 0037436   NcU NcD CtY CSmH

The **Tarantula**; or, The dance of fools. A satirical
work … By the author of the "Rising sun," &c. …
London, J. F. Hughes, 1809.
2 v. 17ᶜᵐ.
A satire upon fashionable life in 1809.
Variously attributed to Eaton Stannard Barrett, Edward Dubois and
Sir R. Peel. cf. Brit. mus. Catalogue, Dict. nat. biog., Notes & queries.

I. Barrett, Eaton Stannard, 1786-1820. II. Dubois, Edward, 1774-1850.
III. Peel, Sir Robert, 2d bart., 1788-1850.

18-8474

Library of Congress   PR3991.A7R5

NT 0037437   DLC

La tarantula; or, The spider king
see under   [Talfourd, Francis] 1828-1862.

Tarantule, a comic ballet.   Paris, 1840.

NT 0037439   PPL

Tăranu, Victor N., ed.
… Bibliografia economică română (Bibliographie économique
roumaine) repertoriu bibliografic al lucrărilor relative la
știinţele sociale economice, agricole și industriale (carţi și
articole din ziare și reviste)

București, Cartea românească,

MT6   Taranushchenko, Valentina Alekseevna.
.K975T5
Kudriävfsev, Aleksandr Vasil'evich, *writer on music.*
Теория музыки; основы гармонии, полифонии и форм
музыкальных произведения. Москва, Гос. изд-во куль-
турно-просветительной лит-ры, 195

Taranushenko, Stefan.
Мистецтво Слобожанщини XVII-XVIII в.в. Харків, 1928.
9 p. 36 plates. 27 cm.
At head of title: Музей українського мистецтва.

1. Art—Ukraine—Hist.   I. Title.
Title transliterated: Mystetstvo Slobozhan-
shchyny XVII-XVIII v.v.

N6995.U5T3   51-51370

NT 0037442   DLC

899.63
B456
Taranzano, Charles
… Sur les traces du père Matthieu Ricci;
tables analytiques des principaux ouvrages du
père Henri Bernard S. J. concernant l'Extrême-
Orient, avec une liste bibliographique et différentes cartes. Tientsin, Hautes études, 1939.
vi, 102 p., 1 l. maps, plan. 24ᶜᵐ.

At head of title: R. P. Charles Taranzano de
la Compagnie de Jésus.
"Sigles des références": 1 folded leaf at end.

"Ricci (P. Matthieu-, Li Ma-Teou, S. J.)":
p. 61-76.

1. Ricci, Matteo, 1552-1610.
2. Bernard, Henri   - Bibliography.
3. China - Bibliography.

NT 0037444   NNC MnU InU MH

Taranzano, Charles

Chinese Reference Collection Q123 T37

Vocabulaire dos sciences mathématiques, physiques et naturelles. Sien-Hsien, Impr. de la Mission Catholique, 1914-21.

2 v. illus. 26 cm.

Suppl. to v. 1. bound at beginning of v. 2.

Vol. 1. lacks common title.

Contents. - [I] Vocabulaire français-chinois des sciences mathématiques, physiques et naturelles, suivi d'un index anglais-français. Pref. du R.P. Wieger. Supplément au vocabulaire

français-chinois des sciences. Classifications. Tableaux synoptiques. - II. Vocabulaire chinois-français.

1. Science - Dictionaries - Polyglot. 2. Science - Dictionaries - French. 3. Science - Dictionaries - Chinese. I. Title.

NT 0037446   CtY

Taranzano, Charles

Q123 T3 1923 Physical Sciences Library

Vocabulaire des sciences: mathematiques, physiques et naturelles ... Sien-Hsien, Impr. de la Mission catholique, 1921-23 [v.1, 1923]

2v. 26cm.

Contents.--1. Vocabulaire français-chinois suivi d'un Index anglais-français.--2. Vocabulaire chinois-français.

----Supplement: Classifications. Tableaux synoptique. [n.p., n.d.] 120p. incl. plates. 26cm.

Two fold. charts in pocket. Errata laid in.

NT 0037448   RPB NIC IaU

TARANZANO, Charles.

Vocabulaire des sciences mathematiques, physiques et naturelles. Sien-Hsien, Imp. de la Mission catholique, 1923-36.

2 vol. 25 cm.

Vol. II: "2e éd."

Added title-pages in Chinese.

Contents: 1. Vocabulaire français-chinois, suivi d'un index anglais-français.-11. Vocabulaire chinois-français.

Supplément au Vocabulaire français-chinois des sciences; classifications, tableaux synaptiques. Sien-Hsien, Imp. de la Mission catholique, 1920.

25 cm. Illustr.

2 folded plates in pocket at end.

Chinese title-page on verso of English title-page.

Supplément: Radioélectricité par Marcel Lichtenberger. Sien- Hsien, Imp. de la Mission catholique, 1938.

25 cm. pp.(4),36.

Title-page in Chinese on verso of English title-page.

Half-title: Vocabulaire, des principales expressions usitées en radioélectricité.

NT 0037451   MH-HY

Taranzano, Charles.

Vocabulaire des sciences mathématiques, physiques et naturelles. Sien-Hsien, Impr. de la Mission catholique, 1936-

v. illus. 26 cm.

Contents. — 1. Vocabulaire français-chinois, suivi d'un index anglais-français. 3. éd.

1. Science—Dictionaries—Polyglot. 2. French language—Dictionaries—Chinese. 3. English language—Dictionaries—French. I. Title.

Q123.T3   62-56380

NT 0037452   DLC WaU NIC

Gest 8018 .895

Taranzano, Charles.

Vocabulaire français-chinois de sciences mathématiques, physiques et naturelles, suivi d'un index anglais-français. Préface du R.P. Wieger. Sien-hsien, Impr. de la mission catholique, 1914.

455,19 p. illus. 25 cm.

Added t.-p. in Chinese.

NT 0037453   NjP CU

Taranzano, Charles.

...Vocabulaire français-chinois, suivi d'un index anglais-français. Sien-Hsien, Impr. de la Mission catholique, 1923. xi, 950 p. 25cm. (His: Vocabulaire des sciences mathematiques, physiques et naturelles. Tome 1.)

—— Supplément au Vocabulaire français-chinois des siences. Classifications. Tableaux synoptiques. Sien-Hsien, Impr. de la Mission catholique, 1923. 120* p. illus. 25cm. (His: Vocabulaire des sciences mathematiques, physiques et naturelles. Tome 1.)

294750-1B.   1. Science—Diction-   aries, French-Chinese.   N. Y. P. L.   March 13, 1945

NT 0037454   NN

Tarao, Hanso, tr.

Okamoto, Kidō, 1872-

The mask-maker, a drama in three acts, by Kido Okamoto; adapted and prepared for stage production by Zoë Kincaid from the translation of Hanso Tarao ... New York, S. French; London, S. French, ltd., *1928.

Tarao, Tadarō.

(Chishima tanken jikki)

千島探檢實紀 / 多羅尾忠郎著. — [大阪]：松雲堂：發賣元　鹿田書店, 明治26 [1893]

2, 6, 121 p., [9] leaves of plates : ill. (5 fold.) ; 23 cm.

気象觀測表　明治24年12月 – 明治25年9月 [5 fold. leaves] inserted.

1. Kuril Islands—Description and travel.   2. Kuril Islands—Natural history.   3. Tarao, Tadarō.   I. Title.

DS895.3.K86T37 1893   77-813118

NT 0037456   DLC

Taroré, Moussa

see **Travélé, Moussa.**

Tarapaca, pseud.

see

Young, Walter H.

Tarapacá, *Chile (Province)*

Peru and Chile, the question of Tarapaca. Memorial address to President Harding. Washington, D. C., 1922.

cover-title, 65 p. map. 21½cm.

1. Tacna-Arica question.   I. Title.

Library of Congress   F3097.3.T5   22-13939

—— Copy 2.

NT 0037459   DLC NIC Or

Chile Ove70 T4 +A22

Tarapacá, Chile (Province) Concejo Departamental.

Memoria. Iquique, Chile, Impr. de El Comercio de Modesto Molina.

27cm.

NT 0037460   CtY

Tarapacá, Chile (Province) Concejo departamental.

Reglamento interior del concejo departamental de la provincia litoral de Tarapaca. Iquique, "El Comercio", 1876.

39 p. D. [In, Miscelaneas, V. 23]

NT 0037461   NcD

338.2764 T1764a LATIN AMERICA

Tarapacá, Chile (Province). Delegación Fiscal de Salitreras.

Avaluos y registros de cateos de las salitreras fiscales de Tarapacá. Tercer grupo. Inquique, Establecimiento Tip. de R. Bini, 1894.

xvi, 47 p. 1 col., fold. map. 22cm.

1. Saltpeter, Chile. I. Title.

NT 0037462   FU

Tarapacá, *Chile (Province) Delegación fiscal de salitreras y guaneras.*

Avaluos y rejistros de cateos de los terrenos salitrales del estado en Tarapacá. Iquique, Tip. y lit., R. Bini.

v. tables (partly fold.) fold. charts. 25½cm.

1. Saltpeter, Chile.

CA 8-507 Unrev'd

Library of Congress   TN911.T3

NT 0037463   DLC

Tarapada Basu

see

Basu, Tarapada.

Tarapada Bhattacharyya

see

Bhattacharyya, Tarapada

Tarapada Chowdhury

see **Chowdhury, Tarapada.**

Tārāpada Vandyopādhyāya

see

Banerji, Tarapada.

Tārāpade Dāsa Gupta

see

Das Gupta, Tarapada.

Tarapani (Anna). *Beiträge zur physiologisch-
pathologischen Wirkung und therapeutischen
Anwendung der Radiumstrahlen. 37 pp. 8°.
Zürich. A. Schereschewsky, 1910.

NT 0037469　DNLM

Tarapani, Helena
　　Zur entwickelungsgeschichte des hyobranchialskel-
ettes,...
　　Inaug. diss.　　　Zurich, 1909
　　Bibl.

NT 0037470　ICRL

　　Tarapanoff, Edmund, 1898–
　　　Die statistik der konsumgenossenschaften ...
　　Würzburg, 1933.　　69 p.
　　Inaug. Diss. —Berlin, 1933.
　　Lebenslauf.
　　Bibliography.

NT 0037471　ICRL PU CtY

F3097　Los tarapaqueños en la Conferencia de Washington;
.3　　　exposición y memorial presentados al Presidente
.T24　　Harding y otros documentos relativos a la ges-
　　　tión de los tarapaqueños para sostener la
　　　nulidad del tratado de Ancón y la reincorpora-
　　　ción al Perú de los territorios detentados por
　　　Chile. Lima, Sanmartí, 1922.
　　　225p. 24cm. (Biblioteca del Mercurio peruano,
　　Serie B, v.2)

　　1. Tacna-Arica question. 2. Peru – Boundaries.

NT 0037472　PSt TNJ

　　Tarapha, Francisco
　　see **Tarafa, Francisco,** *fl.* 1550.

　　Taraphae, Francisci
　　　see Tarafa, Francisco, fl. 1550.

　　　　**Tarapore, J　　C　　** ed. & tr.
Frd84　　Pahlavi Andarz-Nāmak containing Chītak
T17　　　Andarz ī Pōryōtkaeshān; or, The selected ad-
　　　monitions of the Pōryōtkaeshān and five other
　　　Andarz texts. Transliteration and translation
　　　into English and Gujarati of the original Pah-
　　　lavi texts with an introd. by J. C. Tarapore.
　　　Bombay, Trustees of the Parsee Punchayet Funds
　　　and Properties, 1933.
　　　xxi, 94 p. 25 cm.
　　　At head of title: Printed from the Sir
Jamsetjee Jejeebhoy Translation Fund.

NT 0037475　CtY NNC CLU CU RPB IU

　　Tarapore, J　　C
　　　Vijarishn i Chatrang; or, The explanation of Chatrang,
and other texts. Transliteration and translations into English and Gujarati of the original Pahlavi texts with an
introd., by J. C. Tarapore. Bombay, Trustees of the Parsee
Punchayet Funds and Properties, 1932.
　　xiv, 41 p. 25 cm.
　　At head of title: Printed from the Sir Jamsetjee Jejeebhoy Translation Fund.

　　1. Pahlavi language—Texts.　　I. Title.

　PK6199.4.E1T3　　　　　　70-292698
　　　　　　　　　　　　　　　MARC

NT 0037476　DLC CLU CtY OCl

　Tarapore, Pheroze Kharsedji, 1879–
　　Prison reform in India, with a foreword by Bhulabhai
Desai. London, Oxford University Press [1936]
　　xx, 182 p. 20 cm.

　　1. Prisons—India. I. Title.

　HV9793.T37　　　　365.954　　　52-49666

NT 0037477　DLC MiU CU

　　Taraporevala, D. B., sons & co., Bombay.

People of Bombay; 86 pictures of Indian life & characters depicting Indian costumes, manners, customs, ceremonies, etc.
Bombay, D. B. Taraporevala sons & co. [n. d.]

DS421
.5
.P5

　　Taraporevala (D. B.) sons and company, Bombay.

Pictures of Indian life and characters. An album of reproductions from photographs and drawings, depicting the people
of India, their costumes, life, manners, habits, customs, etc.
Bombay, D. B. Taraporevala sons & co. [1920?]

　　Taraporevala's Indian literary review
　　　see The Indian literary review.

Taraporevala's up-to-date guide to Poona and environment,
with maps. [Poona? foreword 1934]
　　iii, 120 p. fold. map. 21 cm.
　　Cover title.
　　"The major portion of editorial responsibility was ... undertaken
... by M. R. Paranjpe."

　　1. Poona, India (City)—Descr.—Guide-books.　　I. Paranjpe,
Madhav Ramkrishna, ed.
　DS486.P6T35　　　　　　　60-59478

NT 0037481　DLC

295.5
T171

　　Taraporewala, Irach Jehangir Sorabji, 1884–
　　　Apologia del Parsismo.　Roma, A. Formíggini, 1928.
　　131 p. 17 cm.

　　1. Parsees.　I. Title.

NT 0037482　NNG CtY

1884-1956
Taraporewala, Irach Jehangir Sorabji, ed. and tr.
　　The divine songs of Zarathushtra
　　　see under Avesta. Yasna. Gathas.

Taraporewala, Irach Jehangir Sorabji, 1884–1956.
　　Elements of the science of language, by Irach Jehangir Sorabji Taraporewala ... [Calcutta] The University of Calcutta,
1932.
　　xxviii p., 1 l., 484 p. illus., fold. map, tables (part fold.) diagrs.
(part fold.)　22cm.
　　"List of authors and books quoted": p. [478]–481.

　　1. Language and languages.

　　　　　　　　　　　　　　　　　　　　33-34073
　Library of Congress　　　　P121.T3

　　　　　　　　　　　　[2]　　　　400

NT 0037484　DLC CtY NN

Taraporewala, Irach Jehangir Sorabji, 1884-1956.
　　The eternal pilgrim and the voice divine and
some hints on the higher life
　　　see under Jehangir Sorabji, 1857-1916.

Taraporewala, Irach Jehangir Sorabji, 1884-1956,
comp. & tr.
　　A few daily prayers from the Zarathoshti
scriptures
　　　see under Avesta. English. Selections.
1940.

Taraporewala, Irach Jehangir Sorabji, 1884-1956,
Gatha ahunavaiti
　　　see under Avesta. Yasna. Gathas.
1944 and later.

Taraporewala, Irach Jehangir Sorabji, 1884-
1956, ed. and tr.
　　The gathas of Zarathushtra
　　　see under Avesta. Yasna. Gathas.
1947.

Taraporewala, Irach Jehangir Sorabji, 1884-1956.

Munshi, Kanaiyalal Maneklal, 1887–
　　Gujarāta and its literature, a survey from the earliest times,
by Kanaiyalal M. Munshi ... with a foreword by Mahātmā
Gandhi. London, New York [etc.] Longmans, Green & co.,
ltd., 1935.

BC25
.V5

Taraporewala, Irach Jehangir Sorabji, 1884-1956.

Vidyabhusana, Satis Chandra, 1870-1920.
　　A history of Indian logic (ancient, mediæval and modern
schools.) By Mahāmahopādhyāya Satis Chandra Vidyabhusana ... Calcutta, Calcutta university, 1921.

BL
1570
T37

Taraporewala, Irach Jehangir Sorabji, 1884-1956.
　　The religion of Zarathushtra. Adyar, Theo-
sophical Publishing House, 1926.
　　ix, 180 p.

　　1. Zoroastrianism　I. Title.

NT 0037491　WaU MH CtY OCl OBlC

Taraporewala, Irach Jehangir Sorabji,
1884-1956, ed. and tr.
　　Selections from Avesta and Old Persian
　　　see under Avesta. Selections. 1922.

Taraporewala, Irach Jehangir Sorabji, 1884–　　ed.
　　Selections from classical Gujarati literature ... edited by
Irach Jehangir Sorabji Taraporewala ... Calcutta, The University of Calcutta, 1924-36.
　　3 v. 24½cm.

　　CONTENTS.—I. Fifteenth century.—II. Sixteenth and seventeenth centuries.—III. Seventeenth, eighteenth and nineteenth centuries.

　　1. Gujarati literature.　I. Calcutta. University.

　　　　　　　　　　　　　　　　　　　　43-36329
　Library of Congress　　　　PK1855.T3

NT 0037493　DLC OCl MU CU

Taraporewala, Irach Jehangir Sorabji, 1884–   *ed.*
Selections from classical Gujarati literature ... edited by Irach Jehangir Sorabji Taraporewala ...   Calcutta, The University of Calcutta, 1924–36.
3 v. 24½ᵐ.
CONTENTS.—I. Fifteenth century.—II. Sixteenth and seventeenth centuries.—III. Seventeenth, eighteenth and nineteenth centuries.

1. Gujarati literature. I. Calcutta. University.
43–36329
Library of Congress   PK1855.T3

NT 0037493   DLC OC1 MU CU

Tarapur, J   C
        see Tarapore, J   C

Tārāpūrvālā, Ïrach Jahāngïr Sorābjï
        see
Taraporewala, Irach Jehangir Sorabji, 1884– 1956.

¡**Tarapygin, Fedor Andreevich**¡
Краткій историческій очеркъ пятидесятилѣтней дѣятельности Пріюта принца Петра Георгіевича Ольденбургскаго, 1846–1896 г. С.-Петербургъ, Тип. П. П. Сойкина, 1896.
v, 420, 129 p. plates, fold. plans, fold. tables. 25 cm.
Preface signed: Θ. А. Тарапыгинъ.

1. Leningrad. Priิût prin£a Petra Georgievicha Ol'denburgskogo.
Title transliterated: Kratkii istoricheskii ocherk p£atidesûatilⅰⅇtnei dⅰⅇûatel'nosti Priiûta.

HV783.L4T3   21–4628 rev

NT 0037496   DLC

Taraqqī, Muḥammad ʿAlī.
فرهنگ خیام عربی و فارسی، شامل ۳۰ هزار واژه مستعمل از عربی، فارسی، ترکی، اروپائی، با ترجمه صحیح فارسی. تألیف م. ع. ت. چاپ ۱. ¡تهران، کتابفروشی خیام،
¡1951 or 2¡ 1330
¡8¡, 529 p. 15 cm.
Bibliography: 3d prelim. page.
1. Arabic language—Dictionaries—Persian. I. Title.
Title romanized: Farhang-i Khayyām-i ʿArabī va Fārsī.

PK6381.A7T3 1951   79–222571

NT 0037497   DLC

Taraqqī, Muḥammad ʿAlī.
فرهنگ خیام فرانسه ـ فارسی.
Petit dictionnair¡e¡ Khayyam français-persan.
شامل ۳۵ هزار واژه صحیح و مصطلح فرانسه و واژه‌های علمی، ادبی، کلاسی. تألیف م. ع. ت. چاپ ۳. ¡تهران،
کتابخانه خیام، ¡1950 or 51¡ 1329
480 p. 14 cm.
1. French language—Dictionaries—Persian. I. Title.
II. Title: Petit dictionnaire Khayyam français-persan.
Title romanized: Farhang-i Khayyām-i Farānsah-Fārsī.

PK6381.F7T3 1950   74–222578

NT 0037498   DLC

Taraqqī, Muḥammad ʿAlī.
فرهنگ خیام فارسی ـ فرانسه.
Petit diction¡n¡aire Khayyamm ¡sic¡ persan-français.
شامل ۳۰ هزار واژه اقتصادی، ادبی، کلاسی. تألیف
م. ع. ت. چاپ ۳. ¡تهران، کتابفروشی خیام ¡1951 or 2¡ 1330
444 p. 15 cm.
1. Persian language—Dictionaries—French. I. Title.
II. Title: Petit dictionnaire Khayyam persan-français.
Title romanized: Farhang-i Khayyām-i Fārsī-Farānsah.

PK6381.F7T32 1951   74–222594

NT 0037499   DLC

Tarare, Jean Paul le
        see
Le Tarare, Jean Paul.

Kress Room   **Tarare.** Chambre consultative des arts et manufactures.
Mémoire sur la situation de la fabrique de Tarare et ses besoins, publié par la Chambre consultative des arts et manufactures de Tarare ... ¡Paris, Imprimerie de A.Coniam, 1829¡
8 p.incl. table. 22.5 cm.

Caption title.
Signed: Auguste Caquet, Alexandre Simonet, Varinay jeune ¡and others¡

NT 0037501   MH–BA

Tarare, an opera, in five acts ...
        see under ¡Salieri, Antonio¡ 1750–1825.

Tararua. no. 1–
June 1947–
¡Wellington, N. Z.¡
v. illus., maps. 21 cm.
Annual magazine of the Tararua Tramping Club.

1. Mountaineering—Yearbooks. I. Tararua Tramping Club, Wellington, N. Z.
G505.T32   796.52058   51–16813

NT 0037503   DLC NN

TARARUA Tramper.
Wellington, N. Z.
v.21–32, 1948–1960

NT 0037504   NhD

G505 .T32   **Tararua Tramping Club, Wellington, N. Z.**
Tararua. no. 1–
June 1947–
¡Wellington, N. Z.¡

Tararua tramping club, Wellington, N. Z.
Safe climbing; published by the Tararua tramping club...with the assistance of the Physical welfare branch of the Department of internal affairs. Edited by L. D. Bridge. ¡Wellington¡ 1947.
30 p. illus. 18cm.
"Bibliography," 1 page following p. 30.

1. Mountaineering. I. Bridge, L. D., ed. II. New Zealand. Internal affairs department. Physical welfare branch.
N. Y. P. L.   December 16, 1949

NT 0037506   NN

Tararua Tramping Club, *Wellington, N. Z.*
Tararua story; pub. in commemoration of the silver jubilee of the Tararua Tramping Club, 1919–1944; ed. by B. D. A. Greig. ¡2d ed.¡ Wellington, 1946.
108 p. illus., ports., fold. map. 25 cm.

1. New Zealand—Descr. & trav. I. Greig, Bernard David Arthur, ed. II. Title.
G505.T3 1946   796.52062931   47–28944*

NT 0037507   DLC NN

Tararyko, Petr Mikhaĭlovich.
Экономика, организация и планирование угольной промышленности; сборник примеров и задач. Утверждено в качестве учеб. пособия для учащихся горных техникумов. Рекомендовано в качестве учеб. пособия для техн. и специальных горнотехн. училищ. Москва, Углетехиздат, 1955.
127 p. diagrs. 23 cm.
Bibliography: p. ¡126¡
1. Coal mines and mining—Accounting. 2. Coal mines and mining—Russia. I. Title.
Title transliterated: Ekonomika, organizatsiíâ i planirovanie ugol'noĭ promyshlennosti.

HF5686.M6T3   56–37839

NT 0037508   DLC

Taras, Mrs. John
        see Stahl, Helene J., ¡ʺMrs. John Tarasʺ,¡ 1907–

Taras, Richard: Die Entwicklung der Besteuerung des Verbrauchs von Tabak und Tabakerzeugnissen im deutschen Reiche vom Jahr 1906 bis zur Gegenwart. ¡Maschinenschrift.¡ 186 S. m. Taf. 4°. — Auszug: ¡Rostock 1922: Winterberg.¡ 2 Bl. 8°
Rostock, Phil. Diss. v. 15. März 1922 ¡1924¡   ¡U 24.8680

NT 0037510   ICRL

Taras, rivista di demografia statistica e storia.
FOR OTHER EDITIONS SEE MAIN ENTRY *comp.*
Portacci, Niccolò Tommaso, 1872–
... Mario Costa, note di vita e d'arte a cura di Nicc. Tomm. Portacci. Taranto, A. Cressati, 1934.

Taras Schewtschenko, der ukrainische Nationaldichter (1814–1861)
        see under Meyer, Karl Heinrich, 1890–

891.79 855 BN31   **Taras Ševčenko,** 1814–1861; výstava o životě a díle: Zrcadlový sál Klementina, březen 1951. ¡Autoři: Zdeněk Nejedlý i Julius Dolanský. Praha: Svaz československo-sovětského přátelství, 1951.
1v.(unpaged) 21cm.

¡. Shevchenko, Taras, 1814–1861. I. Nejedlý, Zdeněk, 1878–1962. II. Dolanský, Julius.

NT 0037513   IU

Tārāśaṅkar Bandyopādhyāy
        see
Banerjee, Tarasankar, 1898– 1971.

Tarasankar Banerjee
        see
Banerjee, Tarasankar, 1898–1971.

Tārāśaṅkara Bandopādhyāẏa
        see
Banerjee, Tarasankar, 1898– 1971.

Tarasca de los ladrones y prision de medio rey por las declaraciones de los ajusticiados, ó sea segunda parte del papel titulado:
Mientras mas hay comiciones &c. [Colophon:] *Mexico——Imprenta de la calle de la Joya núm. 10, à cargo del ciudadano Mariano Malagon, año de 1831. 8vo, pp. 8.*   Y. 94380
Caption title. Information supplied by Anne S. Pratt.

NT 0037517   CtY

La tarasca de Parto en el Meson del Infierno y
dias de fiesta por la noche
see under   Santos, Francisco, fl. 1663.

TARASCAN and Aztec calendars.

18 pp. 8vo.
The original is in the Bibliotheque National.
Reproduced by W.E.Gates.

NT 0037519   MH-P

Los tarascas de Madrid y Tribvnal espantoso
see under   Santos, Francisco, fl. 1663.

PQ   Taraschi, Giustino
4843   'Mmiez' 'a via. Napoli, G. Starace, 1907.
.A6   92 p.
M55

1. Italian language - Dialects - Naples
I. Title.

NT 0037521   DGU

Taraschi, Nicola
... Dei libretti di colonia; studio
sugli art. 1662 e 1663 del Codice
civile. Con riproduzione in appendice del libretto colonico del senatore Devincenzi. Roma, Uniòne cooperativa editrice, 1893.
2 p.l., ₍3₎-62 p. 22½cm.
Bibliographical footnotes.

NT 0037522   MH-L

Taraschi, Tito Manlio.
... La bancarotta; appunti sul Codice di commercio e sul
progetto di riforma (art. 855–867 Codice di commercio, art.
931–956 del progetto per il nuovo Codice di commercio) Napoli, E. de Simone ₍1929₎
277, ₍1₎ p. 1 l. 22ᶜᵐ.

1. Bankruptcy—Italy.   I. Title.
                                                    35–23678
Library of Congress   ₍2₎   [347.7] 332.750945

NT 0037523   DLC

Taraschi, Tito Manlio, ed.

Italy. *Laws, statutes, etc.*
... Il Codice penale commentato ...
Como, E. Cavalleri, 1934–

Taraschi, Tito Manlio.
... La Libia italiana nella preparazione diplomatica e nella
conquista. Napoli, Eugenio de Simone ₍1932₎
3 p. l., ₍3₎-188, ₍2₎ p. 25ᶜᵐ.
Bibliographical foot-notes.

1. Libya (Italian N. Africa)—History.   2. Turco-Italian war, 1911–
1912.
                                                    A C 34–1120
Title from N. Y. Pub.   Libr. Printed by L. C.

NT 0037525   NN

4PQ   Tarasco, Fara P   de.
Peru-p5   Cantos, poemas, odas ... Lima, 1941.
124 p.

NT 0037526   DLC-P4

W 4   TARASCO CAMINO, Severino
M61   Informe sanitario de la población de
1952   Agua Dulce, municipio de Papantla,
Veracruz, y tratamiento de la hiper-
trofia congénita del píloro. México,
Ortega, 1952.
52 p.
Tesis - Univ. de México.
1. Public health - Mexico - Veracruz
(State)

NT 0037527   DNLM

Tarascon, Louis Anastasius, *b. 1759.*

Considerations, on some of the matters to be acted on, or
worth acting on, at the next session of the General assembly of Kentucky. First, the sphere of powers of
the judiciary. Second, the ways and means by which
the people may extricate themselves from difficulties
and raise to happiness ... Louisville, Printed by A. G.
Hodges and co., 1824.

NT 0037529   InU CSmH

Lilly   TARASCON, LOUIS ANASTASIUS, b.1759
Library   An exposition of some of the reasons
why measures should be taken for the construction of a canal round the falls of
the river Ohio; for the location of the
western armory, near to it ... Louisville,
Printed for the author, 1824.

7 p.   8vo

Author's presentation copy.
Sabin: 94382.
Disbound.

NT 0037530   DNA CSmH

Tarascon, Louis Anastasius, *b. 1759.*
Lewis A. Tarascon, of Shippingport, Ky.
To the people of the United States, on the
propriety of establishing a waggon road, from
the River Missouri to the River Columbia, of
the Pacific Ocean. [Louisville ? Ky. 1824.]
24 x 24 cm. Broadside. Text in 3 cols.

NT 0037531   DLC PPiU ICU CtY NjR

Tarascon, Louis Anastasius, *b. 1759.*
Louis Anastasius Tarascon, to his fellow citizens of the
United States of America; and, through their medium, to all
his other fellow human beings on earth, not anywhere else!!
New York, H. D. Robinson, 1837. ₍Tarrytown, N. Y., Re-
printed, W. Abbatt, 1929₎
(*In* The Magazine of history with notes and queries. Tarrytown,
N. Y., 1929. 26¼ᶜᵐ. Extra number. no. 148 (v. 37, no. 4) p. ₍5₎–42)
Proposing to establish a cooperative settlement, called Startpoint,
on the upper Mississippi.

1. Communism.
                                                    29–16259
Library of Congress   E173.M24 no. 148

Tarascon, Louis Anastasius, *b. 1759.*
L. A. Tarascon, to his friends &c. ... Louisville, 1836.
14 p. 14½ᶜᵐ.

1. Communism.   I. Title.
                                                    CA 18–1677 Unrev'd
Library of Congress   HX654.T3

NT 0037532   DLC NN

Tarascon, Louis Anastasius, *b. 1759.*
L. A. Tarascon, to his friends, &c. &c. &c. Louisville, 1836.
₍Tarrytown, N. Y., Reprinted, W. Abbatt, 1929₎
(*In* The Magazine of history with notes and queries. Tarrytown,
N. Y., 1929. 26¼ᶜᵐ. Extra number. no. 148 (v. 37, no. 4) p. ₍43₎–68)
"First edition printed at Louisville, Ky., in November, 1836. The
second at New York, in September, 1837."—p. ₍45₎ In the present reprint
the t.-p. agrees with the 1st edition, but the text differs slightly.
Proposing to establish a cooperative settlement, called Startpoint,
on the upper Mississippi.

1. Communism.
                                                    29–16258
Library of Congress   E173.M24 no. 148

NT 0037533   DLC OCl MiU

MICD   Tarascon, Louis Anastasius, b. 1759.
335.1   L. A. Tarascon, to his friends &c. ...
Louisville, 1836.
14 p. (Kentucky culture series, 213)
Microcard
#Communism.
L. A. Tarascon, to his friends &c.
S Kentucky culture series. no. 213.

NT 0037534   LU

SPECIAL COLLECTIONS
B974.3
T171
Tarascon, Louis Anastasius, b. 1759.
... Petition of Lewis A. Tarascon, (and
others,) praying the opening of a wagon road,
from the river Missouri, north of the river
Kansas, to the river Columbia. December 13,
1824. Printed by order of the Senate of the
United States. Washington, Printed by Gales
& Seaton, 1824.
12 p. 22cm. (18th Cong., 2d sess. Senate.
₍Doc.₎ 2)

NT 0037535   NNC CaBVaU CaBViPA ICN PPL

₍Tarascon, Louis Anastasius₎ b. 1759.
Raisonie, ou Douce demeure, sweet home de la raison:
établissement le premier de son genre à être formé sur
un beau champ agricole à portée aisée des grandes villes
Philadelphie et New York ... pour l'éducation rationelle,
conséquemment démocratiquement républicaine, de tous
les pauvres orphelins, orphelines et autres enfants, et
pour moyens d'asile, soulagement, instruction et bonheur
de tous les êtres humains malheureux, mais honnêtes ...
New York, Impr. de J. F. Curcy, 1839.
24 (i. e. 42) p., 1 l. 21ᶜᵐ.
Signed: L. A. Tarascon, et autres philanthropes.
1. Communism.   I. Title.
                                                    18–22008
Library of Congress   HX654.T4

NT 0037536   DLC NN CtY

[Tarascon, Louis Anastasius] b. 1759
Republican education, and gradual western
march, or enlightened, laborious, virtuous,
and happy generations, from all the present
and future United States and territories of
North America, through their Rocky
Mountains to their north-west coasts on the
Pacific Ocean ... Louisville, Ky., Printed by
S. Penn, jr., 1836.
24, ₍23₎ p. 20cm.
A project for the settlement of the West
by a series of Utopian communities.

Blank forms for subscriptions: [23]p. at
end.
Pub., with additional material (St. Louis,
1837) with title: Louis Anastasius Tarascon,
to his fellow citizens ...

NT 0037538   CtY

Tarascon, *France (Bouches-du-Rhône)*
Inventaire-sommaire des archives communales antérieures à 1790. ₍n. p., n. d.₎
₍101₎ p. 31 cm. (Collection des inventaires-sommaires des archives communales antérieures à 1790)
At head of title: Département des Bouches-du-Rhône. Ville de Tarascon.
Caption title.
Running title: Archives de la ville de Tarascon.
Binder's title: Inventaire des archives communales, Tarascon (Bouches du Rhône)
Prepared by Paul Meyer. Cf. Bibliothèque de l'École des chartes, 6th ser., v. 1, p. 65–70.
1. Tarascon, France (Bouches-du-Rhône)—History—Sources—Bibliography.   I. Title.   II. Title: Archives de la ville de Tarascon.   III. Title: Inventaire des   archives communales, Tarascon.

CD1217.T3A5   72–212247

NT   0037539   DLC

Tarascon, *France (Bouches des Rhône) Conseil municipal*
Canal de Bouc. Jonction de ce canal à celui du Languedoc, en le prolongeant jusqu'à Tarascon, en face de la prise d'eau du bassin de Beaucaire. Délibération du Conseil municipal de la ville de Tarascon, (Bouches-du-Rhône) en sa session de mai de mil-huit-cent-vingt-deux ... ₍Tarascon, Imprimerie d'É.Aubanel, 1822?₎
10 p. 24.5 x 19.5 cm.
Caption title.
Bound with: À leurs seigneuries les membres de la Chambre de   pairs [1825?]

1.Bouc, Canal de 2.Languedoc, Canal du I.Title.

NT   0037541   MH–BA NjR

Tarascon, France (Bouches-des-Rhône) Église de Sainte-Marthe.
Monumens de l'église de Saint-Marthe à Tarascon ...
see under title

Tarascon, France. Laws, statutes, etc.
Les coutumes de Tarascon
see under   Bondurand, Édouard Bligny, 1845–   ed.

Tarascon-sur-Rhône, *France*
see   Tarascon, *France (Bouches-du-Rhône)*

Tarascon, Berthoud and co., *firm, merchants, Philadelphia.*
An address to the citizens of Philadelphia, on the great advantages which arise from the trade of the western country to the state of Pennsylvania at large, and to the city of Philadelphia in particular ... By Messrs. Tarascon junr., James Berthoud and co. Philadelphia, Printed for the addressers, 1806.
13 p. 20½ᵐ.

1. Ohio Valley—Comm.   5–22898†
Library of Congress   HE394.O4T2
——— Copy 2   ₍Duane pamphlets, v. 89, no. 8₎
——— Copy 3.   ₍Duane pamphlets, v. 93, no. 9₎

PP NN MWA
NT   0037545   DLC MsSM NN MiU–C CSt NN PHi OOxM NRCR

Tarascon, Berthoud and ·Company, *firm, merchants, Philadelphia.*
An address to the citizens of Philadelphia, on the great advantages which arise from the trade of the Western Country to the state of Pennsylvania at large, and to the city of Philadelphia in particular. On the danger of loosing those advantages, and on the means of saving them. By Messrs. Tarascon junr., James Berthoud and Co. [1st ed.] Philadelphia: Printed for the Addressers, 1806.
Microcard edition.
Copy owned by Thomas Jefferson.
Sabin 94381. Sowerby 3340.
1. Ohio Valley—Commerce. I. Title

NT   0037546   ViU

Tarascon sur les Alpes
see under   Daudet, Alphonse, 1840–1897.

Tarasenko, Ivan.
Ганнуся. Лівобережна поэма Івана Тарасенка. Золотоноша, Тип. П. Лепскаго и П. Вурмана, 1891.
148 p. 22 cm.

Title transliterated: Hannusi͡a.

PG3948.T23H3   65–67107

NT   0037548   DLC

Tarasenka, Petras.
Kovotojo mokymas. Kaunas, Vyr. štabo sp. ir švietimo sk. leidinys, 1929.
224 p. illus. 23 cm.

1. Military education.   I. Title.

U405.T3   59–58433 ‡

NT   0037549   DLC

Tarasenka, Petras.
... Lietuvos archeologijos medžiaga. Materialien für litauische archeologie. Kaunas, Švietimo ministerijos knygų leidimo komisijos leidinys, 1928.
358, xxxii p., 1 l. 24½ᵐ.
"Bibliografija": p. ₍270₎–311.
                        DK511.L21T3
——— Archeologinis Lietuvos žemilapis. Archäologische übersichtskarte von Litauen ... Kaunas, Švietimo ministerijos knygų leidimo komisijos leidinys, 1928.
cover-title, fold. map. 24½ᵐ.
1. Lithuania—Antiq.   I. Title.
                        32–25901
Library of Congress   DK511.L21T3 Map   913.475

NT   0037550   DLC PU

Tarasenko, Boris Dmitrievich.
... Эпизод; двадцать дней в контрразведке. ₍Ленинград₎ Ленинградское областное издательство, 1935.
85, ₍3₎ p. 21¼ᵐ.
At head of title: Борис Тарасенко.

1. Russia—Hist.—Revolution, 1917–   —Fiction.   I. Title.
Title transliterated: Ėpizod.
PG3476.T2E6   48–47542

NT   0037551   DLC

Tarasenko, M   P
Основные вопросы методики составления перспективных планов плодовых совхозов. На опыте составления плана совхоза "Агроном." Киев, Держ. вид-во колгоспної і радгоспної літ-ри УСРР, 1936.
59 p. 22 cm.
At head of title: Народный комиссариат земледелия УССР. Украинский научно-исследовательский институт плодово-ягодного хозяйства.
1. Agronom (Sovkhoz)   I. Title.
Title transliterated: Osnovnye voprosy metodiki sostavleniia perspektivnykh planov plodovykh sovkhozov.

SB354.6.R9T3   51–53724

NT   0037552   DLC

Tarasenko, Pavel Nikolaevich.
Какъ богатѣютъ на хуторахъ. С.-Петербургъ, Изд. князя Абамелекъ-Лазарева, 1913.
v, 54 p. 24 cm.

1. Agriculture—Economic aspects—Russia.   I. Title.
Title romanized: Kak bogatei͡ut na khutorakh.

HD1992.T28   77–245865

NT   0037553   DLC

HG289   **Tarasenko-Otreshkov, Narkis Ivanovich.**
.T19   De l'or et de l'argent; leur origine, quantité extraite dans toutes les countrées du monde connu, depuis les temps les plus reculés jusqu'en 1855; accumulation actuelle de ces métaux dans les principaux états, et leur rapport mutuel suivant leur poids et leur valeur. Tome premier·. Paris, Guilaumin, 1856.
349 p.
No more published?
1. Gold. 2. Silver.

NT   0037554   ICU DLC NN NNC CtY PU

Tarasenko-Otreshkov, Narkis Ivanovich.
Посѣщеніе въ Крыму армій союзниковъ и исчисленіе потерь въ людяхъ и деньгахъ, понесенныхъ Франціею, Англіею и Шемонтомъ въ нынѣшнюю войну ихъ противъ Россіи. Санктпетербургъ, Въ тип. Н. Греча, 1857.
1 v. (various pagings) 23 cm.
Bound with Anichkov, V. M. Военно-историческіе очерки Крымской экспедицій. С.-Петербургъ, 18

1. Crimean War, 1853–1856.   I. Title.
Title transliterated: Posi͡eshchenie v Krymu armii soi͡uznikov.
DK215.T32   59–46940

NT   0037555   DLC

Tarasenko-Otreshkov, Narkis Ivanovich.
(Zamětki v poězdku vo Franțíï, Severnui͡u Italii͡u, Bel'gii͡u i Gollandii͡u)
Замѣтки въ поѣздку во Францію, С. Италію, Бельгію и Голландію. Н. И. Тарасенко-Отрѣшковъ. Санктпетербургъ, Тип. М. Хана, 1871.
x, 508 p. 25 cm.

1. Europe—Description and travel—1800–1918.   I. Title.

D919.T18   73–216976

NT   0037556   DLC

Tarasenkov, Aleksei Terent'evich, 1813–1873.
Послѣдніе дни жизни Н. В. Гоголя. Санктпетербургъ, Въ Тип. Королева, 1857.
31 p. 26 cm.

1. Gogol', Nikolai Vasil'evich, 1809–1852.
Title transliterated: Posli͡ednie dni zhizni N. V. Gogoli͡a.
PG3335.T3 1857   53–55476 ‡

NT   0037557   DLC

Tarasenkov, Aleksei Terent'evich, 1813–1873.
Послѣдніе дни жизни Н. В. Гоголя; записки его современника. Изд. 2., доп. по рукописи. Москва, Скоропеч. А. А. Левенсонъ, 1902.
33 p. 27 cm.

1. Gogol', Nikolai Vasil'evich, 1809–1852.
Title transliterated: Posli͡ednie dni zhizni N. V. Gogoli͡a.
PG3335.T3 1902   53–55474 ‡

NT   0037558   DLC

Tarasenkov, An
Идеи и образы советской литературы. Москва, Советский писатель, 1949.
278 p. 21 cm.

1. Russian literature—20th cent.—Hist. & crit.
Title transliterated: Idei i obrazy sovetskoi literatury.
PG3021.T3   50–18296

NT   0037559   DLC

Tarasenkov, An
Микола Бажан; критико-биографический очерк. Москва, Советский писатель, 1950.
74, ₍2₎ p. port. 18 cm.
Bibliography: p. 73-₍75₎

Platonovych, 1904–
1. Bazhan Mykola 1903– *Title transliterated:* Mikola Bazhan.
PG3948.B329   51-36951

NT   0037560   DLC

Tarasenkov, An
О поэзии М. В. Исаковского. Москва, Знание, 1954.
38 p. 22 cm. (Всесоюзное общество по распространению политических и научных знаний. Серия 6, № 14)

1. Isakovskiĭ, Mikhail Vasil'evich, 1900–   I. Title.
Title transliterated: O poėzii M. V. Isakovskogo.
PG2991.V8   1954, no. 14   57-17677 ‡

NT   0037561   DLC CtY FMU CU

Tarasenkov, V   **P**
Охлаждение двигателей (автомобильных, тракторных, танковых) Москва, Воен. изд-во, 1955.
83 p. illus. 20 cm.

1. Gas and oil engines—Cooling.   I. Title.
Title transliterated: Okhlazhdenie dvigateleĭ.
TJ789.T3   56-32676

NT   0037562   DLC

Tarasenkov, V   **P**
Стахановские методы вождения трамвая. Москва, Изд-во Министерства коммунального хозяйства РСФСР, 1952.
22 p. 20 cm.
Microfilm SLAVIC ——— Microfilm copy (negative)
Made in 1956 by the Library of Congress.
Microfilm Slavic 736 AO
1. Street-railroads.   I. Title.
Title transliterated: Stakhanovskie metody vozhdeniîa tramvaîa.
TF707.T3   61-25020 ‡

NT   0037563   DLC

Tarasevich, Ivan IUlianovich, 1871–
Zum studium der mit dem thalamus opticus und nucleus lenticularis in zusammenhang stehenden faserzüge, von dr. Johann Tarasewitsch ... Mit tafel v und vi und 5 abbildungen im text.
(*In* Vienna. Universität. Neurologisches Institut. Arbeiten. Leipzig und Wien. 1902. 26ᶜᵐ. hft. IX, p. ₍251₎-273. illus., pl. v-vI)
"Literatur": p. 272-273.

1. Optic thalamus.   2. ₍Lenticular nucleus₎
A C 34-4442
Title from John Crerar   Libr. Printed by L. C.

NT   0037564   ICJ

Tarasevich, Lev Aleksandrovich, 1868-1927.
*Contagiosité syphilitique tardive; contagiosité tertiaire. Paris, 1897.
104 p., 1 l. 8°.
No. 444.

NT   0037565   DNLM

WCA   **TARASEVICH, Lev Aleksandrovich, 1868-*1927*.**
T177c   Contagiosité syphilitique tardive, con-
1897   tagiosité tertiaire. Paris, Steinheil, 1897.
    104 p.
    Issued also as thesis, Paris.

NT   0037566   DNLM

Tarasevich, Lev Aleksandrovich, 1868-*1927*.
Epidemics in Russia since 1914
see under   League of Nations. Secretariat.
Health Section.

RA421   *Tarasevich, Lev Aleksandrovich, 1868-1927, ed*
.M82
Moscow. Gosudarstvennyĭ nauchnyĭ institut narodnogo zdravookhraneniîa.
Государственный научный институт народного здравоохранения имени Пастера ("ГИНЗ") 1919–1924; организация, деятельность и научные труды. Под ред. Л. А. Тарасевича и В. А. Любарского. Москва, 1924.

Tarasevich, Lev Aleksandrovich, 1868-1927.
... Vaccinations antityphoïdiques dans l'armée russe, par M. le Dʳ L. A. Tarassévitch ... ₍Paris, L. Maretheux, imprimeur, 1916?₎
4 p. 22 cm.
Caption title.
At head of title: Extrait du Bulletin de l'Académie de médecine (Séance du 9 mai 1916)

NT   0037569   CSt-H

Law   **Tarasevičius, V.**

Lithuania. *Krašto Apsaugos Ministerija. Karo Mokslo Skyrius.*
Kariuomenės tiekimas, sanitarija ir veterinarija. Sistematizuotas rinkinys įsakymų, įstatymų ir taisyklių, išleistų kariuomenei iki 1922 m. sausio m. 1 d. Paruošė V. Augustauskas ir V. Tarasevičius. Kaunas, 1923.

Tarasevs'kyĭ, Pavlo, *comp.*
Das Geschlechtleben des ukrainischen Bauernvolkes, folkloristische Erhebungen aus der russischen Ukraina. Einleitung und Parallelennachweise von Volodymyr Hnatjuk, Vorwort und Erläuterungen von Friedrich S. Krauss. 1. T.: Dreihundertneunzehn Schwänke und novellenartiger ₍1₎ Erzählungen, die in der Gegend von Kupjansk und Šebekyno der Gouvernements Charkiv und Kursk gesammelt worden. Leipzig, Deutsche Verlagaktiengesellschaft, 1909.
xi, 457 p. 32 cm. (Beiwerke zum Studium der Anthropophyteia, 3. Bd.)

"Privatdruck ... Zahl: 186."
Part 2 published under title: Das Geschlechtleben des ukrainischen Bauernvolkes in Österreich-Ungarn; Folkloristische Erhebungen von Volodymyr Hnatjuk. 2. T. 1912.
Bibliography: p. xi.

1. Folk-lore, Ukrainian. 2. Erotic literature. 3. Ukrainian wit and humor.   I. Gnatîuk, Volodymyr, 1871-1926.   II. Krauss, Friedrich Salomo, 1859–   III. Title.   IV. Series.
GR203.U5T3   A C 38-1954 rev*
Illinois. Univ. Library
for Library of Congress   ₍r48d1₎†

NT   0037572   IU PPAN IaU CLSU OCl PU DLC

Tarasevs'kyĭ, Pavlo
Das geschlechtleben des ukrainischen Bauernvolkes; folkloristische Erhebungen aus der russischen Ukrainia. Einleitung und Parallelennachweise von Volodymyr Hnatjuk, Vorwort und Erläuterungen von F.S.Krauss. Leipzig, Deutsche verlagaktiengesellschaft, 1909-12
2 v. (Beiwerke zum Studium der Anthropophyteia, 3,5)
Teil 2 has the title: Das Geschlechtleben des ukrainischen Bauernvolkes in Österreich-Ungarn. Folkloristische Erhebungen von Votodymyr Hnatjuk"

NT   0037573   MH CtY

Tarashankar Bandyopadhyay
see
Banerjee, Tarasankar, 1898-1971.

Microfilm
Slavic
715   **Tarashchanskiĭ, E**   **G**
AC   Вакуумированный бетон в дорожном строительстве. Москва, Изд-во дорожно-техн. лит-ры, 1952.
Microfilm copy (negative) made in 1956 by the Library of Congress.
Collation of the original, as determined from the film: 62, ₍2₎ p. illus.
Errata slip inserted.
Bibliography: p. ₍63₎
technology
1. Roads, Concrete. 2. Vacuum.   I. Title.
Title transliterated: Vakuumirovannyĭ beton.
Mic 57-5323

NT   0037575   DLC

Tarashchanskiĭ, S   **M**
Теплосиловые установки американских электрических станций; по материалам заграничной командировки. Харьков, Гос. научно-техн. изд-во Украины, 1936.
204, ₍4₎ p. illus. 26 cm.
Errata slip inserted.
Bibliography: p. ₍207₎

1. Electric power-plants—U. S.
Title transliterated: Teplosilovye ustanovki amerikanskikh ėlektricheskikh stantsiĭ.
TK1223.T3   50-54204

NT   0037576   DLC

Tarasi, Battista.
Appalti e contratti; nozioni generali. Firenze, C. Cya, 1954.
99 p. 26 cm.

1. Contracts—Italy.   I. Title.
A 58-345
New York Univ.   Libraries HF1258
for Library of Congress   ₍8₎

NT   0037577   NNU

Tarasi, Battista.
...Elementi di statistica. 3a. edizione. ₍Firenze: S. a. stab. tip. già G. Civelli₎ 1937. 145 p. incl. tables. illus. (incl. charts.) 18½cm.
"Pubblicato a cura del Collegio nazionale degli ingegneri ferroviari italiani."
Bibliographies included.

1. Statistics—Methods.   I. Collegio nazionale degli ingegneri ferroviari italiani.
N. Y. P. L.   October 26, 1939

NT   0037578   NN

Tarasi, Battista.
Nozioni di legislazione ferroviaria ed ordinamento delle Ferrovie dello Stato. ₍3. ed. n. p.₎ Collegio nazionale degli ingegneri ferroviari italiani, 1941.
155 p. 24 cm.

1. Railroad law—Italy.   I. Title.
55-50418

NT   0037579   DLC

Tarasi, Battista.
... Nozioni generali di diritto. ₍Firenze₎ Collegio nazionale degli ingegneri ferroviari italiani, 1940.
198, ₍2₎ p. 24ᶜᵐ.
At head of title: B. Tarasi.

1. Law—Philosophy.   I. Collegio nazionale degli ingegneri ferroviari italiani.
45-22809

NT   0037580   DLC

BP
1213
H8
T2

Tarasievitch, John
Humility in the light of St. Thomas; thesis presented to the Faculty of Theology, Fribourg University, Switzerland, to obtain the degree of doctor in theology. [Fribourg 1935]

2 l., 310p. 25cm.

1. Humility. 2. Thomas Aquinas, Saint
– Humility.

NT 0037581 IMunS

Tarasiĭ, ieromonakh, d. 1904.
Переломъ въ древнерусскомъ богословіи. Варшава, Сvнодальная тип., 1927.

185 p. 20 cm.

1. Theology—Collected works—16th centruy. 2. Orthodox Eastern Church, Russian—Collected works. I. Title.
Title romanized : Perelom v drevnerusskom bogoslovii.

BX480.T37 1927   76–509625

NT 0037582 DLC

Tarasoff, Leo
see
Troyat, Henri, 1911–

Tarasov, pseud.
see Rusanov, Nikolaĭ Sergeevich, 1859–1939.

Tarasiĭ, Saint, Patriarch of Constantinople
see
Tarasius, Saint, Patriarch of Constantinople, d. 806.

Tarasius, Saint, Patriarch of Constantinople, d. 806.

In: Migne, J. P. Patrologiae cursus completus. Series graeca latine tantum editae, Paris, 1856–1867. 85 v.   t. 51.

NNUT NNC NN NIC RPB CaOTU
MB MH MH-AH MWelC MdBP MeB MiU MnU PHC PBMC OO OC
NT 0037586   DLC CSt CU CtHC CtY DCU ICN ICU IU InU PU

Tarasius, Saint, Patriarch of Constantinople, d. 806.
Scripta quae supersunt

In: Migne, J. P. Patrologiae cursus completus. Series graeca. Paris, 1857–1886. 165 v. t. 98.
BR60. M5

PBMC PU RP RPB CaOTU
NhD NNUT NNC NN NIC MdBP MH-AH NjNbS NjP NjPT OC OO
NT 0037587   DLC CU CtHC CtY DCU ICN ICU MB MH NjMD

Tarasov, A
(Lesnaia kooperatsiia i lesnye tresty)
Лесная кооперация и лесные тресты. Москва, 1922.

15 p. 24 cm.

At head of title: Всероссийский кооперативный лесной союз Всеколес. А. Тарасов.

1. Forestry societies—Russia. I. Title.

SD1.T18   73–216928

NT 0037588 DLC

Tarasov, A   A
... Уничтожай врага в рукопашной схватке. Москва, Военное издательство Народного комиссариата обороны Союза ССР, 1941.

38, [2] p. illus. 20ᵐ.

At head of title : Генерал-майор А. А. Тарасов ...

1. Fighting, Hand-to-hand.   I. Title.   *Title transliterated:*
Unichtozhaĭ vraga v rukopashnoĭ skhvatke.

                                              43–41219
Library of Congress   U167.5. H373

NT 0037589 DLC

D525
.N14

Tarasov, A. G., ed.
На борьбу с империализмом! Сборник материалов к десятилетию империалистической войны для библиотек, клубов и изб-читален. Составили О. Э. Вольценбург и А. Я. Виленкин, под ред. А. Г. Тарасова. Ленинград, Изд-во Книжного сектора Ленинградского ГубОНО, 1924.

Tarasov, Aleksandr Ivanovich, 1900–
(Anna iz derevni Grekhi)
Анна из деревни Грехи; повести и рассказы. Москва, Сов. писатель, 1937.

204 p. illus. 21 cm.

At head of title: А. Тарасов.
CONTENTS: Анна из деревни Грехи.—Отец.—В заповеднике.—Возвращение Ильи.—Подруги.

I. Title.

PG3476.T25A8   73–216662

NT 0037591 DLC

Tarasov, Aleksandr Ivanovich, 1900–
(Budni)
Будни; повесть. Москва, Федерация, 1929.

142 p. 17 cm.

At head of title: А. Тарасов.

I. Title.

PG3476.T25B8 1929   73–216771

NT 0037592 DLC

Tarasov, Aleksandr Ivanovich, 1900–
(Okhotnik Aver'ian)
Охотник Аверьян; повесть. Москва, Сов. писатель, 1941.

187 p. 17 cm.

At head of title: А. Тарасов.

I. Title.

PG3476.T25O4   73–215811

NT 0037593 DLC

Tarasov, Aleksandr Ivanovich, 1900–
Повести и рассказы. [Москва] Советский писатель, 1946.

375 p. 20 cm.

Title transliterated: Povesti i rasskazy.

PG3476.T25P6   52–66692 ‡

NT 0037594 DLC

HD4966
.R12R85

Tarasov, Aleksandr Pavlovich, joint author.

Lemtal', Genrikh Al'bertovich.
Оплата труда работников службы пути и сооружений; справочник. Под общей ред. Юрченко, И. Ф. Москва, Гос. трансп. жел-дор. изд-во, 1955.

Tarasov, Aleksei Vasil'evich.
Авангардная роль коммунистов совхоза. [Москва] Московский рабочий, 1954.

42 p. 20 cm. (Библиотечка сельского партработника)

—— Microfilm copy (negative)
Made in 1955 by the Library of Congress.

1. Kommunisticheskaia partiia Sovetskogo Soiuza—Party work.
2. State farms—Russia. I. Title.
                              Title transliterated: Avangardnaia
                              rol' kommunistov sovkhoza.

JN6598.K7T3   55–44334 ‡

NT 0037596 DLC

PG3337
.N4Z795

Tarasov, Anatoliĭ Fedorovich, comp.
О Некрасове. [Сборник. Ярославль, Кн. изд., 19

Tarasov, Anatoliĭ Vladimirovich.
Хоккей с шайбой. Москва, Физкультура и спорт, 1951.

179 p. illus. 20 cm. (В помощь общественному инструктору физической культуры)

1. Hockey.   I. Title.   *Title romanized:* Khokkeĭ s shaĭboĭ.

GV847.T33   53–28638 rev

NT 0037598 DLC

Tarasov, B. N.
see
Tarusov, Boris Nikolaevich.

Tarasov, Boris Afanas'evich.
Юность Чехословакии. [Москва] Молодая гвардия, 1955.

164 p. illus., ports. 20 cm.

1. Youth—Czechoslovak Republic.   I. Title.
                              Title transliterated: IUnost' Chekhoslovakii.

HQ799.C9T3   56–31011

NT 0037600 DLC

Tarasov, Dmitriĭ Klement'evich, 1792–1866.
(Imperator Aleksandr I)
Императоръ Александръ I : послѣдніе годы царствованія, болѣзнь, кончина и погребеніе / по личнымъ воспоминаніямъ лейбъ-хирурга Д. К. Тарасова. — Петроградъ : Изд. Т-ва А. С. Суворина, 1915.

xvi, 226 p. ; [7] leaves of plates ; 21 cm.

1. Alexander I, Emperor of Russia, 1777–1825.   I. Title.

DK192.T3 1915   74–236726

NT 0037601 DLC MH

Tarasov, Dmitriĭ Klement'evich, 1792–1866.
Записки почетнаго лейбъ-хирурга Д. К. Тарасова. (Воспоминанія моей жизни). 1792–1866. (Оттиски изъ журнала "Русская старина"). Санктпетербургъ, 1872.

1 p. l., 176 p. 23ᶜᵐ.

1. Alexander I, emperor of Russia, 1777–1825. 2. Russia—Hist.—Alexander I, 1801–1825. 3. Wylie, Sir James, bart., 1768–1854.

CA 15–1141 Unrev'd

~~Library of Congress~~ DK190.6.T

NT 0037602 DLC

Tarasov, Fedor Ivanovich.
Детекторные приемники и усилители. Рекомендовано в качестве пособия для радиоклубов и радиокружков. Москва, Гос. энерг. изд-во, 1952.

71 p. diagrs. 20 cm. (Массовая радиобиблиотека, вып. 66)
Includes bibliographies.

1. Radio—Receivers and reception. 2. Amplifiers, Vacuum-tube. I. Title. *Title transliterated:* Detektornye priemniki.

TK9956.T29 51–22375 rev

NT 0037603 DLC

Tarasov, Fedor Ivanovich.
Как построить выпрямитель. Москва, Гос. энерг. изд-во, 1949.

14 p. illus. 20 cm. (Массовая радиобиблиотека, вып. 13)

I. Radio—Rectifiers I. Title. *Title transliterated:* Kak postroit' vypriamitel'.

TK9956.T3 51–15314 rev

NT 0037604 DLC

Tarasov, Fedor Ivanovich.
Простые батарейные радиоприемники. Москва, Гос. энерг. изд-во, 1952.

31 p. illus. 20 cm. (Массовая радиобиблиотека, вып. 148)

1. Radio—Receivers and reception. 2. Storage batteries. 3. Radio—Amateurs' manuals. I. Title. *Title transliterated:* Prostye batareĭnye radiopriemniki.

TK6563.T3 54–18327

NT 0037605 DLC

Tarasov, Fedor Ivanovich.
Простые батарейные радиоприемники. 2. изд., доп. Москва, Гос. энерг. изд-во, 1955.

47, [1] p. illus. 20 cm. (Массовая радиобиблиотека, вып. 231)

1. Radio—Receivers and reception. 2. Storage batteries. 3. Radio—~~Amateurs' manuals.~~ I. Title. *Title transliterated:* Prostye batareĭnye radiopriemniki.

TK6563.T3 1955 56–38998

NT 0037606 DLC

TK9956 .G5

Tarasov, Fedor Ivanovich, jt. auth.

Ginzburg, Zinoviĭ Borisovich.
Самодельные детали для сельского радиоприемника [Москва] Московский рабочий, 1950.

Tarasov, Helen, 1915–
Who does pay the taxes? By Helen Tarasov. With an introduction by Jacob Marschak. New York, The Graduate faculty of political and social science, New school for social research, 1942.

xiii, 48 p., 1 l. incl. tables, diagr. 22½ᵐ.

On cover: Social research. Supplement IV.
A revision of the author's Who pays the taxes? *cf.* p. [1]–2.

1. Taxation—U. S. I. Social research. Supplement. II. Title.

43–1933

Library of Congress HJ2380.T3

[3] 336.2

OCU
NT 0037608 DLC MiU OrU OrCS PSt PU NcD CU ViU MH-BA

[Tarasov, Helen] 1915–
... Who pays the taxes? (Allocation of federal, state, and local taxes to consumer income brackets) ... Washington, U. S. Govt. print. off., 1940.

55 p. incl. tables, diagrs. 23 cm. ([U. S.] Temporary national economic committee. Investigation of concentration of economic power ... Monograph no. 3)

At head of title: 76th Congress } Senate committee print.
 3d session
Running title: Concentration of economic power.
"A study made under the auspices of the Department of commerce for the Temporary national economic committee, Seventy-sixth Congress, third session, pursuant to Public resolution no. 113 (Seventy-

fifth Congress), authorizing and directing a select committee to make a full and complete study and investigation with respect to the concentration of economic power in, and financial control over, production and distribution of goods and services."
By Helen Tarasov. *cf.* Acknowledgment.
Printed for the use of the Temporary national economic committee.
"Selective bibliography": p. 36–37.

1. Taxation—U. S. I. Title. II. Title: Allocation of federal, state, and local taxes to consumer income brackets.

HC106.3.A5127 no. 3 336.20973 40–29253

NT 0037610 DLC PPD PHC OC1 OO OU OrU WaU-L WaTU

[Tarasov, Helen] 1915–
... Who pays the taxes? (Allocation of federal, state, and local taxes to consumer income brackets) ... Washington, U. S. Govt. print. off., 1941.

vii, 55 p. incl. tables, diagrs. 23ᵐ. ([U. S.] Temporary national economic committee. Investigation of concentration of economic power ... Monograph no. 3)

At head of title: 76th Congress } Senate committee print.
 3d session
Running title: Concentration of economic power.
"A study made under the auspices of the Department of commerce for the Temporary national economic committee, Seventy-sixth Congress, third session, pursuant to Public resolution no. 113 (Seventy-fifth Con-

gress), authorizing and directing a select committee to make a full and complete study and investigation with respect to the concentration of economic power in, and financial control over, production and distribution of goods and services."
By Helen Tarasov. *cf.* Acknowledgment.
Printed for the use of the Temporary national economic committee.
"Selective bibliography": p. 36–37.

NT 0037612 MiU PPT OrPS

Tarasov, I A
Часовой график и хозрасчет в поточно-комплексной бригаде А. Н. Потапова. Москва, Гослесбумиздат, 1952.

23 p. illus. 23 cm.
At head of title: Министерство лесной промышленности СССР. И. А. Тарасов, Б. К. Рындин.

1. Lumbering—Russia. I. Ryndin, B. K., joint author. II. Title. *Title transliterated:* Chasovoĭ grafik i khozraschet.

SD538.T3 55–59803

NT 0037613 DLC

Tarasov, Ivan Petrovich.
Ленточные транспортёры. Под ред. и с дополенениями Е. Б. Виткуп. Киев, Гос. научно-техн. изд-во машиностроит. лит-ры, 1950.

166 p. illus. 23 cm.
Bibliography: p. [165]

1. Conveying machinery. I. Vitkup, E. B., ed. II. Title. *Title romanized:* Lentochnye transportery.

TJ1390.T3 50–33922 rev

NT 0037614 DLC

Tarasov, Ivan Trofimovich, 1849–
(Kratkiĭ ocherk nauki administrativnago prava)
Краткій очеркъ науки административнаго права : конспектъ лекцій / И. Т. Тарасова. — [S. l. : s. n.], 1888– ([Ярославль : Тип-лит. Г. Фалькъ)

v. ; 24 cm.

Includes bibliographical references.
CONTENTS: т. 1. Введеніе и общая часть.

1. Administrative law. 2. Administrative law—Russia. I. Title.

75–590313

NT 0037615 DLC

Tarasov, Ivan Trofimovich, 1849–
(Ocherk nauki finansovago prava)
Очеркъ науки финансоваго права : составленъ по лекціямъ, читаннымъ въ Демидовскомъ юридическомъ лицѣ, въ 1878–1881 акад. гг. / И. Тарасовъ. — Ярославль : Тип. Губ. правленія, 1883.

xii, 710 p. ; 24 cm.

Includes bibliographies.
CONTENTS: Введеніе.—Общая часть.—Особенная часть.

1. Finance, Public—Law. 2. Finance, Public—Russia—Law. I. Title.

75–578857

NT 0037616 DLC

Tarasov, Ivan Trofimovich, 1849–
Опытъ разработки программы и конспекта общей части науки полицейскаго права. Ярославль, Тип. Губ. правленія, 1879.

48 p. 22 cm.

1. Administrative law—Russia. *Title transliterated:* Opyt razrabotki programmy.

49–57192

NT 0037617 DLC

HB179 .G47

Tarasov, Ivan Trofimovich, 1849– ed.

Giliarov-Platonov, Nikita Petrovich, 1824–1887.
Основныя начала экономіи. Посмертный трудъ Н. П. Гилярова-Платонова съ предисловіемъ профессора И. Т. Тарасова. [Изд. А. М. Гальперсонъ]. Москва, Типо-лит. "Техникъ", 1889.

Tarasov, K., *pseud.*
see Rusanov, Nikolaĭ Sergeevich, 1859–1939.

Tarasov, L M
Адриан Маркович Волков, 1827–1873. Москва, Искусство, 1955.

40 p. illus. 17 cm. (Массовая библиотека "Искусство")

1. Volkov, Adrian Markovich, 1827–1873. *Title transliterated:* Adrian Markovich Volkov.

ND699.V58T3 57–22700 ‡

NT 0037620 DLC

Tarasov, L M
Александр Иванович Морозов, 1835–1904. Москва, Искусство, 1949.

85 p. plates. 17 cm. (Массовая библиотека)

1. Morozov, Aleksandr Ivanovich, 1835–1904. (Series: Массовая библиотека (Moskva, iskusstvo)) *Title transliterated:* Aleksandr Ivanovich Morozov.

ND699.M65T3 51–18447

NT 0037621 DLC

Tarasov, L   M
Андрей Андреевич Попов, 1832–1896. Москва, Искусство, 1954.
85 p. illus. 17 cm.

1. Popov, Andreĭ Andreevich, 1832–1896.
Title transliterated: Andreĭ Andreevich Popov.

ND699.P64 T3   55–16061

NT 0037622   DLC

Tarasov, L. M.
Moscow. Gosudarstvennaía Tret'íakovskaía galiereía.
... Каталог выставки. Москва, Ленинград ¡Объединенное государственное издательство "Искусство"¡ 1936.

Tarasov, L   M
Константин Егорович Маковский, 1839–1915. Москва, Искусство, 1948.
81 p. plates, port. 17 cm. (Массовая библиотека)

1. Makovskiĭ, Konstantin Egorovich, 1839–1915.
Title transliterated: Konstantin Egorovich Makovskiĭ.

ND699.M25T25   52–67221

NT 0037624   DLC

Tarasov, L   M
Петр Иванович Петровичев, 1874–1947. Москва, Искусство, 1951.
80 p. illus. 17 cm. (Массовая библиотека)

1. Petrovichev, Petr Ivanovich, 1874–1947.
Title transliterated: Petr Ivanovich Petrovichev.

ND699.P45 T3   52–26223 ‡

NT 0037625   DLC

Tarasov, L   M
Василий Федорович Тимм, 1820–1895. Москва, Искусство, 1954.
29 p. illus. 17 cm.

1. Timm, Vasiliĭ Fedorovich, 1820–1895.
Title transliterated: Vasiliĭ Fedorovich Timm.

NC269.T5T3   55–34261 ‡

NT 0037626   DLC

ND699
.M26T3

Tarasov, L. M.
Makovskiĭ, Vladimir Egorovich, 1846–1920.
Владимир Егорович Маковский. Москва, Гос. изд-во изобразительного искусства, 1955.

TARASOV, L   P
Injury in ground surfaces.
Worcester, Mass. Norton co. 1947.
73p. illus. diagrs.

NT 0037628   WaS

Tarasov, Leonid ĪAkovlevich.
Крепильщик. Допущено в качестве учеб. пособия для подготовки в горнопромышл. школах крепильщиков горнорудной промышл. Москва, Гос. научно-техн. изд-во лит-ры по черной и цветной металлургии, 1954.
304 p. illus. 21 cm.
Bibliography: p. 301.

1. Mine timbering.   i. Title.   *Title transliterated:* Krepiľshchik.

TN289.T29   55–22004 rev

NT 0037629   DLC

TN289
.T3

Tarasov, Leonid ĪAkovlevich.
Крепление горных выработок на рудниках. Москва, Гос. научно-техн. изд-во лит-ры по черной и цветной металлургии, 1950.
225, ¡3¡ p. illus. 23 cm. (Технический минимум)
On cover: Крепильщик на рудниках.
Bibliography: p. ¡227¡

1. Mine timbering.   i. Title.   ii. Title: Krepiľshchik na rudnikakh.
Title transliterated: Kreplenie gornykh vyrabotok na rudnikakh.

51–21821 rev

NT 0037630   DLC

Tarasov, M   P
Об итогах Всемирного конгресса профсоюзов в Париже; доклад на XIV пленуме ВЦСПС 8 декабря 1945 г. Москва, Профиздат, 1945.
31 p. 15 cm.

1. World Trade Union Congress. 1st, Paris, 1945.
Title transliterated: Ob itogakh Vsemirnogo kongressa profsoíuzov.

HD6475.A2W67 1945d   58–38915

NT 0037631   DLC

Tarasov, M   P
Об усилении общественного контроля профсоюзных организаций над работой столовых, магазинов и подсобных хозяйств; доклад на XII пленуме ВЦСПС 13 марта 1944 г. Москва, Профиздат, 1944.
39 p. 14 cm.

1. Restaurants, lunch rooms, etc.—Russia. 2. Welfare work in industry—Russia. 3. Trade-unions—Russia. i. Title.
Title transliterated: Ob usilenii obshchestvennogo kontrolía profsoíuznykh organizatsiĭ.

HD7393.T3   51–53684

NT 0037632   DLC

Tarasov, M   P
52 дня в Италии. ¡О поездке делегации советских профсоюзов в Италию¡ Москва, Профиздат, 1945.
55 p. 15 cm.

1. Trade-unions—Italy. i. Title.
Title transliterated: Píať desíat dva dnía v Italii.

HD6709.T3   52–68137 ‡

NT 0037633   DLC

Tarasov, M   P
Забота партии и правительства о подъеме материального благосостояния и культурного уровня трудящихся. ¡Москва¡ Профиздат, 1950.
47 p. 21 cm.

1. Russia—Soc. condit. i. Title.
Title transliterated: Zabota partii i praviteľstva o pod"eme materiaľnogo blagosostoíanिía i kuľturnogo urovnía trudíashchikhsía.

DK268.3.T37   52–42867

NT 0037634   DLC

Tarasov, Mikhail Aleksandrovich.
Очерки транспортного права. Москва, Изд-во Министерства речного флота СССР, 1951.
Law
161 p. 23 cm.

1. Transportation—Russia—Laws and regulations. i. Title.
Title transliterated: Ocherki transportnogo prava.

52–65020

NT 0037635   DLC

Law

Tarasov, Mikhail Aleksandrovich.
Претензии и иски при транспортных операциях. Ростов на-Дону, 1947.
55 p. 21 cm.
On cover: ВНИТОВТ. Азово-Доно-Кубанское отделение.

1. Carriers—Russia. i. Title.
Title transliterated: Pretenziĭ i iski pri transportnykh operatsiíakh.

49–14313*

NT 0037636   DLC

591.92
T171bE

TARASOV, N   I
Biology of the sea and the navy. Editor: ... V. A. Berezkin. Moscow, Main office of the Naval publishing house, 1943.
472 p.

At head of title: Unclassified. The Voroshilov naval academy.
Half-title: ONI translation no. A–496 ... Translated by F. R. Preveden; authenticated by R. T. Jameson ... Dated: 20 Feb. 1952.

NT 0037637   WaU

Tarasov, N   V
Балтийский портъ; историческій очеркъ. С.-Петербургъ, Тип. Морского министерства, 1914.
48 p. illus. 24 cm.

1. Paldiski, Estonia—Hist.
Title transliterated: Baltiĭskiĭ port.

DK511.E7T3   54–49340 ‡

NT 0037638   DLC

Tarasov, Nikolaĭ Grigor'evich, b. 1866.
Изъ исторіи русской культуры. Москва, Изд. В. В. Думнова, 1908–
v. illus. 25 cm.
At head of title: Н. Г. Тарасовъ и А. Ф. Гартвигъ.

1. Russia—Civilization—Hist. i. Gartvig, Andreĭ Fedorovich, joint author. ii. Title.
Title transliterated: Iz istorii russkoĭ kuľtury.

DK32.T3   66–58205

NT 0037639   DLC CSt

Tarasov, Nikolaĭ Grigor'evich, b. 1866.
(Kuľturno-istoricheskiía kartiny iz zhizni Zapadnoĭ Evropy chetvertago-vosemnadtsatago víekov)
Культурно-историческія картины изъ жизни Западной Европы IV–XVIII вѣковъ. ¡Москва, 1903¡
xi, 196 p. illus. 25 cm.
At head of title: Н. Г. Тарасовъ и С. П. Моравскій.
Includes bibliographical references.

1. Civilization, Medieval. 2. Middle Ages—History. 3. Europe—Civilization—History. i. Moravskiĭ, Sergeĭ Pavlovich, b. 1866, joint author. ii. Title.

CB351.T28   73–205446

NT 0037640   DLC CaBVaU

Tarasov, Nikolaĭ Grigor'evich, b. 1866–
Культурно-исторические картины из жизни Западной
Европы IV–XVII веков. ¡Допущено как пособие для
преподавателей. Москва, Гос. изд-во ¡1924;

viii, 146 p. illus. 24 cm.

At head of title: Н. Тарасов и С. Моравский.
Bibliographical footnotes.

1. Civilization, Medieval. 2. Middle ages—Hist. 3. Europe—Civilization—Hist.   I. Moravskiĭ, Sergeĭ Pavlovich, b. 1866, joint author.
II. Title.
Title transliterated: Kul'turno-istoricheskie kartiny.

D127.T33   44–48458 rev

NT   0037641   DLC

Tarasov, Nikolaĭ Petrovich.
Курс высшей математики для техникумов. Допущено в
качестве учебника для техникумов. ¡Москва; Гостехиздат, 1947.

270 p. illus. 20 cm.

L. C. copy imperfect: t. p. wanting: title from cover.

1. Calculus. 2. Geometry, Analytic.
Title transliterated: Kurs vyssheĭ
matematiki dlia tekhnikumov.

QA303.T18 1947   60–18862

NT   0037642   DLC

Tarasov, Nikolaĭ Petrovich.
Курс высшей математики для техникумов. Изд. 6.,
перер. Допущено в качестве учебника для техникумов.
Москва, Гос. изд-во технико-теорет. лит-ры, 1949.

356 p. illus. 21 cm.

Errata slip inserted.

1. Calculus. 2. Geometry, Analytic.
Title transliterated: Kurs vyssheĭ matematiki dlia tekhnikumov.

QA303.T18 1949   50–27509.

NT   0037643   DLC

QA303
.T18
1951

Tarasov, Nikolaĭ Petrovich.
Курс высшей математики для техникумов. Изд. 7. Допущено в качестве учебника для техникумов. Москва,
Гос. изд-во технико-теорет. лит-ры, 1951.

356 p. illus. 21 cm.

1. Calculus. 2. Geometry, Analytic.
Title transliterated: Kurs vyssheĭ
matematiki dlia tekhnikumov.

                           55–19461

NT   0037644   DLC

Tarasov, Nikolaĭ Petrovich.
Курс высшей математики для техникумов. Изд. 8.,
перер. Допущено в качестве учеб. пособия для техникумов. Москва, Гос. изд-во технико-теорет. лит-ры, 1954.

390 p. diagrs. 21 cm.

1. Calculus. 2. Geometry, Analytic.   I. Title.
Title transliterated: Kurs vyssheĭ
matematiki dlia tekhnikumov.

QA303.T18 1954   55–38715

NT   0037645   DLC

Tarasov, P V
Богатства Приморского края. Владивосток, Примиздат,
1947.

49 p. 19 cm.

At head of title: Краевой культурно-просветительный отдел.

1. Natural resources—Maritime Province, Siberia.   I. Title.
Title transliterated: Bogatstva Primorskogo kraia.

HC487.M3T3   62–28401 ‡

NT   0037646   DLC

Tarasov, S V
Бухгалтерский учет внешнеторговых операций и вопросы анализа хозяйственной деятельности внешнеторговых объединений. Москва, Внешторгиздат, 1952.

213 p. 22 cm.

1. Accounting. 2. Russia—Comm.   I. Title.
Title transliterated: Bukhgalterskiĭ
uchet vneshnetorgovykh operat︠s︡iĭ.

HF5653.T26   55–30567

NT   0037647   DLC

Tarasov, Semen Alekseevich.
Пособие по безработице. Москва, Гострудиздат, 1929.

38 p. 18 cm.

1. Insurance, Unemployment—Russia.   I. Title.
Title transliterated: Posobie po bezrabot︠s︡īe.

HD7096.R9T3   51–48070

NT   0037648   DLC

Tarasov, Sergeĭ Vladimirovich.
Подготовка волокна в льнопрядильном производстве.
Москва, Гос. научно-техн. изд-во Министерства промышл.
товаров широкого потребления СССР, 1955.

94 p. illus. 22 cm.

1. Flax.   I. Title.
Title transliterated: Podgotovka volokna
v l'nopriadil'nom proizvodstve.

TS1725.T29   59–47097 ‡

NT   0037649   DLC

Tarasov, V. A.

Anisimova, V N
Дорожные моторные катки. Москва, Гос. научно-техн.
изд-во машиностроит. лит-ры, 1955.

Tarasov, Vasiliĭ Vasil'evich.
Борьба Балтийского флота против немцев в 1914–1918
гг. ¡Москва; Госполитиздат, 1941.

21 p. 20 cm.

1. European War, 1914–1918—Naval operations, Russian. 2. Russia.
Voennyĭ Flot. Baltiĭskiĭ flot.   I. Title.
Title transliterated: Bor'ba Baltiĭskogo flota protiv nem︠t︡sev.

D585.T3   43–35080 rev*

NT   0037651   DLC

Tarasov, Vasiliĭ Vasil'evich.
Борьба с интервентами на Мурмане в 1918–1920 гг. Ленинград, Ленинградское газетно-журнальное и книжное
изд-во, 1948.

305 p. illus., port., maps. 20 cm.

Bibliography: p. 301–¡308;

1. Russia—Hist.—Allied intervention, 1918–1920. 2. Murmansk,
Russia (Province)—Hist.
Title transliterated: Bor'ba s interventami na Murmane.

DK265.4.T29   50–17015 rev

NT   0037652   DLC MU

Tarasov-Agalakov, Nikolaĭ Aleksandrovich.
Приборы и способы тушения пожаров легковоспламеняющихся жидкостей. Москва, Изд-во Наркомхоза
РСФСР, 1944.

71 p. illus. 20 cm.

At head of title: Н. А. Тарасов-Агалаков.
Bibliography: p. 71.

1. Petroleum industry and trade—Fires and fire prevention.
I. Title.
Title romanized: Pribory i sposoby tusheniia pozharov legkovosplameniaiushchikhsia zhidkosteĭ.

TH9446.P4T3   49–53954

NT   0037653   DLC

Tarasov-Agalakov, Nikolaĭ Aleksandrovich.
Противопожарное водоснабжение населенных мест в
условиях военного времени. Москва, Изд-во Наркомхоза РСФСР, 1943.

46, ¡2; p. illus. 22 cm.

At head of title: Н. А. Тарасов-Агалаков.
Bibliography: p. ¡47;

1. Fire extinction—Water-supply.   I. Title.
Title romanized: Protivopozharnoe vodosnabzhenie naselennykh mest v usloviiakh voennogo vremeni.

TH9311.T38   50–43655

NT   0037654   DLC

Tarasov-Rodionov, Aleksandr Ignat'evich, 1885–
Chocolate, a novel by Alexander Tarasov-Rodionov; translated from the Russian by Charles Malamuth. Garden City,
N. Y., Doubleday, Doran & company, inc., 1932.

3 p. l., 311 p. 20ᵐ.

"First edition."

I. Malamuth, Charles, tr.   II. Title.

Library of Congress   PZ3.T168Ch   32–10534
——— Copy 2.
Copyright A 50816   ¡5;   891.73

       MiU IaU OCl ViU MB KMK OKentU
NT   0037655   DLC PSC PBm PP Wa WaWW OrU IU OrU NBuC

TARASOV–RODIONOV, ALEKSANDR IGNAT'YEVICH, 1885–
Chocolate, a novel by Alexander Tarasov–Rodionov; translated from the Russian by Charles Malamuth. London, W.
Heinemann, ltd. [1933]
3 p.l., 276 p. 19 cm.

691225A. 1. Fiction, Russian. I. Malamuth, Charles, translator. II. Title.

NT   0037656   NN OrPR MiU

Tarasov-Rodionov, Aleksandr Ignat'evich, 1885–
Čokolada. ¡S ruskog preveo S. Llandžić; Sarajevo ¡Narodna prosvjeta; 1955.

166 p. 17 cm. (Džepna biblioteka, 21)

I. Title.

PG3476.T3S58   60–19422 ‡

NT   0037657   DLC

Tarasov-Rodionov, Aleksandr Ignat'yevich, 1885–
... Csokoládé. Forditotta: Katona Fedor.   Paris, Éditions
Monde, 1930.   255 p.   19 cm.

At head of title: A. Tarasov-Rodionov.

313132B. 1. No subject. I. Katona,   Fedor, tr. II. Title.
N. Y. P. L.   September 20, 1945

NT   0037658   NN

Tarasov-Rodïonov, Aleksandr Ignat'evich, 1885–
... Februar, roman. Potsdam, G. Kiepenheuer, 1928.

586 p., 1 l. 18½ cm.

At head of title: Tarassow-Rodionow.
"1.–6. tausend."
"Vom verfasser autorisierte übersetzung aus dem russischen von
Olga Halpern."
"Der roman 'Februar' ist der erste teil einer trilogie, deren ge-
samttitel 'Schwere schritte' heisst. Die folkenden bände werden die
titel 'Juni' und 'Oktober' führen. Das gesamtwerk ist eine roman-
chronik der russischen revolution."

1. Russia—Hist.—February revolution, 1917—Fiction.   I. Halpern, Olga, tr. II. Title.

PG3476.T3F44   923.547   30—4617

NT 0037659   DLC NN

Tarasov-Rodïonov, Aleksandr Ignat'evich, 1885–
Februar; der Trilogie erster Teil. [Über-
setzung aus dem Russischen von Olga Halpern]
Berlin, Neuer Deutscher Verlag, 1930.
630 p.   20 cm.   (His Schwere Schritte;
Romantrilogie, 1)
Translation of   (transliterated: Fevral')
No more published.

NT 0037660   IU

DK   Tarasov-Rodionov, Aleksandr Ignat'evich,
265   1885–
.T315   Februar. ¿Atorisierte Übers. aus dem
        Russischen von Olga Halpern¿ Berlin,
        Universum-Bücherei für alle, 1932.
        v.   19cm.

1. Russia. Hist. Revolution, 1917–1921.
I. Halpern, Olga, tr. II. Title.

NT 0037661   KU

Tarasov-Rodïonov, Aleksandr Ignat'evich, 1885–
... February, 1917. Translated by William A. Drake. New
York, Covici-Friede, 1931.

3 p. l., 378 p. 24½ᶜᵐ.

At head of title: A chronicle of the Russian revolution. Aleksei
Tarasov-Rodionov.

1. Russia—Hist.—Revolution, 1917–   I. Drake, William A.,
1899–   tr. II. Title.

Library of Congress   DK265.T3   31—28005

———— Copy 2.

Copyright A 42785   ¡5¿   923.547

CoU CtY MoU
OC1 OO ViU NN NjN MB MH OOxM NlC CU MiU CtW IaU KU
NT 0037662   DLC OrCS PU OrU PSC MoU TxU NcD NNC OCU

Tarasov-Rodïonov, Aleksandr Ignatyevich, 1885 –   G–T
Juli. Berlin: Neuer Deutscher Verlag¡, cop. 1932¿. 748 p.
12°.   (Schwere Schritte, 2.)

Sequel to Februar.

1. Ser. 2. Title.
N.Y.P.L.   February 20, 1933

NT 0037663   NN NjP DLC-P4

PG3476   Tarasov-Rodionov, Aleksandr Ignat'evich,
T3J84   1885–
1933   Juli; roman. [Autorisierte Übersetzung aus dem Russischen
        von Olga Halpern] Berlin, Neuer Deutscher Verlag, 1933.
        747 p.

At head of title: Tarassow-Rodionow.
"Der Trilogie 'Schwere Schritte' zweiter Teil."

I. Schwere Schritte, v.2.   II. Title.

NT 0037664   CU

DK   Tarasov-Rodionov, Aleksandr Ignat'evich,
265   1885–
T3   La Révolution de février 1917; Febral
1930   [par] Tarassow-Rodionov. Traduit du
MAIN   russe par Marc Semenoff. 5. ed.   [Paris]
        Gallimard [1930]
        338p. 19cm.   (Les Documents bleus.
        Notre temps, no.31)

1. Russia – Hist. – Revolution, 1917–
I. Title. II. Series.

NT 0037665   TxU CSt-H IU IaU KMK

Tarasov-Rodionov, Aleksandr Ignatevich, 1885–
Schokolade; eine Erzählung.   [Übersetzt von A.
Ramm] Berlin, Verlag der Zeitschrift Die Aktion,
F.Pfemfert [c1924].

166 p.

NT 0037666   MH InU

Law

Tarasov-Rodïonov, Petr Ignat'evich.
Предварительное следствие; пособие для следователеи.
Под ред. Г. Н. Александрова и С. Я. Розенблита. ¡3.,
перер. и значительно расширенное изд.¿ Москва, Гос.
изд-во юрид. лит-ры, 1955.

246 p. forms. 21 cm.

1. Preliminary examinations (Criminal procedure)—Russia.   I.
Title.   *Title transliterated:* Prevaritel'noe sledstvie.

56—42030

NT 0037667   DLC

Law   Tarasov-Rodïonov, Petr Ignat'evich, joint
        author.

Gromov, Vladimir Ustinovich.
... Расследование хищений и злоупотреблений в торговом
аппарате; пособие для органов расследования, под редакцией ... Б. С. Ошеровича. Москва, Государственное издательство Советское законодательство, 1934.

Tarasov-Rodïonov, Petr Ignat'evich.
... Расследование дел о растратах и подлогах; практи-
ческое пособие для следователей и юридических курсов, под
общей редакцией Б. С. Ошеровича, Г. П. ¡!¿ Рогинского.
¡Москва¿ Огиз, Государственное издательство Советское законодательство, 1935.

78, ¡2¿ p. 22½ᶜᵐ.

At head of title: Государственный институт уголовной политики
при прокуратуре Союза ССР и НКЮ РСФСР. П. Тарасов, М. Ласкин.
Errata slip laid in.

1. Embezzlement—Russia. 2. Forgery—Russia. 3. Criminal investigation—Russia.   I. Laskin, Minei Izrailevich, joint author. II. Oshe-
rovich, B. S., ed. III. Roginskii, Grigorii Konstantinovich, joint ed. IV.
Moscow. Gosudarstvennyi institut ugolovnoi politiki. v. Title.

37—36675

NT 0037669   DLC

Tarasova, M   G
... Français. Част I; учебник французского языка для 5
класса неполной средней и средней школы ... Изд. 4. Москва, Государственное учебно-педагогическое издательство
Наркомпроса РСФСР, 1940.

184, ¡2¿ p. illus., vi pl. (incl. port.) on 8 l. 20½ᶜᵐ.

At head of title: М. Тарасова и О. Городецкая.

1. French language—Text-books for foreigners—Russian.   I. Goro-
detskaia, O. S., joint author.

Library of Congress   PC2129.S4T3 1940   44—21975

NT 0037670   DLC

Tarasova, V. E.

PZ90
.Y5K476
Hebr   Khorol, Dvoyre, 1898–
            (Di bin un der hon)

די בין אונ דער האנ / ד. כאראל ; צייכענונגען פון וו.
מארמאסאווא. — מאסקווע : פארלאג עמעס, 1937.

PN6120
.S5P8   Tarasova, V. E.

Puss in Boots.
Театр теней по сказке Шарля Перро Кот в сапогах
¡Рисунки В. Е. Тарасовой. Москва, Министерство мест
ной промышл., 1946¿

NT (not visible)

Bon.
G   Tarasp-Schuls company.
38
.467   Kurhaus Tarasp-spa. Engadine, Swit-
        zerland.   [Samaden]n.d.

Binder's title: Tarasp-spa.
Cover-title.

NT 0037673   ICN

Tarass Boulba
    see under   Gogol, Nikolaï Vasil'evich,
1809–1852.

Tarasseff Tarossian, Leon
    see   Troyat, Henri, 1911–

Tarassévich, L.A.
    see   Tarasevich, Lev Aleksandrovich,
1868–1927.

Tarassenko-Otreschkoff, N.
    see   Tarasenko-Otreshkov, Narkis
Ivanovich.

[Tarassoff, Leo] 1911–
    see   Troyat, Henri, 1911–

¡Tarassoff, Leo¿ 1911–
... La clef de voûte. Monsieur Citrine. Paris, Plon ¡1937¿

5 p. l., ¡5¿–242 p., 2 l. 19ᶜᵐ.

Author's pseud., Henri Troyat, at head of title.

I. Title. II. Title: Monsieur Citrine.   37—36134 Revised

Library of Congress   PQ2639.A68C5 1937

Copyright A—Foreign   36618

¡r40c2¿   843.91

NT 0037679   DLC

Tarassov, Lev
see
Troyat, Henri, 1911–

Taraszov-Rodionov, A
see Tarasov-Rodionov, Aleksandr
Ignat'evich, 1885–

TARATA, BOLIVIA (City)--Junta municipal
Informe del presidente de la Junta municipal de la provincia, al clausurar las sesiones de 1887. -- Tarata : Imprenta del pueblo, por Juan José Rosa Lopez, 1888.
12, ₍2₎ p. ; 4to(22 cm.)

Cover title.
Not in René-Moreno.
Typesigned at end: Tarata, Enero lo. de 1888. Lucas Pardo de Figueroa.
In wrappers, stitched as issued.

NT 0037695 InU

NT 0037681 DNLM

TARATA, BOLIVIA (City)--Junta municipal
Memoria que el presidente de la Junta municipal de la provincia de Tarata de 1874, dirije a la municipalidad de 1875. -- Tarata : Imprenta del pueblo por M. Nuñez, 1875.
8 p. ; 4to(21.4 cm.)

Cover title.
Not in Gutiérrez, or René-Moreno.
In wrappers, stitched as issued.

NT 0037690 InU

Taratantra
see Tantras. Taratantra.

Tarassow-Rodionow.
See
Tarasov-Rodionov, Aleksandr Ignat' evich, *1885 —*

Taratchkof, Aleksandr (Stepanovitch). Observations sur les époques du développement des plantes indigènes des environs d'Orel, faites pendant les années 1851–1853. Moscou. 1855. 8°. pp. [2], 37.
Reprinted from *Bulletin de la Société impériale des naturalistes de Moscou*, 1855. xxviii. pt. 2, pp. 1–37.

NT 0037697 MH-A

NT 0037683 MnU DLC

TARATA, BOLIVIA (City)--Ordinances, local laws, etc
Ordenanza dictada por la Junta municipal de Tarata para prevenir la propagacion del "colera morbus". -- Tarata : Imp. de Isaac Salinas, 1887.
₍2₎, 6 p. ; 4to(22 cm.)

Not in René-Moreno.
Stitched as issued.

NT 0037691 InU

Taratte, René.
... S. O. S. xxᵐᵉ siècle. Paris, E. Figuière ₍ᶜ1937₎
2 p. l., ₍7₎–245 p. 1 l. 18½ᶜᵐ.
CONTENTS. — Genèse.— Terre, humanité.—Europe.—France.—Travaux humains.—Luttes humaines.—Voyage dans l'Est.—Le tribunal.—Hier, aujourd'hui, demain.

I. Title.
Library of Congress   CB73.T3   37–34167
Copyright A—Foreign   36340
                             ₍3₎   901

NT 0037698 DLC

Law
Tarasti, Aarne, ed.
Finland. *Laws, statutes, etc.*
Sosiaalihuollon lainsäädäntö; sosiaalihuollon lakikokoelma. Toimittanut Aarne Tarasti. Helsinki ₍1965₎

al-Tarasusi
see Jabir ibn Hayyan

TARATA, BOLIVIA (City)--Tesorería municipal
Cuenta general de ingresos y egresos de los tesoros municipal é instruccion de la provincia de Tarata : Gestion fenecida de 1888. -- ₍s.l.₎ : Imprenta de Isaac Salinas, ₍1889?₎
18 p. ; 4to(21.2 cm.)

Cover title.
Not in René-Moreno.
Dated at end: 30 de abril de 1889.
In wrappers, stitched as issued.

NT 0037692 InU

Tarauletti, Joseph Rizzo
see Rizzo Tarauletti, Joseph.

al-Tarasusi, Ibrāhīm ibn 'Alī, 1320–1357.
‏أنفع الوسائل إلى تحرير المسائل‏
‏لنجم الدين إبراهيم بن علي بن أحمد بن عبد الواحد بن عبد المنعم‏
‏ابن عبد الصمد الطرسوسي. صححه وراجع نقوله مصطفى محمد‏
‏خفاجي وعمود إبراهيم. مصر، مطبعة الشرق، ١٩٢٦.‏
355 p. 25 cm.

1. Islamic law. 2. Hanafis. I. Title. II. Title: Anfa' al-wasā'il ilá taḥrīr al-masā'il.

Title romanized: al-Fatāwá al-Ṭarsūsīyah.

73–211159

NT 0037686 DLC WaU

Taraval, Louis Gustave, 1738–1794.
₍Sketchbook: collection of water-color and pencil drawings depicting plans of different kinds of buildings designed by Louis Gustave Taraval. 1781.₎
57 plans (part col.) on 51 l. 14cm.

The sketches include plans of castles, temples, churches, arcs of triomph, etc.
In manuscript on label pasted on inside cover: Esquisse de diferan plan de toutte ganre dédifice composé par Louis Gustave Taravel ... 1781.

NT 0037700 NNC

NT 0037687 DNLM

TARATA, BOLIVIA (City)--Tesorería municipal
Cuenta general del tesoro municipal de Tarata. En el año de 1885. -- Tarata : Imprenta del pueblo, administrada por Juan José Rosa Lopez, 1886.
₍2₎, 21 p. ; 4to(22.8 cm.)

Not in René-Moreno.
Dated at end: Tesoreria Municipal. Tarata marzo 23 de 1886.
Stitched as issued.

NT 0037693 InU

Taraszkiewicz, L.
Teorja darowizn rękodajnych, skreślił L. Taraszkiewicz ... Warszawa, W druk. S. Niemiry synów, 1902.
1 p. l., ₍5₎–111, ₍1₎ p. 22½ᶜᵐ.
"Literatura": p. ₍5₎–6.

1. Gifts. I. Title.

39–17280

NT 0037688 DLC

TARATA, BOLIVIA (City)--Tesorería municipal
Cuenta general del tesoro municipal de Tarata. En 1887. -- Tarata : Imprenta del pueblo administrada por Juan José Rosa Lopez, 1888.
₍2₎, 13 p. ; 4to(21.7 cm.)

Not in René-Moreno.
Typesigned at end: Belisario Velasco.
Stitched as issued.

NT 0037694 InU

Taraval, Sigismundo, 1700–1763.
The Indian uprising in Lower California, 1734–1737, as described by Father Sigismundo Taraval. Translated, with introd. and notes, by Marguerite Eyer Wilbur. Los Angeles, Quivira Society, 1931.
xii, 298 p. illus., facsims., maps. 24 cm. (Quivira Society. Publications, v. 2)
Includes bibliographical references.
Photo-offset. New York, Arno Press, 1967.

1. Baja California—Hist.—Sources. 2. Missions—Baja California. 3. Jesuits in Baja California. 4. Indians of Mexico—Baja California. I. Wilbur, Marguerite Knowlton (Eyer) 1889– tr. II. Title. (Series)

F864.T252 1967   972'.2'02   67–24714

WaSpG
IaU ViU MB DSI NN MH TU CLU RPJCB NBu CaBViPA WaS
NcD WaU CU NBuU InU CoU OCl MU IdU OU OrPS MiU FU
NT 0037701 DLC TxU NSyU MnU CSt OrU FTaSU TNJ MWA GU

Microfilm
Taraval, Sigismundo, 1700-1763.
The Indian uprising in Lower California,
1734-1737, as described by Father Sigismundo
Taraval; translated, with introduction and
notes, by Marguerite Eyer Wilbur. Los
Angeles, The Quivira society, 1931.
(Quivira society, Los Angeles. Publications.
vol. II)
Microfilm copy, made in 1958, of the original.
Negative.
Collation of the original: xii, 298 p. IX p*l*.
(incl. maps,   facsims.)

"Six hundred and sixty-five copies printed
for the Quivira society ... This copy is
no. 476."
"The original Journal ... on which the
following English rendition is based, now
forms part of the Ayer collection of western
Americana in the Newberry library at
Chicago."--Introd.
Bibliography   included in the introduction.

1. California, Lower--Hist.--Sources. 2.
Missions--California, Lower. 3. Jesuits in
Lower California. 4. Indians of Mexico--
California, Lower. I. Wilbur, Mrs. Marguerite
Knowlton (Eyer) tr. II. Title. III. Series:
Quivira society, Los Angeles. Publications.
v. 2.

NT 0037704   MoSU

Taravati, a tale, tr into English by Sourindo
Mohun Tagore. Calcutta. 1881.

75 p.
Written by the translator's mother

NT 0037705   OC1

Taravel, Antoine, 1863-1927
    see   Privas, Xavier, pseud.

Taravel, Antoine Paul, 1863-1927
    see
Privas, Xavier, *pseud.*

Taravel, Francine (Loree)
        See
Loree-Privas, Francine.

Taravellier (Félix) [1884-]. *Contribution à l'étude de l'oblitération des vaisseaux
mésentériques (infarctus hémorragique de l'in-
testin). 54 pp. 1 pl. 8°. Lyon, 1911.

NT 0037709   DNLM

Tarawa [title]
    see under   U.S. Office of War Information.

Tarawa to Tokyo [1943-46; published by the officers
and men of the U.S.S. Lexington as a permanent
record of the ship's activities in World war II.
n.p., 194-?] 1 v. (chiefly illus., ports.,
maps 1 fold.) 29cm.

On spine: The story of the U.S.S. Lexington
(CV-16)
Includes roster.
1. Aircraft carriers,U.S.--Lexington. 2. World war,
1939-1945--Aerial   operations--Pacific.

NT 0037711   NN

AA   **Taraxine family almanac.** Indianapolis,
.T22   A. Kiefer.
        no. 21 cm.

        Library has: 1875.

        1. Almanacs & calendars.

NT 0037712   WHi

Taray, Andor, 1822-1900.
A bankügyről. Írta: Taray Andor. Budapest, A szerző,
1874.
v p., 1 l., 253 p. 22ᵐ.

1. Banks and banking—Hungary.   i. Title.
                                              46-41114
Library of Congress   HG1870.H9T3

NT 0037713   DLC

Taray, Andor, 1822-1900.
Eszmék az igazságszolgáltatási politika
köréből. Irta: Taray Andor. Budapest,
A szerző tulajdona, 1881.
4 p.l., 80 p. 23½cm.

With author's autograph.

NT 0037714   MH-L

[Taray, Andor, 1822-1900]
Magyarország europai hivatása és Deák Ferencz.
2.kiad. Pesten, Rosenberg [1869]

201 p.
Cover title

1. Deák, Ferencz, 1803-76. I. Title

NT 0037715   MH NNC

Taray, Andor, 1822-1900.
Vázlatok az alkotmányozási elmélet
köréből. Irta Taray Andor. Pest, A
szerző tulajdona, 1873.
4 p.l., 198 p. 23cm.

With author's autograph.

NT 0037716   MH-L

Taraye, Gabriel, 1895-
... Les kératites à hypopyon chez les enfants...
Lyon, 1922.
25 cm.
Thèse - Univ. de Lyon.

NT 0037717   CtY

Tarayre, Edmond Guillemin-
    see
Guillemin-Tarayre, Edmond, 1832-1920.

SELIGMAN

Tarayre, Jean Joseph, baron, 1770-1855.
Discours prononcé par M. le général Tarayre
... le 3 juillet 1820, sur le budget des voies
et moyens. Paris, Chez A. Comte, 1820.
16 p. 21cm.

At head of title: Chambre des députés.
Volume of pamphlets.

NT 0037719   NNC

Tarayre (M.-J.) *Considérations rapides des
causes de la supériorité de l'homme sur les autres
animaux, pour éclairer l'opinion sur l'importance
de la liberté de la presse. Iv, 5-16 pp. 8°. Paris,
1814.*

NT 0037720   DNLM

Tarazi, Salah El Dine
Les services publics libano-syriens.
Beyrouth, Société d'impression et d'édition
[1946]
xii, 171 p.

Thesis - Lyon.
Bibliography: p. [163]-166.
1. Public utilities - Syria.
2. Public utilities - Lebanon.

NT 0037721   NNC MH

Tarazona, Alonso de, comp.
Manuale chori
    see under   Catholic Church. Liturgy and
ritual.

Tarazona, Angel
    see
Tarazona, Pedro Angel de.

Tarazona, Antonio
    see   Tarazona y Blanch, Antonio.

Tarazona, D. Ignacio.   S. L.
Treinta años (1864-1893) de observaciones efectuadas y deducidas en la
estacion meteorologica de la universidad de Valencia. Madrid. 1912.
31 p.   24½ cm.
43945

NT 0037725   DAS

Tarazona, Fernando.
Estampas afro-cubanas [por] Fernando Tarazona. [Habana,
Impreso en Cuba, O. Echevarría y cía., °1939]
cover-title, [16] p. illus. (part col.) 23½ x 30ᵐ.

Spanish and English text in parallel columns.
"Translation by Gerardo Bahamonde."
"Juicios críticos": p. [2], [15]-[16]

1. Negroes in Cuba. 2. Voodooism.   i. Bahamonde, Gerardo, tr.
ii. Title.
                                              43-34390
Library of Congress   ND305.T3A44
                              [3]   759.97291

NT 0037726   DLC

Tarazona, Hieronimo, fl. 1580
see   Tarazona, Pedro Jeronimo, 16th c.

Tarazona, J.A. Quintero
see   Quintero Tarazona, J.A.

Tarazona, Martin D   Mendoza
see   Mendoza Tarazona, Martin D

DP302
.C64P8

Tarazona, Pedro Angel de, tr.

Pujades, Jerónimo, 1568–1635.
Cronica universal del principado de Cataluña, escrita a principios del siglo XVII por Geronimo Pujades ...   Barcelona, Impr. de J. Torner, 1829–32.

Tarazona, Pedro Angel de.
El pensador matritense. Discursos críticos sobre todos los asumptos que comprehende la sociedad civil ... Con real privilegio, que tiene don Pedro Angel de Tarazona.   Barcelona, F. Genéars [17--?]
5 v.   15 cm.

NT 0037731   CU

DP
48
T38

Tarazona, Pedro Angel de.
El pensador matritense; discursos críticos sobre todos los asumptos que comprende la sociedad civil.   Barcelona, F. Generas [1775?]
5 v.   16 cm.

1. Spain - Civilization.   I. Title.

NT 0037732   CU-S

Tarazona, Pedro Angel de, ed.
Semanario curioso, historico erudio, comercial..
see under   [Barrellas, Estevan.]

Bonaparte
Collection TARAZONA, Pedro Jerónimo, 16th c.
No.4606   Institvcions dels fvrs, y privilegis del regn de Valencia. Eo svmmari e reportori de aqvells. Avtor micer pere Hieroni Taraçona...   Valencia, Pedro de Guete,1580.
[12],414,[4]p.

Imperfect: t.-p. mutilated.
Armorial device on t.-p.

NT 0037734   ICN MH-L MH NNH

Tarazona, Pedro Jerónimo, 16th c.
Institvcions dels fvrs, y privilegis del regne de Valencia. Eo svmmari e reportori de aqvells. Avtor micer Pere Hieroni Taraçona ... En Valencia, En estampa de Pedro de Guete 1580.
Microfilm copy, made in 1961 of the original in Vatican. Biblioteca vaticana. Positive.
Negative in Vatican. Biblioteca vaticana.
Collation of the original as determined from the film: 5 p.1., 414, [4] p.

1. Law, Valencia (kingdom). (Series: [Manuscripta, microfilms of rare and out-of-print books. List 24, no.22])

NT 0037736   MoSU WaSpG MnU

Tarazona, Policarpo Mingote y.
See
Mingote y Tarazone, Policarpo, 1847–

Tarazona, R. Alfonso, 1904–
... La lutte antilépreuse en Amérique du Sud ..
Montpellier, 1932.
Thèse - Univ. de Montpellier.
"Bibliographie": p. [107]-116.

NT 0037738   CtY

Tarazona, Santiago Grassa y
see   Grassa y Tarazona, Santiago.

Tarazona Caceres, Saul.
... La fianza civil. Tesis presentada para optar el titulo de Doctor en ciencias juricas y economicas.   [Bogota? Universidad Javeriana] 1942.
77 p., 3 p.l.   (Bound with Universidad javeriana: Theses, 1937-1942)
(Republica de Colombia. Universidad javeriana. Facultad de ciencias economicas y juridicas)

NT 0037740   WaU-L ViU-L

Tarazona Gutiérrez, Miguel Ignacio, 1912–
... El estado y la responsabilidad en la justicia penal ...
(In Bogotà. Universidad Javeriana. Tesis. 1943, v. II, p. [371]-421)
"Obras consultadas": p. 421.

NT 0037741   MH-L

Tarazona Prada, Luis Jesús.
... Responsabilidad común y responsabilidad por accidentes de trabajo; tesis de grado para obtener el titulo de doctor en ciencias jurídicas presentada por Luis Jesús Tarazona P.   Bogotá, 1939.
56, [2] p. 24cm.
At head of title: República de Colombia. Universidad javeriana. Facultad de ciencias económicas y jurídicas.
"Bibliografía": p. [58]

1. Employers' liability—Colombia. 2. Legal responsibility—Colombia.
I. Title.

Library of Congress   HD7816.C7T3
                           [2]

42–42714

331.8250986

NT 0037742   DLC RPB

JS2652
.A13
1946

Tarazona S., Justino M., comp.

Peru. *Laws, statutes, etc.*
... Demarcación política del Perú; recopilación de leyes y decretos (1821–1946) por Justino M. Tarazona S. ...   Lima [Taller de linotipia] 1946.

Tarazona Vilas, José María.
Las zoonosis parasitarias transmisibles al hombre en el somontano de Barbastro. Huesca, 1954.
23 p. 25 cm. (Publicaciones del Instituto de Estudios Oscenses, no. 8)
At head of title: Consejo Superior de Investigaciones Científicas. Instituto de Estudios Oscenses.
Includes bibliographies.

1. Protozoa, Pathogenic. 2. Worms, Intestinal and parasitic.
3. Communicable diseases in animals. 4. Communicable diseases.
I. Title.

RC112.T3   57–18332 ‡

NT 0037744   DLC DNAL InLP DNLM

Tarazona y Blanch, Antonio

Madrid. Observatorio.
... Memoria sobre el eclipse total de sol del día 28 de mayo de 1900. [Por el astrónomo D. Antonio Tarazona] Madrid, Estab. tipog. de los sucesores de Cuesta, 1899.

Tarazona, Spain.
Lagrimas de la Fidelidad
see under title

Tarazona y Blanch, Antonio
Madrid. Observatorio.
... Memoria sobre el eclipse total de sol del día 30 de agosto de 1905 [por D. Antonio Tarazona] Madrid, Impr. de Bailly-Bailliere e hijos, 1904.

Tarazona, Spain (Diocese) Bishop   (Damián Martínez de Golinsoga)
see also Martínez de Galinsoga, Damián, bp., d. 1802.

Tarbart, pseud
see De la Rue, Thomas.

Tarbat, Alan Cecil.
"The arrow of gold."   By Alan C. Tarbat.   Yeovil [Eng.] Western gazette co. [1933]   132 p.   illus.   19cm.
2. ed.

377809B.   1. England—Descr. and   trav., 1914–
N. Y. P. L.   March 2, 1949

NT 0037750   NN

Tarbat, Alan Cecil.
England, by Alan C. Tarbat ...   Bristol [Eng.] Arrowsmith [1942]
[8] p. 22cm.
A poem.

1. World war, 1939–   —Poetry. I. Title.
                                               A 42–4807
Harvard univ. Library
for Library of Congress   [2]

NT 0037751   MH

TARBAT,Alan Cecil.
The rider of Mendip and other poems. With a foreword by Elizabeth Goudge. [Bristol],Arrowsmith,[1939].
23 cm. pp.64.

NT 0037752   MH

Tarbat, Alan Cecil.
    Shireways, by Alan Tarbat ... Bristol ₍Eng.₎ Rankin bros.
ltd., printers ₍1946₎
    108 p. illus. 18ᵐ.

    1. England—Descr. & trav.   ɪ. Title.

DA630.T3   914.2   47–20770

NT   0037753   DLC

Tarbat, Alan Cecil.
    Six months of war, by Alan C. Tarbat ("A. C. T.") With a
foreword by Sydney Carroll. ₍London₎ Arrowsmith ₍1940₎
    39 p. 22ᵐ.
    "These poems, with six exceptions, have appeared in the 'Daily
sketch'."—p. ₍2₎

    1. World war, 1939–   —Poetry.   ɪ. Title.

                         A 42–8222

New York. Public library
    for Library of Congress   ₍2₎

NT   0037754   NN

Tarbat, George Mackenzie, viscount.
    See
Cromarty, George Mackenzie, 1st earl of, 1630–1714.

BF   Tarbat, William
1434   Remarks on Mr. Baxter's Narrative of
G7   facts, characterising the supernatural
T3   manifestations in members of Mr. Irving's
HRC   congregation, and other individuals in
           England & Scotland, and formerly in the
           writer himself. In a letter to a friend,
           with an appendix containing extracts
           of letters from individuals who are
           subjects of the manifestations.
           Liverpool, J. Davenport, 1833.
           60p. 19cm.

           Inscribed: E. Mabbs. A. Conan Doyle, 1919.

           1. Baxter, Robert. Narrative of facts.
           2. Occult sciences - Gt. Brit.   3. Super-
           natural. I. Title.   **A.F.:** Mabbs, E .

NT   0037757   TxU NNUT

     Tarbé.
         Rapport sur la vis d'Archimède a double effet
             see under   Tarbé de Vauxclairs, Jean
     Bernard.

     Tarbe,   Eveque de.
         Discours de M. l'eveque de Tarbe, invité par
le parlement à prendre séance aux chambres
assemblées; du 14 nobembre 1775.
         1 p.   4°.
         n. t.-p.

NT   0037759   MH-L

     Tarbé, A   **P**   ed.
         Cour de cassation. Lois et réglements à l'usage de la Cour
de cassation, recueillis et annotés par A.-P. Tarbé ... Paris,
Librairie encyclopédique de Roret ₍etc.₎ 1840.
         viii, 504 p. 25¼ᵐ.
         "Liste des magistrats qui depuis 1790 ont été appelés à siéger au
Tribunal et à la Cour de cassation": p. ₍421₎–436.

         1. France. Cour de cassation. 2. Court rules—France. 3. Judges—
France. ɪ. France. Laws, statutes, etc. ɪɪ. Title.

                         41–39012

NT   0037760   DLC

FR REV
DC   Tarbé, Charles, 1756–1804.
165   Discours contre la suspension du rem-
.5   boursement des créances exigibles & liqui-
R31   dées, excédant 10,000 liv. Prononcé à
₍v.7₎   l'Assemblée Nationale, le 15 mai 1792 ...
no.5   ₍Paris, Impr. Natl., 1792₎
         8 p. 19cm.

         Paris. Bibl. Natl. Dépt. des imprimés.
Cat. de l'histoire de la Révolution française. 4¹, 32189.
         No. 5 in   vol. lettered: Recueil des
         pièces de l'   Assemb. Nationale. ₍v.7₎

NT   0037761   NIC

Tarbé, Charles, 1756–1804.
    Discours prononcé par Ch. Tarbé...sur l'état actuel de la co-
lonie de Saint-Domingue. Séance du 11 prairial, an V.   n. t.-p.
Colophon: A Paris: De l'Imprimerie nationale, prairial, an V
₍1797₎.   18 p.   8°.   (France. Corps législatif, 1795–1814.
Conseil des cinq cents.)

    At head of title: Corps législatif. Conseil des cinq-cents.
    Bibliothèque historique de la Révolution française.   Paris, 1806.   ₍no. 3.₎
Astor Library copy.

    1. Haiti.—History, 1797.   2.   France. Corps législatif, 1795–
1814. Conseil des cinq cents.   1814. Conseil des cinq cents.
N.Y.P.L.   September 8, 1915.

NT   0037762   NN PPAmP RPJCB NIC

     Tarbé, Charles, 1756–1804.
         Mémoire sur le cadastre de la France
           see under   ₍Tarbé, Louis Hardouin₎ 1753–
1806.

     Tarbé, Charles, 1756–1804
         Opinion sur le projet de résolution de la commission
des finances relative à la suspension des délégations
anticipées sur les départemens. Séance du 12 thermidor
an V.   [P, an V]

         8 p.
         At head of title: Corps législatif. Conseil des Cinq-
cents.

NT   0037764   MH

Tarbé, Charles, 1756–1804.
    Pièces justificatives du Rapport sur les troubles de Saint-
Domingue, fait au nom du comité colonial, par Charles Tarbé...
₍Paris₎ De l'imprimerie nationale ₍1792.₎   154 p., 1 fold. table.
8°.

    Caption-title, with colophon reading: De l'imprimerie nationale.
    Bibliothèque historique de la Révolution française. Paris, 1806. ₍no. 2.₎
Astor Library copy.

    1. Haiti.—History, 1791–92. 2.   Negro, Santo Domingo, 1791–
92. 3. France. Comité Colonial.
N.Y.P.L.   March 26, 1917.

NT   0037765   NN PPAmP MB

     Tarbe, Charles, 1756–1804.

         Projets de résolution, présentés par C. Tarbé, à la
suite de son opinion sur les colonies; ₍11 prairial an
5 ₍30 May 1797.₎
         n. t.-p.   ₍Paris, 1797.₎   21b.   pp. 4.

NT   0037766   NIC RPJCB

Tarbé, Charles, 1756–1804.
     Rapport et project de décret présentés au nom
du Comité colonial, sur les difficultés que présente l'exécution du décret du 14 mai dernier
         see under   France. Assemblée Nationale
Législative, 1791–1792. Comité Colonia.
[supplement]

Tarbé, Charles, 1756–1804.
    Rapport et Projet de Décret Relatifs
au debarquement de 217 negres... Paris,
1792

NT   0037768   RPJCB

     Tarbé, Charles, 1756–1804.
         Rapport et projet de résolution présentés au
Conseil des Cinq-Cents par Ch. Tarbé
           see under   France. Commission des
     Colonies, 1795–

Tarbé, Charles, 1756–1804.
    Rapport sur les troubles de Saint-Domingue, fait à l'As-
semblée nationale, par Charles Tarbé ... Au nom du Comité
colonial ... imprimé par ordre de l'Assemblée nationale.
Paris, Imprimerie nationale, 1791–₍92₎
    3 pts. and app. in 1 v. tab. 8°.
    At foot of first page of part one "Colonies, n°. 12," of part three
"Colonies, n°. 19."

    Contents.—₍1. ptie₎ Rapport ... le 10 décembre, 1791.—2. ptie.
Rapport ... le 10 janvier, 1792.—3. ptie. Rapport ... le 29 février,
1792.—Réplique a J. P. Brissot ... par Charles Tarbé ... sur les
troubles de Saint-Domingue; prononcée à l'Assemblée nationale, le 22
novembre 1792.—Pièces justificatives du Rapport ... procès-verbaux,
arrêtés, proclamations, &c. de l'Assemblée coloniale de la partie fran-
çoise de Saint-Domingue.—₍1.₎–3. Suite des pièces justificatives relatives aux troubles de Saint-Domingue ...

    1. Haiti—Hist.—Revolution. 1791–1804. 2. Haiti—Hist.—Sources.
3. Brissot de Warville, Jean Pierre, 1754–1793.

F1921.T17   2—12696

NT   0037771   DLC PPAmP NN RPJCB MB

RARE BOOK
DEPT.   Tarbé, Charles, 1756–1804.
×XH   Rapport sur les troubles de Saint-Domingue,
.716C   fait a l'Assemblée nationale, par Charles Tarbé
.T17R   ... au nom du Comité colonial, le 29 février
no.3   1792. Imprimé par ordre de l'Assemblée nationale.
         Troisième partie.
         A Paris, De l'Imprimerie nationale. ₍1792₎

         31p. 19.5cm.(8vo)
         Caption title; imprint from p₍31.
         At foot of p.₍1₎: Colonies, n°.19. A.

NT   0037772   MB PPAmP

RARE BOOK
DEPT.   Tarbé, Charles, 1756–1804.
×XH   Réplique a J.P. Brissot ... par Charles Tarbé
.716C   ... sur les troubles de Saint-Domingue; prononcée
.T17R   à l'Assemblée nationale, le 22 novembre 1792.
no.4   A Paris, De l'Imprimerie nationale. ₍1792₎

         19p. 19.5cm.(8vo)
         Caption title; imprint from p.19.
         At foot of p.1: Colonies, K.   A.

NT   0037773   MB RPJCB

RARE BOOK
DEPT.   Tarbé, Charles, 1756–1804.
×XH   Suite des Pièces justificatives relatives aux
.716C   troubles de Saint-Domingue. Imprimée par décret
.T17R   de l'Assemblée nationale, du 16 février 1792.
no.6   A Paris, De l'Imprimerie nationale. ₍1792₎

         ₍161₎–215p. 19.5cm.(8vo)
         Caption title: imprint from p.215.
         Continues Charles Tarbé's Pièces justificatives
         du Rapport sur les troubles de Saint-Domingue ...

NT   0037774   MB

     Tarbé, E., & Cie.
         Épreuves de caractères. E. Tarbé & Cⁱᵉ
           see under   Fonderie générale des caractères
     français et étrangers, Paris.

Tarbé, E., & Cie.
Premier cahier; caractères romains et ita-
liques, lettres de titres et d'affiches. Paris,
Béthune et Plon, 1835.
[100] l. 27cm.

Price list bound in at front.

1. Printing - Specimens. 2. Type and type-
founding.

NT 0037776 NNC

Tarbé, Edmond, 1838-1900.
Angele, tr. from the French of Edmond Tarbé, by
H. W. Bartol. Philadelphia and London, J. B. Lippincott
company [1917]
302 p. 19½ᶜᵐ. $1.25

I. Bartol, H. W., tr. II. Title.
[Full name: Edmond Joseph Louis Tarbé des Sablons]
Library of Congress   PZ3.T17A   17-7814

NT 0037777 DLC TxU MB

Tarbé, Edmond, 1838-1900.
The city of pleasure
see under Sims, George Robert,
1847-1922.

Tarbé, Edmond, 1838-1900.
Martyre!
see under Dennery, Adolphe Philippe,
1811-1899.

MUSIC
LIBRARY
M   Tarbé, Eugène, comp.
+1730   Album du Gaulois; oeuvres inédites. Recueil-
+T3   lies par Eugène Tarbé & Armand Gouzien. [Paris,
Impr. Becquet, 1869?]
score (2 v.) illus. 33cm.
Cover title.

1. Songs, French I. Gouzien, Armand, comp.
II. Title

NT 0037780 WU

Tarbé, Louis.   No. 26 in **M.391.28.2
Serments envolés. Chanson du vieux temps [T. Accomp. de piano.
3 pp. Fac-simile].
(In Album du Gaulois. Vol. 2. [Paris.] 1869.)

F1458 — T.r. — Songs. With music.

NT 0037781 MB

[Tarbé, Louis Hardouin] 1753-1806.
Lettre écrite à m. le president de
l'Assemblée nationale, par le ministre des
contributions publiques, pour rendre compte à
l'Assemblée nationale de l'état des opérations
relatives à la fabrication des différentes
espèces de monnoies, au 19 août 1791. Imprimée
par ordre de l'Assemblée nationale ...
[Paris, Impr. nationale, 1791]
7 p. 22.5 cm. (In Finances françaises,
1791-94, no. 14)

Caption title.
Signed by the author.

NT 0037783 MH-BA NIC

FR REV
DC
165   Tarbé, Louis Hardouin, 1753-1806.
.5   Mémoire et états relatifs à la fabrication
R31   des monnoies; présentés à l'Assemblée.Na-
[v.5]   tionale le 6 fév. 1792. [Paris, 1792]
no.36   54 p. 19cm.

Paris. Bibl. Natl. Dépt. des imprimés.
Cat. de l'histoire de la Révolution française. 4¹, 32212.
No. 36 in vol. lettered: Recueil des
pièces de   l'Assemb. Nationale.
[v.5]

NT 0037784 NIC

FR REV
DC
165   Tarbé, Louis Hardouin, 1753-1806.
.5   Mémoire lu à l'Assemblée Nationale, le
R31   12 oct. 1791, sur l'administration des con-
[v.7]   tributions publiques. [Paris, Impr. Natl.,
no.21   1791?]
19 p. 19cm.

Paris. Bibl. Natl.. Dépt. des imprimés.
Cat. de l'histoire de la Révolution française. 4¹, 32211.
No. 21 in vol. lettered: Recueil des
pièces de l'   Assemb. Nationale. [v.7]

NT 0037785 NIC

[Tarbé, Louis Hardouin] 1753-1806.
Mémoire sur le cadastre de la France, lu par
le ministre des contributions publiques, à
l'Assemblée nationale, le lundi 21 mai 1792;
imprimé par ordre de l'Assemblée nationale ...
[Paris, Impr. nationale, 1792]
6 p. fold.table. 23 cm. (In Finanzen
der französischen revolution, v.2, no. 8)

Caption title.
"Division du royaume, no. 4."

NT 0037786 MH-BA

Tarbé, Louis Hardouin Prosper.
See
Tarbé, Prosper, 1809-1871.

Tarbé, Louise Marie Victoire Guyot
see Guyot-Tarbé, Louise Marie Victoire.

Tarbé, Prosper, 1809-1871.
La ballade des trois états de France, chantée
et dansée à Reims, sous Louis XI. 28p. Reims,
1847.

NT 0037789 OCl

Tarbé, Prosper i. e. Louis Hardouin Prosper,
1809-1871.
Reims. *Archives municipales.*
[Catalogue des manuscrits de la] Collection P. Tarbé;
par M. L. Demaison.
(*In* France. Ministère de l'instruction publique et des beaux-arts. Catalogue général des manuscrits des bibliothèques publiques de France. Départements. Paris, 1909. 25ᶜᵐ. t. 39ᵗᵗ)

[Tarbé, Prosper] 1809-1871, ed.
Les chansonniers de Champagne aux XIIᵉ et XIIIᵉ siècles
... Reims [Impr. de P. Regnier] 1850.
lvi p., 1 l., 163 p., 1 l. 22ᶜᵐ. (Collection des poètes de Champagne an-
térieurs au XVIᵉ siècle, t. 9)
"Tiré à 225 exemplaires, dont 16 sur papier de couleur."
"Recherches sur la vie & les oeuvres des chansonniers de Champagne aux
XIIᵉ & XIIIᵉ siècles" (signed P. Tarbé): p. [vi]-lvi.
1. French poetry—Old French. 2. French literature—Champagne.
I. Title.
[Full name: Louis Hardouin Prosper Tarbé]
25-15115
Library of Congress   PQ1303.T3 t. 9

NT 0037791 DLC MiU OCU NjP ICU

Tarbé, Prosper, 1809-1871, ed.
Thibaud I, king of Navarre, 1201-1253.
Chansons de Thibault IV, comte de Champagne et de Brie,
roi de Navarre ... Reims [Imp. de P. Regnier] 1851.

Tarbé, Prosper, 1809-1871.
Description of Reims Cathedral for the use
of the visitors
see under title   [supplement]

Tarbé, Prosper, 1809-1871.
L'épistre de monsieur Saint Estienne ...
see under Catholic Church. Liturgy and
ritual.

Tarbé, Prosper i. e. Louis Hardouin Prosper, 1809-187L
... Examen critique et analytique de diverses chartes
des Xᵉ, XIᵉ, XIIᵉ et XIIIᵉ siècles, relatives à la Touraine.
<Communiqué par M. Prosper Tarbé.> [Paris? 1837?]
63 p. 22ᶜᵐ.
Caption title.
At head of title: Extrait de la Revue rétrospective, nᵒ de janvier 1837.

I. Touraine—Hist.—Sources.

Library of Congress   DC611.T722T3   7-27276

NT 0037795 DLC

Tarbé, Prosper, ed.
Inventaire après le décès de Richard Picque
archeveque de Reims. 1389. Reims, 1842.
(2) xvii, 168 p. 16°. [Société des bibliophiles de Reims. 8]

NT 0037796 MB NN MH

944.32
So 13   [TARBÉ, PROSPER] 1809-1871, ed.
no.4   [Les lépreux a Reims. Quinzième siècle.
[Reims] Société des bibliophiles de Reims, 1842.
xx, 23p. 17cm.

Preface signed: Prosper Tarbé.
"No. 24."
Bound in: Société des bibliophiles de
Reims. [Mémoires, no.4]

NT 0037797 PU NN

Tarbé, Prosper, 1809-1871, ed.
Louis XI et la sainte ampoule
see under France. Sovereigns, etc.,
1461-1483 (Louis XI)

---

*Tarbé, Prosper, 1809-1871, ed.

Deschamps, Eustache, d. 1406?
Le miroir de mariage; poème inédit d'Eustache Deschamps; publié par P. Tarbé ... Reims, Brissard-Binet,
1865.

Tarbé, Prosper, 1809-1871, ed.
Le noble et gentil jeu de l'arbaleste à Reims
see under title

Tarbé, Prosper, 1809–1871, ed.
Notice sur la vie et les œuvres de Blondel de
Néele
Blondel *de Néele, 12th cent.*
Les œuvres de Blondel de Néele ... Reims ⸢P. Dubois⸣ 1862.

Tarbé, Prosper, *1809-1871.*   4098.111
Notre-Dame de Reims.
= Reims. Quentin-Dailly. 1845. 139, (5) pp. Plates. 12°.

D5841 — Rheims Cathedral.

NT 0037802   MB

Tarbé, Prosper, 1809–1871.
Notre-Dame de Reims. 2. éd. rev'et augm.
par l'auteur. Illustrée d'un plan, de 6 gravures
sur acier et de 25 gravures sur bois. Reims,
Quentin-Dailly, 1852.
159 p. illus.
1. Reims. Notre-Dame (Cathedral) I. Title.

NT 0037803   CLU PP CtY NjP

---

*Tarbé, Prosper, 1809–1871, ed.

Coquillart, Guillaume, 1450 (*ca.*)–1510.
Les œuvres de Guillaume Coquillart ... Reims, Brissard-Binet; Paris, Techener, 1847.

---

*Tarbé, Prosper', 1809–1871, ed.

Guillaume *de Machaut, d.* 1377.
Les œuvres de Guillaume de Machault. Reims, Chez
tous les libraires; Paris, Techener, 1849.

---

*Tarbé, Prosper, 1809–1871, ed.

⸢Ovide moralisé⸣
Les œuvres de Philippe de Vitry. Reims ⸢Impr. de P.
Regnier⸣ 1850.

Tarbé, Prosper, 1809–1871, ed.

Deschamps, Eustache, *d.* 1406?
Œuvres inédites d'Eustache Deschamps ... Paris, Techener; ⸢etc., etc.⸣ 1849.

---

*Tarbe, Prosper, 1809–1871, ed.

⸢Guillaume *de Machaut*⸣ *d.* 1377.
Poésies d'Agnès de Navarre-Champagne, dame de Foix
... Paris, A. Aubry; ⸢etc., etc.⸣ 1856.

⸢Tarbé, Prosper⸣ 1809–1871, *ed.*
Poètes de Champagne antérieurs au siècle de François
1er. Proverbes champenois avant le xvie siècle ... Reims
⸢impr. de P. Regnier⸣ 1851.
xlviii (i. e. xlviii), 176 p. 22 cm. ⸢Collection des poètes de
Champagne antérieurs au xvie siècle, t. 13⸣
"Tiré à 250 exemplaires, dont 16 sur papier de couleur."
CONTENTS.—Recherches sur la vie et les œuvres de quelques poètes
de Champagne antérieurs au règne de François 1er.—Proverbes champenois avant le xvie siècle.—Le roman du Renard contrefait par le
clerc de Troyes; Fragments.—Glossaire.
1. French poetry — Old French — Hist. & crit. 2. French literature—Champagne. 3. Proverbs, French. I. Renart le contrefait.
II. Title: Proverbes champenois.

PQ1303.T3 t.13   25—15116

NT 0037809   DLC NjP NN GU MiU OC1 ICU MB

Tarbé, Prosper, 1809–1871.
Recherches sur l'histoire du langage et des patois de Champagne. ⸢Par⸣ P. Tarbé ... Reims ⸢Impr. de P. Regnier⸣ 1851.
2 v. in 1. fold. tab. 21cm. ⸢Collection des poètes champenois antérieurs au xvie siècle, t. xiv–xv⸣
"Cette édition se tire à 350 exemplaires, dont 16 sur papier de couleur."
CONTENTS.—t. 1. Recherches sur l'histoire du langage du langage et
des patois de Champagne. Monuments de l'ancien langage en Champagne et dans la province ecclésiastique de Reims. Monuments des
patois de Champagne.—t. 2. Glossaire de Champagne ancien et moderne.
1. French language—Dialects—Champagne. 2. French literature—
Champagne.
⸢*Full name:* Louis Hardouin Prosper Tarbé⸣
11—8087
Library of Congress   PC3012.T3 t. xiv–xv

NT 0037810   DLC PBm MiU MB NN NjP ViU

Tarbé, Prosper, 1809–1871, *ed.*
Recueil de poésies calvinistes (1550–1566) pub. par P.
Tarbé ... 2. éd. ... Reims ⸢Impr. de P. Dubois et cie⸣ 1866.
xliij, 210 p. 22 cm.
From the manuscript compilation in the Bibliothèque nationale
(mss. fr. 22560–65) known under title, "Collection de Rasse de Nœux,
guerres civiles"; with additions from other sources.
1. French poetry—16th cent. 2. France—Hist.—Wars of the Huguenots, 1562–1598. 3. Lorraine, Charles, cardinal de, 1525–1574—
Poetry. 4. Guise, François de Lorraine, 2. duc de, 1519–1563—Poetry.
I. Rasse des Nœux, François, fl. 1562–1575, comp.

PQ1173.T3   18—13851

                    NjPT NjP NN NNH
NT 0037811   DLC NIC NcD CtY PU MiU OC1W OC1 ScU NcU

Tarbé, Prosper i. e. **Louis Hardouin Prosper,** 1809–1871.
Reims. Ses rues et ses monuments, par Prosper Tarbé.
Reims, Quentin-Dailly, 1844.
494 p. front., 3 pl., 2 fold. plans. 20cm.
Cover-title: Reims; essais historiques sur ses rues et ses monuments ...
Reims, 1845.

1. Reims.
10–25466
Library of Congress   DC801.R36T3

NT 0037812   DLC NjP MH

---

*Tarbé, Prosper, 1809–1871, ed.

Auberi le Bourgoing (*Chanson de geste*)
Le roman d'Aubery le Bourgoing. Reims ⸢Impr. de P.
Regnier⸣ 1849.

Tarbe, Prosper, 1809–1871, ed.
Leduc, Herbert, *de Dammartin, 13th cent.*
Le roman de Foulque de Candie, par Herbert Leduc, de
Dammartin ... Reims ⸢P. Dubois, imprimeur⸣ 1860.

Tarbé, Prosper, 1809–1871, ed.

PQ1303
.T3
t. 10   **Girard de Viane** (*Chanson de geste*)
Le roman de Girard de Viane, par Bertrand de Bar-sur-
Aube. Reims ⸢Imp. de P. Regnier⸣ 1850.

---

*Tarbé, Prosper, 1809–1871, ed.

Quatre fils Aimon.
Le roman des quatre fils Aymon, princes des Ardennes.
Reims ⸢Impr. de P. Dubois⸣ 1861.

---

*Tarbé, Prosper, 1809–1871, ed.

Chrestien *de Troyes, 12th cent.*
Le roman du Chevalier de la Charrette, par Chretien
de Troyes et Godefroy de Laigny. Reims ⸢Impr. de P.
Regnier⸣ 1849.

⸢Tarbé, Prosper⸣ 1809–1871, *ed.*
Romancero de Champagne ... Reims ⸢Impr. de P.
Dubois⸣ 1863–64.
5 v. 21½ cm. (*Half-title:* Collection des poètes de Champagne
antérieurs au xvie siècle. ⸢t. 20–24⸣)
CONTENTS.—⸢t. I⸣ 1. ptie. Chants religieux.—t. II, 2. ptie. Chants
populaires.—t. III, 3. ptie. Chants légendaires et historiques, 420–
1550.—t. IV, 3. ptie. Chants historiques, 1550–1750.—t. V, 3. ptie.
Chants historiques, 1750–1829.
1. French poetry—Old French. 2. French literature—Champagne.
I. Title.

PQ1303.T3 t. 20–24   25—15117

NT 0037818   DLC PPT OC1 MiU NjP NN ICU IU CU TNJ OC1

Folio
J
385   Tarbé, Prosper, 1809–1871.
Saint-Remi de Reims; dalles du XIIIe siècle.
Reims, Typographie de Assy, 1847.
1 v. (chiefly plates) 53 cm.
1. Reims. Saint-Remi (Church) 2. Decoration and ornament, Architectural. I.Title.

NT 0037819   CtY

RARE BOOK
DEPT
*XG
.841
.A10D
v.9   Tarbé, Prosper, 1809–1871.
Les sépultures de l'église Saint-Remi de
Reims. Par Prosper Tarbé.
Reims, Chez Brissart, libraire de la Société
des bibliophiles. M DCCC XLII. ⸢1842⸣
2p.l.,115,⸢23⸣p. 17.5cm.
Title vignette.
No.9 of 65 numbered copies; imprinted for
Auguste Duchesne.

NT 0037820   MB CtY NjP

---

*Tarbé, Prosper, 1809–1871, ed.

Huon *de Méri, fl.* 1234.
Le tornoiement de l'Antéchrist, par Huon de Mery (Sur
Seine.) ... Reims ⸢Impr. de P. Regnier⸣ 1851.

Tarbé, Prosper, 1809–1871.   331.04 T172
Travail et salaire, par Prosper Tarbé. Paris, Chez l'auteur;
⸢etc., etc.⸣ 1841].
⸢4⸣, 491, ⸢2⸣ p. 22½cm.

NT 0037822   ICJ NcD MH-BA PU

Tarbé, Prosper, 1809–1871.
Trésors des églises de Reims ... Ouvrage
orné de planches dessinées et lithographiées par
J.-J. Maquart. Reims, Assy, 1843.
338 p. plates. 30 cm.
1. Reims. 2. Church decoration and ornament
in France—Reims.

NT 0037823   NjP

J18
P622
859T   Tarbé, Prosper, 1809–1871
La vie et les œuvres de Jean-Baptiste Pigalle
sculpteur. Paris, Ve J. Renouard, 1859.
268p. fold. geneal. table. 25cm.
Bibliographical footnotes.

1. Pigalle, Jean Baptiste, 1714–1785.

        MB CLSU FMU MoU PPPM NSbSU WaU TNJ AU ViU
NT 0037824   CtY OC1MA InU NN IU MH NNC MdBP NjP NcD

Tarbé, S   A
see Tarbé des Sablons, Sebastien André,
1762–1837.

Tarbé, Théodore.
    Recherches historiques et anecdotiques sur la ville de Sens, sur son antiquité et ses monuments; recueillies et rédigées par M. Théodore Tarbé.   Sens, T. Tarbé, 1838.
    1 p. l., iv, 516 p.   18½ᵐᵐ.

    1. Sens, France.   4-14999

    Library of Congress   DC801.S5T2

NT 0037826   DLC

Tarbé, Théodore.   *4630.26
    Recherches historiques et anecdotiques sur la ville de Sens, son antiquité et ses monuments. 2e édition illustrée de 120 dessins par Marie Guyot ... Préface de Camille Doucet.
    =   Paris. Quantin. 1888. (3), x, (1), 227, 4 pp. Illus. Portrait. Plates. 4°.

    *D5558 — Sens, France. Antiq. — Guyot, Louise Marie Victorine, illus.

NT 0037827   MB OU MH

Tarbé de Saint-Hardouin, François Pierre H   1813?-
    ... Notices biographiques sur les ingénieurs des ponts et chaussées depuis la création du corps, en 1716, jusqu'à nos jours, par F.-P.-H. Tarbé de Sᵗ-Hardouin ... Paris [etc.] Baudry et cⁱᵉ, 1884.

    276 p.   24½ᶜᵐ.   (Encyclopédie des travaux publics)

    1. Engineers, French.
                                                               5-24742
    Library of Congress   TA139.T2

NT 0037828   DLC ICJ

Tarbé de Saint Hardouin, François Pierre H.,
1813?-
    Rapport d'une commission spéciale d'ingénieurs du Corps Royal des ponts et chaussées sur la situation des travaux du Canal de l'Ourcq
    see under   France. Administration générale des ponts et chaussées et des mines.

Tarbé de Vauxclairs, Jacques Binet
    see
Binet Tarbé de Vauxclairs, Jacques.

Tarbé de Vauxclairs, Jean Bernard.
    Dictionnaire des travaux publics, civils, militaires et maritimes, considérés dans leurs rapports avec la législation, l'administration et la jurisprudence ... par M. le chevalier Tarbé de Vauxclairs ...   Paris, 1835.
    27 cm.

NT 0037831   CtY

Tarbé de Vauxclairs, Jean Bernard
    Rapport sur la vis d'Archimède a double effet, lu a la Société d'encouragement pour l'industrie nationale.   Caen, Poisson, 1816.
    12 p.

NT 0037832   PPAmP

Tarbé des Sablons, Edmond Joseph Louis

                    See

Tarbé, Edmond, 1838-1900

Tarbé des Sablons, Michelle-Catherine-Josephine Gvespereau.
    Onésie, ou Les soirees de l'abbaye, par Madame*** auteur D'Eudolie, Enguerrand, Sidonie, et la Marquise de Valcour.   Paris, Pigoreau, 1833.
    2 v.

NT 0037834   PPCCH

    [Tarbé des Sablons, Michelle-Catherine-Josephine Gvespereav]
    Sidonie; ou, L'abus des talens.   Par Madame***.   Paris, Maradan, H. Nicolle, 1820.
    4 v.   17.5 cm.

NT 0037835   CtY

PᵗQ
2450
.T585
1844
    Tarbé des Sablons, Michelle-Catherine-Josephine Gvespereau
    Onésie, ou Les soirées de l'abbaye; suivie de Enguerrand, ou Le duel.   Paris, Waille, 1844.
    436p.   19cm.
    Published anonymously in 1733 and 1825 respectively by the wife of Sebastien-André Tarbé des Sablons, (1762-1837) a civil administrator.

    I.Title. II. Title: Enguerrand.

NT 0037836   LLafS

848
T171rX
    Tarbé des Sablons, Michelle Catherine Josephine Guespereau.
    Roseline, ou de la nécessité de la religion dans l'education des femmes. 2. éd.   Paris, A. Canuet, 1840.
    431 p.   20cm.
    By Mme. Sebastien André Tarbé des Sablons.

NT 0037837   LU

843.7
T179z
RARE BOOK
COLLECTION
    Tarbé des Sablons, Michelle-Catherine-Josephine Gvespereau
    Zoé, ou La femme légère, suivie du curé de Bérilès; par l'auteur d'eudolie. Bibliothèque Catholique de la Belgique. 7ᵉ ouvrage pour 1825. Prix: Fr. I. 50. [Religious ornament] A Louvain, Vanlinthout et Vandenzande, 1825.
    [4], ii, 228 p.   22cm.

    Publisher's catalogue inserted before title. Imprimatur and publisher's stamp verso title. Unbound, in paper cover.
    T. Title.

NT 0037838   FU

    Tarbé des Sablons, Mme. Sebastien André
    see   Tarbé des Sablons, Michelle Catherine Josephine Gvespereav.

    Tarbé des Sablons, Sebastien André, 1762-1837.
    Manuel pratique et élémentaire des poids et mesures et du calcul décimal ...   Paris, Rondonneau, 1801.
    235 p.

NT 0037840   PPAmP

    Tarbé des Sablons, Sebastien André, 1762-1837.
    Manuel pratique et élémentaire des poids et mesures, et du calcul décimal... Avec la nouvelle nomenclature... Nouv. éd.;exactement rev.,corr. et augm... Paris,Chez Rondonneau... et Merlin,nivose an XII [1803 or 4]
    xvi,395p.incl.tabs.   15cm.

    1.Weights and measures. 2.Calculus. 3.Weights and measures - Nomenclature.

NT 0037841   CtY-M

    Tarbé des Sablons, Sébastien André, 1762-1837.
    Manuel pratique et élémentaire des poids et mesures, des monnaies, et du calcul décimal; contenant les tables et instructions les plus propres à étendre la connaissance du système métrique et des mesures usuelles. Ouvrage utile à tous les banquiers, marchands ... Nouvelle éd., entièrement refondue, et augmentée ... Par S. A. Tarbé ... Paris, J. S. Merlin, 1813.
    viii, 532 p.   tables.   14 cm.

NT 0037842   NNC DBS MB

QC
89
F7T3
1826
    Tarbé des Sablons, Sébastien André, 1762-1837.
    Manuel pratique et élémentaire des poids et mesures, des monnaies, et du calcul décimal; contenant les tables et instructions les plus propres à étendre la connaissance du système mètrique et des mesures usuelles. Ouvrage utile à tous les banquiers, marchands, entrepreneurs, arpenteurs, notaires, propriétaires, employés des administrations, instituteurs et élèves des écoles du royaume, et aux étrangers. 12. éd. rev. et corr.

    d'après les nouvelles lois et ordonnances et augm. de plusieurs articles importans. Paris, Roret, 1826.
    464 p.   tables.   14 cm.

    1. Weights and measures--France. I. Title.

NT 0037844   LU

    Tarbe des Sablons, Sébastien André, 1762-1837.
    Manuel pratique et élémentaire des poids et mesures, et du calcul décimal; contenant les instructions les plus propres à familiariser avec la connaissance du nouveau système, et un grand nombre de tables de comparaison, basées sur le mètre et le kilogramme définitifs. Avec la nouvelle nomenclature. Ouvrage utile à tous les banquiers, marchands, entrepreneurs, arpenteurs, notaires, propriétaires, et particulièrement aux instituteurs et élèves des écoles nationales Nouvelle éditions, exactement revue, corrigée et augmentée. Par S.-A. Tarbé. A Paris, Chez Rondonneau; et Merlin, Nivose an XII [1804]
    2 v.
    v.2 has no t.-p.

NT 0037845   PMA

389
T171m
1809
    Tarbé des Sablons, Sebastian Andre, 1762-1837.
    Manuel pratique et élémentaire des poids et mesures, et du calcul décimal; contenant les instructions les plus propres à familiariser avec la connaisance du nouveau système, et un grand nombre de tables de comparaison, basées sur le mètre définitif   9.ed. exactement rev., cor. et augm. par S. A. Tarbe.   Paris, Chez Merlin, 1809.
    420p.

    1. Weights and measures.

NT 0037846   IU RPB

Tarbé des Sablons, Sebastien André, 1762-1837.
Nouveau manuel complet des poids et mesures, des monnaies, du calcul décimal, et de la vérification. Nouv. éd., entièrement refondue... Paris, Roret, 1840.
480p. (Manuels-Roret)

NT 0037847   ScU

Tarbé des Sablons, Sebastien Andre, 1762-1837.
Nouveau manuel complet des poids et mesures, des monnaies, du calcul decimal, et de la verification. Nouvelle edition ... Paris, 1845.
480 p. 9 x 15 cm. (Manuels Roret)

NT 0037848   DBS DP NN

Tarbé des Sablons, Sebastien André, 1762-1837.
... Nouveau petit manuel des poids et mesures; a l'usage des ouvriers et des ecoles. Extrait du manuel complet des poids et mesures et de la verification approuve par M. le ministre du commerce. Par M. Tarbe nouv. ed. Paris, Roret, 1839.
72 p. 15.5 cm.

NT 0037849   DBS NN

1003   Tarbeaux, Frank, 1852-
.8947   Adventurer, being the autobiography of
.1933   one Frank Tarbeaux. London, Long, 1933
254 p. 23 cm

Pub., 1930, under title: The autobiography of Frank Tarbeaux

1. ADVENTURE AND ADVENTURES I. T

NT 0037850   NjP GU

Tarbeaux, Frank, 1852-
...Autobiographie de Frank Tarbeaux. Tr. et présenté par Marcel Duhamel. (In: L'Arbalète; revue de littérature. Lyon, 1944. ₍t., 9, p. 51-68.₎)

At head of title: Donald Henderson Clarke.

L. Clarke, Donald Henderson,   1887-   , ed. II. Duhamel, Marcel, tr. III. Ser.
N. Y. P. L.   June 20, 1949

NT 0037851   NN

Tarbeaux, Frank, 1852-
The autobiography of Frank Tarbeaux as told to Donald Henderson Clarke ... New York, The Vanguard press, 1930.
ix, ₍1₎ p., 3 l., 3-286 p., 1 l. 21½ cm.
Maps on lining-papers.

1. Adventure and adventurers. i. Clarke, Donald Henderson, 1887- ed.
                               30-8243
Library of Congress   G530.T3

    MoU NcD ICU OC1 OC1U CoU NN MH MWA
NT 0037852   DLC WaU OrCS IdB OrU CaBVaU UU PP TxU MB

Tarbeev, D
Море Лаптевых и его побережье. Ленинград, Изд-во Главсевморпути₍etc.₎ 1940.
76, ₍2₎ p. illus. 21 cm.
"Использованная литература": p. 76-₍77₎

1. Arctic regions. 2. Siberia—Descr. & trav. 3. Nordenskjöld sea. i. Title. *Title transliterated:* More Laptevykh i ego poberezh'e.

G820.T3   49-33816

NT 0037853   DLC

Tarbel, Guy, tr.

Wallace, Edgar, 1875-1932.
... Un outsider du Derby; "le 55" (The flying fifty-five) traduit par Guy Tarbel. ₍Paris₎ Hachette ₍1934₎

Tarbel, Jean
    see   Delorme-Jules Simon, Mme. J

Tarbell, Arthur Wilson, 1872-1946, ed.
The Brown book of Boston. v. 1-10, v. 11, no. 1; May 1900-May 1905. Boston, The Bernard-Richards co., ltd. ₍etc.₎ 1900-05.

Tarbell, Arthur Wilson, 1872-1946.
Cape Cod ahoy! A travel book for the summer visitor, by Arthur Wilson Tarbell. Boston, R. G. Badger ₍°1932₎
347 p. front., plates. 19½ᶜᵐ.
Map on front lining-paper.

1. Cape Cod—Descr. & trav. i. Title.
Library of Congress   F73.C3T25   32-30369
—— Copy 2.   MB
Copyright A 56618   ₍3₎   917.449

NT 0037857   DLC MH WaE OEac NN MB

F72   Tarbell, Arthur Wilson, 1872-1946.
C3T25   Cape Cod ahoy! A travel book for the
1932   summer visitor. Boston, A.T. Ramsey ₍1933, c1932₎
347 p. illus. 20cm.

1. Cape Cod - Descr. & trav. I. Title.

NT 0037858   GU

Tarbell, Arthur Wilson, 1872-1946.
Cape Cod ahoy! A travel book for the summer visitor, by Arthur Wilson Tarbell. New and rev. ed. Boston, Little, Brown, and company, 1934.
xiii p., 2 l., ₍3₎-367 p. front., plates. 19½ᵐ.
"First printing, July, 1932 ... Fifth printing, November, 1934."

1. Cape Cod—Descr. & trav. i. Title.
Library of Congress   F72.C3T25 1934   34-39883
—— Copy 2.
Copyright A 78367   ₍5₎   917.449

NT 0037859   DLC MeB PP PPL OLak OO OC1h NN

Tarbell, Arthur Wilson, 1872-1946.
917.449   Cape Cod ahoy! A travel book for the summer visitor, by
T179c   Arthur Wilson Tarbell. Rev. ed. Boston, Little, Brown, 1935.
xiii p., 2 l., ₍3₎-367 p. front., plates. 19½ᵐ.
"First printing, July, 1932 ... Sixth printing, June, 1935."

NT 0037860   NcD

Tarbell, Arthur Wilson, 1872-1946.
Cape Cod ahoy! A travel book for the summer visitor, by Arthur Wilson Tarbell. Rev. ed. Boston, Little, Brown and company, 1937.
xiii p., 2 l., ₍3₎-379 p. front., plates. 19½ᵐ.
"First printing. July, 1932 ... New edition, seventh printing, May, 1937."

1. Cape Cod—Descr. & trav. i. Title.
                                 37-19334
Library of Congress   F72.C3T25 1937
—— Copy 2.
Copyright A 109209   ₍5₎   917.449

NT 0037861   DLC MB WaTU OC1

Tarbell, Arthur Wilson, 1872-1946.
I retire to cape Cod, by Arthur W. Tarbell. New York, S. Daye inc. ₍1944₎
xiv p., 1 l., 143 p. incl. front., illus. 21ᵐ.
Map on lining-papers.

1. Cape Cod. i. Title.
                                 44-40167
Library of Congress   F72.C3T26
           ₍8₎   917.449

    OLak OC1
NT 0037862   DLC CoU PP PPL OrU CaBVa CaBViP Or WaS

Tarbell, Arthur Wilson, 1872-1946, ed.

National magazine ... v. 1-60, v. 61, no. 1-2; Oct. 1894-May/ June 1933. Boston, The Bostonian publishing company ₍etc.₎, 1894-1903₎; Chapple publishing company, limited ₍1903-33₎

Tarbell, Arthur Wilson, 1872-1946.
The story of Carnegie tech; being a history of Carnegie institute of technology from 1900 to 1935, by Dean Arthur Wilson Tarbell ... Pittsburgh, Pa., Carnegie institute of technology, 1937.
2 p. l., 3-270 p., 1 l. plates, ports. (incl. col. front.) 24½ᵐ.
Illustrated lining-papers.

1. Pittsburgh. Carnegie institute. Institute of technology.
Library of Congress   T171.C289T3   38-5728
—— Copy 2.
Copyright A 111567   ₍3₎   607.74886

NT 0037864   DLC PSC MH MiU WaS OO OC1 OC1W ICJ

Cst   Tarbell, Arthur Wilson, 1872-1946.
C21Et   The story of Carnegie tech; being a history of Carnegie institute of technology from 1900 to 1935, by Dean Arthur Wilson Tarbell ... Pittsburgh, Pa., Carnegie institute of technology, 1937.
2 p. l., 3-270 p., 1 l. plates, ports. (incl. col. front.) 24½ᵐ.
Illustrated lining-papers.
"Second edition."

√1. Carnegie Institute of Technology, Pittsburgh

NT 0037865   IU

TARBELL, Arthur W₍ilson₎, 1872-1946.
Tommy Atkins off for the Transvaal. [Boston, 1900].

pp.(6). 2 illustr.
Cut from the "National Magazine" Jan.1900, pp.[363]-367.

NT 0037866   MH

CT275
.T3A3　Tarbell, Daniel, b. 1811.
　　　Incidents of real life; dedicated to the
　　instruction of youth, and elevation of morality,
　　true religion, and politics. Montpelier, Vt.,
　　Argus and Patriot Book and Job Print. House,
　　1883.
　　　92 l.

　　Reproduced by xerography.

　　1. Tarbell, Daniel, b. 1811. I. Title.

NT　0037867　　NbU MH-BA NNC

Tarbell, Edmund Charles.
　　William Badger, 1752-1830, master shipbuilder of Maine.
　　Illus. by L. A. Avery. New York, Newcomen Society in
　　North America, 1955.
　　28 p. illus. 23 cm. (Newcomen address, 1955)

　　1. Badger, William, 1752-1830.

　　VM140.B3T3　　　　　　　　　　56-58447 ‡

NT　0037868　　ViU OClWHi FTaSU NmU MH LU NcRS CaBViP IdU OrCS WaPS
　　　　　　　　DLC NSyU MoU MiU OU CU AAP FU NN IU WHi

Tarbell, Emily.
　　The development of character thru extra-curricular activi-
　　ties ₍by₎ Emily Tarbell.
　　(*In* National education association of the United States. Addresses
　　and proceedings, 1932. p. 313-315)

　　1. Character—₍Study and₎ teaching. 2. Student activities. ₍2. Extra-
　　curricular activities₎ I. Title.　　　　　　　　　E 33-849
　　Library, U. S. Office of　　　　　Education L13.N212 1932
　　Library of Congress　　　　　　　L13.N4 1932

NT　0037869　　DHEW DLC

Tarbell, Frank Bigelow, 1853-1920.
De Cou, Herbert Fletcher, d. 1911.
　　... Antiquities from Boscoreale in Field museum of natural
　　history. By Herbert F. De Cou. With preface and cata-
　　logue of iron implements by F. B. Tarbell ... Chicago, 1912.

Tarbell, Frank Bigelow, 1853-1920.
Bibliography of Greek art
Heermance, Theodore Woolsey, 1872-1905.
　　Greek art, by T. W. Heermance ... Boston and New
　　York, A. W. Elson and company, 1901.

Tarbell, Frank Bigelow, 1853-1920.
　　A cantharus from the factory of Brygos in the
　　Boston Museum of Fine Arts.
　　5 p.　　2 pl.　　(In: The University of Chicago.
　　The decennial publications.　　Chicago, 1904.
　　4°.　Ser. 1., v. 6, p. 5-9)

NT　0037872　　NN PPL

Tarbell, Frank Bigelow, 1853-1920.
　　... Catalogue of bronzes, etc., in Field museum of natu-
　　ral history reproduced from originals in the National
　　museum of Naples. By F. B. Tarbell ... Chicago, 1909.
　　1 p. l., p. 93-144. pl. xxxvi-cxvii. 24½ᶜᵐ. (Field museum of natural his-
　　tory. Publication 130. Anthropological series. vol. vii, no. 3)

　　1. Bronzes, Ancient.

　　Library of Congress　　　　GN2.F4 vol. 7, no. 3　　10-2861

　　MoU NBuU WaU
　　CtY OCU MiU OCl ViU ICJ MH MdBWA OrPS KEmT OOxM GU
NT　0037873　　DLC CtY　　OrP OrU CaBVaU PP PSC PPPM OU

Tarbell, Frank Bigelow, 1853-1920.
Gc3.1　　... The decroos of the Demotionidai. A study
　　of the Attic phratry, by F.B.Tarbell.　Boston,
　　New York₍etc.₎Ginn & company₍1889₎
　　cover-title,19p.　25cm.
　　At head of title: Preprints of the American
　　journal of archaeology, June, 1889. Papers of
　　the American school of classical studies at
　　Athens.

NT　0037874　　CtY MB MH

Tarbell, Frank Bigelow, 1853-1920.
　　The direction of writing on Attic vases. By F. B. Tar-
　　bell.
　　(*In* Chicago.　University.　Studies in classical philology.　Chicago
　　₍etc.₎ 1895. 23ᶜᵐ. v. 1, p. 114-123)
　　Bibliographical foot-notes.

　　1. Inscriptions, Greek. 2. Vases, Greek.　　　　　A 34-331
　　Title from Univ. of Chi-　　　cago PA25.C55 vol. 1
　　Library of Congress　　　　　[PA25.C5 vol. 1]

NT　0037875　　ICU NIC NcD OCU OU MH CtY

Tarbell, Frank Bigelow, 1853-1920.
　　Form of the chlamys.　Chicago [1906]

NT　0037876　　NjP

Tarbell, Frank Bigelow, 1853-1920.
　　... A Greek hand-mirror in the Art institute of Chicago,
　　accompanied by a half-tone plate and A cantharus from the
　　factory of Brygos in the Boston museum of fine arts, accom-
　　panied by two heliotype plates, by Frank Bigelow Tarbell ...
　　Chicago, The University of Chicago press, 1902.
　　1 p. l., 4, 5 p.　illus., pl.　28¼ᶜᵐ.
　　Printed from First series, v. 6 (p. 1-9) of the Decennial publications
　　of the University of Chicago.

　　1. Art objects, Greek.　I. Title.

　　Library of Congress　　　　NK670.T12　　　2-24406

NT　0037877　　DLC OrP WaS MdBWA OCU OCl

Tarbell, Frank Bigelow, 1853-1920.　　*3363.4.Ser.1.6
　　A Greek hand-mirror in the Art Institute of Chicago. A cantharus
　　from the factory of Brygos in the Boston Museum of Fine Arts.
　　Plates.
　　(In University of Chicago. Decennial publications. Series 1.
　　Vol. 6, pp. 1-9. Chicago. 1904.)

　　F5788 — Greece. Antiq. — Mirrors. — Brygos. — Drinking cups.

NT　0037878　　MB PPL MiU OU NN

Tarbell, Frank Bigelow, 1853-1920.
　　... A history of Greek art, with an introductory chapter on
　　art in Egypt and Mesopotamia, by F. B. Tarbell ... Mead-
　　ville, Pa., New York ₍etc.₎, Flood and Vincent, 1896.
　　xiii, ₍1₎, 15-295 p.　front., illus. (incl. plans)　20ᶜᵐ.　₍Chautauqua lit-
　　erary and scientific circle₎
　　At head of title: Chautauqua reading circle literature.

　　1. Art, Greek—Hist.
　　　　　　　　　　　　　　　　　　　　　　4—11658
　　Library of Congress　　　　N5630.T2
　　　　　　　　　　　　　　　　　₍a44q1₎　　　　-709.38

　　OO NcD CaBViP CaBVaU OrMonO OrSaW
　　OCl OClMA IU NN MB DNW NjP NBB PPL IdU OCX PSC KMK
NT　0037879　　DLC PPLas PPMoI OrPR WaE NcD ODW OU OClU

Tarbell, Frank Bigelow, 1853-1920.
　　A history of Greek art, with an introductory
　　chapter on art in Egypt and Mesopotamia, by
　　F. B. Tarbell. New York, Macmillan ₍1896₎
　　xiii, ₍1₎, 15-295 p.　front., illus. (incl.
　　plans)　20cm.

　　1. Art, Greek—Hist.

NT　0037880　　ViU TU WaWW OrCS MeB FMU MdBJ

709.38　Tarbell, Frank Bigelow, 1853-1920.
T179h　　A history of Greek art, with an introductory chapter
　　on art in Egypt and Mesopotamia.　New York, Macmil-
　　lan, 1899₍ᶜ1896₎
　　295p.　front.,illus. (incl. plans)

　　1. Art, Greek - History.

NT　0037881　　FTaSU NjP MH MB OOxM

Tarbell, Frank Bigelow, 1853-1920.
　　A history of Greek art, with an introductory
　　chapter on art in Egypt and Mesopotamia, by
　　F. B. Tarbell ...　New York, The Macmillan
　　company; London, Macmillan & co., Ltd., 1902.
　　2 p.l., ii-xiii, 15-295 p.　front., illus.
　　(incl. plans)　20.5 cm.

NT　0037882　　PSt MeB NjP WaSpG

N
5630　Tarbell, Frank Bigelow, 1853-1920.
.T2　　A history of Greek art, with an introductory
1904　chapter on art in Egypt and Mesopotamia.
Collection　New York, Macmillan, 1904 [c1896]
　　295 p.　illus.　20 cm.
　　Includes bibliography.

　　1. Art, Greek - History.

NT　0037883　　NBuU Vi PP MH

Tarbell, Frank Bigelow, 1853-1920.
　　A history of Greek art, with an introductory
　　chapter on art in Egypt and Mesopotamia, by
　　F. B. Tarbell ... New York, The Macmillan co.;
　　London, Macmillan & co., ltd., 1905. ₍c1896₎
　　2 p.l., iii-xiii, 15-295 p. front., illus.
　　(incl. plans)　20 cm.

NT　0037884　　ViU PSC NcD MH PBa NjP NcD OLak

N
5630　Tarbell, Frank Bigelow, 1853-1920.
T2　　A history of Greek art, with an introductory chapter
1906　on art in Egypt and Mesopotamia, by F. B. Tarbell. New
　　York, Grosset & Dunlap [1906, ᶜ1896]
　　295 p. illus., plans. 20 cm. (Macmillan's standard library)

　　Bibliography: p. 291-292.

　　1. Art, Greek.

NT　0037885　　Vi WaS IdU MtU MH

733　Tarbell, Frank Bigelow, 1853-1920.
T17h　　A history of Greek art, with an introductory
1896.1　chapter of art in Egypt and Mesopotamia.
　　New York, Macmillan, 1907 ₍cl896₎
　　xiii,295p.　front., illus.　20cm.

　　1.Art, Greek - Hist.

NT　0037886　　NcU

Tarbell, Frank Bigelow, 1853-1920
　　A history of Greek art, with an
　　introductory chapter on art in Egypt
　　and Mesopotamia. N. Y., Grosset &
　　Dunlap, ₍1908₎
　　xiii, 15-295 p. front., illus. 19cm.
　　(On cover: Macmillan's Standard Library)

　　"Copyright, 1896"

NT　0037887　　NcD MH NBuU

Tarbell, Frank Bigelow, 1853–1920.
    A history of Greek art, with an introductory chapter on art in Egypt and Mesopotamia, by F. B. Tarbell ... New York, The Macmillan company, 1908.
    xiii, [1], 15–295 p. front., illus. (incl. plans) 19 cm. (*On cover:* The Macmillan standard library)

NT   0037888   MdBWA

Tarbell, F[rank] B[igelow] 1853–1920.   709.38
    A history of Greek art, with an introductory chapter on art in Egypt and Mesopotamia. New York: The Macmillan Co., 1910.
1 p. l., xiii, 15–295 p., 1 pl.   illus.   8°.

1. Greece.—Art.
N. Y. P. L.   March 18, 1911.

NT   0037889   NN PHC MH OC1W

TARBELL, Frank Bigelow, 1853–1920.
    A history of Greek art, with an introductory chapter on art in Egypt and Mesopotamia. New York, Macmillan company, etc., etc., 1912, [
[cop.1896].

    Illustr.

NT   0037890   MH-FA MiU

Tarbell, Frank Bigelow, 1853–1920.
    A history of Greek art, with an introductory chapter on art in Egypt and Mesopotamia, by F. B. Tarbell ... New York, The Macmillan company, 1913.
    xiii, [1], 15–295 p. front., illus. (incl. plans) 19 cm. (*On cover:* The Macmillan standard library)

1. Art, Greek—Hist.
    [N5630.T   ]   A 13—2298
The Booklist
for Library of Congress   [a52n½]

NT   0037891   PV PIm OrAshS Wa PRosC PBa OC1ND NN MU

Tarbell, Frank Bigelow, 1853–1920.
    (A) history of Greek art, with an introductory chapter on art in Egypt and Mesopotamia, by F. B. Tarbell ... New York, The Macmillan company, 1916.
    xiii [1] 15–295 p. front., illus. (incl. plans) 19 cm. (On cover: The Macmillan standard library)
    Greece - Ancient - Antiquities & fine arts.

NT   0037892   NcU OEac

TARBELL, F[rank] B[igelow], 1853–1920.
    A history of Greek art, with an introductory chapter on art in Egypt and Mesopotamia. New York, The Macmillan Co., etc., etc., 1919, [cop.1896].

    Plans and other illustr.

NT   0037893   MH

Tarbell, Frank Bigelow, 1853–1920
    A history of Greek art...N.Y. 1920.

    295 p.

NT   0037894   OO

TARBELL, Frank Bigelow, 1853–1920.
    A history of Greek art, with an introductory chapter on art in Egypt and Mesopotamia. New York, Macmillan company, etc., etc., 1922.

    Front. and other illustr.

NT   0037895   MH-SD

N
5630
TZ
1923
UGL
    Tarbell, Frank Bigelow, 1853–1920.
    A history of Greek art : with an introductory chapter on art in Egypt and Mesopotamia / by F. B. Tarbell. -- New York : Macmillan, 1923, c1896. 295 p. : ill. ; 20 cm. Bibliographical footnotes.
"Short list of books recommended ... " p. 291-292.

1. Art, Greek - History.

NT   0037896   TxU

Tarbell, Frank Bigelow, 1853–1920.   4077-456
    A history of Greek art. With an introductory chapter on art in Egypt and Mesopotamia.
 — New York. The Macmillan Co. 1924. 295 pp. Illus. Plates. Plans. 19 cm.

N1275 — Greece. F.a. Hist.

NT   0037897   MB ViU

N
5630
.T2
1926
    Tarbell, Frank Bigelow, 1853–1920.
    A history of Greek art, with an introductory chapter on art in Egypt and Mesopotamis, by F. B. Tarbell. New York, The Macmillan company, 1926 [1896]
    15–295 p. illus. 20 cm. (Chautauqua literary and scientific circle)

1. Art, Greek—Hist.

NT   0037898   OKentU

Tarbell, Frank Bigelow, 1853–1920.
    A history of Greek art, with an introductory chapter on art in Egypt and Mesopotamia, by F. B. Tarbell ... New York, The Macmillan company, 1927.
    xiii, [1], 15–295 p. front., illus. (incl. plans) 19 cm. (On cover: The Macmillan standard library)

NT   0037899   ViU MH PRosC

Tarbell, Frank Bigelow, 1853–1920.
    History of Greek Art.   1930.
    illus.

NT   0037900   WaT

N
5630
.T2
    Tarbell, Frank Bigelow, 1853–1920.
    A history of Greek art; with an introductory chapter on art in Egypt and Mesopotamia, by F. B. Tarbell. New York, Macmillan, 1936 [c1896] 295 p. illus., plans. 20 cm. Bibliographical footnotes.

1. Art, Greek—History.

NT   0037901   MSohG PPD PU-FA Or

Tarbell, Frank Bigelow, 1853–1920.
    FOR OTHER EDITIONS SEE MAIN ENTRY
Elson, A. W., & company, Boston.
    Illustrated catalogue of carbon prints on the rise and progress of Greek and Roman art. With descriptions by Prof. F. B. Tarbell ... and an introduction by T. W. Heermance ... 3d ed. Boston, U. S. A., A. W. Elson & co., 1899.

Tarbell, Frank Bigelow, 1853–1920.
    Inscriptions from Thisbe. By Frank Bigelow Tarbell, & J. C. Rolfe.
    (In Archaeological institute of America. American school of classical studies at Athens. Papers. 1892. v. 5)

NT   0037903   PU

Tarbell, Frank Bigelow, 1853–1920.
    New fragment of the preamble to Diocletian's edict, De pretiis rerum venalium. By Frank Bigelow Tarbell, J. C. Rolfe.
    (In Archaeological institute of America. American school of classical studies at Athens. Papers. 1892. v. 5)

NT   0037904   PU

TARBELL, Frank Bigelow, 1853–1920.
    A new fragment of the preamble to Diocletian's edict "De pretiis rerum venalium." Boston, etc. [1889].

    Reprints of the American journal of Archeolog. Dec.1889.
    By Frank Bigelow Tarbell and John Carew Rolfe

NT   0037905   MH

Tarbell, Frank Bigelow, 1853–1920.
    The palm of victory. F. B. Tarbell ... Chicago, The University of Chicago press [1908] cover-title, 264–272 p.   25.5 cm.
    Reprinted from Classical philology, vol. III, no. 3, July, 1908.

NT   0037906   CtY

Tarbell, Frank Bigelow, 1853–1920, ed.

Demosthenes.
    The Philippics of Demosthenes. Edited by Frank B. Tarbell ... Boston, Ginn & Heath. 1880.

Tarbell, Frank Bigelow, 1853–1920.
    Report on excavations near Stamata in Attika. By Frank Bigelow Tarbell, & Sir Charles Waldstein.
    (In Archaeological institute of America. American school of classical studies at Athens. Papers. 1892. v. 5)

NT   0037908   PU

Tarbell, Frank Bigelow, 1853–1920.   *7916.102.3
    Some present problems in the history of Greek sculpture.
    (In Congress of Arts and Science ... St. Louis, 1904. Vol. 3, pp. 605–617. Boston. 1906.)

G1836 — Greece. Fine arts. Sculp.

NT   0037909   MB

Tarbell, Frank Bigelow, 1853– *1920.*
... Three Etruscan painted sarcophagi, by F. B. Tarbell ... Chicago, 1917.
1 p. l., p. 63–71. 1 illus., pl. xxix–xxxvii. 24½ᶜᵐ. (Field museum of natural history. Publication 195. Anthropological series. vol. vi, no. 4)

1. Etruria—Antiq. 2. Sarcophagi.

Library of Congress   GN2.F4 vol. 6, no. 4

17—28742

MoU OrPS MiU OCl OCU OU ViU ICJ NN GU CaBVaU
NT   0037910   DLC WaS WaTU WaPS OrU ICJ PU PU–Mu NBuU

Tarbell, G. E.
"Believe in yourself".   n.p. [190 ?]

NT   0037911   NjP

HG
8018
I59
v.2
no.9
   Tarbell, Gage E.
     Modern life insurance: its development
     and its present problems; an address before
     the Massachusetts Reform Club, Dec. 20, 1905.
     [n. p., 1905]
     30 p. 23cm.

     1. Insurance,   Life.

NT   0037912   NIC

Law
Thesis
JX
1425
T17
1894
   Tarbell, George Schuyler.
     The Monroe Doctrine with reference to
     the Clayton-Bulwer Treaty.   [Ithaca, N.Y.]
     1894.
     52 l. 27cm.

     Thesis (LL.B.) - Cornell University,
     1894.

     1. Monroe Doctrine. 2. Clayton-Bulwer
     Treaty, 1850.   I. Title.

NT   0037913   NIC

Tarbell, Grace Elizabeth (Butler)
History of the Daughters of the American revolution of Colorado, 1894–1941, by Mrs. Winfield Scott Tarbell (Grace E. Butler) ... [n. p., 1941?]
64 p. 18ᶜᵐ.

"Compiled to celebrate the Golden Jubilee of the Daughters of the American revolution of Colorado."—Author's note.

1. Daughters of the American revolution. Colorado.

42–15623

Library of Congress   E202.5.C6ST3

[2]   369.135

NT   0037914   DLC MiD NcD

Tarbell, Harlan E., *1890 - 1960.*
Chalk talk stunts, by Harlan Tarbell ... illustrated by the author. Chicago, T. S. Denison & company [ᶜ1926]
100 p. front., illus., pl. 18½ᶜᵐ.

1. Chalk-talks.   I. Title.

26—19816

Library of Congress   NC865.T24

NT   0037915   DLC ICRL CU OrP WaT ICJ Or CaBVa OC1

Tarbell, Harlan E., *1890 - 1960.*
Chalk talks for Sunday schools, by Harlan Tarbell ... Chicago, T. S. Denison & company [ᶜ1928]
152 p. front. (port.) illus. 18½ᶜᵐ.

1. Chalk-talks. 2. Sunday-schools.   I. Title.

Library of Congress   BV1535.T3

28–21079

NT   0037916   DLC PU–Penn TxU WaT IdB

EDUCATION
BV1535 Tarbell, Harlan E., *1890 - 1960.*
T3   Chalk talks for Sunday schools, by Harlan
194-   Tarbell. Minneapolis, T. S. Denison [194-?]
     152 p. illus. 22 cm.

     1. Chalk-talks. 2. Sunday-schools. I. Title.

NT   0037917   OU

Tarbell, Harlan E   1890– *1960.*
Comedy stunts for laughing purposes, by Harlan Tarbell ... illustrated by the author. Minneapolis, T. S. Denison & company [1944]
95 p. illus., diagrs. 18 cm.

1. Amateur theatricals. 2. Amusements.   I. Title.

PN6120.S8T36   793.8   44—47661

NT   0037918   DLC Or WaSp

Tarbell, Harlan E., *1890 - 1960.*
Crazy stunts for comedy occasions, by Harlan Tarbell ... illustrated by the author. Chicago, T. S. Denison & company [ᶜ1929]
102 p. illus. 18½ᶜᵐ.

1. Amusements.   I. Title.   II. Title: Stunts for comedy occasions.

29–10866

Library of Congress   GV1471.T25

NT   0037919   DLC TxU InU NcD

Tarbell, Harlan E., 1890–1960.
Crazy stunts for comedy occasions, by Harlan Tarbell ... illustrated by the author. Minneapolis, T. S. Denison & company [1929]
102 p. illus. 18.5 cm.
Title within line border.

NT   0037920   NcD

Tarbell, Harlan E   1890– *1960.*
Fun with chalk talk, by Harlan Tarbell ... illustrated by the author. Chicago, T. S. Denison & company [ᶜ1931]
106 p. illus. 18½ cm.

1. Chalk-talks.   I. Title.

NC865.T245   793.9   31—22218

NT   0037921   DLC TxU MB OrP WaS WaT OC1

Tarbell, Harlan E., *1890 - 1960.*
Fundamental character analysis, by Doctors Harlan E. Tarbell, John B. Rolle, Carl Loeb. Chicago, The Metaphor system of character anaylsis [ᶜ1922]
5 p. l., 220 p., 1 l. plates. 18½ᶜᵐ.

Cover-title: Fundamental character analysis uncovers the hidden treasures of personality.

1. Characters and characteristics.   I. Rolle, John B., joint author. II. Loeb, Carl, joint author.

Library of Congress   BF831.T3

22–14368

NT   0037922   DLC

Tarbell, Harlan E., illus.

Hilliard, John Northern, 1872–1935.
Greater magic; a practical treatise on modern magic, by John Northern Hilliard ... his manuscripts and notes edited by Carl W. Jones and Jean Hugard; 1111 illustrations by Harlan Tarbell. Minneapolis, C. W. Jones, Priv. print. for professional & amateur magicians [ᶜ1938]

Tarbell, Harlan E., *1890 - 1960.*
Here's power; practical physiognomy, by Harlan E. Tarbell and John B. Rolle; based on the Metaphor system of colors, numbers and languages (Harry Daniels) Chicago, Metaphor system college [ᶜ1923]
128 p. illus. 20½ᶜᵐ.

1. Physiognomy. 2. Characters and characteristics.   I. Rolle, John B., joint author. II. Title.

Library of Congress   BF851.T3

23–12466

NT   0037924   DLC

Tarbell, Harlan E., 1890–*1960*
How to chalk talk, by Harlan Tarbell, illustrated by the author. Chicago, T. S. Denison & company [ᶜ1924]
94 p. incl. front., illus. 18½ cm.

1. Chalk-talks.

Library of Congress   NC865.T25

24—15647

CaBVa
NT   0037925   DLC CU OrU WaS Or PWcS OC1 OO MB WaSp

[Tarbell, Harlan E   ] 1890–1960.
... Magic
     see his   Tarbell system incorporated.
Magic.

Tarbell, Harlan E., *1890 - 1960.*
Mississippi minstrel first-part, a complete routine for the circle, by Harlan Tarbell. Chicago, T. S. Denison & company [ᶜ1930]
49 p. diagr. 18ᶜᵐ.

I. Title.

CA 36–1397 Unrev'd

Library of Congress   PN4305.N6T3
Copyright   D pub. 391   [2]   791.1

NT   0037927   DLC

Tarbell, Harlan E., *1890 - 1960.*
The Tarbell course in magic, written and illustrated by Harlan Tarbell. Rev. ed. ... New York, N. Y., Nat Louis magic company [ᶜ1941–
v. front. (port.) illus. 23ᶜᵐ.

"Revised, edited and published in printed form for the first time."—Leaf at end, v. 1.

1. Conjuring.   I. Title.

42–5557

Library of Congress   GV1547.T28 1941
[2]   791.1

NT   0037928   DLC CLU FTaSU CU OC1 OLak

Tarbell, Harlan E   1890–1960.
　　The Tarbell course in magic, written and illustrated by Harlan Tarbell. Rev. ed. ... New York, N. Y., L. Tannen ₁1944–73, c1943–72₎
　　7 v. front. (port.) illus. 23 cm.
　　Vol. 7 written and edited by H. Lorayne.

　　1. Conjuring.　I. Read, Ralph Wesley, 1882–　ed. II. Lorayne, Harry. III. Title.
　　GV1547.T26　　　　791.1　　　　44–24931

NT 0037929　DLC NN TxU

791.1　**Tarbell, Harlan E**   1890–1960.
T17t　　The Tarbell course in magic, written and
1943　illustrated by Harlan Tarbell, edited by Ralph W. Read. Rev. ed. ... New York, L. Tannen ₍c1953–54₎; v.1, c1953₎
　　6v. illus. ports. 23cm.
　　Vol. 3: c1943, 3d printing 1965; v.6 (without rev. ed. note) edited by B. Elliott.

　　✓1. Conjuring.　✓I. Read, Ralph W., ed. ✓II. Title.

NT 0037930　IU

Tarbell, Harlan E   1890–1960.
　　Tarbell System, incorporated ₍Magic₎ Chicago, ʿ1926–
　　1 v. (loose-leaf) illus. 20 x 27 cm.

　　1. Conjuring.
　　GV1547.T3　1926　　　　58–53088

NT 0037931　DLC

Tarbell, Harlan E   1890–1960.
　　Tarbell System, incorporated: Magic. 3d ed. Chicago, Tarbell System, ʿ1927.
　　1 v. in 3. illus. 20 x 27 cm.
　　Bound with Thurston, Howard. The Thurston magic lessons. ₍n. p.₎ ʿ1928.

　　1. Conjuring.
　　GV1547.T3　1927　　　　58–53090

NT 0037932　DLC NN IMunS

GV1547　Tarbell, Harlan E   1890–1960.
T28　　Tarbell System incorporated: Magic. 4th ed.
1927　Chicago, Tarbell System, c1927.
　　1 v. in 3. illus.
　　Some later editions published under title: The Tarbell course in magic.

　　1. Conjuring.

NT 0037933　CU

Tarbell, Harlan E., *1890–1960.*
　　Tarbell's chalk talk book, by Harlan E. Tarbell ... Chicago, H. S. Paine, ʿ1920.
　　40 p. incl. front. (port.) illus. 20½ᵐ.　$2.00

　　1. Chalk-talks.
　　Library of Congress　　　NC865.T3
　　　　　　　　　　　　　　　　　20–18940

NT 0037934　DLC

---

　　10 magical after dinner stunts easy to perform, by Harlan Tarbell... Chicago: Tarbell system, inc., c1930.　11 f.　illus.　26½cm.

　　Reproduced from typewritten copy; captions printed.

　　1. Legerdemain.

NT 0037935　NN

Tarbell, Horace Sumner, 1838–1904
　　City school supervision. IV.　[New York, H. Holt and co., 1892]
　　p. 65–69.　24 cm.
　　Article in Educational review, January, 1892.
　　v. 3, no. 1.

NT 0037936　RPB

Tarbell, Horace Sumner, 1838–1904.
　　... The complete geography, by Horace S. Tarbell ... and Martha Tarbell ... New York, Chicago ₍etc.₎ Werner school book company ₍1899₎
　　152 p. illus. (incl. maps)　32½ x 25½ᵐ.　(Tarbell's geographical series)
　　Illustrations on lining-papers.
　　"References": p. 3.
　　CONTENTS.—pt. I. The earth as a whole.—pt. II. Continents and countries.—pt. III. Geography generalized.—Appendix.

　　1. Geography—Text-books—1870–　I. Tarbell, Martha, joint author.
　　Library of Congress　　　G127.T175
　　　　　　　　　　　　　　　　　0–18

NT 0037937　DLC DHEW MH

Tarbell, Horace Sumner, 1838–1904
　　The complete geography...
　　New York, Cincinnati, etc., c1913

G127
T3

NT 0037938　DLC

Tarbell, Horace Sumner, 1838–*1904.*
　　Essentials of English composition, by Horace S. Tarbell ... and Martha Tarbell, PH. D. Boston, Ginn & company, 1902.
　　xv, 281 p.　19ᶜᵐ.
　　Largely taken from the author's Second book of lessons in language and grammar.

　　1. English language—Rhetoric.　I. Tarbell, Martha, joint author. II. Title.
　　Library of Congress　　　PE1408.T3
　　　　　　　　　　　　　　　　　2–22421

NT 0037939　DLC DHEW OCl PPT

Tarbell, Horace Sumner, 1838–1904.
　　Introductory geography.　New York, American, c1898.

NT 0037940　PWcS

Tarbell, Horace S₍umner₎ 1838–*1904.*
　　The Tarbell introductory geography.　New York, Chicago ₍etc.₎ Werner school book co. ₍1900₎
　　187 p. illus. 8°.　(Tarbell's geographical series)
　　　　　　　　　　　　　　　　　July 5, 1900–301

NT 0037941　DLC ICRL DHEW NN

Tarbell, Horace Sumner, 1838–1904
　　The introductory geography...
　　New York, Cincinnati, c1913

G127
T172

NT 0037942　DLC

Tarbell, Horace Sumner, 1838–1904.
　　Lessons in language.

NT 0037943　PG1B

Tarbell, Horace Sumner, 1838–1904.
　　Tarbell's lessons in language, by Horace S. Tarbell ... 1st₍–2d₎ book.　Boston, Ginn & company, 1890–91.
　　2 v. illus. 18½ᵐ.
　　"English derivation. An appendix": vi, 38 p. at end of 2d book.

　　1. English language—Composition and exercises.
　　Library of Congress　　　PE1111.T3　1890
　　　　　　　　　　　　　　　　　11–18049

NT 0037944　DLC PPD OClWHi PBa MB MiU OO OCl

Tarbell, Horace Sumner, 1838–*1904.*
　　Lessons in language.　Boston, Ginn & co., 1892.
　　2 v.

NT 0037945　MH

Tarbell, Horace Sumner, 1838–*1904.*
　　Tarbell's lessons in language, by Horace S. Tarbell .. 1st₍–2d₎ book.　Boston, Ginn & company, 1893.
　　2 v. illus. 18½ᵐ.
　　"English derivation. An appendix": vi, 38 p. at end of 2d book.

NT 0037946　ViU RPB MH MiU ODW

PE1111　**Tarbell, Horace Sumner,** 1838–*1904.*
.T3　　Tarbell's lessons in language, by Horace S. Tarbell ...
1894　1st₍–2d₎ book.　Boston, Ginn & company, 1894.
　　2 v. illus. 18½ᵐ.

NT 0037947　ViU MoU MH OO

Tarbell, Horace Sumner, 1838–1904.
　　Lessons in language. First book.　Boston, Ginn & co., 1895.

NT 0037948　MH OClW

Tarbell, Horace Sumner, 1838–1904.
　　Lessons in language. 2d book.　Boston, Ginn & co., 1896.

NT 0037949　MH

Tarbell, Horace Sumner, 1838–1904.
　　Lessons in language.　First book.　Boston, Ginn & co., 1897.

NT 0037950　MH

Tarbell, Horace Sumner, 1838–*1904*.
Tarbell's lessons in language, by Horace S. Tarbell ...
1st[-2d] book. Boston, Ginn & company, 1898.
2 v. illus. 18¼ᶜᵐ.

NT 0037951 ViU

Tarbell, Horace Sumner, 1838–1904.
Lessons in language, by Horace S. Tarbell, L. L. D. ...
and Martha Tarbell, PH. D. Boston, Ginn & company,
1899.
2 p. l., 117 p. illus. 18¼ᶜᵐ.

1. English language—Composition and exercises. I. Tarbell, Martha,
joint author. II. Title.

99—4021

Library of Congress   PE1111.T3 1899

NT 0037952 DLC PU MH

Tarbell, Horace Sumner, 1838–*1904*.
Lessons in language and grammar. Book I. Boston,
Ginn & co., 1899–
12°.

I. Tarbell, Martha, joint author.

Library of Congress   Sept. 7, 99–258

NT 0037953 DLC

Tarbell, Horace Sumner, 1838–1904.
Lessons in language and grammar ... by Horace S. Tarbell
... and Martha Tarbell, PH. D. Boston, Ginn & company, 1899.
2 v. 19ᶜᵐ.

1. English language—Composition and exercises. I. Tarbell, Martha, joint author. II. Title.

99–3692 Revised

Library of Congress   PE1111.T32 1899
Copyright 1899 : 39823,   45096

NT 0037954 DLC

Tarbell, Horace Sumner, 1838–1904.
Lessons in language and grammar; book 1[-2] by
Horace S. Tarbell ... and Martha Tarbell, PH. D. Boston,
Ginn & company, 1900.
2 v. 19ᶜᵐ.
Vol. 1 illustrated.

1. English language—Composition and exercises. I. Tarbell, Martha,
joint author. II. Title.

0–2347 Revised

Library of Congress   PE1111.T32 1900

NT 0037955 DLC OO

Tarbell, Horace Sumner, 1838–1904.
Lessons in language & grammar by
H. & Martha Tarbell. Boston, Ginn, 1901.

NT 0037956 PWcS

Tarbell, Horace S[umner] 1838–*1904*.
Manual to accompany lessons in language and grammar, by Horace S. Tarbell, LL. D. and Martha Tarbell,
PH. D. Boston, Ginn & company, 1903.
1 p. l., 68 p. 18¼ᶜᵐ.

8–10715

NT 0037957 DLC DHEW

Tarbell, Horace Sumner, 1838–1904.

National education association of the United States.
Committee of fifteen on elementary education.
Report of the Committee of fifteen, by W. T. Harris,
LL. D., A. S. Draper, LL. D., and H. S. Tarbell, read at the
Cleveland meeting of the Department of superintendence,
February 19–21, 1895, with the debate. Boston, The New
England publishing company, 1895.

Tarbell, Horace Sumner, 1838–1904.
Report on geography presented to the New
England association of school superintendents
at the meeting held November 15, 1901
       see under New England association
of school superintendents.

Tarbell, Horace Sumner, 1838–*1904*.
A teachers' manual of lessons in language. By Horace
S. Tarbell. Boston, Ginn & company, 1892.
1 p. l., 111 p. 19ᶜᵐ.

1. English language—Study and teaching.

10–18463†

Library of Congress   LB1576.T25

NT 0037960 DLC PPT PU

Tarbell, Horace Sumner, 1838–1904.
A teachers' manual of lessons in language.
Boston, Ginn, 1895, c1892.
111 p.

NT 0037961 PP

Tarbell, Horace Sumner, 1838–1904.
The Werner grammar school geography ... By Horace S.
Tarbell ... New York, Chicago [etc.] Werner school book company [1896]
351 p. illus. 20ᶜᵐ. *and* atlas of 153 p. (p. 8, 63–153 : illustrations ;
p. 9–62, maps) 32 x 25ᶜᵐ.
CONTENTS.—pt. I. [Text]—pt. II. The world in map and picture.

1. Geography—Text-books—1870–

6—1245

Library of Congress   G126.T17

                    MiU MH
NT 0037962 DLC MH PP MtU WaS OrU DHEW OClWHi OCl OO

Tarbell, Horace S[umner] 1838–*1904*.
The Werner introductory geography; by Horace S.
Tarbell ... New York, Chicago [etc.] Werner school book
company [1896]
188 p. illus. 23ᶜᵐ.

1. Geography—Text-books—1870–

5–28556†

Library of Congress   G127.T17

NT 0037963 DLC PPT MtU DHEW OO

Tarbell, Ida Minerva, 185*7*–*1944*, ed.

... Abraham Lincoln. Edited by Ida M. Tarbell.
(In McClure's magazine. New York, 1895–96. 24ᶜᵐ.
v.5,no.6, Nov.1895; v.6,no.1–4, Dec.1895–March 1896; v.6,
no.6, May 1896; v.7,no.1–5, June–Oct.1896; v.8,no.1, Dec.
1896. p.483,–512.[1]–24, [115]–136, 213,–240.[307]–
448.[526]–549.[79]–88.[171]–181,272–281.[319]–331.[401]–
413,[43]–56. illus., ports. maps, facsims.)
Detached copy.
Extracted from the periodical and bound with other
miscellaneous articles contained in the same issues and
with binder's title: Lincoln's childhood.
Interleaved with newspaper clippings mounted on blank
pages.

1. Lincoln, Abrah   am, pres. U.S., 1809–1865.
I.Ser.

NT 0037964 ViU

Tarbell, Ida Minerva, 1857–*1944*.
Abraham Lincoln; an address delivered by Miss Ida
Tarbell for the Students' lecture association of the University of Michigan, Friday evening, February the
twelfth, 1909, in commemoration of the centennial anniversary of Lincoln's birth. [no imprint, 1909†]
35 numb. l. 28½ᶜᵐ.
Caption title.
Typewritten.

1. Lincoln, Abraham, pres. U. S., 1809–1865—Addresses, essays, lectures.

NT 0037965 MiU

Tarbell, Ida Minerva, 1857–*1944*. **FOR OTHER EDITION[S]
SEE MAIN ENTRY**
Abraham Lincoln: The battle of the giants, by Frede-
vor Hill; The parents of Lincoln, by Ida M. Tarbell; An
appeal to patriotism, by Richard Lloyd Jones ... A souvenir
of Lincoln's birthday, February 12, 1907, published by the
Lincoln farm association. [n. p., 1907]

E457
.T156   Tarbell,Ida Minerva,1857–1944.
Lincoln   ...Abraham Lincoln;szkic. Chicago,W.
           Dyniewicza,1909.
           28 p. 17½cm.
           Text in Polish.

1.Lincoln,Abraham,pres.U.S.,1809–1865.

NT 0037967 ICU MiDW CSmH RPB

Tarbell, Ida Minerva, 1857–1944.
Abraham Lincoln's money sense.
     Pam. (In American. Sept. 1923)

NT 0037968 KyBgW

Tarbell, Ida Minerva, 1857–[19]44
All in the day's work; an autobiography by Ida M. Tarbell.
New York, The Macmillan company, 1939.
6 p. l., 412 p. front., ports. 24ᶜᵐ.
"First printing."

I. Title.

39–27284

Library of Congress   PS3539.A58Z5 1939
———— Copy 2.
Copyright A 128021   [15]   928.1

           MtU IdPI MsSM MoU OrCS CaBVa KEmT InNd Wa
           OClW OOxM OFH ViU WaSpG NN NIC IdU GU   KyLx Or
           OrPR OrP WaTU PBm PPT PHC PPLas MB TxU OU OCU OO
NT 0037969 DLC WaE IdB WaS OrSaW OrMonO OrU WaSp

Tarbell, Ida Minerva, 1857–*1944*.
The American woman. n.p. n.d.
[15] p.
Excerpt.

NT 0037970 OClWHi

Tarbell, Ida Minerva, 1857–*1944*.
Boy scouts' life of Lincoln, by Ida M. Tarbell. New York,
The Macmillan company, 1921.
6 p. l., 247 p. front., illus. (map, facsim.) plates, ports. 19½ᶜᵐ.

1. Lincoln, Abraham, pres. U. S., 1809–1865.

21—18596

Library of Congress   E457.T15

           DI Or OEac OLak MiU OCl MB NN
NT 0037971 DLC WaT WaSp WaSpG PLF PSC PPT ICarbS

Tarbell, Ida Minerva, 1857–1944.
Boy scouts' life of Lincoln, by Ida M. Tarbell. New York,
The Macmillan company, 1922.
6 p. l., 247 p. front., illus. (map, facsim.) plates, ports. 19¼ᵐ.

NT 0037972   OrP WaSp

TARBELL,Ida Minerva,1857–1944.
Boy scouts life of Lincoln. New York,The Mac
millan Company,1925.
19 cm. Map,ports.,plates and facsims.

NT 0037973   MH

Tarbell, Ida Minerva, 1857–1944.
Boy scouts' life of Lincoln. New York,
Macmillan, 1943 [c1921]
247 p. illus. (map, facsims.) plates, ports.
20 cm.

NT 0037974   OO

Tarbell, Ida Minerva, 1857–1944.
The business of being a woman, by Ida M. Tarbell ... New
York, The Macmillan company, 1912.
ix, 242 p. 18¼ᵐ.
Reprinted from the American magazine.
CONTENTS.—The uneasy woman.—On the imitation of man.—The busi-
ness of being a woman.—The socialization of the home.—The woman and
her raiment.—The woman and democracy.—The homeless daughter.—
The childless woman and the friendless child.—On the ennobling of the
woman's business.
1. Woman—Social and normal questions. I. Title.
                  12—24007
Library of Congress   HQ1419.T3

WaT Wa PPL PBa CoU OCU WaE NjR OrP OCU
MiU ViU ICJ MB NN OC1 DHEW NcRS NcGU IdU-SB WaSp WaS
NT 0037975   DLC KMK PWcS PBm OC1h OEac ODW OCU OOxM

HQ
1419
T3   **Tarbell, Ida Minerva,** 1857–1944.
The business of being a woman, by Ida M Tarbell ... New
York, The Macmillan company, **1913, ᶜ1912.** New
ix, 242 p. 18¼ cm.
Reprinted from the American magazine.
CONTENTS.—The uneasy woman.—On the imitation of man.—The
business of being a woman.—The socialization of the home.—The
woman and her raiment.—The woman and democracy.—The homeless
daughter.—The childless woman and the friendless child.—On the ennobling of the woman's business.

NT 0037976   LU PP Vi MtU IdU

HQ
1419
T3   **Tarbell, Ida Minerva,** 1857–1944.
The business of being a woman, by Ida M. Tarbell ... New
York, The Macmillan company, 1914 ₍c1912₎
ix, 242 p. 18¼ cm.
Reprinted from the American magazine.
CONTENTS.—The uneasy woman.—On the imitation of man.—The
business of being a woman.—The socialization of the home.—The
woman and her raiment.—The woman and democracy.—The homeless
daughter.—The childless woman and the friendless child.—On the ennobling of the woman's business.

NT 0037977   NBuC NRU OC1W

.96
'17b   Tarbell, Ida Minerva, 1857–1944.
Business of being a woman. N.Y.Mac-
millan,1916. 242p.

NT 0037978   KEmT MtBC

Tarbell, Ida Minerva, 1857–1944.
The business of being a woman. New York,
Macmillan, 1921.
242 p. 18.5 cm.
Reprinted from the American magazine.

NT 0037979   PPT CU NcD

Tarbell, Ida Minerva, 1857–1944.
Early life of Abraham Lincoln. New York,
1894.

NT 0037980   PU-L

Tarbell, Ida Minerva, 1857–1944.
The early life of Abraham Lincoln; containing many un-
published documents and unpublished reminiscences of
Lincoln's early friends, by Ida M. Tarbell assisted by J.
McCan Davis. New York, S. S. McClure, 1896.
240 p. illus., ports., maps, facsims. 25 cm.

1. Lincoln, Abraham, Pres. U. S., 1809–1865.

E457.3.T17 1896a   55–52616
Library of Congress   ₍†₎

NT 0037981   DLC WaU PPF Or WaWW

Tarbell, Ida Minerva, 1857–1944.
The early life of Abraham Lincoln, containing many unpublished documents and unpublished reminiscences of Lincoln's early friends. By Ida M. Tarbell, assisted by J. Mc-
Can Davis ... New York, S. S. McClure, 1896.
2 p. l., 240 p. incl. front., illus., ports. 24½ᵐ. (McClure's magazine
library. No. 3)

1. Lincoln, Abraham, pres. U. S., 1809–1865. I. Davis, John McCan,
1866–1916, joint author.
Library of Congress   E457.3.T17   12–7443

NjP NN OC1 MH WaT MB PPL NIC MoU-C OrU DAU OkU
NT 0037982   DLC PU NRCR WaS OC1JC OU OCU OC1WHi CSmH

Tarbell, Ida Minerva, 1857–1944.
Father Abraham, by Ida M. Tarbell ... with illustrations
by Blendon Campbell. New York, Moffat, Yard and company, 1909.
5 p. 1 l., 3–39 p. col. front., 5 pl. 19½ x 12½ cm.

1. Lincoln, Abraham, pres. U. S.—Personality. 2. Lincoln, Abraham, pres. U. S.—Fiction. I. Title.
                9—9450
Library of Congress   E457.2.T17

MiU WaT Wa DI WaU CLSU OKentU
NT 0037983   DLC NcD NIC PPL PHC ViU OC1W OC1WHi OC1

Tarbell, Ida Minerva, 1857–1944.
Mizner, Addison, 1872–
Florida architecture of Addison Mizner; introduction by
Ida M. Tarbell; one hundred and eighty-five illustrations.
New York city, William Helburn, inc. ₍ᶜ1928₎

E
457
.15
.T173
1907   Tarbell, Ida Minerva, 1857–1944.
He knew Lincoln, by Ida M. Tarbell.
New York, Doubleday, Page & company
[1907]
39 p. illus. 20 cm.

1. Lincoln, Abraham, pres. U.S.—
Anecdotes. I. Title

NT 0037985   OKentU WaE

E
457
.15
.T184   Tarbell, Ida Minerva, 1857–1944
He knew Lincoln, by Ida M. Tarbell.
New York, The Macmillan company, [1907]
39 p. illus. 18 cm.

1. Lincoln, Abraham, pres. U.S.—
Anecdotes. I. Title

NT 0037986   OKentU

Tarbell, Ida Minerva, 1857–1944.
He knew Lincoln, by Ida M. Tarbell ... New York, McClure,
Phillips & co., 1907.
5 p. l., 3–39, ₍1₎ p. col. front., 6 pl. 20ᵐ.

1. Lincoln, Abraham, pres. U. S.—Anecdotes. I. Title.
              7—12636
Library of Congress   E457.15.T17

MiU-C PPF
OC1W OC1WHi OC1 CSmH OC1H OCU ViU MB NN OkU ICU MH
NT 0037987   DLC IdPI Or WaWW WaS OrSaW PPLas PPL NNC

Tarbell, Ida Minerva, 1857–1944.
He knew Lincoln. New York, McClure Co., 1908 ₍ᶜ1907₎
39 p. ports. 20 cm.

1. Lincoln, Abraham, Pres. U. S., 1809–1865—Anecdotes. I. Title.

E457.15.T172   68–38416

NT 0037988   DLC NcD NIC NN DI TxU FTaSU NcU NjP

Tarbell, Ida Minerva, 1857–1944.
He knew Lincoln, by Ida M. Tarbell ... New York, Doubleday, Page & company, 1909.
5 p. l., 3–39, ₍1₎ p. col. front., plates. 19½ cm.

1. Lincoln, Abraham, pres. U. S.—Anecdotes. I. Title.
              37—38777
Library of Congress   E457.15.T173
              ₍a49c1₎   923.173

OWibfU
NT 0037989   DLC PHi OC1W ViU MtHi MiU WaSp NcRS CSmH

Tarbell, Ida M₍inerva₎, 1857–1944.   C2
He knew Lincoln. New York: Doubleday, Page, & Co.,
1910. 4 p.l., 40 p., 7 pl. (1 col'd). 12°.

1. Lincoln, Abraham.—Stories.   2. Title.
N. Y. P. L.   June 7, 1911.

NT 0037990   NN

Tarbell, Ida Minerva, 1857–1944.
He knew Lincoln. New York, Macmillan co.,
1917.
39 p. plates. 19.5 cm.

NT 0037991   MH OO

Tarbell, Ida Minerva, 1857–1944.
He knew Lincoln, by Ida M. Tarbell ... New York, McClure,
Phillips & co., 1919.
5 p. l., 3–39, ₍1₎ p. col. front., 6 pl. 20ᵐ.

NT 0037992   WaTU MtU

Tarbell, Ida Minerva, 1857–1944.
He knew Lincoln, by Ida M. Tarbell ... New York, The
Macmillan company, 1926.
5 p. l., 3–39, ₍1₎ p. plates. 17½ cm.
First published 1907.

1. Lincoln, Abraham, pres. U. S.—Anecdotes. I. Title.
              30—28443
Library of Congress   E457.15.T184
              ₍a48d1₎   923.173

NT 0037993   DLC NNC OC1C

973.709   Tarbell. Ida Minerva, 1857-1944.
L7t213   He knew Lincoln. New York, Macmillan,
1907   1929 [°1907]
       39 p. illus. 20 cm.

1. Lincoln, Abraham, Pres. U.S. Anecdotes. I. Title.

NT   0037994   N

Tarbell, Ida Minerva, 1857-1944.
    He knew Lincoln, and other Billy Brown stories, by
Ida M. Tarbell ... New York, The Macmillan company,
1922.
     xix, 179 p. plates. 19½ᶜᵐ.

    1. Lincoln, Abraham, pres. U. S.—Anecdotes.   ɪ. Title.
                         E457.15.T18   22—3092

      OC1h
NT   0037995   DLC PPT MtBC PHC KEmT OU OEac MB OC1WHi

973.7L63
B2T17h Tarbell, Ida Minerva, 1857-1944
1924   He knew Lincoln, and other Billy Brown stories, by
Ida M. Tarbell ... New York, The Macmillan company,
1924.
     xix, 179 p. plates. 19½ᶜᵐ.

    Lincoln, Abraham, Pres U. S.—Anecdotes.   ɪ. Title.

NT   0037996   IU

HD   Tarbell, Ida Minerva, 1857-1944.
7269   The history of the Standard Oil Company
O4   [New York] McClure [1902-1905]
T2a   1 v. (various pagings) illus. 25 cm.
       Articles detached from McClure's Maga-
zine 1902-1905.
       Contents.—The history of the Standard Oil
Company.—John D. Rockefeller, a character study.
—Kansas and the Standard Oil Company.

       1. Standard Oil Company. 2. Rockefeller,
John Davison, 1839-1937. I. Title.

NT   0038001   AkU

HD2769
S7T3   Tarbell, Ida Minerva, 1857-1944.
1903   The history of the Standard Oil Company, part
R   2. [n.p., 1903-04]
       6 pts. illus., ports., map. 25cm.
       Chapters 1-5 and the announcement of Tarbell's
History, detached from McClure's magazine Nov.
1903-Apr. 1904.

       1. Standard Oil Company.

NT   0038002   DI

Tarbell, Ida Minerva, 1857-1944.
    The history of the Standard oil company, by Ida M.
Tarbell ... New York, McClure, Phillips & co., 1904.
    2 v. fronts., illus., plates, ports., diagrs. 23ᶜᵐ.

    1. Standard oil company.
    Library of Congress   HD7269.O4T2   4—35331

    Or Wa
    OU DAU I CoU PPLas KEmT InU NIC DI CU DAL WaS WaT
    TU ViU WaSpG OEac MiU OO OC1h OC1 MB IN NjP ODW OFH
NT   0038003   DLC PSC NcD ICJ OrP IdB PHC PU PBa WaSp

HD2769
S7T3   Tarbell, Ida Minerva, 1857-1944.
1905   The history of the Standard Oil Company.
   London, W. Heineman, 1905.
       2 v. plates, ports., map. 23 cm.

       1. Standard Oil Company.

NT   0038004   DI PPT

Tarbell, Ida Minerva, 1857-1944.   338.8
    The history of the Standard Oil Company.   New York:
McClure, Phillips & Co., 1905.   2 v.   illus., pl., port.   8°.

1. Standard Oil Co.   2. Trusts.
N. Y. P. L.   February 20, 1911.

NT   0038005   NN NWM NBuHi OrPR

HD
2769
O4   **Tarbell, Ida Minerva, 1857-1944.**
T2   The history of the Standard oil
1912a   company, by Ida M. Tarbell ...
KNOPF   Illustrated with portraits, pictures
NonCirc   and diagrams ... London, W.
     Heinemann, 1912 [c1904]
       2 v. fronts., illus., plates,
ports., diagrs. 23cm.
       Published November, 1904. N. Secon
impression."

       1. Standard Oil Company.
   DA   1912.

NT   0038006   TxU

Tarbell, Ida Minerva, 1857-1944.
    The history of the Standard oil company, by Ida M. Tar-
bell ... New York, The Macmillan company, 1925-
     v. fronts., illus., plates, ports., diagrs. 24ᶜᵐ.
    "Published November, 1904. Reissued June, 1925."

    1. Standard oil company.   26—7672
    Library of Congress   HD2769.O4T2 1925

      CaBVa OLak
NT   0038007   DLC MU OU CLU NBuU WaTU OrP IdU WaE OCU

    Tarbell, Ida Minerva, 1857-1944.
       The history of the Standard oil co., by
Ida M. Tarbell ... N. Y., McClure, Phillips
& co., 1904-26.
       2 v.

NT   0038008   OOxM

Tarbell, Ida Minerva, 1857-1944.   338.8-T
    The history of the Standard Oil Company; illustrated with
portraits, pictures and diagrams.   New York: The Macmillan
Co., 1933[, cop. 1902-33].   2 v. in 1.   chart, facsim., map, pl.,
port., tables.   8°.

1. Trusts.   2. Standard Oil Company.
N. Y. P. L.   October 28, 1933

NT   0038009   NN KyU ViU KyU-A FMU OC1 Ok WaS OC1CC

Tarbell, Ida Minerva, 1857-1944.
    The history of the Standard oil company, by Ida M.
Tarbell ... Illustrated with portraits, pictures and diagrams ... New York, The Macmillan company, 1937.
     2 v. in 1. fronts., illus. (incl. maps, facsims.) plates, ports., diagrs.
22 cm.
     Vol. 2 has half-title only.

    1. Standard oil company.
   [HD2769.O4T   ]   A 40—1979
   North Carolina. Univ.   Library
   for Library of Congress   [a58f¹]

NT   0038010   NcU PHi NcU CLSU IdU-SB FMU

338.8
T172h
1950   Tarbell, Ida Minerva, 1857-1944.
    The history of the Standard oil company.
   New York, P. Smith, 1950.
       2v. in 1. fronts., illus.(incl. maps,
facsims.) plates, ports.,diagrs. 22cm.

       "Published November, 1904 by McClure ...
reprinted, 1950."

      1. Standard oil company.

NT   0038011   TxU DI ViU KEmT CaBVaU WaWW

    Tarbell, Ida Minerva, 1857-1944.
       How Chicago is finding herself. By Ida M.
Tarbell... pt. 1.
       (American magazine [Nov. 1908?] p. 29-41.
illus. (incl. ports.) 25 cm.)

       Concerns the traction question.

NT   0038012   ICHi

    Tarbell, Ida Minerva, 1857-1944.
       ... How I twice eloped
          see under   Eaves, Catherine [pseud.]

    Tarbell, Ida Minerva, 1857-1944.
       Identification of criminals. The scientific
method in use in France. With illustrations from
photographs furnished by M. Bertillon, inventor
of the system. [New York, 1894]
       [1,355]-369 p. front. (diagr.) illus.   24 cm.
       Caption title.
       From McClures magazine March 1894.

NT   0038014   CtY

Tarbell, Ida Minerva, 1857-1944.
    In Lincoln's chair, by Ida M. Tarbell ... New York, The
Macmillan company, 1920.
    3 p. l., 3-55 p. 19½ᶜᵐ.

    1. Lincoln, Abraham, pres. U. S.—Fiction.   ɪ. Title.
                               20—5208
    Library of Congress   E457.9.T17

      ICN
      OO MiU OC1WHi MB NN MiU-C OC1 NRU KyHi TxU NSyU GU
NT   0038015   DLC Or OrP WaS WaTU Wa KEmT PPLas OEac

    TARBELL, IDA MINERVA, 1854-1944.
       In the footprints of Abraham Lincoln.
   [Williamsport, Pa., The Sun, 1923.
       Clippings from The Sun, Williamsport,
Sept. 24-Dec. 13, 1923.
       Numbered 1-69. Nos. 3, 7, 11, 25, 54,
65 wanting.

NT   0038016   InU

Tarbell, Ida Minerva, 1857-1944.
    In the footsteps of the Lincolns, by Ida M. Tarbell ... New
York and London, Harper & brothers, 1924.
    xi, [2], 418 p. front., illus. (map, facsims.) plates, ports. 24½ᶜᵐ.

    1. Lincoln, Abraham, pres. U. S., 1809-1865. 2. Lincoln family (Samu-
el Lincoln, 1619?-1690) ɪ. Title.
                              24—3279
    Library of Congress   E547.3.T175

      TU KyU OKentU NjNbS OC1WHi
      WaT WaWW WaS IdPI CaBVaU ViU NIC KyLxT DI AAP OrPS
      OC1 OEac OU OCX OOxM MiU NN MB OO MiU-C Or WaSpG
NT   0038017   DLC OrP WaSp WaE PBa WaTU PPT PV PRosC

Tarbell, Ida Minerva, 1857-1944.
The irresponsible woman
and the friendless child. pp. 49-53. 8°. New
York, 1912.
Cutting from: Am. Mag., N. Y., 1912, lxxiv.

NT   0038018   DNLM

Tarbell, Ida Minerva, 1857-1944.
Joan of Arc.   New York, 1915.   11(1) p., 6 pl.   illus.
8°.   (Mentor. no. 98.)

1. Arc, Jeanne d'.
N. Y. P. L.   February 2, 1916.

NT   0038019   NN

Tarbell, Ida Minerva, 1857-1944.
Life of Abraham Lincoln. 2 vols.
New York, n.d.

NT   0038020   NjNbS

Tarbell, Ida Minerva, 1857-1944.
The life of Abraham Lincoln. drawn from original sources
and containing many speeches, letters and telegrams hitherto
unpublished. by Ida M. Tarbell ... New York. Lincoln
memorial association [19——]
2 v. fronts. (v.1:port) illus. maps. facsims. 21½ᵐ.

NT   0038021   ViU IdPI WaT Or

Tarbell, Ida Minerva, 1857-1944.
Life of Abraham Lincoln.   1900.
2 v.

NT   0038022   PPFr PHi PPWe DN

Tarbell, Ida Minerva, 1857-1944.
The life of Abraham Lincoln, drawn from original sources
and containing many speeches, letters, and telegrams hitherto
unpublished, by Ida M. Tarbell ... New York, The Doubleday & McClure co., 1900.
2 v. fronts., illus., plates. ports. facsims. 23ᵐ.

1. Lincoln, Abraham, pres. U. S., 1809-1865.
Library of Congress   E457.T17   0—1357

NT   0038023   DLC PV PBa PPL WaT MtU NcD OCU MiU OLak
DNW OC1U OC1h OC1W MiU-C
OO NjN CSmH NjP MdBP MB OC1WHi PWcS MH TU IHi MB MH

Tarbell, Ida Minerva, 1857-1944.
The life of Abraham Lincoln, drawn from original sources
and containing many speeches, letters and telegrams hitherto
unpublished, by Ida M. Tarbell ... New York, The Doubleday & McClure co., 1900.
2 v. fronts., illus., plates, ports., maps, facsims. 26½ cm.
"Of this special illustrators' edition there were printed in May,
1900, seventy-five copies, of which this is no. 53."

1. Lincoln, Abraham, pres. U. S., 1809-1865.
Library of Congress   E457.T172   19—4965

NT   0038024   DLC WaE OrPR

Tarbell, Ida Minerva, 1857-1944.
The life of Abraham Lincoln; drawn from original sources
and containing many speeches, letters and telegrams hitherto
unpublished. New York, Lincoln Memorial Association
[*1900]
2 v. illus., port. maps, facsims. 22 cm.

1. Lincoln, Abraham, Pres. U. S., 1809-1865.

E457.T174   55-52915

NT   0038025   DLC Or WaSpG WaWW NcU ViU NIC NBuC IdPI
OKentU OU IU DAU OrPS

Tarbell, Ida Minerva, 1857-1944.
The life of Abraham Lincoln; drawn from original
sources and containing many speeches, letters and telegrams
hitherto unpublished. New York, McClure, Phillips, 1900.
2 v. illus., ports., maps, facsims. 24 cm.

1. Lincoln, Abraham, Pres. U. S., 1809-1865.

E457.T173   55-52617

NT   0038026   DLC

E
457
.T37
Tarbell, Ida Minerva, 1857-1944.
The life of Abraham Lincoln drawn
from original sources and containing
many speeches, letters, and telegrams
hitherto unpublished, and illustrated
with many reproductions from original
paintings, photographs, etc., by Ida M.
Tarbell. New York, McClure, Phillips
and Co. [c1900]
4 v. illus. 23 cm.

1. Lincoln, Abraham, pres. U. S.,
1809-1865. I. Title

NT   0038027   OKentU NIC MH

Tarbell, Ida Minerva, 1857-1944.
The life of Abraham Lincoln drawn from original sources
and containing many speeches, letters and telegrams hitherto
unpublished, and illustrated with many reproductions from
original paintings, photographs, etc., by Ida M. Tarbell. New
York, Lincoln history society, 1902.
4 v. fronts., illus., plates, ports., facsims. 23ᵐ.

NT   0038028   ViU MtBC OC1WHi ODW OC1FC

Rare
E
457
T17
1902
Tarbell, Ida Minerva, 1857-1944.
The life of Abraham Lincoln. Drawn from
original sources and containing many speeches, letters and telegrams hitherto unpublished, and illus. with many reproductions
from original paintings, photos., etcetera.
New York, McClure, Phillips, 1902.
2 v. illus. 24cm.

With book-plate of William A. Carr.

NT   0038029   NIC PV MWA NN

TARBELL, Ida M[inerva], 1857-1944.
The life of Abraham Lincoln drawn from
original sources and containing many speeches
letters and telegrams hitherto unpublished.
New York, The Lincoln History Society, 1903.
4 vol. Ports., plates, and facsimile plates.

NT   0038030   MH IU OC1StM NjP OLak

B
L638t
Tarbell, Ida Minerva, 1857-1944.
The life of Abraham Lincoln, drawn from
original sources and containing many speeches, letters and telegrams hitherto unpublished, and illustrated with many reproductions
from original paintings photographs, et
cetera, by Ida M. Tarbell. New York,
McClure, Phillips, 1904 [c1900]
2 v.   illus., facsims., maps, plates,
ports.   24 cm.

NT   0038031   KyU

Tarbell, Ida Minerva, 1857-1944.
The life of Abraham Lincoln drawn from original sources
and containing many speeches, letters, and telegrams hitherto
unpublished, and illustrated with many reproductions from
original paintings, photographs, etc., by Ida M. Tarbell. New
York, Lincoln history society, 1905.
4 v. fronts., illus., plates, ports., facsims. 23ᵐ.

NT   0038032   OrStbM OrPR

Tarbell, Ida Minerva, 1857-1944.
The life of Abraham Lincoln drawn from original sources
and containing many speeches, letters, and telegrams hitherto
unpublished, and illustrated with many reproductions from
original paintings, photographs, etc., by Ida M. Tarbell.
New York, Lincoln historical society, 1906.
4 v. fronts., illus., plates, ports., facsims. 23 cm.

1. Lincoln, Abraham, Pres. U. S., 1809-1865.

E457.T175   A 13—1484
Bangor, Me. Public   Library
for Library of Congress   [a57e½]†

OrStbM
NT   0038033   MeB AAP PU OLak IdB IU WaU DI ViU DLC Wa

E457
.T175
1907
Tarbell, Ida Minerva, 1857-1944.
The life of Abraham Lincoln drawn from original sources and containing many speeches,
letters, and telegrams hitherto unpublished,
and illustrated with many reproductions from
original paintings, photographs, etc. New
York, Lincoln Historical Society, 1907 c°1900⊃
4 v. illus., facsims., plates, ports. 23cm.

1. Lincoln, Abraham, Pres. U. S., 1809-1865.

NT   0038034   OrPS OO NcD

E
457
T173x
Tarbell, Ida Minerva, 1857-1944.
The life of Abraham Lincoln, drawn from
original sources and containing many speeches
letters and telegrams hitherto unpublished,
and illustrated with many reproductions from
original paintings, photographs, etc., by
Ida M. Tarbell. New York, McClure, Phillips,
1908.
2v. illus.

1. Lincoln, Abraham, pres. U. S., 1809-
1865. I. Title.

NT   0038035   NbU OC1FC PPPL

Tarbell, Ida Minerva, 1857-
The life of Abraham Lincoln drawn from original sources
and containing many speeches, letters, and telegrams hitherto
unpublished, and illustrated with many reproductions from
original paintings, photographs, etc., by Ida M. Tarbell. New
York, Lincoln history society, 1908-09.
4 v. fronts., illus., plates, ports., facsims. 23ᵐ.
v.1, 1909; v.2-4, 1908.

NT   0038036   MiU-C OC1W OCX MtHi

Tarbell, Ida Minerva, 1857-1944.   B-L
The life of Abraham Lincoln; drawn from original sources
and containing many speeches, letters and telegrams hitherto
unpublished, and illustrated with many reproductions from original paintings, photographs, etc.   New York: Doubleday Page
& Co., 1909. 2 v. fac., pl., port. 8°.

1. Lincoln, Abraham.
N. Y. P. L.   January 14, 1915.

NT   0038037   NN OrSaW OrP IdU MiU PHC MB MH

Tarbell, Ida Minerva, 1857-1944.   4342.213
The life of Abraham Lincoln. Drawn from original sources and
containing many speeches, letters, and telegrams hitherto un-
published ...
New York. Lincoln History Society. 1909. 4 v. Illus. Portraits.
Plates. Maps. Facsimiles. 22 cm., in 8s.

D7725 — Lincoln, Abraham. Biog. — Lincoln History Society. Publications.

NT   0038038   MB NmLcU PV MeB NcRS OU

Tarbell, Ida Minerva, 1857–1944.

The life of Abraham Lincoln, drawn from original sources and containing many speeches, letters, and telegrams hitherto unpublished, by Ida M. Tarbell ... New York, The Doubleday & McClure co., 1910.

2 v. fronts. illus. plates, ports., facsims. 23ᶜᵐ.

NT   0038039   CaBVaU WaS

Tarbell, Ida Minerva, 1857–1944.

The life of Abraham Lincoln, drawn from original sources and containing many speeches, letters and telegrams hitherto unpublished, and illustrated with many reproductions from original paintings, photographs, et cetera. New ed., with new matter, by Ida M. Tarbell ... New York, The Macmillan company, 1917.

2 v. fronts. illus. (incl. maps) plates, ports., facsims. 22½ᶜᵐ.

1. Lincoln, Abraham, pres. U. S., 1809–1865.

17—25788

Library of Congress   E457.T18

PP OOxM OC1 OC1W NN
NT   0038040   DLC WaWW CaBVaU PPLas KyLx OCU NmU

E
457
T18
1920
KNOPF
NonCirc

Tarbell, Ida Minerva, 1857–1944.

The life of Abraham Lincoln, drawn from original sources and containing many speeches, letters and telegrams hitherto unpublished, and illustrated with many reproductions from original paintings, photographs, et cetera. New ed., with new matter, by Ida M. Tarbell ... New York, The Macmillan company, 1920 [c1917]

2 v. fronts., illus. (incl. maps) plates, ports., facsims. 22 1/2cm.

1. Lincoln, Abraham, President United States, 1809–1864.
DA 1920.

NT   0038041   TxU

Tarbell, Ida Minerva, 1857–1944.

The life of Abraham Lincoln, drawn from original sources and containing many speeches, letters and telegrams hitherto unpublished, and illustrated with many reproductions from original paintings, photographs, et cetera. New ed., with new matter, by Ida M. Tarbell ... New York, The Macmillan company, 1923.

2 v. in 1. fronts. illus. (incl. maps) plates, ports., facsims. 22½ᶜᵐ.

1. Lincoln, Abraham, pres. U. S., 1809–1865.

23—26468

Library of Congress   E457.T183

NT   0038042   DLC IdU IdB OCX OC1JC OC1C

Tarbell, Ida Minerva, 1857–1944.

... The life of Abraham Lincoln, drawn from original sources and containing many speeches, letters, and telegrams hitherto unpublished; profusely illustrated with many reproductions from original photographs, paintings, etc., by Ida M. Tarbell ... New York, Lincoln history society, 1924.

4 v. fronts., illus. (incl. maps) plates (part double) ports., facsims. (1 double) 23 cm.

At head of title: Sangamon edition.

1. Lincoln, Abraham, pres. U. S., 1809–1865.

25—7

E457.T184

NcU OC1W MiU-C CLSU ViHarEM KyU-A OU IEN ViU
NT   0038043   DLC IU NSyU CaBVaU Wa IdB NcU PPLT PPT

TARBELL, IDA MINERVA, 1857–1944.

The life of Abraham Lincoln; drawn from original sources, and containing many speeches, letters and telegrams hitherto unpublished. New ed. with new matter. New York, MacMillan, 1924[c1917] 2 v. plates,ports,facsims. 23cm.

1 Lincoln, Abraham,   16th pres. U. S.

NT   0038044   NN OC1h

Tarbell, Ida Minerva, 1857–1944.

The life of Abraham Lincoln; drawn from original sources and containing many speeches, letters and telegrams, hitherto unpublished, and illustrated with many reproductions from original paintings. New York: The Macmillan Co., 1925. 2 v. facsims., maps, pl. (some fold.), port. 8°.

1. Lincoln, Abraham.   2. United   States—Hist.: Civil war.
N. Y. P. L.   December 21, 1926

NT   0038045   NN CaBVaU WaTU

Tarbell, Ida Minerva, 1857–1944.

... The life of Abraham Lincoln. drawn from original sources and containing many speeches, letters, and telegrams hitherto unpublished; profusely illustrated with many reproductions from original photographs paintings, etc., by Ida M. Tarbell... N. Y. Macmillan co., 1927.

2 v.

NT   0038046   OFH WaS

Tarbell, Ida Minerva, 1857–1944.

The life of Abraham Lincoln; drawn from original sources and containing many speeches, letters, and telegrams hitherto unpublished. [New ed.] New York, Macmillan, 1928 [*1924]

2 v. illus., ports., maps, facsims. 22 cm.

1. Lincoln, Abraham, Pres. U. S., 1809–1865.

55–52615

E457.T187

OrSaW CaBVaU
NT   0038047   DLC WaSp PPD CLSU NN OC1ND MeB KEmT DI

Tarbell, Ida Minerva, 1857–1944.

The life of Elbert H. Gary; the story of steel, by Ida M. Tarbell ... New York, London, D. Appleton and company, 1925.

xii p., 1 l., 361 p. front., plates, ports. 23ᶜᵐ.

1. Gary, Elbert Henry, 1846–1927.   2. United States steel corporation.

25–22357

Library of Congress   HD9520.G3T3

NcD PHC WaTC PSC MtU PU-W
CU WaWW MB ICJ ViU DL NN OOxM ODW OEac OC1C OC1 OU
WaSpG NBuC OO OrSaW NWM NIC DAU Or OrPS NBuU-L TU
NT   0038048   DLC Wa IdB WaS PP OrPR OrP GU KEmT IdPS

HD9520
G3T3

Tarbell, Ida Minerva, 1857–1944.

The life of Elbert H. Gary; a story of steel. New York, Appleton, 1926 [c1925]

xii, 361 p. illus. 23cm.

1. Gary, Elbert Henry, 1846–1927.   2. United States Steel Corporation.

NT   0038049   MB PU MiHM

Tarbell, Ida Minerva, 1857–1944.

The life of Elbert H. Gary; the story of steel, by Ida M. Tarbell ... New York, London, D. Appleton-Century company, 1933.

xii p., 1 l., 361 p. front., plates, ports. 23 cm.

NT   0038050   ViU

Tarbell, Ida Minerva, 1857–1944.

A life of Napoleon Bonaparte; with a sketch of Josephine, empress of the French. Illustrated from the collection of Napoleon engravings made by the late Hon. G. G. Hubbard, and now owned by the Congressional library, Washington, D. C., supplemented by pictures from the best French collections. By Ida M. Tarbell. [2d ed.] New York, McClure, Phillips & co., 1901.

485 p. incl. illus., ports. 24½ cm.

Originally appeared in v. 3–4 of McClure's magazine. 1st ed., 1895.
1. Napoléon ɪ, emperor of the French, 1769–1821. 2. Joséphine, empress consort of Napoleon ɪ, 1763–1814.

1—31066

Library of Congress   DC203.T17

OC1C DN OC1h N IdB WaSp WaS PP PU
NT   0038051   DLC Or CaBVaU WaWW PG1B OCU OC1W OC1JC

DC203
.T17
1903

Tarbell, Ida Minerva, 1857–1944.

A life of Napoleon Bonaparte; with a sketch of Josephine, empress of the French. Illustrated from the collection of Napoleon engravings made by the late Hon. G. G. Hubbard, and now owned by the Congressional library, Washington, D. C., supplemented by pictures from the best French collections. By Ida M. Tarbell. [2d ed.] New York, McClure, Phillips & co., 1903.

485 p. incl. illus., ports. 23ᶜᵐ. p. 1–2: wanting.
Originally appeared in v. 3–4 of McClure's magazine. 1st edition, 1895. "Third impression May, 1903."
1. Napoléon ɪ, emperor of the French, 1769–1821. 2. Joséphine, empress consort of Napoleon ɪ, 1763–1814.

NT   0038052   ViU DNW PPT MtHi

Tarbell, Ida Minerva, 1857–1944.

A life of Napoleon Bonaparte... [2d ed.] N.Y., McClure, Phillips & co., 1904[c1901]

485 p. incl.illus., ports.

NT   0038053   PMA

DC
203
.T17
1906

Tarbell, Ida Minerva, 1857–1944.

A life of Napoleon Bonaparte; with a sketch of Josephine, Empress of the French. Illustrated from the collection of Napoleon engravings made by the late Hon. G. G. Hubbard, and now owned by the Congressional library, Washington, D. C., supplemented by pictures from the best French collections. By Ida M. Tarbell. New York, McClure, Phillips, 1906.

485 p. illus., ports.
Originally appeared in v. 3–4 of McClure's magazine. 1st

edition, 1895.
#Napoleon I. Emperor of the French, 1769–1821.
#Josephine, Empress consort of Napoleon I, 1763–1814.
(A)A life of Napoleon Bonaparte.

NT   0038055   MoU MH TU

DC203
T2
1901

Tarbell, Ida Minerva, 1857–1944.

A life of Napoleon Bonaparte; with a sketch of Josephine, Empress of the French. Illustrated from the collection of Napoleon engravings made by the late G.G. Hubbard, and now owned by the Congressional Library, Washington, D.C., supplemented by pictures from the best French collections. [2d ed.] New York, Moffat, Yard, 1909 [c1901]

485 p. illus., ports. 24cm.

Originally   appeared in v. 3–4 of McClure's magazine

NT   0038056   GU OC1 NcRS

Tarbell, Ida Minerva, 1857–1944.

Life of Napoleon Bonaparte, with a sketch of Josephine, empress of the French, illustrated from the collection of Napoleon engravings made by G.G. Hubbard ... New York, Macmillan, 1914 [c1894–1901]

485 p.

NT   0038057   PU

DC
203
T17
1918

Tarbell, Ida Minerva, 1857–1944.

A life of Napoleon Bonaparte; with a sketch of Josephine, empress of the French. Illustrated from the collection of Napoleon engravings made by the late Hon. G. G. Hubbard, and now owned by the Congressional library, Washington, D. C., supplemented by pictures from the best French collections. By Ida M. Tarbell. [2d ed.] New York, The Macmillan Co., 1918 [c1901]

485 p. incl. illus., ports. 20½ cm.

NT   0038058   NIC FTaSU Wa MH

Tarbell, Ida Minerva, 1857-1944.
A life of Napoleon Bonaparte, with a sketch of Josephine, empress of the French. Illustrated from the collection of Napoleon engravings made by the late Hon. G.G. Hubbard, and now owned by the Congressional library, Washington, D.C., supplemented by pictures from the best French collections, by Ida M. Tarbell.   New York, The Macmillan company, 1926.
485 p.   incl. front., illus. (incl. ports.) 20.5 cm.

NT   0038059   OrSaW Wa

Tarbell, Ida Minerva, 1857-1944.
Lincoln and the emancipation proclamation.
(In Dandridge, Clay, Starlight)

NT   0038060   RPB

Tarbell, Ida Minerva, 1857-1944.
Lincoln's first love.   Collier's, February 8, 1930.
7, 8, 36, and 38 p.

NT   0038061   MiKW

Tarbell, Ida Minerva, 1857-1944.
Madame Roland: a biographical study ...
London, Lawrence, 1896.
12, 328 p.   front., plates, ports., facsim.
19.5 cm.
Bibliography: p. 313-319.
1. Roland de la Platière, Marie Jeanne (Phlipon) 1754-1793. 2. France-Hist. - Revolution, 1789-1799.

NT   0038062   NjP MiU OOxM

Tarbell, Ida Minerva, 1857-1944.
Madame Roland: a biographical study; by Ida M. Tarbell. New York, C. Scribner's sons, 1896.
xii p., 1 l., 328 p.   front., plates, ports., facsim.   19½ᵐ.
Bibliography: p. 313-319.

1. Roland de la Platière, Marie Jeanne (Phlipon) 1754-1793.
2. France—Hist.—Revolution.

Library of Congress   DC146.R7T2   4—10841
———— Copy 2.   ₍a30k1₎   -920.7

OC1 MB NN NIC FU LU PPL PPFr KyU
NT   0038063   DLC MeB NcD MCE PU PPA PPT DN OrP WaS Or

Tarbell, Ida Minerva, 1857-1944.
Madame Roland; a biographical study, by Ida M. Tarbell.
New York: McClure, Phillips & co., 1905.   xii, 328 p.   facsim., front., plates, ports.   19½cm.
Bibliography, p. 313-319.

912127A. 1. Roland de la Platière,   Marie Jeanne (Philpon), 1754-1793.
2. France—Hist.—Revolution, 1789-   1793.
N. Y. P. L.   November 12, 1937

NT   0038064   NN OKentU OrSaW Wa WaE MtBC ODW

Tarbell, Ida Minerva, 1857-1944.
Madame Roland: a biographical study; by Ida M. Tarbell.   New York, Moffat, 1909.
xii p., 1 l., 328 p.   front., plates, ports., facsim.   19.5 cm.
Bibliography: p. 313-319.

NT   0038065   WaSp NcRS

Spec
Col
q
E
767
.T3
1922

Tarbell, Ida Minerva, 1857-1944.
The man they cannot forget / Ida M. Tarbell. [New York] : Collier's, The National Weekly, 1922.
1 l. ; 35.5 cm.
Essay on Woodrow Wilson, reprinted from Collier's, February 18, 1922.
Broadside.
Signed by the author.
From the library of P. George Ulizio.

1. Wilson, Woodrow, Pres. U. S., 1856-1924--Addresses, essays, lectures. I. Title

NT   0038066   OKentU

Tarbell, Ida Minerva, 1857-1944, ed.

Napoléon I, *emperor of the French*, 1769-1821.
Napoleon's addresses; selections from the proclamations, speeches and correspondance of Napoleon Bonaparte; ed. by Ida M. Tarbell.   Boston, J. Knight company, 1897.

Tarbell, Ida Minerva, 1857-1944.
... The nationalizing of business, 1878-1898, by Ida M. Tarbell.   New York, The Macmillan company, 1936.
xvi p., 1 l., 313 p.   front., plates (1 double) ports.   22ᵐ.   (A History of American life, vol. IX)
Illustrated lining-papers.
"Critical essays on authorities": p. 278-293.

1. U. S.—Indus.—Hist. 2. Trusts, Industrial—U. S. 3. Monopolies—

Library of Congress   E169.1.H67   vol. 9   36-28966
————— Copy 2   HC105.T3
₍a44q7₎   (973) 330.97⁹

Wa WaE IdPS
KyU WaU KEmT TNJ OrSaW OrLgE MtU-M OrU-M CaBVaU
WaT WaTC WaWW WaSpG WaPS OrPR OrCS MtBC OC1JC OrStbM
OrPS WaS MtU-M WaSp NcC NcD NcRS IdU MtU OrP OrU
MtBC DFT ViU-L OCU OO OC1 Ck MB NN MiHM ViU MiU OU
NT   0038068   DLC PWcS PV MtU IdB PIm PHC Or CaBVa AU

Tarbell, Ida Minerva, 1857-1944.
... The nationalizing of business, 1878-1898, by Ida M. Tarbell.   New York, The Macmillan company, 1940.
xvi p., 1 l., 313 p.   front., plates (1 double) ports.   22 cm.   (A History of American life, vol. IX)
Illustrated lining-papers.
"Critical essays on authorities": p. 278-293.

NT   0038069   PRosC

Tarbell, Ida Minera, 1857-1944.
The nationalizing of business, 1878-1898.   NY, Macmillan [1944]
xvi, 313 p.   illus.   (A history of American life, 9)

NT   0038070   MH-L

Tarbell, Ida Minerva, 1857-1944.
New ideals in business, an account of their practice and their effects upon men and profits, by Ida M. Tarbell ... New York, The Macmillan company, 1916.
5 p. l., 339 p.   illus. (facsim.) diagrs.   20 cm.

1. Welfare institutions for laborers.   I. Title.

HD7654.T3   16—23449

PP PHC FTaSU DHU OrCS
ViU OC1W ODW OC1 OCU OOxM MiU LU OKentU DHEW NN MB
NT   0038071   DLC MtU OrP IdB OrPR WaSpG WaS Or ICJ OU

Tarbell, Ida Minerva, 1857-1944.
New ideals in business, an account of their practice and their effects upon men and profits by Ida M. Tarbell... New York, The Macmillan company, 1917.
5 p.l., 339 p. illus. (facsim) diagrs. 20 cm
92158

NT   0038072   DNW NRCR NcRS NjP PPFr OU OCX OC1W

Tarbell, Ida Minerva, 1857-1944.
New ideals in business, an account of their practice and their effects upon men and profits. New York, The Macmillan company, 1917, [c1916]
339 p. 1. illus. (facsim.) diagrs.
Microfiche.

NT   0038073   PSt

Tarbell, Ida Minerva, 1857-1944.
Owen D. Young, a new type of industrial leader, by Ida M. Tarbell ...   New York, The Macmillan company, 1932.
xiv, 353 p. front., illus., plates, ports., facsim. 23 cm.
"Published June, 1932."
"Catalogue of the Owen D. Young fundamental library of English literature for college students": p. 330-342.

1. Young, Owen D.

E748.Y74T3   923.373   32—26673

PU PBm
PPT MsSM GAuA NN MB OC1M OCU MiU OC1 ViU OO OFH PP
OrSaW WaSpG AAP CoU OrP Or MtU IdB WaS OrCS   NcD
NT   0038074   DLC KEmT CU-I MeB OrU OKentU CaBVaU OrU

Tarbell, Ida Minerva, *1857-1944*.   *4349a-355
The parents of Lincoln.
(*In* Abraham Lincoln. A souvenir of Lincoln's birthday. Pp. 17-24. Plates. Map. [New York. 1907.])

D7655 — Lincoln, Abraham. Family history.

NT   0038075   MB

Tarbell, Ida Minerva, 1857-1944.
Peacemakers—blessed and otherwise; observations, reflections and irritations at an international conference, by Ida M. Tarbell. New York, The Macmillan company, 1922.
5 p. l., 227 p. 19½ᵐ.

1. Washington, D. C. Conference on the limitation of armament, 1921-1922. 2. World politics. I. Title.
Library of Congress   JX1974.5.T3   22—7444

NJN OC1 ViU PPFr WaS KEmT Jo FTaSU IdPI MB NN
NT   0038076   DLC Or OrP PPT PP PPL AAP DAU IU OOxM OU

Tarbell, Ida Minerva, 1857-1944.
[Prospectus of Ida M. Tarbell's "Life of Abraham Lincoln", including specimen pages, etc.]
see under   Lincoln history society, New York.

Tarbell, Ida Minerva, 1857-1944.
A reporter for Lincoln. Story of Henry E. Wing, soldier and newspaperman. ₍c1926₎

NT   0038078   OC1

Tarbell, Ida Minerva, 1857-1944.
A reporter for Lincoln; story of Henry E. Wing, soldier and newspaperman, by Ida M. Tarbell. New York, The Macmillan company, 1927.
5 p. l., 78 p. col. front. 19½ᶜᵐ.

1. Lincoln, Abraham, pres. U. S., 1809-1865. 2. Wing, Henry Ebeneser, 1839-1925. I. Title.
27-4861

Library of Congress   E457.15.T2

IdPI CaBVaU NcU
OCU OEac MiU NN MB MWA MiU-C FMU GU NIC FU WaT PPFr
NT 0038079   DLC WaTU PPL PP PU OrP WaE NmU KEmT OU Or

973.7L63 **Tarbell, Ida Minerva,** 1857-1944.
B2T17r   A reporter for Lincoln; story of Henry E.
1929   Wing, soldier and newspaperman.   New York,
Book League of America, 1929.
78p. col.front. 20cm.

1. Lincoln, Abraham, Pres. U.S., 1809-1865.
2. Wing, Henry Ebeneser, 1839-1925. I. Title.

NT 0038080   IU ViU

Tarbell, Ida Minerva, 1857-1944.
The rising of the tide; the story of Sabinsport, by Ida M. Tarbell. New York, The Macmillan company, 1919.
2 p. l., 277 p. 20ᶜᵐ.

1. European war, 1914-1918—Fiction. I. Title.
19-5278

Library of Congress   PZ3.T1725R

OEac MiU MsU NcD
NT 0038081   DLC Or OrCS WaS PBa PU PP PSt MB NN OO

Tarbell, Ida Minerva, 1857-1944, comp.
[Scrapbook: Lincoln material containing clippings from The Boston daily globe 1909]
Boston, 1909.
1 v. 22 cm.

NT 0038082   RPB

Tarbell, Ida Minerva, 1857-1944, ed.

Lincoln, Abraham, *pres. U. S.,* 1809-1865.
Selections from the letters, speeches, and state papers of Abraham Lincoln, ed. with introduction and notes, by Ida M. Tarbell ... Boston, New York [etc.] Ginn and company [*1911]_

Tarbell, Ida Minerva, 1857-1944,
A short life of Napoleon Bonaparte, by Ida M. Tarbell. With 250 illustrations from the Hon. Gardiner G. Hubbard's collection of Napoleon engravings, supplemented by pictures from the collections of Prince Victor Napoleon, Prince Roland Bonaparte, Baron Larrey and others. New York: S. S. M⁶Clure, Ltd., 1895. viii, 248 p. incl. front. illus. (incl. fac., port.) 4°.

On cover: M⁶Clure's life of Napoleon...

I. Napoleon I., emperor of the   French, 1769-1821.
N. Y. P. L.   December 27, 1917.

IEdS WaU OEac FU AzU PHi PPD
NT 0038084   NN WaWW MiU OU OCU OC1W MB MH ViU NIC CU

— **Tarbell, Ida Minerva,** 1857-1944.
A short life of Napoleon Bonaparte, by Ida M. Tarbell; with 250 illustrations from the Hon. Gardiner G. Hubard's collection of Napoleon engravings, supplemented by pictures from the collections of Prince Victor Napoleon, Prince Roland Bonaparte, Baron Larrey and others. New York, The S. S. McClure co., 1896.
viii, 248 p. incl. front., illus., ports. 24½ cm.

Forms, combined with another work, uniform in makeup, a volume in cloth with title lettered on front cover: M⁶Clure's biographies : Napoleon, Gladstone, Bismarck, Grant, Dana, Stevenson and others.

Continued in next column

Continued from preceding column

The second work has title: Human documents: portraits and biographies of eminent men; articles by Robert Louis Stevenson, Herbert Spencer, Professor Drummond, Edward Everett Hale, H. H. Boyesen, Gen. Horace Porter, Hamlin Garland, Robert Barr and others; with 275 illustrations. New York, The S. S. McClure co., 1896. (viii, 248 p. incl. front., illus., ports.)

1. Napoléon I, emperor of the French, 1769-1821. 2. Biography. I. Title. II. Title: McClure's biographies. III. Title: Human documents.
CT119.T4   24-16882

NT 0038086   DLC NcU ICRL MoU IU CoU WaSpG WaS OrCS

Tarbell, Ida Minerva, 1857-1944.
A short life of Napoleon Bonaparte. With 250 illustrations from the Hon. Gardiner G. Hubbard's collection of Napoleon engravings, supplemented by pictures from the collections of Prince Victor Napoleon, Prince Roland Bonaparte, Baron Larrey and others. New York, Doubleday & McClure co., 1898.

viii, 248 p. ports., plates, illus., facsims. 24.5 cm.

NT 0038087   MH

Tarbell, Ida Minerva, 1857-1944.

Mullett, Mary B   d. 1932.
Singing memories, by Mary B. Mullett. Printed for private distribution. [New York, Print. by Ledell press, ᶜ1933]

Tarbell, Ida Minerva. 1857-1944.   9385-973a62
Standard Oil rebates.
(In Railway problems ... Pp. 62-77. Boston. [1907.])
Reprinted from her History of the Standard Oil Company [9338.77a49].

G4250 — Standard Oil Company. — Railroad rebates.

NT 0038089   MB

Tarbell, Ida Minerva, 1857-1944.
The story of the Declaration of independence
847   ...
1
From McClure's magazine, v.17, p. [223-235], July, 1901.

NT 0038090   CtY MWA MiU

Tarbell, Ida Minerva, 1857-1944.
The tariff in our times, by Ida M. Tarbell ... New York, The Macmillan company, 1911.
ix, 375 p. 20 cm.

1. Tariff—U. S.—Hist. I. Title.
HF1753.T2   11-26206

MB NN PPL NcD KEmT KyU-A MH-PA NBuU
PWcS PSC CU ODW ViU OO OCU ScU KyU OU OFH OC1 ICJ
NT 0038091   DLC WaTU ICJ Or CaBVaU WaS WaWW OrP PPT

Tarbell, Ida Minerva, 1857-1944.
The tariff in our times, by Ida M. Tarbell ... New York, The Macmillan company, 1912.
ix, 375 p. 20ᶜᵐ.

NT 0038092   MtU OrPR NjP PHC

Tarbell, Ida Minerva, 1857-1944.
The ways of woman, by Ida M. Tarbell ... New York, The Macmillan company, 1915.
vii, 135 p. 18½ᶜᵐ. $1.00

"All of these essays have appeared in the Woman's home companion."
"They supplement the author's earlier book, 'The business of being a woman.' "—Pref.
CONTENTS.—What women are doing.—Give the girl a chance.—That's her business.—The talkative woman.—The culture chasers.—The twenty-cent dinner.—A young girl's thoughts.

1. Woman—Social and moral questions. I. Title.
Library of Congress   HQ1221.T2
15-22289

NcC ODW CU ViU OC1W MiU OC1 MB NN
NT 0038093   DLC MtU WaSp Or WaS ICJ KMK OCU KEmT NcU

Tarbell, Ida Minerva, 1857-1944.
What shall we do with the young prostitute? Reform her or neglect her? By Ida M. Tarbell. [n.p., 1912?]
cover-title, 28 p. illus., ports. 23 cm.
"Reprinted from the American magazine, December, 1912".
1. Prostitution - New York City. 2. Defective and delinquent classes.

NT 0038094   ViU PU NjR OO OU

CT99   **Tarbell, Ida Minerva,** 1857-1944.
.D139T3   A wonderful truth seeker, by Ida M. Tarbell.
[New York city, 1914]
8 p. 15½cm.

"Reprinted from The American magazine December, 1914."

1. Dale, Samuel Sherman, 1859-

NT 0038095   DLC

Tarbell, J
Zc28   The emigrant's guide to California; giving a
853t   description of the overland route from the
Council Bluffs ... by South Pass, to Sacramento
city; including a table of distances ... Keokuk:
Printed at the Whig book and job office, 1853.
18p. 17½cm.
Original wrappers.

NT 0038096   CtY ICN

Tarbell, J
The emigrant's guide to California; giving a description of the overland route, from the Council Bluffs, on the Missouri River, by the South Pass, to Sacramento City. Keokuk, Whig Book and Job Office, 1853.
1 card. (Plains and Rockies, 232a)

Collation of original: 18 p. 17 cm.

NT 0038097   NjP IdPI IdU TxFTC MoU C

Tarbell, J. Horace Greeley's practical advice on reconstruction in Mississippi. 5 pp. (*Mag. Am. Hist.* v. 18, 1887, p. 423.)

NT 0038098   MdBP

Tarbell, John Adams, 1810-1864.
Homoeopathy simplified; or, Domestic practice made easy ... 2d ed. Boston, Sanborn, Carter, and Bazin, 1856.
360 p. 20 cm.

1. Homeopathy.
Med 47-1981

U. S. Army medical library   [WB1330T179h 1856]
for Library of Congress   [2]

NT 0038099   DNLM CtY MB ICJ

Tarbell, John A₍dams₎ 1810-1864.
Homœopathy simplified; or, Domestic practice made easy.
Containing explicit directions for the treatment of disease, the man-
agement of accidents, and the preservation of health.   Boston:
O. Clapp, 1859.   360 p.   3. ed.   12°.

1. Homœopathy.—Materia medica and   therapeutics. 2. Medicine (Domestic).
N. Y. P. L.   March 5, 1912.

NT   0038100   NN

WBK   TARBELL, John Adams, 1810-1864
T179h   Homœopathy simplified; or, Domestic
1856a   practice made easy. Containing explicit
           directions for the treatment of disease,
           the management of accidents, and the
           preservation of health. 4th ed. Boston,
           Clapp, 1859 ₍c1856₎
           360 p.

NT   0038101   DNLM OO OClW-H

Tarbell, John Adams, 1810-1864.
Homœopathy simplified; or, Domestic practice made
easy. Containing explicit directions for the treatment of
disease, the management of accidents, and the preservation of health. By John A. Tarbell ... Rev. ed. Boston,
O. Clapp, 1863.
vii, 372 p. 20ᶜᵐ.

1. Homœopathy—Popular works.

Library of Congress   RX76.T19   7-13671†

NT   0038102   DLC MB NN

Tarbell, John Adams, 1810-1864.
Homœopathy simplified; or, Domestic practice made easy
Containing explicit directions for the treatment of disease, the
management of accidents, and the preservation of health. By
John A. Tarbell ... Rev. ed. Boston, O. Clapp. 1864.
vii, 372 p. 19½ᶜᵐ.

1. Homœopathy—Popular works.

                                                   33-35583
Library of Congress   RX76.T19 1864   615.53

NT   0038103   DLC MB

615.53 Tarbell,John Adams,1810-1864.
T179   Homoeopathy simplified;or,Domestic
          practice made easy. Containing explicit
          directions for the treatment of disease,
          the management of accidents,and the pres
          ervation of health. By John A.Tarbell...
          Rev.ed.   Boston,O.Clapp;etc.,etc.₎ 1866.

NT   0038104   N

Tarbell, John Adams, 1810-1864.
Homeopathy simplified. Revised ed.   Boston,
Otis Clapp, 1874.
372 p.

NT   0038105   PPHa

Tarbell, John Adams, 1810-1864.
Homeopathy simplified. Revised ed.   Otis
Clapp, 1876.
372 p.

NT   0038106   PPHa

RX
76
T17
1890
MHT   Tarbell, John Adams, 1810-1864.
             Homœopathy simplified; or, Domestic
             practice made easy. Containing explicit
             directions for the treatment of disease,
             the management of accidents, and the pre-
             servation of health. Rev. ed. Boston, O.
             Clapp, 1890.
             vii, 372 p. 20 cm.

             1. Homeopathy - Popular works.
             I. Title.

NT   0038107   DSI

RX76
849T   TARBELL, John Adams, 1810-1864.
             The pocket homoeopathist and family
             guide. Boston,O.Clapp,1849.
             63p. 13cm.

NT   0038108   CtY-M PPC DNLM

Tarbell, John Adams, 1810-1864.
Pocket homoeopathist and family guide. Ed. 3
enl.   Boston, Clapp, 1855, [c'49]
71 p.

NT   0038109   PU

---

613   Tarbell, John Adams, 1810-1864.
T179s   The sources of health and the prevention of
          disease; or, Mental and physical hygiene.   Bos-
          ton, O. Clapp, 1850.
          170p. 18cm.

          1. Hygiene.

NT   0038110   IU ICRL MiU

Tarbell, John H.
**My experiences photographing the negro in
the south.**

Extract from New Eng. magazine,   Dec.1903.

NT   0038111   NcU

Tarbell, John Parker.
An oration delivered before the Democratic citizens of the
north part of Middlesex county, at Groton, July fourth, 1839.
By John P. Tarbell. Lowell, A. Watson, 1839.
35 p. 21ᶜᵐ.

1. Fourth of July orations.
                                                   37-14187
Library of Congress   E286.G89 1839
                              ₍2₎   973.361

NT   0038112   DLC N CtHT-W MH CSmH MB PHi

Tarbell, Lyle E
Determination of means to safeguard aircraft
from power plant fires in flight. Part IV.
The Boeing B-29, by Lyle E.Tarbell and H.R.
Keeler. Indianapolis, Civil Aeronautics
Administration Technical Development and
Evaluation Center, 1950.
35 p. illus., fold.chart. (Technical
development report no. 107)

Cover-title.

NT   0038113   MH-BA

Tarbell, Lyle E
Determination of the air speed required to control landing
gear fires, by Lyle E. Tarbell and Burnett C. Street. Indianapolis, Civil Aeronautics Administration, Technical Development and Evaluation Center, 1949.
8 p. 27 cm. (Technical development report no. 100)
Cover title.

1. Aeroplanes—Fire and fire prevention.   I. Street, Burnett C.,
joint author. II. Title: Landing gear fires.   (Series: U. S. Civil
Aeronautics Administration. Technical development report no. 100)

TL521.A374 no. 100   *629.144 629.1344   50-60669
——— Copy 2.   TL697.F5T3

NT   0038114   DLC

Tarbell, Martha, joint author.
Tarbell, Horace Sumner, 1838-1904.
... The complete geography, by Horace S. Tarbell ...
and Martha Tarbell ... New York, Chicago ₍etc.₎ Werner
school book company ₍1899₎

Tarbell, Martha, joint author.
Tarbell, Horace Sumner, 1838-
Essentials of English composition, by Horace S. Tarbell ... and Martha Tarbell, PH. D. Boston, Ginn & company, 1902.

Tarbell, Martha.
Geographical pamphlet. Palestine in the time of
Christ ₍by₎ Martha Tarbell ... Indianapolis, The Bobbs-
Merrill company ₍1907₎
1 p. l., 43, ₍2₎ p. incl. maps. front., plates, maps. 23ᶜᵐ. (*On cover:* Tar-
bell's geographical manual for 1908)

1. Bible—Geography.   I. Title.

Library of Congress   DS104.3.T3   7—37962

NT   0038117   DLC PSt PPLT NNUT OO NN

Tarbell, Martha.
The German ballad: history, four great writers,
characteristics. Thesis offered by... candidate
for the degree of Doctor of philosophy, Brown
university, March 31, 1897.   [Providence] 1897.
33 cm.

NT   0038118   RPB

Tarbell, Martha.
In the Master's country: a geographical aid to the study
of the life of Christ ₍by₎ Martha Tarbell ... New York,
Hodder & Stoughton, George H. Doran company ₍ᶜ1910₎
1 p. l., x, 43, ₍2₎ p. front., illus., plates, maps. 23½ᶜᵐ.

1. Bible—Geography. 2. Palestine—Descr. & trav.   I. Title.

Library of Congress   DS104.3.T4   10—16186

NT   0038119   DLC NN NBuU NjPT CPFT ViU OCl ABS

Tarbell, Martha, joint author.   FOR OTHER EDITIONS
Tarbell, Horace Sumner, 1838-1904.   SEE MAIN ENTRY
Lessons in language and grammar; book 1₍-2₎ by Horace S.
Tarbell ... and Martha Tarbell, PH. D. Boston, Ginn & com-
pany, 1900.

Tarbell, Martha, joint author.
Tarbell, Horace Sumner, 1838-1904.
Manual to accompany lessons in language and grammar,
by Horace S. Tarbell, LL. D. and Martha Tarbell, PH. D. Boston, Ginn & company, 1903.

BV1560
.T3

Tarbell, Martha, ed.

Tarbell's teachers' guide to the International Bible Lessons for Christian teaching of the uniform course. [1st]– 1906–
Westwood, N. J. [etc.], F. H. Revell Co. [etc.]

NT 0038123   IU Nh

027.22   Tarbell, Mary Anna.
H765t   The Homefield library: its work and its helpers.   [Homefield, 190 ?]
10p.

NT 0038123   IU Nh

Tarbell, Mary Anna.
The minutemen who lived in Brimfield. Their preparation for the coming struggle. List of those who enrolled... By Mary Anna Tarbell. [Brimfield, Mass.? 1924?]   3 l.   illus.   12°.
Caption-title.

1. Brimfield, Mass.—Hist. 2. Brown   family.
N. Y. P. L.   September 10, 1925

NT 0038124   NN MWA

Tarbell, Mary Anna.
Stage days in Brimfield, a century of mail and coach [by] Mary Anna Tarbell. [Springfield, Mass., The F. A. Bassette company, printers, °1909]
32, [2] p. incl. front., illus.   23½ᶜᵐ.

1. Brimfield, Mass. 2. Coaching—Massachusetts.   I. Title.
                                                        9–29350
Library of Congress   F74.B75T2

NT 0038125   DLC PP WHi ICN MB MWA MiU

Tarbell, Mary Anna.
... A village library [by] Mary Anna Tarbell ... [Boston, 1905]
19 p. 19¼ᶜᵐ. (Leaflets, Massachusetts civic league. no. 3)
An account of the Brimfield, Mass., public library.

1. Brimfield, Mass. Public library.
                                                        8–36829
Library of Congress   Z733.B845

NT 0038126   DLC NN MWA NRCR PPD C

Tarbell, Mary Anna.
... A village library in Massachusetts; the story of its upbuilding. By Mary Anna Tarbell ... Boston, A. L. A. Publishing board, 1905.
19 p. 19ᶜᵐ. (American library association. Publishing board. Library tract, no. 8)
An account of the Brimfield public library. "A reprint of Leaflet no. 3 of the Massachusetts civic league."

1. Brimfield, Mass. Public library.
                                                        5–36917
Library of Congress   Z665.A51
——— Copy 2.   Library of Congress   Z733.B8451

NT 0038127   DLC WaS MiU OU OC1W NBuG OC1 ICJ

Tarbell, Robert W.
Robert Lawrence Cooley-Educator.   [n. p., 1944]
8 p.
1. Cooley, Robert Lawrence, 1869-1944.

NT 0038128   WHi

HG
9678
.T18

Tarbell, Thomas F.
The combined fire and casualty annual statement blank. [n.p., 1951]
[74]-140 p.   23 cm.
Cover title.
"Reprinted from the Proceedings of the Casualty Actuarial Society, vol. XXXVII, part II, no. 68, November, 1950 and vol. XXXVIII, part II, no. 69, November, 1951."

1. Insurance, Fire--Accounting. 2. Insurance, Casualty.

NT 0038129   MiU

Tarbell, Thomas F.
Effect of influenza on insurance.   Hartford, Conn., 1919.
17 p.

NT 0038130   PPProM

Tarbell, Thomas F.
Legal requirements and state supervision of fire insurance, by Thomas F. Tarbell ... New York, The Insurance society of New York, 1927.
38, [1] p. 23ᶜᵐ.
Cover-title.
Bibliographical foot-notes.

1. Insurance law—U. S. 2. Insurance, Fire—U. S.   I. Insurance society of New York. II. Title.
                                                        27–17324
Library of Congress   HG9734.U6T3

NT 0038131   DLC CU NN

Tarbell, Warren E
Workmen's compensation insurance, employers robbed, injured workers swindled, workers forced to pay $15.60 per capita tax, state fund only remedy; address delivered by Hon. Warren E. Tarbell on floor of Massachusetts Senate. [Brookfield? Mass., 1922]
[32] p. 23½ᶜᵐ.

1. Employers' liability—Massachusetts.
                                                        46–28909
Library of Congress   HD7816.U7M46

NT 0038132   DLC

Tarbell, *Mrs.* Winfield Scott
see
Tarbell, Grace Elizabeth (Butler)

Tarbell's teachers' guide to the International Bible Lessons for Christian teaching of the uniform course. [1st]– 1906–
Westwood, N. J. [etc.], F. H. Revell Co. [etc.]
v. illus. 23 cm. annual.

Title varies slightly.
Editors: 1906-49, M. Tarbell (with W. G. Chanter, 1948-49)— 1951– F. S. Mead.

1. International Sunday-school lessons.   I. Tarbell, Martha, ed. II. Mead, Frank Spencer, 1898-   ed.

BV1560.T3   268.61   5–40811 rev*‡

KyLxCB KyLx KyU NcD OU
CaBVaU OrU ICU ODW OEac   Wa WaS OC1 MH NN AAP MB
NT 0038134   DLC NjNbS NcC PP PPLT OO NcD OLak CaBVa

W 4
L99
1954/55
no. 69

TARBÉS, André, 1927-
Intérêt du test d'immobilisation du tréponème pour le diagnostic étiologique de manifestations morbides, paraissant cliniquement de nature syphilitique.
Lyon, 1954.
104 p. (Lyons. [Université] Faculté de médecine et de pharmacie. Thèse, 1954/55, no. 69)
1. Syphilis - Diagnosis

NT 0038135   DNLM

Tarbés (Roch). Manuel de la saignée, ou dialogue sur l'art de pratiquer cette opération. xxi, 300 pp. 16°. *Paris, Croullebois, an V* [1797].

NT 0038136   DNLM

Tarbés, Roch.
Mémoire historique et pratique sur la vaccine, contenant un procès-verbal de la contre-épreuve faite authentiquement. Nouv. éd, corr. et augm. Toulouse, Manavit, 1801.
58, 21 p.   21 cm.
"Observations sur le meilleur mode d'exécution": 21 p. at end.

1. Vaccines. I. T.

NT 0038137   NjP

TARBÉS, Roch
Mémoire sur la vaccination pratiquée avec l'aiguille à coudre, et sur la manière d'employer utilement les croûtes vaccines; suivi de quelques corollaires relatifs à la vaccine. Paris, Croullebois, 1809.
31 p.   WCH T179m
Author's autograph presentation copy.

NT 0038138   DNLM

Tarbes (Diocese) Bishop (Gain-Montaignac)
see also   Gain-Montaignac, François de, Bp. of Tarbes, 1744-1812.

Tarbes (Diocese) Bishop,
(Bertrand Sévère Laurence)
see also   Laurence, Bertrand Sévère, Bp. of Tarbes, 1790-1870.

Z6945
.T35

Tarbes, France. Bibliothèque municipale.
Liste des périodiques français et étrangers en cours concernant les bibliothèques et centres de documentation des départements (à jour au 1er janvier 1953) : Hautes-Pyrénées. Tarbes, 1953.
20 l. 27 cm.
Cover title.
L.C. copy imperfect: leaf 13 wanting.

1. French periodicals—Bibl. 2. Periodicals—Bibl.—Catalogs.
                                                        A 54–5873
Illinois. Univ. Library
for Library of Congress   [3]

NT 0038141   IU DLC

Film
791.45013
T179c

Tarbet, Donald Gentry, 1917-
A comparison of achievement in current affairs of television and non-television groups.
140p. tables, map.

Thesis (Ph.D.) - University of Missouri, 1952.
Positive microfilm by University Microfilms.
Bibliography: p. [116]-122.
Vita.

NT 0038142   NcU KMK

Tarbet, Marie Lorimer.
Swing of the sea, by Marie L. Tarbet. London, Hodder and Stoughton [1939]
287, [1] p. 19ᶜᵐ.
"First printed 1939."

I. Title.
                                                        39–11258
Library of Congress   PZ3.T1726Sw

NT 0038143   DLC

Tarbet, Roy E

Report on design and construction of the Baker River bridge, Baker River highway. The first bridge in the northwest having a precast concrete deck and A discussion of the precast stringers in trestles, Turnagain Arm Project, Alaska [and] Plans for proposed precast deck design eliminating all "on job" form work and including precasting of curbs. Portland, Bureau of Public Roads, 1950.
17 [8] p. illus., plans.
Prepared for Bureau of Public Roads, Portland. Washington Forest Highway project 25-C4.

NT 0038144   OrP

Tarbet, W   G.
Fighting for favour; a romance, by W. G. Tarbet. New York, H. Holt and company, 1898.
viii, 312 p. 19ᵐ.

i. Title.
8—25562

Library of Congress   PZ3.T1728F

NT 0038145   DLC PPL CtY

---

813   [Tarbet, W   G   ]
T1731   Ill-gotten gold.   Chicago, W. B. Conkey company, c1902.
309p.

NT 0038146   IU PPL

Tarbet, W   G.
... In oor kailyard, by W. G. Tarbet. Bristol & London, J. W. Arrowsmith; [etc., etc., 1897]
226 p. 19½ᵐ.

8-25561†

Library of Congress   PZ3.T1728I

NT 0038147   DLC

[Tarbet, William]
Spiritual manifestations in the present day.
Liverpool, 1855.
12 p.   8   (In v. 310, College pamphlets).

NT 0038148   CtY OK

Spec.
E   Tarbet, William L
286   An address delivered on the Fourth of
.V56   July, 1860, at Virden, Illinois. Pub. by
1860   request.   Carlinville,Ill.,H.M.Kimball, 1860.
16p.

1. Fourth of July orations.

NT 0038149   DeU

Tarbet, William L
Description and discussion of the recent decisions of the United States supreme court in the Kentucky franchise tax cases. [National tax association] 1918.
p. 206-17.

NT 0038150   Or

Tarbett, Ralph Edwin, joint author.

Goldberger, Joseph, 1874-1929.
... A study of endemic pellagra in some cotton-mill villages of South Carolina, by Joseph Goldberger, and G. A. Wheeler, surgeons, Edgar Sydenstricker, statistician, and Wilford [!] I. King, special consultant in statistics, with the cooperation of Wm. S. Bean, jr., R. E. Dyer, J. D. Reichard, P. M. Stewart, surgeons, M. C. Edmonds, assistant surgeon, R. E. Tarbett, sanitary engineer, Dorothy Wiehl, assistant statistician, and Jennie C. Goddard, senior statistical clerk, U. S. Public health service. Washington, U. S. Govt. print. off., 1929.

Tarbett, Ralph Edwin, joint author.

Goldberger, Joseph, 1874–
... A study of the relation of factors of a sanitary character to pellagra incidence in seven cotton-mill villages of South Carolina in 1916, by Joseph Goldberger, surgeon, G. A. Wheeler, passed assistant surgeon, and Edgar Sydenstricker, statistician, with sanitary ratings by R. E. Tarbett, sanitary engineer, United States Public health service ... Washington, Govt. print. off., 1920.

Tarbett, Ralph Edwin, joint author.

Hommon, Harry Britton, 1879–   FOR OTHER EDITIONS SEE MAIN ENTRY
... Treatment and disposal of sewage. Brief descriptions of methods, processes, and structures used in the treatment and disposal of sewage in the United States, with bibliography, by H. B. Hommon, J. K. Hoskins, H. W. Streeter, R. E. Tarbett and H. H. Wagenhals, associate sanitary engineers, United States Public health service ... Washington, Govt. print off., 1920.

An tarbh breac
see under [Fegan N   ] ed.

Tarbiat, Gholam Ali
see
Tarbiyat, Ghulām ʻAlī.

Tarbiat, Reza
see Tarbiyat, Riza.

Tarbiet, Mirza Reza Khan
see Tarbiyat, Riza.

Tarbill, Von Valjean.
Mountain-moving in Seattle.   n.p., 1930.
8 p.   maps.
Reprinted from Harvard business review, July, 1930, pages 482-89.

NT 0038158   WaS

QL482
.R9T3
Tarbinskiĭ, S   P   ed.
Определитель насекомых Европейской части СССР. Под ред. С. П. Тарбинского и Н. Н. Плавильщикова. Москва, Сельхозгиз, 1948.
1127 p. illus. 27 cm.

1. Insects—Russia.   i. Plavil'shchikov, Nikolaĭ Nikolaevich, 1892–   joint ed.   ii. Title.
Title transliterated: Opredelitel' nasekomykh Evropeĭskoĭ chasti SSSR.

51–38348

NT 0038159   DLC

תרביץ; רבעון למדעי היהדות. שנת 1– ; תשרי 630–
1929– [etc.]
ירושלים. הוצאת הספרים ע"ש י. ל. מאגנס. האוניברסיטה העברית
v. in   illus., facsims. 24-26 cm.
Subtitle varies: v. 1-23 למדעי חרות
Added t. p.: Tarbiz.
Summaries in English. v. 24–
INDEXES:
Vols. 1-10, 1929-39, *with* v. 10.
Vols. 1-20, 1929-49.   1 v.
Vols. 1-30, 1929-61.   1 v.
1. Jews—Hist.—Period. 2. Judaism—Hist.—Period.   i. Title: Tarbiz.
Title romanized: Tarbits.
DS101.T35   HE 67-1804
PL 480: Is-S-196

NT 0038160   DLC TxU OrPS UU InU CLSU TNJ-R

التربية الاسلامية.
(al-Tarbiyah al-Islāmīyah)
[بغداد، جمعية التربية الاسلامية.]
v. 24 cm. monthly.

1. Islam—Periodicals. 2. Islam—Education—Periodicals.
I. Jam'iyat al-Tarbiyah al-Islāmīyah.
BP1.T28   77-647034
(MARC-S)

NT 0038161   DLC

التربية الجديدة.
(al-Tarbiyah al-jadīdah)
[بيروت، مكتب اليونسكو الاقليمي للتربية في البلاد العربية.]
v. ill. 24 cm. 3 no. a year.
Other title   : L'Éducation nouvelle.
Summaries in English or French.

1. Education—Arab countries—Periodicals.   I. United Nations Educational, Scientific and Cultural Organization. Regional Office for Education in the Arab Countries. II. Title: L'Éducation nouvelle.
LA1490.T37   77-648280
(MARC-S)

NT 0038162   DLC

Tarbiyat, Ghulām ʻAlī.
فرهنگ جیبی تربیت، آلمانی – فارسی، حاوی بیست هزار واژه. تألیف غلامعلی تربیت. چاپ 2. تهران، ابن سینا، 1331 [1952]
[A]–C, 752 p. 14 cm.
Added t. p.: Deutsch-Persisches Taschenwörterbuch, enthaltend ca. 20000 Wörter u. Redensarten, von Gholam Ali Tarbiat.

1. German language—Dictionaries—Persian.   i. Title.
Title romanized: Farhang-i jaybī-i Tarbiyat, Almānī-Fārsī.
PK6381.G4T3 1952   70-222585

NT 0038163   DLC CU

Tarbiyat, Ghulām ʻAlī.
Farhange Tarbiat; iranisch-deutsches wörterbuch, enthaltend über 25.000 wörter und redensarten. Von Gholam Ali Tarbiat ... Teheran, Druck. von Gebrüder Fardine, 1315/1937.
5 p. l., 568 p. 1 l. 17½ᵐ.
Added t.-p. and paging in Persian.

1. Persian language—Dictionaries—German.   i. Title.
A C 38-2209

New York. Public library
for Library of Congress   [2]

NT 0038164   NN MH

---

tPK6381   Tarbiyat, Ghulām ʻAlī
T37   Farhange Tarbiat; persisch-deutsches
1953   Wörterbuch, enthaltend über 25.000 Wörter
und Redensarten.   Teheran, Buchhandlung
Ebné-sina, 1332/1953.
568 p. 14cm.

Added title-page in Persian.

1. Persian language – Dictionaries – German.

NT 0038165   CU

⸝ Tarbiyat, Mohammad-'Alí, 1827 or 8–1939 or 40.

Browne, Edward Granville, 1862–
The press and poetry of modern Persia; partly based on the manuscript work of Mírzá Muḥammad 'Alí khán "Tarbiyat" of Tabríz, by Edward G. Browne ... Cambridge, University press, 1914.

NT 0038167   CLU NN OC1

Tarbiyat, Riza.
Deutsch-persisches Taschen-wörterbuch. Berlin-Charlottenburg, Kaviani [1923]
292 p.
Added t.p. in Persian.
1. German language – Dictionaries – Persian.

NT 0038168   TxU

491.5533   Tarbiyat, Riza.
T1715d   Deutsch-Persisch-Französisches Taschen-
1927   Wörterbuch. Bearb. von Mirza Reza Khan Tarbiet[!] 2. Aufl. Berlin, Persepolis (R. Tarbiet) 1927.
526p. 14cm.
Added t.p., in Persian.
On cover: Deutsch-Persisch-Französisches Wörterbuch.

NT 0038168   TxU

AP91   TARBIZ; a quarterly review of the humanities ...
.T17   v.1–
Oct.1929–
Jerusalem,The Hebrew university press association,1929–
v. plates,plans,facsims. 25½cm.
Title-pages also in Hebrew;text in Hebrew.
Editor:Oct.1929–   J.N.Epstein.
––– ––––– Supplement to Tarbiz. I–
Jerusalem,1930–
v. plates.   25½cm.
Title-pages also   in Hebrew;text in Hebrew.

CU OrU
NT 0038169   ICU NcU TxU TxDaM CaBVaU OU CSt OC1 MiU

Tarble, E   F.
Tarble's self-instructor in writing and its uses ... By E. F. Tarble ... Terre-Haute, R. N. Hudson & I. M. Brown, printers, 1856.
28 p. 14 pl. 24½ x 20ᶜᵐ.
The 14 plates (copy slips) are accompanied by blank leaves.
Contents.—pt. I. Penmanship.—pt. II. Book-keeping.—pt. III. Letter writing.

1. Penmanship. 2. Bookkeeping. 3. Letter-writing.
13–24245
Library of Congress   Z43.T17

NT 0038170   DLC

F8077   Tarble, Helen Mar (Paddock), 1843–
.T179   The story of my capture and escape during the Minnesota Indian massacre of 1862, with historical notes, descriptions of pioneer life, and sketches and incidents of the great outbreak of the Sioux or Dakota Indians as I saw them. St. Paul, Abbott print, 1904.
65 p. ports. 23 cm.

1. Dakota Indi-   ans – Wars, 1862–1865
2. Minnesota –   History.

NT 0038171   WHi ICN

Turboché (Jean-Baptiste) [1754–1824]. Réponse à la seconde lettre de M. Guérin, membre du Collège de chirurgie de Bordeaux. 62 pp. 8°. [Toulouse], 1789.
For Biography, see Notice d. trav. Soc. roy. de méd. de Bordeaux, 1824, 48–51.

NT 0038172   DNLM

Tarbor, Joseph.
Dartmouth, Mass. Address to the Quakers. Boston, 1784.

NT 0038173   PSC-Hi

Tarboro, N. C.   Board of trustees.
Annual report. 1st.
1891/92
(n.p.) 1892
1 v.

NT 0038174   DHEW

Tarboro, N.C. Calvary Episcopal Church
History of Calvary Church.   [Tarboro, 1938?]   [15]p. illus. O.

1. Tarboro, N.C. Calvary Episcopal Church
2. N.C.--Church history--Episcopal

NT 0038175   NcU

Tarboro,N.C. Commissioners.   N.p.,n.d.
Patrol regulations for the town of Tarboroug

NT 0038176   NcU

Tarbor, N. C. Ordinances, etc.
Ordinances for the government of the town of Tarboro. [Tarboro, N.C., C. F. Clayton's print., 1900]
cover-title, 56 p. 22.5 cm.

NT 0038177   NcD NcU

Tarboro, N. C. Ordinances, etc.
Ordinances, [1907].   Tarboro, n.d.
(2), xiv, 52 p.   8 vo.

NT 0038178   MH-L

Tarboro, N.C. Ordinances, etc.
Revised ordinances of the town of Tarboro (Adopted April meeting 1934). [N.P., n.p., 1934?]
53 p. 23 cm.

1. North Carolina - Ordinances, etc.

NT 0038179   NcU-L

Tarboro, N. C. School Board.
Report of the public schools of Tarboro, N. C.
1911/12–   Tarboro, 1913–
Library has: 1911/12.
1. Tarboro, N. C. - Schools.

NT 0038180   NcU

975.646   Tarboro and Edgecombe County. [Charlotte,
T179   N. C., Queen City Printing Co., 1913]
Sutro   48 p. illus. 24cm.

NT 0038181   C

Tarboro scaevola.   Tarborough, 1837–

NT 0038182   NcU

Tarborough southerner.   Tarboro, 1852–

Preceded by Free press, 1824–1851.

NT 0038183   NcU

Tarbot, Jerry.
Jerry Tarbot, the living unknown soldier. New York, Tyler publishing co. [1928].
iv, vii–viii, 182 p. 2 port. (incl. front.) 20ᶜᵐ.
War and post-war experiences of an amnesia victim who is trying to identify himself. cf. Publisher's note.

1. European war, 1914–1918—Personal narratives, American. 2. Amnesia. I. Title. II. Title: The living unknown soldier.
28-2951
Library of Congress   D570.9.T3

NT 0038184   DLC ViU MB

Lilly
GT 3450   TARBOTT, TIFFANY
.T179 M935   The moving market : or, Cries of London :
Copy 1   for the amusement and instruction of good children : decorated with twenty-four cuts from the l[ife] by the author / Tiffanny Tarbott. -- London : John Marshall, [18--?]
[26] p. : ill., front. ; 10 cm.

Title page and many leaves damaged affecting text. Lacks p.9, 10, 19, 20.
Publisher's ads 3 p. at end.
Stitched in   green wrappers.

NT 0038185   InU

DA   Tarbotton, Marriott Ogle.
690   History of the old Trent bridge, with a
N92   descriptive account of the new bridge, Nottingham.
T3   By M.O.Tarbotton. Nottingham, Richard Allen
f   and Son, 1871.
28p.[1]l. plates. 29cm.
As issued in brown cloth.

1.Nottingham (Eng.)--Hist. 2.Nottingham (Eng.)--Description I.Title

NT 0038186   NSyU TxU

Tarbotton, Marriott Ogle
House drainage. Regulations to be observed in the drainage & water supply of town and country houses ... By M. Ogle Tarbotton ... London, New York, E. and F.N. Spon, 1877.
8 p. 5 fold.pl. 21 1/2cm.

1. Drainage, House.

NT 0038187   DP DNLM

Tarbotton, Harriott Ogle.
—— & Rawlinson (Robt.) Report to the Nottingham and Leen Valley sewerage board, on the utilization of the sewage, and the purification of the river Trent and its tributaries, with descriptions of various modes of treating sewage. 56 pp., 2 charts, 2 tab. roy. 8°. London, E. & F. N. Spon, 1875.

NT 0038188   DNLM

D628.3
T17
    Tarbotton, Marriott Ogle
        Sanitary legislation & science, with especial
    regard to sewage & water supply (forming a ré-
    sumé of the sewage question) being the substance
    of two lectures delivered before the Literary &
    philosophical society, Nottingham, by M. O. Tar
    botton ... London, Spon, 1872.
        45 p.   21½cm.

        1. Sewage disposal.

NT 0038189   NNC DNLM NN

Tarbouriech, chanoine.
    ... Notice sur Beaulieu, 1194–1918.   Montpellier: Impri-
merie de la Charité, 1929.   98 p.   8°.

553640A. 1. Beaulieu, France—Hist.
N. Y. P. L.   November 10, 1931

NT 0038190   NN

Tarbouriech (A.-P.) * Des euphorbiacées,
leurs laticifères, leur latex. 45 pp., 1 l. 4°.
Montpellier, 1886, No. 303.

NT 0038191   DNLM

Tarbouriech, Amédée Caprais, 1834–1870.
    Une Bible manuscrite et enluminée de la
Bibliotheque d'Auch. Ses nombreuses miniatures,
et en particular l'initiale de la Genèse 'XIIIe siecle)
Auch, Foix, 1862.
    12 p.

NT 0038192   PP

Tarbouriech, Amédée Caprais, 1834–1870.
    Bibliographie politique du département du Gers pen-
dant la période révolutionnaire. Pub., pour la première
fois, d'après les imprimés et les documents authentiques,
par Amédée Tarbouriech ... 2. tirage avec additions et
corrections nouvelles ... Paris, A. Aubry, 1867.
    74 p.   25cm.

    1. Gers, France (Dept.)—Bibl. 2. France—Hist.—Revolution—Bibl.
                                              7–10138 Revised
    Library of Congress   Z2184.G4T2

NT 0038193   DLC

Soc
DC
195
G47
T3
    Tarbouriech, Amédée Caprais, 1834–1870.
        Curiosités révolutionnaires du Gers, par
    A. Tarbouriech. Avec une préface de Paul
    Bénétrix.   Auch, Aux Archives départe-
    mentales ₍1892₎
        102p.

        1. Gers, France (Dept.) – Hist. 2. France –
    Hist. – Revolution. I. Title.

NT 0038194   FTaSU MH

Tarbouriech, Amédée Caprais, 1834–1870.
    Documents sur quelques faïenceries du sud-ouest de la
France, par Amédée Tarbouriech ... Paris, Chez A. Aubry,
1864.
    24 p. 18½cm.
    "Extrait de la Gazette des beaux-arts."
    No. 2 in a volume lettered: Pamphlets on china ware. 1857.

    1. Pottery—France.
                                              32–33308
    Library of Congress   NK3760.P3 no. 2   738

NT 0038195   DLC

DC
195
A89
T17
    Tarbouriech, Amédée Caprais, 1834–1870.
        La justice révolutionnaire à Auch:
    histoire de la Commission extraordinaire
    de Bayonne, d'après les documents origi-
    naux. Paris, J. Baur, 1869.
        xii, 99 p. 22cm.

        Only 100 copies printed.
        Contents.—I. La Commission extra-
    ordinaire.—II. L'affaire Delong.—
    III. Le procès.

NT 0038196   NIC CtY

Tarbouriech, Amédée Caprais, 1834–1870.
    ... Les livres d'heures au seizième siècle.
Paris, Chez Auguste Aubry, 1865.
    3 p. l., ₍3₎–23 p. 22cm.

    At head of title: Amédée Tarbouriech.

    1. Hours, Books of.

NT 0038197   NNC NjP

FILM
11633
BX
Library
School
    Tarbouriech, Amédée Caprais, 1834–1870.
        Les livres d'heures au seizième siècle.   Paris, A. Aubry,
    1865.
        23 p. On film (Negative)

        Microfilm. Original in Bibliothèque Nationale.

        1. Hours, Books of.

NT 0038198   CU

Tarbouriech, Ernest, 1865–
    ... La cité future; essai d'une utopie scientifique ..
Paris, P. V. Stock, 1902.
    3 p. l., 484 p. 19cm. (Bibliothèque des recherches sociales. no. 7)
    Contents.—Généralités.—La consommation.—Production.—Équilibre de
la production et de la consommation.
                                                            3–6912

NT 0038199   DLC ICU NcD NIC MiEM ICJ MB CaBVaU

Tarbouriech, Ernest, 1865–
    ... La cité future; essai d'une utopie scientifique.
Paris, P. V. Stock, 1910.
    3 p. l., 484 p. 19 cm. (Bibliothèque des
recherches sociales. no. 7)
    "Deuxième édition".

NT 0038200   OU

TARBOURIECH, Ernest, 1865–
    Contribution à la théorie de la cause; dans la
cause dans les libéralités. Paris, 1894.

    8°. 21p.

NT 0038201   MH-L

Tarbouriech, Ernst, 1865–
    ... De la responsabilité contractuelle
et délictuelle ... Des assurances contre
les accidents du travail, assurance collective et de responsabilité civile ...
Besançon, Millot frères et cie., 1889.
    4 p. l., 102 p., 1 l., lxxii, 318 p.   25cm.
    Thèse – Faculté de droit de Paris.

NT 0038202   MiU-L

TARBOURIECH, Ernest, 1865–
    Des assurances contre les accidents du tra-
vail, assurance collective et de responsabilité
civile. Paris, 1889.

    8°.

NT 0038203   MH-L

Tarbouriech, Ernest, 1865–
    Essai sur la propriété, par Ernest Tarbouriech ...   Paris:
V. Giard & E. Brière, 1904. 3 p. l., 356 p.   fold. tables.   16°.
(Bibliothèque socialiste internationale.)

    1. Property. 2. Series.
N. Y. P. L.   November 24, 1920.

NT 0038204   NN CaBVaU KU InNd MH

Tarbouriech, Ernest, 1865–
    ... La responsabilité des accidents dont les ouvriers
sont victimes dans leur travail. Histoire, jurisprudence
et doctrine, bibliographie, travaux parlementaires jusqu'à
la date du 24 mars 1896, par E. Tarbouriech ... Paris,
V. Giard & E. Brière, 1896.
    xv, 516 p. 23cm. (Bibliothèque du Collège libre des sciences sociales)
    "Bibliographie": p. ₍459₎–471.

    1. Labor and laboring classes—Accidents. 2. Employers' liability.
                                                            10–15472

    Library of Congress   HD7816.F8T3

NT 0038205   DLC CtY CU ICJ

Tarbouriech, J   547·5 Q400
    ... Contribution à l'étude des amides secondaires et tertiaires.
... Par J. Tarbouriech, ... Montpellier, Impr. Delord-
Boehm et Martial, 1904.
    62, ₍2₎ p. 25cm.
    Thèse — École supérieure de pharmacie, Montpellier.
    "Bibliographie," 1 p. at end.

NT 0038206   ICJ DNLM

Tarbouriech, J   547.54
                                                        Q400
    ... La purine et ses dérivés, par J. Tarbouriech ... Montpellier,
Imprimerie Delord-Boehm et Martial, 1904.
    [2, 5]–212 p. 25cm.
    At head of title: École supérieure de pharmacie de Paris. [Concours d'agré-
gation. (Section de physique, chimie et toxicologie.)]
    Bibliographical foot-notes.

NT 0038207   ICJ DLC DNLM

Tarbouriech, J
    Technique des analyses chimiques, médicales,
industrielles, des produits alimentaires et
pharmaceutiques à l'usage des pharmaciens. Paris,
A. Maloine, 1903.
    509p. illus.

NT 0038208   ICRL DNLM

Tarbouriech, J
    Technique des analyses chimiques, médicales,
industrielles, des produits alimentaires et
pharmaceutiques à l'usage des pharmaciens. 2e
éd. rev. et augm. Paris, A. Maloine, 1906.
    579p. illus.

NT 0038209   ICRL ICJ

Tarboux, Joseph Galluchat, 1898–
    Alternating-current machinery. 1st ed. Scranton, Inter-
national Textbook Co., 1947.
    xii, 652 p. illus., diagrs. 24 cm. (International texts in electrical
engineering)

    1. Electric machinery—Alternating current.
    TK2712.T3   621.3133   47–11699*

NT 0038210   NNC MB FU FTaSU PPF PSC CaBVaU WaS WaSpG OrCS
               DLC NcRS PU-EI PP TU OU MiHM ViU TxU UU

TK2715
.T3
Tarboux, Joseph Galluchat, 1898–
Alternating current theory: electrical circuits. Norman, Okla., University Litho Publishers ₍1933₎
2 v. illus. 28 cm.

1. Electric currents, Alternating.
I. Title.

NT 0038211 TU NcRS

Tarboux, Joseph Galluchat, 1898–
Electric power equipment, by J. G. Tarboux ... 1st ed. New York ₍etc.₎ McGraw-Hill book company, inc., 1927.
xi, 455 p. illus., diagrs. 23½ᶜᵐ. $5.00

1. Electric engineering. I. Title.
Library of Congress   TK145.T3   27–17540

OC1FC OC1 NN ICJ MB
NT 0038212 DLC PPF CU PU–EI NcD TU OCU OC1W OU MiU

Tarboux, Joseph Galluchat, 1898–
Electric power equipment, by J. G. Tarboux ... 2d ed. New York and London, McGraw-Hill book company, inc., 1932.
xiii, 493 p. illus., diagrs. 23½ᶜᵐ. $5.00

1. Electric engineering. I. Title.
Library of Congress   TK145.T3 1932   32–14968
—— —— Copy 2.
Copyright A 51666   ₍2₎   621.3

MiHM OC1 ICJ TU
NT 0038213 DLC PPD PPPEC PP PSC PV NcRS OC1W MiU

Tarboux, Joseph Galluchat, 1898–
Electric power equipment ₍by₎ J. G. Tarboux ... 3d ed. New York and London, McGraw-Hill book company, inc., 1946.
xiii, 493 p. illus., diagrs. 23½ᶜᵐ.

1. Electric engineering. I. Title.
TK145.T3 1946   621.3   46–7949

CaBVaU OrP
NcD NcRS TxU MB ViU OC1FC OC1 IdU MtB–U OrCS WaT
NT 0038214 DLC CU NRU MsSM FTaSU PP TU PPD PCW PPT

Tarboux, Joseph Galluchat, 1898–
Introduction to electric power systems, by J. G. Tarboux ... 1st ed. Scranton, Pa., The International textbook company, 1944.
xiii, 385 p. incl. front., 1 illus., tables, diagrs. fold. pl. 21½ᶜᵐ. (*Half-title:* International texts in electrical engineering; E. E. Dreese ... consulting editor)

1. Electric circuits.   44–5475
Library of Congress   TK3226.T3
          ₍2₎621.319

WaS OrP
OC1 OU MiHM OCU CU CaBVaU CaBVa IdU MtBC OrCS WaSp
NT 0038215 DLC PCW TU PPD PSt PHC NcD NcRS NIC MB

Tarboux, Joseph Galluchat, 1898–
Introduction to electric power systems, by J. G. Tarboux ... 1st ed. Scranton, Pa., The International textbook company, ₍1949₎
xiii, 395 p. incl. front., 1 illus., tables, diagrs. fold. pl. 21½ᶜᵐ. (*Half-title:* International texts in electrical engineering; E. E. Dreese ... consulting editor)

ScC1eU
NT 0038216 ViU MiU AAP MsSM TxU OC1W PSt NcD WaSp

621.342
T17
1950
Tarboux, Joseph Galluchat, 1898–
Introduction to electric power systems. Rev. ed. Scranton, Penn., The International Textbook Co. ₍1950₎
395p. illus. 22cm. (International texts in electrical engineering)

1. Electric   uits. (Series)

NT 0038217 KU IU

Law
Thesis
KF
645
T17
Tarbox, C   O
The law of underground waters. ₍Ithaca, N.Y.₎ 1896.
21 l. 27cm.

Thesis (LL.B.) – Cornell University, 1896.

1. Water, Underground. 2. Riparian rights.
I. Title.

NT 0038218 NIC

VM
1
F 91
no.334
TARBOX, CHARLES SMITH.
March. The United States wheel... Chicago, The Chicago stamping co. ₍c1895₎
3p. 35½cm.

Piano solo.

NT 0038219 ICN

Tarbox, E   E.
... Quality and growth of white pine as influenced by density, site, and associated species, by E. E. Tarbox, with field assistance by P. M. Reed. Petersham, Mass., Harvard forest, 1924.
30 p. plates, diagrs. 23½ᶜᵐ. (Harvard forest. Bulletin no. 7)

1. White pine. I. Reed, Paul M.   24—20956
Library of Congress   SD1.H3 no. 7
—— —— Copy 2.   SD397.P65T3

NT 0038220 DLC OrP MiU NN MH–A

Tarbox, Frank Green, 1887–
Brookgreen gardens... Brookgreen, S. C., Printed by order of the Trustees, 1936.
1 p. l., 18 p. D.

NT 0038221 PP

Tarbox, Frank Green, 1887–
Brookgreen gardens; list of plants ₍by₎ F. G. Tarbox, jr. Brookgreen, S. C., Printed by order of the Trustees, 1940.
iv, 72 p. 18½ᶜᵐ.

1. Brookgreen, S. C. 2. Plants, Cultivated—South Carolina.
Library of Congress   SB466.U7B77   41–7780
          581.9757

NT 0038222 DLC IaAS NcRS

Tarbox, Frank Green, 1887–
Milkweeds of the Southeast in Brookgreen gardens ... Brookgreen, S. C., 1946.
12 p. front., illus. 18ᶜᵐ.

1. Milkweed. 2. Brookgreen gardens, Brookgreen, S. C.
QK495.A815T3   583.73   47–20322
          Brief cataloging

NT 0038223 DLC ScC1eU NcD

Tarbox, Frank Green, 1887–
Some native hollies, rare and common, in Brookgreen gardens, by F. G. Tarbox, jr. Brookgreen, S. C., Printed by order of the trustees, 1944.
19 p. incl. front., illus. 18½ᶜᵐ.

1. Holly. 2. Brookgreen gardens, Brookgreen, S. C.
U. S. Dept. of agr. Library   97.31T17   Agr 45–123
for Library of Congress   QK495.I 3T3
          ₍3₎†   583.2781

NT 0038224 DNAL PP DLC NcD ICJ

Tarbox, Glennie.

U. S. *Hydrographic office.*
... The coast of British Columbia from Juan de Fuca Strait to Portland canal, together with Vancouver and Queen Charlotte islands. 2d ed. Washington, Govt. print. off., 1907

Tarbox, Increase Niles, 1815–1888.
An address delivered before the citizens of Framingham ... at the consecration of the cemetery ... October 13th, 1848 ... To which is added some account of the establishment of the cemetery, and the order of the exercises at the consecration .. Boston, 1849.
"Printed by vote of the town."

NT 0038226 CtY RPB

Tarbox, Increase Niles, 1815–1888.
An address on the origin, progress & present condition of philosophy, delivered before the Hamilton Chapter of the Alpha Delta Phi Society, on its eleventh anniversary at Clinton, N. Y., by I. N. Tarbox. Utica, N. Y.: R. W. Roberts, 1843. 31 p. 8°.

1. Philosophy.—History.
N. Y. P. L.   August 26, 1919.

RPB NUt
NT 0038227 NN NNC CtY CSmH NcD NBuU NBu NIC WHi MH

Tarbox, Increase Niles, D.D. 1815–88. Beliefs that dishonor God. 13 pp. (*New Englander,* v. 48, 1888, p. 103.)—Graduates of Yale College, 1701–45. 16 pp. (*New Englander,* v. 45, 1886, p. 65.)

NT 0038228 MdBP

Tarbox, Increase Niles, 1815–1888.
A biographical sketch, by Increase N. Tarbox. To which is added the Funeral address by Hon. H. Barnard, LL. D. Cambridge, 1884.
23 p. Portrait.

NT 0038229 PBL MWA

PZ263
.T17C3
1855
₍Tarbox, Increase Niles₎ 1815–1888.
The carrier pigeon, and other stories. New York, Leavitt & Allen, 1855.
64 p. illus.

NT 0038230 ICU DLC OO NBuG NN

TARBOX, Increase Niles, 1815–1888.
A chapter of Connecticut reminiscences. ₍New Haven, 1883₎.

pp. ₍26₎.
New Englander, 1883, 42, 697–722.

NT 0038231 MH

813.39
T179c   Tarbox, Increase Niles, 1815-1888.
     The child's book of true stories. New-York,
     Leavitt & Allen, 1853.
       64 p. plates. 15 cm. (Uncle George's juveniles)

       1. Children's books. L. Title.

NT   0038232   N NNC ICU

Tarbox, Increase Niles. 1815-1888.   **4447-400**
   Commemorative sketch [of Ebenezer Alden, M.D.].
   (In Memorial. Ebenezer Alden, M.D. Pp. 3-16. Boston. [1881.])

NT   0038233   MB NN

Tarbox, Increase Niles, 1815-1888.   ***4451.51.3=**G.300.52.3**
   The Congregational (Trinitarian) churches of Boston since 1780.
   (In Winsor, J., editor. The memorial history of Boston. Vol. 3,
   pp. 401-420. Portrait. Table. Autograph facsimiles. Boston.
   1881.)
   Includes a table showing succession of Congregational churches of Boston with their ministers from 1780 to 1880, pp. 415-420.

L2677 — Congregational Church in the United States. Massachusetts. — Boston. Hist. Relig.

NT   0038234   MB

Spec.   Tarbox, Increase Niles, 1815-1888.
Coll.   A correct apprehension of God, essential to
BT   true worship; or, A view of the Doctrine of the
111   Trinity, as it stands connected with the whole
T3   Gospel scheme. Boston, J. P. Jewett, 1849.
       39 p.   21 cm.
       In box.   25 cm.
       Bound with Edson, Theodore. The rector's library. Lowell, 1844.
       Stevens, William Bacon. A sermon delivered before The Bishop White
       Prayer Book Society. Philadelphia, 1849. Putnam, George. A sermon
       delivered before His Excellency George N. Briggs. Boston, 1846.

       Fuller, Samuel. Characteristic excellences of the liturgy. Andover
       [Mass.] 1843. Preston, William. "Oxfordism." Pittsburgh, 1843.
       Barnes, Albert. The missionary enterprise dependent on the religion
       of principle for success. Boston, 1844. Smith, Sydney. A fragment
       on the Irish Roman Catholic Church. Boston, 1845. Waterson, Robert
       Cassie. An address on Pauperism. Boston, 1844. Cheever, George
       Barrell. The inheritance of principles, character and power received
       from our pilgrim and puritan   ancestors, and the only means of

NT   0038236   IEdS RPB MWelC Nh CtY

Spec.   Tarbox, Increase Niles, 1815-1888.   A correct
Coll.   apprehension of God...1849.   (Card 3)
BT
111   perpetuating it. New York, 1851. Storrs, Richard Salter. The
T3   obligation of man to obey the civil law. New York, 1850. Thompson,
       Joseph Parrish. The Fugitive Slave Law; tried by the Old and New
       Testaments. New York, 1850. Weld, Theodore Dwight. The Bible
       against slavery. New York, 1838. Sumner, Charles. White slavery
       in the Barbary States. Boston, 1847. Tracy, Joseph. Colonization
       and missions. Boston, 1844. Furness, William Henry. An address
       delivered before a meeting of the members and friends of the

       Pennsylvania Anti-Slavery Society. Philadelphia, 1850.

       1. Trinity—Biblical teaching. 2. Sermons, American. I. Title.

NT   0038238   IEdS

E
185   Tarbox, Increase Niles, 1815-1888.
.6   The curse; or, The position in the world's
T37   history occupied by the Race of Ham.   Boston,
       American Tract Society [1864]
       vi, 160p. illus. 15cm.

       1. Negroes—History. 2. Slavery in the U.S.
     3.U.S.—Race question. I. T. II.T.: The position in the world's history occupied by the Race
     of Ham.

NT   0038239   CtU MB MH NcU CtY CtHC

[Tarbox, Increase Niles] 1815-1888.
   [Dedicatory hymn] n. t. p.   [1847]
     2 p.   D.   ([Fugitve poetry])
      In— Order of exercises at dedication of
   Hitchcock hall, 1874.

NT   0038240   RPB

Tarbox, Increase Niles, 1815-1888, ed.

   Robbins, Thomas, 1777-1856.
     Diary of Thomas Robbins, D. D., 1796-1854. Printed
   for his nephew. Owned by the Connecticut historical
   society ... Ed. and annotated by Increase N. Tarbox ...
   Boston, T. Todd, printer, 1886-87.

TARBOX, Increase Niles, 1815-1888.
   Ebenezer Alden. [Commemorative sketch].

   Port. of Alden.
   (In the New England hist. and geneal. register,
   Oct. 1881; 35. 309-318).

NT   0038242   MH DNLM PPC

Tarbox, Increase Niles, 1815-1888.
   Festival of Congregational club. Forefathers' day,
   Boston, December, 1880.   [Boston, 1880]
     6 p.   D.   ([Occasional poems.])

NT   0038243   RPB MB

[TARBOX, Increase Niles, 1815-1888].
   Forefathers' day, Boston, Dec., 1880. [Poem
   read at the festival of the congregational
   club.] Boston, 1880.

     p. 6.

NT   0038244   MH

Tarbox, Increase Niles, 1815-1888.
   George Hayward Allan. By Increase N. Tarbox, D. D.
   [Boston, 1886]
     broadside. 24½ x 15½ cm.
     "Reprinted from the Necrology of the New England historic genealogical society, in the Historical and genealogical register for October, 1886."

     1. Allan, George Hayward, 1832-1886.

                    5-14273

NT   0038245   DLC

TARBOX, Increase Niles, 1815-1888.   54
   The Hebrew worshiper.
     [New Haven, 1862.]   406-426 pp.   8°.
   From The New Englander [*7454.1.21].

NT   0038246   MB

285.8744
T179h Tarbox, Increase Niles, 1815-1888.
Theol.   Historical survey of churches, 1776 and 1876
    [1877]
     [29]-49p. 23cm.

       1. Congregational churches in Massachusetts.
   I. Title.

NT   0038247   TxDaM

Tarbox, Increase Niles, 1815-1888.
   John Tarbox and his descendants.   Boston,
   1888.
     15 p.   8°.   (Rep't. N. E. Hist. and Gen. Reg.
   Jan. 1888)

NT   0038248   MWA

Tarbox, Increase Niles, 1815-1888.
   Life of Israel Putnam ("Old Put"), major-general in
   the Continental army. By Increase N. Tarbox ... Boston, Lockwood, Brooks, and company, 1876.
     389 p. front. (port.) 4 pl., fold. map. 22 cm.
     Below frontispiece: This fac-simile is from a bond given by Israel Putnam to his brother David in 1743.

     1. Putnam, Israel, 1718-1790.

   Library of Congress   E207.P9T2

                         12-26150

MdBP
   PHi PBm OO DN OU MiU OCl NjP MWA Nh WaWW OrP OrCS
NT   0038249   DLC IEN GEU NBuHi MB PP NN I NIC MU PPL

Tarbox, Increase Niles, 1815-1888.
   Memoirs of James H. Schneider and Edward M.
   Schneider. (Missionary Patriots) Boston,
   Massachusetts Sabbath School Society, 1867.

NT   0038250   DLC

Tarbox, Increase Niles, 1815-1888.
   Memorial. Ebenezer Alden, M. D.
   see under title

Tarbox, Increase N. Niles, 1815-1888.
   Memorial address on the ministers of
   the Old south church, Boston. Sunday October 26, 1884. On the occasion of the
   erection of tablets in the church, commemorative of its line of ministers, and
   of Samuel Sewall and Samuel Adams. Bost.
   David Clapp & Son, 1885.
     15 p. 26cm.

NT   0038252   OClWHi MiD MB OO CtY

Tarbox, Increase Niles, 1815-1888.
   Missionary patriots. Memoirs of James H. Schneider
   and Edward M. Schneider. By Increase N. Tarbox ...
   Boston, Massachusetts Sabbath school society, 1867.
     iv, 7-357 p. 2 port. (incl. front.) 17¾ cm.
     J. H. Schneider served as chaplain of the 2d regt., U. S. colored troops;
     E. M. Schneider, in Co. K, 57th Mass. infantry.

     1. Schneider, James Henry, 1839-1864. 2. Schneider, Edward M., 1846-
   1864. 3. U. S. infantry. 2d colored regt., 1863-1866. 4. Massachusetts
   infantry. 57th regt., 1864-1865.

                         12-7435

   Library of Congress   E492.94.2d

NT   0038253   DLC NcD IEdS CtY OO NjP MB

[Tarbox, Increase Niles] 1815-1888.
   The mocking-bird and other stories.   New York,
   Leavitt & Allen, 1855.
     64 p. front., plates.   (On cover: Uncle
   George's juveniles)

NT   0038254   ICU

Tarbox, Increase Niles, 1815–1888.
Musical history.
In– Lynn, Mass. – First Church of Christ
Celebration of the two hundred and fiftieth anniver-
sary ... June 8, 1882. Lynn, 1882. p. 80–93.

NT 0038255 RPB

Tarbox, Increase Niles, 1815–1888.
Nineveh; or, The buried city. Boston, [c1863]
16°.

NT 0038256 CtY

F
94
.5
C75   [Tarbox, Increase Niles] 1815–1888.
v.2   Old Connecticut vs. the Atlantic
no.7   monthly. [New Haven? 1865?]
            46 p. 23cm.
            "From the New Englander for April,
        1865."

        1. Connecticut--Intellectual life.
    I. Title

NT 0038257 NIC MWA MB

Tarbox, Increase Niles, 1815–1888.
Boston. Old South church.
Old South church (Third church) Boston. Memorial
addresses, Sunday evening, October 26, 1884. Boston,
Cupples, Upham & co., 1885.

NT 0038259 MB

Tarbox, Increase Niles, 1815–1888.
The Pilgrims and Puritans: or, Plymouth and the
Massachusetts Bay.
(Old Colony historical society. Collections.
No. 1, p. 23–58. Taunton, 1879.)

NT 0038259 MB

Tarbox, Increase Niles, 1815–1888.
Rambles in old pathways... By Increase N. Tarbox...
Written for the Congregational Sabbath School and Publishing
Society, and approved by the Committee of Publication. Bos-
ton: Congregational Sabbath School and Publishing Soc. [1868]
2 v. fronts., plates. 15½cm. (Uncle George's series.)

730729–30A. 1. Bible. O. T.—Hist.   of events, Juvenile. I. Congregational
Sabbath School and Publishing   Society. II. Title.
N. Y. P. L.   May 6, 1935

NT 0038260 NN

Tarbox, Increase Niles, 1815–1888.
The religious and ecclesiastical contrast within the bounds of
Suffolk West Conference, between the years 1776 and 1876. An
address read before the Suffolk West Conference at its meeting in
Auburndale, October 11, 1876. By Increase N. Tarbox... Bos-
ton: Published by vote of the conference, 1876. 23 p. 23cm.

Cover-title: Contrasts.

830936A. 1. Congregational Churches   in Massachusetts—Hist. 2. Suffolk
County, Mass.—Churches, Congrega-   tional.
N. Y. P. L.   July 1, 1936

NT 0038261 NN CtY PHi NIC MB MH-AH

[TARBOX, Increase Niles,1815–1888].
Richard Salter Storrs. [Boston?1874?]

pp.27. Port.
Cover title.
Signed: Increase N.Tarbox.
"Reprinted from the Congregational Quarterly
July 1874."

NT 0038262 MH

Tarbox, Increase Niles, 1815–1888, *ed.*
Sir Walter Ralegh and his colony in America. Including
the charter of Queen Elizabeth in his favor, March 25, 1584,
with letters, discourses, and narratives of the voyages made to
America at his charges, and descriptions of the country, com-
modities, and inhabitants. With historical illustrations, and a
memoir by the Rev. Increase N. Tarbox, D. D. Boston, The
Prince society, 1884.

    4 p. l., 329 p. front. port. 22 x 18cm. (*Added t.-p.:* The publications
of the Prince society ... [v. 15])
    "Two hundred and fifty copies."

    The charter and various narratives are taken from v. 3 of Hakluyt's
Collection of early voyages.
    "The first voyage to America under the charge and direction of Sir
Walter Ralegh, knight, 1584" (p. [107]–127) is supposed to be by Capt.
Arthur Barlow. The first part of "The second voyage ... 1585" (p. [129]–
142) is probably by Sir Richard Grenville; the remainder (p. 143–181) is
by Ralph Lane. "The third voyage ... 1586" (p. [183]–186) is anonymous.
"A briefe and true report of the new found land of Virginia ... by Thomas
Heriot," p. [187]–244. "The fourth voyage ... 1587" (p. [245]–270) is given
anonymously by Hakluyt. A letter from White to Hakluyt, accompanying his account of the fifth voyage, is here appended to the fourth voyage
(p. 270–273) "The fifth voyage ... 1590" (p. [275]–296) is by "Governor"
John White.

    1. Virginia—Hist.—Colonial period. 2. Virginia—Descr. & trav. 3.
Indians of North America—Virginia. 4. Raleigh, Sir Walter, 1552–1618.
I. Gt. Brit. Laws, statutes, etc., 1558–1603 (Elizabeth) II. Barlow,
Arthur, 1550 (ca.)–1620. III. Grenville, Sir Richard, 1542–1591. IV. Lane,
Sir Ralph, 1530?–1603. V. Harriot, Thomas, 1560–1621. VI. White, John,
fl. 1585–1593.
                                                                3–24567 Revised
    Library of Congress   E186.P85 vol. 15

        OC1WHi Vi MH MiU-C MU PHi GEU FTaSU
NT 0038265   DLC WaS NjR CaBVaU FMU ViU MiU OFH OC1

GROSVENOR Tarbox, Increase Niles, 1815–1888.
LIBRARY
BX7260   Sketch of Selah Burr Treat, by Increase N.
T8T2   Tarbox. Reprint from "The Congregational
            quarterly" for July, 1877. Boston, Alfred
            Mudge & son, 1877.

            31p. front. 23½cm.

NT 0038266   MWA MH NN WaWW RPB MH-AH ICN OO OC1WHi

Tarbox, Increase Niles, 1815–1888.
Sketch of William Alfred Buckingham. By Increase
N. Tarbox ... Boston, A. Mudge & son, printers, 1876.
24 p. front. (port.) 24cm.
"Reprinted from 'The Congregational quarterly' for April, 1876."

    1. Buckingham, William Alfred, 1804–1875. I. Title.
                                                    15–5278
    Library of Congress   E499.B17

NT 0038267   DLC OO MWA Nh

Tarbox, Increase Niles, 1815–1888.
Songs and hymns for common life. By Increase N. Tarbox.
Boston, Printed for the author by D. Clapp & son, 1885.
xi, 258 p. 17cm.

    I. Title.

                                                    31–12884
    Library of Congress   PS2969.T7

NT 0038268   DLC NIC OCH MH

CT99
.R636T3   Tarbox, Increase Niles, 1815–1888.
            Thomas Robbins. By the Rev. Increase
        N. Tarbox ... [Boston, 1884]
            8 p. 24cm.

            Caption title.
            "Reprinted from the N. E. historical
        and genealogical register for October,
        1884."
            1. Robbins, Thomas, 1777–1856.

NT 0038269   DLC MH OC1W OO PHi

Tarbox, Increase Niles, 1815–1888.
Tyre and Alexandria: the chief commercial cities of
Scripture times. By Increase N. Tarbox ... Boston,
Massachusetts Sabbath-school society [1865]
362 p. front. plates. 17½cm.

    1. Tyre. 2. Alexandria, Egypt. 3. Commerce—Hist.
                                                    5–3471
    Library of Congress   DS104.T2

NT 0038270   DLC ViU FU NjP MB

Tarbox, Increase Niles, 1815–1888.
[Uncle George's series] Boston [1868]
4 v. 15.5 cm.
Contents. [v. 1–2] Rambles in old pathways.
[v. 3] Uncle George's stories. [v. 4] The old meeting house.

NT 0038271   CtY DLC

[Tarbox, Increase Niles] 1815–1888.
When I was a boy. A story of real life ...
Boston [1862]
15.5 cm.
Written for the Mass. Sabbath school society,
and approved by the committee of publication.

NT 0038272   CtY

TARBOX,Increase Niles,1815–1888.
William Cogswell. [Boston,1883].

pp.(12). Port.of Cogswell.
New England Historical and Genealogical
Register,1883,117–128.

NT 0038273   MH

[TARBOX, INCREASE NILES] 1815–1888.
Winnie and Walter's Christmas stories. Boston: J. E.
Tilton and Co., 1861. 124 p. front., plates. 15½cm.

775761A. 1. Juvenile literature—Fiction, American.
2. Christmas —Fiction. I. Title.

NT 0038274   NN

[TARBOX, INCREASE NILES] 1815–1888.
Winnie and Walter's evening talks with their father about
old times. Boston: J.E.Tilton and Co., 1867. iii, 5–142 p.
front., plates. 15½cm. (His: Winnie and Walter books.
[v.3])

776786A. 1. Juvenile literature, American I. Title.

NT 0038275   NN IEN CoU

Tarbox, John W
New York checklists of procedure for common transactions; edited by the editorial staff of the Lawyers Co-operative Pub. Co. [New York, 1953]
41 p. 25 cm.
"Prepared for use with Summary of American law, New York
notes, under the direction of George L. Clark."

    1. Civil procedure—New York (State) I. Clark, George Luther,
1877–   New York notes to Summary of American law. II. Title.
                                                    347.9   53–4454 ‡

NT 0038276   DLC

1951
T1797
L45p

Tarbox, Lela (Prescott)
Poems and illustrations, with prose supplement. New Bern, N.C., O. G. Dunn Co., ₍1954₎
63 p.   illus.   23 cm.

On cover: Inspirations.
Includes To the Lincoln memorial, a poem, and the Gettysburg address.

NT   0038277   RPB

Tarbox, Russell.
[Tomboy. Libretto. English]
Tomboy, a musical comedy in two acts. Book and lyrics by Charles O. Locke; music by Russell Tarbox.   [New York] c1925.   1 v. (unpaged) 30cm.

Typescript.
Without music.
1. Musical comedies—Librettos. Tomboy. I. Locke, Charles O. Tomboy.   II. Title.

NT   0038278   NN

TH5604
T3

Tarbuck, Edward Lance.   ed.
The encyclopaedia of practical carpentry and joinery ... Leipzig, A. H. Payne; London, J. Hagger [18--]
236, xiv p.   illus., plates.

1. Carpentry.   2. Joinery.   I. Title.

NT   0038279   CU TxU NN DSI N

Tarbuck, Edward Lance.
Handbook of house property; a guide to the purchase, mortgage, tenancy & compulsory sale of houses and land, including the law of dilapidations and fixtures. 3rd ed.   London, 1883.

NT   0038280   PU-L

Tarbuck, Edward Lance.   3667.77
Handbook of house property: a popular and practical guide to the purchase, mortgage, tenancy & compulsory sale of houses and land: including the law of dilapidations and fixtures: with examples of all kinds of valuations, useful information on building, and suggestive elucidations of fine art. 4th edition, enlarged. London. Lockwood & Co. 1887. xi, 9-278 pp. 17½ cm., in 12s.

L6098 — T.r. — Building. — Real property. — Conveyancing.

NT   0038281   MB

Tarbuck, Edward Lance.
Handbook of house property; a guide to the purchase, mortgage, tenancy & compulsory sale of houses and land, including the law of dilapidations and fixtures. 7th ed.   London, 1904.

NT   0038282   PU-L

Tarbuck, Edward Lance.
Handbook of house property; a popular and practical guide to the purchase, mortgage, tenancy & compulsory sale of houses and land including dilapidations and fixtures, with examples of all kinds of valuations, information on building and on the right use of decorative art, by Edward Lance Tarbuck ...   9th ed.   London, The Technical press ltd., 1938.

xi, ₍9₎-299 p.   18½ᶜᵐ.

1. Real property—Gt. Brit.   2. Real property—Valuation.   3. Architecture, Domestic.   I. Title.

39-12000

NT   0038283   DLC

NA200
T37
Arch.
Library

Tarbuck, Edward Lance
A popular account of the styles of architecture; their rise, progress, and present condition.   London, J. Hagger, 1855.
80 p.

"Prize essay for the 'Institute medal' of the Royal Institute of British Architects."

1. Architecture - Hist.

NT   0038284   CU PPFr

Tarbuk, Johann.
Sprengübungen der Genie-Regimenter im Jahre 1892.   (In: Austria. Technisches Militär-Comité. Mittheilungen über Gegenstände des Artillerie- und Genie-Wesens. Wien, 1893.   8°. Jahrg. 24, 1893.   p. 405-412.)

1. Military engineering.   2. Explosives in war.
N.Y.P.L.   December 23, 1911.

NT   0038285   NN

Tarbun, Ludwig.
Ueber die einstweilige zulassung eines unlegitimierten vertreters.
Inaug. diss. Tuebingen, 1899.

NT   0038286   ICRL

₍Tarbutt, William₎
The annals of Cranbrook church; its monuments. ₍Cranbrook, Printed by G. Waters, 1873₎
cover-title, 90 p.   illus., geneal. tab.   21½ᶜᵐ.
"Second lecture, read before the Cranbrook literary association on the 13th of January, 1870."
Pedigree of the descendants of Walter Roberts, fl. 1442-1522: geneal. tab.

1. Cranbrook, Eng. (Parish)   2. Epitaphs—Cranbrook, Eng.   3. Roberts family.   I. Title.

15-21495

Library of Congress   CS439.R56

NT   0038287   DLC

D
245192
.9

₍TARBUTT, WILLIAM₎
The annals of Cranbrook church; its monuments. Cranbrook, Printed by G. Waters, 1875.
90p.   illus., geneal. table.   22cm.
Cover-title.
"Third lecture, read before the Cranbrook literary association on the 7th & 14th of April, 1870."

NT   0038288   ICN MdBP

Tarbutt, William.
Haslewood, Francis, 1840-1900.
The parish of Benenden, Kent: its monuments, vicars, and persons of note. Also a reprint of an exceedingly rare pamphlet, entitled This winter's wonders, dated 1673. By the Rev. Francis Haslewood ...   Priv. print., Ipswich, The author, 1889.

Lmg62
C465
836t

Tarbutt, William Brackstone
Letter the first to the governors of Christ's hospital, and the public, on the use and abuse of this splendid institution, and on the mismanagement which has so long prevailed within its walls; on the distribution of its charities, the application and misapplication of its funds, &c. &c. &c. By William Brackstone Tarbutt ...   London, E.Wilson, 1836.
2p.₤.,47p.   23½cm.

1.Christ's hospital, Horsham.

NT   0038290   CtY

Tarbutton, Grady, 1902-
Lead-mercurous acetate voltaic cell with acetic acid as the solvent, by Grady Tarbutton and Warren C. Vosburgh. ₍Easton, Pa.,1933₎
cover-title, p. ₍618₎-624 incl. tables. 23½ᶜᵐ.
Part of thesis (PH. D.)—Duke university, 1933.
"Reprint from the Journal of the American chemical society, 55 ... (1933)"
Bibliographical foot-notes.

1. Electric batteries.   2. Acetic acid.   I. Vosburgh, Warren Chase, 1894-   joint author.   II. Title.

A 40-2396

Duke univ. Library
for Library of Congress   ₍2₎

NT   0038291   NcD

Tarbutton, Grady, 1902-
The system lead acetate, acetic acid, water, by Grady Tarbutton and Warren C. Vosburgh. Durham, N. C.,n.p., 1932.
p. 4537-4544.   diagr.   24 cm.
Part of thesis (Ph. D.) = Duke University, 1933.
"Reprint from the Journal of the American Chemical Society, 54, 4537 (1932)."

1. Solubility.   I. Title.   II. Vosburgh, Warren Chase, 1894-

NT   0038292   NcD

Tarbut Héber Kulturegyesület. Iskolái
Évkönyve.
[no.] 1(1945/46).
Budapest: A Magyarországi Tarbut Héber Kulturegyesület,1946.   v.   8.

NT   0038293   OCH

Bd22
682

Tarcagnota, Giovanni, d.1566.
L'Adone di Giovanni Tarcagnota da Gaeta, ristampato a cura di Angelo Borzelli. Napoli,Gennaro M.Priore,1898.
xi,18p.,1₤.   23½cm.
Pages [1]-18 reprinted as p.[307]-324 of Borzelli's Il cavalier Giovanbattista Marino ... Napoli,1898.

NT   0038294   CtY

Tarcagnota, Giovanni, d. 1566.
Del sito, et lodi della citta di Napoli, con vna breve historia de gli re svoi, & delle cose piu degne altroue ne' medesimi tempi auenute di Giouanni Tarchagnota di Gaeta. ₍In Napoli, Appresso G. M. Scotto, 1566₎
12 p. l., 174 numb. l.   16ᶜᵐ.
Title vignette (coat of arms)
With this is bound Loffredo, F., marchese di Trivico. Antichita di Pozzvolo. 1590.

1. Naples (City)—Hist.   2. Naples (City)—Descr.

NT   0038295   MiU ICN

Case
F
09
.862

TARCAGNOTA, GIOVANNI, d.1566.
Delle historie del mondo di M. Gio. Tarchagnota, lequali contengono quanto dal principio del mondo fino a tempi nostri e successo... Venetia,Per M.Tramezzino,1562.
v.   22cm.
Printer's device on t.-p.; initials.

NT   0038296   ICN DLC PPL

Case
F
09
.863

TARCAGNOTA, GIOVANNI, d.1566.
Delle historie del mondo, lequali con tutta quella particolarità, che bisogna, contengono quanto dal principio del mondo fino à tempi nostri è successo... In Venetia,Per M.Tramezzino, 1573.
v.   24cm.
Titles within engraved border; initials.

NT   0038297   ICN MiU-C

Tarcagnota, Giovanni, *d.* 1566.
Delle istorie del mondo di M. Giovanni Tarcagnota. Lequali contengono quanto dal principio del mondo è successo, sino all' anno 1513, cauate da piu degni, & piu graui autori, & che habbino nella lingua greca, ò nella latina scritto ... Con l'aggiunta di M. Mambrino Roseo. & dal Reuerendo M. Bartolomeo Dionigi da Fano, sino all' anno 1582 ... Venetia, Appresso i Giunti, 1585–92.
3 pts in 4 v. 25½ᶜᵐ.
Pt. 1, 1592; pt. 2–3, 1585.
Printer's mark. Side-notes.
Subject entries: History, Universal.

2–9797

Library of Congress, no.   D18.T18.

NT 0038298   DLC NIC

D.   Tarcagnota, Giovanni, d.1566.
18   Delle historie del mondo... Lequali contengono
T2   quanto dal principio del mondo è successo, sino
1598   all'anno 1513... Con l'aggiunta di M. Mambrino
Cage   Roseo, & del... M.Bartolomeo Dionigi da Fano,
         sino all'anno 1582. Seguitata vltimamente sino à
         tempi nostri dal... Cesare Campana. Parte prima
         ₍-terza₎,... In Venetia, Appresso i Giunti, 1598.

         3 pts. in 5 v. 4to.
         Without the continuation by Campana.

NT 0038299   DFo NNH MH

D18   Tarcagnota, Giovanni, d.1566.
.T18   Delle historie del mondo. Lequali contengono,
Rare   quanto dal principio del mondo è successo sino
Bk   all'anno della nostra salute 1513. Cavate da
         piu' degni, e gravi auttori, che habbiano, ò
         nella lingua Greca, ò nella Latina scritto.
         Aggiuntoui la quinta parte di B. D. da Fano;
         laquale, ripigliando dall'anno sudetto 1513
         contiene quanto è successo sino all'anno 1606.
         Venetia, Appresso G. & V. Varischi, 1617.
         4 pts. in 2 v.

         Printer's mark. Side notes.
         Each part has special t.-p.

         1. World history--Early works to 1800.

NT 0038301   ICU

TARCALI, ROBERT.
Quand Horthy est roi. Illustrations de Marcel Vértès.
Paris, Edition "Astra", 1922.   128 p. illus. 24cm.

No. 1 of 100 copies printed.

1. Jews in Hungary—Anti-Semitism. 2. Hungary—Anti-Semitism.
3. Hungary—Hist.—Revolution of 1918–1920. 4. Jews—Persecution.
5. Persecution. I. Title.

NT 0038302   NN NjP CLU

Tarcali & Medioni.
The owner of the copyright in a motion pic-
ture, France (1939) Tarcali & Medioni vs.
Société Tobis Sascha. ₍Comp. by₎ Edwin P.
Kilroe. 1942.
184 l

Reproduced from typewritten copy.

NT 0038303   NNC

Tarcan, Selim Sirri, 1875–
Beden terbiyesi, oyuncimnastik-spor ₍yazan₎ Selim Sirri ...
İstanbul, Devlet matbaasi, 1932.
2 p. l., 435, ₍1₎ p. illus. 24ᶜᵐ.

1. Physical education and training—Turkey. I. Title.
40–37936

Library of Congress   GV279.T3

NT 0038304   DLC

Tarcan, Selim Sirri, 1875–
... Bugünkü Almanya (yardimci kiraat) ... İstanbul, Devlet matbaasi, 1930.
vii, 116 p., 2 l. illus. 19½ᶜᵐ.
At head of title: Selim Sirri.

1. Germany. 2. Germany—Descr. & trav.—1919–   I. Title.
40–24095

Library of Congress   DD18.T3

NT 0038305   DLC

Tarcan, Selim Sirri, 1875–
... Garpta hayat, yardimci kiraat ... İstanbul, Devlet matbaasi, 1929.
2 p. l., 157 p. illus. 20ᶜᵐ.
At head of title: Selim Sirri.

1. Europe—Descr. & trav.—1919–   2. Turkish language—Chrestomathies and readers. I. Title.
40–24364

Library of Congress   D921.T27

NT 0038306   DLC

Tarcan, Selim Sırrı, 1875–
Hatıralarım. İstanbul, Türkiye Yayinevi, 1946.

72 p. ports. (In Canlı tarihler [4])

NT 0038307   MH

Tarcan, Selim Sirri, 1875–
Köy mekteplerinde beden terbiyesi. ₍Yazan₎ Selim Sirri.
Köy mekteplerinde tatbik edilmek üzere tertip edilmiştir.
İstanbul, Devlet matbaasi, 1933.
2 p. l., 102 p., 1 l. illus. 19½ᶜᵐ.

1. Physical education and training—Turkey. I. Title.
40–37937

Library of Congress   GV279.T33

NT 0038308   DLC

Tarcan, Selim Sirri, 1875–
Müziğin dili. Ankara, Millî Eğitim Basımevi, 1945.
62 p. illus. 18 cm. (İyi yaşama serisi, 7)

1. Music. I. Title.

ML64.T37   N E 62–1412 ‡

NT 0038309   DLC NNC

4PQ   Tarceno, Salome, 1854–1903.
Span.   Ortigas y jazmines; poesias [por] Salome Tarcena
Am.   (El Negro Melenudo) Juicio literario de Francisco
954   J. Santamaría.   Villahermosa, Tab., 1948.
         118 p. (Publicaciones del Gobierno del Estado.
         Escritores tabasqueños, 30)

NT 0038310   DLC-P4

Tarceso, Max.
Schneeflocken; drei Erzählungen.   Magdeburg,
In Commission bei W. Heinrichshofen, 1826.
176 p.   19 cm.

NT 0038311   CaBVaU

Tarchaniota Marullus, Michael
see Marullo Tarcaniota, Michele, *d.* 1500.

Tarchanjanz, Tarchan: Aus d. Chir. Univ.-Klinik. Blutige
Naht oder primäre conservative Behandlung der Olekranon-
fraktur. (Berlin 1910: Blanke.) 33 S. 8°
Berlin, Med. Diss. v. 21. Juni 1910, Ref. Bier
[Geb. 28.(15.) Jan. 84 Schuscha; Wohnort: Baku; Staatsangeh.: Rußland;
Vorbildung: Gymn. Baku Reife 05; Studium: Berlin 10 S.; Rig. 3. Juni 10.]
[U 10. 104

NT 0038313   ICRL NNC DNLM

Tarchanoff, Jean de
see Tarkhanov, Ivan Romanovich, *knîaz'*, 1846?–1908?

Tarchanoff (Paul llich). *Materialy dlja
pharmakologii hidrastinina. [Pharmacology
of hydrastinine.] 60, 71 pp., 1 tab. 8°. St.
Petersburg, V. F. Komaroff, 1891.

NT 0038315   DNLM

Tarchetti, Andrea.
... L'aratura meccanica in risaia. Relazione della giuria
sulle prove d'aratura eseguite a Sali Vercellese nella primavera
1914 promosse ed organizzate dalla Stazione sperimentale di
risicoltura di Vercelli ... Vercelli, Premiata tipo-litografia
Gallardi & Ugo, 1914.
162 p., 1 l. incl. illus., map. 29½ᶜᵐ.

1. Plow, ₍Motor₎ 2. Rice ₍and rice culture₎
Agr 15—846

U. S. Dept. of agr. Library   59T17
for Library of Congress   ₍a41b1₎

NT 0038316   DNAL

Tarchetti, Andrea.
...Per una migliore lavorazione in risaia,1916.
1916.
25p.

NT 0038317   DNAL

Tarchetti, Andrea.
...Trebbiatura e pulitura de cereali. 1916.
26p. 24 1/2cm.

NT 0038318   DNAL

TARCHETTI,Anton-Giuseppe.
Orazione in lode del santo martire Calimero,arcivesco-
vo di Milano,detta nella basilica parrocchiale del santo
...1758. In Milano,nella stamperia di Antonio Agnelli,
[1758].

17 cm. pp.30,(1).
Too closely trimmed at top.

NT 0038319   MH

QY   TARCHETTI, C
T179m   Manuale di microscopia e batteriologia
1907   clinica ₍di₎ C. Tarchetti ₍e₎ C. P. Goggia.
         Milano, Vallardi ₍1907₎
         xv, 532 p. illus.
         I. Goggia, Carlo Paola

NT 0038320   DNLM

TARCHETTI, I[gino] Ugo, 1841-1869.
Disjecta; versi. Bologna, N. Zanichelli, 1879.

nar. 16°.

NT 0038321   MH

PQ
4733
T3
D5
1882

Tarchetti, Iginio Ugo, 1841-1869.
Disjecta; versi. 2. ed. Bologna,
N. Zanichelli, 1882.
168p. 17cm.

NT 0038322   CtU

Tarchetti, Iginio Ugo, 1841-1869.
... La leggenda del castello nero, e altri racconti. ₍Roma₎
D. de Luigi ₍1944₎
3 p. l., 9-171 p., 2 l. 20ᶜᵐ. (Half-title: Romanzo nero, v. 3 ₍4. e. 4₎)
"Prima edizione: Roma, agosto 1944."
"Nuova edizione a cura di Umberto Bosco."
CONTENTS.—Introduzione: Il Tarchetti e la scapigliatura, di Umberto Bosco.—I fatali.—La leggenda del castello nero.—La lettera U.—Un osso di morto.—Uno spirito in un lampone.

I. Bosco, Umberto, 1900-   ed.   II. Title.
PQ4733.T3L4 1944   853.89   A F 47-253
Princeton univ. Library
for Library of Congress   ₍4₎†

NT 0038323   NjP IU CtY DLC

Tarchetti, Iginio Ugo, 1841-1869.
Paolina. Milano, Lombarda, 1875.
192 p. front. (port.)

NT 0038324   MBU

TARCHETTI, Igino Ugo, 1841-1869.
Racconti fantastici. Milano, 1869.

(Biblioteca amena)

NT 0038325   MH

Tarchetti, Iginio Ugo, 1841-1869.
Racconti fantastici, Prefazione di Eugenio
Giovannetti. Milano, Jandi ₍1944₎
108 p. front. (port.)

At head of title: I. U. Tarchetti.

NT 0038326   NNC

TARCHETTI, Igino Ugo, 1841-1869.
Racconti umoristici. Milano, 1869.

(Biblioteca amena).

NT 0038327   MH

Tarchetti, Iginis Ugo, 1841-1869.
Storia di un ideale. -L'innamorato del montagua -
Storia di una gamba. Milano, 1877.
sm. 8°.

NT 0038328   CtY

Tarchetti (Maurizio). Sul tifo epidemico nel
1870 in Mandrogne, borgata della città di Alessandria. 41 pp. 8°. Milano, De Cristoforis, 1871.
Repr. from : Ann. univ. di med., Milano, 1871, ccxviii.

NT 0038329   DNLM

Tarchetti, Pietro
—— Rendiconto statistico sanitario della sessione medica dell' Ospedale civile di Alessandria nel sessennio 1886-91. 11 pp., xvi l. fol.
Alessandria, G. Panizza, 1893.

NT 0038330   DNLM

Tarchetti (Pietro). Rivista storico-clinica delle principali epidemie d' influenza dal secolo xvi ai nostri giorni. 15 pp. 8°. Alessandria, G. Panizza, 1892.

NT 0038331   DNLM

Tarchetti (Pietro). La sezione medica del civico ospedale di Alessandria nel 1883. Agli onorevoli membri della Congregazione di carità,
rendiconto clinico. 39 pp. 8°. Alessandria, Jacquemod, 1884.

NT 0038332   DNLM

Tarchi, Angelo, 1760-1814.
₍Adrasto, re d'Egitto. Libretto. Italian₎

Adrasto, re d'Egitto; dramma per musica, da rappresentarsi nel Teatro alla scala, il carnevale dell' anno 1792. ₍La poesia è del De Gamerra₎ Milano, G. B. Bianchi ₍1792₎
96 p. 17 cm.
Vol. 8, no. 1, of a collection with binder's title: Drammi per musica.

1. Operas—To 1800—Librettos.   I. Gamerra, Giovanni de, 1743-1803. Adrasto, re d'Egitto.   II. Title.
ML48.A5   vol. 8, no. 1   76-207980

NT 0038333   DLC

Tarchi, Angelo, 1760-1814.
Une aventure de Saint-Foix
For libretti see under   Duval, Alexandre,
1767-1842.

[Tarchi, Angelo] 1760-1814.
La congiura pisoniana
For libretti see under   [Salfi, Francesco]
1759-1832.

Tarchi, Angelo, 1760-1814.
₍Il conte di Saldagna. Libretto. Italian₎

Il conte di Saldagna; tragedia per musica, da rappresentarsi nel Teatro grande alla scala, la primavera dell' anno 1787. Milano, G. B. Bianchi ₍1787₎
68 p. 17 cm.
Vol. 7, no. 4, of a collection with binder's title: Drammi per musica.
Libretto by Ferdinando Moretti. Cf. L. C. Cat. opera librettos.
1. Operas—To 1800—Librettos.   I. Moretti, Ferdinando. Il conte di Saldagna.   II. Title.
ML48.A5   vol. 7, no. 4   72-208010

NT 0038336   DLC

Rare
ML
50
.2
A888
T179

Tarchi, Angelo, 1760-1814.
[D'auberge en auberge. Libretto. French]
D'auberge en auberge, ou Les préventions.
Comédie en 3 actes, mêlée de chant. Par Emmanuel Dupaty. Musique de Tarchy [i.e. Tarchi] Représentée, pour la première fois, sur le Théâtre de l'Opéra-Comique, rue Favart, le six floréal an '. (Samedi 26 avril 1800)
... Paris, Chez Vente, An X. [1802]
[2], 73 p. 20 cm.

Bookplate: Yale University Library. Bought with the income of the Edward Wells Southworth Fund, 1915.

1. Operas—Librettos. I. Mercier-Dupaty, Emanuel, 1775-1851. D'auberge en auberge.
II. Title. III. Title: Les préventions.

NT 0038338   CtY-Mus

Tachi, Angelo, 1760-1814.
D'auberge en auberge
For editions without music see under Dupaty,
Louis Emmanuel Félicité Charles Mercier, 1775-1851.

---

*
Ml
.S444
v.163
no.11

Tarchi, Angelo, 1760-1814.
De puri affetti miei, song with an accompaniment for the piano forte or harp composed by Sigr. Tarchi. Price 2 s. London, Printed by Rt. Birchall, No. 133 New Bond Street ₍180-?₎
7 p. 30cm. ₍Sheet music collection, v. 163, no. 11₎
Caption title.

1. Songs with various accompaniment.
I. Title.

NT 0038340   ViU

Tarchi, Angelo, 1760-1814.
Il disertore: a serious opera, [founded on L.S. Mercier's Deserteur.] ... Music [not here] by [A.] Tarchi. [Ital. and Eng.] London, 1789.
63 p. 8°. (In "Librettos," 18.)

NT 0038341   CtY

Tarchi, Angelo, 1760-1814.
₍Alessandro nell' Indie. Lodi agli dei₎
Duett: Lodi agli dei, sung by Sigra. Guiliane ₍i. e. Giuliani₎ & Sigr. Marchesi in the opera Generosita d'Alessandro, composed by Sigr. Tarchi... London, Printed by Longman and Broderip ₍1789₎ 27 p. 33cm.

Duet for soprano and tenor with orchestra.

1. Scenas, etc., Secular (2 voices)   —Orch. acc. I. Tarchi, Angelo,
1760-1814. Lodi agli dei. II. Title: Alessandro nell' Indie. III. Title:
La generosità d'Alessandro.

NT 0038342   NN

Tarchi, Angelo, 1760-1814.
La generosità d'Alessandro [same as his "Alessandro nell' Indie," the name of Metastasio's work from which it is adapted] ... [Libretto, Ital. & Eng.]
London, 1789.
51 p. 8°. (In "Librettos," 18.)

NT 0038343   CtY

---

*
Ml
.S444
v.163
no.10

Tarchi, Angelo, 1760-1814.
Io ti lascio o mia speranza, a song with accompaniment for the piano forte, composed by Tarchi. Price 2 s. London, Printed by Rt. Birchall, No. 133 New Bond Street.
₍180-?₎
7 p. 30cm. ₍Sheet music collection, v. 163, no. 10₎
Caption title.

1. Songs with piano. I. Title.

NT 0038344   ViU

Tarchi, Angelo, 1760-1814.

Nel lasciarti amato bene. Sung by Sigr. Marchesi, in the opera Iffigenia ₍i. e. Ifigenia in Aulide by Cherubini₎ Composed by Sigr. Tarchi. London, Printed by Longman and Broderip ₍1789?₎ 17 p. 33cm.

Score: solo baritone, vocal trio (STBar) and orchestra.

1. Scenas, etc., Secular (4 voices)   —Orch. acc. I. Cherubini, Luigi,
1760-1842. Ifigenia in Aulide. Nel   lasciarti amato bene.

NT 0038345   NN

M
1497
018(11)
Cage

Tarchi, Angelo, 1760-1814.
Non lagrimar ben mio. Sung by Madam Mara & Sigr. Rubinelli in the opera of Virginia ... London, Printed by Longman & Broderip [1786]

12 p. Fo.
Score.

NT 0038346   DFo

Tarchi, Angelo, 1760-1814.
[Alessandro nell' Indie. Or che il cielo]
Or che il cielo ameti; rondo sung by Sigr. Marchesi, in the opera La generosita d'Alesandro. Composed by Sigr. Tarchi... London, Printed by Longman and Broderip [1789] 13 p. 33cm.

Score: one voice and orchestra.

I. Scenas, etc., Secular (1 voice) 1760-1814. Or che il cielo ameti. III. Title: La generosità d'Alessandro.   —Orch. acc. I. Tarchi, Angelo, II. Title: Alessandro nell' Indie.

NT 0038347   NN

Tarchi, Angelo, 1759?-1814
Recit, Forza echio [i.e.Forza e ch'io ceda] & Air, In un mardie tante [i.e.In un mar ti tante pene] L, Goulding [1802?]

Score (10 p.) (Periodical Italian song, 31)
Bd.with Ferrari, G.G. Rinaldo d'Asti. Selections: In amor ci vuol pazienza, et al.

NT 0038348   MH-Mu

Tarchi, Angelo, 1760-1814.
[Alessandro nell' Indie. Se mai più sarò geloso]
"Se mai pici [sic], saro geloso," sung by Sigr. Marchesi, in the opera Generosita d'Alessandro, composed by Sigr. Tarchi... London, Printed by Longman and Broderip [1789] 5 p. 33cm.

Score: one voice and orchestra.

I. Scenas, etc., Secular (1 voice) 1760-1814. Se mai più sarò geloso. III. Title: La generosità d'Alessandro.   —Orch. acc. I. Tarchi, Angelo, II. Title: Alessandro nell' Indie.

NT 0038349   NN

Tarchi, Angelo, 1760-1814.
[Alessandro nell' Indie. Se possono tanto]
Se possono tanto, sung by Sigr. Marchesi in the opera Generosita d'Alessandro. Composed by Sigr. Tarchi... London, Printed by Longman and Broderip [1789] 8 p. 33cm.

Score: one voice and orchestra.

I. Scenas, etc., Secular (1 voice) 1760-1814. Se possono tanto. III. Title: La generosità d'Alessandro   —Orch. acc. I. Tarchi, Angelo, II. Title: Alessandro nell' Indie.

NT 0038350   NN

Tarchi, Angelo, 1760-1814.
[Alessandro nell' Indie. Son prigionier]
Terzetto in the opera La generosita d'Alessandro, sung by Sigra. Giuliani, Sigrs. Marchesi and Forlivesi, composed by Sigr. Tarchi. The words by Mr. Badini... London, Printed by Longman and Broderip [1789] 22 p. 33cm.

Score: 3 solo voices and orchestra.
First line: Son prigionier lo vedo.

I. Scenas, etc., Secular (3 voices) II. Title: Alessandro nell' d'Alessandro.   —Orch. acc. I. Badini, Carlo Francesco. Indie. III. Title: La generosità

NT 0038351   NN

ML
50
.T18
T8

[Tarchi, Angelo] 1760-1814.
[Le trente et quarante. Libretto. French]
Le trente et quarante, ou, Le portrait, comédie en un acte, prose et arriettes [sic]: par le citoyen, Alexandre Duval. Représenté, pour la première fois, sur le Théâtre de la rue Feydeau, le 29 floréal, an 8 [18 mai 1800(!)] Paris, Barba, an X [1802?]
35 p. 22 cm.
I. Duval, Alexandre, 1767-1842. Le trente et quarante. II. Title.

NT 0038352   MiU NN MB

Tarchi, Angelo, 1760-1814.
Le trente et quarante
For editions without music see under Duval, Alexandre, 1767-1842.

M
1505
P149M

Tarchi, Angelo, 1760-1814.
[Virginia] Idol mis [sic. mio] quest' alma amante. Sung by Sigr. Rubinelli in the opera of Virginia. Composed by Sigr. Tarchi. London, Longman & Broderip [1786]
11p. 33cm. (Bound with: Paisiello, G., Il marchese Tulipano)

Full score.
Engraved.

NT 0038354   NRU-Mus PPL

Tarchi, Angelo, 1897-
... Autarchia dei carburanti ... Firenze, Casa editrice poligrafica universitaria del dott. C. Cya, 1938.
3 p. l., [9]-202 p., 3 l. 25½ᶜᵐ.

1. Fuel.   I. Title.

                   45-53927
Library of Congress   TP317.I 8T3

NT 0038355   DLC NN CSt-H

Pam.
Coll.
15874

Tarchi, Angelo, 1897-
... Premesse per la creazione della nuova struttura economico-sociale. [n.p., 19 47?]
15 p. 18cm.

1. Italy. Economic policy

NT 0038356   NcD

Tarchi, Angelo, 1897-
... Prospettive autarchiche ... Firenze, C. Cya, 1939-
v. diagrs. 25½ᶜᵐ.
At head of title of v. 1: Angiolo Tarchi.
"Ricerca e coordinazione statistica [nel v. 1-] a cura di Andrea de Mitri."

1. Italy—Indus. 2. Italy—Economic policy.   I. Mitri, Andrea de. II. Title.
                  44-12337 Revised
Library of Congress   HC305.T27 1939
              [r45c2]   330.945

NT 0038357   DLC CtY CU NN IU MH NcD

Tarchi, Angelo, 1897-
... Prospettive autarchiche ... 2. ed. [Firenze] C. Cya, 1939-
v. 25½ᶜᵐ.
"Ricerca e coordinazione statistica [nel v. 1-] a cura di Andrea de Mitri."

1. Italy—Indus. 2. Italy—Economic policy.   I. Mitri, Andrea de. II. Title.
                  45-31146
Library of Congress   HC305.T27 1939 a
              [2]   330.945

NT 0038358   DLC CtY NN

---

fNA380
T35
Arch.
Library

Tarchi, Ugo
L' architettura e l'arte musulmana in Egitto e nella Palestina. Torino, C. Crudo [1922]
18 p. illus., 166 plates, plans. 48cm.

1. Architecture, Mohammedan. 2. Art, Mohammedan. 3. Architecture - Egypt. 4. Architecture - Palestine.

      NcGU IaU MiU OO MiD NN PP OU ICU ViU MWiW NBrockU
NT   0038359   CU NBuG CoU CtY KyU CaBVaU CLU CLSU DDO

Tarchi, Ugo.
...L'architettura e l'arte nell'antico Egitto... Torino: C. Crudo & C. [1924?] 28 p. illus. (incl. plans), A.-G., 100 pl. f°.

1. Egypt—Archaeology. 2. Architecture—Egypt. 3. Art, Egyptian. N.Y.P.L.   June 12, 1925

      CtY MiD NNU-W
NT   0038360   NN OO MB MA OCl NIC IU MH OU DLC-P4 RPB

Tarchi, Ugo
... L'arte cristiano-romanica nell'Umbria e nella Sabina; con 232 tavole. Milano, Treves [1937]
3 p. l., 8 p. 232 plates (incl.plans) on 116 l. 35ᶜᵐ. (His L'arte nell'Umbria e nella Sabina, v. 2)

1. Art - Sabina. 2. Art - Umbria. 3. Art, Early Christian. 4. Art, Romanesque.

NT 0038361   NNC MH

WE
2390

Tarchi, Ugo
L'arte del Rinascimento (e secoli posteriori) nell'Umbria e nella Sabina. Architettura civile. Milano, A.Garzanti [1942]
1v.(chiefly illus.) (L'arte nell'Umbria e nella Sabina, v.5)

1. Art - Umbria.
x.His series

NT 0038362   CtY NNC

Tarchi, Ugo.
L'arte del Rinascimento nell'Umbria e nella Sabina. Con 481 tavole. Appendice: I calchi michelangioleschi nell'Accademia di Perugia e i marmi nella Cappella medicea. [Milano] Garzanti [1954 or 5]
1 v. (chiefly plates) 35 cm.
Includes bibliographical references.
"500 esemplari, di cui 470 numerati."

1. Art—Umbria. 2. Art, Italian.
                   A 55-5387
Harvard Univ. Library
for Library of Congress   [3]

NT 0038363   MH CtY CU

Tarchi, Ugo
... L'arte etrusco-romana nell'Umbria e nella Sabina; con 280 tavole. Milano, Treves [1936]
3 p. l., 15 p. 280 plates on 140 l. 35ᶜᵐ. (His L'arte nell'Umbria e nella Sabina, v. 1)

1. Etruria - Antiquities. 2. Art - Sabina. 3. Art - Umbria. 4. Art, Etruscan. 5. Art, Roman.

NT 0038364   NNC MH OClMA NNU-W

Tarchi, Ugo
L'arte medioevale nell'Umbria e nella Sabina, architettura civile, dalla metà del sec.XIII al principio del sec.XV. Milano, Treves [1938]
6 p., 202 plates (His L'arte nell'Umbria e nella Sabina, 3)

NT 0038365   MH NNC

Tarchi, Ugo
L'arte medioevale nell'Umbria e nella Sabina; architettura religiosa, dalla metà del sec.XIII al principio del sec.XV. Milano, Garzanti [1940]
11 p. 264 plates (incl.plans) (His L'arte nell'Umbria e nella Sabina, 4)

NT 0038366   MH NNC

Tarchi, Ugo.
L'arte nell' Umbria e nella Sabina ... v. 1–   Milano: S. a.
Fratelli Treves ₁1936–   v.   map, plans, plates.   35cm.

Each volume has also special t.-p.
CONTENTS.—v. 1. Periodo etrusco-romano.—v. 2. Periodo cristiano-romanico.

1. Architecture—Italy—Umbria.   2. Art, Italian—Umbria.   I. Title.
N. Y. P. L.   January 24, 1940

     OU MB MoU
NT   0038367   NN MH CU CLU IU MiU DDO CaBVaU MiD NNC

Tarchi, Ugo.
I calchi michelangioleschi nell'Accademia di Perugia e
marmi nella Cappella medicea. ₁Milano₎ Garzanti ₁1954₎
₁54₎ p. (p. ₁18₎–₁51₎ illus.) 35 cm.
First published in the author's L'arte del Rinascimento nell'Umbria
e nella Sabina (1954)
Bibliography: p. ₁17₎

1. Buonarroti, Michel Angelo, 1475-1564.   2. Perugia. Accademia
di belle arti.   3. Florence.   San Lorenzo (Church)   Sagrestia nuova.
NB623.B9T3   A 57–1878
Harvard Univ. Library
for Library of Congress   ₁3₎†

NT   0038368   MH DLC-P4 DLC

Tarchi, Ugo.
Studi e progetti della scuola di architettura
perugina...
       see under   Perugia. Accademia di Belle
Arti. Scuola di Architettura.

ſ NA7756   Tarchi, Ugo
P44T3   Sul ripristino e restauro del Palazzo del capitano del popolo in
         Perugia (oggi Palazzo di giustizia) e sulla nuova facciata dell'
         adiacente sede della Corte d'assise con aggiunta di altri progetti
         riguardanti monumenti o località della città di Perugia.   Milano,
         Bestetti & Tumminelli ₁1917₎
         88 p.   illus. ₁17 plates, plans. 33cm.

         1. Perugia. Palazzo di giustizia.

NT   0038370   CU

Tarchi, Ugo.
Sul ripristino e restauro del Palazzo del capitano
del popolo in Perugia (oggi Palazzo di giustizia) e
sulla nuova facciata dell'adiacente sede della Corte
d'assise: con aggiunta di altri progetti riguardanti
monumenti o località della città di Perugia / Ugo
Tarchi.   Milano, Bestetti & Tumminelli, [1920]
88 p.   ill., plans.   33 cm.
Author's autographed presentation copy to Ugo
Ojetti.

NT   0038371   NNC

Tarchi, Ugo, *ed.*
La villa detta "La Simonetta" nel suburbio di Milano.
Roma, La Libreria dello Stato, 1953.
16 p. illus., 20 plates (incl. plans) 50 cm. (I Monumenti italiani.
ser. 2, fasc. 2)
Bibliography: p. 14.

1. Milan. La Simonetta.   (Series: I Monumenti italiani, ser. 2,
fasc. 2)
NA7595.S5T3   A 54–2234
Columbia Univ.   Libraries
for Library of Congress   ₁1₎†

     DDO NcU DLC
NT   0038372   NNC FMU InU MoSW   CLU GU CtY NN NjP TxU

Tarchiani, Alberto, 1885–
America–Italia, le dieci giornate di De Gasperi negli
Stati Uniti. Milano, Rizzoli ₁1947₎
163 p. plates, ports. 22 cm.

1. Gasperi, Alcide de, 1881–   2. Italy—For. rel.—U. S.
3. U. S.—For. rel.—Italy.

DG575.G3T35   49–22634*

NT   0038373   DLC CSt-H MH NjP NNC ICU

TARCHIANI, ALBERTO, 1881-
    America-Italia; le dieci giornate di DeGasperi negli
Stati Uniti.   Milano, Rizzoli [1947]   163 p.   illus., ports.
22cm.

    Film reproduction. Positive.

1. Visits of state--U. S.   2. Gasperi, Alcide de, 1881-
1954.

NT   0038374   NN

ſarchiani, Alberto, 1885–
    Dieci anni tra Roma e Washington. Con 32 illustrazioni
fuori testo, 3 autografi e 4 carte geografiche. ₁1. ed. Milano₎
Mondadori ₁1955₎
356 p. illus., ports., fold. col. maps. 21 cm. (Le Scie)

1. U. S.—For. rel.—Italy.   2. Italy—For. rel.—U. S.   ₁. Title.

E183.8.I 8T3   56–32301

NT   0038375   DLC OrU NN WHi TNJ MiU MH-L

D763   **Tarchiani, Alberto,** 1885–
I8T35   Il mio diario di Anzio.   ₁1. ed., ed. provvi
        soria.   Verona₎ A. Mondadori ₁1947₎
        138 p.   (Arianna; diari, memorie, episto-
        lari, 8)

        1. World war, 1939–1945 - Campaigns -
        Italy. 2. World War, 1939–1945 - Personal
        narratives, Italian. I. Title. II. Title:
        Anzio.

NT   0038376   CU ICRL CSt-H MB MH NN NNC

720.945   Tarchiani, Nello, 1878–
T179a   L'architettura italiana dell' ottocento.
        Firenze, Novissima enciclopedia monografica
Art   illustrata ₁1937₎
        72p. front.,illus. O. (Novissima
        enciclopedia monografica illustrata. 72)

        1.Architecture. Italy.

NT   0038377   IaU CtY NN NjP

Tarchiani, Nello.
    ... Firenze; con 177 illustrazioni e 3 tavole. Bergamo,
Istituto italiano d'arti grafiche ₁1915₎
170 p. front, illus. 2 pl. 26½ᶜᵐ. (Half-title: Collezione di monografie
illustrate. ser. 1.ᵃ—Italia artistica, 77)

1. Art—Florence. 2. Florence—Descr.

                              16–20185
Library of Congress   N6921.F7T3

    MiU CtY   OO MB NjP NN
NT   0038378   DLC ViU NSyU MWiCA FU PP OClW DDO NjR

N6921   Tarchiani, Nello, 1878-
F7T3   Firenze; con 177 illustrazioni e 3 tavole.
1920   (2. ed.) Bergamo, Istituto italiano d'arti
        grafiche ₁192-?₎
        164 p. illus. ₎3 plates. (Collezione di
        monografie illustrate. Ser.1a - Italia
        artistica, 77)

        1. Art - Florence. 2. Florence, Italy -
        Descr.

NT   0038379   CU MH

Tarchiani, Nello, 1878–
    ... Firenze; con 181 illustrazioni e 3 tavole.   (3. ed.) Ber-
gamo, Istituto italiano d'arti grafiche ₁193-?₎
2 p. L. ₁7₎–168 p. front., illus., 2 pl. 26ᶜᵐ. (Half-title: Collezione di
monografie illustrate. Ser. 1.ᵃ—Italia artistica, 77)

1. Art—Florence. 2. Florence—Descr.

                              45–42313
Library of Congress   N6921.F7T3
                              709.45

NT   0038380   DLC

709.455   Tarchiani, Nello, *1878-*
T179   Firenze; con 177 illustrazioni e 3 tavole
        (11ᵃ ed.) Bergamo, Istituto Italiano d'Arti
        Grafiche ₁194-?₎
        164 p. illus., plates. 26ᶜᵐ. (Collezione di
        monografie illustrate. Ser. 1ᵃ- Italia artistica,
        77)

        1.Art - Florence. 2.Florence - Descr.

NT   0038381   CSt

N   Tarchiani, Nello, 1878-
6911   Florence. Translated by Alethea Wiel.
I871   Bergamo, Istituto italiano d'arti grafiche
v.2   ₁1915₎
        168 p. illus. 26cm. (Collection of
        illustrated monographs. 1st ser.: Artistic
        Italy ₁2₎)

        1. Art--Florence. 2. Florence--Descr.

NT   0038382   NIC CaBVaU NNC

Tarchiani, Nello, *1878-*
    ...Florence. (Translated by Alethea Wiel)...   Bergamo:
"Istituto italiano d'arti grafiche", 1921. 168 p.   illus.
26cm. (Collection of illustrated monographs. ser. 1: Artistic
Italy. 3.)

252856B. 1. Florence—Descr.   2. Art, Italian—Florence.
N. Y. P. L.   February 16, 1944

     PU
NT   0038383   NN OOxM MeB DCU PU IU OKentU DSI-GA CSt

N6921   Tarchiani, Nello, 1878-
.F7T32   Florence. Translated by Alethea Wiel.
1926   With three plates and 181 illustrations.
        Bergamo, Istituto Italiano d'Arti Grafiche
        ₁1926₎
        168 p. illus. 26cm. (Artistic Italy)

        1. Art--Florence. 2. Florence--Descr. I. Wiel,
        Hon. Alethea Jane (Lawley) 1851-   tr.

NT   0038384   ViU MWiCA TU

Art   Tarchiani, Nello, 1878-
N 6921   Florence. Translated by Alethea
F 7   Wiel. Bergamo, Istituto italiano d'arte
T 313   grafiche [1939?]
        168 p. 18? illus., 3 plates.

          Art - Florence.
          Florence - Descr.

NT 0038385   MoSW

Tarchiani, Nello, 1878-
   ...La Galleria degli Uffizi a Firenze ...   Milano: Fratelli
Treves[, 192-?]. xxxi p. illus., 60 pl. 16°. (Il fiore dei
musei e monumenti d'Italia. no. 11.)
   Letter-press descriptive of each plate on verso of preceding plate.

452298A. 1. Art—Collections—   Italy—Florence. 2. Ser.
N. Y. P. L.   December 26, 1929

NT 0038386   NN CLCM

Tarchiani, Nollo, 1878-
   ...La R. Galleria Pitti in Firenze. (137
illustrazioni) Roma, La Libreria dello Stato
[1934]
   77 p., 1 l. incl. plates. 18½cm. (Itinerari
dei musei e monumenti d'Italia. [n. 41.])
   At head of title: Ministero della educazione
nazionale. Direzione generale delle antichità
e belle arti ...
   Plans on p. [2] and [4] of cover.

   1. Florence. P   Galleria Palatina.

NT 0038387   NNC NN DDO

Tarchiani, Nello, 1878-
   ... La R. Galleria Pitti in Firenze (137 illustrazioni) 2. ed.
Roma, La Libreria dello stato, a. XVII E. F. [1939]
   76 p. incl. plates. 18½cm. (Itinerari dei musei e monumenti d'Italia.
[N. 41])
   At head of title: Ministero della educazione nazionale. Direzione
generale delle antichità e belle arti ...
   Plans on p. [2], [4] of cover.

   1. Florence. Galleria Palatina.
                                               45–42303
   Library of Congress   N2560.T3 1939
                           [2]   708.5

NT 0038388   DLC CU

Tarchiani, Nello, 1878-
   Italia medievale, con 96 tavole in zinco-
tipia. Bologna, Casa editrice Apollo, 1925.
   29 p. 95 plates on 48 l. 25cm.

NT 0038389   NNC DLC NjP MB IdU

Tarchiani, Nello, 1878-
   Letture artistiche; pagine scelte da d'artic-
ti sull'arte loro, con cenni biografici e note
di N. Tarchiani ... Firenze, Barbèra, 1915.
   vi, 364 p. incl. front., illus. (On cover:
Collezione scolastica; secondo: I programmi
governativi)
   1. Art - Addresses, essays, lectures. 2. Artists, Italian.

NT 0038390   NNC IU

Tarchiani, Nello, 1878-
   Le logge [testo di Nello Tarchiani]
      see under   Raphael, 1483-1520.

Tarchiani, Nello, 1878-
   Le madonne [testo di Nello Tarchiani]
      see under   Raphael, 1483-1520.

Tarchiani, Nello, 1878-
   ... The Medici-Riccardi palace and the Medici museum;
translated by Klyda R. Steege. Firenze, A cura dell' Amministrazione della provincia, 1931.
   1 p. l., [5]–53 p., 3 l. front., xx pl. (incl. ports.) on 10 l. 18mm.

   1. Florence. Palazzo Medici-Riccardi.   I. Steege, Klyda Richardson, tr.

   Library of Congress   NA7756.F65T33   32–34219
                                                   708.5

NT 0038393   DLC CtY ViU

NA   Tarchiani, Nello, 1878-
1113   ... Das mittelalterliche Italien ... Mün-
.T18   chen, Allgemeine verlagsanstalt [C1925]
        28[?] p. 95 pl. on 48 l. 25cm. [Schriften
        und abhandlungen zur kunst- und kulturgeschichte. 3]
        "Deutsche übersetzung von dr. L. Zahn."

          1. Architecture—Italy. 2. Architecture, Medieval.
        I. Zahn, Leopold, 1890-   tr. II. Title.

NT 0038394   MiU WaS KyLoU PSC

TARCHIANI, NELLO, 1878-
   ...Il Palazzo Medici Riccardi e il Museo mediceo.
Firenze: A cura dell' Amministrazione della provincia,
1930. 49 p. 20 pl. on 10 l. 12°.

629729A. 1. Art—Collections—Italy—Florence.

NT 0038395   NN MiDA MWelC TxDaM MoU

Tarchiani, Nello, 1878-
   Ojetti, Ugo, 1871-
   ... La pittura italiana del seicento e del settecento alla
Mostra di palazzo Pitti. Milano-Roma, Bestetti e Tumminelli
[1924]

Tarchiani, Nello, 1878-
   Raffaello; le Logge
      see   Raphael, 1483-1520.
   Le Logge.

Tarchiani, Nello, 1878-
   Raffaello; le madonne
      see   Raphael, 1483-1520.
   Le Madonne.

Tarchisni, Nello, 1878-
   Raffaello; ritratti dipinti vari
      see   Raphael, 1483-1520.
   Ritratti e dipinti vari.

TARCHIANI, NELLO, 1878-
   ...La scultura italiana dell'ottocento. Firenze [1936]
64 p. front., illus. 24cm. (Novissima enciclopedia
monografica illustrata. 64.)

   1. Sculpture, Italian. 19th cent. I. Ser.

NT 0038400   NN IaU

Tarchiani, Nello, 1878-
   Il settecento italiano ... Milano-Roma, Bestetti & Tumminelli, 1932.

Tarchiani, Nello, 1878-
   Le Stanze
      see under   Raphael, 1483-1520.

Art   Tarchiani, Nello, 1878-
Library   The Uffizi Gallery in Florence [di]
J465   Nello Tarchiani. Milan, Treves-Treccani-
F69X   Tumminelli [1928]
928Tg   xxxvi p. illus., 60 plates. 17 cm.
        (The "Fiore" collection, 11)

          I. Tarchiani, Nello, 1873-

NT 0038403   CtY MH

BT   Tarchier, L
1326   Le sacrement de l'Eucharistie d'après Saint
.T17   Augustin. Lyon, A. Rey, 1904.
        115 p. 25 cm.
        Thesis - Lyon.
        Bibliographical footnotes.

          1. Eucharist. 2. Augustine, Saint, Bp. of
        Hippo, 354-430. I. Title.

NT 0038404   DCU

TARCHINI, Antonio.   279.
   Antonio Sellajo. Novella. [Anon.]
      Pavia. Zenoni. 1832. 50 pp. 16°.

NT 0038405   MB

Tarchini, Gian Carlo.
   La giurisdizione amministrativa per il cantone Ticino ... da
Gian Carlo Tarchini ... Bellinzona, Lugano, Istituto editoriale
ticinese [1942]
   109 p., 1 l. 24cm.
   Tesi di laurea—Bern.
   "Letteratura": p. [9]

   1. Administrative courts—Ticino (Canton)
                                               45–29079

NT 0038406   DLC CtY

Tarchini-Bonfanti (Antonio). Atti peri-
tali medici relativi al processo di omicidj contro
Antonio Boggia. 79 pp. 8°. Milano, G. Chiusi,
1862.
   Repr. from: Gazz. med. ital. lomb., Milano, 1862, 5. s., 1.

NT 0038407   DNLM

Tarchini-Bonfanti, Antonio.
———. Estasi ed itinoci. 18 pp. 12°. *Milano,*
frat. Rechiedei, 1883.
Repr. from: Arch. ital. per le mal. nerv., Milano, 1883, xx.

NT 0038408   DNLM

Tarchioni, Zoraide Sandri
see   Sandri Tarchioni, Zoraide.

935.4
Os7
no.9   Tarchnisvili, Michael
Die byzantinische liturgie als verwirklichung
der einheit und gemeinschaft in dogma, von p.
Michael Tarchnisvili ... Würzburg, Rita-verlag
und -druckerei, 1939.
76 p.   22ᶜᵐ.   (Added t.p.: Das Östliche
christentum ... hrsg. von Georg Wunderle ...
hft. 9)
Bibliographical foot-notes.
1. Byzantine empire - Church history. 2. Eastern
churches. Liturgy and ritual.

NT 0038410   NNC MH

Tarchnišvili, Michael.
Geschichte der kirchlichen georgischen Literatur, auf
Grund des ersten Bandes der georgischen Literaturgeschichte
von K. Kekelidze. Bearb. von Michael Tarchnišvili in Verbindung mit Julius Assfalg. Città del Vaticano, Biblioteca
apostolica vaticana, 1955.
xv, 521 p.   26 cm.   (Studi e testi, 185)

1. Religious literature, Georgian. 2. Georgian literature—Hist. &
crit.   i. Kekelidze, Kornilii Semenovich. K'art'uli literaturis
istoria, dzveli mc'erloba. (Series: Vatican. Biblioteca vaticana.
Studi e testi, 185)

PK9164.T3   57-30782

     DCU NIC WaU CtY NjPT TNJ-R CU ICN OU NcD
     MoSCS OCU OrU CU-S NBuU MH NIC TxU DDO MH-AH ICU IU
NT   0038411   DLC ODaU NNC CSt ICMcC InStme RPB TNJ NN

GL35   Tarchnišvili, Michael, ed.
C82   ... Liturgiae ibericae antiquiores
(1-2)   ... Lovanii,e Typographeo linguarum
orientalium,apud L.Durbecq,1950.
2v.   26cm.   (Corpus scriptorum
christianorum orientalium, 122-123.
Scriptores iberici (1-2₁)
Original serial numbering: ser.1,
t.1.
Iboric (Georgian) and Latin; ed.
and tr. by Michael Tarchnišvili.

NT 0038412   NNUT CBGTU IMunS RPB MH OCl

Tarchnišvili, Michael, ed. and tr.

Gregorius *Pacurianus, d.* 1086.
Typicon. Edidit (et interpretatus est₁ Michael Tarchnišvili. Louvain, L. Durbecq, 1954.

Tarchov, Todor
The vision, and other poems. Translated by J.Kirkup and
L.Sirombo. L, Newman & Harris [1953]
37 p.

NT 0038414   MH

Tarchow, V   A
Ehe und Familie in der sozialistischen Gesellschaft und die
Grundprinzipien des sowjetischen sozialistischen Familien-
rechts. Leipzig, Urania-Verlag, 1955.
56 p.   17 cm.

1. Marriage. 2. Women and socialism.   i. Title.

HX546.T3   56-34899 ‡

NT 0038415   DLC NN

Tarchow, V   A
Vorlesungen über das sowjetische Zivilrecht. (Übers. von
A. Walter₁ Berlin, Deutscher Zentralverlag, 1955.
152 p.   24 cm.   (Deutsches Institut für Rechtswissenschaft.
Schriftenreihe Zivilrecht, Heft 1)

1. Civil law—Russia.

56-31283 ‡

NT 0038416   DLC IU DS MH-L

Tarchy, Angelo
see   Tarchi, Angelo, 1760-1814.

QL157
.L5
T3   Tarcia, Salvador
Cultura de variedades de linho destinadas à
produção de óleo de linhaça. Rio de Janeiro,
Ministério da Agricultura, Serviço de Informa-
ção Agrícola, 1948.
63 p. illus. 23 cm.
Cover title.

1. Linum usitatissimum.   i.t.

NT 0038418   NNBG DNAL

Tarcici, Adnan, *1912-*
... L'éducation actuelle de la jeune fille musulmane au Liban,
par Adnan Tarcici ... Vitry-sur-Seine, Mariale, 1941.
173 p., 1 l. 24ᶜᵐ.
Thèse—Univ. de Paris.
"Index des ouvrages cités" : p. (167₁-169.

1. Education of women—Lebanon. 2. Women, Mohammedan.
                     46-43011
Library of Congress   LC2410.L4T3
            o.   376.9569

NT 0038419   DLC CtY ICU NNC NNC-T

Tarcici, Adnan, 1912-
Yemen. (Akkar? Lebanon, 1947₁
96 p. illus., ports., maps. 26 cm.
Cover title.
Text in French; issued also in English.

1. Yemen.

DS247.Y4T3   915.33   48-21932*

NT 0038420   DLC

Tarcici, Adnan, *1912-*
Yemen. (New York, 1947₁
cover-title, 96 p. illus., ports., maps. 26 cm.
"Original text in French."

1. Yemen.
DS247.Y4T315   915.33   48-12744*

NT 0038421   DLC

Tarcisia, *sister*
(of the Sisters of the Third order of Saint Francis, Syracuse, N. Y.)
see   Ball, Mary Tarcisia, *sister,* 1894-

Tarcisio, Padre, C. P.
Il dramma dell'amore; quadri della
passione. Milano, Editrice Ancora, (1952₁
253 p.

NT 0038423   DCU

Tarciussus: the boy martyr of Rome
see under   [Rolfe, Frederick William] 1860-
1913.

D766   Tarco, L.
.4
.L79   **Lupăşteanu, A**
Inimi de viteji. Bucureşti, Editura Militară, 19

Tarcov, Oscar.
Bravo, my monster. Chicago, H. Regnery Co., 1953.
133 p. 22 cm.

i. Title.

PZ4.T179Br   53-8794 ‡

NT 0038426   DLC GU CoU OCl

Tarcsay, Izabella.
Grundriss der psychodiagnostik; eine praktische einführung
in die Rorschach-methode und ihre klinische anwendung, von
dr. Isabella Tarcsay. Mit abbildungen auf 14 ganzseitigen
tafeln. Zürich, Rascher, 1944.
391 p. incl. plates (2 col.) diagrs. 23ᶜᵐ.
"Zweite auflage."
"Der ungarische originaltitel dieses buches lautet: Pszichodiagnosz-
tika, a Rorschachvizsgálat és klinikai alkalmazása."

1. Rorschach test. 2. Nervous system—Diseases—Diagnosis.

RC348.T315   Med 47-1789

NT 0038427   DLC PSt TxU OCU ICU PPC IaU

Tarczai, György, pseud.
see   Divald, Kornél, 1872-1931.

Tarczali, Paul de, fl. 1672-1677.
Disputatio Medica Inauguralis De Arthritide ...
Lugduni Batavorum, J. Elzevier, 1677.
Copinger 4639.

NT 0038429   PU

Tarczay, Erzsébet.
A jobbágyság története Horvátországban, 1650-1848. Irta
Tarczay Erzsébet.   Budapest: J. May könyvnyomda, 1913.
118 p.   8°.

' 1. Serfdom—Croatia.
N. Y. P. L.   September 25, 1928

NT 0038430   NN PU

Tarczay, Isabella
  see Tarcsay, Izabella.

615.853   **Tarczay, Kálmán.**
T17k   Der Kurort Bartfeld in Ungarn, seine
1877   Topographie, Geschichte und therapeutische
     Bedeutung. 2.Aufl.   Kaschau, A. Maurer,
     1877.
       viii, 184p.   22cm.

       Bibliography: p.40-44.

       1. Baths--Bardejov, Slovakia. 2. Bardejov,
     Slovakia--Descr. & trav. I. Title.

NT   0038432   IU

Tarczyc, Janusz.   3061.158
Świętorbliwa Jadwiga, królowa polska. Wydanie przeznaczone dla
szerokich kół z powodu zamierzonej kanonizacji. Wydanie 2.
— Warszawa. Przegląd katolicki. 1912. (3), 102, ii pp. Illus. Portraits. 31 cm.

L2460 — Poland. Hist. — Hedwig, Q., of Poland. 1371–1399. — Poland. Lang.
Works in Polish.

NT   0038433   MB

PG   **Tarczyński, Rudolf A.**
7014   Dzieje literatury polskiej w najogólnie-
.T17   jszym zarysie; dla polskich wyższych szkół
     i kolegjów w Ameryce. [n.p.] 1933.

       1. Polish literature – Hist. & crit.

NT   0038434   DCU

---

436   **Tarczyński, Stefan.**
T17   Pasożyty wewnętrzne ludzi i zwierząt.
     Warszawa, Książka i Wiedza, 1949.
     107 p.   (Świat i człowiek)

       1. Parasites.

NT   0038435   DNAL DLC-P4

Tarczyński-Alf, Tadeusz.
     ... Homage to Chopin. Hołd Chopinowi. Glasgow,
Książnica polska, The Polish library [1942]
     31 p.   14½ x 23ᶜᵐ.

       1. Chopin, Fryderyk Franciszek, 1810–1849.   I. Title.   II. Title:
Hołd Chopinowi.
                              44-49227
Library of Congress   ML410.C54T19
         [2]   927.8

NT   0038436   DLC NcU

Tard, G
  see Tarde, Gabriel de, 1843–1904.

Tard, Henri.
     Économie & politique du caoutchouc, le plan Stevenson, ses
résultats, études des éléments du marché futur, par Henri Tard
... Préface de m. R. d'Argila ... Paris, Imprimerie Les
Presses modernes, 1928.
     200 p. plates (1 fold.) fold. map, diagrs. 24ᶜᵐ.
     "Bibliographie" : p. [196]–197.

       1. Rubber industry and trade.   [1. India-rubber]
     HD9161.A2T3   Agr 29–148 rev †
     U. S. Dept. of agr.   Library   305T17
     for Library of Congress   [r46c2]†

NT   0038438   DNAL DLC MH-A CtY MH

Tard, Robert DeCourcy
     Recent foreign studies of thunderstorms. Cambridge.
1896.
     10 p.   8.
     P.2765

NT   0038439   DAS

Tardáguila, Manuel.
     ... El estado ... Montevideo, 1882.
     103 p. 20½ᶜᵐ.
     Tésis—Univ. de Montevideo.
     At head of title: Universidad de la Republica.

       1. State, The.
                                 10-4286†
     Library of Congress   JC219.T24

NT   0038440   DLC

Tardan, K   I
    see
    Tardent, Charles, 1812–1856.

Tardani, Gaetano
    [——.] Appendice all' articolo pubblicato col
supplemento al n. 211 del Giornale di Roma relativo ad un nuovo metodo di curare il cholera
morbus. 8 pp. 8°. [Roma, T. Ajani, 1854.]
[P., v. 872.]

NT   0038442   DNLM

Tardani, Gaetano
    [——.] Nuovo metodo di ravvisare il cholera
morbus e relativo metodo di cura. 8 pp. 8°.
[Roma, T. Ajani, 1854.] [P., v. 872.]
Repr. from: Gior. di Roma. [1854], no. 211.

NT   0038443   DNLM

Tardani (Gaetano). Osservazioni sopra alcune
memorie intorno all' analisi delle orine di recente
pubblicate dal Prof. Pietro Peretti. 32 pp. 8°.
Firenze, 1846. [P., v. 872.]
Repr. from: Gazz. tosc. d. sc. med.-fis. Firenze, 1846, iv.

NT   0038444   DNLM

WCB   **TARDANI, Gaetano**
T181r   Risoluzione del problema sul cholera-
1855   morbus; memoria chimico-patologica.
     Roma, Monaldi, 1855.
     37 p.

NT   0038445   DNLM NN

[**Tardani Ciani, Francesca**] 1890–
     ... Il giuoco della musica. Illustrazioni di Sto [pseud.]
Roma, A. Signorelli [1936]
     49, [1] p. incl. illus. (part col., incl. music) 3 fold. pl. (part col., incl.
music) fold. col. pl. 26 x 37½ᶜᵐ.
     Author's pseud., Zia Franca, at head of title.
     Preface signed : Francesca Tardani Ciani.
     Illustrated cover and lining-papers.

       1. Music—Instruction and study. 2. Games.   I. Tofano, Sergio,
1886–   Illus.   II. Title.
                               37-37931
     Library of Congress   MT740.T18G5
         [3]   781.21

NT   0038446   DLC

Tardas, Jean Élie, 1906–
     ... Le risque invalidité dans la législation des assurances
sociales ... par Tardas Jean-Élie ... Paris, Librairie technique et économique, 1938.
     2 p. l., [7]–231 p. incl. tables. 24ᶜᵐ.
     Thèse—Univ. de Paris.
     "Bibliographie" : [p. 223]–226.

       1. Insurance, Health—France. 2. Insurance, State and compulsory—
France.   I. Title.
                               42-25098
     Library of Congress   HD7106.F8T28

NT   0038447   DLC CtY

Tarde, Alfred de, 1880–1925.
     For works written jointly with Henri Massis
under the pseudonym Agathon see under   Massis,
Henri, 1886–

Tarde, Alfred de, 1880–1925.
     ... Avant-postes (chronique d'un redresse-
ment) 1910–1914 ...
       see under   Massis, Henri, 1886–

Tarde, Alfred de, 1880–1925.
     Éloge de Edmond Rousse; discours prononcé à
l'ouverture de la Conférence des avocats, le 5 déc.
1908.   Paris, Alcan-Lévy, 1908.
     38 + p.
       At head of title: Barreau de Paris.

NT   0038450   MH

Tarde, Alfred de, 1880–1925.
     L'esprit de la nouvelle Sorbonne [par] Agathon
[pseud. of Henri Massis and Alfred de Tarde]
       see under   [Massis, Henri], 1886–

Tarde, Alfred de, 1880–
     L'Europe court-elle à sa ruine?   Paris: A. Colin, 1916.
     2 p.l., 76 p.   12°.
     Author's name at head of title.

       1. European war, 1914– .—Finance.   2. European war, 1914– .—Eco-
nomic aspects.
N. Y. P. L.   December 18, 1916.

NT   0038452   NN CtY

Tarde, Alfred de, 1880–1925.
     L'idée du juste prix ... par Alfred de Tarde.
     Sarlat, Michelet, 1906.
     (4) 372 p.   26 cm.
     Thèse – Univ. de Paris.

NT   0038453   CtY-L NcD

Tarde, Alfred de, 1880–1925.
   L'idée du juste prix; essai de psychologie économique, par Alfred de Tarde ... Paris, F. Alcan, 1907.
   3 p. l., 372 p.   25½ cm.
   "Bibliographie": p. ₍359₎–366.

   1. Prices. 2. Value. 3. Economics—Hist. 4. Wages. 5. Interest and usury.
                                                              8—4471
   Library of Congress   HB221.T2

NT 0038454   DLC OO ICJ NN CU KU

Tarde, Alfred de, 1880–   joint author.

Massis, Henri, 1886–   FOR OTHER EDITIONS
   ... Les jeunes gens d'aujourd'hui;   SEE MAIN ENTRY
le goût de l'action, la foi patriotique, une renaissance catholique, le réalisme politique ... Paris, Plon-Nourrit et cⁱᵉ ₍1919₎

D⁷ 317 .T16 1923
   Tarde, Alfred de, 1880–1925.
   ... Le Maroc, école d'énergie, par Alfred de Tarde. Paris, Plon-Nourrit et cⁱᵉ ₍1923₎
   127, ₍1₎ p. pl. 19ᶜᵐ. (Les problèmes d'aujourd'hui)
   "4ᵉ édition."
   "J'assemble sous ce titre ... quelques études écrites à des dates différentes ... Elles se rapportent toutes à un seul problème: quel est le sens de notre effort colonisateur?"—Avant-propos.

   1. France—Colonies—Africa, North. 2. Morocco. ɪ. Title.
   Library of Congress   DT317.T3 1923
                                                    26-8340

NT 0038456   DLC MH NN DW InU

Tarde, Alfred de, 1880–1925.
   ... L'organisation des intellectuels en France, par Alfred de Tarde ... Rapport au Congrès international du travail intellectuel (août 1921) ₍Bruxelles, 1921₎
   26 p. 24½ᶜᵐ. (Union des associations internationales. Publication n° 100)

   1. France—Intellectual life. 2. Intellectual cooperation. ɪ. Title.
   ɪɪ. Title: Intellectuels en France.
                                                    23-14620
   Library of Congress   AZ656.T3

NT 0038457   DLC

DC393 T3
   Tarde, Alfred de, 1880–1925.
   La politique d'aujourd'hui; enquête parmi les groupements et les partis, par Alfred de Tarde er ₍1₎ Robert de Jouvenel. Paris, La Renaissance du livre ₍1925₎
   343 p.

   1. France - Pol. & govt. - 1914–
   2. Political parties - France. ɪ. Jouvenel, Robert de.

NT 0038458   CU IU ICU CSt-H

Tarde, Alfred de, 1880–1925, and R. de Jouvenel.
   La politique d'aujourd'hui; enquête parmi les groupements et les partis, par Alfred de Tarde et Robert de Jouvenel. Paris: La renaissance du livre ₍, 1925?₎.   343 p.   12°.
   Bibliographical footnotes.
   Contents: Avertissement. TARDE, A. DE, and R. DE JOUVENEL. Comment les problèmes se posent. TARDE, A. DE. Le Bloc national ou la politique de la majorité. JOUVENEL, R. DE. Le Bloc des gauches. Essai d'une doctrine. TARDE, A. DE, and R. DE JOUVENEL. Où les thèses se confrontent.

235107A. 1. France—Politics, 1919–   1923. 2. Finance—France, 1919–1923.
3. European war, 1914–1918—Repara-   tions 4. Jouvenel, Robert de, d. 1924,
jt. au.   jt. au.
N. Y. P. L.   May 10, 1926

NT 0038459   NN ViU

---

*Tardé, Gabriel de, 1843–1904, ed.

   Archives d'anthropologie criminelle, de médecine légale et de psychologie normale et pathologique ... t. 1–29; 1886–1914. Paris, G. Masson; ₍etc., etc.₎, 1886–1915₎

NT 0038461   DLC-P4

4K 3013
   Tarde, Gabriel de, 1843–1904
   La criminalidad comparada. Traduccion castellana de Jorge Argerich. Buenos Aires, F. Lajouane, 1888.
   212 p.

NT 0038462   MiU-L

Tarde, Gabriel de, 1843–1904.
   La criminalidad comparada por G. Tarde. Prologo y notas de Adolfo Posada ... Con una carta del autor escrita para la edición española. Madrid, La España moderna ₍1893?₎
   379 p.   17ᶜᵐ.
   Editor's foreword dated March, 1893.

---

ar V 9235
   Tarde, Gabriel de, 1843–1904.
   La criminalité comparée. Paris, F. Alcan, 1886.
   214 p. 19cm.

   Contents.—Le type criminel. La statistique criminelle. Problèmes de pénalité. Problèmes de criminalité.

   1. Crime and criminals. 2. Criminal anthropology.   3. Punishment.

NT 0038463   NIC MoSU ICJ MH IU

Tarde, Gabriel, 1843–1904.
   La criminalité comparée, par G. Tarde. 2. éd. rev. Paris, F. Alcan, 1890.
   viii, ₍9₎–215 p. 18ᶜᵐ.
   Contents.—Le type criminel.—La statistique de pénalité.—Problèmes de criminalité.

   1. Crime and criminals. 2. Criminal anthropology. 3. Punishment.
                                    ₍Full name: Jean Gabriel Tarde₎
                                                    8—26158
   Library of Congress   HV6036.T18

NT 0038464   DLC MH TxU CtY

Tarde, Gabriel, 1843–1904.
   La criminalité comparée, par G. Tarde ... 3. éd. rev. Paris, F. Alcan, 1894.
   viii, [9]–215 p.   18 cm.

NT 0038465   CtY

TARDE, G₍abriel₎ de, 1843–1904.
   La criminalité comparée. 4me éd. Paris, 1898.
   12°.

NT 0038466   MH-L

Tarde, Gabriel de, 1843–1904.
   La criminalité comparée, par G. Tarde ... 5. éd. Paris, F. Alcan, 1902.
   viii, ₍9₎–215 p. 18½ cm. (On cover: Bibliothèque de philosophie contemporaine)
   Contents.—Le type criminel.—La statistique criminelle.—Problèmes de pénalité.—Problèmes de criminalité.

   1. Crime and criminals. 2. Criminal anthropology. 3. Punishment.
   ɪ. Title.
   HV6036.T2   5—3799

NT 0038467   DLC MsSM FMU ICJ NjP NcD

HV6036 .T2 1907
   Tarde, Gabriel ɪ. ₑ. Jean Gabriel de, 1843–1904.
   La criminalité comparée, par G. Tarde ... 6. éd. Paris, F. Alcan, 1907.
   — viii, ₍9₎–215 p. 18½ cm. (On cover: Bibliothèque de philosophie contemporaine)

   CONTENTS.—Le type criminel.—La statistique criminelle.—Problèmes de pénalité.—Problèmes de criminalité.

   1. Crime and criminals. 2. Criminal anthropology. 3. Punishment. I. Title. II. Ser..

NT 0038468   ViU CU

Tarde, Gabriel, 1843–1924.
   La criminalite comparee. Ed. 7. Paris, Alcan 1910.
   215 p.

NT 0038469   PU

4HV 702
   Tarde, Gabriel 1843–1904.
   La criminalité, comparée. 8. éd. Paris, F. Alcan, 1924.
   215 p.

NT 0038470   DLC-P4 TxU DCU LU RWoU OClW

394.8 T172dTS
   Tarde, Gabriel de, 1843–1904.
   ... El duelo, por G. Tarde. Madrid, La España moderna [n.d.]
   350p.,1l. tables. 16½cm. (Colección de libros escogidos)
   Translation of Le duel, one of the Études pénales et sociales.
   "El delito político" (translation of Le délit politique, another of the Études pénales et sociales) p.₍263₎–350.
   1. Dueling. 2. Political crimes and offenses.

NT 0038471   TxU

Tarde, Gabriel de, 1843–1904.
   ... Essais et mélanges sociologiques, par G. Tarde. Lyon, A. Storck; Paris, G. Masson, 1895.
   2 p. l., 429 p., 1 l. 24½ᶜᵐ. (Bibliothèque de criminologie)
   Contents.—Foules et sectes au point de vue criminel.—Les crimes des foules.—Les crimes de haine.—La sociologie criminelle et le droit pénal.—Pro domo mea. (Réponse à M. Ferri)—Questions sociales.—Les délits impoursuivis.—Histoire des doctrines économiques.—La croyance et le désir.—Monadologie et sociologie.—La variation universelle.—Appendice (Psychologie des foules)
   1. Crime and criminals. 2. Criminal anthropology. 3. Crowds.
                                    ₍Full name: Jean Gabriel de Tarde₎
   Library of Congress   HV6015.T3
                                           F-2776 Revised

NT 0038472   DLC TU MoSU NcD MiU OClW NjP MB

HV 6036 T18E7 1900
   Tarde, Gabriel de, 1843–1904.
   Essais et mélanges sociologiques. Lyon, A. Storck, 1900.
   429 p. 25cm. (Bibliothèque de criminologie)

   Contents.—Foules et sectes au point de vue criminel. Les crimes des foules. Les crimes de haine. La sociologie criminelle et le droit pénal. Pro domo mea. (Réponse à M. Ferri) Questions sociales. Les délits impoursuivis. Histoire des doctrines

économiques. La croyance et le désir. Monadologie et sociologie. La variation universelle. Appendice (Psychologie des foules)

   1. Crime and criminals. 2. Criminal anthropology. 3. Crowds.

NT 0038474   NIC ICJ

Tarde, Gabriel de, 1843–1904.
... Études de psychologie sociale, par G. Tarde ... **Paris,**
V. Giard & E. Brière, 1898.

3 p. l., 326 p., 1 l. 23ᶜᵐ. (Bibliothèque sociologique internationale ...
xiv)

CONTENTS.—La sociologie.—Les deux éléments de la sociologie.—Le
transformisme social.—L'idée de l'"organisme social."—Criminalité et
santé sociale.—La criminalité professionnelle.—La jeunesse criminelle.—
Souvenirs de transports judiciaires.—La graphologie.—Sympathie et syn-
thèse.—La sociologie de M. Giddings.—Crimes, délits, contraventions.

1. Sociology—Addresses, essays, lectures. 2. Social psychology.
3. Crime and criminals.

⟨Full name: Jean Gabriel de Tarde⟩

Library of Congress   HM251.T3   9–20197 Revised

NjP ICJ MH NN

NT   0038475   DLC CaBVaU NIC MB NcD CU OCU OC1W PHC

MICROFILM
F3100

Tarde, Gabriel de, 1843–1904.
Études de psychologie sociale. Paris, V. Giard & E. Brière, 1898.
326 p. (Bibliothèque sociologique internationale. 14)

Microfilm (negative) of copy at Columbia University. N. Y., Columbia University Libraries,
1965. 1 reel.

NT   0038476   NNC

Tarde, Gabriel de, 1843–1904.
... Études pénales et sociales, par G. Tarde. Lyon, A.
Storck; ⟨etc., etc.⟩ 1892.

3 p. l., 460 p. 24½ᶜᵐ. (Bibliothèque de criminologie. ⟨t. vi⟩)
"Ce livre est composé, en majeure partie, de morceaux détachés qui
ont déjà paru dans différentes revues ⟨la Revue philosophique, la Revue
des deux mondes, les Archives de l'anthropologie criminelle, la Revue
scientifique; à des dates plus ou moins récentes."—Avant-propos.
CONTENTS.—Le duel.—Le délit politique.—L'atavisme moral.—L'amour
morbide.—Quatre crimes passionels.—L'archéologie criminelle en Péri-
gord.—La crise du droit moral et la crise de droit pénal.—Études criminelles et pénales.—L'idée de culpabilité.—Les lois de l'imitation.—Dé-
population et civilisation.—Les idées sociologiques de Guyau.—Le suffrage dit universel.
1. Crime and criminals. 2. Criminal anthropology.

⟨Full name: Jean Gabriel de Tarde⟩

Library of Congress   HV6036.T4   12–30279 Revised

NT   0038477   DLC ICJ MH PBm NcD

Microfilm
F4281

Tarde, Gabriel de, 1843–1904.
... Études pénales et sociales, par G. Tarde. Lyon, A.
Storck; ⟨etc., etc.⟩ 1892.

3 p. l., 460 p. 24½ᶜᵐ. (Bibliothèque de criminologie. ⟨t. vi⟩)
"Ce livre est composé, en majeure partie, de morceaux détachés qui
ont déjà paru dans différentes revues ⟨la Revue philosophique, la Revue
des deux mondes, les Archives de l'anthropologie criminelle, la Revue
scientifique; à des dates plus ou moins récentes."—Avant-propos.
CONTENTS.—Le duel.—Le délit politique.—L'atavisme moral.—L'amour
morbide.—Quatre crimes passionels.—L'archéologie criminelle en Péri-
gord.—La crise du droit moral et la crise de droit pénal.—Études criminelles et pénales.—L'idée de culpabilité.—Les lois de l'imitation.—Dé-
population et civilisation.—Les idées sociologiques de Guyau.—Le suffrage dit universel.
1. Crime and criminals. 2. Criminal anthropology.

⟨Full name: Jean Gabriel de Tarde⟩

NT   0038478   NNC

Tarde, Gabriel de, 1843–1904.
Estudios penales y sociales. Madrid, La España Moderna
⟨189–?⟩
308 p. 17 cm. (Colección de libros escogidos)

1. Crime and criminals. 2. Criminal anthropology.

Full name: Jean Gabriel de Tarde.

HV6036.T256   54–47416 ‡

NT   0038479   DLC MH-L

Tarde, Gabriel de, 1843–1904.
Fragment d'histoire future, par G. Tarde ... Lyon ⟨etc.⟩
A. Storck & cie, 1904.

1 p. l., 188 p., 2 l. 19½ cm.

1. Utopias.

⟨Full name: Jean Gabriel de Tarde⟩

A 11–140

Harvard Univ. Librar⟨
for Library of Congress   ⟨a48b1⟩

NT   0038480   MH CU MiU WU PSt NcD

HM
55
T373
1909

Tarde, Gabriel de, 1843–1904.
Gabriel Tarde; introduction et pages
choisies par ses fils. Suivies de poésies inédites de G. Tarde. Préf. de H.
Bergson. Paris, Michaud ⟨1909?⟩
223 p. illus. 19 cm. (Les grands
philosophes)
Bibliography: p. ⟨68⟩–70.

NT   0038481   CaBVaU MiU MH NcD

B
2411
A14
1917

Tarde, Gabriel de, 1843–1904.
Gabriel Tarde : suivies de poésies inédites de G. Tarde /
introduction et pages choisis par ses fils ; préf. de H. Bergson. --
Paris : Louis-Michaud, ⟨1917?⟩.
223 p. : ill. -- (Les grands philosophes français et étrangers)

Bibliography: pp. 68-70.

NT   0038482   CLU

Tarde, Gabriel de, 1843–1904.
Gabriel Tarde; introduction et pages
choisies par ses fils, suivies de poésies
inédite de G. Tarde. Préface de H. Bergson...
Paris, Louis Michaud ⟨1939⟩
223 ⟨1⟩p. illus., ports.   18 1/2cm.
(Les grands philosophes)
"Bibliographie": p. ⟨68⟩–70.

I. Bergson, Henri Louis, 1859–

NT   0038483   NNF DCU–IA

Tarde, Gabriel, 1843–1904.
L'idee de culpabitites.   n.p., n.d. ⟨c1891⟩
28 p.

NT   0038484   PU-L

TARDE, Gabriel, 1843–1904.
L'invention considérée comme moteur de
l'évolution sociale.   Paris, 1902.

pp.12.
"Extrait de la Revue internationale de
sociologie."

NT   0038485   MH

Tarde, Gabriel de, 1843–1904.
The laws of imitation, by Gabriel Tarde ... tr. from the
2d French ed., by Elsie Clews Parsons ... with an introduction by Franklin H. Giddings ... New York, H. Holt and
company, 1903.

xxix, 404 p. 22½ᶜᵐ.

1. Imitation. 2. Sociology.   I. Parsons, Mrs. Elsie Worthington
(Clews) 1875–   tr. II. Title.
⟨Full name: Jean Gabriel de Tarde⟩

Library of Congress   HM55.T3   3–24233 Revised

——— Copy 2.

Copyright A 67725

⟨r29j2⟩

NN PP TU WaWW CaBVaU WaTU NcD
OU OO OCU OOxM MiU ViU OC1W OCl ODW PPT PHC ICJ NjP
NT   0038486   DLC KMK MtU OrP Or WaE TxU GAuA NIC DHEW

Tarde, Gabriel *i. e.* **Jean Gabriel de,** 1843–1904.
La logique sociale, par G. Tarde.   Paris, F. Alcan, 1895.

xiv p., 1 l., 464 p. 22½ᶜᵐ.

CONTENTS.—1. ptie. Principes.—2. ptie. Applications.

1. Sociology.   I. Title.

16–12036

Library of Congress   HM55.T34

NT   0038487   DLC OrCS PU PSt CU TxU NIC CtY MiU NjP MB

Tarde, Gabriel *i. e.* **Jean Gabriel de,** 1843–1904.
La logique sociale, par G. Tarde.   2. éd., rev. et augm.
Paris, F. Alcan, 1898.

xvi p., 1 l., 466 p. 22ᶜᵐ.

1. Sociology.   I. Title.

17–17910

Library of Congress   HM55.T34 1898

NT   0038488   DLC CtY PBm NcD TxU ICJ

Tarde, Gabriel.
La logique sociale; 3ᵉ édition, revue et
augmentée.   Paris, 1904.
16,466p.

NT   0038489   ICRL OC1W OCU OO ViU WaU

HM55
T22
1913

Tarde, Gabriel de, 1843–1904.
La logique sociale, par G. Tarde.   4. éd.   Paris,
F. Alcan, 1913.

xvi p., 1 l., 466 p. 22ᶜᵐ.

NT   0038490   CU

Tarde, Gabriel *i. e.* **Jean Gabriel de,** 1843–1904.
Les lois de l'imitation; étude sociologique, par G.
Tarde. Paris, F. Alcan, 1890.

viii, 431, ⟨1⟩ p. 22½ᶜᵐ.

1. Imitation. 2. Sociology.

15–8402

Library of Congress   HM55.T24 1890

NT   0038491   DLC NIC IU PU NjP MH

Tarde, Gabriel *i. e.* **Jean Gabriel de,** 1843–1904.
Les lois de l'imitation; étude sociologique, par G. Tarde.
2. éd., rev. et augm.   Paris, F. Alcan, 1895.

xxiv, 428 p. 22ᶜᵐ.

1. Imitation. 2. Sociology.

8—29054

Library of Congress   HM55.T24

ICJ
NT   0038492   DLC NjR CU NcU ViU PU CtY TxU MiU ODW

Tarde, Gabriel de, 1843–1904.
Les lois de l'imitation, étude sociologique par G. Tarde.
3. éd., rev. et augm.   Paris, F. Alcan, 1900.

xxiv, 428 p. 23ᶜᵐ.

1. Imitation. 2. Sociology.

⟨Full name: Jean Gabriel de Tarde⟩

Library of Congress   HM55.T24 1900   4–1413 Revised

NT   0038493   DLC MH ViU TxU PBm OC1W

Tarde, Gabriel, 1843–1904.
Les lois de l'imitation; étude sociologique. 4.éd.,
revue et augmentée.   Paris, Alcan, 1904.

xxiv, 428 p. (Bibliothèque de philosophie contemporaine)

NT   0038494   MH-Lm

Tarde, Gabriel de, 1843-1904.
　　Les lois de l'imitation; étude sociologique par
G. Tarde. 5. éd.   Paris, F. Alcan, 1907.
　　xxiv, 428 p.
　　Microfilm (positive) New York, Columbia
University Libraries, 1972. 1 reel.
　　Master negative 0163.

NT   0038495   NNC

HM55
T24
1911
Tarde, Gabriel de, 1843-1904.
　　Les lois de l'imitation, étude sociologique par G. Tarde.
6. éd.   **Paris, F. Alcan, 1911.**
　　xxiv, 428 p. 23ᶜᵐ.

NT   0038496   CU

Tarde, Gabriel, 1843-1904.
　　Les lois de l'imitation; étude sociologique,
par G. Tarde ... 7. éd.   Paris, Alcan, 1921.
　　xxiv, 428 p.   23 cm.   (On cover: Bibliothèque
de philosophie contemporaine)

NT   0038497   NNR CaBVaU TU PPT

301
T17Lo
Tarde, Gabriel de, 1843-1904.
　　Les lois sociales; esquisse d'une socio-
logie.   Paris, F. Alcan, 1898.
　　172 p. 19 cm.

　　1. Sociology. I. Title.

NT   0038498   LU RPB MB MH-L MH TU InU TxU MsSM

301
T172toi
1899
Tarde, Gabriel de, 1843-1904.
　　Les lois sociales; esquisse d'une sociologie, par G. Tarde. 2. éd.   Paris, F.
Alcan, 1899.
　　165 p.,1l. 18½cm.   (On cover: Bibliothèque
de philosophie contemporaine)

　　1. Sociology. I. Title. II. Series.

NT   0038499   TxU ICJ NjP PBm PLatS

HM201
T39
1902
Tarde, Gabriel, 1843-1904.
　　Les lois sociales; esquisse d'une sociologie. 3. éd.
Paris, F. Alcan, 1902.
　　165 p.

　　1. Sociology.

NT   0038500   CU MoSU

HM201
.T39
1905
Tarde, Gabriel, 1843-1904.
　　Les lois sociales; esquisse d'une sociologie. 4. ed.   Paris, F. Alcan, 1905.
　　165 p.

　　1. Sociology. I. T.

NT   0038501   NBuU

Tarde, Gabriel, 1843-1904.
　　Les lois sociales; esquisse d'une sociologie
... 6. éd.   Paris, F.Alcan, 1910.
　　165, [1] p.

NT   0038502   MH-BA IU

HM
201
.T18
1921
Tarde, Gabriel de, 1843-1904.
　　Les lois sociales; esquisse d'une sociologie.
8. éd. Paris, F. Alcan, 1921.
　　165 p. 19 cm.

　　1. Sociology. I. Title.

NT   0038503   DCU

Tarde, Gabriel de, 1843-1904.
　　... Összehasonlitó tanulmányok a krimino-
lógia köréből. Paul Cuche előszavával.
Forditotta s a bevezetést irta Dʳ Lengyel
Aurél. Budapest, Athenaeum irodalmi és
nyomdai részvénytársulat, 1908.
　　186 p. 22½cm.   (A Magyar jogászegylet
könyvkiadó vállalata. I. évfolyam. 3. köt.)

　　At head of title: ... Tarde.
　　Bibliographical footnotes

NT   0038504   MH-L

HM
221
T3165
Tarde, Gabriel de, 1843-1904.
　　Opinia i tłum / G. Tarde ; Przekład
Kazimiery Skrzyńskiej. Warszawa :
Gebethner i Wolff, 1904.
　　155 p. ; 18 cm.   (Biblioteka
Tygodnika illustrowanego ; nr. 9)
　　Translation of L'opinion et la foule.

　　1. Crowds. 2. Public opinion.
3. Social psychology. I. Title

NT   0038505   NBuC IEdS MB NN

Tarde, Gabriel de, 1843-1904.
　　L'opinion et la foule; par G. Tarde ... Paris, F. Alcan,
1901.
　　vii, 226 p., 1 l. 22½ᶜᵐ.   (On cover: Bibliothèque de philosophie contemporaine)
　　CONTENTS.—Avant-propos.—I. Le public et la foule.—II. L'opinion et
la conversation.—III. Les foules et les sectes criminelles.

　　1. Crowds. 2. Public opinion. 3. Social psychology.   I. Title.
　　　　　　　　　　　　　　　　　　　　　　 [Full name: Jean Gabriel de Tarde]
　　　　　　　　　　　　　　　　　　　　　　　　 2-24518 Revised 2
Library of Congress   HM281.T3

NT   0038506   DLC CaBVaU NBuU NIC NcD MiU ICJ NjP NBC

TARDE, GABRIEL DE, 1843-1904.
　　L'opinion et la foule.   Paris, F. Alcan, 1901.
　　vii, 226 p. 22cm.   (Bibliothèque de philosophie contemporaine)

　　Microfilm.

　　1. Crowds--Psychology.   2. Public opinion.
3. Psychology, Social.

NT   0038507   NN

Tarde, Gabriel de, 1843-1904.
　　L'opinion et la foule; par G. Tarde ... *Paris, F. Alcan,
1904.
　　vii, 226 p., 1 l. 22½ᶜᵐ.   (On cover: Bibliothèque de philosophie contemporaine)
　　CONTENTS.—Avant-propos.—I. Le public et la foule.—II. L'opinion et
la conversation.—III. Les foules et les sectes criminelles.
　　*2. éd.

NT   0038508   ViU MsSM TxU

Tarde, Gabriel, 1843-
　　L'opinion et la foule. Paris, F. Alcan, 1910,
226p.

NT   0038509   ICRL CU

Tarde, Gabriel, 1843-1904.
　　L'opinion et la foule. 3e éd.   Paris, F. Alcan,
1910.
　　226 p.   (Bibliothèque de philosophie contemporaine)

NT   0038510   MH OU OCU

Tarde, Gabriel de, 1843-1904.
　　L'opinion et la foule; par G. Tarde ... 4. éd.
Paris, F. Alcan, 1922.
　　vii, 226 p., 1 l. 22½ᶜᵐ. (On cover: Bibliothèque
de philosophie contemporaine)
　　Contents.—Avant-propos.—I. Le public et la foule.
—L'opinion et la conversation.—III. Les foules et
les sectes criminelles.

　　1. Crowds. 2. Public opinion. 3. Social psychology.
Title.   Full name: Jean Gabriel de

NT   0038511   ViU DCU TxU MH WaU NNC OO

Tarde, Gabriel de, 1843-1904.
　　L'opposition universelle; essai d'une théorie des contraires,
par G. Tarde.   Paris, F. Alcan, 1897.
　　viii, 451 p. 22½ᶜᵐ. (On cover: Bibliothèque de philosophie contemporaine)

　　1. Opposition, Theory of.   I. Title.
　　　　　　　　　　　　　　　　　　　　　　 34-7197
Library of Congress   B2411.O6   194.9

　　　　 MB ViU OO ICRL PSt PBm PU
NT   0038512   DLC OrU NIC TxU CU NcD MiU OCU DHEW MH

Tarde, Gabriel de, 1843-1904.
　　... Penal philosophy, by Gabriel Tarde ... tr. by Rapelje
Howell ... with an editorial preface by Edward Lindsey ...
and an introduction by Robert H. Gault ... Boston, Little,
Brown, and company, 1912.
　　xxxii, 581 p. 23½ᶜᵐ. (The Modern criminal science series published
under the auspices of the American institute of criminal law and crimi-
nology)
　　Translated from the 4th French edition.
　　1. Crime and criminals. 2. Punishment. 3. Criminal anthropology.
I. Howell, Rapelje, 1878-   tr. II. Title.
　　　　　　　　　　　　　　　　　 [Full name: Jean Gabriel de Tarde]
　　　　　　　　　　　　　　　　　　　　　　 12-27951
Library of Congress   HV6036.T33

　　　 CoU CU-AL OC1W IdPI WaTU NcD MHU
　　 NN PU PSC PBm GU FMU NBuU-L MsSM ICRL NIC GU-L DAU
　　 OrPR TU ODW OO OU OCU OC1W OOxM MiU OC1 ViU-L ICJ
NT   0038513   DLC MtU OrP IdU WaU-L OrCS Or CaBVaU CU

Tarde, Gabriel de, 1843-1904.
　　... La philosophie pénale, par G. Tarde. Lyon, A. Storck;
Paris, G. Masson, 1890.
　　4 p. l., 566 p. 24½ᶜᵐ. (Bibliothèque de criminologie)

　　1. Crime and criminals. 2. Criminal anthropology. 3. Criminal law.
　　　　　　　　　　　　　　　　　　　 [Full name: Jean Gabriel de Tarde]
　　　　　　　　　　　　　　　　　　　　　　 43-33905
Library of Congress   HV6036.T29   1890

NT   0038515   DLC MH PU-L TxU DNLM

4HV
440
Tarde, Gabriel de, 1843-1904
　　La philosophie pénale. 2. éd. rev.
et corrigée. Lyon, A. Storck, 1891.
　　578 p.

　　(Bibliothèque de criminologie)

NT   0038516   DLC-P4 NjP MH PBm NcU MiU

HV
6036
T17p
1892

Tarde, Gabriel de, 1843–1904.
La philosophie pénale / par G. Tarde.
-- 3. éd., rev. et corr. -- Lyon : A. Storck,
1892.
578 p. -- (Bibliothèque de criminologie)

1. Crime and criminals. 2. Punishment.
3. Criminal anthropology. I. Title.

NT   0038517   CLU PU

Tarde, Gabriel de, 1843–1904.
La philosophie pénale. 4e édition. Lyon,
Storck, 1895.
(7) 578 p.   8°.   [Bibliothèque de criminologie]

NT   0038518   MB

Tarde, Gabriel de, 1843–1904.
... La philosophie pénale, par G. Tarde ... 5 éd. (rev. et
cor.) Lyon, A. Storck & cⁱᵉ; ⎣etc., etc.⎦ 1900.
4 p. l., 578 p. 23¼ᶜᵐ. (Bibliothèque de criminologie)

1. Crime and criminals. 2. Criminal anthropology. 3. Criminal law.
I. Title.
⎣Full name: Jean Gabriel de Tarde⎦
12–33763 rev.

Library of Congress   HV6036.T3

NT   0038519   DLC MH

Tarde, Gabriel de, 1843–1904.
... La philosophie pénale, par G. Tarde ... 4. éd. (rev. et
cor.) Lyon, A. Storck & cⁱᵉ, 1903.
3 p. l., 578 p. 24ᶜᵐ. (Bibliothèque de criminologie)

1. Crime and criminals. 2. Criminal anthropology. 3. Criminal law.
I. Title.
⎣Full name: Jean Gabriel de Tarde⎦
38–21788

NT   0038520   DLC

Tarde (Gabriel) [1843–1904]. Positivisme et
pénalité. 22 pp. 8°. Lyon, A. Storck. 1887.

NT   0038521   DNLM

Tarde, Gabriel de, 1843–1904.
Преступникъ и преступление. Переводъ Е. В. Выстав-
киной, подъ ред. М. Н. Гернета и съ предисл. Н. Н. Полян-
скаго. Москва, Тип. Т-ва И. Д. Сытина, 1906.
xx, 324 p. 20 cm. (Библиотека для самообразования, 29)
L. C. copy imperfect: p. ⎣i⎦–ii wanting.
Translation of 2 chapters from the author's La philosophie pénale.

1. Crime and criminals. 2. Criminal anthropology. 3. Criminal law.
I. Title. (Series: Biblioteka dlia samoobrazovaniîa, 29)
Title transliterated: Prestupnik i prestuplenie.
Full name: Jean Gabriel de Tarde.

H V6036 T298   53–55901

NT   0038522   DLC

Tarde, Gabriel de, 1843–1904.
Преступленія толпы. Переводъ И. Ѳ. Іорданскаго, подъ
ред. А. И. Смирнова. Казань, Типо-лит. Имп. Университета, 1893.
44 p. 24 cm.

1. Lynch law. I. Title. Title transliterated: Prestuplenîìa tolpy.
Full name: Jean Gabriel de Tarde.

H V6455 T38   55–54298

NT   0038523   DLC DNLM

Tarde, Gabriel de, 1843–1904.
(Proiskhozhdenie sem'i i sobstvennosti)
Происхожденіе семьи и собственности, съ прибавле-
ніемъ очерка Л. Е. Оболенскаго: О происхожденіи
семьи и собственности по теоріи эволюціонистовъ и
экономическихъ матеріалистовъ. С.-Петербургъ, Изд.
В. И. Губинскаго ⎣1897⎦
147 p. 21 cm.
At head of title: Г. Тард.
Includes bibliographical references.
1. Family. I. Obolenskiĭ, Leonid Egorovich, 1845–1906. O prois-
khozhdenii sem'i i sobstvennosti po teorii ėvoliûtsionistov i ėkono-
micheskikh materialistov. II. Title.

HQ503.T3718   74–201776

NT   0038524   DLC

Tarde, Gabriel de, 1843–1904.
Psychologie économique, par G. Tarde ... Paris, F. Alcan,
1902.
2 v. 22½ᶜᵐ. ⎣Bibliothèque de philosophie contemporaine⎦
Contents.—t. 1. Partie préliminaire. livre 1. La répétition économique.—t. 2. livre 2. L'opposition économique. livre 3. L'adaptation économique.

1. Economics. I. Title.
⎣Full name: Jean Gabriel de Tarde⎦
2–14161 Revised

Library of Congress   HB173.T18

NT   0038525   DLC CSt CU FMU WaU TxU CLU NcD MiU OClW   ViU PBm ICJ MB NjP NN

Tarde, Gabriel de, 1843–1904.
La psychologie intermentale. Paris, Giard,
1901. 15 p.

NT   0038526   OClW

Tarde, Gabriel de, 1843–1904.
Social laws; an outline of sociology by G. Tarde. Translated
from the French by Howard C. Warren ... with a preface by
James Mark Baldwin. New York, The Macmillan company;
London, Macmillan & co., ltd., 1899.
xi, 213 p. 17½ᶜᵐ.

1. Sociology. I. Warren, Howard Crosby, 1867–1934, tr. II. Title.
⎣Full name: Jean Gabriel de Tarde⎦
99—4329

Library of Congress   HM201.T4

NT   0038527   DLC GAuA NBuU KU TxU MiU KEmT CU DL MH   MiU NcD PSC PSt WaE OrSaW WaSpG MCE WaTU NN ViU WaU NN OU MdBP OOxM ICJ OCl NjP Nh OO OCU

HM
201
.T4

Tarde, Gabriel de, 1843–1904.
Social laws, an outline of sociology
by G. Tarde. Translated from the
French by Howard C. Warren ... with a
preface by James Mark Baldwin. New
York, The Macmillan company; London,
Macmillan & co., ltd., 1899.
xi, 213 p. 17 1/2 cm.

Photocopy. Ann Arbor, Mich., University Microfilms, 1968.

#Sociology.
(A)Warren, Howard Crosby, 1867–1964,
tr.
(A)Social laws.

NT   0038529   MoU NBuC

Tarde, Gabriel i. e. Jean Gabriel de, 1843–1904.
Social laws; an outline of sociology by G. Tarde.
Tr. from the French by Howard C. Warren ...
with a preface by James Mark Baldwin. New York,
The Macmillan company; ⎣etc., etc.⎦ 1907.
xi, 213 p. 17.5 cm.

NT   0038530   CU PHC PP

Tarde, Gabriel de, 1843–1904.
Las transformaciones del derecho. Traducción, prólogo
y 120 notas, por Adolfo Posada. Madrid, España Moderna
⎣1893?⎦
325 p. 23 cm. (Biblioteca de jurisprudencia, filosofía é historia)

1. Law—Hist. & crit. 2. Jurisprudence—Hist. I. Posada, Adolfo,
1860–1944, ed. and tr. II. Title.
Full name: Jean Gabriel de Tarde.
60–57419

NT   0038531   DLC CtY TxU

Tarde, Gabriel de, 1843–1904.
Las transformaciones del derecho, traducción prólogo y
notas de Adolfo Posada. Buenos Aires, Editorial Atalaya
⎣1947⎦
211 p. 24 cm.

1. Law—Hist. & crit. 2. Jurisprudence—Hist. I. Posada, Adolfo,
1860–1944, ed. and tr. II. Title.
Full name: Jean Gabriel de Tarde.
48–15593

NT   0038532   DLC

4K
1916

Tarde, Gabriel de, 1843–1904.
Les transformations du droit;
étude sociologique. Paris, F. Alcan,
1893.
212 p.

NT   0038533   DLC-P4 NNC

Tarde, Gabriel, 1843–1904.
Les transformations du droit. Etude sociologique.
2e édition. Paris, Alcan, 1894.
(3), viii, 208 p. [Bibliothèque de philosophie
contemporaine.] 12⁷
Contents. – Droit criminel. – Procédure. –
Régime des personnes. – Régime des biens. –
Obligations. – Le droit naturel. – Le droit et la
sociologie.

NT   0038534   MB CtY

Tarde, Gabriel i.e. Jean Gabriel de, 1843–1904.   340.1 Q303
Les transformations du droit. Étude sociologique, par G. Tarde
... . Quatrième édition revue. Paris, F. Alcan, 1903.
[4], viii, 208 p. 19ᶜᵐ. (On cover: Bibliothèque de philosophie contemporaine.)

NT   0038535   ICJ

K
.T173t
1906

Tarde, Gabriel de, 1843–1904
Les transformations du droit; étude sociologique par G. Tarde. 5. ed. rev. Paris, F.
Alcon, 1906.
viii,208p. 19cm. (Bibliothèque de philosophie
contemporaine)

Includes bibliographical references.

1. Law - History and criticism. 2. Jurisprudence - History. I. Title.

NT   0038536   PSt ViU MoSU

TARDE, Gabriel, 1843–1904.
Les transformations du droit; étude sociologique. 6e éd., revue. Paris, 1909.
208 p.
(Bibliothèque de philosophie contemporaine).

NT   0038537   MH ICRL CU OCU

Tarde, Gabriel de, 1843–1904.
Les transformation du droit; etude
sociologique. 7. ed. Paris, Alcan, 1912.
208 p.

NT 0038538   OOxM

Tarde, Gabriel de, 1843–1904.
Les transformations du droit; étude sociologique par G.
Tarde... 8. éd. Paris, F. Alcan, 1922.
2 p. l., viii, 208 p. 18½ᶜᵐ.

1. Law—Hist. & crit. 2. Jurisprudence—Hist.   I. Title.
⟨Full name: Jean Gabriel de Tarde⟩
32–14520 Revised

NT 0038539   DLC IU NIC CtY NcD

Tarde, Gabriel de, 1843–1904.
Les transformations du pouvoir par G. Tarde. Paris, F.
Alcan, 1899.
x, 266 p. 22ᶜᵐ. (Half-title: Bibliothèque générale des sciences sociales)
"Ce livre n'est en grande partie que la substance de deux séries de
conférences qui ont été faites en 1896, à l'Ecole libre des sciences politiques, et, en 1898, au Collège libre des sciences sociales."—Avant-propos.

1. Political science.   I. Title.
⟨Full name: Jean Gabriel de Tarde⟩
Library of Congress   JC336.T2
1–21084 Revised 2

NT 0038540   DLC NIC PU NcD CU TxU MB OOxM MiU

Tarde, Gabriel de, 1843–1904.
Les transformations du pouvoir ...   Paris F.
Alcan, 1909.
266 p.
2 ed.

NT 0038541   OC1W OU

Tarde, Gabriel i. e. **Jean Gabriel de, 1843–1904.**
Underground man, by Gabriel Tarde ... Tr. by Cloudesley Brereton, M. A., L. ès L. With a preface by H. G.
Wells. London, Duckworth & co., 1905.
vii, 198 p. 19½ᶜᵐ.
CONTENTS.—Dedication.—Preface. By H. G. Wells.—Introductory.—
Prosperity.—The catastrophe.—The struggle.—Saved !—Regeneration.—
Love.—The æsthetic life.—Note on Tarde. By Joseph Manchon.

I. Brereton, Cloudesley, tr.   II. Wells, Herbert George, 1866–
6–2286

NT 0038542   DLC TxU NcD NcU OTU CtY ICJ

Tarde, Gabriel de, 1843–1904.
Законы подражанія. (Les lois de l'imitation). Ж. Тарда.
Переводъ съ французскаго ... С.-Петербургъ, Изданіе Ф.
Павленкова, 1892.
2 p. l., iv, 370 p. 19½ᶜᵐ.
Bibliographical foot-notes.

1. Imitation. 2. Sociology.   Title transliterated: Zakony po-
drazhanīīa.
⟨Full name: Jean Gabriel de Tarde⟩
Library of Congress   HM55.T32
43–43498

NT 0038543   DLC

Tarde, Jean, 1561/62–1636.
Les astres de Borbon, et apologie pour le
soleil, montrant & verifiant que les apparences
dans la face du soleil sont des planettes,...
Paris, 1627.
diagr. 8°

NT 0038544   NN

Tarde, Jean. 1561–1636.
Les Astres de Bourbon, et apologie pour le
soleil, montrant et verifiant que les apparences
dans la face du Soleil sont des planettes et non
des taches, trad. du Latin. Paris, 1727.
4°

NT 0038545   NN

Tarde, Jean. 1561/62–1636.
Borbonia sidera, id est, Planetæ qvi solis limina circvmvolitant motv proprio ac regulari, falsò hactenus ab helioscopis maculæ
solis nuncupati. Ex nouis obseruationibus Ioannis Tarde...
Parisiis: Apud Ioannem Gesselin, 1620.   87 p.   diagrs.   23cm.
Title vignette.

—— —— ⟨Another issue⟩   1621.   24cm.

1. Planets—Theory.   I. Title.   *Revised*
N. Y. P. L.   *May 8, 1935*

NT 0038546   NN CtY-M

Tarde, Jean, 1561/62–1636.
Les chroniques de Jean Tarde ... contenant l'histoire
religieuse et politique de la ville et du diocèse de Sarlat,
depuis les origines jusqu'aux premières années du XVIIᵉ
siècle, annotées par le Vte Gaston de Gérard ..., précédées
d'une introduction par M. Gabriel Tarde ... Paris, H.
Oudin, A. Picard, 1887.
xliv, ⟨3⟩, liii, 432 p.   fold. map.   29 cm.

NT 0038547   NjP DLC

TARDE, Jean. 1561/62–1636.
Les usages du quadrant a l'esguille aymantee.
Divisé en deux livres. Le premier donne la
cognoissance du quadrant. Le second, les usages,
utilitez & services qui en peuvent estre tirez..
A. Paris, chez Jean Gesselin, 1621.

23 cm.   Diagrs. and other illustr.

NT 0038548   MH

Tarde, Jean. 1561/62–1636.
Les usages du Quadrant a l'esguille
anymantee. Paris, 1627.
4to.

NT 0038549   NN

Tarde, Jean. 1561–1636.
Les vsages dv qvadrant a l'esgville aymantee, divise' en
devx livres. Le premier donne la cognoissance du quadrant.
Le second, les vsages, vtilitez & seruices qui en peuuent
estre tirez; comme de mesurer toutes distances, hauteurs &
profondeurs; prendre & rapporter au petit pied toutes
sortes de plans; faire la carte & description d'vn pays;
& toutes les autres operations de la boussole. Paris,
Chez Iean Gesselin, 1638.
5p. l., 118p. illus.

NT 0038550   NNE

Tarde, Jean Gabriel de
see
Tarde, Gabriel de, 1843–1904.

693.5   **Tarde, Maurice.**
T17r   La résistance des bétons en fonction de
leur dosage ...   Paris, 1932.
160p. illus., diagrs. (1 fold.)

NT 0038552   IU

He77   Una tarde en Ocaña; ó, El reservado por
O27   fuerza, juguete cómico en tres actos
12   arreglado al teatro español. [Madrid, 1851]
14p.   27cm.   (Biblioteca dramatica)
Binder's title: Teatro español. 3.ser.,
v.12.
Caption title.

NT 0038553   CtY

La tarde y siguientes hasta concluir.
Primeros egericios literarios
see under title

Tardebigge, Eng. (Parish)
Psalms and hymns, for the use of the parish
church of Tardebigge
see under title

Tardel, Hermann, 1869–
"Der arme Heinrich" in der neueren dichtung. Von
dr. Hermann Tardel. Berlin, A. Duncker, 1905.
3 p. l., 69 p. 23½ᶜᵐ. (Added t.-p.: Forschungen zur neueren literaturgeschichte. Hrsg. von dr. F. Muncker ... ⟨bd.⟩ xxx)
CONTENTS.—Einleitung.—I. Hartmann von Aue. Illustrationen von Jos.
v. Führich. Uhland (Fragmente). Übersetzungen: Simrock, Chamisso,
Fr. Koch, Hans v. Wolzogen, G. Bornhak, Th. Ebner, Aug. Hagedorn.—
II. Epen: Longfellow ("The golden legend"), Dante Gabriel Rossetti.—
III. Dramen: Josef Weilen, Anonyma (1861), Betty Fischer, Hans Pöhnl,
Carl Schultes, Hermann Hanau, Käthe Becher.—IV. Novelle: (Xav. de
Maistre; Wilh. Raabe), Ricarda Huch; Musik-drama: Hans Pfitzner.—
V. Gerhart Hauptmann (Anm. Ernst Hammer.)—VI. Arthur Fitger ("San
Marcos tochter").—Schluss.
1. Hartmann, von Aue, 12th cent.   Der arme Heinrich.
Library of Congress   PN35.F7 vol. 30
5–40075

NjP NN
NT 0038556   DLC CU LU IaU OU CU KyU PU PBm NcU MiU

Tardel, Hermann, 1869–
Bremen im sprichwort, von Hermann Tardel. Bremen,
G. Winter, 1929.
68 p. 23½ᶜᵐ. (On cover: Bremische weihnachtsblätter, hrsg. von
der Historischen gesellschaft des Künstlervereins zu Bremen, hft. 2)
Bibliography included in "Anmerkungen" (p. 55–63)

1. Proverbs, German.   I. Title.
⟨Full name: Hermann August Heinrich Tardel⟩
35–33017
Library of Congress   PN6465.B7T3   398.90943520

NT 0038557   DLC OC1 OrU

Tardel, Hermann, 1869–
Bremen im Sprichwort, Reim und Volkslied. ⟨Bremen⟩
Bremer Schlüssel Verlag, 1947.
120 p. 21 cm.
"Der erste Teil dieser Arbeit 'Bremen im Sprichwort' erschien
zuerst in den Bremischen Weihnachtsblättern ... Heft 2 im Jahre
1929, der zweite Teil 'Bremen im Volksreim und Volkslied' in der
Niederdeutschen Zeitschrift für Volkskunde Jahrg. ix. 1931, S. 26–67.
Beide eng zusammenhängende Abschnitte konnten hier mit Erweiterungen als Stück einer bremischen Volkskunde vereinigt werden."
Bibliography included in "Anmerkungen" (p. 109–120)
1. Bremen in literature. 2. Proverbs, German.   I. Title.
Full name: Hermann August Heinrich Tardel.
PT149.G4B77   398   49–54957*

NT 0038558   DLC CSt MH OC1 NN

Tardel, Hermann, 1869–
Der Bremer Schlüssel, zur Geschichte des Wahrzeichens.
⟨Bremen⟩ Bremer Schlüssel Verlag, 1946.
40 p. (p. 32–40 advertisements) illus. 21 cm. (Bremer Schlüssel-Bibliothek, ⟨Bd. 1⟩)
Bibliographical references included in "Anmerkungen" (p. 30)

1. Heraldry—Germany—Bremen. 2. Emblems. 3. Devices.
I. Title.
Full name: Hermann August Heinrich Tardel.
CR554.B7T3   A F 48–3588*
Wisconsin. Univ. Libr.
for Library of Congress   ⟨2⟩†

NT 0038559   WU DLC

Tardel, Hermann, 1869–
Der Bremer Schlüssel, zur Geschichte des Wahrzeichens. ₁Bremen₎ Bremer Schlüssel Verlag, 1946.
40 p. (p. 82–40 advertisements) illus. 21 cm. (Bremer Schlüssel-Bibliothek, ₁Bd. 1₎)
Film reproduction. Negative.
Bibliographical references included in "Anmerkungen" (p. 30)

. Heraldry--Germany--Bremen. 2. Emblems, German. 3. Devices.
Bremer Schlüssel-   Bibliothek.

NT 0038560   NN

834H293
DO
Tardel, Hermann, 1869–
Gerhart Hauptmanns "Schluck und Jau" und verwandtes, von Hermann Tardel ...

(In Studien zur vergleichenden litteraturgeschichte ... 2. bd., heft II. Berlin, Duncker, 1902. ₁184,–202 p.)
Bound with Ohmann, Fritz. Das tragische in Gerhart Hauptmanns dramen. ₁1908₎

1. Hauptmann, Gerhart, 1862–
Schluck und   Jau

NT 0038561   NNC

Tardel, Hermann, 1869–
Goethes beziehungen zu bremischen zeitgenossen, von Hermann Tardel. ₁Bremen₎ A. Geist, 1935.
24 p. 23½ᶜᵐ. (On cover: Bremische weihnachtsblätter ... hft. 5)
With special reference to Georg von Gröning, Amalie (Kotzebue) Gildemeister and Johann Carl Friedrich Gildemeister.
"Die folgenden abschnitte sind stücke einer grösseren arbeit über 'Goethe und Bremen'."—p. 3.
Bibliographical foot-notes.

1. Goethe, Johann Wolfgang von--Contemporaries.   I. Title.
₁Full name: Hermann August Heinrich Tardel₎
41–32710

Library of Congress   PT2068.T3
832.62

NT 0038562   DLC CtY

Tardel, Hermann, 1869–
Handschriftliche Nachträge zu Heinrich Smidts bremischen Kinderliedern (1836), von Hermann Tardel. (In: Volkskundliche Gaben; John Meier zum siebzigsten Geburtstage dargebracht. Berlin, 1934. 28cm. p. 269–279.)

739960A. 1. Smidt, Heinrich, 1768–   1867: Kinder- und Ammen-Reime.
N. Y. P. L.   January 11, 1935

NT 0038563   NN

Tardel, Hermann, 1869–   ed.
Niederdeutsche volkslieder aus Schleswig-Holstein und den Hansestädten. Herausgegeben mit unterstützung des Deutschen volksliedarchivs, von Hermann Tardel. Bilder von Ingwer Paulsen. Münster i. W., Aschendorff, 1928.
94 p. illus. 17½ᶜᵐ. ₁Landschaftliche volkslieder ... 10. hft.₎
"Musikalische sätze von Hans Dagobert Bruger."

1. Folk-songs, German--Schleswig-Holstein. 2. Folk-songs, Low German.   I. Title.
₁Full name: Hermann August Heinrich Tardel₎
A C 36–4886

Title from Univ. of Chi-   cago PT1205.A1L3   no. 10
Library of Congress   ₁M1736.L2 hft. 10₎
₁2₎   (784.4943)

NT 0038564   ICU IU OCl NN MH

Tardel, Hermann, 1869–   ed.
Niederdeutsche zeitschrift für volkskunde ...
Bremen, C. Schünemann ₁192

Tardel, Hermann, 1869–
... Patriotische lyrik von Friedrich dem grossen bis Wilhelm II.   [Leipzig, B. G. Teubner, 1915]
p. [57]–64.   24 cm.

NT 0038566   OrU

PT 1834
.Z5 T2
TARDEL, HERMANN, 1869–
Quellen zu Chamissos Gedichten.   Graudens, 1896.
22 p.

"Wissenschaftliche Beilage zum Programm der städtischen Realschule in Graudens."

1. Chamisso, Adelbert von, 1781–1838.

NT 0038567   InU NjP NIC MiU

Tardel, Hermann, 1869–
Die sage von Robert dem Teufel in neueren deutschen dichtungen und in Meyerbeers oper. Von dr. Hermann Tardel. Berlin, A. Duncker, 1900.
3 p. l., 82 p. 23ᶜᵐ. (Forschungen zur neueren litteraturgeschichte ... ₁bd.₎ XIV)

1. Robert le Diable. 2. Meyerbeer, Giacomo, 1791–1864. Robert le Diable. 3. German literature--19th cent.--Hist. & crit.

Library of Congress   PN35.F7   vol. 14
G–2823

NjP
NT 0038568   DLC PBm PU CU PSt MoU OU NcD MiU OCH MB

Tardel, Hermann, 1869–
Studien zur bremischen Theatergeschichte. Oldenburg, G. Stalling, 1945.
173 p. illus. 24 cm. (Schriften der Wittheit zu Bremen, Reihe D: Abhandlungen und Vorträge, Bd. 16, Heft 2)
Includes bibliographies.

1. Bremen. Staatstheater. 2. Theater--Bremen--Hist. 3. Wagner, Richard, 1813–1883.
Full name: Hermann August Heinrich Tardel.

PN2656.B64T3   57–35383 ‡

NT 0038569   DLC MH CtY CU

Hct
x194t
Tardel, Hermann, 1869–
Studien zur Lyrik Chamissos. Bremen, 1902.
64p. 22cm.
"Beilage zum Programm der Handelsschule (Oberrealschule) zu Bremen, Ostern 1902."

1. Chamisso, Adelbert von, 1781–1838.

NT 0038570   CtY CU InU

Microfilm
R 1959 Tardel, Hermann, 1869.

Untersuchungen zur mittelhochdeutschen Spielmannspoesie. Schwerin, 1894.

72 p.

Inaug.-Diss. - Schwerin.
Includes bibliography.
Microfilm copy (negative)

NT 0038571   CaBVaU TxU

TARDEL, Hermann, 1869–
Untersuchungen zur mittlehochdeutschen spielmannspoesie. 1. Zum Orendel. 2. Zum Salman-Morolf. Inaug.-diss., Rostock. Schwein i.M., 1894.

pp. 72.

NT 0038572   MH

PT2355
.H5A17
1909
Herwegh, Georg, 1817–1875.
Herweghs Werke in drei Teilen, hrsg. mit Einleitungen und Anmerkungen versehen von Hermann Tardel. Berlin, Bong & Co. ₁1909₎

PN
1341
T172z
Tardel, Hermann, 1869–
Zum Problem der Entstehung und Wesensart des Volksliedes.   [Bremen] Bremer Wissenschaftliche Gesellschaft [1935?]
[221]–256 p.
Cover title.
"Sonderdruck aus den Abhandlungen und Vorträgen der Bremer Wissenschaftlichen Gesellschaft, Jahrg. 8/9 der Festschrift zur Feier des zehnjährigen Bestehens der Bremer Wissenschaftlichen Gesellschaft."

1. Folk-songs --   Hist. & crit. I. Title.

NT 0038574   CLU

PN1341 Tardel, Hermann, 1869–
.T2   Zwei liedstudien. I. Die englisch-schottische rabenballade. II. Das lammerstraten-lied ... Bremen, 1914
70 p. 22½ᶜᵐ.
Contains music.
Separate, from Programm--Real-gymnasium, Bremen.

1. Folk-songs--Hist. & crit.

NT 0038575   ICU NcU CU InU

Tardent, Charles, 1812–1856.
(Vinogradstvo i vinodĕlīe) Виноградство и винодѣліе. Составлены примѣнительно къ Новороссійскому краю и Бессарабіи. К. И. Тарданомъ. Съ политичными рисунками. Перевели съ французскаго В. Делла-Восъ и А. Де-Брюксъ. Одесса, Въ Тип. Францова и Нитче, 1854.
222 p. 25 cm.
L. C. copy imperfect: illus. wanting.

1. Viticulture--Russia, Southern. 2. Wine and wine making--Russia, Southern.   I. Title.

SB396.5.T28   75–561626

NT 0038576   DLC

TARDENT, HENRY ALEXIS.
...In freedom's cause; Australia's contribution to the World war, by Henry A. Tardent ("Anzacophil")...
Brisbane: Watson, Ferguson & Co., Ltd., 1923.   60 p. illus. (incl. ports.)   8°.

"First prize Maryborough, 1922, Eisteddfod."
"Publications by the same author," p.60.

625537A. 1. European war, 1914–1918--Australia.

NT 0038577   NN

4N
383
Tardent, Henry Alexis.
The life and works of Richard John Randall, Australia's greatest artist, and other essays on art. Brisbane, A. J. Cumming, Govt. printer [pref. 1916]
52 p.

NT 0038578   DLC-P4

YA
15626
Tardent, Henry Alexis.
Science as applied to agriculture and other essays. [n.p., 1906]
60 p.

NT 0038579   DLC

Tardes Americanas: Gobierno Gentil y Catolico: breve y particular noticia de toda la historia Indiana
  see under Granados y Gálvez, José Joaquín.

Tardes de Abril y Mayo
  see under Fernandez Shaw, Carlos, 1865–1911.

Tardes de estio
  see under Rico, Jose Adrian Maria.

Las tardes de la Granja
  see under Ducray-Duminil, Francois Guillaume, 1761–1819.

Greenlee
4504
P855
TARDES de mayo; ou, Tardes de passeyo, passadas em conversação erudita em que se tratão todas as materias uteis e necessarias para a instrucção da mocidade portugueza. num. 1-8. [n.p. 182-]
  62p. 20cm.

NT 0038584 ICN

868
T172
Las Tardes de Roque Pio y don Rufo de Alfarache: obra periodica, publicada en Murcia dos veces cada mes, dirigida a manifestar los graves perjuicios que causa la ociosidad en todos los estados, clases, y profesiones de la vida. Por D.M.C. ... Murcia, Oficina de la Viuda de Felipe Teruel, 1794.
  v. 20cm.

  [I. C., D.M. II. Title: Roque Pio y don Rufo de Alfarache.

NT 0038585 TxU

Tardes Entretenidas
  see under Castillo Solorzano, Alonso de, 1584–1647.

Tardes grises
  see under Durbán, Orozco, Jose.

Tardes masonicas de la aldea. Dialogo. Telesforo masón, Mauricio y Jacinta profanos. Tarde primera [-undecima, y suplemento] [Bogotá, Impr. de la Rep. por Nicomedes Lora, 1823]
  108 p. 21cm.

  Posada: Bibliografía bogotana, II, 677.
  Dialogues against freemasonry.
  Dated Aug. 1 - Oct. 12, 1823.
  Imperfect: p. 41-50 (tarde 5) wanting.

  55R0248. 1. Freemasons. Anti.   2. Freemasons—Colombia.

NT 0038588 NN

475
V81Y4
T1
Tardi, L'Abbé Dominique.
  Les epitomae de Virgile de Toulouse, essai de traduction critique avec une bibliographie, une introduction et des notes. These complementaire pour le Doctorat des lettres. Paris, Boivin & Cie, Éditeurs, 1928.
  151p. 26cm.

  "Les Epitomae: French and Latin on opposite pages."

  1. Virgilius Maro, the grammarian. Les Epitomae. I. Tit

NT 0038589 TNJ MH

PA6389 Tardi, Dominique.
.F25Z8   ... Fortunat. Étude sur un dernier représentant de la poésie latine dans la Gaule mérovingienne. Paris, Boivin & c[ie], 1927.
  xvi, 288 p. 25cm.
  "Bibliographie": p. [vii]-xvi.

  1. Fortunatus, Venantius Honorius Clementianus, bp. of Poitiers, ca. 530-ca. 600.

  OCU MH DDO CtY CSt
NT 0038590   ICU NcD WaU DCU CU TNJ-R TNJ NIC MiU OU

Tardi, Dominique.
  La sainte messe. Paris, Éditions Spes, 1945.
  80 p. 18 cm. (Collection "Prends et lis")

  1. Mass. I. Title. (Series)

  BX2230.T3   265.3   48–41849*

NT 0038591 DLC

M
219
.5
T181 ‡
Gmaj.
Tardi, Francesco.
  [Sonata, violin & piano, G major]
  Sonata in sol maggiore, per violino e pianoforte. Libera elaborazione di Ettore Bonelli. Padova, G. Zanibon, 1939.
  score (14 p.) and part. 34 cm.
  Ed. from MS. in the National Library Marciana of Venice.

  1. Sonatas (Violin and piano)

NT 0038592 CtY-Mus

Law   Tardi, István, ed.

  Budapest. *Ordinances, etc.*
    Nagy-Budapest közlekedési szabályai (1000/1949. fk. II. számú főkapitányi rendelet) és a legújabb közlekedési rendeletek. Összeállította és magyarázatokkal ellátta: Tardi István és Madarász Aladár. [Budapest] Cserépfalvi, 1949.

Tardi, Laurence
  see Tardy, Lorenzo.

Law   Tardi, Pál, ed.

  Hungary. *Laws, statutes, etc.*
    A külkereskedelem hatályos jogszabályai. [Lezárva: 1955. április 15.] A Külkereskedelmi Minisztérium hivatalos kiadványa. [Összeállították: Katona Péter és Tardi Pál] Budapest, Közgazdasági és Jogi Könyvkiadó, 1955.

Tardi, Pierre, 1897–

International geodetic and geophysical union. *Association of geodesy.*
  ... Bibliographie géodésique internationale ... t. 1–   ;
  1928/30–
  Paris, Secrétariat de l'Association, 1935–

Tardi, Pierre, 1897–
  La lecture des cartes célestes. Ouvrage comportant en annexe cinq cartes des constellations et deux cartes concernant les positions des quatre principales planètes. Paris, Gauthier-Villars, 1947.
  30 p. illus., fold. col. charts. 23 cm.

  1. Astronomy—Observers' manuals. I. Title.

  QB65.T2   64–52402

NT 0038597 DLC

QB321
.B7
Tardi, Pierre, 1897–
  Brazil. *Diretoria do Serviço Geografico do Exercito.*
    Projeção conforme de Gauss; manual para os cálculos a máquina com as fórmulas do comandante Tardi. Trabalho organizado pelo Gabinete Técnico de Geodésia. Rio de Janeiro, 1946.

Tardi, Pierre, 1897–
  Titres et travaux scientifiques. Paris, 1955
  32 p.

NT 0038599 MH

Tardi, Pierre, 1897–
  Traité de géodésie, par le capitaine P. Tardi. Préface par le général G. Perrier ... Paris, Gauthier-Villars, 1934–
  v. illus., diagrs. 25½cm.
  Paged continuously.
  Bibliographical references included in the preface.
  CONTENTS.—fasc. I. Généralités sur la géodésie, géodésie mathématique, triangulations.—fasc. II. Astronomie géodésique de position, géodésie dynamique, la figure de la terre.

  1. Geodesy.
                [Full name: Pierre Antoine Ernest Tardi]
                                    36–14693
  Library of Congress   QB301.T3

NT 0038600 DLC CU CtY NIC OU OC1W

Tardi, Pierre, 1897–
  Traité de géodésie. 2. éd. entièrement refondue, par Pierre Tardi [et] Georges Laclavère. Paris, Gauthier-Villars, 1951–
  v. in illus. 26 cm.
  CONTENTS.—t. 1. Triangulations. fasc. 1. Les fondements mathématiques de la géodésie. Opérations sur le terrain.

  1. Geodesy. I. Laclavère, Georges, joint author.
                Full name: Pierre Antoine Ernest Tardi.

  QB301.T32   526   51–33210

NT 0038601 DLC CaBVaU TxU NN DSI NNC CU MoSU OU

Tardi, Pierre Antoine Ernest
  see
  Tardi, Pierre.

Tardiani, Héctor Raúl.
... Hacia un mejoramiento del bienestar económico-social debido al notariado de los territorios nacionales. Quemú ¡República argentina¡ Imp. Fava ¡1941?¡

cover-title, 13 p. 17ᵐ.

1. Notaries—Argentine republic.   I. Title.

44–22717

NT 0038603   DLC

¡Tardieu, A   ¡
Charlotte Tardieu de Malleville, 829–1890. ¡Compiègne, Imprimé par H. Lefebvre, 1890?¡

19 p., 1 l. 23ᶜᵐ.
Signed: A. T.

1. Tardieu de Malleville, Charlotte, 1829–1890.

12–2630

Library of Congress   ML417.T17

NT 0038604   DLC

TARDIEU (A.). *Intoxication aiguë par le véronal et les autres dérivés de la malonyl-urée (barbiturisme)... 8°.. Paris, 1924.

NT 0038605   DNLM

Tardieu, A   Philippe Saint Marcel
see Saint Marcel, A   Philippe Tardieu.

Tardieu, Alexandre.
Notice sur les Tardieu, les Cochin et les Belle, graveurs et peintres.
(*In* Archives de l'art français ... Paris, 1855/56. 21½ᶜᵐ. ¡t. 7¡ Documents t. 4. p. ¡49¡–68)

Signed: Alexandre Tardieu.
Also includes information concerning the Horthemels family of engravers.

1. Artists, French. 2. Tardieu family. 3. Horthemels family. 4 Cochin, Charles Nicolas, 1688–1754. 5. Cochin, Charles Nicolas, 1715–1790. 6. Belle family.

A C 38–1651

Newberry library
for Library of Congress   ¡N6841.A8 vol. 7¡
¡3¡   (704)

NT 0038607   ICN DLC

Tardieu, Alexandre, defendant.

Law

Delamalle, Gaspard Gilbert, 1752–1834.
Réplique pour le sieur Baudelocque ... chirurgien en chef accoucheur de l'Hospice de la maternité ... contre Alexandre Tardieu ... Jean-François Sacombe ... la femme Bridif; et le sieur Lefebvre ... prononcée par mʳ. Delamalle, à l'audience du 5 fructidor an XII; recueillie par le sténographe. Paris, Impr. de Delance et Lesueur, an XIII–1804.

Tardieu, Ambroise, 1788–1841.
Atlas de geografía universal para uso de las escuelas de América, adaptado al curso de geografía de M. Letronne. Nueva ed., aumentada con un texto que abraza la descripción particular de cada mapa. Paris, C. Bouret, 1878.

64 p. 23 col. maps. diagr. 23 x 30 cm.

1. Atlases, Mexican. 2. Geography—Text-books—1870–1945.
I. Letronne, Antoine Jean, 1787–1848.

G1019.T24 1878   Map 51–340 rev

NT 0038609   DLC MH

GA
319   **Tardieu, Ambroise,** 1788–1841.
1821   Atlas pour servir à l'intelligence de l'Histoire
T18   générale des voyages, de LaHarpe. Paris, E.
       Ledoux, 1821.
       15 col. maps (11 double)

1. Atlases.   I. LaHarpe, Jean François de, 1739–1803. Abrégé de l'Histoire générale des voyages.

NT 0038610   MiU

Beinecke   **Tardieu, Ambroise,** 1788–1841.
Library   Atlas pour servir à l'intelligence de
1974   l'histoire générale des voyages de La Harpe,
Folio   dressé par Ambroise Tardieu. Paris, Chez
73   Le Dentu, libraire, 1825.
          2 p.l., 15 maps (part fold.) 45 cm.

1. Voyages and travels – 1700–1800.   I. La Harpe, Jean François de, 1739–1803. Abrégé de l'Histoire générale des voyages.

NT 0038611   CtY NNG

Tardieu, Ambroise, 1788–1841.
Atlas universel de géographie, ancienne et moderne. Pour l'intelligence de la Géographie universelle par Malte-Brun. Paris, Furne, 1842.

¡3¡ p., 27 double col. maps. 42 cm.

1. Atlases, French.   I. Malte-Brun, Conrad, 1775–1826. Précis de la géographie universelle.   II. Title.

G1019.T25 1842   Map 56–702

NT 0038612   DLC

Tardieu, Ambroise, 1788–1841.
Atlas universel de géographie, ancienne et
EE23   moderne, dressé et gravé par Ambroise Tardieu
850T   ... pour la intelligence de La géographie
       universelle par Malte-Brun. Paris, Furne; New-
       York, R. Lockwood & son, 1850.
       2 p.l., 30 double maps. 43 cm.

NT 0038613   CtY

G1319   **Tardieu, Ambroise,** 1788–1841.
f1853a   Atlas universel de géographie ancienne et mo-
(Ge)   derne, dressé et gravé par Ambroise Tardieu ...
        Pour l'intelligence de la Géographie universelle
        par Maltebrun. Paris, Furne, 1853.
        ¡4¡ p. 30 double maps. 40 cm.

1. Atlases.

NT 0038614   ICU CtY

Tardieu, Ambroise, 1788–1841.
Atlas universel de géographie, ancienne et moderne. Revu et corrigé par A. Vuillemin pour l'intelligence de la Géographie universelle de Malte-Brun Lavallée. Paris, Furne, 1861.

¡3¡ p., 31 fold. col. maps. 43 cm.

1. Atlases, French.   I. Vuillemin, Alexandre A., b. 1812.   II. Malte-Brun, Conrad, 1775–1826. Précis de la géographie universelle.   III. Title.

G1019.T25 1861   Map 56–703

NT 0038615   DLC

Tardieu, Ambroise, 1788–1841.
Atlas universel de géographie ancienne et moderne. Revu et corrigé par A. Vuillemin, pour l'intelligence de la Géographie universelle de Malte-Brun Lavallée. Paris, Furne, 1863.

¡3¡ p., 31 fold. maps (part col.) 43 cm.

1. Atlases, French.   I. Vuillemin, Alexandre A., b. 1812, ed.   II. Malte-Brun, Conrad, 1775–1826. Précis de la géographie universelle.

G1019.T25 1863   Map 59–556

NT 0038616   DLC ViU

Tardieu, Ambroise, 1788–1841.
Carte de France, pour le service du genie militaire
see under Achin,

Tardieu, Ambroise, 1788–1841.
La colonne de la grande armée d'Austerlitz, ou de la victoire, monument triomphal érigé en bronze, sur la Place Vendôme de Paris. Description... par Ambroise Tardieu...   Paris: A. Tardieu, 1822.   75 p.   38 pl.   4°.

Bookplate of George Phillips Parker.

1. Monuments (Historical), France: Paris.
N. Y. P. L.   April 16, 1923.

NT 0038618   NN CtY FTaSU NjP N MB PBL

TARDIEU, Ambroise, 1788–1841.
La colonne de la grande armée d'Austerlitz, ou de la Victoire; monument triomphal élévé a la gloire de la grande armée par Napoleon. Paris, Chez tous les libraires, 1837.

4°. pp. (1), 4. 4°. [i.2.39] plates.

NT 0038619   MH NWM

Tardieu, Ambroise, 1788–1841.
Entretiens sur la minéralogie d'après la méthode du célébré Hauy par Ambroise Tardieu. Paris, 1823.

NT 0038620   PPAN

530.4   **Tardieu, Amboise,** 1788–1841.
T17c   Entretiens sur la physique et sur
        l'astronomie. Paris, C. A. Boulland,
        1825.
        viii, 415 p. plates. 18 cm.

1. Physics—Addresses, essays, lectures.
2. Astronomy—Addresses, essays, lectures.
I. Title.

NT 0038621   LU OkU

TARDIEU, Ambroise, 1788–1841, engraver.
Galerie des uniformes des Gardes nationales de France. Paris, A. Tardieu, etc., 1817.

1. 8°. 28 plates (colored and partly folded).
                                    Fr 357.15*

NT 0038622   MH

TARDIEU, Ambroise, *1788– 1841.*   **K.6**
[Généraux français.]

[Paris, 182–?] 152 portrs. 8°.
This forms the 5th series of Tardieu's Iconographie universelle, and is a supplemes Panckoucke's Victoires et conquêtes.

NT 0038623   MB

Tardieu, Ambroise, 1788–1841.
Un mois en Espagne voyage artistique a Madrid. L'escorial, Tolède, Cordoue, Grenade, Séville, Cadix, Barcelone, etc. Avec quatroze vues de Villes, de Monuments, des Portraits, etc. par Ambroise Tardieu. Historiographe de l'auvergne membre de l'academie royale d'histoire de Madrid, de l'institut archéologique d'Allemagne, a Rome, des académies. De Toulouse, Rouen, Marseille, Clermont–Ferrand, etc., Officier et Chevalier de divers ordres, etc.

[Vignette, Cvncta cvm Labore] Chez L'Auteur (Puy-de-Dome) M D CCC L XXX V.

NT 0038625   NNH

Tardieu, Ambroise, 1788–1841.
Monument national. Portraits des députés, écrivains et pairs constitutionnels, défenseurs invariables de la Charte et de la Loi des élections du 5 février 1817; dessinés et gravés par Ambroise Tardieu; et précédés de la Charte et de la Loi des élections du 5 février 1817. Paris: A. Tardieu, 1820–21.   16 p.   pl., 151 ports.   30cm.

1. Portraits, French. 2. Portraits,   Engraved, French. I. Title.

NT   0038626   NN DLC-P4 NcU ICN

944.05   Tardieu, Ambroise, *1788–1841.*
L549o   Relation anglaise de la bataille de Waterloo, ou de Mont Saint-Jean, ... Traduit sur la 2me. éd. pub. à Londres en septembre 1816. 3. éd.   Bruxelles, P.J. de Mat, 1816. 88p.   col. illus., fold. col. map.
Bound with LeMayeur, A.J.J. Ode sur la bataille de Waterloo; and, Relation fidèle et détaillée de la dernière campagne de Buonaparte, par un Témoin oculaire.

1. Waterloo, Battle of, 1815. I. Title.

NT   0038627   FTaSU

Tardieu, Ambroise, 1788–1841.
Victoires, conquestes, désastres, revers et guerres civiles des Francais, de 1792 à 1815 see under   Beauvais de Préau, Charles Theodore, 1772–1830.

Tardieu, Ambroise, 1818–
see   Tardieu, Ambroise Auguste, 1818–

Tardieu, Ambroise, 1840–   Fr 3028.4F
Dictionnaire iconographique de l'ancienne Auvergne, c'est-à-dire Liste générale de tous les portraits gravés, lithographiés, dessinés concernant cette province. Avec une suite de personnages vivants dignes de mémoire. Clermont-Ferrand, P. Raclot, 1904.
4°.   pp. (4), 227 +.   Ports. and other illus.
The title-page has ornamental border.
"Cet ouvrage, tiré à petit nombre, n'a pas été mis dans le commerce. Les exam plaires sont signés de la main de l'auteur."

Auvergne

NT   0038630   MH NNC NNU-W

Tardieu, Ambroise, 1840–
Dictionnaire iconographique des Parisiens, c'est-à-dire liste générale des personnes nées à Paris, dont il existe des portraits gravés et lithographiés, avec une biographie de chaque nom cité (environ 3000) ouvrage orné de curieux et rarissimes portraits par Thomas de Leu, Léonard Gaultier, etc., reproduits par la photogravure, par Ambroise Tardieu ... Herment (Puy-de-Dome) L'auteur, 1885.
2 p. l., iii, (1) p., 308 col., 1 p., 1 l. front., 1 illus., 16 port. 25cm.
"Cet ouvrage n'a été tiré qu'à 390 exemplaires, numérotés et signés." This copy neither numbered nor signed.
1. Paris—Biog.—Portraits—Catalogs. 2. Paris—Hist. 3. Engravings—Catalogs.   I. Title.   13–5236

Library of Congress   NE270.T3

NT   0038631   DLC CU NNGr MB

Tardieu, Ambroise, 1840–
Grand dictionnaire historique du département du Puy-de-Dôme, comprenant l'histoire complète des villes, bourgs, hameaux, paroisses, abbayes, prieurés ... situés sur ce territoire et faisant jadis partie de l'ancienne Basse-Auvergne, par Ambroise Tardieu ... Moulins, Impr. de C. Desrosiers, 1877.
2 p. l., iii, (1), 380 p. front., illus., plates (1 col., 1 double) fold. map, plans. 36½cm.
Initials; head-pieces.
"Cet ouvrage n'a été tiré qu'à 315 exemplaires numérotés et signés. no. 276."
"Bibliographie historique et archéologique du Puy-de-Dôme": p. [367]–378.
1. Puy-de-Dôme   (Dept.)—Gazetteers.   5–17424
Library of Congress   DC611.P98T3

NT   0038632   DLC

Tardieu, Ambroise, 1840–
Histoire illustrée de la ville et du canton de Saint-Gervais d'Auvergne, par Ambroise Tardieu et Augustin Madebène. [Clermont-Ferrand, Typ. A. Richet] 1892

232 p. illus.

1. St. Gervais d'Auvergne, France. I. Madebène, Augustin

NT   0038633   MH

TARDIEU, Ambroise, 1840–
La ville gallo-romaine de Beauclair, commune de Voingt, près d'Herment (Puy-de-Dôme). Fouilles et découvertes par Ambroise Tardieu et François Boyer. Clermont-Ferrand, F. Boyer, etc., etc., 1882.

f°. Plates and map.

NT   0038634   MH MB

DG431   Tardieu, Ambroise, 1840–
3   Voyage archéologique en Italie et en Tunisie; Rome, Naples, Pompéi, Messine, Catane, Syracuse, Palerme, Malte, Tunis et Utique.   Herment, chez l'auteur, 1885.
28 columns. illus.

1. Italy – Antiq. 2. Tunisia – Antiq. I. Title.

NT   0038635   CU CtY

Tardieu, Ambroise Auguste, 1818–1874.
—— & Lasègue (Ernest-Charles). Consultation médico-légale sur l'état mental et le mariage in extremis de M. Achille Humbert. 8 pp. fol. [*Paris*], Noël, [1870].
Lithograph.

NT   0038636   DNLM

TARDIEU, Ambroise *Auguste, 1818–1879.*
Contribution à l'histoire des monstruosités considérés au point de vue de la médicine légale à l'occasion de l'exhibition publique du monstre pygopage Millio-Christine. Paris, 1874.

8°. (2), 32p. Illustr.
I. Laugier, Maurice, joint author

NT   0038637   MH-L DNLM

TARDIEU, *Ambroise Auguste, 1818–1879.*
De la morve et du farcin chroniques chez l'homme et chez les solipèdes.   Paris. Baillière. 1843. 187 pp. 4°.

NT   0038638   MB PPC DNLM

Tardieu, *Ambroise Auguste, 1818–1879.*   '85.63.3
The diagnosis of hanging, a medico-legal study.
(In Medico-Legal Society of New York. Papers. Series 3, pp. 40–46. New York. 1886.)

K1878 — Hanging.

NT   0038639   MB

Tardieu, Ambroise Auguste, 1818–1879.
Dictionnaire d'hygiène publique et de salubrité, ou, Répertoire de toutes les questions relatives à la santé publique, considérées dans leurs rapports avec les substances, les épidémies, les professions, les établissements et institutions d'hygiène et de salubrité, complété par le texte des lois, décrets, arrêtés, ordonnances et instructions qui s'y rattachent, par Ambroise Tardieu ... Paris, Chez J. B. Baillière; [etc., etc.] 1852–54.

3 v. 22cm.
1. Hygiene, Public—Dictionaries. 2. France—Sanit. aff.   I. France. Laws, statutes, etc.   8–8238†

Library of Congress   RA423.T18

NT   0038640   DLC DNLM NN

Tardieu, Ambroise Auguste, 1818–1879.
Dictionnaire d'hygiène publique et de salubrité; ou, Répertoire de toutes les questions relatives à la santé publique ... par Ambroise Tardieu. 2. éd., considérablement augm. Paris, J.-B. Baillière; New-York, Baillière, 1862.
4 v. 23cm.

1. Public health, Encyc. 2. Public health, France. 3. Sanitation.

NT   0038641   NcD-MC GU ICJ MdBF NN PPC DNLM T

Tardieu, Auguste Ambroise, 1818–1879.
Dictionnaire d'hygiène publique et de salubrité; ou, Repertoire de toutes les questions relatives a la sante publique. Ed. 2.   Paris, Baillière, 1863. 4 v.

NT   0038642   PU

Tardieu, Ambroise Auguste, 1818–1879.

Blyth, Alexander Wynter.
A dictionary of hygiene and public health, comprising sanitary chemistry, engineering, and legislation, the dietetic value of foods, and the detection of adulterations, on the plan of the "Dictionnaire d'hygiène publique" of Professor Ambroise Tardieu. By Alexander Wynter Blyth ... London, C. Griffin and company, 1876.

WCB   TARDIEU, Ambroise Auguste, 1818–1879
T184d   Du choléra épidémique; leçons pro-
1849   fessées à la Faculté de médecine de Paris.   Paris, Baillière, 1849. viii, 216 p.

NT   0038644   DNLM MB PPC

Tardieu, *Ambroise Auguste, 1818–1879.*
——, Loran (P.) & Roussin (Z.) Empoisonnement par la strychnine, l'arsenic et les sels de cuivre, observations et recherches nouvelles. 28 pp. 8°. *Paris, J.-B. Baillière & fils,* 1865.
Repr. from: Ann. d'hyg. Par., 1865, 2. s., xxiv.

NT   0038645   DNLM

Tardieu, Ambroise Auguste, 1818–1879.
... Estudio médico-legal sobre el colgamiento, la extrangulacion y la sofocacion, por Ambrosio Tardieu ... tr. de la 2ª. ed. francesa, anotado y adicionado con el importante capitulo del profesor Hofmann (de Viena) sobre la asfixia por el licenciado en medicina y cirurgia Prudencio Sereñana y Partagás ... Edicion ilustrada con varios grabados. (Va comprendida la legislacion actual española) Barcelona, F. Perez; [etc., etc.,] 1883.
xvi, [17]–544 p. illus. 21½cm.
At head of title: Biblioteca Tardieu.
1. Violent deaths. 2. Hanging. 3. Asphyxia. 4. Medical jurisprudence.   I. Hofmann, Eduard ritter von, 1837–1897. II. Sereñana y Partagás, Prudencio, 1842–   1902, tr.
     32–13720
Library of Congress   RA1071.T25   340.6

NT   0038646   DLC NNC DNLM

Tardieu, Ambroise Auguste, 1818–1879.
... Estudio médico-legal sobre el infanticidio, por Ambrosio Tardieu ... Traducido y anotado según las más recientes teorías de la ciencia, por ... Prudencio Sereñana y Partagás ... (Va comprendida en la legislación española vigente) Barcelona, D. Cortezo y c.ª, 1883.

2 p. l., 372 p. 21cm.

At head of title: Biblioteca Tardieu.

1. Infanticide. 2. Medical jurisprudence. I. Sereñana y Partagás, Prudencio, 1842–1902, tr

32–8391

Library of Congress   RA1067.T34   340.6

NT   0038647   DLC CtY MH-L

Tardieu, Auguste-Ambroise, 1818–79.
——. Estudio médico-legal sobre la locura. Traducido de la segunda edición por ... Prudencio Sereñana y Partagas, y anotado por Arturo Galcerán. (Va comprendida la legislación actual española.) xxxiii, 632 pp. 8°. *Barcelona, F. Pérez; Madrid, Simón y Osler,* 1883.

NT   0038648   DNLM

Tardieu, Ambroise Auguste, 1818–1879.
... Estudio médico-legal sobre las enfermedades producidas accidental ó involuntariamente por imprudencia, negligencia ó transmissión contagiosa, comprendiendo la historia médico-legal de la sífilis y de sus diversos modos de transmisión, por Ambrosio Tardieu ... traducido y anotado según las más recientes teorías de la ciencia, por ... Prudencio Sereñana y Partagás ... (Va comprendida la legislación española vigente) Barcelona, D. Cortezo y c.ª, 1884.

ix, (11)–228 p. 21½cm.

At head of title: Biblioteca Tardieu.
1. Medical jurisprudence. 2. Contagion and contagious diseases.
I. Sereñana y Partagás, Prudencio, 1842–1902, tr.

32–8392

Library of Congress   RA1051.T16   340.6

NT   0038649   DLC

W
600
T182e
1883

Tardieu, Ambroise Auguste, 1818–1879
Estudio médico-legal sobre las heridas, comprendiendo las heridas en general y las heridas por imprudencia, los golpes y el homicidio involuntarios. Tr. y anotado según las más recientes teorías de la ciencia por Prudencio Sereñana y Partagás. Va comprendida la legislación española vigente. Barcelona, Pérez, 1883.
486 p.

I. Sereñana y Partagás, Prudencio, 1842–1902

NT   0038650   DNLM

W
600
T182e
1882

TARDIEU, Ambroise Auguste, 1818–1879
Estudio médico-legal sobre los delitos contra la honestidad. Tr. de la 7. ed. francesa ... por Prudencio Serenana y Partagas. Barcelona, La Popular, 1882.
vii, 422 p. illus. (Biblioteca Tardieu)
Translation of Étude médico-légale sur les attentats aux moeurs.

NT   0038651   DNLM

RA
1231
.P6
C5

Tardieu, Ambroise Auguste, 1818–1879
Étude hygiénique et médico-légale sur la fabrication et l'emploi des allumettes chimiques; rapport fait au Comité consultatif d'hygiène publique. Paris, J.-B. Baillière; New York, H. Baillière, 1856.
54 p. 21 cm.

Bound with Chevallier, Alphonse. Sur la nécessité dans un but de sécurité publique d'interdire la fabrication des allumettes chimiques avec le phosphore ordinaire. (Paris, 1856)

NT   0038652   WU DNLM

Tardieu, Auguste Ambroise, 1818–79.
——. Étude hygiénique sur la profession de mouleur en cuivre pour servir à l'histoire des professions exposées aux poussières inorganiques. 74 pp. 12°. *Paris, J.-B. Baillière,* 1855. *Repr. from: Ann. d'hyg. Par., 1854, 2. s., ii.*

NT   0038653   DNLM

Tardieu, Ambroise Auguste, 1818–1879.
Étude médico-légale et clinique sur l'empoisonnement, par Ambroise Tardieu ... avec la collaboration de Z. Roussin ... pour la partie de l'expertise médico-légale relative à la recherche chimique des poisons ... Paris, Baillière (etc.), 1867.

xxii, 1072 p. illus. 22 cm.

1. Poisons. 2. Medical jurisprudence. I. Roussin, Zacharie, 1827–1894. II. Title.

Med 47–2537

U. S. Army Medical Library   [WC590T182e 1867]
for Library of Congress   (2)

NT   0038654   DNLM NIC WaU IU MH MB GU PP PPC

Tardieu, Ambroise Auguste, 1818–1879.
Étude médico-légale et clinique sur l'empoisonnement, par Ambroise Tardieu ... avec la collaboration de Z. Roussin ... pour la partie de l'expertise médico-légale relative à la recherche chimique des poisons. 2. éd., revue et considérablement augm. Avec deux planches et 54 figures intercalées dans le texte. Paris, J.-B. Baillière et fils; (etc., etc.) 1875.

xx, 1236 p. illus. plates. 22cm.

1. Poisons. 2. Medical jurisprudence. I. Roussin, Zacharie, 1827–II. Title.

35–24605

Library of Congress   RA1211.T23 1875   615.9

NT   0038655   DLC MBCo MnU-B NIC CtY-M NcD-MC MH-L

Older
N.L.M.

W
867
T182E
1864

Tardieu, Ambroise Auguste, 1818–1879.
Étude médico-légale sur l'avortement suivie d'observations et de recherches pour servir à l'histoire médico-légale des grossesses fausses et simulées. Paris, J. B. Baillière, 1864.
208 p. 21 cm.

1. Abortion, Induced. 2. Pseudopregnancy.
I. Title.

NT   0038656   WU-M PPC CtY WaU ICJ NIC DNLM

Tardieu, Ambroise Auguste, 1818–1879.
Étude médico-légale sur l'avortement; suivie d'une note sur l'obligation de déclarer à l'état civil les foetus mort-nés et d'observations et recherches pour servir à l'histoire médico-légale des grossesses fausses et simulées. 3. éd., rev. et augm. Paris, J.-B. Baillière; Londres, Hippolyte Baillière, 1868.
vii,280p. 22cm.

NT   0038657   NcD-MC CU-M MH-L DNLM

614.23
T182av4

Tardieu, Ambroise Auguste, 1818–1879.
Étude médico-légale sur l'avortement suivie d'une note sur l'obligation de déclarer à l'état civil les foetus mort-nés et de recherches pour servir à l'histoire médico-légale des grossesses fausses et simulées. 4.éd., rev. et augm. Paris, J. B. Baillière et fils; (etc., etc.) 1881
290p.

Bibliographical foot-notes.

1. Jurisprudence, Medical. 2. Abortion.

NT   0038658   IU-M ICRL MiU

Tardieu, Ambroise Auguste, 1818–1879.   618.39 Q700
70038 Étude médico-légale sur l'avortement, suivie d'une Note sur l'obligation de déclarer à l'état civil les fœtus mort-nés et d'observations et recherches pour servir à l'histoire médico-légale des grossesses fausses et simulées, par Ambroise Tardieu, ... Nouvelle édition, revue et augmentée de rapports médicaux sur l'affaire Boisleux et La Jarrige. Par MM. Brouardel, Thoinot et Maygrier. Paris, J.-B. Baillière et fils, 1907.
vii, 336 p. 23½cm.

NT   0038659   ICJ

W
867
T182e
1939

TARDIEU, Ambroise Auguste, 1818–1879
Étude médico-légale sur l'avortement.
Nouv. éd. Paris, Baillière, 1939.
vii, 335 p.
1. Abortion - Criminal
2. Pseudocyesis

NT   0038660   DNLM

W
600
T182ee
1868

TARDIEU, Ambroise Auguste, 1818–1879
Étude médico-légale sur l'infanticide.
Paris, Baillière, 1868.
viii, 342 p. illus.

NT   0038661   DNLM PU NcD-MC CtY-M

Tardieu, Ambroise Auguste, 1818–1879.
Étude médico-légale sur l'infanticide, par Ambroise Tardieu ... 2. éd. augm. avec 3 planches coloriées. Paris J. B. Baillière et fils; (etc., etc.) 1880.

viii, 370 p. 3 pl. (1 fold.) 21½cm.

1st edition, 1868.

1. Infanticide. 2. Medical jurisprudence.

16–12673

Library of Congress   RA1067.T3 1880

NT   0038662   DLC DNLM NcD-MC ICRL ICJ

Tardieu, Ambroise Auguste, 1818–1879.
Étude médico-légale sur la folie, par Ambroise Tardieu ... Avec quinze fac-similé d'écriture d'aliénés. Paris, J.-B. Baillière et fils; (etc., etc.) 1872.

xxii, 610 p. incl. facsims. 22cm.

Contains legislation.

1. Insanity—Jurisprudence. 2. Insane—Laws and legislation—France.

32–34187

Library of Congress   RA1151.T3   (347.1) 340.6

NT   0038663   DLC MnU WU-M NcD-MC PPC DNLM MH

14.23
173e

TARDIEU, Ambroise Auguste, 1818–1879.
Étude médico-légale sur la pendaison, la strangulation et la suffocation ... Paris, J.-B. Baillière et fils, 1870.
xii, 352 p. illus., 1 col. plate.

Translated into Spanish under title: Estudio médico-legal sobre el colgamiento, la extrangulacion y la sofocacion.

NT   0038664   WaU MH MB DNLM DLC-P4 PPC NcD-MC

614.23
T182p2

Tardieu, Ambroise Auguste, 1818–1879.
Étude médico-légale sur la pendaison, la strangulation, et la suffocation 2.éd. augm. Paris, J. B. Baillière et fils; (etc., etc.) 1879
364p. illus., col.pl.

Bibliographical foot-notes.

1. Hanging. 2. Asphyxia. 3. Strangulation.
4. Jurisprudence, Medical.

NT   0038665   IU-M MiU ICRL

W
600
T182et
1864

TARDIEU, Ambroise Auguste, 1818–1879
Étude médico-légale sur la strangulation.
Paris, Baillière, 1859.
90 p.
Bound with his Étude médico-legale sur les maladies provoquées ou communiquées. Paris, 1864.
Reprinted from Annales d'hygiène publique et de médecine légale, 2. sér., 1859.

NT   0038666   DNLM

W
600
T182e

TARDIEU, Ambroise Auguste, 1818-1879
Étude médico-légale sur les attentats
aux moeurs. ⌈1.⌉ éd. Paris,
Bailliére ⌈185-?⌉-
v. illus.

NT 0038667   DNLM

Tardieu, Auguste Ambroise, 1818-1879.
Étude médico-légale sur les attentats aux moeurs.
2 ed. Paris, Baillière, 1858.
176 p.

NT 0038668   PPC PPPH

Tardieu, Ambroise, 1818-1879.
Étude médico-légale sur les attentats aux
moeurs. 3e.édition. Paris, Baillière, 1859.

vi, 188 p. plates. 21 1/2 cm.

viii, 263 p. plates. 21 1/2 cm.

NT 0038669   MBCo PPC

RA
1141
T373
1862
HRC

Tardieu, Ambroise Auguste, 1818-1879.
Etude médico-légale sur les attentats aux
moeurs, par Ambroise Tardieu. 4ème éd., accompagnée de trois planches gravées. Paris, J.-
B. Baillière et Fils ⌈etc.⌉ 1862.
224p.

1. Sex crimes - France. 2. Sex and law.
I. Title.

NT 0038670   TxU DNLM PU

340.6
T173

Tardieu, Ambroise Auguste, 1818-1879.
Étude médico-légale sur les attentats aux
moeurs...5.éd. Paris, Baillière, 1867.
VIII, 265 p. plates. 22 cm.

Provenance: E.A.Dalrymple, Maryland
Diocesan Library.

1,Medical jurisprudence. 2. Crime & criminals. I, Title: Attentats aux moeurs.

NT 0038671   NNG WaU MH DNLM

4K
4294

Tardieu, Ambroise Auguste, 1818-1879
Étude médico-légale sur les attentats aux moeurs. 6. éd. accompagnée
de 4 planches gravées. Paris,
Librairie J.-B. Baillière, 1873.
303

NT 0038672   DLC-P4 CtY PPC

Tardieu, Ambroise Auguste, 1818-1879.
Étude médico-légale sur les attentats aux mœurs, par
Ambroise Tardieu ... 7. éd. accompagné de cinq planches
gravées. Paris, J. B. Baillière et fils; ⌈etc., etc.⌉ 1878.

viii, 296 p. v pl. 22½ᶜᵐ.

1. Medical jurisprudence. 2. Crime and criminals. ɪ. Title: Attentats
aux mœurs, Étude médico-légale sur les.

16-12682

Library of Congress   RA1141.T3

NT 0038673   DLC MH DNLM ICRL NcD-MC NIC

W
600
T182ea
1871

TARDIEU, Ambroise Auguste, 1818-1879
Étude médico-légale sur les blessures
par imprudence; l'homicide et les coups
involontaires. Paris, Baillière, 1871.
196 p.
Reprinted from Annales d'hygiène
publique et de médecine légale, 2. série,
1871.

NT 0038674   DNLM OClM MB

NON-
CIRC.

Tardieu, Ambroise Auguste, 1818-1879.
Étude médico-légale sur les maladies produites
accidentellement ou involontairement par imprudence, négligence ou transmission contagieuse,
comprenant l'histoire médico-légale de la syphilis
de ses divers modes de transmission, par Ambroise
Tardieu. Paris, J.B. Baillière, 1879.
x, 288 p. 23 cm.

Includes bibliographical references.

266203   1. Communicable diseases. 2. Diseases--Causes
and theories of causation. 3. Syphillis. I.
Title.

ICJ PPC ICRL
NT 0038675   CU-M CtY MH-L IU-M NcD-MC IU MB DNLM

614.2
T182et
1879

Tardieu,Ambroise Auguste,1818-1879.
Étude médico-légale sur les maladies provoquées ou communiquées,comprenant l'histoire
médico-légale de la syphilis et de ses divers
'odes de transmission,par Ambroise Tardieu ...
Paris, J.-B.Baillière et fils; New-York, Baillière brothers; ⌈etc.,etc.⌉ 1864.
2 p.ℓ.,128 p. 21½cm.
Caption-title: Etude médico-légale sur les maladies
accidentellement et involontairement produites par
imprudence,négligence ou transmission contagieuse,
comprenant l'histoire médico-légale de la syphilis et
de ses divers modes de transmission.

"Extrait des Annales d'hygiène publique et de
médecine légale,1861,2ᵉ série,t.XV,et 1864,2ᵉ série,
t.XXI."
With his Etude médico-légale sur la pendaison,la
strangulation et la suffocation. 1879.

1.Contagion and contagious diseases. 2.Syphilis.
3.Medical jurisprudence.

NT 0038677   MiU DNLM

Tardieu, Ambroise Auguste, 1818-1879.
Jusqu'a quel point le diagnostic anatomique peut-
éclairer le traitement des névroses... Paris,
Bourgogne, 1844.
60 p.

NT 0038678   PPC

Hist.
19th c.
WB
T182M
1848

Tardieu, Ambroise Auguste, 1818-1879.
Manuel de pathologie et de clinique
médicales. Paris, G. Baillière, 1848.
xiv, 736 p. 18 1/2 cm.

1. Medicine. I. Title.

NT 0038679   WU-M DNLM MB PPC

WB
T182m
1857

TARDIEU, Ambroise Auguste, 1818-1879
Manuel de pathologie et de clinique
médicales. 2. éd., rev., corr., augm.
Paris, Baillière, 1857.
xvi, 776 p.

NT 0038680   DNLM PPC ICJ NN

RB
110
.T3
1866

Tardieu, Ambroise Auguste, 1818-1879
Manuel de pathologie et de clinique médicales. 3. ed., rev., corr., augm. Paris,
New York, G. Baillière, 1866.
915 p. 19 cm.

Includes bibliographies.

1. Pathology.

NT 0038681   WU PPC CtY ICJ

Tardieu, Ambroise Auguste, 1818-1879.
Manuel de pathologie et de clinique medicales.
Paris, Baillière, 1898.
736 p.

NT 0038682   PU

WB
100
T182m
1880

TARDIEU, Ambroise Auguste, 1818-1879
Manual de patología y de clínica
médicas. Tr. al castellano de la 4.
ed. francesa por R. Ibañez Abellán.
Madrid, Calleja, 1880-
v.
Translation of Manuel de pathologie et
de clinique médicals.

NT 0038683   DNLM

W
600
T182et
1864

TARDIEU, Ambroise Auguste, 1818-1879
Mémoire sur l'empoisonnement par la
strychnine, contenant la relation médico-
légale complète de l'affaire Palmer.
Paris, Baillière, 1857.
104 p.
Bound with his Étude médico-légale
sur les maladies provoquées ou communiquées. Paris, 1864.
Reprinted from Annales d'hygiène et de
médecine légale, 2. ser., 1856 and 1857.

NT 0038684   DNLM MH

Tardieu, Ambroise Auguste, 1818-1879.

Mémoire sur la coralline et sur le danger que
présente l'emploi de cette substance dans la teinture de certains vêtements; suivi du rapport de
M. P. Schützenberger sur un procédé meilleur de
préparation du rouge d'aniline. 22 pp. 8°.
Repr. from: Ann. d'hyg., Par., 1869, 2. s. xxxi

NT 0038685   DNLM

Tardieu, Ambroise Auguste, 1818-1879.
Observations et recherches nouvelles sur la
morve chronique et les ulcérations morveuses des
voies aériennes. Paris, Locquin, 1841.
32 p. Pl. 8°.

NT 0038686   MB

WX
T182p
1865

TARDIEU, Ambroise Auguste, 1818-1879
Projet de construction du nouvel
Hotel-Dieu de Paris; rapport fait au
Conseil municipal de Paris. Paris,
Baillière, 1865.
44 p.
1. Paris. Hôtel-Dieu

NT 0038687   DNLM

W
600
T182q
1872

TARDIEU, Ambroise Auguste, 1818-1879
Question médico-légale de l'identité,
dans ses rapports avec les vices de
conformation des organes sexuels,
contenant les souvenirs et impressions
d'un individu dont le sexe avait été méconnu.
Paris, Baillière, 1872.
159 p.
Reprinted from Annales d'hygiène
publique et de médecine légale, t. 38,
2. sér., no. 77-78, juil.-oct. 1872.

NT 0038688   DNLM

614.23
T182q2

Tardieu, Ambroise Auguste, 1818-1879.
Question médico-légale de l'identité dans ses
rapports avec les vices de conformation des organes sexuels, contenant les souvenirs et impressions d'un individu dont le sexe avait été méconnu 2.éd., rev. corr. et augm. Paris, J. B.
Baillière et fils, 1874.
174p.

Bibliographical foot-notes.

1. Hermaphroditism. 2. Jurisprudence, Medical.

NT 0038689   IU-M NcD-MC PPC ICRL DNLM WaU MH-L

Tardieu, Ambroise Auguste, 1818-1879.
———. Question médico-légale de la pendaison;
destinction du suicide et de l'homicide. 31 pp.
8°. Paris, J.-B. Baillière & fils, 1865.

NT 0038690   DNLM

W
600
T182r
1864

TARDIEU, Ambroise Auguste, 1818-1879
Relation médico-légale de l'affaire
Armand (de Montpellier) Simulation de
tentative homicide, commotion cérébrale
et strangulation.   Paris, Baillière, 1864.
84 p.
Reprinted from Annales d'hygiène
publique et de médecine légale, 2. sér.,
1864.

NT 0038691   DNLM

Tardieu, Ambroise Auguste, 1818-1879.
Treatise on epidemic cholera; being lectures delivered under
the authority of the Faculty of medicine of Paris. By Am-
broise Tardieu ... Translated from the French by Samuel
Lee Bigelow, M. D. With an appendix by a fellow of the
Massachusetts medical society. Boston, Ticknor, Reed, and
Fields, 1849.
xi, 286 p. 20cm.
"Appendix" (p. [171]-277) by William W. Morland.

1. Cholera, Asiatic.   I. Bigelow, Samuel Lee, 1826-1862, tr.
II. Morland, William Wallace, 1818-1876.

35-32077

Library of Congress   RC126.T372

NT 0038692   DLC MsSM NcD-MC CtY ICRL DNLM RPB MB ICJ
MH NN MiU

W
600
T182e
(860

TARDIEU, Ambroise Auguste, 1818-1879
Die Vergehen gegen die Sittlichkeit in
staatsärztlicher Beziehung. Nach der
dritten französischen Aufl. ins Deutsche
übertragen von Fr. Wilh. Theile. Weimar,
Voigt, 1860.
x, 188 p. illus.
Translation of Étude médico-légale
sur les attentats aux moeurs.

NT 0038693   DNLM MH-L

W
600
T182ec
(868

TARDIEU, Ambroise Auguste, 1818-1879
Die Vergiftungen in gerichtsärztlicher
und klinischer Beziehung. Der gerichtlich-
chemische Theil bearb. von Z. Roussin.
Autorisirte deutsche Ausg. von Fr. Wilh.
Theile und Hermann Ludwig.   Erlangen,
Enke, 1868.
xiii, 598 p. illus.
Translation of Étude médico-légale
et clinique sur l'empoisonnement.
I. Roussin, Zacharie, 1827-1894

NT 0038694   DNLM MH-L

Tardieu, Ambroise Auguste, 1818-1879.
Voiries et cimetières. Thèse présentée au
concours pour la Chaire d'hygiène à la Faculté
de médecine de Paris, et soutenue le 1er mars
1852. Paris, J.B. Baillière, 1852.
271p. 21cm.

1.Mortuary   practice. 2.Sewage.

NT 0038695   NcD-MC DNLM PPC NN

Tardieu (Amédée). L'asthme et les eaux du
Mont-Dore. 18 pp. 8°. Clermont-Ferrand,
Malleval, 1900.

NT 0038696   DNLM CtY

Tardieu, Amédée.
Huitième ambulance de campagne de la Société
de secours aux blessés...
see under   Red Cross. France. Croix-
Rouge française. Société française de secours
aux blessés militaires.

Tardieu, Amedee, 1822-1893
Geographie de Strabon... t. 1.   Paris, Hachette
1867.

NT 0038698   DPU

Tardieu, Amédée, 1822-1893.
Sénégambie et Guinée, par m. Amédée Tardieu ... Nubie,
par m. S. Chérubini ... Abyssinie, par m. Noël Desvergers
... Paris, Firmin Didot frères, 1847.
2 p. l., 386, [2], 136, 190 p. plates, fold. maps. 21 cm. (*Half-title:*
L'univers. [t. 15])

1. Senegambia. 2. Guinea. 3. Ethiopia—Hist.—1490-1889. 4. Nu-
bia.   I. Chérubini, S.   II. *Desvergers, Noël, 1805-1867.
[Full name: Eugène Amédée Tardieu]

D20.U58   t. 15   3-10098

NT 0038699   DLC NNC InU OU CSt OCU NBuU DS MB NN GU

Tardieu, André, dr., joint author.
Caussade, Georges Gabriel, 1861-
Manifestations pleuro-pulmonaires et thérapeutique du rhu-
matisme articulaire aigu, médication salicylée, par G. Caus-
sade ... et A. Tardieu ... avec graphiques dans le texte. Paris,
G. Doin & cie, 1931.

Tardieu, Andre Louis-Amedee
see   Tardieu, A

Tardieu, André Pierre Gabriel Amédée, 1876-1945.
A la jeunesse française, discours sur le traité de paix
prononcé le 22 juin 1919, par M. André Tardieu ... à la
fête des Éclaireurs unionistes ... [Paris] Union des
grandes associations françaises [1919]
8 p. 22cm.

1. European war, 1914-1918—Peace.   I. Title.

Library of Congress   D646.T35   25-21239

NT 0038702   DLC

Tardieu, André Pierre Gabriel Amédée, 1876-1945
... Alerte aux Français. [Paris] E. Flammarion [1936]
47, [1] p. 18cm.

1. France—Pol. & govt.   I. Title.

Library of Congress   JN2593.1936.T3   36-33754
Copyright A—Foreign   32920
[2]   342.44

NT 0038703   DLC CtY NIC NcD

D
619
T35

Tardieu, André Pierre Gabriel Amédée, 1876-1945
... L'Amérique en armes. 2. mille. Paris, E. Fas-
quelle, 1919.
ix, 320 p. 19cm.
At head of title: André Tardieu.
Bibliothèque-Charpentier.

1. European war, 1914-1918—U. S. 2. European war, 1914-1918—France.
3. France. Haut commissariat aux États-Unis. 4. European war, 1914-1918—
Economic aspects.   I. Title.

Library of Congress   D619.T35   19-26556

NT 0038704   DLC CaBVaU NN NjP ICJ

Tardieu, André Pierre Gabriel Amédée, 1876-1945
... L'Amérique en armes. 3. mille. Paris, E. Fas-
quelle, 1919.
ix, 320 p. 19cm.
At head of title: André Tardieu.
Bibliothèque-Charpentier.

1. European war, 1914-1918—U. S. 2. European war, 1914-1918—France.
3. France. Haut commissariat aux États-Unis. 4. European war, 1914-1918—
Economic aspects.   I. Title.

19-26556

Library of Congress   D619.T35

NT 0038705   DLC MiU

DC389
T182

Tardieu, André Pierre Gabriel Amédée, 1876-
1945.
L'année de Munich; notes de semaine 1938.
Paris, Flammarion [1939]
252 p. 19cm.

1. France - Pol. & govt. - 1914-1940.   2.
France - For. rel. - 1914-1940. 3. Europe -
Hist. - 1938-   4. Munich
Four Power Agree   ment, 1938.

NT 0038706   CSt-H

Tardieu, André Pierre Gabriel Amédée, 1876-1945.
... Avec Foch (août-novembre 1914) Notes de campagne
accompagnées de quatre cents ordres et comptes rendus du Haut
commandement.   Paris, E. Flammarion [1939]
283 p., 1 l. 18½cm.
At head of title: André Tardieu.

1. European war, 1914-1918—Personal narratives, French. 2. European war, 1914-1918—Campaigns—Western. 3. Foch, Ferdinand, 1851-
1929. 4. European war, 1914-1918—Documents, etc., sources.   I. Title.

Library of Congress   D548.T25   39-25469
Copyright A—Foreign   [3558
[2]   940.48144

NT 0038707   DLC NcD CtY CLU NIC KyLoU GU OCl

Tardieu, André Pierre Gabriel Amédée, 1876-1945.
Le communisme et l'Europe. Avec un avant-propos de
Louis Guitard. Paris, Éditions G. D. [1948]
30 p. port. 21 cm.

1. Communism—Hist. 2. Communism—Europe.   I. Title.

HX40.T3   335.4   49-17751*

NT 0038708   DLC CtY

Tardieu, André Pierre Gabriel Amédée, 1876-1945.
La conférence d'Algésiras; histoire diplomatique de la
crise marocaine (15 janvier-7 avril 1906) par André Tardieu ... Paris, F. Alcan, 1907.
1 p. l., iii, 554 p. 22½ cm. (*On cover:* Bibliothèque d'histoire contemporaine)
"Acte général de la Conférence internationale d'Algésiras": p. 504-531.

1. Algeciras. International conference on Moroccan affairs, 1906. 2. Morocco—Pol. & govt. 3. Morocco—For. rel.

Library of Congress   DT317.T28 1907   20-22483

NT 0038709   DLC PHC NjP MB MH NN

F
9297

Tardieu, André Pierre Gabriel Amédée, 1876-1945.
La conférence d'Algésiras; histoire diplomatique de la
crise marocaine (15 janvier-7 avril 1906) par André Tardieu ... Paris, F. Alcan, 1907.
1 p. l., iii, 554 p. 22½cm. (*On cover:* Bibliothèque d'histoire contemporaine)
"Acte général de la Conférence internationale d'Algésiras": p. 504-531.
Microfilm (negative) Washington, Library
of Congress, 1973. 1 reel.

NT 0038710   NNC

Tardieu, André Pierre Gabriel Amédée, 1876–1945.
La conférence d'Algésiras; histoire diplomatique de la crise marocaine (15 janvier–7 avril 1906) par André Tardieu ... 2. éd. Paris, F. Alcan, 1908.
2 p. l., x, iii, 554 p. 23cm.
"Acte général de la Conférence internationale d'Algésiras": appendix XII, p. 504–531.

1. Algeciras. International conference on Moroccan affairs, 1906. 2. Morocco—Pol. & govt. 3. Morocco—For. rel.

7—38523
Library of Congress DT317.T28

NT 0038711 DLC NcD CU IEN MiU

Tardieu, André Pierre Gabriel Amédée, 1876–1945.
La conférence d'Algésiras; histoire diplomatique de la crise marocaine (15 janvier–7 avril 1906) par André Tardieu ... 3. éd., rev. et augm. ... Paris, F. Alcan, 1909.
2 p. l., iii, 604 p. 23cm. (*On cover:* Bibliothèque d'histoire contemporaine)
"Acte général de la Conférence internationale d'Algésiras": appendix XII, p. 504–531.
"Le Maroc après la conférence (1906–1909)": p. [541]–590.

1. Algeciras. International conference on Moroccan affairs, 1906. 2. Morocco—Pol. & govt. 3. Morocco—For. rel. I. Title.

21–1468
Library of Congress DT317.T28 1909

NT 0038712 DLC PU OClW NjP

D
505
W92
v.12
no.7

Tardieu, André Pierre Gabriel Amédée, 1876-1945.
La coopération américaine et la guerre / André Tardieu. Paris : Société des études économiques, 1918.
20 p. ; 21 cm.
Cover title.
No. 7 in vol. lettered: World War, 1914-1918. Pamphlets, 12.

NT 0038713 NIC

Tardieu, André Pierre Gabriel Amédée, 1876–1945.
... Devant l'obstacle; l'Amérique et nous. Paris, Émile-Paul frères, 1927.
2 p. l., [vii]–xii, 311, [1] p. 20½cm.
At head of title: André Tardieu.
On cover: Dix-neuvième édition.
Published also in English under title: France and America; some experiences in coöperation.

1. France—Relations (general) with U. S. 2. U. S.—Relations (general) with France. 3. France—Hist. 4. European war, 1914–1918—U. S. 5. Reconstruction (1914–)—France. I. Title.

28–14077
Library of Congress DC59.8.U6T2

TNJ NcU OClC OCU OO OCl NN CSt-H
NT 0038714 DLC OrPR PBm PU CtY TxU MB MiU OKentU

DC
59
.8
U58
T18
1929

Tardieu, André Pierre Gabriel Amédée, 1876-1945.
Devant l'obstacle; l'Amérique et nous. Paris, Émile-Paul frères, 1929.
2 p. l., [vii]-xii, 311, [1] p. 21cm.
At head of title: André Tardieu.
Published also in English under title: France and America; some experiences in coöperation.
1. France--Relations (general) with U. S. 2. U. S.--Relations (general) with France. 3. France--Hist. 4. European war, 1914-1918--U. S. 5. Reconstruction (1914-)--France. I. Title. II. His France and America.

NT 0038715 NIC TNJ OU CU-I MoSU

Tardieu, André Pierre Gabriel Amédée, 1876–1945
... Devant le pays. Paris, E. Flammarion [1932]
xxvii, [29]–247, [2] p. 18½cm.
A collection of addresses delivered by the author in 1932.
CONTENTS.—Les devoirs immédiats.—La paix française.—Aristide Briand.—Le travail de quatre ans.—La tâche de la prochaine Chambre.—Veille de scrutin.—Le drame du cartel.—Paul Doumer.

1. France—Pol. & govt.—1914– I. Title.

32–23598
Library of Congress DC395.T3
Copyright A—Foreign 17615
[2] 944.08

NT 0038716 DLC ViU NN CLU WU OClW

Tardieu, André Pierre Gabriel Amédée, 1876–1945.
La doctrine de Monroe et le panaméricanisme. Conférence. (In: Les questions actuelles de politique étrangère dans l'Amérique du Nord... Paris, 1911. 12°. p. 187-227.)

1. Monroe doctrine.
N. Y. P. L. September 26, 1911.

NT 0038717 NN

Tardieu, André Pierre Gabriel Amédée, 1876–1945.
... L'épreuve du pouvoir. [Paris] E. Flammarion [1931]
xix, [21]–282 p., 2 l. 19cm.
At head of title: André Tardieu.
Fourteen speeches delivered between November 7, 1929, and December 4, 1930.
CONTENTS.—Vers une politique neuve.—L'appel aux citoyens.—La France et l'Europe.—Le bilan.

1. France—Pol. & govt.—1914– 2. France—For. rel.—1914– I. Title.

32–22970
Library of Congress DC394.T3
Copyright A—Foreign 12404
[2] 944.08

NT 0038718 DLC CtY PU MH NIC NN

Tardieu, André Pierre Gabriel Amédée, 1876–1945.
France and America; some experiences in coöperation, by André Tardieu. Boston and New York, Houghton Mifflin company, 1927.
vii, [1], 311, [1] p. 21½cm.
Published also in French under title: Devant l'obstacle: l'Amérique et nous.

1. France—Relations (general) with U. S. 2. U. S.—Relations (general) with France. 3. France—Hist. 4. European war, 1914–1918—U. S. 5. Reconstruction (1914–1939)—France. I. Title.

27—10224
Library of Congress DC59.8.U6T3
——— Copy 2. E183.8.F8T3
[a45r37o1] 327.440973

WaT OrPR IdU WaSp WaS Or
OClW OClWHi OCl ViU NjN MB NN CLU NcC TU DAU NcRS
NT 0038719 DLC NcU NIC PPPL KEmT PPD PPA PP OEac OO

Tardieu, André Pierre Gabriel Amédée, 1876–1945.
France and the alliances; the struggle for the balance of power, by André Tardieu ... New York, The Macmillan company, 1908.
x, 314 p. 21cm.

1. France—For. rel.—1870– 2. Europe—Politics—1871– 3. Balance of power. I. Title.

8—31144
Library of Congress DC341.T3

OrPR WaS PU NjP MB NN
NIC NcU ODW OCl OCU DNW DN ViU OU OOxM MiU OO N WaT
NT 0038720 DLC PPT PHC PSC MtU OKentU ICRL CoU CLU

DC
341
T18

Tardieu, André Pierre Gabriel Amédée, 1876-
La France et les alliances; la lutte pour l'équilibre. Paris, F. Alcan, 1909.
iii, 365 p. 19cm. (Bibliothèque d'histoire contemporaine)

1. France--For. rel.--1870-1940.
2. Europe--Politics--1871-1918.
3. Balance of power. I. Title.

NT 0038721 NIC MiDW MH NBC

Tardieu, André Pierre Gabriel Amédée, 1876–1945.
La France et les alliances; la lutte pour l'équilibre (1871–1910) par André Tardieu ... 3. éd., refondue et complétée. Paris, F. Alcan, 1910.
2 p. l., iii, [1], 428 p. 19cm. (*On cover:* Bibliothèque d'histoire contemporaine)
"Ouvrage couronné par l'Académie des sciences morales et politiques."

1. France—For. rel.—1870– 2. Europe—Politics—1871– 3. Balance of power. I. Title.

19–6533
Library of Congress DC341.T3 1910

NT 0038722 DLC ICU ICJ MiU

Tardieu, André Pierre Gabriel Amédée, 1876–1945.
... France in danger! A great statesman's warning; translated from the French by Gerald Griffin. London, D. Archer, 1935.
4 p. l., 13–256 p. front., ports. 22½cm.
At head of title: André Tardieu.

1. France—Pol. & govt.—1914– 2. Germany—Pol. & govt.—1918– 3. France—For. rel.—Germany. 4. Germany—For. rel.—France. 5. Versailles, Treaty of, June 28, 1919 (Germany) I. Griffin, Gerald, tr. II. Title. *Translation of* L'heure de la décision.

35–17810
Library of Congress DC389.T32
[3] 944.08

NT 0038723 DLC NcD OU CtY NN OCl

4DD-
1443

Tardieu, André Pierre Gabriel Amédée, 1876-1945.
Fürst von Bülow. Berlin, H. Bondy, 1910.
336 p.

NT 0038724 DLC-P4

Tardieu, André Pierre Gabriel Amédée, 1876–1945.
... L'heure de la décision. [Paris] E. Flammarion [°1934]
viii, [9]–281 p., 2 l. 19cm.
At head of title: André Tardieu.

1. France—Pol. & govt.—1914– 2. Germany—Pol. & govt.—1918– 3. France—For. rel.—Germany. 4. Germany—For. rel.—France. 5. Versailles, Treaty of, June 28, 1919 (Germany) I. Title.

34–10227
Library of Congress DC389.T3
Copyright A—Foreign 23976
944.08

NT 0038725 DLC PBm OrPR ViU KyLoU NN

DA644
.T293
D644
.T293

Tardieu, André Pierre Gabriel Amédée, 1876–1945.
... Мир; перевод с французского под редакцией и с вступительной статьей Б. Е. Штейна. [Москва] Огиз, Госполитиздат, 1943.
xxiv, 430, [2] p. 22½cm. (Библиотека внешней политики)
At head of title: ... А. Тардье.
"Русский перевод ... сверен по французскому изданию A. Tardieu 'La paix,' Paris 1921 ... Перевод с французского сделан Н. П. Довгалевской."

1. Versailles. Treaty of June 28, 1919 (Germany) I. Stein, Boris Efimovich, 1872– ed. II. Dovgalevskaia, N. P., tr. III. Title.
Title transliterated: Mir.

44-24871

NT 0038726 DLC

Tardieu, André Pierre Gabriel Amédée, 1876–1945.
... Le mystère d'Agadir. Paris, Calmann-Lévy [°1912]
3 p. l., 619 p. fold. maps. 23 cm.

1. Morocco—For. rel.—Germany. 2. Germany—For rel.—Morocco. 3. Agadir, Morocco. I. Title.

DT317.T3 12—10654

PU PHC OKentU OU CU
NT 0038727 DLC MB IEN N MU OClW NN NjP MiU NcD CtY

Tardieu, André Pierre Gabriel Amédée, 1876–1945.
... La note de semaine, 1936. [Paris] E. Flammarion [1937]
viii, [9]–245 p., 2 l. 18½cm.
At head of title: André Tardieu.
"Je groupe ici mes articles de Gringoire de 1936."—Avant-propos.

1. France—Pol. & govt.—1914– 2. France—For. rel.—1914– I. Title.

37–5537
Library of Congress DC396.T28
Copyright A—Foreign 34874
[3] 944.08

NT 0038728 DLC PU NNC

Tardieu, André Pierre Gabriel Amédée, 1876-1945.
... La note de semaine, 1937. ₍Paris₎ E. Flammarion ₍1938₎
248 p., 1 l. 18½ᶜᵐ.
At head of title: André Tardieu.
"Pour la seconde fois, je réunis, en fin d'année mes articles hebdomadaires de Gringoire."—Avant-propos.

1. Europe—Politics—1914-   2. France—Pol. & govt.—1914-
I. Title.

                              38-37730
Library of Congress   DC396.T282
Copyright A—Foreign   38842
                      ₍3₎   944.08

NT   0038729   DLC NNC NIC

Tardieu, André Pierre Gabriel Amédée, 1876-1945.
... Notes de semaine 1938. L'année de Munich. Paris, Flammarion ₍1939₎
252 p., 1 l. 18½ᶜᵐ.
At head of title: André Tardieu.

1. France—Pol. & govt.—1914-1940. 2. France—For. rel.—1914-1940.
3. History—Year-books—1938. 4. Munich four-power agreement, 1938.
I. Title. II. Title: L'année de Munich.

   DC389.T33   944.08   40-2480

NT   0038730   DLC OrU CtY RPB OC1 PU MiU MH

Tardieu, André Pierre Gabriel Amédée, 1876-1945.
Notes sur les États-unis: la société, la politique,
la diplomatie. Paris, Calmann-Levy, n. d.
381 p.

NT   0038731   PP

Tardieu, André Pierre Gabriel Amédée, 1876-
... Notes sur les États-unis: la société—la politique, la diplomatie. Paris, Calmann-Lévy ₍1908₎
2 p. l., iii, 381 p. 18½ᶜᵐ.
On cover: Troisième édition.

1. U. S.—Soc. life & cust. 2. U. S.—Pol. & govt.—1901-1909. 3. U. S.—
For. rel.—1901-1909.

                            9-3114
Library of Congress   E168.T18

     OO ICJ NWM NjR NjP DPU
NT   0038732   DLC ICU GU NIC NN TNJ PU UU CtY NcD OC1

Tardieu, André Pierre Gabriel Amédée, 1876-
... La paix, préface de Georges Clemenceau. Paris, Payot & cⁱᵉ, 1921.
2 p. l., ₍vii₎-xxxii, 520 p. 23ᶜᵐ. (On cover: Collection de mémoires, études et documents pour servir à l'histoire de la guerre mondiale)
At head of title: André Tardieu.
On cover: 10ᵉ mille.

1. Versailles, Treaty of, June 28, 1919 (Germany) I. Title.

                           22-13160
Library of Congress   D644.T29

NT   0038733   DLC NbU OkentU MH PU DNW MeB FMU IU MiU

DC
373
.T2   Tardieu, André Pierre Gabriel Amédée, 1876-
A44   Paroles réalistes. Paris, E.Figuière, 1928.
        229 p. port. (Les Paroles du XXᵉ siècle)

       1.France—Pol. & govt.—1914-1940.
       I.Title.

NT   0038734   MiU

Tardieu, André Pierre Gabriel Amédée, 1876-
The policy of France.

From FOREIGN AFFAIRS, Sept. 15, 1922, p.11-29
88298

NT   0038735   DNW

Tardieu, André Pierre Gabriel Amédée, 1876-
... Le prince de Bülow; l'homme et le milieu, la politique extérieure, la politique intérieure. Paris, Calmann-Lévy ₍1909₎
3 p. l., ₍3₎-373, ₍1₎ p. 19ᶜᵐ.

1. Bülow, Bernhard Heinrich Martin Karl, fürst von, 1849-
            2. Germany—Pol. & govt.—1888-
many—For. rel.—1888-   3. Germany—Pol. & govt.—1888-

                              9-30053
Library of Congress   DD231.B8T3

     OC1W OC1 CtY
NT   0038736   DLC OrPR NIC TU UU PPL PU OKentU NcD NN

Tardieu, André Pierre Gabriel Amédée. 1876-1945.   2819.75
Le prince de Bülow. L'homme et le milieu. La politique extérieure.
La politique intérieure.
Paris. Calmann-Lévy. [1910.] (3), 373, (1) pp. 18½ cm., in
12s and 6s.
Relates to the contemporary political history of Germany.

H3309—Germany. Pol. hist.—Buelow, Bernhard Heinrich Martin Carl, Fuerst von. 1849-

NT   0038737   MB

Tardieu, André Pierre Gabriel Amédée, 1876-1945.
Questions diplomatiques de l'année 1904, par André Tardieu
... France et Italie; France et Angleterre; Siam; Maroc;
Saint-Siège: Tunisie; Macédoine; Serbie; Crète; Russie et
Japon; la Chine et la guerre. Paris, F. Alcan, 1905.
2 p. l., 319 p. 19ᶜᵐ. (On cover: Bibliothèque d'histoire contemporaine)
CONTENTS.—Introduction.—1. ptie. Politique française.—2. ptie. Question d'Orient.—3. ptie. La guerre russo-japonaise.—Appendice: I. Traité franco-siamois du 15 février 1904. II. L'accord franco-anglais.

1. France—For. rel.—1870-   2. Eastern question. 3. Russo-
Japanese war, 1904-1905. 4. Europe—Politics—1871-   I. Title.

                            5-34222
Library of Congress   D443.T2

NT   0038738   DLC NcD OC1W NjP NN

342.44   **Tardieu, André Pierre Gabriel Amédée,** 1876-
T17r8Pp   La reforma del estado. Su problema en
      España, preámbulo de José María Gil Robles.
      Traducción española ₍por₎ Luis de Pedroso y
      Madan₎ Madrid, Librería Internacional de
      Romo ₍1935₎
        209p. fold.illus. 19cm.

      Translation of La réforme de l'état.

      1. France—Pol. & govt.—1914-1940. I. Title.

NT   0038739   IU MH IEN

Tardieu, André Pierre Gabriel Amédée, 1876-1945
... La réforme de l'état; les idées maîtresses de "L'heure de la décision". ₍Paris₎ E. Flammarion ₍1934₎
viii, ₍9₎-142 p. 18ᶜᵐ.
At head of title: André Tardieu.

1. France—Pol. & govt.—1914-   I. Title.
                              35-2191
Library of Congress   JN2593.1934.T3
Copyright A—Foreign   26356
                  ₍2₎   342.44

NT   0038740   DLC MiU PU CtY TU

Tardieu, André, 1876-1945.
La réforme de l'état; les idées maîtresses de
L'heure de la decision. [Paris] Flammarion [1934]
viii, 142 p.
Microfilm, positive, of Harvard College Library copy
                    Film Mas 368
———. Microfilm, master copy, of Harvard College
Library copy

NT   0038741   MH

Tardieu, André Pierre Gabriel Amédée, 1876-
... La révolution à refaire ... ₍Paris₎ E. Flammarion ₍1936-
v. 18½ᶜᵐ.
At head of title: André Tardieu.

1. France—Pol. & govt.—1870-   I. Title.
                              36-14259
Library of Congress   DC340.T3
Copyright A—Foreign   31497
                              944.08

     OU NNC MU OC1 OO NN CaBVaU ICU
NT   0038742   DLC InU CSt-H ViU FU PU MB WU CtY NcD

Tardieu, André Pierre Gabriel Amédée, 1876- , and **F. C. von
Jessen.**
Le Slesvig et la paix, janvier 1919 - janvier 1920, par André
Tardieu en collaboration avec F. de Jessen. Paris: J. Meynial,
1928. xvi, 393 p. 4°.

4Z7072A. 1. Schleswig. 2. European   war, 1914-1918—Territorial questions
—Schleswig. 3. Jessen, Franz   Christopher von, 1870-1926, jt. au.
                              September 23, 1929

     CtY ICU DCE
NT   0038743   NN MiU RPB NjR PU OC1 NRU OC1W CSt-H MH

D
651   Tardieu, André Pierre Gabriel Amédée, 1876-1945
S4   Slesvig paa fredskonferencen januar 1919-januar
T3   1920. I samarbejde med Franz v. Jessen. København, Slesvigsk forlag, 1926.
        518p. illus. 24cm.

       1. European War, 1914-1918 - Territorial
       questions - Schleswig 2. Paris. Peace Conference, 1919 I. Jessen, Franz Christopher
       von, 1870- jot author II. Title

NT   0038744   WU MnU NN

Tardieu, André Pierre Gabriel Amédée, 1876-1945.   F354.44-T
Le souverain captif ₍by₎ André Tardieu. ₍Paris₎ Ernest Flammarion ₍cop. 1936₎ 282 p. 12°. (La Révolution à refaire, 1.)

1. France—Govt. and politics.   2. France—Hist. 3. Title. 4. Ser.
N. Y. P. L.   September 8, 1936

NT   0038745   NN

Tardieu, André Pierre Gabriel Amédée, 1876-1945
... Sur la pente. ₍Paris₎ E. Flammarion ₍1935₎
lxx, 250, ₍2₎ p. 18½ᶜᵐ.
At head of title: André Tardieu.
Consists principally of speeches made in the Chamber of deputies,
1932-33.
"Avant-propos. Histoire de trois ans ₍1932-1935₎": p. ₍vii₎-lxx.

1. France—Pol. & govt.—1914-   2. Stavisky, Serge Alexandre,
1886-1934. I. Title.
                              35-13965
Library of Congress   DC396.T3
Copyright A—Foreign   28274
                  ₍3₎   944.08

NT   0038746   DLC CaBVaU CtY ICU MiU NN

Tardieu, André Pierre Gabriel Amédée, 1876-1945.
The truth about the Treaty, by André Tardieu, foreword
by Edward M. House, introduction by Georges Clemenceau.
Indianapolis, The Bobbs-Merrill company [*1921]
11 p. l., 473 p. 23½ cm.

1. Versailles, Treaty of, June 28, 1919 (Germany)   I. Title.

       21—7504

Library of Congress   D644.T3

PBa

NT   0038747   DNW ViU OC1WHi OC1W OC1h OCU NNUN PSt TxU PBm UU
NjN NjP NcC KEmT MiHM MB NN ICJ OU OK OC1 WaU MiU
OrSaW WaT MtBC WaSp MtU OrP IdB PPLas PHC WaTU DN
DLC WaSpG IdU CaBVa CaBVaU Or WaWW WaS

Tardieu, Antoine Charles Marie Anne de,
marquis de Maleissye, 1764-1851

See

Maleissye, Antoine Charles Marie Anne de
Tardieu, marquis de, 1764-1851

912
T17
2ed

Tardieu, Antoine François.
Atlas de tableaux et de cartes gravé par
P.F. Tardieu. Pour Le cours complet de cosmo-
graphie, de géographie, de chronologie et d'histoire ancienne et moderne, par Edme Mentelle.
2d édition.   Paris, chez Bernard, 1804.
20 fold maps & plans, 26cm

NT   0038749   MnCS

Cm912
1800c2

[Tardieu, Antoine François, 1757-
Carta delle provincie meridionali degli
Stati-Uniti. [n.p., 1800?]
34 x 49cm.
Scale of miles about 40 to the inch.
Based on Carte des provinces méridionales
des Etats-Unis, engraved by P. F. Tardieu.

1. N.C.--Maps   2. Southern States--Maps
I. Title.

NT   0038750   NcU

Tardieu, Antoine François, 1757-   No. 31 in *Map 129.3
Carte de l'isle de Cuba et les Isles Lucayes.
—   [Paris, 1789.] Size, 12 × 16⅛ inches. Scale (computed),
39 geographical miles to 1 inch.

*D6663 — Cuba. Geog. Maps. — Bahama Islands. Geog. Maps.

NT   0038751   MB

Tardieu, Antoine Francois, 1757-
Carte de l'Ile de Martha's Vineyard...
8 7/16 x 10 1/4 in. (In Crevecoeur's
Lettres d'un Cultivateur Americain. Paris,
1787. v2 p147.
Grave par P. F. Tardieu.(ie. A. F.
Tardieu, cf Phillips Atlas 706.)

NT   0038752   MiU-C

Tardieu, Antoine Francois, 1757-
Carte de L'Ile de Nantucket...
7 13/16 x 10 3/4 in. (In Crevecoeur's
Lettres d'un Cultivateur Americain. Paris,
1787. v2 p99.
Grave par P. F. Tardieu. (ie. A. F.
Tardieu, cf Phillips Atlas 706.)

NT   0038753   MiU-C

Cm912
1775t

Tardieu, Antoine François, 1757-
Carte de la Caroline Méridionale et Septentrionale et de la Virginie.   [Paris, ca.
1775]
32 x 43 cm. (No. 135)
Scale of British miles 33 to an inch.
Probably from atlas published by Edme Mentelle.

Cm912
1775t.1

--- -----Another edition, with many place
names added.

NT   0038754   NcU

Cm912
1800c.1

Tardieu, Antoine François, 1757-
Carte de la partie méridionale des Etats-
Unis gravé par P. F. Tardieu. [n.p., ca.
1800]
38 x 51 cm. (Pl. IX à fin du Tom II)
Scale of miles about 38 to an inch.
Another edition of his Carte des provinces
méridionales, with added place names and details.

1. N.C.--Maps. 2. Southern States--Maps
I. Title.   Card for Map Room.

NT   0038755   NcU

Tardieu, Antoine Francois, 1757-
Carte de la partie méridionale des Etats-Unis,
gravé par P. F. Tardieu.   n.p.,n.d. (circa 1830)
1 p.   (Photostat)

NT   0038756   PHi

Tardieu, Antoine Francois, 1757-1822.
Carte de la Russie d'Europe ...
see under   Lapie, Pierre, 1779-1850.

Tardieu, Antoine François. 1757-1822.   No. 42 in *Map 129.1
Carte des Antilles.
[Paris. 1789.] Size, 11¹⁵/₁₆ × 16¾ inches. Scale (computed),
32 geographical miles to 1 inch.

I15468 — West Indies. Geog. Maps.

NT   0038758   MB

Tardieu, Antoine François. 1757-1822.   No. 43 in *Map 129.1
Carte des Isles de la Jamaique et de Sᵗ. Domingue.
[Paris. 1789.] Size, 11⅞ × 16⅛ inches. Scale (computed), 38
miles to 1 inch.

H5469 — Hayti. Geog. Maps. — Jamaica. Geog. Maps.

NT   0038759   MB

Cm912
1800c

Tardieu, Antoine François, 1757-
Carte des provinces méridionales des Etats-
Unis. [n.p., ca. 1800]
34 x 49 cm. (Plate III)
Scale of French miles 40 to an inch.

1. N.C.--Maps   2. Southern States--Maps
I. Title.   Card for Map Room.

NT   0038760   NcU

Tardieu, Antoine François. 1757-1822.   No. 41 in *Map 129.1
Carte du Golfe du Mexique et des Isles Antilles.
[Paris. 1789.] Size, 12 × 16¾ inches. Scale (computed), 161.3
miles to 1 inch.

H5469 — Mexico. Gulf of. Geog. Maps. — West Indies. Geog. Maps.

NT   0038761   MB

Tardieu, Antoine François, 1757-1822.
Extrait d'une carte manuscrit du cours
de fleuve St.Louis... Paris le 30 mars
1846.
56.8 x 37.3 cm.
Vignaud.
2 copies.

NT   0038762   MiU-C

GN789
.U5T18

TARDIEU, ANTOINE FRANÇOIS,1757-1822
Fortifications des anciens indigenes sur la
riviere Huron ou Aigle Chauve. Cette esquisse
fut envoyeé au Général Washington par A.Steiner
le 28 Mai 1789. n.p.,n.pub. [1790?]   2 plans
on 1 sheet.   15x22cm.fold.to 20 x12 cm.

NT   0038763   InU

Tardieu, Antoine François, 1757-1822.
A map of Louisiana and Mexico. Paris,1820.
99x67 cm.
Phillips maps of America p. 373.
Gravee par P.A. F. Tardieu, pere.
in two sections.
Vignaud.

NT   0038764   MiU-C

Tardieu, Antoine François. 1757-1822.   No. 1 in *Map 117.2
United States of Nᵗʰ. America. Carte des États-Unis de l'Amérique
Septentrionale copiée et gravée sur celle d'Arrowsmith corrigée
et considérablement augmentée . . . Par P. F. Tardieu [pseud.],
gravenr.
Paris. L'an XI (1802). Size, 46¾ × 54 inches. Scale (com-
puted), 25 geographical miles to 1 inch. Vignette. Folded.
Submap. — Plan de la ville de Washington.
The vignette is a view of Niagara Falls, with explanatory text in French
and English.

H1575 — United States. Geog. Maps. — Niagara Falls.

NT   0038765   MB MdBP

Tardieu, Antoine Francois,1757-1822.
United States of Nth America. Carte des
Etats-unis de l'Amerique Septentrionale
copiee et gravee sur celle d'Arrowsmith
corrigee et considerablement augmentee d'
apres les renseignemens les plus authentique
par P.F.Tardieu, graveur, editeur-proprie-
taire. Place de l'Estrapade No.18. A Paris
1808.
Inset: Plan de la ville de Washington
situee sur le territoire de Columbia, cede
par les Etats de Virginie et Maryland aux
Etats Unis de Amerique...1800.

NT   0038766   MiU-C

Tardieu, Antoine Francois,1757-1822.
United States of Nth America. Carte des
Etats-Unis de Amerique septentrionale,
copiee et gravee sur celle d'Arrowsmith
corrigee... par P.F.Tardieu...a Paris 1812.
Atlas alcove. Green cloth case.

NT   0038767   MiU-C

HS   Tardieu, Armand Louis, 1807-1867.
397   La justice de la franc-maçonnerie; appel
T18   á l'opinion publique. Bruxelles, Office de
J9   publicité, 1858.
    73 p. 21cm.

    "Post-scriptum" signed: A. L. Tardieu.

    1. Freemasons. I. Title.

NT 0038768   NIC

Tardieu, Auguste Ambroise
    see
    Tardieu, Ambroise Auguste, 1818-1879.

RC343   Tardieu, C., 1916-   joint author.
T3   **Tardieu, Guy,** 1914-
    Le système nerveux végétatif, par G. Tardieu et C. Tardieu. Paris, Masson, 1948.

Tardieu (Charles). *Des appareils inamovibles. 114 pp., 1 L, 1 pl. 4°. Paris, 1844, No. 32, v. 49*

NT 0038771   DNLM PPC

Tardieu, Charles.   F940.9-T
    Sous la pluie de fer; impressions d'un marsouin; les Marquises (1914) — Massiges (1915); préface de Alfred Capus. Paris: Calmann-Lévy ₍cop. 1917₎. 272 p. 12°.

1. Title. 2. European war.
N. Y. P. L.   September 18, 1917.

NT 0038772   NN MiU CSt-H MU NjP MiU

Tardieu, Charles, *novelist*
    ... Cinq à sept, roman. Paris, J. Ferenczi et fils ₍ᶜ1923₎
    2 p. l., ₍7₎-254 p. 19ᶜᵐ.

    I. Title.
    Library of Congress   PQ2639.A7C5 1923   23-15620

NT 0038773   DLC

Tardieu, Charles, *novelist.*
    ... La maison du bout du quai, roman. Paris, J. Ferenczi ₍ᶜ1922₎
    252 p. 19ᶜᵐ.   fr. 6.75

    I. Title.
    Library of Congress   PQ2639.A7M3 1922   22-18848

NT 0038774   DLC PU

Tardieu, Charles Henri, 1838-   ed.
L'Art; revue mensuelle illustrée ... 1.-
année (t. 1-   ); 1875-
Paris, Librairie de l'Art ₍etc., etc.₎ 1875-

Tardieu, Charles Henri, 1838-
    ... Lettres de Bayreuth. L'Anneau du Nibelung de Richard Wagner; représentations données en août 1876 ... Bruxelles, Schott frères, 1883.
    175, ₍1₎ p. 17½ᶜᵐ.
    Extrait de l'Indépendance belge.
    "Richard Wagner, oeuvres publiées par Schott frères": p. ₍169₎-175.

    1. Wagner, Richard. Der ring des Nibelungen.
                            9-4434
    Library of Congress   ML410.W2T18

NT 0038776   DLC MiU MB

         Tardieu, E.
NA1047   **Gourlier, Charles Pierre,** 1786-1857.
.G67   Choix d'édifices publics projetés et construits en France depuis le commencement du xixᵐᵉ siècle; publié avec l'autorisation
Folio   du Ministre de l'intérieur, par mm. Gourlier, Biet, Grillon, et feu Tardieu ... Paris, L. Colas ₍etc.₎ 1825-50.

Tardieu (Émile). *De l'état local et de l'état général dans les maladies. 124 pp. 4°. Lyon, 1885, No. 249.*

NT 0038778   DNLM

Tardieu, Émile.
    L'ennui, étude psychologique, par Émile Tardieu. Paris, F. Alcan, 1903. vii, 297 p. 23cm. (Bibliothèque de philosophie contemporaine.)

299525B. 1. Ennui.
N. Y. P. L.   June 29, 1945

NT 0038779   NN ICRL CU MBCo ICJ MB

BF   Tardieu, Émile
323   L'ennui; étude psychologique. 2. éd. rev.
.E5   et corr. Paris, F. Alcan, 1913.
T18   ₍vi₎ 283 p. 22 cm.

    Bibliographical footnotes.

    1. Interest (Psychology) I. Title.

NT 0038780   DCU PU MiU OU NIC NcD-MC

Tardieu, Émile.
    Znudzenie. ₍n. p., 1903?₎ 239 p. 12°.
    t.-p. missing.
    Translated by M. Massonius.

1. Ennui. 2. Massonius, Marjan,   1859-   , translator. 3. Title.
N. Y. P. L.   November 17, 1926

NT 0038781   NN

Tardieu, Eugène.
    ... L'industrie du vêtement pour hommes à Bruxelles et dans l'agglomération bruxelloise, par Eugène Tardieu ... ₍Bruxelles, J. Lebègue et cⁱᵉ, 1899₎
    ₍197₎-276 p. incl. tables. 25ᶜᵐ. (Belgium. Office du travail. Les industries à domicile en Belgique, vol. I ₍no. 2₎)
    "Débouchés": p. 244-246.
    "La législation du travail": p. 270.
    "Annexe ... un type de règlement d'atelier": p. 271-273.

    1. Clothing trade—Brussels. 2. Tailors—Brussels. I. Title.
                            15-2303
    Library of Congress   HD2336.B4A3 vol. 1, no. 2

NT 0038782   DLC MiU NN

Tardieu, Eugène, 1851-
    Psychologie militaire. Notions de psychologie et leurs applications a l'éducation militaire, par Eugène Tardieu ... Bruxelles, P. Weissenbruch, 1898.
    110 p. 18 cm.
    1. Psychology. 2. War. 3. Military education.

NT 0038783   CU

Tardieu (Eugène) ₍1881- ₎. *Étude sur le massage du cœur, expérimental et clinique. Une observation inédite. vii, 9-45 pp., 1 L. 8°. Montpellier, 1905, No. 82.*

NT 0038784   DNLM

Tardieu, Eugène Amédée
    see
Tardieu, Amédée, 1822-1893.

Tardieu, Frézal, 1814-1871.
    Missions catholiques des îles Sandwich, ou Hawaii, par serviteur de Dieu, le r. p. Frézal Tardieu ... Notice annotée complétée par le r. p. Ildefonse Alazard ... Paris ₍etc.₎ Bureaux des Annales des Sacrés-cœurs, 1924.
    78, ₍2₎ p. front., illus. (incl. double map) plates, ports. 23ᵐᵐ.

    1. Missions—Hawaiian islands. 2. Catholic church—Missions.
    I. Alazard, Ildefonse, ed.
                 ₍Secular name: Jean Pierre Eugène Tardieu₎
                          31-20475
    Library of Congress   BV3680.H3T3   ₍266.2₎ 279.69

NT 0038786   DLC NN

Tardieu, G.
    ...Les limites naturelles de la Provence. Marseille: A. Tacussel, 1926. 11 p. 8°.

1. Provence—Bound.
N. Y. P. L.   June 1, 1927

NT 0038787   NN DLC

Tardieu, Gustave-Jean, 1910-
    ... Contribution à l'étude de l'hémoglobinurie paroxystique "a frigore" du cheval ... Paris, 1935.
    At head of title: École nationale vétérinaire d'Alfort, année 1935, no. 31.
    Thèse - Univ. de Paris.
    "Bibliographie": p. ₍63₎-68.

NT 0038788   CtY

Tardieu, Guy, 1914-
    ... Le coma, étude clinique, recherches expérimentales et anatomiques ... Paris, Imprimerie R. Foulon, 1942.
    368 p.
    Thèse.

NT 0038789   DNLM CtY DLC-P4 MnU

Tardieu, Guy, 1914-
    Le système nerveux végétatif, par G. Tardieu et C. Tardieu. Paris, Masson, 1948.
    742 p. illus. 26 cm.
    "Bibliographie": p. ₍709₎-728.

    1. Nervous system, Sympathetic. 2. Nervous system—Diseases.
    I. Tardieu, C., 1916-   joint author. II. Title.
               RC343.T3   48-25750*

     NcD-MC
NT 0038790   DLC OrCS OrU-M PPC CtY NcD OU DNLM ICU

Tardieu, H., joint author.

Boizard, Émile, 1850–
Histoire de la législation des sucres (1664–1891) suivie d'un résumé général des lois et règlements en vigueur, d'annexes, de tableaux statistiques et d'une table chronologique et analytique des lois, règlements et décrets depuis l'origine; par E. Boizard ... et H. Tardieu ... Paris, Bureaux de la "Sucrerie indigène et coloniale," 1891.

TARDIEU,J. ,ancien capitaine d'artillerie.
Explication de la déviation apparente du plan d'oscillation du pendule dans,les expériences de M.Foucault et recherche de la formule qui donne la loi de cette déviation,le tout fondé sur des considérations purement géometriques. Paris,1851.

po.14.

NT 0038792 MH

Tardieu, Jacques, 1861–
... Traité théorique et pratique de la legislation des pensions de retraite, par J. Tardieu ... Avec la collaboration de MM. Basset, Smet et Carrière ... Paris, P. Dupont, 1906.
380 p. 28½ x 22½ᶜᵐ.
Extrait du "Répertoire du droit administratif."

1. Pensions—France. I. Basset, Frédéric, joint author. II. Smet, Tony, joint author. III. Carrière, Gabriel, joint author.

7—32573

Library of Congress   JN2748.T2

NT 0038793 DLC ICJ

Tardieu, Jacques, 1861–
Traité théorique et pratique des contributions directes, par J. Tardieu ... Paris, L. Larose, 1896.
2 p. l., 498 p. 28 x 23ᶜᵐ.
Extrait du Répertoire général alphabétique du droit français.

1. Taxation—France—Law.

13—24016

Library of Congress   HJ3476 1896

NT 0038794 DLC

Tardieu, Jacques, 1861–
Traité théorique et pratique des patentes, par J. Tardieu ... Paris, L. Larose, 1902.
2 p. l., ₇7₎–258 p. 28½ᶜᵐ.
"Extrait du Répertoire général alphabétique du droit français."

1. Business tax—France.
₍Full name: Jacques León Jules Amedée Tardieu₎

12–30113

NT 0038795 DLC ICRL ICJ

Tardieu, Jacques, 1861–
Traité théorique et pratique des patentes, par J. Tardieu ... Paris, L. Larose, 1902.
2 p. l., ₇7₎–258 p. 28½ᶜᵐ.
"Extrait du Répertoire général alphabétique du droit français."

1. Business tax—France.
₍Full name: Jacques León Jules Amedée Tardieu₎

12–30113

NT 0038795 DLC ICRL ICJ

Tardieu, Jean, 1903–
... Accents. Paris, Gallimard ₍1939₎
2 p. l., 7–94 p., 1 l. 19ᶜᵐ.
Poems.
"Transposition en rythmes français de L'archipel de Hölderlin": p. ₍65₎–92.

I. *Hölderlin, Friedrich, 1770–1843. Der archipelagus. II. Title.

Library of Congress   PQ2639.A72A7 1939   39–24270
Copyright A–Foreign   42873
₍2₎   841.91

NT 0038796 DLC CtY MiU

ND552
.F7

Frénaud, André.
Bazaine, par André Frénaud. Estève, par Jean Lescure. Lapicque, par Jean Tardieu. Paris, L. Carré ₍ᶜ1945₎

Tardieu, Jean, 1903–   ed
Choix de rondeaux
see under   Charles d'Orleans, 1394–1465.

Hfp
tal2j
Tardieu, Jean, 1903–
Le démon de l'irréalité. Neuchâtel,Ides et calendes[1946]
83p. 25cm. (Ides poétiques)
No. 855 in an ed. of 1056 copies.

NT 0038799 CtY NN PU PHC CLU IEN

PQ2639
.A72D5
TARDIEU,JEAN,1903–
Les dieux étouffés. Paris, P. Seghers, 1946.
41 p.
Poems.
"650 exemplaires sur vélin du marais."
This is no. 170.

NT 0038800 InU DLC-P4 CLU CtY PU OCU

Tardieu, Jean, 1903–
Il était une fois, deux fois, trois fois ... ; ou, La table de multiplication en vers, avec des images d'Élie Lascaux. Paris, Gallimard ₍1947₎
₍35₎ p. illus. 31 cm.

I. Lascaux, Élie, 1888– II. Title.

PZ24.3.T3   48–18394 rev*

NT 0038801 DLC

Tardieu, Jean, 1903–
Figures. ₍Paris₎ Gallimard ₍1944₎
116 p. 19 cm.

1. Artists, French. 2. Musicians, French. I. Title.

PQ2639.A72F5   848.91   47–15098 rev*

NT 0038802 DLC NN CtY

Tardieu, Jean, 1903–
Jours pétrifiés, 1942–1944. Poèmes. ₍Paris₎ Gallimard ₍1948₎
115 p. 19 cm.

I. Title.

PQ2639.A72J6   841.91   48–20905 rev*

NT 0038803 DLC OrU IU CtY OOxM MU OrU AU

PQ2639
.A5J8
1948
Tardieu, Jean, 1903–
Jours pétrifiés, 1942–1944; poèmes. 4. éd. ₍Paris₎ Gallimard ₍c1948₎
115 p.

NT 0038804 ICU NBuU

Tardieu, Jean, 1903–
Mi-figue, mi-raisin; quatre esquisses comiques extraites de Les jeux de la langue et du hasard Spectacle de Michel de Ré au Théâtre du quartier latin.

(In Opera. Supplément théâtral, 55. Jan., 1952, p.23–36₎

NT 0038805 MH

Tardieu, Jean, 1903–
Monsieur, monsieur; poèmes. ₍Paris₎ Gallimard ₍1951₎
118 p. 19 cm.

I. Title.

PQ2639.A72M6   841.91   51–30539 rev

IEN IU CtY MH NN MU
NT 0038806 DLC OrU OU MiU IaU TU WaU TxU OrU ICU

Tardieu, Jean, 1903–
Un mot pour un autre. ₍Paris₎ Gallimard ₍1951₎
147 p. 20 cm.

1. French language—Idioms, corrections, errors. I. Title.

PC2460.T3   52–29719 rev ‡

NT 0038807 DLC OrU IU TxU ICU MiU IaU OCU

Hfp
tall
Tardieu, Jean, 1903–
Poèmes. Burin de Roger Vieillard. [Paris] Éditions du Seuil[1944]
57p. illus. 25cm.
No. 183 in an ed. of 210 copies.

NT 0038808 CtY

Tardieu, Jean, 1903–
La première personne du singulier. ₍Paris₎ Gallimard ₍1952₎
125 p. 20 cm.
Essays.

I. Title.

PQ2639.A72P7   844.91   53–15505 rev ‡

CSt CU MU IaU PU CtY IU
NT 0038809 DLC OrU MtU NBuU MiU OU OrU ICU VtMiM

Tardieu, Jean, 1903-
Le témoin invisible. ₍Paris₎ Gallimard ₍1943₎
78 p. 20 cm. (Collection Métamorphoses. ₍15₎)
Poems.
CONTENTS.—Le témoin invisible.—Suite mineure.—Dialogues à voix basse.—Les épaves reconnues.—Nuit.

PQ2639.A72T4   841.91   A F 48–331*
New York. Public Libr.
for Library of Congress   ₍1₎†

NT 0038810   NN DLC

Tardieu, Jean, 1903–
Théâtre de chambre. Paris, Gallimard ₍1955–
v. 18 cm. (*His* Théâtre ₍1₎

I. Title.
PQ2639.A72A19 1955   55–42066 rev ‡

IaU NN NcD CtY IU C OO OU CU OrU
NT 0038811   DLC NcU MU MH NBuU FTaSU MB TU CtY PU

Tardieu, Jean, 1903–
Une voix sans personne. ₍Paris₎ Gallimard ₍1954₎
124 p. 20 cm.
Poems and prose.

I. Title.
PQ2639.A72V6   54–29240 rev ‡

PPT LU NN MU
NT 0038812   DLC OrU FU OOxM NNU PSt MiU MH OrU IaU

Tardieu, Jean A
La Legion étrangère. Couverture de M-Th.
Auffray. Illustrations de Carter. Paris, Willeb
[1946]
94 p. (Collection "Trois couleurs", 4)

NT 0038813   MH

Tardieu, Jean Baptiste Pierre, 1746–1816.   *Map 1036.27
Carte du royaume de France divisée en 86 départements d'après le
traité de paix de Paris.
= Paris. Jean. 1818. Size, 20½ × 25½ inches. Scale (computed),
27 geographical miles to 1 inch. Folded.
Submap. — Corse.

F9636 — France. Geog. Maps.

NT 0038814   MB

Tardieu, Jean Baptiste Pierre. 1746–1816.   *Map 1036.40
Carte l'Italie.
Paris. Flocquart. 1835. Size, 28 × 18¾ inches. Scale (com-
puted), 32.3 geographical miles to 1 inch. Folded.

111320 — Italy. Geog. Maps

NT 0038815   MB

Tardieu, Jean Baptiste Pierre. 1746–1816.   *Map 1036.41
Map of Italy with the ancient and modern names; compiled from
Cramer, Wahl, Danville [sic], Malte-Brun, Lapie and Brué.
Paris. Galignani. 1833. Size, 19¼ × 15¼ inches. Scale (com-
puted), 49.3 miles to 1 inch. Folded.

H1320 — Italy. Geog. Maps.

NT 0038816   MB

Tardieu, Jean Baptiste Pierre, 1746–1816.

Notice sur l'île d'Elbe, contenant la description de ses
villes, ports, places fortes, villes, bourgs, villages, l'état
de sa population, de ses productions; son étendue, sa distance de Paris, etc.; la description des mœurs et usages
de ses habitants; un coup-d'œil sur l'histoire de cette île
qui est devenue la résidence de Buonaparte. Paris, Tardieu-Denesle, 1814.

G1840   Tardieu, Jean Baptiste Pierre, fl. 1820–1870.
.P42   FOR OTHER EDITIONS
1845   Perrot, Aristide Michel, 1793–1879.   SEE MAIN ENTRY
Map   Atlas géographique, statistique et progressif des départe-
mens de la France et de ses colonies, par A. Perrot et
Achin, sous la direction de P. Tardieu. Accompagné d'un
texte historique sur la France par Bory de St. Vincent.
Paris, A. Boulland ₍1845?₎

Tardieu (Joseph-Rémy) [1885–]. *De la
tuberculine dans le traitement des tuberculoses
oculaires atypiques. 52 pp. 8°. *Bordeaux,*
1908, No. 38.

NT 0038819   DNLM

TARDIEU, JULES.
L'affaire Leplat; ou, La lettre de cachet en 1931;
ce que contient le fameux rapport des docteurs Claude,
Truelle et Rogues de Fursac, qui conclurent à "la
folie" de Madame Leplat. Lille, Éditions du Furet
du Nord ₍1931?₎ 59 p. 22cm.

Microfiche (neg.) 2 sheets. 11 x 15cm. (NYPL FSN 12,781)

1. Leplat, Alice Adrienne   (Courdet). 2. Criminals, Insane—France—Lille.

NT 0038820   NN

Tardieu (Jules). *De la transmission hérédi-
taire de l'épilepsie. 43 pp. 4°. *Paris,* 1868,
No. 255.

NT 0038821   DNLM

[Tardieu, Jules Romain] 1805–1868.
L'art d'etre malheureux; legende par J. T. de
Saint-Germain, [pseud] Paris, 1856.
S.

NT 0038822   RPB

843.7   Tardieu, Jules Romain, 1805–1868.
T182a   L'art d'être malheureux; légende par J.-T.
de Saint-Germain [pseud.] Paris, J.Tardieu,
1857.
228p. 17cm.

Bibliography: p.[217]–220.

NT 0038823   IEN ViU PPL MH

Tardieu, Jules Romain, 1805–1868.
L'art d'etre malheureux. Ed. 3. Paris,
Tardieu, 1859.
239 p.

NT 0038824   PU

Tardieu, Jules Romain, 1805–1868.
The art of suffering. Translated from the
French by Edmond Butler. New York, D. & J.
Sadlier, 1860.
6–192 p. 13 cm.
3 copies.

NT 0038825   PLatS OClJC

Tardieu, Jules Romain, 1805–1868.
Le Chalet d'Auteuil, legende.
Paris: J. Tardieu, 1863.   2d ed.
2 p.l., 174 p. 16°.

NT 0038826   NN

Y   ₍TARDIEU, JULES ROMAIN₎ 1805–1868.
762   Contes et légendes de J.T. de Saint-Germain
.T 17   ₍pseud.₎ Paris, Charpentier et cie,1876.
v. 18½cm.

Contents.—t.I. La légende de Mignon. Pour
une èpingle. La fontaine de Mèdicis. La feuille
de coudrier. La roulette.

NT 0038827   ICN MWelC

TARDIEU, Jules Romain, 1805–1868.
De la perpétuitée en matière de littérature
et d'art; lettre à l'Académie impériale des
sciences, belles-lettres et arts de Rouen.
Paris, 1858.
8°

NT 0038828   MH-L

[TARDIEU, Jules Romain, 1805–1868].
Les extrèmes; légende. Par J.T. de Saint-
Germain, [pseud.] Paris, etc., 1866.

NT 0038829   MH

PQ2449   ₍TARDIEU, JULES ROMAIN₎ 1805–1868.
.T43F4   La feuille de coudrier et la fontaine de Médicis;
1863   légendes, par J.T. de Saint-Germain₍pseud.₎... Paris,
J. Tardieu, 1863.
₍3₎, 176 p. illus. 14¼cm.

NT 0038830   ICU

844T171   ₍Tardieu, Jules₎ 1805–1868.
U53   En knappenaals erindringer, af M. J.-T. de
Saint-Germain ₍pseud.₎ Oversat fra fransk ved
Max Rolf. Kjöbenhavn, G. E. C. Gad ₍1858?₎
179 p.

I. Rolf, Max,   tr. II. Title.

NT 0038831   NNC

PZ   Tardieu, Jules Romain, 1805–1868.
3   Lady Clare : légende / par J. T. de
.T1735   Saint-Germain. 2d ed. Paris : J. Tardie
L   , 1859.
212 p. ; 17 cm.
Imperfect: brittle pages; faded;
worn.

NT 0038832   MsSM PU

Tardieu, Jules Romain, 1805-1868.
   Lady Clare. Legend.
   Paris: J. Tardieu, 1862.
    1 p.l., 212 p.   16°.

NT 0038833   NN

Tardieu, Jules Romain, 1805-1868.
   Manuel des vegetaux, ou, Catalogue Latin et
François de toutes les plantes, arbres & arbrisseaux
connus sur le Globe de la terre jusqu'a ce jour ...
par M. J. J. de St. Germain.   Paris, 1784.

NT 0038834   PPAN

Tardieu, Jules Romain, 1805-1868.

   Martin Bossange, 1766-1865 ... Paris ₍Impr. Jouaust₎
1865.

Tardieu, Jules Romain.
   Mignon, legende par J. T. de Saint Germain.
   Paris, Tardieu, 1857.
    218 p.

NT 0038836   PU PPL

[TARDIEU, Jules Romain, 1805-1868].
   Mignon; légende par J.T de Saint-Germain,
₍pseud.₎ 4e éd. Paris, 1860.

NT 0038837   MH

₍Tardieu, Jules Romain₎ 1805-1868.
   Mignon. A tale. Tr. from the French. New York, P.
O'Shea, 1868.
    1 p. l. ₍5₎-202 p. 18½ᶜᵐ.

   I. Title.

                                 7-25765
Library of Congress   PZ3.T1735M

NT 0038838   DLC

[TARDIEU, Jules Romain, 1805-1868].
   Mignon. Legende par J.T.de Saint-Germain.
13e éd. Paris, 1871.

The cover reads:- "14e éd."

NT 0038839   MH

Tardieu, Jules Romain, 1805-1868.
   Le miracle des roses, opérette de salon...
    see under   Bordese, Luigi, 1815-1886.

Tardieu, Jules Romain, 1805-1868.
   ... Money. A tale. By Jules Tardieu ... ₍New York,
G. Munro, 1879₎
   25 p. 32½ᶜᵐ. ₍Seaside library. v. 28, no. 586₎

                                    8-20100†
Library of Congress   PZ3.T1735Mo
— — — — Copy 2   (Copyright 1879: 12326)
                           Library of Congress PZ1.S55

NT 0038841   DLC MB MH PPL OC1

PZ3
.T1735   Tardieu, Jules Romain, 1805-1868.
 Mo 2   Money. By Jules Tardieu, tr. from the
    French by Margaret Watson. London, W. H.
    Allen and co., 1879.
     iv, 245, [1] p. 18 1/2ᶜᵐ.

   I. Watson, Margaret, tr.   II. Title

NT 0038842   MB CtY NN

₍Tardieu, Jules Romain₎ 1805-1868.
   Only a pin! An instructive moral story. Tr. from the
French of J. T. de Saint-Germaine ₍pseud.₎ By P. S. ...
New York, The Catholic publication society, 1873.
   206 p. 17½ᶜᵐ.

   I. Stump, Pauline.
Library of Congress   PZ3.T1735O
                    (Copyright 1873: 4253)
                            8-20099†

NT 0038843   DLC

Tardieu, Jules Romain, 1805-1868.
   Pour parvenir. Paris, Tardieu, 1861.
    222 p.

NT 0038844   PU PPL

Tardieu, Jules Romain, 1805-1868.
   Pour parvenir: légende. Paris, J. Tardieu,
1869.
    2 p. l., (1) 4-222 p., 1 l.   16°.
    4. ed.

NT 0038845   NN

Tardieu, Jules Romain, 1805-1868.
   Pour une epingle. Paris, Tardieu, 1856.
    204 p.

NT 0038846   PU

[TARDIEU, Jules Romain] 1805-1868.
   Pour une épingle; légende par J.T.de Saint
Germain, [pseud.] 3 éd. Paris, J.Tardieu, 1857.

**Prefixed are extracts from newspapers,
criticising the work.**

NT 0038847   MH PPL PU

TARDIEU, Jules Romain, 1805-1868.
   Pour une épingle. Légende. Par J. T. de Saint-Germain
5e édition.
    Paris. Tardieu. 1859. (3), 224 pp. Pl. 18?.   66

NT 0038848   MB MH

₍Tardieu, Jules Romain₎ 1805-1868.
   Pour une épingle, légende par J. T. de Saint-Germain
₍pseud.₎ ... 7. éd. Paris, J. Tardieu, 1860.
   4 p. l., 5-224 p. incl. front. 16ᵐ.

   I. Title.
                         34-29979
Library of Congress   PQ2449.T6P6 1867   843.79

NT 0038849   DLC N

Tardieu, Jules Romain, 1805-1868.
   Pour une Epingle; legende. Neuvième édition.
   Paris, 1861.
    224 p.

NT 0038850   PHi

TARDIEU, JULES ROMAIN, 1805-1868
   POUR UNE ÉPINGLE. ... 13.ÉD. PARIS, [1865]

   [FRENCH NOVELS. No.1]

NT 0038851   MdBJ

₍Tardieu, Jules Romain₎ 1805-1868.
   Pour une épingle. Légende. Par J. T. de Saint-Germain ₍pseud.₎ ... Avec vocabulaire. 14. éd. française ...
1. éd. américaine. Boston, S. R. Urbino; New York, Ley-
poldt & Holt ₍etc.₎ 1866.
   174 p. 18½ᶜᵐ.

   I. Title.
                         12-30434
Library of Congress   PQ2390.S4P6 1866

NT 0038852   DLC OrCS NN CtY

---

ar V
5233   ₍Tardieu, Jules Romain₎ 1805-1868.
    Pour une épingle. Légende. Par J. T.
    de Saint-Germain ₍pseud.₎ Avec vocabulaire.
    19th ed.   New York, H. Holt ₍1866₎
    224 p. illus. 19cm.

NT 0038853   NIC MH OOxM

₍Tardieu, Jules Romain₎ 1805-1868.
   Pour une épingle, légende par J. T. de Saint-Germain
₍pseud.₎ ... 14. éd. Paris, J. Tardieu, 1867.
   4 p. l., 5-224 p. incl. front. 16ᵐ.

   I. Title.
                         34-29979
Library of Congress   PQ2449.T6P6 1867   843.79

NT 0038854   DLC MH MB

Tardieu, Jules Romain 1805-1868
   Pour Une Epingle. Legende par J. T.
De Saint-Germain. ed. 19 Bost., Urbans 1870.
   174 p.   D

NT 0038855   OO NcD

₍Tardieu, Jules Romain₎ 1805-1868.

   Pour une épingle. Légende. Par J. T. de Saint
Germain ₍pseud.₎ Avec vocabulaire. 19. ed.
New York, H. Holt ₍1887?₎
   174 p. 19ᶜᵐ. (Bibliothèque d'instruction et de
récréation)

NT 0038856   ViU MH

Tardieu, Jules Romain, 1805-1868.
Pour une épingle, or The memoirs of a pin
with grammatical and explanatory notes by
V.Kastner. New ed. London, Lib. Hachette &
cie., etc., etc., 1895.

At head of title: J.T.de Saint-Germain [pseud]

NT 0038857 MH

Tardieu, Jules Romain, 805-1868.
[Curmer, Henri Léon]? 1801-1871.
La propriété intellectuelle est un droit. À M. J.-T. de
Saint-Germain [i. e. Jules Romain Tardieu] ... Paris.
E. Dentu, 1858.

[Tardien, Jules Romain] 1805-1868.
Les roses de Noël, dernières fleurs, par J. T.
de Saint-Germain [i. e. Jules Romain Tardieu.]
3. ed. aug. Paris, J. Tardieu, 1844.
179 p. 16°.

NT 0038859 NN

[Tardieu, Jules Romain] 1805-1868.
Les roses de Noël, dernières fleurs; par J. T.
de Saint-Germain [pseud] Paris, 1860.
17 cm.

NT 0038860 CtY

Tardieu, Jules Romain, 1805-1868.
La treve de Dieu; souvenirs d'un dimanche d'ete
par J. T. de Saint-Germain... Paris, Tardieu,
1862.
176 p.

NT 0038861 PU

Tardieu, Jules Romain, 1805-1868.
La veilleuse. Paris, Tardieu, 1859.
235 p.

NT 0038862 PU PPL

TARDIEU, LUCY.
Poèmes. [Poèmes. [Paris, Imp. E. Thouvenin, 195-?]
42 p. 24cm.

NT 0038863 NN

---

aD
1265
A7
J362   Tardieu, Mauricio A
LAC-2   [Expropiacion por causa de utilidad
publica, por Mauricio A. Tardieu.
Buenos Aires, 1903.
39p. 23cm.
Tesis - Universidad Nacional de
Buenos Aires.

1. Eminent domain - Argentine
Republic. I. TITLE.

NT 0038864 TxU

TARDIEU,P. A. F.

See TARDIEU,Antoine François,1757.

Tardieu, P   E
Sciences appliquées [par] P. E. Tardieu, G. Dumesnie [et]
J. Haumesser. À l'usage des classes du 2ᵉ cycle des écoles
primaires (arrêté du 16 août 1941) Écoles de garçons. Éd.
urbaine. Paris, Istra [1943]
350 p. illus. 25 cm.

1. Science.

Q161.T3   600   50-42224

NT 0038866 DLC

D59
T3   Tardieu, Pierre
Atlas pour l'Histoire universelle par le
Comte de Ségur. Partie ancienne, romaine
et du Bas-Empire. Dirigé, dessiné et gravé
par P. Tardieu. Avec le texte explicatif
[par P. Tardieu] Paris, A. Eymery, 1822.
23 p. col.plates,col.maps.

1. History, Ancient - Maps. 2. Atlases.
I. Ségur, Louis Philippe, comte de, 1753-
1830. / Histoire universelle. II. Title.

NT 0038867 CU

Tardieu, Pierre.
Atlas pour servir à l'Histoire ancienne romaine
et du Bas-Empire, des oeuvres de M. le Comte de
Ségur...; dirigé, dessiné et gravé par P. Tardieu.
Avec le texte explicatif. Paris, A. Eymery, 1827.
25 p. 20 plates. 20 x 26 cm.
1. Classical geography - Maps. 2. Geography,
Ancient - Maps. I. Ségur, Louis Philippe, comte de,
1753-1830.

NT 0038868 NcU

Tardieu, Pierre.
Carte de l'Allemagne; ou, Confédération
Germanique. Paris, 1833.
1 p.

NT 0038869 PHi

Tardieu, Pierre.
Cartes des Routes de Poste de France. n. p.,
1834.
1 p.

NT 0038870 PHi

Tardieu, Pierre.
Ségur, Louis Philippe, comte de, 1753-1830.
Histoire universelle, ancienne et moderne; par M. le comte
de Ségur ... Avec atlas par P. Tardieu ... Paris, A. Eymery,
1821-22.

Tardieu, Pierre.
Ségur, Louis Philippe, comte de, 1753-1830.
Œuvres complètes de M. le comte de Ségur ... ornées
de son portrait, d'un fac simile de son écriture, et de deux
atlas composés de 32 planches, par P. Tardieu ... Paris,
A. Eymery, 1824-27.

Tardieu, Pierre, and F. Ecoffey.
...Soleil d'automne; comédie en un acte. Paris: Librairie
théâtrale, cop. 1930. 38 p. 12°.

567186A. 1. Drama, French.   I. Ecoffey, Francis, jt. au.
II. Title.
N. Y. P. L.   February 9, 1932

NT 0038873 NN DLC

Tardieu, Pierre François [pseud.]
see Tardieu, Antoine Francois, 1757-

Tardieu, Pierre Gabriel Amédée
see Tardieu, André Pierre Gabriel A.,
1876-1945.

Tardieu, Suzanne.
Images populaires du Mans, de Chartres et
d'Orléans
see under Paris. Musée National des arts
et traditions populaires.

NK2547
.T3   Tardieu, Suzanne.
Meubles régionaux datés. Paris, Vincent, Fréal, 1950.
31 p. illus. 29 cm.
"Bibliographie sommaire": p. 28-29.

1. Furniture—France. I. Title.
A 51-5742
Oregon. Univ. Libr.
for Library of Congress   [1]

NT 0038877 OrU OU ICU NN CU DLC

Tardieu, Suzanne.
Objets domestiques

see under

Paris. Musée national des arts et traditions
populaires.

Tardieu (V.) *De la résection du coude et
d'un nouveau procédé opératoire. 52 pp. 4°.
Montpellier, 1866, No. 75.   C.

NT 0038879 DNLM

587.3   Tardieu-Blot, Laure.
T17a   Les aspléniées du Tonkin. Toulouse, Imp. H.
Basuyau [1933]
190p. illus. 25cm.

"Ouvrage couronné par l'Académie des sciences."
Bibliography: p.186-190.

1. Ferns—Tonkin. I. Title.

NT 0038880 IU NIC CtY MiU

Tardieu-Blot, Laure.
Essai sur les affinités et la répartition des
Fougères d'Indochine (A l'exclusion des Polypodia-
ceae) [Paris, Masson, 1935]
[595]-600 p. 29 cm.
Caption title.
From "Archives du Muséum. 6e Série. T. XII."
1. Filicies - Inochina.

NT 0038881   NNBG

Tardieu-Blot, Laure.
... Fougeres, par Mme. Tardieu-Blot et Carl
Christensen. Paris, Masson et cie, 1939-1941.
v. Illus. 25.5 cm.
4 pts.

NT 0038882   OU

EQ
1170   Tardieu-Blot, Laure.
T182n   Natalité et obstétrique en Indochine.
1934   Paris, Le François, 1934.
135 p.

Also published as thesis.
Bibliography: p. [123]-135.

1. Birth (Folklore, customs, etc.) -
Indo-China, French 2. Maternal and infant
welfare - Indo-China, French

NT 0038883   DNLM

Tardieu-Blot, Laure.
Les pteridophytes de l'Afrique intertropicale française.
[Dakar, IFAN] 1953.
241 p. illus. 28 cm. (Mémoires de l'Institut français d'Afrique
noire, nº 28)
Bibliography : p. [227]-231.

1. Pteridophyte. 2. Ferns—Africa, French Equatorial.   (Series:
Institut français d'Afrique noire. Mémoires, nº 28)

QK530.T3   55-17845

LU MiEM NcD FU MiU NIC MH PPAN NN
NT 0038884   DLC GU DAU NNBG TEN CU-S CSt GASU ViU

QK
523   Tardieu-Blot, Laure
.T3   Ptéridophytes; fougères et plantes alliées.
Paris, Société d'édition d'enseignement
supérieur, 1954.
106 p. illus. (Cryptogamia)

Includes bibliography.

1. Ferns. 2. Pteridophyta. I. Title.

NT 0038885   MiEM CaBVaU InU OkU MiU

Tardieu-Blot, Mme. M.L.

See

Tardieu-Blot, Laure.

Wing   TARDIEU-DENESLE, HENRI
Z   Almanach typographique, ou Répertoire de
3039   la librairie. Paris, H. Tardieu [1793]
.864   229p. 18cm.

"Décret de la Convention nationale, du
17 juillet, l'an second de la République
française. Relatif aux droits de propriété
des auteurs d'écrits en tout genre, des com-
positeurs de musique, des peintres et des
dessinateurs," p.[9]-16.

NT 0038887   ICN ICJ

Tardieu-Denesle, Henri;
Almanach typographique, ou Répertoire de la librairie   ...   [A
Paris: Chez H. Tardieu, l'an VII de la République Française [1798]
228 p.   18cm.

Annual supplements were intended, but never published.—cf. "Avertissement" signed:
Henry Tardieu.

12146B. 1. Booksellers and book   trade—Direct.—France. 2. Book
industries—France—Paris. I. Title.
N.Y.P.L.   January 31, 1941

NT 0038888   NN

Tardieu-Denesle, Mme. Henri.
Atlas portatif....
see under   Maire, N   M

GV1471
.T26   [Tardieu- Denesle, Mme Henri]
Les jeux innocents de société, par
Madame T*** D *** [pseud.]   Édition ornée
de six jolies figures. Paris, Tardieu
Denesle [1817]
3 p.l., [3]-300 p. incl. front. plates.
14cm.

Incomplete.

1. Games.   I. Title.

NT 0038890   DLC MB NjP

Tardieu-Denesle, Mme Henri.
Nouvelle mythologie de la jeunesse ... par
demandes et par réponses ... Tome 1. Paris,
Tardieu-Denesle, 1816.
1 v. illus. nar, 12°.

NT 0038891   NN

Tardieu-Denesle, Mme. Henri.
Nouvelle mythologie de la jeunesse, contenant les divinités ....
les héros ... un abrégé de la vie des poètes qui ont le plus
contribué à nous faire connaitre la mythologie; les emblêmes
des fleurs et des couleurs; les symboles des animaux ... par
mme Tardieu-Denesle. 3. éd., avec 83 figures en taille-douce ...
Paris, Tardieu-Denesle, 1826.
2 v. fronts. 20 pl. 18°.
I. C. copy imperfect : pt. 8, 12, 14 wanting.

1. Mythology, Classical—Juvenile literature. 2. French poetry (Selections: Extracts, etc.) 3. Symbolism.

31-29548

Library of Congress   BL725.T3 1826   292

NT 0038892   DLC MWA

Tardieu Pereira,
... Pontos de direito constitucional, organizado pelo dr.
Tardieu Pereira. Rio de Janeiro, Editora Getulio Costa [1942]
76 p., 2 l. 19cm. (Pontos para concursos oficias, orientação e revisão
do prof. A. Tenorio d'Albuquerque)

1. Brazil—Constitutional law.

45-13814

Library of Congress   J1.2418.T3   342.8103
[2]

NT 0038893   DLC

Tardieu Saint-Marcel, A   P
see   Saint-Marcel, A   Philippe
Tardieu.

Tardieu-Saint-Marcel, A. Ph.
see   Saint Marcel, A   Philippe
Tardieu.

Tardieu-Saint-Marcel, M
see   Saint Marcel, A. Philippe Tardieu.

Tardieu Commission
see   France. Haut commissariat
aux Etats Unis.

Tardif,
Nouvelle méthode d'encaissement, pour fonder
facilement et solidement... dans les rivières,
dans les maraes, etc. Paris, 1759.
fol.

NT 0038898   NWM

Tardif (A.-H.-Anthelme). * Quelques mots sur
le diagnostic des étranglements herniaires. 4'
pp. 4°. Paris, 1860, No. 18

NT 0038899   DNLM

Tardif, Adolphe François Lucien, 1824-1890.

Dubreuil, Joseph, 1747-1824.
Analyse raisonnée de la législation sur les eaux, par Dubreuil ... Nouv. éd. Mise en rapport avec le dernier état de
la législation et de la jurisprudence, augm. d'un supplément,
par MM. Tardif & Cohen ... avec des notes de M. J. J. Estran-
gin ... et précédée d'une notice sur Dubreuil, par M. Ch. Giraud ... Aix, Aubin, 1842-43.

Tardif, Adolphe François Lucien, 1824-1890,
ed.
Lorris, France. Laws, statutes, etc.
... Coutumes de Lorris, publiées d'après le registre original
du Parlement de Paris, par Ad. Tardif ... Paris, A. Picard,
1885.

Tardif, Adolphe Francois Lucien, 1824-1890, ed.
Toulouse. Laws, statutes, etc.
... Coutumes de Toulouse, publiées d'après les manuscrits
9187 et 9993 fonds latin de la Bibliothèque nationale, par
Ad. Tardif ... Paris, A. Picard, 1884.

Tardif, Adolphe François Lucien, 1824-1890, ed.
Artois. Laws, statutes, etc.
... Coutumier d'Artois, publié d'après les manuscrits 5248
et 5249, fonds français de la Bibliothèque nationale, par Ad.
Tardif ... Paris, A. Picard, 1883.

Tardif, Adolphe François Lucien, 1824-1890.
Des origines de la communauté de biens entre époux, par
Adolphe Tardif ... Paris, A. Durand, 1850.
40 p. 25cm.

1. Community property—France. 2. Husband and wife—France.
I. Title.

30-25776

NT 0038904   DLC

KE
1130
T18

Tardif, Adolphe François Lucien, 1824-1890
  Le droit privé au xiiie siècle d'après les coutumes de Toullouse et de Montpellier. Paris, A. Picard, 1886.
    iii, 109 p.

  1. Customary law - Toulouse. 2. Customary law - Montpellier. I. Title: Le droit privé au xiiie siècle.

NT 0038905   CU-L PU-L OC1 MnU PU MH-L

Tardif, Adolphe François Lucien, 1824-1890.
  Histoire des sources du droit canonique, par Adolphe Tardif ... Paris, A. Picard, 1887.
    2 p. l., iii, 409, ₁1₎ p. 23ᶜᵐ.

  1. Canon law—Bio-bibl.

  Library of Congress   Z7776.T28   13-15468

NT 0038906 CU MH DLC NIC OO KU CtY PU PBm GU OC1W WaU-L

Tardif, Adolphe François Lucien, 1824-1890.
  Histoire des sources du droit français, origines romaines, par Adolphe Tardif ... Paris, A. Picard, 1890.
    2 p. l., v, 527, ₁1₎ p. 23ᶜᵐ.
    "Titres des ouvrages cités en abrégé dans les notes": p. ₁iii₎-v.

                                        6-13707

NT 0038907   DLC OCU CtY TxU   OC1 MB MH

Tardif, Adolphe François Lucien, 1824-1890.
Tardif, Jules, 1827-1882.
  Une minute de notaire du ixᵉ siècle en notes tironiennes, d'après la lecture donnée en 1849 par Jules Tardif. Paris, A. Picard, 1888.

Tardif, Adolphe François Lucien, 1824-1890.
  Notions élémentaires de critique historique, par Ad. Tardif ... Paris, Alphonse Picard, 1883.
    30 p., 1 l. 24cm.
    "Les dernières leçons du cours d'histoire du droit civil et du droit canonique professé à l'École des chartes, pendant l' année scolaire 1882-1883."
    Bibliography: p. 8

NT 0038909   MH-L MH ICU OC1W

TARDIF, Adolphe.
  Practica forensis de Jean Masuer. Paris, 1883.
    8°. 12 p.
    "Extrait de la Nouvelle revue historique de droit français et étranger."

NT 0038910   MH-L

Tardif, Adlophe François Lucien, 1824-1890, ed.
  Privilèges accordés à la couronne de France par le Saint-Siège
      see under Catholic Church. Pope.

Tardif, Adolphe François Lucien, 1824-1890.
  La procédure civile et criminelle aux xiiᵉ et xivᵉ siècles ou procédure de transition, par Adolphe Tardif ... Paris, A. Picard ₁etc.₎ 1885.
    2 p. l., 167 p. 22½ᶜᵐ.

                                        11-12339

NT 0038912   DLC PU NIC

Tardif, Adolphe François Lucien, 1824-1890, ed.
  Recueil de textes pour servir à l'enseignement de l'histoire du droit ... par Ad. Tardif ... Paris, A. Picard, 1883-85.
    3 v. 24ᶜᵐ.
    CONTENTS.—₁1₎ Coutumier d'Artois, publié d'après les manuscrits 5248 et 5249, fonds français de la Bibliothèque nationale.—₁2₎ Coutumes de Toulouse, publiées d'après les manuscrits 9187 et 9993, fonds latin de la Bibliothèque nationale.—₁3₎ Coutumes de Lorris, publiées d'après le registre original du Parlement de Paris.
    I. Artois. Laws, statutes, etc. II. Toulouse. Charters. III. Lorris, France. Charters. IV. Title. V. Title: Coutumier d'Artois. VI. Title: Coutumes de Toulouse. VII. Title: Coutumes de Lorris.

                                        22-10430

NT 0038913   DLC MH

Tardif (Albert). *De la fracture transversale de la rotule au point de vue surtout de son traitement par le caoutchouc. 56 pp. 4°. *Paris,* 1873, No. 123.

NT 0038914   DNLM

TARDIF, Alexandre, b. 1801
  Essais dramatiques. Paris, Everat, impr., 1835.

  Contents:- Louis VII à Vitry.- Une Espagnole D'étranger.- Les amans suisses.- Le Parisien et les Normandes.

NT 0038915   MH

---

*FC8
T1733
842v

Tardif, Alexandre, b. 1801.
  Variétés poétiques, par Alexandre Tardif ... Paris, Librairie de Dauvin et Fontaine, passage des Panoramas, 35, et galerie de la Bourse, 1. 1842.
    222p. 18cm.
    Contents: Optimis parentibus. Sonnet.--L'art de ne plus aimer; poème traduit d'Ovide.--Hermann.--Contes.--Les saisons de Paris.--Les voyages classiques.--Improvisations artistiques

NT 0038916   MH CtY

Tardif (Antoine) [1857-   ]. *Contribution à l'étude des accidents consécutifs aux lésions du nerf sous-orbitaire. 53 pp., 1 l. 4°. *Paris,* 1885, No. 189.

NT 0038917   DNLM

HIST SCI
RL
151
T18

Tardif, Antoine Auguste.
  Dissertation sur la plique polonoise, présentée... par Ant. Aug. Tardif. Strasbourg, De l'impr. de Levrault, 1812.
    22 p. 25cm.

  Diss.--Strasbourg.

  1. Plica polonica.

NT 0038918   NIC DNLM

Tardif, Antoinette
    see Desrosiers, Marie Antoinette (Tardif)

Tardif, C., ed.   FOR OTHER EDITIONS
                       SEE MAIN ENTRY
Fournel, Jean François, 1745-1820.
  Traité du voisinage, considéré dans l'ordre judiciaire et administratif, et dans ses rapports avec le Code civil; par m. Fournel ... 4. éd., rev. et considérablement augm. par M. Tardif ... Paris, B. Warée, oncle, 1827.

Tardif, Edmond
  Leçons de droit social naturel données à la Conférence des études sociologiques. Paris, etc., Delhomme & Briguet, 1894.
    323 p. 18 cm.

NT 0038921   MH

Tardif, Edmond
  Système rationnel des sciences expérimentales. iv, 5-47 pp. 8°. *Paris, Garnier frères,* 1891.

NT 0038922   DNLM

Tardif (E[douard-Alphonse-Joseph]). *Les anastomoses viscérales sans sutures. 63 pp., 1 nl. 4°. *Paris,* 1894. No. 228.

NT 0038923   DNLM

Tardif (Émile). * Des complications des kystes de l'ovaire pendant la grossesse. 108 pp. 8°. *Paris,* 1906. No. 362.

NT 0038924   DNLM

Law

Tardif, Ernest Joseph, 1855-1922, joint ed.
France. *Échiquier de Normandie.*
  ... Atiremens et jugiés d'Eschequiers, publiés par R. Génestal ... ₁et₎ J. Tardif ... Caen, L. Jouan, 1921.

Tardif, Ernest Joseph, 1855-1922.
  Les auteurs présumés du Grand coutumier de Normandie, par E.-J. Tardif ... Paris, L. Larose et Forcel, 1885.
    55, ₁1₎ p. 22½ᶜᵐ.
    "Extrait de la Nouvelle revue historique de droit français et étranger."
    "Cette étude est extraite de l'introduction qui accompagnera la nouvelle édition du texte latin du Grand coutumier de Normandie, préparée pour la Société de l'histoire de Normandie."—p. ₁5₎

  1. Usage and custom (Law)—Normandy. ₁1. Customary law—Normandy₎ 2. Normandy. Laws, statutes, etc. Grand coutumier. I. Title. II. Title: Grand coutumier de Normandie.

                                        31-23072

NT 0038926   DLC MH

TARDIF, E[rnest] J[oseph], 1855-1922
  Les chartes mérovingiennes de l'abbaye de Noirmoutier avec une étude sur la chronologie du règne de Dagobert II. Paris, L. Larose, 1899.

  On cover:- Études mérovingiennes, 1.
  "Extrait en partie de la Nouvelle Revue historique de droit français et étranger, t. XXII, p. 763-790."

NT 0038927   MH NNU-W CtY

Tardif, Ernest Joseph, 1855-1922, ed.
Normandy. *Laws, statutes, etc.*
  Coutumiers de Normandie; textes critiques publiés avec notes et éclaircissements, par Ernest-Joseph Tardif ... Rouen, Impr. de E. Cagniard, 1881-

Tardif, Ernest Joseph, 1855-1922.
... La date et le caractère de l'
ordonnance de Saint Louis sur le duel
judiciaire, par E.-J. Tardif ...
Paris, L. Larose et Forcel, 1887.
cover-title, 12 p. 21½cm.
At head of title: Études sur les
ordonnances des rois de France.
Bibliographical footnotes.
With author's autograph.

NT 0038929   MH-L CtY

TARDIF, Ernest Joseph.
Étude sur la litis contestatio en droit
romain et les effets de la demande en justice
en droit français. Paris, A. Lahure, 1881.

NT 0038930   MH

TARDIF, E[rnest] J[oseph].
Étude sur les sources de l'ancien droit normand et spécialement sur la législation des
ducs de Normandie. Rouen, 1911.
4°. 50p.
"Extrait du Congrès du millénaire normand."

NT 0038931   MH

Tardif, Ernest Joseph, 1855-1922.
[Jus romanum: De receptis arbitris, qui ar-
bitrium receperunt, ut sententiam dicant. Droit
civil français: Des transactions. Droit commercial: Du concordat] ... par Ernest-Joseph Tardif
... Paris, Moquet, 1877.
91 p. 21 cm.
Thesis, Paris, 1877.

NT 0038932   NNC

Tardif, Étienne, 1875-
Les abeilles; poème lyrique en 4 actes et
5 tableaux. Paris, E. Sansot & Cie, 1908.
162 p., 1 l. 12°.
Date on cover. 1909.

NT 0038933   NN

Wason
PG2639
A21A5
Tardif, Etienne.
Amours tonkinoises. [Vienne, Ternet-
Martin, 1947]
250 p. 19cm.

NT 0038934   NIC

Tardif (Étienne) [1875-   ]. *Étude critique des odeurs et des parfums, leur influence
sur le sens génésique. 120 pp. 8°. Bordeaux,
1898, No. 38.

NT 0038935   DNLM

Tardif, Étienne.
Madame Première. [Roman. Vienne, Isère, Ternet-
Martin, 1948]
407 p. 19 cm.

ɪ. Title.
                       A 50-4481
Illinois. Univ. Library
for Library of Congress   [3]

NT 0038936   IU NIC

Tardif, Étienne.
Le mirage. Comédie en trois actes et en prose.
Vienne, H. Martin, 1907.
27 p. 4°.

NT 0038937   NN

Tardif, Étienne.
Mon Capharnaüm, contes de la France d'outre-mer.
[Vienne (Isère) Ternet-Martin, 1948]
377 p. 19 cm.
CONTENTS.—Quinine préventive.—Parole d'honneur.—La légende du
bienheureux Saint-Grobo.—Toufiane.—L'affaire de Dunakalé.—Un
fait divers. — Un peu la viande. — Une veillée. — Trois histoires de
Bouzous.—Procession nocturne.

ɪ. Title.
                       A 50-5665
Illinois. Univ. Library
for Library of Congress   [3]

NT 0038938   IU NN

Wason
DS557
A5T18
Tardif, Etienne.
La naissance de Dalat (Annam), 1899-1900,
capitale de l'Indochine, 1946.   [Vienne
(Isère) Ternet-Martin, 1949]
274 p. illus., map. 19cm.

1. Indochina, French--Descr. & trav.
2. Annam--Descr. & trav. I. Title.

NT 0038939   NIC CU

Tardif, Étienne, 1875-
...Nos P. C. R. Moeurs de guerre. [Vienne (Isère) Ternet-
Martin, 1949] 331 p. 19cm.

560495B. 1. World war, 1939-1945—   War work—Red Cross. 2. World
war, 1939-1945—Medical and sanitary   affairs—France.
N. Y. P. L.   February 5, 1951

NT 0038940   NN

TP983
.T2
TARDIF, ÉTIENNE, 1875-
...Les odeurs et les parfums: leur influence sur
le sens génésique... Paris, J.B. Baillière et fils,
1899.
114 p. incl. facsim., diagrs. 25cm.
"Index bibliographique": p. [9]-12.

1. Perfumery.

NT 0038941   ICU DNLM FMU NN

Tardif, Étienne, 1875-
Gli odori ed i profumi loro influenze sul
senso genesico... Roma, F. Capaccini. 1900.
127 p.

NT 0038942   MiU

Tardif, Étienne.
Péchés de jeunesse. [Vienne, Impr. Ternet-Martin, 1949]
277 p. 19 cm.
CONTENTS.—Les sentimentales.—Les abeilles.—Tonton Crésus.

ɪ. Title.
                       A 50-6682
Illinois. Univ. Library
for Library of Congress   [3]

NT 0038943   IU

Tardif, Etienne, 1875-
——. La peste à Quang-Tchéou-Wan (épidémie
de janvier-juin 1901). 60 pp., 12 pl. 8°. Paris, J.-B. Baillière & fils, 1902.

NT 0038944   DNLM

Tardif, Etienne, 1875-
——. Un sanatorium en Annam. La mission
du Lung-Bian. 2 p. l., 139 pp., 1 plan. 8°.
Vienne, Ogeret & Martin, 1902.

NT 0038945   DNLM

Tardif (Étienne-St. Hilaire) [1805-   ]. *Le
lichen de Wilson de la bouche. 64 pp. 8°.
Paris, 1926. No. 325.

NT 0038946   DNLM CtY

Tardif (Eugène). *De la pustule maligne observée à Paris. 1 p. l., 70 pp. 4°. Paris, 1873,
No. 287.

NT 0038947   DNLM

Tardif (Félix) [1870-   ]. *Contribution à
l'étude clinique de quelques analgésies viscérales
profondes dans l'ataxie locomotrice progressive;
analgésies trachéale, mammaire, épigastrique et
testiculaire. 92 pp. 8°. Paris, 1899, No. 299.

NT 0038948   DNLM

WB
T183i
1907
TARDIF, Félix, 1870-
Indications respectives du Mont-Dore
et de La Bourboule, parallèle climatique,
technique et clinique des deux stations
[par] Félix Tardif [et] Gilbert Sersiron.
Paris, Doin, 1907.
98 p. illus.
I. Sersiron, Gilbert

NT 0038949   DNLM

Tardif, Fernand.
...Un département pendant la guerre. La Roche-Sur-Yon:
Guigné-Hurtaud, 1917.   2 p.l., 281 p., 1 l.   3. ed.   12°.

1. European war, 1914-   , France: Vendée. 2. Vendée.—History, 1914-
3. Title.
N. Y. P. L.   May 31, 1919.

NT 0038950   NN NjP

TARDIF, FERNAND.
Un département pendant la guerre. 3. ed.   La
Roche-Sur-Yon, Guigné-Hurtaud, 1917.   281 p.   19cm.
Microfiche (neg.) 6 sheets. 11 x 15cm. (NYPL FSN 10,143)

1. European war, 1914-1918--France--Vendée (Département). 2. Vendée,
France (Department)--Hist.,   1914-1918. I. Title.

NT 0038951   NN

Tardif (Gilles-François). *Des principaux soins
hygiéniques que réclament les enfans au-dessous
de sept ans dans l'état de santé. 31 pp. 4°.
Paris, 1819, No. 64, v. 146.

NT 0038952   DNLM

TARDIF, Guillaume, b. ca. 1400
Basis grammaticae, cum Commento.* [Strassburg, Heinrich Eggestein, cir. 1474.]

[24] leaves. 4°. 21.8 cm. Rubricated and initials supplied in red.
Hain, Repertorium, 15240. Goff T-16
Fully described in this Library's sheet Catalogue of Incunabula.

NT 0038953   MH

Tardif, Guillaume, b. ca. 1400, tr.

Incun.
1490
.A2   Æsopus.
Rosen-
wald Coll.   Fabulae. French. [Paris, Antoine Vérard, ca. 1490]

Tardif, Guillaume, b. ca. 1400, tr.

Poggio-Bracciolini, 1380-1459. FOR OTHER EDITIONS SEE MAIN ENTRY
Les Facéties de Pogge Florentin; traduction nouvelle et intégrale, accompagnée des Moralitez de Guillaume Tardif, suivie de la Description des bains de Bade (xv⁰ siècle) et du dialogue Un vieillard doit-il se marier? Édition annotée, précédée d'une notice sur Pogge, sa vie, son œuvre, ses traducteurs, par Pierre des Brandes [pseud.] Paris, Garnier frères [19—]

Tardif, Guillaume, b. ca. 1400
La favconnerie de Iean de Franchieres
see under   Franchières, Jean de, 15th cent.

Tardif, Guillaume, b. ca. 1400.
Le livre de l'art de faulconnerie et des chiens de chasse, par Guillaume Tardif. Réimprimé sur l'édition de 1792 avec une notice et des notes par Ernest Jullien. Paris: Librairie des bibliophiles, 1882. 2 v. in 1. 16°. (Cabinet de vénerie. [no.] 4.)

no. 155 of 340 copies printed.
First edition printed in 1492.
With this is bound: G. Dubois. Débat entre deux dames. Paris, 1882. 16°.

1. Falconry. 2. Dog (Hunting). 3. Jullien, Ernest, 1829- editor. 4. Series.
N. Y. P. L.   May 13, 1916.

NT 0038957   NN CtY OClW NcU

Tardif, H.
*Quelques considérations sur l'hématémèse.
Montpellier, 1874.
vii, 9-58 p., 3 l. 4°.

NT 0038958   DNLM

Tardif, Henri.
Christiani populi sacramenta. (Etudes de pastorale sacramentaire) Paris, Les Editions ouvrières [1952]
141 p. 19 cm. (Collection "Piscatores hominum")
1. Liturgy and theology. 2. Sacraments (Theology)

NT 0038959   IMunS

Tardif, Henri
La victoire du nouvel Adam (Études evangeliques)
Paris, Les Editions Ouvrières. [c1952]

8-223 p. 19 cm. (Collection "Piscatores hominum")

NT 0038960   PLatS MnCS

---

qM786.3 Tardif, Hilary Marie, ed.
T173c
Catholic hymns. Approved by the Commission on Church Music of the Archdiocese of New York. New York, C. H. Hansen Music Co., c1952.
17p. 31cm. (Jumbo note)

At head of title: For the elementary pianist.

NT 0038961   IU

Tardif, Hilary Marie   (2)
Introduction, fugue et grand choeur sur Ave Maria.
NY, Belwin [195-]

Score (8 p.)
For organ

NT 0038962   MH-Mu

Tardif, J.
Essai sur le rythme en général et ses principales applications au chant, par J. Tardif... Angers: Germain et G. Grassin, 1886. 28 p. illus. (music.) 24½cm.

Bibliographical footnotes.

1. Musical meter and rhythm.   2. Chant [plain, Gregorian, etc.].
N. Y. P. L.   May 11, 1934

NT 0038963   NN

Tardif, J.
Méthode élémentaire et pratique de plain-chant, approuvée par Monseigneur l'évêque d'Angers pour l'usage des séminaires, collèges et écoles de son diocèse, par l'abbé J. Tardif ... Angers, E. Barassé, 1860.
xvi, [2], 267 p., 1 l. 3 pl. 24ᶜᵐ.

1. Chant (Plain, Gregorian, etc.)

9-11342†

Library of Congress   MT860.T183

NT 0038964   DLC

Tardif (Jacques-Jean). *Sur le mal de mer. 1 p. l., 32 pp. 4°. *Strasbourg, 1828, v. 57.*

NT 0038965   DNLM

Tardif, Joseph.
... Des pouvoirs de police municipale en matière de commerce... Caen, 1917.
25 cm.
Thèse - Univ. de Caen.
Bibliographie: p. [v]-viii.

NT 0038966   CtY

ML174 Tardif, Jules, 1827-1882.
T35   Essai sur les neumes. Paris, A. Durand, 1853.
Music   24 p. (Extrait de la Bibliothèque de l'École des chartes,
Library 3e série, t. 4; mars 1853)

1. Neumes.

NT 0038967   CU

Tardif, Jules, 1827-1882.
Études sur les institutions politiques et administratives de la France. Période mérovingienne. [1] Paris, A. Picard, 1881.
224 p. 25 cm.
No more published.

1. France—Pol. & govt.—To 987.

Full name: Léon Jules Amédée Tardif

JN2331.T3   A 12-1517 rev*
Chicago. Univ. Libr.
for Library of Congress   [r52e⅓]†

NT 0038968   ICU DLC NcU CaBVaU NjP MH CtY NjR

Tardif, Jules, 1827-1882.
... Fac-similé de chartes et diplômes mérovingiens et carlovingiens sur papyrus et sur parchemin compris dans l'inventaire des Monuments historiques, par M. Jules Tardif ... Paris, J. Claye, 1866.
49 pl. (i. e. 62 facsim. on 52 pl.) 70½ x 55½ᶜᵐ. (Ministère de la maison de l'empereur et des beaux-arts. Archives de l'empire. Inventaires et documents publiés par ordre de l'empereur sous la direction de M. le marquis de Laborde)
"Chartes et diplômes publiés en fac-similé par la Direction générale des Archives de l'empire (première et seconde séries)" the first series being a reissue of "Diplomata et chartæ mérovingicæ ætatis in Archivo Franciæ asservata delineanda curavit A. Letronne ... Parisiis, ex officina Kæpplini [1844-49]."

1. Manuscripts—Facsimiles. 2. Diplomatics. 3. Paleography. 4. France—Hist.—Sources. 5. France—Hist.—Carlovingian and early period to 987.—Sources. I. Tardif, Jules, 1827-1882. Monuments historiques. II. Letronne, Antoine Jean, 1787-1848. Diplomata et chartæ ... III. France. Archives nationales. IV. Title. V. Title: Chartes et diplômes.

[Full name: Léon Jules Amédée Tardif]

6-7003 Revised 2
Library of Congress   CD132.T35

NT 0038970   DLC ICU PPTU

Tardif, Jules, 1827-1882.
... Introduction à l'inventaire du fonds d'archives dit les monuments historiques. Paris, J. Claye, 1866.
cxiv p. 30.5 cm. (With this is bound: Huillard-Bréholles, J. L. A. Titres de la Maison ducale de Bourbon)
At head of title: Les archives de la France pendant la revolution.

NT 0038971   NcD

Tardif, Jules, 1827-1882.
Mémoire sur les notes tironiennes, par Jules Tardif.
([In Académie des inscriptions et belles-lettres, Paris. Mémoires présentés par divers savants. Paris, 1854. 29½ᶜᵐ. 2. sér., t. III, p. [104]-171. tables) .

1. Tironian notes.   [Full name: Léon Jules Amédée Tardif]

A C 40-679
Hamilton college. Library
for Library of Congress   [DC31.1 G. vol. 3]
[2]   (913.44)

NT 0038972   NCH MB OU

Tardif, Jules, 1827-1882.
Une minute de notaire du IX⁰ siècle en notes tironiennes, d'après la lecture donnée en 1849 par Jules Tardif. Paris, A. Picard, 1888.
15, [1] p. 23½ᶜᵐ.
Pub. by Adolphe F. L. Tardif from the first chapter of the second (inedited) part of Jules Tardif's thesis "Des notes tironiennes," 1850.

1. Tironian notes.   I. Tardif, Adolphe François Lucien, 1824-1890.
[Full name: Léon Jules Amédée Tardif]

11-15230 Revised
Library of Congress   Z81.T18

NT 0038973   DLC OCU

Tardif, Jules, 1827–1882.
Une minute de notaire du IX siècle en notes tironiennes d'après la lecture données en 1849.   Paris, A. Picard, 1888.   15 p. 24cm.

Film reproduction.   Negative.

I. Tiro, Marcus Tullius.   2. Short-   John Robert Gregg Shorthand Coll.

NT 0038974   NN

Tardif, Jules, 1827–1882.
... Monuments historiques (Cartons des rois, 528–1789) par M. Jules Tardif ...   Paris, J. Claye, 1866.

2 p. l., cxiv p., 1 l., xix, 711, (1) p.   31 x 24ᶜᵐ.   *and* atlas of 14 facsims. (7 double) 70½ x 55½ᶜᵐ.   (Ministère de la maison de l'empereur et des beaux-arts. Archives de l'empire. Inventaires et documents publiés par ordre de l'empereur sous la direction de M. le marquis de Laborde)

Text has half-title and running title: Monuments historiques. Cartons des rois.
Atlas has title: ... Fac-similé de chartes et diplômes mérovingiens et carlovingiens sur papyrus et sur parchemin compris dans l'inventaire des Monuments historiques par M. Jules Tardif ...

The Library of Congress has no copy of the atlas in the form noted. The facsimiles were however issued together with a reissue of those pub. at an earlier date, "Diplomata et chartæ merovingicæ ætatis in Archivio Franciæ asservata delineanda curavit A. Letronne. Parisiis, ex officina Kæppelini (1844–49)." The two series of facsimiles are arranged in one chronological sequence, preceded by a list which has caption: Table des chartes et diplômes publiés en fac-simile par la Direction générale des Archives de l'empire (première et seconde séries)
A copy of this volume is in the Library of Congress.

1. France—Hist.—Sources. 2. Diplomatics.   I. France. Archives nationales.   II. Title.   III. Title: Cartons des rois.
(*Full name:* Léon Jules Amédée Tardif)

6–7002 Revised

Library of Congress   CD132.T3

NT 0038976   DLC PU MdBP IEN NIC MB OCU

Tardif, Léon Jules Amédée
see
Tardif, Jules, 1827–1882.

Tardif (Léonard). *1. Quels sont les signes fournis par l'augmentation et par la diminution des forces musculaires? II. (etc.). 30 pp. 4°. Paris, 1839, No. 412, v. 350.*

NT 0038978   DNLM

ML50
T27B6   **Tardif, Lucien**
(Bouton d'or. Libretto)
Bouton d'or, opéra comique en trois actes. Paroles et musique de Lucien Tardif.
(Paris?) 1877.
38 p., music (33 p.)

Cover title.
At head of title: Le petit théâtre.

NT 0038979   CU

PQ
1262   **Tardif, O**
I29+   Les captifs d'Hanambougou.   (Paris,
1898   1898)
no.4   102–104 p. 30cm. (Supplément à l'Illustration du 6 août 1898. Romans)

Caption title.

NT 0038980   NIC

PQ
1262   **Tardif, O**
I29+   Croquis du Soudan. Frères ennemis.
1898   (Paris, 1898)
no. 7   62–64 p. 30cm. (Supplément à l'Illustration du 27 août 1898. Romans)

Caption title.

NT 0038981   NIC

Tardif, René, 1915–
... Une maison d'aliénés et de correctionnaires sous l'ancien régime au XVIIIᵉ siècle; (histoire de la charité de Chateau-Thierry)...   Paris, 1939.
Thèse - Univ. de Paris.

NT 0038982   CtY

Tardif, Robert, 1903–
... Diagnostic différentiel du chancre syphilitique de l'amygdale et de l'angine de Vincent...   Paris, 1930.
Thèse - Univ. de Paris.
"Bibliographie": p. 55–58.

NT 0038983   CtY

Tardif, Thérèse.
...Désespoir de vieille fille. Montréal, L'Arbre, 1943.
124 p., 1 l. 19ᶜᵐ.

I. Title.
Library of Congress   PQ3919.T26D4

44–23903
848.91

NT 0038984   DLC NIC CaOTU CaBVaU

Tardif, Thérèse.
La vie quotidienne, roman. (Éd. préliminaire. Ottawa, 1951)
180 p. 20 cm.

I. Title.
PQ2639.A728V5 1951   51–29254

NT 0038985   DLC CaOTU NNC NcU NN WaS CaBVaU

PQ2639
.A7306x
        Tardif, Yanette Delétang.
La colline / Y. Delétang-Tardif. -- Paris : R. Debresse, 1935.
14 p. ; 19 cm. -- (Cahiers des poètes : 2. série ; 3)
Cover title.
Poems.
Author's autograph presentation copy to René Lacôte.
I. Title.

NT 0038986   MB

Tardif, Yanette (Delétang)
Confidences des îles [par] Yanette Delétang-Tardif.   Paris, Editions R.A. Correa, 1934.
92 p.   20 cm.

NT 0038987   IU NN

Tardif, Yanette (Delétang)
L'éclair et le temps [par] Yanette Delétang-Tardif, Roger Belluc, Louis Emié. [Limoges] Rougerie [1951?]
[30] p.

NT 0038988   MH

Tardif, Mme. Yanette (Deletang)
Eclats; poèmes.   Paris, A. Quillet, 1929.

NT 0038989   MH

Tardif, Yanette (Delétang)
Edellina, ou Les pouvoirs de la musique. Niort, Nicolas [1943]
43 p. (Collection Les amis de Rochefort, 10)

NT 0038990   MH

Tardif, Yanette (Delétang)
Edmond Jaloux. Paris, Table ronde (1947)
234 p. port., facsim. 19 cm.
"Œuvres (de Jaloux)": p. 232–234.

1. Jaloux, Edmond, 1878–

PQ2619.A4Z8   843.91   48–42873*

CaBVaU
NT 0038991   DLC INS OU MB IU NjP IEN NN NNC MiU

PQ2639
.A7304x
        Tardif, Yanette Delétang.
Générer : poèmes / Yanette Delétang-Tardif. -- Paris : A. Quillet, 1930.
157 p. ; 20 cm.

NT 0038992   MB

Tardif, Yanette (Delétang)
La nuit des temps [par] Yanette Delétang-Tardif. Paris, P. Seghers (1951)
34 p. 18 cm. (Poésie 51.136)

I. Title.
A 52–6413

Illinois. Univ. Library for Library of Congress   (3)

NT 0038993   IU ICN MH NN

845T175 **Tardif, Yanette (Delétang)**
Os   Sept chants royaux, ornés par Survage.
[Paris] Éditions du Rond-Point [1945]
42p. illus. 24cm.

NT 0038994   IU

Tardif, Yanette (Delétang)
Les séquestrés; roman. Paris, Table ronde (1945)
162 p. 19 cm.

I. Title.
PQ2639.A73S4   843.91   A F 49–1248 rev*
New York. Public Libr. for Library of Congress   (r51b3)†

NT 0038995   NN PBm ICU ICRL DLC CLU

Tardif, Yanette (Delétang)
Tenter de vivre, poèmes. Paris, Éditions Denoël (1943)
171 p. 19 cm.

I. Title.
PQ2639.A73T4   A F 48–3711*
Chicago. Univ. Libr. for Library of Congress   (1)†

NT 0038996   ICU IU ICRL NN MB DLC

Tardif, *Mme.* Yanette (Delétang)
... Vol des oiseaux. Parir, A. Quillet, 1931.

83 p., 1 l. 19½ᵐ.

At head of title: Yanette Delétang-Tardif.
"Il a été tiré de cet ouvrage trois cent cinquante exemplaires sur velin
blanc numérotés de 1 à 350. Exemplaire n° 131."
Poems.

ɪ. Title.

38-12266

Library of Congress   PQ2639.A73V6 1931

₍2₎   841.91

NT 0038997   DLC

Tardif d' Hamonville, Jean Charles Louis, baron,
1830-1899
     see   Hamonville, Jean Charles Louis
Tardif d', baron, 1830-1899.

Tardif de Mello, Achille.
     Des peuples européens, leur état social
sous leurs divers gouvernements. Esprit de
ˡᵃ démocratie de 1789 à 1840. Paris, 1840. 8°.
                                          3734

NT 0038999   MdBP

Tardif de Mello, Achille.   2951.50
Dictionnaire littéraire et historique de la Grèce, de Rome et du
   moyen âge. Enrichi de tableaux synoptiques embrassant l'histoire
   de tous les siècles avant et après Jésus-Christ.
Paris. Delagrave & cⁱᵉ. 1873. iv, 592 pp. 4 folded plates. L. 8°.

G6451 — Greece. Lit. Dict. — Greece. Hist. Dict. — Rome. Hist. Dict. — Latin
literature. Dict. — Middle Ages. Hist. Dict. — Middle Ages. Lit. Dict.

NT 0039000   MB

Tardif de Mello, Achille.
     Histoire intellectuelle de l'empire de Russie. Paris,
Amyot, 1854.

iii, 374 p. 27 cm.

Includes selections and extracts of Russian poetry and prose
works.

1. Russian literature—Translations into French. 2. French literature—Translations from Russian. 3. Russian literature—Hist. &
crit.   ɪ. Title.

PG3214.T3   68-43053

NT 0039001   DLC WaU OU NN

Tardif de Moidrey, René, 1828-1879.
     ... Introduction au "Livre de Ruth"; texte intégral de l'ou-
vrage de l'abbé Tardif de Moidrey. Paris, Desclée, de Brou-
wer et cie ₍1938₎

236 p., 1 l. incl. front. (port.) 20½ᵐ.

At head of title: Paul Claudel.

1. Bible. O. T. Ruth—Criticism, interpretation, etc. 2. Bible—Criticism, interpretation, etc.—O. T. Ruth.   ɪ. *Claudel, Paul, 1868-
ɪɪ. Title.

38-31544

Library of Congress   BS1315.T3

Copyright A—Foreign   40072

₍3₎   222.3

NT 0039002   DLC KyTrA NNC CtY NjP ICN InStme

222.35   Tardif de Moidrey, René, 1828-1879.
T183i   Introduction au "Livre de Ruth"; texte
            intégral de l'ouvrage de l'abbé Tardif de
            Moidrey. ₍Paris₎ Gallimard ₍1952₎
            236p. 21cm.

               At head of title: Paul Claudel.

            √1.Bible.   O.T.   Ruth - Criticism inter-
            pretation, etc.-2.Bible - Criticism, inter-
            pretation, etc. - O.T.   Ruth.√I.Claudel,
            Paul, 1868-   1955.₎

NT 0039003   CLSU IaU FTaSU TU IEN CU MH OrU

Tardif-Desvaux,
     Angers pittoresque, par Tardif-Desvaux. Texte
par E. L.   Angers, Cosnier et Lachèse, 1843.
v. p.   plates (incl. plans) 36 cm.
Ornamented half-title.
1. Anjou- Descr. & tr. ɪ. L., E.

NT 0039004   CU

Tardiff, Alfredo Lima
     see   Lima, Alfredo.

4PN-   Tardiff, Guillermo.
427   El verbo de la juventud mexicana a traves de
            los concursos de oratoria, 1926-1930. Tomado
            de los reportajes y versiones taquigráficas publi-
            cadas con ese motivo por "El Universal".
            Colaboró César Liekens [19   ]
            252 p.

NT 0039006   DLC-P4 TxU CU-BANC

Tardiff B   , Guillermo
     see
Tardiff, Guillermo.

Tardiff de Moidrey, Joseph
     see
Moidrey, Joseph Tardif de, 1858-1937.

Tardin, Jean.
     Disquisicio physiologica de pilis. Tvrnoni, Exc.
Claud. Michael, 1619.
8p. l., 280, [22]p. 18cm.

1. Medicine - Early works to 1800. 2. Hemorrhoids.

NT 0039009   CtY-M

B618.23   Tardin, Jean.
N144   Disquisitio medica, de ea quae undecimo mense
v.1   peperit. In qua, sententia Hippocratis de summo
            gestationis termino examinatur. A Joanne Tar-
            dino. Juxtà exemplar Turnoni impressum anno
            1640. Parisiis, Excudebat Joannes-Thomas
            Herissant, 1765.

               (In Naissance tardive. Paris, 1764-65.
            20cm.   v.1)
                  1. Pregnancy, Protracted.

NT 0039010   MnU PU WaU PPC DNLM

WZ   TARDIN, Jean
250   ... Disquisitio physiologica de pilis. Turnoni, Claudius
T1825d   Michael, 1609.
1609   [16], 280, [22] p. 17 cm.
               Imperfect? Last leaf (blank?) wanting.

NT 0039011   DNLM PPC NNNAM MnU CtY-M

X
QA528
T3   Tardin, Jean
               Histoire natvrelle. De la fontaine qui
            brusle pres de Grenoble. Avec la recherche
            de ses causes, & principes, & ample traicte
            des feux soussterrains ... Tournon, G.
            Linocier, 1618.
            ₍22₎,379p. 17cm.

NT 0039012   TxDaM

BP   [Tardini, Domenico] cardinal, 1888-1961
639   De natura et ratione peccati personalis.
T18   Romae [in Pont. Universitate de propaganda
1917   fide] 1917-18.
               1 l., 107p. 25cm.
               Planographed.

               1. Sin.

NT 0039013   IMunS MBtS

BP   [Tardini, Domenico] cardinal, 1888-1961
639   De poenitentia. Romae [in Pont. Univer-
T18   sitate de propaganda fide] 1918.
1917   [1] 208, viii p. 25cm.
               As issued, with author's De natura et
            ratione peccati...

               1. Penance (Sacrament).

NT 0039014   IMunS MBtS

BX   Tardini, Domenico, Cardinal.
2260   De poenitentia. Romae, 1922.
T3   215 p. 25cm.

               Reproduced from handwritten copy.

               1. Penance.   I. Title.

NT 0039015   CMenSP

BS1236 Tardini, Domenico, cardinal, 1888-1961.
T37   Praelectiones dogmaticae de sacramentis in
1916   genere. Romae, Pont. Universitate de Propaganda
            Fide, 1917.

               339 p. 25 cm.

               Typescript.

               1. Sacraments. I. Title.

NT 0039016   MBtS

BX   Tardini, Domenico, Cardinal, 1888-1961
2200   Praelectiones dogmaticae: De sacramentis in genere.
T3   Romae, Typis Polyglottis Vaticanis, 1932.
               207 p. 21cm.

               "Ad privatum auditorum usu pro manuscripto."

               1. Sacraments--Catholic Church.   I. Title: De Sacramentis
            in genere.

NT 0039017   CMenSP

BS1312 Tardini, Domenico, cardinal, 1888-1961.
T37   Praelectiones dogmaticae de ss. eucharistia.
1915   Romae, Pont. Universitate de Propaganda Fide,
            1916.

               386 p. 25 cm.
               Typescript.

               1. Eucharist. I. Title.

NT 0039018   MBtS IMunS

BX 2215 .T3
Tardini, Domenico, Cardinal.
Praelectiones dogmaticae: De SS. Eucharistia. Romae, 1923.
503 p. 25cm.

Reproduced from handwritten copy.

1. Lord's Supper--Catholic Church. I. Title: De SS. Eucharistia.

NT 0039019   CMenSP

f DG816 .3 P5T3
Tardini, Giulio, 1908-
Basilica vaticana e borghi; dati storici raccolti ... Roma, Istituto grafico tiberino [1936]
114 p. illus., plans. 35cm.

Bibliography: p. [105]-110.

1. Vatican (City) San Pietro in Vaticano (Basilica) 2. Rome, Italy (City) Ager vaticanus. 3. Rome, Italy (City) - Suburbs. 4. Architecture - Rome.

NT 0039020   CU NNC DCU CSt InStme MH

Tardini, Luigi Vincenzo
... I fondamenti della concezione giuridica di L.A. Muratori; studio sul trattato La filosofia morale. Modena, Società tipografica modenese, 1937.
111 p., 1 l. 25cm.

Bibliographical footnotes.

NT 0039021   MH-L

Tardini, Vincenzo.
... I teatri di Modena : contributo alla storia del teatro in Italia ... Modena, G. T. Vincenzi e nipoti, 1899-1902.
3 v. 25ᶜᵐ.
At head of title: V. Tardini.
Paged continuously.
Vol. III has imprint: Modena, Forghieri, Pellequi e c.
Vol. I was first published independently in 1898 under title: La drammatica nel nuovo teatro comunale di Modena.
CONTENTS.—I. La drammatica nel nuovo teatro comunale. 1899.—II. Il teatro Aliprandi. 1899 (i. e. 1900)—III. Opere in musica rappresentate dal 1594 al 1900. 1902.
1. Theater—Modena—Hist. 2. Opera—Modena. 3. Opera, Italian. I. Title.
                                                    25-15569
Library of Congress   ML1733.8.M6T2

NT 0039022   DLC CtY NcU

Tardinus, Joannes
see   Tardin, Joan.

Lilly BX 1756 .T 182 Mendel
TARDÍO, FERNANDO, 1636-1714.
Sermones varios / predicados por el Rdo. Padre Fernando Tardio, de la Compañia de Iesus, en el Nueuo-Reyno del Perù. — Barcelona : Antonio la Caualleria, 1678.
[8], 475, [1] p. ; 4to(20.5 cm.)

Medina, BHA, 1660.
Bound in vellum.

NT 0039024   InU

Tardit, Michel, ed.

France. *Laws, statutes, etc.*
Bulletin annoté des lois et décrets ...
Paris, Société anonyme des publications périodiques de l'Imprimerie P. Dupont

Tardit, Michel, and Ripert, André.
Traité des octrois municipaux. Paris, 1904.
476 p.

NT 0039026   IU

4PA Lat 161
Tarditi, Giovanni
I diminutivi nel Satyricon di Petronio. Genova, Typis [1951]
23 p.

NT 0039027   DLC-P4 CU NjP

Tarditi, Giovanni, 1857-   , arr.
Ruy Blas. Fantasia
see under   Marchetti, Filippo, 1831-1902.

Tarditi, José Rodríguez
see
Rodríguez Tarditi, José.

Case -VM 1549 T 18c
TARDITI, ORAZIO, d.ca.1670.
...Canzonette amorose, libro secondo, a doi, e tre voci concertate per cantare nel cimbalo, spinetta, tiorba, ò altro simile instrumento...
Venetia, A.Vincenti, 1647.
[2],17,[1]p. 22cm.

At head of title: Basso.
Title vignette; initials.
Italian words.
Complete in 4 books.

NT 0039030   ICN

Tarditi, Orazio, d. ca. 1670
Missa, Et Psalmi In Vespertinis Laudibus Decantandi Tribvs Vocibvs Ad Organi concentum concertarim accomodati Cum Litaniis in fine beatissime Mariae Virginis Avctore Horatio Tardito Opvs Decimvm Septimvm Ad Per Illustrem, & Admodum Reu. Dominum d'Hyacintvm Paradisvm A'Verona Congregationis Camaldulensis Abbatem Optime meritum. Superiorvm Permissv. Et Privilegiis.

In Venetia, Apresso Alessandro Vincenti MDCXXXX. (1640).

(Basso part only).

NT 0039031   CU-MUSI

333.38 T17b
Tarditi, Pascual.
Breve estudio de los problemas fundamentales de las empresas fraccionadoras de terrenos. Mexico, Instituto Politecnico Nacional, 1943.
72 p. illus. 22cm.

"Tesis...[presentado en el] examen profesional de Contador Público y Auditor."
With author's autograph.

1. Land   subdivision.

NT 0039032   LU

Tardiu, Jean, 1901-
... La périchondrite laryngée syphilitique...
Lyon, 1926.
25.5 cm.
Thèse - Univ. de Lyon.
Bibliographie: p. 61-63.

NT 0039033   CtY

Tardivaux, René
see   Boylesve, René, 1867-1926.

Tardiveau, A
Fleurs d'antan et fleurs nouvelles cueillies par A. Tardiveau. [1.ser.] Paris, Libr. Lavauzelle, 1892
vii, 235 p.

NT 0039035   MH

Tardiveau (Ferdinand). *Essai sur la transpiration cutanée. 31 pp. 4°. Paris, 1829, No. 102, v. 223.

NT 0039036   DNLM

Tardiveau, François Alexandre
Rapport sur une pétition de la commune de Strasbourg relative aux lettres écrites le 11 juin 1792 par le ministre de l'intérieur aux administrateurs du département du Bas-Rhin et au maire de Strasbourg. [Strasbourg, 1792]
4 p.

NT 0039037   MH

Tardiveau (J.-A.) *Sur les maladies de la glande thyroïde. vi, 7-39 pp. 8°. Paris, an XI [1803]. v. 98.

NT 0039038   DNLM

Tardiveau, Jean Pierre Piet
see   Piet Tardiveau, Jean Pierre.

Tardiveau (Simon-A.-J.) *Essai sur la mélodie aiguë simple, ou l'inflammation des reins. 16 pp. 4°. Paris, 1830, No. 74, v. 251.

NT 0039040   DNLM PPC

Tardiveaux, M
Discours Chretien, a l'Occasion de la Guerre entre la France & les Isles Britanniques, par M. Tardiveaux. n.p., 1780.
34 p.

NT 0039041   PHi

Tardivel (Achille) [1854-   ]. *Contribution à l'étude de la tuberculose d'origine cutanée. 125 pp. 4°. Paris, 1890, No 184.

NT 0039042   DNLM

Tardivel, Emile Hyacinthe, 1859-   *comp.*
The amended license law of New Hampshire in force May 1, 1905; comp. in handy form, with annotations, by Emile H. Tardivel ... Berlin, N. H., The Weston press, 1905.
4 p. l., 116 p. 23½ᶜᵐ.

1. New Hampshire. Laws, statutes, etc.   5-17232
Library of Congress   (Copyright 1905 A 114317)

NT 0039043   DLC ICJ

⌐Tardivel, Emile Hyacinthe¬ 1859–   *ed.*
⌐-⌐Le guide canadien-français de Manchester, ⌐N. H. pour 1894–
95, contenant un almanach complet des adresses, le mouvement
de la population canadienne depuis 23 ans, un aperçu historique de la ville de Manchester, des paroisses et des sociétés canadiennes ... 1. année. Manchester, N. H., La Cⁱ⁸ John B.
Clarke, 1894.

300 p.   plates, ports.   23ᶜᵐ.

Advertising matter interspersed.

1. French Canadians in Manchester, N. H.   2. Manchester, N. H.—
Direct.   I. Title.

Library of Congress   F44.M2T2   7—39287

NT 0039044   DLC

Tardivel, Fernande.
... J. H. Newman, éducateur ... par Fernande Tardivel.
Paris, Imprimeries Les Presses modernes, 1937.

236 p.   24ᶜᵐ.

Thèse complémentaire—Univ. de Paris.
"Index bibliographique": p. ⌐229¬–232.
"Errata": 1 leaf, inserted.

1. Newman, John Henry, cardinal, 1801–1890.   2. Education—Philosophy.

Library of Congress   LB675.N45T3 1937 a   41—25889
                               ⌐2¬   370.1

NT 0039045   DLC CtY OCX

Tardivel, Fernande.
J. H. Newman, éducateur, par Fernande Tardivel ... ⌐Paris,
G. Beauchesne et ses fils¬ 1937.

236 p.   25¼ᶜᵐ.

"Index bibliographique": p. ⌐229¬–232.

1. Newman, John Henry, cardinal, 1801–1890.   2. Education—Philosophy.

Library of Congress   LB675.N45T3   40—1978
                               ⌐2¬   370.1

NT 0039046   DLC LU ICU OC1JC

Tardivel, Fernande.
... La personnalité littéraire de Newman ... par Fernande
Tardivel. Paris, G. Beauchesne et ses fils, 1937.

3 p. l., ⌐9¬–444 p., 2 l.   22¼ᶜᵐ.

Thèse—Univ. de Paris.
"Bibliographie": p. ⌐427¬–437.

1. Newman, John Henry, cardinal, 1801–1890.   I. Title.

Library of Congress   42—1383
                               BX4705.N5T3 1937 a
                               ⌐2¬   922.242

NT 0039047   DLC CtY NNUT

Tardivel, Fernande.
... La personnalité littéraire de Newman. Paris, G. Beauchesne et ses fils, 1937.

3 p. l., ⌐9¬–444 p., 1 l.   23ᶜᵐ.   (*On cover:* Bibliothèque des Archives de
philosophie)

"Bibliographie": p. ⌐427¬–437.

1. Newman, John Henry, cardinal, 1801–1890.   I. Title.

Library of Congress   39—3210
                               BX4705.N5T3
                               ⌐2¬   922.242

NT 0039048   DLC IEG TxU ICU OC1JC NN ICN OCX

Tardivel, Jules, Paul, 1851–1905.
L'anglicisme voilà l'ennemi; causerie faite
au Cercle catholique de Québec, le 17 décembre
1879 par J. P. Tardivel... Québec, Impr. du
"Canadien", 1880.
28 p.   19 cm.
1. French language - Foreign words and
phrases - English.   2. French language in Canada.
I. Cercle catholique de Québec.

NT 0039049   MiU CtY CaNSWA MH CaOTU OO CaBVaU

Tardivel, Jules Paul, 1851–1905.
Borrowed and stolen feathers; or, A glance through Mr.
J. M. Lemoine's latest work "The chronicles of the St.
Lawrence." My J. P. Tardivel.   Quebec, "Le Canadien"
steam printing office, 1878.

33 p.   22 cm.

1. Le Moine, Sir James MacPherson, 1825–1912.   The chronicles
of the St. Lawrence.   I. Title.

F1050.L56   2—503M2

NT 0039050   DLC CaNSWA CtY CaOTU TxU CaBVaU

Tardivel, Jules Paul, 1851–1905.
La langue française au Canada; conférence lue devant
l'Union catholique de Montréal, le 10 mars 1901, par J.-P.
Tardivel ...   Montréal, La Compagnie de publication de la
Revue canadienne ⌐1901¬

2 p. l., ii p., 2 l., iii–xvii, 69 p. front., 5 port. 16¼ cm.

1. French-Canadian dialect.   2. French Canadians.   I. Title.
PC3608.T2   8—25838

         FU NcD
NT 0039051   DLC CaBVaU CtY RWoU TxU NN MB OC1 CaOTU

Tardivel, Jules Paul, 1851–1905.
Mélanges; ou, Recueil d'études religieuses,
sociales, politiques et littéraires, par J. P.
Tardivel... Première série... Québec, Impr.
de la Vérité, 1887–1903.
3 v.   22 cm.
Vol. 2 printed by L. J. Demers & frère, v. 3
by S. A. Demers.
A selection of articles from la Vérité.
1. Catholic church in Canada.   2. Education -
Canada.   3. Canada - Hist. - 1867–1914.   I.
I. La Vérité.

NT 0039052   MiU MnU MH CtY CaBVaU

         D
         919
         .T18
Tardivel, Jules Paul, 1851–
Notes de voyage en France, Italie, Espagne,
Irlande, Angleterre, Belgique et Hollande, par
J.-P. Tardivel ... Montréal, E. Senécal & fils,
1890.

460 p. incl. front.   plates, ports.   22½ᶜᵐ.

1. Europe—Descr. & trav.

NT 0039053   MiU CaOTU RWoU CaBVaU

         LB
         2537
         .Q3
         T18
Tardivel, Jules Paul, 1851–1905.
Polémique à propos d'enseignement entre m. J.
-P. Tardivel ... et m. C.-J. Magnan ... Quebec,
Impr. de L.-J. Demers & frère, 1894.
110 p., 1 l.   22 cm.
Debate on the education laws of the province
of Quebec reprinted from the periodicals la
Vérité and l'Enseignement.
1. Educational law and legislation—Quebec
(Province)   I. Magnan, Charles Joseph, 1865–1942.

NT 0039054   MiU CaBVaU CaOTU

Tardivel, Jules Paul, 1851–
Pour la patrie; roman du xx⁸ siècle, par J. P. Tardivel
... Montréal, Cadieux & Derome, 1895.

2 p. l., ⌐3¬–451 p. 19 cm.

I. Title.

PQ3919.T3P7 1895   2—8145

NT 0039055   DLC CtY CaBVaU

         PS
        *8489
         A74P6
         1936
Tardivel, Jules Paul, 1851–
Pour la patrie; roman du XXe siècle.
⌐2. éd.¬ Montreal, La "Croix", 1936.
379 p.

NT 0039056   CaOTU

Tardivel, Jules Paul, 1851–1905.
La situation religieuse aux États-Unis; illusions et réalité par Jules Tardivel ... Lille, Paris, Desclée, De Brou-
wer et cie, 1900.

2 p. l., ⌐v¬–viii, 302 p., 1 l.   19 cm.

1. Catholic Church in the U. S.   2. U. S.—Religion—19th century.
I. Title.

BX1406.T3   F 2499

NT 0039057   DLC MB RWoU CtY-D NRU IEdS InStme

         BX
         4397
         .T183
Tardivel, Jules Paul, 1851–1905.
La situation religieuse aux États-Unis;
illusions et réalité. Lille, Desclée, 1900.
Microfilm copy. Negative.
Collation of the original: viii, 302 p.
19 cm.

1. Catholic Church - U. S.   I. Title.

NT 0039058   DCU

         WG
         33793
Tardivi, Henri
Action des iodures métalliques sur les
sels d'alcaloides. Montpellier, 1902.
139 p.
Thèse - Ecole supérieure de pharmacie de
Montpellier.
"Bibliographie": pp. [135]–136.

NT 0039059   CtY DNLM

Tardivo, Renato
... L'erede apparente, per il dott.
Renato Tardivo ... Padova, A. Milani,
1932.
1 p. l., 136 p.   25ᶜᵐ. (Studi di
diritto privato italiano e straniero
diretti da Mario Rotondi ... v. IV)
"Pubblicazione dell'Istituto di
diritto commerciale comparato della
R. Università di Pavia".

NT 0039060   MiU-L

Tardjan Hadidjaja
   see
Hadidjaja, Tardjan, 1905–

Tardo, Lorenzo.
... L'antica melurgia bizantina nell'interpretazione della
Scuola monastica di Grottaferrata. Grottaferrata, Scuola
tip. italo orientale "S. Nilo," 1938.
xx, 402 p., 1 l.   illus. (music) facsims., diagrs. 31 cm. (Collezione
meridionale diretta da U. Zanotti-Bianco. Ser. III: Il Mezzogiorno
artistico)
At head of title: Lorenzo Tardo jeromonaco.
Errata slip laid in.
"Bibliografia": v. 1, p. ⌐xvii¬–xx.
CONTENTS.—Genesi e sviluppo della melurgia e della semiografia
bizantina.—Testi teoretici di melurgia bizantina.
1. Music, Byzantine.   2. Church music—Orthodox Eastern church.
3. Paleography, Musical.   I. Grottaferrata, Italy (Basilian monastery)   II. Title.

ML188.T17A5   780.9495   41—3027

         IU IaU
NT 0039062   DLC OrStbM CaBVaU TU DDO WU OU MH NcU

M 41
.T365

TARDO, LORENZO.
I codici melurgici della Vaticana e il contributo alla musica bizantina del monachismo greco
della Magna Grecia.

Reprinted from: Archivio storico per la Calabri-
a e la Lucania. v.1(1931) p.225-248.
Xerocopy.

NT 0039063   DDO

M2
.M639
vol. 1
Case

Tardo, Lorenzo, ed.

Catholic Church. *Byzantine rite (Greek) Liturgy and
ritual. Hirmologion.*
Hirmologium e codice Cryptensi E. γ. II, edendum curavit
Laurentius Tardo. Roma, Libreria dello Stato, 1950.

NT 0039065   DDO

TARDO, LORENZO.
La musica bizantina e i codici di melurgia della
Biblioteca di Grottaferrata.

Reprinted from: Accademie e Biblioteche d'Italia
v.4, no.4-5(Aprile 1931) p.355-369.
Xerocopy.

NT 0039065   DDO

Tardo, Lorenzo, ed.
Musicae byzantinae monumenta cryptensia.
Phototypice expressa.   Roma, La Libreria dello
stato, 1950-
¡v.

NT 0039066   OrU

Tardo, Lorenzo, ed.
L'ottoeco nei mss. melurgici
see under   Orthodox Eastern Church.
Liturgy and ritual.

Tardoire, Jean de la
see   Magog, Henri Jeanne, 1877-

---

g
BQV
197
H58

Tardolus, Laomedon
Oratio de ivstitiae ac Divi Ivonis lavdibvs
ad Senatum Apostolicvm. n.p., n.d. [Romae?
1520?]
[14] p. 20 cm.

At head of title: Laomedontis Tardoli Camertis
...
In box with title: Miscellaneous pamphlets.
1. Justice. 2. Ivo Hélory, Saint, 1253-1303.

NT 0039069   CU-L

Tardon, Joaquin Vijil
see
Vijil Tardon, Joaquin.

TARDON, RAPHAËL, 1911-
Bleu des îles. Paris, Fasquelle [1946] 209 p. 19cm.
(Écrits français d'outre-mer)

Short stories.

NT 0039071   NN MB IEN NBuU FU

Tardon, Raphaël, 1911-
La caldeira, roman. Paris, Fasquelle [1949]
264 p. 23 cm.

I. Title.

PQ2639.A734C3   843.91   50-28176

NT 0039072   DLC NNC NBuU IU MU

Tardon, Raphaël, 1911-
Christ au Poing, roman. Paris, Fasquelle [1950]
267 p. 21 cm.

I. Title.

PQ2639.A734C48   843.91   A 51-4993
Illinois. Univ. Library
for Library of Congress   [3]†

NT 0039073   IU NNC CtY NBuU MB NN MU DLC

Tardon, Raphaël, 1911-
Le combat de Schœlcher. Paris, Fasquelle [1948]
127 p. 19 cm.

1. Schœlcher, Victor, 1804-1893.   I. Title.

A 49-2305*
Harvard Univ. Library
for Library of Congress   [1]

NT 0039074   MH NBuU CU IU CtY CLU

Tardon, Raphaël, 1911-
Starkenfirst, roman. Paris, Fasquelle [1947]
201 p. 23 cm.

I. Title.

PQ2639.A734S7   843.91   48-21372*

NT 0039075   DLC NBuU CtY MB

Tardon, Raphaël, 1911-
Toussaint Louverture, le Napoléon noir. Paris, Bellenand
[1951]
254 p. 19 cm.

1. Toussaint Louverture, François Dominique, 1743-1803.
F1923.T953   52—32270 ‡

NT 0039076   DLC NcD NN NIC CU CtY FU TxU DHU

Tardos (Jean-Émile-Alfred) [1865-   ]. *Critique du traitement abortif de la syphilis par la
cautérisation et l'excision du chancre. 34 pp.
4°. Bordeaux, 1891, No. 9.

NT 0039077   DNLM

¥
4
L99
1943/44

Tardos, René, 1919-
Sur les tumeurs cérébrales à évolution
aiguë et à symptomatologie d'abcès du
cerveau ... Auch, Bouquet, 1944.
50, [1] p. (Lyons. Université. Faculté
mixte de médecine et de pharmacie. Thèse.
1943/44. no. 113)

NT 0039078   DNLM

4HD
1246
[

Tardos, Tibor
Gyári belépő. [Budapest] Athenaeum

233 p.

NT 0039079   DLC-P4 MH

Tardos, Tibor.
Igaz történetek nagy építkezésekről. [Budapest] Művelt
Nép Könyvkiadó, 1952.
107 p. illus. 20 cm.

1. Building—Hungary.   I. Title.

TH65.5.T3   56-43199

NT 0039080   DLC

4PH
Hung
675

Tardos, Tibor
Izgalmas órák; mindenki Sajókútra!
Filmregény. [   ] Szépirodalmi Könyvkiadó, 1954.
140 p.

NT 0039081   DLC-P4

PQ2639
.A735U6

Tardos, Tibor.
A U. S. writling boy-chronicle of America sop. Paris,
Réclame, 1949.
[80] p. 20 cm.

I. Title.

A 51-4430
Illinois. Univ. Library
for Library of Congress   [3]

NT 0039082   IU NN DLC

QA
621
.T18

Tardos, Vida
Térgörbék szinguláris pontjairól. Pannonhalma,
1934.
30 p. 23 cm. (Közlemények a Debreceni
Tudományegyetem Matematikai Szemináriumából,
9.füzet)
Title also in German on cover. Summary in
German.

1. Curves.

NT 0039083   MiU

Tardos, Viktor.
Nero anyja; tragédia öt felvonásban.
Budapest, Wodianer F. és Fiai [1903]
175 p.

NT 0039084   CLU

Tardov, Mikhail S
Фронт. Киев, Держ. літ. вид-во, 19

v. illus., port. 20 cm.

1. Russia—Hist.—Revolution, 1917-1921—Fiction.   I. Title. *Title transliterated:* Front.

PG3476.T34F7   52-39926

NT 0039085   DLC

Tardov, Mikhail S
קאסאווסקי. קיעוו, מעלוכעפֿארלאַג פֿאַר די נאַצ׳
אָמלע מינדערהייטן אין אוסער, ₍Киъ₎ 1940

170 p. illus. 15 cm.

Portrait on cover.

1. Kotovskiĭ, Grigoriĭ Ivanovich, ₍₁₈₁₎-1925. *Title transliterated:* Kotovski.

DK254.K66T3   52-49238

NT 0039086   DLC

Tardov, V   G
Домъ; трагическая комедія въ 4-хъ дѣйствіяхъ. Петроградъ, Изд. журнала "Театръ и искусство," ₍191-₎

68 p. 23 cm.

I. Title.   *Title transliterated:* Dom.

PG3470.T315D6   54-19932 ‡

NT 0039087   DLC

Tardov, V   G
Судьба Россіи; избранные очерки (1911-1917). Москва, Изд. Д. Я. Маковскаго, 1918.

viii, 546, iv p. 23 cm.

At head of title: Т. Ардовъ (В. Г. Тардовъ).

1. Russia—Politics and government—1894-1917—Addresses, essays, lectures. I. Title.   *Title romanized* Sud'ba Rossii.

DK262.T275   76-288401

NT 0039088   DLC

Tardres (Jean-Pierre) [1881-]. *Contribution à l'étude des troubles nerveux à topographie radiculaire. 46 pp., 1 l. 8°. *Montpellier, 1907.*

NT 0039089   DNLM

Tardu, Bedii
Tabiat ve fen bilgisi, yazanlar Bedii Tardu. Istanbul, Maarif Basımevi ₍1955₎.

5 v. (Ilkögretmen okullari kitaplari)

1. Zoology. 2. Botany. 3. Physics. 4. Hygiene, Public.

NT 0039090   NNC

Tarducci, Achille.
Delle machine, ordinanze et qvartieri antichi et moderni ... discorsi d'Achille Tardvcci. Aggiuntoui dal medesimo Le fattioni occorse nell'Ongaria ... nel 1597 e la battaglia in Transiluania contra il Valacco, 1600, fatte dal signor Giorgio Basta ... Venetia, G. B. Ciotti, 1601.
202 ₍i. e. 203₎, 40 p. illus., port. 21 cm.
The second group of pages has special t.-p. with title: Svccesso delle fattioni occorse nell'Ongaria vicino a Vacia nel M. D. XCVII. et la battaglia ₍sic₎ faita in Transiluania ... nel 1600 dal signor Giorgio Basta, generale ...
1. Military art and science—Early works to 1800. I. Tarducci, Achille. Successo delle fattioni occorse nell'Ongaria vicino a Vacia nel MDXCVII. 1601. II. Title.

U101.T27   77-502583

NT 0039091   DLC MH MiU

Tarducci, Achille. Successo delle fattioni occorse nell'Ongaria vicino a Vacia nel MDXCVII. 1601.

Tarducci, Achille.
Delle machine, ordinanze et qvartieri antichi et moderni ... discorsi d'Achille Tardvcci. Aggiuntoui dal medesimo Le fattioni occorse nell'Ongaria ... nel 1597 e la battaglia in Transiluania contra il Valacco, 1600, fatte dal signor Giorgio Basta ... Venetia, G. B. Ciotti, 1601.

U101 .T27 Rare Bk Coll

16cm. (8°.)

Tarducci, Achille.
Il Tvrco Vincibile In Vngaria Con mediocri aiuti di Germania, Discorso Appresentato a i tre supremi Capitani dell'Essercito confederato contra Il Tvrco. E doppo mandato alli suoi amici d'Italia Da Achille Tarducci... Diuiso in tre parti... Ferrara, Per Vittorio Baldini, Stampator Ducale, 1597. 8 p.l., 174 p., 1 l. fold. plan. 16cm. (8°.)

Grässe, VI, 28.
Last leaf blank.
With label of Biblioteca Banzi.

1. Hungary—Hist., 1301-1683.   2. Turkey—Hist.—Muhammad III, 1595-1603. I. Title.   i. ₍Title₎ Turce.

NT 0039093   NN MH

Tarducci, Achille.
Il tvrco vincibile in Vngaria, con mediocri aiuti di Germania. Discorso appresentato a i supremi capitani dell'essercito confederato contra il tvrco. E doppo mandato alli suoi amici d'Italia da Achille Tarducci ...
In Ferrara, Per Vittorio Baldini, stampatore camerale. 1600. Con licenza de'superiori.

*IC5 T1735. 597tb

8°. 8p.l., 174p. fold. plan. 16cm.
Printer's mark on t.-p.

Another copy. 16cm.
Prelim. leaf 8 misbound following t.-p. in this copy.
Bound with J. Geuder's Tvrca νιϰητος, 1601.

NT 0039095   MH NjP CtY MnU

TARDUCCI, Armando
La fisiopatologia del senso cromatico. Firenze, Spinelli, 1917.
v, 149 p. illus.

WW 150 T183f 1917

NT 0039096   DNLM

Tarducci, Filippo
Collezione delle similitudini contenute nelle Iliade di Omero estratte fedelmente da dalle due piu celebri versioni; latina di Cunioli, italiana del cav. Vinc. Monti. Roma, 1830.
8vo.

NT 0039097   NN

[Tarducci, Filippo]
Ferdinand, in Mexico. A serious opera, in two acts. As performed at the King's theatre in the Haymarket. The music by Portogallo. London, J. Brettell [180-?]
49p. 20cm.
Without the music.
English and Italian on opposite pages.

Vg14 1 F40

I. Portogallo, i. e. Marcos Antonio da Fonseca, known as, 1762-1830. II. Title.

NT 0039098   CtY NIC

Tarducci, Filippo.
Nel convito de' primarj artisti ed impiegati municipali nel Tempio di Roma e Venere, in occasione delle pubbliche feste per la nascita del re di Roma; canzone anacreontica. Roma: ₍Romanis e figli,₎ 1805. 1 p.l., 15 p., 1 l. 8°.

1. Poetry (Italian).
N. Y. P. L.   March 26, 1913.

NT 0039099   NN

TARDUCCI, Filippo.
Nel convito de' primarj artisti ed impiegati municipali nel tempio di Roma e venere in occasione delle pubbliche feste per la nascita del re di Roma; canzone Anacreontica. Roma, 1811.

Pamphlet.

NT 0039100   MH

[Tarducci, Filippo]
La vedova contrastata, dramma giocoso per musica da rappre[s]entarsi nel regio teatro di via della Pergola nella primavera del 1815 ...
Firenze 1815. Presso Giuseppe Fantosini con approvazione.

*IC7 A100 B750 v.81

61p. 17cm.
Author named on p.2.
Device of the Accademia degli Immobili on t.-p.

"La selva d'Hermanstadt, ballo eroico spettacoloso" by Alessandro Fabbri: p.[45]-61.
The "s" in "rappresentarsi" in title has failed to print.
Without the music by P. C. Guglielmi.
No.3 in v.81 of a collection of Italian plays.
Based on Leonardo Buonavoglia's La scelta dello sposo.

NT 0039102   MH

Tarducci, Francesco, 1842-
Cecilia Gonzaga e Oddantonio da Montefeltro; narrazione e documenti. Mantova, G. Mondovi, 1897.
45 p. 24cm.

DG 463 .7 T18

1. Gonzaga, Cecilia. 2. Montefeltro, Odd'Antonio conte de.

NT 0039103   NIC

Tarducci, Francesco, 1842-
Finali, Gaspare, 1829-1914.
... Cristoforo Colombo e il viaggio di Ulisse nel poema di Dante; saggio d'interpretazione e carteggio tra l'autore e F. Tarducci, con prefazione di Giovanni Franciosi. Città di Castello, S. Lapi, 1895.

PQ4332 .P3 vol. 23

Tarducci, Francesco, 1842-
Di Giovanni e Sebastiano Cabote. Memorie raccolte e documentate da F. Tarducci. Venezia, Prem. stabilimento tip. fratelli Visentini, 1892.
₍4₎, 429 p. 24¼ᶜᵐ. (R. Deputazione veneta di storia patria)

1. Cabot, Sebastian. 2. Cabot, John, d. 1498.

Library of Congress   E129.C1T18
                   2—1581

NT 0039105   DLC DeU CU NIC MiU-C MB MdBP NN

973.17
T183dYh   Tarducci, Francesco, 1842–
    H. Harrisse e la fama di Sebastiano Caboto.
Torino, Fratelli Bocca, 1894.
    13 p. 24cm.

    Bound with Harrisse, Henry. Sébastien Cabot,
navigateur vénitien. Paris, 1895.
    "Estratto dalla Rivista storica italiana,
vol.XI, fasc IV, anno 1894."

    1. Harrisse, Henry, 1829-1910. Jean et
Sébastien Cabot. I. Title.

NT 0039106   FU

Tarducci, Francesco, 1842–
    ... L'Italia dalla discesa di Alboina alla morte di
Agilulfo. Città di Castello, S. Lapi, 1914.
    1 p. l., (v)-xi, 388 p. 25½cm.
    Bibliographical foot-notes.
    Presentation copy with autograph of the author.

    1. Italy—Hist.—476-1268.

NT 0039107   MiU MH

Tarducci, Francesco, 1842–
    John and Sebastian Cabot. Biographical notice with
documents. By Francesco Tarducci. Tr. from Italian
by Henry F. Brownson. Detroit, H. F. Brownson, 1893.
    viii, ii, 409 p. front. (port.) map. 23½cm.

    1. Cabot, Sebastian, ca. 1474-1557. 2. Cabot, John, d. 1498? I. Brown-
son, Henry Francis, 1835-1913, tr.

    Library of Congress   E129.C1T19   2-1580

      MiU OClStM WaU NIC Nh MH
NT 0039108   DLC PU PP PPL AU NBuC NjN MiU-C DN MU

Tarducci, Francesco, 1842–
    The life of Christopher Columbus by Francesco Tarducci,
after the latest documents. Translated from the Italian by
Henry F. Brownson ... Detroit, H. F. Brownson, 1890.
    2 v. fronts., plates, ports. 23½cm.
    Italian original published at Milan in 1885.

    1. Colombo, Cristoforo.   I. Brownson, Henry Francis, 1835-1913, tr.

    Library of Congress   E111.T19   2-7939 Revised

      MiU-C NjN DN NIC MiU OCX ODW ScU PV PPLas OClJC WaS
NT 0039109   DLC CU PPG MChB ViU I NN MB DPU PPL NjP

Tarducci, Francesco, 1842–
    The life of Christopher Columbus, by Francesco Tar-
ducci, after the latest documents. Translated from Italian
by Henry F. Brownson ... Detroit, H. F. Brownson, 1891.
    2 v. in 1. fronts., plates, ports. 23½ cm.
    Italian original published at Milan in 1885.

    1. Colombo, Cristoforo.   I. Brownson, Henry Francis, 1835-1913,
tr.

    E111.T192   25—21363

      MChB WaTU
NT 0039110   DLC UU PPD PP ICN MiU-C TxU OClStM ICU

MX56
G449   Tarducci, Francesco, 1842–
Xt17   Il P. Giusto da Urbino, missionario in
Abissinia e le esplorazioni africane.
Faenza, Stab. Tipo-lit. di G. Montanari, 1899.
    227 p. port. 19 cm.

    Bibliographical references included in
footnotes.

    1. Giusto da Urbino, 1814-1856. 2. Ethiopia -
Missions. 3.   Catholic church -
Missions -   Ethiopia.

NT 0039111   CtY-D

TARDUCCI, Francesco, 1842–
    La patria di Giovanni Caboto. [With notes and
an appendix,—containing extracts from letters
and public records.] Torino,etc.,1892.

    pp.39.
    "Estratto dalla Revista storica italiana,
vol.ix,fasc.1,1892."

NT 0039112   MH

Tarducci, Francesco, 1842–
    La strega, l'astrologo, e il mago,
monografie... Milano, Treves, 1886.
    vii,198 p. 19cm.

    Bibliographical foot-notes.

    1.Astrology. 2.Witchcraft.

NT 0039113   NjP MH

TARDUCCI,Francesco,1842–
    Usi nuziali. [Modena,1888].

    pp.(15).
    Rassegna emiliana,1888,1.148-162.

NT 0039114   MH

Tarducci, Francesco, 1842–
    Vita di Cristoforo Colombo, narrata da Francesco Tar-
ducci secondo gli ultimi documenti ... Milano, Fratelli
Treves, 1885.
    2 v. front. (port.) 2 maps. 19cm.

    1. Colombo, Cristoforo.

    Library of Congress   E111.T18   2—7938

NT 0039115   DLC CtY PU LNT MiU MiU-C

Tarducci, Francesco. Vita di Cristoforo Colombo, narrata da Francesco Tarducci secondo gli ultimi documenti ... Milano,
Fratelli Treves, 1892. 2v. in 1. front.(port.)
maps. 19cm.

NT 0039116   CU

Tarducci, Francesco.
    Vita di S. Francesco d'Assisi.
Mantova. Mondovi. 1904. xx, 433 pp. 24 cm., in 8s.
Contains a presentation inscription from Tarducci to M. Sabatier, also
Sabatier MS. note.

E3583 — Francesco d'Assisi, Saint, 1182-1226. Biog.

NT 0039117   MB MdSsW

Tarducci, Francesco, 1842–
    ... Vita di S. Francesco d'Assisi...   Roma: Desclée e Ci,
1923. 467 p. front. (port.), plates. 2. ed., rev. 8°.
    Bibliography, p. (12)-(23).

1. Francis of Assisi, Saint, 1182-1226.   2. Franciscans.—History.
N. Y. P. L.   September 19, 1924

NT 0039118   NN MdSsW MB

Tarducci, Icilio.
    In memoria di Icilio Tarducci
see under Perugia. Università.

Tarduchy, Emilio Rodriquez
    see   Rodriguez Tarduchy, Emilio.

Tardy,
    Cours d'Arabe parlé. n.p.
    235 p.
    At head of title: Ecole spéciale militaire.

NT 0039121   OCl

Tardy,
    Travaux publiés par M. Tardy.
    Ann. Inst. nat. agron. sér. 2, tome 1, p. 333.   Paris, 1903.

    Library, U. S. Dept. of   Agriculture   Agr 13-703

NT 0039122   DNAL

Tardy,   of Breslau.
    ... Goethe's Verhältnis zu Vaterland und Staat...
Breslau, 1874.
    1 p. l., 46 p. 25.5 cm.
    Program - Gymnasium zu St. Maria-Magdalena,
Breslau.

NT 0039123   CtY NIC CU

Tardy   of Virginia , defendant.
    ... Cameron's ex'ix v. Goode's ex'r, &c. Note
for Tardy and others, defendants. (n.p., 186-?)
    22 p. 22½cm.
    Title from caption.
    At head of title: In the Circuit court of Albemarle.
    Signed: James Alfred Jones (state reporter).

    1. Hot Springs, Va. I. Virginia. Circuit court (8th
district). II. Albemarle Co. Va. Circuit court. III.
Goode, Thomas, d. 1858. IV. Williams,   defendant.
V. Cameron,   VI. Jones, James Alfred.
1820-1594

NT 0039124   ViU

Tardy,   fl. 1799.
    An explanatory pronouncing dictionary of the French
language, (in French and English); wherein the exact
sound and articulation of every syllable are distinctly
marked (according to the method adopted by Mr. Walker,
in his Pronouncing dictionary). To which are prefixed,
the principles of the French pronunciation ... and the
conjugation of the verbs ... By l'abbé Tardy ... London, Printed for the author, sold by l'Homme (etc.) 1799.
    44, (318) p. 15½cm.
    T.-p. mutilated.
    1. French language—Dictionaries—English. 2. English language—Dic-
tionaries—French.

    Library of Congress   PC2640.T3   CA 11-1464 Unrev'd

NT 0039125   DLC

Tardy, fl. 1799.
    An explanatory pronouncing dictionary of
the French language, (in French and English);
wherein the exact sound and articulation of
every syllable are distinctly marked (as in
Walker's Pronouncing dictionary). To which are
prefixed, the principles of the French
pronunciation ... and the conjugation of the
verbs...By L'Abbé Tardy. Carefully revised and
corrected by Malcom Campbell. New Brunswick,
N. J., Printed by William Elliot, 1808.
    318 p. 16 cm.

Continued in next column

Continued from preceding column

Imperfect copy: p. 107-110 mutilated.

1. French language. Dictionaries. English.
2. English language. Dictionaries. French.
I. Title.

NT 0039127   NcD NN MB PU MH OClWHi OO

443   Tardy, fl. 1799.
T17e   An explanatory pronouncing dictionary
         of the French language (in French and
         English) ... A new ed., rev.   London,
         1814.
           40 [218]p.

NT 0039128   IU MH

PC2640
.T183e   Tardy,   fl. 1799.
           An explanatory pronouncing dictionary of
         the French language (in French and English);
         wherein the exact sound and articulation of
         every syllable are distinctly marked, to
         which are prefixed the principles of the
         French pronunciation; prefatory directions
         for using the spelling representative of
         every sound and the conjugation of the verbs,
         regular, irregular and defective, with their
         true pronuncia-   tion. A new edition, rev.

         London, Longman, Hurst, Rees, Orme and
         Brown, 1817.
           40, [315]p.

           1. French language - Dictionaries -
         English. 2. English language - Dictionaries
         - French.

NT 0039130   TNJ-R MH

Tardy,   fl. 1799.
  An explanatory pronouncing dictionary of the French
language, in French and English ... To which are prefixed, the principles of the French pronunciation ... and
the conjugation of the verbs ... By l'abbé Tardy ...
New ed., carefully rev. London, Longman, Rees, Orme,
Brown, and Green, 1831.
  iv, [5]-347, [1] p. 17 cm.

  1. French language—Dictionaries—English. 2. English language—Dictionaries—French.

                                        14-20088
  Library of Congress   PC2640.T33

NT 0039131   DLC

Tardy (A.) * De l'ergotisme. 60 pp. 4°. *Paris,
1858, No. 183, v. 624.*

NT 0039132   DNLM

Tardy (A.) * Étude rationnelle sur le fonction-
nement des diaphragmes en électrolyse. 51 pp.
8°. *Genève, H. Kündig,* 1904.

NT 0039133   DNLM

Tardy, A   Charles.
  Esquisse géologique de la Bresse et des régions circonvoisines. Abrégé de Géologie à l'usage des Bressans.
Par Ch. et Fréd. Tardy. Bourg, Impr. du "Courrier de
l'Ain," 1892.
  118, [2] p. 22 cm.

  1. Geology—France—Ain.   I. Tardy, Frédéric, joint author.

                                        G S 7-1084
  Library, U. S. Geol.   survey

NT 0039134   DI-GS

Tardy (Alexandre). * Quelques considérations
sur la fièvre typhoïde (putride), la phthisie, etc.
16 pp. 4°. *Paris,* 1850, No. 195, v. 234.

NT 0039135   DNLM PPC

Tardy, André.
  ... Action du formol sur les fonctions alcooliques de quelques
glucides ... Lyon, Imprimerie Noirclerc & Fénétrier, 1937.
  108 p., 2 l. incl. tables, diagrs. 24 cm.
  Thèse—Univ. de Lyon.

  1. Acetals. 2. Formaldehyde. 3. Cellulose.
                                        42-45686
  Library of Congress   QD321.T28

NT 0039136   DLC CtY

Tardy, Anne Southerne.
  Sun through window shutters, by Anne Southerne Tardy.
Brattleboro, Vt., Stephen Daye press, 1935.
  100 p. front. 21 cm.
  Poems.

  I. Title.
                                        35-19694
  Library of Congress   PS3539.A688 1935
  —————— Copy 2.
  Copyright A 87669   [2]   811.5

NT 0039137   DLC AAP NNR AU

Tardy, Charles
  see   Tardy, A. Charles.

W 6   TARDY, Claude, 1607-1670?
P3   ... An biliosis purgatio ante cibum? [Paris? 1661?]
v.2503   4 p. 22 cm.
no. 2   Caption title.
           Imperfect: p. 3-4 mutilated
           "Quaestio medica. Cardinalitiis disputationibus mane discu-
         tienda in scholis medic. die Jovis X. Martii. M. Claudio Tardy
         ... moderatore."
             At end: Probonebat Lutetiae Joannes Baptista Ferrand ...
         M. DC. LXI.

           I. Ferrand, Joannes Baptista, fl. 1647-1678

NT 0039139   DNLM

WZ   TARDY, Claude, 1607-1670?
250   ... An morbi omnes à vitiato circulari
T183t   motu sanguinis? [Paris? 1660?]
1654   8 p. 23 cm.
           Caption title
           "Quaestio medica. Quodlibetariis
         disputationibus mane discutienda, in
         scholis medicorum, die Jovis 22. Januarii.
         M. Claudio Tardy, doctore medico, modera-
         tore."
             "Proponebat Lutetiae Petrus Pourret,
         Baudoniensis, baccalaureus, etsi doctor

         Monspeliensis eruditissimus. A. R. S. H.
         M. DC. LX."
           Bound with the author's Traitté du
         mouvement circulaire du sang et des
         esprits. Paris, 1654.
           I. Pourret, Petrus

NT 0039141   DNLM

WZ   TARDY, Claude, 1607-1670?
250   Hippocratica purgandi methodus ...
T183t   Parisiis, Apud Carolum Chastelain, 1646.
1654   [8], 40 p. 23 cm.
           Caption title, p. 2: An morbis à pituita,
         vomitus? à bile, dejectio?
           "Quaestio medica, quodlibetariis dis-
         putationibus mane discutienda, in scholis
         medicorum, die Jovis 18. Januarii. M.
         Claudio Tardy, doctore medico, praeside."
           "Proponebat Lutetiae Tussanus Foucault

         Paris. A. R. S. H. M. DC. XLVI."
           Bound with the author's Traitté du
         mouvement circulaire du sang et des
         esprits. Paris, 1654.
           1. Hippocrates. I. Foucault, Toussain

NT 0039143   DNLM

WZ   TARDY, Claude, 1607-1670?
250   In libellos Hippocratis De septimestri
T183i   et octimestri partu. Commentarii quibus
1651   universa partuum doctrina propriis
         rationibus demonstratur ... Parisiis,
         Apud Carolum Du Mesnil, 1651.
           48 p. 23 cm.
WZ   — — Another copy.
250   Bound with the author's Traitté du
T183t   mouvement circulaire du sang et des
1654   esprits. Paris, 1654.

           1. Hippocrates. De octimestri partu
           2. Hippocrates. De septimestri partu

NT 0039145   DNLM

WZ   TARDY, Claude, 1607-1670?
250   In libellum Hippocratis De virginum
T183t   morbis commentatio paraphrastica. Ubi
1654   de morbis capitis et aliis qui prodeunt
         ex intercepto, imminuto, depravato &
         adaucto circulari motu sanguinis. Ac
         eorum curatione. Idque expositione
         continua difficillimorum contextuum ex
         variis Hippocratis libris ... Parisiis,
         Apud Jacobum de Senlecque [etc.] 1648.
           40 p. 23 cm.

           Bound with the author's Traitté du
         mouvement circulaire du sang et des
         esprits. Paris, 1654.
           I. Hippocrates. De virginum morbis.
         Latin

NT 0039147   DNLM

Tardy, Claude, 1607-1670?
  Lettre escrite a monsieur Le Breton... Pour
confirmer les vtilitez de la transfusion du
sang, & respondre à ceux qui les estendent
trop. [Paris, Chez l'Avtevr... 1667]
  8 p. 23 cm.
  Caption title.

  1. Blood - Transfusion. I. Le Breton,
medecin ordinaire de monseigneur le prince.

NT 0039148   CtY-M NNNAM

WZ   TARDY, Claude, 1607-1670?
250   Observationes anatomicae ... [Paris?
T183t   165-?]
1654   7 p. 23 cm.
           Caption title.
           Bound with the author's Traitté du
         mouvement circulaire du sang et des
         esprits. Paris, 1654.

NT 0039149   DNLM

Tardy, Claude, 1607-1670?
Les opérations chirvrgiqves esclairées des experiences dv movvement circvlaire dv sang et des esprits ... Paris, Chez l'avthevr, Iean dv Bray [et] C. Barbin, 1665.
140, [4] p.   24 cm.

1. Surgery. Early works to 1800. 2. Surgery. Operative. 3. Blood. Circulation.

NT 0039150   MnU-B NNNAM

W 6
P3
v.2503
no.3
TARDY, Claude, 1607-1670?
Tempus infusionis animae ... [Paris? 165-?]
8 p. 22 cm.

NT 0039151   DNLM

[Tardy, Claude] 1607-1670?
Traitte' de l'ecovlement du sang d'vn homme dans les venes d'vn autre, & de ses vtilitez. [Paris, Chez l'Avtevr... Iean dv Bray... Clavde Barbin... 1667]
15, [1] p. 23 cm.
Caption title.
In his Lettre escrite a monsieur Le Breton, Paris, 1667 (October), Tardy speaks of having published this tract 6 months previously, thus establishing its date.
1. Blood - Transfusion.

NT 0039152   CtY-M NNNAM

WZ
250
T183t
1654
TARDY, Claude, 1607-1670?
Traitté de la monarchie du coeur en l'homme, des quatre humeurs & de leurs sources, des usages du foye, et des vaisseaux qui contiennent le chyle ... Paris, La vefve Du Puys [etc.] 1656.
[2], 12 p. 23 cm.
Bound with the author's Traitté du mouvement circulaire du sang et des esprits. Paris, 1654.

NT 0039153   DNLM NNNAM

W 6
P3
v.2503
no.1
TARDY, Claude, 1607-1670?
Traitté des moyens de conserver en santé les hommes bilieux ... [Paris? 165-?]
8 p. 22 cm.
Caption title.

NT 0039154   DNLM

WZ
250
T183t
1654
TARDY, Claude, 1607-1670?
Traitté du mouvement circulaire du sang et des esprits. Qui est le principal des trois moyens dont la nature se fert à perfectionner l'homme ... Paris, Charles Du Mesnil [etc.] 1654.
[16], 119, 32, [2] p. 23 cm.
"Seconde partie du traitté du mouvement circulaire du sang et des esprits" (32, [2] p. at end) includes, Commentaire avec paraphrase du troisième livre de la diette du grand Hippocrate and Commentaire avec paraphrase du livre des songes du grand Hippocrate.
With this are bound the author's Traitté de la monarchie du coeur en l'homme. Paris, 1656. —In libellos Hippocratis De septimestri et octimestri partu commentarii. Parisiis, 1651. — Hippocratica purgandi methodus. Parisiis, 1646. —In libellum Hippocratis De virginum morbis commentatio paraphrastica. Parisiis, 1648.—An morbi omnes à vitiato circulari motu sanguinis? [Paris? 1660?]—Observationes anatomicae. [Paris? 165-?]
1. Hippocrates. De insomniis 2. Hippocrates. De victus ratione

NT 0039157   DNLM

Tardy, Edwin.
Saved, a temperance sketch, in one act, by Edwin Tardy... Clyde, O., A. D. Ames [18—]   6 p.   19cm. (Ames' series of standard and minor drama.   no. 59)

1. Temperance—Drama.   2. Drama, American.   December 20, 1951

NT 0039158   NN RPB CtY

Tardy, Emmanuel, 1720-1793.
Dissertation sur le transport des eaux de Vichy, avec la manière de se conduire avec succès dans leur usage. Moulins, 1755.

NT 0039159   WU

Tardy, Ernest Jacques.   L547.831 Q200
.... Étude analytique sur quelques essences du genre anisique. .... Par Ernest-Jacques Tardy .... Paris, imprimerie de la Faculté de médecine, 1902.
58, [2] p. 25½ cm.
Thèse — Univ. de Paris.

NT 0039160   ICJ

Tardy, Fernand, 1904–
...Histoire de la pharmacie à Bourges et en Berry, des origines à la loi de germinal an XI (1803)...par Fernand Tardy... Paris, Éditions Occitania [1937]   238 p. illus. 24cm.
Thèse — Lyon.
"Index bibliographique," p. 234-238.

425313B. 1. Pharmacy—France.
N. Y. P. L.   October 25, 1951

NT 0039161   NN CtY DNLM WU

Tardy, Frédéric, joint author.
Tardy, A Charles.
Esquisse géologique de la Bresse et des régions circonvoisines. Abrégé de Géologie à l'usage des Bressans. Par Ch. et Fréd. Tardy. Bourg, Impr. du "Courrier de l'Ain," 1892.

W 4
M79
1784
T. 1
TARDY, Gaspard Mathurin
Dissertatio medico-chirurgica de abusu amputationis membrorum ... Monspelii, Apud Joannem-Franciscum Picot, 1784.
76 p. 19 cm.
Diss. - Montpellier.

NT 0039163   DNLM

PQ2639
.A736P6
Tardy, Georges.
Pour n'en point perdre l'habitude. Paris, R. Lacoste [1950]
155 p. 19 cm. (Collection Les Heures sombres)
Poems.

1. Title.

Illinois. Univ. Library   A 51-6039
for Library of Congress   [2]

NT 0039164   IU DLC

Tardy, Gustave, b.1861.
Notice sur l'abbé J.Jallet, curé de Chérigné, député du clergé de Poitou aux États généraux de 1789. Publiée sous les auspices du Conseil municipal à l'occasion de l'inauguration du buste de Jallet à la Mothe-Saint-Heray, le 7 septembre 1884. Niort, L.Clouzot, 1884.
26 p.

NT 0039165   MH

TARDY, Gustave, b. 1861
Notice sur l'abbé J.Jallet curé de Chérigné, député du clergé de Poitou aux états généraux de 1789. Publiée sous les auspices du Conseil municipal à l'occasion de l'inauguration du buste de Jallet à la Mothe-Saint-Heray, le 7 septembre 1884. Niort, L.Clouzot, 1884.
pp.37. Port.and facsimile plates.
"700 exemplaires."

NT 0039166   MH

Tardy, Henry Gabriel, 1871–
A treatise on the law and procedure of receivers, with forms; being a greatly enl., newly classified, and entirely rewritten 2d ed. of Smith on receivers, by Henry G. Tardy ... San Francisco, Calif., Bender-Moss company, 1920.
2 v. 25 cm.

1. Receivers—U. S.   I. Smith, John Wilson. The law of receiverships ...

20—17817

WaU-L
NT 0039167   DLC PPB NcD OCX PPT-L GASU MtU IU FU

Tardy, Henri Gaspard.
Essai sur la nature de l'inflammation. Paris, Didot, 1814.
27 p.

NT 0039168   PPHa DNLM

---

z Tardy, Herman, 1832-1917, ed.
Bibli Svatá
see under Bible. Czech. 1887.
Kralická bible.

[Tardy, Jean]
Premiers pas vers Jésus [par Jean, Jacques et Pierre Tardy] Illus. de G. Sassier. Bourges, A. Tardy [1942]
188 p. col. illus., col. maps. 16 cm.

1. Religious education—Text-books for children—Catholic. I. Title.

BX930.T3   268.432   49-43957*

NT 0039170   DLC

---

*FC7
I5213
B704a
[Tardy, Jean Charles]
Ad reverendum patrem Franciscum Antonium Le Febvre e Societate Jesu. Ode. [Paris, 1704?]
4p. 16.5cm.
Caption title; signed on p.4: Joannes C. Tardy.
No.7 in a volume of Le Febvre's works.

NT 0039171   MH

Tardy (Jean-Louis). ***De l'empoisonnement thébaïque. 37 pp. 4°. *Strasbourg,* 1858, 2. a., No. 444, v. 25.

NT 0039172   DNLM

TARDY, Joseph.
La Savoie de 1814 à 1860. Chambéry, A. Perrin, 1896.

NT 0039173   MH

Tardy, Joseph.
La vérité. Désorganisation de toutes les sociétés anciennes prouvée par un fait matériel; régénération des société nouvelles sur un base fondamentale stable; solution d l'importante question de l'organisation du travail; suppression totale de l'impot. Dijon, Lamarche, Décailly et Molland, 1848.
29 p. 8°.
2. ed.

NT 0039174   NN

4JN Fr. 58   Tardy, Jules de
Essais critiques, historiques, politiques et philosophiques sur la constitution de 1848 et sur les périls de l'ordre social. Nantes, Impr. L. Guéraud, 1849.
226 p.

NT 0039175   DLC-P4 CtY ICJ

Tardy, Jules de.
Miscellanées politiques, philosophiques et littéraires, pour faire suite à l'essai sur la Constitution de 1848. Par m. de Tardy ... Nantes, Imprimerie Guéraud, 1850–
v. 17½ᵐ.

1. France—Pol. & govt.—1848–1852. I. Tardy, Jules de. Essais critiques, historiques, politiques et philosophiques sur la Constitution de 1848. II. Title.
Library of Congress   DC272.5.T3   42-51327

NT 0039176   DLC

[TARDY, Jules de.]
La particule nobiliaire. Réplique à quelques magistrats. Paris, chez Ledoyen, 1861.
pp. 36.
Signed: "Jules de Tardy".

NT 0039177   MH

Tardy, Lajos, 1914-
Balugyánszky Mihály. Budapest, Akadémiai Kiadó, 1954
256 p. illus.
Summary in Russian

1. Balug'ianskii, Mikhail Andreevich, 1769-1847.

NT 0039178   MH NNC DLC-P4

Tardy, Lajos, 1914- joint author.

Névai, László.
Русско-венгерский юридический и административный словарь. Будапешт, Изд-во юрид. и административной лит-ры, 1951.

Tardy, Lajos, 1914- ed. and tr.

Russia (1917–   *R. S. F. S. R.*) *Laws, statutes, etc.*
A szovjetorosz Büntetötörvénykönyv, írta és a törvényt fordította Olti Vilmos, Tardy Lajos és, Villányi András. Készült as Igazságügyminisztérium hozzájárulásával. Budapest, Egyetemi Nyomda, 1949.

NT 0039181   DNLM

Tardy (Lazare) [1846-]. *Essai sur les altérations des nerfs crâniens dans la paralysie générale. 35 pp. 4°. *Paris,* 1877, No. 465.

NT 0039181   DNLM

WB 24193   Tardy, Lorenzo
Life of St. Clare of Montefalco, professed nun of the Order of Hermits of St. Augustine. Translated from the Italian of Lawrence Tardy, by Joseph A. Locke. New York, Benziger Bros. [c1884]
219p. illus.

1. Chiara, of Montefalco, Saint, d. 1308.

NT 0039182   CtY DLC PV

Tardy, Lorenzo.
Life of St. Rita of Cascia, O. S. A. O. S. Translated from the Italian of L. T. by Rev. Richard Connolly, O. S. A. London, Washbourne, 1903.

NT 0039183   PV

Tardy, Lorenzo.
Vita della B. Chiara di Montefalco, O. S. A. Roma, Mordacchini, 1821.

NT 0039184   PV

Tardy, Lorenzo.
Vita della B. Rita di Cascia, O. S. A. Fuligno, Giov. Tomassini, 1805.

NT 0039185   PV

Tardy, Lorenzo.
Vita di Santa Chiara di Montefalco, dell' Ordine degli eremiti di S. Agostino, scritta dal Rᵐᵒ· P. maestro Lorenzo Tardy ... Roma, Tip. della Pace, 1881.
270 p., 1 l. 23ᶜᵐ.

1. Chiara, of Montefalco, Saint, d. 1308.   4-23348

NT 0039186   DLC NjP PV

Tardy, Louis.
Comment les coopératives agricoles peuvent-elles se procurer le crédit dont elles ont besoin? Paris, Commission internationale d'agriculture, 1936.
20 p.

1. Agricultural credit. France. 2. Agricultural cooperative credit associations. France. 3. France. Caisse nationale de crédit agricole.

NT 0039187   DNAL

334.5 T183c   Tardy, Louis.
La coopération dans les colonies [par] Louis Tardy [et] Maurice Colombain. Préf. de G. Angoulvant. Paris, Fédération nationale des coopératives de consommation [1930]
93p. 22cm.

1. Cooperative societies. I. Colombain, Maurice, joint author. II. Title.

NT 0039188   IEN

Tardy, Louis.
La coopération vinicole en France.
Ann. Inst. nat. agron. sér. 2, tome 23, p. 275–288.   Paris, 1930.

1. Cooperation—France. 2. Wine and wine making. [Cooperative]
     Agr 31-571
Library, U. S. Dept. of   Agriculture 105.3 In8 sér. 2, no. 23
Library of Congress   [85.P3 ser. 2, no. 23]

NT 0039189   DNAL

Tardy, Louis.
Le crédit agricole international.
Ann. Inst. nat. agron. sér. 2, tome 23, p. 289–302.

1. Agricultural credit.
     Agr 31-572
Library, U. S. Dept. of   Agriculture 105.3 In8 sér. 2, no. 23
Library of Congress   [85.P3 ser. 2, no. 23]

NT 0039190   DNAL

Tardy, Louis.
L'organisation actuelle des établissements nationaux de crédit agricole et l'organisation du crédit agricole international. Par M. Louis Tardy ... Agen, Imprimerie moderne (Association coopérative ouvrière) 1926.
60 p. 24½ᵐ.

1. Agricultural cooperative credit associations. 2. Agricultural cooperative credit associations—France.
     Agr 29-456
Library, U. S. Dept. of   Agriculture 284.2T17Or

NT 0039191   DNAL NcU

Tardy, Louis.
... Report on systems of agricultural credit and insurance, submitted by M. Louis Tardy ... [Geneva, League of nations, 1938]
viii, 116 p. 24ᶜᵐ.
At head of title: [Communicated to the Council and the members of the League.] Official no.: C. 479. M. 322. 1938. II. A. Geneva, December 14th, 1938.
Series of League of nations publications. II. Economic and financial. 1938. II. A. 24.
"Agricultural credit institutions in various countries": p. 49–116.
1. Agricultural credit. 2. Insurance, Agricultural. 3. Agricultural cooperative credit associations. I. League of nations. II. Title: Systems of agricultural credit and insurance.
(L. of N. author file Biv; topic file C: Agricultural credit, Agricultural insurance)
     39-7926
Library of Congress   HG2041.T3
   [8]   332.71

OU ViU
NT 0039192   DLC CaBVaU GU FTaSU IdU OrU PPT OC1 OO

[TARDY, Marc Louis de].
Fables et tragédies. Par M. le Mis de T.... Paris, Sagnier et Bray, 1847.

Contents: - Cromwel; Sylla; Fables.

NT 0039193   MH NjP

Tardy, Marcel.
... La Conference internationale du travail.
(Paris, 1922)
cover-title, 22 p. 24 cm.

NT 0039194   DL

Tardy, Marcel.
... Le corporatisme. Paris, Société d'études et d'informations économiques (1935)
cover-title, 2 p. l., 78 p. 27ᶜᵐ. (Supplément au Bulletin quotidien (de la Société d'études et d'informations économiques; avril 1935)
At head of title: Marcel Tardy, Édouard Bonnefous.
Lithographed.

1. Association and associations. 2. Industry—Organization, control, etc. 3. Industry and state. I. Bonnefous, Édouard, joint author. II. Title.
35–19211
Library of Congress   HD3611.T3
(2)   338.7

NT 0039195   DLC NN

Tardy, Marcel.
... Le problème de la socialisation en Allemagne. Paris, Société d'études et d'information économiques; M. Rivière, 1921.
232 p. 19ᶜᵐ. (Bibliothèque de la Société d'études et d'information économiques)

1. Socialism in Germany. 2. Industry and state—Germany. I. Title. II. Title: Socialisation en Allemagne.
L 22–306
Library, U. S. Dept. of   Labor

NT 0039196   DL CSt-H ICJ NN MB

(Tardy, Mrs. Mary T   ) ed.
The living female writers of the South. Ed. by the author of "Southland writers". Philadelphia, Claxton, Remsen & Haffelfinger, 1872.
xxx, 568 p. 21ᶜᵐ.
Revised edition of the author's Southland writers. 2 v. 1870.

1. American literature—Southern states. 2. Authors, American. 3. Authors, Women. I. Title.
Library of Congress   PS551.T35   1–3811

   ODW ViU NBuG Vi NjP MdBP MH NN ICN.
NT 0039197   DLC OrP NcGU TU NcD PHC PPL CLSU GU OU

(Tardy, Mrs. Mary T   ) ed.
The living female writers of the South. Ed. by the author of "Southland writers." Philadelphia, Claxton, Remsen & Haffelfinger, 1872. xxx, 568 pp. 8°.

Microprint. Louisville, Ky., Lost Cause Press, 1956. 14 cards. 7½ x 12½ cm. (Nineteenth century American literature on microcards)

NT 0039198   MiU MsU UU ICRL

PS
551   Tardy, Mary T
T18   Southland writers. Biographical and critical sketches of the living female writers of the South. With extracts from their writings. By Ida Raymond (pseud.) Philadelphia, Claxton, Remsen & Haffelfinger (cl869)
2 v. illus. 22cm.

Introd. by Charles Dimitry.

1. Authors,   American. 2. Authors, Women. 3. Amer   ican literature--Southern states. I. Title.

NT 0039199   NIC

(Tardy, Mrs. Mary T   )
^ Southland writers. Biographical and critical sketches of the living female writers of the South. With extracts from their writings. By Ida Raymond (pseud.) ... Philadelphia, Claxton, Remsen & Haffelfinger, 1870.
2 v. 22ᶜᵐ.
Vol. 1: Added t.-p., illus., and illuminated.
Introduction by Charles Dimitry.
Later edition published 1872 under title: The living female writers of the South.

1. Authors, American. 2. Authors, Women. 3. American literature—Southern states. I. Title.
Library of Congress   PS551.T3   22–1828

   TKL NN
NT 0039200   DLC TxH Vi CtY MiU GMW NcD WaS ViU MB MH

TARDY, Maurice.
Les tabellions romains depuis leur origine jusqu'au xe siècle. Angoulême, 1901.

Thèse---Bordeaux.

NT 0039201   MH-L

Tardy (Paul-Edouard) [1888–]. *De la tuberculose basale post-pleurétique. 80 pp. 8°. Lyon. 1913. No. 26.

NT 0039202   DNLM CtY

Tardy, R.
Der lateinische Aufsatz. Breslau, 1890.

NT 0039203   NjP

Tardy, S.C.
An account of the Hot Springs, Bath county, Va., and an analysis of the waters ...
see under title

Tardy, S. C.   FOR OTHER EDITIONS SEE MAIN ENTRY

Hot Springs, Bath county, Virginia, with some account of their medicinal properties, and an analysis of the waters, with cases of cure of gout, rheumatism, diseases of the liver ... Richmond, Clemmitt & Jones, printers, 1871.

Tardy (Théodomir). *I. Définir la maladie. Examiner si l'on peut tracer une ligne de démarcation bien tranchée entre l'état de maladie et l'état de santé. II. [etc.]. 28 pp. 4°. Paris, 1841, No. 209, v. 392.

NT 0039206   DNLM

Tardy, Tony.
Profession libérale; fantaisie juridique en deux tableaux. Lyon-Villeurbanne, D. Valentin, 1926.
32 p.
At head of title: Répertoire du nouveau Guignol.

NT 0039207   MH

Tardy, William Thomas, 1874–1919.
The man and the message, by William Thomas Tardy; with a foreword by Rev. J. B. Gambrell ... Marshall, Tex., Mrs. W. T. Tardy, 1920.
2 p. l., 200 p. front. (port.) 20 cm.

I. Title.

BX6217.T3   20—15400

NT 0039208   DLC NRCR

Tardy, William Thomas, 1874–1919.
Trials and triumphs, an autobiography, by Rev. W. T. Tardy, with a foreword by Rev. George W. Truett, D. D. Ed. by J. B. Cranfill, LL. D. Marshall, Tex., Mrs. W. T. Tardy (1919)
5 p. l., 116 p. 2 port. (incl. front.) 19½ᶜᵐ.

I. Cranfill, James Britton, 1858– ed. II. Title.
Library of Congress   BX6495.T3A3   19–8641

NT 0039209   DLC NcD LU TxU NRCR

Tardy, William Thomas, 1896–
Composiciones ilustradas. Dallas, Banks, Upshaw and co. [c.1930]

NT 0039210   MH PPT DPU

Tardy, William Thomas, 1896–
Easy Spanish reader, by William T. Tardy ... Dallas, B. Upshaw and company (1929)
xiv, 201 p. incl. front., illus. 19½ᶜᵐ.

1. Spanish language—Chrestomathies and readers.
Library of Congress   PC4117.T3   29–28818

NT 0039211   DLC TxU PPT OrP

Tardy, William Thomas, 1896–
Easy Spanish reader. New and enl. ed. Dallas, B. Upshaw (1942)
234 p. illus. 20 cm. and phonotape (1 reel (7 in.) 3¾ in. per sec.)

1. Spanish language—Chrestomathies and readers.
   468.64   61–44119 ‡
———— Copy 2. 234 p. illus. 20 cm. and phonotape (1 reel (7 in.) 7½ in. per sec.)

NT 0039212   DLC IU KEmT AU PP

Tardy, William Thomas, 1896–
El libro de oro; an anthology of Spanish lyrical poetry compiled by William T. Tardy. Dallas, Tex., Tardy publishing company (1934)
4 p. l., 102 p. 18ᶜᵐ.

1. Spanish poetry (Collections) 2. Lyric poetry. I. Title.
Library of Congress   PQ6176.T3   39–2276
———— Copy 2.   (3)   861.04

NT 0039213   DLC TxU OCl

Tardy, William Thomas, 1896–
Money-making ideas for school yearbooks. Dallas, B. Upshaw (1954)
81 p. 18 cm.

1. College and school journalism. I. Title.
LB3621.T3   371.805   55–3541 ‡

NT 0039214   DLC NN TxU

Tardy, William Thomas, 1896–
Second Spanish reader, by William T. Tardy ... Dallas, B. Upshaw and company ₍°1930₎
3 p. l., v–vi, 187 p. illus. 19½ᶜᵐ.

1. Spanish language—Chrestomathies and readers.

Library of Congress   PC4117.T35   30–31405
Copyright A 30554   ₍2₎   468.6

NT 0039215   DLC WaSp FMU PPT DHEW IU OOxM OC1

Tardy, William Thomas, 1896–   joint author.
Stigler, William Alonzo.
Workers and wealth of Texas, by W. A. Stigler ... and William T. Tardy ... Dallas, B. Upshaw and company ₍°1931₎

W 4
L99
1953/54
no. 169
TARDY, Yvon, 1928–
Mortalité fœtale et vitalité du nouveau-né en fonction de l'emploi de divers analgésiques au cours du travail. Lyon, 1954.
66 p. (Lyons. ₍Université₎ Faculté de médecine et de pharmacie. Thèse, 1953/54, no. 169)
1. Anesthesia - Obstetrics 2. Fetal death - Causes

NT 0039217   DNLM

French
Rev.
DC
141
F87+
v.140
Tardy de la Carrière, Jean Philibert Antoine, 1741–1813.
Rapport...sur un projet de loi relatif à l'achèvement d'une route de Rouen à Saint-Valéry. 13 avril 1810. ₍Paris, Hacquart, 1810₎
3 p. 22cm.
At head of title: Corps législatif.
Reprinted in Archives Parlementaires, 2e série, v. 10, p. 716.

NT 0039218   NIC

French
Rev.
DC
141
F87+
v.140
Tardy de la Carrière, Jean Philibert Antoine, 1741–1813.
Rapport...sur un projet de loi relatif à la réparation et achèvement de routes... 12 avril 1810. ₍Paris, Hacquart, 1810₎
8 p. 22cm.
At head of title: Corps législatif.
Reprinted in Archives Parlementaires, 2e série, v. 10, p. 706.

NT 0039219   NIC

₍**Tardy de Montravel, A**   A.₎
Essai sur la théorie du somnambulisme magnétique. Par Mr. T. D. M. Novembre 1785. À Londres, 1785. xxxii, 86 p. illus. 20cm.

1. Somnambulism. 2. Hypnotism.   I. T. D. M. II. M., T. D.
N. Y. P. L.   May 4, 1942

NT 0039220   NN CtY-M DNLM NNE NcD-MC WU

BF
1132
T18
₍**Tardy de Montravel,** A. A.₎
Essai sur la théorie du somnambulisme magnétique. Par Mr. T. D. M. Novembre 1785. Londres, 1786.
xii, 74 p. 17cm.

1. Animal magnetism. I. T. D. M. II. M., T. D. III. Title.

NT 0039221   NIC PU

154.72
T173
Tardy de Montravel, A   A
Essai sur la théorie du somnambulisme magnétique. Par M. T. D. M. Nouvelle édition. A Londres, [n.p.], 1787.
[1] leaf, xxx, 84 p. 20 cm.
Title vignette. Head & tail pieces.
Provenance: Rev. Edwin A. Dalrymple, Maryland Diocesan Library.

1. Mesmerism. 2. Animal magnetism. 3. Hypnotism. I. Title. II. Title: Somnambulisme magnetique

NT 0039222   NNG NNUT DNLM

₍**Tardy de Montravel, A**   A.₎
Journal du traitement magnétique de la Demoiselle N., lequel a servi de base à l'Essai sur la théorie du somnambulisme magnétique. Par M. T. D. M. ... A Londres, 1786. xxxii, 255 p. illus. 20cm.

1. Somnambulism. 2. Hypnotism.   I. T. D. M. II. M., T. D.
N. Y. P. L.   May 4, 1942

NcD-Mc
NT 0039223   NN MH NNE CtY-M DNLM PPG WU PPAmP ICU

₍**Tardy de Montravel, A**   A.₎
Journal du traitement magnétique de Madame B..... Pour servir de suite au Journal du traitement magnétique de la Dᵉ N. ...& de preuve à la théorie de l'Essai. Par M. T. D. M. Janvier 1787. A Strasbourg: A la Librairie académique ₍1787₎ xxiv, 279 p. 20cm.

141092B. 1. Somnambulism.   2. Hypnotism. I. T. D. M. II. M., T. D.
N. Y. P. L.   May 4, 1942

NT 0039224   NN NNE MH DNLM CtY-M

18th
cent.
[**TARDY DE MONTRAVEL, A. A.**]
Lettres pour servir de suite a l'Essai sur la théorie du somnambulisme magnétique. Par M.T.D.M. Londres,1787.
65p. 20cm.

NT 0039225   CtY-M

[**Tardy de Montravel, A**   A]
Suite du traitement magnétique de la Demoiselle N., lequel a servi de base à l'Essai sur la théorie du somnambulisme magnétique. Par M. T. D. M...
A Londres, 1786.
206 p. 20 cm.
1. Somnambulism. 2. Hypnotism.
I. T. D. M. II. M. T. D.

NT 0039226   NN ICU

Tardy de Montravel, Jean François, 1744–
supposed author.
Réflexions d'un habitant de Besançon, addressées aux troupes nationales de cette ville, le 3 sept. 1789
see under title

Tardy de Montravel, ₍**Louis Marie François**₎
Campagne de la Constantine. Instructions sur la Nouvelle-Calédonie, suivies de renseignements hydrographiques et autres sur la mer du Japon et la mer d'Okotsk, par M. Tardy de Montravel ... commandant la Constantine. Publié sous le ministère de S. Exc. l'amiral Hamelin. Extrait des Annales hydrographiques. Paris, Impr. administrative de P. Dupont, 1857.
viii, 188 p. 12 pl. (partly fold. incl. maps) tables. 24½ x 14½ᶜᵐ.

1. Constantine (Ship) 2. New Caledonia. 3. Sailing directions — Pacific Ocean.

1–25915* Cancel
Library of Congress   VK933.N5T2

NT 0039228   DLC

Tardy de Montravel, L₍**ouis Marie François**₎
La Plata au point de vue des intérêts commerciaux de la France. Par L. Tardy de Montravel ... Paris, Impr. de Schiller aîné, 1851.
2 p. l., 60 p. 21¼ᶜᵐ.

1. France—Comm.—Argentine Republic. 2. France—Comm.—Uruguay. 3. Argentine Republic—Comm.—France. 4. Uruguay—Comm.—France.

4–6222
Library of Congress   F2808.T18

NT 0039229   DLC TxU

2.790F
L569
Tardy-Durozet
Programme d'un ouvrage ayant pour titre: Le domaniste de bonne foi, ou essai d'un plan de réforme provisoire de l'impôt du contrôle des actes et droits y joints ... présenté au Comité des impositions par M. Tardy-Durozet ... A Paris, Chez Regent et Bernard, 1790.
1 p. l., 22 p. 21cm.

Volume of pamphlets.

NT 0039230   NNC

Tardy-Pigelet (V.) and Sons, Bourges.
Bourges; a practical guide for American and English people. Patronized by the "Syndicat d'initiative du centre. Bourges, 1918.
32 p. illus. 18 cm.
Includes advertising matter.
1. Bourges. Descr. Guide-books. I. Title.

NT 0039231   OrU

Tardy.
Bibliographie générale de la mesure du temps, suivie d'un essai de classification technique et géographique. Préf. de Paul Ditisheim. Paris ₍1947₎
352 p. 25 cm.

1. Horology—Bibl.

A 49–1170*
Harvard Univ. Library
for Library of Congress   ₍1₎

NT 0039232   MH OU PU NN IaU ICJ ICU CtY ViU MB MiU

Tardy.
Les coqs de montres de la collection de M. E. Coinon. 660 modèles de coqs français, allemands, anglais, autrichiens, hollandais, suisses. Paris ₍n.d.₎
30 p. illus. 27cm.

1. Clocks and watches - Private collections.
I. Coinon, M   E   I. Title.

NT 0039233   DSI

Tardy.
Les faïences françaises; ₍historique, caractéristiques du décor, couleurs, pâtes, émail, production, marques. Suivi d'un répertoire des noms cités, des marques classées par ordre alphabétique, et d'un index analytique des décors. Avant propos de Jean Joire. Paris ₍1949₎
289 p. 19 cm.

1. Pottery, French. 2. Pottery—Marks.

NK4305.T35   738.88   49–29935*

NT 0039234   DLC OrU MiU

Tardy.
    Les monnaies d'or, d'argent et de platine,
internationales, 3. ed.   Paris, 1947.
    126 p.   pl.   S.

NT   0039235   PP

Tardy.
    Les monnaies d'or internationales, réunies par **Tardy.**
Paris [194–?]
    24 p.   col. illus.   16 cm.

    1. Money.   I. Title.

    HG289.T3   49–32245*‡

NT   0039236   DLC ICRL

Tardy.
    Origine de la mesure du temps, du gnomon a
la montre.   Avant propos de Alfred Chapuis.
Paris, Chez l'Auteur [1950]
    118 p.   illus.   27 cm.

    1. Time measurements.   2. Sun-dials.
3. Clocks and watches.   I. Title.   II. Title:
Du gnomon a la montre.

NT   0039237   DSI PPF

Tardy.
    La pendule française, des origines à nos jours; documenta-
tion recueillie auprès de nos penduliers.   Paris [194–]
    1 v. (unpaged)   illus.   32 cm.
    Contents.—L'horloge gothique.—L'horloge renaissance.—L'horloge
Louis XIII.—Le style Louis XIV, la pendule Louis XIV, la pendule religieuse.—La Régence. Louis XV, la pendule Louis XV, la pendule Louis XV.—
Transition entre les styles Louis XV et Louis XVI.—Le style Louis XVI,
la pendule Louis XVI.—Le Directoire, la pendule directoire.—Le style
empire, la pendule empire.—Le style Louis Philippe et Napoléon III,
la pendule Louis Philippe et Napoléon III.—Modern' style, le style
1900–1925.—Les provinces.—Les styles étrangers et influence de l'art
français.
    1. Clock and watch making—France.

    TS543.F8T32   681.11   50–39884

NT   0039238   DLC NN

Tardy.
    La pendule française; documentation recueillie auprès de
nos penduliers.   Paris [194–]
    6 pts.   illus.   32 cm.
    Contents.—[1] Gothique. Renaissance. Louis XIII. Louis XIV.—
[2] Régence. Louis XV.—[3] Louis XVI. Directoire.—[4] Consulat.
Napoléon. Louis XVIII. Charles X. Louis Philippe. Napoléon III.
Modern' style, 1925.—[5] Art régional. Styles étrangers. Influence
de l'art français.—[6] Liste des horlogers français.

    1. Clock and watch making—France.

    TS543.F8T3   681.11   49–41035*

NT   0039239   DLC PP

Tardy.
    Les pierres précieuses, les perles, l'écaille, l'ivoire et la
répression des fraudes; documentations réunies par Tardy.
106 illus.   Paris [1945]
    252 p.   illus.   17 cm.
    On cover: Pierres, perles.

    1. Precious stones.   2. Precious stones—France.   3. Ivories.

    QE392.T2   A F 50–224
    Iowa. State Coll. Libr.
    for Library of Congress   [2]†

NT   0039240   IaAS NjP NN PP DLC

Tardy.
    Les pierres précieuses, les perles, l'écaille, l'ivoire et la
répression des fraudes; documentations réunies par Tardy.
106 illus.   Paris [1945]
    252 p.   illus.   17 cm.
    Film reproduction.   Negative.
    On cover: Pierres, perles.

    1. Gems.   I. 1945.

NT   0039241   NN

Tardy.
    Les pierres précieuses, les perles, l'écaille, l'ivoire et la répres-
sion des fraudes, par Tardy. 2. éd.   Paris, L'auteur [1951]
324 p.   illus.   18 cm.

    1. Gems.

NT   0039242   NN

Tardy.
    Le poinçons de garanite internationaux pour
l'argent, 3. ed.   Paris [194?]
    151 p.   illus. pl.   S.

NT   0039243   PP

HD9747
.A3A1
1944   **Tardy.**
    Les poinçons de garantie internationaux pour l'argent.
2. éd.   Paris [1944]
    148 p.   illus.   17 cm.

    1. Coins.   2. Silver.   3. Money—Tables, etc.   I. Title.
                                  A 48–8640*
    Iowa. State Coll. Libr.
    for Library of Congress   [1]

NT   0039244   IaAS NN DLC

TARDY.
    Les poinçons de garantie internationaux pour l'argent. 4. éd.
Paris. [1951]   353 p.   illus.   17 cm.

    1. Hall-marks.

NT   0039245   NN PPPM PP

Tardy.
    Les poinçons de garantie internationaux pour l'or.   2. éd.
Paris [1943]
    95 p.   illus.   16 cm.

    1. Gold—Standards of fineness.   I. Title.
    HD9747.A3A1   1943   52–58049

NT   0039246   DLC

Tardy.
    Les poinçons de garantie internationaux pour l'or.   3. éd.
Paris [1945]
    108 p.   illus.   17 cm.

    1. Coins.   2. Gold.   3. Money—Tables, etc.   I. Title.
                                  A 48–8641*
    Iowa. State Coll. Libr.
    for Library of Congress   [1]

NT   0039247   IaAS NN

Tardy.
    Les poinçons de garantie internationaux pour l'or.   3. éd.
Paris [1945]
    108 p.   illus.   17 cm.
    Film reproduction.   Negative.

    1. Hall-marks.

NT   0039248   NN

739.218
T173g   **Tardy.**
    Les poinçons de garantie internationaux
pour l'or.   5th ed.   Paris, 1952.
    171 p.   illus. (pt. folded)

    1. Hall-marks.   2. Goldsmithing.   I. Title.

NT   0039249   MiDA

Tardy.
    Les poinçons de garantie internationaux
pour le platine.   2e ed.   Paris [n.d.]
36 p.

    1. Hall-marks.   2. Platinum.   I. Title.

NT   0039250   MiDA PP

NK4497
.T3   **Tardy.**
    Les porcelaines françaises; historique, caractéristiques,
décor, couleurs, production, contrefaçons, copies, marques.
Suivi d'un répertoire des noms cités, des marques classées
par ordre alphabétique.   Avant-propos de Marc H. Gobert
et de M. Leyendecker.   Documentation réunie par **Tardy.**
Paris [1950]
    407 p.   illus.   20 cm.

    1. Porcelain, French.   2. Porcelain—Marks.   I. Title.
                                A 51–1176
    Oregon. Univ. Libr.
    for Library of Congress   [3]

NT   0039251   OrU MiU NN MiDA DLC

Tardy.
    Les poteries, les faïences et les porcelaines européennes.
Paris [1953–1955]
    3 v. in 2 (1125 p.)   illus.   20 cm.
    Vols. 2–3 have sub-title: France exceptée.
    Contents.—1. ptie. Allemagne, Autriche, Hongrie, Belgique, Dane-
mark, Espagne, Estonie, Finlande, Grande Bretagne.—2. ptie. Hollande, Hongrie, Italie, Luxembourg, Malte, Norvège, Pologne, Portugal,
Roumanie, Russie, Suède, Suisse.—3. ptie. Notes complémentaires sur:
l'Allemagne, la Belgique, le Danemark, l'Espagne, la Finlande, la Hollande.   Tables.
    1. Pottery, European.   2. Pottery—Marks.   I. Title.

    NK4083.T3   62–32073 rev

NT   0039252   DLC CtY NN NIC MH

Tardy.
    Les principaux calibres de montres...
Paris [Duclos] n.d.
    2 v.   diagrs.   O.

NT   0039253   PP

Tardy act of justice. Monument proposed to
the man who planned this city. [By F.J.O. anon.]
n.p., clipping.
    5 l.   12 l.   mounted.   [Toner excerpt].

NT   0039254   DLC

Tardy George
see under [Boker, George Henry] 1823–1890.

T655.4764
T1731 Tardy Publishing Company, Dallas.
An innovation in book publishing. Dallas
[19—]
14p. 18cm.

NT 0039256 TxU

Tardy Publishing Company, Dallas.
Tardy's periodical and book news
see under title

Tardyová, Jiřina.
Stín padal na Evropu. Praha, Svoboda, 1946.
108 p. 21 cm. (3. sv. Knihovny českých autorů)
Short stories.

I. Title.

PG5038.T3S8   53–15795

NT 0039258 DLC IEdS NN

Tardy's periodical and book news. Dallas,
Texas.

NT 0039259 PP

Taré (GÉRARD JOHAN). and others.
Memorie, gedaan maaken en aan de... Staaten Generaal
der vereenigde Neederlanden overgegeven [5. April 1793]
door de ondergete Kenden, Mr. G. T. Taré,... Mr. A.
Reigersman... en L. Pels... allen van Breda; mitsgaders
door Mr. A. G. van Doorn en D. Ruyssenaers. . beiden
van Geertruidenberg. [Exhibitum den 8. April, 1793,
relative to their arrest by order of General Dumouriez as
hostages]. n. p., [1793?] 11 pp. f°.

NT 0039260 NN

Tareas de un solitario ó Nueva colección de
novelas
see under [Montgomery, George Washington] 1804–1841.

Tareev, Boris Mikhaĭlovich.
Электротехнические материалы. Утверждено в качестве учеб. пособия для подготовки рабочих кадров и сред-
нетехн. персонала. Москва, Гос. энерг. изд-во, 1946.
231 p. illus. 20 cm.

1. Electric engineering—Materials.
   Title transliterated: Élektrotekhnicheskie materialy.

TK453.T3   50–19007

NT 0039262 DLC

Tareev, Boris Mikhaĭlovich.
Электротехнические материалы. Утверждено в качестве учеб. пособия для подготовки рабочих кадров и сред-
нетехнического персонала. Изд. 3., перер. Москва, Гос.
энерг. изд-во, 1949.
282 p. illus. 21 cm.

1. Electric engineering—Materials.
   Title transliterated: Élektrotekhnicheskie materialy.

TK453.T3 1949   50–22181

NT 0039263 DLC

Tareev, Boris Mikhaĭlovich.
Электротехнические материалы. Изд. 4., перер. Допущено в качестве учеб. пособия для ремесленных и жел-
дор. училищ, курсов подготовки рабочих кадров и курсов
мастеров. Москва, Гос. энерг. изд-во, 1952.
288 p. illus. 21 cm.
Bibliography: p. [281]–282.

1. Electric engineering—Materials. I. Title.
   Title transliterated: Élektrotekhnicheskie materialy.

TK353.T3 1952   54–17507

NT 0039264 DLC

Tareev, Boris Mikhaĭlovich.
Электротехнические материалы. Изд. 5. перер. Допущено в качестве учеб. пособия для техн., ремесленных и
жел-дор. училищ электротехн. специальностей. Москва,
Гос. энерг. изд-во, 1955.
256 p. illus. 21 cm.
Bibliography: p. [252]–253.

1. Electric engineering—Materials. I. Title.
   Title transliterated: Élektrotekhnicheskie materialy.

TK453.T3 1955   56–28282

NT 0039265 DLC

Tareev, Boris Mikhaĭlovich, ed.
Akademiiâ nauk SSSR. *Fizicheskiĭ institut.*
Научная литература по диэлектрикам. [Ответственный
редактор Б. М. Тареев] Москва, Изд-во Академии наук
СССР, 1952.

Tareev, Boris Mikhaĭlovich.
Производство остеклованных резисторов. Москва, Гос.
энерг. изд-во, 1944.
26, [2] p. diagrs. 20 cm.
Bibliography: p. 26–[27]

1. Electric resistors.
   Title transliterated: Proizvodstvo
   osteklovannykh rezistorov.

TK2851.T38   50–44428

NT 0039267 DLC

TK3351
.P72
1945
Tareev, joint author.
Boris Mikhaĭlovich.
Privezentsev, Vladimir Alekseevich.
Производство силовых кабелей и обмоточных проводов.
Допущено в качестве учебника для электротехнических
техникумов. Изд. 4., перер. Москва, Гос. энерг. изд-во,
1945.

Tareev, Boris Mikhaĭlovich.
Стеклянная изоляция. Москва, Гос. энерг. изд-во,
1943.
142, [2] p. illus. 20 cm.
At head of title: Н. В. Александров [и др.]
Bibliography: p. 139–[143]

1. Electric insulators and insulation. 2. Glass. I. Title.
   Title transliterated: Stekliânnaiâ izoliâtsiiâ.

TK3441.G5T3   51–50749

NT 0039269 DLC

Tareev, V M
Теплотехника. Допущено в качестве учебника для
механических факультетов ин-тов жел-дор. транспорта.
Москва, Гос. трансп. жел-дор. изд-во, 1951.
716 p. diagrs. 27 cm.
At head of title: В. М. Тареев, Г. А. Матвеев, С. Н. Григорьев.

1. Thermodynamics. I. Title.
   Title transliterated: Teplotekhnika.

QC311.T2   52–26839

NT 0039270 DLC

DK651
.K12258
A63
Orien
Armen
Tarēgirkʻ Hayotsʻ Ilakhatsʻ ew Ōlakhatsʻerkri.
Selections. 1896.
Alishan, Ghewond, 1820–1901, comp.
Կամենից. Տարեկիրք Հայոց Իլխանատեր եւ Ֆոււլխանե,
Հատասելալ յասքրումարդեր։ Վենետիկ, Ս. Ղազար, 1896։

W 4
L99
TAREL, André, 1923–
De la splénectomie dans la maladie
d'Osler et spécialement dans l'infarctus
de la rate. Lyon, Bosc, 1948.
52 p. (Lyons. [Université]
Faculté [mixte] de médecine et de
pharmacie. Thèse. 1948/49. no. 48)
1. Endocarditis - Infectious
2. Spleen - Surgery

NT 0039272 DNLM CtY-M

Tarel, Jean.
... Essai sur la condition juridique des sociétés russes en
France ... par Jean Tarel ... Grenoble, Imprimerie Boissy &
Colomb, 1938.
241 p., 1 l. 25ᶜᵐ.
Thèse—Univ. de Grenoble.
"Bibliographie": p. 235–238.

1. Corporations, Foreign—France. 2. Corporations—Russia. 3. Corporation law—France.

41–23608

NT 0039273 DLC CtY

Tarel, Pierre Jacques Jean, 1904–
... Contribution à l'étude du traitement de
la tuberculose des enfants par l'aurothérapie
... Bordeaux.
Thèse - Univ. de Bordeaux.
"Bibliographie": p. [93]–107.

NT 0039274 CtY

Tarelli, Charles Camp, 1870–
... Persephone, and other poems. New York, London,
The Macmillan company, 1898.
viii, 96 p. 16ᶜᵐ.
Title within ornamental border.

I. Title.
Library of Congress   ✸ PR6039.A62P4 1898

12–39249

NT 0039275 ICN TNJ NIC IU

Tarello, Camillo.
Ricordo d'agricoltvra, di m. Camillo Tarello da Lonato ...
In Venetia, appresso F. Rampazetto, 1567.
4 p. l., 76 numb. l. 15ᶜᵐ.
Signatures: A⁴, A–I⁸, K⁴.

1. Agriculture—[Early works to 1800]

Agr 31–766

Library, U. S. Dept. of   Agriculture 30.8T17

NT 0039276 DNAL

S.61 Tarello, Camillo.
Ricordo d'agricoltura. Mantova, Appresso G. Ruffinello,
1577.
16°. ff. 72.

NT 0039277   MH-A DeU

Tarello, Camillo
Ricordo d'agricoltvra. Di nuouo corretto,
& ristampato. Venetia, G. Bizzardo, 1609.
141p. 15cm.
Title vignette.
Signatures: 7.

NT 0039278   WU

WD
10939   Tarello, Camillo
Ricordo d'agricoltura ... Bergamo,
G. Santini, 1756.
70 p.

1. Agriculture - Early works to 1800.
2. Agriculture - Italy - Hist.

NT 0039279   CtY

6908 Tarello, Camillo.
Ricordo d'agricoltura ... cor., illus., aumentato con
note, aggiunte, e tavole, dal padre maestro Gian-Fran-
cesco Scottoni ... Venezia, G. Bassaglia, 1772.
6 p.l., 296 p. front., fold. tab., fold. diagr. 19½
cm.
First edition [?] Venezia 1567.

NT 0039280   MH-BA

4K
It
1602   Tarello, Mario
Le società civili. Torino, Fratelli Bocca, 1932.
117 p.

(Nuova collezione di opere
giuridiche, n. 267)

NT 0039281   DLC-P4

Tarello, Pierre Paul, 1907-
... Considérations sur le chlorhydrate de
choline, étude expérimentale... Bordeaux,
1931.
Thèse - Univ. de Bordeaux.
"Bibliographie": p. [35]-36.

NT 0039282   CtY

Tarello, Renato.
Unen a Venezuela. Schizzi di Arturo Tarrida. Caracas,
1952-
v. Illus. 24 cm.
"Una raccolta di bozzetti venezuelani ... ho riportato il dialogo
nella parlata originale."
Italian or Spanish.

I. Title.

PQ4843.A66U5   60-30893 ‡

NT 0039283   DLC TxU MH NN

Tarelo, Miguel Miramón y
see
Miramón, Miguel, 1831-1867.

A42
+Ak136M
28   Tarenetskii, Aleksandr Ivanovich, 1845-1905.
Beiträge zur Anatomie des Darmkanals.
St.-Pétersbourg,Eggers,1881.
55 p. 32cm. (Mémoires de l'Académie
Impériale des Sciences de St.-Pétersbourg,
VII.sér., t. 28, no. 9)

NT 0039285   CtY DNLM

Nk97
A2
+890t   Tarenetskii, Aleksandr Ivanovich, 1845-
... Beiträge zur Craniologie der Ainos
auf Sachalin ... St.Pétersbourg,1890.
1p.l.,55p.incl. tables. 34cm. (Mémoires
de l'Académie impériale des sciences de St.
Pétersbourg, VII.sér., t.XXXVII, no.13 et
dernier)

1. Ainos - Craniology. x ser.^

NT 0039286   CtY DNLM MB MdBP

GN
qT184b
1884   TARENETSKII, Aleksandr Ivanovich,
1845-
Beiträge zur Craniologie der gross-
russischen Bevölkerung der nördlichen
und mittleren Gouvernements des europäischen Russlands. St.-Pétersbourg,
Eggers, 1884.
81 p.
Read before the Akademiia nauk,
Petrograd, on Aug. 28, 1884.

Reprinted from the Mémoires of the I.
Akademiia nauk, Petrograd, 7th ser.,
t. 32, no. 13.

NT 0039288   DNLM CtY

506.47
.A33   Tarenetskii, Aleksandr Ivanovich
Beiträge zur skelet- und schädelkunde der
Aleuten, Konaegen, Kenai und Koljuschen mit
vergleichend anthropologischen bemerkungen.
S.-Petersbourg, Imperatorskaia Akademiia
Nauk, 1900.
73 p. IV pl., tables. 34 cm. (Akademiia
Nauk SSSR. Otdelenie Fiziko-matematicheskikh
Nauk. Zapiski. 8. ser. vol. 9, No. 4)

NT 0039289   MB DSI

A42
+Ak136M
41   Tarenetskii, Aleksandr Ivanovich, 1845-1905.
Weitere Beiträge zur Craniologie der
Bewohner von Sachalin - Aino, Giljaken
und Oroken. St.-Pétersbourg,Eggers,1893.
45 p. 32cm. (Mémoires de l'Académie
Impériale des Sciences de St.-Pétersbourg,
VII sér., t. 41, no. 6)

1. Ainos - Craniology. 2. Craniology-
Sakhalin.

NT 0039290   CtY

Tarenghi, Mario, 1870-
Inno, hymn, op.62, no.4. Transcribed by
Pietro A. Yon. G. Schirmer, c1924.
9 p.

Organ.

I.Yon, Pietro Alessandro, 1886-1943, arr. II.
Title.

NT 0039291   OrP

Tarenghi, mario, 1870-
[Pages intime, op. 56.]
Pages intime, pour piano. Milan, A. & G.
Carisch [c1911-12] 2 v. 30 cm.

CONTENTS. - Op. 56. Simple mélodie. Heure
solitaire. Aspiration. Arabesque. Cavalcade.
- Op. 60. Réponses d'amour. Souvenir
lointain. Reve. Joie intime. Noces du
chasseur.

1. Piano music. (1) Tarenghi, Mario,
1870- Pages intime, op. 60. (TITLE)

NT 0039293   NN

TARENGHI, MARIO, 1870-
Scena orientale per orchestra, op. 17. Milano,
R. Fantuzzie (190-?] Pl. no. F 601 R. score (35 p.) 34cm.

1. Orchestra. I. Title.

NT 0039294   NN

Tarenghi, Paolo.
Pauli Tarenghi Romani ... Odarum libri iv. Quarum
singulæ singulis Horatianis tam metris, quam versibus
respondent. Accedit Epodon liber eodem modo elabo-
ratus. Vilnæ, typis Iosephi Zawadzki, 1805.
3 p. l., 174, [6] p. 14½ᵐ.

22-9317

NT 0039295   DLC

Tarenghi, Paolo, tr.
I quattordici canti del poema o sia del
supplimento alla Iliade
see under   Quintus Smyrnaeus.

Tarenne, George.
La cochliopérie, recueil d'expériences très-curieuses sur les
hélices terrestres, vulgairement nommés escargots; avec une
instruction sur la guérison radicale des hernies ou descentes,
sans dépense, ni aucun secours étranger. Par George Tarenne
... Paris, De l'impr. de Delance, 1808.
171 p. 16½ᵐ.

NT 0039297   ICJ DNLM

PT1205
.S9T2
Rare bk
room   TARENNE,GEORGE
Recherches sur les ranz des vaches,ou sur les chan-
sons pastorales des bergers de la Suisse;avec musique.
Par George Tarenne... Paris,F.Louis,1813.
84,[1]p. 21½cm.

1.Ranz des vaches.

NT 0039298   ICU MH CtY IaU

2648. TARENNE, GEORGE. Vers sur Dieu, et sur
la trinité de la nature. Paris: chez Leblanc,
et chez tous les marchands de nouveautés [de
l'imprimerie de Gillé], an VIII. 15 p.

NT 0039299   NN

TX765 ⟨Tarenne de Laval, G   P   ⟩ 1763-
T3   1847.
1838   Le pâtissier à tout feu; ou, Nouveaux
principes économiques de pâtisserie ... par
G.P.L.   2. ed. considérablement aug.   Paris,
Audot, 1838.
282 p. illus.

1 Baking. 2. Pastry. I. Title.

NT 0039300   CU

Tarenta, Valescus de
see Balescon de Tarente, fl. 1380-1418.

Tarente, Henri-Charles de La Trémoille, *prince de*
see La Trémoille, Henri-Charles de,
prince de Tarente.

Tarente, Jacques Etienne Joseph Alexandre,
Macdonald, duc de
see Macdonald, Jacques Etienne Joseph
Alexandre, duc de Tarente, 1765-1840.

DC146 TARENTE, LOUISE EMMANUELLE(DE CHÂTILLON)LA
.T2A3   TRÉMOÏLLE, *princesse* DE, d.1814.
Souvenirs de la princesse de Tarente 1789-1792.
Nantes, E.Grimaud et fils, 1897.
vi,236,⟨1⟩p. front.(port.) 26cm.
Edited by Louis de La Trémoïlle.
Contents.--Souvenirs de la princesse de Tarente.--
Lettres de la princesse de Tarente.--Extraits des comp-
tes.--Notes sur ma vie, par le duc de La Trémoïlle.

1.France--Hist.--Revolution--Personal narratives.

NT 0039304   ICU WaU MH NIC NN

Tarente, Louise Emmanuelle (de Châtillon) prin-
cesse de, d.1814.
... Souvenirs de la princesse de Tarente,
1789-1792, accompagnés de deux portraits inédits
de Louis XVII et de la princesse de Tarente.
Paris, H.Champion, 1901.
vi,244 p.,1 *l*. 2 port.   20½ cm.
Editor's name, Louis de la Trémoïlle, at head of title.
First published in 1897.
CONTENTS.--Souvenirs de la princesse de Tarente.--
Extrait des mémoires de m.de la Trémoïlle.--Lettres de
la princesse de Tarente.--Extraits de comptes.
1.France--Revolution--Personal narratives. I.La
Trémoille, Louis, duc de, 1838-1911, ed.

NT 0039305   MiU MH CtY NjP LU

Tarente, Napoléon Alexandre Fergus MacDonald,
3. duc de
see MacDonald, Napoléon Alexandre
Fergus, 3. duc de Tarente.

*FC6   La tarentele escrasee ov L'imprecation de
M456m   l'impie Mazarin.
3750   A Roüen.M. DC. XLIX.
7p. 22cm., in case 28cm.
Moreau 3750.
Poem.
In folder; in case labeled: Mazarinades.

NT 0039307   MH ICN

Tarentelle ⟨and Angelus⟩ from the ballet of Ondine
see under ⟨Pugni, Cesare⟩ 1805-1870.

PG65   Tarentino, Jimmie.
T5   ... 6 years of Hollywood life, by Jimmie
Tarentino and Hollywood life staff...
⟨Los Angeles, Hollywood life office, c1952.
169 p. ports. 27cm.
Chiefly editorials by Jimmie Tarentino,
editor of Hollywood life.

NT 0039309   CU-BANC

PQ   Tarentino, Secondo
4634   Il capitan Bizzarro. Comedia ... recitata in
T35   Taranto, in casa del Signor Trolio Suffiano.
C3   In Vineggia, Appresso di Agostino Bindoni.
1551   Colophon: ... 1551.
Cage
38 ⟨2⟩ 1. A-E⁸ (E8, blank, lacking). 8vo.
Baron Horace Landau-Gustavo Camillo Galletti
copy.

NT 0039310   DFo

x853T17 Tarentino, Secondo.
Oc1567   Il capitan Bizzarro, comedia.   Vinegia,
A. Rauenoldo, 1567.
⟨39⟩*l*. 16cm.

Signatures: A-E⁸ (A8 blank)
Some leaves numbered.

NT 0039311   IU

La Tarentule. Pas de deux
see under ⟨Gide, Casimir⟩ 1804-1868.

Tarentum, Pa. Central Presbyterian Church.
Dedication... Oct. 18, 1914. n.p.

NT 0039313   PPPrHi

Taretum, Pa. First Presbyterian Church.
One hundredth anniversary program, December
12-18, 1932.
Pamphlet.

NT 0039314   PPPrHi

Tarentum, Pa. St. Clement's church.
Golden jubilee, St. Clement's Church, Tarentum,
Penna., 1903-1953
see under ⟨Lovasik, Lawrence George⟩ 1913-

... Tarentum, Brackenridge, Natrona, Creighton, Glassmere directory ...
Binghamton, N. Y., The Calkin-Kelly directory company,
c19
v. 24½ᵐ.

1. Tarentum, Pa.—Direct. 2. Brackenridge, Pa.—Direct. 3. Natrona,
Pa.—Direct. 4. Creighton, Pa.—Direct. 5. Glassmere, Pa.—Direct.
CA 31-54 Unrev'd

Library of Congress   F159.T2A18

NT 0039316   DLC PP

Tares. ⟨Poems.⟩   *A.8739
= London. Kegan Paul, Trench & Co. 1884. (5), 27, (1) pp.
Sm. 8°.

NT 0039317   MB

Taresti, Aarne, 1906-   comp.
Sosiaalihuollon lainsäädäntö.

see under

Finland. Laws, statutes, etc.

Law   Tarey, G. S., ed.

Bombay (State) Laws, statutes, etc.
The Bombay tenancy and agricultural lands act, 1948, by
G. S. Tarey. ⟨2d ed. rev. & enl. Erandol? M. D. Kale, 1953⟩

Tarfán, Gerardo, and J. Pérez-López.
Rosiña; zarzuela dramática de costumbres gallegas en un
acto...en prosa. original. Música del maestro J. Cristóbal.
Madrid: R. Velasco. 1909.   37 p.   8°.

In: NPL p. v. 289, no. 13.

1. Drama (Spanish). 2. Pérez-   Lopez, José, jt. au. 3. Cristóbal.
Julio, composer. 4. Title.   March 16, 1911.
N. Y. P. L.

NT 0039320   NN

Lilly
AC 88   TARFIA ⟨SIC⟩ JENERAL DE LOS DERECHOS DE
.C7 T 18   encomiendas. Bogotá, Impª por J.A.
1834   Cualla, 1834.
Mendel   Broadside 43.5 x 31.2 cm.

1. Encomiendas (Latin America)—Colombia.
I. Title: Tarifa.

NT 0039321   InU

Targ, Alojzy, ed.
Księga o Śląsku, wydana z okazji jubileuszu 35-letn.
istnienia "Znicza." Cieszyn, Nakł. "Znicza," 1929.
288 p. illus., ports. 25 cm.
Errata slip inserted.

1. Silesia. 2. Znicz. I. Title.

DD491.S422T3   62-57615

NT 0039322   DLC

Targ, Alojzy.
...Śląsk w okresie okupacji niemieckiej (1939-1945) Poznań,
Wydawnictwo zachodnie, 1946. 92 p. 21cm.

1. World war, 1939-1945—   Poland—Silesia. 2. Silesia, Poland—
Hist.

NT 0039323   NN MH NNUN

Targ, J. I., ed.

Polska na morzu; praca zbiorowa pp. doktora Mieczysława
Boguckiego, licencjata Kazimierza Demela, b. wicemarszałka
Jana Dębskiego ¡i. i.¡ ... pod redakcją J. I. Targa ... War-
szawa, Główna księgarnia wojskowa, 1935 ¡i. e. 1934¡

Targ, Semen Mikhaĭlovich.
Основные задачи теории ламинарных течений. Мо-
сква, Гос. изд-во технико-теорет. лит-ры, 1951.
420 p. illus. 20 cm.
At head of title: C. M. Тарг.
Bibliographical footnotes.

1. Laminar flow.   I. Title.   *Title romanized: Osnovnye zadachi*
                                        teorii laminarnykh techeniĭ.

QA929.T3   53–37196

NT   0039325   DLC

---

531   Targ, Semen Mikhaĭlovich
T174kEt   Theoretical mechanics, a short course.
         ¡Translated from the Russian by V. Talmy¡
         Moscow, Foreign Languages Pub. House ¡n.d.¡
         421p. diagrs., tables. 22cm.

         Translation of Краткий курс теоретической
         механики (transliterated: Kratkiĭ kurs
         teoreticheskoĭ mekhaniki)

         1. Mechanics.   I. Title.

NT   0039326   IU

Targ, William, 1907–
     Adventures in good reading, by **William Targ.** Chicago,
The Black archer press, 1940.
     ix p., 2 l., 95 p. 20ᶜᵐ.

1. Bibliography—Best books.   I. Title.
                                                          41–5737
Library of Congress   Z1035.T17
———— Copy 2.
Copyright   ¡3¡   016

     OCl OLak
NT   0039327   DLC WaSp TxU PPD OrU ICN NBuU NmLcU OU

Targ, William, 1907–
     American books and their prices; a handbook for collectors,
booksellers and librarians, by William Targ. Chicago, The
Black archer press, 1941–
     v. fronts., pl., facsims. 18½ᶜᵐ.
     "Limited edition of five hundred copies."
     "An enlargement and complete revision of American first editions and
their prices ... published in 1931. ¡First edition published 1930 under
title: Targ's American first editions & their prices.¡"—v. 1, p. 6–7.
     "Reference": v. 1, p. 12; v. 2, p. 11.
     1. American literature—Bibl. 2. American literature—Bibl.—First
editions. 3. America—Bibl. 4. Books—Prices.   I. Title.
                                                  42–11160 Revised
Library of Congress   Z1231.F5T2 1941
                            ¡r42¡4¡   016.0944

     PP ScU CoU NbU CU OU ViU NN OrCS
NT   0039328   DLC WaSp WaS Or IdU CtY WaU OCl NcGU PSt

Targ, William, 1907–
     Targ's American first editions & their prices; a checklist of
the foremost American firsts. Chicago, W. Targ, 1930.
     6 p. l., 15–114 p., 1 l. 17½ᶜᵐ.
     "Five hundred copies have been printed for subscribers only."

1. American literature—Bibl.—First editions. 2. Books—Prices.
I. Title: American first editions & their prices.
                                                  30–19156 Revised 2
Library of Congress   Z1231.F5T2 1930
                            ¡r42h2¡   016.0944

     OrU IEN
NT   0039329   DLC NBuU MWA TxU LU OCl NjP FMU Or ViU

Targ, William, 1907–
     American first editions and their prices, 1931; a checklist of
the foremost American first editions from 1640 to the present
day, together with a few prefatory remarks, by William Targ
... Chicago, The Black archer press, 1931.
     4 p. l., vii, ¡1¡ p., 122 numb. l. incl. front., facsims. 18½ᶜᵐ.
     Half-title: Targ's American first editions and their prices.
     "Four hundred and forty-five copies have been issued for subscribers."
     First edition published 1930 under title: Targ's American first editions
& their prices.
     I. Title.
     1. American literature—Bibl.—First editions. 2. Books—Prices.
     I. Title.
                                                          42–10561
Library of Congress   Z1231.F5T2 1931
                            ¡3¡   016.0944

     WaS
NT   0039330   DLC PBm NSyU NN NBuU MB MH MWA ICN InU

Targ, William, 1907–   ed.
     The American West, a treasury of stories, legends, narra-
tives, songs & ballads of western America, edited with an introduction by William Targ. Cleveland and New York, The
World publishing company ¡1946¡
     xii, 595 p. illus. 21½ᶜᵐ.
     "First published April 1946."

1. The West. 2. American literature (Collections) 3. American literature—The West.   I. Title.
                                                          46–25163
Library of Congress   PS561.T3
                            ¡10¡   810.82

     OC1W TxU NBuHi TU MB NcGU MtU CaBVaU Or Wa WaE MH
NT   0039331   DLC IdU WaSp WaS WaT NBuU MtBC PP PWcS

Targ, William, 1907–   ed.
     Bouillabaisse for bibliophiles; a treasury of bookish lore,
wit & wisdom, tales, poetry & narratives & certain curious
studies of interest to bookmen & collectors. Edited, with an
introd. and notes. ¡1st ed.¡ Cleveland, World Pub. Co.
¡1955¡
     506 p. illus., facsims. 25 cm.

1. Bibliomania. 2. Literature—Miscellanea.   I. Title.

Z992.T16   010.82   55–9750

     OrCS OrAshS WaSp OrU Wa WaE WaS
     NN PPD PPT OO OCl AU OrMonO DAU CaBVaU MtU CaBVa Or
     PSC OCU TU MiD TxU MB NcC CU OU KEmT TxU NcD OOxM
NT   0039332   DLC WaSpG WaT FU ICN MU CU–S ViU MiU PLF

Targ, William, 1907–   ed.
     Carrousel for bibliophiles, a treasury of tales, narratives,
songs, epigrams and sundry curious studies relating to a
noble theme, edited, with an introduction by William Targ.
New York, P. C. Duschnes, 1947.
     xii, 400 p., 2 l., 13, ¡2¡ p., 1 l. 24½ cm.

1. Book collecting. 2. Bibliomania. 3. Literature—Miscellanea.
I. Title.
Z992.T17   010.82   47–3040

     WaT WaTU
     ViU PSC PPT PPD PU Or DHU KEmT MU NSyU OrU CU–S IU
NT   0039333   DLC MeB WaS IdB WaSp NcD ICU MH TxU TU

Targ, William, 1907–
     The case of Mr. Cassidy; a murder mystery about a Chicago
book collector ¡by¡ William Targ and Lewis Herman. New
York, Phoenix press ¡*1939¡
     255 p. 20ᶜᵐ.

I. Herman, Lewis, 1905–   joint author. II. Title.
                                                          39–31414
Library of Congress   PZ3.T174Cas

NT   0039334   DLC

813.5   Targ, William, 1907–
T185c   The case of Mr. Cassidy, a mystery.
1944   Cleveland and New York, The World Publishing
         Company ¡1944, c1939¡
         224p. (A Tower mystery)

NT   0039335   ICarbS CaOTP

Targ, William, 1907–   ed.
     Great western stories; a western story omnibus. New
York, Penguin Books ¡1947¡
     183 p. 18 cm. (Penguin books, 654)
     A revision of the editor's Western story omnibus, first pub. in 1945.

1. Western stories.   I. Title.

PZ1.T158Gr   48–2860*

NT   0039336   DLC KU–RH KU OrU

Targ, William, 1907–
     Lafcadio Hearn: first editions and values; a checklist for
collectors, by William Targ ... Chicago, The Black archer
press, 1935.
     51, ¡1¡ p. front. (facsim.) 20½ᶜᵐ.
     Descriptive letterpress on verso of frontispiece.
     "Published in a strictly limited edition of 550 copies for subscribers,
50 copies of which are printed on Inomachi vellum and signed by the
compiler." This copy not signed.
     CONTENTS.—Introduction.—First editions.—Books about Lafcadio
Hearn.—Index.
     1. Hearn, Lafcadio, 1850–1904—Bibl.
                                                          36–1080
Library of Congress   Z8393.7.T18
———— Copy 2.
Copyright A 90194   ¡3¡   012

     WaT WaTU WaWW Or OrStbM OrSaW OrU–M MtBuM
     MtU OrCS OrP OrPR OrU Wa WaE WaPS WaS WaSpG
     TxU NcD NIC ViU OU OCl MB CaBVaU IdB IdPI IdU MtBC
NT   0039337   DLC NBuU DeU CoU OOxM NBu CU–S PSt PSC

Targ, William, 1907–
     The making of the Bruce Rogers World Bible. Cleve-
land, World Pub. Co. ¡1949¡
     19 p. illus., group ports., facsim. 30 cm.

1. Rogers, Bruce, 1870–   2. Bible. English. 1949. Authorized.
I. Title.
Z232.R67T3   094.3   50–7794 rev
———— Copy 3. Rosenwald Coll.

     FMU IU I
     TxDaM–P TxU MeB LU KEmT MH–AH OKentU ViW NcU KyU
NT   0039339   DLC NIC CSt PSC PP OC1W OCl NN WU ICU

Targ, William, 1907–
     Modern English first editions and their prices. 1931–
A check-list of the foremost English first editions from 1860
to the present day, with a preface by William Targ ... Chicago, The Black archer press, 1932–
     v. front., facsims. 18½ᶜᵐ.
     "Five hundred copies ... issued for subscribers."

1. English literature—Bibl.—First editions. 2. Books—Prices.
I. Title.
Library of Congress   Z2014.F5T2   32–7334
———— 2d set.
Copyright A 50001   ¡5¡   016.0944

     OU OO MiU OCl NN MB
NT   0039340   DLC WaTU WaSp PP OrU KyLx CtW InU ViU

Targ, William, 1907–
     999 books worth reading; a checklist of the world's best
books, compiled by William Targ. Chicago, Black archer
press, 1934.
     43, ¡1¡ p. 19ᶜᵐ.

1. Bibliography—Best books.   I. Title.
                                                          35–1710
Library of Congress   Z1035.T18
                            ¡2¡   016

NT   0039341   DLC PPD OU OCl

Targ, William, 1907–
     The pauper's guide to book collecting, being a series of
random notes and informal jottings on a noble hobby, by William Targ. Chicago, Black archer press, 1933.
     31 p. 18½ᶜᵐ.
     "Books recommended": p. 31.

1. Book collecting.   I. Title.
                                                          34–2432
Library of Congress   Z992.T21
———— Copy 2.
Copyright A 70191   ¡2¡   025.2

NT   0039342   DLC PSC IdPI OCl

[Targ, William] 1907–
Poems of a Chinese student, by Charles Yu [pseud.] Chicago, Ill., W. Targ, The Black archer press [1941]
2 p. l., 7–28 p., 1 l. 20°.

"Limited edition of two hundred fifty copies issued."
"Most of the poems ... first appeared in Front views and profiles in the Chicago Tribune during 1941."

I. Title.
42–13336
Library of Congress   PS3539.A63P6
[2]   811.5

NT 0039343   DLC NIC PSC NN RPB IEN

Targ, William, 1907–   *ed.*
... Rare American books, valued from $50.00 to $25,000.00; a checklist of the scarcest & most valuable American first editions, edited by William Targ. Chicago, The Black archer press, 1935.
24 p. 18¼ x 10¼°.
At head of title: "The book-hunter's guide."

1. American literature — Bibl.— First editions. 2. Bibliography — Bibl.—Rare books. I. Title. II. Title: "The book-hunter's guide".
Library of Congress   Z1231.F57T22   36–1081
———— Copy 2.
Copyright A 90193   [3]   016.0944

NT 0039344   DLC OrU Or NcU NSyU PP OO OClW OCU OCl

Targ, William, 1907–
Rare book guide for beginners, by William Targ ... Chicago, The Black archer press, °1942.
[1], 14 p. 21¼ x 9¼°.

1. Book collecting. I. Title.
44–9258
Library of Congress   Z987.T3
[3]   025.2

NT 0039345   DLC

Targ, William, 1907–   *ed.*
A reader for writers. New York, Hermitage House [1951]
322 p. 21 cm. (Professional writers library)

1. Authorship—Collections. I. Title.
PN137.T3   029.6   51–12726 ‡

WaE CaBViP
NT 0039346   DLC IdPI WaS OrCS OrU ViU NN MB TxU MiU

Targ, William, 1907–   *comp.*
Ten thousand rare books and their prices, compiled by William Targ and Harry F. Marks. A handbook for collectors, dealers and librarians.
Chicago, The Black archer press, 1936
viii, 360, [23] p. fold. front., illus. (incl. port.) facsims. 20°.

"Limited to 370 copies for subscribers."
Blank pages for "Notations" ([23] at end)

NT 0039347   MiU-C OCl OU

Targ, William, 1907–   *comp.*
Ten thousand rare books and their prices, compiled by William Targ and Harry F. Marks. A handbook for collectors, dealers and librarians. New York, N. Y., H. F. Marks, inc. [1936]
viii, 360, [23] p. fold. front., illus. (incl. port.) facsims. 20°.

"Limited to 370 copies for subscribers."
Blank pages for "Notations" ([23] at end)

1. Bibliography—Rare books. 2. Books—Prices. I. Marks, Harry F., joint comp. II. Title.
Library of Congress   Z1012.T18   36–27470
———— Copy 2.   [10–5]   016.09

MiU-C ViU ODW MiU
NT 0039348   DLC NcD PHi OrCS Or WaS NN ViW NSyU NN

Targ, William, 1907–   *comp.*
Ten thousand rare books and their prices, a dictionary of first editions and valuable books. A handbook for collectors, dealers and librarians. Chicago, William Targ, 1940.
viii, 360 p., 1 l. front., plates, facsims. 21°.

"Reprint of the 1936 limited edition."
On cover: Popular edition.

1. Bibliography—Rare books. 2. Books—Prices. I. Title.
Wellesley college. Library   A 43–2821
for Library of Congress   [Z1012.T   ]
[3]   016.09

NT 0039349   MWeIC OrU WaSp PPT WU CU-S CU ICN

Targ, William, 1907–   *ed.*
Western story omnibus, a collection of short stories edited by William Targ. Cleveland and New York, The World publishing company [1945]
320 p. 20½°.

"Tower books edition ; first printing January 1945."

1. Short stories, American. I. Title.
45–2150
Library of Congress °   PZ1.T158We

NT 0039350   DLC PP OCl

---

*
AC8   Targ, William, 1907–   , ed.
.A5
no.686   Western story omnibus. New York, Editions
1945   for the Armed Services, °1945.
383 p. 12 x 17cm. (Armed Services ed. 686)

NT 0039351   ViU

Targa, Carlo
Ponderazioni sopra la contrattatione maritima, opera del dottor Carlo Targa ... Ricauata dalla legge ciuile, e canonica, dal Consolato di mare, e dalli vsi maritimi, con le formule de contratti attinenti à questa contrattazione, di profitto, non solo de pratticanti nel foro; mà anchora d'ogni sorte de mercanti, e marinari ... In Genova, Per A.M.Scionico, M.DC.LXXXXII.
6 p.l., 450 (i.e.460) p. 21½cm.
Page 344 wrongly numbered 334, and error continued.

NT 0039352   MiU-L NcU OCU CtY NN MH-BA

Targa, Carlo.
Ponderazioni sopra le contrattazioni marittime ... colla giunta delle leggi navali, e del gius navale de' rodii gre. lat. Degli statuti degli ufiziali di sicurta' della cità' di Firenze. Nuova ed. ricorretta, e i illustrata. Livorno, Stamperia di G.P.Fantechi e com., 1755.
xii, 368, vi, 59 p. 23 cm.

Title-page mutilated at imprint.
First edition Genova 1692 - Palau.

NT 0039353   MH-BA NcU MH

Targa, Carlo.
Ponderazioni sopra le contrattazioni marittime ... colla giunta delle leggi navali, e del gius navale de' Rodii Gre. Lat. Degli statuti degli ufiziali di sicurta della citta di Firenze. Nuova ed. ricorr. e illustrata. Livorno, G. P. Fantechi [1755]
Microfilm copy, made in 1966, of the original in Vatican. Biblioteca vaticana. Positive.

Negative film in Vatican. Biblioteca vaticana.
Collation of the original, as determined from the film: xii, 368, vi, 59 p.
1. Maritime law. (Series: [Manuscripta, microfilms of rare and out-of-print books. List 63, no. 15])

NT 0039355   MoSU

Targa, Carlo
Ponderazioni sopra la contrattazione marittima. Ricavate dalla legge civile e canonica, dal Consolato di mare, e dagli usi marittimi, con le formole di tali contratti, profittevoli non solo a' praticanti del foro, ma ancora ad ogni sorta di mercadanti e marinari dal dottissimo Carlo Targa ... Accresciuta questa nuova ed. di materia molto interessante. Genova, Dagli eredi di Adamo Scionico ... (A spese di Pietro Paolo Pizzorno) 1787.
4 p.l., 259 p.   22cm.

NT 0039356   MiU-L CLL

Targa, Carlo.
Ponderazioni sopra la contrattazione marittima ricavate dalla legge civile e canonica, dal consolato del Mare, e dagli usi marittimi con le formole di tali contratti, profittevoli non solo a praticanti nel foro ma ancora ad ogni sorta di mercadanti e marinari. Venezia, Gnoats, 1802.
99 p.

NT 0039357   PU

Targa, Carlo
Ponderazioni sopra la contrattazione marittima. Genova, 1803.
4to.

NT 0039358   NN

Targa, Carlo
Ponderazioni sopra la contrattazione marittima. Ricavate dalla legge civile e canonica, dal Consolato del mare, e dagli usi marittimi con le formole di tali contratti, profittevoli non solo a'praticanti nel foro, ma ancora ad ogni sorta di mercadanti e marinari, dal dottissimo Carlo Targa ... Trieste, appresso Giovanni Orlandini libraio, 1805.
2 p.l., 163 p.   26cm.

NT 0039359   MiU-L

Targa, Carlo
Reflexiones sobre los contratos maritimos, sacadas del derecho civil, y canonico, del consulado del mar, y de los usos maritimos, con las formulas de los tales contratos. Obra muy util, y aun necessaria para la práctica de los tribunales, y no menos para los consules, comerciantes, capitanes de navios, corredores, y qualesquiera otras personas empleadas en el trafico del mar ... Traducida del idioma italiano al español por Juan Manuel Giron.

Madrid, Francisco Xavier Garcia, 1753.
14 p. l., 330, [6] p.

NT 0039361   NNC NcD CU-L TxU MH-L TU MH-BA

Targa, Domingo.
El modus operandi de las artes electorales en Puerto Rico, por Domingo Targa ... [San Juan de Puerto Rico, Imprenta Puerto Rico, inc., 1940]
1 p. l., [5]–111, [3] p. 17½°.

"Informando el resultado del concurso electoral celebrado según anuncios publicados en 'El Imparcial' y 'La Correspondencia' de Puerto Rico."
"Fe de erratas": p. [3] of cover.

1. Elections—Puerto Rico. 2. Election law—Puerto Rico. I. Title.
Library of Congress   JL1058.T3   42–47108
[2]   324.7295

NT 0039362   DLC NN

Targa, Leonardo, 1730-1815.

Celsus, Aulus Cornelius.
A. Corn. Celsi Medicinae libri octo, ex recensione Leonardi Targae. Quibus accedunt tituli marginales perpetui, capitum librorumque; annotationes criticae. medicae. physicae: tabulae characterum, ponderum, mensurarum. aliae; indices materiae medicae Celsianae, rerumque: praefixa de Celsi vita dissertatione. Concinnavit, indice jam delphiniano auxit Eduardus Milligan ... Ed. 2., auctor et castigator. Edinburgi, veneunt apud Maclachlan et Stewart; ¡etc., etc.¡ 1831.

Targa, Leonardo, 1730-1815.

Celsus, Aulus Cornelius.
Aur. Cor. Celsus on medicine, in eight books, Latin and English. Translated from L. Targa's edition, the words of the text being arranged in the order of construction. To which are prefixed, a life of the author, tables of weights and measures, with explanatory notes, etc. designed to facilitate the progress of medical students, By Alex. Lee, A. M., surg. In two volumes ... London, E. Cox, 1831-36.

Targa, Pietro, pseud.
    see   Pavesi, Cesare, 16th cent.

(TARGAN,————)
- La manufacture impériale des tabacs. [Paris,imp.Ballée,1867.]

1.8°. 4to. pp.(48). Illustr.
Extracted from vol.2 of a larger work.

NT 0039366   MH

Targarona, Peter.
Petition of Peter Targarona to the Congress of the United States for the recovery of the value of his steamboats "Capitol" and "Live Oak" taken from him by the officers of the United States, since the late war. Also, the evidence, brief and argument in behalf of claimant. ¡Washington?¡ W. H. Moore ¡1876¡. ii, 73 p. 8°.

1. Claims, U. S.
N. Y. P. L.   January 8, 1913.

NT 0039367   NN

Targe, Antoine Louis, 1865–
...La garde de nos frontières; constitution et organisation des forces de couverture... Paris: Charles-Lavauzelle & cie.¡, 1930.¡ 134 p. 8°.

       1. Defence—France.
N. Y. P. L.   October 16, 1931.

NT 0039368   NN DS DNW CU NjP

F
456
.862
   TARGE, JEAN BAPTISTE, 1714-1788.
     Histoire d'Angleterre, depuis le traité d'Aix-la-Chapelle en 1748, jusqu'au traité de Paris en 1763. Pour servir de continuation aux histoires de MM. Smollett et Hume. Londres,1768.
     5v. 18cm.

NT 0039369   ICN

946.05 **Targe, Jean Baptiste,** 1714-1788.
T17h   Histoire de l'avénement de la maison de Bourbon au trone d'Espagne, dédiée au roi. Paris, 1772.
     6v.

NT 0039370   IU MdBP MH

Targe, Maxime.
     Professeurs et régents de collège dans l'ancienne Université de Paris (XVIIe et XVIIIe siècles) par Maxime Targe... Paris, Hachette et cie, 1902.
     viii, 318 p. 23 cm.
     Thèse - Université de Paris, 1902.

NT 0039371   CtY NcD

Targe, Maxime.
     Professeurs et régents de collège dans l'ancienne Université de Paris (xviie et xviiie siècles) par Maxime Targe ... Paris, Hachette et cie, 1902.
     viii, 318 p. 23cm.   4-2605

NT 0039372   DLC PU KU ICN NIC DHEW ICJ MB NNUnC

Targé, P.
     Ueber schneeverwehungen auf eisenbahnen und mittel dawider. Von P. Targé ... Leipzig, J. J. Weber, 1847.
     23, ¡1¡ p. illus. 22cm.

     1. Railroads—Snow-plows.

Library of Congress   TF542.T18   6-29493†

NT 0039373   DLC

Target, Felix.
     On the main drainage of Paris, and the utilisation of its sewage... London, W. Clowes & Sons, 1878.
     25 p. 1 map. 2 pl. 8°.
     Excerpt: Minutes of proceedings of the Institution of Civil Engineers, Vol. liii. Session 1877-78. Part iii.

NT 0039374   NN

[TARGET, GUY JEAN BAPTISTE] 1733-1807.
     La censure. Lettre a **... [Paris?] 1775. 28 p. 21½cm.

     1. Censorship—France, 1775. I. Title.

NT 0039375   NN NIC

Target, Guy Jean Baptiste, 1733-1807, tr.

Mirabeau, Honoré Gabriel Riquetti, comte de, 1749-1791.
     Considerations on the order of Cincinnatus; to which are added, as well several original papers relative to that institution, as also a letter from the late M. Turgot ... to Dr. Price, on the constitutions of America; and an abstract of Dr. Price's Observations on the importance of the American revolution; with notes and reflections upon that work. Tr. from the French of the Count de Mirabeau ... London, Printed for J. Johnson, 1785.

Target, Guy Jean Baptiste
     Discours prononcés... 10 mars 1785

     see under

Académie française, Paris.

Target, Guy Jean Baptiste, 1733-1807.
     L'Esprit des cahiers ...
     see under title

Target, Guy Jean Baptiste, 1733-1806.
     Les États-généraux convoqués par Louis XVI. 1788.
     54 p. D.

NT 0039379   NcU NN

DC
163.7
T35   [Target, Guy Jean Baptiste]
     Les états-généraux convoqués par Louis XVI. [Paris? 1789?]
     3 v. in 1. 21 cm.
RARE: Each vol. has half-title only.
SPECIAL   Ms. note on half-title: De Mr. Target. Cf.
COLLECTIONS   Bib. Nat. Cat. gen.
     Title on spine: Les états-généraux du 1789.

     ⟍1. France. États généraux, 1789.⟍2. France—Politics and government—Revolution, 1789-1799. ⟍I. Title.

NcU
NT 0039380   CU-A WU ViU NIC MiDW KU MnU NcD MB NNC

Target, Guy Jean Baptiste, 1733-1806.
     Les États généraux ...
     see also   Mémoire sur le choix de la deliberation par tete ou par ordre.

French Rev.
DC
141
P87+   ¡Target, Guy Jean Baptiste, 1733-1806
v.6   Lettre d'un homme à un autre homme, sur l'extinction de l'ancien Parlement et la création du nouveau. ¡n.p., 1771¡
     16 p. 18cm.

     1. France—Pol. & govt.—1715-1774. I. Title.

NT 0039382   NIC MH

¡Target, Guy Jean Baptiste¡ 1733-1806.
     Instruction, ou si l'on veut, cahier de l'assemblée du bailliage de***. 28 février 1789. ¡1789¡
     32 p. 22cm.

     Volume of pamphlets.

NT 0039383   NIC NN

DC
141   Target, Guy Jean Baptiste, 1733-
     Instruction, ou si l'on veut, Cahier de l'assemblée du bailliage de *** .
     ¡n.p.¡ 28 février 1789.
     1 card. (Hayden, French revolutionary pamphlets, 1261)

     Microcard copy.
     Collation of the original: 32 p.

NT 0039384   MiEM

Target, Guy Jean Baptiste
— Levée des scellés, mausolée et résur-
rection de M. Target. 1790.

NT 0039385   NIC

Target, Guy Jean Baptiste.
Mémoire de m. Target, sur l'exécution des
lettres de convocation pour les Etats-généraux.
1789.
52 p.   D.
[Etats généraux, no. 6]

NT 0039386   NcU

[Target, Guy Jean Baptiste] 1733-1807.
Mémoire sur l'amélioration des domaines et
bois du Roi, sur les vices de l'administration
actuelle, & sur les moyens d'en tirer un
parti plus avantageux au profit de l'état, en
procurant la tranquilité aux détempteurs.
Berlin et Paris, Chez Gattey, 1788.
58 p.   19½ cm.

DC 142
.P 18 C   No. [1] in a volume with binder's title:
v. 3   Pamphlets. French Revolution. v.3.
1. France - Forest policy.   I. Title.   II.
Series.

NT 0039387   MdBJ

Target, Guy Jean Baptiste, 1733-1807.
Mémoire sur les demandes formées contre le
Général et la Société des Jésuits, au sujet des
engagemens qu'elle a contracté par le ministere
du P. de Lavalette [Memoire pour le Sr. Cazotte,
commissaire général de la Marine et pour la
demoiselle Fouque...]   Paris, 1761.
70 p.   17 cm.
Signed, Mes. Rouhette & Target fils, avoc.

NT 0039388   CtY

Target, Guy Jean Baptiste, 1733-1807
— Mort, testament et enterrement de M.
Target. 1790.

NT 0039389   NIC

Target, Guy Jean Baptiste, 1733-1807.
La nouvelle constellation, ou l'apothéose de
M. Target.   [1790?]

NT 0039390   NIC

Target, Guy Jean Baptiste, 1733-1807.
Observations de Target sur le procès de Louis
XVI.   [Paris, 1792]
7 p.   20 cm.
Caption title.
[Bound with Journal des débats, [III, 3] at
end of volume]

NT 0039391   CtY PU

Target Guy Jean Baptiste, tr.

Price, Richard, 1723-1791.
Observations sur l'importance de la révolution de
l'Amérique, et sur les moyens de la rendre utile au monde. Par Richard Price ...
(*In* Mirabeau, Honoré Gabriel Riquetti, comte de. Considérations sur
l'ordre de Cincinnatus. Londres, 1788. 20ᶜᵐ. p. 203-299)

Target, Guy Jean Baptiste,

,1262. —— Observations sur la manière d'exécuter les Lettres de convocation des États-
généraux. n. p. [1789.] 51 p.

NT 0039393   NN

DC
141   Target, Guy Jean Baptiste, 1733-
Observations sur la manière d'exécuter les
Lettres de convocation des États-généraux.
[n.p., 1789]
1 card.   (Hayden, French revolutionary
pamphlets, 1262)

Microcard copy.
Collation of the original: 51 p.

NT 0039394   MiEM

[Target, Guy Jean Baptiste] 1733-1806.
Observations sur le commerce des grains,
écrites en décembre 1769. Par M..... avocat.
A Amsterdam, et se trouve à Paris, Chez L.
Cellot, 1775.
46 p.   21cm.

Bound with Condorcet, Marie Jean Antoine Nicolas Caritat, marquis de. Lettres sur le commerce des grains. 1774 [i.e. 1775]

NT 0039395   NNC NcD

FR REV
DC
141   Target, Guy Jean Baptiste, 1733-1806.
R4543   Opinion sur la division du royaume, à la
no.18   séance du 10 nov. 1789. [Paris, Baudouin,
1789]
28 p.   21cm.

No. 18 in vol. lettered: Révolution française. Féodalité. Mélanges.
Paris. Bibl. Natl. Dépt. des imprimés.
Cat. de l'histoire de la Révolution française. 4¹, 32262.

NT 0039396   NIC PU

[Target, Guy Jean Baptiste, 1733-1806]
*FC7   Plaidoyer pour la demoiselle Sara-Mendés
P3596   d'Acosta,] epouse du sieur Peixotto; contre le
Z7/9t -   sieur Peixotto, son mari.
A Paris,De l'imprimerie de L.Cellot,rue
Dauphine.M.DCC.LXXIX.
4°. 58p. 25cm.
Signed at end: Monsieur de Saint-Fargeau,
avocat du roi. Mᵉ Target, avocat. Charier,
procureur.

NT 0039397   MH NNJ

Target,Guy Jean Baptiste,1733-1807.
Projet de Déclaration des droits de
l'homme en société; par m.Target. [Paris,
Baudouin, 1789]
7 p.   20ᶜᵐ.
Caption title.
No.[2] in a volume of pamphlets with
binder's title: Révolution française. Mémoires.

NT 0039398   MiU NN MH NIC PU

Target, Guy Jean Baptiste, 1733-1807.
Projet de Déclaration des droits de l'homme
en société; par M. Target. [Versailles, Baudouin, imprimeur de l'Assemblée nationale,
1789]
8 p.   19 cm.   [Mélanges politiques. v.40,
no.6]
Caption title.

I.Title. II.Title. Déclaration des droits de
l'homme en société.

NT 0039399   MnU NIC CLL

Target, Guy Jean Baptiste, 1733-1807.
Rapport fait à l'Assemblée nationale
see under France. Assemblée nationale
constituante, 1789-1791. Comité de constitution.

Target, Guy Jean Baptiste, 1733-1807.
Rapport fait au nom du Comité de constitution
see under France. Assemblée nationale
constituante, 1789-1791. Comité de constitution.

DC   Target, Guy Jean Baptiste, 1733-1806.
141   Rapport fait le 29 septembre 1789.
F87+   [Paris, Baudouin, 1789]
v.49   8 p. 22cm.

On the organization of the legislative
body.
Reprinted in the Archives Parlementaires,
v. 9, p. 210-211.

NT 0039402   NIC

Target, Guy Jean Baptiste, 1733-1807, supposed
author.
Réflexions succintes sur ce qui s'est passé
au parlement de Paris depuis déc. 1770
see under title

Target, Guy Jean Baptiste.
Reflexions sur la destitution de l'universalite
des offices du parlement de Paris par voie de
suppression
see under   Mirabeau, Andre Bonif
Louis Riquette, vicomte, 1754-1792.

Target, Guy Jean Baptiste, 1733-1807.
Relevailles, rechûte et nouvelle
conception de mᵉ Target
see under title

Target, Guy Jean Baptiste, 1733-1807.
Second mémoire pour le Sr. Cazotte & la Dlle
Fouque contre le Général et la Société des
Jésuites. [Paris, 1761]
72 [4] p.   17 cm.
Caption title.
Binders title: Affai. des Jesuites Amerique.

NT 0039406   CtY

Target, Guy Jean Baptiste, 1733-1807

Price, Richard, 1723-1791.
A short abstract of a work lately printed by Dr. Price, on the importance of the American revolution, and the means of making it a blessing to the world: to which are added, Reflections and notes upon that work.

(*In* Mirabeau, Honoré Gabriel Riquetti, comte de. **Considerations on the order of Cincinnatus.** London, 1785. 21½ᶜᵐ. p. 175-284)

Target, Paul Louis, 1821-1908, ed.
Un avocat du XVIIIᵉ siècle
see under title

Target, Paul Louis, 1821-1908.
*FC9   In condamnation du régime, par P. - L.
D8262   Target ... Troisième édition.
Z900t2c   Librairie nationale, Paris, 29, rue de Penthièvre, 29, Paris[1900?]
cover-title, 32p. 17cm.
Dated at end: 25 octobre 1900.
Original printed gray wrappers preserved; bound in half red cloth and marbled boards.

NT 0039409   MH

Microfilm
9212
DC   **Target, Paul Louis, 1821-1908.**
Dix ans de République (1879-1889) par P. L. Target ... Paris, H. Chapelliez et cⁱᵉ, 1889.
2 p. L, 147 p. 21½ᶜᵐ.

L. C. Copy Replaced by Microfilm

1. France—Hist.—Third republic, 1870-1940.   I. Title.
                                                           S D 21-49 Revised
U. S. Dept. of state. Libr.   [DC335.T17]
for Library of Congress   [r42b2]

NT 0039410   DS DLC

DC335   **TARGET, PAUL LOUIS, b.1821.**
.T2   Feuillets d'histoire. Vingt ans de république(1880-1900)par P.-L.Target ... 2.éd. ... Paris, Librairie nationale, 1901.
[1],iv,[5]-277,33,38 p. 18½cm.
"Une nouvelle édition des diverses brochures que j'ai publiées depuis 1880."

1. France—Pol. & govt.—1870-

NT 0039411   ICU

DC
252.5   **Target, Paul Louis, 1821-1908.**
.G9   Législation électorale. Droits et devoirs des électeurs ... Paris, Michel-Lévy, frères, v.60   1863.
16 p. 24ᶜᵐ.

No. [1] in [Guizot collection of pamphlets. v.60]
(Binder's title: Brochures diverses)

1. Election law—France. 2. Suffrage—France.

NT 0039412   MiU

TARGET, PAUL LOUIS.
Législation électorale; droits et devoirs des électeurs. Paris, M. Lévy, 1863. 16 p. 23cm.

Film reproduction. Negative.

1. France—Elections—Jurisp.

NT 0039413   NN

Target, Paul Louis, 1821-1908.
La révision de la constitution par une assemblée constituante par P. L. Target...   Paris, De Soye et fils, 1899.
24 p. 24 cm.
"Extrait du Correspondant."

NT 0039414   CtY

Target, Roland, 1912-
... Contribution à l'étude de l'asthme professionnel...   Paris, 1938.
Thèse - Univ. de Paris.
"Bibliographie": p. [38]

NT 0039415   CtY

AP201
.T3   **The Target; a paper for boys.** Continuing the Sunday school advocate.
Cincinnati, O. [The Methodist book concern, 19
v. illus. 34cm. weekly.

1. Methodist Episcopal church—Period.

NT 0039416   DLC PP IEG

Target; the bulletin on productivity. v. 1-
June, 1948-
[London] 1948-   illus.   43cm.
Monthly.
Subtitle varies.
Issued by the Central office of information of Great Britain for the Economic information unit of the Treasury.

I. Great Britain. Information,   Central office of. II. Great Britain.
Treasury. Economic information   unit.
N. Y. P. L.   December 1, 1950

NT 0039417   NN

TARGET; the bulletin on productivity. v. 1-[22];
June, 1948-1969
[London]   v.   illus.   43cm.
Microfilm (negative, 1948-62; positive, 1963-69)
Monthly.
Subtitle varies.
Published by the Central office of information of Great Britain for the Economic information unit of   the Treasury, 1948-50; by the

Information division of the Treasury, 1951-July, 1953; by the Central office of information for the Board of trade and other agencies, Aug./Sept. 1953-1959; by the British productivity council, 1960-69.
Absorbed B. P. C. bulletin, Jan. 1960.
Includes supplements.
Ceased publication with Mar. 1971.

1. Labor productivity—Per. and soc. publ. I. Great Britain. Information,
Central office of. II. Great   Britain. Treasury. III. British
productivity council.

NT 0039419   NN

Target comics ... v. 1-
Feb. 1940-
[Philadelphia, Novelty press, inc., 1940-
v. col. illus. 26½ᶜᵐ. monthly.
Editorial office, New York.
Consists chiefly of illustrations.
No number was issued for Feb. 1941.

42-41067
Library of Congress   AP101.T25

NT 0039420   DLC

Target for tomorrow.
no. 1
London: The Pilot press ltd., 1943   26cm.
no. illus.
Editor : no. 1   Charles Madge.
Editorial board: no. 1   , Sir William Beveridge, Julian Huxley, Sir
J. B. Orr.

1. No subject. I. Madge,   Charles, 1912-   , ed.
N. Y. P. L.   January 31, 1944

NT 0039421   NN NcD

UxL36   **The target;** or, A treatise upon a branch
+756t   of art military. By a gentleman, who has resided some time in England ... London, Printed for R.and J.Dodsley, 1756.
vii,[2],183p. plans. 29½x23cm.

1 Military art and science - Early works to 1800. I.A Gentleman who has resided some time in England.

NT 0039422   CtY PPL ICN

La Targétade, tragédie un peu burlesque; parodie d'Athalie, de Racine
see under [Huvier des Fontenelles, Pierre Marie François] 1757-1823.

Targets in reading...
see under Barry, Linda E.

Targett (James H.) Appendix V to the second edition of the Descriptive catalogue of the pathological specimens contained in the Museum of the Royal College of Surgeons of England. ix, 36 pp. 8°. *London, Taylor & Francis,* 1891.
Appendix VI. ix, 42 pp.
8°. *London, Taylor & Francis,* 1892.

NT 0039425   DNLM

[Targett, W   ]
Ed   A month on the continent in the year 1854,
854s   with brief sketches in Ireland, in the year 1855, by a servant. Bristol, I.Arrowsmith, 1855.
vii, 76p. 16cm.

NT 0039426   CtY

Targetti, Ferdinando.
... Per l'unità proletaria. Milano, A. Corticelli [1945]
110, [2] p. 18½ᶜᵐ.
CONTENTS.—L'avvento del fascismo ed il Partito socialista italiano.—Per l'unità proletaria.—Il fascismo e l'assassinio di Giacomo Matteotti.

1. Socialism in Italy. 2. Fascism—Italy. I. Title.
HX287.T3   A F 47-297
Columbia univ. Libraries
for Library of Congress   [4]†

NT 0039427   NNC MH-PA CU DLC

Targetti, Ferdinando.
... Per l'unità proletaria. Milano, A. Corticelli ₁1945₁
110 ₍?₎ p. 18¹ᵐ
Film reproduction. Negative.
CONTENTS.—L'avvento del fascismo ed il Partito socialista italiano.—
Per l'unità proletaria.—Il fascismo e l'assassinio di Giacomo Matteotti.

1. SOCIALISM--ITALY   2. FASCISM--ITALY

NT 0039428   NN

Targetti, Ferdinando
... Per la riforma degli art. 393, 394
del Codice penale ... Roma, Bocca, 1908.
    cover-title, 23 p. 25cm.
    Caption title: Il "Libello famoso" del
Fulci e il progetto dei giornalisti per
la riforma della diffamazione; critiche
e previsioni.

NT 0039429   MH-L

Targetti, Lodovico.
... Satire clandestine; prefazione di Leonida Règaci, disegni
di Giammusso. Milano, A. Corticelli ₁1946₁
4 p. l., 11-146 p., 3 l. illus. (incl. music) 24ᵐ.
"Di questo volume ... sono state impresse 500 copie di cui ... 484
numerate da 17 a 500. Esemplare n. 95"
Poems.

1. Mussolini, Benito, 1883-1945—Poetry.   I. Title.
PQ4843.A67S3   851.91   A F 47-3661
Yale univ. Library
for Library of Congress   ₁2₁†

NT 0039430   CtY NN IU NjP DLC

Targetti, Raimondo, 1869 –
...Il dazio comunale di consumo sui manufatti. \ Relatore:
ing. Raimondo Targetti...   Roma: Provveditorato generale
dello stato, 1927. 14 p. 8°.
    At head of title: Ministero dell'economia nazionale. Consiglio superiore dell'
economia nazionale.
    "Estratto dagli Atti dal Consiglio superiore dell' economica nazionale — sessione
maggio 1927 — V."

419201A. 1. Industrial and mechanic   arts—Taxation—Italy. 2. Italy.
Economia nazionale, Consiglio su-   periore dell'.
N. Y. P. L.   June 22, 1929

NT 0039431   NN

Targetti, Raimondo, 1869–
...Problemi attuali dell'industria:\la produzione della lana ed
i mercati regionali. Relazione dell' ing Targetti.   Roma: Provveditorato generale dello stato, 1928. 22 p. 8°.
    At head of title: Ministero dell'economia nazionale. Consiglio superiore dell' eco-
nomia nazionale. Sessione dicembre 1927 — anno VI.

410120A. 1. Wool—Trade and stat.   —Italy. 2. Italy. Economia nazionale,
Consiglio superiore dell'.
N. Y. P. L.   May 9, 1929

NT 0039432   NN

Targetti, Raimondo, 1869–
... Scritti di economia laniera. Roma, G. Bardi, 1942.
2 p. l., ₍7₎-314 p., 1 l. 24½ᵐ.
"Note bibliografiche": p. ₍281₎-312.

1. Wool trade and industry—Italy.
45-34762
Library of Congress   HD9005.I 72T3
₍2₁   338.4767731

NT 0039433   DLC NN

Targgart, Raymond P
    Back in the old Sunday school. Accompaniment
by Marie Culver.   [Portland, Ore., c1954]
    [2] p. illus. 29 cm.
    For voice and piano.
    1. Songs (Medium voice) with piano.

NT 0039434   OrU

Targhetta (J. Peppino) [1876-   ]. *Étude
sur le thymus envisagé spécialement au point
de vue de la médecine légale. 147 pp. 8°.
Paris, 1902, No. 160.

NT 0039435   DNLM

Targhetta (Jean) [1842-   ]. *Des dévia-
tions de l'utérus; leur traitement, valeur de la
méthode Alquié-Alexandre. 110 pp. 4°. *Paris*,
1893, No. 297.

NT 0039436   DNLM

Targi poznańskie, Posen
    see   Posen. Targi poznańskie.

W 4   TARGIER, Joachim, fl. 1687, respondent
U92   Exercitationis medicae specimen inaugurale de abortu ...
1687   Trajecti ad Rhenum, Ex officina Francisci Halma, 1687.
T. 1   22, [2] p. 22 cm.
            Diss. - Utrecht.

NT 0039438   DNLM

Targini, Francisco Bento Maria, +r.
    Ensaio sobre o homem ...
        see under   Pope, Alexander, 1688-1744.

Targini, Francisco Bento Maria, +r.
    Paraiso perdido ...
        see under   Milton, John, 1608-1674.

Targioni, Giovanni, 1712-1783
    see   Targioni-Tozzetti, Giovanni, 1712-1783.

Targioni, Giovanni Luigi.
    ——, Della vera natura dell' aria fissa e della
di lei influenza nell' arte medica. Discorso i
e ii.
    In: Rac. di opusc. med.-prat. 8°. *Firenze*, 1775, iii, 229-
298.

NT 0039442   DNLM

Targioni, Giovanni Luigo.
    ——, Esame del veleno dei carciofi.
    In: Rac. di opusc. med.-prat. 8°. *Firenze*, 1775, iv, 161-
180.

NT 0039443   DNLM

Targioni (Giovanni Luigi). Istoria della cura
di uno scorbuto.
    In: Rac. di opusc. med.-prat. 8°. *Firenze*, 1775, i, 273-
296.

NT 0039444   DNLM

Targioni, Giovanni Luigi.
    ——, Istoria di un anasarca succeduto ad una
febbre intermittente.
    In: Rac. di opusc. med.-prat. 8°. *Firenze*, 1775, iii, 196-
218.

NT 0039445   DNLM

Targioni (Giovanni Luigi)
    ——, Istoria di alcune malattie nelle quali fu
usata l'acqua impregnata di aria fissa.
    In: Rac. di opusc. med.-prat. 8°. *Firenze*, 1775, ii, 262-
272.

NT 0039446   DNLM

Targioni, Giovanni Luigi.
    Istorie di malattie del basso ventre.
    IN: Rac. di opusc. med. prat. 8°. Firenze,
1775, iii, 61-123.

NT 0039447   DNLM

Targioni, Giovanni Luigi.
    ——, Osservazione fatte in Firenze nella costi-
tuzione vajnolosa dell' anno 1773.
    In: Rac. di opusc. med.-prat. 8°. *Firenze*, 1775, iv, 229-
248.

NT 0039448   DNLM

Targioni, Giovanni Luigi, ed.
    Raccolta di opuscoli fisico-medici
    see under title

Targioni, Giovanni Luigi, ed.
    Raccolta di opuscoli medico-pratici...
    see under title

Targioni, Giovanni Luigi.
    ——, Relazione di una complicata malattia di
occhi.
    In: Rac. di opusc. med.-prat. 8°. *Firenze*, 1775, ii, 227-
238.

NT 0039451   DNLM

Targioni, Giovanni Luigi.
    ——, Storia ragionata delle febbre putride, lo
quale nell' anno 1775 hanno regnato nelle persone addette al servizio del Regio Arcispedale di
Santa Maria Nuova di Firenze.
    In: Rac. di opusc. med.-prat. 8°. *Firenze*, 1775, iv, 99-
148.

NT 0039452   DNLM

Kress·
Room
  Targioni, Luigi
    Saggi ‡fisici politici ed economici ...
Napoli, Stamperia di D.Campo, 1786.
XLII p., 1 *l*., 448 p. 20.5 cm.

  Bibliographical footnotes.

  1.Sheep - Apulia. 2.Wool - Apulia.

NT 0039453   MH-BA ICU

  Targioni-Tozzetti, Adolfo, 1823-1902.
    Ancora sulla melata e la sua origine. 1877.
  E. T. v. 7a.

NT 0039454   PPAN

  Targioni-Tozzetti, Adolfo, 1823-1902.
    Animali ed insetti del tabacco in erba e del
tabacco secco, di Ad. Targioni Tozzetti... e per
incarico della R. Direzione generale delle gabelle...
Firenze-Roma, F. Bencini, 1891.
  lxiii [1] 346 p., 1 l. illus., plates. 25 cm.
  "Indice bibliografico di scrittori, opere o
articoli speciali per gli insetti del tabacco":
p. [xxxv]-lx.
  1. Tobacco - Diseases and pests.

NT 0039455   CU MH PPAN NcD

QL
1
S67
v.5
no.6
  Targioni-Tozzetti, Adolfo, 1823-1902.
    Aonidia blanchardi, nouvelle espèce de
cochenille du dattier du Sahara.
  (In Société zoologique de France.
Mémoires. Paris. 25cm. v. 5 (1892),
p. 69-82. illus.)

NT 0039456   NIC

  Targioni Tozzetti, Adolfo. Bibliographia botanica Tar-
gioniana. Florentine. 1874. l. 8°. pp. 23.

NT 0039457   MH-A PPAN

  Targioni Tozzetti, Adolfo, 1823-1902.
    La bocca ed i piedi dei Tetranychus. 1877.
  E. T. v. 7a.

NT 0039458   PPAN

  Targioni-Tozzetti, Adolfo.

  Florence. R. Museo di fisica e storia naturale.
  Catalogo della collezione di insetti italiani del R. Museo di Firenze ... coleotteri. Firenze, Tip. Cenniniana,
1876-79.

  Targioni Tozzetti, Adolfo, 1823-1902.
    Catalogo di Crostacei podottalmi brachiuri e
anomouri raccolti nel viaggio di circumnavigazione
della Fregate Italiana Magenta. 1872.
  E. T. v. 7a

NT 0039460   PPAN

Mann
QL
462
T18
  Targioni-Tozzetti, Adolfo, 1823-1902.
    [Collected papers. v. p.]
    v. illus. 25 cm.

NT 0039461   NIC

  Targioni-Tozzetti, Adolfo, –1902.   **594-5 Mg00**
  Commentario sui cefalopodi mediterranei del R. Museo di Firenze
del prof. Adolfo Targioni-Tozzetti. Pisa, Tip. Nistri, 1869.
  67 p. pl. vi-vii. 23¼cm.
  "Estratto dal Bullettino malacologico italiano, anno II."

NT 0039462   ICJ PPAN

  Targioni Tozzetti, Adolfo, *1823–1902.*
    ...Crostacei brachiuri e anomouri, per Adolfo Targioni Toz-
zetti. [Firenze: Coi tipi dei successori Le Monnier, 1877] xxix,
257 p. illus., 13 pl. 27½cm. (Florence «City». Università.
Scienze matematiche, fisiche e naturali, Facoltà di. Pubblicazioni.
no. 1.)
  Half-title.
  At head of title: Zoologia del viaggio intorno al globo della r. pirocorvetta Magenta
durante gli anni 1865–68.

Astor 941.   1. Crustacea. I. Ser.   *Revised*
N. Y. P. L.   August 21, 1936

NT 0039463   NN PPF PPPCPh

  Targioni-Tozzetti, Adolfo.
    Degli alimenti freschi e conservati a diversi gradi di
preparazione. Classe LXVII. Relazioni del Prof. Cav.
Adolfo Targioni-Tozzetti. (*In* Italy. R. Commissione,
Esposizione universale, Paris, 1867. Relazioni dei giurati
italiani sulla Esposizione universale del 1867. Firenze,
1868–69. 24¼ᶜᵐ. v. 3 (1869) p. 213–286)

  1. Food.

  Library of Congress   T801.G1I8   5–28706†

NT 0039464   DLC

  Targioni-Tozzetti, Adolfo, *1823–1902.*
    Del pidocchio o della fillossera della vite e delle specie del
genere Philloxera in Europa e in America, per Adolfo Targioni
Tozzetti. [Firenze, Tip. Cenniniana nelle Murate, 1875?]
  54 p., 1 l. fold. pl. 21½ᶜᵐ. [*With his* Della malattia del pidocchio
(*Phylloxera vastatrix* Planch.) ... Roma, 1875]
  Caption title.
  "Dal Bullettino entomologica, anno VII."

  1. Phylloxera.

                               31–20276
  Library of Congress   SB608.G7T3

NT 0039465   DLC

  Targioni-Tozzetti, Adolfo, *1823–1902.*
    ... Della malattia del pidocchio (*Phylloxera vastatrix*
Planch.) nella vite secondo gli studi **fatti** in Europa e in
America e discussi al Congresso internazionale dei viticultori
convocato a Montpellier nell'ottobre 1874, per Ad. Targioni
Tozzetti ... Roma, Stab. tip. alle Terme diocleziane, 1875.
  156 p., 2 l., iv p. illus., fold. pl., 2 fold. maps. 21½ᶜᵐ.
  At head of title: Annali del Ministero di agricoltura, industria e
commercio, parte i—Agricoltura.
  With this are bound the author's Del pidocchio o della fillossera
della vite ... [Firenze, 1875?] and Notizie e indicazioni sulla malattia
del pidocchio della vite o della fillossera ... Roma, 1875.
  1. Phylloxera.   I. Italy. Ministero di agricoltura, industria e commercio. Annali.

                               31–20275
  Library of Congress   SB608.G7T3   632.75

NT 0039466   DLC

  Targioni-Tozzetti, Adolfo.
    Di una specie nuova in un nuovo genere di cirripedi
lepadidei ospitante sulle penne addominali del *Priofinus
cinereus* dell' Atlantico australe e dell' oceano Indiano,
raccolta nel viaggio intorno al mondo della fregata italiana la Magenta dai professori F. de Filippi ed E. Gi-
glioli. Nota di Ad. Targioni Tozzetti. [Firenze, Tip.
Cenniniana, 1872]
  13, [2] p. pl. 22½ᶜᵐ.
  Caption title.
  "Dal Bullettino entomologico, anno IV."
  1. Ornitholepas australis.

                        CA 8–210 Unrev'd
  Library of Congress   QL444.C5T2

NT 0039467   DLC PPAN

  Targioni Tozzetti, Adolfo, 1823-1902.
    Discurso inaug. letto nella prima Adunanza
pubblica nella Societa Entomologica Italiana.
n. d.
  ~~E. T. v. 7a~~

NT 0039468   PPAN

  Targioni-Tozzetti, Adolfo, 1823-1902.
    Esperienze tentate per determinare la tolleranze
delle giovani vegetazioni della vita, verso
l'azione di vari miscugli insetticidi. Studi della
R. Stazione di entomologia agrata de Firenze
per il prof. Ad. Targioni-Tozzetti e dott. C del
Buercio. [Torin, 1892?]
  cover-title, 18 p. 23.5 cm.
  From Le Stazioni sperimentali agrarie
italiane, Giornale. v. 20, fasc. 6.

NT 0039469   PPAN

  Targioni-Tozzetti, Adolfo, 1823-1902.
    Esperienze tentate per distruggere la
Schizoneura lanigera Hausm. sul Melo e la
Chionaspie con l'Aspidiotus, sull' Evonimo...
A. T. Tozzetti & G. del Guercio.
  (Studi della R. Stazione di Entomologia
Agraria di Firenze. 1891)
  E. T. v. 20a

NT 0039470   PPAN

  Targioni-Tozzetti, Adolfo, 1823-1902.
    Esperienze tentate per distruggere la
Tignuola del Pruro e dell'Evonimo... A. T.
Tozzetti & G. del Guercio. 1891.
  Ent. T. v. 20a.

NT 0039471   PPAN

  Targioni-Tozzetti, Adolfo, 1823-1902.
    Estratto di un catalogo sistematico e
critico dei molluschi cefalopodi del Mediterraneo,
posseduti da R. Mus. di Firenze con alcune specie
nuovo. 1869.
  C. T. v. 15.

NT 0039472   PPAN

  Targioni-Tozzetti, Adolfo, 1823-1902.
    La fillossera a Valmadrera. 1880.
  E. T. v. 7a.

NT 0039473   PPAN

  Targioni-Tozzetti, Adolfo, 1823-1902.
    Korallen von der Insel S. Iago. Eine neue art
korallen.
  (Intern. Fisch. Ausst. in Berl. Italien. Abth.
auszug aus dem Ital.)
  Ichth. T. v.

NT 0039474   PPAN

  Targioni Tozzetti, Adolfo, 1823-1902.
    La letta contra la fillossera in Isvizzora.
1880.
  E. T. v. 7a.

NT 0039475   PPAN

Targioni Tozzetti, Adolfo, 1823-1902.
    Myxolecanium Ribarae Beccari (Lecanitl)
1877.
    E. T. v. 7a.

NT 0039476   PPAN

Targioni Tozzetti, Adolfo, 1823-1902.
    Nota anatomiche intorno agli insetti.
1872.
    E. T. v. 7a

NT 0039477   PPAN

Targioni Tozzetti, Adolfo, 1823-1902.
    Nota sopra alcuni parasiti del Gelso
e dell'Olivo.   1863.
    E. T. v. 7a

NT 0039478   PPAN

Targioni-Tozzetti, Adolfo, 1823-1902.
    ... Notizie e indicazioni sulla malattia del pidocchio della
vite o della fillossera (*Phylloxera vastatrix*) da servire ad uso
degli agricoltori, per il prof. Adolfo Targioni Tozzetti. Roma,
Stab. tip. alle Terme diocleziane, 1875.
    24 p. illus. 21¼ᶜᵐ. ₍With his Della malattia del pidocchio (*Phyllox-
era vastatrix* Planch) ... Roma, 1875₎
    At head of title: Annali del Ministero di agricoltura, industria e
commercio.

    1. Phylloxera.   I. Italy. Ministero di agricoltura, industria e com-
mercio. Annali.

                                        31-18810
    Library of Congress   SB608.G7T3

NT 0039479   DLC

Targioni Tozzetti, Adolfo.
    ... Notizie e indicazioni sulla malattia del pidocchio della
vite o della fillossera (*Phylloxera vastatrix*) da servire ad
uso degli agricoltori, per il professore A. Targioni-Tozzetti ... Roma, Tipografia eredi Botta, 1879.
    39 p. col. pl. 23ᶜᵐ. ₍Italy₎ Ministero di agricoltura, industria e com-
mercio. Direzione dell' agricoltura. Annali di agricoltura 1879. num. 11)

    1. Phylloxera.

    Library, U. S. Dept. of   Agriculture 16An7 Agr 9-1713
                                                            no. 11

NT 0039480   DNAL DLC

Targioni Tozzetti, Adolfo, 1823-1902.
    Notizie sommarie de due specie di cecidomidei,
una consociata ad un phytoplus ad altri acari e ad
una thrips in alcune galle del nocciolo (corylus
avelana L.) una gregaria sotto la scorza dei rama
di olivo, nello stato larvale.   1886.
    13 p.   plates.   23 cm.
    Caption title.

NT 0039481   RPB

Targioni, Tozzetti, Adolfo, 1823-1902.
    Notizie sulla fillossera delle Viti.   1881.
    E. T. v. 7a.

NT 0039482   PPAN

Targioni-Tozzetti, Adolfo, 1823-1902.
    La nuova cocciniglia dei gelsi... by ad
Targioni Tozzetti and F. Franceschini.   1890.
    12 p.   plates.   23 cm.
    Caption title.

NT 0039483   RPB

Targioni-Tozzetti, Adolfo, 1823-1902.
    Nuove emulsioni insetticidi... A. T. Tozzetti &
G. del Guercio.
    (Giorn. Le Stazion. Sperim. Agrar. Ital.
XX, 5)
    Ent. t. v. 19a.

NT 0039484   PPAN

Targioni-Tozzetti, Adolfo, 1823-1902.
    Nuovo metode par tirare la seta. Memoria letta
all' I. e. R. Accademia dei Georgofili.   Firenze,
dai Torchi della Galileaian, 1848.
    13 p.   fold. chart.   22 cm.
    Provenance: Bp. Whittingham, Maryland
Diocesan Library.

NT 0039485   NNG

Targioni Tozzetti, Adolfo, 1823-1902.
    Orthopterorum Italiae species novae in
collectione R. Musei Florentine digestae.
1881.
    E. T. v. 7a.

NT 0039486   PPAN

Targioni Tozzetti, Adolfo.
    ... Ortotteri agrari cioè dei diversi insetti dell' **ordine**
degli ortotteri nocivi o vantaggiosi all' agricoltura o al-
l'economia domestica e principalmente delle **cavallette,**
per Ad. Targioni Tozzetti. Firenze-Roma, Tipografia **dei**
fratelli Bencini, 1882.
    vii, 238 p. illus. 23ᶜᵐ. ₍Italy₎ Ministero di agricoltura, industria e
commercio. Direzione dell' agricoltura. Annali di agricoltura 1882. mo.
55₎
    "Saggio bibliografico di scrittori di opere relative agli ortotteri e special-
mente alle cavallette": p. 216-222.

    1. Orthoptera. 2. Locust.

                                        Agr 3-818* Cancel
    ⌐ Library, U. S. Dept. of   Agriculture 423T17O

NT 0039487   DNAL CU DLC

Targioni Tozzetti, Adolfo, 1823-1902.
    Osservazioni di entomologia agraria.   1877.
    E. T. v. 7a

NT 0039488   PPAN

Targioni Tozzetti, Adolfo, 1823-1902, compiler.
    ...La pesca in Italia. Documenti raccolti per cura del Mini-
stero di Agricoltura, Industria e Commercio del regno d'Italia
ordinati da Ad. Targioni Tozzetti... Genova: R. Istituto Sordo-
Muti, 1871-74. 2 v. in 5. tables (part fold.). 8°.

    At head of title: Annali del Ministero di Agricoltura, Industria e Commercio.

    1. Fish, Italy. 2. Italy. Agri-   coltura, Industria e Commercio,
    Ministero di.   June 21, 1921.
    N. Y. P. L.

NT 0039489   NN IU

Targioni-Tozzetti, Adolfo, 1823-1902.
Florence. R. Stazione di entomologia agraria.
    ... Relazione intorno ai lavori della Stazione di entomo-
logia agraria di Firenze ... per gli anni 1876-83/85 per
Ad. Targioni Tozzetti ... Firenze, Roma, Tipografia
Bencini, 1878-88.

NT ———

Targioni Tozzetti, Adolfo.
    ——— Relazione sopra la seta moogha delle Indie, e sopra
    un opuscolo intorno alla rincelimasione del gelso. ₍Firenze.
    1867.₎ 8°. pp. 24.
    "*Estratto dagli Atti dei georgofili,*" 1866, nuov. ser., xiii.

NT 0039491   MH-A

Targioni-Tozzetti, Adolfo, 1832-1902.
    Relazioni d'alcune viaggi fatti in diversi parti
della Toscana per osservare le produzioni
naturali e gli antichi monumenti di Essa dal
Dottor G. T. Tozzetti. 2nd ed. Firenze,
1768-70.
    12 v.

NT 0039492   PPAN

Targioni Tozzetti, Adolfo, 1823-
    Relazioni sulla pesca a S. E. il ministro di agricoltura,
industria e commercio di Adolfo Targioni Tozzetti, professore di zoologia e anatomia comparata al R. Istituto
di studi superiori in Firenze. Genova, Tip. del R. Istituto
sordo-muti, 1872.
    72 p. 23ᶜᵐ.
    "Elenco dei pesci riportati dai viaggi di Taranto, di Sicilia, di Sardegna":
p. 23-27.

    1. Fisheries—Italy. I. Italy. Ministero di agricoltura, industria e
commercio. II. Title.

                                        15-12614
    Library of Congress   SH277.T3

NT 0039493   DLC PPAN

Targioni Tozzetti, Adolfo, 1823-1902.
    Relazioni sulla sezioni pesca salati e in
conserva quale era rappresentata all' esposizioni
Universale di Vienna nelgiugno 1873.
    Ichth. T. v. 3a.

NT 0039494   PPAN

Targioni Tozzetti, Adolfo, 1823-1902.
    Riassente ed emendamento del prospetti dei
generi e delle speci degli Ortotterie secondo la
fauna Italiana.   1878.
    E. T. v. 7a

NT 0039495   PPAN

Targioni Tozzetti, Adolfo.
    ——— Le scienze naturali e le loro più recenti questioni.
    ₍Firenze. 1866.₎ 8°. pp. 28.
    "*Estratto dalla Nuova antologia,* 31 luglio, 1866."

NT 0039496   MH-A

Targiono-Tozzetti, Adolfo.
    Sostanze alimentari all' Esposizione di Londra nel 1862.
Firenze: Stamperia reale, 1867. 156 p. 12°.

    1. Food.—Exhibitions, Gt. Br.: Eng.:   London, 1862. 2. Exhibitions, Lon-
don, 1862.   don, 1862.
    N. Y. P. L.   November 18, 1913.

NT 0039497   NN PPAN CU IU

Targioni-Tozzetti, Adolfo, 1823–1902.
Sulla malattia delle uve; rapporto generale della commissione della R. Accademia dei georgofili, compilato dal dott. Adolfo Targioni-Tozzetti ... Firenze, Coi tipi di M. Cellini e c., 1856.

viii, 320 p. fold. pl. 20½ᶜᵐ.

"Indice bibliográfico": p. ₍299₎–313.

1. Grapes—Diseases ₍and pests₎

Agr 33–209

Library, U. S. Dept. of   Agriculture 464.05T17

NT   0039498   DNAL CU CU-A

MANN
QK
625
O 3
T18

Targioni-Tozzetti, Adolfo, 1823–1902.
Sulle relazioni degli Oidium e delle Erysiphe colla nuova forma vegetabile osservata dal Cav. Amici (i) **e sulle relazioni di questi esseri collo stato delle piante autosite.**
₍Florence?₎, Tip. Galileaiana, 1853?₎
20 p. 23 cm.

Caption title.
"Estr. dagli Atti dei Georgofili, ₍2. ser. ₎ vol. XXXI."
"Letta alla R.   Accademia dei Georgofili nel- l'Adunanza   del di 13 febbrajo 1853."

1. Oidium. 2. Erysiphaceae. ₍I. Title₎ ₍II. Series: I Georgofili, ser. 2, v. 31₎

NT   0039500   NIC

Targioni Tozzetti, Adolfo, 1823–1902.
Sunto della conferenza sulla Fillosera.   1874. E. T. v. 7a.

NT   0039501   PPAN

Targioni Tozzetti, Adolfo, 1823–1902.
Gli Uccelli, gli insetti parasiti e le trattative per gli accordi internazionali intorno alle leggi di Caccia.
G. N. H. T. v. 4a.

NT   0039502   PPAN

Targioni-Tozzetti, Adolfo, 1823–1902.
Zoologia del viaggio intorno al globo della R. pirocorvetta Magenta ... 1865–68. Crostacei brachiuri e anomouri, per Adolfo Targioni Tozzetti. ₍Firenze, Successori Le Monnier, 1877₎

xxix, 257 p. 13 pl. 27½ᶜᵐ. (*Added t.-p.:* Pubblicazioni R. Istituto di studi superiori pratici e di perfezionamento in Firenze. Sezione di scienze fisiche e naturali. ₍no. 1₎)

1. Crustacea.
Q54.F6   vol. 1   I–271
——— Copy 2.   QL441.T18

NT   0039503   DLC PPAN PSt CU OU OCU

Targioni-Tozzetti, Antonio, ₍1785₎–1856.
——— Acqua minerale magnesiaca purgativa delle piagge di Bibbona, esaminata chimicamente. 11 pp. 8°. *Firenze, M. Cecchi,* 1852.

NT   0039504   DNLM

Targioni Tozzetti, Antonio, 1785–1856.
Acqua salsojodica di Castrocaro. [Forlì, 1846, vel subseq.]
1 l.   8°.   [P. v. 1430]

NT   0039505   DNLM

615.79
T17a

Targioni Tozzetti, Antonio, 1785-1856.
Acque minerali e termali dei rr. stabilimenti balneari di Montecatini in Valdinievole, illustrate con nuova analisi chimica dai professori Antonio Targioni-Tozzetti, cav. Gioacchino Taddei, e Raffaele Piria.   Firenze, Tipografia di M. Cecchi, 1853.
86p. fold.tables.
Bibliographical foot-notes.
1. Mineral waters--Montecatini, Italy (Lucca)
I. Taddei, Gioacchino, 1792-1860, joint author.
II. Piria, Raffaele, 1813-1865, joint author.

NT   0039506   IU DNLM NjP

RA
872
A7
T3

Targioni-Tozzetti, Antonio, d. 1856
Le acque minerali e termali di Armajolo nella provincia senese e loro chimica analisi. Siena, Tip. dell'Ancora, 1843.
40p. 22cm.
Bibliographical footnotes.

1. Mineral waters – Armajolo, Italy I. Title

NT   0039507   WU

543.3
T17a

Targioni Tozzetti, Antonio, 1785-1856.
Analisi chimica delle acque minerali di Chianciano eseguita nel 1832   Firenze, G. Galletti, 1833.
222p. pl.

Bibliographical foot-notes.

1. Water--Analysis.   2. Mineral waters--Chianciano.

NT   0039508   IU DNLM

Targioni-Tozzetti ₍Antonio₎
——— Analisi chimica delle acque minerali e termali dei Bagni d'Aqui, altrimente detti di Casciana nelle colline Pisane. 19 pp. 8°. *Firenze,* 1849.

NT   0039509   DNLM

Targioni-Tozzetti, Antonio. Cenni storici sulla introduzione di varie piante nell' agricoltura ed orticoltura toscana. Firenze. 1853. 8°. pp. viii, 324+.
"Errori," at end.

NT   0039510   MH-A

Targioni-Tozzetti, Antonio, d. 1856.
... Cenni storici sulla introduzione di varie piante nell' agricoltura ed orticoltura toscana. Nuova ristampa arricchita di note lasciate manoscritte dall' autore e fatta dalla R. Società toscana di orticultura, per cura del dott. Eugenio Baroni. Firenze, Tipografia M. Ricci, 1896.

viii, 270 p. 26½ᶜᵐ.

1. Gardening—Italy.   I. R. Società Toscana di orticultura. II. Baroni, Eugenico, ed.   III. Title.

Library of Congress   SB87.1 8T3

2—2652

NT   0039511   DLC MBH ICU

Targioni Tozzetti, Antonio. [–1856]
——— Compendio delle osservazioni ed analisi chimiche sull' acqua salsojodica di Castrocaro e suo uso in medicina prodigiosa, specialmente nelle malattie scrofolose e glandulari. 8 pp. 8°. *Forlì, tipog. Casali.* 1845.

NT   0039512   DNLM

QV
766
q7185c
1847

Targioni Tozzetti, Antonio, 1785–1856
Corso di botanica medico-farmaceutica e di materia medica.   2. ed. accresciuta e rifusa. Firenze, Batelli, 1847.
785 p.

First ed. issued under title: Sommario di botanica medico-farmaceutica e di materia medica.

NT   0039513   DNLM NIC MH-A

Targioni Tezzetti, Antonio, 1785–1856.
Dei bagni di Montalceto.   Firenze, 1835.

NT   0039514   NjP

RA
872
C5
T3

Targioni-Tozzetti, Antonio, d. 1856
Delle acque minerali acidule di Cinciano e loro analisi chimica, eseguita nel 1845. Firenze, Tip. di M. Cecchi, 1845.
38p. 23cm.
Bibliographical footnotes.

1. Mineral waters – Chianciano, Italy I. Title

NT   0039515   WU DNLM

WBI
T185g
1854

TARGIONI TOZZETTI, Antonio, 1785-1856
La grotta di Monsummano; osservazioni chimiche del prof. A. Targioni-Tozzetti e cenni storici sull'uso dei suoi bagni a vapore del dott. Tersizio Vivarelli.   Firenze, Tip Galileiana, 1854.
92 p.
I. Vivarelli, Tersizio

NT   0039516   DNLM

Targioni-Tozzetti, Antonio, –1856.
——— Indagini sulla composizione chimica dell' acqua minerale Arcangioli, fatte nel 1850. 15 pp. 8°. *Firenze, M. Cecchi,* 1850.

NT   0039517   DNLM

Targioni-Tozzetti, Antonio, –1856.
——— Osservazioni sopra due diverse qualità di terreno vecchio e nuovo e sulla respettiva fertilità loro. 15 pp. 8°. *Firenze* 1846.

NT   0039518   DNLM

Targioni-Tozzetti, Antonio.
——— Raccolta di fiori, frutti ed agrumi più ricercati per l'odornamento dei giardini, disegnati al naturale da vari artisti, illustrati e descritti. Firenze. 1825 ₍'22-29₎. f°. 45 colored plates.

NT   0039519   MH-A MBH

HC307
.T92T2

Targioni-Tozzetti, Antonio, 1785-1856.
Rapporto delle adunanze tenute dalla terza classe dell'I. e R. Accademia delle belle arti e dei perfezionamenti delle manifatture in Toscana. Firenze, G. Galletti, 1838.
viii, 106 p.

1. Italy--Indus. 2. Tuscany--Indus.
I. Florence. Accademia di belle arti. Terza classe, arti e mestieri.

NT   0039520   ICU NN

QV
T185s
1830

TARGIONI TOZZETTI, Antonio, 1785-1856
Sommario di botanica medico-farmaceutica e di materia medica per uso
degli studenti di farmacia.   Firenze,
Galletti, 1828-30.
2 v. in 1.

NT 0039521   DNLM

615.79   Targioni Tozzetti, Antonio, 1785-1856.
T17s   Storia ed analisi chimica delle acque minerali
1839   delle terme leopoldine dette di S. Agnese nella
           terra di S. Maria in Bagno   2.ed., con osserva-
           zioni sulle proprietà medicinali di dette acque
           del dott. Cammillo Zannetti   Firenze, Tipo-
           grafia della Speranza, 1839.
           143p.
           Bibliographical foot-notes.

           1. Mineral waters--Bagno di Romagna. 2. Water
           --Analysis. I. Zannetti, Cammillo.

NT 0039522   IU DNLM NjP

Targioni-Tozzetti, Giovanni, 1712-1783.
Alimurgia, o sia Modo di render meno gravi le carestie
proposto per sollievo de' poveri ... dal dottor Giovanni
Targioni Tozzetti. Tomo primo. Firenze, Per il Moücke,
a spese di G. Bouchard, 1767.
viii, 376 p. pl. 30ᶜᵐ.
Engr. title vignette (coat of arms)
No more published.
"Osservazioni meteorologiche fiorentine notate dal Signor dottor Luca
Martini": p. 131-170.
1. Agriculture—Tuscany. 2. Crops and climate. 3. Meteorology—Italy—
Florence. 4. Agriculture—Early works to 1800. I. Martini, Luca.

                                                  18-11653
Library of Congress   S515.T3

NT 0039523   DLC MH-BA

Q111
.A23

Targioni-Tozzetti, Giovanni, 1712-1783, ed.

Accademia del cimento.
Atti e memorie inedite e notizie aneddote dei progressi
delle scienze in Toscana, contenenti, secondo l'ordine delle
materie e dei tempi, memorie, esperienze, osservazioni, sco-
perte e la rinnovazione della fisica celeste e terrestre, comin-
ciando da Galileo Galilei, fino a Francesco Redi ed a Vincenzo Viviani inclusive. Pubblicate dal dottore Gio.
Targioni Tozzetti. Firenze, G. Tofani stampatore, L.
Carlieri librajo, 1780.

TARGIONI-TOZZETTI, Giovanni, 1712-1783.
Joannis Targioni Tozetti catalogus vegetabili-
um narinorum susei sui. Florentiae, typis
Attilii de Tofanis, 1826.

NT 0039525   MH

FILM
6971
QK

Targioni-Tozzetti, Giovanni, 1712-1783.
Catalogus vegetabilium marinorum musei sui;
opus postumus ad secundum partem novorum ge-
nerum plantarum ...   Petri Antonii Micheli
inserviens, cum notis Octaviani Targioni-
Tozzetti. Florentiae, A. de Tofani, 1826.
91 p. plates. On film (Negative)

Microfilm. Original in British Museum.

1. Marine flora - Italy. I. Micheli,
Pierantonio, 1679-1737. II. Targioni-Toz-
zetti, Ottaviano,   1755-1829, ed.
III. Title.

NT 0039526   CU MH

Targioni-Tozzetti, Giovanni, 1712-1783.

Micheli, Piero Antonio, 1679-1737.
Cl. Petri Antonii Michelii. Catalogvs plantarvm horti
caesarei florentini opvs postvmvm, ivssv societatis bota-
nicae editvm, continvatvm, et ipsivs horti historia loev-
pletatvm ab Io. Targionio Tozzettio ... Florentiae, ex
typographia B. Paperinii, 1748.

---

*IC6
M2735
Y745c
(A)

[Targioni-Tozzetti, Giovanni, 1712-1783, ed.]
Clarorvm Belgarvm ad Ant. Magliabechivm
nonnvllosqve alios epistolae ex autographis in
Biblioth. Magliabechiana, quae nunc publica
Florentinorum est, adservatis descriptae ...
Florentiae.MDCCXLV.ex typographia ad insigne
Apollinis in platea Magni Ducis. Superiorum
permissu.
8°. 2v. 17.5cm.
Editor's name at head of dedication.
Volume 1 contains letters by Gijsbert Kuiper,

*IC6
M2735
Y745c
(B)

Nicolaas Heinsius & J. G. Graevius; v.2, by
Jacobus Gronovius, Anthony van Leeuwenhoek,
Pieter Burman, Jacobus Perizonius, Adriaan
Reeland, Willem Goes and others.
Another copy. 19.5cm.
Contemporary half blue and white boards.
Imperfect: slightly wormed throughout.

NT 0039529   MH MnU MU ScU NcU

---

*IC6
M2735
Y746c

[Targioni-Tozzetti, Giovanni, 1712-1783, ed.]
Clarorvm Germanorvm ad Ant. Magliabechivm
nonnvllosqve alios epistolae ex autographis in
Biblioth. Magliabechiana, quae nunc publica
Florentinorum est, adservatis descriptae. Tomvs
primvs.
Florentiae.MDCCXLVI.ex typographia ad insigne
Apollinis in platea S.C.M. Superiorum permissu.
8°. 2p.ℓ.,vii-xlviii,391p. 19cm.
Editor's name at head of dedication.
No more published.

Letters from Johannes Bohn, R. J. Camerarius,
F. B. Carpzov, Christian Daum, H. F. Heckel, H.
C. von Hennin, G. C. Kirchmaier, G. W. Leibniz,
Heinrich Meibom, J. B. Mencke, Otto Mencke, W.
E. Tentzel, & J. C. Wagenseil and others.
Contemporary half blue and white boards.
Imperfect: many leaves wormed.

NT 0039531   MH MnU NNC

---

*IC6
M2735
Y745c2

[Targioni-Tozzetti, Giovanni, 1712-1783, ed.]
Clarorvm Venetorvm ad Ant. Magliabechivm
nonnvllosqve alios epistolae ex autographis in
Biblioth. Magliabechiana, quae nunc publica
Florentinorum est, adservatis descriptae ...
Florentiae.MDCCXLV-XLVI.ex typographia ad
insigne Apollinis in platea Magni Ducis.
Superiorum permissu.
8°. 2v. 19cm.
Editor's name at head of dedication.
Volume 1 contains letters by D. A. Gandolfo,
Giusto Fontanini, Francesco Bianchini, M.

V. Coronelli, Lorenzo Patarolo and others;
v.2, by G. M. Merati, Stefano Cosmi, Carlo
de'Dottori, Niccolò Biffi, A. M. Quirini,
Stefano degli Angeli and others.
Contemporary half blue and white boards.
Imperfect: slightly wormed throughout.

NT 0039533   MH MU NIC MnU MiU ICU PU NjP ScU NNC ICN

460.21
T17

Targioni-Tozzetti, Giovanni, 1712-1783.
Le collezioni di Giorgio Everardo Rumpf
acquistate dal Granduca Cosimo III de'Medici
una volta esistenti nel Museo di fisica e
storia naturale di Firenze, estratto da un
catalogo manoscritto. Firenze, 1903.
213 p.

NT 0039534   DNAL MH-A

Targione-Tozzetti, Giovanni, 1712-1783.
Dei vulcani o monti ignivomi piu noti ...
see under title

Targioni-Tozzetti, Giovanni, 1712-1783.
Disamina d'alcuni progetti fatti nel secolo XVI. per sal-
var Firenze dalle inondazioni dell' Arno ... dal dottor
Giovanni Targioni Tozzetti. Firenze, Stamp. di S. A. R.
per G. Cambiagi, 1767.
vii, 79 p. fold. map. 18½ᶜᵐ.
Engr. head-piece.
Appended: Analisi della memoria idrometrica sopra l'Arno pub. in
Firenze l'anno MDCCLXXVIII. Pescia, G. T. Masi, e compagni, 1778: xl
p. at end.
1. Arno River and Valley. 2. Florence—Floods.

                                                  18-8598
Library of Congress   DG975.A75T3

NT 0039536   DLC NN

Targioni-Tozzetti, Giovanni. [1712-83].
—— Istoria di una vomica polmonare, con la
sezione del cadavere.
In: Rac. di opusc. med.-prat. 8°. Firenze, 1775, ii, 59-96.

NT 0039537   DNLM

TX
351
T1751
1767
Rare

TARGIONI-TOZZETTI, Giovanni, 1712-1783
Istruzione...circa le varie maniere d'accrescere il pane con l'uso da alcune sostanze
vegetabili...coll'esposizione di gran copia di
altre frutta, ed erbe capaci di somministrare
un sostanzioso, salubre, e ancor piacevole ali-
mento. Si aggiungono alcune nuove...regole
per bene scegliere i semi del grano. Ed. 2.
Pisa, Presso Agostino Pizzorno, 1767.
iii, 64 p. 17.5 cm.
In portfolio.
1. Food 2. Food supply I. Title

NT 0039538   CLU-M

Targioni-Tozzetti, Giovanni, 1712-1783.
Lettera di Giovanni Targioni ... all'illustrissimo Sig.
barone Gio: Batista de Bassand ... sopra una numerosis-
sima specie di farfalle vedutasi in Firenze sulla metà di
luglio 1741. Firenze, Nuova stamperia di G. B. Bruscagli
e compagni, 1741.
1 p. l., 32 p. 21½ᶜᵐ.
Title vignette.
1. Butterflies—Italy—Florence.
                                                  25-3920
Library of Congress   QL555.I 8T3

NT 0039539   DLC MH-Z

Targioni-Tozzetti, Giovanni, 1712-1783.
Notizie degli aggrandimenti delle scienze fisiche ac-
caduti in Toscana nel corso di anni LX. del secolo XVII,
raccolte dal dottor Gio. Targioni-Tozzetti ... Firenze,
Si vende da G. Bouchard, 1780.
4 pts. in 3 v. diagrs. on XI fold. pl. 24ᶜᵐ.
Tome 2 is in 2 parts, paged continuously.
Published later under title: Atti e memorie inedite dell' Accademia del cimento ... The latter is a duplicate of this, with new title-pages.
1. Science—Hist.—Italy—Tuscany.

NT 0039540   MiU OkU NNC RPB PPAmP MB

MANN
QK
31
M6
T18

Targioni-Tozzetti, Giovanni, 1712-1783.
Notizie della vita e delle opere di
Pier' Antonio Micheli, botanico
fiorentino di Giovanni Targioni-
Tozzetti. Pubblicate per cura di Adolfo
Targioni-Tozzetti. Firenze, F. Le
Monnier, 1858.
vi, 446 p. port. 19 cm.
"Catalogus operum Petri Antonii
Micheli": p. [337]-360.

1. Micheli, Pierantonio, 1679-1737.
2. Micheli, Pierantonio, 1679-1737--
Bibliography. I. Targioni-Tozzetti,
Adolfo, 1823-1902. II. Title

NT 0039541   NIC MiU CU MH-A OkU NNC NN

Targioni-Tozzetti, Giovanni, 1712–1783.
Notizie sulla storia della scienze fisiche in Toscana, cavate da un manoscritto inedito di Giovanni Targioni-Tozzetti. Firenze, Dalla I. e. R. Biblioteca palatina, 1852.
xxvii, 335 p. 32 x 24cm.
"Discorso intorno a Giovanni Targioni-Tozzetti, al suo ms. intitolato Selva di notizie e alla presente pubblicazione." [By Francesco Palermo]: p. [v]–xxvii.
1. Science—Hist.—Italy. I. Palermo, Francesco, ed.
5–22473†
Library of Congress Q127.I8T2

NT 0039542 DLC CU NIC NjP MB

Targioni-Tozzetti, Giovanni, 1712-1783.
Notizie sulla storia delle scienze fisiche in Toscana, cavate da un manoscritto inedito. Firenze, Dalla I. e. R. Biblioteca palatina, 1852.
Microfilm copy, made in 1966, of the original in Vatican. Biblioteca vaticana. Positive.
Negative film in Vatican. Biblioteca vaticana.
Collation of the original, as determined from the film: xxvii, 335 p.
"Discorso intorno a Giovanni Targoni-Tozzetti, al suo ms. intitolato Selvo di notizie e alla presente pubblicazione." [By Francesco Palermo]: p. [vi]-xxvii.
1. Science--Hist.--Italy. I. Palermo, Francesco, d. 1874, ed. (Series: [Manuscripta, microfilms of rare and out-of-print books. List 62, no. 19])

NT 0039545 MoSU OU

Targioni-Tozzetti, Giovanni, 1712–1783.
Prima raccolta di osservazioni mediche del dottor Giovanni Targioni Tozzetti ... Firenze, Stamperia imperiale, 1752.
xvi, 176 p. 22cm.
"Informazione intorno al medicamento praticato nel vener. Arcispedale degl' incurabili di Firenze ...": p. [141]–176.
1. Medicine—15th–18th cent.
18–13784
Library of Congress R128.7.T3

NT 0039546 DLC NIC NNNAM PPJ DNLM

Targioni-Tozzetti, Giovanni, 1712–1783.
Prodromo della corografia e della topografia fisica della Toscana, opere del dottor Giovanni Targioni Tozzetti ... Firenze, Stamperia imperiale, 1754.
210 p. 19½cm.
1. Tuscany—Descr. & trav.
18–9332
Library of Congress DG733.T28

NT 0039547 DLC MH

Targioni-Tozzetti, Giovanni, 1712–1783.
Raccolta di teorie, osservazioni, e regole per ben distinguere, e prontamente dissipare le asfissie o morti apparenti dette anche morti repentine, o violente, prodotte da varie cause sì interne, che esterne formata per istruzione del pubblico dal dottor Giovanni Targioni Tozzetti. Firenze, G. Cambiagi, 1773.
411 p. 18½cm.
"Riflessioni sopra l'infelice sorte di quelle persone. che sotto l'apparenza di morte sono state sepolte vive. Mezzi da mettersi in pratica per prevenire un tale accidente ... Del Sig. Janin ... traduzione dal francese dell' abate Luigi Semplici": p. [359]–407.
1. Asphyxia. 2. Death, Apparent. 3. Burial, Premature. I. Janin de Combe-Blanche, Jean, b. 1731. II. Semplici, Luigi, tr.
18–11255
Library of Congress RA1071.T3

NT 0039548 DLC NIC DNLM CtY-M MnU-B

Targioni-Tozzetti, Giovanni, 1712–1783.
Ragionamenti del dottor Giovanni Targioni Tozzetti sull' agricoltura toscana. Lucca, Stamperia di J. Giusti, 1759.
viii, 216 p. 18½cm.
1. Agriculture—Tuscany. 2. Agriculture—Early works to 1800.
18–11641
Library of Congress S469.T8T3

NT 0039549 DLC MH-BA NIC

Targioni-Tozzetti, Giovanni, 1712–1783.
Ragionamento del dottor Giovanni Targioni Tozzetti sopra le cause, e sopra i rimedj dell' insalubrità d'aria della Valdinievole ... Firenze, Stamperia imperiale, 1761.
2 v. 2 fold. maps, fold. diagr. 29½cm.
Paged continuously.
Engr. title vignette.
1. Florence—Sanit. affairs.
18–9343
Library of Congress RA507.F5T3

NT 0039550 DLC WU-M DNLM

TARGIONI TOZZETTI, Giovanni, 1712-1783.
Reisen durch verschiedene gegenden des grossherzogthums Toskana in einem auszuge, von J.C.Tagemann. 2 vols.in 1. Leipzig, Weygand, 1787.
12mo. Map.

NT 0039551 MH-Z

Targioni Tozzetti, Giovanni. [1772-83].
——. Relazione d'un enorme tumore vessicolare del peritoneo.
In: Rac. di opusc. med.-prat. 8°. *Firenze,* 1775, iii, 124-138.

NT 0039552 DNLM

Targioni Tozzetti, Giovanni. [1712-83].
——. Relazione dell' ultima malattia, morte, e sezione del cadavere del Rev. P. F. Gio. Batista Fourcault.
In: Rac. di opusc. med.-prat. 8°. *Firenze,* 1782, vi, 73-91.

NT 0039553 DNLM

Targioni-Tozzetti, Giovanni, 1712–1783.
Relazioni d'alcuni viaggi fatti in diverse parti della Toscana, per osservare le produzioni naturali, e gli antichi monumenti di essa dal dottor Giovanni Targioni Tozzetti ... Firenze, Stamperia imperiale, 1751–54.
6 v. 3 fold. pl., fold. geneal. tab. 18½cm.
"Relazione del viaggio fatto l'anno 1733 ... per diversi luoghi dello Stato senese dal celebre bottanico Pier' Antonio Micheli e dal Signore dottore Gio. Batista Mannaioni ... distesa dal medesimo Micheli, con alcune annotazioni di Giovanni Targioni Tozzetti": v. 6, p. 173–250.
"Relazione di un viaggio fatto da Pier' Antonio Micheli nell' estate dell' anno 1734, per le montagne di Pistoia": p. 250–268.
"Indice generale": v. 6, xii, 135 p. at end.
1. Tuscany—Descr. & trav. I. Micheli, Pierantonio, 1679–1737.
18–9342
Library of Congress DG733.T3

NT 0039554 DLC MH-A NN

Targioni-Tozzetti, Giovanni, 1712–1783.
Relazioni d'alcuni viaggi fatti in diverse parti della Toscana per osservare le produzioni naturali, e gli antichi monumenti di essa, dal dottor Gio. Targioni Tozzetti. Ed. 2., con copiose giunte ... Firenze, Stampería granducale. Per G. Cambiagi, 1768–79.
12 v. fold. plates, fold. maps, fold. plans, fold. tables. 18½cm.
"Relazione del viaggio fatto l'anno 1733 ... per diversi luoghi dello Stato senese dal celebre bottanico Pier' Antonio Micheli e dal Signor dottore Gio. Batista Mannaioni ... Distesa dal medesimo Micheli, con alcune annotazioni di Giovanni Targioni Tozzetti": v. 9, p. 333–456; v. 10, p. 1–118. "Relazione di un viaggio fatto da Pier' Antonio Micheli nell' estate dell' anno 1734. per le montagne di Pistoia": v. 10, p. 159–178.
"Lettera geologica di sua eccellenza il Signor Giovanni Strange": v. 10, p. 119–158.
"Indice generale": v. 12, p. 419–446.
1. Tuscany—Descr. & trav. 2. Natural history—Tuscany. I. Micheli, Pierantonio, 1679–1737.
Library of Congress DG733.T3 1768 21–20821

NT 0039555 DLC NIC MH IaU MH-A CtY PKsL

Targioni-Tozzetti, Giovanni, 1712–1783.
Relazioni d'innesti di vaiuolo fatti in Firenze nell' autunno dell' anno MDCCLVI. distese dal dottor Giovanni Targioni Tozzetti. Firenze, Appresso A. Bonducci, 1757.
2 p. l., 97 p. 17½cm.
1. Smallpox, Inoculation of.
18–13783
Library of Congress RM786.T3

NT 0039556 DLC NIC DNLM

Targioni Tozzetti, Giovanni. [1712-83].
——. Riflessioni sopr' all' osservazione [del dott. M. Gonnelli] di tumore della glandola timo. [Con supplemento.]
In: Rac. di opusc. med.-prat. 8°. *Firenze,* 1775, ii, 106-163.

NT 0039557 DNLM

6304 [Targioni-Tozzetti, Giovanni] 1712-
Sitologia ovvero raccolta di osservazioni, di esperienze e ragionamenti sopra la natura e qualità dei grani e delle farine per il panificio con l'aggiunta di altri trattati utilissimi agli agricoltori ed ai mercanti . . . Livorno, M. Coltellini, 1765.
2 v. in 1. 24 cm.
Dissertazione sopra gli ordinamenti degli antichi Romani relativi al commercio e distribuzioni del grano e del pane, pubblicata in francese nel trattato politico civile da Mr. de Lamare . . . tr. in toscano da G. G. F. M. D. S.: v. 2, p. [110]-140.

NT 0039558 MH-BA

Targioni-Tozzetti, Giovanni, 1712–1783.
True nature, causes and sad effects of the rust, the bunt, the smut, and other maladies of wheat, and of oats in the field. Part v of Alimurgia; or, Means of rendering less serious the dearths. Proposed for the relief of the poor. With a biography and evaluation by Gabriele Goidànich. Translated from the Italian by Leo R. Tehon. [Ithaca, N. Y., American Phytopathological Society, 1952]
xxiv, 139 p. illus., port., facsim. 25 cm. (Phytopathological classics, no. 9)
Bibliographical footnotes.
1. Grain—Diseases and pests. I. Goidànich, Gabriele, 1912– II. Title. (Series)
[SB608.G6T] A 53–7026
Iowa. State Coll. Libr. for Library of Congress [3]

ScCleU GU NNBG IEN DNAL NjR MtBC
NT 0039559 IaAS IU IdU OU CaBVaU OrCS PSt OOxM CU

Targioni-Tozzetti, Giovanni, 1712–1783.
... Vera natura, cause, e tristi effetti della ruggine, della volpe, del carbonchio, e di altre malattie del grano, e delle biade in erba, dall' opera Alimurgia (1767) con presentazione, annotazioni e biografia dell' autore di Gabriele Goidànich. Roma, Reale accademia d'Italia, 1943.
xxiv p., 2 l., 160 p., 2 l. incl. front. (port.) pl., facsim. 25cm. (Reale accademia d'Italia. Studi e documenti, 12)
Part 5 of the author's Alimurgia.
1. Grain—Diseases and pests. I. Goidànich, Gabriele, 1912– ed. II. Title.
45–17199
Library of Congress SB608.G6T3
[2] 632.4

NT 0039560 DLC CU MiU DNAL NN

Targioni-Tozzetti, Giovanni, 1712-1783.
    Voyage minéralogique, philosophique, et his-
914.55 torique, en Toscane.   Paris, Lavilette,
T185   1792.
    2 v. 23ᶜᵐ.
    Account of a journey in the fall of 1742.

    1. Tuscany - Description.   2. Natural his-
tory - Tuscany.

NT 0039561   CSt ICU CU OkU CtY ICN IU

Targioni-Tozzetti, Giovanni, 1863-1934.
    ... Il canto XXII dell' Inferno, letto da Giovanni Targioni-
Tozzetti nella sala di Dante in Orsanmichele. Firenze, G. C.
Sansoni ₁1912₎
    30 p. 24½ᶜᵐ. (Lectvra Dantis)
    Title vignette.
    "Letto ... il dì XVII gennaio MCMVII."

    1. Dante. Divina commedia. Inferno. Canto XXII.
                                           27–643

    Library of Congress   PQ4445.C22T3

NT 0039562   DLC PU CtY CoU ICU

Targioni-Tozzetti, Giovanni, 1863-
    Cavalheirismo rustico; melodrama em 1 acto ...
    see under   Mascagni, Pietro, 1863-1945.

Targioni-Tozzetti, Giovanni, 1863-1934.
M1503
.M389C32 Mascagni, Pietro, 1863-1945.
1891   ₁Cavalleria rusticana. Piano-vocal score. English & Italian₎

    Cavalleria rusticana. Rustic chivalry, melodrama in one
act, by G. Targioni- Tozzetti and G. Menasci, English version by Nathan Haskell Dole; vocal and piano-score by L.
Mugnone. Authorized ed. New York, G. Schirmer, ᶜ1891.

TARGIONI-TOZZETTI, Giovanni, 1863-1934.
    Fantasie liriche. Milano, E. Sonzogno, 1891.

    1.8°.

NT 0039565   MH

TARGIONI-TOZZETTI, Giovanni, 1863-1934.
    In Ciociaria; ricordi di usanze popolari.
Livorno, 1891.

    pp. 62.
    Contents:- A Ceccano.- Le nozze. - La festa
della "Radica." - "Gli reconsulo." - La giostra
della bufala.- Un delitto.

NT 0039566   MH

Targioni-Tozzetti, Giovanni, 1863-1934.
ML50
.M39N4 Mascagni, Pietro, 1863-1945.
1935   ₁Nerone. Libretto. Italian₎

    Nerone; dalla "commedia" di Pietro Cossa. Tre atti
(quattro quadri) di Giovanni Targioni-Tozzetti. Livorno,
Arti grafiche Belforte, 1935.

Targioni-Tozzetti, Giovanni. 1863-. No-
vellina popolare della Ciociaria. 4 pp. (Archic. studio
tradiz. popolari, v. 10, 1891, p. 870.)

NT 0039568   MdBP

Targioni-Tozzetti, Giovanni, 1863-1934.
    Paa Sicilien
    see under Mascagni, Pietro, 1863-1934.
    ₍supplement₎

Targioni-Tozzetti, Giovanni, 1863-1934.
ML50
.M39P4 Mascagni, Pietro, 1863-1945.
1921   ₁Il piccolo Marat. Libretto. Italian₎

    Il piccolo Marat, libretto in 3 atti di Giovacchino Forzano,
per la musica di Pietro Mascagni. Milano, Sonzogno, 1921.

Targioni-Tozzetti, Giovanni, 1863-1934.
    Pinotta; idillio in 2 atti
    see under   Mascagni, Pietro, 1863-1945.

TARGIONI-TOZZETTI, Giovanni, 1863-   ed.
    Le poesie. A cura di G. Targioni Tozzetti.
Firenze, G. C. Sansoni, [1922].

    32°.

NT 0039572   MH

Targioni-Tozzetti, Giovanni, 1863-1934.
    Die Rantzau; Oper in 4 Akten ...
    see under   Mascagni, Pietro, 1863-
1945.

Targioni-Tozzetti, Giovanni, 1863-
    ... I Rantzau; opera in quattro atti ...
    see under   Mascagni, Pietro, 1863-

Targioni-Tozzetti, Giovanni, 1863-1934.
ML50
.M39C32 Mascagni, Pietro, 1863-
1891 b   ₁Cavalleria rusticana. Libretto. English & Italian₎

    Rustic chivalry (Cavalleria rusticana), melodrama in one
act. By Pietro Mascagni. English version by J. C. Macy.
Boston, Oliver Ditson company; New York, C. H. Ditson &
co.; ₁etc., etc.₎ ᶜ1891.

Targioni-Tozzetti, Giovanni, 1863-1934.
    Saggio di novelline, canti ed usanze popolari della Ciociaria.
Palermo, C. Clausen, 1891.
    pp. viii, 108. (Curiosità popolari tradizionali, 10.)
    "Edizione di soli 200 esemplari. N. 181."

    Folklore–Italy–Cio   ciarla|Ballads–Italian–Ciociarla

NT 0039576   MH CtY OCl ICN NjP PU   NN MiU

Targioni-Tozzetti, Giovanni, 1863-1934.
    Silvano, dramma marinaresco in due atti
    see under   Mascagni, Pietro, 1863-1945.

Targioni-Tozzetti, Giovanni, 1863-1974, and G. Menasci.
    Vistilia, scene liriche. ₍In four acts and in verse.₎ Per la
musica di P. Mascagni. Livorno: S. Belforte & C., 1902. 110 p.
2. ed. 12°.

    1. Drama (Italian). 2. Menasci,   Guido, jt. au. 3. Mascagni, Pietro,
composer. 4. Title.
N. Y. P. L.   October 26, 1912.

NT 0039578   NN

Targioni-Tozzetti, Giovanni, 1863-1934.
ML50
.M39Z3 Mascagni, Pietro, 1863-1945.
1896   ₁Zanetto. Libretto. Italian₎

    Zanetto (Le passant, di F. Coppée) Riduzione di G.
Targioni-Tozzetti e G. Menasci. Milano, E. Sonzogno ₁1896₎

Targioni-Tozzetti, Giovanni, 1863-1934.
    ... Zanetto and Cavalleria rusticana. Italian
librettos ...
    see under   Mascagni, Pietro, 1863-1945.

Targioni Tozzetti, Ottaviano, Catalogus plantarum medi-
cinalium in Etruria sponte nascentium, systemates Linneano
distributus. [London. 1829.] 8°.
    Transactions of the Medico-botanical society of London, 1829, ii, 40–60.₎

NT 0039581   MH-A

₁Targioni-Tozzetti, Ottaviano₎ 1755-1829.
    Catalogus seminum collectorum in Horto botanico-
agrario florentino anno MDCCCXVII. ₍Florentiae, 1817?₎
    29 p. 15ᶜᵐ.
    Caption title.
    Signed: Octavianus Targioni Tozzetti.

    1. Florence. Orto botanico fiorentino.
                                     Agr 12–1710

    Library, U. S. Dept. of   Agriculture 61.5T17

NT 0039582   DNAL PPAN

Targioni Tozzetti, Ottaviano, 1755-1829.
    Delle cognizioni botaniche di Dante...   1829.

NT 0039583   NIC

Targioni Tozzetti, Ottaviano, 1755-1829.
    Di alcuni prodotti naturali del territorio di Colle
in Valdelsa, dis Gimignano, e di Volterra.
Lettera al Signor C. G. B.
    (In Opuscoli scientifici. Vol. 4, p. 142-157.
Bologna, 1823)

NT 0039584   MB

Targioni-Tozzetti, Ottaviano, 1755-1829.
Dizionario botanico Italiano, che comprende i nomi volgari Italiani, specialmente Toscani, e vernacoli delle piante, raccolti da diversi autori, e dalla gente di compagna, col corrispondente latino linneano... Firenze, G. Piatti, 1809.
2 v.
1. Botany - Dictionnaires.

NT 0039585   KMK

Targioni-Tozzetti, Ottaviano, 1755-1829.
Dizionario botanico italiano che comprende i nomi volgari italiani specialmente toscani e vernacoli delle piante raccolti da diversi autori e dalla gente di campagna, col corrispondente latino botanico comp. dal dottore Ottaviano Targioni Tozzetti ... 2. ed. ... Firenze, Presso G. Piatti, 1825.
2 v. 21½ᶜᵐ.

1. Botany—Dictionaries. 2. Botany—Italy. [2. Italy—Botany]

Agr 17-1077

U. S. Dept. of agr. Library   452.1T17
for Library of Congress   [u37b1-]

NT 0039586   DNAL PPAN

QK45
.T3
1802   Targioni-Tozzetti, Ottaviano, 1755-1829.
Istituzioni botaniche. 2. ed., con molte aggiunte e figure in rame. Firenze, Nella stamperia Reale, Vendesi da G. Piatti, 1802.
3 v. 12 plates. 22 cm.

Copy 1, v. 1, inscribed: L. A. Mongiardini.
9106 Pritzel.

1. Botany. i.t. a. Mongiardini, L   A.

NT 0039587   NNBG

Targioni-Tozzetti, Ottaviano, 1755-1829.
Istituzioni botaniche del dottore Ottaviano Targioni Tozzetti ... 3. ed. Firenze, G. Piatti, 1813.
3 v. 14 pl., 3 tab. 21½ᶜᵐ.

1. Botany.   4—14943

Library of Congress   QK45.T18

NT 0039588   DLC NNBG MiU ICJ MH-A OkU

Targioni Tozzetti, Ottaviano, 1755-1829.
Lezioni di agricoltura, specialmente toscana ... Firenze, Presso G.Piatti, 1802-4.
6 v. in 3. 16.5 cm.

Bibliographical foot-notes.

NT 0039589   MH-BA

QV
T185L   TARGIONI TOZZETTI, Ottaviano, 1755-1826
1821   Lezioni di materia medica. Firenze,
Piatti, 1821.
360 p.

NT 0039590   DNLM PPG

Targioni Tozzetti, Ottaviano, 1755-1829.
Novella allegorica
see under Jacopone da Todi, 1230-1306.

RARE BK
DEPT   Targioni-Tozzetti, Ottaviano, 1755-
CA 5567   Opuscoli / del Dott. Ottaviano
Targioni-Tozzetti. [Firenze?] :
Targioni-Tozzetti, [1801?].
[21] p., 1 leaf of plates : ill. ; 20 cm.

1. Rocks. I. Title

NT 0039592   WU

Targioni-Tozzetti, Ottaviano, 1755-1829.
Sulle cicerchie, memoria letta nell' adunanza della R. Accademia dei Georgofili di Firenze il di' 3 agosto 1785. Dal Dott. Ottaviano Targioni Tozzetti ... Firenze, Nella stamperia sulla Piazza de Pitti per L. Carlieri, 1793.
72 p. fold. table. 20 cm.
Imperfect: browned.
James Smithson collection.
In Smithson pamphlet case no. 3.

NT 0039593   DSI

Targioni Tozzetti, Ottaviano, 1833-1899.
Antologia della poesia italiana. Livorno, 1883.

NT 0039594   PPD NIC

PQ
4208   Targioni-Tozzetti, Ottaviano, 1833-1899,
T3   comp.
1886   Antologia della poesia italiana, compilata e annotata da Ottaviano Targioni Tozzetti. 2.ed., notevolmente accresciuta. Livorno, Tip.R.Giusti, 1886.
xxix,878p. 20cm.

Includes bibliographical references.

NT 0039595   CLSU

PQ
4208   Targioni Tozzetti, Ottaviano, 1833-1899,
T18   comp.
1893   Antologia della poesia italiana, compilata e annotata da Ottaviano Targioni Tozzetti. 7. ristampa, riv. ed aumentata. Livorno, R. Giusti, 1893.
xxviii, 823 p. 20cm.

1. Italian poetry (Selections: Extracts, etc.)

NT 0039596   NIC

Targioni-Tozzetti, Ottaviano, 1833-1899.
... Antologia della poesia italiana. 1. ristampa della 8. ed., curata da Francesco C. Pellegrini. Livorno, R. Giusti, 1901.
vii, 1079 p. 19 cm.
L. C. copy replaced by microfilm.

Microfilm 11480 PQ

1. Italian poetry (Selections: Extracts, etc.) I. Pellegrini, Francesco Carlo, ed. II. Title.

[PQ4208.T3]   1—26979

NT 0039597   DLC OrU NBuC PU

Targioni-Tozzetti, Ottaviano, 1833-1899.
Antologia della poesia italiana; nona edizione, curata da Francesco C. Pellegrini. Livorno, Giusti, 1904.
xxvii, 1064 p.   D.

NT 0039598   PP

PQ
4208   Targioni-Tozzetti, Ottaviano, 1833-1899.
T18   Antologia della poesia italiana. 11. ed.
1909   curata da F. C. Pellegrini. Livorno, R. Giusti, 1909.
xxvii, 1064 p. 19cm.

Imperfect copy: p. 1057-1064 wanting.

1. Italian poetry (Selections: Extracts, etc.) I. Pellegrini, Francesco Carlo, ed. II. Title.

NT 0039599   NIC MiD MH

PQ4207   Targioni Tozzetti, Ottaviano, 1833?-1899, comp.
.T2   ...Antologia della poesia italiana. 14. ed., riveduta e migliorata per cura di Francesco C. Pellegrini. Livorno, R.Giusti, 1914.
[1], xxvii, 1094 p. 18½ᶜᵐ.
At head of title: Ottaviano Targioni Tozzetti.

NT 0039600   ICU NN

TARGIONI TOZZETTI, Ottaviano, 1833-
Antologia della poesia italiana. 16a ed. Curata da F.C.Pellegrini. Livorno, R.Giusti, 1918.

pp.(2), xxvii, 1094.

NT 0039601   MH

851.08   Targioni-Tozzetti, Ottaviano, 1833-1899.
T174a6   Antologia della poesia italiana. 17.
1920   ed. curata da Francesco C. Pellegrini.
Livorno, R. Giusti, 1920.
1094p. 19cm.

Bibliographical footnotes.

1. Italian poetry (Selections: Extracts, etc.) I. Pellegrini, Francesco Carlo, ed. II. Title.

NT 0039602   KU NcD

PQ4208   TARGIONI-TOZZETTI, OTTAVIANO, 1833-1899
.T18   Antologia della poesia italiana. 20ᵃ ed.
curata da F.C.Pellegrini. Livorno, R.Giusti, [1924]. 27+1094 p.

NT 0039603   InU PPT

Targioni Tozzetti, Ottaviano, 1833-1899.
... Antologia della poesia italiana. [2]. ed., curata da Francesco C. Pellegrini. Livorno, Raffaello Giusti, 1927.
xxvii, 1094 p. 19½ᶜᵐ.

1. Italian poetry - Collections. I. Pellegrini, Francesco Carlo, 1856-1929, ed. II. Title.

NT 0039604   NNC MH MiU OClW

Targioni-Tozzetti, Ottaviano, 1833-1899.
... Antologia della poesia italiana. 23. ed.,
curata da Francesco C. Pellegrini. Livorno,
R. Giusti, 1932.
1 p.l., xxxvii, 1094 p.   19 cm.

NT 0039605   CU

Targioni Tozzetti, Ottaviano, 1833-1899, comp.
Antologia della prosa Italiana. Ed. 3, enl.
Livorno, Giusti, 1887.
2 v.

NT 0039606   PPD

Targioni-Tozzetti, Ottaviano, 1833-1899, *ed.*
Antologia della prosa italiana, comp. e annotata da
Ottaviano Targioni Tozzetti. 6. ristampa. Livorno, R.
Giusti, 1892.
1 p. l., [vi]-xxiv, 773 p.   19ᵐᵐ.

1. Italian prose literature (Selections: Extracts, etc.)   I. Title.

Library of Congress   PQ4248.T3   1-26978

NT 0039607   DLC

TARGIONI TOZZETTI, Ottaviano, 1833-1899, compiler.
Antologia della prosa italiana. 7ª ed. intieramente rifatta. Livorno, tip. de r. Giusti, 1897.

NT 0039608   MH

Targioni-Tozzetti, Ottaviano, 1833-1899, ed.
Antologia della prosa italiana, comp. e annotata
da Ottaviano Targioni Tozzetti. 10ed. riv.
Livorno, R. Giusti, 1908.
xxi, 787 p.   19 cm.

NT 0039609   PSC PPL

Targioni Tozzetti, Ottaviano, 1833-

Antologia della prosa italiana; compilata e annotata da Ottaviano Targioni Tozzetti. Livorno: Raffaello Giusti, 1913.
787 p.   12°.

1. Title. 2. Italian literature.
N. Y. P. L.   November 21, 1917.

NT 0039610   NN MiD

Targioni Tozzetti, Ottaviano, 1833-1899
Antologia della prosa italiana, compilata e
annotata da Ottaviano Targioni Tozzetti. 18.
ed. Livorno, Raffaello Giusti [1924]
xxii, 787 p. 19ᶜᵐ.

1. Italian prose literature.

NT 0039611   NNC CtY

Targioni-Tozzetti, Ottaviano, 1833-
... Antologia della poesia italiana.
24. ed. Curata da Francesco C. Pellegrini.
Livorno. R. Giusti [1938]
2 p. l., [iii]-xxvii, 1094 p.

NT 0039612   OU

Targioni-Tozzetti, Ottaviano, 1833-1899, ed.

Novelletta del mago e del Giudeo, scrittura del secolo
XIV. 2. ed., coll' aggiunta di due brevi prose del secolo
XIII. Ferrara, Tip. di D. Taddei, 1869.

HQ   Targioni-Tozzetti, Ottaviano, 1833-1899.
744   Strenne nuziali del secolo XIV.   Livorno,
T18   F. Vigo, 1873.
         xii, 69 p.   24cm.

1. Marriage. I. Title.

NT 0039614   NIC

[Targioni-Tozzetti, Ottaviano] 1833-1899, ed.
Trattati della virtù delle pietre scrittura del
secola. [4. Livorna, 1871.
24 p.   8°.

NT 0039615   CtY MH

[Targioni-Tozzetti, Ottaviano] 1833-1899
Bml2e   Il XXIX maggio, 1848 ... Firenze, 1859.
1

NT 0039616   CtY MH

Targioni-Tozzetti, Teresa, 1826-1880.
... Confidenze di Massimo d'Azeglio ...
see under Azeglio, Massimo Tapparelli,
marchese d', 1789-1866.

WZ   TARGIRUS, Joachimus, fl. 1697
250   ... Medicina compendiaria, in qua, propositis veterum
T185m   sententiis, nova & verissima artis medicae forma et ratio breviter
1698   & dilucide explicatur. Lugduni in Batavis, Apud Fredericum
          Haringium, 1698.
          [20], 696 p. 17 cm.

NT 0039618   DNLM PPC

DB 919 TARGO, R
.T2   Vyhubit; obraz slovenského utrpení. V
          Telči, Nakl. E. Šolce [1908?]
          63 p.

1. Slovaks in Hungary.

NT 0039619   InU

WF   Targon, Luigi
553   Asma bronchiale e sistema nervoso.
T185a   Padova, Zannoni, 1937.
1937   141 p.

Bibliography: p. [127]-141.

1. Asthma - Etiology and pathogenesis
2. Nervous system, Autonomic

NT 0039620   DNLM

Targonski, A.
... Effet du bombardement moléculaire sur de très petites par-
ticules liquides suspendues dans un gaz, par A. Targonski. ...
Genève: Soc. générale d'imprimerie, 1917.   27 p. incl. tables.
8°. (Geneva. Université. — Laboratoire de physique. Travaux du laboratoire de physique. sér. 5, fasc. 6.)

Repr.: Archives des sciences physiques et naturelles. Tome 43, avril - mai,
1917.

177557A. 1. Physics, Molecular.   2. Adsorption.   3. Ser.
N. Y. P. L.   September 17, 1925

NT 0039621   NN

Targonski, A.
... La question des sous-électrons et le mouvement brownien
dans les gaz, par A. Targonski. ... Genève: Soc. générale d'imprimerie, 1916.   66 p. incl. tables.   8°. (Geneva. Université.
— Laboratoire de physique. Travaux du laboratoire de physique.
sér. 4, fasc. 12.)

Repr.: Archives des sciences physiques et naturelles. Tome XLI, mars, avril et
mai 1916.

177556A. 1. Electrons. 2. Brownien   movements. 3. Ser.
N. Y. P. L.   June 28, 1926

NT 0039622   NN

Targoński, H
Przyczyny wypadków kolejowych w świetle psychofizjo-
logii. Warszawa, Wydawn. Komunikacyjne, 1952.
40 p. 21 cm.
At head of title: Polskie Koleje Państwowe.

1. Accidents—Psychological aspects. 2. Railroads—Accidents.
I. Title.

HV675.T35   65-52457 ‡

NT 0039623   DLC

Targosz, Stanisław.
... Polonia katolicka w Stanach Zjednoczonych w przekroju;
przedmowa: j. e. ksiądz biskup Stefan S. Woźnicki ... Detroit,
Mich., Nakładem autora [Czcionkami Drukarni kooperatywnej
Barc bros.] 1943.
xv, 99 p. tables (1 fold.) 24ᵐᵐ.

1. Poles in the U. S. 2. Catholics in the U. S.   I. Title.
                                             45-1654
Library of Congress °   E184.PTT3

NT 0039624   DLC NN OC1

Targow, Abram Morris, 1907-
... The effect of a growth-promoting extract of the anterior
pituitary on the early growth of the albino rat ... by A. M.
Targow ... [New York, 1934]
1 p. l., p. 699-710 incl. tables. 25¼ᵐᵐ.
Thesis (PH. D.)—University of Chicago, 1933.
"Private edition, distributed by the University of Chicago libraries,
Chicago, Illinois."
"Reprinted from the Journal of experimental medicine, vol. 59, no. 6,
1934."
Bibliography: p. 710.

1. Pituitary extract. 2. Growth. 3. Rats.
                                                    35-1758
Library of Congress   QP187.T3 1933
Univ. of Chicago Libr.
————— Copy 2.   [2]   612.492

NT 0039625   ICU DLC OU OCU

A1
T174o
  Targowiasko, Johannes de
     Oratio ad Innocentium VIII. [Rome, Bartholomaeus Guldinbeck, after 26 May 1486]
    [2]ℓ., verso of final leaf blank. 4⁰.
    21cm. Goff T-18a
     Leaf [1ª]: Iohãnis de Targowiasko electi premisliẽn. Serenissimi Regis Polonie Oratoris ad Innocencium octauum põtificem summũ Oratio.
     Brit. Mus. Cat. (XV cent.) IV, p.72 (IA. 18190)

     Speech delivered on May 26, 1486.
     Capital letter supplied in manuscript on leaf [1ª] Manuscript marginal note in an early hand on same page, also a few words on the page underlined in ink.
     Modern decorated boards.

     1. Incunabula — Specimens. I. Guldinbeck, Bartholomaeus, printer.

NT 0039627   CLU

Targowiasko, Johannes de
Rocznik. [Lat.] 9 pp. (Bielowski, A., *Monumenta Polon. hist.* v. 3, p. 282.)

NT 0039628   MdBP

WL
T185e
1890
  TARGOWLA, Jacques
     Essai sur les fibres nerveuses à myéline intracorticales du cerveau dans la paralysie générale et dans la démence. Paris, Baillière, 1890.
    104 p.

NT 0039629   DNLM

Tck25
931t
  Targowla, René Jacques, 1894-
    ... L'intuition délirante, par R.Targowla ... et J.Dublineau ... Paris,N.Maloine,1931.
    2p.ℓ.,[7]-316p. 19cm. (Bibliothèque de neuro-psychiatrie)
    "Références bibliographiques": p.305-311.

NT 0039630   CtY NcD-MC DNLM CU

Targowla (René-Jacques) [1894-]. *Le syndrome humoral de la paralysie générale, ses modalités, sa valeur sémiologique.* 192 pp. 8°, Paris, 1922. No. 281.

NT 0039631   DNLM CtY

TARGOWSKI, JÓZEF.
  Tradition et révolution dans le rythme de la vie. Varsovie, Edition de l'Institut polonais de collaboration avec l'étranger, 1934. 19 p. 17cm.

1. Tradition. 2. Change. I. Polski instytut współpracy z zagranicą, Warsaw.

NT 0039632   NN

  Targowski, Zdzisław.
    Rada Spółdzielcza, 1921-1936. Warszawa, Spólnota Pracy, 1936.
    viii, 99 p. 25 cm.

    1. Poland. Rada Spółdzielcza.

HD3517.7.A4T3   59–55577

NT 0039633   DLC DS

  Targuebayre, Claire.
    Cordes-en-Albigeois; précédé de textes d'Albert Camus et Pierre de Gorsse. Toulouse, Privat [1954]
    150 p. illus. 19 cm. (Sites de France)

    1. Cordes, France (Tarn)—Descr.

DC801.C79T3   55–17588 ‡

NT 0039634   DLC UU WU CU NN MH IU OCU

Targul'îàn, O. M., ed.
  Akademiîà nauk SSSR. *Komitet po prazdnovaniîù îùbileîà akademika V. R. Vil'îàmsa.*
    Академик Василий Робертович Вильямс; 50 лет научной, педагогической и общественно-политической деятельности. [Юбилейный сборник, 1884–1934, под общей ред. В. П. Бушинского и др. Отв. ред. О. М. Таргульян] Москва, Гос. изд-во колхозной и совхозной лит-ры, 1935.

S494
.V8
  Targul'îàn, O. M., ed.
  Vsesoîùznaîà akademiîà sel'skokhozîàĭstvennykh nauk imeni V. I. Lenina.
    Достижения советской селекции; работы IV сессии 19–26 декабря 1936 г. Ответственный редактор О. М. Таргульян. Москва, 1937.

SB123
.V9916
  Targul'îàn, O. M., ed.
  Vsesoîùznaîà akademiîà sel'skokhozîàĭstvennykh nauk imeni V. I. Lenina.
    Спорные вопросы генетики и селекции; работы IV сессии 19–27 декабря 1936 года. Ответственный редактор О. М. Таргульян. Москва, 1937.

Targum
  see
  Bible. *O. T. Aramaic.*

Targum Jonathan to the Pentateuch
  see
  Bible. *O. T. Pentateuch. Aramaic. Targum Pseudo-Jonathan.*

Targum Jonathan to the Prophets (Nevi'im)
  see
  Bible. *O. T. Prophets (Nevi'im). Aramaic. Targum Jonathan.*

Targum Ketuvim
  see
  Bible. *O. T. Hagiographa. Aramaic.*

Targum Nevi'im
  see
  Bible. *O. T. Prophets (Nevi'im). Aramaic.*

Targum Onḳelos to the Pentateuch
  see
  Bible. *O. T. Pentateuch. Aramaic. Targum Onḳelos.*

Targum Palestinense
  see
  Bible. *O. T. Pentateuch. Aramaic. Targum Pseudo-Jonathan.*
  Bible. *O. T. Pentateuch. Aramaic. Targum Yerushalmi.*

Targum Pseudo-Jonathan
  Bible. *O. T. Pentateuch. Aramaic. Targum Pseudo-Jonathan.*

Targum sheni
  see
  Bible. *O. T. Esther. Aramaic. Targum sheni.*

Targum to Chronicles
  see
  Bible. *O. T. Chronicles. Aramaic.*

Targum to Hosea (Targum Jonathan)
  see   Bible. O.T. Hosea. Aramaic.

Targum to Job
  see   Bible. O.T. Job. Aramaic

Targum to Malachi
  see   Bible. O.T. Malachi. Aramaic.

Targum to Ruth
  see
  Bible. O.T. Ruth. Aramaic.

The Targum to the book of Ruth   (In Studia orientalia. Helsingforsiae, 1928)
  see under   Bible. O.T. Ruth. English. 1928.

Targum to the Hagiographa
  see
  Bible. *O. T. Hagiographa. Aramaic.*

Targum to the Prophets
    see
    Bible. *O. T. Prophets (Nevi'im). Aramaic.*

'The Targum to the Song of songs.' Translated
    from the Aramaic, by Hermann Gollancz...
    London, 1909
            see under   Bible. O. T. Song of
    Solomon. English. 1909. Gollancz.

Targum Yerushalmi I
    see
    Bible. *O. T. Pentateuch. Aramaic. Targum Pseudo-*
    Jonathan.

Targum Yerushalmi to the Pentateuch
    see
    Bible. *O. T. Pentateuch. Aramaic. Targum Yerushalmi.*

Das Targum zu Josua in jemenischer überlieferung
        see under   Bible. O. T. Joshua. Aramaic.
    1899.

Das Targum zu Koheleth nach südarabischen
    Handschriften
        see under   Bible. O. T. Ecclesiastes.
    Aramaic. 1905.

Das Targum zum Propheten Jeremias in jemenischer
    Überlieferung ... Halle, 1902
        see under   Bible. O.T. Jeremiah. I-XII.
    Aramaic. 1902.

The targums of Onkelos and Jonathan Ben
    Uzziel on the Pentateuch; ... from the Chaldee
        see under   Bible. O.T. Pentateuch.
    English. 1862-65. Etheridge.

The Targums on the books of Ruth and Jonah,
    literally translated from the Chaldee
        see under   Bible. O.T. Ruth. English.
    1886. Crane.

TARGUSE, V.
    Ebb and flow, by V.Targuse... (In: Seven one—act plays,
    1934. Wellington, 1934. 21½cm. p. 81—91.)

    Caption-title.

765427A. 1. Drama, New Zealand. I. Title.

NT   0039663   NN

TARGUSE, V.
    Fear, by V. Targuse...   (In: Seven one—act plays [1933]
    Wellington, 1933. 21½cm.   p. 30—42.)

    Caption-title.

765428A. 1. Drama, New Zealand. I. Title.

NT   0039664   NN

TARGUSE, V.
    Rabbits, by V. Targuse...   (In: Seven one—act plays [1933]
    Wellington, 1933. 21½cm.   p. 121—132.)

    Caption-title.

765428A. 1. Drama, New Zealand. I. Title.

NT   0039665   NN

TARGUSE, V.
    The touchstone, by V. Targuse...   (In: Seven one—act plays
    [1933] Wellington, 1933. 21½cm.   p. 13—27.)

    Caption-title.

765428A. 1. Drama, New Zealand. I. Title.

NT   0039666   NN

PL   Tarhan, Abdülhak Hâmit, 1852-1937.
250   Abdülhak Hâmid Tarhan. [Hazırlayan] Kunt
T174A14   Ozan. [Istanbul, Arkadaş Basımevi] 1937.
1937   119 p. illus., ports. (Türk edip ve şairle-
            ri serisi, 4)

    I. Ozan, Kunt.

NT   0039667   CLU

PL   Tarhan, Abdülhak Hâmit, 1952-1937.
250   Abdülhak Hâmid Tarhan ve şiirleri. [Yazan]
T174A17   Ziya Karamuk. Istanbul [Kâğıt ve Basım işleri
1948   Anonim Şirketi Matbaası] 1948.
                79 p.

    I. Karamuk, Ziya.

NT   0039668   CLU

Tarhan, Abdülhak Hâmit, 1852-1937.
    'Abdülhaqq Ḥāmids dramatische Dichtung Ruḥlar ("Gei-
    ster") Deutsche Übersetzung mit beigegebenem türkischen
    Texte von A. Fischer. Leipzig, F. A. Brockhaus, 1941.
        72 p.; 61 p. 24 cm. (Abhandlungen für die Kunde des Morgen-
    landes, xxvi, 4)

        Bibliographical footnotes.

        I. Fischer, August, 1865-1949, ed. and tr. II. Title: Rublar. (Se-
    ries: Deutsche Morgenländische Gesellschaft. Abhandlungen für die
    Kunde des Morgenlandes, xxvi, 4)

    [PJ5.D5 xxvi, 4]   A 51-7661 rev
    New York. Public Libr.
    for Library of Congress   [r59c¾]

NT   0039669   NN IU CLU ICarbS

PL235   Tarhan, Abdülhak Hâmit, 1852-1937.
.A8
Orien   **Atatürk'e** şiirler. [Yazanlar] Abdülhak Hâmit Tarhan [et al.
Turk   1. bası] İstanbul, Nebioğlu Yayınevi [1943]

NT   0039671   CLU MiU

PL   Tarhan, Abdülhak Hâmid, 1851-1937.
250   Hakan. Istanbul, Akşam Matbaası, 1935.
T174h   98 p.

NT   0039671   CLU MiU

PL   Tarhan, Abdülhak Hâmit, 1852-1937.
248   Hâmid'in son yılları ve son şiirleri [müellifi.
.T28   Hıfzı Tevfik Gönensay. İstanbul, Vakıt Matbaası,
H3   1943.
                87 p. 20cm.

    1. Tarhan, Abdülhak Hâmit, 1852-1937.
    I. Gönensay,   Hıfzı Tevfik, 1892-1949.

NT   0039672   NNC

PL248   Tarhan, Abdülhak Hâmit, 1852-1937.
.K4H8
Orien   **Kemal, Namık,** 1840-1888.
Turk   Hususî mektuplarına göre Namık Kemal ve Abdülhak
            Hâmid. [Hazırlıyan] Fevziye Abdullah Tansel. Ankara,
            Güneş Matbaası, 1949.

PL   Tarhan, Abdülhak Hâmit, 1852-1937.
250   İbn-i Musa yahut Zat ül-cemal. [Yazan] Abdül-
T174i   hak Hâmit. Istanbul, Sanayii Nefise Matbaası,
1928   1928.
                415 p.

NT   0039674   CLU

Tarhan, Abdülhak Hâmit, 1852-1937.
    Makber. [Yazan] Abdülhak Hâmid. Makber mühimesi
    Fatma Hanımın bir resmini ve İsmail Hami Danişmend'in
    bir yazısını muhtevidir. [2. tabı. İstanbul] Kanaat Kita-
    bevi [1944]
        143 p. ports. 18 cm.
        Poem.

    I. Title.

    PL248.T28M3 1944   61-56671 ‡

NT   0039675   DLC

Tarhan, Abdülhak Hâmit, 1852-1937.
    Makber. [Yazan] Abdülhak Hâmid. Makber mühimesi
    Fatma Hanımın bir resmini ve İsmail Hami Danişmend'in
    bir yazısını muhtevidir. [İstanbul] Kanaat Kita-
    bevi c1948]
        143 p. ports. 18 cm.
        Poem.

NT   0039676   CU

Tarhan, Abdulhak Hamit, 1852–1937.
...Tarik. (Osvojenje Španjolske.) Drama u šest činova i četiri dodatka. S turskog preveo Salih Bakamović. Mostar: Prve Muslim. nakladne knjižare i štamparije, 1915).   ix, 136 p. facsim., port.   8°.   (Muslimanska biblioteka.)

Added t.-p. in Turkish.
Dvije tri o autoru, by S. Bakamović.

489410A. 1. Turkish literature— lations from Turkish. I. Bakamović, N. Y. P. L.   Drama. 2. Drama, Croatian. Trans- Salih, translator. II. Title.   March 19, 1931

NT   0039677   NN

Tarhan, Abdülhak Hâmit, 1852–1937.
Tezer; yahut, Melik Abdurrahmân-is-Sâlis. ¡Yazan, Abdülhak Hâmid. Müellifin el yazısıyla tâdil ve tashih edilen nüsha esas ittihaz edilerek İsmail Hami Danşimend tarafından nesrolunmuş ve sonuna bir lûgatçe ilâve edilmiştir. ¡İstanbul, Kanaat Kitabevi, 1945.

125 p.   19 cm.   (*His* Abdülhak Hâmid külliyatı, 2)
Ankara kütüphanesi, 53.

I. Title.

PL248.T28T4   59–53261

NT   0039678   DLC

Tarhan, Lucienne Abdülhak Hâmit.
DR592   Lettres à Abdulhak Haamit, 1920–1927.
T25A3   Istanbul, Matbaaçilik ve Neşriyat Türk, 1932.
192 p.   18cm.
At head of title: Lüsiyen Abdulhak Haamit.

I. Tarhan, Abdülhak Hâmit, 1852–1937.
II. Title.

NT   0039679   CSt-H

Tarhan, Servet.
La monnaie turque pendant la deuxième guerre mondiale. Neuchâtel, 1952.

146 p.   diagrs.   24 cm.
Thesis—Neuchâtel.
Bibliography: p. ¡141,–142.

1. Currency question—Turkey.   I. Title.

HG1164.T3   54–25920

NT   0039680   DLC NN OU CtY

Tarhan, Zühdü.
De la responsabilité de l'administration et des fonctionnaires en France et en Turquie (en dehors de la sphère contractuelle). Toulouse, Boinseau, 1941.
208 p.

Thesis, Toulouse.
"Bibliographie": p. ¡204,–206.

NT   0039681   NNC

Tarhe - the Crane
    see under [Meek, Basil], 1829–1922.

Tarheel ...
    see also   Tar heel...

HG1501   Tarheel banker.
T27   v.1-   1922-
      Raleigh, N. C., North Carolina Bankers Association.
       v. illus. 30cm.

1. Banks and   banking - N. C. - Period.
I. North   Carolina Bankers
Association

NT   0039684   NcRS NcU ICJ MdBJ NN OClFRB NcDurC

FC364   The Tarheel boy, v.1-   May, 1940-
W13t
      Rocky Mount, N.C., Eastern Carolina Train-
ing School.
       v. illus. 30cm. bimonthly.
Published monthly, 1940-

NT   0039685   NcU

W 1   **The TARHEEL cassette.**
TA581   ¡Charlotte, N. C., 194
      v. illus.
      Official organ of the North Carolina Society of X-ray Technicians.
      I. North Carolina Society of X-ray Technicians

NT   0039686   DNLM

S560   Tarheel farm economist.
T25   1952-
      Raleigh, North Carolina State University, Agricultural Extension Service.
       v. illus. 28cm.

1. Agriculture - Econ. aspects - N. C.
I. North   Carolina. State University
at Raleigh.   Agricultural Extension
Service

NT   0039687   NcRS DNAL

TX356   Tarheel food shopper.
T25
      Raleigh, North Carolina State University, Agricultural Extension Service.
       v. 28cm.

1. Marketing (Home Economics) - Period.
2. Marketing (Home Economics) - N. C.
I. North   Carolina. State University
at Raleigh.   Agricultural Extension
Service

NT   0039688   NcRS NcU

C383   The Tarheel postmaster, v.1-
T18
      Red Springs ¡etc., North Carolina Chapter,
National Association of Postmasters.
       v. illus., ports. 22cm.
Frequency varies, monthly to bi-monthly.
Library has:

v.14-17, 1959-62;

1. N.C.--Postmasters   I. National Assoc.
of Postmasters.   North Carolina Chapter.
(Serials)

NT   0039689   NcU

C333   The Tarheel realtor, v.1-
T18
      Greensboro, North Carolina Association of Realtors.
       v. illus., ports. monthly.

1. N.C.--Real estate business   I. North Carolina Association   of Realtors   (Serials)

NT   0039690   NcU

Tarheel wheels.
      v.1-
      Raleigh, N. C., North Carolina Motor
Carriers Association, 1944-
       v. illus. 30cm.

Title varies: v.1-10 North Carolina Motor
Carriers Association. ¡Digest.

NT   0039691   NcRS NcD

SB211   Tarheel Yambassador.
Y3T37   v.1-
      Raleigh, N.C., North Carolina Yam
Commission.
       v. illus. 28cm.

1. Yams - N.C.
I. North Carolina Yam Commission

NT   0039692   NcRS

Tari (Achille). Le acque potabili di Cassino; ricerche sperimentali. 25 pp. 8°. *Napoli, F. Giannini & figli,* 1890.

NT   0039693   DNLM

Tari, Antonio, 1809–1884.
... Saggi di estetica e metafisica, a cura di B. Croce. Bari, G. Laterza & figli, 1911.
ix, 336 p., 1 l. front. (port.) 20½ᶜᵐ. (*On cover:* Biblioteca di cultura moderna. ¡n. 42,)

"Antonio Tari—discorso di Giovanni Borio": p. ¡325,–336.
CONTENTS.—Lo stato degli studii estetici e il compito dell' Italia.— Dei sistema delle arti.—Critica accademica e critica storico-filosofica dell' arte.—Sull' essenza della musica secondo Schopenhauer ed i wagneriani.—Avvenire ed avveniristi.—Vincenzo Bellini.—Beethoven e la sua Sinfonia pastorale.—Ente, spirito e reale, confessioni filosofiche.— Lettere quattro a complemento delle confessioni.
1. Esthetics—Addresses, essays, lectures. 2. Art—Philosophy. 3. Mu-sic—Philosophy and esthetics. 4. Metaphysics—Addresses, essays, lec-tures. 5. Bellini, Vincenzo, 1801–1835. 6. Beethoven, Ludwig van, 1770–1827. I. Croce,   Benedetto, 1866–   ed.

Library of Congress   BH194.T3   35–21122

NT   0039694   DLC CtY ICU MH CU

Tari, Georges.
... Des moyens d'assurer l'exécution des jugements rendus centre l'administration et principalement du systeme d'astreinte consacrè par l'article 7 de la loi roumaine sur le con-tentieux administratif du 23 décembre 1925... Paris, Les Editions demat-Montchrestien, 1933.
127 p.   24 cm.
Thèse - Faculté de droit de Paris.
Bibliographical foot-notes.

NT   0039695   CtY-L

Tari, John C
    see
Tarr, John Charles.

Tarí, José
see Tarí Navarro, José.

Tarí Navarro, José.
Miscelánea alicantina. ¡Efemérides, anécdotas y tradiciones¡ Alicante, Vda. de J. Rovira López, 1951.
239 p. 23 cm.
Pref. signed: Juan Martínez Blanquer.

1. Alicante, Spain (Province)—Descr. & trav. 2. Alicante, Spain (Province)—Hist. I. Title.
A 53–3840
Illinois. Univ. Library
for Library of Congress ¡2¡

NT 0039698 IU NN

Taria, Bruno
The forms of poetry. n. p., c1933.
Folded chart.

NT 0039699 OC1

Tarible (Joseph). *Sur les combinaisons du bromure de bore, avec les composés halogénés du phosphore, de l'arsenic et de l'antimoine. 51 pp. 8°. *Paris*, 1899, No. 6. Ecole de pharmacie.

NT 0039700 DNLM

Tarible, Louis.
Les industries graphiques; mémento du chef de fabrication. Préf. de Charles Peignot. ¡5. éd.¡ Paris ¡1952¡
2 v. Illus. 22 cm.
First ed. published in 1925 under title: Mémento du chef de fabrication.

1. Printing, Practical. I. Title.
Z244.T27 1952
58–46488 ‡

NT 0039701 DLC NN

Taric, Abul Kasin Tarif Aben, pseud.
see Luna, Miguel de, fl. 1600.

Taricat, Jacques
Médailles; poèmes. Paris, Debresse [1954]
126 p.

NT 0039703 MH

Taricco (Francesco Antonio). Osservazioni sul colera morbus che imperversò in Piemonte nel 1835, con alcuni suggerimenti per prevenire questa spaventevole malattia e curarla con successo. 28 pp. 8°. *Torino, tipog. Castellazzo & Degaudenzi, 1849.*

NT 0039704 DNLM

Taricco, Michele.

Italy. *Ufficio geologico.*
... Note illustrative della carta geologica d'Italia alla scala 1 : 100.000 ¡dell'¡ ing. dott. Michele Taricco. Fogli 232 e 232 bis isola di S. Pietro e capo Sperone, con sette figure e tre tavole. Roma, Istituto poligrafico dello stato, Libreria, 1934.

Tarich; h.e. series regvm Persiae, ab Ardschir-Babekan usq¡ ad Iazdigerdem à chaliphis expulsum per annos ferè 400, cum procoemio longiori in quo vetusti quidam Asiae magnates, maximè reges Adarbigan, item genealogia Christi Salvatoris, quantum de illâ tenent Saraceni; omnia ex fide manuscripti voluminis authentici apud Musulmanos, quod à Turcis ex archivo Fillekensi reportavit & primus in Germaniam invexit Vitvs Marchtaler...indicibus quoq¡ ornatum authore Wilhelmo Schikardo. 248p. Tubingae, typis T. Werlini, 1628.

NT 0039706 OC1 NN

Tarich, h. e. series regvm Persiae¡ ab Ardschir-Babekan usque ad Iazdigerdem à chaliphis expulsum, per annos ferè 400, cum procoemio longiori in quo vetusti quidam Asiae magnates, maximè reges Adarbigan, item genealogia Christi Salvatoris, quantum de illâ tenent Saraceni; omnia ex fide manuscripti voluminis... quod à Turcis ex Archivo Fillekensi reportavit... Vitvs Marchtaler... authore Wilhelmo Schikardo. [2]-8 numb.l. [9]-248p. Tubingae, S. Michelspacher, 1631.
Preliminary leaf and pp. 241-248 lacking.

NT 0039707 OC1

Law
Tariche Llaguno, Leonardo, ed.
Cuba. *Laws, statutes, etc.*
FOR OTHER EDITIONS
SEE MAIN ENTRY
Ordenanzas de aduanas de la república de Cuba, para el régimen y guía de los empleados de aduanas, con todas las disposiciones y modificaciones introducidas desde su promulgación, en 22 de junio de 1901, hasta el 30 de junio de 1944, intercaladas con circulares y resoluciones de hacienda y otras, más las instrucciones y leyes consular relacionadas con la misma, y el reglamento de la zona franca del puerto de Matanzas, reglas para el despacho de las aeronaves dedicadas al servicio regular de transporte aereo internacional, sus pasajeros y el expreso aereo; reglas para el abastecimiento a los buques
surtos en el puerto de la Habana, con mercancías procedentes de depósito mercantil, etc., por el doctor Leonardo Tariche y Llaguno ... La Habana, Cultural, s. a., 1945.

Tariche Llaguno, Leonardo.
Tratado de práctica de aduanas y aplicación de aranceles, redactado y compilado especialmente para las escuelas profesionales de comercio de Cuba, de acuerdo con el Decreto-ley no. 75 de 15 de marzo de 1934 ... Prólogo del doctor Miguel A. Varona y Guerrero. Por dr. Leonardo Tariche Llaguno ... ¡y¡ dr. Miguel A. Varona Galbis ... Habana, Cultural, s. a., 1938.
xiv, 471 p. 24½ᵐ.
"Bibliografía": p. ¡v¡
1. Tariff—Cuba—Law. 2. Customs administration—Cuba. I. Varona Galbis, Miguel A., joint author.
41–22323
Library of Congress HJ6801.T3
¡2¡ 336.26097291

NT 0039710 DLC

Tariche y Llaguno, Leonardo
see
Tariche Llaguno, Leonardo.

Tarics, Sándor.
Előmetszések és hátrametszések megoldása számológéppel; a Mérnöki Továbbképző Intézet 1944. évi tanfolyamainak anyaga. Budapest, Egyetemi Nyomda, 1947.
40 p. 25 cm. (A Mérnöki Továbbképző Intézet kiadványai, M. 66. sz.)
Bibliographical footnotes.

1. Geodesy—Observations. I. Title.
QB296.A1T37
75–572553

NT 0039712 DLC

PK 2910
.S3 T2
1904
Táriðr. Smásaga eftir J. C. S. Akureyri, Kostnaðarmaður Oddur Björnsson, Prentað hjá Oddi Björnssyni, 1904.

With this are bound Jóhannesson, Þ. Dalurinn minn, Winnipeg, 1905 and Skáld-Helga saga. Sagan af Skáld-Helga. Reykjavík, 189?.

NT 0039713 MdBJ WaS

Taride (A.) publisher
see Taride, Paris, publishers.

Taride, Alice Marie, 1889–
Works by Alice Marie Taride, published under the name Tante Marie, are entered in this catalog under Marie, Tante, pseud.

914.436
T174a
Taride, Paris, publisher
Album photographique; exposition 1900. Paris ¡1900¡
folder (18p. of illus) 22cm.
Cover title.

1. Paris. Descr. Views. 2. Paris. Exposition universelle, 1900.

NT 0039716 OrU IU

Taride, Paris, pub.
Album souvenir. Malmaison, Versailles, Rambouillet, Fontainebleau. Paris, Editions Taride [193–?]
cover-title, 30 pl. on 15 l. 18 cm.
Plates are mainly views of Paris.
1. Paris, France (City)— Descr. - Views.

NT 0039717 CU

D12
T28
Taride, Paris, pub.
Carte d'Europe. ¡ Paris ¡1934?¡
col.map. 90 x 101cm. fold. to 22½ x 17cm.

1. Europe.-Desc.-Maps.

NT 0039718 NBuG

Taride, Paris, publisher
Carte de France et de Belgique. ¡
n.d.

NT 0039719 DN

Taride, *Paris, publisher*
Carte de France, routes & plans de villes. Paris, Cartes Taride, 1948.
col. map 145 x 118 cm. on 2 sheets 80 x 120 cm. (Carte Taride, no. 76–77)
Scale 1 : 1,000,000; 10 klm au centimetre.
Includes 74 insets showing routes through towns.

1. France—Road maps.

G5831.P2 1948.T3 Map 51-154

NT 0039720 DLC

G
6030
1910
T375
HRC-MOK
Noncirc

Taride, Paris, pub.
Carte routière de l'Allemagne du sud, Autriche, Tyrol; grands itinéraires. À l'usage des cyclistes, automobiles, tourists, etc. Paris [1910?]
col. map 66x95cm. fold. to 18x13cm.
"No.35."
Scale 1:900,000 or 1 cm. to 8.7 kilometers.

1. Central Europe - Maps.
2. Germany - Maps. 3. Austria - Maps.
CC+ MOK

NT 0039721 TxU

Map
G
5831
P2
192-
T3

Taride, Paris, publisher
Carte routière pour automobilistes & cyclistes. Paris [n.d., ca. 1920]
col. maps 68 x 89 cm.

Scale 1:250,000.
Contents: 1. Nord de la France et Belgique.-1a. Belgique, section est.-2. Nord-est de la France.- 3. Environs de Paris, section nord-est.-6. Est de la France.

NT 0039722 NIC NBuC DNW PBL MB ICU CLSU NN

Taride, *Paris, pub.*
Le Code de la route actuellement en vigueur. Textes officiels des ministères des travaux publics et de l'intérieur après le décret du 17 janvier 1935 clairement exposés et expliqués ... Paris, Cartes Taride [1935]
vi, [7]–202 p. illus., col. diagrs. 21 x 11½cm.

1. Highway law—France. 2. Automobiles—Laws and regulations—France. I. France. Laws, statutes, etc. II. France. Ministère des travaux publics. III. France. Ministère de l'intérieur. IV. Title.

35-36355

NT 0039723 DLC

Taride, Paris, publisher
Dardanelles — Mer de Marmara — Bosphore. Paris: A. Taride [1915].

Size within outer border: →15¾ × ↑26½ in.
Printed in color.
5 maps on 1 sheet, folded, in cover with headline reading, "Cartes Taride." 12°.
[1] Roumanie, Bulgarie, Turquie, Grèce, etc. Scale 1 = 3 850 000 (61 m. = 1 in.). Size, 11¼ × 11¾ in. Inset map, Smyrne.
[2] Bosphore. Scale, 1 = 200 000 (3⅛ m. = 1 in.). Size, →4 × ↑6¼ in.
[3] Mer Noire. Scale, 1 = 9 300 000 (145 m. = 1 in.).

[4] Dardanelles. Scale, 1 = 250 000 (18½ m. = 1 in.). Size, →7¾ × ↑9⅝ in. Inset map, Iles des Princes.
[5] Mer de Marmara. Scale, 1 = 750 000. Size, →15¼ × ↑9 in.

1. European war, 1914– .—Maps. 2. Dardanelles.—Maps, 1915. 3. Sea of Marmora.—Maps, 1915. 4. Bosporus.—Maps, 1915. 5. Black Sea.—Maps, 1915. 6. Balkan states.—Maps, 1915.
N. Y. P. L. September 23, 1915.

NT 0039725 NN NjP

Taride, Paris, pub.
France, Belgique, bords du Rhin, Suisse, etc. Paris [1914?]

NT 0039726 NjP

Taride, Paris, publisher.
... Grande carte des Etats-Unis d'Amérique. Paris. [n.d.]
1 sheet. 34 1/4 x 40 3/4 in. (Collection des cartes Taride)
Scale: 400 miles to 5 inches.

NT 0039727 MH-BA

Taride, Paris, pub.
Grande carte routière de la Hollande (Pays Bas, Neederland) à l'usage des automobilistes, cyclistes, touristes, etc. Paris, Cartes Taride [192-?]
33 x 28.5 inches.
Scale: 1:4000.000.
1. Roads. Netherlands. Maps.

NT 0039728 OrU

Taride, Paris, publisher
Grande carte routière; est de la France: Lorraine, Alsace, Vosges. [Paris, 190–.] 1 map in pocket. 12°. (Cartes Taride. no. 6.)

Title from cover.

1. France.—Maps.
N. Y. P. L. September 7, 1912.

NT 0039729 NN

Taride, Paris, publisher
Grande carte routière; frontière nord-est: Ardennes belges, Luxembourg, Lorraine. [Paris, 190–.] 1 map in pocket. 12°. (Cartes Taride. no. 2.)

Title from cover.

1. France.—Maps.
N. Y. P. L. September 7, 1912.

NT 0039730 NN

Taride, Paris, pub.
Guide illustré de Paris avec plans et indicateur des rues. Circuits pour la visite de Paris en 3 jours. Execusions à Saint-Cloud, Versailles, la Malmaison, Saint-Germain-en-Laye, Chantilly, Rambouillet, Fontainebleau. (Modèle déposé) Paris, Cartes Taride [193-?]
128 p. illus. (incl. plan) plates, fold. map. 17 cm.
Plates printed on both sides.
Référence no. 309.
1. Paris, France (City) - Descr. - Guide-books.

NT 0039731 CU

Taride, publisher, Paris.
Guide pratique du vétérinaire et du parfait couvier
see under title

Taride, *Paris, pub.*
Guide Taride des environs de Paris pour automobilistes, motocyclistes & cyclistes. Les 60 plus belles promenades du dimanche autour de Paris avec itinéraires détaillés, kilométrés et documentés circuits de 30 à 250 kilomètres — (adaptés pour cyclistes) — avec schémas d'orientation. Modèle déposé. Paris, Cartes Taride [°1925]
2 p. l., 243, [1] p. illus. (maps) 17cm.

1. France—Descr. & trav.—Guide-books. I. Title.
Library of Congress DC708.T3 26-4177

NT 0039733 DLC

Taride, *Paris, publisher.*
Guide Taride des environs de Paris pour automobilistes, motocyclistes & cyclistes. Les 60 plus belles promenaden du dimanche autour de Paris; itinéraires détaillés, kilométrés et documentés; circuits de 30 à 250 kilomètres adaptés pour cyclistes. Avec schémas d'orientation. 10. éd. Paris, Cartes Taride, °1948.
xviii, 252 p. maps. 17 cm.

1. France—Descr. & trav.—Guide-books. I. Title.

DC708.T3 1948 52-26336

NT 0039734 DLC

Taride, Paris, publisher.
Guide-Taride. Les routes de France
see its Les routes de France.

Taride, Paris, pub.
... Guide touristique Taride & plans Taride des villes de France. Traversées et sorties des villes avec routes numérotées; curiosités touristiques & Taride [1929]
viii, 860 [2] p. illus. (incl. plans) maps (2 fold.) 17 cm.
At head of title: Référence no. 504.
Added t.-p. has title: ... Le véritable dictionnaire touristique de la France.
Advertising matter including in paging.

1. France - Descr. & trav. - Guide-books.
2. Cities and towns - France.

NT 0039737 CU

Taride, *Paris, publisher.*
Handy alphabetical guide to Paris, commentated & illustrated with map and street guide. Plans for the visit of Paris in 3 days. Historical excursions to Saint-Cloud, Versailles, La Malmaison, Saint-Germain-en-Laye, Chantilly, Rambouillet, Fontainebleau. Paris [191-?]
x, 90, 89 p. illus., maps (1 fold. col.) 18 cm. (Collection des guides & plans Taride)

1. Paris—Descr.—Guide-books.

DC708.T32 49-39188*

NT 0039738 DLC CU

Taride, Paris, publisher
Indicateur de toutes les rues de Paris. Paris: A. Taride [191-?]. 79 p. map. 12°.

Cover-title: Plan de Paris.

1. Paris.—Maps. 2. Title.
N. Y. P. L. March 21, 1923.

NT 0039739 NN

Taride, Paris, publisher
Indicateur des rues de Paris. Métropolitain — Nord-Sud — Autobus — Tramways... Paris, Cartes Taride [190–] 171 p. map. 13cm. (Collections des guides & plans Taride.)

Cover-title: Plan de Paris.

313587B. 1. Paris—Maps.
N. Y. P. L. February 7, 1946

NT 0039740 NN

Taride, Paris, publisher
Indicateur des rues de Paris...　　Paris, Cartes Taride ₁1923₎
130 p.　map.　13cm.

Cover-title: Plan de Paris.

289173B.　1. Paris—Maps.
N.Y.P.L.　　　　　　　　　　　　　　　　May 16, 1945

NT　0039741　NN MH

Map
G
6711
P2
1920
T3

Taride, Paris, publisher
Italie. Section₁₋₋es, Nord, Centrale,
Sud.　Paris, 1919–1920.
3 col. maps 87 x 68cm. or smaller.

Scale 1:600,000.

1. Italy—Road maps.

NT　0039742　NIC

Taride, Paris, pub.
Manuel Taride de la circulation dans Paris.
Sens unique, plan et règlements, parcs de sta-
tionnement, signalisation...　Paris [1937?]
cover-title, 40 p.　fold. map.　20 cm.
Caption title:　Plan Taride du sens unique,
résumé des règlements sur la circulation à Paris
des voitures et des piétons...
1. Traffic regulations - Paris. I. Title
II. Title: Plan Taride du sens unique.

NT　0039743　CU

Taride, Paris, publishers.
Nouveau guide Taride. Les routes de France.
Nouvelle ed. Revue et considérablement augmentee.
Indispensable aux automobilistes.　Paris, A. Tari-
de [1912]

NT　0039744　MH

4DC
1586

Taride, Paris publisher.
Nouveau guide Taride: les routes de
France. Nouv. éd., rev. et considérablement augm. Indispensable aux automobilistes. Ouvrage contenant 4,800
itinéraires français recommandés. Nomenclature détaillée des localités,
kilométrage, état de la route, sorties
de villes, pourcentage des cotes.　250
grands itinéraires étrangers.　Deux
cartes index: France et étranger.　Paris ₁1921₎
1 v. (various pagings)

NT　0039745　DLC-P4 NN

Taride, Paris, pub.
Nouveau plan de Paris/avec toutes les lignes
du métropolitain.　Paris, 1951.
26 ½ x35 inches.

Scale: 1:14,500.
Inset: Paris, 20 arrondissements, 80
quartiers.

1. Paris.　Maps.　xParis.　Description.
Maps.

NT　0039746　OrU

Map
G
5834
P3
1918
T3

Taride, Paris, publisher
Nouveau plan de Paris avec toutes les
lignes du Métropolitain et du Nord-Sud.
Paris ₁ca. 1918₎
col. map 69 x 90cm.

Scale 1:15,000.

1. Paris—Maps.

NT　0039747　NIC

Map
G
5834
P3
1925
T3

Taride, Paris, publisher
Nouveau plan de Paris avec toutes les
lignes du Métropolitain et du Nord - Sud.
Paris, Cartes Taride ₁1925₎
col. map 46 x 57cm.

Scale 1:21,000.
On verso: Tramways de Paris, Antobus,
Tramways de la Banlieu, Chemins de fer.

1. Paris—　　　Maps.

NT　0039748　NIC

MAP
G
5834
P3
1930
T3

Taride, Paris, pub
Nouveau plan de Paris avec toutes les
lignes du Métropolitain et du Nord-Sud.
Paris ₁ca. 1930₎
col. map 69 x 90 cm.

Scale 1:15,000.

1. Paris—Maps.

NT　0039749　NIC

Taride, Paris, publisher.
Nouveau plan monumental de Paris; nomenclature des édifices, palais, musées, promenades,
théâtres, cirques, concerts, etc. Indication de
chaque emplacement avec renvoi au plan, jours et
heures d'entrée.　Paris, A. Taride [18--?]
cover-title [4] p.　fold. map.　16.5 cm.
Another folded map of Paris, published by
Librairie Chaix, inserted.

NT　0039750　NNC

Taride, Paris. pub.
Nouveau plan Taride. Paris par arrondissement.
Indicateur des rues. - Autobus. - Tramways. -
Métropolitain. - Nord-Sud. - Plans des bois de
Boulogne et de Vincennes. - Plan d'ensemble de
Paris.　Paris,Cartes Taride[1927]
171,[1]p.　double maps(incl.front.)　14½cm.
(Collection des guides & plans Taride)
Folded map mounted on inside front cover.

NT　0039751　CtY NNR MBSi

Taride, Paris, publisher.
Nouveau plan Taride
see also its　Paris par arondissement.

MAP
G
5832
P2
1912
T3

Taride, Paris, publisher
Nouvelle carte cycliste et automobile
des environs de Paris.　Paris, 1912.
4 col. maps 51 x 60 cm.

Scale 1:80,000.

1. Paris—Road maps. 2. France—
Road maps. I. Title.

NT　0039753　NIC

Map
G
5830
1900?
T3

Taride, Paris, publisher
Nouvelle carte de France, Belgique,
Bords du Rhin, Suisse, etc.　Paris,
ca. 1900.
col. map 82 x 92 cm.

Scale 1:1,265,000.

1. France—Maps.

NT　0039754　NIC

Taride, Paris, pub.
... Paris - monumental. St.-Denis - Ecouen -
Chantilly - Compiègne - St-Cloud - Malmaison -
St-Germain en Laye - Fontainebleau - Rambouil-
let - Versailles. Notices en Français - English -
Español - Deutsch - Italiano.　(Modèle déposé)
Paris, "Cartes Taride" [1938]
160 p.　illus. (maps, plans) plates.　17 cm.
At head of title: Le véritable guide international
du visiteur.
Plates printed on both sides.
Reference no. 318
1. Paris, France (City - Descr. - Guide-books.

NT　0039755　CU

Taride, Paris, pub.
Paris par arrondissement. Indicateur des
rues.—Autobus. Tramways.—Metropolitain.
Nord-Sud.—Plans des Bois de Boulogne et de
Vincennes. Plan d'ensemble de Paris.　Paris,
Cartes Taride, 1923.
127 p. illus.

At head of title: Nouveau plan Taride.

1. Paris—Streets. 2. Paris—Maps. I. Title.

NT　0039756　CaOTP

Taride, Paris, publisher.
Paris par arrondissement
see its　Nouveau plan Taride.
also

Taride, Paris, publisher.
Paris, ses monuments guide pratique du visiteur.　Paris, Taride, n.d.

NT　0039758　PU PHi

Taride, Paris,　　publisher.
Paris sous Napoléon 1.: la topographie de
Paris ou plan détaillé de la ville de Paris et
de ses faubourgs publié par Maire en 1808; cette
reimpression est accompagnée d'une nomenclature
générale des rues de Paris sous la révolution,
par Alfred Franklin...　Paris, A.Taride [1908]

16 p.　6 plates.　49.5 x 33 cm.

NT　0039759　MH-FA

914.436
T174

Taride, Paris, publisher.
Paris, Versailles, 1900.　Paris ₁1900₎
folder (18p. of illus.)　22cm.

Cover title.

1. Paris.　Descr.　Views.

NT　0039760　OrU

DC737 Taride, Paris, publishers.
T3   Plan and guide of Paris. ₍Paris, 1903₎
          62, 53 p. illus. 18cm.

1.Paris - Description. I.Title.

NT 0039761   OrCS

Map
G   Taride, *Paris, publisher*
5834   Plan de Paris, nouvelle édition.
P3   Paris, ca. 1920.
ca. 1920   col. map 70 x 91 cm.

Scale 1:15,000.
Shows "Lignes du Métropolitain."

1. Paris--Maps.

NT 0039762   NIC NjP

DC709 Taride, Paris, pub.
T28   Plan de Paris. Paris, Cartes Taride
        ₍1937?₎
          col.map. 96x44cm.fold. to 19x12cm.

1. Paris.-Description.-Maps.

NT 0039763   NBuG

Taride, Paris, pub.
    Plan de Paris contenant l'indicateur de toutes
les rues. Paris [1898]
    50 p. fold. map. 18 cm.

NT 0039764   CtY

Taride, *Paris,*   pub.
    Plan & guide de Paris ... [Paris,
1908?]
    64p. illus., fold.map.

Map in pocket on back cover.
On cover: Paris monumental.

NT 0039765   IU KMK

Taride, *Paris* , publisher
  Plan & guide de Paris; avec Indicateur des rues.
Circuits pour la visite de Paris en 3 jours. Paris,
Cartes Taride [1926?]

    x, 82, 92 p. Illus.

NT 0039766   MH

DC
708   Taride,Paris,pub.
.T19   Plan-guide de Paris; répertoire des rues
1937 métropolitain autobus ... Paris, Cartes
      Taride ₍1937?₎

        160,64 p. illus.

1.Paris--Descr.--Guide-books.

NT 0039767   MiU

Taride, *Paris, publisher.*
    Plan-guide de Paris. │ Répertoire des rues; métropolitain;
renseignements indispensables. Paris, Cartes Taride ₍1949₎
    223 p. 34 fold. col. maps. 14 cm. (Collection des guides & plans
    Taride)

    Cover title: Paris par arrondissement ...

    1. Paris—Maps.   I. Title: Paris par arrondissement.

G1844.P3T3 1949   Map 55–1030

NT 0039768   DLC PPT

G1844 Taride, Paris, publisher
P3T3   Plan-guide de Paris. Répertoire des rues -
1950 métros - autobus; renseignements indispensables.
      Paris, Cartes Taride, ₍1950?₎
         √ 304p. col.maps(part fold.) 14cm. (Col-
      lection des guides & plans Taride)

        Cover title: Paris par arrondissement...

        1. Paris - Maps. I. Title. II. Title:
      Paris par arrondissement.

NT 0039769   IaU

Pam.   Taride, Paris, publisher.
Coll.   Plan-guide de Paris; repertoire des rues,
        métros, autobus, renseignements indispensables
41102   ... Index to streets, metros, bus, indispensa-
        ble addresses ... Paris, Cartes Taride [1955]
           240, a-c p. maps (2 fold. col.) 14 cm.
        (Collection des guides & plans Taride)

        At head of title: Modèle déposé.
        1. Paris. Streets. 2. Paris. Maps. I.
      Title.

NT 0039770   NcD

Taride, *Paris, publisher*
    Reproductions d'anciens plans de Paris.
Paris [1908]
        see under title

Taride, *Paris, publisher*   ed
    (Les) routes de France à l'usage des conducteurs
d'automobiles et cyclistes., 4,000 itinéraires
Français...250 grands itinéraires étrangers...Paris
Taride, (1905)
    v. maps 18 cm

NT 0039772   DNW

Taride, *Paris, publisher*   *4669a.87
    Les routes de France à l'usage des conducteurs d'automobiles et
    cyclistes. Nouvelle édition pour 1907, revue et considérablement
    augmentée.
=   Paris. 1907. Variously paged. Maps. 17½ cm., in 16s.
    · At head of title: Guide-Taride.

M6222 — France. Geog. Guide-books. — Road-books. France. —
Automobile journeys.

NT 0039773   MB

Taride, Paris, publisher.
    Les routes de France
        see also its Nouveau guide Taride. Les
routes de France.

Taride, Paris, pub.
    Sud-est de la France. Vallée du Rhone, Alpes
françaises (Savoie et Dauphiné) Provence, Cote
d'azur, Corse... Paris, Cartes Taride [1935]
    64, 224 p. illus. (incl. plans) maps (1 double)
20 x 11 cm. (Les grands itinéraires Taride des
routes de France... région no. 5)
    On cover: *Guide* Taride (Volume no. 5)
    Référence no. 525.
    Advertising matter included in paging.
    Blank pages for "Notes personnelles."

1. France - Descr. & trav. - Guide-books.
2. Corsica - Descr. & trav. - Guide-books.

NT 0039776   CU

GV1025 Taride, *Paris,*   pub.
.T25   Tableau d'assemblage de la carte routière
        de France, avec les distances kilométriques
        d'après les cartes de l'État-major et du
        Ministère de l'intérieur ... divisée en 25
        sections à l'usage des automobiles, cyclistes,
        voyageurs, touristes, etc. Paris, A. Taride,
        1907.
           map. 38½x37cm. fold. to 14½x10½cm.

NT 0039777   NBuG

Taride, Paris, publisher.
    Le véritable guide international du visiteur
        see its Paris-monumental.

HF2151 Tarief-vereeniging.
.T55   Aan de leden der Tarief-vereeniging.
        ₍2₎ 1.
          Amsterdam? 1910₎

          Caption title.

          Has bound in: Its Lijst van leden der
        Tarief-vereeniging. (Februari 1909)
        ₍Amsterdam? 1909?₎ (Caption title. 4 p.)
        and its Reglement der Tarief-vereeniging.
        ₍Amsterdam? n.d.₎ (Caption title. 2 p.)

NT 0039779   CU

Tarief voor het vervoer van bestelgoederen ...
        see under Maatschappij tot exploitatie
van staatsspoorwegen.

Tariefwet Nieuw-Guinea
    see under Netherlands (Kingdom, 1815-
Departement van Zaken Overzee.

Tariel, Édouard, joint author.

Tariel, Louis.
    Étude sur les surfaces portantes en aéroplanie, par Louis
Tariel ... ₍et₎ Édouard Tariel ... Paris, H. Dunod et
É. Pinat, 1909.

Tariel, Louis.
Étude sur les surfaces portantes en aéroplanie, par Louis Tariel ... [et] Édouard Tariel ... Paris, H. Dunod et É. Pinat, 1909.
vi, 62 p., 1 l. diagrs. 23ᶜᵐ.

1. Aerofoils. I. Tariel, Édouard, joint author.

34–13086

Library of Congress TL574.A4T3 629.1323

NT 0039783 DLC

Tariel (Paul-Julien) [1864–]. *De la hernie inguinale étranglée chez l'enfant. 64 pp. 4°. Paris, 1894, No. 220.

NT 0039784 DNLM

Tariel (Pierre-Jules).
rinée dans l'accouchemen
1854, No. 164, v. 566.

NT 0039785 DNLM

4DS
China
79
Tariel, Victor Esther
La campagne de Chine (1900–1901) et le matériel de 75. Paris, Berger-Levrault, 1902.
109 p.

NT 0039786 DLC-P4 DNW

Tarieven, te rekenen van 1 Augustus 1917 af, tot een nader te bepalen datum geldig voor herstellingen aan schoeisel. (Vastgesteld bij beschikking van den Minister van Oorlog van 24 Augustus 1917, VIe afd. no. 127.) 's-Gravenhage: De Gebroeders van Cleef, 1917. 16 p. 8°.

1. Prices.—Shoe repairing, Netherlands. 2. European war, 1914– .
—Economic aspects, Netherlands. 3. Netherlands (Kingdom, 1815–). Oorlog, Departement van.
N. Y. P. L. November 8, 1920.

NT 0039787 NN

Tarif Aben Taric, Abul Kasim, pseud.
see
Luna, Miguel de, fl. 1600.

Tarif Abentarique, Abulcacim, pseud.
See
Luna, Miguel de, fl. 1600.

تعريف القدماء بابي العلاء، جمعه وحققه لجنة من رجال وزارة المعارف العمومية باشراف طه حسين. القاهرة، مطبعة دار الكتب المصرية، 1944.

14, 695 p. 28 cm. (1 سفر، العلاء المعري إبي آثار)
At head of title: المصرية المعارف وزارة. المصرية المملكة

1. Abū al-'Alā, al-Ma'arrī, 973–1057. I. Egypt. Wizārat al-Tarbiyah wa-al-Ta'līm. *Title transliterated: Ta'rif al-qudamā' bi-Abī al-'Alā'.*

PJ7750.A25Z875 N E 65–1635

NT 0039790 DLC CU NN

Tarif d'encaissement des effets entré en vigueur le 1ᵉʳ Janvier 1886. Florence, J. Pellas,, 1886.
3 p. l. , 1–79 p. 8°.

NT 0039791 NN

2193 Tarif de la reduction des monnoyes de France et de Lorraine. Nancy, P. Antoine [17—?]
1 p.l., [37] p. 13½ cm.

NT 0039792 MH-BA MH

4k
Fr.
810
Tarif de la solde, des accessoires de la solde, des masses et des fournitures en vivres, fourrages et chauffage, faisant suite à l'Ordonnance du 19 mars 1823, concernant la solde, les revues et l'administration intérieure des Corps de troupe de l'armée de terre. [ ]
1 v (unpaged)

NT 0039793 DLC-P4

Tarif décimal, ou, Réduction de la livre tournois de France, en francs, en argent de Brabant et en argent de change; suivie des réductions de l'argent courant de Brabant, en monnaie républicaine et livres tournois de France, et en argent de change de Brabant. ... , etc., etc. Nouvelle édition, très-exacte, considérablement augmentée, et avec empreintes. Bruxelles, A. Stapleaux, [179–?]
[2], 72 p. illus. 17½ᶜᵐ.

NT 0039794 ICJ

Tarif des accises pour la ville de Berlin, les villes de la marche electorale
see under Prussia. Laws, statutes, etc.

Tarif des bois propres au service de la Maime royale
see under [Sane, Jacques Noël, baron]
1740–1831.

Tarif des denrées et marchandises de première nécessité avec le décret de la Convention nationale, du 29 septembre. Paris, Lepetit [1794]
23 p. 22cm.

1. Price regulation—France. 2. Prices—France.

NT 0039797 NIC

... Tarif des droits d'entrée; suivi de la réglementation concernant les droit de statistique, taxe de transmission, taxe de luxe, droits d'accise et taxe de consommation, licences, publiés d'après les documents officiels.
Bruxelles, Editorial-office [19
v. 21½ cm. annual.
Publication began in 1928?
At head of title, 19 : Royaume de Belgique.

1. Tariff—Belgium. 2. Taxation—Belgium.

HJ6240.T3 336.265 48–39046

NT 0039798 DLC OU

Tarif des droits d'entrée et de sortie des cinq grosses fermes ordonnés etre percus par l'edit de 1664
see under France. Laws, statutes, etc.

French
Rev.
DC
141
F87+
v.465
Tarif des droits d'entrée ou de sortie dans le royaume des Pays-Bas. Bruxelles, Weissenbruch, 1819.
44 leaves. 22cm.

Bound with: Loi du 12 mai 1819. Bruxelles, 1819.

1. Tariff—Netherlands.

NT 0039800 NIC

Tarif des droits de quatrième sur les vins & boissons qui se vendent en détail dans les villes, bourgs & paroisses de la province de Normandie. Revü corrigé & considérablement augmenté. Avec l'instruction sur la jauge par M. Leger, pour la facilité des personnes qui veulent apprendre à jauger. On y a joint aussi le tarif des droits sur les papiers & parchemins timbrés. A Rouen, Chez J. J. Le Boullenger, 1755.
293, [4] p. (chiefly tables) 17cm.

NT 0039801 NNC

French
Rev.
DC
141
F87+
v.465
Tarif des droits des douanes sur les marchandises importées de France en Piémont et sur celles exportées du Piémont pour la France. [Turin, Impr. phylantropique, an X, i.e. 1802]
95 p. 20cm.

Title and text also in Italian.

1. Tariff—France. 2. Tariff—Piémont.

NT 0039802 NIC

Kress
Room
Tarif des droits du sceau tant de 1672, 1674, 1691, que de l'augmentation de 1704 ... 1704?
52 l. (102 p.) 17.5 cm.

Manuscript.

1. Taxation - France. I. France - Laws, statutes, etc., 1643-1715 (Louis XIV)

NT 0039803 MH-BA

Tarif des droits qve l'entrepreneur du magazin de grand pain bourgeois, estably dans la ruë des Rosiers au petit Hostel Do [i.e. d'O], à costé de la vieille ruë du Temple, prend tant pour le déchet ordinaire de la farine au moulin ou ailleurs, que pour les frais dudit moulin, & de la fabrique & cuisson tu pain.
[Paris, 1650]
4°. 4 p. 21.5cm., in case 28cm.
Another edition of Moreau 3751, described with title reading "pour le détail

ordinaire ..."
Caption title.
In folder; in case labeled: Mazarinades.

NT 0039805 MH

Tarif des glaces de la Manufacture royale, avec
le tarif de la vaiselle d'argent platte,
poincon de Paris et des, autres provinces
& c.   Paris, C.P. Gueffier [1753] 122
unnumbered pages.   10 cm.

Second part: "Tarif du marc" has half-title.

1234. 1. Glassware--Prices.

NT 0039806   NCorniM NCorniC

ar U   Tarif des monnaies ayant cours en Égypte.
919   Le Caire, Imprimerie Centrale J. Barbier,
             1888.
             42 p. 13cm.

             1. Money--Egypt--Tables, etc. 2. Foreign
           exchange--Tables.

NT 0039807   NIC

       Tarif du marc, avec les fractions de l'once
     & du gros, des matieres d'or & d'argent, sui-
     vant le prix auquel elles doivent être reçues
     au change des hôtels des monnoyes; en exécu-
     tion de l'arrêt du conseil d'etat du roi &
     des lettres-patentes du 13 septembre 1771,
     registrées en la Cour des monnoies le 27 dudit
     mois. A Paris, Chez Knapen & Delaguette, 1771.
     62, [3] p. 15cm.

       Bound with Nouveau tarif du prix des glaces.
     1758.

NT 0039808   NNC

*C
HJ2653   Tarif du prix des glaces, calculé conformément
I18   aux deux styles, et dressé sur la derniere
             édition; a l'usage des Officiers Publics, et
             généralement de tous ceux qui sont obligés
             de parler le langage de la loi.   Paris, Chez
             Aubry, Libraire, quai des Augustins, près la
             rue Pavée, no. 42, An VI de la République
             [1798] 35 p. tables (1 fold.) 15 cm.

             8749. 1. Glass--Taxation.

NT 0039809   NCorniM NCorniC

       3495 Tarif du prix des glaces de la manufacture royale à
            Paris. [Paris] C. Chevillard, 1722.
              70, [2] p. 13 cm.

NT 0039810   MH-BA

       Tarif dv prix dont on est conuenu dans vne
         assemblée de notables ...
           see under [Marigny, Jacques Carpentier
     de] d. 1670.

       Tarif du prix qui sera payé és hostels des monnoyes,
       des barres et autres matieres d'or & d'argent qui y
       seront portées. Fait en la Cour des monnoyes le 10.
       jour d'octobre 1679. en exécution de l'arrest de ladite
       Cour du 28. septembre audit an. Paris, S. Mabre-
       Cramoisy, 1679.
         13, [1] p. 24½ cm.

NT 0039812   MH-BA

Tarif général de l'empire de Russie
et du royaume de Pologne.   St. Petersburg, 1819.

NT 0039813   PPL

Tarif général de toutes les contributions, tant
directes qu'indirectes, décrétées par l'Assemblée nationale en 1790 et 1791
  see under Goguillot,   comp.

DC   Tarif général de toutes les denrées de
141   première nécessité taxées par le Corps
F87+   municipal de Paris, d'après un décret de la
v.358   Convention nationale. [Paris, Galletti,
        1794]
          8 p. 16cm.

          1. Price regulation--France. 2. Prices
        --France.

NT 0039815   NIC

Tarif général des denrées et marchandises de|
première nécessité; avec le décret de la Convention
nationale, du 29 sept. [1793].
Paris. [1793]. 23½ cm.

NT 0039816   NIC

Tarif général des droits de Douane des Etats-
  Unis d'Amerique ...
    see under Campbell, James, deputy col-
lector of the port of New York.

Kress   Tarif general des droits de sorties et
Room   entrées du Royaume, & des provinces esquelles
           les bureaux ne sont establis, ordonnez estre
           levez sur toutes les marchandises & denrées.
           Arresté au Conseil royal, le 18. septembre
           1664. Avec l'edit du Roy du mesme mois & an.
           Portant conversion et diminution de plusieurs
           droits de sorties & entrées, sur les denrées
           & marchandises; reglement pour la perception
           d'iceux: suppression de la nouvelle imposition
           d'Anjou, & des tabliers establis pour la
           levée d'icelle; & des droits appellez de

           massicault, & autres.   Nouv. ed., augm.
         des nouveaux arrests & reglemens.   Paris,
         T.Charpentier [etc.] 1715.
           112 p. 23.5 cm.

           Interleaved, with manuscript notes.

NT 0039819   MH-BA

HJ6245   Tarif général des Provinces Unies pour les
.A2   droits d'entre'e & de sortie, [que payent les
1718   marchandises, tant en ce païs qu'à la mer Bal-
           tique, au passage du Sond. Ensemble l'aprécia-
           tion des marchandises sur laquelle les droits
           d'entrée & de sortie sont reglé, suivant les
           derniers ordonnances. Amsterdam, P. de la
           Feuille, 1718.
             123 p.

             1. Tariff--   Netherlands--Rates
           and tables.

NT 0039820   ICU ICJ

Tarif general et perpetuel pour les monnoyes
de France, de Rome, de Venise, d'Espagne,
de Flandre, d'Holande, d'Angleterre, et
d'Allemagne, courantes et de banque
    see under La Mothe,   de, sieur.

Tarif général, ou Comptes faits pour faire et
recevoir des paiemens en monnaies et espèces
des Pays-bas, de Brabant...
    see under Rampelbergh, M.E.

q659.1 Tarif media.
T17
          Paris.
            v. illus., tables. 31cm. 4 no. a year.

          Includes special no.

NT 0039823   IU

DC   Tarif ou tableau général de la diminution
141   du prix des principales denrées et comes-
F87+   tibles par la suppression de tous les droits
v.358   aux entrées de Paris, conformément au décret
           de l'Assemblée nationale. [Paris, Cordier
           et Meymac, 1791]
             8 p. 21cm.

             1. Prices--France. 2. Food supply--
           France--Paris.

NT 0039824   NIC

RARE BK
DEPT   Tarif pour diferents prix de la viande
CA 5546   de boucherie. [s.l. : s.n.], 1698.
             169 p. ; 13 cm.

             1. Tariff--France.

NT 0039825   WU

Tarif pour faciliter le change des pièces étrangères
en monnaies françaises, à l'usage des militaires,
des voyageurs, des négociants et des marchands.
Paris, Tiger [1814?]
  2 l., 7 plates.   21 x 26 cm.
  Introductory text signed: M.C.T.

NT 0039826   NNC

Tarif pour faciliter les comptes de réduction du
papier-monnoie en numéraire métallique ...
    see under Isère, France (Dept.)

Tarif pour l'evaluation des vaisseles et bijonx ...
    see under France. Assemblée nationale
constituante, 1789-1791.

French
Rev.
DC
141
F87+   Tarif pour l'intérêt des assignats.
v.164   Lausanne, Hignou, 1790.
     [16] p. 15cm.

     1. Assignats.

NT   0039829   NIC

Kress
Room   Tarif pour la façon des ouvrages en menui-
     serie ... [Marseille, Imprimerie de J.-F.
     Achard, 183-?]
     20 p. 15.5 cm.

     Caption title.

     1.Carpentry. 2.Prices - France. 3.Furni-
ture.

NT   0039830   MH-BA

DC
141
F87+   Tarif pour le rachat des droits féodaux
v.208   et fonciers précédé d'une instruction
     nécessaire pour faire la liquidation
     desdits rachats.   Chartres, Lacombe, 1792.
     80 p. 22cm.

     1. Land tenure--France. 2. France--
Hist.--Revolution--Economic aspects.

NT   0039831   NIC MH

     The tarif settled by the French king and
council, September 18,1664. Shewing the duties
agreed to be paid upon the several sorts of
merchandizes, goods, wares, &c. being the
growth, product and manufactures of Great
Britain, which should be imported from England
into France.   London, Printed for the author,
1713.
     23 p. 15.5 cm.
     An extract from Colbert's famous Tarif of
1664. -- Foxwell.

NT   0039832   MH-BA MnU NNC PU

---

*C
HJ2669
T18   Tarif suivant les differentes mesures des
     verres à vitre qui se fabriquent à la
     Verrerie Royale des Sieur & Dame Libaude,
     à Romesnil, près Blangis, par Abbeville
     Comté d'Eu, Privilégies de S.A.S. Mon-
     seigneur le Duc de Penthièvre [n.p.,
     1774?] sheet. 24 x 18 cm.

     4516. 1. Glass——ation. I. Libaude.

NT   0039833   NCorniM

Tarif van rechtskosten in het Fransche rijk: zoo bij de vre-
degerechten en vrederechters, als bij de rechtbanken van
eerste instantie en de hoven van appél, derzelver **griffiers**,
deurwaarders, praktizijns, notarissen, zaakkundigen, ge-
tuigen en toezienders; benevens de kosten van alle acten,
rekwesten, tegenspraken, pleidooijen, verhooren, **vonnissen**,
vacatien, kopijen en uitleveringen van stukken: alles naar
de waarde van het hollandsche geld berekend. Amsterdam,
J. Allart, 1811.

     viii, 132 p., 1 l. 21 x 12½ᶜᵐ.

     1. Costs (Law)—France.

                           36-34470

NT   0039834   DLC

Tarifa,   *marqués de*
     see   Enriquez de Rivera, Fadrique,
marqués de Tarifa, d. 1539?

Tarifa, pseud.
     Facts *vs.* sophisms. [*Washington, D. C.*, 1880]
   22 pp. 8°.

NT   0039836   NN

HF2601
.T3   [Tarifa] pseud.
     ...Statements in the Cobden club's recent pam-
     phlet, reviewed and disproven by official figures...
     Relation of our tariff laws to the agriculturalists
     and producers of the United States. [Washington?
     1880]
     22 p. tables. 22cm.
     Caption title.
     Signed:Tarifa.
     "Written to the Chicago 'Inter ocean,' October
10,1880."

NT   0039837   ICU CSmH

Tarifa, Carlos Sánchez
     see   Sánchez Tarifa, Carlos.

Tarifa das alfandegas do Brasil ...
     see under   Brazil. Laws, statues, etc.

Tarifa de Buenos Ayres.   1817.

NT   0039840   PPL

Tarifa de exportacion. Tabla ajustada a la unidad
     con deduccion y aumento del 25 y 10
     respectivamente.   Habana, La Propaganda
     Literaria, 1882.
     16 l. 16°.
     By R.M.y.J.
     I. M.y.J., R.

NT   0039841   NN

Tarifa de honorarios vigente en el año de 1876.
Texto comparado de las dos ediciones publicadas.
15 pp. 8°.   *Madrid, L, Maroto y Roldan.* 1876.

NT   0039842   DNLM

DP3
S48   Tarifa de los precios a que indispensablemente, y
v.8:45   sin la menor alteración se ha de cobrar por los balcones, tendidos,
x   nichos, y demás asientos que se ocupen en la segunda fiesta de
     toros, que se ha de celebrar en la plaza mayor de esta villa en el
     dia 24 del presente mes de septiembre por mañana y tarde.
     Madrid, 1789.
     broadside, 42x28 cm. fold. to 24x19 cm. [Spain. Laws, statutes,
     etc. Reales ordenes, v. 8, no. 45]

     1. Bull-fights.

NT   0039843   CU-BANC

PQ
6171
.A195   Tarifa general de la loteria nacional
T186   primitiva, por A. G. C. V.   Barcelona,
     Impr. de J. M. de Grau, 1842.
     50 p. 15cm.

     I. V., A. G. C.

NT   0039844   WU

Tarifa general para averiguar el valor de
     muchas cosas, dado que sea el de una, y dado
     el de muchas cosas averiguar el de una
     see under   [Cortada, Juan] 1805-1868.

Tarifa jeneral de los derechos de encomiendas
     see   Tarifa jeneral ...

Tarifa ó arancel que para la esaccion del derecho
     nacional de alcabalas
     see under   Mexico. Laws, statutes, etc.

F1222
.32   Tarifa; ó Prontuario de posturas de carnero, desde 10 onzas hasta
T36   30 por 1 real, y precio de arrobas en cada una desde 1 hasta
x   1000. México, Impr. de L. Abadiano y Valdés, 1851.
     56 p. (incl. cover) 15cm.

     Cover title.
     "Tarifas de precios de carne de res, desde 4 reales hasta 3
pesos arroba, 1851, " p. [37]-56.

     1. Sheet - Mexico. 2. Sheep - Prices. 3. Beef - Mexico. 4.
Beef - Prices.

NT   0039848   CU-BANC

Tarifa, o regulacion de los precios de los
     medicamentos ...
     see under   Madrid.

**Tarifa para el cobro de la alcabala en el
departamento del Istmo.** [n. p., n. d.]
[2] p. 50cm. in cover 47cm. [Miscellaneous
papers; Pinart collection. no. 8]

     Caption title.

NT   0039850   CU-BANC

Tarifa para el cobro de los derechos de
     alcabalas conforme al decreto de 2 de junio de
     1853
     see under   Jalisco, Mexico. Laws, statutes,
                              etc.

TARIFA para el transporte de paquetes postales
entre España y varios países extranjeros. Precios y condiciones de aplicación. Nomenclatura
alfabética de las estaciones y localidades de
España y de los paises extranjeros que partici-
pan del servicio de paquetes postales. Madrid,
1904.
     4°.
     At head of title: Ferrocarriles del norte, ...

NT   0039852   MH-L

Tarifa para las aduanas de la Neuva Granada
    see under   Colombia. Laws, statutes, etc.

HE 7065 .H6 LAI

Tarifa vigente para transmisión de mensajes
inalámbricos. Tegucigalpa, Tipografía
nacional, 1922.
    10p.   19 cm.
    Signed: D. Almendares, Director Gral. de
Telégrafos y Teléfonos.

    1. Telegraph service - Honduras - Rates.

NT   0039854   LNT

Tarifa zoè noticia dy pexi e mexure di Luogi
e Tere che s'adovra marcadantia per el mondo ...
Venezia, C.Ferrari, 1925.
    75 p.   32 cm.   (Pubblicata dal R. Istituto
superiore di scienze economiche e commerciali di
Venezia celebrandosi l'XI centenario dell'
Università di Pavia (21 maggio 1925)

    Bibliographical foot-notes.

NT   0039855   MH-BA

Tarifas de los precios de todas clases de obra
de albanileria
    see under   Havana. Maestro mayor.

Tarifas del correo de Honduras e itinerario de la administra-
ción central, Tegucigalpa, 1936. En vigencia desde el 1° de
marzo de 1936. Tegucigalpa, Talleres tipográficos nacionales
₁1936?₎
    cover-title, 54 p, 1 l. 27¼°°.
    Half-title: Tarifas postales aprobadas por el Poder ejecutivo según
Acuerdo no. 1211 del 4 de marzo de 1936.
    Includes advertising matter.

    1. Postal service—Honduras—Rates.

		43–21255
Library of Congress	HE6707 1936	
	₍2₎	383.497283

NT   0039857   DLC

Tarifas para sesvicio [!] telefónico de las empresas Cía. telefónica y telegráfica mexicana
y Empresa de telefonos ericsson, s.a.
    see under   ₍Mexico. Ministerio de comuni-
caciones y obras públicas₎

Tarifas que rigen el los ferrocarriles y muelles de
la República
    see under   ₍Peru. Dirección de Obrás
Públicas₎

Tarifbestimmungen für die Arbeitnehmer des öffentlichen
Dienstes (ATO) (TO.A) (TO.B) einschliesslich Lemgoer
und Königsteiner Vereinbarungen mit einem Anhang
(Kr.T) (FKr.T) (RKT) (RKTTr.), und für die bei der
Mil. Reg. beschäftigten deutschen Angestellten. Düsseldorf-
Lohausen, Werner-Verlag, 1949.
    240 p.   17 cm.

    1. Germany—Officials and employees—Salaries, allowances, etc.

                 51–39212

NT   0039860   DLC

Tarifbestimmungen für die Arbeitnehmer des öffentlichen Dienstes (ATO) (TO.A) (TO.B) einschliesslich der
bischer ergangenen zusätzlichen Vereinbarungen, mit einem
Anhang für den öffentlichen Krankendienst (Kr.T) (F
Kr.T) (RKT) (RKT Tr.) und für die bei der Besatzungs-
macht beschäftigten deutschen Angestellten. 3. erweiterte
Aufl. Düsseldorf-Lohausen, Werner-Verlag, 1951.
    304 p.   15 cm.

    1. Germany (Federal Republic, 1949-   )—Officials and em-
ployees—Salaries, allowances, etc.

                 52–64751 ‡

NT   0039861   DLC

HG 8061 T186

TARIFE und Bedingungen der privaten
Krankenversicherung. 1.-   Aufl.;
1929-
Berlin.
     v.
     Editor: 1939, Erik Schülke
     1. Health insurance - Germany
     2. Health insurance - Rates & tables
     I. Schülke, Erik. ed.

NT   0039862   DNLM

Tarife und Bedingungen der privaten Krankenversicherung
    see also under   Schülke, Erik.

Tarif-Erhöhung oder Reichs-Eisenbahnen? Eine volkswirtn-
schaftliche Studie, von einem Fachmann.   Berlin: I. Guttentag,
1876.   61 p.   8°.

1. Freight—Rates—Germany, 1876.	2. Railways—Gov. ownership—Ger-
many, 1876.	
N.Y.P.L.	April 8, 1925

NT   0039864   NN

The **Tariff**.
    v.

Newark, N. J., 19   4°.
    v.   illus.
    Monthly.
    Published by the Traffic Club of Newark, N. J.

I. Transportation—Per. and soc. publ.	
N.Y.P.L.	April 30, 1925

NT   0039865   NN

... The tariff. Extracts from the speeches of
Hon. Wm. J. Bryan ...
    see under   Bryan, William Jennings, 1860-
1925.

The **tariff**. Martin Van Buren, the people's friend and
candidate ... Henry Clay, the candidate of politicians and
speculators ... Whiggery exposed. ₁Columbus, Ohio,
1844?₎
    8 p.   23 cm.
    Caption title.
    At head of title: Ohio Statesman, supplement.

    1. Campaign literature, 1844—Democratic.   2. Van Buren, Martin,
Pres. U. S., 1782–1862.   I. Columbus Press.   Supplement.

E400.T3	48–41092*

NT   0039867   DLC

Tariff (The). no. 1: its injustice on principles of revenue.
Remarks on the injustice of our system of indirect taxation, by a tariff of duties on imported goods, for the support of the general government, and for the protection of
American industry. *New York: J. B. Liddle*, 1843.   18
pp.   8°.   (₍Plebeian tracts ?   no. 1.₎)
    In : **10** p. v. 2.

          DLC: YA8492

NT   0039868   NN PHi DLC

The Tariff; a collection of odd numbers of Tariff
reform ...
    see under   New York Reform Club. Tariff
Reform Committee.

The tariff: its true character and effects, practically illustrated. Charleston, Printed by A. E. Miller, 1830.
    2 p. l, 52 p.   21°°.
    Originally published in the Southern patriot.

    1. Tariff—U. S.   2. Free trade and protection—Free trade.

Library of Congress	HF1754.T3	7–792†
—— Copy 2.		₍Financial pamphlets, v. 35, no. 2₎

NT   0039870   DLC ScU GU MWA NN M

The tariff: the rates of duty on imports in force
July 1, 1877. [n.p., 1877]
55p.

          YA 18076

NT   0039871   DLC

The **tariff**, a tract for the times, by a citizen of Virginia.
Prepared by order of Hon. Willis Green, chairman of the
executive committee of the Whig members of Congress.
₁Washington? 1844?₎
    20 p.   24½°°.

    1. Tariff—U. S.   2. Free trade and protection—Protection.

	CA 7—2758 Unrev'd
Library of Congress	HF1754.T28

NT   0039872   DLC NcD ICN OClWHi CSmH

The tariff act of 1842 ...
    see under   U.S. Laws, statutes, etc.

The tariff act of 1897
    see under   ₍Taussig, Frank William₎ 1859-
1940.

Tariff act of 1922, with index
    see under   U.S. Laws, statutes, etc.

Tariff acts passed by the Congress of the United
States from 1789 to 1895
   see under   U.S. Laws, statutes, etc.

NT 0039877   PPL

The Tariff adds untold wealth to the nation.
Speeches in Congress.   Washington, 1884.
[American Politics]

The tariff and administrative customs act of 1890
   see under   U.S. Laws, statutes, etc.

The tariff and how it effects the woolen cloth
manufacture and wool growers
   see under   [Harris, Edward] 1801-1872.

Tariff and miscellaneous documents.   1889.

NT 0039880   PPLL

Tariff and prices.
Bost., 1892.

NT 0039881   Nh

ar W   [Tariff and taxation. Miscellaneous speeches
5743   and essays. Washington, etc. 1888-97]
           22 pamphlets in 1 v. 23cm.

           Binder's title: Speeches. Tariff and
           taxation. Wm. Sulzer.

           1. Tariff—U.S. 2. Taxation—U.S.

NT 0039882   NIC

The tariff as it affects the workshop
   see under   [Mann, Jonathan B

Tariff as it is and as it should be.   New York.
12 p.

NT 0039884   PHi

Tariff association of New York.
   Tariff rates for steam vessels, promulgated by the
Tariff association of New York, September 10, 1895.
N.Y. Tariff assoc. 1895. 102 p.   D.
   Pages 98-102 reversed.

NT 0039885   OC

... Tariff bargaining under the new deal...
   see under   [Stewart, Maxwell Slutz] 1900-

... The Tariff – British Imposture and Political
Humbug
   see under   [Mansfield, Edward Deering]
1801-1880.

The tariff ? Cartoons and comments from Puck. The
revenue issue in a nutshell ... [New York, Keppler &
Schwarzmann] *1888.
   31, [1] p. illus. 18 x 27cm.

   1. Tariff—U.S. 2. Caricatures and cartoons—U.S.   I. Puck.

   Library of Congress   HF1755.T185   11—3336

NT 0039888   DLC CU-S MiD MiD-B MU

Tariff circulars
   see   U.S. War dept.

Tariff Commission League
   Tariff tinkering must stop. In thirty years of
"tariff tinkering" we had five years revisions of the
tariff and two attemps at revision... How the tariff
can be taken out of politics. Tariff Commission
League.. [Chicago,1915]
   16p.

NT 0039890   OC1WHi

Tariff commission, *London.*
   ... The abandonment of Cobdenism: a seven years'
survey of fiscal developments in the United Kingdom
and the British empire ... Westminster, P. S. King &
son [1913]
   32 p. 28cm.
   CONTENTS.—A. Comparative decline of British trade and its implications.—B. Alternatives to tariff reform and their breakdown.—C. Continuous growth of preference in the empire.—D. Abandonment of Cobdenism.
   1. Tariff—Gt. Brit. 2. Free trade and protection—Protection. 3. Imperial federation.   I. Title. II. Title: Cobdenism, The abandonment of.

   Library of Congress   HF2046.T2   14-2589

NT 0039891   DLC ICJ

Tariff commission, *London.*
   ... Calculations bearing upon various schemes of reciprocal tariff preference. [London, 1907]
   8 p. 28cm.

   1. Tariff—Gt. Brit. 2. Imperial federation.
                                              7-37958
   Library of Congress   HF3506.T2

NT 0039892   DLC

Tariff commission, *London.*
   ... The economic position of Ireland and its relation to
tariff reform ... [London] Pub. for the Tariff commis-
sion by P. S. King & son [printed by Wightman Mountain
& Andrews, ltd.] 1912]
   43 p. 27½cm.
   At head of title: The Tariff commission.
   CONTENTS.—A. Range of Irish industry.—B. External trade of Ireland.—
C. Course of Irish agriculture in the last fifty years.—D. Irish linen and
shipbuilding industries.—E. Economic interdependence of England and
Ireland.—F. Fiscal provisions of the Irish home rule bill, 1912.
   1. Ireland — Econ. condit. 2. Tariff — Ireland. 3. Tariff — Gt. Brit.
I. Title.
   Library of Congress   HF2076.T3   12-16989

NT 0039893   DLC NN

Tariff Commission, *London.*
   The engineering industries; including structural, electrical,
marine, and shipbuilding, mechanical and general industrial engineering...with analysis and summary of evidence and statistical tables.   London: P. S. King & Son, 1909.   160 l.   4°.
(Great Britain. Tariff Commission. Report. v. 4.)

   1. Engineering (Electrical), Gt. Br.   2. Marine engineering, Gt. Br.
3. Shipbuilding, Gt. Br. 4. Engineer-   ing (Mechanical), Gt. Br. 5.
Tariff, Gt. Br., 1909.
N. Y. P. L.   November 27, 1917.

NT 0039894   NN

Tariff commission, London.
   ...Evidence on the flax, hemp and jute industries...
Lond., 1905.
   1 v. 4°

NT 0039895   DLC

Tariff Commission, *London.*
   ...The export trade in manufactures of the United Kingdom,
Germany and the United States.   Westminster: P. S. King &
Son [1909].   51 p. incl. tables.   4°.

   Caption-title.
   At head of title: The Tariff Commission.

   1. Commerce, Gt. Br., 1883-1907.   2. Commerce, Germany, 1883-1907.
3. Commerce, U. S., 1883-1907.
N. Y. P. L.   December 14, 1921.

NT 0039896   NN

Tariff Commission, *London,*   TK quarto
   The glass industry, with analysis and summary of evidence
and statistical tables.   London: P. S. King & Son, 1907.   36 l.
4°.   (Great Britain. Tariff Commission. Report. v. 6.)

   1. Glass.—Trade, etc., Gt. Br. 2.   Glass.—Tariff, Gt. Br., 1907.
3. Series.
N. Y. P. L.   November 23, 1917.

NT 0039897   NN

HF1534 Tariff commission, London.
1921   ...Imperial preference; chronological statement
.T2   of the progress of the movement. Westminster,
           Pub. for the Tariff commission by P.S. King & son
           [1921]
              14 p. 22cm.

           At head of title: The Tariff commission.

              1. Gt.Brit.—Commercial policy. 2. Imperial fed-
           eration.

NT 0039898   ICU PBm MH IU

308
Z
Box 845
           Tariff commission, London.
              The import and export trade of the United
           Kingdom in 1905 and 1906. [London, 1907]
              8 p. tables.

           At head of title: MM 29. 19/1/07.

              1. Gt. Brit. - Comm. - Stat.

NT 0039899   NNC

TARIFF COMMISSION, London.
The industrial crisis and British policy.
Westminster, S.W.,P.S:King & Son,[1921].

4°. (Its Memorandum,59).

NT 0039900   MH PBm

Tariff Commission, *London.*
The iron and steel trades, with appendix.   London: P. S.
King & Son, 1904.   vii p., 108 l.   diagr., tables.   4°.   (Great
Britain. Tariff Commission. Report... v. 1.)

1. Steel.—Trade, etc., Gt. Br.   2. Iron.—Trade, etc., Gt. Br.
3. Steel.—Tariff, Gt. Br., 1904.   4. Iron.—Tariff, Gt. Br., 1904.
5. Series.
N. Y. P. L.   November 20, 1917.

NT 0039901   NN

308
Z
Box 845

Tariff commission, London.
Memorandum on the new German commercial
treaties and the new German tariff. [London,
1905]
14 p.

At head of title: Proof. MM23. 8/4/05.
"Abstract of the treaty of 6th December,
1891, between Austria-Hungary and Germany,
with the modifications and additions introduced by the treaty of 25th January, 1905":
p. 7-14.

NT 0039902   NNC

Tariff commission, *London.*
... Most-favoured-nation arrangements and British trade
...   Westminster, P. S. King & son [1910]
26 p.   27cm.
Caption title.
CONTENTS.— Character of the most-favoured-nation arrangement.—
Amount of British trade affected.—Evasions of the most-favoured-nation
clause.—Some results of direct negotiation.—The status of the dominions.—
Statements by traders.

1. Favored nation clause. 2. Gt. Brit.—Commercial treaties.

Library of Congress   HF1721.T3   11-7465

NT 0039903   DLC

Tariff commission, *London.*
Most-favored-nation arrangements and British trade.
Prepared by the Tariff commission, London, England.
Printed for Committee on finance, United States Senate.
Washington [Govt. print. off.] 1911.
34 p.   23½cm.

1. Favored nation clause. 2. Gt. Brit.—Commercial treaties. I. U. S.
Congress. Senate. Committee on finance.
                                                    11-35530
Library of Congress   HF1721.T32

NT 0039904   DLC ICJ

Tariff commission, *London.*
... The new Canadian tariff and preferential trade with
the Empire. [London, Vacher & sons, printers, 1907]
24 p.   28cm.
CONTENTS.— A. The new Canadian tariff.— B. The general course of
Canadian trade: 1. Total trade. 2. Free and dutiable imports. 3. Operation of the preference in detail. 4. Experiences of manufacturers and
merchants.—C. Appendix: 1. Canadian import duties under the old and
new tariffs. 2. "Empire" free list in the new Canadian tariff. 3. Rebates
in the new Canadian tariff.

1. Tariff—Canada. 2. Canada—Comm.   I. Canada. Laws, statutes,
etc.
                                                    7-20510
Library of Congress   HF2041.T3
———— Copy 2.   Library of Congress HF1765.T3

NT 0039905   DLC ICJ

308
Z
Box 845

Tariff commission, London.
The new continental tariffs. [London, 1906]
15 p.   tables.

At head of title: MM 27. 10/3/06.

1. Tariff - Germany. 2. Gt. Brit. - Comm. -
Germany.

NT 0039906   NNC

Tariff commission, *London.*
... The new tariff of the United States and its relation
to the trade and policy of the United Kingdom and the
British empire...   Westminster, Pub. for the Tariff
commission by P. S. King & son [1914]
35 p. incl. tables.   28cm.

1. Tariff—U. S. 2. U. S.—Comm.—Gt. Brit. 3. Gt. Brit.—Comm.—U. S.
I. Title.
                                                    14-5325
Library of Congress   HF1756.T3

NT 0039907   DLC ICJ

Tariff commission, *London.*
... Notes on imperial preference ...   Westminster, Pub. for
the Tariff commission by P. S. King & son, ltd. [1917]
1 p. l., 28 p.   28cm.
At head of title: The Tariff commission.
CONTENTS.—Chronological statement.—The colonial desire.—Dominion
and inter-dominion preferences. — Other inter-imperial preferences.—
Appendix: Imperial conference resolutions.

1. Imperial preference.
                                                    24-6198
Library of Congress   HF2046.T215

NT 0039908   DLC

Tariff Commission, *London.*
The pottery industries, with analysis and summary of evidence and statistical tables.   London: P. S. King & Son, 1907.
49 l.   4°.   (Great Britain. Tariff Commission. Report. v. 5.)

1. Pottery.—Trade, etc., Gt. Br. 2.   Pottery.—Tariff, Gt. Br. 1907.
3. Series.
N. Y. P. L.   November 23, 1917.

NT 0039909   NN

308
Z
Box 845

Tariff commission, London.
Preference in relation to the trade between
the United Kingdom and Canada. [London, 1906]
10 p.   charts.

At head of title: MM 26. 11/1/06.

1. Gt. Brit. - Comm. - Canada.

NT 0039910   NNC

Tariff commission, *London.*
... The problems of the Imperial conference and the policy
of preference ...   Westminster, Pub. for the Tariff commission by P. S. King & son [1911]
47 p. incl. tables.   28cm.
CONTENTS.—A. General scope of the conference and its relation, direct
and indirect, to the tariff question.—B. The proposal of free trade within
the empire.—C. The development of the policy of preference.—D. Treaty
relations of the empire as affected by recent developments.—E. Alternative
policies.—Appendix: Statistical tables showing the course of empire trade
under preference.

1. Imperial preference. 2. Gt. Brit.—Commercial policy.
                                                    11-12837
Library of Congress   HF2046.T18

NT 0039911   DLC ICJ ICU

Tariff commission, *London.*
... The proposed reciprocal trade arrangement between
Canada and the United States of America ... [2d ed.]
[London] P. S. King & son [1911]
38 p.   27½cm.
At head of title: 2nd edition ...
The Tariff commission.
CONTENTS.—Character and origin of the arrangement.—Analysis of the
schedules.—Effect of the arrangement upon British food supplies and
British industry.—Bearing of the arrangement upon the trade and policy
of the British Empire.—Statements by British authorities.

1. Canada—Comm.—U. S. 2. U. S.—Comm.—Canada. 3. Reciprocity.
4. Tariff—Gt. Brit.
                                                    11-7343
Library of Congress   HF1732.C2T2

NT 0039912   DLC ICJ

Tariff commission, *London.*
Proposed reciprocal trade arrangement between Canada and the United States. Prepared by the Tariff commission, London, England. [2d ed.] Printed for Committee on finance United States Senate. Washington [Govt.
print. off.] 1911.
56 p. incl. tables.   23½cm.

1. Canada—Comm.—U. S. 2. U. S.—Comm.—Canada. 3. Reciprocity.
4. Tariff—Gt. Brit.   I. U. S. Congress. Senate. Committee on finance.
                                                    11-35531
Library of Congress   HF1732.C2T22

NT 0039913   DLC Or CaBVaU NN ICJ

Tariff commission, *London.*
... The reciprocal trade arrangement between Canada
and the West Indies ...   Westminster, Pub. for the Tariff commission by P. S. King & son [1912]
28 p. incl. tables.   28cm.
CONTENTS.—Origin and character of the agreement.—Analysis of the
schedules.—Course of trade between Canada and the West Indies.—Development of the colonial trade of the United States under preference.

1. Canada—Comm.—West Indies, British. 2. West Indies, British—
Comm.—Canada. 3. Reciprocity.
                                                    12-26009
Library of Congress   HF1733.C3W5

NT 0039914   DLC ICJ

Tariff commission, London.

Chapman, S[ydney] J[ohn] 1871–
A reply to the report of the Tariff commission on the
cotton industry, written for the Free trade league. By
S. J. Chapman ... Manchester and London, Sherratt &
Hughes, 1905.

Tariff commission, *London.*
... Report of British tariff commission. Reciprocity
with Canada. Most-favored-nation agreements in relation to the proposed reciprocal trade agreement between
Canada and the United States of America ... Washington [Govt. print. off.] 1911.
19 p.   23½cm.   ([U. S.] 62d Cong. 1st sess. Senate. Doc. 66)
Presented by Mr. Lodge. Ordered printed July 14, 1911.
1. Canada—Comm.—U. S. 2. U. S.—Comm.—Canada. 3. Reciprocity.
4. Tariff—Gt. Brit. 5. Favored nation clause.   I. Lodge, Henry Cabot,
1850-1924.
                                                    11-35612
Library of Congress   HF1732.C2T25

NT 0039916   DLC MiU OO ICN NN

Tariff commission, *London.*   L337.5
Report of the Tariff commission ... London, P. S. King & Q400
son, 1904-09.
7 v. in 4   tables, diagrs., forms. 27½cm.

A commission "to examine the fiscal proposals ... submitted to the
country" by Hon. Joseph Chamberlain; "and to report as to:—A. Their
probable effect on present conditions. B. Whether any modifications are
desirable. C. The best way in which, where there are conflicting interests, those interests can be harmonised. D. What duties, if any, should
be recommended."
Index to v. 1 issued separately.

Continued in next column

Continued from preceding column

Vol. 1, pt. 1 of v. 2, and v. 3 are complete reports. The remaining volumes are each an analysis and summary of the industry studied. Full reports on these industries were not published.
CONTENTS.—v. 1. The iron and steel trades.—v. 2. The textile trades: pt. 1. The cotton industry. pt. 2. Evidence on the woollen industry. pt. 3. Evidence on the hosiery industry. pt. 4. Evidence on the lace industry. pt. 5. Evidence on the carpet industry. pt. 6. Evidence on the silk industry. pt. 7. Evidence on the flax, hemp and jute industries.—v. 3. Report of the Agricultural committee.—v. 4. The engineering industries.—v. 5. The pottery industries.—v. 6. The glass industry.—v. 7. Sugar and confectionery.
1. Tariff—Gt. Brit. 2. Gt. Brit.—Econ. condit. 3. Gt. Brit.—Indus. 4. Agriculture—Gt. Brit. I. Chamberlain, Joseph, 1836–1914.

Library of Congress   HF2041.T2   5–37152 Revised

NT 0039918   DLC DL OU

Tariff commission, *London.*
Report of the Tariff commission ... London, P. S. King & son, 1904–09.
7 v. in 13. tables, diagrs., forms. 27½ᶜᵐ.
A commission "to examine the fiscal proposals ... submitted to the country" by Hon. Joseph Chamberlain; "and to report as to:—A. Their probable effect on present conditions. B. Whether any modifications are desirable. C. The best way in which, where there are conflicting interests, those interests can be harmonised. D. What duties, if any, should be recommended."
Index to v. 1 issued separately.

Vol. 1, pt. 1 of v. 2, and v. 3 are complete reports. The remaining volumes are each an analysis and summary of the industry studied. Full reports on these industries were not published.
CONTENTS.—v. 1. The iron and steel trades.—v. 2. The textile trades: pt. 1. The cotton industry. pt. 2. Evidence on the woollen industry. pt. 3. Evidence on the hosiery industry. pt. 4. Evidence on the lace industry. pt. 5. Evidence on the carpet industry. pt. 6. Evidence on the silk industry. pt. 7. Evidence on the flax, hemp and jute industries.—v. 3. Report of the Agricultural committee. 2d ed.—v. 4. The engineering industries.—v. 5. The pottery industries.—v. 6. The glass industry.—v. 7. Sugar and confectionery.
1. Tariff—Gt. Brit. 2. Gt. Brit.—Econ. condit. 3. Gt. Brit.—Indus. 4. Agriculture—Gt. Brit. I. Chamberlain, Joseph, 1836–1914.

Library of Congress   HF2041.T2   5–37152 Revised

NT 0039920   DLC MdBJ NjP ICJ NNC CU

Tariff Commission, *London.*
...The status of the dominions and their relations with foreign countries... [London:] Published for the Tariff Commission by P. S. King & Sons [1920]. 21 p. 4°.
Cover-title.
At head of title: The Tariff Commission.

1. Diplomatic service, Canada.   2. Commerce, Gt. Br.: Colonies. 3. Tariff, Gt. Br.: Colonies.
N. Y. P. L.   February 2, 1922.

NT 0039921   NN

Tariff Commission, *London.*
Sugar and confectionery, with analysis and summary of evidence and statistical tables. London: P. S. King & Son, 1907. 61 l. diagr. 4°. (Great Britain. Tariff Commission. Report. v. 7.)

1. Sugar.—industry and trade, Gt. Br. 2. Confectionery.—Trade, etc., Gt. Br. 3. Sugar.—Tariff, Gt. Br., 1907. 4. Confectionery.—Tariff, Gt. Br., 1907. 5. Series.
N. Y. P. L.   November 20, 1917.

NT 0039922   NN

308
Z
Box 845
Tariff commission, London.
The tariff system of Europe and America. [London, 1905]
3 p.

1. Tariff.

NT 0039923   NNC

Tariff Commission, *London.*
The textile trades. London: P. S. King & Son, 1905. 4°. (Great Britain. Tariff Commission. Report. v. 2.)
Part 1. The cotton industry... 1 p.l. [vii–]viii p., 113 l. diagr., tables.
Part 2. Evidence on the woollen industry... 1 p.l. [vii–]viii p., 145 l. diagr., tables.
Part 3. Evidence on the hosiery industry... 1 p.l. [vii–]viii p., 42 l. diagr., tables.

Part 4. Evidence on the lace industry... 1 p.l. [vii–]viii p., 39 l. diagr., tables.
Part 5. Evidence on the carpet industry... 1 p.l. [vii–]viii p., 32 l. diagr., tables.
Part 6. Evidence on the silk industry... 1 p.l. [vii–]viii p., 80 l. diagr., tables.
Part 7. Evidence on the flax, hemp and jute industries. 1 p.l., [vii–]viii p., 97 l. diagr., tables.

1. Tariff, Gt. Br., 1905. 2. Textile   trade, etc., Gt. Br. 3. Series.
N. Y. P. L.   November 27, 1917

NT 0039925   NN

Tariff commission, *London.*
... Trade aspects of the war with Germany ... Westminster, Pub. for the Tariff commission by P. S. King & son [1914]
24 p. incl. tables. 28ᶜᵐ.
CONTENTS.—Introductory.—A. The British home market.—B. German trade with the British empire outside the United Kingdom.—C. German trade with foreign countries outside Europe.—Appendices: 1. German exports to the British empire and foreign countries outside Europe. 2. German goods competing with British products.

1. Gt. Brit.—Comm. 2. Germany—Comm. 3. European war, 1914–1918—Economic aspects. I. Title.
14–15481

Library of Congress   HF3506.2.T3

NT 0039926   DLC ICJ

Tariff commission, *London.*
... Trade aspects of the war with Germany ... Westminster, Pub. for the Tariff commission by P. S. King & son [1914]
24 p. incl. tables. 28ᶜᵐ.
At head of title: Second edition ...

1. Gt. Brit.—Comm. 2. Germany—Comm. 3. European war, 1914–1918—Economic aspects. I. Title.
24–4443

Library of Congress   HF3506.2.T3   1914 a

NT 0039927   DLC

Tariff Commission, *London.*
... The trade relations of India with the United Kingdom, British possessions, and foreign countries. Part 1– Westminster: P. S. King & Son [1908–] part. 4°.
Caption-title.
At head of title: The Tariff Commission.

1. Commerce, India, 1885–1907.
N. Y. P. L.   November 15, 1921.

NT 0039928   NN

Tariff Commission, *London.*
...The treaty position as it affects the Empire... [London:] P. S. King & Son [1911]. 19 p. 4°.
At head of title: The Tariff Commission.

1. Tariff.—Treaties, Gt. Br.   2. Tariff (Colonial), Gt. Br.
N. Y. P. L.   December 14, 1921.

NT 0039929   NN

Tariff commission, *London.*
... The war and British economic policy ... Westminster, Pub. for the Tariff commission by P. S. King & son, ltd. [1915]
cover-title, 174 p. 28ᶜᵐ.
CONTENTS.—pt. 1. British finance and industry under war conditions and the basis of future policy.—pt. 2. Iron and steel and engineering industries.—pt. 3. Textile industries.—pt. 4. The aniline dye industry.—pt. 5. Other industries—Appendix I. Enemy patents.—Appendix II. British dyes limited.
1. European war, 1914–1918—Economic aspects—Gt. Brit. 2. Gt. Brit.—Economic policy. 3. Tariff—Gt. Brit. I. Title.
15—6127

Library of Congress   HC256.2.T3

NT 0039930   DLC PBm CU ICJ NN

Tariff Commission, London. Agricultural Committee.
Report of the Agricultural Committee... London: P. S. King & Son, 1906–[1914].
[no. 1.] With appendix. 272 l. 2. ed. 4°. (Great Britain. Tariff Commission. Report... v. 3.)
no. 2. 24 p. 4°.

1. Agriculture, Gt. Br. 2. Tariff, Gt. Br. 3. Agriculture.—Economics,
N. Y. P. L.   November 17, 1917.

NT 0039931   NN DNAL ICU

Tariff commission, *London. Agricultural committee.*
... Second report of the Agricultural committee. Westminster, Pub. for the Tariff commission by P. S. King & son [1914]
24 p. 28½ᶜᵐ.
At head of title: The Tariff commission.
Signed: Henry Chaplin, chairman, Agricultural committee, W. A. S. Hewins, secretary, Tariff commission.
CONTENTS.—A. National importance of agriculture.—B. Changes since 1906 [date of First report].—C. Policy in relation to the present position.—D. Agricultural rates.—Appendix [tables]
1. Agriculture—Gt. Brit. 2. Agriculture—Economic aspects. 3. Tariff—Gt. Brit. I. Chaplin, Henry, 1841– II. Hewins, William Albert Samuel, 1865–
14–13681

Library of Congress   HF2601.T2

NT 0039932   DLC NIC

Tariff Commission, U. S.
see U.S. Tariff Commission.

Tariff Commission on the Dumping of Foreign Art-Products in the United Kingdom. Artistic Sub-Committee.
Report ...
see Merrill, Eugene.
Art in the dumps ...

---

q368.1 Tariff committee of Russian insurance
T17cE   companies.
Company fire insurance in Russia. 1827–1910. Tr. from the Russian by G. Dobson. St. Petersburg, 1912. 142p.

NT 0039935   IU

The Tariff controversy. [Book reviews] n. p. [1904?]
28 p.
Without title-page.
Caption title.

NT 0039936   MH

Tariff convention, 1831
see
Friends of domestic industry.

Tariff conventions. v.1– v.p., 1828–

NT 0039938   PPAmP

A Tariff creed.   n.p., n.d.
4 p.   15 cm.

NT 0039939   RPB OClWHi

HF1946   The Tariff curse in Brazil ...   [London, 1914?]
.T3   1 pam.   12°.

NT 0039940   DLC

1904 The tariff dictionary. A compendious handbook to the fiscal   337 Q403
question. London, Simpkin, Marshall, Hamilton, Kent and Co.,
[1904].
iv, 262, [2] p. incl. tables. 18½cm.

NT 0039941   ICJ DL PPF DLC-P4

Tariff doctrine
        see under   Whig Congressional Committee,
1843-1845.

Tariff facts for speakers and students ...
        see under   American Tariff League.

Tariff facts for the farmer, the workman and the
manufacturer. n.p., n.d.
11 p.

NT 0039944   PHi

A tariff for protection with revenue as the incident, vs. a tariff for revenue with protection as
the incidetn. An analysis of Hon. William McKin-
ley Jr.'s great tariff speech. [Boston, 1890]
27p.

                    YA 18055

NT 0039945   DLC

A tariff for revenue
        see under   [Wells, David Ames] 1828-1898.

"Tariff for revenue only" is free trade.   9337-373²⁷
Democracy's surrender to alien interests.
= [N. p., 1892.] (2) pp. Caricature. 8°.
A caricature of Grover Cleveland as: The star-eyed goddess of reform.

F4727 — Presidential elections. 1892. - Free trade. In opposition to. — Caricature. — Cleveland, Grover.

NT 0039947   MB

"Tariff for revenue only" vs. Canada's national
policy
        see under   Mackintosh, Charles Herbert,
1843-

1844A   A tariff for revenue, with discrimination in
T17   favor of protection. [1844]
          515-532 p. 25cm.

          "Art. IV."
          Vol. 1, no. 4, Oct. 1844.
          Name of periodical clipped off; article not
in Poole's Index.

          1. Tariff - U. S. - Addresses, essays, lec-
tures.

NT 0039949   NNC

HE2122 Tariff guide.
T5   no. 1-
         19
         New York, Academy of Advanced Traffic.
         v. 28 cm. (An Academy traffic aid)

         By E. Albert Ovens.

NT 0039950   OU

Tariff hearings before the committee on ways and
means ...
        see under   U.S. Congress. House.
Committee on Ways & Means.

The tariff humbug. When Cleveland is elected and
another Democratic House...
small card, 2 p.

NT 0039952   OClWHi

Tariff investigation, 1885.   Providence, 1885.
6 p.   22 cm.
Clippings from the Providence journal ...

NT 0039953   RPB

The Tariff issue
        see under   Freed, Augustus Toplady,
1835-

Kress   Tariff meeting. Pursuant to previous notice
Room   a numerous meeting of the friends of a protec-
tive tariff in the county of Windsor, was held
at the court house in Woodstock, on the 15th of
March, 1842, and the following memorial and
resolutions were adopted ...   [n.p., 1842]
8 p. 27.5 cm.

          Caption title.

          1.Tariff - U.S. 2.Free trade and protection -
Protection.

NT 0039955   MH-BA

The Tariff of conscience; free trade in slave
produce considered and condemned; a dialogue.
[London, C. Gilpin, 185-?]
12 p.   O.

NT 0039956   NcU

R
347.76335 Tariff of costs: Parish of Ørleans.
T18   Civil District Court, First and Second
City Courts, Recorder of Mortgages,
Register of Conveyances. [New Orleans]
West Pub. Co., 1953.
16 p.

          1. Courts - New Orleans, La. I.
Orleans Parish, Civil District Court.

NT 0039957   LN

Tariff of duties ...
        see under   U.S. Treasury Dept.

Kress   Tariff of duties on imports and exports
Room   for the island of Java, and the Dutch East
India colonies ... Boston, Printed by
S.N.Dickinson, 1844.
8 p. 22.5 cm.

          "Printed for Paine, Stricker & co. of
Batavia."

          1.Tariff - Java. 2.Java. I.Netherlands
(Kingdom, 1815-   ) Laws, statutes, etc.

NT 0039959   MH-BA

The Tariff of 1883. Rates of duty fixed by the tariff of 1883,
and now in force, compared with the previous rates, and
accompanied by a detailed statement of the importations of
foreign goods and duties paid on the same in the two years
ending June 30th, 1883, and June 30th, 1887, reprinted in
part from the Tribune almanac for 1884. New York, The
Tribune, 1888.
cover-title, 3-19 p. 27½ x 21cm.
Page 19 is 3d page of cover.
1. Tariff—U. S.—Law. 2. U. S.—Comm.   I. U. S. Laws, statutes,
etc. II. The Tribune almanac and political register. III. New York
tribune.
                                                    S-16133
Library of Congress   HJ6085 1888.S3

NT 0039960   DLC

The tariff of 1883 and the Mills bill. Rates of duty fixed
by the tariff of 1883, and now in force, compared with
the previous rates and those of the Mills bill, and accompanied by a detailed statement of the importations of
foreign goods and duties paid on the same in the two
years ending June 30th, 1883, and June 30th, 1887,
reprinted in part from the Tribune almanac for 1884.
2d ed. New York, The Tribune, 1888.
cover-title, 3-22 p. 27½ x 21½cm.
"Imports and duties from 1791 to 1887" printed on inside of back cover.
1. Tariff—U. S.—Law. 2. U. S.—Comm.—Stat. 3. Mills bill.   I. U. S.
Laws, statutes, etc. II. The Tribune almanac and political register. III.
New York tribune.
                                              8-17493†
Library of Congress   HJ6085.1888.S4
                            (Copyright 1888: 25931)

NT 0039961   DLC

*BROAD-   Tariff of fees adopted by the medical
SIDE   profession for Richmond city. Richmond,
1850   Ritchie & Dunnavant, Prs., 1850.
.T375   broadside. 43 x 36cm.

          1. Medical care, Cost of—Richmond.

NT 0039962   ViU

*
R728
.T37   Tariff of fees, adopted [sic] by the
1858   medical profession of the County of Mecklen-
1950ed.burg Va. Boydton, ⟨Job Office⟩ Print.,
1858. [i. e., 195-?]
10 p. (photocopy) 17cm.
Photocopy (positive) made in [195-?] from the
original in the possession of the Virginia
Historical Society.

          1. Medical fees—Mecklenburg Co., Va.

NT 0039963   ViU

TARIFF of Fees made by the Judges of the
Superior Courts of Common Law,...1871.
Toronto,1872.

14 p.

NT 0039964   MH-L

Tariff of minimum rates for the state of Texas. Dallas, Tex., Press of J. F. Worley, 1903.

254 p. incl. tables, col. diagrs. 20ᶜᵐ.

1. Insurance, Fire—Texas. 2. Insurance, Fire—Rates and tables.

Library of Congress   HG9769.T18   7–28032†

NT 0039965   DLC

Tariff of rates for insurance against fire,
with rules and regulations, adopted at Chicago,
October, 1854. Chicago, F. H. Bacon, printer.
1854.

84 p.   23 cm.

NT 0039966   ICHi

Tariff of the colony of Victoria, including **excise**
duties. Corrected to March, 1893.
Melb., 1893.
38 p.

NT 0039967   CSt

Tariff of the Confederate States of America
approved by Congress,... Charleston, 1861.

NT 0039968   MBAt

Tariff of the United States. [1882]
    see under   The Metropolitan industrial
league, New York.

The tariff on lumber. Several reasons **why**
the present tariff should not be repealed.
Proceedings of a meeting of lumbermen of the
Saginaw valley, held at East Saginaw, March 10
1870. Facts and statistics of the lumber
business of the Saginaw valley. East Saginaw,
Mich., Daily enterprise steam print, 1870.
14 p.

NT 0039970   MiD-B

337.3
D865p   The tariff on salt.   n.p. [1872?]
32p.

No.20 in a volume of pamphlets lettered: Tracts on political economy;
no.1 being: Dudley, T. H. Protection to
home industry. 1880.

NT 0039971   IU

Tariff, or Free trade. Which is up?
    N.Y., 1888

HF1755
.T187

NT 0039972   DLC

Tariff, or rates of duties, payable from and
after the 3rd of March 1833
    see under   Lincoln, Levi R

Tariff, or rates of duty, after the thirtieth of June, 1816, on
all goods, wares and merchandise, imported into the United
States of America; as established by act of Congress of the
twenty-seventh of April, one thousand eight hundred and
sixteen, entitled "An act to regulate the duties on imports and
tonnage". Washington, D. C., 1816.

23 p. 22½ᶜᵐ.

1. Tariff—U. S.—Law.   I. U. S. Laws, statutes, etc.   II. Title.

Library of Congress   HJ6085.1816.R2   8–21092

NT 0039974   DLC MB PHi NIC

HJ608
1824
.R2   **Tariff, or rates of duty, after the thirtieth
day of June 1824, on all goods, wares & merchandise, imported into the United States of
America, carefully compiled and corrected, by
a person well acquainted with custom-house
business. New-York, Printed and published
by S. Gould and son, 1824.
108 p. table. 19 cm.

1. Tariff - U.S. - law. I. U. S. Laws,
statutes, etc.

NT 0039975   NjR PPL

Tariff; or, Rates of duty on goods, wares and merchandise, imported into the United States of America ... 1814
    see under   U. S. Laws, statutes, etc.

TARIFF,or rates of duty,on all goods,**wares,**
and merchandizes imported into the United
States. [New York?,1817?].

pp.21.

NT 0039977   MH

Tariff, or rates of duties, on all goods, wares,
and merchandise, imported into the United
States of America ... Philadelphia, 1823
    see under   Mortimer & Vallette, ed.

Tariff; or, Rates of duty on goods, wares and
merchandise, imported into the United States of
America, as established by acts of Congress and
treasury decisions, from and after September,
1841
    see under   U. S. Laws, statutes, etc.

Tariff; or, Rates of duty payable, according to the existing laws and Treasury decisions, on the first day of
July, 1828 ... Washington, Printed by E. De Krafft,
1828.

1 p. l., [35]–111 p. 28 x 22ᶜᵐ.
Large paper edition.

1. Tariff—U. S.—Law.   I. U. S. Laws, statutes, etc.

8–33403†

Library of Congress   HJ6085.1828.E2

NT 0039980   DLC MB

BR   382.70971 T13
   **Tariff or rates of duty, payable on goods,
wares & merchandise, imported into Canada,
in conformity with an Act of Parliament
assented to on the 15th August, 1866.
Alphabetically arranged by an Officer of
the Customs. Montreal, Printed by A.A.
Stevenson, 1866.
24 p.

In original pink paper covers.

NT 0039981   CaOTP

Tariff pamphlets.
   v. p.
   n. t.-p.

NT 0039982   PU

The TARIFF policy of the government [of Canada];the two trade policies compared. Splendid
results from the liberal policy. n.p.,[1911?]

pp.28.

NT 0039983   MH

Tariff problems, British and American
    see under   American Academy of Political
and Social Science, Philadelphia.

Tariff protection
    see under   Committee of the Democratic
Members of Congress.

Tariff, protection; extracts from periodicals.
7 pamphlets in box.

NT 0039986   DNW

The tariff protects American from inundation during
economic storm
    see under   Republican Party. National Committee, 1932-1936.

The Tariff question; a few questions to intelligent
voters. n.d.
    [2] p. T. [Dawson pamphlets, v. 29,
no. 17]

NT 0039988   NcU

[The Tariff question, 1820–1828]
    29 pams. in 2 v.
    [V. 1. 1820–1827] includes Memorial of the merchants ... in Salem to the Congress of the U. S.; Report of a committee of the citizens of Boston ... opposed to a further increase of duties; The American system, by Nathan Hale, and 18 other similar pamphlets. [V. 2. 1827–1828] includes Minutes of evidence taken before the Committee of manufactures, 1st sess. 20th Cong., and 7 other similar pamphlets.

NT   0039989   MiD

The tariff question. How it affects working men and business men
    see under   Republican Party. New York (State). State Committee.

337.3   [The tariff question in the U.S.: pamphlets
T1742   pro and con.   Boston, etc., 1865–90]
       5 pamphlets in 1v.   23cm.

NT   0039991   IU

The tariff question, or, Protection and free trade considered, in a series of articles, addressed to the American public. By a Mohawk Valley farmer. Utica, Beardsley & Lyon, printers, 1852.
    32 p. 22cm.

    1. Tariff—U. S. 2. Free trade and protection—Protection.   I. Mohawk Valley farmer.

                                 A 17–421

    Title from Univ. of Chicago   HF1714.T2   Printed by L. C.

NT   0039992   ICU NHi OO NN

The tariff questions; how it affects American jobs...
    see under   Republican Party. National Committee, 1948–1952.

... Tariff rates on principal agricultural products
    see under   [Wells, Clarence Floyd] 1892–

The Tariff record. v. 1, no. 1–   July 16, 1885– Washington.

NT   0039995   PHi

Tariff reform.   Published semi-monthly by the Tariff reform committee of the Reform club.

New York,
    v. 23½cm.   semimonthly.

    1. Tariff—U. S.—Period. 2. Free trade and protection—Free trade. I. New York reform club.

                             CA 8—1642 Unrev'd
    Library of Congress   HF1750.T2

NT   0039996   DLC WaSp OFH ICJ NN NcU DNW RPB MdBP

Tariff reform.
    [Numbers containing special discussions ...
    see under   New York Reform Club. Tariff Reform Committee.

Tariff reform. A plain talk to the working men of Lancashire and Yorkshire. [London: Tariff reform league, 1911?] 61 p. 16cm.

    Cover-title.
    Signed: D. L. B. S.
    "Revised and reprinted...from 'The Manchester Courier'."

    1. Free trade—Gt. Br. I. S, D.   L. B.
    N. Y. P. L.   November 5, 1941

NT   0039998   NN

Tariff reform and taxation [1909]
    see under   [Guernsey, Rocellus Sheridan] 1836–1918.

Tariff Reform League, *London.*
    The cost of living under "free trade" and protection. [London: J. Truscott & Son, 1910] 32 p. 16°.

    1. Tariff, Great Britain, 1910.   2. Living expenses, Great Britain,
    N. Y. P. L.   February 14, 1911.

NT   0040001   NN

Tariff Reform League, *London.*
    Employment under "free trade" and protection. [London: J. Truscott & Son, 1910] 20 p. 16°.

    1. Labor, Great Britain.
    N. Y. P. L.   February 7, 1911.

NT   0040002   NN

Tariff Reform League, *London.*
    The "exports pay for imports" argument. [London: J. Truscott & Son, 1910.] 12 p. 16°.

    1. Tariff, Great Britain, 1910.
    N. Y. P. L.   February 7, 1911.

NT   0040003   NN

Tariff reform league, London.
    Fiscal facts. "Every picture tells its own tale." 64 cartoons dealing, with "free trade" and tariff reform by E. Huskinson. London, The Tariff Reform League, 1909.
    64 p. 32°.
    Title from cover.
    I. Huskinson, E., illus.

NT   0040004   NN MH

Tariff reform league, *London.*
    ... Fiscal facts ... "Every picture tells its own tale." 64 cartoons dealing with "free trade" and tariff reform by E. Huskinson. (8th 100,000 ed.) [London] The Tariff reform league [1909]
    cover-title, 64 p. illus. 12 x 15cm.

    1. Tariff—Gt. Brit. 2. Free trade and protection—Protection.   I. Huskinson, E., illus.

                                         10–6590
    Library of Congress   HF2046.T3 1909 fi

NT   0040005   DLC

Tariff Reform League, *London.*
    The food tax bogey. [London: J. Truscott & Son, 1910.] 32 p. 16°.

    1. Food.—Taxation of, Great   Britain, 1910.
    N. Y. P. L.   February 7, 1911.

NT   0040006   NN

Tariff Reform League.
    "Free traders" and Germany. An "exposure" exposed. Letters of a "tariff tripper" and other light on Cobdenite "errors in perspective." [London: J. Truscott & Son, 1910] 52 p. 16°.

    1. Labor.—History, Germany.   2. Free trade, Germany.
    N. Y. P. L.   February 14, 1911.

NT   0040007   NN

Tariff reform league, *London.*
    A handbook for speakers and students of the policy of tariff reform and imperial preference. New (6th) ed., 1910. [London] The Tariff reform league, 1910.
    xx, 290 p., 1 l., xxxv p. 21cm. (On cover: Tariff reform league. Speakers' handbook)

    1. Gt. Brit.—Commercial policy. 2. Tariff—Gt. Brit. 3. Free trade and protection—Protection.

                                       A 11–477
    Title from Univ. of Minn.   Printed by L. C.

NT   0040008   MnU IEN OCIW MiU ICJ

---

337   **Tariff reform league,** *London.*
T17lh   A handbook for speakers and students of the policy of
1910   tariff reform and imperial preference. New (6th) ed., 1910. [London] The Tariff reform league, 1910.
    xx, 290 p., 1 l., xxxv p. 21cm. (On cover: Tariff reform league. Speakers' handbook)

    Errata slip inserted.

NT   0040009   IU NcU

Tariff reform league, *London.*
    A handbook for speakers and students of the policy of tariff reform and imperial preference. 7th ed., 1912. Westminster, The Tariff reform league, 1912.
    xx, 328, xxviii p. 21½cm.
    On cover: Tariff reform league. Speakers' handbook.

    1. Gt. Brit.—Commercial policy. 2. Tariff—Gt. Brit. 3. Free trade and protection—Protection.

                                       12–12753
    Library of Congress   HF2046.T22 1912

NT   0040010   DLC ICJ CaBViP CtY MH-BA

HC255   **Tariff reform league,** London.
.T2   The keys of industry. A handbook to the new British and "Key" industries exhibition. Organized by the Industrial section of the Tariff reform league. 1918. [London] 1918]
    x, 102 p. diagrs. (1 fold.) 24cm.
    p. 94–102 blank for "Memoranda".

    1. Gt. Brit.—Indus. 2. European war, 1914– — Economic aspects—Gt. Brit. 2. Mines and mineral resources—Gt. Brit.

NT   0040011   ICU

Tariff Reform League, London.
The menace to imperial preference. [London: J. Truscott & Son, 1910] 32 p. 16°.

1. Tariff, Great Britain, 1910.   2. Reciprocity, Great Britain.
N. Y. P. L.   February 14, 1911.

NT 0040012   NN

Tariff Reform League, London.
Monthly notes on tariff reform
see under title

Tariff Reform League, London.
Progress under "free trade" and protection. A comparison.
[London: J. Truscott & Son, 1910] 16 p. 16°.

1. Commerce.—Statistics.
N. Y. P. L.   February 7, 1911.

NT 0040014   NN

Tariff reform league, London.
The policy of tariff reform. London, J. Truscott & son, ltd. [1904]
cover-title, [204] p. illus. 21½ cm.
A collection of Tariff reform league leaflets.

1. Tariff—Gt. Brit. 2. Free trade and protection—Protection. I. Title.
                                              CA 18–228 Unrev'd
Library of Congress   HF2046.T3 1904

NT 0040015   DLC

Tariff Reform League.
Our imperial heritage. [London: Hill, Siffken & Co., 1910]
27 p., 1 map. 16°.

1. Reciprocity, Great Britain.   2. Tariff, Great Britain.
N. Y. P. L.   February 14, 1911.

NT 0040016   NN

Tariff reform league, London.
[Publications] London, Tariff reform league [1910]–1911.
4 nos. illus., tables. 16–24.5 cm.
Numbered arbitrarily.
Contents: – [no. 1] Who pays an import duty.–
[no. 2] A handbook for speakers ... 6th ed.,
1910. – [no. 3] What a tariff has done for the
American workman; facts and figures from the
official Board of trade report ... 1911. – [no. 4]
Price list [of] tariff reform posters.

NT 0040017   PHC

Tariff reform league, London.
Reports on labour and social conditions in Germany
... London, The Tariff reform league, 1910–
v. front., plates. 21½ cm.
Plates printed on both sides.
"The arrangements in connection with the itinerary ... were supervised
by the Tariff reform league, and the League also arranged for the collec-
tion and publication of the reports of the delegates."—Pref.

1. Labor and laboring classes—Germany. 2. Germany—Soc. condit.
                                              10–28486
Library of Congress   HD8450.T2

NT 0040018   DLC NcD N ICJ OClW

Tariff Reform League, London.
The shipping trade question. [London: J. Truscott & Son, 1910.] 16 p. 16°.

1. Shipping, Great Britain, 1910.
N. Y. P. L.   February 7, 1911.

NT 0040019   NN

Tariff reform league, London.
A short handbook for speakers and students of the policy
of preferential tariffs. [London] The Tariff reform league
[1903]
117, xi p. 21 cm.

1. Gt. Brit.—Commercial policy. 2. Tariff—Gt. Brit. 3. Free trade
and protection—Protection.
                                              4–32166
Library of Congress   HF2046.T22

NT 0040020   DLC

337.0942   Tariff Reform League, London.
T187s   A short handbook for speakers and
           students of the policy of preferential
           tariffs. 2d ed. [London, 1905]
           165, xxvi p. 22cm.

           1. Gt. Brit. Commercial policy.
           2. Tariff, Gt. Brit. 3. Free trade
           and protection. Protection.

NT 0040021   IEN

HF   Tariff reform league, London.
2046   A short handbook for speakers and students of the pol-
T22   icy of preferential tariffs (5th ed.) [London] The Tariff
1909   reform league, 1908.
         xx, 256, xxvi p. 21 cm.
         On cover: Tariff reform league. Speakers' handbook.
                                              HF2046.T22 1908
         —— Supplement to the Speakers' handbook (5th ed.) ...
         London, The Tariff reform league [1909]
         1 p. l., 43, iii p. 21 cm.
         1. Gt. Brit.—Commercial policy. 2. Tariff—Gt. Brit. 3. Free trade and
         protection—Protection.
                                              10–6588–9
         Library of Congress   HF2046.T22 1909

NT 0040022   WU

Tariff Reform League, London.
A tariff reform catechism. Questions and answers. [Lon-
don: J. Truscott & Son, 1910.] 16 p. 16°.

1. Tariff, Great Britain, 1910.
N. Y. P. L.   February 7, 1911.

NT 0040023   NN

Tariff Reform League, London.
The tariff reformer's Enquire within. 100 questions and answers on tariff reform. A reprint, with additions, of the results of
the prize competitions published during the year 1913, in "Monthly
notes on tariff reform"... Published by the Tariff Reform
League. London, 1914. 1 p.l., 62 p. 16°.

1. Protection, Gt. Br., 1914.
N. Y. P. L.   October 5, 1914.

NT 0040024   NN

HF2046   Tariff reform league, London.
.T3   The tariff reformer's enquire within; ...
1914   London, 1914–

NT 0040025   DLC

Tariff reform league, London.
The **Tariff** reformer's pocket book and vade mecum ...
London, The Tariff reform league

Tariff reform league, London.
... Things one ought to know. (Illustrated) [New and
rev. ed.] [London] Tariff reform league [1909?]
cover-title, 30, [2] p. illus. 12 x 15½ cm.

1. Tariff—Gt. Brit. 2. Free trade and protection—Protection.
                                              10–6591
Library of Congress   HF2046.T3 1909 th

NT 0040027   DLC

HF2046   [Tariff reform league, London]
.T3   The truth about tariff reform and free trade.
1909tr   [London, 1909]

NT 0040028   DLC

Tariff Reform League, London.
Wages under "free trade" and protection. [London: J.
Truscott & Son, 1910] 16 p. 16°.

1. Wages, Great Britain.
N. Y. P. L.   February 7, 1911.

NT 0040029   NN

Tariff Reform League, London.
What a tariff has done for the American workman. Facts and
figures...on the cost of living, rates of wages, &c., in American
towns. London: the league, 1911. 23(1) p. 8°.

1. Living expenses, U. S., 1900-11.   2. Wages, U. S.
N. Y. P. L.   October 19, 1911.

NT 0040030   NN WU

Tariff Reform League, London.
Who pays an import duty? [London: J. Truscott & Son,
1910] 24 p. 16°.

1. Tariff, Great Britain, 1910.
N. Y. P. L.   February 2, 1911.

NT 0040031   NN

The **Tariff** reformer's pocket book and vade mecum ...
London, The Tariff reform league
v. ports. 12½ cm.
Editor: G. G. Anderson.

1. Tariff—Gt. Brit. 2. Free trade and protection—Protection. I. Anderson, G. Graham, ed. II. Tariff reform league, London.
                                              CA 12–293 Unrev'd
Library of Congress   HF2046.T4

NT 0040032   DLC IU

The Tariff review ...
see   American economist.

Tariff revision. Annals of the American
Academy of Political and Social Science
see under   American Academy of Political
and Social Science, Philadelphia.

Tariff revision, 1912-1915. — Peking : Waichiaopu
Press, 1921.
ix, 86 p. — (Diplomatic documents)
At head of title: Ministry of Foreign Affairs.
Microfilm (positive)

I. China. Wai chiao pu.

NT   0040035   ICRL

Tariff revision, reciprocity and the farmer
see under   Harris, William Alexander,
1841-1909.

The Tariff settled by the French king ...
September 18, 1664 ...
see   The Tarif settled ...

Tariff Silver Mining Company.
Report [by the superintendent.   New York,
K. Tompkins, 1879]
16 p.   1 map., 3 pl.   4°.

NT   0040038   NN

... **Tariff statistics.** Statistical tables of the imports and
exports of the United States, and production of various
articles of commerce in the United States and foreign
countries for the years 1909, 1910, 1911, and 1912 ...
Washington ₍Govt. print. off.₎ 1913.
22 p. 23½ᶜᵐ.   (₍U. S.₎ 63d Cong. 1st sess. Senate. Doc. 180)
Presented by Mr. Bristow. Ordered printed September 6, 1913.

1. U. S.—Comm. 2. Tariff—U. S.   ɪ. Title.

Library of Congress   HF3001.A45 1913

13-35720

NT   0040039   DLC OO MiU

A tariff symposium. The ethics of patriotism.
By Prof. George Gunton ... The morality of
protection. By Rev. Cyrus Hamlin ...
see under   Home Market Club, Boston.

329.3
T174   Tariff texts by James G. Blaine and others.
New York, 1888.
16p. 22cm.

At head of title: No.17.

1. Campaign literature, 1888.   Democratic.

NT   0040041   OrU

... Tariff texts. Republicans against the republican platform. Speeches of Blaine, Grant,
Garfield, Hamson, Morton and other republican
leaders ...   [n.p., 1889?]
16 p.   20 cm.   [Pamphlets on free trade,
v. 3]
At head of title: no. 26.

NT   0040042   CU

337.05
A519t   Tariff tract, no.1–
no.1–
1880–
Philadelphia, American iron and steel assoc.,
1880–
v. 22cm.

1. Tariff – U.S. I. Title.

NT   0040043   LNT MB PPL MiGr NcU Nh PP

Tariff vs. distribution. [n.p., 18-   ]
8p.

YA 8491

NT   0040044   DLC

Tariffa de pesi e mesure ...
see under   [Pasi, Bartholomeo di] 16th cent.

Tariffa de pexi e mesvre ...   Venesia, 1503
see under   [Paxi, Bartholomeo di]

Tariffa de tvtte le marcǎcie da ogni precio ...
see under   [Manenti, Giacomo] 16th cent.

Tariffa de tvtti li ori che correno per il mõdo
redutti da li suoi pretij in ducati correnti
da £ 6 β 4 p et calando & crescendo
di pretio questa seruirà in perpetuo
see under   [Mariani, Giovanni] 16th cent.

Tariffa dei dazi doganali ...
see under   Italy. Laws, statutes, etc.

Tariffa delle analisi chimicho-microscopiche e
batteriologiche. 43pp. 8°. [Ferrara, G. Mon-
fanari, 1895.]

NT   0040050   DNLM

Tariffa delle gabelle, che devono pagarsi
alla magnifica dogana, alle porti della città,
& alli passaggieri dello stato di Siena, per
le mercantie, e robbe, che si traono, mettono,
ò passano. In Siena, Nella Stamperia del
Pubblico, 1664.
91 p. 30cm.

1. Tariff - Italy.

NT   0040051   NNC

Tariffa delle Gabelle per Firenze. Firenze, Cambiagi,
1781.   312 p.   DLC : YA 3209

NT   0040052   DLC

La Tariffa delle puttane di Venegia (XVIe siècle)
Texte italien et traduction littérale.   Paris,
Isidore Liseux, 1883.
viii, 87 [1] p.   16 cm.
Attributed to Pietro Aretino by Gershon
Legman in his Advance List, 50.
"Tiré à cent cinquante exemplaires
numérotés, 41".
I. Aretino, Pietro, 1492-1556. II. Title.

NT   0040053   OU

**Tariffa delle puttane di Venegia, accompagné d'un catalogue des
principales courtisanes de Venise,** tiré des archives vénitiennes
(XVIe siècle) et traduit pour la première fois en français. Introd.,
essai bibliographique par Guillaume Apollinaire. Paris, Bibliothèque des curieux ₍1911₎
175 p. 15 cm. (Le Coffret du bibliophile)
At head of title: Les poèmes arétinesques.
Italian text with French translation.

1. Prostitution—Venice—Poetry.   I. Series.

PQ4561.A1T3514 1911   76-453365
MARC

NT   0040054   DLC MiDW NIC

274.5311
T174   Tariffa delle spese, e cere che occorrono
in cadauna fonzione, e processione di ogni
genere della veneranda scola di San Rocco e
sua chiesa. ₍Venezia₎ P. Zerletti, stampator di scola, 1784.
116p. 27cm.

1. Venice. San Rocco (Church) 2. Venice.
Scuola di San Rocco.

NT   0040055   IU

Tariffa di ogni sorta di monete in corso con l' apposizione dell'
agio alle monete di oro; aggiuntovi le tavole monetarie dal num.
1 fino al 50 di ciascuna specie.   Fuligno: G. Tomassini, 1823.
40 p. 12°.

ɪ. Money.—Tables, Italy.
N. Y. P. L.   November 24, 1913.

NT   0040056   NN

18th
cent.   TARIFFA, eonovredes, en los prevs de las
medicines, tant simples, com compostes
segons lovs antich y modern. Feta per
los consols y Collegi de Apothecaris de
Barcelona. Barcelona, A. y B. Ferrer [1705]
[4], 35, 20p. 20cm.
1. Drugs - Prices and sale.

NT   0040057   CtY-M

Tariffa generale delle imposte di consumo
compresi i generi tassati in base al
valore e in vigore a datare dal...195...
Cuneo, Tip. Casa Editrice "I.C.A.",
1952.
40p.

NT   0040058   NNU

337
T1741

Tariffa generale, o siano, Conti fatti per qualunque sorta di cose a rubbi, libbre, ed oncie, aune, o rasi, od emine, o qualunque altra cosa a numero, peso, e misura. Pavia, Stamperia del R. I. monastero di S. Salvatore, 1785.
340p. incl.tables.

"Fiere principali che si fanno ne'stati di S. R. M. di qua da'monti rettificate a norma de'nuovi stabilimenti": p.59-71 inserted at end; "Tariffa delle monete correnti negli stati di S. R. M.

di qua dal mare a tenor de'r. editti de'15 febbrajo 1755, e 30 dicembre 1785, e manifesti camerali de'30 giugno 1755 ... 4 e 25 gennajo 1786": p.72-81 inserted at end.

1. Tariff-Italy. 2. Italy--Fairs.

NT 0040060   IU

Tariffa perpetva con le ragion fatte per scontro di qualunque ... 1553
see under [Mariani, Giovanni] 16th cent.

Kress
Room

Tariffa sopra il corso delle monete d'oro, e d'argento dello Stato Pontificio, e forastiere. [Perugia, Stamperia del Costantini, 1787]
[8] p. 21.5 cm.

1.Foreign exchange - Tables. 2.Money - Italy.

NT 0040062   MH-BA

Wing
fZP
635
.B 435

TARIFFE della gabella grossa di Bologna. Bolona [ ], Per A. Benacci, 1580, e ristampate da l'herede del Benacci, 1647.
[14],43,[3]p. front. 33cm.

Title vignette.
Typographic front.; initials; head and tail pieces.

NT 0040063   ICN

Tariffe Du Presage universel des Providences de La France ... Nismes, 1583.

NT 0040064   PU

HF
5698
T3
1571
Cage

Tariffe et concordance des poids de plusieurs prouinces les plus pratiquez au temps present, par les marchãs françoys, allemans & plusieurs autres ... A Lyon, Par Charles Pesnot, 1571.

2 pts in 1 v. Pt.1: [8] 100 l. *⁸ a-m⁸, n⁴; pt.2: [2] 9-83 [1] 84-189 l. A², B-K⁸, L⁴, M-2A⁸, 2B². 8vo.
Half title-page on sig. *4r: Tables pour sauoir la valeur de la cane et du pan ... Le tout ... calculé par Mammes Gisse, de Lengres.

NT 0040065   DFo

... Tariffe et distribution du prix des grains à toutes les petites mesures à proportion de la charge ... [Aix? 1635?]
12, [4] p. 15 cm.

Caption title.
Imperfect: p.1-2 wanting.
Bound with Minuti, Joseph, Tariffes contenant liquidation des droits de disme ... 1635.

NT 0040066   MH-BA

Beinecke
Library
1972
+64

Tariffe generalle dv diocese dv Pvy, et pays de Velay. Av Pvy, [ar François Varolles, imprimeur de la ville, 1649.
1 p.[ ]., 5-198+ p. 33 cm.

Signatures: A-Q⁶R²⁺ (A1 blank)
Imperfect: p. 85-86 and all after p. 198 wanting.
1. Costs (Law) - Puy, France. 2. Costs (Law) - Velay, France. 3. Taxation - Velay, France. I. Puy, France. II. Velay, France.

NT 0040067   CtY

... Tariffe per il facchinaggio delle merci varie
see under Genoa. Ordinances, etc.

Tariffe postali e telegrafiche e disposizioni complementari sul carteggio dei sindaci ...
see under [Italy. Ministero delle poste e delle telecomunicazioni]

Tariffe postali, telegrafiche e telefoniche: interno, estero, aerea
see under [Italy. Ministero delle poste e delle telecomunicazioni]

Tariffi, Natalia Rosi de
see Rosi de Tariffi, Natalia.

Tariffi, Terzo.
Caracas; guía histórico-artística e indicador general [por Terzo Tariffi y Natalia Rosi de Tariffi] Caracas, Editorial "Nueva Venezuela" [195-]
366 p. illus. (part fold.) ports., fold. map. 18 cm. (Guías venezolanas)

1. Caracas—Descr.—Guide-books.   I. Rosi de Tariffi, Natalia, joint author.

F2341.C2T3   53-19298

NT 0040072   DLC TxU LU OC1 CtY FU NN

Tariffi, Terzo.
Los clásicos griegos de Francisco Miranda. Caracas, Tip. Americana, 1950.
26 p. 23 cm.

1. Greek literature—Bibl.—Catalogs.   I. Venezuela. Biblioteca Nacional, Caracas.

Z907.T3   51-27412

NT 0040073   DLC IU NN OC1 TxU NNC NcD CtY DPU

Tariffs. 1840-1841. [v. p., 1840-1841]
5 pamphlets in 1 v. 31 cm.
Binder's title.
CONTENTS.
1. Vandenbussche, C. Nouveau tarif des douanes belges ... Bruxelles, 1840.
2. Portugal. Laws, statutes, etc., 1834-1853 (Maria II) Carta de lei [de 9 de outubro de 1841] [Lisbon, 1841]
3. Spain. Laws, statutes, etc., 1833-1868 (Isabella II) Ley de aduanas, aranceles é instruccion ... Madrid, 1841.
4. Portugal. Laws, statutes, etc., 1834-1853 (Maria II) Pauta geral das alfandegas. Lisbon, 1841.
5. Spain. Laws, statutes, etc., 1833-1868 (Isabella II) Ley de aduanas, aranceles é instruccion ... Madrid, 1841.
1. Tariff—Collections.

HJ6041.T35   48-36546

NT 0040074   DLC

Tariffs and trade barriers
see under Academy of Political Science, New York.

Tariffs benefit the Farmer
see under [American Tariff League]

The tariffs of 1883 and 1890 on imports into the United States
see under U.S. Laws, statutes, etc.

The tariffs of 1890 and 1894 on imports into the U.S., and customs administrative act of June 10, 1890
see under U.S. Laws, statutes, etc.

Tariflöhne der Beschäftigten im Organisationsbereich des Verbandes ...
see under Verband der Gemeinde- und Staatsarbeiter, Berlin.

Tariflohnkatalog für betriebe der privatkapitalistischen wirtschaft
see under
Balling, Heinz.

Tarifní věstník. roč. 1-   1945-
V Praze [Dopravní nakl.]
v. in   illus., tables. 30 cm. weekly.
Issued by Ministerstvo dopravy.

1. Railroads—Czechoslovak Republic—Rates.   I. Czechoslovak Republic. Ministerstvo dopravy.

HE1887.C9A3   61-36284

NT 0040081   DLC

Tarifno-kvalifikatsionnyi spravochnik dlia rabochikh lesozagotovok
see under [Cherniaev, S   N   ] ed.

Tarifnoe otdielenie Departamenta tamozhennykh sborov
see
Russia. *Departament tamozhennykh sborov. Tarifnoe otdelenie.*

Тарифное руководство.
Москва, Трансжелдориздат [etc.]
nos. in   v. 25-27 cm.
At head of title, 19   : Народный комиссариат путей сообщения СССР; 19   : Министерство путей сообщения СССР.
A few nos. in 1931 were issued by Народный комиссариат водного транспорта СССР.
Most of the issues were pub. as supplements to Сборник тарифов железнодорожного и водного транспорта.
L. C. set incomplete: scattered nos. are wanting.

1. Tariff—Russia.   I. Russia (1923-   U. S. S. R.) Narodnyi komissariat putei soobshcheniia. II. Russia (1923-   U.S.S.R.) Ministerstvo putei soobshcheniia.
Title transliterated: Tarifnoe rukovodstvo.

HE1895.T3   49-24961*

NT 0040084   DLC

Tarifnyĭ sˮezd predstaviteleĭ russkikh zheleznykh dorog, *Leningrad*
see
Obshchiĭ tarifnyĭ sˮezd predstaviteleĭ russkikh zheleznykh dorog, *Leningrad.*

Tarifnyĭ sˮezd predstaviteleĭ zheleznykh dorog i sudokhodnykh predpriĭatiĭ.
... Протоколы ... Тарифного съезда представителей железных дорог и судоходных предприятий ...
Москва, 1ʋ
_ _ ʌ v. 26-27 cm.
At head of title: Народный комиссариат путей сообщения.
1. Railroads—Russia—Rates. 2. Railroads—Russia—Freight. 3. Inland navigation—Russia. I. Russia (1923—. U. S. S. R.) Narodnyĭ komissariat puteĭ soobshchenii͡a.
Title transliterated: Protokoly.
HE2175.T3   47-44475

NT 0040086   DLC

Tarifordnung B für Gefolgschaftsmitglieder
see
Germany. Reichstreuhänder für den Öffentlichen Dienst.

Tarifordnung für die OT.
see
Germany. Organisation Todt.

Tarifordnungen, Reichstarifordnung für die Heimarbeit im deutschen Kunstblumengewerbe
see
Germany. Laws, statutes, etc.

Die tarifreform im Deutschen Reiche nach dem gesetze vom 15. juli 1879. B-E ... Jena, G. Fischer, 1880.
2 v. 22ᶜᵐ. (Supplement v-vi der Jahrbücher für nationalökonomie und statistik)
"A. Die getreidezölle. Von dr. J. Conrad" appeared in Jahrbücher für nationalökonomie und statistik, 34. bd., 1879.
CONTENTS.—(1) B. Die neuen deutschen holzzölle. Von dr. J. Lehr. c. Die rohstoffe und erzeugnisse der textil-industrie im zolltarife vom 15. juli 1879. Von dr. J. Gensel.—(2) D. Die eisenzölle. Von F. Ritschl. E. Die zölle auf droguen, glas, leder, papier und materialwaaren. Von A. Bayerdörffer.
1. Tariff—Germany. I. Lehr, Julius, 1845-1894. II. Gensel, Julius *i. e.* Walther Julius, 1835- III. Ritschl, F. IV. Bayerdörffer, A.
14-15906
Library of Congress   HB5.J3 vol. 34

NT 0040090   DLC CtY CU MiU OU OCU

Tarifs de confection et de réparation des effects d'habillement, de chaussure et de grand équipment. 12 juillet, 1900. 3ᵉ édition, à jour jusqu' en juin 1904. Paris, H. Charles-Lavauzelle [1904]
130 p. 9°.
n. t.-p.
Title from cover.

NT 0040091   NN

Tarifs des droits d'aydes, pour la generalité de Rouen. A Paris, Chez la Veuve Saugrain, & P. Prault, Imprimeur des fermes & droits du roy, 1724 [i.e. 1691-1724]
14 pts. in 1 v. 26cm.
Each part has separate title-page and paging. Parts are not bound in order as shown on p. [3].

Continued in next column

Continued from preceding column

Contents.--Election de Rouen. 1724.--Election d'Arques et d'Eu. 1724.--Election de Neuf-Chastel. [1724]--Election de Lyons. [1724]--Election de Gisors. 1724.--Election de Chaumont et Magny. 1724.--Election de Pont-De-L'Arche. [1723]--Election de Ponteau-De-Mer. [1723]--Election de Pont-L'Evesque.

[1696]--Election de Caudebec. 1723.--Election de Montivilliers. 1723.--Election d'Andely. [1691]--Election d'Evreux. [1723]--Election d'Eu. 1723.

NT 0040094   NNC

[Tarifs, modèle de bordereau et instruction see under [France. Assemblée nationale constituante, 1789-1791. Comité des monnoies]

336.23
T174   Tarifs pour établir la contribution personnelle dans les différentes municipalités. Paris, 1790.
19p. tables(part fold.)

NT 0040096   IU NNC

Tarifschema. Tarifvorschriften für den Transport von Gütern. [Berlin, G. Bernstein, 1876?]
12 p. f°.
n. t.-p.
In: TPG p. v. 7.

NT 0040097   NN

Tarifsko-transportni vesnik (TTV); zvanična saopštenja tarifske i transportne službe.
Beograd.
v. 30 cm. irregular.
Issued by various governmental agencies of Yugoslavia; Jan. 1954- by the association Jugoslovenske železnice.
Includes legislation.
1. Railroads—Yugoslavia—Rates. I. Jugoslovenske železnice. II. Yugoslavia. Laws, statutes, etc.
HE3241.T3   55-36203

NT 0040098   DLC ICRL

305.3 21 v.9
***** .... Tarifverträge. 1. bis 5. Tausend. M. Gladbach, Verlag der Westdeutschen Arbeiter-Zeitung, 1905.
32 p. 21ᶜᵐ. (*In* Arbeiter-Bibliothek, 9. Heft.)

NT 0040099   ICJ

Tarifverträge des deutschen Holzarbeiter-Verbandes.
See under
Deutscher Holzarbeiter-Verband, Berlin.

HD
4966
M52   Die Tarifverträge im Bauschlosser- und
G47   Anschlägergewerbe. [Einleitung vom Vorstand des Deutschen Metallarbeiter-Verbandes] Stuttgart, A. Schlicke, 1913.
200p. 19cm.
1. Wages - Metal workers - Germany
2. Metal workers - Germany I. Deutscher Metallarbeiter-Verband

NT 0040101   WU

Tarifvertrag der graphischen Arbeitnehmer ...
see under
Hauptverband der Graphischen Unternehmungen Osterreichs.

Tarifvertrag über die betriebsverfassung in den betrieben des baugewerbes
see under
Fitting, Karl, 1912-

Wason   Tarih araştırmaları, 1940-1941. Istanbul,
DS748.4   Cumhuriyet Matbaası, 1941.
K16   [145]-296,4 p. 25cm. (Ankara Universitesi. Dil ve Tarih-Coğrafya Fakültesi. Tarih Enstitüsü. Neşriyatı. No. 4)
1. Historical research. I. Series.

NT 0040104   NIC

Tarih dergisi. v.1- 1949- Istanbul.
v. 25 cm. Irregular.
Issued by: Istanbul Üniversitesi Edebiyat Fakültesi.
1. Turkey - Hist. - Period. I. Istanbul. Universite. Edebiyat Fakültesi.

NT 0040105   MiU

DR
401   Tarih dünyası.
T12   1-   1949-
Istanbul.
v. in
Editor: 1949-   Niyazi Ahmet Banoğlu.
1. Turkey - Hist. - Period. I. Banoğlu, Niyazi Ahmet.

NT 0040106   CLU InU

DR
401   Tarih hazinesi.
T14   1-   1950-
Istanbul.
v. in
Editor: 1950-   Ibrahim Hakkı Konyalı.
"Sayı" 1-   also called "Yıl" 1-
and "Cilt" 1-
1. Turkey - Hist. - Period. I. Konyalı, Ibrahim Hakkı.

NT 0040107   CLU InU

Tarih vesikaları.
cilt 1-3. (sayı 1-15) Haz. 1941-May. 1949.
Yeni seri. cilt 1- (sayı 1 (16)-Ağ. 1955-
[Ankara. 1941-
v. plates, facsims. (part fold., some in pockets) maps (part fold.) 28ᶜᵐ.
Published by Maarif Vekâleti Türk Kültür Eserleri Bürosu.
Editors: H. İlaydın and A. S. Erzi.
Publication suspended between Ekim 1944-May. 1949, and between May. 1949-Ağ. 1955.

NT 0040109   NNC NIC

DR 741 TÂRÎH-İ EDİRNE;HİKÂYET-İ BEŞİR ÇELEBİ ₍HAZIR-
.E4 T18 layan₎ Ismail Hikmet Ertaylan.   Istanbul,
Ayaydın Basımevi, 1946.
facsim: 21 p.   (Türk Edebiyatı Örnekleri,
3)

Istanbul--Üniversitesi. Yayınlar: Edebiyat
Fakültesi--Türk dil ve Edebiyatı Dalı, no.3.

1. Edirne--Hist. 2. Manuscripts--Turkish--
Facsimiles. I. Ertaylan,Ismail,Hikmet,1899-
ed. II. Tc.: Hikâ   yet-i Beşir Çelebi.

NT   0040110   InU NNC

Tarihi Osmani Encümeni
see
Türk Tarih Encümeni.

DR   **Tarihten sesler.**
401   1-   1943-
T174   Istanbul.
v. illus.

No. 1-   also called v. 1-
Editor: 1943-   Iskender F. Sertelli.

1. Turkey - Hist. - Period. I. Sertelli, Iskender Fahri.

NT   0040112   CLU

Tarija, *Bolivia. Alcaldía.*
Informe del desenvolvimiento municipal de Tarija, período
de 1933 al primer trimestre de 1941, administración del sr. Isaác
S. Attié ... Tarija, Imprenta "Renacimiento," 1941.
1 p. l., 41 p. incl. tables. plates. 30ᵐ.

1. Tarija, Bolivia—Pol. & govt.   i. Attié, Isaác S., 1894–

Library of Congress   JS15.T3
45–50200

NT   0040113   DLC

Tarija, Bolivia. Colegio de propaganda fide.

Tamajuncosa, Antonio.
Descripción de las misiones, al cargo del Colegio de
Nuestra Señora de los angeles de la villa de Tarija, por
fray Antonio Tamajuncosa ... 1. ed. Buenos-Aires, Imprenta del estado, 1836.

Tarija, Bolivia. Colegio franciscano
see
Tarija, Bolivia. Colegio de propaganda fide.

**Tarija, Bolivia. Colegio Nacional "Juan Misael
Saracho".**
Monografía del Colegio Nacional "Juan
Misael Saracho"
see under   Pacheco Loma, Misael.

G352.0842   **Tarija, Bolivia. Ordinances, etc.**
T174a   Acuerdos, reglamentos y ordenanzas municipales.
Ed. municipal.   Tarija, Tip. de "El Trabajo",
1888 [cover 1889]
68p. 20cm.

Cover title: Reglamentos, ordenanzas y acuerdos
municipales dictados en 1,888.

1. Tarija, Bolivia - Pol. & govt.

NT   0040117   TxU

Lilly   **Tarija,Bolivia(City).   Ordinances,local laws,
RA 644   etc.**
.S6 T18   Ordenanzas municipales sobre higiene y
Mendel   salubridad. -- Tarija : Tipografía Guadal-
quivir, ₍1908?₎.
11 p. ; 20.4 cm.

Cover title.
Not in Pané-Moreno,Bibl.bol.
Dated at end: Diciembre de 1908.
In original wrappers.

NT   0040118   InU

**Tarija, Bolivia. Universidad Autónoma "Juan Misael Sa-
racho"**
see
Tarija, Bolivia. Universidad "Juan Misael Saracho."

Tarija, Bolivia. Universidad "Juan Misael Saracho."
Informe de labores.
Tarija.
v. 20 cm.

Continued by: Universidad Boliviana Juan
Misael Saracho. Informe de labores - Universidad Boliviana "Juan Misael Saracho."

LE27.T3A28
58–46445

NT   0040120   DLC

**Tarija, Bolivia. Universidad "Juan Misael
Saracho"**
see also   Tarija, Bolivia. Colegio Nacional
"Juan Misael Saracho."

Tarija, Bolivia. Universidad "Misael Saracho"
see
Tarija, Bolivia. Universidad "Juan Misael Saracho."

9.1   Tarija, Bolivia (Province) Junta Agropecuaria
T17   Departamental.
Circular.
Tarija

1. Tarija, Bolivia (Province) Agriculture.

NT   0040123   DNAL

PL248   **Tarik Dursun, K.,** 1931-
.T9H3   Hasangiller; iki hikâye.   Ankara, Seçilmiş
1955   Hikâyeler Dergisi Kitapları ₍1955₎
130 p. (SHD kitapları, sayı 20)

NT   0040124   ICU

Tarik Halulu
see   Halulu, Tarik.

Tarik Kitai
see   Banakati, Davud ibn Muhammad, d.
1329 or 30.
Abdallae Beidavaei Historia sinensis.

Tārika zi' aḥōmū lanegūśna 'Iyāsū walanegūśna 'Iyō'as.
Annales regum Iyāsū II et Iyo'as. Edidit ₍et interpretatus
est₎ Ignatius Guidi. Parisiis, E Typographeo Reipublicae,
1910–12.
2 v. 25 cm. (Corpus scriptorum Christianorum orientalium, v. 61,
66. Scriptores Aethiopici, ser. 2, t. 6)
Ethiopic and French.

1. Ethiopia—Kings and rulers.   i. Guidi, Ignazio, 1844–1935, ed.
and tr.   (Series)

[BR60.C5A4 ser. 2, vol. 6]
A 53–5447

Catholic Univ. of   America. Library
for Library of Congress   ₍2₎

NT   0040127   DCU ViU CSt WU TNJ-R PPiPT OCU CtY UU

Tarika zi' ahomu lanegusna 'Iyasau walanegusna
'Iyo'as.
Annales regum Iyasu II et Iyo'as. Edidit
₍et interpretatus est₎ Ignatius Guidi.
Louvain, L. Durbecq, 1954.
2v.   25cm. (Corpus scriptorum Christiano-
rum orientalium, v.61,66. Scriptores
Aethiopici, t.28,29)

1. Ethiopia - Kings and rulers. i. Guidi,
Ignazio, 1844-1935, ed. and tr. Series.

NT   0040128   MoSC CtY-D OU MCW

BR 60   **TĀRĪKA ZI' AḤŌMŪ LANEGŪŚNA 'IYĀSŪ WALANEGŪŚNA**
.C83   **'Iyō'as**
v.61,66   Annales regum Iyāsū II et Iyo'as. Edidit
₍et interpretatus est₎ I. Guidi. Louvain,
Secrétariat du CorpusSCO, 1954-62 ₍v.1, 1962₎.
2 v. (Corpus scriptorum Christianorum
orientalium, v. 61, 66. Scriptores Aethiopici, t. 28-29)

Ethiopic and French.
Publisher varies: v. ₍2₎ L. Durbecq.

"Réimpression anastatique" of the
Paris ed. of 1910-12, issued as Scriptores
Aethiopici, ser. 2, t. 6.

1. Ethiopia--Kings and rulers. I. Adyām
Sagad II,Negus of Ethiopia. II. 'Iyo'as,
Negus of Ethiopia. III. Guidi,Ignazio,
844-1935,ed.   and tr. IV. Title.

NT   0040130   InU

PJ7538   **Ta'rikh al-adab al-'Arabī al-ḥadīth.**
.S25
Orien   **Sa'īd, Jamīl.**
Arab   تاريخ الأدب العربي الحديث للصفوف الثالثة المتوسطة؛ تأليف
جميل سعيد وعبد الرزاق محيي الدين وأحمد حامد الشربتي.
الطبعة ١ بغداد، مطبعة بغداد، ١٩٤٩.

Ta'rīkh al-dawlah al-Sa'dīyah.
تاريخ الدولة السعدية الدرعية التاكمادرتية، لؤلف جمول
الاسم. اعتنى بنشره جورج كولان. رباط، الطبعة الجديدة،
١٩٣٤.
5, 112, 13 p. 26 cm. ₍المجموعة ٢₎ (مطبوعات معهد العلوم العليا المغربية ؛
(Institut des hautes-études marocaines. Collection de textes arabes,
v. 2)
Added t. p.: Chronique anonyme de la dynastie sa'dienne.
1. Sa'adi dynasty. 2. Morocco—History—1516-1830. I. Colin,
Georges Séraphin, 1888-   ed. II. Series: Rabat, Morocco. Institut des hautes-études marocaines. Publications, v. 2. III. Series:
Rabat, Morocco. Institut des hautes-études marocaines. Collection
de textes arabes, v. 2.
DT321.T3
54–52224

NT   0040132   DLC ICU

D161   **Tārīkh al-Firinjah, Gesta Fracorum et aliorum
.9   Hierosolymitanorum. Arabic.**
.H3
Orien   **Ḥabashi, Ḥasan.**
Arab   الحرب الصليبية الأولى، تأليف حسن حبشى. الطبعة ١
مصر، دار الفكر العربي ١٩٤٧،

DS247
.K85R29
Orien
Arab

Tārīkh al-Kuwayt.
al-Rashīd, 'Abd al-'Azīz, 1883 or 4–
(Tārīkh al-Kuwayt)

تاريخ الكويت، لعبد العزيز الرشيد. بغداد -يطلب من
الكتبة العربية -1926.

Târîkh è gozîdè ... Les dynasties persanes
pendant la période musulmane depuis les
Saffârîdes jusques ...
see under   Hamd Allāh Mustawfī Qazīnī,
fl. 1330–1340.

تاريخ حياة طيب الذكر الامير علي بن الامير عبد القادر ملك الاقطاع
المغربي وسلطان الارياض الجزائرية. وضعه نخبة من افاضل
الكتاب تحت رعاية الامير محمد سعيد. دمشق، مطبعة الترقى،
.1918

176 p. 21 cm.

1. 'Alī ibn 'Abd al-Qādir, b. 1859 or 60.   I. Title: Ḥayāt al-Amīr
'Alī ibn al-Amīr 'Abd al-Qādir.
Title romanized: Tārīkh ḥayāt ṭayyib al-dhikr
al-Amīr 'Alī ibn al-Amīr 'Abd al-Qādir.

DT324.3.A33T3   N E 68–2936

NT   0040136   DLC

Ta'rīkh-d afghan.
See under
•Krusinski, Judass Tadeuss, 1675–1756.

Tarikh-i asham; récit de l'expédition de Mir-
Djumlah au pays d'Assam
see under   [Ahmad ibn Muhammad Vali]
fl. 1663.

The Tārīkh-i-guzīda, or "Select history" of
Hamdu'llāh Mustawff-i-Qazwīnī
see under   Hamd Allāh Mustwaff Qazvīnī,
fl. 1330–1340.

Tārīkh-i sayyah hoc est : *Chronicon peregrinantis...*
see under   [Krusinski, Judasz Tadeusz]
1675–1756.

Ta'rīkh-i-Sīstān.
A critical and explanatory translation of portions of the
anonymous Ta'rīkh-i-Sīstān ⌈by⌉ R. Park Johnson. Ann
Arbor, University Microfilms ⌈1941⌉;
(⌈University Microfilms, Ann Arbor, Mich.⌉ Publication no. 2986)
Microfilm copy of typescript. Positive.
Collation of the original, as determined from the film: xv, 380 l.
The translator's thesis—Princeton University.
Bibliography: leaves ix–xv.

I. Johnson, Roswell Park, tr.

Microfilm AC–1 no. 2986   Mic 56–4233

NT   0040141   DLC NNC

Tārīkh-i Sīstān.

تاريخ سيستان، تأليف در حدود ٤٤٥-٧٢٥، بتصحيح
ملك الشعراء بهار. طهران، محمد رمضانى ⌈1935⌉ .1914

36, 486 p. 26 cm.

1. Sistan—History.   I. Bahār, Malik al-Shu'arā Muḥammad
Taqī, 1886–1951, ed.
Title romanized: Tārīkh-i Sīstān.

DS324.S5T37   73–209915

NT   0040142   DLC

(Tārīkh ummah fī ḥayāt rajul, 17 Āb 1943–1947)

تاريخ امة في حياة رجل، ١٧ آب ١٩٤٢ - ١٩٤٧ : اربع سنوات
من العهد الوطني / انشاء وجمع وثائقه واصوله هيئة من الكتاب
المؤرخين - - - ⌈s. l. : s. n., 1947⌉ (دمشق : مطلبة اليقظة العربية)

470 p., ⌈43⌉ leaves of plates : ill. ; 24 cm.

1. Syria—Politics and government.   2. al-Qūwatlī, Shukrī, 1891–
1967.

DS98.T37   75–587042

NT   0040143   DLC

Tarikiainen, Viljo, 1879–
Aleksis Kivi, elämä ja teokset. 5.painos. Helsinki,
Söderström [1950]

561 p. illus., ports.

NT   0040144   MH

BX 3746
.G8T2
(Rare)

Tarillon, François, 1666–1735.
Lettre a Monseigneur le comte
dePontchartrain ... sur l'état
present des missions des peres jesuites
dans la Grece. Paris, N. Le Clerc,
1715.
[2], 173, [3] p. fold. map. 16 cm.
(Nouveaux memoires des missions de la
Compagnie de Jésus dans le Levant)
Caption title.
"Relation en forme de journal de la
nouvelle isle sortie de la mer dans le
Golfe de Santorin": p. 126–173.
1. Jesuits in Greece. 2. Santorin. I.
Jesuits. Letters from missions. II.
Series.

NT   0040145   ICU

2562
272
L561

Tarillon, François, 1666–1735.
Lettre du P. Tarillon à Monseign. le Comte de
Pontchartrain, Secr. d'Etat, sur l'état present des
Missions des Pp. [Jésuites dans la Grèce.
Lettres Edifiantes et Curieuses etc. Vol. 1. p. 1.
Paris, J.G. Merigot, 1780.

NT   0040146   DCU-H

Tarillon, François, 1666–1735.
Namurcum a Ludovico Magno expugnatum. Parisiis,
Apud Viduam S. Bénard, 1692.

12 p. 15 cm.
Poem.

I. Title.

PA8585.T23A7   52–50029

NT   0040147   DLC

Tarillon, François, 1666–1735.
Pulvis Pyrius, carmen. ⌈n. p., 16—⌉

21 p. 15 cm.

PA8585.T23A72   52–50028

NT   0040148   DLC

DS
51
K63T17ki

Tarīm, Cevat Hakkī
Kīrşehir tarih ve coğrafya lūgatī. [Kīrşehir] Kīrşehir
V[ilâyet] Matbaasī, 1940.
96 p. map.

1. Kīrşehir, Turkey.

NT   0040149   CLU NNC

Tarım, Cevat Hakkı
Kırşehir; tarihi üzerinde araştırmalar.
[Kırşehir] Kırşehir Vilâyet Matbaası, 1938

251 p. illus. (Kırşehir halkevi kitapsaray
yayın kolu neşriyatından, 1)

NT   0040150   MH CLU

DS51
.K47T2
(Or)

Tarim, Cevat Hakkı.
Kirşehir tarihi üzerinde araştırmalar. Kirşehir Vilâyet matbaası, 1938–40.
2 v. in 1. plates, map, facsims. (Kırşehir
halkevi kitapsaray. Yayın kolu neşriyatından, 1)
Contents.—v.1. Kirşehir tarihi.—v.2. Kirşehir tarih ve coğrafya lugati.

1. Kirşehir, Turkey.

NT   0040151   ICU

Tarım, Cevat Hakkı.
Tarihte Kirşehir-Gülşehri ve babailer, ahiler,
bektaşiler. İstanbul, Yeniçağ Matbaası, 1948.

124 p. illus.

NT   0040152   MH

Tarım, Cevat Hakkı.
Tarihte Kirşehri-Gülşehri ve Babailer-Ahiler-Bektaşler.
3. baskı. İstanbul, Yeniçağ Matbaası, 1948.
124 p. illus., facsims. 24 cm.

1. Kirşehri, Turkey—Hist.   2. Islamic sects—Turkey.   I. Title.

DS51.K43T3 1948   55—25457

NT   0040153   DLC ICU WU CLU MiU CU

DS
51
K63T17tu

Tarım, Cevat Hakkı
Türkiye Radyosunda Kırşehir Gecesi. [Hazır-
layan] C. H. Tarım. Kırşehir, Köybasımevi,
1942.
16 p.

1. Kırşehir, Turkey - Soc. life & cust.

NT   0040154   CLU

S16
.T8C5
Orien
Turk

Tarıman, Celâl.

Çiftçi.
⌈Ankara⌉

Tarin, ⌈E.⌉
Nouvelle géométrie pratique, au l'on donne les notions pré-
liminaires, les pratiques de géométrie sur le papier & sur le terrein,
la trigonométrie-rectiligne, la planimétrie & la stéréométrie...
La Haye: P. Paupie, 1755.   2 p.l., viii, (1)10–20, 359(1) p., 16
diagr. 12°.

1. Geometry.—Textbooks, 1755.
N. Y. P. L.   February 26, 1912.

NT   0040156   NN

Tarin, Gil, merino de Zaragoza.

Saragossa. *Merino*, 1291-1312.
El registro del merino de Zaragoza, el caballero don Gil
Tarin, 1291-1312. Transcrito, anotado y acompañado de
apuntes biográficos de la familia de Tarin, por don Manuel de
Bofarull y de Sartório, jefe del Archivo de la corona de Ara-
gón. Zaragoza, Impr. del Hospicio provincial. 1889.

Cocked Press
Wason
MSS.
BV.
T18+

Tarin, Jaime.
Historia y relacion breue de la entrada en
el reyno de China la mission que truxo de
España nuestro Hº Comissario Fr. Buenaventura
Ybañez. Escrita por Fr. Iaime Tarin religioso
de nro. Padre S. Francº y compañero de la
misma mission. Año de 1689.
₍36₎ p. 30cm.

1. Missions--China. 2. Franciscans in
China. 3. Ibáñez. Buenaventura, 1610-
1691. I. Title.

NT   0040158   NIC

Tarin, Jean, 1586-1666, tr.
De anima celebres opiniones
see under title

Tarin, Jean, 1586-1666.   TF
De monetarvm avgmento, variatione, et diminvtione,
tractatus varij. Hisce temporibus admodum vtiles, &
necessarij. Ex bibliotheca perillustris senatoris Gasparis
Antonii Thesavri in hoc volumen redacti. Hic accessit
locvpletissimvs index, cum nota valoris cuiuscunque
monete ad hec vsque tempora.   Avgvstæ Tavrinorvm,
1609.   [45], 914[10] p.   22cm.

Caption of dedication: Illvstr, mo et excell. mo Francisco Provanæ...
Io. Dominicus Tarinus S.P.

1. Money, to 1800.   I. Tesauro, Gaspero Antonio, 17th cent.   II. Title.

NT   0040161   NN

BR65
.O 6
1624
Jefferson
coll.

Tarin, Jean, 1586-1666, ed. and tr.

Origenes.
Origenis Adamantii Philocalia, de obscvris S. Scriptvræ
locis, a ss. pp. Basilio Magno, & Gregorio theologo, ex variis
Origenis commentariis excerpta ... Omnia nunc primum
græcè edita ... opera & studio Io. Tarini Andegaui, qui &
latina fecit & notis illustrauit. Lvtetiæ Parisiorvm, apud
Sebastianvm Cramoisy, 1624.

Tarin, Jean Henri
Spinoza théologien. Genève, Imprimerie
P. Richter, 1909.
96 p. 24cm.

Thesis, Geneva.
Bibliography: p. ₍5₎

NT   0040163   NNC OCH

Tarin, Joaquin Gonzalo y
see Gonzalo y Tarin, Joaquin.

Tarín, José.
See
Tarín-Iglesias, José.

TARIN, Maurice.
De l'albuminurie dans l'amygdalite
chronique. Thèse. Paris,1913.

NT   0040166   MBCo

Tarin, Petro
see Tarin, Pierre, 1725-1761.

---

f
QM
455
T17

TARIN, Pierre, 1725-1761
Adversaria anatomica, de omnibus corporis
humani partium, tum descriptionibus, cum
picturis. Adversaria anatomica prima, de
omnibus cerebri, nervorum & organorum func-
tionibus animalibus inservientium, descriptionibus & iconismis. Autore Petro Tarin,
Medico ... Parisiis, Ex typis Joannis
Francisci Moreau, MDCCL.
4to 4 p. ℓ., 46, ₍2₎ p. 18 fold. plates
(part col.)   29 cm.

NT   0040168   MBCo PPC CtY-M DNLM

611.09
T174a

₍TARIN, Pierre₎ 1725-1761.
Anthropotomie; ou L'art de disséquer
les muscles, les ligamens, les nerfs,
& les vaisseaux sanguins du corps humain; auquel on a joint une histoire
succincte de ses vaisseaux avec la
maniere de faire les injections, de
preparer, de blanchir les os & de
dresser les squelettes; de preparer
toutes les differentes parties & de les
conserver preparées, soit dans une

liqueur propre à ses effet, soit en
les faisant secher; celle d'ouvrir &
d'embaumer les cadavres; on y donne
aussi la description des matieres
propres a chacune de ses preparations
& la figure des instrumens. Paris,
Briasson, 1750.
2 v. 4 fold. plates.

NT   0040170   WaU DNLM

Tarin, Pierre, 1725-1761.
Dictionaire anatomique suivi d'une
bibliotheque anatomique et physiologique.
Paris, Briasson, 1753.
2ℓ.,102p.;ℓ.,107p. 252mm. 4to.

1.Anatomy. 2.Dictionaries, Medical. 3.
Bibliography of medicine. (Chronol: 1753.
Printer: Briasson)

NT   0040171   NcD-MC PPAmP DNLM KU-M PPiD OC1W-H NIC

MF
2078
b

Tarin, Pierre, c. 1725-1761.
Dictionnaire anatomique suivi d'une bibliotheque anatomique.   Paris, chez Briasson,
1753.
102p

Microfilm. Positive.

1. Anatomy. Early works to 1800.--2. Anatomy.
Dictionaries.

NT   0040172   MnCS OU

B611.73
T174

Tarin, Pierre, 1725-1761.
Myo-graphie; ou, Description des muscles
du corps humain.   Paris, Briasson, 1753.

xxxiv, 56, 171 p.   47 plates (part
fold.)   26cm.

1.Muscles. I.Title.

NT   0040173   MnU

---

xQM101
T37

Tarin, Pierre, 1725-1761.
Ostéo-graphie; ou, Description des os de
l'adulte, du foetus, &c. Precedée d'une introduction a l'étude des parties solides du
corps humain.   Paris, Briasson, 1753.
xxxiv, 24, 56, 126p. plates (part fold.)
26cm.

Text in Latin and French on opposite pages;
introd. in French.

1. Bones. 2. Skeleton. 3. Fetus. I.
Title.

NT   0040174   IaU NNNAM DNLM DSI CLU-M WU-M NIC

Tarin (Pierre) [1725-61]. Problema anatomi-
cum, utrum inter arterias meseraicas venasque
lacteas immediatum detur commercium. [*Parisiis,* 1748.]
In: Haller. Disp. anat. [etc.]. 4º. *Gottingœ,* 1751.
vii, 239-260.

NT   0040175   DNLM

4BX
Cath.
704

Tarín-Iglesias, José
L'Abat Marcet; mig segle de vida
montserratina. Amb una carta-próleg
de l'Excm. i Revdm. Dom. Aureli M.
Escarré. [1. ed.] Barcelona, Aymà
S. L. ₍1955₎
228 p.

NT   0040176   DLC-P4

Tarín-Iglesias, José.
Apeles Mestres, el último humorista del siglo xix. Prólogo
de Joaquín Renart. Barcelona, Editorial Políglota, 1954.
62 p. illus. 26 cm.

1. Mestres, Apeles, 1854-1936.

PC3941.M4Z9   57-31815 ‡

NT   0040177   DLC NIC

4BX
Cath
524

Tarín-Iglesias, José
Josefina Viñaseca, la niña que
supo defender su pureza. Prólogo
del Excmo. y Rvmo. P. Juan Perelló
Pou. Barcelona, Ediciones Betis,
1953.
107 p.

NT   0040178   DLC-P4

GR910
.A49

Tarín-Iglesias, José.

Amades, Joan.
Leyendas y tradiciones marineras ₍por₎ Juan Amades ₍y₎
José Tarín. ₍Barcelona₎ Sección de Prensa de la Diputación
Provincial de Barcelona ₍1954₎

DP269.8   Tarín Iglesias, José
R4T27   Los martires de Montserrat. Prólogo
de Luis Sola Escofet. Barcelona, Editorial La Hormiga de Oro, 1950.
118 p. illus., ports.

1. Spain--Hist.--Civil War, 1936-1939--
Religious aspects. 2. Montserrat, Spain--
Hist. 3. Montserrat (Benedictine Abbey)
I. Title.

NT 0040180   PPiU

3189   Tarín-Iglesias, José
.25   Milá y Fontanals, periodista y poeta.
.944   Prólogo de José Maria Castro y Calvo. Vila-
franca del Panadés, 1950.
₍60₎ p. 19 cm.

1.Milá y Fontanals, Manuel, 1818-1884.

NT 0040181   NjP MH

D763   Tarín-Iglesias, José, joint author.
.N6D64
Doltra Oliveras, Esteban.
... Narvik (una página para la historia) Madrid, Ediciones
Afrodisio Aguado, 1941.

Tarín-Iglesias, Manuel.
Pierre Laval. Madrid, A. Climent ₍1945₎
187, xxxii p. plates, ports. 19 cm. (Actualidad y reportajes,
no. 3)

1. Laval, Pierre, 1883-1945.   (Series)

A 48-5946*

Yale Univ. Library
for Library of Congress   ₍1₎

NT 0040183   CtY IU IEN FU

Tarín-Iglesias, Manuel.
... Pierre Laval. Madrid-Barcelona,
A. Climent [1946]
3 p.l. [9]-187 p., 2 l. [xiii]-xxxiii p., 1 l.,
[14] p., 1 l. facsims. 19 cm. (On cover:
Actualidad y reportajes [no. 3])
1. Laval, Pierre, 1883-1945. 2. France -
Pol. & govt. - 1914 - 3. World war, 1939-
1945 - France.

NT 0040184   CSt-H

BX2656   Tarin y Juaneda, Francisco.
.V2T2   La cartuja de Porta-Coeli (Valencia), apuntes
históricos. Ilustraciones de Vicente Soriano
Mari. Valencia, Establecimiento Tip. de M. Alu-
fre, 1897.
viii, 222 p. illus.

1. Valencia (City) Porta-Coeli (Carthusian
monastery)

NT 0040185   ICU

Tarin y Juaneda, Francisco
La real cartuja de Miraflores, Burgos, su historia y
descripción. Burgos, Santiago Rodríguez, 1896

623 p. illus.

NT 0040186   MH

NA   Tarín y Juaneda, Francisco.
5811   La Real Cartuja de Miraflores (Burgos);
M67T3   su historia y descripción. 2.ed. ilustrada
1896a   (Compendio de la edición 1.a de 1896). Burgos,
Hijos de Santiago Rodríguez,n.d.
243p. illus. 18cm.

1. Miraflores (Carthusian Monastery). I.
Title.

NT 0040187   MU ICU NNU CU

TARÍN Y JUANEDA,Francisco.
La real cartuja de Miraflores (Burgos);su
historia y descripción. 2a ed.ilustrada.
Compendio de la edición 1ª de 1896. Burgos,
Hijos de S.Rodríguez,[1925].

Illustr.

NT 0040188   MH

Tarini Charan Chaudhuri.
See
Chaudhuri, Tarini Charan.

Tarini Prasad Sinha
see   Sinha, Tarini Prasad.

Tarini Sankar Chakravorty
see
Chakravorty, Tarini Sankar.

Tārinī-śaṅkara Chakravartī
see   **Chakravorty, Tarini Sankar.**

Tāriṇīśaṅkara Cakrabartī
see
Chakravorty, Tarini Sankar.

F   Tarino,
2781   Montevideo desde las nubes./ Fotografías
T18+   obtenidas por los aviadores Tarino y Lorenzo.
¿Montevideo? A. Barreiro y Ramos ₍19--₎
₍1₎ l., 16 plates. 21 x 29cm. (Colección de vistas aéreas. 1. serie)

1. Montevideo--Descr.--Views.
I. Lorenzo,   II. Title.

NT 0040194   NIC

274.5114 Tarino, Pietro.
T174n   La Nostra Signora d'Oropa; operetta divisa in
due parti, una storica e l'altra pratica —
Biella, G. Amosso, 1892.
415p. illus.

NT 0040195   IU

Tarino, Pietro.
Nozioni elementari sopra i doveri e i diritti ad
uso massime delle scuole tecniche pel cav. Pietro
Tarino ... Biella, 1873.
24.5 cm.

NT 0040196   CtY

Tarinus, Io. Dominicus
see   Tarin, Jean, 1586-1666.

Tarinus, Johannes
see   **Tarin, Jean,** 1586-1666.

Tario, Francisco, 1911–
Acapulco en el sueño. Con fotografías de Lola Alvarez
Bravo. ₍1. ed.₎ México, 1951.
1 v. (chiefly illus.) 30 cm.

1. Acapulco, Mexico—Descr.—Views.   I. Title.

F1391.A15T3   917.27   51-30934

NT 0040199   DLC NN TxU CLU CU-BANC

Tario, Francisco, 1911–
... Aquí abajo, novela. México, Antigua librería Robredo,
1943.
3 p. l., 9-250 p., 1 l. 20½ᵐ.
"Primera edición."

I. Title.   44-47105

Library of Congress   PQ7297.T36A75
₍2₎   863.6

NT 0040200   DLC CtY TxU MA NcU TU NIC

Tario, Francisco, 1911–
Breve diario de un amor perdido. México, Ediciones Los
Presentes, 1951.
90 p. illus. 25 cm.
"Se han impreso quinientos ejemplares en papel Corsican antique,
de los cuales, doscientos numerados, se reservan a los suscriptores.
Ejemplar núm. 52."

I. Title.

PQ7297.T36B7   868.6   51-35362

NT 0040201   DLC IU CU NN TxU CU-I

Tario, Francisco, 1911–
...Equinoccio. México, 1946. 113 p. 17cm.

1. Mexican literature—Misc.

NT 0040202   NN TxU CtY CoU NjP IU NIC

Tario, Francisco, 1911–
... La noche. México, Antigua librería Robredo ₍1943₎
2 p. l., 7-213 p., 1 l. 20½ᵐ.
Short stories.

I. Title.

     43-10400

Library of Congress   PQ7297.T36N6
₍2₎   863.6

NT 0040203   DLC CtY TxU NcU MB MiU

Tario, Francisco, 1911–
La puerta en el muro, viñetas de F. Castro Pacheco. México, 1946.
58 p. illus. 21 cm. (Colección "Lunes," 24)

    ɪ. Title.   (Series)

    PQ7297.T36P8   863.6   48–24681*

NT   0040204   DLC CU–I KyU NcD IU

Tario, Francisco, 1911–
Tapioca Inn, mansión para fantasmas. [1. ed.] México, Tezontle [1952]
259 p. illus. 21 cm.
Short stories.

    ɪ. Title.

    PQ7297.T36T3   863.6   52–66915 ‡

         MiU
NT   0040205   DLC CaBVaU NcU TU CSt CoU NN CU TxU PSt

Tario, Francisco, 1911–
Yo de amores qué sabía. [México, 1950]
[11] p. 25 cm. (Los Presentes, 2)
"Se tiraron cien ejemplares numerados del 1 al 100, con firma del autor ... y 25 ejemplares fuera de comercio, marcados del ɪ al xxv ... Ejemplar no. 80."

    ɪ. Title.

    PQ7297.T36Y6   52–18290

NT   0040206   DLC CU

Tariot, Alexandre Joseph Désiré.   No. 14 in **M.260.10.4
O Salutaris pour T. Avec accomp. de piano ou d'orgue. Paris. Lassalle & Thuillier. [186–?] 5 pp. F°.

F1193 — T.r. — Church music. Anthems, &c.

NT   0040207   MB

Tariot, Jules, b. 1813.
Fantaisie dramatique, pour la harpe, sur le célèbre choral protestant, intercalé par Giacomo Meyerbeer dans Les Huguenots, arrangée...par Jules Tariot...d'après la fantaisie à 4 mains de Korbach... Paris, Prilipp et cie. [1835?] Pl.no. C.191 P. 9 p. 34cm.

Movements.—Introduction.—Rondo.—Choral.

ʃ. Harp. ɪ. Korbach. Fantasia.   ɪɪ. Title: Ein' feste Burg.

NT   0040208   NN

Tariote (Antoine). *Considérations sur les occlusions intestinales en général et sur le traitement des occlusions à début rapide en particulier par l'opium. 40 pp. 4°. *Paris*, 1874, No. 392.

NT   0040209   DNLM

Tariq, Abdul Rahman
     see   Tariq, 'Abdurrahman, 1915–

Ṭāriq, 'Abdurraḥmān, 1915–

اشارات اقبال؛ جس میں حکیم الامت علامہ اقبال کے اردو
تصنیفات میں سے جملہ اشارات و تلمیحات کو ہر جہت سے مکمل
و مفصل صورت میں حل کیا گیا ہے۔ مرتبہ و مؤلف عبدالرحمن
طارق۔ لاہور، کتاب منزل [1951]

215 p. port. 21 cm.
In Urdu.
1. Iqbal, Sir Muhammad, 1877–1988. ɪ. Iqbal, Sir Muhammad, 1877–1938. ɪɪ. Title.
Title romanized: Ishārāt-i Iqbāl.

     PK2199.I 65Z895   S A 68–13247

NT   0040211   DLC

(al-Ṭarīq)

الطريق۔
[بيروت ، دار الغارابي]
v. ill. 22 cm.
«مجلة فكرية سياسية»

     AP95.A6T34   76–647155
           (MARC-S)

NT   0040212   DLC

طريق الحق۔ السنة ۱۱–٤
مايو ۱۹٦۲۰ [القاهرة]
v. 25 cm. monthly.
Began publication in 1951. Cf. Cairo. Dār al-Kutub al-Miṣrīyah. Qism al-Fahāris al-'Arabīyah wa-al-Ifranjīyah. Fihris al-dawrīyāt al-'Arabīyah, v. 1, 1961.

1. Islam—Period.   *Title transliterated:* Ṭarīq al-ḥaqq.

     BP1.T3   N E 65–412
     Library of Congress   [2½]   PL 480: UAR-C-78

NT   0040213   DLC

Taris, Étienne.   623.6 Q8o1
T9410 L'automobile et les armées modernes. Par Étienne Taris ... . Paris, H. Dunod et E. Pinat, 1908.
[2], 351 p. 144 illus. incl. diagrs. 22½ᶜᵐ.

NT   0040214   ICJ MiD DNW

Taris, Étienne.
     ... Les moteurs d'aviation. [By] Étienne Taris [and] Émile Berthier. 2nd ed. Paris [n. d.]
[248] p.   O.

NT   0040215   DSI

Taris, Étienne.
     ... Les moteurs d'aviation. Paris, Librairie aéronautique [1911]
2 p. l., [286] p. illus., diagrs. 24ᶜᵐ.
At head of title: Étienne Taris ... Émile Berthier ...

1. Aeroplanes—Motors.   ɪ. Berthier, Émile, joint author.

                    31–22476
     Library of Congress   TL701.T3 1911   629.13

NT   0040216   DLC ICJ NN

Taris, Étienne.   5964.179
     Les moteurs d'aviation.
— Paris. Librairie aéronautique. [1912?] (289) pp. Illus. Plans. Diagrams. 24 cm., in 8s.
The preface is by Aimé Witz.

By Étienne Taris and Émile Berthier.

H8997 — Flying machines. —Motors. — Witz, Aimé, pref. 1849–. — Jt. auth.

NT   0040217   MB

Taris, Étienne.
     ... Les moteurs d'aviation. Paris, Librairie aéronautique [1913]
2 p. l., [356] p. illus., diagrs. 23½ᶜᵐ.
At head of title: Étienne Taris ... Émile Berthier ...
On cover: Préface de m. Aimé Witz ... 2. édition, augmentée et mise à jour.
"Supplément. Nouveaux moteurs et perfectionnements": p. [285–354]

1. Aeroplanes—Motors.   ɪ. Berthier, Émile, joint author.

                    31–22957
     Library of Congress   TL701.T3 1913   629.13

NT   0040218   DLC DSI ICJ

Taris, Étienne.
     ... La Russie et ses richesses, par Étienne Taris ... 24 photogravures hors texte, une carte. Paris, P. Roger & cᵉ [1912]
2 p. l., 252 p. plates, maps (1 fold.) 20ᶜᵐ. (Collection "Les pays modernes")

1. Russia—Descr. & trav. 2. Russia—Econ. condit. ɪ. Title.

     Library of Congress   DK27.T3   27–22965

NT   0040219   DLC KU NN

Taris, Étienne.
     La Russie et ses richesses, par Étienne Taris...   Paris: P. Roger et Cie., 1916.   2 p.l., 280 p., 20 pl.   Maps.   5. ed., rev. 12°.   (Collection "Les pays modernes.")

1. Russia.—Description and travel,   1910– . 2. Economic history, Russia. 3. Title. 4. Series.
N. Y. P. L.   September 7, 1917.

NT   0040220   NN DNW CaBVaU MH NNC

914.7
T174r   **Taris,** Étienne.
1920   La Russie et ses richesses. 7. ed. Paris, P. Roger [1920]
     252p. illus. 20cm. (Collection "Les pays modernes")

     1. Russia - Descr. & trav. 2. Russia - Econ. condit. I. Title.

NT   0040221   TxU

Tarissan, 1850–
     *Essai sur le beribéri au Brésil. Paris, 1881. 84 p. 4°. No. 110.

NT   0040222   DNLM

Tarissan (J.-B.) *Considérations pathologiques sur les calculs dans les voies urinaires. vi. 7–41 pp. 4°. *Paris*, 1822, No. 117. v. 173.

NT   0040223   DNLM PPC

Tarit, E
     ... La princesse captive. Paris, Saint-Étienne, Dumas [1945]
142 p., 1 l. illus. 19ᶜᵐ. (On cover: Collection Jeunes de France)

     ɪ. Title.

     PQ2639.A74P7   A F 47–4855
     Chicago. Univ. Library
     for Library of Congress   [2]†

NT   0040224   ICU ICRL NN DLC

Tarixa, *Bolivia*
    see
Tarija, *Bolivia*.

Tarizzo, Antonio Francesco
    see   Tarizzo, Francesco Antonio.

TARIZZO, *FRANCESCO ANTONIO.*
Compendio della vita del gloriosissimo
patriarca, S. Giovanni di Matha. Torino, per
D. Paulino, 1598. Ristampato in Roma da G.
Olivieri, tipog. 1848.

NT   0040227   MH

945.111 Tarizzo, Francesco Antonio.
T174r   Raggvaglio istorico dell'assedio,
difesa, e liberazione della città di
Torino.   Torino, 1707.
103p.

NT   0040228   IU

(Tarjamät mukhtärah min al-majallät al-'askariyah al
-'älamiyah)
ترجمات مختارة من المجلات العسكرية العالمية.

،القاهرة؛
     no.   illus.   24 cm.   bimonthly.
Issued by Wizárat al-Harbiyah, Hay'at al-Buḥūth al-'Askariyah of
Egypt (June 1971–   under the earlier name of the jurisdiction:
United Arab Republic)
   1. Military art and science — Periodicals.   2. Naval art and sci-
ence — Periodicals.   3. Egypt — Armed Forces — Periodicals.   I.
United Arab Republic.   Wizárat al-Harbiyah.   Hay'at al-Buḥūth al
-'Askariyah.   II. Egypt.   Wizárat al-Harbiyah.   Hay'at al-Buḥūth al
-'Askariyah.
U4.T3   74–643280
                      MARC-S

NT   0040229   DLC

Tarjan, Armen Charles, 1920–
   Pathogenic behavior and life histories of the root-knot
nematodes, *Meloidogyne* spp., on snapdragon, *Antirrhinum
majus.* ¡College Park, Md., 1951¡
   iv, 70 l.   mounted illus., tables.   28 cm.
   Thesis—University of Maryland.
   Typescript (carbon copy)
   Vita.
   "Literature cited": leaves ¡52¡–53.
   1. Root-rot.   2. Snapdragons—Diseases and pests.   3. Meloidogyne.
I. Title.   II. Title: Root-knot nematodes.
     SB608.S57T3   A 52–4873
    Maryland.   Univ.   Libr
    for Library of Congress   ¡2¡†

NT   0040230   MdU DLC

949.6   Tarján, Edmond
T174h   Hongrois, Slovaques et Ruthènes dans
la Vallée Danubienne par Edmond Tarján
at André Fall. Budapest, S. A. V.
Hornyánszky, 1938.
61 p.   fold. maps (part. col.)

   1. Danube Valley - History. I. Fall,
André. II. Title.

NT   0040231   WaU

HV941   Tarján, Ferenc.
H9T18   ... A gyermeknyaraltatás problémája. Függelék:
Vezérfonal a gyermekek gondozásával megbízott
vezetők és felügyelők részére, irta Tarján
Ferenc ... Budapest, "Patria" irodalmi vállalat és nyomdai részv.-társ., 1919.
   62,¡2¡ p.   illus.   23ᵐ.
   At head of title: A nagyvárosi szegény
gyermekek megmentéséről.
   "Forrásmunkák": p. ¡64¡
   1. Fresh-air charity - Hungary. 2. Vacations.
I. Title. II.   Title: A nagyvárosi
szegény gyermek   -ek megmentéséről.

NT   0040232   CSt-H

Tarján, Ferenc.
   Hogyan születik a találmány; a technika és tudomány legújabb
vívmányai, irta Tarján Ferenc.   Budapest: Lampel R. (Wodianer
F. és fiai), 1935.   181 p.   plates, ports.   24cm.

832909A.   1. Science—Popular works,   1935.   2. Scientists, Hungarian.
3. Industrial arts.
N. Y. P. L.   November 6, 1936

NT   0040233   NN OC1

Tarján, Ferenc.
   Uj találmányok és felfedezések lexikona, szerkesz-
tették: Tarján Ferenc [és] Braun Pál.   [Budapest]
Fővárosi könyvkiadó, 1947.   200 p.   21cm.

   1. Inventions. I. Braun Pál, joint author.
II. Braun, Pál.   t. 1947.

NT   0040234   NN

PF
3025
.M45   Tarján, Jenő.
no.3   A vasércbányászat szaknyelvének szókincse
Rudabányán. Budapest, Pázmány P. Tud. Egyetem
Német Nyelvészeti és Néprajzi Intézete, 1939.
82 p.   24cm.   (Német nyelvészeti dolgozatok,
3)

   German title: Wortschatz der Bergmannssprache
des Eisenerzbergbaues in Rudabánya.
   Summary in German.
   Bibliography: p. ¡74¡–76.

NT   0040235   NNC

Tarján, Nándor, joint author.

Berényi, Sándor, 1865–
   Der erwerb und der verlust der ungarischen staatsbürger-
schaft.   Für den praktischen gebrauch bearbeitet von dr.
Alexander Berényi und dr. Ferdinand Tarján ... Aus dem
ungarischen übersetzt und mit einem vorwort versehen von dr.
Isidor Schwartz ... Leipzig, Duncker & Humblot, 1906.

DB953   Tarján, Ödön.
T187   Háborus tanulságok, irta Tarján Ödön.
¡Budapest¡ Kármán Zsigmond könyvnyomdai műin-
tézetének nyomása, 1917.

   cover-title, 12 p.   22½ᶜᵐ.

   1. European war, 1914-1918 - Hungary. I. Title.

NT   0040237   CSt-H

Tarján, Ödön.
   Hungarians, Slovaks and Ruthenians in the Danube-valley,
by Ödön Tarján and Dr. A. Fall. Budapest, V. Hornyánszky
co. ltd., 1938.
   59, ¡1¡ p.   III fold. maps.   21ᶜᵐ.

   1. Hungary—For. rel.   2. Slovaks.   3. Ukrainians in Czechoslovak
republic.   4. Hungarians in Czechoslovak republic.   5. Czechoslovak
republic—Pol. & govt.   I. Fall, A., joint author.

    Library of Congress   DB926.T3   39–6787
    ——— Copy 2.   ¡3¡   943.7

NT   0040238   DLC InU PHi IEdS CtY ICJ NNC NN OC1

4DB   Tarján, Ödön
Cz   Die Tschechoslowakei Ende 1935;
233   Situationsbericht. Budapest, Druck
der Sárkány-Druckerei, 1936.

NT   0040239   DLC-P4

4DB   Tarján, Ödön
Cz.   Die Tschechoslowakei; Anfang Mai
184   1934. Budapest, Druck der Sárkány
-Druckerei Aktiengesellschaft, 1934.
16 p.

NT   0040240   DLC-P4

DB926   Tarján, Ödön.
T1873   Ungarn, Slowaken und Ruthenen im Donau-
becken, von Ödön Tarján und Dr. Andreas
Fall. Budapest, V. Hornyánszky, 1938.
66 p.   maps fold.   21cm.
   Published also in English.

   1. Hungary - For. rel.   2. Slovaks.   3.
Ukrainians in Czechoslovak Republic.   4.
Hungarians in Czechoslovak Republic.   5.
Czechoslovak   Rep   ublic - Pol. & govt.
I. Fall, Endre.   II. Title.

NT   0040241   CSt-H DLC-P4 NN MH

Tarján, Ödön.
   ... The ways of Czechoslovakia and its Magyar minority.
¡n. p., 1934?¡
   84 p.   III fold. maps, II fold. tab.   21ᶜᵐ.

   1. Hungarians in the Czechoslovak republic.   2. Minorities.   3. Czechoslovak republic—Pol. & govt.   I. Title.

                               36–14474
    Library of Congress   DB215.T3
                     ¡2¡   943.7

NT   0040242   DLC

325.437   Tarján, Ödön.
T187w   Der Weg der Tschechoslowakei und die
ungarische Minderheit. ‹Budapest, O'Tarján,
1932›
   8?p.   tables(fold.)maps(fold.)   21cm.

   1. Hungarians in the Czechoslovak Republic.
2. Minorities. I. Title.

NT   0040243   NcU

DB215   Tarján, Ödön
T37   Der Weg der Tschechoslowakei und die ungarische Minderheit. [n. p., 1934?]
83 p.   maps.   21 cm.

   1. Czechoslovak Republic - Pol. & govt.
2. Hungarians in the Czechoslovak Republic.
3. Minorities - Czechoslovak Republic.
cdu

NT   0040244   CtY CSt-H IaU

TX   TARJÁN, Róbert
820   Élelmezés és gyógyélelmezés, írta:
T186e   Tarján Róbert, Soós Aladár, Somogyi
1952   Lászlóné. Budapest, Egészségügyi
Kiadó, 1952.
192 p.   illus.
   1. Diet in disease 2. Cookery -
Institutional

NT   0040245   DNLM DLC-P4

WS
115
T187h
1952

TARJAN, Róbert
    Helyes gyermektáplálás és napközi
élelmezés. [Irták] Tarján Róbert [és]
Fekete László. Budapest, Könyv- é&
Lapkiadó Vállalat, 1952.
    205 p. illus.
    1. Children - Nutrition 2. School
children - Food I. Fekete, László

NT   0040246   DLC-P4 DNLM

4TX
178

Tarján, Róbert
    Közétkeztetési áruismeret, ki-
egészítés az "Élelmiszer áruismeret"
c. könyvhöz. Budapest, Közgazdasá-
gi és Jogi Könyvkiadó, 1955.
    100 p.

NT   0040247   DLC-P4

W 6
P3

TARJÁN, Róbert, comp.
    Tápanyagtáblázat. Az Országos
Élelmezés= és Táplálkozástudományi
Intézet munkaközösségének vizsgálatai
alapján. 3. bőv. és átdolg. kiad.
Budapest, Művelt Nép, 1955.
    31 p.
    1. Nutrition - Tables

NT   0040248   DNLM

DB955
T187

Tarján, Vilmos, 1881-1947.
    A terror; Fényes László előszavával. Feiks
Jenő rajzaival. Irta Tarján Vilmos. 1.rész.
Budapest, "Ujságüzem" részvénytársaság [1919]
    62 p.,1 l. illus.(ports.)   22ᶜᵐ.
    On cover: Censurat: Spida.
    Published during the Rumanian occupation of
Hungary.
    No more published?
    1.Hungary - Hist. - Revolution, 1918-1919.
I.Title.

NT   0040249   CSt-H

DB
868
.T3

Tarján, Vilmos, 1881-1947.
    Pesti éjszaka. Budapest, 1940.
    110 p.

    1. Budapest - Soc. life & cust. 2. Buda-
pest - Music-halls (Variety-theaters, caba-
rets, etc.) I. Title.

NT   0040250   NNC

LA847
.A5
1920

Tarjanne, Artturi Johannes, 1866-
Finland. *Kouluhallitus.*
    Finlands skolväsen 1910-1920. Kortfattad redogörelse
utarbetad för det 11:te Nordiska skolmötet i Kristiania 1920.
Helsingfors, Statsrådets tryckeri, 1920.

Tarjanne, Artturi Johannes, 1866-
Finnlands Schulwesen, 1920-1925 ...
    see under   Nordiska Skolmötet,
12th Helsinki, 1925.

Tarjanne, Artturi Johannes, 1866-
Kansakoulun piiritarkastaja kokous. *7th, Helsingfors,* 1912.
    Pöytäkirja jonka Helsingissä 15-18 p: nä tammikuuta 1912
pidetystä seitsemännestä Kansakoulujen piiritarkastajain ko-
kouksesta, laati A. J. Tarjanne. Helsingissä, Keisarillisen senaatin kirjapainossa, 1912.

Tarjanne, Artturi Johannes, 1866-
Kansakoulun piiritarkastaja kokous. *8th, Helsingfors,* 1916.
    Pöytäkirja jonka Helsingissä 10-13 p: nä tammikuuta 1916
pidetystä kahdeksannesta Kansakoulujen piiritarkastajain ko-
kouksesta, laati A. J. Tarjanne. Helsingissä, Keisarillisen senaatin kirjapainossa, 1916.

Tarjanne, Artturi Johannes, 1866-
    Seminaarien kirjastot ja kirjastonhoidon opetus, muistiin-
panoja v. 1916 toimitetuista tarkastuksista A. J. Tarjanne.
Helsingissä, Keisarillisen senaatin kirjapaino, 1917.
    43 p. 22ᶜᵐ.

    1. Libraries—Finland. 2. Pedagogical libraries.

                                    CA 27-70 Unrev'd

Library of Congress   Z821.A1T2

NT   0040255   DLC

4K
Fin.-
54

Tarjanne, Tapio, 1901-1941.
    Asianosaisseuraanto Suomen siviili-
prosessissa. Helsinki, 1929.
    212 p.

NT   0040256   DLC-P4

Tarjanne, Tapio, 1901-1941.
Asianosaisseuraanto suomen siviiliproses-
sissa, kirjoittanut Tapio Tarjanne ...
Helsinki [Seuran kirjapainon] 1929.
    xix, 242 p. 24½cm.
    Diss. - Helsinki.
    Bibliography: p. [ix]-xix.

NT   0040257   MH-L

Tarjanne, Tapio, 1901-1941.
    Asianosaisseuraanto suomen siviiliprosessissa,
kirjoittanut Tapio Tarjanne ... Yliopistollinen
väitöskirja, joka Helsingin yliopiston lainopillisen
tiedekunnan suostumuksella esitetään julkisesti
tarkastettavaksi historiallis-kielitietellisessä
oppisalissa toukokuun 22 päivänä 1929 kello 12
päivällä. Helsinki [Suomal. Kirjall. Seuran
Kirjapainon Oy] 1929.
    xix, 242 p. 24.5 cm.
    "Kirjallisuusluettelo": p. [ix]-xix.

NT   0040258   CtY-L

Finland
46
Su75
no.23

Tarjanne, Tapio, 1901-1941
    Kirjoituksia ja lausuntoja. [Vammala]
Suomalainen Lakimiesyhdistys [1943]
    xii,301p. 25cm. (Suomalaisen Lakimies-
yhdistyksen julkaisuja, A-sarja, n:o 23)

    "Muistosanoja Tapio Tarjanteesta".- V.
Merikoski.
    "Luettelo Tapio Tarjanteen Julkaisuista.":
p.[297]-301.
    Bibliographical footnotes.

NT   0040259   CtY-L DLC-P4 MH-L

4K-
621

Tarjanne, Tapio, 1901-1941.
    Vero-oikeus. Lainopillisen Ylioppilastiede-
kunnan Kustannustoimisto; jakaja: Akateeminen
Kirjakauppa [1939]
    379 p.

NT   0040260   DLC-P4

4JN
Fin
22

Tarjanne, Tapio, 1901-1941.
    Virkasuhteen lakkaaminen Suo-
men valtionhallinnossa. Helsingissä, Otava [1934]
    284 p.

    (Suomalaisen Lakimiesyhdistyksen
Julkaisuja, n:o 1)

NT   0040261   DLC-P4

Tarjanne, Johannes Tapio
    see   Tarjanne, Tapio, 1901-1941.

Tarjei Vesaas; serprent av 50-årsheftet i Syn og segn.   Oslo,
Det Norske samlaget, 1947.   115 p.   illus.   21cm.

N. Y. P. L   1. Vesaas, Tarjei, 1897-   I. Syn og segn.   February 28, 1952

NT   0040263   NN

Tarjem, Kåre, *ed.*
    Sandefjord turn- og idrettsforening gjennem 50 år. [Re-
daktører: Kåre Tarjem og Ole Lind.   Sandefjord, 1950]
    143 p. illus., ports. 27 cm.

    1. Sandefjord turn- og idrettsforening.   I. Lind, Ole, joint ed.

Harvard Univ. Library   A 51-5979
for Library of Congress   [2]

NT   0040264   MH

তর্জমাঘুল-হাদীছ.
[ঢাকা]
        v. 25 cm. monthly.
    In Bengali.

    1. Islam—Periodicals.
                                Title romanized: Tarjumānula-hādīcha.
BP1.T343   S A 68-19273
                                                  PL 480: EP-D-B-33

NT   0040265   DLC

Tark talutüdruk; Eesti muinasjutte kogust "Tuulesõlmed."
[Illustreerinud E. Okas;   Tallinn, Ilukirjandus ja kunst,
1947.
    52 p. illus. 24 cm.

    CONTENTS.—Tuulesõlmed.—Tark talutüdruk.—Ilus minia.—Talutü-
druk ja vaeslaps.—Noor sepp.

    1. Tales, Estonian.

PZ90.E7T35   54-24670 ‡

NT   0040266   DLC

Tarkabāchaspati, Tārā Nāth
    see
Tarkavachaspati, Taranatha, 1812-1885.

... The Tarkabhasa; or, Exposition of reasoning
    see under   [Keśava Miśra]

Tarkabhūṣaṇa, Pramathanātha, ed.

Jimūtavāhana.
    The Kāla-vivĕka (a part of Dharmaratna) a treatise on Hindu law and rituals, by Jimūtavāhana, edited by Paṇḍita Pramathanātha Tarkabhūṣaṇa ... Calcutta, The Asiatic society of Bengal, 1905.

Tarkachuramony, Jogindranath
    see   Jogindranath Tarkachuramony.

SOCIAL
STUDIES
D
11
+T3
    Tarkalankar, Girish Chandra
    Chronological tables containing Christian, Bengalee, Moolkee...eras with their corresponding dates. Bhowanipore, S. Banerjee, 1894-1901.
    2 v. in 1. illus. 27cm.
    Vol. 1 by Girish Chandra Tarkalankar and Pran Nath Saraswati.
    Contents: [v.1] From 1764-1900.-v.2.1901-1910.
    1. Chronology, Historical - Tables I. Saraswati, Pranna... d. 1892 II. Title

NT   0040271   WU

PK3791
.B188K3
1850
Orien
Sans
    Tarkalankar, Madanmohan, 1815-1857.

Bāṇa.
    (Kādambarī)
    কাদম্বরী / শ্রীবাণভট্টবিরচিত: ; edited by Madana Mohana Tarkālaṁkāra. — [Calcutta : Sanskrit Press, 1850]

PK3796
.K6
1850
Orien
Sans
    Tarkalankar, Madanmohan, 1815-1857.

Kālidāsa.
    (Kumārasambhava)
    কুমারসম্ভবম্ / শ্রীকালিদাসকৃতম্, শ্রীমল্লিনাথসূরিবিরচিতয়া সঞ্জীবনী-সমাখ্যয়া ব্যাখ্যয়ানুগতম্, শ্রীমদনমোহন শর্ম্মতর্কালঙ্কারেণ সংস্কৃতম্. — কলিকাতা : সংস্কৃতযন্ত্রে মুদ্রিতম্, 1907 [1850]

PK3798
.K74C3
1867
Orien
Sans
    Tarkalankara, Jaganmohana.

Kṣemīśvara.
    (Caṇḍakauśika)
    চণ্ডকৌশিকম্ / আর্য্যক্ষেমীশ্বর প্রণিতম্, শ্রী জগন্মোহন তর্কালঙ্কারেণ কৃতয়া টীকয়া প্রাকৃতানুবাদেন চ সহিতম্ তেনৈব সংস্কৃতম্. — কলিকাতা : শ্রীকেদার-নাথবন্দ্যোপাধ্যায়েন প্রকাশিতম্, সংবৎ 1924 [1867]

PK3621
.K3
1873
Orien
Sans
    Tarkalankara, Jaganmohana, ed.

Purāṇas. *Kalkipurāṇa.*
    Kalki-purana. Edited by Jaganmohana Tarkalankara. Calcutta, Printed for K. Banerjee at the Kavyaprakasha Press, 1873.

PK3635
.B4
1862
Orien
Ben
    Tarkalankara, Jaganmohana, tr.

Mahābhārata. *Bengali.*
    মহাভারত. শৌল শ্রীযুক্ত বর্দ্ধমানাধিপতি মহারাজাধিরাজ মহতাবচন্দ বাহাদুর কর্তৃক শ্রীযুক্ত জগন্মোহন তর্কালঙ্কার-দ্বারা বঙ্গভাষায় অনুবাদিত ও শ্রীযুক্ত শ্যামাচরণ তত্ত্ববাগীশ-দ্বারা পরিশোধিত. বর্দ্ধমান, 1862-

---

Tarkalankara, Krishna
    see
    Kṛṣṇa Tarkālaṅkāra, *18th cent.*

Tarkālankara, Mrityunjaya
    see
    Mṛityuñjaya Vidyālaṅkāra, *b. 1762.*

956.17
T17
    Tarkan, Faruk
    Türk hukuk ve teamüllerine göre umumî banka muameleleri, muhasebesi ve riyaziyesi. Istanbul, Pulhan Matbaasi, 1951.
    xii, 299 p. (Sümerbank Umum Müdürlüğü neşriyatî, 20-29)

    1. Banks and banking - Turkey. 2. Banks and banking - Accounting. Banking law. Turkey.

NT   0040280   NNC

Tarkanian, Lois.
    Suggested policies for the education of aurally handicapped children in special day classes
    see under   San Bernardino Co., Calif. Office of Superintendent of Schools.

---

al-Tarkantī, Abū Bakr ibn Aḥmad
    see
    al-Sūsī, Abū Bakr ibn Aḥmad.

Hun
190
T17
    Tárkány Szücs, Ernő.
    Mártély népi jogélete. Kolozsvár, Nagy Jenő Könyvnyomdája, 1944.
    148 p. illus. 25 cm. (Régi magyar jog, 1)

    Title also in German and French. Summary in German and French.

NT   0040283   NNC-L

Tarkányi, Béla.
    Nagybőjti kalauz Krisztus kinszenvedésének és halálának negyvennapi magszentelésére, a nagyhéti ajtatossággal együtt. Pest, Kiadja Heckenast Gusztáv, 1866.
    viii, 312 p. front.(col. plate) 17 cm.

NT   0040284   PLatS

Tarkapanchanan, Jagannath
    see   Jagannatha Tarkapanchanana, d. 1806.

Tarkapañchanana, Jagannatha
    see   Jagannatha Tarkapañchanana, d. 1806.

Tarkapanchanana, Jayanarayana
    see
    Jayanarayana Tarkapanchanana

Tarkaratna, Rajkumar.
    Student's Sanskrit grammar ... Calcutta, Jadu Nath Seal, 1888.
    x, 236 p. 18.5 cm.
    1. Sanskrit language - Grammar.

NT   0040288   CtY

Tarkaratna, Rāmanārāyaṇa.
    (Kulina kulasarbbasva)
    কুলীন কুলসর্ব্বস্ব : নাটক / রামনারায়ণ তর্করত্ন প্রণীত. — কলিকাতা : সংস্কৃত যন্ত্র, 1913.
    2, 110 p. ; 19 cm.
    In Bengali.

    I. Title.

PK1729.T37K8   75-986123

NT   0040289   DLC

PK3798
.N277V412
1913
Orien
Ben
    Tarkaratna, Rāmanārāyaṇa.

Nārāyaṇa Bhaṭṭa.
    (Veṇīsaṃhāra. Bengali)
    বেণীসংহার নাটক / নারায়ণ ; রামনারায়ণ তর্করত্ন কর্তৃক অনুবাদিত. [s.l. : s.n.], 1913 (কলিকাতা : সত্যার্ণব)

PK
1771
.E9
.R3
1904
    Tarkaratna, Rāmanārāyaṇa.
    Ratnavali: a drama in four acts. Translated from the Bengali by Michael M. S. Dutt. Calcutta, N. Roy, 1904.
    71 p.
    "A reprint of the first edition, 1858."
    Based on the Sanskrit play of the same name by Harsavardhana.
    #Bengali drama--Translations into English.
    #English drama--Translations from Bengali.
    (A) Dutt, Michael Madhusudan, 1824-1873, tr.

    (A) Harsavardhana, King of Thanesar and Kanauj, fl. 606-64. Ratnavali.
    (A) Ratnavali.

NT   0040292   MoU ICU

Tarkaratna, Rāmanātha.
    ... Sri Bhāshyam
    see under   Ramanuja, founder of sect.

Tarkasāṃkhyabedāntatīrtha, Yogendranātha
    see
    Bagchi, Jogendranath.

Tarkasiddhanta Kunjabihari
    see   Kunjabihari Tarkasiddhanta.

Tarkatirtha, Amarendra Mohan, comp.
 A brief catalogue of Sanskrit manuscripts in the
Post-Graduate Department of Sanskrit
  see under   Calcutta. University. Sanskrit
College. Dept. of Post-graduate of Sanskrit.

Tarkatirtha, Amarendra Mohan, ed.
 Kavyaprakaśa... 1936
  see under   Mammatācārya.

Tarkatirtha, Parvati Charana, ed.
 ... Kalivilasa tantra
  see under   Tantras. Kalivilasa tantra.

PK3799
.K29D5
1857
Orien
Sans

Tarkavachaspati, Taranatha, 1812-1885.
 Kāñcanācāryya.
  [Dhanañjayavijaya]
  धनञ्जयविजयः / श्रीकाञ्चनाचार्य्यविरचितः ; श्रीतारानाथ तर्कवाचस्पति
  संस्कृतः. — Calcutta : H.C. Banerjee, 1857.

Tarkavachaspati, Taranatha, 1812-1885.
Gayashradhadipadhati. Calcutta,1872.

NT   0040300   MH

Tarkavachaspati, Taranatha, 1812-1885.
 Rajaprasti, a Sanscrit poem in praise of the late
H.R.H. Prince Alfred Ernest Albert, composed by Sri
Taranatha Tarkavachaspati Bhattacharya. Translated into
Sinhalese by C.A.Seelakkhanda Mahathera, and translated
into English by N.H.Jinadasa. Pub. under the patronage
of Henry Amarasuriya, Galle. [Colombo] Buddhist Press,
1911.

 various paging. ports.
 Sinhalese and English texts.

NT   0040301   MH CU

Fpg57
+T17

Tarkavachaspati, Taranatha, 1812-1885.
 ... Sabdastomamahanidhi; a Sanscrit
dictionary compiled by Táránátha Tarka-
váchaspati ... Calcutta,The New Sanskrit
press[etc.,etc.]1870.
 3p.l.,[2,526]p. 28½x23cm.
 Paged in Sanskrit numerals; title also in
Sanskrit.

NT   0040302   CtY

Tarkavachaspati, Taranatha, 1812-1885, ed.
 Sisulpalavadham ... 1869
  see under   Magha.

PK925
.B57

Tarkavachaspati, Taranatha, 1812-1885.
 Vachaspatya; a comprehensive Sanscrit diction-
ary. Calcutta, Printed at the Kavya Prakasha
Press, 1873-84.
 22 pts. in 7 v. (2, 5442 p.) port.
 Title in Sanskrit at head of t.p.
 Pts.9-22 have imprint: Calcutta, Saraswati
Press.

 1. Sanskrit language--Dictionaries.

NT   0040304   ICU PPULC PU

Tarkavagisa, Abhinanda
 see   Abhinanda Tarkavagisa. [Supplement]

Tarkavāgīsa, Harirāma, supposed author.
 Mangalavādah; ossia, Ragionamento sulla
felicita
  see under   Mangalavādah.

Tarkavāgīsa, Mathurānātha
 see   Mathurānātha Tarkavāgīsa.

PK3708
.K572R3
1854
Orien
Sans

Tarkavagisa, Premachandra. Kapātavipātikā. 1854.
 Kavirāja, 12th cent.
  [Rāghavapāndaviya]
  राघवपाण्डवीयम् / श्रीकविराजपण्डित विरचितम् ; श्रीप्रेमचंद्रतर्कवागीशभट्टा-
  चार्य विरचितया कपाटविपाटिकास्यया टीकया सहितम्. — [s.l. : s.n.], संवत्
  1910 [1854] (कलिकाता : संस्कृतयंत्रे मुद्रितम्)

Tarkavāgīśa, Rāmacarana
 see
Rāmacarana Tarkavāgīśa, *fl.* 1700.

Tarkhad, Jnanesvara Atmarama
 see   Jñanesvara Ātmārāma Tarkhad.

Tarkhadkar, Dadoba Pandurauga
 see   Dadoba Pandurauga Tarkhadkar.

Tarkhan-Mouravov, Ivan Romanovich, *kniaz'*
 see Tarkhanov, Ivan Romanovich, *kniaz'*, 1846?-1908?

Tarkhaniants (Sophie) [1871-   ]. *Contribution à l'étude du foie dans la chlorose. 75
pp. 8°. *Paris, 1900. No. 265.*

NT   0040313   DNLM

Tarkhanoff, Ivan Romanovich, *kniaz'*
 see Tarkhanov, Ivan Romanovich, *kniaz'*, 1846?-1908?

BF
T187g
1891

TARKHANOV, Ivan Romanovich, kniaz,
  1846?-1908?
  Hypnotisme, suggestion et lecture
des pensées. Tr. du russe par Ernest
Jaubert, Paris, Masson, 1891.
  vii, 163 p. illus.
  Translation of Gipnotizm, vnushenie i
chtenie myslei.

NT   0040315   DNLM MH

BF
T187g
1893

TARKHANOV, Ivan Romanovich, kniaz,
  1846?-1908?
  Hypnotisme, suggestion et lecture
des pensées. Tr. du russe par Ernest
Jaubert. 2. éd. Paris, Masson, 1893.
  vii, 163 p. illus.
  Translation of Gipnotizm, vnushenie i
chtenie myslei.

NT   0040316   DNLM NN

ND699
.R4A36

Tarkhanov, Ivan Romanovich, kniaz', 1846?-1908?
 Repin, Il'ia Efimovich, 1844-1930.
  Письма к Е. П. Тархановой-Антокольской и И. Р. Тар-
ханову. [Под общей ред. К. И. Чуковского; вступ. статья
и примечания И. А. Бродского и Я. Д. Лещинского] Ленинград, Искусство, 1937.

Tarkhanov, Ivan Romanovich, kniaz', 1846?-1908?
 jt. author.
 Poehl, Aleksandr Vasil'evich, 1850-
  Rationelle organotherapie mit berücksichtigung der
urosemiologie von Prof. Dr. A. v. Poehl, Prof. Dr. fürst
J. v. Tarchanoff und Dr. P. Wachs. Uebers. aus dem russischen ...   St. Petersburg, 1905

HX19
.O18

Tarkhanov.
 (O sisteme politobrazovaniia)
 О системе политобразования; [тезисы к докладу т. Тарха-
нова на Полит. просвет. секции VI с'езда РКСМ. Мо-
сква] Молодая гвардия, 1924.

Tarkhanov, O., *pseud.*
 see
Razumov, Sergeï Petrovich.

ND699
.R4A36

Tarkhanova-Antokol'skaia, E. P.
 Repin, Il'ia Efimovich, 1844-1930.
  Письма к Е. П. Тархановой-Антокольской и И. Р. Тар-
ханову. [Под общей ред. К. И. Чуковского; вступ. статья
и примечания И. А. Бродского и Я. Д. Лещинского] Ленинград, Искусство, 1937.

Tarkhnishvili, Ivan Ramazovich
 see
Tarkhanov, Ivan Romanovich, *kniaz'*, 1846?-1908?

Tarkhov, A   G
  Геофизическая разведка методом индукции. Москва,
Гос. научно-техн. изд-во лит-ры по геологии и охране
недр, 1954.
  92, [4] p. illus. 22 cm.
  Errata slip inserted.
  Bibliography: p. [94]
 ---- Microfilm copy (negative)
Made in 1955 by the Library of Congress.
  [Prospecting—Geophysical methods.   I. Title.
                Title transliterated: Geofizicheskaia
                razvedka metodom indukfsii.
TN269.T3   55-37898

NT   0040323   DLC

Tarkiainen, Maria (Haggren)
 see   Jotuni, Maria, 1880-1943.

Tarkiainen, Maria Kustaava (Jotuni)
see
Jotuni, Maria, 1880–1943.

Tarkiainen, Tuttu Vilho, 1912–
Tasavallan presidentin asema Suomen parlamenttaarisessa hallitusjärjestelmässä. Jyväskylä, K. J. Gummerus ₁1938₎

353 p. 25 cm.

Thesis—Helsingfors.
Bibliography: p. ₁341₎–353.

1. Finland—Presidents.

JN6711.T3   50–48202

NT 0040326   DLC NjP NNC CtY

Tarkiainen, Viljo, 1879–1951.
Äänneopillinen tutkimus Javan murteesta, tehnyt V. Tarkiainen. Helsingissä, Suomal. kirjallis. seura; kirjapainon osakeyhtiö, 1903

138 p.
Eripainos aikakauskirjasta Suomesta

NT 0040327   MH

Tarkiainen, Viljo, 1879–1951.
Aapinen. Kuvittanut T. K. Sallinen. 3. painos. Helsingissä, Osakeyhtiö Valistus [1921]

123 p. illus.

NT 0040328   MH

PH
325   **Tarkiainen, Viljo,** 1879–1951.
T17a   Aino ja muut Kalevalan naiset. Porvoo, Söderström, 1911.
103 p.

1. Kalevala. I. Title.

NT 0040329   CLU InU MH

Tarkiainen, Viljo, 1879–1951.
Aleksis Kiven maineen kaikuja; poimintoja koti- ja ulkomaisten arvostelijoiden lausunnoista, koonnut V. Tarkiainen. Helsinki: Suomalaisen kirjallisuuden seura, 1934. 25 p. 24½cm.

835944A. 1. Stenvall, Alexis,   1834–1872.   August 14, 1936
N. Y. P. L.

NT 0040330   NN DSI

Tarkiainen, Viljo, 1879–1851, comp.
Aleksis Kiven muisto, runoilijan syntymän 85-vuotispäiväksi. 1919.
In Finnish.

NT 0040331   RP

Hza94   **Tarkiainen, Viljo,** 1879–1951.
St42X   Aleksis Kiven muisto, runoilijan syntymän
T175   85-vuotispäiväksi. [Helsinki] Kustannusosa-keytiö Ahjo [1919]
354 p. illus. 26 cm.

1. Stenvall, Aleksis, 1834–1872. I. Title(1)

NT 0040332   CtY DLC-P4

Tarkiainen, Viljo, 1879–1951.
Aleksis Kiven oleskelusta Siuntiosta. Alexis Kivis vistelse i Sjundeå. Der Aufenthalt Alexis Kivis in Sjundeå. Helsinki, Suomalaisen Kirjallisuuden Seura, 1934.

32 p. illus., ports. 23cm.

Summaries in Swedish and German.
"Eripainos juhlajulkaisusta 'Aleksis Kiven satavuotismuisto 10.X. 1934'."

1. Stenvall, Aleksis, 1834–1872.

NT 0040333   MnU

Hza94   **Tarkiainen, Viljo,** 1879–1951.
St44   Aleksis Kiven "Seitsemän veljestä";
T17   kirjallinen tutkimus ... Porvoossa, 1910.
3p.l., 164p. 21cm.
Thesis – Helsinki.

NT 0040334   CtY ICRL

Tarkiainen, Viljo, 1879–1951.
Aleksis Kivi. ₁Helsingissä, 1917₎
187 p. illus., ports. 17 cm. (Kansanvalistusseuran elämäkertoja, 24)

1. Kivi, Aleksis, 1834–1872.   I. Series: Kansanvalistusseura.
Elämäkertoja, 24.

PH355.K548Z9   71–275661

NT 0040335   DLC

Tarkiainen, Viljo, 1879–1951.
Aleksis Kivi; elämä ja teokset. 2. painos. Porvoo, W. Söderström ₁1915₎
vi, 640 p. illus., map, ports. 22 cm.
Bibliography: p. ₁636₎–640.

1. Stenvall, Aleksis, 1834–1872.

PH355.S8Z88 1915   65–82274

NT 0040336   DLC

Tarkiainen, Viljo, 1879–1951.
Aleksis Kivi; elämä ja teokset. Söderström [1923]
illus., ports.

NT 0040337   OrP

PH355
.S827   **Tarkiainen, Viljo,** 1879–1951.
Aleksis Kivi, elämä ja teokset. 5. painos. Helsinki, W. Söderström ₁1950₎
561 p. illus., ports. 21cm.
Bibliography: p. ₁538₎–552.

1. Stenvall, Aleksis, 1834–1872. 2. Finnish language—Texts.

NT 0040338   MB OC1 NN

895.1St42
BT
Tarkiainen, Viljo, 1879–1951.
Aleksis Kivi; elämä ja teokset. 5. painos. Porvoo, Söderström ₁1950₎
561 p. plates, ports., facsims.

Bibliography: p. ₁538₎–552.

1. Stenvall, Aleksis, 1834–1872. 2. Stenvall, Aleksis, 1834–1872 – Bibliography.

NT 0040339   NNC DLC-P4 CtY InU MiU

PH   **Tarkiainen, Viljo,** 1879–1951, ed.
124   Arwidssonista Snellmaniin. Kansallisia kirjoitelmia vuosilta
T17a   1817–44. Suunnitelman laatineet V. Tarkiainen ja Aarne Anttila. Suomentanut E. V. I. Karjalainen. Helsinki, Suomalaisen Kirjallisuuden Seura, 1929.
448 p. (Suomalaisuuden syntysanoja, 3)

Suomalaisen Kirjallisuuden Seura, Helsinki. Toimituksia, 105.

1. Finnish language - Addresses, essays, lectures. I. Anttila, Aarne, 1892–1952. II.   Title. III. Series. IV. Series: Suomalaisen Kirjalli-   suuden Seura, Helsinki.
Toimituksia.

NT 0040340   CLU MH

4PH   **Tarkiainen, Viljo,** 1879–1951.
Fin   Eino Leinon runoudesta; tutkielmia.
597   Helsingissä, Otava ₁1954₎
229 p.

NT 0040341   DLC-P4

PH 353 TARKIAINEN, VILJO, 1879–1951
.A27 Z853   Eskatologisia piirteitä Mikael Agricolan teoksissa. Helsinki, Suomalaisen Kirjallisuuden Seura, 1943.
248–264 p.

Reprint: Suomi-Kirjan eripainoksia 14. Uusi sarja.

1. Agricola, Michael Olavi, Bp., 1508?–1557. Folkl. cds.

NT 0040342   InU

4PH   **Tarkiainen, Viljo,** 1879–1951.
Fin   Finsk litteraturhistoria.
249   [Översättningen har utförts av E. N. Tigerstedt] Helsingfors, Söderström [1950]
390 p.

NT 0040343   DLC-P4 NN CU MnU

Tarkiainen, Viljo, 1879–1951.
Finsk litteraturhistoria. ₁Översättningen har utförts av E. N. Tigerstedt₎ Stockholm, H. Geber ₁1950₎
390 p. 22 cm.
"De viktigaste källorna": p. 368–371. "Finsk litteratur i svensk översättning": p. 373–382.

1. Finnish literature—Hist. & crit.   A 51–6094

Harvard Univ. Library
for Library of Congress   ₁1₎

NT 0040344   MH CtY

Tarkiainen, Viljo, 1879–1951.
Fredrik Cygnaeus runoilijana. Porvoossa, W. Söderström, 1911.
101 p. 21 cm.
1. Cygnaeus, Fredrik, 1807–1881.

NT 0040345   MnU DLC-P4 MH

Tarkiainen, Viljo, 1879–1951.
Gustaf von Numers; elämä ja teokset, kirjallisuushistoriallinen tutkielma. Helsingissä, Kustannusosakeyhtiö Otava [1922]

208 p. illus.

1. Numers, Gustaf Adolf   von, 1848–1913

NT 0040346   MH DLC-P4

Tarkiainen, Viljo, 1879- 1951.
Henrik Gabriel Porthan. Helsinki, Suomalaisen Kirjallisuuden Seura, 1948.
84 p. illus., port. 21 cm. (Tietolipas no. 6)
Bibliography: p. ₍82₎-84.

1. Porthan, Henrik Gabriel, 1739-1804.   (Series)

PH117.P6T3   52-67313

NT   0040347   DLC NN InU MH TxU

Tarkiainen, Viljo, 1879-1951.
Holberg Suomessa. Helsinki, Suomalaisen Kirjallisuuden Seura ₍1930₎

28 p. 23cm. (Vähäisiä kirjelmiä,
70)

"Eripainos Suomi V, 10:stä."

1. Holberg, Ludvig, Baron, 1684-1754.

NT   0040348   MnU

PH
301
T17k
Tarkiainen, Viljo, 1879-1951.
Kansankirjailijoita katsomassa. Porvoo,
Söderström, 1904.
83 p.

1. Finnish literature - Hist. & crit.
I. Title.

NT   0040349   CLU

Tarkiainen, Viljo, 1879-   ed.
Karjalan laulu; valikoima Suomen Karjalan, Vienan,
Aunuksen ja Inkerin runoutta. Helsingissä, Kustannusosakeyhtiö Otava ₍1941₎
296 p. 19 cm.

1. Finnish poetry. 2. Poetry of places—Finland—Karelia. 3. Karelia—Descr.—Poetry. I. Title.

PH346.T3   57-53438 ‡

NT   0040350   DLC

PH
301
T17ka
Tarkiainen, Viljo, 1879-1951.
Kaunokirjallisuus ja kirjallisuuden tutkimus.
Helsinki, Suomalaisen Kirjallisuuden Seura,
1931.
57 p. (Vähäisiä kirjelmiä, 72)

1. Finnish literature - Hist. & crit.
I. Title. II. Series.

NT   0040351   CLU

PH355
.K548
1944
Tarkiainen, Viljo, 1879-1951, ed.

Kivi, Aleksis, 1834-1872.
Kootut teokset. ₍Julkaissut E. A. Saarimaa. 4. painos.
Helsinki, Suomalaisen Kirjallisuuden Seura, 1944-51₎

PQ
6337
T175m
Tarkiainen, Viljo, 1879-1951.
Miguel de Cervantes Saavedra; elämä ja teokset.
Porvoo, Söderström, 1918.
400 p. illus., port.

1. Cervantes Saavedra, Miguel de, 1547-1616.

NT   0040353   CLU MiU

PH355
.S8Z57
Tarkiainen, Viljo, 1879-   ed.

Aleksis Kiven Seura.
Minä elän; Aleksis Kivi ajan kuvastimessa. ₍Toimitus-
kunta: V. Tarkiainen et al.₎ Helsingissä, Kustannusosakeyhtiö Otava ₍1945₎

4PH
Fin.
484
Tarkiainen, Viljo, 1879-1951.
Minna Canth. Helsingissä, Otava
₍1921₎
108 p.

NT   0040355   DLC-P4

Tarkiainen, Viljo, 1879-1951.
O. Manninen runoilijana. Porvoo,
W. Söderström ₍1933₎

63 p. 20cm.

1. Manninen, Otto, 1872-1950.

NT   0040356   MnU InU MH

Tarkiainen, Viljo, 1879-1951.
Piirteitä suomalaisesta kirjallisuudesta. Porvoossa, W. Söderström
₍1922₎

286 p. illus. 21cm.

1. Finnish literature. History and
criticism.

NT   0040357   MnU

4PH
Fin.-
53
Tarkiainen, Viljo, 1879-1951.
Poimintoja vanhemmasta suomalaisesta
kirjallisuudesta; koulujen tarpeeksi toimit-
tanect V. Tarkiainen ja O. J. Brummer.
5. painos. Helsingissä, Kustannusosakeyhtiö
Otava [1947]
172 p.

NT   0040358   DLC-P4 NN

PH
329
T17r
Tarkiainen, Viljo, 1879-1951
Ritvalan helka juhla ja virret. Porvoo,
Söderström, 1922.
105 p. (Kalevalaseura. Julkaisuja, 1)

1. Helkavirret. 2. Ballads, Finnish.
I. Title.

NT   0040359   CLU MH

TARKIAINEN, Viljo, 1879-1951.
Die Studien Michael Agricolas in Wittenberg;
Vortrag, gehalten am 9 IV. 1945. (IN: Suomalainen
tiedeakatemia, Helsingfors. Sitzungsberichte. Proceedings. Helsinki.
25cm. 1945. p. [185]-139)

Bibliographical footnotes.
1. Agricola, Mikael, bp.,   ca. 1510-1557.

NT   0040360   NN

PH308
.T37
Tarkiainen, Viljo, 1879-1951.
Suomalaisen kirjallisuuden historia. Helsingissä, Otava ₍1934₎
346 p. illus. 26cm. (Yleinen kirjallisuuden historia)
"Aikataulukko": p. ₍331₎-336. Bibliography:
p. ₍337₎-338.

1. Finnish literature—Hist. & crit.
2. Finnish language—Texts.   I. Title.

NT   0040361   MB PU OC1 NN

Tarkiainen, Viljo, 1879-1951.
Suomalaisen kirjallisuuden historia; toinen,
korjattu ja lisätty painos 55 liitekuvaa, hen-
kilöhakemisto ja kirjallisuusluettelo.
Helsinki, Otava, 1934.
398p. illus.,ports.

At head of title: V. Tarkiainen - Eino
Kauppinen.
Finnish

NT   0040362   OC1

Fke4
943T
Tarkiainen, Viljo, 1879-1951, ed.
Suomen kansan kannel; vanhaa kansanrunoutta,
julkaistuna alkuperäisten kirjaanpanojen mu-
kaan. Toimittaneet V. Tarkiainen ja Hertta
Harmas. Helsingissä, Kustannusosakeyhtiö
Otava [1943]
576 p. illus., ports. 21 cm. (Suomen
kansalliskirjallisuus, 3. osana)

1. Folk-songs, Finnish. I. Harmas, Hertta
joint ed.
cdu

NT   0040363   CtY MnU

Tarkiewicz, Wladyslaw, 1886-
Dominik Merlini. [Wyd. 1. Warszawa]
Budownictwo i Architektura, 1955.
193 p. illus. 25 cm. (Mistrzowie
architektury polskiej)

At head of title: Instytut Urbanistyki i
Architektury.
Bibliography: p. 32-[33]

1. Merlini, Dominik, 1730-1797.   SSL NUC EX

NT   0040364   CSt

Tarkington, Booth, 1869-1946.
The works. Garden City, N.Y., Doubleday, Page, ₍19--?₎
12v. illus. 22cm.

Autograph edition limited to 565 copies.

NT   0040365   KU

810.8
T17w
Tarkington, Booth, 1869-1946.
Works. Seawood edition. Garden City,
N.Y., Doubleday ₍1902₎
16 v.

Contents: v.1 The Gentleman from Indiana.-
v.2 The two vanrevels.- v.3 Guest of Quesnay.-
v.4 Flirt.- v.5 Penrod.- v.6 Penrod and Sam.-
v.7 In the arena.- v.8 Harlequin and Columbine
and other stories.- v.9 Monsieur Beaucaire;
The beautiful lady; His own people and other

stories.- v.10 Turmoil.- v.11 Conquest of
Canaan.- v.12 Seventeen.- v.13 Magnificent
Ambersons.- v.14 Ramsey Milholland.- v.15
Alice Adams.- v.16 Gentle Julia.

NT   0040367   KEmT

PS
2970
.A2
1902
Tarkington, Booth, 1869-1946.
The works of Booth Tarkington.
Seawood edition. Garden City, N.Y.,
Doubleday, Page & Company, [c1902-1932]
27 v. fronts. 22 cm.
"This edition is strictly limited to
1075 numbered and registered copies
each with a portrait signed by the
author in volume one. No. 152."
CONTENTS.--v. 1. The gentleman from
Indiana.--v. 2. The two Vanrevels.--v.
3. The guest of Quesnay.--v. 4. The
flirt.--v. 5. Penrod.--v.6 Penrod and
Sam.--v. 7. In the arena.--v. 8.
Harlequin and Columbine and other
stories.--v. 9. Monsieur Beaucaire. The
beautiful lad y. His own people and
other stories   --v. 10. The turmoil.
--v. 11. The   conquest of Canaan.--

Continued in next column

Continued from preceding column

v. 12. Seventeen.--v. 13. The
magnificent Ambersons.--v. 14. Ramsey
Milholland.--v. 15. Alice Adams.--v.
16. Gentle Julia.--v. 17. The
fascinating stranger and other stories.
--v. 18. The midlander.--v. 19. Women.
--v. 20. The plutocrat.--v. 21. Claire
Ambler.--v. 22. Looking forward and
others.--v. 23. The world does move.--
v. 24. Young Mrs. Greeley.--v. 25. The
new Penrod book, Penrod Jashber.--v.
26. Mirthful haven.--v. 27. Mary's
neck.

NT 0040369   OKentU

Tarkington, Booth, 1869-
    The works of Booth Tarkington.
Garden City, N.Y., Doubleday, Page,
1918-1919.
    13 v. illus.
    "Autograph edition, limited to five
hundred and sixty-five copies. This is
no.333."

    Contents.- v.1. The gentleman from
Indiana.- v.2. The two vanrevels.- v.3.

The quest of Quesnay.- v.4. The flirt.-
v.5. Penrod.- v.6. Penrod and Sam.-
v.7. In the arena.- v.8. Harlequin and
Columbine and other stories.- v.10. The
turmoil.- v.11. The conquest of Canaan.-
v.12. Seventeen.- v.13. The magnificent
Ambersons.- v.14. Ramsey Milholland.

NT 0040371   WaSpG

Tarkington, Booth, 1869-1946.
    The works of Booth Tarkington ... Garden City, New York,
Doubleday, Page and company, 1918-19.
    14 v. fronts. (v. 1: port.) illus. 22ᶜᵐ.
    Vol. 5 only has illustrations.
    "Autograph edition, limited to five hundred and sixty-five copies. This
is no. 67; no. 1 signed by author.
    CONTENTS.—I. The gentleman from Indiana.—II. The two Vanrevels.—
III. The guest of Quesnay.—IV. The flirt.—V. Penrod.—VI. Penrod and
Sam.—VII. In the arena.—VIII. Harlequin and Columbine, and other stories.—IX. Monsieur Beaucaire. The beautiful lady. His own people, and
other stories.—X. The turmoil.—XI. The conquest of Canaan.—XII. Seventeen.—XIII. The magnificent Ambersons.—XIV. Ramsey Milholland.
                    ₍Full name: Newton Booth Tarkington₎
                                18-20474 Revised 2
    Library of Congress   PS2970.A2 1918

NT 0040372   DLC PP InU TxU

20th   Tarkington, Booth, 1869-1946.
Cent   The works of Booth Tarkington. Garden
Am   City, N.Y. Doubleday, Page, 1918-28.
T 187   21 v. fronts. (v.1: port.) illus. 22 cm.
IN: Vol. 5 only has illustrations.
spec   "Autograph edition, limited to five
        hundred and sixty-five copies. This is no.
        480". Vol. 1 signed by author.
           CONTENTS: I. The gentleman from
        Indiana.--II. The two Vanrevels.--III. The
        quest of Quesnay.--IV. The flirt.--V.
        Penrod.--VI. Penrod and Sam.--VII. In the
        arena.--VIII. Harlequin and Columbine, and

other stories.--IX. Monsieur Beaucaire.
The beautiful lady. His own people,
and other stories.--X. The turmoil.--
XI. The conquest of Canaan.--XII.
Seventeen.--XIII. The magnificent
Ambersons.
    --XIV. Ramsey Milholland.--XV. Alice
Adams.--XVI. Gentle Julia.--XVII. The
fascinating stranger, and other stories.--
XVIII. The Midlander.--XIX. Women.--XX.
The plutocrat.--XXI. Claire Ambler.
    Vol. 1-14: fro   nt. in two states, one
colored. Vol. 17   -21 have no front.

NT 0040374   IEN

Tarkington, Booth, 1869-1946.

    The works of Booth Tarkington...
Garden City, N.Y., Doubleday, Page and
company, 1918-32.
    27 v. illus. 22 ᶜᵐ.

    Autograph edition limited to 565
copies, signed by the author.

NT 0040375   NjP

812T17   Tarkington, Booth, 1869-1946.
I3   ₍The works of Booth Tarkington₎ Garden City,
        New York, Doubleday, Page, 1920-24.
           10 v. front., illus.

           Each volume has special t.-p. only.
           Contents.--₍v. 1₎ The two Vanrevels.--₍v. 2.₎
        The flirt.--₍v. 3₎ The guest of Quesnay.--₍v. 4₎
        The gentleman from Indiana.--₍v. 5₎ Penrod.--₍v. 6₎
        Penrod and Sam.--₍v. 7₎ In the arena.--₍v. 8₎
        Monsieur Beaucaire. The beautiful lady. His own
        people.--₍v. 9₎   The magnificent Ambersons.
        --₍v. 10₎ Ramsey   Milholland.

NT 0040376   NNC

Tarkington, Newton Booth.
    Works. Garden City, Doubleday, 1922
[c1899-22]
    v. 1-   (Seawood edition)

NT 0040377   PU

Tarkington, Booth, 1869-1946.
    Works. Garden City, N.Y., Doubleday, Page &
co., 1922.

    16 v. port., plates, illus. 22 cm.
    Half-title: Seawood ed.
    Contents: 1.The gentleman from Indiana.- 2.
The two Vanrevels.- 3.The guest of Quesnay.- 4.
The flirt.- 5.Penrod.- 6.Penrod and Sam.- 7.
In the arena.- 8.Harlequin and Columbine and
other stories.- 9.Monsieur Beaucaire. The
beautiful lady. Hi   own people, and other

stories.- 10.The turmoil.- 11.The conquest of
Canaan.- 12.Seventeen; a tale of youth and
summer time and the Baxter family, especially
William.- 13.The magnificent Ambersons.- 14.
Ramsey Milholland.- 15.Alice Adams.- 16.Gentle
Julia.

NT 0040379   MH ViU

---

813   Tarkington, Booth, 1869-1946.
T17   The works of Booth Tarkington ...
1922   Garden City, 1922.
           21v. fronts., illus.   (Lettered on
        cover: Seawood ed.)

           "This edition is strictly limited to
        1075 numbered and registered copies ...
        [This copy is] no.579."

NT 0040380   IU

---

818   Tarkington, Booth, 1869-1946.
I174   The works of Booth Tarkington.   Garden
Sel   City, N. Y., Doubleday, Page, 1922-24.
           18 v. illus., port. 22cm.   (Seawood
        edition.

           Contents.--v.1. The gentleman from Indiana.--
        v.2. The two Vanrevels.--v.3. The guest of
        Quesnay.--v.4. The flirt.--v.5. Penrod.--v.6.
        Penrod and Sam.--v.7. In the arena.--v.8. Harle-
        quin and Columbine, and other stories.--v.9.
        Monsieur Beaucaire. The beautiful lady. His own

        people, and other stories.--v.10. The turmoil.--
        v.11. The conquest of Canaan.--v.12. Seventeen.--
        v.13. The magnificent Ambersons.--v.14. Ramsey
        Milholland.--v.15. Alice Adams.--v.16. Gentle
        Julia.--v.17. The fascinating stranger, and
        other stories.--v.18. The midlander.

NT 0040382   AU OCU

Tarkington, Booth, 1869-1946.
    The works of Booth Tarkington...   New York: Double-
day, Page & Co., 1922-28.   21 v. fronts. (v. I, port.) illus.
(v. 5, 14.) 8°.   (Seawood edition.)

    no. 814 of 1075 copies printed.
    Frontispieces are drawings by the author, by Arthur William Brown, Gordon
Grant, Worth Brenn, C. A. Gilbert, and others.
    v. 18-21 have no frontispieces.
    With author's autograph.
    Contents: v. 1. The gentleman from Indiana. v. 2. The two Vanrevels. v. 3.
The guest of Quesnay. v. 4. The flirt. v. 5. Penrod. v. 6. Penrod and Sam. v. 7. In

the arena. v. 8. Harlequin and Columbine, and other stories. v.9. Monsieur Beaucaire.
The beautiful lady. His own people, and other stories. v. 10. The turmoil. v. 11. The
conquest of Canaan. v. 12. Seventeen. v. 13. The magnificent Ambersons. v. 14.
Ramsey Milholland. v. 15. Alice Adams. v. 16. Gentle Julia. v. 17. The fascinating
stranger, and other stories. v. 18. The midlander. v. 19. Women. v. 20. The plutocrat.
v. 21. Claire Ambler.

470482-502A.   1. American litera-   ture—Collected works.
N. Y. P. L.   April 24, 1930

NT 0040384   NN CtY

RARE BOOK
DIVISION
PLN

PS   Tarkington, Booth, 1869-1946.
2970   The works of Booth Tarkington ₍Seawood edition₎
A2   Garden City, N.Y., Doubleday, Page & co., 1922-
1922   1932.
           27 v. fronts.(v.1, port.) 22 cm.
           "This edition is strictly limited to 1075
        numbered and registered copies each with a por-
        trait signed by the author in volume one. No.315"
        Signed: Doubleday, Page.
           Publication initiated by Doubleday, Page and
        completed by Doubleday, Doran.

           cf. Russo and Sullivan, p. 221.
           Contents.-v.1. The Gentleman from Indiana.-
        v.2. The two Van Revels.-v.3. The guest of
        Quesnay.-v.4. The Flirt.-v.5. Penrod.-v.6. Penrod
        and Sam.-v.7 In the Arena.-v.8. Harlequin and
        Columbine and other stories.-v.9. Monsieur
        Beaucaire, The beautiful lady, His own people
        and other stories.-v.10. The turmoil.-v.11. The
        conquest of Canaa v.12. Seventeen...-v.13. The

        magnificent Ambersons.-v.14. Ramsey Milholland.-
        v.15. Alice Adams.-v.16. Gentle Julia.-
        v.17. The fascinating stranger and other stories.
        -v.18. The midlander.-v.19. Women.-v.20. The
        plutocrat.-v.21. Claire Ambler.-v.22. Looking
        forward and others.-v.23. The world does move.
        -v.24. Young Mrs. Greeley.-v.25. The new book
        of Penrod Jashber.-v.26. Mirthful haven.-v.27.
        Mary's neck.

NT 0040387   PPT WaS PP OO InU MB MWelC

Lilly   TARKINGTON,BOOTH,1869-1946
PS 3539   About Fred C. Kelly, author of Kelly-
.A7 A15   grams ... ₍Cleveland, Ohio, Printed by
        Horace Carr for Editor's Future Service,
        1926?₎
           Broadside.   30 x 19.2 cm.

           Caption title. Imprint from Russo &
        Sullivan, Bibl. of Booth Tarkington, p. 134.
           First edition.
           From the library of J. K. Lilly.
           Unbound; mar- ginal tears.

NT 0040388   InU

Tarkington, Booth, 1869-1946.

₍Clemens, Samuel Langhorne₎ 1835-1910.
    The adventures of Huckleberry Finn, by Mark Twain
₍pseud.₎ with the original illustrations by E. W. Kemble, and
a new introduction by Booth Tarkington. New York, The
Limited editions club, 1933.

Tarkington, Booth, 1869–1946.

　　Alice Adams. Garden City, N. Y.,
Doubleday, Page, 1921.
　　434 p. 4 pl. 20cm.
　　First edition.—Johnson.

　　　I. Title.
　　　　　　　　　　　　Full name: Newton Booth
　　　　　　　　　　　　Tarkington.

NT　0040390　　ViU WU InU CaOTP ICU

Tarkington, Booth, 1869– 1946.

　　Alice Adams, by Booth Tarkington; illustrated by Arthur William Brown. Garden City, N. Y., and Toronto, Doubleday, Page & company, 1921.
　　5 p. l., 3–434 p. front., plates. 19¼ᶜᵐ.

　　　I. Title.
　　　　　　　　[Full name: Newton Booth Tarkington]
　　　　　　　　　　　　　　　　21–26561
　　　Library of Congress　　PZ3.T175A1

　　OrSaW OrPS MtU PHC PV Or WaSpG
MH　　　ODW OO OCU ViU NIC NcD NBuC PBm PBa CaBVa
TxU CaBVaU IdPI WaE OrP Wa WaSp IdU WaS NN MB OC1JC
NT　0040391　DLC OC1W　　　OrLgE OrAshS UU KEmT CU–S

Tarkington, Booth, 1869–1946.
　　Alice Adams.　New York, 1921.

NT　0040392　　PPL PWcS DAU PPHPI

PZ
3
.T175　Tarkington, Booth, 1869–1946
A12　　Alice Adams.　　New York, Grosset &
　　　　Dunlap [1921]
　　　　434 p. 20 cm.

　　　I. Title.

　　OO ICU TxU
PU KyU MB PPT NcU ViU OU NBuC MB KEmT NBuU OCU MiU
NT　0040393　NBrockU Vi MU IU PPAp PU MsU NcD PP PPD

Tarkington, Booth, 1869–1946.
　　Alice Adams, by Booth Tarkington.　New York, The Odyssey Pr. [c1921]
　　5 p. l., 3–434 p. 19.5 cm.
　　"Educational Edition".
　　I. Title.
　　[Full name: Newton Booth Tarkington]

NT　0040394　　NjP

---

*
PS2972
.A5
1921b　Tarkington, Booth, 1869–1946.

　　　Alice Adams. New York, Scribner, 1921.
　　　434 p. plates. 20cm.

　　　I. Title.　　Full name: Newton Booth Tarkington.

NT　0040395　　ViU MH

Tarkington, Booth, 1869–1946.
　　Alice Adams. By Booth Tarkington.　Toronto, London, New York, Hodder and Stoughton Ltd. [1921]
　　9–316 p.

NT　0040396　　CSmH

Tarkington, Booth, 1869–
　　Alice Adams, by Booth Tarkington...　Garden City, N. Y.: Doubleday, Page & Co., 1922.　434 p.　front., plates.　12°.

341497A. 1. Fiction, American.　　2. Title.
N. Y. P. L.　　　　　　　　　　　　　　January 26, 1928

NT　0040397　　NN WaTU WaChenE OrCS MH PP

Tarkington, Booth, 1869–1946.
　　Alice Adams, by Booth Tarkington; illustrated by Arthur William Brown.　Garden City, N. Y., and Toronto, Doubleday, Page & company, 1922 [c1921]
　　5 p. l., 3–434 p. front., plates. 19¼ cm.

NT　0040398　　OU MsU TxU MoU ViU

Tarkington, Booth, 1869–1946.
　　Alice Adams, by ...　New York, Doubleday, Page, 1926.
　　434 p. front. 19.5 cm.

NT　0040399　　OWorP

813
T17a　Tarkington,　　Booth, 1869–1946.
1930　　Alice Adams, by Booth Tarkington ...　New York, Grosset & Dunlap [1930?]
　　　434p.

　　　"Copyright 1921."

NT　0040400　　IU

813
T17a　Tarkington,　　Booth, 1869–1946.
1935　　Alice Adams, by Booth Tarkington ...　New York, Grosset & Dunlap [1935?]
　　　434p.

　　　"Copyright 1921."

NT　0040401　　IU

813
T17a　Tarkington,　　Booth, 1869–1946.
1937　　Alice Adams　　New York, Grosset & Dunlap
　　　[1937]
　　　434p.

　　　On cover: Pulitzer prize novel.

NT　0040402　　IU

Tarkington, Booth, 1869–　　Alice Adams.

Hawthorne, Nathaniel, 1804–1864.
　　... The house of the seven gables [by] Nathaniel Hawthorne, including also passages from So big [by] Edna Ferber, and Alice Adams [by] Booth Tarkington.　Syracuse, N. Y., The L. W. Singer company [1942]

　　　　　　　　Tarkington, Booth, 1869–　　Alice Adams.
PS2972
A42T7
　　　Trotter, Elizabeth.
　　　Alice Adams, a play in three acts, by Elizabeth Trotter. Adapted from the novel of the same name by Booth Tarkington. Boston, Mass., Los Angeles, Cal., Baker's plays [1945]

AC–L
T174al　Tarkington, Booth, 1869–1946.
1947　　... Alice Adams.　New York, Grosset & Dunlap, 1947 [c1921]
　　　4p. l., 3–434p. 19½cm.

　　　At head of title: Booth Tarkington.

　　　I. Title.　Br.: Payne Collection

NT　0040405　　TxU

UF
T187a　Tarkington, Booth, 1869–1946.
1952　　Alice Adams.　New York, Grosset & Dunlap
　　　[1952?]
　　　434p. 20cm.

NT　0040406　　IU

Tarkington, Booth, 1869–1946.
　　... Les Amberson, roman traduit de l'anglais par Jacqueline Duplain.　Genève–Paris, Édition Jeheber [1946]
　　2 p. l., [7]–306 p., 1 l. 18¼ᵐ.
　　"Cet ouvrage a été publié en langue anglaise sous le titre: The magnificent Ambersons."

　　　I. Duplain, Jacqueline, tr.　II. Title.
　　　　　　　　　　　　[Full name: Newton Booth Tarkington]

　　　PS2972.M25F7　　　　　　　　47–15326

NT　0040407　　DLC RPB NjP

⊁Tarkington, Booth, 1869–　　illus.

Roberts, Kenneth Lewis, 1885–
　　Antiquamania, edited by Kenneth L. Roberts; the collected papers of Professor Milton Kilgallen [pseud.], F. R. S., of Ugsworth college, elucidating the difficulties in the path of the antique dealer and collector, and presenting various methods of meeting and overcoming them.　With further illustrations, elucidations and wood-cuts done on feather-edged boards, by Booth Tarkington.　Garden City, N. Y., Doubleday, Doran & company, inc., 1928.

Rare
PS
2972　Tarkington, Booth, 1869–1946.
A76　　Aromatic Aaron Burr; a play.　[Kennebunkport, Me.?, 1938?]
　　　1 v. 30cm.

　　　Original typescript of the play.

NT　0040409　　NIC

AC–L
qT174Esat Tarkington, Booth, 1869–1946.
1941a　　As I seem to me.　[Philadelphia, 1941]
　　　[74]p. illus. 34½cm.

　　　Various paging.
　　　Detached from the Saturday evening post, v.214, nos. 1, 2, 3, 5, 6, 7, 8; July 5, 12, 19, Aug. 2, 9, 16, 23, 1941.

　　　I. Title.　II. The Saturday evening post.

NT　0040410　　TxU

Rare
PS
2972　Tarkington, Booth, 1869–1946.
A79++　　As I seem to me, by Booth Tarkington. [Philadelphia, Pa., Curtis Publishing Company, 1941]
　　　7 nos. illus. (incl. ports.) 35cm.

　　　A series of articles which appeared in the Saturday evening post from July 5, 1941 to Aug. 23, 1941.

NT　0040411　　NIC

PS3539
.A64
B38y
Tarkington, Booth, 1869-1946.
Beasley's Christmas party.
Illustrated by Ruth Sypherd Clements.
New York, Harper 1909.
99 p. col. front., col. illus.
Title-page decorated in colors.

NT 0040412   OCU PV PP PG1B PPD

Tarkington, Booth, 1869-1946.
Beasley's Christmas party, by Booth Tarkington ; illustrated by Ruth Sypherd Clements. New York and London, Harper & brothers, 1909.
3 p. l., 99, [1] p. col. front., col. illus. 20½ cm.
Title-page decorated in colors.
$1.25
—— Another issue. 1911, c1909. Illus. in black and white. Harper & bros., New York, N. Y.
PS2972.B3 1911
I. Title.
PZ3.T175B   9-28111
—— —— Copy 3.   PS2972.B3 1909

NT 0040413   OrCS ViU WaTU
OO NjP OEac OCl MH MiU NIC MB ViU NIC MH AAP MoSW
DLC MtBC CLU InU TxCM Wa Or OrP WaSp TxU

Tarkington, Booth, 1869-1946.
Beasley's Christmas party.   New York,
Harper, 1911.
99 p.

NT 0040414   PU PHC

AC-L
T174be
1911
Tarkington, Booth, 1869-1946.
Beasley's Christmas party, by Booth Tarkington; illustrated by Ruth Sypherd Clements. New York and London, Harper & brothers [1911, c1909].
3 p. l., 99, [1] p. front., illus. 19½cm.
"Published October, 1911."
Title-page decorated.

NT 0040415   TxU

Tarkington, Booth, 1869-1946.
Beaucaire. Opera in 4 acts and 11 scenes
see under   MacColl, Hugh Frederick,
1885-1953.

PS2972
B35
Tarkington, Booth, 1869-1946.
The beautiful lady.   London, J. Murray,
1905.
143 p. illus. 20 cm.

NT 0040417   CU-A

Tarkington, Booth, 1869-1946.
The beautiful lady [by] Booth Tarkington. New York, McClure, Phillips & co., 1905.
5 p. l., 3-143, [1] p. front. 6 pl. 20ᶜᵐ.
I. Title.
[Full name: Newton Booth Tarkington]
5—16519
Library of Congress   PZ3.T175Be
—— —— Copy 2.   PS2972.B35 1905

NT 0040418   Wa WaSp OrU KU WaU CoU NcRS CaOTP   VtU OKentU
OCU MiU OCl MH   NN NjP MB TxU ViU InU IdPI WaSpG
DLC PBa PPD PPL FMU MtU NIC ViU OClW

TARKINGTON, Booth, 1869-1946.
The beautiful lady. Garden City, New York,
Doubleday, Page & Co., 1913.

NT 0040419   MH

TARKINGTON, Booth, 1869-1946.
The beautiful lady. Garden City, New York,
Garden City Publishing Co., Inc., 1923.

Cover: Famous authors series.

NT 0040420   MH IU

Tarkington, Booth, 1869-1946.
The beautiful lady. Garden City, New York,
Garden City publishing co., inc., 1924.

Cover: Famous author series.

NT 0040421   MH OU

813
T17b
1925
Tarkington, Booth, 1869-1946.
The beautiful lady.   Garden City, N.Y.,
Garden City Pub. Co., 1925.
120p. illus. 20cm.

"A pocket copyright."

NT 0040422   IU

Tarkington, Booth, 1869-
Beauty and the Jacobin; an interlude of the French revolution, by Booth Tarkington; with illustrations by C. D. Williams. New York and London, Harper & brothers, 1912.
I. Title.
[Full name: Newton Booth Tarkington]
12—24644
Library of Congress   PS2972.B4 1912

NT 0040423   OrP IdB WaSp CaBVaU KEmT FTaSU TxU MsSM RPB
OCl NjP NN MB MH OClW OEac PP PPL Or WaS WaE OrLgE
DLC TxCM CoU OU IU PU TNJ NIC NjP NRU MiU

Tarkington, Booth, 1869-1946.
Beauty and the Jacobin; an interlude of the
French revolution, by Booth Tarkington; with
illustrations by C. D. Williams. New York
and London, Harper & brothers, 1912.
4 p. l., 99, [1] p. front., plates. 20cm.
Microcard

NT 0040424   MsU

Lilly
Library
PS 3539
.A7 B45
TARKINGTON, BOOTH, 1869-1946.
Beauty and the Jacobin. An interlude
of the French revolution ... With illustrations
by C.D. Williams. New York and London,
Harper & Brothers, 1912.
4 p.l., 99, [1] p. front., illus.
(tinted) 8vo (19.4 cm.)

First edition; Russo & Sullivan, p.
26-27.
Incomplete: lacks dust jacket.

Bound in original cloth, spine faded.
From the library of J.K. Lilly, with
his book plate.
For text see Works, Seawood edition,
v. 9.

NT 0040426   InU

812.5
T187b
Tarkington, Booth, 1869-1946.
Beauty and the Jacobin; an interlude of
the French revolution; with illustrations by
C. D. Williams.   New York and London,
Samuel French [c1912]
4 p.l., 99, [1]p. front., plates. 20cm.
(French's standard library edition)

NT 0040427   ICarbS

TARKINGTON, Booth, 1869-1946.
Beauty and the Jacobin.

(In COHEN, Helen L., editor. One-act plays by
modern authors. 1921, pp.1-49)

NT 0040428   MH ODW OU OClJC OC1C

Tarkington, Booth, 1869-1946.
Beauty and the Jacobin, by Booth Tarkington.   (In: Dickinson, A. D., editor. Drama. Garden City, N. Y., 1922. 16°.
p. [17-]86.)

1. Drama (American). 2. Title.
N. Y. P. L.   August 21, 1923.

NT 0040429   NN

Tarkington, Booth, 1869-1946.
Betty et ses amoureux, par Booth Tarkington; traduction de Marc Helys [pseud.] [Paris] Hachette [c1936]
252 p., 1 l. incl. front., 1 illus. 18ᶜᵐ. [Bibliothèque bleue]

I. Léra, Mme. Maria, tr. II. Title.   *Translation of* The two
Vanrevels.   [Full name: Newton Booth Tarkington]
37—6560
Library of Congress   PS2972.T85F7
Copyright A—Foreign   34586

NT 0040430   DLC

PS
2972
.B5
1924
Tarkington, Booth, 1869-1946.
Bimbo, the pirate. New York, S. French,
c1924.
175-221p. 24cm.

NT 0040431   TNJ

PS
2972
B61f
Tarkington, Booth, 1869-1946.
Bimbo, the pirate; a comedy in one act.
New York, S. French [c1924]
175-221p. 20cm. (French's standard library
edition)

I. Title.
Full name: Newton Booth Tarkington.

NT 0040432   NRU OrCS

Tarkington, Booth, 1869-1946.
Bimbo, the pirate; [a comedy] by Booth Tarkington. N. Y., S. French; London, S. French, c1924.
221p. 19cm.

i. Title.
[Full name: Newton Booth
Tarkington]

NT 0040433   FMU MiU

---

*fAC9
T174t
B925g
Tarkington, Booth, 1869-
... Bimbo the pirate.
[Philadelphia, 1924]
8l. 58 x 15cm., folded, in case 31.5cm.
Caption title.
Galley proofs for the play's publication in
the Ladies' home journal, June, 1924.
Rubber stamps at head: File proof [&] Jan 29
1924.
In case lettered: Booth Tarkington. Galley
proofs ...

NT 0040434   MH

Tarkington, _____ Booth, 1869-1946.　　　　6257.422
　Bimbo, the pirate.
　(*In* Ladies' Home Journal. The Ladies' Home Journal One-act
plays. Pp. 173-221. Garden City, N. Y. 1925.)

N1884 — T.r. Play.

NT　0040435　　MB OEac OLak OCl OOxM MH

812.5, T13.4
　Tarkington, Booth, 1869-1946.
　　Bimbo, the pirate; a comedy in one act.
　Boston, Baker's Plays [c1926]
　　39 p. illus.

NT　0040436　　caOTP

Tarkington, Booth, 1869-1946.
　Bimbo, the pirate; a comedy by **Booth Tarkington**.
New York, London, D. Appleton and company, 1926.
　3 p. l., 39, [1] p. illus. 19ᵐᵐ. (*Half-title:* Appleton Little theatre plays,
no. 11)

　　I. Title.
　　　　　　　　　　　　　　　　 ⟨*Full name:* Newton Booth Tarkington⟩
Library of Congress　　PS297²B5 1926　　26-8439

　　OCl MH CSmH NjP InU
NT　0040437　　DLC PU WaE TxU ViU NIC OClh OEac OLak

Tarkington, Booth, 1869-1946.
　Bimbo, the pirate; a comedy by Booth
Tarkington.　New York, London, D. Appleton
and company, 1931.
　3 p.l., 39 [1] p.　illus.　19 cm.　(Half-
title: Appleton Little theatre plays, no. 11)
　With this are bound his The ghost story,
Station YYYY, The Travelers, The trysting place,
and A dramatization of Monsieur Beaucaire, by
Ethel Hale Freeman.
　I. Title.

NT　0040438　　NcU

Tarkington, Booth, 1869-1946.
　Booth Tarkington on dogs.　　Nappanee [Ind.] Private print,
James Lamar Weygand [194-]　2 p.l., 4 p.　16cm.

343312B. 1. Dog.
N.Y.P.L.　　　　　　　　　　　　June 20, 1946.

NT　0040439　　NN MH ICN

PS2973　Tarkington, Booth, 1869-1946.
.A4　　　Booth Tarkington on dogs. Nappanee, J. L.
1944　　Weygand [1944?]
　　　　　[3], 4 p.
　　　　　"Private print."
　　　　　A letter to the City council of Indianapolis.

　　　1. Dogs.

NT　0040440　　ICU

Rare
PS　　　Tarkington, Booth, 1869-1946.
2972　　　Bridewater's half dollar.　[New York?]
B85　　1942.
1942　　　8 fold. sheets.　26cm.

　　　Galley proof of contribution to "This is
my best", edited by Whit Burnett.

NT　0040441　　NIC

TARKINGTON, BOOTH, 1869-1946.
　Bristol glass, by Booth Tarkington and Harry Leon
Wilson.　[Cleveland, 1923]　48, 40, 39 l.　29cm.
　Typescript.
　Promptbook.
　Cast added in ms.
　Produced at the Ohio theatre, Cleveland, Ohio, April 1923; later pro-
duced at the Frazee theatre, N. Y., 13 August, 1923 under the title of
Tweedles.

NT　0040442　　NN

Tarkington, Booth, 1869-1946.
　Business and pleasure; photoplay title of The
plutocrat; a novel. NY, Grosset & Dunlap [c1927]
　543 p. plates. 20 cm.

　I. T.　II. T.: The plutocrat.

NT　0040443　　NjP CaBVaU NIC PSt PP NN

Tarkington, Booth, 1869-1946.
　"Cameo Kirby," by Booth Tarkington and Harry Leon Wilson.
(First outline of plot.)　[n. p., n. d.]　21 f.　33cm.
　Typewritten.

————　————　[New York? 1907?]　3 parts in 1 v.
Prompt-book; typewritten, with ms. notes.
Play in four acts; act 3 wanting.
"Script used in try-out with Nat Goodwin as Cameo Kirby." —*Ms. note on cover.*
Bound with the above.

Act 2 only.
Typewritten, with ms. notes and autograph of Booth Tarkington.
Bound with the above.

973835A. 1. Drama, American.　　　2. Prompt-books. I. Wilson, Harry
Leon, 1867- , jt. au. II. Title.
N. Y. P. L.　　　　　　　　　　　　January 16, 1939

NT　0040445　　NN

PS2972　[TARKINGTON, BOOTH] 1869-
f.C2　　Cameo Kirby.　[19-?]
19-　　　2 l., 28 numb. l.　37cm.
Rare bk　Typewritten.
room　　"A 4 act comedy drama."

NT　0040446　　ICU

Tarkington, Booth, 1869-1946.
　"Cameo Kirby;" a play in four acts, by Booth Tarkington and
Harry Leon Wilson.　[New York? 1907?]　4 parts in 1 v.
28cm.
　Typewritten, with ms. notes.

————　————　32, 27, 23, 15 f.
　Typewritten.
　"As done in N. Y. with Dustin Farnum in the title role." —*Ms. note on cover.*
Light and property plots included.
Bound with the above.

973834A. 1. Drama, American.　　　I. Wilson, Harry Leon, 1867-
jt. au. II. Title.
N. Y. P. L.　　　　　　　　　　　　January 10, 1939

NT　0040447　　NN

Tarkington, Booth, 1869-1946.
　Cherry, by Booth Tarkington ... New York & London,
Harper & brothers, 1903.
　4 p. l., 178, [1] p. col. front., 2 col. pl. 20½ cm.

　I. Title.

PZ3.T175Ch　　　　　　　　　　　3-25882
————　Copy 5.　　　　　PS2972.C45 1903

WaS CU-S WaWW MoU CoU　　NjP CSmH IdU
OEac OU MiU CU TxU WaU CaOTP NN CoU WaSp CLSU Or
NT　0040448　　DLC MH OCl PBm PBa PHC PV NIC ViU MB

Lilly
Library
PS 3539　TARKINGTON, BOOTH, 1869-1946
.A7 C52　　Cherry ...　London and New York, Harper
　　　　　& Brothers, 1903.
　　　　　5 p.l., 178, [1] p.　col. front., col.
plates.　8vo (19.6 cm.)

　　　First edition. Russo & Sullivan, p. 12-
13; at p. 13 a similar copy, with London
preceding New York in imprint, is described
as "a trial issue."
　　　Integral publisher's ads, 4 p. at end.
　　　Incomplete: lacks dust jacket.

　　　Pasted to blank p. [iv], photo of sketch
by Tarkington, for a projected frontispiece,
inscribed by author with initials, further
inscription on facing page. Signed by author
on recto of frontispiece with date 1905 (?).
Tipped in at back, carte de visite of Mrs.
O. B. Jameson (author's sister) with ms.
message on verso, in envelope addressed to
Mrs. J. K. Lilly

　　　Bound in original cloth, some spotting
of covers. In quarter red morocco slipcase.
From the library of J. K. Lilly, with
his bookplate.

　　　I. Assn. cd.: Jameson, Mary Booth (Tarkington)
d. 1937. II. Assn. cd.: Author.

NT　0040451　　InU

SPECIAL COLLECTIONS
B812T17
P3
1903　　　Tarkington, Booth, 1869-1946.
　　　　Cherry. Illustrated. New York & London,
Harper [c1903]
　　　　5 p. l., 3-178 p. illus., col. plates.
20cm.

　　　Title within ornamental border.
　　　First state of first edition

NT　0040452　　NNC

---

*
PS2972
.C3　　　Tarkington, Booth, 1869-1946.
1903a
　　　　Cherry.　London & New York, Harper &
Brothers, 1903.
　　　　5 p. l., 3-178 p., 1 l., [4] p. col. plates.
20½cm.
　　　　Publisher's advertisements: [4] p. at end.
　　　　"Published October, 1903."
　　　　Second state, Johnson, p. 489.

NT　0040453　　ViU

AC-L　　**Tarkington, Booth**, 1869- 1946.
T174ch　　**Cherry**, by Booth Tarkington ... New York & Lon-
1916　　don, Harper & brothers [1916, c1903]
　　　　4 p. l., 178, [1] p. front., plates. 20cm.

　　　Code date of printing on verso of t.-p.: E-Q
[i.e. May, 1916]

NT　0040454　　TxU

813.49　　**Tarkington, Booth**, 1869-1946.
T17　　　**Cherry, and Beasley's Christmas party**.
Och　　New York, Harper, 1925.
1925　　　268p.　front.　20cm.

　　　I. Title. II. Title: Beasley's
Christmas party.

NT　0040455　　KU PU PPL PP

Tarkington, Booth, 1869–
Cherry, and Beasley's Christmas party, by Booth Tarkington. New York and London, Harper & brothers, 1925.

5 p. l., 3–268 p. front. 20ᶜᵐ.

I. Title. II. Title: Beasley's Christmas party.
⟨*Full name:* Newton Booth Tarkington⟩

Library of Congress   PZ3.T175Ch 5   26–3002

NT 0040456   DLC WaS NjP KEmT ViU NIC OU MH OCl NN

Rare
PS
2972
C551++   **Tarkington, Booth,** 1869–1946.
Christmas this year. Written for Mr. Bernheimer with the best wishes of Booth Tarkington.

The holograph manuscript of the printed edition.

NT 0040457   NIC

Rare
PS
2972
C55++   **Tarkington, Booth,** 1869–1946.
Christmas this year. Written for Mr. Bernheimer — with the best wishes of Booth Tarkington. ⟨Los Angeles, Calif., 1945⟩
⟨6⟩ l. plate. 32cm.

On cover: Season's greetings for the year 1945 from Earle J. Bernheimer.
"Printed for Earle J. Bernheimer by the Ward Ritchie Press, Los Angeles, California. Limited to 52 copies ... Christmas, 1945."

Copy 1 is No. 43, copy 2 is No. 44.
Reproduced in facsimile from the holograph manuscript.

NT 0040459   NIC

Tarkington, Booth, 1869–1946.

Christmas this year... ⟨Los Angeles, Calif., W.Ritchie press, 1945⟩
facsim.: 5 numb. l. 1 illus. 29½ ᶜᵐ.
On cover: Season's greetings for the year 1945 from Earle J. Bernheimer.
Limited ed.

NT 0040460   NjP NcD InU

Rare
PS
2972
C56   **Tarkington, Booth,** 1869–1946.
Cider of Normandy, by Booth Tarkington.

(In O. Henry memorial award prize stories of 1931. Garden City, New York. 20cm. p. ⟨299⟩–327)

NT 0040461   NIC

Tarkington, Booth, 1869–1946.
Claire. [Overs. til dansk...af Aage v. Kohl] København [etc., etc.] Jespersens of Pios forlag c1928?⟩
219 p. 22 cm. (Moderne verdensliteratur)

Trans. of Claire Ambler.

NT 0040462   NjP

PS
2972
.C55   **Tarkington, Booth,** 1869–1946
Claire Ambler, by Booth Tarkington. Garden City, N. Y., Doubleday, Doran & Company, inc., 1928.
5 p. l., 253 p.

"First edition."

NT 0040463   INS NBu TxU OO MH NIC InU MH

Tarkington, Booth, 1869–1946.
Claire Ambler, by Booth Tarkington. Garden City, N. Y., Doubleday, Doran & company, inc., 1928.
5 p. l., 253 p. 19½ cm.

I. Title.

PZ3.T175Cl   28–3166

OKentU MoSW KEmT OrCS CoU VtU CaOTP TxU PV MB
Wa CaBVa IdB IdPI Or OrU WaS MtU IdU WaT OrP NN PRos
PEm NcD NIC MiU OLak OClh OClJC OU MoU ViU NBuU WaSp
NT 0040464   DLC OClW WaWW OCl OrPS OEac WaTU WaE PHC

PN
35
T3
HRC   **Tarkington, Booth,** 1869–1946.
Claire Ambler, by Booth Tarkington. Copyright ed. Leipzig, B. Tauchnitz, 1928.
269p. 16cm. (Collection of British authors.
v.4815   Tauchnitz ed., v.4815)

NT 0040465   TxU

AC–L
T174cl   **Tarkington, Booth,** 1869–1946.
1929   Claire Ambler, by Booth Tarkington ...   New York, Grosset & Dunlap [1929, c1928]
5 p. l., 253 p. 19½ᶜᵐ.

Publisher's advertisements ([9]p.) beginning on verso of p.253, bound in at end.
Reprinted 1929 by Grosset & Dunlap. Cf. Russo and Sullivan, p.86.

NT 0040466   TxU

Tarkington, Booth, 1869–1946.
Claire Ambler.   Doubleday, Doran, 1929.

NT 0040467   PV

810.82
G253b   **Tarkington, Booth,** 1869–1946.
Sup.   Clarence.
Theol.
(In Gassner, John. Best American plays, supplementary volume, 1918–1958)

NT 0040468   TxDaM

Tarkington, Booth, 1869–*1946.*
Clarence; a comedy in four acts, by Booth Tarkington ... New York, S. French; ⟨etc., etc.⟩ *1921.
124 p. plates, plans. 19½ᶜᵐ.
On cover: French's standard library edition.

I. Title.
⟨*Full name:* Newton Booth Tarkington⟩

Library of Congress   PS2972.C6 1921   21–18009

PPT PU PPL MH NcD OU ViU MsSM KEmT MeB FTaSU OClW
OrCS InU OCl OClh OEac OO ODW TU NIC MB PU PBm TxU
NT 0040469   DLC WaS WaWW WaSp WaU OrP Or OrU WaE Wa

---

*AC9
T1747
921cb   **Tarkington, Booth,** 1869–*1946.*
Clarence; a comedy in four acts, by Booth Tarkington ...
[Ottawa, Can.] New York, Samuel French, 28–30 West 38th street, publisher; London, Samuel French, ltd., publisher, 26 Southampton st., Strand [1921]
104p. 20.5cm., in case 22cm.
On back cover: Printed in Canada by Geo. H. Popham, limited, 124 Queen st., Ottawa, Can. September 1921.
Original red-brown printed wrappers; in cloth case.

NT 0040470   MH

Tarkington, Booth, 1869–*1946.*
Clarence [with scenario by Clara Beranger] [1922]

[317] leaves. 34cm.

Various paging.
Reproduced from type-written copy.
Paramount pictures.

NT 0040471   CLSU

Tarkington, Booth, 1869–*1946.*
Clarence; a comedy in four acts. New York, etc., S.French [1925?]

124 p. plates, plans. 19 cm.
On cover: French's standard library edition.

NT 0040472   MH

PS2972
.C6
1948   **Tarkington, Booth,** 1869–1946.
Clarence; a comedy in four acts. New York, S. French ⟨1948?⟩ ᶜ1921.
124p. illus. 19cm. (French's standard library edition)

NT 0040473   OrPS

Tarkington, Booth, 1869–1946.
Clarence, by Booth Tarkington; scenario by Clara Beranger
see under title

Lilly
PS 3539
.A16
1948   TARKINGTON,BOOTH,1869–1946
[A collection of ephemeral writings (many political), and contributions to secondary magazines and to programs for various functions, by Tarkington; ephemeral comment and contributions to periodicals and other works, about Tarkington. 1895–1948] 36 pieces.

Size of pieces varies.
From the library of J.K. Lilly.
In tan cloth   case.

NT 0040475   InU

⟨Tarkington, Booth⟩ 1869–*1946.*
The collector's whatnot; a compendium, manual, and syllabus of information and advice on all subjects appertaining to the collection of antiques, both ancient and not so ancient. Compiled by Cornelius Obenchain Van Loot, Milton Kilgallen, and Murgatroyd Elphinstone. Boston and New York, Houghton Mifflin company, 1923.
xx, 147 p., 4 l. front., illus. plates. 21ᶜᵐ.

I. Roberts, Kenneth Lewis 1885–   joint author. II. Kahler, Hugh MacNair, 1883–   joint author. III. Title.
⟨*Full name:* Newton Booth Tarkington⟩

Library of Congress   PN6231.C35T3   23–17751

ICN ViU WaS WaSp TU OrP IU NcU TxU
NT 0040476   DLC PP CoU MH NN MB NjP NIC Wa IaU PU MU

AC-L
T174co
1923a
₁Tarkington, Booth₁ 1869– 1946.
The collector's whatnot; a compendium, manual, and syllabus of information and advice on all subjects appertaining to the collection of antiques, both ancient and not so ancient. Compiled by Cornelius Obenchain Van Loot, Milton Kilgallen and Murgatroyd Elphinstone. Boston and New York, Houghton Mifflin company, 1923.

xx, 147 p., 4 l. front., illus., plates. 21ᶜᵐ.

"The first edition ... consists of 3127 copies, as follows:
Twenty-seven on choicest domestic leaf, bound in teakwood. with leather hinges."

numbered A to &, with the author's thumbprints in red ink in each copy.
Three thousand one hundred copies on American antique wove, bound in manila boards."
"Other books for the antique-lover." 4ℓ. at end.

NT 0040478 TxU

PN6231
C35T3
₁Tarkington, Booth₁ 1869–1946.
The collector's whatnot; a compendium, manual, and syllabus of information and advice on all subjects appertaining to the collection of antiques, both ancient and not so ancient. Compiled by Cornelius Obenchain Van Loot, Milton Kilgallen, and Murgatroyd Elphinstone. Boston and New York, Houghton Mifflin ₁c1923₁.

xx, 147 p., 4 l. front., illus., plates. 21ᶜᵐ.

NT 0040479 MeB

AS36
A473
no. 96
Tarkington, Booth, 1869–1946. FOR OTHER EDITIONS SEE MAIN ENTRY
American academy of arts and letters.
Commemorative tributes to: Gillette and Howard, by William Lyon Phelps; Lie, by Royal Cortissoz; Garland, by Booth Tarkington; Finley, by Nicholas Murray Butler; Markham, by William Lyon Phelps. Prepared for and published by the American academy of arts and letters. New York, 1940.

Lilly
PS 3539
.A7 C7572
TARKINGTON,BOOTH,1869–1946
The conquest of Canaan, a novel ... Illustrations by Lucius W. Hitchcock. Melbourne, Sidney [etc.], George Robertson & Co. [1905]
v, [3], 388 [1] p. front., 5 plates. 8vo (19.4cm.) (Colonial library)

Sheets apparently of the first edition, early state of type at p. 378, with cancel title-leaf substituting Australian imprint for Harper imprint as above; the copyright

page has added line Printed in United States of America not present in Lilly copy of the first edition.
Imperfect: lacking plates facing pages 196 and 246, front end paper excised. Bound in original ribbed green cloth.

NT 0040482 InU CtY

Tarkington, Booth, 1869–1946.
The conquest of Canaan ... illustrated by Lucius W. Ritchcock. New York, 1905.
388 p.

NT 0040483 PHC PPL

PS2972
C6
1905a
Tarkington, Booth, 1869–1946.
The conquest of Canaan. Illustrated by Lucius W. Hitchcock. New York, A.L. Burt [c1905]
388 p. illus. 20cm.

NT 0040484 CoU LU MB ViU OClJC MH ODW OClW OrU

Tarkington, Booth, 1869-1946.
The conquest of Canaan, a novel, illus. by Lucius W. Hitchcock.   New York, Harper, 1905.
v, 388 p. 8 pl. 20 cm.
First edition. cf. Johnson, Merle. American first editions.
I. Title.
Full name: Newton Booth Tarkington.

NT 0040485 ViU

Tarkington, Booth, 1869-1946.
The conquest of Canaan, a novel by Booth Tarkington ... illustrations by Lucius W. Hitchcock.   New York and London, Harper & brothers, 1905.
v p., 2 l., 388, ₁1₁ p. front., 7 pl. 19½ cm.
——— Another issue. ₁1905₁
v, ₁1₁ p., 2 l., 388, ₁1₁ p. front., plates. 19½ cm.
——— ——— Copy 2.   PS2972.C65 1905a
I. Title.   PZ3.T175Co 2
                       ᵂull name: Newton Booth Tarkington

PZ3.T175Co   5–35295 rev 2

       CU-S NcD NjP
       WaS WaTU OrP MtU IdPI OEac OClW IdU MH CSmH OrPR
       PRosC PBa PU Wa MoU MsSM NN OrPS WaWW MB WaSp Or
NT 0040486   DLC TxU ViU MiU OCl MoSW NIC OO OCU PIm

AC-L
T174Eha
1905a
Tarkington, Booth, 1869-1946.
The conquest of Canaan, by Booth Tarkington ... New York and London, Harper & brothers publishers, c1905.
[118] p. col. front.,illus.,plates. 24½cm.

Various pagings.
On front cover: Advance copy for private distribution. Not for sale – Harper & brothers publishers, New York and London. Consists of sheets from the plates of

Harper's magazine, v.111-112, nos. 661-667, June 1905-Dec. 1905. Cf. Russo and Sullivan, p.18.

I. Title.   II. Harper's magazine. A.F.: Grant, J.E. A.F.: McCutcheon, George Barr 1866-1928.

NT 0040488 TxU InU ViU

Tarkington, Booth, 1869–1946.
The conquest of Canaan, by Booth Tarkington ... Illustrated by Lucius W. Hitchcock. New York, A. L. Burt company ₁191–?₁
4 p. l., 388, ₁1₁ p. front., plates. 19¼ᶜᵐ.

I. Title.
                       ₁Full name: Newton Booth Tarkington₁
                               20–15608 Revised
Library of Congress   PZ3.T175Co 6

NT 0040489 DLC PPLas OrPS

Tarkington, Booth, 1869–
The conquest of Canaan, by Booth Tarkington ... Illustrated by Lucius W. Hitchcock. New York, A. L. Burt company ₁1912₁
₁₂₁1 p., 1 l., 388 ₁1₁ front., plates. 19¼ᶜᵐ.

NT 0040490 ViU

AC-L
T174con
192–
Tarkington, Booth, 1869-1946.
The conquest of Canaan, by Booth Tarkington ... New York, A.L. Burt company [192-?]
vp.,1ℓ.,388,[1]p. 19¼cm.

Letters "M-X" beneath copyright box on verso of t.-p.
Publisher's advertisements ([13]p.) bound in at end.

NT 0040491 TxU

Tarkington, Booth, 1869-1946.
The conquest of Canaan.   Garden City, New York, Doubleday, 1922, c1905.
425 p. (Seawood ed.)

NT 0040492 PP

Tarkington, Booth, 1869–1946.
The conquest of Canaan, a novel, by Booth Tarkington ... New York and London, Harper & brothers, 1935.
x p., 2 l., 315, ₁1₁ p. front., plates. 21ᶜᵐ.

I. Title.   ₁Full name: Newton Booth Tarkington₁
                                         35–2535
Library of Congress   PZ3.T175Co 14

NT 0040493 DLC NN NjP

Rare
PS
2972
C81
Tarkington, Booth, 1869-1946.
Cornelia's mountain, by Booth Tarkington.

(In O. Henry memorial award prize stories of 1925. Garden City, New York. 20cm. p. 259-282)

NT 0040494 NIC

Tarkington, Booth, 1869–1946.
The country cousin; a comedy in four acts, by Booth Tarkington and Julian Street ... New York, S. French; ₁etc., etc.,₁ ᵉ1921₁
141 p. plates, diagrs. 20ᶜᵐ.
Published 1916 under title: The Ohio lady.
On cover: French's standard library edition.
I. Street, Julian Leonard, 1879– joint author. II. Title.
                       ₁Full name: Newton Booth Tarkington₁
                               21–19878 Revised
Library of Congress   PS2972 C7 1921

       TxU CaOTP NcD PPT PP KU Wa WaWW MsSM AzU WaS
NT 0040495 DLC Or NIC OrCS OrU MB OCl ODW MH ViU OU

Tarkington, Booth, 1869-1946.
El cuarto mandamiento. [Versión castellana: Fernando Santos] Madrid [1944?]
379 p. 16 cm. (Ediciones La Nave. Serie, B,46)

Trans. of The Magnificent Ambersons.
Added t.p., illus.
Ex copy 2. In variant binding.

NT 0040496 NjP

813
T17magSs
Tarkington, Booth, 1869–1946.
El cuarto mandamiento ... (premio Pulitzer) Madrid, Ediciones "La Nave" [1945?]
379p. front., illus. (Added t.-p.: Ediciones "La Nave." ser.B, no.46)

"Título inglés: 'The magnificent Ambersons'; versión castellana: Fernando Santos."

I. Santos, Fernando, 1892- tr. II. Title.

NT 0040497 IU

4FZ
225
Tarkington, Booth, 1869-1946.
El cuarto mandamiento. ₁Traducción del inglés y notas de Fernando Santos₁ Madrid, Aguilar Ediciones, 1951.
490 p.

(Colección Crisol, núm. 329)

NT 0040498 DLC-P4

Tarkington, Booth, 1869–1946.
Da la piel del diablo; novela. Trad. del inglés
por Emilio M. Martínez Amador. Barcelona, G.
Gili, 1926.
242, [1] p. illus. 20 cm. (Biblioteca Emporium
29)

Trans. of Penrod.

NT   0040499   NjP

4PS-   Tarkington, Booth, 1869–1946.
359   Da la piel del diablo. [Traducción del inglés
por Ramón D. Peres. 1. ed.   Barcelona, 1950]
234 p.   (Al monigote de papel)

NT   0040500   DLC-P4

Lilly   TARKINGTON, BOOTH, 1869–1946.
PS 3539   Dance music. (In the Flower Mission
.A7 D17   Magazine for November, 1896, p. 5–8. In-
dianapolis, 1896.   31.8 cm.)

Russo & Sullivan, A bibl. of Booth
Tarkington, p. 156.
On cover: A November leaf.
Tarkington's contributions include also
cover design, untitled poem on title, poem
Proud lover signed H.D.W., and anonymous
poem In winter.

Other contributors include James Whit-
comb Riley (Song for November), Meredith
Nicholson (Romance), and Susan E. Wallace
(Women in the Orient).
Copious ms. notes by Mary Booth (Tark-
ingtcn) Jameson, the author's sister.
From the library of J. K. Lilly.
In printed wrappers; in green cloth
folder.

NT   0040502   InU NIC

PS2972   Tarkington, Booth, 1869–1946.
.D6
1920   A dog does not know that he wags his tail
(In McAuley, Mary E., ed. The wanderer. New
York. 1920. 21cm. p. 289)

I. McAuley, Mary Ethel,
vanderer. II. Title.

NT   0040503   ViU

Tarkington, Booth, 1869–1946.
Dollarmanden. [Overs. af Aage v. Kohl] København [etc.,etc.] E. Jespersens forlag [1927]
340 p.   22 cm. (Moderne verdensliteratur)

Trans. of The plutocrat.

NT   0040504   NjP

Tarkington, Booth, 1869–1946.
"Dolling", - a story from "Women".
(In the week-end library. 1927. 51 p.)

NT   0040505   PPT

* Tarkington, Booth, 1869–1946.

Art association of Indianapolis, Indiana. *John Herron art
institute.*
Dutch paintings, etchings, drawings, Delftware of the
seventeenth century, February 27 to April 11, 1937, John
Herron art museum, Indianapolis, Indiana. [Indianapolis,
Printed by Hammel & McDermott, inc., 1937]

Tarkington, Booth, 1869–1946.
Egoistka…Przekł. autoryzowany Janiny Sujkow-
skej. Warszawa, Bibljoteka Groszowa [1928?]
214, [1] p. 18 cm.

On spine: 642.
Trans. of Claire Ambler.

NT   0040507   NjP

Tarkington, Booth, 1869–1947.
Exhibition of first editions and inscribed copies
of the works of Booth Tarkington at the Indiana
Historical Society Library
see under   Indiana Historical Society.
William Henry Smith Memorial Library.

Tarkington, Booth, 1869–1946
…Exhibition of the Booth Tarkington
collection of paintings. March 20-April
30, 1948 at the Newhouse Galleries

New York, Newhouse, 1948

5p.   23.5cm.

NT   0040509   MdBWA

Tarkington, Booth, 1869–1946.
En familjeflicka…Bemyndigad övers. av Vera
V. Kraemer. Stockholm, Wahlström & Widstrand
[1925]
256 p. 20 cm.

Trans. of Alice Adams.

NT   0040510   NjP

Tarkington, Booth, 1869–1946.
The fascinating stranger, and other stories, by Booth
Tarkington. Garden City, N. Y., Doubleday, Page &
company, 1923.
5 p. l., 492 p. 19½ᵐ.
"First edition, after the printing of 377 de luxe copies."
CONTENTS.—The fascinating stranger.—The party.—The one-hundred-
dollar bill.—Jeannette.—The spring concert.—Willamilla.—The only child—
Ladies' ways.— Maytime in Marlow.—"You."—"Us."—The tiger.—Mary
Smith.
I. Title.
[Full name: Newton Booth Tarkington]
23—8938
Library of Congress   PZ3.T175Fa

OrStbM
ViU NIC CoU PHC MeB WaSp Or PU FU OrCS CU-S PBm TxU
InU NN MB NcD OClh OCl OClJC MH OO OCU OEac OU NjP
NT   0040511   DLC MtU TNJ CaOTP KU NvU NIC WaS CaBVaU

Tarkington, Booth, 1869–1946.
The fascinating stranger & other stories.
Garden City, New York, Doubleday, 1924, c1923.
492 p.   (Seawood ed.)

NT   0040512   PP

Rare   Tarkington, Booth, 1869–1946.
PS   The fighting Littles.   Garden City,
2972   N. Y., Doubleday, Doran and Company,
F47   Inc., 1941.
1941a   [4] l., 304 p. 21cm.

NT   0040513   NIC PPPCPh PPL PU PP KMK PNt NIC

Tarkington, Booth, 1869–
… The fighting Littles. Garden City, N. Y., Doubleday,
Doran and company, inc., 1941.
4 p. l., 304 p. 20½ᵐ.
"First edition."

I. Title.
[Full name: Newton Booth Tarkington]
41–21285
Library of Congress   PZ3.T175Fi

GAuA WaSp MiU WaT OrU WaS Wa Or TxU OKentU NBuC
OLak OClW OEac MH OCU OOxM IdPI CaBVaU WaE TNJ
NT   0040514   DLC InU KU ICN CLU NcD OU OClh OCl OO

Tarkington, Booth, 1869–   The fighting
Littles.

Francke, Caroline.
The fighting Littles, a play in three acts, by Caroline Francke,
adapted from the novel of the same name by Booth Tarkington.
New York, N. Y., Los Angeles, Calif., S. French; [etc., etc.,
1943]

Rare Book Coll.   Tarkington, Booth, 1869–1946.
Barrett   The flirt … [vignette] Illustrations by
PS2708   Clarence F. Underwood. Garden City, N. Y.,
.Z9T36   Doubleday, Page & Co., 1913.
1913   [4] l., 378 p. plates. 18.7cm.

First ed.; Russo and Sullivan, p. 27–28.
Previously published in the Saturday Evening
Post, Dec. 21, 1912-Feb. 15, 1913.
Original red cloth, gilt stamped; d.j. want-
ing.

Inscr.: "For Dr. James Whitcomb Riley,
with evergreen affection from Newton Booth
Tarkington. April 2nd. 1913. Indianapolis"

I. Riley, James Whitcomb, 1849–1916.
II. Title.

NT   0040517   ViU INS

Tarkington, Booth, 1869–1946.
The flirt. Illustrated. 278 p., front, plates.
New York, Charles Scribner's sons, [1913]

NT   0040518   OCl

Tarkington, Booth, 1869–
The flirt, by Booth Tarkington … illustrated by Clar-
ence F. Underwood. Garden City, N. Y., Doubleday,
Page & company, 1913.
5 p. l., 3–378 p., 1 l. front., plates. 19½ᵐ. $1.25
Illustrated t.-p.

I. Title.
[Full name: Newton Booth Tarkington]
13–4422 Revised
Library of Congress   PZ3.T175Fl

WaSp WaS WaWW WaE MB OU
NIC   TxU CSmH ViU MH OEac NjP   InU Or OrP
NT   0040519   DLC NBuC TNJ PPLas PPL PP PU KU OCl IU

PS   Tarkington, Booth, 1869–1946.
2972   The flirt, by Booth Tarkington. New
.F5   York, P. F. Collier and son company
1913   [c1913]
378 p.   20 cm.
Hoosier edition.

NT   0040520   OKentU

Tarkington, Booth, 1869–1946.
The flirt, by Booth Tarkington … Illustrated
with scenes from the photoplay, a Universal-Jewel
production. New York, Grosset & Dunlap [c1913]
4 p.l., 3–378 p. front., plates. 19½ᵐ.
Title within line border.

I. Title.
[Full name: Newton Booth
Tarkington]

NT   0040521   ViU GAuA PHC CLSU MH NN MiU OClND

Tarkington, Booth, 1869–
    The flirt, by Booth Tarkington ... Illustrations by Clarence
F. Underwood. New York, Grosset & Dunlap [1915]
    4 p. l., 3–378 p. front., plates. 19½ cm.
    Title vignette.

    I. Title.
                                    [Full name: Newton Booth Tarkington]
                                                    21–13947 Revised
    Library of Congress   PZ3.T175F13

NT 0040522   DLC MB

813.5
T18f1   Tarkington, Booth, 1869–
    The flirt. Illustrated. New York, Scribner's,
1915.
    378p. front., plates. 20cm.

NT 0040523   TNJ MoU MB

Tarkington, Booth, 1869–1946.
    Flirt. Göteborg, Elanders boktryckeri, 1916
    272 p. 19 cm.

NT 0040524   NjP

813.5
T187FL   Tarkington, Booth, 1869–1946.
    The flirt. New York, C. Scribner's Sons,
    1916 [c1913]
    378 p. plates. 20 cm.

NT 0040525   NcD LU ViU IU

813.5 T13.102
    Tarkington, Booth, 1869–1946.
    The flirt. New York, Scribner, 1917.
    378 p. illus.

NT 0040526   CaOTP

Tarkington, Booth, 1869–1946
    The flirt. 1919.

    13–4422

NT 0040527   NjP

Tarkington, Booth, 1869–1956.
    Flirt, by ... New York, Charles Scribner's
sons, 1919.
    378 p.

NT 0040528   PPLas

Tarkington, Booth, 1869–1946.
    The flirt, by Booth Tarkington ... Illustrations by Clar-
ence F. Underwood. Garden City, N. Y., Doubleday, Page
& company, 1920.
    4 p. l., 3–378 p. front. 19½ cm.
    Title vignette.
    On cover: Royalty edition.

    I. Title.

    PZ3.T175F16   22–16014

NT 0040529   DLC Wa OC1JC OC1W

Tarkington, Booth, 1869–1946.
    Flirt. Overs. fra engelsk efter "The flirt" af
G. Holck. Kjøbenhavn og Kristiania, Gyldendalske
boghandel [etc., etc.] 1920.
    189 p. 22 cm.

NT 0040530   NjP

Tarkington, Booth, 1869–1946.
    Flirt; novela trad. del inglés por Guillermo de
Bolaçres. Barcelona. Seguí [1927?]
    327 p. 18 cm. (Colección obras selectas)

NT 0040531   NjP

Tarkington, Booth, 1869–1946.
    [Foreign exchange] A play in four acts, by Booth Tarkington
and Harry Leon Wilson. [New York, 1909?]   4 parts in 1 v.
28cm.
    Typewritten.
    Title changed in ms. from Nancy Baxter, to Foreign exchange.

    ———— 3 parts in 1 v.

    Imperfect: act 1 incomplete, act 4 wanting.
    Bound with the above.

972254A. I. Drama, American.   I. Wilson, Harry Leon, 1867–
jt. au. II. Title. III. Title: Nancy Baxter.
N. Y. P. L.   January 31, 1939

NT 0040532   NN

ND237
.R68A4   Tarkington, Booth, 1869–1946.
Rare bk.
Coll.   [Rockwell, Norman] 1894–
    The four freedoms ... [Philadelphia, 1943?]

Lilly
PS 3539   TARKINGTON, BOOTH, 1869–1946.
.A7 F8   A free camp in the land of the free.
2 cops.   [n.p.,1945]
        Single sheet. 27.2 x 21.2 cm.

    Copy 1, multigraphed on Hammermill bond
    paper; copy 2, reissued on Weston Waverly Lod-
    ger (28 x 21.5 cm). Russo & Sullivan, Bibli-
    ography of Booth Tarkington, p. 147.
    Copy 1, signed in facsimile by the author.
    Written July 7, 1945, for Rev. James A.

    Carey, in tribute to the Free Camp for Chil-
    dren on Sabbathday Lake, Maine.
        Third paragraph on copy 2,has some vari-
    ants from copy 1.
        From the library of J.K. Lilly.

    1. New Gloucester,Me.--Free Camp for Children.
    2. Carey,James A.

NT 0040535   InU

AC–L
T174Eim   Tarkington, Booth, 1869–1946.
1894a   Gay fragments. [Indianapolis, 1894]
        p.24–29. illus. 28cm.

    In a whole no. of the Impromptu, 1894.
    Cover design by Bruce Rogers.

    I. Rogers, Bruce, 1870–1957, illus.
    II. Title. III. Impromptu. A.F.: McCutcheon,
    George Barr, 1866–1928.

NT 0040536   TxU

Za
T175   Tarkington, Booth, 1869–1946.
9220ec   Gentle Julia ... Bruxelles, London [etc.]
        Wm. Collins Sons & Co., ltd., 1922.
        213 p. 17 cm. (Collins' standard col-
        lection of British and American authors,
        v. 231)

    "Copyright edition."

NT 0040537   CtY

---

*
PS2972
.G38   Tarkington, Booth, 1869–1946.
1922a
        Gentle Julia. Illustrated by C. Allan
    Gilbert and Worth Brehm. Garden City,
    N. Y., Doubleday, Page, 1922.
    375 p. 20cm.

    I. Title.
                Full name: Newton Booth Tarkington.

NT 0040538   ViU MB TxU MoU ViU PSt

Tarkington, Booth, 1869–1946.
    Gentle Julia, by Booth Tarkington; illustrated by C. Allan
Gilbert and Worth Brehm. Garden City, N. Y., and Toronto, Doubleday, Page & company, 1922.
    5 p. l., 375 p. col. front., plates. 19½ cm.
    "First edition."

    I. Title.
                                    [Full name: Newton Booth Tarkington]
                                                    22–9877
    Library of Congress   PZ3.T175Ge

        WaT WaE OrP IdU IdB WaS WaWW Or IdPI CaBVa OrSaW
        OC1W MH OEac OO NN MB IU NIC PRosC PBm PHC Wa PPLas
NT 0040539   DLC CaBVaU CU-S KEmT TNJ TxCM CtU NjP TxU

Tarkington, Booth, 1869–1946.
    Gentle Julia. New York, 1922.

NT 0040540   PPL PPCCH PPPH-I

PS
2972   Tarkington, Booth, 1869–1946.
G39   Gentle Julia. Hoosier ed.   New York,
1922   P.F. Collier [c1922]
        375 p. 20cm.

NT 0040541   CoU

PS
2972   Tarkington, Booth, 1869–1946.
G3   Gentle Julia, by Booth Tarkington ...
1922   illustrated by C. Allan Gilbert and
        Worth Brehm. New York, Grosset &
        Dunlap [c1922]
        4 p. l., 375 p. col. front., plates.
        19 cm.

NT 0040542   NBuU OKentU PP PU PPT PWcS

Tarkington, Booth, 1869–1946.
    Gentle Julia, by Booth Tarkington ... illustrated by C.
Allan Gilbert and Worth Brehm. New York, Grosset &
Dunlap [193–]
    4 p. l., 375 p. col. front., plates. 19 cm.

    I. Title.
                            Full name: Newton Booth Tarkington.

    PZ3.T175Ge 11   35–33397

NT 0040543   DLC NIC OC1h MH ViU TxU

Tarkington, Booth, 1869–1946.
    Gentle Julia ... Screen play
        see under Gentle Julia (Motion picture) script.

Tarkington, Booth, 1869-1946.
    Gentleman from Indiana.

NT 0040545   PPCCH

Tarkington, Booth, 1869-1946.
    The gentleman from Indiana, by Booth Tarkington.
New York, Doubleday & McClure co., 1899.
    viii p., 1 l., 384 p. 20½ cm.

      I. Title.

    (PZ3)   -813.5   99—5008

OKentU NNC
OU OCl WaU NcU ViU IEN TxU WaWW Or WU ICU IU IEN
NT 0040546   DLC MH MB NjP OClh OLak PWcS PPL PP OEac

PN6157 **Tarkington, Booth,** 1869- 1946
K6T188g   The gentleman from Indiana, by Booth Tarkington.
1899a New York, Doubleday & McClure co., 1899.
    viii p., 1 l., 384 p. 20½ᶜᵐ. [Koundakjian collection]

    First ed., variant state.
    Page 245, line 12, last word is "glance" rather than "eye". Cf.
Johnson, Merle. American first editions.

      I. Title.   ₍Full name: Newton Booth Tarkington₎

NT 0040547   CU-BANC MoSW TxU GEU InU

Lilly
Library
PS 3539 TARKINGTON,BOOTH,1869-1946
.A7 0337   The gentleman from Indiana ... New York,
1899f Doubleday & McClure Co., 1899.
    viii p., 1.l., 384 p. 8vo (20.3 cm.)

    Third state of text, later (?) state of
binding (ear of corn upside down): Russo &
Sullivan, p. 3-6.
    Bound in original cloth, in cloth case.
    Name on front endpaper, with date 1900.
    From the library of J.K. Lilly, with his
bookplate..

NT 0040548   InU

Lilly
Library
PS 3539 TARKINGTON, BOOTH, 1869-1946
.A7 0337   The gentleman from Indiana ... New York
Doubleday & McClure Co., 1899.
    viii p. ₍1₎ l., 384 p. 8vo (20.4 cm.)

    First edition, first state text, first
(?) binding (ear of corn on spine upright);
Russo & Sullivan, p. 3-6
    Inscription to "Miss Smith" on front end-
paper, signed Newton Booth Tarkington.
    Imperfect; lacks free back endpaper.
    Bound in original green cloth, tinted

in is a typed slip on states of text with
note in hand of Whitman Bennett.
    Bound in original cloth, in quarter
morocco case.
    From the library of J.K. Lilly, with
his book plate.

NT 0040550   InU MH ViU

MICROFILM
F **Tarkington, Booth,** 1869-1946.
5200   The gentleman from Indiana, by Booth **Tarkington.**
New York, Doubleday & McClure co., 1899.
    viii p., 1 l., 384 p. 20½ cm.

    (Wright American Fiction, v. III, 1876-1900,
no. 5369, Research Publications, Inc, Microfilm, Reel T-3)

NT 0040551   NNC CU

Rare
PS **Tarkington, Booth,** 1869-1946.
2972   The gentleman from Indiana; a novel,
G333b+ by Booth Tarkington.

    (In McClure's magazine. May-October,
1899. Vol. 13, nos. 1-6)

    This is the serialized version of the
novel.

NT 0040552   NIC

Tarkington, Booth, 1869-
    The gentleman from Indiana, by Booth Tarkington. **New**
York, Doubleday & McClure co., 1900.
    viii p., 1 l., 384 p. 20½ᵐ.

      I. Title.
        ₍Full name: Newton Booth Tarkington₎

Library of Congress   PZ3.T175Gen 2   20-23137 Revised

    ViU InU TxU MiU OClJC NjP MH NN WaSpG OrU WaS WaTU
NT 0040553   DLC MsU IEN MH PBm PBa MB PU OU DAU MsU

Beinecke **Tarkington, Booth,** 1869-1946.
Library   The gentleman from Indiana ... Toronto,
Za William Briggs, 1900.
T175   1 p.l., vii-viii p., 1 l., 384 p. 20 cm.
899D   Original wrappers.

NT 0040554   CtY

Tarkington, Booth, 1869-1946.
    The gentleman from Indiana. New York,
Doubleday & McClure co., 1901.

NT 0040555   MH

PS2972 **Tarkington, Booth,** 1869-1946.
G4   The gentleman from Indiana. New York,
1902 Grosset & Dunlap ₍c1902₎
    viii,303p. front. 20cm.

NT 0040556   IaU

Tarkington, Booth, 1869-1946.
    The gentleman from Indiana, by Booth Tarkington...
New York: Grosset & Dunlap ₍cop. 1902₎. viii p., 1 l., 383(1) p.,
front. 12°.

    1. Fiction (American). 2. Title.
    N. Y. P. L.   May 11, 1915.

NT 0040557   NN NcU MB NIC OClW OO OClC MH

PS2972 **Tarkington, Booth,** 1869-1946.
G39   The gentleman from Indiana. New York,
Grosset & Dunlap ₍c1902₎
    504 p. front. 19cm.

NT 0040558   OrCS WaE MtU MiU PPT PU PSC OrStbM

PS 2972 **Tarkington, Booth,** 1869-1946.
G4   The gentleman from Indiana, by Booth Tarkington ...
1902 New York, McClure, Phillips & co., 1902.
    viii p., 1 l., 384 p. incl. front. 19½ᵐ.

      I. Title.
        ₍Full name: Newton Booth Tarkington₎

NT 0040559   OU ViU LU TxU OClWHi

Booth, 1869-1946.
    Gentleman from Indiana. New York, 1903.

NT 0040560   NjP

Tarkington, Booth, 1869-
    The gentleman from Indiana. New York,
McClure, Phillips & co., 1903.

NT 0040561   MH

Tarkington, Booth, 1869-
    The gentleman from Indiana, by Booth Tarkington ...
New York, McClure, Phillips & co., 1904.
    viii p., 2 l., 384 p. incl. front. 19½ᵐ.

      I. Title.
        ₍Full name: Newton Booth Tarkington₎

              22-14538
        PZ3.T175Gen 4

NT 0040562   DLC MoU OrP ODW

Tarkington, Booth.
    The gentleman from Indiana. New York: McClure, Phil-
lips & Co., 1907. viii p., 2 l., 384 p. 12°.

NT 0040563   NN TxU MH

Tarkington, Booth, 1869-1946.
    The gentleman from Indiana, by Booth Tarkington ...
frontispiece by Henry Hutt. New York, Grosset & Dunlap
₍1910₎
    2 p.l., vii-viii p., 1 l., 383, ₍1₎ p. front.
19½cm.

    Frontispiece wanting.

NT 0040564   ViU

AC-L **Tarkington, Booth,** 1869- 1946.
T174gen   The gentleman from Indiana, by Booth Tarkington ...
1910 New York, Grosset & Dunlap [1910? c1902₎
    4p.l.,504p. front. 19½cm.

NT 0040565   TxU IaU

Tarkington, Booth
    Gentleman from Indiana. Garden city, Doubleday,
1912.
    384p. front. D. (Royalty ed.)

NT 0040566   OClW ViU

Tarkington, Booth, 1869-1946.
    The gentleman from Indiana, by Booth
Tarkington ... Garden City, New York,
Doubleday, Page & Company, 1913.
    viii p., 2 l., 383 [2] p. incl. front. 19.5 cm
    On cover: Royalty edition.
    I Title.

NT 0040567   PPT MiU MH

Tarkington, Booth, 1869-1946.
 The gentleman from Indiana. New York,
C.Scribner's sons, 1915.

   504 p. port., plate. 19.5 cm.

NT   0040568   MH PPT IdU NcD GAuA

813.5   Tarkington, Booth, 1869-1946.
T187GE   The gentleman from Indiana. New York, C.
         Scribner's Sons, 1916 [c1902]
            504 p. plates. 20 cm.

NT   0040569   NcD OClU

Tarkington, Booth, 1869-1946.
 The gentleman from Indiana. New York, C.
Scribner's sons, 1917.

NT   0040570   MH

Tarkington, Booth, 1869-1946.
 The gentleman from Indiana ... New York,
Doubleday, Page & company, 1919 [c1899]

NT   0040571   PU

---

*AC9   Tarkington, Booth, 1869-1946.
T1747   The gentleman from Indiana, by Booth
899gm   Tarkington.
            Garden City,New York,Doubleday,Page &
         company,1919.
            5p.l.,3-504p.,1l. front.(port.),pl. 18.5cm.
         Publisher's device on t.-p.
         Original brown limp leather; top edges gilt.
         Inscribed: Dear Quinby:-Here's an old-Timer
         Doubleday includes--surely not for reading!
         It must be he thought it might have value as a
         trade-mark. Yours   as ever, Booth Tarking-
         ton. New York.   Dec. 1914.   ME44-1460

NT   0040572   MH

PS2972   Tarkington, Booth, 1869-1946.
.G4
1920   The gentleman from Indiana. New York,
         Grosset & Dunlap [192-]
            viii, 384 p. front. 20cm.

NT   0040573   ViU

Tarkington, Booth, 1869-1946.
 The gentleman from Indiana, by Booth Tarkington. Garden City, N. Y., Doubleday, Page & company, 1920.
    4 p. l., 3-504 p., 1 l. front. 19¼ cm.
    On cover: Royalty edition.

    I. Title.
                        Full name: Newton Booth Tarkington.
    PZ3.T175Gen 8   22—16013

NT   0040574   DLC WaSp OU OFH OClW Wa PRosC PV PPLas

Tarkington, Booth, 1869-
 The gentleman from Indiana. New York, C.
Scribner's sons, 1920.

   504 p. port., plate. 20 cm.

NT   0040575   MH TxU ICU OO

PZ   Tarkington, Booth, 1869-1946.
3   The gentleman form Indiana. Garden City,
T175   N.Y., Doubleday, Page & co., 1921.
Gen   504p.
1921
HRC

NT   0040576   TxU

Tarkington, Booth, 1869-1946.
 The gentleman from Indiana, by Booth Tarkington... New
York: C. Scribner's Sons, 1921.   504 p. front. (port.), pl.
12°.

341993A. 1. Fiction, American.   2. Title.   February 27, 1928
N. Y. P. L.

NT   0040577   NN MH

812T17   Tarkington, Booth, 1869-1946.
R2   ... The gentleman from Indiana ... Garden
         city, New York, Doubleday, Page, 1922.
            5 p. l., 504 p. front. (port.) 22cm.
         (The works of Booth Tarkington. v. 1)

            "Seawood edition. This edition is strictly
         limited to 1075 numbered and registered copies
         each with a portrait signed by the author in
         volume one. No. 102."

NT   0040578   NNC PP

PZ   Tarkington, Booth, 1869-1946.
3   The gentleman from Indiana. Garden City,
T175   N.Y., Doubleday, Page & co., 1924.
Gen   504p.
1924
HRC

NT   0040579   TxU OCU

Tarkington, Booth, 1869-1946.
 The gentleman from Indiana. New York,
Published by Doubleday, Page for P. F. Collier,
1925 [c1902]
   504p. front. 20cm.

NT   0040580   NcU OClUr

813.5
T187g.d Tarkington, Booth, 1869-1946.
          The gentleman from Indiana, by ... N.Y.,
         Doubleday, Page, 1926.

            504p. front. 19½cm.

NT   0040581   OWorP PHC MH

---

d13
T174ge
1902rl TARKINGTON, BOOTH, 1869-1946.
          The gentleman from Indiana, by Booth
         Tarkington. Garden City, N.Y., Doubleday,
         Page & company, 1927 [c1902]
            4p.l.,504p.,1l. front. 19½cm.

NT   0040582   TxU

---

*PS2972
.G42   Tarkington, Booth, 1869-1946.
1929   The gentleman from Indiana. Garden
         City, N.Y., Doubleday, Doran, 1929.
            504 p. front. 18cm.

            I. Title.
              Full name:Newton Booth Tarkington

NT   0040583   MB PU

Tarkington, Booth, 1869-1941.
 The gentleman from Indiana, by Booth Tarkington ...
frontispiece by Henry Hutt. New York, Grosset & Dunlap
[1931?]
    5 p. l., 3-504 p. front. 19¼ cm.

    I. Title.

    PZ3.T175Gen 11   35—28562

NT   0040584   DLC WaWW ViU LU OCU

Tarkington, Booth, 1869-1946.
 ... The gentleman from Indiana. One-by-one ed. Garden
City, N. Y., Doubleday, Doran & company, inc., 1935.
    5 p. l., 3-504 p. 19¼cm.

    I. Title.
                                [Full name: Newton Booth Tarkington]
                                                 35-17775
    Library of Congress   PZ3.T175Gen 15

NT   0040585   DLC OCU

Tarkington, Booth, 1869-1946.
 The gentleman from Indiana, by Booth
Tarkington. Garden City, New York,
Doubleday, Page & company, 1944 [c1902]
   4 p.l., 3-504 p., 1 l. front. 19.5 cm.

NT   0040586   NcGU

Tarkington, Booth, 1869-1946.
 Gentleman z Indiany; powieść. Przekład autoryzowany J. Zydlerowej. Warszawa, Wydawn.
Współczesne [1930?]
   332 p. 20 cm.

NT   0040587   NjP

An   Tarkington, Booth, 1869-1946.
Ta   George Ade, one of our own kind. [Chicago]
         1944.
            5-6p. ports. 24cm. (His Tarkington mis-
         cellany [no. 6])

            Detached from The Magazine of Sigma Chi,
         v. 63, no. 4, Oct./Nov. 1944.

            1. Ade, George. 1866-1944.

NT   0040588   IEN

(2x)
3952   Tarkington, Booth, 1869- 1946.
.75   The ghost story; a one-act play for persons of no great
.339   age, by Booth Tarkington.
1922   Boston, W.H. Baker Co. [c1922]
            42 p. 19ᵐ

NT   0040589   NjP OrCS

Tarkington, Booth, 1869-
 The ghost story; a one-act play for persons of no great
age, by Booth Tarkington. Cincinnati, Stewart Kidd
company [c1922]
    42 p. 19ᶜᵐ. (Half-title: Stewart Kidd little theatre plays, ed. by Grace
Adams. no. 1)

    I. Title.
                                [Full name: Newton Booth Tarkington]
                                                 22-11037
    Library of Congress   PS2972.G45 1922

    OCl NN MB WaT Or WaE
NT   0040590   DLC InU OrP AzU TxU IU NIC PPPL MH ODW

Tarkington, Booth, 1869-
  The ghost story; a one-act play for persons
of no great age, by Booth Tarkington. Cincinnati, Stewart Kidd company ₍c1922₎
    42 p. 19cm. (Half-title: Stewart Kidd
little theatre plays, ed. by Grace Adams.
no. 1)

NT 0040591   MsU

AC-L   Tarkington, Booth, 1869-1946.
T174gh   The ghost story; a one-act play for persons of no great
1923   age, by Booth Tarkington. Cincinnati, Stewart Kidd
    company [1923? c1922]
        42 p. 19ᶜᵐ· (Half-title: Stewart Kidd little theatre plays, ed. by Grace
    Adams. no.1)
        Five titles of "Stewart Kidd Little Theatre
    Plays" listed on verso of front paper wrapper.
    "Stewart Kidd Dramatic Anthologies" listed on
    recto of terminal paper wrapper.
        Publisher's advertisements (₍5₎p.) bound in
    at end.   22-110:7

NT 0040592   TxU

Y   TARKINGTON, BOOTH, 1869-1946.
235   The ghost story, a one-act play for persons
.T 168   of no great age. New York, D. Appleton and Co.,
    1925.
        42p. 20cm.   (Appleton little theatre
    plays. no.1)

NT 0040593   ICN

Tarkington, Booth, 1869-1946.
  The ghost story; a comedy for persons of no great age, by
Booth Tarkington. (In: Nicholson, K., editor. The Appleton
book of short plays. New York, 1926. 8°. p. ₍331-366.₎)
    Drama in one act.

246135A. 1. Drama, American.   2. Title.
N. Y. P. L.   August 26, 1926

NT 0040594   NN MH

PS2972   Tarkington, Booth, 1869-1946.
G45   The ghost story, a one-act play for persons
1931   of no great age. New York, D. Appleton,
    1931 ₍ᶜ1922₎
        42 p. 19cm. (Appleton little theatre plays.
    plays, no.1)

NT 0040595   OrCS

Tarkington, Booth, 1869-1946.
  The ghost story; a one-act play for persons
of no great age. Boston, Baker's Plays [1946]
    42 p. 19 cm. (Baker's royalty plays)

NT 0040596   CoU

Lilly
Library
PS 3539
.A7 G44   TARKINGTON, BOOTH, 1869-1946
    The Gibson upright ... by Booth Tarkington
    and Harry Leon Wilson ... n.p., Eastman
    Kodak Co., 1919.
        44 p. one fold, stapled (22.9 cm.)
        First book printing, privately printed
    for employees of Eastman; Russo & Sullivan,
    p. 51-52.
        Cover title.
        Inscription signed by author, and note
    signed with   initials, both on front
    cover.

        Bound in original wrappers, in case.
    From the library of J. K. Lilly, with
    his bookplate.

    I. Wilson, Harry Leon, 1867-1939, jt. auth.

NT 0040598   InU

Tarkington, Booth, 1869-1946.
  The Gibson upright, by Booth Tarkington and Harry
Leon Wilson. Garden City, New York, Doubleday, Page &
company, 1919.
    4 p., 3-117, ₍1₎ p. 19½ cm.

    I. Wilson, Harry Leon, 1867-1939, joint author. II. Title.

PS2972.G5 1919   19-15770

        FU OKentU Or OrP IdB Wa NN PU PP PPL PPT
        NjP OC1 MiU AU FMU KEmT CU-BANC InU WaS WaSp KMK
NT 0040599   DLC MH NIC NcU NjP TxU OLak ViU MB OC1W

Ex
3952   Tarkington, Booth, 1869-1946.
.75   The Gibson upright. By Booth Tarkington
.338   and Harry Leon Wilson. ₍Rochester, N.Y.,
.11   Eastman kodak co., 1919₎
        44 p. 23 cm.
        "Copyright 1919 by the Curtis publishing
    co."
        "First printed...in the Saturday evening
    post."
        Reprinted for distribution to the employees
    of the Eastman   Kodak company.

NT 0040600   NjP

Tarkington, Booth, 1869-   , and H. L. Wilson.
  The Gibson upright, by Booth Tarkington and Harry Leon
Wilson. (In: Webber, J. P., and H. H. Webster, editors. Typi-
cal plays for secondary schools. Boston₍, cop. 1929₎. 12°.
p. ₍146-₎212.)
    Caption-title.
    In three acts.

456128A. 1. Drama, American.
N. Y. P. L.   jt. au. 3. Title.   2. Wilson, Harry Leon, 1867-
                                            April 21, 1930

NT 0040601   NN

Tarkington, Booth, 1869-1946.
  The great German bluff about America, by Booth Tarkington... London: W. H. Smith & Son ₍1918₎. 16 p. nar. 16°.

1. European war, 1914-   , U.S.   2. Title.
N. Y. P. L.   May 7, 1919.

NT 0040602   NN

Tarkington, Booth, 1869-1946.
  A great man's wife.
  (In Three yarns. New York. 1924. 18 cm.
p. 43-88. port.)
    I. Title. II. Title: Three yarns.

NT 0040603   ViU

PS
2972   Tarkington, Booth, 1869-1946.
.G7   Growth, by Booth Tarkington. Garden
1923   City, N. Y., Doubleday, Page & company
    [c1923]
        887 p. 20 cm.

        I. Title II. Title: The magnificent
    Ambersons. III. Title: The turmoil.
    IV. Title: National avenue.

NT 0040604   OKentU PWcS MtU

Tarkington, Booth, 1869-1946.
  Growth, by Booth Tarkington. Garden City, N. Y.,
Doubleday, Page & company, 1927.
    4 p. l., 887 p. 19½ cm.
    CONTENTS.—The magnificent Ambersons.—The turmoil.—National
avenue.

    I. Title. II. Title: The magnificent Ambersons. III. Title: The
turmoil. IV. Title: National avenue.

PZ3.T175Gr   27-27696

        WaSp WaT Wa MB OrP CU-A IdPI IdU FTaSU
        NIC OEac OO MiU ViU OC1 KEmT KyU KyLxT IU WaChenE
NT 0040605   DLC CaOTP NN OC1JC NcD MH PHC PU PV PPD

Tarkington, ₍Newton₎ Booth, 1869-1946.   51-734
  Growth. [1st edition.] By Booth Tarkington.
— Garden City, N. Y. Doubleday, Page & Co. 1927. 19 cm.
    Contents.—The god. The magnificent Ambersons.—The turmoil.—
    National Avenue.
    The magnificent Ambersons and The turmoil have been published sepa-
rately.

N5027 — T.r. — Magnificent Amber. ., The. — Turmoil, The. — National
Avenue. — God, The.

NT 0040606   MB InU TxU

Tarkington, Booth, 1869-1946.
  Growth, by Booth Tarkington. London, W.
Heinemann, 1927.
    4 p. ℓ., 887 p. 20 cm.

    Contents. - The magnificent Ambersons. - The
turmoil. - National avenue.
    Presentation copy to Barton Currie with inscrip-
tion by the author.

    I. T. II. T.: The magnificent Ambersons.
III. T: The turmoil. IV. T: National avenue.

NT 0040607   NjP

Tarkington, Booth, 1869-1946.
  The guardian; a play in four acts, by Booth Tarkington and
Harry Leon Wilson. New York, 1907. 245 p. 19cm.
    Prompt-book, with ms. and typewritten notes. Additional scene, 2 typewritten l.,
inserted at end.
    Title changed in ms. from The guardian, to The man from home.
    "The guardian (The man from home). Printed (but not published) 1907...
One hundred copies were printed...for copyright purposes for the authors before
the selection later of the title, The man from home."—Currie, B. W. Booth Tarkington; a bibliography. 1932. p. 125.

976276A. 1. Drama, American.   2. Prompt-books. I. Wilson,
Harry Leon, 1867-   , jt. au.   II. Title. III. Title: The man
N. Y. P. L.   from home.
                                         January 5, 1939

      ViU
NT 0040608   NN InU MH CtY NjP DeU InU NNC NIC RPB

Rare
PS   Tarkington, Booth, 1869-1946.
2972   A guess at George Ade, by Booth
G92   Tarkington.
        (In The American spectator year
    book, 1934. New York. 23cm. p. 64-
    67)

NT 0040609   NIC

Tarkington, Booth, 1869-1946.
  The guest of Quesnay. New York, McClure,
1906.
    335 p.

NT 0040610   PPCCH

Tarkington, Booth, 1869-1946.
  The guest of Quesnay, by Booth Tarkington ...
illustrations by W.J. Duncan. London,
Heinemann, 1908.
    310 [1] p. 20 cm.

NT 0040611   NjP

PS
1279   Tarkington, Booth, 1869-1946.
.G8   The guest of Quesnay, by Booth
1908a   Tarkington...illustrations by W. J.
    Duncan. New York, Grosset and Dunlap
    [c1908]
        335 p. illus. 20 cm.

NT 0040612   OKentU MH PSt GAuA

Tarkington, Booth, 1869–1946.
The guest of Quesnay, by Booth Tarkington ... illustrations by W. J. Duncan. New York, The McClure company, 1908.
5 p. l., 3–335 p. col. front., 4 pl. 20 cm.

I. Title.

Full name: Newton Booth Tarkington.

PZ3.T175Gu
—— Copy 3.   PS2972.G8 1908   8—27810

MiU OClW OO OClh OCl OLak MH
MB WaWW NjP OrP Or TxU CoU IEN NcU OEac OCU OClW-H
CaOTP PBa PSt PPD PPL PP PNt InU ViU MtBC NIC IdB
NT   0040613   DLC WaSp WaS MtU OU ScU LU IaU AAP VtU

PS
2972   Tarkington, Booth, 1869–1946.
.G8   The guest of Quesnay, by Booth
1908   Tarkington. New York, C. Scribner's
     sons [c1908]
     321 p. illus. 20 cm.

NT   0040614   OKentU WaS

TARKINGTON, Booth, 1869–1946.
The guest of Quesnay. Illustrations by W. J.
Duncan. New York, Doubleday, Page & Co., 1909.
19.5 cm. Front. (colored), plates.

NT   0040615   MH

Tarkington, Booth, 1869–1946.
The guest of Quesnay. Illustrations by W. J. Duncan.
New York: Doubleday, Page & Co., 1909. 5 p. l., 3–335 p., 5 pl.
12°.

1. Fiction (American). 2. Title.
N. Y. P. L.   August 29, 1914.

NT   0040616   NN

Tarkington, Booth i.e. Newton Booth, 1869–
The guest of Quesnay, by Booth Tarkington...illustrations by W. J. Duncan. New York. The McClure company, 1908. Garden city, Doubleday, 1912.
(Royalty ed.)

NT   0040617   OClW

Tarkington, Booth, 1869–1946.
The guest of Quesnay. Illustrations by W. J.
Duncan. Garden City, N. Y., Doubleday, Page &
Co., 1913.
335 p. front. 19.5 cm.
Lettered on spine: Royalty edition.

NT   0040618   MH

PS2972   Tarkington, Booth i. e. Newton Booth, 1869–1946.
.G8   The guest of Quesnay, by Booth Tarkington ... New
1915   York, C. Scribner's sons, 1915.
     [7], 321, [1] p. front., plates. 20ᵐᵐ.

NT   0040619   ICU IEN LU TxU NjP NcD PU

Tarkington, Booth, 1869–1946.
The guest of Quesnay, by Booth Tarkington ... New
York, C. Scribner's sons, 1916.
5 p. l., 3–321, [1] p. front., plates. 20ᵐᵐ.

I. Title.

[Full name: Newton Booth Tarkington]

Library of Congress   PZ3.T175Gu 6
     22–14553 Revised

NT   0040620   DLC NcD MB MsU WaTU CaBVaU OU

TARKINGTON, Booth, 1869–1946.
The guest of Quesnay. New York, C. Scribner's
sons, 1917, [cop. 1908].
Illustr.

NT   0040621   MH

Tarkington, Booth, 1869–1946.
The guest of Quesnay, by Booth Tarkington ... Illustrations by W. J. Duncan. Garden City, N. Y., Doubleday, Page & company, 1920.
4 p. l., [3]–321, [1] p. front. 19¼ cm.
On cover: Royalty edition.

I. Title.

PZ3.T175Gu 8   22—16012

NT   0040622   DLC Wa NjP

Tarkington, Booth.   T
The guest of Quesnay.   Garden City, N. Y.: Doubleday,
Page & Co., 1922.   321 p.   front.   8°.
Seawood edition.

NT   0040623   NN

Tarkington, Booth, 1869–1946.
The guest of Quesnay. Garden City,
New York, Doubleday, 1923, c1908.
321 p. (Seawood ed.)

NT   0040624   PP

Tarkington, Booth, 1869–1946.
The guest of Quesnay, by Booth Tarkington...
Garden City, N. Y., Doubleday, Page & company, 1925.
4 p.l., [3,–321 p. front. 19½cm.
Lettered on cover: Royalty edition.
Defective: front wanting.

I. Title.

[Full name: Newton Booth Tarkington]

NT   0040625   ViU OClUr

Tarkington, Booth, 1869–1946.
The guest of Quesnay, by Booth Tarkington ... illustrations by W. J. Duncan. New York, Grosset & Dunlap [1925]
4 p. l., 3–335 p. front., 3 pl. 19½cm.

NT   0040626   ViU

Tarkington, Booth, 1869–
The guest of Quesnay. Garden City, N.Y.,
Doubleday, Page & co., 1927.
321 p. 19.5 cm.
Lettered on spine: Royalty edition.

NT   0040627   MH WaChenE

Tarkington, Booth i. e. Newton Booth, 1869–
... Harlequin and Columbine, and other stories ...
Garden City, N. Y., Doubleday, Page and company, 1918.
5 p. l., 3–403, [1] p. 22ᵐᵐ. (The works of Booth Tarkington. vol. VIII)
"Autograph edition. Limited to five hundred and sixty-five copies. This is no. ——."

CONTENTS.—Harlequin and Columbine.—Mary Smith.—Truth is stranger than fiction.—Marjorie Jones' picnic.—Penrod—zoölogist.—The fairy coronet.—The second name.—Brudie's pickle.

I. Title.

Library of Congress   PZ3.T175Ha
     21–8687

NT   0040628   DLC CaBVaU OEac

Tarkington, Booth, 1869–1946.
Harlequin and Columbine, by Booth Tarkington, frontispiece by E. Stetson Crawford. Garden City, N. Y. & Toronto, Doubleday, Page & company, 1921.
4 p. l., 3–188 p. front. 19ᵐᵐ.

I. Title.

[Full name: Newton Booth Tarkington]

Library of Congress   PZ3.T175H
     21–22104 Revised

TxU
IdU Or Wa WaSp OrCS PU CoU KU NcU IU IdB TNJ OrU
NT   0040629   DLC WaS NcD OO OCl MH NN MiU NIC CaOTP

AC-L   Tarkington, Booth, 1869–1946.
T174ha   Harlequin and Columbine, by Booth Tarkington, frontis
1921a   piece by E. Stetson Crawford. Garden City, N. Y. & Toronto,
     Doubleday, Page & company, 1921.
     4 p. l., 3–188 p. front. 19ᵐᵐ.
     "First edition."

NT   0040630   TxU ViU InU

Tarkington, Booth, 1869–1946.
Harlequin and Columbine. New York,
Doubleday, 1921, c1918.

NT   0040631   PPL PRosC

Tarkington, Booth.   T
Harlequin and Columbine, and other stories.   Garden City,
N. Y.: Doubleday, Page & Co., 1922.   403 p.   front.   8°.
Seawood edition.
Contents: Harlequin and Columbine. Mary Smith. Truth is stranger than fiction.
Marjorie Jones' picnic. Penrod—zoölogist. The fairy coronet. The second name.
Brudie's pickle.

1. Titles. 2. Theater—Fiction.
N. Y. P. L.   April 22, 1930

NT   0040632   NN PP OO

Tarkington, Booth, 1869–1946.
The Help each other club, by Booth Tarkington. New
York, London, D. Appleton-Century company, incorporated, 1934.
3 p. l., 25, [1] p. 19ᶜᵐ. (Half-title: Appleton short plays, no. 27)

I. Title.

Library of Congress   PS2972.H4 1934   34–32919
Copyright D pub. 31416   [2]   812.5

NT   0040633   DLC NBu InU ViU WaS Or OCl

Tarkington, Booth, 1869–1946.
... The heritage of Hatcher Ide. London,
Toronto, W. Heinemann [1941]
4 p.l., 288 p. 20.5 cm.
Published serially under title: The man of the family.
"First edition".
I. Title.
[Full name: Newton Booth Tarkington]

NT   0040634   NjP

Tarkington, Booth, 1869–
... The heritage of Hatcher Ide. New York, Doubleday,
Doran and company, inc., 1941.
4 p. l., 310 p. 20¼ cm.
Published serially under title: The man of the family.
"First edition."

I. Title.

PZ3.T175He   41—2817

MH ICU
OrP CaBVa PWcS NIC ViU OOxM OEaC OIak OO OClh OClW
MoU InU AAP OCl TNJ GAuA TxU WaTU WaE WaWW IdB WaS
NT   0040635   DLC OU OCU MiU PU OKentU PPT NcD FTaSU OI

Lilly
PS 3539
.A7 H67
1907

TARKINGTON, BOOTH, 1869-1946
His own people ... Illustrated by Lawrence Mazzanovich and F.R. Gruger. Decorated by Wm. St. John Harper. London,
John Murray, 1907.
5 p.ℓ.,3-150 p. illus.,front. 8vo
(18.8 cm.)

Russo & Sullivan, A bibl. of Booth Tarkington, p. 20; first edition, N.Y., 1907.
Decorated title page.

NT 0040636   InU NjP

Tarkington, Booth i.e. Newton Booth, 1869-1946.
His own people, by Booth Tarkington; illustrated by
Lawrence Mazzanovich and F. R. Gruger, decorated by
Wm. St. John Harper. ₍New York₎ Doubleday, Page & Co.
c1907.
(Royalty ed.) Garden city.

NT 0040637   OClW

Tarkington, Booth, 1869-1946.
His own people, by Booth Tarkington; illustrated by Law-
rence Mazzanovich and F. R. Gruger, decorated by Wm. St.
John Harper. New York, Doubleday, Page & co., 1907.
5 p. L, 3-150 p. col. front, 5 pl. (1 col.) 20 cm.
Illustrated end-papers in color.

I. Title.

PZ3.T175Hi   7—30869

CaOTP DAU IEN InU OKentU TNJ CoU CU-S INS WaWW WaSpG
OEac ViU OCl PPT LU PJA PP PBa TxU NcU ICarbS OU MoU
NT 0040638   DLC NjP WaS NIC MH WaSp OClW NN OrP MoSW

PS
2972
H5
1907a

Tarkington, Booth, 1869-1946.
His own people. Illustrated by Lawrence
Mazzanovich and F.R. Gruger. Decorated
by Wm. St. John Harper. New York,
Grosset & Dunlap ₍1907₎
150 p. col. illus. 20cm.

NT 0040639   CoU KyU MH OU ViU

PS
2972
H67
1912

Tarkington, Booth, 1869-1946.
His own people. Illus. by Lawrence
Mazzanovich and F. R. Gruger, decorated
by Wm. St. John Harper. Garden City,
N.Y., Doubleday, Page & co., 1912.
226 p. illus. 20cm.

Contents.--His own people.--Mrs.
Protheroe.--Great men's sons.

NT 0040640   NIC

818
T187h1
1912

Tarkington, Booth, 1869-1946.
His own people. Illus. by
Laurence Mazzanovich and F.R. Gruger,
decorated by Wm. St. John Harper.
₍Royalty ed.₎ Garden city, N.Y.,
Doubleday, 1912.
226p. D.

NT 0040641   IaU MiU

Tarkington, Booth, 1869-1946.
His own people, by Booth Tarkington. Decorated by Wm.
St. John Harper. Garden City, N. Y.: Doubleday, Page & Co.,
1915. 4 p.l., 3-150 p., 1 l. 12°.

1. Fiction (American). 2. Harper,   William St. John, illustrator.
3. Title.
N. Y. P. L.   February 10, 1916.

NT 0040642   NN IU MH

Tarkington, Booth, 1869-1946.
The Hon. Julius Caesar; a travesty with
music
see under   Harris, Erdman, 1898-

Rare
PS
2972
H78

Tarkington, Booth, 1869-1946.
Hoosier thoughts on the state of Maine.

(In The old farmers almanac, by
Robert B. Thomas. Maine edition,
144th year, 1936)

NT 0040644   NIC

Lilly
PS 3539
.A7 H8

TARKINGTON, BOOTH, 1869-1946
How America lives. (In Ladies' Home Journal. vol. LXII, no.4, April. Philadelphia,
1945. p. 131-134. 34.5 cm.)

Russo & Sullivan, Bibl. of Booth Tarking-
ton, p. 254.
Title in table of contents, "How America
lives: meet the Ecks."
From the library of J.K. Lilly.
In colored printed wrapper.

NT 0040645   InU

TARKINGTON, BOOTH, 1869-1946
"How's your health?" [by Booth Tarkington and
Harry Leon Wilson] [New York, Rosenfield, 192-?]
51, 34, 34 l. 28cm.

Typescript.
Produced at the Vanderbilt theatre, New York, Nov. 26, 1929.

1. Drama, American. I. Wilson, Harry Leon, 1867-1939, joint author.
II. Title.

NT 0040646   NN

TARKINGTON, BOOTH, 1869-1946.
How's your health, by Booth Tarkington and Harry
Leon Wilson. [New York, 1928] 5 v. 29cm.

Typescripts of 5 versions.
Produced at the Vanderbilt theatre, N.Y., 26 November 1929.

1. Drama, American. 2. Drama--Promptbooks and typescripts.
I. Wilson, Harry Leon, 1867-   1939, joint author. II. Title.
i. Subs for cards dated 4. 58

NT 0040647   NN

812
T17ho
1930

Tarkington, Booth, 1869-1946.
How's your health? A comedy in three
acts, by N. Booth Tarkington and Harry
Leon Wilson. Rewritten and rev. New
York, N.Y., S. French, c1930.
105 ₍2₎p. diagrs. 19cm.
On cover: French's Standard library
edition.

I. Wilson, Harry Leon, 1867-1939, joint
author. II. Title.

NT 0040648   IU

Tarkington, Booth, 1869-1946.
How's your health? A comedy in three acts, by N. Booth
Tarkington and Harry Leon Wilson ... New York, N. Y.,
Los Angeles, Calif., S. French, inc.: London, S. French, ltd.,
ᶜ1930.
3 p. l., 5-105, ₍2₎ p. diagrs. 19ᶜᵐ. (On cover: French's standard library edition)

I. Wilson, Harry Leon, 1867- joint author. II. Title.
₍Full name: Newton Booth Tarkington₎

Library of Congress   PS2972.H7 1930   31—17892
Copyright D pub. 671   ₍3₎   812.5

NBuG ICU NN
NT 0040649   DLC TxU OU ViU Or OrP Wa OEac OCl MH

---

*BROAD-
SIDE
1940
.C632

Tarkington, Booth, 1869-1946.
I am for Willkie because of facts ...
New York ₍1940₎
broadside (postcard). 9 x 14cm.
Reproduced from manuscript copy and distributed
by American Writers for Wendell L. Willkie.
In folder with Cobb, Irvin S. I am supporting
Willkie₍sic₎ ... New York ₍1940₎

1. Willkie, Wendell Lewis, 1892-1944. 2.
Presidents--U. S.--Election--1940. I. American
Writers for Wendell L. Willkie.

NT 0040650   ViU

P
T1741

Tarkington, Booth, 1869-1946.
... Image of Josephine. Garden City, New York, Doubleday,
Doran and company, inc., 1945.
4 p. l., 275 p. 20ᶜᵐ.

I. Title.
₍Full name: Newton Booth Tarkington₎
45-2270

Library of Congress   PZ3.T175 Im

ViU NNC TxU
NT 0040651   DLC CoU MoU FTaSU WU NIC KEmT NjP NBuU

Tarkington, Booth, 1869-
... Image of Josephine. Garden City, New York, Doubleday,
Doran and company, inc., 1945.
4 p. l., 275 p. 20ᶜᵐ.
"First edition"

I. Title.
₍Full name: Newton Booth Tarkington₎
45-2270

Library of Congress   PZ3.T175 Im

PV NBuC OKentU
NcGU OrU WaSp Wa WaT IdU WaE IdPI Or OrP WaS InU PU
OCU OClW OO OCl OEac OOxM OC1C WaU MoU MB CaBVa MsU
NT 0040652   DLC PSt PRosC PSC OrCS OU NIC TxU ViU ODW

Tarkington, Booth, 1869-1946.
Image of Josephine ... New York, 1945.

NT 0040653   PU

Rare
PS
2972
I31
1945

Tarkington, Booth, 1869-1946.
Image of Josephine. ₍New York, 1945₎
78 sheets. 24cm.

Galley proofs.

NT 0040654   NIC

Tarkington, Booth, 1869-1946.
Image of Josephine. London, Hammond, Hammond & Co. [1948]
253 p. 19 cm.

NT 0040655   NjP

---

*
PS2972
.I 495
1943

Tarkington, Booth, 1869-1946.
"In extenuation" a foreword by the author
of the eight plays of the Ninth Annual
Midsummer Drama Festival

(In Pasadena Playhouse Association. Eight hit
plays by Tarkington. Pasadena. 1943. 24cm.
1 p. port.)

NT 0040656   ViU

PS
2972
.I37
1905

Tarkington, Booth, 1869-1946
In the arena; stories of political
life [by] Booth Tarkington; illustrated
by A. I. Keller, Power O'Malley and J.
J. Gould. Garden City, Doubleday, Page
and Co. [c1905]
278 p. illus. 20 cm.

NT 0040657 OKentU

Lilly
PS 3539
.A7 I 35
1905

TARKINGTON,BOOTH,1869-1946
In the arena; stories of the political
life ... London, John Murray, 1905.
7 p.l., [3]-276 p. illus., front. 8vo
(19.3cm.) (Murray's Imperial Library)

Russo & Sullivan, A bibl. of Booth Tarkington, p. 15.
Inserted publisher's ads at end: 8 p.
In original printed wrappers. Frontispiece and title stained.
ι. Title.

NT 0040658 InU NjP

Tarkington, Booth, 1869-1946.
In the arena; stories of political life [by] Booth Tark-
ington; illustrated by A. I. Keller, Power O'Malley and
J. J. Gould. New York, McClure, Phillips & co., 1905.
7 p. l., 278 p. front., 7 pl. 20 cm.
CONTENTS.— Boss Gorgett. — The aliens. — The need of money. —
Hector.—Mrs. Protheroe.—Great men's sons.

ι. Title.

PZ3.T175 In   5—3791

                    ViU CU-S MB
        OEac NIC IU KU TxU IEN OU NcD Or WaSp WaChenE IdPI
NT 0040659 DLC CaOTP PP PPL MB NjP NBuG MH CtY OC1

PS
2972
.I 5

Tarkington, Booth, 1869-1946
In the arena; stories of political life
[by] Booth Tarkington; illustrated by A. I.
Keller, Power O'Malley and J. J. Gould. New
York, McClure, Phillips & Co., 1905.
276p. front., 7 pl.

First edition.
Contents.-Boss Gorgett.-The aliens.-The
need of money.-Hector.-Mrs. Protheroe.-Great
men's sons.

NT 0040660 INS InU

Lilly
PS 3539
.A7 I 35
2 cops.

TARKINGTON,BOOTH,1869-1946
In the arena; stories of political life
... Illustrated by A.I. Keller, Power O'
Malley and J.J. Gould. New York, McClure,
Phillips & Co., 1905.
8 p.l.,[3]-276 p. front.,plates.
8vo(19.2 cm.)

First edition; Russo & Sullivan, A bibl.
of Booth Tarkington, p. 14.
Copy 2, presentation inscription by the

author to Henry Hutt, and a later explanatory note about it, also in the author's
hand.
Bound in original green grained cloth
with gilt lettering on front and spine.
Copy 2, in quarter green morocco slipcase.

ι. Title. II. Assoc. cd.: Author.

NT 0040662 InU

818
T187i
1912

Tarkington, Booth, 1869-1946.
In the arena; stories of political
life. Illus. by A.I. Keller, Power
O'Malley and J.J. Gould. [Royalty ed.]
Garden City, N.Y., Doubleday, 1912.
202p. front. D.

NT 0040663 IaU OC1W MiU WaSpG

Tarkington, Booth, 1869-1946.
In the arena; stories of political life by Booth
Tarkington; illustrated by A. I. Keller, Power O'Mal-
ley and J. J. Gould. Garden City, N.Y. Doubleday,
Page & company, 1919.
3-278 p. front 19 1/2cm.

NT 0040664 OU

Tarkington, Booth, 1869-1946.
In the arena; stories of political life [by] Booth Tarkington; illustrated by A. I. Keller, Power O'Malley and J. J.
Gould. Garden City, N. Y., Doubleday, Page & company,
1920.
6 p. l., [3]-278 p. front. 19¼ cm.
On cover: Royalty edition.
CONTENTS.—Boss Gorgett.—The aliens.—The need of money.—Hector.—Mrs. Protheroe.—Great men's sons.

ι. Title.

PZ3.T175 In 5   22—16011

            NBuU ViU
NT 0040665 DLC MtBC MB MH OC1W NN PPD Wa WaSpG OU

Tarkington, Booth.   T
In the arena; stories of political life; illustrated by A. I. Keller.
Garden City, N. Y.: Doubleday, Page & Co., 1922.   278 p.
front. 8°.

Seawood edition.
Contents: Boss Gorgett. The aliens. The need of money. Hector. Mrs. Pro-
theve. Great men's sons.

... political life—Fiction. 2. Titles.
N.Y.P.L.   April 22, 1930

NT 0040666 NN CaBVaU OO

PS
2972
I5
1925

Tarkington, Booth, 1869-1946.
In the arena; stories of political life.
New York, Published by Doubleday, Page for
P.F. Collier, 1925 [c1905]
278 p. front. 20 cm.

Contents:- Boss Gorgett.- The aliens.- The
need of money.- Hector.- Mrs. Protheroe.-
Great men's sons.

NT 0040667 LU TxU OC1Ur

Tarkington, Booth, 1869-1946.
In the arena; stories of political life.
New York, Doubleday, Page for P. F. Collier
1926 [c1905]
278 p. 20cm.

NT 0040668 ViU NjP PHC OWorP

Tarkington, Booth, 1869-1946.
In the arena; stories of political life.
Garden City, N.Y., Doubleday, Page & co., 1927.

278 p. front. 19.5 cm.
Spine: Royalty ed.

NT 0040669 MH OU

PS2972
.I 52
1904

Tarkington, Booth, 1869-1946.
In winter [poem]
(In Fosdick, R. 3., ed. Princeton verse.
Buffalo. 1904. p. 45)
"This edition limited to one thousand copies,
of which this is number 179."
Other poems by Tarkington in this issue: The
stupid people; The proud lover.

I. Fosdick, Raymond Blaine, 1883-   ed.
Princeton verse. II. Title.

NT 0040670 ViU

Rare
PS
2972
139

Tarkington, Booth, 1869-1946.
Indiana in literature and politics.

(In Modern eloquence, founded by
Thomas B. Reed. Vol. 3. After dinner
speeches. New York, c1923. 22cm.
p. 314-318)

NT 0040671 NIC

Tarkington, Booth, 1869-1946.
The intimate strangers; a comedy in three acts, by Booth
Tarkington... New York: S. French, cop. 1921. 116 p.
plates. 12°. (French's standard library edition.)

1. Drama, American. 2. Title.   3. Ser.
N.Y.P.L.   January 25, 1926

            NBuU
NT 0040672 NN MiD ICU CLSU RPB ViU NNC InU AzU NcC

Tarkington, Booth, 1869-
The intimate strangers; a comedy in three acts,
by Booth Tarkington ... New York, S. French; London, S. French, ltd., c1921.
118 p. plates. 20cm. (On cover: French's standard
library edition)

        Wa WaE OrCS KMK Or MtU ICarbS
NT 0040673 ViU OC1 OCX NRU MiU CLU NIC PPT TxU FTaSU

Tarkington, Booth, 1869-1946.
The intimate strangers; a comedy in three
acts, by Booth Tarkington ... New York,
Samuel French; London, Samuel French, ltd.,
1921.
118p. 19cm.

First edition.
Original wrappers; in case.
Ex libris: Charles F. Nugent, jr.

NT 0040674 NBu NIC IU

Rare
PS
2972
I61
1922

Tarkington, Booth, 1869-1946.
The intimate strangers, by Booth Tar
kington.

(In Cohen, Helen Louise, ed. Longer
plays by modern authors. New York,
c1922. 20cm. p. [249]-345)

NT 0040675 NIC

812.1
T187i

Tarkington, Booth, 1869-
The intimate strangers, a comedy in
three acts... New York, French [1924
118p. plates. D. (On cover: French's
standard library edition)

NT 0040676 IaU

Rare
PS
2972
I88

Tarkington, Booth, 1869-1946.
Italian old masters: Frescobaldi di
Tutti Frutti, 1392-1620.

(In Golden-rod: the magazine of the
Indianapolis Flower Mission. Indianapolis, November 3, 1891. p. 13-17)

NT 0040677 NIC

Lilly
PS 3539
.A7 I 8
TARKINGTON,BOOTH,1869-1946
... It's time to be afraid. (In Los Angeles Times,"This week magazine," Nov. 11, 1945. 32.2 cm. p. 2.)

Caption begins: Booth Tarkington says.
From the library of J.K. Lilly.
In printed wrappers.

NT 0040678   InU

Tarkington, Booth, 1869-1946.
"Just Princeton" the place and the idea ...
see under   Princeton University.
Graduate Council.

Tarkington, Booth, 1869-1946.
Kate. [Version castellana: Miguel Rivera] Madrid [1945?]
396 p. illus.,port. 16 cm. (Ediciones La Nave. Serie B, 62)

Trans. of Kate Fennigate.

NT 0040680   NjP

Tarkington, Booth, 1869-
... Kate Fennigate. Garden City, New York, Doubleday, Doran & co., inc., 1943.
4 p. l., 359 p. 20¾".
"First edition."

I. Title.
                        ⟨Full name: Newton Booth Tarkington⟩
                                          43-51197
Library of Congress   PZ3.T175Kat

ICarbS
OrSaW OrU WaS Wa WaSp OKentU TNJ Or GAuA OU CLU NBuC
CaBVa CoU MB MtBC InU MoU PBm TxU NBuU MtU OrCS OrP
OClh OClFC PSt WaT PHC PBa   WaTU IdPI NcD CaOTP
NT 0040681   DLC NIC ICU OCU OO OClW OLak OCl OEac ViU

Rare
PS
2972
K19
1943
Tarkington, Booth, 1869-1946.
Kate Fennigate, by Booth Tarkington.
⟨New York, 1943⟩
114 sheets. 25cm.

Original galley sheets.

NT 0040682   NIC

Tarkington, Booth, 1869-1946.
Kate Fennigate. Garden City, N.Y., Sun Dial Pr. [1944]
[8],359 p. 21 cm.

Presentation copy to Barton Currie with inscription by the author.

NT 0040683   NjP IdU

Lilly
PS 3539
.A7 K2
1946
TARKINGTON,BOOTH,1869-1946
Kate Fennigate ... London,Hammond, Hammond & Co. Ltd., [1946]
398 p. 8vo (18.5cm.)

Russo & Sullivan, A bibl. of Booth Tarkington, p. 118; first edition N.Y., 1943.
Bound in red buckram, with printed jacket.

NT 0040684   InU NjP

*
PS2972
.J6
1896
Tarkington, Booth, 1869-1946.

The kisses of Marjorie, a brief play
(In John-a-Dreams. New York. 26cm. Vol. 1, no. 4 (Dec. 1896) p. 147-157. illus.)
Illustrations by the author.

I. Title. II. John-a-Dreams.

NT 0040685   ViU

Tarkington, Booth, 1869-1946.
The kisses of Marjorie. A play by Booth Tarkington.   ⟨Indianapolis? 190-?⟩ 20 f. 26cm.
Cover-title.
Typewritten, with author's ms. additions and corrections. Interleaved.
With bookplate of Louisa and Booth Tarkington.

976448A. 1. Drama, American.   2. United States—Hist.—Revolution—Drama. I. Title.
N. Y. P. L.   December 28, 1938

NT 0040686   NN

Rare
PS
2972
K61
Tarkington, Booth, 1869-1946.
Kisses of Marjorie ⟨by⟩ Booth Tarkington.

(In Werner's readings & recitations. New York, 1905. No. 34, p. 17-23)

NT 0040687   NIC

4PS-52
Tarkington, Booth, 1869-1946.
Der kleine Orvie. [Ubertragung von Georg Bojkowsky] Linz, Pittsburgh, Ibis-Verlag [c1948]
336 p.

NT 0040688   DLC-P4 NjP

Tarkington, Booth, 1869-1946.
Kobiety; powieść.

NT 0040689   OCl

Tarkington, Booth, 1869-1946.
Kobiety; powieść. [Przekł. autoryzowany J. Sujkowskiej] Warszawa, Bibljoteka Groszowa [1935?]
335 p. 20 cm.

Trans. of Women.

NT 0040690   NjP

Tarkington, Booth, 1869-1946.
Książę krwi (Monsieur Beaucaire). Warszawa, Bibljoteka Groszowa [1927?]
122, [1] p. 18 cm.

I. T. II. T.: Monsieur Beaucaire.

NT 0040691   NjP

Tarkington, Booth, 1869-1946.
Kvinnor. Övers. från engelskan av Lisa Ringenson. Stockholm, Ahlén & Åkerlunds förlag [1929]
362 p. 20 cm.

Trans. of Women.

NT 0040692   NjP

Tarkington, Booth, 1869-1946.
Lady Hamilton and her Nelson ⟨by⟩ Booth Tarkington. New York, House of books, ltd., 1945.
⟨43⟩ p. 20ᶜᵐ. ⟨The Crown octavos, no. 9⟩
"First edition is limited to three hundred copies signed by the author."

1. Hamilton, Emma, lady, 1761?-1815—Drama. 2. Nelson, Horatio Nelson, viscount, 1758-1805—Drama. I. Title.
                        ⟨Full name: Newton Booth Tarkington⟩
                                          46-3706
Library of Congress   PS2972.L3 1945
                        ⟨12⟩   812.5

NN MB NNC InU MH IU IaU WU MiEM
NT 0040693   DLC MoSW ViU NIC DeU ICN ICU PSC TxU NjP

Tarkington, Booth, 1869-1946.
Lányok és asszonyok; regény; forditotta Benedek Rószi. ⟨286⟩ Budapest, Singer és Wolfner kiadása. n.d.
A regény angol címe: Women.

NT 0040694   OCl

Tarkington, Booth, 1869-1946.
Lányok és asszonyok; regény. Forditotta Benedek Rószi. Budapest, Singer és Wolfner [1935?]
286 p. 19 cm.

Trans. of Women.

NT 0040695   NjP

*
PS2972
.J6
1896
Tarkington, Booth, 1869-1946.

A letter of regrets. (Left at Giles's Coffee-House; to be Given by ye Waiter to Mr. Richard Rakell, Sir Thomas Wilding, or Lord Townbrake.)
(In John-a-Dreams. New York. 26cm. Vol. 1, no. 3 (Sept. 1896) p. 65-68. illus.)
Illustrations by the author.
Written under the pseudonym Cecil Woodford.

I. Title. II. John-a-Dreams.

NT 0040696   ViU

Rare
PS
2972
L77
Tarkington, Booth, 1869-1946.
Little gentleman, arranged from Booth Tarkington's book "Penrod". Sioux City, Iowa, Wetmore Declamation Bureau, 1926.
6 p. illus. 19cm.

NT 0040697   NIC

Tarkington, Booth, 1869-
Little Orvie, by Booth Tarkington; illustrated by George Brehm. Garden City, N. Y., Doubleday, Doran & company, inc., 1934.
x p., 1 l., 383, ⟨2⟩ p. illus. 21ᶜᵐ.
"First edition."

I. Title.
                        ⟨Full name: Newton Booth Tarkington⟩
                                          35-27014
Library of Congress   PZ3.T175Li

OKentU CaOTP AAP NIC
MiU MH OCl NN MB IdPI OrP WaSp IdB WaS Or WaE
NT 0040698   DLC PSt PWcS TNJ InU CaBVaU TxU OO OEac

Tarkington, Booth, 1869-1946.
Little Orvie. by Booth Tarkington; illustrated
by George Brehm. NY, The Council on Books in
Wartime, 1934.
319 p. illus. 12 x 16 cm. (Armed Services
edition, 844)

Printed in double columns.

NT 0040699   NjP ViU

---

*
PS2972
.L5   Tarkington, Booth, 1869-1946.
1934
Little Orvie. Illustrated by George
Brehm. New York, Doubleday, Doran & Company,
Inc., 1934.
x p., 1 l., 383, [2] p. illus. 21cm.
Illustrated t. p.
Author's inscription: "Inscription for Mr. C. W.
Barrett, Booth Tarkington. March 5, 1940."

NT 0040700   ViU KU

---

j810   Tarkington, Booth, 1869-1946.
T187   Little Orvie. Illustrated by George
tL   Brehm. New York, Grosset & Dunlap [c1934]
1934   x,383p. illus. 19cm.

NT 0040701   CLSU GAuA

PS2972
.L5   Tarkington, Booth, 1869-1946.
1936
Little Orvie; illus. by George Brehm.
New York, Grosset & Dunlap [1936]
x, 383 p. illus. 20cm.

I. Title.
Full name: Newton Booth Tarkington.

NT 0040702   ViU

---

*
PS2972
.L5   Tarkington, Booth, 1869-1946.
1944
Little Orvie; illustrated by George Brehm.
New York, Armed Services, Inc. [1944?]
319 p. illus. 11½ x 17cm. (Armed Services
edition, 844)

NT 0040703   ViU MsSM

Tarkington, Booth, 1869-1946.
Looking forward, and others, by Booth Tarkington.
Garden City, N. Y., Doubleday, Page & company, 1926.
4 p. l., 198 p. 19½ cm.

CONTENTS. — Looking forward to the great adventure.—Nipskil-
lions.—The hopeful pessimist.—Stars in the dust-heap.—The golden
age.—Happiness now.

I. Title.
Full name: Newton Booth Tarkington.

PS2972.L6 1926   26—23673

PU IdU-SB IdU Wa OrP ViU PPT PPL
OCU OLak OOxM OC1 NN MB MH OC1h MiU CSmH NIC CaOTP
NT 0040704   DLC KMK NcU FTaSU MoU WaU TU TNJ AAP TxU

Lilly
Library
PS 3539   TARKINGTON,BOOTH,1869-1946
.A7 L83   Looking forward and others ... Garden
City, N.Y., Doubleday, Page & Company, 1926.
4 p.l., 193 p. 8vo (18.8 cm.)

First edition; Russo & Sullivan, p. 78-80.
Incomplete: lacks dust jacket.
Bound in original green cloth.
From the library of J. K. Lilly, with his
bookplate.

NT 0040705   InU NcD TxU

Lilly
PS 3539   TARKINGTON,BOOTH,1869-1946
.A7 L 83   Looking forward & others ...   London,
1927   William Heinemann Limited, 1927.
4 p.l., 193 p. 8vo (19cm.)

Russo & Sullivan, A bibl. of Booth
Tarkington, p. 79; first edition N.Y.,
1926.
Bound in original blue cloth.

NT 0040706   InU OrCS ScU

Tarkington, Booth, 1869-
...Looking forward, and others ... Garden City,
N.Y., Doubleday, Doran & company, inc., 1932 [1926]
5 p.l. 193p. O (His works ... Seawood ed.
1922-1932. v. 22)

NT 0040707   OO

813.49   Tarkington, Booth, 1869-1946.
T17   The Lorenzo bunch. Garden City, N.Y.,
OLo   Doubleday, Doran, 1936.
.936   294p. 21cm.

NT 0040708   KU NN MoU MB NIC KyU-E MsU CaOTP ViU

Tarkington, Booth, 1869-
... The Lorenzo bunch. Garden City, N. Y., Doubleday,
Doran & company, inc., 1936.
4 p. l., 294 p. 20½cm.
"First edition."

I. Title.
[*Full name: Newton Booth Tarkington*]
36-27082
Library of Congress   PZ3.T175Lo

Or WaSp OrCS
PHC TNJ OU PPL TxU PU IdB OEac OCU OO MiU OrP OrU
NT 0040709   DLC MH ViU OC1 OKentU NcD NvU InU PBm

Tarkington, Booth, 1869-1946.
... The Lorenzo bunch. London, Toronto,
W. Heinemann [1936]
259 p. 20 cm.

NT 0040710   NjP

Rare
PS
2972   Tarkington, Booth, 1869-1946.
L865   The Lorenzo bunch. New York,
1936a   Doubleday, Doran & Company Inc.,
1936.
[4] l., 294 p. 21cm.

NT 0040711   NIC

Lilly
PS 3539   TARKINGTON,BOOTH,1869-1946
.A7 L 87   Love and the moon. Words by Booth
2 cops.   Tarkington. Music by Jerome Kern. Sung
by Billie Burke in Florenz Ziegfeld Jr's
production of Booth Tarkington's latest
comedy "Rose Briar." New York, T. B.
Harms Company [c1922.
5,[1] p. incl. covers. port. 31.4 cm.
(copy 1)

Cover title and imprint.

Russo & Sullivan, A bibl. of Booth
Tarkington, p. 132. Plate mark T.B.H. Co.
222-3.
For voice and piano.
Pictorial front cover from a painting
of Billie Burke signed H. Cheney Johnston.
Original sheet music as issued.
Copies vary in colors of front cover,
and in height.

Copy 1 from the library of J.K. Lilly,
in green cloth folder.

I. Title. II. Kern,Jerome,1885-1945.

NT 0040714   InU

Rare
PS
2972   Tarkington, Booth, 1869-1946.
L934   Lucius Brutus Allen Stories.

(In Everybody's magazine. New York,
1916-17. 26cm. Oct.-Dec., 1916, Jan.,
1917)

Contents.—The spring concert.—Maytime in Marlow.—Maud and Bill.—The
only child.

NT 0040715   NIC

TARKINGTON,BOOTH,1896-1946
The magnificent Ambersons by Booth
Tarkington ... Toronto, William Briggs
[n.d.]
vii, 516 p., [1] l. plates 18.7 cm.

Bound in brown cloth.

NT 0040716   InU

Tarkington, Booth, 1869-1946.
The magnificent Ambersons, by Booth Tarkington; illustrated by Arthur William Brown. Garden City, New York,
Doubleday, Page & company, 1918.
vii, 516 p., 1 l. front., plates. 19½cm.

I. Title.
[*Full name: Newton Booth Tarkington*]
18-20166
Library of Congress   PZ3.T175Ma
———— Copy 2.   PS2972.M25 1918
                                     [2]

OrCS OrU OrLgE Or
OCU WaS PRosC OrP ViU OEac CaOTP WaSp NBuU CU-S IdU
MB NjP   MiU OC1 TxU InU NIC NcU Wa PSC PBa MH
NT 0040717   DLC PG1B WaWW WaE OC1W ViU OO NN OC1WHi

---

*AC9   Tarkington, Booth, 1869-1946.
T1747   The magnificent Ambersons, by Booth Tarkington.
918mad   Hodder and Stoughton,London,New York,Toronto.
[c.1918]
320p. incl. front. 19cm.
Original green-gray cloth.
With long signed autograph inscription from
the author to [W. D.] Howells, dated:
Kennebunkport, Aug. 14, '19.

NT 0040718   MH

Tarkington, Booth, 1869-1946.
The magnificent Ambersons ... New York,
1918.

NT 0040719   PPL PV PPCCH PWeS

PS2972
M3   Tarkington, Booth, 1869-1946
1918   The magnificent Ambersons. Illus. by
Arthur William Brown. New York, Doubleday,
Page, 1918.
516 p. illus. 20 cm.

NT 0040720   MeB OKentU

UNDERGRAD LIB
PS2972   Tarkington, Booth, 1869-1946.
M3   The magnificent Ambersons. New York,
1918a   Grosset & Dunlap [c1918]
516 p. 22 cm.

NT 0040721   OU IU OC1StM OC1U IaU MtBC

Tarkington, Booth, 1869-1946.
    The magnificent Ambersons, by Booth
Tarkington; illustrated by Arthur William Brown.
Garden City, New York, Doubleday, Page &
company, 1919 [c1918]
    vii, 516 p., 1 l.   front., plates.   19.5 cm.
    I. Title.
    [Full name: Newton Booth Tarkington]

NT 0040722   PPT PU

---

*AC9
T1747
918mb
    Tarkington, Booth, 1869-1946.
    The magnificent Ambersons, by Booth Tarkington
Illustrated by Arthur William Brown.
    Garden City, New York, Doubleday, Page & company,
1919.
    vii, 516 p., 1l. front., 7 pl. 18.5 cm.
    Title vignette; publisher's device on last
leaf.
    Original brown limp morocco; top edges gilt.
    Inscribed: Inscribed for Henry C. Quinby, with
the heartiest appreciation of the time and energy he has expend-   ed to the large benefit of
Booth Tarkington. New York. December. 1919.

NT 0040723   MH

TARKINGTON, Booth, 1869-
    The magnificent Ambersons. Illustrated by
Arthur William Brown. Garden City, N.Y., Doubleday, Page & Co., 1919.
    19 cm. Front.
    Spine: Royalty edition.

NT 0040724   MH MiU

Y
255
T 175
    TARKINGTON, BOOTH, 1869-1946.
    The magnificent Ambersons... New York, C.
Scribner's sons, 1919.
    516 p. 19½ cm.

NT 0040725   ICN OrSaW

Tarkington, Booth, 1869-
    The magnificent Ambersons, by Booth Tarkington;
illustrated by Arthur William Brown. Garden City,
N. Y., Doubleday, Page & company, 1920.
    4 p. l., 3–516 p., 1 l. front. 19¼ᶜᵐ.
    Lettered on cover: Royalty edition.

    I. Title.
                   [Full name: Newton Booth Tarkington]

Library of Congress   PZ3.T175Ma 4   22–16010

NT 0040726   DLC OrAshS NcD DGU Wa WaE OC1W OrStbM

Tarkington, Booth, 1869-1946.
    The magnificent Ambersons, by Booth Tarkington
New York, Charles Scribner's sons, 1920.
    vii, 516 p., 1 l. front., plates. 19.5 cm.
    I. Title.
    [Full name: Newton Booth Tarkington]

NT 0040727   NcD

Tarkington, Booth, 1869-1946.
    The magnificent Ambersons, by Booth Tarkington ...
Illustrated by Arthur William Brown, New York, Grosset
& Dunlap [1920]
    4 p. l., 3–516 p. front., plates. 19½ cm.

    I. Title.
                  Full name: Newton Booth Tarkington.

PZ3.T175Ma 3   21—13724

NT 0040728   DLC PPLas OC1JC TxU

(Ex)
3952
.75
.358
1920
    Tarkington, Booth, 1869-1946.
    The magnificent Ambersons, by Booth Tarkington. Paris,
L. Conard, 1920.
    351 p. 16 cm. (Standard collection of British
and American authors, 171).

NT 0040729   NjP

Tarkington, Booth, 1869-1946.
    The magnificent Ambersons. New York, C.
Scribner's Sons, 1921.
    19.5 cm. Plates.

NT 0040730   MH

Tarkington, Booth, 1869-1946.
    The magnificent Ambersons.   c1922.
    illus.

NT 0040731   PPPH -I PU

Tarkington, Booth, 1869-1946.
    The magnificent Ambersons, by Booth Tarkington. Gar-
den City, New York, Doubleday, Page & company, 1922.
    3 p. l., ix–xvi, 516 p. 19½ cm.

    I. Title.
              Full name: Newton Booth Tarkington.

PZ3.T175Ma 5   22—9197

NT 0040732   DLC ODW MtU ViU MoU

PS2972
.t5
.1922
    Tarkington, Booth, 1869-1946.
    The magnificent Ambersons. Illustrated by
Arthur William Brown. New York, Grosset & Dunlap [c1922]
    516 p. plates. 20 cm.

NT 0040733   OU IdPI WaTU

Tarkington, Booth, 1869-
    The magnificent Ambersons, by Booth Tarkington.
Garden City, N.Y. Doubleday, Page & company, 1924.
    516 p. [Lambskin Library]

NT 0040734   OCU

PS2972
M3
1922
    Tarkington, Booth, 1869-1946
    The magnificent Ambersons. New York,
Doubleday, Page, 1924 [c1922]
    516 p. illus. 20 cm.

NT 0040735   MeB ViU

813
.5
T187
73-2952
    Tarkington, Booth, 1869-1946.
    The magnificent Ambersons, by Booth
Tarkington. Garden City, New York,
Doubleday, Page & Company, 1925 [c1918]
    516 p. 20 cm.

NT 0040736   N OC1U

813
T17mag
1926
    Tarkington, Booth, 1869-1946.
    The magnificent Ambersons. New York, Pub.
by Doubleday, Page for P. F. Collier, 1926.
    516 p. plate. 20 cm.

NT 0040737   IU TxU OWorP PHC OC1Ur

Tarkington, Booth, 1869-1946.
    The magnificent Ambersons, by Booth
Tarkington. Garden City, New York, Doubleday,
Doran & Co., 1933.
    3 p. l., 516 p. 19.5 cm.
    "One-by-one edition".
    I. Title.
    Full name: Newton Booth Tarkington.

NT 0040738   OrSaW

Tarkington, Booth, 1869-
    The magnificent Ambersons, by Booth Tarkington
Garden City, New York, Doubleday, Page & company, 1934.
    516 p.

NT 0040739   MiU WaChenE OrCS

F
T174ma
    Tarkington, Booth, 1869-1946.
    The magnificent Ambersons. Garden City,
N. Y., Doubleday, Doran, 1945 [c1918]
    516 p. illus.

NT 0040740   KEmT

Tarkington, Booth, 1869-1946.
    De magnifika Ambersons... Bemyndigad övers.
av H. Flygare. Stockholm, Fahlcrantz & Co. [1919]
    381 p. 20 cm.
    Imprint on cover: Helsingfors, Söderström &
Co.

NT 0040741   NjP

Tarkington, Booth
    The MAN from home; [a play in four acts].
    4°. Typewritten.
    By Booth Tarkington and H.L.Wilson.
    Cut and altered for acting, with stage direc-
tions pencilled in.
    Contains property plot.

NT 0040742   MH

Tarkington, Booth, 1869-1946.
    The man from home, by N. Booth Tarkington and Harry
Leon Wilson. [New York, 1907]
    4 pts. 29 cm.
    Typewritten (carbon copy)
    Drama.

    I. Wilson, Harry Leon. 1867–1939, joint author. II. Title.
               Full name: Newton Booth Tarkington.

PS2972.M3 1907   49–36344*

NT 0040743   DLC

[Tarkington, Booth] 1869-
    "The man from home." [New York? 1908] 112 f. 27½ cm.
    Caption-title.
    Prompt-book; typewritten, with ms. corrections.
    By Booth Tarkington and Harry Leon Wilson.
    First New York production, Aug. 17, 1908, at the Astor theatre.

    962276A. 1. Drama, American.   Prompt-books. I. Wilson, Harry
Leon, 1867–1939, jt. au. II. Title.
N. Y. P. L.   September 20, 1940

NT 0040744   NN

PS2972
M3
1908

Tarkington, Booth, 1869-1946.
The man from home, by Booth Tarkington and Harry Leon Wilson; with illustrations from scenes in the play. New York, Harper, 1908.
175 p. illus. 21cm.
The illustrations are from photographs of scenes in the play made by Luther S. White.

I. Wilson, Harry Leon, 1867-1939.
II. Title.

NT 0040745   CoU CaOTP GASU NcC NBuU MB

Tarkington, Booth, 1869-
The man from home, by Booth Tarkington and Harry Leon Wilson; with illustrations from scenes in the play. New York and London, Harper & brothers, 1908.
7 p. l., 13-175, [1] p. front., 7 pl. 21ᶜᵐ.
The illustrations are from photographs of scenes in the play made by Luther S. White.

I. Wilson, Harry Leon, 1867-1939, joint author. II. Title.
[Full name: Newton Booth Tarkington]
Library of Congress   PS2972.M3 1908   8—32634

TxU CU-BANC MtU OrP IdB WaT WaWW WaSp Or
OU OEac ODW MiU MB NN NIC VtU OC1 OC1h MH FTaSU
NT 0040746   DLC PU OrCS WaS OrPR PBa KEmT ViU NjP

Tarkington, Booth, 1869-1946.

Wilson, Harry Leon, 1867-
The man from home; a novel by Harry Leon Wilson founded upon the play by N. Booth Tarkington and Harry Leon Wilson; illustrated by C. H. Taffs. New York and London, D. Appleton and company, 1915.

Tarkington, Booth, 1869-
The man from home, a play in four acts [by] Booth Tarkington and Harry Leon Wilson (completely rewritten and revised) ... New York, N. Y., Los Angeles, Calif., S. French, inc.; London, S. French, ltd.; [etc., etc.] °1934.
97 p. plates, diagrs. 18½ᶜᵐ. (On cover: French's standard library edition)

I. Wilson, Harry Leon, 1867- joint author. II. Title.
[Full name: Newton Booth Tarkington]
Library of Congress   PS2972.M3 1934   34-20746
Copyright D pub. 29651   [3]   812.5

OU
NT 0040748   DLC CU-BANC OrCS OrP CU ViU PU InU TNJ

Tarkington, Booth, 1869-1946.
Manden fra Indiana. Overs. fra engelsk...af Margrethe John-Hansen. Kjøbenhavn [etc., etc.] Gyldendalske boghandel [etc., etc.] 1922.
248 p. 18 cm.

Trans. of The gentleman from Indiana.

NT 0040749   NjP

Tarkington, Booth, 1869-1946.
Der Mann mit den Dollars; Roman...Übertragen von Georg Schwarz. Leipzig, Wien, E.P. Tal & Co., 1929.
285, [1] p. 19 cm.

Trans. of The plutocrat.

NT 0040750   NjP

Tarkington, Booth, 1869-1946.
Mannen från Indiana. Övers. av. A Berg. 2.uppl. Stockholm, Holmquists boktryckeris förlag [1928]
192 p. 20 cm.

Trans. of The gentleman from Indiana.

NT 0040751   NjP

Tarkington, Booth, 1869-1946.
Mary's neck. Garden City, Doubleday, 1929.

NT 0040752   AU

Tarkington, Booth, 1869-
Mary's Neck, by Booth Tarkington; frontispiece by Wallace Morgan. Garden City, N. Y., Doubleday, Doran and company, inc., 1932.
4 p. l., 318 p. col. front. 20ᶜᵐ.
"First edition."

I. Title.
[Full name: Newton Booth Tarkington]
Library of Congress   PZ3.T175Mar   31-28691

OrU WaT OrPR InU WaS CaOTP
PP INS CoU OKentU WaSp IdPI OrAshS Or OrCS CaBVaU
NcD OU OO OCU MiU OC1W ViU OC1 OEac MH MoU MB PBm
NT 0040753   DLC NN Wa NBuC MeB PHC VtU OrU TxU NIC

Tarkington, Booth, 1869-1946.
Mary's Neck, by Booth Tarkington; frontispiece by Wallace Morgan. Garden City, N. Y., Doubleday, Doran and company, inc., 1932.
4 p. l., 318 p. col. front. 20 cm.
Book-of-the-Month Club. ed.
Presentation copy to Mr. Fisher with inscription and illus. by the author.

NT 0040754   NjP

Tarkington, Booth, 1869-1946.
Maud and Cousin Bill, by Booth Tarkington. [Indianapolis? 1932?] 37 (i. e. 36) parts in case. 28cm.

Caption-title; parts 1-4 have title: Maud and Bill.
Reproduced from typewritten copy.
Dramatic episodes as presented in studios of station WJZ, New York, December 1932 to February 28, 1933.
Accompanied by ms. letter of author.
Advertising matter interspersed.

652761A. 1. Drama, Radio.   I. Title.
N. Y. P. L.   July 5, 1933

NT 0040755   NN

Tarkington, Booth, 1869-1946.
Mary's Neck, by Booth Tarkington. London, W. Heinemann, 1932.
viii, 304 p. 20 cm.

NT 0040756   NjP NcU

PS
2972
M3

Tarkington, Booth, 1869-1946.
Mary's Neck. New York, Grosset & Dunlap [c1932]
318 p. 20½cm.

I. Title.
Full name: Newton Booth Tarkington.

NT 0040757   CU-I

Tarkington, Booth, 1869-1946.
Mary's neck. New York, Garden city, '33.

NT 0040758   PPCCH

Lilly
PS 3539
.A7 M5
2 cops.

TARKINGTON, BOOTH, 1869-1946
Memorial tribute to President Roosevelt. Read by B. Howard Caughran, for the Indiana Committee for victory at W F B M. Inc. [Indianapolis?]1945.
1 p.l., 3 p., [1] l. 28 cm.

Caption title.
Russo & Sullivan, Bibl. of Booth Tarkington, p.154.
Typescript.
From the   library of J.K. Lilly.
Unbound.

NT 0040759   InU

Tarkington, Booth, 1869-1946.
The midlander, by Booth Tarkington. Garden City, N. Y., Doubleday, Page & company, 1923.
5 p. l., 493, [1] p. 22½ᶜᵐ.
"This edition, signed by the author, is limited to three hundred and seventy-seven copies." This copy not numbered.

I. Title.
[Full name: Newton Booth Tarkington]
Library of Congress   PZ3.T175Mi   24—535

NjP OEac OC1JC MH DeU TxU CU-A
NT 0040760   DLC PWcS WaE PBm IdB OrP TNJ InU OKentU

Rare
PS
2972
M62
1923a

Tarkington, Booth, 1869-1946.
The Midlander, by Booth Tarkington. London, W. Heinemann, Ltd., 1923.
[5], l., 493 p. 23 cm.

Title-page on stub, with statement on verso that it was printed in the U.S.A.; imprint of Doubleday, Page on spine; the limitation notice is unnumbered and unsigned.

NT 0040761   NIC

---

*fAC9
T1747
B925g

Tarkington, Booth, 1869-
The midlander, by Booth Tarkington. [Philadelphia,1923]
3-6 numb.l. illus. 40 x 34.5cm.,folded, in case 31.5cm.
Page proofs of the opening portion first instalment of the novel in the Ladies' home journal, October 1923.
Illustrations by Frank Street.
In case lettered: Booth Tarkington. Galley proofs ...

NT 0040762   MH

Tarkington, Booth, 1869-1946.
The midlander, by Booth Tarkington. Garden City, N. Y., Doubleday, Page & company, 1924.
4 p. l., 493 p. 19½ cm.

I. Title.
[Full name: Newton Booth Tarkington]
Library of Congress   PZ3.T175Mi 2   24—5810

WaTU OrCS MtU OrU IdPI IdU
ViU GAuA PSC PU PPT PPL MH NcGU NcD CaBVaU WaS
NT 0040763   DLC CoU TxU MU MiU OC1W OCU OO MB NN

(Ex)
3952
.75
.359
1924

Tarkington, Booth, 1869-1946.
The midlander, by Booth Tarkington. London, W.Heinemann, 1924.
493 p. 20 cm.

NT 0040764   NjP

Tarkington, Booth, 1869-1946.
Millionaersønnen Bibbs; roman. Overs. of M.K. Nørgaard. Kjøbenhavn og Kristiania, Gyldendalske boghandel [etc., etc.] 1918.
219 p. 22 cm.

Trans. of The turmoil.

NT 0040765   NjP

PS
2972
.M5
1930

Tarkington, Booth, 1869-1946.
Mirthful Haven [by] Booth Tarkington. Garden City, N. Y., Doubleday, Doran & company, inc. [c1930]
319 p. 21 cm.

NT 0040766   OKentU CaOTP NN OC1h OC1

Tarkington, Booth, 1869–
Mirthful Haven ₍by₎ Booth Tarkington.　Garden City,
N. Y., Doubleday, Doran & company, inc., 1930.
4 p. l., 319 p.　21ᶜᵐ.

"First edition."

ɪ. Title.　　　　　　₍Full name: Newton Booth Tarkington₎
　　　　　　　　　　　　　　　　　30–25307
Library of Congress　　　_ PZ3.T175Mir

MiU OCU OO NjP NcD NcU CoU MU PHC TxU PRosC PPLas Or
OrStbM MB PU KyLoU KEmT INS InU OU TNJ MH OEac OOxM
NT　0040767　　DLC NNC ViU WaSp WaS OrCS WaWW IdPI OrP

Ay
T174
930ma
Rare
Books
Col
　Tarkington, Booth, 1869–1946.
　Mirthful Haven [by] Booth Tarkington.　Garden
City, N.Y., Doubleday, Doran & company, inc.,
1930.
　4 p. l., 319 p.　21cm.

A reprint; lacks "First edition" note on verso
of t.-p. and has corrections noted by Currie.

I. Title.　Sp.: DeGolyer Collection.

NT　0040768　　TxU AU

Tarkington, Booth, 1869–1946.
Mirthful Haven ₍by₎ Booth Tarkington.　Garden City,
N. Y., Doubleday, Doran & company, inc., 1931.
4 p. l., 319 p.　21 cm.

ɪ Title.　　　　　Full name: Newton Booth Tarkington.

PS2972.M5 1931　　813.5　　34—8427

NT　0040769　　DLC NjP NIC ViU

Tarkington, Booth, 1869–1946.
Mirthful Haven ₍by₎ Booth Tarkington.
Heinemann, 1931.　　　　London, W.
4 p l. 319 p. 21ᶜᵐ.

NT　0040770　　NjP

Rare
PS
2972
M671
　Tarkington, Booth, 1869–1946.
　₍Miscellaneous items containing
material by and about Booth Tarkington₎
1 v.　23cm.

NT　0040771　　NIC

Rare
PS
2972
.1
M67++
　Tarkington, Booth, 1869–1946.
　₍Miscellaneous magazines containing
Booth Tarkington material₎　In seven
volumes₎

NT　0040772　　NIC

AC–L
T174Eha
1917a
　Tarkington, Booth, 1869–1946.
　Mister Antonio, parts I [and] II.　[New
York, 1917₎
　p. [187]–203 (v.134, no.800); p. [374]–387
(v.34, no.801) illus. 25cm.

　Detached from Harper's magazine, v.134,
nos. 800–801, Jan.–Feb. 1917.

　I. Title.　II. Harper's magazine.　A.F.:
McCutcheon, George Barr, 1866–1928.

NT　0040773　　TxU

Tarkington, Booth, 1869–1946.
Mister Antonio; a play in four acts, by Booth
Tarkington... N.Y., French, c1925.
118 p.

NT　0040774　　OCX

PS
2972
M55
　Tarkington, Booth, 1869–1946.
　Mister Antonio; a play in four acts.　New
York, S. French, c1935.
　118p.　illus. 19cm. (French's standard
library edition)

NT　0040775　　WU NIC

Tarkington, Booth, 1869–
Mister Antonio; a play in four acts, by Booth Tarkington
... New York, N. Y., Los Angeles, Calif., S. French, inc.;
London, S. French, ltd.; ₍etc., etc.₎ *1935.
118 p. plates, diagrs. 19ᶜᵐ.　(On cover: French's standard library
edition)

ɪ. Title.　　　　　　₍Full name: Newton Booth Tarkington₎
　　　　　　　　　　　　　　　35–14061
Library of Congress　　　PS2972.M55 1935
Copyright　D pub. 36563₎　₍3₎　　　　　812.5

NT　0040776　　DLC Wa　　TxU ViU IU OCl TU

Rare
PS
2972
M675+
　Tarkington, Booth, 1869–1946.
　Mr. Howells, by Booth Tarkington.

　(In Harper's magazine.　New York,
26cm.　Vol. 141, August, 1920.　p. ₍346₎–
350)

　1. Howells, William Dean, 1837–1920.

NT　0040777　　NIC

Tarkington, Booth, 1869–
Mr. White, The red barn, Hell, and Bridewater, by Booth
Tarkington.　Garden City, N. Y., Doubleday, Doran & company, inc., 1935.
xviii, 126 p. 19½ᶜᵐ.

"First edition."

ɪ. Title.　ɪɪ. Title: The red barn.　ɪɪɪ. Title: Hell.　ɪᴠ. Title: Bridewater.
　　　　　　　　　₍Full name: Newton Booth Tarkington₎
　　　　　　　　　　　　　35–27454
Library of Congress　　PZ3.T175Mr

OClW OEac ViU NIC NcD PSt PU PPL KMK OU InU FU IU
NT　0040778　　DLC NN OrPS Or CaBVa MB TxU MH OCl OCU

Tarkington, Booth, 1869–1946.
Mr. White. The red barn. Hell, and Bridewater, by Booth
Tarkington.
₍1937₎　　　　　London, Toronto, W. Heinemann
xxiv,164 p.　20 cm.

NT　0040779　　NjP

Tarkington, Booth, 1869–1946.
Monsieur Beaucaire.

For a musico-dramatic work based on this see Messager, André
Charles Prosper, 1853–1929. Monsieur Beaucaire.

Tarkington, Booth, 1869–1946.
Monsieur Beaucaire, by Booth Tarkington.　London: Hodder
and Stoughton ₍190–?₎　129 p.　19cm.

69565B.　1. Fiction, American.
N. Y. P. L.　　　　　　　　　　November 8, 1940

NT　0040781　　NN

Tarkington, Booth, 1869–1946.
Monsieur Beaucaire.　c1900.
illustrated.

NT　0040782　　PPPH–I

Rare
PS
2972
M75
1900a
　Tarkington, Booth, 1869–1946.
　Monsieur Beaucaire; a story of English
life in the last century.

　(In McClure's magazine.　Vol. 14, no.
2, December, 1899–Vol. 14, no. 3, January,
1900)

NT　0040783　　NIC

813
T17m
1900
　Tarkington, Booth, 1869–1946.
　Monsieur Beaucaire.　Garden City, N.Y.,
Doubleday ₍ac1900₎
　115p.　22cm.

NT　0040784　　IU OLak MiD CoU KEmT MB

PS
2972
M6
1900
　Tarkington, Booth, 1869–1946.
　Monsieur Beaucaire.　Illustrated by C.D.
Williams.　New York, Grosset & Dunlap ₍c1900₎
　127 p.　6 col. plates.　20 cm.

　"The decorations of this book were designed
by Chas. Edw. Hooper."

NT　0040785　　LU NRU CoU ViU

Tarkington, Booth, 1869–
... Monsieur Beaucaire, by Booth Tarkington, illustrated
with scenes from the photoplay.　A Paramount picture.　New
York, Grosset & Dunlap ₍1900₎
5 p. l., 115, ₍1₎ p.　front., plates.　19½ᶜᵐ.

At head of title: Rudolph Valentino edition.
Photographs on lining-paper.

ɪ. Title.　　　　　　₍Full name: Newton Booth Tarkington₎
　　　　　　　　　　　　　28–17920
Library of Congress　　PZ3.T175Mo 6

TxU WaChenE OClStM OClUr OCU MtU
NT　0040786　　DLC CaBVa MtBC OrCS ViU KyLx KyU CLSU

Tarkington, Booth, 1869–1946.
Monsieur Beaucaire, by Booth Tarkington; illustrated by
C. D. Williams.　New York, McClure, Phillips & co., 1900.
6 p. l., 3–127, ₍1₎ p. incl. front., plates.　19ᶜᵐ.

ɪ. Title.　　　　　　₍Full name: Newton Booth Tarkington₎
　　　　　　　　　　　　　0–3289 Revised 2
Library of Congress　　PZ3.T175Mo 2

IEN TxU Or WaT LU NcD
CU–S OrPS CaBVaU FTaSU NcU InU MoSW AAP CoU
OClJC LNT MB OU OClW OCU MiU OO PP PPT MtBC WaS OrP
NT　0040787　　DLC PBm PRosC PHC CaOTP NIC NjP MH ViU

Spec.
PS 2972   Tarkington, Booth, 1869-1946.
M 6   Monsieur Beaucaire, by Booth Tarkington;
1900a   illustrated by C. D. Williams. New York,
McClure, Phillips & Co., 1900.
            6 p. l., 3-127, [1] p. incl. front.,
plates. 19 cm.
            First edition, 1st state. cf. Russo
and Sullivan, pp. 6-7.
            Signed by the author.
            George N. Meissner collection.
            I. Title.

NT   0040788   MoSW ODaU MWiW-C

Lilly
Library
PS 3539   TARKINGTON,BOOTH,1869-1946.
.A7 M75   Monsieur Beaucaire by Booth Tarkington.
1900   Illustrated by C. D. Williams. New York,
McClure, Phillips & Co., 1900.
            5 p.l., 3-127, [2] p. incl. plates
8vo (19.3 cm.)

            First edition, second state. Russo,
p. 6-9. Large Gilliss Press Seal on page
following text.
            Lacks pale green dust jacket.
            Bound in red grained cloth with gilt

stamping on front and spine. In green case.
From the J. K. Lilly library.

NT   0040790   InU TxU MoSW

Tarkington, Booth, 1869–
    Monsieur Beaucaire, by Booth Tarkington; illustrated by
C. D. Williams. New York, McClure Phillips & co., 1900.
    6 p. l., 3-127, [1] p. incl. front., plates. 19 cm.
    Fifth impression, October 1900.

    I. Title.

    PZ3.T175Mo 5   8—25560

NT   0040791   DLC OC1W NSyU

FILM   Tarkington, Booth, 1869–1946.
4274   Monsieur Beaucaire, by Booth Tarkington; illustrated by
FR   C. D. Williams New York, McClure, Phillips & co., 1900.
v.3   6 p. l., 3-127, [1] p. incl. front., plates. 19 cm.
reel
T3   (Wright American Fiction, v. III, 1876-1900,
no. 5370, Research Publications, Inc. Microfilm, Reel T-3)

NT   0040792   CU

Tarkington, Booth, 1869–
    Monsieur Beaucaire, by Booth Tarkington; illustrated by C. D.
Williams. London, J. Murray, 1901. 129 p. illus. 19cm.

NT   0040793   NN

Tarkington, Booth, 1869–1946.
    Monsieur Beaucaire, by Booth Tarkington; illustrated by
C. D. Williams. New York, McClure, Philips & co., 1900
[1901]
    6 p. l., 3-127, [1] p., 1 l. incl. front., plates. 20cm.

    I. Title.
                            [Full name: Newton Booth Tarkington]

    Library of Congress   (❋) PZ3.T175Mo 9   8—25591

NT   0040794   MH MiU MH NBuU ICU MB CSmH ViU

LE
T1878mon   Tarkington, Booth, 1869-1946.
                Monsieur Beaucaire. Illustrated by C.D
            Williams. Toronto, Publisher's Syndicate,
            1901.
                127p. illus.

NT   0040795   CaOTU

PZ   Tarkington, Booth, 1869- 1946.
3   Monsieur Beaucaire, by Booth Tarkington; illustrated
T175   by C. D. Williams. New York, McClure, Phillips & co.,
Mo10   1902.
HRC   6 p. l., 3-127, [1] p., 1 l. incl. front., plates. 20cm.

            Inscribed: Mary A. Walters, 1903.

NT   0040796   TxU

Tarkington, Booth, 1869–
    Monsieur Beaucaire, by Booth Tarkington.
Illustrated by C. D. Williams. New York,
Grosset & Dunlap [1903]
    5 p. l., 3-127, [1] p.   19 1/2 cm.

NT   0040797   ViU KAS MoU PHC PPT PBa IU MB MH

Tarkington, Booth, 1869–
    Monsieur Beaucaire, by Booth Tarkington; illustrated
by C.D. Williams. New York, McClure Philips & co.,
1903.

NT   0040798   OC1W

Tarkington, Booth, 1869-1946.
    Monsieur Beaucaire ...   New York,
Grosset, 1905 [c1899-1900]
    128 p.

NT   0040799   PU

Tarkington, Booth, 1869-1946.   2-T
    Monsieur Beaucaire. London: John Murray, 1907. 130 p.
pl.   12°.

NT   0040800   NN

Tarkington, Booth.   C2
    Monsieur Beaucaire; illustrated by C. D. Williams.   New
York: The McClure Co., 1908. 5 p.l., 128 p. illus. 12°.

NT   0040801   NN TxU

Tarkington, Booth, 1869–1946.

    Monsieur Beaucaire; illus. by C. D. Wil-
iams. New York, Grosset & Dunlap [1910]
    127 p. plates. 20cm.

    I. Title.   Full name: Newton Booth Tarkington.

NT   0040802   ViU

Tarkington, Booth.
    Monsieur Beaucaire.   Garden City, N. Y.,
Doubleday, Page, 1911.

NT   0040803   MA

TARKINGTON,Booth,1869–
    Monsieur Beaucaire. Illustrated by C.D.
Williams. Garden City,New York,Doubleday,
Page,& Co.,1913.

    Front.

NT   0040804   MH MtBC

Tarkington, Booth, 1869-1946.
    Monsieur Beaucaire, by Booth Tarkington; illustrated by
C. D. Williams. Garden City, N. Y., Doubleday, Page &
co., 1915.
    6 p. l., 3-127, [1] p., 1 l. incl. front., plates. 19½ cm.

    I. Title.   Full name: Newton Booth Tarkington.

    PZ3.T175Mo 15   16—6988

NT   0040805   DLC OrLgE OrPS ViU

Tarkington, Booth, 1869–
    Monsieur Beaucaire. The beautiful lady. His own people,
by Booth Tarkington ... New York, C. Scribner's sons, 1915.
    5 p. l., 3-252 p., 1 l. front., plates. 19½cm.

    I. Title. II. Title: The beautiful lady. III. His own people.
                            [Full name: Newton Booth Tarkington]
                                        20–4018 Revised
    Library of Congress   PZ3.T175Mo 16

NT   0040806   DLC NjP OU ICU

Tarkington, Booth, 1869-1946.
    Monsieur Beaucaire / by Booth Tarkington ; illustrated by C.
D. Williams. — Garden City, N.Y. : Doubleday, Page, 1916,
c1900.
    127 p., [1] leaf of plates : ill. ; 20 cm.
    Author's typescript note to and portrait of Haute Tarkington Jameson in-
serted.

    I. Title.
    PS2972.M6   1916   76-373719
                                              MARC

NT   0040807   DLC

Tarkington, Booth, 1869–1946.
813.5   Monsieur Beaucaire. The beautiful lady. His own peo-
T187BA   ple, by Booth Tarkington ... New York, C. Scribner's sons,
1916 [c1907]
            5 p. l., 3-252 p., 1 l. front., plates. 19½ cm.

NT   0040808   NcD PPLas PSt

Tarkington, Booth, 1869-1946.
    Monsieur Beaucaire. The beautiful lady. His own
people. N.Y. Scribn., 1917.
    252p.

NT   0040809   OC1W

Tarkington, Booth, 1869–
    ... Monsieur Beaucaire, The beautiful lady, His own
people, and other stories ... Garden City, N. Y., Doubleday, Page and company, 1918.
    6 p. l., 3-427, [1] p. front. 22cm. (The works of Booth Tarkington,
vol. IX)
    "Autograph edition, limited to five hundred and sixty-five copies. This
is no. ——."

    I. Title. II. Title: The beautiful lady. III. Title: His own people.
                            [Full name: Newton Booth Tarkington]
                                        24—20469
    Library of Congress   PZ3.T175Mo 18

NT   0040810   DLC PV

Tarkington, Newton Booth.   68.150==Z.F.29t 2
Monsieur Beaucaire. By Booth Tarkington. Illustrated by C. D.
Williams.
Garden City. Doubleday, Page & Co. 1919. Plates. 19 cm.
The scene is laid in Bath during the régime of Beau Nash.

N6825 — T.r. — Great Britain. Hist. ict. George II., 1727-1760. — Nash,
Richard, 1674-1762.

NT   0040811   MB PU MH PHC

PS   Tarkington, Booth, 1869-1946.
2972   Monsier Beaucaire. The beautiful lady.
M66   His own people. New York, Scribner, 1919
1907a   [c1907]
                252 p.   illus.   20cm.

              I. Title. II. Title: The beautiful lady.
        III. Title: His own people.

NT   0040812   CoDCC OClU

---

*
PS2972
.M6   Tarkington, Booth, 1869-1946.
1920
        Monsieur Beaucaire, illustrated with
        scenes from the photoplay. A Paramount
        picture. New York, Grosset & Dunlap [192-]
        115 p. plates.   20cm.
        At head of title: Rudolph Valentino edition.
        Photographs on lining-paper.

        I. Title.
              Full name: Newton Booth Tarkington.

NT   0040813   ViU

---

813   Tarkington, Booth, 1869-1946.
T187mon   Monsieur Beaucaire. Garden City, New
1920.2   York, Doubleday, [c1920]
             115p. 22cm.
Under-
grad.
lib.

NT   0040814   NcU

Tarkington, Booth, 1869–
    Monsieur Beaucaire. The beautiful lady. His own people,
by Booth Tarkington. Garden City, N. Y., Doubleday, **Page**
& company, 1920.
    4 p. l., 3-252 p., 1 l. front. 19½ᶜᵐ.
    Lettered on cover: Royalty edition.

    I. Title. II. Title: The beautiful lady. III. Title: His own people.
                                   [Full name: Newton Booth Tarkington]

                                                    22—16009
    Library of Congress   PZ3.T175Mo 21

NT   0040815   DLC PPD PP Wa LU OrStbM NIC OCU MH ODW

Tarkington, Booth, 1869–
    Monsieur Beaucaire, by Booth Tarkington. **Illustrated by**
C. D. Williams. New York, Grosset & Dunlap [1920]
    5 p. l., 3-127, [1] p. front., plates. 19½ cm.
    "The decorations of this book were designed by Chas. Edw.
Hooper."

    I. Title.

    PZ3.T175Mo 20   21—13949

NT   0040816   DLC OrStbM DAU MH

PS
2972   Tarkington, Booth, 1869-1946.
M6   Monsieur Beaucaire ; The beautiful lady ;
1920   His own people / by Booth Tarkington. -- New
          York : Scribner, 1920, °1907.
            252 p., [6] leaves of plates : ill. ; 20 cm.

            I. Tarkington, Booth, 1869-1946. The
        beautiful lady. II. Tarkington, Booth, 1869-
        1946. His own people. III. Title. IV. Title:
        The beautiful lady. V. Title: His own people.

NT   0040817   LU MH

Tarkington, Newton Booth.   68.148
Monsieur Beaucaire. The beautiful lady. His own people. By Booth
Tarkington.
— Garden City. Doubleday, Page & Co. 1921. Plates. 18 cm.
    The scene of the first story is laid in Bath during the régime of Beau Nash.

N6199 — T.r. (3) — Great Britain. i . Fict. George II., 1727-1760. — Nash,
Richard, 1674-1762.

NT   0040818   MB

Tarkington, Booth, 1869-1946.
    Monsieur Beaucaire. Övers. från engelskan av
Nelly Lindblad. Helsingfors, H. Schildts förlags-
aktiebolag [1921]
    77 p.   19 cm.
    Presentation copy to Howard S. Fisher with in-
scription by the author.

NT   0040819   NjP

Tarkington, Booth, 1869–
    Monsieur Beaucaire. The beautiful lady. His
own people. New York, C.Scribner's sons, 1921.

    20 cm.

NT   0040820   MH

Tarkington, Booth.   T
    Monsieur Beaucaire, The beautiful lady, His own people, and
other stories. Garden City, N. Y.: Doubleday, Page & Co., 1922.
427 p. front. 8°.
    Seawood edition.
    Contents: Monsieur Beaucaire. The beautiful lady. His own people. Beauty and
the Jacobin. The kisses of Marjorie. Mr. Brooke. Lord Jerningham.

NT   0040821   NN PP PU

Tarkington, Boot , 1869–
    ...Monsieur Beaucaire... and other stories...
Garden City, N.Y., Doubleday, Page & company, 1923
[c1918]
    6 p.l., 3-427 p. front. O (His Works...[Seawood ed.]
1922-1932. v 9.)

NT   0040822   OO

Rare
PS   Tarkington, Booth, 1869-1946.
2972   ... Monsieur Beaucaire, by Booth
M75   Tarkington. Illustrated with scenes from
1924   the photoplay, a Paramount picture. New
          York, Grosset & Dunlap [1924]
            [5] l., 3-127, [1] p., [1] l. front.,
          plates. 20cm.

            At head of title: Rudolph Valentino
          edition.

NT   0040823   NIC

PS2972
.M6   Tarkington, Booth, 1869-1946.
1925   Monsieur Beaucaire. The beautiful
        lady. His own people. New York,
        Doubleday, Page for P. F. Collier,
        1925.
          252 p. fronts. 20cm.

            I. The beautiful lady. II. His own
        people.

NT   0040824   AAP MH   OClUr

Tarkington, Booth, 1869–
    Monsieur Beaucaire, by Booth Tarkington...
Garden City, N.Y., Doubleday, Page & company, 1926.
    115 [1] p.

NT   0040825   MiU MH IdU

813.5
T187m.b Tarkington, Booth, 1869-1946.
        Monsieur Beaucaire. The beautiful lady.
        His own people, by ... N.Y., Doubleday, Page,
        1926.
          252p. front. 19½cm.

            I.Title. II.Title: The beautiful lady.
        III.Title: His own people.

NT   0040826   OWorP PP

Tarkington, Booth, 1869–
    Monsieur Beaucaire, by Booth Tarkington.   (In: Pence, R.
W., editor. Dramas by present-day writers.   New York[, cop.
1927].   12°. p. [567,–670.)
    In five acts.

346069A. 1. Drama, American.   2. Title.
N. Y. P. L.   January 26, 1928

NT   0040827   NN MH

Tarkington, Booth, 1869-1946.
    Monsieur Beaucaire. ...La bella lady (The beauti-
ful lady); romanzi. Trad. dall'inglese da G. Rossi
Milano, Sonzogno [1928?]
    96 p. 22 cm. (Romantica economica, 85)

    I. T. II. T.: La bella lady.

NT   0040828   NjP

Tarkington, Booth, 1869-1946.
    Monsieur Beaucaire.   Doubleday, Doran, 1929.

NT   0040829   PV

3952   **Tarkington, Booth**, 1869-1946.
.75   Monsieur Beaucaire.
.36   By Booth Tarkington. Garden City, N. Y., Doubleday,
1932   1932.
            xvi,115 p. front.,plates. 19 cm.

            I. Title.

NT   0040830   NjP

U
813.5   Tarkington, Booth, 1869-
T187MB   Monsieur Beaucaire. New York, Doubleday,
          Doran & Co., 1941 ₍c1900₎
               xvi, 115 p. 20 cm.

               "One-by-one edition."

NT 0040831   NcD

          Tarkington, Booth, 1869-1946.
               Monsieur Beaucaire. Illustrated by C. D. Williams.
          New York, Grosset & Dunlap ₍1941,°1900₎
               115 p. 6 col. plates. 22 cm.

               I. Title.
          PS2972.M6 1941   77-207478
                                                       MARC

NT 0040832   DLC

---

813   Tarkington, Booth, 1869-1946.
T17m   Monsieur Beaucaire. One-by-one ed.   Garden
1944   City, N.Y., Doubleday, Doran & company, inc.,
          1944.
               115p.

NT 0040833   IU NjP

---

818   Tarkington, Booth, 1869-1946.
T174moXa   Monsieur Beaucaire.   New York, Doubleday,
          1950 ₍°1900₎
               xvi, 115 p. 20 cm.

NT 0040834   LU Vi

          Tarkington, Booth, 1869-1946.
               Monsieur Beaucaire. [Drama]
               see under   Freeman, Ethel H.

Rare
PS   Tarkington, Booth, 1869-1946.
2972   My boy friends.
M99++
               (In The Ladies home journal. Phila-
          delphia, October 1917. 41cm.)

NT 0040836   NIC

          Tarkington, Booth, 1869- 1946₍?₎

Riley, James Whitcomb, 1849-1916.
          The name of Old glory, poems of patriotism, by James
     Whitcomb Riley; with an appreciation of the poet by
     Booth Tarkington, frontispiece by Howard Chandler
     Christy. Indianapolis, The Bobbs-Merrill company
     ₍°1917₎

Rare
book
coll.   Tarkington, Booth, 1869-1946.
PS2972   The new Penrod book: Penrod Jashber, by
.N4   Booth Tarkington. Illustrations by Gordon
also   Grant.   Garden City, N.Y., Doubleday,
Main   Doran, 1929.
813   321p. illus. 21cm.
T187pen
               I. Title. II. Title: Penrod Jashber.

NT 0040838   NcU OCl OClh MH

          Tarkington, Booth, 1869-1946.
               The new Penrod book, Penrod Jashber, by
          Booth Tarkington. Illustrations by Gordon Grant.
          New York, Grosset, c1929, c1915.
               321 p. illus.

NT 0040839   PBa

TARKINGTON,BOOTH,1869-1946
          Newton Booth. ₍n.p., 1892₎
          35 p. front.(port) 8vo

          A memorial volume issued in a private
     printing by Elizabeth Booth Tarkington.
     Russo and Sullivan: 155.
          Bound in white cloth with gilt letter-
     ing on front cover.
          From the library of Josiah Kirby Lilly.

NT 0040840   InU-L

Rare
PS   Tarkington, Booth, 1869-1946.
2972   Now, Ripley, please!
N94
               (In Post stories of 1939. Boston,
          1940. 22cm. p. ₍180₎-197)

NT 0040841   NIC

          Tarkington, Booth.
               Oh, Florence! Tr. by de Pedro de Olazabal.
          1945.
               280 p.

NT 0040842   DPU

Tarkington, Booth i. e. Newton Booth, 1869-
          The Ohio lady, by N. Booth Tarkington and Julian
     Street. ₍New York, Ebert press, °1916₎
          cover-title, 1 p. l., 179 p. 27ᶜᵐ.

     "A play in four acts."
     "Printed, but not published, for the authors."

          I. Street, Julian Leonard, 1879-   joint author. II. Title.
     Library of Congress   PS2972.O4 1916   16-9153

NT 0040843   DLC ViU NjP ICU NIC TxU MH

Lilly
PS 3539   TARKINGTON,BOOTH,1869-1946
.A7 O 3   The Ohio lady, by N. Booth Tarkington
vault   and Julian Street. ₍New York₎ Printed,
          but not published, for the authors ₍Elbert
          Press, °1916₎
               1 p.ℓ.,179 p. gathered and sewn in
          tens (27 cm.)

               Cover title. A play in four acts. Re-
          written in 1917, and produced and published
          under the title "The Country Cousin."

               First edition; Russo & Sullivan, Bibl.
          of Booth Tarkington, p. 40. Limitation
          usually stated to be only 60 copies; ours
          numbered 62 in red ink as in Russo & Sul-
          livan's note.
               Collates: inserted title ₍-₎1, ₍1-9₎10;
          4to in tens?
               From the library of J. K. Lilly.

               Bound in original white wrappers, mounted
          on cloth; in quarter grey morocco slipcase.

          I. Street,Julian Leonard,1879-1947,jt. auth.
          II. Title. III. Title: Country cousin.

NT 0040846   InU MWiW-C

          Booth, 1869-1946.
               Old gray eagle.   n.p., 1901.
               94 p.

NT 0040847   NjP

Rare
PS   Tarkington, Booth, 1869-1946.
2972   On behalf of man's best friend.
O57
               (In Coronet. June, 1943. Vol. 14,
          no. 2, p. 143)

NT 0040848   NIC

          Tarkington, Booth, 1869-1946.
               On dogs. Nappanee ₍Ind.₎ Priv. print., J. L.
          Weygand ₍n.d.₎
               4p. 16cm.

               1. Dogs. I. Title.

NT 0040849   IEN InU

Rare
PS   Tarkington, Booth, 1869-1946.
2972   The one hundred dollar bill, by Booth
O58   Tarkington.

               (In O. Henry memorial award prize
          stories of 1923. New York, 1924. 20cm.
          p. 211-228)

NT 0040850   NIC

          Tarkington, Booth, 1869-1946.
               An overwhelming Saturday; a "Penrod" story.
          New York, International Magazine Company
          ₍c1913₎
               30 p. 18 cm.

NT 0040851   NNC InU TxU NjP NIC MoSW

          Tarkington, Booth, 1869-1946.
               Pani Stella, powieść.   Warszawa, Swiat, n.d.
               199 p.

NT 0040852   PP

Tarkington, Booth, 1869-
          ... Pani Stella, powieść. Warszawa, "Świat" ₍1934₎
          199 p. 17¼ᶜᵐ.

     At head of title: B. Tarkington.
     Translation, by J. Sujkowska, of Young Mrs. Greeley
     Published also under title: Sukces pani Stella. Warszawa, Wydaw
     nietwo współczesne.

          I. Sujkowska, Janina, tr.
                                                       37-10412
     Library of Congress   PS2972.Y6P6 1934
                                        ₍2₎   813.5

NT 0040853   DLC

Lilly
PS 3539   TARKINGTON,BOOTH,1869-1946
.A7 P26   Partly a woman-hater. The love log of a
          (coast) wise sailor.
               (In Redbook Magazine. New York. 29.3 cm.
          vol.60,no.4 (Feb.1933),p.25-29)

               Russo & Sullivan, A bibl. of Booth Tark-
          ington, p. 263.
               From the library of J. K. Lilly.

          I. Title. II. Redbook Magazine,vol.60,no.4
          (Feb.1933). III. Provenance: Lilly,J.K.

NT 0040854   InU

Tarkington, Booth, 1869-1946.
En penningfurste; roman... Övers. från engelskan av Elin Palmgren... Stockholm, P.A. Norstedt & Söners förlag [1928]
396 p. 20 cm.

Trans. of The plutocrat.

NT 0040855 NjP

Tarkington, Booth, 1869-1946.
Penrod, by Booth Tarkington; illustrated by Gordon
Grant. Garden City, N. Y., Doubleday, Page & company,
1914.
6 p. l., 3-345, ₁1₎ p. incl. front., illus. 19½ cm

I. Title.

PZ3.T175Pe   14—5820

PPL PWcS
NjP ViU OO PPLas PHC PBm PP TxU KEmT MB CU-S PHC
WaS WaWW ICU CoU OKentU NN MB OClW OEac OClJC MH
NT 0040856 DLC ViU DCU OrPR Or MtBuM MtU OrP WaSp

Lilly
PS 3539
.A7 P4
1914
TARKINGTON, BOOTH,1869-1946
Penrod. By Booth Tarkington...Illustrated
by Gordon Grant. Garden City, New York,
Doubleday, Page & Company, 1914.
5 p.l., 345, ₁1₎ p. illus. 18.8 cm.

First editon, second state. Russo,
p. 29-33 Number viii omitted from page; page
19, line 23 has word spelled sence.
Lacks illustrated, cream-colored dust
jacket.
Bound in blue mesh cloth with white

lettering. In green cloth case.
From the J. K. Lilly library.

I. Grant, Gordon, 1875-1962, illus. II. Title.

NT 0040858 InU

Rare
PS
2972
P41
1914a
Tarkington, Booth, 1869-1946.
Penrod, by Booth Tarkington. Illus-
trated by Gordon Grant. Garden City,
N. Y., Doubleday, Page & Company, 1914.
₁6₎ l., 3-345, ₁1₎ p. front., illus. 19cm.

First edition, state 3.

NT 0040859 NIC

Tarkington, Booth i.e. Newton Booth, 1869-1946.
Penrod (by Booth Tarkington;) illustrated by
Gordon Grant. Garden City, New York, Doubleday,Page
& company c 1914. (royalty ed.)

NT 0040860 OClW

O'Hegarty
B1632
Department of Special Collections
Tarkington, Booth, 1869-1946.
Penrod. London, Hodder and Stoughton
c1914₎

NT 0040861 KU

Tarkington, Booth, 1869-1946.
Penrod, by Booth Tarkington. NY, Council on Books in
Wartime, 1914.
288 p. 10 x 14 cm. (Armed Services editions,
C-70)

Printed in double columns.

I. Title.
₁Full name: Newton Booth Tarkington₎

NT 0040862 NjP ViU

PS2972
.P45
1914
Tarkington, Booth, 1869-1946.
Penrod. Illustrated by Gordon Grant. New
York, Grosset & Dunlap [c1914]
306 p. illus. 21cm.
"A Thrushwood book."

I. Title.
Full name: Newton Booth Tarkington.

NT 0040863 MB KU MoU TxCM CU

370.002
T187p
IN:
curr
Tarkington, Booth, 1869-1946.
Penrod, by Booth Tarkington.
Illustrated by Gordon Grant. New York,
Grosset & Dunlap [1914]
345p. front.,illus. 19cm.

NT 0040864 IEN MB MiU PU PG1B PWcS MH TxU OClW

PS2972
P4
1914a
Tarkington, Booth, 1869-1946.
Penrod. Illustrated by Gordon Grant.
New York, Grosset & Dunlap [c1914]
345, 11p. illus. 20cm.

Includes bibliographical sketch of the
author by Asa Don Dickinson (11p. at end).

1. Tarkington, Booth, 1869-1946. I. Dickinson, Asa Don, 1876- II. Title.

NT 0040865 IaU CLSU InU TxU

Tarkington, Booth.   C2-T
Penrod; illustrated by Gordon Grant. Garden City, N. Y.:
Doubleday, Page, and Co., 1915. 5 p.l., 345 p. illus. 12°.

NT 0040866 NN TxCM WaTU ViU OClW CoU IEN

Tarkington, Booth, 1869-
Penrod, by Booth Tarkington. Illustrated by Gordon Grant.
Garden City, N. Y.: Doubleday, Page & Co., 1915. 6 p.l., 3-345,
15 p. illus. ₁8. ed.₎ 12°.

60. thousand.
Appended: "Booth Tarkington," by A. D. Dickinson, p. 1-10.
Bibliography, p. 12-15.

1. Fiction (American). 2. Grant, Gordon, illustrator. 3. Dickinson,
Asa Don. 4. Title.
N. Y. P. L.   February 5, 1916.

NT 0040867 NN

Tarkington, Booth, 1869-
Penrod, by Booth Tarkington; illustrated by Gordon
Grant. Garden City, New York, Doubleday, Page &
company, 1916.
6 p. l., 3-345, ₁5₎ p. incl. front., illus., facsims. 19½cm.
"Booth Tarkington, a gentleman from Indiana ... by Asa Don Dickinson," p. 1-11 at end.
"Bibliography" and "List of published works";
p. 12-15 at end.

NT 0040868 ViU MiU

Tarkington, Booth, 1869-
Penrod, by Booth Tarkington. Illustrated by Gordon
Grant. New York, Grosset & Dunlap ₁1916₎
5 p. l., 3-345 p. front., illus. 19½cm.
Illustrated t.-p.

I. Title.
₁Full name: Newton Booth Tarkington₎

Library of Congress   PZ3.T175Pe 2

             21—13946

NT 0040869 DLC MsSM CaBVa IdU

Tarkington, Booth, 1869-1946.
Penrod. New York, C. Scribner's Sons, 1916
[c1914]
345 p. illus.

NT 0040870 OClU MoU

Tarkington, Booth, 1869-
Penrod, by Booth Tarkington; illustrated by Gordon
Grant. Garden City, New York, Doubleday, Page &
company, 1918.
6 p. l., 3-345, 11 p. incl. front., illus., facsims. 19½ᶜᵐ.
"Booth Tarkington, a gentleman from Indiana ... by Asa Don Dickinson": 11 p. at end.

1. Dickinson, Asa Don, 1876- II. Title.
₁Full name: Newton Booth Tarkington₎

Library of Congress   PZ3.T175Pe 4 19-370 Revised

NT 0040871 DLC MH

Tarkington, Booth, 1869-1946.
Penrod. Övers. av A.R.E. Stockholm, Åhlén
& Åkerlunds förlags a.-b. [1918]
238 p. 19 cm.

Presentation copy to Howard S. Fisher with
inscription by the author.

NT 0040872 NjP

---

*AC9
T1747
914pg
Tarkington, Booth, 1869-1946.
Penrod, by Booth Tarkington. Illustrated by
Gordon Grant.
Garden City,New York,Doubleday,Page & company,
1919.
6p.l., 3-345, [1]p.incl.front.,illus. 18.5cm.
Title vignette.
Original brown limp leather; top edges gilt.
Inscribed: Inscribed most gratefully, for
Henry C. Quinby. Booth Tarkington, New York,
December, 1919.

NT 0040873 MH

Tarkington, Booth, 1869-1946.
Penrod by Booth Tarkington. New York,
Charles Scribner's sons, 1919.

NT 0040874 PPLas NCD

Tarkington, Booth, 1869-1946.
Penrod ... Illus. by Gordon Grant. New York,
Doubleday, Page & company, 1919.

NT 0040875 PU

Tarkington, Booth, 1869-1946.
Penrod, by Booth Tarkington; illustrated by Gordon
Grant. Garden City, N. Y., Doubleday, Page & company,
1920.
5 p. l., 3-345, ₁1₎ p. front., illus. 19½ᶜᵐ.
Lettered on cover: Royalty edition.

I. Title.
₁Full name: Newton Booth Tarkington₎

Library of Congress   PZ3.T175Pe 6 22-16015

NT 0040876 DLC MtBuM OClW

Tarkington, Booth, 1869-1946.
Penrod. New York, C. Scribner's sons, 1921.

345 p. front., illus. 19.5 cm.

NT 0040877 MH

Tarkington, Booth, 1869- Penrod.

Rose, Edward Everett, 1862-
Penrod; a comedy in four acts, adapted for the stage from
Booth Tarkington's Penrod stories, by Edward E. Rose ...
New York, S. French; [etc., etc.] [1921.]

Tarkington, Booth, 1869-1946.
Penrod. Garden City, New York, Doubleday,
1922, c1914.
345 p. (Seawood ed.)

NT 0040879 PP PU

Tarkington, Booth, 1869-1946.
Penrod, by Booth Tarkington; illustrated by Gordon
Grant. Garden City, N. Y., Doubleday, Page & company,
1922.
6 p. l., 3-345 p. incl. front., illus. 19¼ cm.

I. Title. *Full name: Newton Booth Tarkington.*

PZ3.T175Pe 8 24—20477

NT 0040880 DLC OrMonO Wa OC1C

Tarkington, Booth i.e. Newton Booth
Penrod. N.Y. Doubleday, Page, 1925, c14.
345p. front. illus.

NT 0040881 OC1Ur PPD

Tarkington, Booth, 1869-1946.
Penrod. Illustrated by Gordon Grant. Garden City,
Doubleday, Page, 1926.

345 p. illus.

NT 0040882 MH-Lm OWorP

TARKINGTON, Booth, 1869-1946.
Penrod. Garden City, N.Y., Doubleday, Doran &
Company, Inc., 1928.

Illustr.

NT 0040883 MH

Tarkington, Booth, 1869-1946.
Penrod. Trad.: Saint-Just Péquart, dessins
d'Y. Bosc. Paris, Librairie Stock, 1930.
281, [1] p. illus. 19 cm. (Collection Maïa.
Sér. B, 13)

NT 0040884 NjP

Tarkington, Booth, 1869-1946.
... Penrod. One-by-one ed. Garden City, N. Y., Doubleday, Doran & company, inc., 1935.
6 p. l., [3]-345 p. incl. front., illus. 20 cm.

I. Title. *Full name: Newton Booth Tarkington.*

PZ3.T175Pe 20 35—17776

NT 0040885 DLC

PZ27
T17P4
1936
Tarkington, Booth, 1869-1946.
Penrod. Illustrated by Gordon Grant.
New York, Grosset & Dunlap [1936?]
5 p. l., 306 p. illus. 24ᵐ
Illustrated t.p. and lining-paper.
Yellow cloth, lettered in red; top
edges stained red.
Presentation inscription for Philip
von Blon [from his mother]

I. Grant, Gordon, 1875- illus.
II. Title. 8 + 1

NT 0040886 CSt

(Ex)
3952
.75
.368
1939
Tarkington, Booth, 1869-1946.
Penrod, by Booth Tarkington.

Hodder & Stoughton [1939] London
316 p. front. 20 cm.

7.ed.

NT 0040887 NjP

PS
2972
P41g
Tarkington, Booth, 1869-
... Penrod. Illustrated by Gordon
Grant ... New York, Grosset & Dunlap
[1946?c1914]
6 p. l., 3-306p. illus. 21cm.
"A Thrushwood book."

[Full name: Newton Booth Tarkington]

NT 0040888 NRU

Tarkington, Booth, 1869-1946.
Penrod. A school ed., by Lou P. Bunce. New York,
Globe Book Co. [1954]
271 p. illus. 21 cm.

I. Title. *Full name: Newton Booth Tarkington.*

PZ3.T175.Pe23 54-2676 ‡

NT 0040889 DLC

Tarkington, Booth, 1869-1946.
Penrod; en fortaelling om en dreng af hans
hund. Overs. af David Grünbaum. København, V.
Pios boghandel, 1924.
228 p. illus. 20 cm.

Presentation copy to Howard S. Fisher with
inscription by the author.

NT 0040890 NjP

Tarkington, Booth, 1869-
...Penrod...suomentanut Väinö Nyman. [1924]

NT 0040891 OC1

Tarkington, Booth, 1869-1946.
Penrod and Sam. New York, Grosset &
Dunlap, n.d.
356 p. 18.5 cm.

NT 0040892 PPLas

Tarkington, Booth, 1869-1946.
Penrod and Sam. Grosset [c1910]
356 p.

NT 0040893 PWcS

Tarkington, Booth, 1869-1946.
Penrod & Sam. New York, Grosset [c1914-16]
356 p.

NT 0040894 PU

Tarkington, Booth, 1869-1946.
Penrod and Sam, by Booth Tarkington ... illustrated by
Worth Brehm. Garden City, N. Y., Doubleday, Page &
company, 1916.
ix, 356 p. front., plates. 19½ cm.

I. Title.
PZ3.T175Pen 16—22263
————Copy 2. PS2972.P45 1916

WaSpG WaSp MH OU OC1W
FTaSU TxU MU PBa PP PU NNC WaSp IdU WaS OrP IdB
NT 0040895 DLC NN MB NjP OEac NNR KU IEN NcU ViU

Rare
PS
2972
P412
1916a
Tarkington, Booth, 1869-1946.
Penrod and Sam, by Booth Tarkington
... Illustrated by Worth Brehm. Garden
City, N. Y., Doubleday, Page & Company,
1916.
ix, 356 p. front., plates. 20cm.

First edition, status unestablished.

NT 0040896 NIC InU

Lilly
PS 3539
.A7 P28
TARKINGTON, BOOTH, 1869-1946
Penrod and Sam. By Booth Tarkington...
Illustrated by Worth Brehm... Garden City,
New York, Doubleday, Page & Co., 1916.
ix, 356 p. front., plates. 18.7 cm.

First edition; first state of binding.
Russo, p. 41-44. Bound in light green cloth
with black-stamped imprint at foot of spine.
Lacks off-white dust jacket with repro-
duction of frontispiece.
From the J. K. Lilly library.
I. Brehm, Worth, 1883-1928, illus. II. Title

NT 0040897 InU NIC

Tarkington, Booth, 1869-1946.
Penrod and Sam ... illustrated by Worth
Brehm. New York, c1916.
356 p.

NT 0040898 PHC PPPH-I PPL

813
T174ps
1946rl
TARKINGTON, BOOTH, 1869-1946.
Penrod and Sam. New York, Grosset & Dunlap
[c1916]
iv, 249p. 20cm.

NT 0040899 TxU WaPS OO OU MH OrCS WaChenE

PZ
3
T175
Pen4
Tarkington, Booth, 1869-1946.
Penrod and Sam. New York, Grosset &
Dunlap [c1916]
249p. 20cm. (A Thrushwood book)

NT 0040900 NBuC

Tarkington, Booth, 1869-1946.
. Penrod and Sam. Illustrated by Worth Brehm, and with scenes from the photoplay ... New York, Grosset & Dunlap [c1916]
356 p. plates. 20cm.

NT 0040901   NNC IEN CaOTP CaBVa NcD MtU Or

(Ex)
3952
.75
.371
1918

Tarkington, Booth, 1869-1946.
Penrod and Sam, by Booth Tarkington . Paris, L.Conard, 1918.
295 p. 16 cm. (Standard collection of British and American authors, 112)

i. Title.   [Full name: Newton Booth Tarkington]

NT 0040902   NjP

Tarkington, Booth, 1869-1946.
Penrod and Sam, by Booth Tarkington ... Illustrated by Worth Brehm. New York, Grosset & Dunlap [1918]
5 p. l., 3-356 p. front., plates. 19½ cm.

i. Title.

PZ3.T175Pen 3   20—15606

NT 0040903   DLC PRosC PPLas OC1JC GAuA ViU

Tarkington, Booth, 1869-
Penrod and Sam, by Booth Tarkington ... illustrated by Worth Brehm. Garden City, N. Y., Doubleday, Page & company, 1920.
5 p. l., 3-356 p., 1 l. front. 19 cm.
On cover: Royalty edition.

i. Title.
     Full name: Newton Booth Tarkington.

PZ3.T175Pen 5   22—16008

NT 0040904   DLC PPT PPD

Tarkington, Booth, 1869-1946.
Penrod & Sam. Garden City, New York, Doubleday, 1922, c1916.
356 p. (Seawood ed.)

NT 0040905   PP

Tarkington, Newton Booth.   48.166=Z.F.2gt 4
Penrod and Sam. By Booth Tarkington.
Garden City, N. Y. Doubleday, Page & Co. 1924. Plates. 19 cm.

N640 — T.r.

NT 0040906   MB MiU

Tarkington, Booth i.e. Newton Booth
Penrod and Sam. N.Y. Doubleday. Page,1925,c14-16.
356p.

NT 0040907   OC1Ur

Tarkington, Booth, 1869-1946.
Penrod & Sam. 1926.
356 p.

NT 0040908   PPFr

813
T17pe
1930

Tarkington, Booth, 1869-1946.
Penrod and Sam ... New York, Grosset & Dunlap [193-?]
356p.

"Copyright 1914 ... 1916."

NT 0040909   IU

Lilly
Library
PS 3539
.A7 P28
1931

TARKINGTON,BOOTH,1869-1946
Penrod and Sam. By Booth Tarkington ... Illustrated by Worth Brehm ... New York, Grosset & Dunlap [1931]
5 p.l., [3]-356, [2] p. front., plates. 18.8 cm.

Russo, p. 42. Plates are scenes from First National's photoplay.
Publisher's advertisement: [2] p. at end.

Bound in green cloth with black lettering on front and spine.
From the J.K. Lilly library.

NT 0040911   InU

813
T17pe
1943

Tarkington, Booth, 1869-1946.
Penrod and Sam ... New York, Grosset & Dunlap [1943?]
356p.

NT 0040912   IU

Tarkington, Booth, 1869-1946.
Penrod and Sam. Illustrated by Gordon Grant. Garden City, N. Y., Junior Deluxe Editions [195-]
220 p. illus. 22 cm.

i. Title.
     Full name: Newton Booth Tarkington.

PZ7.T1657Pe   57-41976 ‡

NT 0040913   DLC

Tarkington, Booth, 1869-
Penrod : his complete story ... by Booth Tarkington; illustrated by Gordon Grant. Garden City, N. Y., Doubleday, Doran & company, inc., 1931.
xii, 590 p. incl. illus., plates. col. front., col. plates. 23½ᶜᵐ.
Illustrated t.-p. and lining-papers.
"First edition."
Contents.—pt. 1. Penrod.—pt. 2. Penrod and Sam.—pt. 3. Penrod Jashber.
i. Grant, Gordon, 1875- illus. ii. Title. iii. Title: Penrod and Sam. iv. Title: Penrod Jashber.
     [Full name: Newton Booth Tarkington]

Library of Congress   31—28239
———— Copy 2.   PZ3.T175Pep

NT 0040914   InU NjP OC1 OEac OOxM MH MB ViU FTaSU IaU PPD PPFr DLC NN KEmT OrStbM IdPI Or WaSp WaT TxU

TARKINGTON,Booth,1869-
Penrod;his complete story:Penrod,Penrod and Sam,Penrod Jashber. Illustrated by Gordon Grant. New York,Doubleday,Doran & Co.,Inc.,1938,cop.1931].
24 cm. pp.xii,590. Colored plates,and other illustr.
Illustration on title-page.
Illustrated end-papers.

NT 0040915   MH

(Ex)
3952
.75
.368
1939
.2

Tarkington, Booth, 1869-1946.
Penrod : his complete story ... by Booth Tarkington; illustrated by Gordon Grant. Garden City, N. Y., Doubleday, Doran & company, inc., 1931. 1939.
xii, 590 p. incl. illus., plates (part col.). 24 cm.
Contents.—pt. 1. Penrod.—pt. 2. Penrod and Sam.—pt. 3. Penrod Jashber.
i. Grant, Gordon, 1875- illus. ii. Title. iii. Title: Penrod and Sam. iv. Title: Penrod Jashber.
     [Full name: Newton Booth Tarkington]

NT 0040916   NjP

(Ex)
3952
.75
.368
1943

Tarkington, Booth, 1869- 1946.
Penrod : his complete story ... by Booth Tarkington; illustrated by Gordon Grant. Garden City, N. Y., Doubleday, Doran & company, inc., 1943.
xii, 590 p. incl. illus., plates. col. front., col. plates. 23½ᶜᵐ.
Illustrated t.-p. and lining-papers.
Contents.—pt. 1. Penrod.—pt. 2. Penrod and Sam.—pt. 3. Penrod Jashber.
i. Grant, Gordon, 1875- illus. ii. Title. iii. Title: Penrod and Sam. iv. Title: Penrod Jashber.
     [Full name: Newton Booth Tarkington]

NT 0040917   NjP

PS2972
.P4
1945

Tarkington, Booth, 1869-1946.
Penrod : his complete story ... by Booth Tarkington: illustrated by Gordon Grant. Garden City, N. Y., Doubleday, Doran & company, inc., 1945, ᶜ1931.
xii, 590 p. incl. illus., plates. col. front., col. plates. 23½ cm.
Illustrated t.-p. and lining-papers.
Contents.—pt. 1. Penrod.—pt. 2. Penrod and Sam.—pt. 3. Penrod Jashber.

NT 0040918   OrPS

961
T187
penr
1931
Educ.
Library

Tarkington, Booth, 1869-
Penrod : his complete story ... by Booth Tarkington; illustrated by Gordon Grant. Garden City, N. Y., Doubleday, 1946,c1931.
xii, 590 p. incl. illus., plates. col. front., col. plates. 23½ᶜᵐ.
Illustrated t.-p. and lining-papers.
Contents.—pt. 1. Penrod.—pt. 2. Penrod and Sam.—pt. 3. Penrod Jashber.
i. Grant, Gordon, 1875- illus. ii. Title. iii. Title: Penrod and Sam. iv. Title: Penrod Jashber.
     [Full name: Newton Booth Tarkington]

NT 0040919   CU WaS NcU WaU LU MiU

Rare
PS
2972
P413
1929

Tarkington, Booth, 1869-1946.
... Penrod Jashber, by Booth Tarkington. Illustrations by Gordon Grant. Garden City, N. Y., Doubleday, Doran & Company, Inc., 1929.
x p., [1] l., 321 p. incl. front., illus. 20cm.

At head of title: A new Penrod book.

NT 0040920   NIC MoU CaOTP NN MB MU KU

Tarkington, Booth, 1869-1946.
... Penrod Jashber, by Booth Tarkington, illustrations by Gordon Grant. Garden City, N. Y., Doubleday, Doran & company, inc., 1929.
x p., 1 l., 321 p. incl. front., illus. 19½ cm.
At head of title: The new Penrod book.
"First edition."

i. Title.

PZ3.T175Per   29—18939

WaS OrCS CaBVa NBuU InU WaSpG TxU WaSp
NcD InU TNJ IEN NjR OU FTaSU CoU NNC CU-S WaT Wa
NT 0040921   DLC PHC PU PP ViU MH OEac OCU OO MiU

PS2972
P48x
1929
   Tarkington, Booth, 1869-1946.
     Penrod Jashber. New York, Grosset &
   Dunlap [c1929]
     x, 245 p. illus. 20 cm.

NT   0040922   GAuA

PZ3
.T175Per3 Tarkington, Booth, 1869-1946.
     Penrod Jashber. New York, Grosset &
   Dunlap [c1929]
     245 p. 20 cm. (A Thrushwood book)

NT   0040923   MB

370.002 Tarkington, Booth, 1869-1946.
T187pen   Penrod Jashber, by Booth Tarkington,
    illus. by Gordon Grant. New York,
IN: Grosset & Dunlap [1929]
curr   x, 321 p. illus. 20 cm.
    At head of title: The new Penrod book.

NT   0040924   IEN

    Tarkington, Booth, 1869-1946.
      Penrod og Sam. Autoriseret overs. af Ingeborg
    Vollquartz. København, V. Pios boghandel, 1924.
      230 p. 21 cm.

      Trans. of Penrod and Sam.

NT   0040925   NjP

    Tarkington, Booth, 1869-1946.
      Penrod som opdager...Overs. af Palline Bagge
    København [etc., etc.] Jespersen of Pios [1918?]
      192 p. 21 cm.

      Trans. of Penrod Jashber.

NT   0040926   NjP

J
PZ90
.G7T25
   Tarkington, Booth, 1869-1946.
     Penront; mythistorēma. Metaphrasē: Natas Kok-
   kolē. [Athēnai] Ikaros [1953]
     202 p. 19 cm.

NT   0040927   MB

    Tarkington, Booth, 1869-1946.
      The plutocrat; a novel by Booth Tarkington. Garden
   City, N. Y., Doubleday, Page & company, 1927.
      4 p. l., 543 p. 19½ cm.

      I. Title.
                  Full name: Newton Booth Tarkington.

      PZ3.T175Pl   27—26118

    WaTU KyLx CoU KU PHC PRosC PSC WaWW MU MtU
    IdPI CaBVa WaS Wa ViU MoU KyU KEmT WaT IdU OrP WaE
    NjP MB NN ViU CaBVaU OrCS NIC MoU CoU NBuU OrPR Or
NT   0040928   DLC PBa OCl OEac OO ViU OClW CSmH MiU MH

813
T174pl
   TARKINGTON, BOOTH, 1869-1946.
     The plutocrat; a novel by Booth Tarkington.
   Garden City, N.Y., Doubleday, Page & company,
   1927.
     4p l.,543p. 19½cm.

     "First edition."

NT   0040929   TxU InU NcD

    Tarkington, Booth, 1869-1946.
      The plutocrat, a novel. Leipzig, B. Tauchnitz, 1927.
      338 p. 17 cm. (Collection of British authors. Tauchnitz ed.,
   v. 4774)

      I. Title.
                  Full name: Newton Booth Tarkington.

      PS2972.P55   1927   60-58478

NT   0040930   DLC NIC NN

    Tarkington, Booth, 1869-1946
      The plutocrat; a novel by Booth Tarkington.   London: W.
   Heinemann, Ltd., 1927.   543 p.   12°.

   459199A. 1. Fiction, American.   2. Title.   April 18, 1930
   N. Y. P. L.

NT   0040931   NN NjP

813
T17pl
1927
   Tarkington, Newton Booth, 1869-
     The plutocrat, a novel by Booth Tarkington
   New York, Grosset & Dunlap [1927]
     543p.

NT   0040932   IU ODW TU

AC-L   Tarkington, Booth, 1869-1946.
T174pl   The plutocrat; a novel by Booth Tarkington.   Toronto,
1927c S.B. Gundy; Garden City, N.Y., Doubleday, Page &
   company, 1927.
     4 p. l., 543 p. 19½cm.

     "First edition."
     "Printed in the United States."
     Errors in running heads corrected. Mis-
   spelling on p.438, line 2, "hed."

NT   0040933   TxU

    Tarkington, Booth, 1869-1946.
      The plutocrat. Garden City, New York,
   Doubleday, 1928, c1927.
      543 p. (Seawood ed.)

NT 0040934   PP

813
T17pl
1929
   Tarkington, Booth, 1869-
     The plutocrat, a novel ...   New York, Grosset
   & Dunlap [1929]
     543p.

NT   0040935   IU NjP

    Tarkington, Booth, 1869-1946.
      Plutokrat. Přel. W.F. Waller. Praha, Sfinx
   Janda, 1931.
      313, [1] p. 19 cm. (Nové cíle, 381)

      Trans. of The plutocrat.
      On book jacket: "Kniha 53" and "První díl".

NT   0040936   NjP

    Tarkington, Booth,1869-1946.
      Plutokrata. 2v. [1928]

NT   0040937   OCl

    Tarkington, Booth, 1869-1946.
      Plutokrata; powieść. [Przekład... Zofji Popław-
   skiej] Warszawa, Bibljoteka Groszowa [1928]
      2 v. 19 cm.

      Ex copy 2: "Printed in Poland" stamped on wrap-
   per.

NT   0040938   NjP

Rare
PS
2972
P93
1933
   Tarkington, Booth, 1869-1946.
     Presenting Lily Mars. Garden City,
   N. Y., Doubleday, Doran and Company,
   Inc., 1933.
     [4,]1., 321 p. 21cm.

NT   0040939   NIC OKentU TxCM NjP GAuA

    Tarkington, Booth, 1869-1946.
      ... Presenting Lily Mars. Garden City, N. Y., Doubleday,
   Doran and company, inc., 1933.
      4 p. l., 321 p. 20½ cm.
      Illustrated lining-papers.
      "First edition "

      I. Title.

      PZ3.T175Pr   33—21388

    IdPI NjP WaSp OrP Or WaS IdB WaTU
    PPLas PU OEac OCU OO OCl MB MH IEN VtU CU-S WaSpG
NT   0040940   DLC NN TxU InU CaOTP WaE ViU PHC PSt

PS
2972
P7
1934
   Tarkington, Booth, 1869-
     Presenting Lily Mars / by Booth Tarkington.
   -- London : Heinemann, 1934.
     327 p. ; 19 cm.

NT   0040941   CU-S NjP

    Tarkington, Booth, 1869-
      ... Presenting Lily Mars. New York, Triangle books [1943]
      4 p. l., 321 p. 19½ cm.
      First published in 1932.

      I. Title. II. Title: Lily Mars.
                [*Full name:* Newton Booth Tarkington]
                           43-9930
      Library of Congress   PZ3.T175Pr 3

NT   0040942   DLC

    Tarkington, Booth, 1869-
      Presenting Lily Mars ... New York, N. Y. [1944]
      259 p. 16ᵐ. (New Avon library. [55])

      I. Title. II. Title: Lily Mars.   [*Full name:* Newton Booth Tarkington]
                                              44-51244
                                         Brief cataloging
      Library of Congress   PZ3.T175Pr 5

NT   0040943   DLC NjP TxU

    Tarkington, Booth, 1869-1946, ed. and illus.
      Princeton University Bric-a-Brac
      see under title

Rare
PS
2972
A761
Tarkington, Booth, 1869-1946.
    Prologue to Aromatic Aaron Burr.
₍Kennebunkport, Me.?₎ 1938.
    ₍16₎ p. 22cm.

    A playbill of the Garrick Players,
Booth Tarkington Drama Festival, August
1-14, 1938, Kennebunkport, Me.

NT 0040945   NIC

---

*
PS2972
.J6
1896
Tarkington, Booth, 1869-1946.

    The proud lover ₍poem₎
(In John-a-Dreams. New York. 26cm. Vol. 1,
no. 2 (Aug. 1896) p. 58)
Published under the pseudonymn Cecil Woodford.

    I. Title. II. John-a-Dreams.

NT 0040946   ViU

Rare
PS
2972
P97+
Tarkington, Booth, 1869-1946.
    The public is not an ass. ₍Indianapo-
lis?, 1945?₎
    ₍6₎ l. 28cm.

    Carbon copy of a typewritten statement
read before the Republican Postwar Policy
Association, May 12, 1945.

NT 0040947   NIC

---

*
PS2972
.P401
1946
Tarkington, Booth, 1869-1946.

    Radioteatro de America. "Penrod".
Recorded: 7/30/46; broadcast: 8/8/46.
₍n. p., 1946₎
    31 p. 28cm.
Reproduced from typescript.
"The National Broadcasting Company presents ...
highlights from one of the great novels of Booth
Tarkington."

    I. Radioteatro de America.

NT 0040948   ViU

Tarkington, Booth, 1869-
    ...Raharuhtinas (The plutocrat); romani; suomentanut
Aune Suomalainen. ₍1939₎

NT 0040949   OC1

Tarkington, Booth, 1869-1946.
    Ramsey Milholland. Illustrated by Gordon
Grant. Toronto, S.R.Gundy [19-]

    218 p. plates, illus. 19.5 cm.

NT 0040950   MH

Tarkington, Booth, 1869-1946.
    Ramsey Milholland. New York, Grosset,
c1918-19.
    218 p.

NT 0040951   PU

B812T17
V5
1919
Tarkington, Booth, 1869-1946.
    Ramsey Milholland. Illustrated by Gordon
Grant. Garden City, N. Y., Doubleday, Page,
1919.
    218 p. illus. 20cm.

    First edition with author's inscription
tipped in. Caricature of Booth Tarkington
pasted on fly-leaf.

NT 0040952   NNC InU

Tarkington, Booth, 1869-1946.
    Ramsey Milholland. New York, 1919.

NT 0040953   PPL PPCCH

Tarkington, Booth, 1869-1946.
    Ramsey Milholland, by Booth Tarkington; illustrated by
Gordon Grant. Garden City, New York, Doubleday, Page &
company, 1919.
    5 p. l., 3-218 p., 1 l. front., illus., plates. 19½ cm.

    I. Title.

    PZ3.T175Ra   19—13300

    NIC PLF PBa PRosC PHC LU MB GAuA
    OrP WaT Wa TxU ViU NN MH OC1 OEac MiU OC1W OO OU
NT 0040954   DLC WaWW Or WaSp IdB OrCS   WaChenE

813.5 T13.7
Tarkington, Booth, 1869-1946.
    Ramsey Milholland. Illustrated by Gordon
Grant. New York, Grosset & Dunlap [1919]
    218 p. illus.

NT 0040955   CaOTP

Tarkington, Booth, 1869-1946.
    Ramsey Milholland, by Booth Tarkington; illustrated by
Gordon Grant. Garden City, N. Y., Doubleday, Page & com-
pany, 1920.
    5 p. l., 3-218 p., 1 l. front., plates. 19½ cm.
On cover: Royalty edition.

    I. Title.
                              Full name: Newton Booth Tarkington.
    PZ3.T175Ra 3   22—16007

NT 0040956   DLC ViU OC1W WaSp

PS
2972
R34
1920
Tarkington, Booth, 1869-1946
    Ramsey Milholland. Illustrated by Gordon
Grant. Toronto, S.B. Gundy ₍1920?₎
    218 p. illus.

NT 0040957   CaOTU

PS2972
.R3
1921
Tarkington, Booth, 1869-1946.

    Ramsey Milholland. Illustrated by Gordon
Grant. New York, Grosset & Dunlap ₍1921₎
    218 p. illus. 20cm.

    I. Title.
        Full name: Newton Booth Tarkington.

NT 0040958   ViU

Tarkington, Booth, 1869-1946.
    Ramsey Milholland.   Garden City,
New York, Doubleday, 1922, c1919.
    218 p.   (Seawood ed.)

NT 0040959   PP CaBVaU

Tarkington, Booth
    Ramsey Milholland. N.Y.
Doubleday, Page & co., 1925.
Illus.

NT 0040960   OC1Ur

Tarkington, Booth, 1869-1946.
    ... O romance de duas vidas; tradução de Tina Canabrava.
São Paulo, Editora universitária ₍194-₎
    360 p. 21½ᵐ.

    I. Canabrava, Tina, tr. II. Title.   *Translation of* Kate Fenni-
gate.   ₍Full name: Newton Booth Tarkington₎

    PS2972.K3P6   47-33147

NT 0040961   DLC

Tarkington, Booth, 1869-1946.
    ... Rumbin galleries; illustrated by Ritchie Cooper. Gar-
den City, N. Y., Doubleday, Doran & co., inc., 1937.
    5 p. l., 305 p. plates. 21 cm.
    "First edition."

    I. Title.

    PZ3.T175Ru   37—28787

    TxU IdPI
    WaTU WaT WaSpG OrU OrCS PPL PPA PU NIC OO
    NcD OKentU TNJ FTaSU InU WaS Wa IdB WaE CaBVa Or
NT 0040962   DLC ViU OC KU KyU KyLx OCU OEac OC1 MH

PS2972
.R8
1937a
Tarkington, Booth, 1869-1946.

    Rumbin galleries. Illustrated by Ritchie
Cooper. New York, The Literary Guild of
America, 1937.
    305 p. illus. 21cm.

    OC1Ur CLSU LU
NT 0040963   ViU MsSM IEN MH PU CoU WaWW PSC NIC

Tarkington, Booth, 1869-1946.
    Rumbin galleries.
                                            London,
    Toronto, W. Heinemann ₍1938₎
    4 p. l., 279 p. 20 cm.
    "First edition."

NT 0040964   NjP

Lilly
PS 3539
.A7 848
TARKINGTON, BOOTH, 1869-1946.
    The serious moment. (In The Flower
Mission Magazine for November, 1899,
p. 6-13. Indianapolis, 1899.   36.3 cm.)

    Russo & Sullivan, A bibl. of Booth
Tarkington, p. 157.
    Includes contribution (four poems) by
Meredith Nicholson.
    On front cover and title page: Once
a year.
    From the library of J.K. Lilly.

    In original printed wrappers; in
green cloth folder.

    I. Nicholson, Meredith, 1866-1947.
    II. Title.

NT 0040966   InU MH

Tarkington, Booth
　　Seventeen. N.Y., Crosset & Dunlap, 1915.
　　329p.

NT　0040967　　OC1W

Tarkington, Booth, 1869-1946.
　　Seventeen. New York, Grosset & Dunlap [*1916]
　　249 p.　22 cm.　(A Thrushwood book)

　　I. Title.
　　　　　　　　　　　　Full name: Newton Booth Tarkington.

PZ3.T175Se 2　　　　　　　　　　　61-1710 ‡

NT　0040968　　FTaSU CLSU LU CoGuW
　　　　　　　　DLC IdPI TxU KEmT NcU MB CaOTP NBuU NcD

Lilly
PS 3539　　TARKINGTON,BOOTH,1869-1946
.A7 S49　　... Seventeen ... Paris, Louis Conard,
1917a　　1917.
　　　　　280 p.　small 8vo (15.4 cm.)　(Standard
　　　　　collection of British and American authors,
　　　　　v. 72)

　　　　　At head of title: author's name. Series
　　　　　information from half-title. On front cover:
　　　　　Copyright secured for Continental circulation
　　　　　only.

　　　　　Russo & Sullivan, A bibl. of Booth
　　　　　Tarkington, p. 37.
　　　　　From the library of J. K. Lilly.
　　　　　Bound in original printed limp cloth.

NT　0040970　　InU

Tarkington, Booth, 1869-1946.
　　Seventeen; ...
　　New York and London, [1922]

PZ3
.T175
Se
6

NT　0040971　　DLC

Tarkington, Booth, 1869-1946.
　　... Seventeen. New York, French, c1924.
　　　111 p.　19 cm.

NT　0040972　　PPT

Tarkington, Booth, 1869-1946.
　　... Seventeen. New York, Harper C1932]
　　　303 p.　19 cm.　(Harper's modern
　　classics)

NT　0040973　　PPT

813　　Tarkington,　　Booth, 1869-1946.
T17s　　Seventeen ... Frontispiece by Arthur William
1940　　Brown. New York, Grosset & Dunlap [1940]
　　　328p.

　　　"Copyright 1915, 1916."

NT　0040974　　IU

PS2972
.S4　　Tarkington, Booth, 1869-1946.
1946　　　Seventeen. New York, Grosset & Dunlap,
　　　[1946? c1916]
　　　249 p.　22 cm.　(A Thrushwood book)

　　I. Title.
　　　　　　　　　　Full name: Newton Booth Tarkington

NT　0040975　　MB

Tarkington, Booth, 1869-1946.
　　Seventeen. New York, Grosset & Dunlap [1947?,
　　c1916]
　　3 p.ℓ., 249 p.　21 cm.　(Thrushwood books)

NT　0040976　　NjP

Tarkington, Booth, 1869-1946.
　　Seventeen; a musical comedy
　　see under Kent, Walter, 1911-

*Tarkington, Booth, 1869-

Stange, Hugh Stanislaus.
　　Booth Tarkington's Seventeen, a play of youth and love and
　　summertime, in four acts, by Hugh Stanislaus Stange and
　　Stannard Mears, in collaboration with Stuart Walker ... New
　　York, S. French; [etc., etc.] *1924.

PS2972
.S43　　Tarkington, Booth, 1869-
1915　　　Seventeen; a tale of youth and summer time.
　　　London, Hodder and Stoughton [1915]
　　　328 p.　illus.　20cm.

NT　0040979　　ScCleU

PZ3　　Tarkington, Booth, 1869-1946.
T175　　Seventeen; a tale of youth and summer time and
Se 9　　the Baxter family especially William, by Booth
　　　Tarkington.　New York, Grosset and Dunlap
　　　Publisher, [1915,1916]
　　　328 p.　front., plate. 19 cm.

　　I. Title.
　　　　　　　　　　Full name : Newton Booth
　　　　　　　　　　Tarkington.

NT　0040980　　NcRS PPL PHC PU PPT PP

Tarkington, Booth, 1869-1946.　　　　　2-T
　　Seventeen; a tale of youth and summer time and the Baxter
family, especially William.　New York: Harper & Bros. [cop.
1915-16.]　329 p.　pl. (some col'd.)　12°.

NT　0040981　　NN NcU

Tarkington, Booth, 1869-1946.
　Seventeen; a tale of youth and summer time and the Baxter
family, especially William.

　　　London, Hodder and Stoughton [1916]
　　　320 p.　20 cm.

　　I. Title.
　　　　　　　　　　[Full name: Newton Booth Tarkington]

NT　0040982　　NjP

*
PS2972
.S4　　Tarkington, Booth, 1869-1946.
1916a
　　　Seventeen; a tale of youth and summer time
　　　and the Baxter family, especially William.
　　　Illustrated by Arthur William Brown. New
　　　York, Grosset & Dunlap [1916]
　　　5 p. l., 328, [1] p. plates.　20cm.

　　　I. Title.　Full name: Newton Booth Tarkington.

NT　0040983　　ViU LU IEN NcD

UGL
PS　　Tarkington, Booth, 1869-1946.
2972　　　Seventeen: a tale of youth and summer
S3　　　time and the Baxter family especially
1916　　　William. New York, Harper & Bros. [c1916]
　　　329 p.　19 cm.

NT　0040984　　NBuU CoU

Tarkington, Booth, 1869-1946.
　　Seventeen; a tale of youth and summer time and the
　　Baxter family, especially William, by Booth Tarkington
　　... New York and London, Harper & brothers [1916]
　　6 p. l., 328, [1] p. front., plates (part double) 19 cm.

　　I. Title.
　　　　　　　　　　　[Full name: Newton Booth Tarkington]

　　Library of Congress　　PZ3.T175Se　　16—6604

　　　OO OU OC1 NN PSC PRosC
　　WaE WaS TxU MeB MB LU NIC NjP MH MiU ViU OC1W ODW
NT　0040985　　DLC PU PP WaSp IdB WaTU OrP Or OrPS IdU

Lilly
Library
PS 3539　　TARKINGTON, BOOTH, 1869-1946.
.A7 S49　　　Seventeen. A tale of youth and summer
　　　time and the Baxter family especially William
　　　... Illustrated. New York and London, Har-
　　　per & Brothers [1916]
　　　6 p.ℓ., 328, [1] p.　front., 11 plates
　　　(part double)　8vo (18.5 cm.)

　　　First edition, cloth-bound copy; Russo &
　　　Sullivan, p. 36-40. Binding in presumed ear-
　　　lier style with gilt lettering and decoration.

NT　0040986　　InU

Lilly
Library
PS 3539　　TARKINGTON, BOOTH, 1869-1946
.A7 S49　　　Seventeen ... New York and London,
1917　　　Harper & Brothers [1917]
　　　6 p.ℓ., 328, [1] p.　front., 11 plates
　　　8vo (18.5 cm.)

　　　Not first edition. Code A-R (Jan. 1917,
　　　according to Boutell) on copyright page.
　　　Incomplete: lacks dust jacket.
　　　Bound in original light red cloth, covers
　　　soiled.
　　　From the library of J. K. Lilly, with his
　　　bookplate.

NT　0040987　　InU

(Ex)
3952　　Tarkington, Booth, 1869-1946.
.75　　　... Seventeen; a tale of youth and summer time and the
.385　　Baxter family, especially William, by Booth Tarkington.
1917　　Paris, L. Conard, 1917.
　　　280 p.　17 cm.　(Standard collection of British
　　　and American authors, 72)

　　　Imperfect: 7-8 wanting, p.9 mutilated.

NT　0040988　　NjP

Tarkington, Booth, 1869–
    Seventeen; a tale of youth and summer time and the **Baxter** family, especially William, by Booth Tarkington. **Illustrated** by Arthur William Brown. New York, Grosset & Dunlap ₁1918₎
    5 p. l., 328, ₁1₎ p. front., plates. 19¾ᶜᵐ.

    I. Title.
                                    ₁Full name: Newton Booth Tarkington₎

    Library of Congress   PZ3.T175Se 3
                                              21—13948

        OC1C OC1JC
NT 0040989   DLC OrAshS WaSpG CaBVa Wa PV TxU ViU

Tarkington, Booth, 1869–1946.
    Seventeen, a tale of youth & summer time & the Baxter family especially William.   Garden City, Doubleday, 1922 [c1915-16]
    358 p.

NT 0040990   PU PP

AC–L   Tarkington, Booth, 1869–1946.
T174se   Seventeen; a tale of youth and summer time and the
1930   Baxter family, especially William, by Booth Tarkington. Illustrated by Arthur William Brown. New York, Grosset & Dunlap ₁1930, c1916₎
        4 p. l. 328, ₁1₎ p. front., plates. (part double) 19½ᶜᵐ.
        "Published by arrangement with Harper & brothers."
        Code date of printing on verso of t.-p.: D–E [i.e. April, 1930]   ₁Full name: Newton Booth Tarkington₎

        Publisher's advertisements (₍12₎p.) bound in at end.
        Page 235, third from last line, "in" for "it." Cf. Russo and Sullivan, p.37.

        I. Title. Br.: Payne Collection.

NT 0040992   TxU

Tarkington, Booth, 1869–1946.
    Seventeen; a tale of youth and summer time and the Baxter family, especially William, by Booth Tarkington; illustrated by Edwin Tunis. New York and London, Harper & brothers, 1932.
    3 p. l., v–x p., 1 l., 288 p. col. front., 1 illus., plates. 23½ cm.

    I. Tunis, Edwin, 1897–   illus. II. Title.
                                    ₁Full name: Newton Booth Tarkington₎
                                              32—25850

    Library of Congress   PZ3.T175Se 10

NT 0040993   DLC OrMonO OrCS OrPR MB OKentU NcRS NjP

Tarkington, Booth, 1869–1946.
    ... Seventeen; a tale of youth and summer time and the Baxter family, especially William, by Booth Tarkington; edited by Mabel Dodge Holmes ... New York and London, Harper & brothers, 1932.
    xiv p., 1 l., 303 p. front., plates. 19 cm. (Harper's modern classics)

    I. Holmes, Mabel Dodge, 1883–   ed. II. Title.
                                    Full name: Newton Booth Tarkington.

    PZ3.T175Se 9
                                              32—11118

NT 0040994   DLC NjP

813   Tarkington,   Booth, 1869–*1946*
T17s   Seventeen; a tale of youth and summer time
1939   and the Baxter family, especially William ...
        New York, Grosset & Dunlap ₍1939?₎
        328p.

        "Copyright 1915, 1916."

NT 0040995   IU

PS   Tarkington, Booth, 1869–1946.
2973   Seventeen; a tale of youth and summer
S4   time and the Baxter family, especially
1944   William. Edited by Mabel Dodge Holmes.
        New York, Harper [c1944]
in   xii, 288 p. 21cm. (Harper's modern
College   classics)

        I. Holmes, Mabel Dodge, 1883–   ed.
        II. Title.

NT 0040996   CoU NIC

PS   Tarkington, Booth, 1869–
2972   ... Seventeen; a tale of youth and summer time and the
.S5   Baxter family, especially William, by Booth Tarkington;
1944   edited by Mabel Dodge Holmes ... New York and London,
        Harper & brothers, ₁1944?₎
        xiv p., 1 l., 303 p. front., plates. 19ᶜᵐ. (Harper's modern classics)

NT 0040997   MiU AU TxU Vi

Za   Tarkington, Booth, 1869–1946.
T175   Seventeen; a tale of youth and summer time
916sd   and the Baxter family especially William. [By]
        Booth Tarkington. New York, Bantam books[1945].
        254p. 16½cm. (Bantam books, 17)
        "Bantam edition published November, 1945."

NT 0040998   CtY NjP

Rare   Tarkington, Booth, 1869–1946.
PS   She was right once.
2972
S53   (In O. Henry memorial award prize
        stories of 1932. New York, 1932. 21cm.
        p. ₍243₎–268)

NT 0040999   NIC

Rare   Tarkington, Booth, 1869–1946.
PS   The show piece. Introduction by
2972   Susanah Tarkington. Garden City, N. Y.,
S55   Doubleday & Company, Inc., 1947.
1947a   x p., ₍1₎ l., 212 p. 20cm.

        Advance sheets before binding.

NT 0041000   NIC

Tarkington, Booth, 1869–1946.
    ... The show piece; introduction by Susanah Tarkington. Garden City, N. Y., Doubleday & company, inc., 1947.
    x p., 1 l., 212 p. 20½ᶜᵐ.

    "First edition."
    A condensed version appeared in Hearst's International Cosmopolitan for December 1946.
    I. Title.
                                    ₁Full name: Newton Booth Tarkington₎
    PZ3.T175Sh
                                              47—1180

                NcD OC1 ICU MH PWcS PSt PIm PP ViU KU MB TxU InU
NT 0041001   DLC WaSp WaT OKentU OrP Or CaBVa Or CLSU

Tarkington, Booth, 1869–
    ... Siedemnasta wiosna ... Warszawa, Bibljoteka groszowa ₍1937?₎
    2 v. in 1. 19ᶜᵐ.
    "Przekład autoryzowany J. Sujkowskiej."

    I. Sujkowska, Janina, tr. II. Title.   *Translation of Seventeen.*
                                              40–38920
    Library of Congress   PS2972.S4P6
                                              813.5

NT 0041002   DLC

Tarkington, Booth, 1869–1946.
    Sjutton år; roman. Övers. av Ulla Ell. Stockholm, Wahlström & Widstrand [1927]
    238 p. 20 cm.

NT 0041003   NjP

N   Tarkington, Booth, 1869–1946.
7598   Some old portraits; a book about art and human beings
T3   ₁by₎ Booth Tarkington. New York, Doubleday, Doran & co., inc., 1939.
        4 p. l., vii–xx, 249 p. ports. (part col.) 26 cm.

NT 0041004   NBuC ViU CU

Tarkington, Booth, 1869–1946.
    Some old portraits; a book about art and human beings ₁by₎ Booth Tarkington. New York, Doubleday, Doran & co., inc., 1939.
    4 p. l., vii–xx, 249 p. ports. (part col.) 26 cm.
    Issued in case.
    Colored portrait mounted on cover.
    "This edition is limited to two hundred and forty-seven copies ... numbered and signed by the author." This copy not numbered.
    Bibliography: p. 239-249.
    1. Portraits. 2. Biography.   I. Title.
                                    Full name: Newton Booth Tarkington.

    N7598.T3   757   39—29474

            TxU WaS WaSp WaT
            NBB MH OEac OC1 OU NjP NIC OrP OrCS MelB PPFr OLak
NT 0041005   DLC WaSpG OrP Or IdU MoSW GAuA OC1SA PP

Lilly   TARKINGTON, BOOTH, 1869–1946.
PS 3539   Some old portraits. A book about art
.A7 S69 and human beings ... New York, Doubleday,
        Doran & Co. Inc., 1939.
        4 p. l., vii–xx, 249 p. ports. (part col.)
        8vo (25.3 cm.)

        Limited edition prepared before the
        first trade edition; Russo & Sullivan, Bibl.
        of Booth Tarkington, p. 112-113.
        Bibliography: p. ₍239₎–249.

        Limitation on inserted leaf before
        half-title: no. 41 of 247 copies; signed
        by the author.
        From the library of J. K. Lilly.
        Bound in original tan buckram, with
        colored reproduction pasted on front cover.
        In blue cloth slipcase.

NT 0041007   InU

Lilly   TARKINGTON, BOOTH, 1869–1946.
Library   Some old portraits. A book about art
PS 3539 and human beings ... New York, Doubleday,
.A7 S69 Doran & Co., Inc., 1939.
1939   xx, 249 p. plates (part col.)
        large 8vo (25.4 cm.)
        title printed on tinted background.

        First trade edition, issued after the
        printing of a limited edition. Russo &
        Sullivan, p. 112-113.

        Incomplete: lacks dust jacket.
        Bound in original russet cloth.
        From the collection of J.K. Lilly.

NT 0041009   InU PPA TxU PU

Tarkington, Booth, 1869–1946.
    Some old portraits; a book about art and human beings. NY, Doubleday, Doran & Co., 1939.
    249 p. plates. 26 cm.

    Ex copy 1. Presentation copy to Dr. and Mrs. Erwin Panofsky with inscription by the author.
    Ex copy 2. Presentation copy to " Big" Murray with inscription by the author.
    Ex copy 3. Presentation copy (with self-portrait) to Howard S. Fisher with inscription by the author.

    Ex copy 4. Presentation copy to Barton Carrie with inscription by the author.
    Ex copies 1-4 signed (in ms.) by the author.
    Bibliography: p. [237]-249.
    Limited ed.

NT 0041011   NjP

Rare
PS
2972
S693

Tarkington, Booth, 1869-1946.
 Some ways like Washington.

(In Post stories of 1936. Boston, 1937.
22cm. p. ₍19₎-42)

NT 0041012 NIC

Lilly
PS 3539
.A7 S72

TARKINGTON,BOOTH,1869-1946
 The son of the bead. (In the Flower
Mission Magazine for November, 1897,
p. 21-[26]. Indianapolis, 1897.
31.3 cm.).

 Russo & Sullivan, A bibl. of Booth
Tarkington, p. 157.
 Includes contributions by James Whit-
comb Riley (An old-home song) and Meredith
Nicholson (The wind patrol).
 On front cover and title page: Once a
year.

 From the library of J.K. Lilly.
 In original printed wrappers; in green
cloth folder.

 I. Riley,James Whitcomb,1849-1916--An old-
home song. II. Nicholson,Meredith,1866-
1947--The wind patrol. III. Title.

NT 0041014 InU

SPECIAL COLLECTIONS
B812T17
W3
1910

Tarkington, Booth, 1869-1946.
 The spring concert. New York, Ridgway Company ₑc1910₎
 31 p. 18cm.

NT 0041015 NNC

Rare
PS
2972
S76
1916

Tarkington, Booth, 1869-1946.
 The spring concert ₍by₎ Booth Tarkington.
New York, The Ridgway Company ₍c1916₎
 31 p. 19cm.

 H CSmH CoU
NT 0041016 NIC ICU NNC IU IEN TxU CtY CLSU InU NjP

PS
2972
S7

Tarkington, Booth, 1869-1946
 Station YYYY. New York, S. French [c1927]
 43p. illus. 19cm.

NT 0041017 WU NRU

Tarkington, Booth, 1869-
 Station YYYY, by Booth Tarkington. New York, London, D. Appleton and company, 1927.
 3 p. l., 43, ₍1₎ p. illus. (plan) 19ᵐ. (*Half-title:* Appleton short
plays, no. 19)

 I. Title.
                    ₍*Full name:* Newton Booth Tarkington₎
 Library of Congress   PS2972.S7   27-15534

 NIC OC1h OC1 OO MH NN
NT 0041018 DLC InU OrCS OrP Or WaE NjP TxU MiU ViU

PS
2972
S7
1928

Tarkington, Booth, 1869-
 Station YYYY. New York,Appleton,1928.
 44p. plan. 19cm. (Appleton short plays,
no. 19)

NT 0041019 MU

Rare
PS
2972
S82

Tarkington, Booth, 1869-1946.
 Stella Crozier, by Booth Tarkington.

(In O. Henry memorial award prize
stories of 1926. Garden City, N. Y.,
1927. 20cm. p. 245-268)

NT 0041020 NIC

Tarkington, Booth, 1869-1946.
 Die stolzen Ambersons. ₍Übers. von N. O. Scarpi₎ Zürich,
Morgarten-Verlag ₍1945₎
 362 p. 20 cm.
 Translation of The magnificent Ambersons.

 I. Title.

 PS2972.M25G4   50-44723

NT 0041021 DLC NjP

Tarkington, Booth, 1869-
 Strack selections from Booth Tarkington's stories, arranged by Lilian Holmes Strack. Boston, Walter H. Baker company, 1926.
 138 p. 19ᵐᵐ.

 1. Readers and speakers—1870-   I. Strack, Lilian Holmes.
                    ₍*Full name:* Newton Booth Tarkington₎
 Library of Congress   PZ3.T175St   26-17112

NT 0041022 DLC NjP OrCS NcD NIC OEac

Am
Ta

Tarkington, Booth, 1869-1946.
 Tarkington miscellany. ₍n.p.₎ 1916-45₎
 7 pamphlets (in portfolio) 25cm.

 Title from spine.
 Contents.- ₍no. 1₎ The ghost story. [1922]-
₍no. 2₎ The wren. 1922.- ₍no. 3₎ Clarence.
1921.- ₍no. 4₎ The spring concert. [1916]- ₍no.
5₎ Freeman, E. H. A dramatization of Monsieur
Beaucaire. [1916]- ₍no. 6₎ George Ade, one of
our own kind. 1944.- ₍no. 7₎ Young literary
Princeton fifty years ago. 1945.

NT 0041024 IEN

---

*
PS2972
.T86
1940

Tarkington, Booth, 1869-1946.
 ₍Testimonial letter₎
 (In Grumbacher, M. Wayman Adams painting a
portrait. New York. 1940? 28cm. port.)
 Advertisement for a Kodachrome silent film.

 1. Adams, Wayman, 1883-

NT 0041025 ViU

Rare
PS
2972
T37

Tarkington, Booth, 1869-1946.
 'Thea Zell, by Booth Tarkington.

(In The World's best short stories of
1926; sixteen tales selected by the editors
of the leading American magazines.
New York, c1926. 21cm. p. 13-40)

NT 0041026 NIC

Tarkington, Booth, 1869-1946.
 Three selected short novels. ₍1st ed.₎ Garden City, N. Y.,
Doubleday, 1947.
 ₍4₎ l., 3-341 p. 21 cm.
 CONTENTS.—Walterson.—Uncertain Molly Collicut.—Rennie Peddigoe.

 I. Title: Walterson. II. Title: Uncertain Molly Collicut. III. Title:
Rennie Peddigoe.
                    Full name: Newton Booth Tarkington.
 PZ3.T175Th   47-5078*
 Library of Congress

 NcD ViU CaBVa Or OrP WaE WaT
NT 0041027 DLC PU PP PPL NIC OU InU ICU MH KEmT TxU

Lilly
PS 3539
.A7 T6

TARKINGTON,BOOTH,1869-1946
 To a golf orphan. (In The Flower Mission
Magazine for November, 1898, p. 27-₍29₎.
Indianapolis, 1898. 31.3 cm.)

 Russo & Sullivan, A bibl. of Booth
Tarkington, p. 157.
 Includes verse contributions by Meredith
Nicholson.
 On front cover and title page: Mother
goose for all.

 From the library of J. K. Lilly.
 In original printed wrappers; in green
cloth folder.

 I. Nicholson,Meredith,1866-1947. II. Title.

NT 0041029 InU

PS
2972
T77b

Tarkington, Booth, 1869-1946.
 The travelers, a one-act play. Boston
₍W. H. Baker, ᶜ1927₎
 51 p. plan. 20cm. (Baker's royalty
plays)

 I. Title.
     Full name: Newton Booth Tarkington.

NT 0041030 NRU

Tarkington, Booth, 1869-
 The travelers, by Booth Tarkington. New York, London,
D. Appleton and company, 1927.
 3 p. l., 51, ₍1₎ p. illus. (plan) 19ᵐ. (*Half-title:* Appleton short
plays, no. 20)

 I. Title.
                    ₍*Full name:* Newton Booth Tarkington₎
 Library of Congress   PS2972.T65   27-15533

 OC1h OC1 NN InU IU ViU MiU
NT 0041031 DLC Or WaE TxU NjP ICN NIC OLak OEac MH

(Ex)
3952
.75
.3893
1927

Tarkington, Booth, 1869-1946.
 The travelers, by Booth Tarkington. New York, London,
S.French ₍1927₎
 3 p. l. 51 ₍1₎ p. illus. plan 19ᵐ. (*Half-title:* Appleton short
plays, no. 20)
 Presentation copy to Howard S.Fisher with inscription by the author.

 I. Title.
                    ₍*Full name:* Newton Booth Tarkington₎

NT 0041032 NjP

PS
2972
T65
1928

Tarkington, Booth, 1869-
 The travelers. New York,Appleton,1928.
 52p. plan. 19cm. (Appleton short plays,
no. 20)

NT 0041034 MU

Rare
PS
2972
T82+
Tarkington, Booth, 1869-1946.
Tribute to a man's friend. ₍A letter₎
₍Indianapolis, 1944₎
i sheet. i illus. 29cm.

This portfolio also contains Tarkington's original manuscript of the letter
and a clipping from the Los Angeles
Evening herald and express in which the
letter appeared, Tuesday, March 16, 1943.

NT 0041035 NIC

Tarkington, Booth, 1869-1946.
Tribute to man's friend... [Indianapolis? 1943]
broadside. illus. 28 x 22 cm.

NT 0041036 NjP

AP2
.L16
v.39
no.2
Tarkington, Booth, 1869-1946.
The trysting place; a farce in one act; by
Booth Tarkington. Illustrations by William
Meade Prince...
(In The Ladies' home journal. Philadelphia,
1922. 27ᵐ. vol.39, pt.2, p.3-6, 137-145)

Caption title.

NT 0041037 ICU MH

PS
2972
T87b
Tarkington, Booth, 1869-1946.
The trysting place, a farce in one act.
Boston ₍W.H.Baker, ᶜ1923₎
51p. plan. 20cm. (Baker's royalty plays)

I. Title.
Full name : Newton Booth Tarkington.

NT 0041038 NRU

Tarkington, Booth, 1869-1946.
The trysting place; a farce in one act. Boston,
Mass.; Los Angeles, Calif., Baker's Plays [c1923]
51 p. plan. 19 cm.

NT 0041039 NjP

Tarkington, Booth, 1869-1946.
The trysting place; a farce in one act, by Booth Tarkington. Cincinnati, Stewart Kidd company ₍1923₎
51 p. 19½ cm. (*Half-title:* Stewart Kidd little theatre plays, ed.
by Grace Adams, no. 4)

I. Title.

PS2972.T7   23—6892

        NIC ViU MiU PPPL InU
NT 0041040   DLC CaBVaU Or TxU NjP PU MH MB OC1 OC1h

Rare
PS
2972
T87
1923a
Tarkington, Booth, 1869-1946.
The trysting place; a farce in one act,
by Booth Tarkington. ₍New York, 1923₎
7 fold. sheets. 17 x 17cm.

NT 0041041 NIC

Tarkington, Booth, 1869-
The trysting place; a farce in one act. (In: Cohen, H. L.,
editor. The junior play book. New York ₍1923₎. 12°.
p. ₍191-₎223.)

NT 0041042 NN

812.5
T187try
Tarkington, Booth, 1869-1946.
The trysting place; a farce in one act.
New York, London, Samuel French ₍c1923₎
51p.

NT 0041043 ICarbS

*fAC9
T1747
B925g
Tarkington, Booth, 1869-
The trysting place; a farce in one act, by
Booth Tarkington.
D. Appleton and company, New York::1925::London
51p. 19cm., in case 31.5cm. (Appleton
Little theatre plays; ed. by Grace Adams, no.4)
Publisher's device on t.-p.
Original printed wrappers; [1]p. of advts. at
end; in case lettered: Booth Tarkington. Galley
proofs ...

NT 0041043-1 MH MoU

812.5 T13.3
Tarkington, Booth, 1869-1946.
The trysting place; a farce in one act.
New York, S. French [1926]
51 p.

NT 0041044 CaOTP

PS
2972
T7
1927
Tarkington, Booth, 1869-1946
The trysting place : a farce in one act
/ by Booth Tarkington. -- New York : S.
French, c1927.
51 p. ; 22 cm.

NT 0041045 WU

Tarkington, Booth, 1869-
The trysting place; a farce. (In: Tucker, S. M., editor.
Twelve one-act plays for study and production. Boston₍, cop.
1929₎. 12°. p. 53-83.)

NT 0041046 NN

TARKINGTON, Booth, 1869-
The trysting place.

(In CLARK, B.H., editor. The American scene
1930, pp. [357]-[388].)

NT 0041047 MH OC1C OC1W OO OC1 OC1h

Tarkington, Booth, 1869-1946.
The trysting place; a farce in one act.
Boston, Baker's Plays ₍c1949₎
51p. 19cm.

Acting edition.

NT 0041048 MtU IdPI OrCS

*
PS2972
.T78
1914
Tarkington, Booth, 1869-1946.
The turmoil. New York and London, Harper
& Brothers, 1914.
1 v. (v. p.) plates (part. col.) 25cm.
Detached from issues of Harper's magazine, vol.
CXXIX-CXXX "Advance copy for private distribution,
not for sale Compliments of Harper & Brothers"
(Signed)

NT 0041049 ViU

Tarkington, Booth.
The turmoil; illustrated by C. E. Chambers. ₍cop. 1914-15.₎

NT 0041050 NN

Tarkington, Booth 1869-
The turmoil; a novel by Booth Tarkington...illus-
trated by C.E. Chambers. New York, Grosset & Dunlap.
₍c1914, c1915₎.
348, ₍1₎p.

NT 0041051 MiU AU

Lilly
PS 3539
.A7 T9
2 cops.
TARKINGTON, BOOTH, 1869-1946
The turmoil ... Advance copy for private
distribution, not for sale. New York,
Harper & Brothers ᶜ1914, ᶜ1915.
₍135₎ p. front., illus.(part. col.)
8vo (24.2 cm.) (Harper's Monthly Magazine,
nos. 771-₍778₎, Aug. 1914-March 1915)

Advance issue from the Harper's Magazine
plates; Russo & Sullivan, Bibl. of Booth
Tarkington, p. 34-35.

Illustrated by C. E. Chambers.
Magazine excerpts paged irregularly
following the order of the magazine issues
and with some text of other pieces, except
for the eighth installment which was apparently preprinted without added material appearing in the magazine.
On copy 2 extensive manuscript note by

the author, on recto of front., about illus-
tration facing p. 400.
Inscribed on end paper by Harper &
Brothers.
From the library of J. K. Lilly.
Bound in original red boards with paper
label on front cover.
I. Title. II. Assoc. cd.: Tarkington, Booth,
1869-1946.

NT 0041054 InU

AC-L
T174Eha
1914a
Tarkington, Booth, 1869-1946.
The turmoil, by Booth Tarkington ... New
York and London, Harper & brothers publishers,
c1914-15.
₍133₎p. col. front., plates (part. col.)
24½cm.

Various pagings.
On front cover: Advance copy for private
distribution. Not for sale - Harper &
brothers publishers, New York and London.
Consists of sheets from the plates of

Harper's magazine, v.129-130, nos. 771-777,
Aug. 1914-Mar. 1915. Cf. Russo and Sullivan,
p.34.

I. Title. II. Harper's magazine. A.F.:
McCutcheon, George Barr, 1866-1928.

NT 0041056 TxU

Tarkington, Booth, 1869-
The turmoil, a novel, by Booth Tarkington ... illustrated by
C. E. Chambers. New York, Grosset & Dunlap ₍1915₎
3 p. l. 348, ₍1₎ p. front., plates. 20ᵐ.

I. Title.

₍*Full name:* Newton Booth Tarkington₎

Library of Congress   PZ3.T175Tu 2

                                    21-4145 Revised 2

        CoU OCU GU ViU CoGuW
        MiDW NBuU TNJ OC1W NN NjP DN MH PSt PSC PRosC PU
NT 0041057   DLC CaOTP IdPI IdB OrPR WaSpG I   TxU

Lilly
Library
TARKINGTON, BOOTH, 1869-1946
The turmoil, by Booth Tarkington ...
New York, Harper & brothers, c1915.
₍135₎ p. plates (part col.) 8vo

Various pagings.
"Advance copy for private distribution,
not for sale."
Excerpts from Harper's magazine, v. 129,
no. 771-v. 130, no. 777 (Aug.,1914-Feb.,1915)
In boards with paper label on front cover

Title page (which is front fly leaf) has
manuscript note: Compliments of Harper
and brothers.

NT 0041059 InU CSt CLSU

Tarkington, Booth, 1869-1946.
The turmoil; a novel, by Booth Tarkington ... illustrated
by C. E. Chambers. New York and London, Harper &
brothers, 1915.
4 p. l., 348, ₍1₎ p. col. front., plates, 19 cm.

I. Title.

PZ3.T175Tu   15—3643

WaS CaBVa Or Wa
OClW OO MH TxU ViU OU NIC WaTU MtU WaE OrP WaWW
NT 0041060 DLC CU-I CoU NjR NN NjP NcD OEac CU OCU

Tarkington, Booth, 1869-
The turmoil; ...
New York and London, 1915-
PZ3
.T175
Tu
4

NT 0041061 DLC

---

813   Tarkington,   Booth, 1869-
T17tu   The turmoil, a novel, by Booth Tarkington ...
1918   New York, Grosset & Dunlap ₍1918₎
348p.

NT 0041062 IU

Tarkington, Booth.   T
The turmoil. Garden City, N. Y.: Doubleday, Page & Co.,
1922. 453 p. front. 8°.

Seawood edition.

NT 0041063 NN PU PP

Tarkington, Booth, 1869-
... The turmoil, by Booth Tarkington, edited by Elizabeth
W. Baker ... and Mary V. Baker ... New York and London,
Harper & brothers ₍1929₎
xxiii p., 1 l., 363 p. front. (port.) plates. 19¼ᵐ. (Harper's modern
classics)

"Other novels of American life": p. 358-360.
"The historical and industrial background of The turmoil": p. 361-
363.
I. Baker, Elizabeth Whitemore, ed. II. Baker, Mary V., joint ed.
III. Title.
₍Full name: Newton Booth Tarkington₎
Library of Congress   PZ3.T175Tu 6   29—22142

NT 0041064 DLC OrU CoU NjP PPT ViU

Tarkington, Booth, 1869-1946.
The turmoil. Edited by Elizabeth W. Baker and Mary
V. Baker. New York, Harper ₍1943₎
273 p. 21 cm. (Harper's modern classics)

I. Title.

PZ3.T175Tu 10   60—4713 ‡

NT 0041065 DLC IdU AU FTaSU OU CoU PU

Tarkington, Booth, 1869-1946.
Två män om ett namn. Stockholm, Vårt Hems
förlag [1926]
152 p. 19 cm.

Trans. of The two Vanrevels.

NT 0041066 NjP

Tarkington, Booth, 1869-
Tweedles, a comedy by Booth Tarkington and Harry
Leon Wilson ... New York, S. French; London, S.
French, ltd., ₍1924.
112 p. plates. 19½ᶜᵐ. (On cover: French's standard library edition)

I. Wilson, Harry Leon, 1867-   joint author. II. Title.
₍Full name: Newton Booth Tarkington₎
24—12859
Library of Congress   PS2972.T8 1924

OrCS CaBVaU
NcD NIC ViU OC1 MH MB MoU Or WaE CLU IdU MsSM OrP
NT 0041067 DLC PU Wa ViU MsU CU TxU InU PPT NcC OU

₍Tarkington, Booth₎ 1869-
Two gentlemen from Indiana. ₍n.p.,
1942₎
4 l. 1 illus.
In portfolio.
Limited ed.
A letter from Booth Tarkington about
Wayman Adams, who painted the portrait of
Tarkington, reproduced in this leaflet.

1. Adams, Wayman, 1883-

NT 0041068 NjP CtY

Rare
PS
2972   Tarkington, Booth, 1869-1946.
T96   Two gentlemen from Indiana. ₍New
York, 1942₎
₍4₎ p., French fold. 14cm.

"One hundred copies printed for the
friends of Gabriel Engel, Christmas 1942."
Signed typescript reproduced in facsimile. (Copy 1 only)

NT 0041069 NIC

---

*
PS2972
.T96   Tarkington, Booth, 1869-1946.
1942
Two gentlemen from Indiana. ₍New York,
Gabriel Engel, 1942₎
folder. port. 14 x 11cm.
Port. by Wayman Adams, with testimonial letter.
"One hundred copies printed for the friends of
Gabriel Engel, Christmas, 1942."

I. Adams, Wayman, 1883-   . II. Title.

NT 0041070 ViU

---

*
PS2972
.T9   Tarkington, Booth, 1869-1946.
1902b
The two Vanrevels. Illustrations by
Henry Hutt. London, Grant Richards, 1902.
4 p. l., 351 p. plates. 20cm.

Book plate of Robert Temperley.

NT 0041071 ViU

Lilly
Library
PS 3539   TARKINGTON, BOOTH, 1869-1946
.A7 T923   The two Vanrevels ... Montreal, The
1902   Montreal News Company, Limited, 1902.
vii,₍1₎ p., ₍2₎l., 351 p. front.,
6 plates (part col.) 8vo (18.9 cm.)

Canadian issue; Russo & Sullivan, p. 11.
Imperfect?: lacking dust jacket?
Bound in original green cloth.
From the library of J. K. Lilly.

NT 0041072 InU

PS
2972   Tarkington, Booth, 1869-1946.
.T85   The two Vanrevels. New York, A.L. Burt
1902   ₍1902₎
viii,351p. illus. 20cm.

NT 0041073 OrU OU IEN

PZ3
.T175Tw3 Tarkington, Booth, 1869-1946.
The two Vanrevels. Illustrations by Henry
Hutt. New York, Grosset & Dunlap ₍c1902₎
313 p. front. 20 cm.

NT 0041074 MB

Tarkington, Booth, 1869-
The two Vanrevels, by Booth Tarkington ... illustrations
by Henry Hutt. New York, McClure, Phillips & co., 1902.
viii p., 2 l., 351 p. front. plates. 19¼ᵐ.

I. Title.
₍Full name: Newton Booth Tarkington₎
Library of Congress   PZ3.T175Tw   2—22845

OKentU CaOTP OrU OrP Or NcCU OU NBuU
MB MoSW FTaSU CSmH ICU CoU GU TNJ NmU CLSU TxU NIC
InU NcD WaWW NjP ViU OEac OC1W MiU OC1 MH NjP NN
NT 0041075 DLC ScU MdBP IdU PPL WaSp PPD PP PPT

Rare
PS
2972   Tarkington, Booth, 1869-1946.
T97   The two Vanrevels, by Booth Tarkington
1902   ... Illustrated by Henry Hutt. New York,
McClure, Phillips & Co., 1902.
viii p., ₍2₎ l., 351 p. front., plates.
20cm.

First edition, 1st state.

NT 0041076 NIC

Lilly
Library
PS 3539   TARKINGTON, BOOTH, 1869-1946
.A7 T921   The two Vanrevels ... Illustrations by
1902c   Henry Hutt. New York, McClure, Phillips
& Co., 1902.
viii p., ₍2₎ l., 351 p. front., 6 plates
(part col.) 8vo (18.8 cm.)

First edition, 3rd state of terminal ads,
earlier state of binding; Russo & Sullivan,
p. 9-12.
Imperfect: lacks integral blank

preceding half-title, lacks dust jacket.
Publisher's ads, 10 p. at end.
Bound in original green cloth, spine
badly soiled.
From the library of J. K. Lilly.

NT 0041078 InU NIC

Lilly
Library
PS 3539   TARKINGTON, BOOTH, 1869-1946
.A7 T921   The two Vanrevels ... New York,
1902e   McClure, Phillips & Co., 1902.
viii p., ₍2₎l., 351 p. front.,
6 plates (part col.) 8vo (17.8 cm.)

First edition, 5th state of terminal
ads, later state of binding; Russo & Sul-
livan, p. 9-12.
Incomplete?: lacking dust jacket?
Publisher's ads: 8 p. at end.
Bound in   original dark red cloth.

NT 0041079 InU

Lilly
Library
PS 3539   TARKINGTON,BOOTH,1869-1946
.A7 T922   The two Vanrevels ...   New York,
1902a   McClure, Phillips & Co., 1902.
viii p., ₍2₎l., 351 p.   front.,
6 plates   8vo (20 cm.)

Limited edition, issued after first
edition. Limitation, no. 753 of 500
copies numbered 500 to 1,000. Russo &
Sullivan, p. 11.
Bound in original drab boards with
label.
From the   library of J. K. Lilly,
with his book-   plate.

NT   0041080   InU NjP

Tarkington, Booth i.e. Newton Booth, 1869-
The two Vanrevels, by Booth Tarkington...illustra-
tions by Henry Hutt. New York, McClure, Phillips &
co. c1902.
Garden city, Doubleday, (Royalty ed.)

NT   0041081   OCIW

PS2972
.T9   Tarkington, Booth, 1869-1946.
1910   The two Vanrevels. New York, A. L.
Burt ₍191-₎
351 p. front. 20cm.

NT   0041082   ViU

PS
2972   Tarkington, Booth, 1869-1946.
T93   The two Vanrevels. Illustrations by Henry
1912   Hutt. Garden City, Doubleday, Page, 1912
[c1902]
viii,351 p. illus.

On spine: Royalty edition.

NT   0041083   CLU MiU

Tarkington, Booth i. e. Newton Booth, 1869-1946.
The two Vanrevels, by Booth Tarkington ... Illustrations by Henry Hutt. Garden City, New York, Doubleday, Page & company, 1913.
viii p., 1 l., 351, ₍1₎ p. front. 19½ᶜᵐ.

ɪ. Title.

Library of Congress   PZ3.T175Tw 5   20-15607

NT   0041084   DLC MB

PS2972 **Tarkington, Booth** i. e. Newton Booth, 1869-1946.
.T93   The two Vanrevels, by Booth Tarkington ...   New York,
1915   C. Scribner's sons, 1915.
₍9₎, 313, ₍1₎ p. front., plates. 20ᵐᵐ.

NT   0041085   ICU PU MB NjP AAP CoU MsU IEN

---

818   Tarkington, Booth, 1869-1946.
T174twX   The two Vanrevels, by Booth Tarkington... illustrations by Henry Hutt.   New York, Scribner's, 1916₍c1902₎
313 p. front., plates. 20 cm.

NT   0041086   LU

PS2972
.T9   Tarkington, Booth, 1869-1946.
1917   The two Vanrevels. New York, C. Scribner's Sons
1917.
313 p. illus. 20cm.

NT   0041087   ViU MH

Tarkington, Booth, 1869-1946.
The two Vanrevels, by Booth Tarkington ... illustra-
tions by Henry Hutt. Garden City, N. Y., Doubleday,
Page & company, 1920.
5 p. l., 3–313, ₍1₎ p. front. 19½ᶜᵐ.
Lettered on cover: Royalty edition.

ɪ. Title.

₍Full name₎: Newton Booth Tarkington₎

Library of Congress   PZ3.T175Tw 9   22-16006

MH NN
NT   0041088   DLC PSt Wa WaTU lCarbS TxU NIC OCIW OO

Tarkington, Booth.   T
The two Vanrevels; illustrated by Henry Hutt.   Garden
City, N. Y.: Doubleday, Page & Co., 1922.   313 p.   front.
8°.

Seawood edition.

NT   0041089   NN CaBVaU

Tarkington, Booth, 1869-
The two Vanrevels, by Booth Tarkington ...
Garden City, N. Y., Doubleday, Page & com-
pany, 1925.
4 p. l., 3–313,   19½ᶜᵐ.
On cover: Royalty edition.

NT   0041090   ViU OCIUr MH

Za   Tarkington, Booth, 1869-1946
T175   ...An unacceptable peace. [n.p., 1944]
+944U   broadside. 17x23cm.

Caption title.
"Reprinted from the February, 1944, issue
of The American Legion."
"Distributed by the Society for the Prevention of World War III, Inc."

NT   0041091   CtY ViU

Tarkington, Booth, 1869-1946.
An unacceptable peace. [NY] 1944.
broadside. 20 x 23 cm.

At head of title: Distributed by the Society for
the prevention of World War III, Inc.
"Reprinted from the February, 1944, issue of
The American Legion."
In double columns.

NT   0041092   NjP

Lilly
PS 3539   TARKINGTON,BOOTH,1869-1946
.A7 U52   Unconditional surrender--from whom?. (In
Society for the Prevention of World War III,
Inc. No. 8., March-April 1945. New York,1945.
28 cm. p. 9-10)

Russo & Sullivan, Bibl. of Booth Tarking-
ton, p. 262.
From the library of J.K. Lilly
In printed wrappers.

NT   0041093   InU

Tarkington, Booth, 1869-1946.
The vocal score of Seventeen
see under Kent, Walter, 1911-

PS   Tarkington, Booth, 1869-1946.
2972   Wanton Mally. With drawings by Joseph
W25   Simont. Garden City, N.Y., Doubleday,
1932a   Doran & company, 1932.
280 p. illus. 20cm.

NT   0041095   NIC CaOTP MoU NN

Tarkington, Booth, 1869-1946.
Wanton Mally, by Booth Tarkington; with drawings by
Joseph Simont. Garden City, N. Y., Doubleday, Doran &
company, inc., 1932.
5 p. l., 280 p. incl. 1 illus., plates. col. front. 20 cm.
Illustrated lining-papers.
"First edition."

ɪ. Title.

PZ3.T175Wan   32—28094

waS IdB
IdPI VtU InU OU OrPS KEmT TxU OKentU OrP CaBVa OrU
WaT WaSpG WaSp AAP KU MsU MoSW ViU OLak OCIh OCI
NT   0041096   DLC PSt PBa Or NcD OCIW WaSp MH MB PHC

Tarkington, Booth, 1869-1946.
Wanton Mally; a romance of England in the days
of Charles II. London, W. Heinemann, 1933.
263 p. 19 cm.

NT   0041097   NjP

Tarkington, Booth, 1869-1946.
Wanton Mally. With drawings by Joseph
Simont. New York, Grosset & Dunlap ₍1935₎
280 p. illus., col. port. 20ᶜᵐ.

I. Title   Full name: Newton Booth Tarkington.

NT   0041098   ViU

Rare
PS   Tarkington, Booth, 1869-1946.
2972   Wednesday madness. ₍n. p., 1915₎
P412   3 fold. sheets. 22cm.
1915
Part of original manuscript of Penrod
and Sam.

I. Tarkington, Booth, 1869-1946.
Penrod and Sam. II. Title.

NT   0041099   NIC

---

*
PS2972
.W46   Tarkington, Booth, 1869-1946.
1948   "Who'll be the clerk?" " I!" said the
lark: ₍New York, Lee and Gabriel Engel,
1948₎
folder. 11 x 14cm.
Remarks and limerick on the autobiography of
S. S. McClure, reprinted from McClure's, June 1914.
"One hundred copies printed for the friends of
Lee and Gabriel Engel, Christmas, 1948."

1. McClure, Samuel Sidney, 1857-1949.

NT   0041100   ViU

Tarkington, Booth, 1869-1946.
Women, by Booth Tarkington. Garden City, N. Y., Doubleday, Page & company, 1925.
ix, 415 p. 19½ cm.

ɪ. Title.

PZ3.T175Wo   25—27730

OrCS IdPI
WaT INS WaU WaSp WaS TxU KEmT WaTU OrP TNJ AAP VtU
PRosC PBa NcD PHC NIC OCI OU IdU AzU OKentU Wa Or
NT   0041101   DLC MB NN CSmH PP MiU OO OCIW OEac OCIU

Lilly
PS 3539
.A7 W87
TARKINGTON, BOOTH, 1869-1946
Women. By Booth Tarkington... Garden
City, New York, Doubleday, Page & Company,
1925.
ix, 415 p.   8vo(18.8 cm.)

First edition. Russo, p. 74-76.
Lacks pictorial colored dust jacket.
Bound in green grained cloth with gilt
stamped panel on front.
From the J. K. Lilly library.
I. Title.

NT 0041102   InU MH TxU ViU

Tarkington, Booth, 1869-1946.
Women, by Booth Tarkington. New York, Grosset
[°1925]
ix, 415 p. 19½ cm.

NT 0041103   OrPS NNC

Lilly
Library
PS 3539
.A7 W87
1925
TARKINGTON, BOOTH, 1869-1946
Women, by Booth Tarkington. Toronto,
S. B. Gundy; Garden City, N.Y., Doubleday,
Page & Co., 1925.
ix, 415 p.   18.7 cm.

First Canadian edition.
Bound in green cloth.

NT 0041104   InU

TARKINGTON, Booth, 1869-
Women. Garden City, N.Y., Doubleday, Page &
Company, 1926.

NT 0041105   MH

813
T17w
1926
Tarkington, Booth, 1869-1946.
Women. Copyright ed.   Leipzig, B. Tauchnitz,
1926.
287p. 17cm. (Tauchnitz edition. Collection
of British and American authors, v.4720)

NT 0041106   IU MH

Tarkington, Booth, 1869-1946.
Women. Garden City, New York, Doubleday,
1928, c1924-1925.
415 p.   (Seawood ed.)

NT 0041107   PP

Tarkington, Booth, 1869-1946.
The world does move, by Booth Tarkington. Garden
City, N. Y., Doubleday, Doran and company, incorporated,
1928.
4 p. l., 294 p. 20 cm.

1. U. S.—Soc. life & cust.   I. Title.

E169.T18   28—28979

PP PU
ViU MB MH OU OC1W OCU OEac NjP OO NN Wa NIC PPA
WaWW FTaSU WaSp CaBVaU Or IdPI WaTU WaT OrP AU GU
NT 0041108   DLC CoU InU TxU CaOTP OKentU OrU WaS

917.3
T174w
1929
Tarkington, Booth, 1869-1946.
The world does move.   Garden City,
N.Y., Doubleday, Doran, 1929.
294p. 20cm.

1. U.S. Social life & customs.
I. Title.

NT 0041109   KU OrPR CaOTP FTaSU

Tarkington, Booth, 1869-1946.
The world does move; an autobiographical
narrative ... London, William Heinemann, ltd.,
1929.
4 p. l., 294 p. 19 cm.

1. U.S. - Soc. life & customs.   I. Title.

NT 0041110   CtY MiU

Tarkington, Booth, 1869-1946.
The world does move.   New York, Doubleday,
Doran, 1929.

NT 0041111   PPPCPh

Tarkington, Booth, 1869-1946.
The wren; a comedy in three acts, by Booth Tarkington
... New York, S. French; [etc., etc.,] °1922.
109 p. plates. 20 cm. (On cover: French's standard library edition)

I. Title.

PS2972.W7 1922   22—20670

                                      OC1 MH PU TxU InU
NT 0041112   DLC NBuU IdU Or Wa NIC PPT NcD ViU MiU OU

Am
Ta
Tarkington, Booth, 1869-1946.
Young literary Princeton fifty years ago.
[Princeton, N. J.] 1945.
1-5p.   23cm.   (His Tarkington miscellany
[no. 7])

Detached from The Princeton University
Library chronicle, v. 7, no. 1, Nov. 1945.

NT 0041113   IEN

PS
2972
Y686
1929
HRC
NON-CIRC
Tarkington, Booth, 1869-
Young Mrs. Greeley, by Booth
Tarkington. Garden City, N. Y.,
Doubleday, Doran & company, inc., 1929.
3 p. l., 205 p. 19 cm.
Inscribed by the author.   With dust
jacket.

NT 0041114   TxU

Tarkington, Booth, 1869-1946.
Young Mrs. Greeley, by Booth Tarkington. Garden City,
N. Y., Doubleday, Doran & company, inc., 1929.
3 p. l., 205 p. 19½ cm.

I. Title.   Full name: Newton Booth Tarkington.

PZ3.T175Yo   813.5   29—12765

                                      OO
CaOTP VtU AAP WaTU WaE WaT WaS OrP TNJ ICRL OkU
OU OCU ViU MiU OEac OC1 MB NN PWcS PPLas PP MsU
NT 0041115   DLC OrU WaSp IdPI Wa Or PV PHC NcD NIC

---

*AC9
T1747
929y
Tarkington, Booth, 1869-
Young Mrs. Greeley, by Booth Tarkington.
1929, Doubleday, Doran & company, inc., Garden
City, N.Y.
3p.l., 205p. 19.5cm.
Title vignette.
"First edition."
Original tan cloth; top edges stained.

NT 0041116   MH FTaSU NjP OKentU InU TxU

813
T174y
1929
Tarkington, Booth, 1869-1946.
Young Mrs. Greeley, by Booth Tarkington
... Copyright ed.   Leipzig, B. Tauchnitz,
1929.
271,[1]p. 16cm. (Collection of British
authors, Tauchnitz edition, vol. 4891)

NT 0041117   TxU CtY NN

Za
T175
929yb
Tarkington, Booth, 1869-1946.
... Young Mrs Greeley. London, W. Heinemann
ltd. [1929]
2l., 246,[1]p. 19cm.

NT 0041118   CtY

Lilly
Library
PS 3539
.A7 Y82
TARKINGTON, BOOTH, 1869-1946
Your amiable uncle. Letters to his nephews
by Booth Tarkington. Illustrated with his
original sketches. Indianapolis, New York,
Bobbs-Merrill Company, Inc. [c1949]
6 p. l., 11-192 p. front. (port.) illus.
8vo (21.4 cm.)

"First [Hoosier] edition."
"Limited to one thousand copies of which
this is no. 673." Signed by the Three nephews:

John Jameson, Donald Jameson and Booth T.
Jameson, to whom the letters were written.
Bound in blue cloth with gilt lettering on
front and spine. Blue end papers with white
illustrations.
From the J. K. Lilly library.

NT 0041120   InU NjP

Tarkington, Booth, 1869-1946.
Your amiable uncle; letters to his nephews by Booth
Tarkington, illus. with his original sketches. [1st ed.] Indianapolis, Bobbs-Merrill Co. [1949]
192 p. illus., port. 23 cm.

I. Title.   Full name: Newton Booth Tarkington.

PS2973.A4   816.5   49—10265*

WaS CaBVa IdB WaT WaWW WaSp NIC NmLcU
ViU MoSW TU ICU PPL PP CSt GU TxU MU PU OrP OrU
NT 0041121   DLC PPFr PBm PPT KyLx MB TxU OO OC1JC Or

TARKINGTON, BOOTH, 1869-1946.
Your humble servant [by Booth Tarkington and Harry
Leon Wilson.   New York, Z. & L. Rosenfield, 1910?]
1 v. (various pagings)   28cm.

Typescript.
Produced by Charles Frohman at the Garrick theatre, New York, 3 Jan.,
1910.

1. Drama, American. 2. Drama—Promptbooks and typescripts. I. Wilson,
Harry Leon, 1867-1939, joint   author. II. Title.

NT 0041122   NN

[Tarkington, John Stevenson] 1832-1923
The auto-orphan, by John Steventon [pseud.] ... Boston, R. G. Badger [°1913]
122 p. 21½cm. $1.00.

CONTENTS.—The auto-orphan.—The boy on horseback.—A boy's sus-
picions.—Scenes of my childhood.—At grandfather's.—The preacher.—Identification.—"If a body kiss a body need a body cry."—The sick tell no tales.—
The schoolmaster.—Boy and dog.—Spare the rod and spoil the child.—As
a father pitieth his child.—The priest.—Home with my father.—The man-
hunt.—Curtain.

I. Title.

Library of Congress   PZ3.T176 A   13-22754 Revised

NT 0041123   DLC NIC InU NN

⟨Tarkington, John Stevenson⟩ 1832–1923.
The hermit of Capri, by John Steventon ⟨pseud.⟩ ...
New York and London, Harper & brothers, 1910.
3 p. l., 135, ⟨1⟩ p. front., plates. 21½ᶜᵐ. $1.25

I. Title.

Library of Congress   BL50.T3

10—8322

NT 0041124   DLC NcU NN ViU MiU OCl MB

BX
8495
T18
A3
Tarkington, Joseph, *1800–1891*.
Autobiography of Joseph Tarkington, one of
the pioneer Methodist preachers of Indiana.
With introduction by T. A. Goodwin.
Cincinnati, Curts & Jennings, 1899.
171 p. 19cm.

I. Goodwin, Thomas A   1818–1906, ed.

NT 0041125   NIC IEG OCl ICN ICU

TARKINGTON, JOSEPH, 1800–1891.
Autobiography of Rev. Joseph Tarkington, one of the
pioneer Methodist preachers of Indiana. With introd.
by Rev. T.A. Goodwin... Cincinnati, Press of Curts
& Jennings, 1899.   171 p.   4 port.(incl. front.)
19cm.

Film reproduction. Negative.
1. Country reminiscences, Clergymen's.
2. Pioneer life--U.S.--   Indiana.

NT 0041126   NN

Tarkington, Kate.
Rex goes to the rodeo. San Antonio, Naylor Co. ⟨*1955⟩
88 p. illus. 20 cm.

I. Title.

PZ7.T17Re   56–22724 ‡

NT 0041127   DLC TxU

Tzz
818
T174m
TARKINGTON, MARGARETE KATHERINE
My thoughts in prose and poetry [by] Margarete
Katherine Tarkington.   San Antonio, Tex., The
Naylor company, 1940.
3p ℓ., 43p. 20½cm.

NT 0041128   TxU

Tarkington, Newton Booth
see
Tarkington, Booth, 1869–

650.7
T17s
Tarkington, Robert N
... State university programs for preparation of
business teachers as compared with programs for
home economics, English, and social science teachers ... edited by Ann Brewington ...   ⟨Chicago?⟩
The National association of commercial teacher-
training institutions, 1939.
35, ⟨1⟩p. (National association of commercial teacher-training institutions. Bulletin
no.18)
Abstract of thesis (Ed.D.)--New York university,
1938.
Bibliographies: p.33–⟨36⟩

NT 0041130   IU OU PPT

Tarkio, Missouri. United Presbyterian Church.
Souvenir and program of the dedication...
⟨Tarkio⟩ Avalanche Prt., 1890.

NT 0041131   PPPrHi

Tarkio, Mo.   School board.
Manual...containing report 1888/89 1894/96
Tarkio, Mo., 1887–95
2 v.

NT 0041132   DHEW

Tarkio college, *Tarkio, Mo.*
... Annual catalogue ... Announcements.

Tarkio, Mo. ⟨etc.⟩
v. illus. 19½–22ᶜᵐ.
At head of title: Tarkio college bulletin ...

cA 9–1524 Unrev'd

Library of Congress   LD5271.T3

NT 0041133   DLC PPF PPPrHi NjP

Tarkio college, *Tarkio, Mo.*
Glimpses of Tarkio ... ⟨Kansas City, Mo., Press of
Hudson-Kimberly pub. co., 1899⟩
40 p. illus., ports. 19ᶜᵐ. (*On cover:* The Tarkio college phoenix,
August 1, 1899)
Blank pages at end for "Convention notes" and "Autographs."
Contents.—The landscape.—The country.—The town.—The college.—
The founder.—The moral.

1. Tarkio college, Tarkio, Mo.—Descr.   E 15–2097

Library, U. S. Bur. of   Education LD5271.T33

NT 0041134   DHEW

Tarkio Valley College and Normal Institute
see Tarkio College, Tarkio, Mo.

⟨Tarkkanen, Antti⟩
Herra tulee ja muttaa maailman; yhdeksässä luennossa
esitti Rasmatun valossa. [by] A·T· [pseud.] Waasassa,
Kirjoittajan kustantama [1898]

129 p.

NT 0041136   MH

MY42
H244
Xt17e
Tarkkanen, Matti
Eräs Afrikan profeetta William Wadé Harris.
⟨Helsinki⟩ Suomen Lähetysseura ⟨1935⟩
22 p. 19 cm.

1. Harris, William Wadé, ca.1865–1929.
2. Liberia - Missions.   I. Title. Afr

NT 0041137   CtY-D

Tarkkanen, Matti.
Nykyajan herätysliikkeet. Porvossa,
Söderström [1905]
108 p. ports.

NT 0041138   MH

Tarkkanen, Matti
Raamattu ja raittiuskysymys. 3., täydellisesti
uudistettu painos. Helsingissä, Raittiuden ystävät,
1904

62 p.

NT 0041139   MH

Tarkkanen, Matti
Raamattu ja raittiuskysymys. 4., täydellisesti
uudistettu painos. Porvoo, Söderström [1931]

83 p.

NT 0041140   MH

Tarkovski, Arseni
see
Tarkovskiĭ, Arseniĭ Aleksandrovich.

PG1418
.S95M6
Tarkovskiĭ, Arseniĭ Aleksandrovich, tr

Stijenski, Radule.
... Моя песня; перевод с сербского Арсения Тарковского,
Аркадия Штейнберга и Игоря Строганова. ⟨Москва⟩ Изда-
тельство ЦК ВЛКСМ "Молодая гвардия," 1942.

Tarkow-Naamani, Jacob
see Naamani, Jacob Tarkow.

Tarkunde, Vithal Mahadev.
The danger ahead; an analysis of Congress capitalist
alignment. ⟨Delhi⟩ Radical Democratic Party ⟨1945?⟩
7 p. 18 cm.
Cover title.

1. Indian National Congress   I. Title.

JQ298.I 5T3   55–44076

NT 0041144   DLC NN

Tarkunde, Vithal Mahadev.
Great Britain and India. ⟨Delhi⟩ Radical Democratic
Party ⟨1946?⟩
8 p. 18 cm.
Cover title.

1. Gt. Brit.—Commercial policy. 2. Gt. Brit.—Comm.—India.
3. India—Comm.—Gt. Brit.   I. Title.

HF1534 1946.T3   382   53–57163

NT 0041145   DLC NcD NN ViU

831W38
DT17
Tarlach, Hans, 1900–
... Veit Weber und seine dichtungen. Ein beitrag
zur erforschung des 15. jahrhunderts ... Greifswald, H. Adler, 1933.
115p.

Inaug.-diss.--Greifswald.
Lebenslauf.
"Literaturverzeichnis": p.⟨5⟩-8.

NT 0041146   IU MiU CtY NjP PU InU TU

Tarlan, Ali Nihad, *1898-*
　　Ali Şir Nevayi. Ali Şir Nevayi'nin beşyüzüncü doğum
yıldönümü münasebetile Üniversitede verilen konferanslar-
dan. İstanbul, Bürhaneddin Matbaası, 1942
　　22 p.　24 cm.　(İstanbul Üniversitesi neşriyatından)

　　1. 'Alī Shīr, Mīr, called al-Nawā'ī, 1441-1501.

　　PL55.U89A675　　　　　　　　　　　　N E 62-715 ‡

NT　0041147　DLC NNC

Tarlan, Ali Nihad, *1891-*
　　Divan edebiyatında muamma. İstanbul, Burhaneddin
Matbaası, 1936.
　　29 p.　24 cm.　(İstanbul Üniversitesi yayınlarından, no. 24)

　　1. Turkish literature—Hist. & crit.　2. Literary recreations.
　　ı. Title.

　　PN6377.T8T3　　　　　　　　　　　　N E 64-2970 ‡

NT　0041148　DLC ICU InU MiU

Tarlan, Ali Nihad, *1898-*
　　Divan edebiyatında tevhidler. İstanbul, Bürhaneddin
Matbaası, 1936.
　　4 v. in 1.　25 cm.　(İstanbul Üniversitesi yayımlarından, no. 24)

　　1. Turkish poetry—Hist. & crit.　ı. Title.

　　PL218.T3　　　　　　　　　　　　　61-56670

NT　0041149　DLC NNC MH CLU MiU

PL
218
.T3
　　Tarlan, Ali Nihad, *1898-*
　　　　Edebî san'atlar.　3 üncü basım.　İstanbul,
Yüksel Yayınevi, 1947.
　　　　88 p.

　　　　1. Turkish poetry.　2. Turkish language -
Style.　I. Title.

NT　0041150　NNC MiU

PL248
.F95
1950
Orien
Turk
　　Tarlan, Ali Nihad, *1898-*　Ed. and tr.
　　Fuzuli, Mehmet, 1494-1555.
　　　　Fuzulî divanı; ¡Türkçe divan¿ Edisyon kritik ve tran-
skripsiyon. ¡Hazırlıyan¿ Ali Nihad Tarlan. İstanbul, Üçler
Basımevi, 1950-

PK6463
.F8
1950
Orien
Turk
　　Tarlan, Ali Nihad, *1898-*　Ed. and tr.
　　Fuzuli, Mehmet, 1494-1555.
　　　　Fuzulî'nin Farsça divanı. Tercümesi: Ali Nihad Tarlan.
İstanbul, Millî Eğitim Basımevi, 1950.

　　Tarlan, Ali Nihad, 1898-
　　Genceli Nizami divani, tercüme eden Ali
Nihad Tarlan
　　　　see under　Niẓāmī, Ganjavī, 1140 or 41-
1202 or 3.

PL
248
.T1
G5
　　Tarlan, Ali Nihad
　　Güneş yaprak.　¡İstanbul, Anıl Matbaası¿,
1963¿
　　132 p.

NT　0041154　NNC NN

PL248
.H33
1945
Orien
Turk
　　Tarlan, Ali Nihad, ed.
　　Hayâlî, d. 1556.
　　　　Hayâlî Bey dîvânı.　¡Hazırlıyan¿ Ali Nihat Tarlan.
İstanbul, B. Erenlar Matbaası, 1945.

　　Tarlan, Ali Nihad.
　　İran edebiyatı. İstanbul, Remzi Kitabevi ¡1944¿
　　4, 168 p.　21 cm.　(Dünya edebiyatına toplu bakışlar, 4)

　　1. Persian literature—Hist. & crit.　ı. Title.

　　PK6406.T3　　　　　　　　　　　　N E 63-1833

NT　0041156　DLC NN

　　Tarlan, Ali Nihad.
　　Metin tamiri. İstanbul, Burhaneddin Basımevi, 1937.
　　30 p.　24 cm.　(İstanbul Üniversitesi yayımlarından)
　　Seminer çalışmalarından, 1.

　　1. Turkish poetry—Hist. & crit.　2. Poetic license.　ı. Title.

　　PL220.T3　　　　　　　　　　　　N E 62-197 ‡

NT　0041157　DLC InU

PK
6483
T17m
　　Tarlan, Ali Nihat, 1898-
　　Mevlânâ Celâleddini Rûmî.　İstanbul, Varoğlu
Yayınevi [1948]
　　62 p.　plates.　(Faydalı kitap, 13)

　　1. Jalāl al-Dīn, Rūmī, Maulānā, 1207-1273.

NT　0041158　CLU

　　Tarlan, Ali Nihad, 1898-
　　Nef'înin Farsça divani tercümesi
　　　　see under　Nef'ī, d. 1634.

PL
248
S555Z5t
　　Tarlan, Ali Nihad, 1898-
　　Şeyhi divanini tetkik.　İstanbul, Sühûlet
Basımevi, 1934.
　　2 v. in 1.

　　1. Şeyhî, Yusuf Sinan, Germiyani, fl. 1400.

NT　0041160　CLU

　　Tarlan, Ali Nihad, *comp.*
　　Şiir mecmualarında XVI. ve XVII. asır divan şiiri. ¡İstan-
bul¿ 1948-49.
　　4 v. in 1.　24 cm.　(İstanbul Üniversitesi yayınlarından, no. 356)
　　At head of title: Edebiyat Fakültesi.　Türk Dili ve Edebiyatı Dalı.
　　Contents.—fasikül 1. Rahmî ve Fevrî.—fasikül 2. Ubeydî, Aşkî,
Şem'î, İşretî.—fasikül 3. Ulvî, Me'âlî, Nihanî, Feyzî, Katibî.—fasikül
4. Revani, Hayreti, Haveri, Ahi, Peyami, Sani.

　　1. Turkish poetry—History and criticism.　ı. Title.

　　PL218.T35　　　　　　　　　　　N E 63-114

NT　NNC
　　0041161　DLC MH NjP ICU MiU CU CLU OCl MiU ICU

NK1120
.K4T3
　　Tarlanov, Mamed.
　　Kerimov, Liatif Guseĭn ogly, 1906-
　　　　Лятиф Керимов.　Автор текста М. Тарланов.　Москва,
Советский художник, 1955.

DG975
.R2T2
　　Tarlazzi, Antonio.
　　　　Appendice ai Monumenti ravennati dei secoli di mezzo
del conte Marco Fantuzzi, pubblicata a cura del canonico
Antonio Tarlazzi... Ravenna, Stab. tip. di G. Angeletti,
1869-76.
　　　　2 v.　33cm. (Half-title: Monumenti istorici pub. dalla
R. Deputazione di storia patria per le provincie della
Romagna, ser. 11)

　　　　1. Ravenna—Hist.

NT　0041163　ICU MdBP MH

　　Tarlazzi, Antonio
　　　　Appendice ai Monumenti ravennati dei secoli
di mezzo del Conte Marco Fantuzzi. Ravenna,
G. Angeletti, 1872-1884.
　　　　2 v. in 4.　(Dei Monumenti istorici perti-
nenti alle provincie della Romagna.　Ser. 2.
Carte)

NT　0041164　NNC

¡TARLAZZI, Antonio, editor¿.
　　Feste ravennati nel luglio dell'anno 1857 per
la venuta e soggiorno in Ravenna del sommo pontefice Pio IX felicemente regnante.　Ravenna,
Tip. del Ven. seminario arciv., 1857.
　　1. 8°.　pp. 96.　7 plates.
　　Dedication signed: Ravenna dalla residenza
municipale: Conte Giulio commendatore Facchi-
netti Pulazzini, Francesco Donati, ¡and others¿.
　　Editor's name given on page 55.

NT　0041165　MH

274.5433 Tarlazzi, Antonio.
T175m　Memorie sacre di Ravenna in continu-
　　azione di quelle pubblicate dal ...
Girolamo Fabri.　Ravenna, 1852.
　　664p.　front. (port.) fold. pl., tables.
　　"Serie cronologica degli arcivescovi
di Ravenna": p. 503-509.

NT　0041166　IU MH

　　Tarlazzi, Antonio.
　　Statuti del comune di Ravenna
　　　　see under　Ravenna. Laws, statutes, etc.

　　Tarlé, Antoine *de.*
　　　　...L'avenir économique de la Macédoine.　Notice de M. de
Tarlé... ¡Lyon: A. Rey¿ 1917.　30 p.　4°.
　　Cover-title.
　　At head of title: Chambre de Commerce de Lyon (séance du 12 juillet 1917).

　　1. Economic history. Macedonia.　　　　2. Lyons, France. Chambre de
Commerce.
N. Y. P. L.　　　　　　　　　　　　　　　　December 23, 1920.

NT　0041168　NN

　　Tarle, Antoine *de*
　　Comment l'Allemagne prepare la guerre.
1913.
　　No. 33334

NT　0041169　DNW

Tarle, Antoine de
   ... Les conseils d'ouvriers.
Revue des deux mondes, 15 fevrier, 1923,
t. 13: (883)-909.

NT   0041170   DL

D
560
T35
    Tarlé, Antoine *de.*
    D'Alsace a la Cerna. Notes et impressions
d'un officier de l'armée d'orient (Octobre 1915
Août, 1916) [Par] Jean Saison [pseud.] Paris,
Plon,1918..
    325p. maps. 19cm.

    1. European War, 1914-1918 - Balkan Pennin-
sula. I. Title.

NT   0041171   MU NN CSt-H MH IU NjP

Tarle, Antoine de.
   ... D'Alsace à la Cerna; notes et impressions
d'un officier de l'armée d'Orient (octobre 1915 - aou
aout 1916)... Paris: Plon-Nourrit et Cie., 1918.
3 p. l., 325 p., 1 l. maps.
3. ed.

NT   0041172   NN PU DNW

Tarle, Antoine de.
   La defense de l'empire Britannique,
L'organisation militaire et navale de
l'Australia. Par Capitaine A.De Tarle.
24987

NT   0041173   DNW

Tarlé, Antoine de.
   Murat. Paris, Chapelot, 1914.

   166 p.
   "Les grands hommes de guerre."

NT   0041174   MH CU OrU

Tarlé, Antoine de.
   ... La préparation de la lutte économique par l'Allemagne. Paris, Payot & cᵉ, 1919.
   3 p. L, ₍9₎–284 p. 19ᶜᵐ. (*On cover:* Bibliothèque politique et économique)   fr. 4.50

   1. Germany—Econ. condit. 2. Germany—Comm. 3. European war, 1914-
1918—Economic aspects—Germany. ɪ. Title. ɪɪ. Title: Lutte économique
par l'Allemagne.
   Library of Congress   HC286.2.T3   19—12651

NT   0041175   DLC CSt-H ICJ

Tarlé, Antoine de.
   ...La préparation industrielle de la guerre en France et en
Allemagne. La métallurgie. Paris: Chapelot, 1922. 53 p.
8°.

   1. Metallurgy, France. 2. Metal-
and statistics, France. 4. Coal.—
N.Y.P.L.   lurgy, Germany. 3. Coal.—Trade
            Trade and statistics, Germany.
            March 13, 1923.

NT   0041176   NN DNW

Tarlé, Antoine Paulin Marie Alexandre de
    see   Tarle, Antoine de.

Tarlé, E.
   *Étude sur les conditions sanitaires de la
grande pêche maritime. Paris, 1938.
   36 p. 8°.

NT   0041178   DNLM CtY

Tarle, Evgeniĭ Viktorovich, 1874-*1955.*
   [Achtzehnhundert zwölf] 1812: Russland und das Schicksal
Europas. Berlin, Rütten & Loening [1951]

   461 p. illus.

NT   0041179   MH OC1W

Tarle, Evgeniĭ Viktorovich, 1874-*1955.*
   Адмирал Ушаков на Средиземном море, 1798-1800 гг.
Москва, Воен. изд-во, 1948.
   289 p. port., fold. maps. 21 cm.
   At head of title: Институт истории Академии наук Союза ССР.
   Bibliography : p. 283–₍285₎

   1. Ushakov, Fedor Fedorovich, 1745-1817. 2. Russia — History,
Naval. 3. Russia—Hist.—Paul ɪ, 1796-1801.   *Title transliterated:* Admiral Ushakov
                                       na Sredizemnom more.
    DK187.T3   51–35400

NT   0041180   DLC NcD UU

D1
.A5
    Tarle, Evgeniĭ Viktorovich, 1874-*1955,* joint ed.

    Анналы; журнал всеобщей истории. № 1–
Петербург, 1922–

HC205 **Tarle, Evgeniĭ Viktorovich, 1874**
.T2
   ... Le blocus continental et le royaume d'Italie; la situation économique de l'Italie sous Napoléon Iᵉʳ, d'après des
documents inédits. Paris, F. Alcan, 1928.
   xii, 377, ₍1₎ p. 23ᶜᵐ. (*On cover:* Bibliothèque d'histoire contemporaine)
   At head of title: Eugène Tarlé.

   1. Continental system of Napoleon. 2. Italy—Econ. condit.

MiU
NT   0041182   ICU TU InU IU CU MA MeB OC1W ICN NN NjP

Tarle, Evgeniĭ Viktorovich, 1874-
   ... Le blocus continental et le royaume d'Italie; la situation
économique de l'Italie sous Napoléon Iᵉʳ d'après des documents
inédits. Nouv. éd. Paris, F. Alcan, 1931.
   xii, 377 p., 1 l. 23ᶜᵐ. (*On cover:* Bibliothèque d'histoire contemporaine)
   At head of title: Eugène Tarlé.

   1. Continental system of Napoleon. 2. Italy—Econ. condit. ɪ.Title.
   Library of Congress   HC305.T3 1931   32–8007
                                               330.945

NT   0041183   DLC CaBVaU NBuU FU NR NcU OU WaU MoU NcD

Tarle, Evgeniĭ Viktorovich, 1874-
   Bonaparte, by Eugene Tarlé; translated from the Russian
by John Cournos. New York, Knight publications, 1937.
   431, ₍1₎ p. 24½ᶜᵐ.
   Maps on lining-papers.

   1. Napoléon ɪ, emperor of the French, 1769-1821. ɪ. Cournos, John,
1881–   tr. ɪɪ. Title.
                                        37–5291
   Library of Congress   DC203.T2
   ——— Copy 2.
   Copyright A 105240   923.144

    OrP WaS OrU OrPR
    NN MB ViU OO OC1 OC1W AAP CU-I CU MoU NBuU NSyU Wa
NT   0041184   DLC PPD ICU PU RPA PU-PSW NcC NcRS OCU OU

Tarle, Evgeniĭ Viktorovich, 1874-
   Der Brand von Moskau. [Aus 1812. Russland
und das Schicksal Europas. Autorisierte
Übersetzung aus dem Russischen. Berlin] Rütten
& Loening [1951]
   105 p.

NT   0041185   OC1W

Tarle, Evgeniĭ Viktorovich, 1874-
   ... La campagne de Russie, 1812. Traduit du russe ...
₍Lagny-sur-Marne₎ Gallimard ₍ᶜ1941₎
   2 p. l., ₍7₎–270 p., 1 l. incl. front. (map) 22¾ᵐ.
   At head of title: E. Tarle.
   Bibliographical foot-notes.

   1. Napoléon ɪ—Invasion of Russia, 1812. ɪ. Title. ***Trans-**
lation of Нашествие Наполеона на Россию, 1812 год. (transliterated:
Nashestvie Napoleona na Rossiĭu, 1812 god)
                                             A 42–698
   Harvard univ. Library
   for Library of Congress

NT   0041186   MH OU DLC MWAC

947.07
T148nIs
1950
    Tarle, Evgeniĭ Viktorovich, 1874-1955.
    La campagne de Russie, 1812. Traduit du
russe par Marc Slonim. 11.ed. ₍Lagny sur
Marne₎ Gallimard ₍c1950₎
    332p. illus. (La suite des temps, 2)

    Translation of: Nashestvie Napoleona na
Rossiiu, 1812 god.
    Bibliographical footnotes.

    1. Napoléon I - Invasion of Russia, 1812.
I. Title.

NT   0041187   FTaSU CU ScU NcD

Tarle, Evgeniĭ Viktorovich, 1874-1955.
   Чесменский бой и первая русская экспедиция в Архи-
пелаг, 1769-1774. Москва, 1945.
   100, ₍1₎ p. 22 cm.
   At head of title: Академия наук Союза ССР.
   Bibliography : p. 107–₍110₎

   1. Çeşme, Battle of, 1770. ɪ. Title.
                     Title transliterated: Chesmenskiĭ boĭ i pervaîa
                              russkaîa ékspediîsiîa v Arkhipelag.
    DR553.T3   51–36817

NT   0041188   DLC CSt OU LU OrU

    Tarle, Evgeniĭ Viktorovich, 1874-   joint ed.

    Akademiîa nauk SSSR. *Institut istorii.*
    ...Двадцать пять лет исторической науки в СССР; под
    редакцией академика Волгина В. П., академика Тарле
    Е. В. и члена-корреспондента Академии наук СССР
    Панкратовой А. М. Москва, Ленинград, Издательство
    Академии наук Союза ССР, 1942.

Tarle, Evgeniĭ Viktorovich, 1874- *1955,*
   ... Две отечественные войны. Москва, Ленинград, Государственное военно-морское издательство НКВМФ Союза
ССР, 1941.
   70, ₍1₎ p. 17 x 13ᵐ.
   At head of title: Академик Е. В. Тарле.
   "Настоящая брошюра является сокращенным изложением моей
книги 'Нашествие Наполеона на Россию'."—p. 4, foot-note.
   Published also under title: Отечественная война 1812 года и разгром
империи Наполеона.
   1. Napoléon ɪ—Invasion of Russia, 1812. ɪ. Title.   *Title trans-*
literated: Dve otechestvennye voĭny.
                                       43–22371
   Library of Congress   DC235.T33 1941 a

NT   0041190   DLC

Tarle, Evgeniĭ Viktorovich, 1874-1955.
   Экспедиция адмирала Д. Н. Сенявина в Средиземное
море, 1805-1807. Москва, Воен. изд-во, 1954.
   165 p. illus. 21 cm.

   1. Senîavin, Dmitriĭ Nikolaevich, 1763-1831. 2. Russia—History,
Naval. 3. Napoléon ɪ, Emperor of the French, 1769-1821—German
and Austrian Campaign, 1805. 4. Napoléon ɪ, Emperor of the French,
1769-1821—Campaigns of 1806-1807. ɪ. Title.
               Title transliterated: Ėkspediîsiîa admirala
                         D. N. Senîavina v Sredizemnoe more.
    DK194.T37   68–130109 ‡

NT   0041191   DLC KU

Tarle, Evgeniĭ Viktorovich, 1874– *1955.*
... Европа в эпоху империализма. 1871–1919 г.г. Москва, Ленинград, Государственное издательство, 1927.

483 p. 23½ᶜᵐ. *(On cover:* Библиотека общественных знаний)

At head of title: Академик Е. В. Тарле.
"Библиография": p. 470–478.

1. Europe—Hist.—1871–1919. 2. Imperialism. 3. European war, 1914–1918. I. Title.
Title transliterated: Evropa v ėpokhu imperializma.
44–48446

Library of Congress   D395.T3

NT   0041192   DLC

Tarle, Evgeniĭ Viktorovich, 1874–1955.
Европа в эпоху империализма, 1871–1919 гг. Изд. 2. доп. Москва, Гос. изд-во, 1928.

511 p. 23 cm.

Bibliography : p. 492–500.

1. Europe—Hist.—1871–1918. 2. Imperialism. 3. European War, 1914–1918. I. Title.
Title transliterated: Evropa v ėpokhu imperializma.

D395.T3 1928   58–54227

NT   0041193   DLC

DT1521
.A4

Tarle, Evgeniĭ Viktorovich, 1874–1955.
Fashistski falsifikatsii na istoriĭata.

Alshekh, Zhak.
Расизмъ предъ съда на науката. Съ приложение: Фашистски фалшификации на историята, отъ Е. Тарле. София ₍Култура, 1945₎

DC161
.V8

Tarle, Evgeniĭ Viktorovich, 1874– *1955,* joint ed.

Volgin, Vi͡acheslav Petrovich, 1879– *ed.*
... Французская буржуазная революция. 1789–1794. Под редакцией акад. В. П. Волгина и акад. Е. В. Тарле. Москва. Ленинград, Издательство Академии наук СССР, 1941.

Tarle, Evgeniĭ Viktorovich, 1874–
Germinal und Prairial. ₍Ins Deutsche übertragen von Hilde Koplenig. 1. Aufl.₎ Berlin, Rütten & Loening ₍1953₎

336 p. 25 cm.

1. France—Hist.—Revolution, 1795. I. Title.

DC185.9.T315   944.042   54–15191 ‡

NT   0041196   DLC FMU VtU TxU ICU

Tarle, Evgeniĭ Viktorovich, 1874–1955.
Город русской славы: Севастополь в 1854–1855 г.г. Москва, Воен. изд-во, 1954.

214 p. 21 cm.

1. Sevastopol—Siege, 1854–1855. I. Title.
Title transliterated: Gorod russkoĭ slavy.

DK215.7.T37   55–33127 ‡

NT   0041197   DLC

Tarle, Evgeniĭ Viktorovich, 1874– *1955₎*
Граф С. Ю. Витте; опыт характеристики внешней политики. Ленинград, Книжные новинки ₍1927₎

92 p. 18 cm. (Царская Россия)

1. Witte, Sergeĭ I͡Ulʹevich, graf, 1849–1915. 2. Russia—For. rel.—1894–1917.   *Title transliterated:* Graf S. IU. Vitte.

DK254.W5T3   54–45490 ‡

NT   0041198   DLC

Tarle, Evgeniĭ Viktorovich, 1874–1955.
La guerra patria y el fin del Imperio de Napoleon. [n. p., n. d.]
[209]–255 p.   24 cm.
El presente folleto es una exposicion breve de [E. Tarle] libro La invasión de Napoleon.
Reprinted from "Dialectica" [Havana, Cuba]
At head of title: E. Tarle.
1. Napoleon I - Invasion of Russia, 1812.
I. Title.

NT   0041199   OKentU

Tarle, Evgeniĭ Viktorovich, 1874–
... How Mikhail Kutuzov defeated Napoleon, by Prof. E. Tarle. ₍London, "Soviet war news" ₍1944₎
cover-title, 15, ₍1₎ p. illus. (map) 18½ᶜᵐ. (Soviet booklets. (No. 4))
Portrait on p. ₍2₎ of cover.

1. Kutuzov, Mikhail Illarionovich, svetleĭshiĭ kni͡azʹ Smolenskiĭ, 1745–1813. 2. Napoléon I—Invasion of Russia, 1812. I. Title.
A 44–1466

Harvard univ. Library
for Library of Congress

NT   0041200   MH CU

Tarle, Evgeniĭ Viktorovich, 1874–
... L'industrie dans les campagnes en France à la fin de l'ancien régime, par E. Tarlé ... Paris, É. Cornély et cᶦᵉ, 1910.

2 p. l., 84 p., 2 l. 25ᶜᵐ. (Bibliothèque d'histoire moderne ... fasc. XI)

1. France—Indus.—Hist. 2. Textile industry and fabrics—France. 3. Peasantry—France.
12–7177

Library of Congress   HC275.T2

NT   0041201   DLC NcU MiU FTaSU OClW

Tarle, Evgeniĭ Viktorovich, 1874–
... La invasión de Napoleón en Rusia—1812. Buenos Aires, Editorial Claridad ₍1942₎

393 p., 1 l. plates. 20½ᶜᵐ. (*Added t.-p.:* Biblioteca de obras famosas, v. 86)

At head of title: Eugenio Tarlé.
"Traducción directa del inglés por C. Siralceta y N. R. Ortiz Oderigo."
"Primera edición ₍argentina₎ noviembre de 1942."

1. Napoléon I—Invasion of Russia, 1812. I. Siralceta, C., tr. II. Ortiz Oderigo, N. R., joint tr. III. Title. IV. *Translation of Nashestvie Napoleona na Rossii͡u, 1812 god* (*transliterated:* Nashestvie Napoleona na Rossii͡u, 1812 god)
Library of Congress   DC235.T337   44–24702
947.07

NT   0041202   DLC MiD

Tarle, Evgeniĭ Viktorovich, 1874–1955.
₍Istorii͡a Italii v novoe vremi͡a₎
Исторія Италіи въ новое время. С.-Петербургъ, Брокгаузъ-Ефронъ, 1901.

190 p. 25 cm. (Исторія Европы по эпохамъ и странамъ въ Средніе вѣка и новое время)

Bound with the author's Исторія Италіи въ средніе вѣка. С.-Петербургъ, 1906.

1. Italy—History. I. Title. II. Series: Istorii͡a Evropy po ėpokham i stranam v Sredne vĕka i novoe vremi͡a.

DG538.T37   73–206127

NT   0041203   DLC KU

Tarle, Evgeniĭ Victorovich, 1874–1955.
₍Istorii͡a Italii v Sredne vĕka₎
Исторія Италіи въ Средніе вѣка. С.-Петербургъ, Брокгаузъ-Ефронъ, 1906.

197 p. 25 cm. (Исторія Европы по эпохамъ и странамъ въ Средніе вѣка и новое время)

Bound with the author's Исторія Италіи въ новое время. С.-Петербургъ, 1901.

I. Title. II. Series: Istorii͡a Evropy po ėpokham i stranam v Sredne vĕka i novoe vremi͡a.

DG538.T37   73–206125

NT   0041204   DLC KU

Tarle, *Evgeniĭ Viktorovich, 1874–* *1955.*
Karl XII och Poltava ₍av₎ Eugen Tarle. ₍Översättning från ryskan av Arthur Magnusson₎ Stockholm, Arbetarkulturs förlag, 1951. 75 p. 19cm. (Kultur och politik)

1. Charles XII, king of Sweden, 1682–1718. 2. Poltava, Battle of, 1709.

NT   0041205   NN

Tarle, Evgeniĭ Viktorovich, 1874– *1955.*
... Континентальная блокада ... Москва, Задруга, 1913–

v. 23½ cm.

At head of title: Е. В. Тарле.
"Источники": v. 1, p. 5–84.
Original documents in French and English: v. 1, p. 699–789.

Contents.—I. Изслѣдованія по исторіи промышленности и внѣшней торговли Франціи въ эпоху Наполеона. Съ приложеніемъ неизданныхъ документовъ.

1. Economic history. 2. Continental system of Napoleon. 3. Blockade. I. Title.   *Title transliterated:* Kontinentalʹnai͡a blokada.

HC53.2.T3   19–11490 rev

NT   0041206   DLC

Tarle, Evgeniĭ Viktorovich, 1874– *1955.*
Крымская война. Москва, Гос. военно-морское изд-во; ₍etc.₎ 1941–43.

2 v. 20 cm.

At head of title: Институт истории Академии наук СССР.
"Источники и литература": v. 1, p. 699–₍726₎; v. 2, p. 582–₍602₎

1. Crimean war, 1853–1856. I. Akademii͡a nauk SSSR. Institut istorii. II. Title.   *Title transliterated:* Krymskai͡a voĭna.

DK214.T3   48–34508

NT   0041207   DLC

Tarle, Evgeniĭ Viktorovich, 1874–
Крымская война. Москва, 1944–45.

2 v. fold. maps. 23 cm.

At head of title: Академия наук Союза ССР.
Bibliography: v. 1, p. 544–₍567₎; v. 2, p. 469–₍485₎

1. Crimean War, 1853–1856. I. Akademii͡a nauk SSSR.
Title transliterated: Krymskai͡a voĭna.

DK214.T33   A 48–1742*
Harvard Univ. Library
for Library of Congress   ₍1₎†

NT   0041208   MH DLC OrU

Tarle, Evgeniĭ Viktorovich, 1874– *1955,*
Крымская война. 2. испр. и доп. изд. Москва, 1950.

2 v. 2 fold. maps. 23 cm.

At head of title: Академия наук СССР.
Bibliography: v. 1, p. 539–₍565₎; v. 2, p. 611–₍634₎

1. Crimean War, 1853–1856.   *Title transliterated:* Krymskai͡a voĭna.

DK214.T34   50–55149

NT   0041209   DLC

Tarle, Evgeniĭ Victorovich, 1874–

DC145
.A67

Arana, A *ed. and tr.*
Marat, Robespierre, Dantón ₍por₎ Tarle ₍et al.₎ Estudios sobre la gran Revolución francesa y selección de discursos y escritos políticos, comp. y tr. por A. Arana. Montevideo, Ediciones Pueblos Unidos ₍1947₎

Tarle, Evgeniĭ Viktorovich, 1874–
1812 ₍una mille ottocento dodici₎ la campagna di Napoleone in Russia. ₍La traduzione dal russo è dovuta ad A. Lyanowa e E. Villoresi₎ Milano, A. Corticelli ₍1950₎
365 p.

Bibliographical footnotes.

NT   0041211   NNC

Tarle, Evgeniĭ Viktorovich, 1874– 1955,
... Нахимов. Москва, Ленинград, Издательство Академии
наук СССР, 1942.
127 p. incl. port. 22½ͫ.
At head of title: Академия наук Союза ССР. Акад. Е. В. Тарле.
"Работа составлена из материалов соответствующих глав моей
двухтомной монографии 'Крымская война,' подготовленной к печати."—p. 7, foot-note.
Bibliographical foot-notes.

1. Nakhimov, Pavel Stepanovich, 1803–1855.   I. Akademii͡a nauk
SSSR.   *Title transliterated:* Nakhimov.
                                                      43–40968

NT   0041212   DLC NcD

Tarle, Evgeniĭ Viktorovich, 1874– 1955,
Нахимов. Москва, Воен. изд-во, 1948.
109 p. port. 20 cm.

1. Nakhimov, Pavel Stepanovich, 1803–1855
                              Title transliterated: Nakhimov.
DK209.6.N3T3 1948   51–28943

NT   0041213   DLC

Tarle, Evgeniĭ Viktorovich, 1874–
...Napoléon. Traduit du russe avec l'autorisation de l'auteur
par Charles Steber. Paris: Payot, 1937.   489 p.   23cm.
(Bibliothèque historique.)
At head of title: ...Eugène Tarlé.

939080A. 1. Napoleon I, em–   peror of the French, 1769–1821.
I. Steber, Charles, tr.
N. Y. P. L.   July 18, 1938

NT   0041214   NN MA KU InU NcU

Tarle, Evgeniĭ Viktorovich, 1874–
... Napoleon ... Warszawa, Wydawnictwo współczesne
[1937]
3 v. illus. (double map) port. 19½ͫ.
At head of title: Profesor Eugeniusz Tarlé.
"Przekład autoryzowany dr. Heleny Winawerowej."
"Bibliografia" : [5] p. at end of v. 3.
Contents.—[1] Wschodzące słońce.—[II] U szczytu chwały.—[III]
Zmierzch.

1. Napoléon I, emperor of the French, 1769–1821.   I. Winawerowa,
Helena, tr. II. Title.
                                                      37–38362
Library of Congress   DC203.T25
                                                      923.144

NT   0041215   DLC CtY

Tarle, Evgeniĭ Viktorovich, 1874– 1955,
Наполеон. Москва, Гос. социально-экон. изд-во, 1939.
340, [2] p. 23 cm.
Errata slip inserted.
Bibliography: p. 332–[350]

1. Napoléon I, Emperor of the French, 1769–1821.
                                Title transliterated: Napoleon.
DC203.T18   53–53627

NT   0041216   DLC CaBVaU

Tarle, Evgeniĭ Viktororich, 1874–1955.
Napoleon. [Z ruského preložil Pavol Ličko.
Bratislava, Pravada, 1949.
461 p.
Slovak.

NT   0041217   OC1

Tarle, Evgeniĭ Viktorovich, 1874-
Napoleon in Russia, by Eugene Tarlé. New York, International publishers [1942?]
64 p. 18½ͫ.
Translation of an abridgment of Nashestvie Napoleona na Rossiĭĭ, 1812
god.

1. Napoléon I–Invasion of Russia, 1812.   I. Title.
                                                      43–17510
Library of Congress   DC235.T334
                                                      947.07

NT   0041218   DLC NcD WU TxU NIC MtU OrCS ICU

Tarle, Evgeniĭ Viktorovich, 1874–
... Napoleon in Russland, 1812. Zurich,
Steinberg verlag [1944]
384 p.

NT   0041219   OC1 MiD

Tarle, Evgeniĭ Viktorovich, 1874–1955.
Napoleone...   Milano, A. Corticelli [1938]
453 [2] p.   map.
Bibliografia: p. 44–445.

NT   0041220   MiD

DC
235
T32
1942
Tarle, Evgeniĭ Viktorovich, 1874–1955.
Napoleon's invasion of Russia, 1812. London,
G. Allen [c1942]
300 p. (plans on lining papers)

Bibliography: p.293.
"Translated by G.M." (pseud. of Norbert
Guterman and Ralph Manheim)
"The original Russian edition published under
title: Nashestvie Napoleona na Rossiiu, 1812 go.'

1. Napoléon I - Invasion of Russia, 1812.
I. Title.

NT   0041221   WaU NcRS NNC MH ICU MtU

Tarle, Evgeniĭ Viktorovich, 1874–
... Napoleon's invasion of Russia, 1812. New York, Toronto,
Oxford university press, 1942.
4 p. l., 3–422 p. 22ͫ.
At head of title: Eugene Tarle.
Maps on lining-papers.
"Translated by G. M." (pseud. of Norbert Guterman and Ralph Man-
heim)
"The original Russian edition ... under the title: Nashestvie Napoleona
na Rossiyu—1812 god."—p. [413]
"A note on the author's sources": p. [413]

1. Napoléon I–Invasion of Russia, 1812. I. *Guterman, Norbert,
1900– tr. II. *Manheim, Ralph. 1907– joint tr. III. Title.
                                                      42–36171
Library of Congress   DC235.T32
                                                      947.07

OrU IdB
IU MiU NIC WaTU NcU CaBViP IdRR OrCS CaBVaU WaT OrP
OC1C OLak OEac ODW OC1 PHC OO OU OCU OC1W CoU CLU
NT   0041222   DLC PP NcC NSyU WaS Or WaSp PSC PBm NcD

944.05
T188
1943
Tarle, Evgenii Viktorovich, 1874–
Napoleon's invasion of Russia, 1812 [by]
Eugene Tarlé. [Translated by G.M., pseud.]
London, Allen & Unwin [1943]
300p. maps (on lining papers) 22cm.

Translation of (transliterated) Nashestvie
Napoleona na Rossiyu - 1812 god.

1. Napoléon I. Invasion of Russia, 1812.
II. Title.

NT   0041223   IEN

Tarle, Evgeniĭ Viktorovich, 1874–1955.
Нашествие Наполеона на Россию; 1812 год. [Москва]
Гос. социально-экон. изд-во, 1938.
279 p. illus., maps. 23 cm.
At head of title: Академия наук СССР. Институт истории.

1. Napoléon I–Invasion of Russia, 1812.   I. Title.
                Title transliterated: Nashestvie Napoleona na Rossii͡u.
DC235.T3 1938   55–49985

NT   0041224   DLC NIC CSt KU WU

Tarle, Evgeniĭ Viktorovich, 1874– 1955.
Нашествие Наполеона на Россию; 1812 год. [Изд. 2.,
испр. и доп.] [Москва] Гос. изд-во полит. лит-ры, 1943.
362, [2] p. plates, ports., fold. map. 20 cm.

1. Napoléon I–Invasion of Russia, 1812.   I. Title.
                Title transliterated: Nashestvie Napoleona na Rossii͡u.
DC235.T3 1943   49–33807

NT   0041225   DLC CaBVaU

Tarle, Evgeniĭ Viktorovich, 1874–   ed.
Akademii͡a nauk SSSR. *Institut istorii.*
Новая история. Допущено в качестве учебника для
исторических фак-тетов гос. университетов и педагог.
ин-тов. Москва, Гос. социально-экон. изд-во, 1939–

NT   0041226   DLC

Tarle, Evgeniĭ Viktorovich, 1874–1955.
(Ocherk noveĭsheĭ istorii Evropy)
Очерк новейшей истории Европы: 1814–1919. 2. изд.
Ленинград, Прибой, 1929.
208 p. 21 cm.

1. Europe—History—1815–1871. 2. Europe—History—1871–1918.
I. Title.

D359.T26 1929   73–216975

NT   0041227   DLC

Tarle, Evgeniĭ Viktorovich, 1874–1955.
Очерки и характеристики изъ исторіи европейскаго
общественнаго движенія въ XIX вѣкѣ. С.-Петербургъ,
Тип. Т-ва М. О. Вольфъ, 1903.
ii, 367 p. ports. 24 cm.

1. Europe—Civilization—Addresses, essays, lectures. 2. Europe—
Politics—1789–1900.   I. Title.
                Title transliterated: Ocherki i kharakteristiki iz isto-
rii evropeĭskago obshchestvennago dvizhenii͡a.

CB113.R8T35   56–54513

NT   0041228   DLC

Tarle, Evgeniĭ Viktorovich, 1874– 1955.
... Отечественная война 1812 года и разгром империи Наполеона. [Москва] Огиз, Госполитиздат, 1941.
67, [1] p. 19½ͫ.
At head of title: Академик Е. Тарле.
"Настоящая брошюра является сокращенным изложением моей
книги 'Нашествие Наполеона'."—p. 3, foot-note.

1. Napoléon I–Invasion of Russia, 1812. I. Title.   *Title
transliterated:* Otechestvennai͡a voĭna 1812 goda ...
                                                      43–34687
Library of Congress   DC235.T33

NT   0041229   DLC

Tarle, Evgeniĭ Viktorovich, 1874– 1955,
Паденіе абсолютизма въ Западной Европѣ; историческіе
очерки Е. В. Тарле. Часть первая. С.-Петербургъ и Москва, Изданіе Т-ва М. О. Вольфъ, [1907]
2 p. l., 208 p., 1 l. 22½ͫ. (Half-title: Свободное знаніе)
No more published?

1. Despotism. 2. Europe—Politics.   I. Title.
                Title transliterated: Padenie absoli͡utizma v Zapadnoĭ Evropi͡e.
                                                      44–28940
Library of Congress   JC381.T25

NT   0041230   DLC

Tarle, Evgeniĭ Viktorovich, 1874– 1955,
... Парижскій мир, 1856. Москва, Ленинград, Издательство Академии наук СССР, 1942.
67, [1] p. 22ͫ.
At head of title: Академия наук Союза ССР. Акад. Е. В. Тарле.
This book forms a chapter in v. 2 of the author's Krymskai͡a voĭna.
cf. p. 3.

1. Paris, Treaty of, 1856. I. Akademii͡a nauk SSSR. II. Title.
                Title transliterated: Parizhskiĭ mir, 1856.
                                                      44–48464
Library of Congress   DK215.T33

NT   0041231   DLC

Tarle, Evgenii Viktorovich, 1874–1955, ed.
... Партизанская борьба в национально-освободительных войнах Запада; сборник статей под редакцией академика Е. В. Тарле. [Москва] Огиз, Государственное издательство политической литературы, 1943.

115, [1] p. 20 cm.

At head of title: Институт истории Академии наук СССР.
Contents.—Неедлы, Зденек. Гуситские партизаны в Чехии.—Лесников, М. Гёзы в борьбе за независимость Нидерландов.—Эргерт, З. К. Методы партизанской борьбы американцев в войне за независимость.—Косорез, Н. Борьба испанского народа против французской оккупации в 1808–1813 гг.—Адамов, Е. Гарибальдийская "тысяча" в Сицилии.—Никитин, С. Из прошлого партизанской борьбы в Болгарии.

1. Guerrillas. I. Akademiia nauk SSSR. Institut istorii. II. Title.   *Title transliterated:* Partizanskaia bor'ba.

U240.T23   48-30916

NT   0041232   DLC

Tarle, Evgenii Viktorovich, 1874–1955.
Павел Степанович Нахимов. [Москва] Молодая гвардия, 1944.

135 p. port. 14 cm. (Великие люди русского народа)

Based on material from the author's Крымская война.
Bibliographical footnotes.

1. Nakhimov, Pavel Stepanovich, 1808–1855. 2. Sevastopol—Siege, 1854–1855. I. Series: Velikie liudi russkogo naroda. *Title transliterated:* Pavel Stepanovich Nakhimov.

DK209.6.N3T34   A 48-1736*
Harvard Univ. Library for Library of Congress   [1]†

NT   0041233   MH DLC

PN5177   **Tarle, Evgenii Viktorovich, 1874–1955.**
T187   ... La presse en France sous le règne de Napoléon I (d'après des documents inédits) Е.В.Тарле. Печать во Франции при Наполеоне I; по неизданным материалам. Петроград, "Былое", 1922.

56 p.   27 cm.
At head of title: E.Tarlé.
Bibliographical foot-notes.

1.Press- France. 2.Napoléon I, emperor of the French, 1769–1821. I.Title.

NT   0041234   CSt-H

Tarle, Evgenii Viktorovich, 1874–   ed.

Akademiia nauk SSSR. *Institut istorii.*
Против фашистской фальсификации истории; сборник статей. Ред. коллегия: Е. В. Тарле, А. В. Ефимов [и др.] Ответственный редактор Ф. И. Нотович. Москва [etc.] 1939.

Tarle, Evgenii Viktorovich, 1874–1955.
Рабочий класс во Франции въ эпоху революціи; историческіе очерки. С.-Петербургъ, Тип. "Слово," 1909–

v. 23 cm. (Записки Историко-филологическаго факультета Имп. С.-Петербургскаго университета, ч. 91

1. Labor and laboring classes—France—Hist. 2. France—Hist.—Revolution, 1789–1791. I. Title. (Series: Leningrad. Universitet. Istoriko-filologicheskii fakul'tet. Zapiski, ch. 91   *Title transliterated:* Rabochii klass vo Frantsii v epokhu revoliutsii.

AS262.L4223 pt. 91, etc.   54-55166

NT   0041236   DLC

Tarle, Evgenii Viktorovich, 1874–
Рабочий класс во Франции в первые времена машинного производства от конца Империи до восстания рабочих в Лионе. Москва, Гос. изд-во, 1928.

iv, 278 p. 24 cm. (Исследования по истории пролетариата и его классовой борьбы, вып. 2)

At head of title: Институт К. Маркса и Ф. Энгельса.

1. Labor and laboring classes—France—Hist. I. Title.   *Title transliterated:* Rabochii klass vo Frantsii.

HD8429.T35   53-51425 ‡

NT   0041237   DLC OU CtY

Tarle, Evgenii Viktorovich, 1874–1955.
... Роль студенчества въ революціонномъ движеніи въ Европѣ въ 1848 г. С.-Петербургъ, Типо-литографія "Энергія," 1906.

28 p. 18½ cm.

At head of title: Книгоиздательство "Свободный трудъ" А. И. Жуковой и М. А. Полубояриновой. Е. Тарле.

1. Europe—Hist.—1848–1849. 2. Students—Europe. I. Title.   *Title transliterated:* Rol' studenchestva v revoliutsionnom dvizhenii v Evropѣ v 1848 g.

Library of Congress   D387.T25   43-33077

NT   0041238   DLC

Tarle, Evgenii Viktorovich, 1874–1955.
Русский флот и внешняя политика Петра I. Москва, Воен. изд-во, 1949.

123 p. 21 cm.

1. Russia—For. rel.—1689–1725. 2. Russia—History, Naval. I. Title.   *Title transliterated:* Russkii flot i vneshniaia politika Petra I.

DK145.T3   51-15404

NT   0041239   DLC

Tarle, Evgenii Viktorovich, 1874–
Studien zur geschichte der arbeiterklasse in Frankreich während der revolution. Die arbeiter der nationalien manufakturen (1789–1799) nach urkunden der französischen archive. Von Eugen Tarle ... Leipzig, Duncker & Humblot, 1908.

xiv, p, 1 l., 128 p. 23 cm. (Added t.-p.: Staats- und sozialwissenschaftliche forschungen; hrsg. von G. Schmoller und M. Sering. hft. 132)

1. Labor and laboring classes—France. 2. France—Hist.—Revolution—Causes and character.

Library of Congress   HB41.S7 hft. 132   9-3398

NT   0041240   DLC ICU CaBVaU NN MB ICJ CU PU

Tarle, Evgenii Viktorovich, 1874–1955.
Талейран. Москва, Молодая гвардия, 1939.

206 p. illus., plates, ports. 18 cm. (Жизнь замечательных людей. Серия биографий, вып. 1 (145))

1. Talleyrand-Périgord, Charles Maurice de, prince de Bénévent, 1754–1838. (Series: Zhizn' zamechatel'nykh liudei [Moskva, Molodaia gvardiia] vyp. 1 (145))   *Title transliterated:* Taleiran.

CT190.Z43 vol.145   49-33278*‡

NT   0041241   DLC

Tarle, Evgenii Viktorovich, 1874–
Талейран. Москва, Изд-во Академии наук СССР, 1948.

294, [10] p. 23 cm. (Академия наук СССР. Научно-популярная серия)

Errata slip inserted.
"Библиография": 7 p. at end.

1. Talleyrand-Périgord, Charles Maurice de, prince de Bénévent, 1754–1838. (Series: Akademiia nauk SSSR. Nauchno-populiarnaia seriia)   *Title transliterated:* Taleiran.

DC255.T3T35 1948   49-16039*

NT   0041242   DLC CaBVaU

Tarle, Evgenii Viktorovich, 1874–1955
Talleyrand [aus dem Russischen (Morkau-Leningrad 1948) von Dr. Richard Ullrich] Leipzig, Koehler & Amelang, 1950.

274p. port. 22cm.

NT   0041243   PV

Tarle, Evgenii Viktorovich, 1874–
La tattica della diplomazia borghese. [Milano] Edizioni sociali [1952]

126 p. 19 cm. (Problemi)

1. International relations. 2. Diplomacy. I. Title.

JX1311.T26   53-38163 ‡

NT   0041244   DLC

HC305   **Tarle, Evgenii Viktorovich, 1874–1955.**
.T316   La vita economica dell'Italia nell'età napoleonica [ver] Evgenij Viktorovic Tarle. [Torino] Einaudi, 1950.

386 p. 22cm. (Biblioteca di cultura storica, 39)

Translation of Ekonomicheskoe polozhenie Italie vo vremia Napoleona.
Bibliographical footnotes.

1. Italy--Econ. condit. I. Title.

NT   0041245   ViU CaBVaU NcU MH ICU NIC MdBJ NjP NRU

Tarle, Evgenii Viktorovich, 1874–1955.
Warum kämpft die Sowjetunion für den Frieden? Wien, 1952.

23 p. 15 cm.

1. Russia—For. rel.—1945– I. Title.

DK267.3 1952.T37   55-23485 ‡

NT   0041246   DLC WU

Tarle, Evgenii Viktorovich, 1874–1955.
Why Soviet Union fights for peace. New Delhi, Representative [of] TASS in India, 1954.

26 p. illus. 19 cm.

1. Russia—For. rel.—1945– I. Title.

DK267.3 1952.T35   56-45269 ‡

NT   0041247   DLC DS

Tarle, Evgenii Viktorovich, 1874–1955.
Жерминаль и Прериаль. Москва, Гос. социально-экон. изд-во, 1937.

274 p. plate. 22 cm.

At head of cover title: Институт истории Академии наук С. С. Р.
Bibliographical footnotes.

1. France—Hist.—Revolution, 1795. I. Title.   *Title transliterated:* Zherminal' i Prerial'.

DC185.9.T3 1937   51-55174

NT   0041248   DLC

DC185   **Tarle, Evgenii Viktorovich, 1874–1955.**
.9   Жерминаль и Прериаль. 2. перер. и доп. изд. Москва,
.T3   Изд-во Академии наук СССР, 1951.
1951   310, [2] p. 23 cm.

At head of title: Академия наук СССР. Институт истории.
Errata slip inserted.
Bibliography: p. 247-[311]

1. France—Hist.—Revolution, 1795. I. Title.   *Title transliterated:* Zherminal' i Prerial'.

DC185.9.T3 1951   51-40102

NT   0041249   DLC

Tarlé (Gustáve) [1882–]. *A propos de l'hygiène du paysan en Bretagne. 75 pp. 8°. Montpellier, 1911. No. 32.

NT 0041250   DNLM CtY

Tarle, IAkov.
Пионы меж небоскребов; стихотворения. Peonies among skyscrapers; poems. New York, Spartacus Pub. House, 1929.
99 p. facsim., music, port. 22 cm.

I. Title.
Title romanized: Piony mezh neboskrebov.

PG3476.T343P5   76–295648

NT 0041251   DLC

Tarlé, J.
see
Tarle, Evgenii Viktorovich, 1874–1955.

Tarle (Jakob) [1889–]. *Die Neuritis retrobulbaris acuta (Neuritis axialis acuta [Wilbrand und Sänger]) und die multiple Sklerose. 51 pp. 8°. Tübingen, G. Schnürlen, 1913.

NT 0041253   DNLM CtY

Tarlé, Jean Josse de, 1739–1813. Conseils à son fils.
Les Tarlé, 1525–1939; précédés par les idées morales d'un maréchal de camp de l'ancien régime, Conseils du chevalier de Tarlé à son fils. Roanne, Impr. Souchier [1945]

CS599
.T3
1945

Tarle, Jevgen Viktor
see Tarle, Evgenii Viktorovich, 1874–1955.

Tarle, Michael: Studien über den Zusammenhang zwischen der Reaktionsfähigkeit und Dissoziation. Weida i. Th. 1912: Thomas & Hubert. 51 S. 8°
Leipzig, Phil. Diss. v. 26. April 1912, Ref. Le Blanc, Beckmann
[Geb. 8./20. Nov. 86 Cherson; Wohnort: Cherson; Staatsangeh.: Rußland; Vorbildung: I. Gymn. Cherson Reife Juni 04; Studium: Odessa 3, Leipzig 11 S.; Rig. 15. Dez. 11.]   [U 12. 3380]

NT 0041256   ICRL OCU PU CtY

Les Tarlé, 1525–1939; précédés par les idées morales d'un maréchal de camp de l'ancien régime, Conseils du chevalier de Tarlé à son fils. Roanne, Impr. Souchier [1945]
142, 49 p. illus. (part col.) ports., maps (part col.) facsims. 26 cm.
"Il a été tiré de cet ouvrage 90 exemplaires hors commerce sur papier Vidalon numérotés de 1 à 90. No. 35."

1. Tarlé family. I. Tarlé, Jean Josse de, 1739–1813. Conseils à son fils.
CS599.T3 1945   49–44663*

NT 0041257   DLC

Tarter (Sigmund). *Bericht über Infectionskrankheiten, die zur Section kamen vom Jahre 1852 bis 1865. 16 pp. 8°. Würzburg, Bonitas-Bauer, 1866.

NT 0041258   DNLM

Tarlet, Francisque, 1899–
... Les formes cliniques de début des tumeurs malignes du naso-pharynx... Lyon, 1927.
24 cm.
Thèse – Univ. de Lyon.
"Bibliographie": p. 71–74.

NT 0041259   CtY

Tarleton, Alfred Henry, 1862–1921.
Nicholas Breakspear (Adrian IV.) Englishman and pope, by Alfred H. Tarleton. London, A. L. Humphreys, 1896.
xvii, 292 p. front., plates, ports., maps, fold. facsim., fold. geneal. tab. 27½cm.
Title in red and black; title vignette; initials; tail-pieces.
Appendix I. Text and translation of the facsimile bull.—Appendix II. Bibliography.—Appendix III. List of cardinals living at the accession of Adrian IV. and of those created by him. Bulls issued by Adrian IV.

1. Hadrianus IV, pope, d. 1159.

Library of Congress   BX1225.T3   2–24027 Revised

CSmH
NT 0041260   DLC FU IU PU TxU MCE CtY OO OCU OClW MB

Tarleton, *Sir Banastre, bart.,* 1754–1833.
A history of the campaigns of 1780 and 1781, in the southern provinces of North America, by Lieutenant-Colonel Tarleton ... Dublin, Printed for Colles [etc.] 1787.
vii, 533 p. 21cm.

1. Southern states—Hist.—Revolution. 2. U. S.—Hist.—Revolution—Campaigns and battles.
2–4503

Library of Congress   E236.T18

VtU MB TKL IC
NcD MdAN AU CtY MiU OU OClWHi Nh RPJCB NIC CaBVaU
NT 0041261   DLC NBuHi MiU-C KyU MeB DeU OO PPL PSC

Tarleton, *Sir Banastre, bart.,* 1754–1833.
A history of the campaigns of 1780 and 1781, in the southern provinces of North America. By Lieutenant-Colonel Tarleton ... London, Printed for T. Cadell, 1787.
vii, [1], 518 p. maps (part fold.) 29 x 22cm.

1. Southern states—Hist.—Revolution. 2. U. S.—Hist.—Revolution—Campaigns and battles.
2–4502

Library of Congress   E236.T17

ViU NjP MnU NjN OrP CaBVaU FTaSC
KyLx DeU MsU MiU CtY NSyU NcGU MWiW-C MiA1bC
PHi OrU OClWHi NjP CtU NcGU MoU GASU OOxM MiU-C
NN CaNSWA OWoC MB MiU Vi OCl ScU RPJCB NcD PP PU
NT 0041262   DLC MWA NcU MdBP PPL MA GSDe NIC NWM IC

Micro
Film
D50
reel
427
no.1

Tarleton, Sir Banastre. 1754–1833
A history of the campaigns of 1780 and 1781, in the southern provinces of North America. By Lieutenant-Colonel Tarleton ... London, Printed for T. Cadell, 1787.
(On American culture series, reel 427, no.1)
Microfilm (positive). 35mm. Ann Arbor, Mich., University Microfilms, 1970.
Collation of the original: vii,[1,]518p. maps (part fold.) 29x22cm.
1. Southern states – Hist. – Revolution. 2. U.S. – Hist. – Re volution – Campaigns and battles. I. Title.

NT 0041263   PSt ViU IaAS FMU KEmT

Tarleton, Sir Banastre, bart., 1754–
History of the campaigns of 1780 and 1781, in the southern provinces of North America. By Major-General Tarleton, commandant of the late British legion. The second edition. Lond, Printed for T. Cadell, jun. & W. Davies, (Successors to Mr. Cadell,) 1796.
17 p., 1 l.,(iii)-vii, (1), 518 p. fold. maps (partly col.) 27.3 cm.
Stevens 2d Addenda 365
Bookplate of Westport House.

NT 0041264   MiU-C CSmH

942.07
B897
v.61
no.8

Tarleton, Sir Banastre, bart., 1754–1833.
Lieut.-General Tarleton's reply to Colonel de Charmilly [with reference to a private quarrel] London, Printed for the Author [1810?]
14p. 24cm. (In Burdett tracts. v.61, no.8)

I. Venault de Charmilly. II. Series.

NT 0041265   OrU OClWHi RPB NN CtY

TARLETON, Sir BANASTRE, bart., 1754–1833.
Substance of a speech, delivered by Lieut.-Gen. Tarleton, in a committee of the House of Commons, on the army estimates, March 4, 1811. London: Printed for J.Ebers, 1811. 56 p. 20½cm.

869430A. 1. Army, British—Hist., 1810. 2. Peninsular war, 1807–1814.

NT 0041266   NN RP OrU CSmH

Tarleton, Sir Banastre, bart., 1754–1833.
Substance of a speech intended for the vote of Credit bill, for 1810. London, Printed for J. Ridgway, 1810.
23 p. 23cm.

1. Gt. Brit. – Hist. – 1789–1820.

NT 0041267   NNC CtY

Tarleton, Charles William, 1844–
The Tarleton family. Comp. by C. W. Tarleton ... 1900. Concord, N. H., I. C. Evans, printer, 1900.
244 p. illus., plates, ports., geneal. tables. 23¾cm.

1. Tarleton family. 2. Tarleton family (Richard Tarleton, d. 1706)
3–3817

Library of Congress   CS71.T188 1900

NT 0041268   DLC PP PHi Nh MWA MB NN

Tarleton, Fiswoode, d. 1931.
Bloody ground; a cycle of the southern hills, by Fiswoode Tarleton. New York, L. MacVeagh, The Dial press; Toronto, Longmans, Green & company, 1929.
4 p. l., 312 p. 20cm.

I. Title.
Library of Congress   PZ3.T178B1   29–3264

OClh
NT 0041269   DLC TNJ MoU WaSp WaS PU NcD ViU OCl MB

Tarleton, Fiswoode, d. 1931, ed.
Modern review. v. 1–2; autumn 1922–July 1924. [Winchester, Mass.] 1922–24.

Tarleton, Fiswoode, d. 1931.
Short story writing for beginners... Girard, Haldeman-Julius publications, [c1927].
64 p.
(Little blue books, no. 1240.)
YA 27822

NT 0041271   DLC

Tarleton, Fiswoode, *d. 1931.*
    Some trust in chariots, by Fiswoode Tarleton ...   New York, L. MacVeagh, The Dial press; Toronto, Longmans, Green and co., 1930.
    5 p. l., 3–308 p.   19½ᶜᵐ.

    I. Title.
    Library of Congress   PZ3.T178So
                                                         30-24347

NT 0041272   DLC NcD ViU OC1

Tarleton, Francis Alexander, 1841–*1920,* **joint author.**
Williamson, Benjamin, 1827–1916.   FOR OTHER EDITIONS
                                        SEE MAIN ENTRY
    An elementary treatise on dynamics, containing applications to thermodynamics, with numerous examples. By Benjamin Williamson ... and Francis A. Tarleton ... 3d ed., rev. and enl. London, New York [etc.] Longmans, Green and co., 1900.

Tarleton, Francis Alexander, *1841–1920.*
    An introduction to the mathematical theory of attraction. By
20692 Francis A. Tarleton, ...   [Vol. I–II.]   London, Longmans,
ᵃ   Green & Co., 1899–1913.
    2 vol.   19½ᶜᵐ.

    NBuG NIC OCU PU CSt MH RPB PU OU NjP PHC DBS
NT 0041274   ICJ CaBVaU CU WaU GU OC1W MiU NN NNC MB

TARLETON, FRANCIS ALEXANDER, 1841–*1920,*
    On chemical equilibrium.   [Dublin, 1880]
12 p.   28cm.

    Microfiche (Negative).   1 sheet.   11 x 15cm.   (NYPL FSN 1111)
    Caption title.
    Offprint transactions of the Royal Irish academy, vol. 28.

    1. Equilibrium, Chemical.   t. 1880.

NT 0041275   NN

        Tarleton, Richard
            see   Tarlton, Richard, d. 1588.

    Tarleton, W. W., ed.

    New South Wales. *Laws, statutes, etc.*
        A collection of the private acts of practical utility in force in New South Wales; embracing the local private legislation from the year 1832 to the year 1885. By W. W. Tarleton ... Published by authority. Sydney, T. Richards, government printer, 1886.

        Tarleton, W.W., reporter.

    New South Wales. *Supreme court.*
        The term reports. Reports of cases argued and determined in the Supreme court of New South Wales. Vol. I [no. 1–12, first term, 1881–fourth term, 1883] Sydney, F. Cunninghame & co. [1881–83]

1620

        Tarleton, William.
            A correspondence between the Lord Bishop of Worcester, the Hon. and Rev. G. M. Yorke, Dr. Evans, and Mr. William Tarleton, relative to certain irregularities in the performance of divine service in St. Philip's Church, Birmingham. Birmingham, W. Grew & Son, 1851.
            16 p.
            Bound with 1608.
            I. Pepys, Her   ry, Bp. of Worcester, 1783–1860. II. (Over)   B.M.

NT 0041279   TxDaM

TARLETON.

    see also TARLTON.

    Tarleton Agricultural College, Stephenville, Tex.
        see   John Tarleton agricultural college, Stephenville, Tex.

    Tarleton's fox hunt
        see under   [Hance, Anthony M.]

23688a   Tarletons tragical treatises, contayning sundrie discourses and prety conceytes, both in prose and verse.   Imprinted at London by Henry Bynneman, An. 1578.
        8* [Incomplete]   8 vo.   12. 9 x 9. 4 cm.
        Black letter.
        Title within border of type ornaments.
        Apparently the only copy known.
        Slightly wormholed.
        "The Epistle Dedicatorie" to Lady Francis Mildmay, sig. *2r–*3v. Commendatory verses by T.A., Ferdinando Freckleton, and Lewis Ph,

        sig. *4r–*5v.
        Britwell Court copy.
        Paper covers.

NT 0041284   DFo

FILM
        Tarletons tragical treatises, contayning sundrie discourses and pretty conceytes, both in prose and verse.   London, Imprinted by H. Bynneman, 1578.
        Imperfect: all after sig. *8 lacking.
        Although the dedication is signed Richard Tarleton, he probably was not the author. Cf. Dict.nat.biog.
        University microfilms no.16920 (carton 718)
        Short–title catalogue no.23688a (Bishop,p.200)
        I. Tarlton, Richard, d.1588, supposed author.

NT 0041285   MiU

TARLIER, André Léon Daniel, 1907–
    L'hypoderma bovis chez le cheval. Thèse. Paris, Vigot frères, 1930.

    pp.(6),47.
    At head of title: École nationale vétérinaire d'Alfort.
    "Bibliographie" pp.45–46.

NT 0041286   MH CtY DNLM

    Tarlier, Hippolyte
    Liste alphabétique des communes de Belgique, conforme à l'orthographe des sceaux officiels, indiquant toutes les circonscriptions territoriales auxquelles ressortit chaque commune. *Bruxelles: G. Stapleaux,* 1852. x, II, 316 pp. 8°.
    In: **TB.** p. v. 24.
    Full name: Alexandre Hippolyte Tarlier

NT 0041287   NN

    Tarlier, Hippolyte
    Nouveau dictionnaire des communes, hameaux, charbonnages, etc. du royaume de Belgique...
    Bruxelles, 1877.
    8°

NT 0041288   NN

Tarlier, J.
    Quelques nots sur la prononciation du Grec. Bruxelles, 1847.

NT 0041289   NjP

Tarlier, *Jules, 1825–1870.*
Atlas general de geographie moderne.
Bruxelles, s. a.
4to.

NT 0041290   NN

TARLIER, JULES, *1825–1870.*
    Atlas général de géographie moderne, extrait des cartes de Lapie, Berghaus, Stieler, Sydow, Bauerkeller, Arrowsmith, etc., etc.   Bruxelles, Société pour l'émancipation intellectuelle, A. Jamar [1854] 14 p.
    18 double maps (part col.) 19cm. (Encyclopédie populaire)

    1. Geography--Atlases, 1854.   I. Société pour l'émancipation
intellectuelle, Brussels.

NT 0041291   NN

DH531   Tarlier, Jules, 1825–1870.
. B4   La Belgique ancienne et moderne, Géographie et histoire des communes belges, par Jules Tarlier... [et] Alphonse Wauters... Ouvrage dédié au roi et pub. sous le patronage du gouvernment...   Bruxelles, A. Decq., 1859–1872.
        6 v. fold. maps. 28 cm.
        "Les 6 livraisons ont été réunies en 2 volumes sous le titre: Arrondissement de Nivelles... 1873.
        For a continuation of this title see Wauters, Alphonse Guillaume Ghislain.

NT 0041292   DLC

Tarlier, Jules. 1825–1870.   No. 1 in 4866.45
    Description géographique de la Belgique. Bruxelles. Jamar. [1854.] 3 parts in 1 v. Maps. [Encyclopédie populaire.] 12°.

F2802 — S.r. — Belgium. Geog.

NT 0041293   MB NjP NN

Tarlier, Jules, 1825–1870.
    Notice bibliographique sur les traductions italiennes, espagnoles, portugaises, françaises, anglaises, allemandes, hollandaises, danoises, polonaises et grecques des satires de Perse, par le docteur Jules Tarlier ... Bruxelles, C. Muquardt [etc.], 1848.
    2 p. l., v–xxiii p. 27½ᶜᵐ.

    1. Persius Flaccus, Aulus—Bibl.
                                                         42–45065
    Library of Congress   Z8674.T3

NT 0041294   DLC

TARLIER, Léon, 1882–
    Contribution à l'étude des troubles et accidents causés par des corps étrangers d'origine gastrique chez les bovins; observations de myocardite traumatique. Thèse. Paris, Lib.le Français, 1927.

    pp.28.
    At head of title: École nationale vétérinaire d'Alfort.

NT 0041295   MH DNLM CtY

TARLING, W   J   , comp.
Café Royal cocktail book, compiled by W.J.Tarling. Illustrated by Frederick Carter, decorated by the Chevron
studio.   London: Publ. from Pall Mall ltd [1937]   134 l.
illus. (incl. port.)   19cm.

"Coronation edition, 1937."

904673A. 1. Alcoholic drink« I. Title.

NT 0041296   NN

Tarliński, Zygmunt, and W. Sikora.
De la Silésie du duché de Cieszyn; essai par le Dr. Sigismond
Tarliński et le professeur Vincent Sikora. [n. p., 1919.]   7 p.
incl. tables.   8°.

Caption-title.

1. Teschen. 2. European war, 1914-   .—Territorial questions, Teschen.
3. Sikora, Wincenty, jt. au.
N. Y. P. L.   September 1, 1920.

NT 0041297   NN

DK432
.D9
Rare bk.   Tarło, Adam, 1713–1744.
Coll.   Dzikowska konfederacja, 1734–1736.
Solennissima manifestatio. Confœderatæ reipublicæ Polonæ,
patriæ suæ insinuata, & universis Europæ potentiis, pro in-
formatione præsentis status sui, exhibita. Die 30. julii 1735.
anno ... Manifesto solenne. Della Republica confederata di
Pollonia diretto alla sua patria, ed a tutte le potenze di Europa
per informarle del presente suo stato. Il dì 30. luglio 1735 ...
[n. p., 1735 ?]

Tarło, Jan Joachim, bp., d. 1733.
Meridies gratiarum inter definitas Apostolico
numero, ac Joannis nomine gratiosis duodecim
Posnaniensibus praesulibus destinatas horas
see under title

Tarlok Singh
see
Singh, Tarlok, 1913–

Tarlov, Isadore M   1905–
Plasma clot suture of peripheral nerves and nerve roots;
rationale and technique. [1st ed.] Springfield, Ill., Thomas
[1950]
[xii, 116 p. illus. 24 cm.
Bibliography: p. 108–107.

1. Nerves—Surgery. 2. Sutures.   I. Title.

RD595.T3   617.48   50–14917 rev

         PWpM
         NcU DNLM ICJ ICU NbU-M OkU-M OrU-M CtY-M TNJ-M
NT 0041301   DLC NBuU PPPCPh OClW MBCo FU-HU ViU MoU

Tarlov, Isadore M   1905–
Sacral nerve-root cysts, another cause of the sciatic or
cauda equina syndrome. Springfield, Ill., Thomas [1953]
134 p. illus. 24 cm.
Includes bibliography.

1. Perineurial cysts, Sacral.   I. Title.

RC422.P4T3   616.83   53–9292 ‡

NT 0041302   DLC OrU-M NBuU OClM OU DNLM ICJ NcU

PL65
.K59
M3417   Tarlovskiĭ, Mark Arkad'evich.
1941
(Manas)
Manas. Russian. Selections.
Манас; киргизский народный эпос; главы из "Вели-
кого похода" (по варианту Сагымбая Орозбакова) Перевод Семена Липкина, Марка Тарловского; редакция
и вступительная статья Е. Мозолькова и У. Джаки-
шева. Москва, Государственное издательство "Худо-
жественная литература," 1941.

M459
.B   Tarlow, Marc, arr.

Beethoven, Ludwig van, 1770–1827.
[Sonata, piano, no. 7, op. 10, no. 3, D major. Menuetto, arranged]

Menuetto from sonata, op. 10, no. 3 [by] L. van Beethoven,
arranged by M. Tarlow. N[ew] Y[ork] M. Witmark & sons,
°1938.

Tarłowski, Cwi.
בײ דער ארבעם ... זאמלונג פון פעדאגאגישע נאמיזן און
ארמיקלען. סים א פאראװארם פון מ. פעקער. ווארשע, פארלאג
[Warszawa] 1934. "דאס קינד."
68 p. 23 cm.

1. Child study.   I. Title.   Title transliterated: Bay der arbet.

LB1119.T3   58–53329 ‡

NT 0041305   DLC

Tarlowsky, Lydia Proskura.
Drusenschlauchähnliche bildungen im perikarditisch
exsudate.
Inaug. Diss.   Zurich, 1908
Bibl.

NT 0041306   ICRL DNLM

Tarlton, B   D
Some reflections on the relations of capital
and labor. Address before the Texas Bar
Association, 1895.
(Bar Addosition reports)

NT 0041307   PU-L

Tarlton, Dewitt Talmage.
The history of the cotton industry in Texas, 1820–1850...
By Dewitt Talmage Tarlton...   Cleburne, Tex., 1923.   iv,
115 f. incl. tables.   4°.

Photostat reproduction of typewritten copy.
Dissertation, Univ. of Texas.
Bibliography, p. 113–115.

1. Cotton plant and culture—U. S.—   Texas, 1820–1850. 2. Cotton-
Trade and stat.—U. S.—Texas, 1820-   1850.
N. Y. P. L.   September 30, 1926

NT 0041308   NN

Tarlton, Edward James
Rearrangements and oxidations in steroids

Thesis - Harvard, 1954

NT 0041309   MH

Tarlton, Gilbert Allen, 1927–
The Oblate library
see under St. John's Abbey, Collegeville,
Minn.

Tarlton, Richard, d. 1588, supposed author.
[A floorish vpon fancie ...
see under [Breton, Nicholas] 1545?–1626?

Tarlton, Richard, d. 1588, supposed author.
A prettie newe ballad, intytuled: The crowe sits
vpon the wall, Please one and please all. To the
tune of, Please one and please all. London, Im-
printed for H.Kyrkham [1592]
Signed at end: R.T. [i.e. Richard Tarlton? Cf.
Dict.nat.biog.]
Broadside.
Short-title catalogue no.23685 (carton 1085)

I.Title. II.Title: The crowe sits vpon the
wall.

NT 0041312   MiU NNC CSmH

Tarlton, Richard, d. 1588.
Story of the two lovers of Pisa, which
Shakespeare employed in his play of The merry
wives of Windsor. n. p., n. d.
24 p.

NT 0041313   PU

Tarlton, Richard, d. 1588.   2597.5.2
Story, The, of the two lovers of Pisa, which Shakespeare employed in
his play of The merry wives of Windsor. Reprinted from "Tarl-
ton's News out of Purgatory." (1), 13–24 pp.
(In Collier, John Payne, compiler. Shakespeare's library ...
Vol. 2. London. [1843.])
Tarlton's work is based upon an Italian tale by Straparola.

G7240— Two lovers, The, of Pisa. Shakespeare, William. Merry wives of
Windsor. Sources. — Tarlton, Richard.

NT 0041314   MB

Tarlton, Richard, d. 1588.
The story of The two lovers of Pisa, which Shakespeare employed in his play of The merry wives of Windsor. [Adapted from
the Italian of Straparola, and] reprinted from "Tarltons news out
of purgatory." (In: J. P. Collier, Shakespeare's library. London, 1850. 8°. v. 2. 2 l., 15-24 p.)

1. Shakespeare, William.—Single   plays: The merry wives of Windsor.
2. Straparola, Giovanni Francesco: Le tredici piacevoli notti. 3. Title.
N. Y. P. L.   April 6, 1911.

NT 0041315   NN

Tarlton, Richard, d. 1588, supposed author.
Tarletons tragical treatises...
see under title

Tarlton, Richard, d. 1588, supposed author.
Tarltons newes out of purgatorie...
see under title

Tarlton, Richard, d. 1588.
A very Lamentable and woful discours of the
fierce fluds, whiche lately flowed in Bedford Shire,
in Lincoln Shire, and in many other places, with
the great losses of sheep and other cattel. The
v. of October... 1570. London, by John Allde,
1570.
Broadside.
Laid no. (84) in same vol. with: Awdelay or
Awdeley, John. ECCLESI. XX. 1569.

NT 0041318   CSmH DFo

Tarlton, Richard, d.1588, supposed author.
A very lamentable and woful discours of the fierce fluds,whiche lately flowed in Bedford shire,in Lincoln shire,and iu . l. many other places,with the great losses of sheep and other cattel. The v.of October ... 1570 ... Jmprinted at London ... by John Allde. 1570.
Signed: Richard Tarlton. "It is unlikely that Tarlton was the author".—Dict.nat.biog.
University microfilms no.15618 (case 67,carton 399)
Short-title catalogue no.23688.

NT 0041319   MiU ViU WaPS

Tarlton, O. Presbyterian Church.
Paper pledging subscriptions for the pastor's salary... April 30, 1832.

NT 0041320   PPPrHi

FILM
Tarlton's Jests.
An excellent iest of Tarlton suddenly spoken.
[n.p., n.d.]
Caption title.
Fragments only of sig.C2-3.
University microfilms no.17687 (carton 671)
Short-title catalogue no.23684a[i.e.Bishop Checklist no.23684.1]

NT 0041321   MiU

23684a   Tarltons iests. Drawne into these three parts.
1. His Court-wittie Iests. 2. His Sound Cittie Iests. 3. His Country prettie Iests. Full of delight, wit, and honest myrth. London, printed for Iohn Budge, and are to be sold at his shop, at the great South doore of Paules, 1613.
A-D^4 (Incomplete)   4 to.   19 x 13.9 cm.
Black letter.
This is apparently the only copy of this edition which is not recorded in the S.T.C.
Slightly stained; slightly wormholed; title-page and one other leaf torn.

NT 0041322   DFo

Tarltons iests. Drawne into these three parts.
1 His court-wittie iests 2 His sound cittie iest: 3 His country prettie iests. Full of delight, wit and honest myrth. London, I.Budge, 1613.
Imperfect: all after sig.D4 lacking.
University microfilms no.17688 (carton 671)
Short-title catalogue no.23684b[i.e.Bishop Checklist no.23684.2]

NT 0041323   MiU

Tarlton's iests, drawing into these three parts.
1. His court-witty iests. 2. His lewd city iests. 3. His countrey pretty iests. Full of delight, with and honest mirth. London, by I.H., for A. Crook, 1638.
sm. 4 to.   Blue morocco, by Riviere.
Lacking: title-page.

NT 0041324   CSmH

Tarlton's jests. [With notices of Richard Tarlton.]
(In Hazlitt, William Carew, editor. Shakespeare jest-books. Vol. 2. pp. 188-260. London, 1864.)

NT 0041325   MB

Tarlton's jests, drawn into three parts: 1.His court-witty jests. 2.His sound city jests. 3.His countrey pretty jests. Full of delight, wit and honest mirth. Lond. by J.H., 1611. Reprinted from the rare originals and edited with introduction and notes by W. Carew Hazlitt. London, 1866.
p.[191]-260, 18 cm. (Old English jest books)

NT 0041326   MH DFo PU-F

TARLTON'S jests; London,1638. From the rare original in the collection of Henry Huth. [London,187-?].
sm.4°. ff.(22)
(ASHBEE,E.W. Fac-simile reproduction)

NT 0041327   MH DLC-P4 PU OClWHi

Tarlton's Jests, and News out of purgatory: with notes, and some account of the life of Tarlton, by James Orchard Halliwell ... London, Printed for the Shakespeare society, 1844.
xlvii, 135, [1] p. incl. front. (port.) 1 illus. 22^{cm}. [Shakespeare society. Publications, no. 20]
Vol. XIII, no. 2, in the L. C. set.
More or less fictitious anecdotes, many of them far older than Tarlton, who probably was in no way responsible for either work. *cf.* Dict. nat. biog., and introd.

CONTENTS. — Introduction.— Tarlton's jests: Court-witty jests, Sound city jests, Pretty country jests.— Tarlton's Newes out of purgatory.— **Appendix**: Extracts from "The cobler of Canterbury (an answer to "The news out of purgatorie") A very lamentable and wofull discours of the fierce fluds whiche lately flowed in, Lincolnshire, and in many other places, with the great losses of sheep and other cattel, the 5. of October, 1570. Extract from Chettle's "Kind-Harts dreame".
1. Tarlton, Richard, d. 1588. 2. English wit and humor. I. Halliwell-Phillipps, James Orchard, 1820-1889, ed. II. Chettle, Henry, d. 1607? Kind-Harts dreame. III. Newes out of purgatorie. IV. Title: Tarlton's News out of purgatory. V. Title: The cobler of Canterburie. VI. Title: A very lamentable and wofull discours ...

Library of Congress   PR2838.L5 vol. 13   16—13793

OrCS
NcU OO OCU MiU OClW OOxM WU NdBP CaBVaU OrU NIC
NT 0041329   DLC PHC PP PPT PSC NcGU NN PU-F MHi ViU

Tarlton's Jests, and News out of purgatory: with notes, and some account of the life of Tarlton, by James Orchard Halliwell ... London, Printed for the Shakespeare society, 1844.
xlvii, 135 [1] p. incl. front. (port.) 1 illus. 22 cm. (Shakespeare society. Publications, no. 20]
More or less fictitious anecdotes, many of them far older than Tarlton, who probably was in no way responsible for either work. cf. Dict. nat. biog., and introd.
Micro-opaque. Washington, D. C. Microcard Editions, 19__ 3 cards.   7.5 x 12.5 cm.

CONTENTS.—Introduction.—Tarlton's jests: Court-witty jests, Sound city jests, Pretty country jests.—Tarlton's Newes out of purgatory.—Appendix: Extracts from "The Cobler of Canterburie (an answer to "The news out of purgatorie") A very lamentable and wofull discours of the fierce fluds whiche lately flowed in Bedfordshire, in Lincolnshire, and in many other places, with the great losses of sheep and other cattel, the 5. of October, 1570. Extract from Chettle's "Kind-Ha rts dreame."

1. Tarlton, Richard, d. 1588. 2. English wit and humor. I. Tarlton, Richard, d. 1588. Jests. II. Tarlton, Richard, d. 1588. News out of purgatory. III. Halliwell-Phillips, James Orchard, d. 1607? Kind-Harts dreame. IV. Title: News out of Purgatory. V. Title: Kind-Harts dreame. VI. Title: The cobbler of Canterburie. VII. Title: A very lamentable and wofull discours of the fierce fluds which lately flowed in Bedfordshire in Lincolnshire ... √VIII. Series: Shakespeare Society, London, Publications, no. 20. acm

NT 0041332   IEdS

FILM
Tarltons newes out of purgatorie. Onely such a iest as his iigge,fit for gentlemen to laugh at an houre,&c. Published by an old companion of his,Robin Goodfellow. London, Printed for T.G[ubbin] and T.N[eewman] 1590.
Tarlton was not responsible for this work. Cf. Dict.nat.biog.
Short-title catalogue no.23685 (carton 1085)
I.Tarlton,Richard,d.1588, supposed author.
II.Title: Newes out of purgatorie.

NT 0041333   MiU CaBVaU NNC

Tarltons newes out of purgatorie. Onelye such a iest as his iigge, fit for gentlemen to laugh at an houre, & c.
Published by an old companion of his, Robin Goodfellow. At London Printed for Edward White [1590]
Tarlton was not responsible for this work. cf. Dict. nat. biog.
University microfilms no. 15617 (case 60, carton 358)
Short-title catalogue no. 23585a.
I. Tarlton, Richard, d.1588, supposed author. II. Title: Newes out of purgatorie.

NT 0041334   MiU NNC CaBVaU WaPS

TARLTONS Newes out of purgatorie. Onelye such a iest as his iigge,fit for gentlemen to laugh at an houre,&c. Published by an old companion of his,Robin Goodfellow. London, printed for Edward White,[1590]. Photostat copy.
Attributed to Richard Tarlton.
Photostat reproduction (positive) of a copy in the Henry E.Huntington Library.
Label: White-Huntington series,6.

NT 0041335   MH PBL CSmH

23686   TARLTONS | NEVVES OVT OF | PVRGATORY. | Onely fuch a Ieft as his Iigge, fit for | Gentlemen to laugh at an houre, &c. | Publifhed by an old Com-
.45 panion of his, | Robin Goodfellow. | [rule; print-
T188(3) er's mark, McKerrow 281; rule] LONDON, | Printed
[n] by George Purflowe, and are to be fold by Fran-cib | Groue, on Snow-hill, at the Signe of the Wind-mill, | neere vnto St. Sepulchres Church. | 1630.
A^2, B-G^4, H^2. (A1, A2, H1 and H2 in facsimile; supplied also by photostat from British Museum copy) 4to. 18x13cm. Black letter.
Modern morocco, by Lortie.

NT 0041337   DFo MH

Tarlton, William S
Somerset Place and its restoration. Prepared for the Division of State Parks, North Carolina Dept. of Conservation and Development. [Raleigh?] 1954.
141 p. 28 cm.
1. Somerset Place, N. C. 2. Collins family. I. North Carolina. Division of State Parks. II. Title.
F262.W3T3   62-62913 ‡

NT 0041338   DLC DSI NN NcU

TARLTON.
See also TARLETON.

Tarma, Peru. Sociedad de beneficencia
see   Sociedad de beneficencia de Tarma.

Tarma, Acobamba, Muruhuay...
See under
•Cardenas, Fortunato E

Tarma, ciudad de los árboles. Lima, Perú, Emp. Schwore [194-]
cover-title, [156] p. illus. (incl. map) ports. 20^m.
"El Touring y automóvil club del Perú ... nos alienta en esta obra turística con sus autorizadas conceptos en pró del turismo por nuestras sierras andinas ... El sr. José G. Otero ... nos he proporcionado ... la mayor parte del material gráfico y literario de esta obra."—Nota editorial.
Includes advertising matter.
1. Tarma, Peru—Descr. I. Touring y automóvil club del Perú. II. Otero, José G.
Library of Congress   F3611.T3T3   44-16273
918.5

NT 0041342   DLC

Tarman, Grover Cleveland, 1885–
The producer's marketing guide, the connecting link between producer and consumer ... Grover C. Tarman, Lawrence Leer, authors. New Paris, Ind., Producer's marketing guide company [1915]

1 p. l., 53 p. illus. 18½ᶜᵐ. $0.50

1. Farm produce—Marketing. 2. Parcels-post—U. S.   I. Leer, Lawrence, joint author. II. Title.

Library of Congress   S571.T3

15–20920

NT   0041343   DLC ICJ

F149
.F76
1953   **Tarman, Harold James,** joint author.
FOR OTHER EDITIONS
SEE MAIN ENTRY
Fortenbaugh, Robert, 1892–
The Pennsylvania story [by] Robert Fortenbaugh [and] H. James Tarman; Lucille Wallower, editorial consultant. State College, Pa., Penns Valley Publishers, 1953.

F149
.F77   **Tarman, Harold James,** joint author.

Fortenbaugh, Robert, 1892–
Pennsylvania, the story of a commonwealth, by Robert Fortenbaugh ... and H. James Tarman ... Harrisburg, Penna., The Pennsylvania book service, 1940.

Tarman, Ömer Rüschtü.
Baklagillerden yem bitkileri yetiştirilmesi

see under

Turkey. Ziraat Vekaleti.

4
Turk.   **Tarman, Ömer Rüschtü**
815   En iyi yem otlarımızdan korunga. [Yazan]:
Ömer Tarman. [19]
[3] p.

(Tarım Vekaleti Çayır Mer'a ve Yem Nebatları Komitesi neşriyatı)

NT   0041347   DLC-P4

4
Turk.   **Tarman, Omer Rüschtü.**
816   Hayvanlara çok yarlıyan yonca.   [Yazan] Omer
Tarman [19]
[3] p.

NT   0041348   DLC-P4

S517
.T8C5   **Tarman, Ömer Rüschtü,** tr.

Christiansen-Weniger, Friedrich Johann Georg, 1897–
Türkiye genel ziraatinin temelleri [yazan] profesör dr. F. Christiansen-Weniger ... Türkçeye çevirenler dr. Ömer Tarman ve dr. Vamık Tayşı ... Ankara, Köyhocası matbaası, 1935.

Tarman, Tevfik.
Rayfayzen (Raiffeisen) kooperatifleri.   Ankara, 1936.

viii, 101 p. illus. 23 cm. (Ziraat Vekaleti. Neşriyat İşleri Direktörlüğü. İlmî araştırmalar serisi, [seri: A] sayı: 2)

Bibliography: p. [iii]

1. Raiffeisen, Friedrich Wilhelm, 1818–1888. 2. Agricultural cooperative credit associations—Germany. 3. Agricultural cooperative credit associations—Turkey. (Series: Turkey. Tarım Bakanlığı. İlmî araştırmalar serisi, seri: A, sayı: 2)

HG2051.T9T3   1936   N E 64–912

NT   0041350   DLC

Tarman, Tevfik.
Rayfayzen (Raiffeisen) kooperatifleri, yazan Tevfik Tarman ...   2. bas.   İstanbul, Devlet basımevi, 1937.

x, 95 p., 1 l. plates. 23ᶜᵐ.

1. Raiffeisen, Friedrich Wilhelm, 1818–1888. 2. Agricultural cooperative credit associations—Germany. 3. Agricultural cooperative credit associations—Turkey. I. Title: Kooperatifler.

Library of Congress   HG2051.T9T3

40–24485

NT   0041351   DLC

Tarmap Pacha-Huaray Azucenas Quechuas (Nuna shimi Chihuanhuai) (Bilingue). Tarma,1905.

see

Azucenas Quechuas

Tarmapap Pachahuarainin. Apologos Quechuas

see

Apologos Quechuas
Tarmapap Pachahuarainin. ...

Tarmess, Gisep.
Le spousa dil solegl; romanza.   Solothurn [
[17--?]
8 p.   8°.

NT   0041354   NIC

Tarmini Almertê.
L'illustre portugais ...
see under   Iturbide, Agustín de, emperor
of Mexico, 1783–1824.

Tarmini Almertê,   Geog 4348.14
Voyages de la reine d'Angleterre et du baron Pergami son chambellan, en Allemagne, en Italie, en Grèce, etc. pendant les années 1814–1820. Paris, Locard et Davi, etc. 1821.
Portraits.

Caroline, *queen consort of George IV, king of Gr. Brit.*

NT   0041356   MH PV

TARMIO, VEIKKO.
Kesäretkien Kuusamo. [Piirrokset Armas Lähteenkorva]
Helsingissä, Otava [1951]   78 p.   illus., map.   21cm.

1. Outdoor life—Finland—Kuusamo.

NT   0041357   NN DLC-P4

HC337
E7R6   **Tarmisto, Vello.**

Rostovtsev, Mikhail Ivanovich.
Эстонская ССР; экономико-географический очерк.
Таллин, Эстонское гос. изд-во, 1955.

Tarn, Adam.
... Obraz ojca w czterech ramach, powieść. Warszawa, Wydaw. J. Przeworskiego, 1934.

2 p. l., 7–267, [1] p. 19½ᶜᵐ.

I. Title.

Library of Congress   PG7158.T3O2   37–36410
Copyright A—Foreign   24640
[2]   891.853

NT   0041359   DLC OC1

Tarn, Adam.
Zebranie w Piotrkowicach.   Warszawa, "Książka i wiedza," 1951.   31 p.   illus.   20cm.

1 Piotrowo, Poland—Soc. condit.

NT   0041360   NN

Tarn, Adam.
Zwykła sprawa, sztuka w trzech aktach.   [Warszawa] "Czytelnik," 1950.   62 p.   21cm.

1. Drama, Polish.   I. Title.

NT   0041361   NN NNC CLU InU

Tarn, Albert
The individual and the state; a brief analysis of political government. London,1891.
Pamphlet

NT   0041362   CtY

TARN, ALBERT.
The state; its origin; its nature, and its abolition.
Birmingham, C.Stocker [1889?]   20 p.   18cm.

Microfiche (neg.) 1 sheet.   11 x 15cm.   (NYPL FSN 10,580)
Imperfect: p.19-20 wanting.

1. Anarchism.

NT   0041363   NN

Tarn, Arthur Wyndham.
The course of legislation, of the teaching of assurance, and of the development of the contract of assurance, since the congress at Vienna.   (In: International Congress of Actuaries, VII. Amsterdam, 1912. Reports, memoirs and proceedings. Amsterdam, 1912.   8°.   v. 2, p. 241-258.)

Contains synopses in French and German.

1. Insurance.—Education.
N. Y. P. L.   September 6, 1913.

NT   0041364   NN

Tarn, Arthur Wyndham.
The educational work of the Institute of Actuaries. (In: International Actuarial Congress. V.   Berlin, 1906.   Berichte, Denkschriften und Verhandlungen.   Berlin, 1906.   8°.   v. 2, p. 387-396.)

With synopses in French and German.

1. Insurance (Life).—Education,   Gt. Br. 2. Institute of Actuaries.
N. Y. P. L.   September 11, 1912.

NT   0041365   NN

Tarn, Arthur Wyndham.
Historical review of life assurance in Great Britain and Ireland, being a supplement to the Insurance guide and hand-book (5th ed.) London, C. and E. Layton, 1912.

Tarn, Arthur Wyndham, ed.
The insurance guide and hand-book
see under   Walford, Cornelius, 1827-1885.

Tarn, Arthur Wyndham, comp.
A record of the Guardian assurance company limited, 1821-1921, comp. by A. W. Tarn and C. E. Byles, with an introduction by the chairman ... Printed for private circulation. [London, Printed by Blades, East & Blades ltd.] 1921.
3 p. l., 153 p. incl. fold. tab. front., plates, ports., fold. facsims. 23cm.
Errata slips inserted.

1. Guardian assurance company limited, London.   i. Byles, Charles Edward, 1873-   joint comp. ii. Title.

Library of Congress   HG8598.Z9G8   22-12409

NT 0041368   DLC ICJ CaBVaU

Tarn, Arthur Wyndham.
The student's guide to life assurance in theory and practice; to which are added chapters on fire and other branches of insurance, by Arthur Wyndham Tarn ... London, Macdonald & Evans, 1912.
vi, [2], 224 p. incl. tables, diagr. 19cm.

1. Insurance. 2. Insurance, Life.
                                                      A 13-664
Title from Univ. of Chicago   HG8051.T2   Printed by L. C.

NT 0041369   ICU CtY ICJ

BX5132
.A1P12   **Tarn,** Arthur Wyndham
no.2   Thirteen centuries of the see of London :
in: a lecture delivered at St. Mark's, Regent's
SWTS   Park, April 21, 1904. - London : Society for
             Promoting Christian Knowledge ; New York :
             Edwin S. Gorham, 1904.
             39p. ; 17cm. - (Pamphlets ;no. 2)

1. London (Diocese)—Hist. I. Title.

NT 0041370   IEG

Tarn, David E.
An architectural monograph on the town of Suffield, Connecticut, with text by David E. Tarn; prepared for publication by Russell F. Whitehead ... [St. Paul, White pine bureau] 1921.
16 p. illus. 28¼cm.   (On cover: The white pine series of architectural monographs, vol. VII, no. 6)
Title within ornamental border.

1. Architecture, Domestic—Suffield, Conn.   i. Whitehead, Russell Fenimore, 1884-   ed. ii. Title.
                                                      22-3198
Library of Congress   NA7238.S9T3
——— Copy 2.   NA1.W6 vol. VII, no. 6

          OC1MA MB
NT 0041371   DLC NcD MsU MU MeB FU WaS OrU ViU MiU

Tarn, Edward Wyndham.
Carpentry & joinery, by E. Tarn and Thomas Tredgold. 1873.

NT 0041372   PPFr

Tarn, Edward Wyndham.   4018.117
An elementary treatise on joinery.
(In Tredgold, Thomas. Elementary principles of carpentry. Pp. 217-288. London, 1880.)

E4670 — Joinery.

NT 0041373   MB

TH
2431   **Tarn, Edward Wyndham.**
T3   An elementary treatise on the construction of
HRC   roofs of wood and iron, deduced chiefly from the
NonCirc works of Robinson, Tredgold, and Humber. By
             E. Wyndham Tarn, M.A., architect,.. With
             numerous illus.   London, Crosby Lockwood and
             Co., 1882.
             viii, 116 p.   illus.   18 cm.   (On cover:
             Weale's rudimentary series, no. 228)
             Armorial bookplate of Royal Institute of
             British Architects, "The Pink Bequest, 1889."
             48 p. advertisement bound in a end.
             Inscribed: Ch: Richard Pink, [?] 1883.

1. Roofs. 2. Roofing, Iron and steel.

NT 0041375   TxU DeU MiD

Tarn, Edward Wyndham.   8097.58
An elementary treatise on the construction of roofs of wood and iron. Deduced chiefly from the works of Robison, Tredgold and Humber. 3d edition, with an appendix.
London. Lockwood. 1893. viii, 128 pp. Illus. Plates. Plans.
[Weale's Rudimentary series.] 17 cm., in 12s.

L6161 — S.r. — Roofs.

NT 0041376   MB TxU

ar V
22486   **Tarn, Edward Wyndham.**
             An elementary treatise on the
             construction of roofs of wood and iron,
             deduced chiefly from the works of
             Robisnon, Tredgold, and Humber, by E.
             Wyndham Tarn. 5th ed. London C.
             Lockwood and Son, 1906.
             viii, 128 p. illus. 18cm. (Weale's
             scientific & technical series.)
             Cover title: Roofs of wood & iron.

1. Roofs I. Title II. Title: Roofs of wood & iron.

NT 0041377   NIC

Tarn, Edward Wyndham.
Light. An introduction to the science of optics. London, C. Lockwood and son, 1890.
viii, 112 p. Sm. 8°. [Weale's rudimentary series]

NT 0041378   MB

Tarn, Edward Wyndham.
The mechanics of architecture. A treatise on applied mechanics especially adapted to the use of architects.
London. Lockwood. 1892. xi, 367 pp. Diagrams. 18½ cm., in 8s.   8097 54

L8979 — T.r. — Building. — Mechanics. Applied.

NT 0041379   MB MiD RPB OC1

Tarn, Edward Wyndham.   690.2 P203
4001 The mechanics of architecture ; a treatise on applied mechanics especially adapted to the use of architects. Second edition, enlarged. xi,374 p. 125 il. D. London: C. Lockwood & Son, 1894.

NT 0041380   ICJ PU CU OCU MB

Tarn, Edward Wyndham
Practical geometry for the architect, engineer, surveyor and mechanic: giving rules for the delineation and application of various geometrical lines, figures, and curves. London, Lockwood, 1871.
xvi, 170p. illus. 22cm.

NT 0041381   NIC PPT MB

Tarn, Edward Wyndham.
Practical geometry for the architect, engineer, surveyor & mechanic; giving rules for the delineation & application of various geometrical lines, figures & curves, with appendices on diagrams of strains & isometrical projection.
London, Lockwood, 1882.
178 p.

NT 0041382   PU-FA MH MB

Tarn, Edward Wyndham
The science of building: an elementary treatise on the principles of construction. Especially adapted to the requirements of architectural students. By E. Wyndham Tarn... London, Lockwood and co., 1870.
viii,120 p. incl. table, diagrs. 22cm.

1. Building. I. Title.

NT 0041383   DP DSI MiU

arV
19680   **Tarn, Edward Wyndham.**
             The science of building: an elementary
             treatise on the principles of construction.
             2d ed. rev. and enl. London, C. Lockwood,
             1882.
             xii, 211 p. illus. 19cm.

NT 0041384   NIC

TH
146
T375   **Tarn, Edward Wyndham.**
1890   The science of building; an
HRC   elementary treatise on the principles
NonCirc of construction. Especially adapted
             to the requirements of architectural
             students, by E. Wyndham Tarn. 3d ed.,
             rev. and enl. London, Crosby
             Lockwood, 1890.
             216p. illus. 19cm.
             (Weale's rudimentary series, 267)
             Publisher's list bound in.
             Inscribed: F.H. Greenaway.
             1. Building. I. TITLE.
AF Greenaway, Francis Hugh, d. 1935.
CO- WEI

NT 0041385   TxU DSI DP MB

Tarn, Edward Wyndham.   690.2 0901
**** The science of building: an elementary treatise on the principles of construction especially adapted to the requirements of architectural students. Fourth edition. xii,216 p. 58 il. nar.D.
[Weale's rudimentary series, no. 267.] London: C. Lockwood & Son, 1896.

NT 0041386   ICJ

Tarn, Edward Wyndham, ed.

Dobson, Edward, ed.
The student's guide to the practice of measuring and valuing artificers' works: containing directions for taking dimensions, abstracting the same, and bringing the quantities into bill; with tables of constants, for valuation of labour. Originally ed. by Edward Dobson ...
New ed., with additions of mensuration and construction, and several useful tables for facilitating calculations and measurements, by E. Wyndham Tarn ... With nine plates and forty-seven woodcuts. London, Lockwood & co., 1871.

Tarn, H   **C**
Magnetism. Part I. of Magnetism and electricity. For the first stage of the specific subject, Educational code; and for the elementary magnetism of the Science and art department. By H. C. Tarn ... London and Edinburgh, W. & R. Chambers, 1884.

58 p. illus., diagrs. 17ᶜᵐ.

1. Magnetism.

QC753.T26   46–44470

NT   0041388   DLC DN

Tarn, H. C.   3969.132
Magnetism and electricity. For the use of students in schools and science classes.
London. Chambers. 1886. viii, 5–188 pp. Illus. Sm. 8°.

H7670 — Electricity. Theory and history. — Magnetism.

NT   0041389   MB OC1

Tarn, H. C.
Magnetism and electricity, for the use of students in schools and science classes. Chambers, 1890.
188 p. illus. maps, diagrs.

NT   0041390   MiD

Tarn , J.
Uber die proteolytischen enzyme der milchsaurebakterien. 1930.
Akademisk avhandling – Helsingfors

NT   0041391   OU

Tarn, Pauline Mary
   see
   Vivien, Renée, 1877-1909.

Tarn, Shirley.
Seven years... Steyning, The Vine press [etc., etc.] 1928.
3 p. l., v–xi, 14 p., 1 l. 20.5 cm. (Half-title: The Hermes books, no. 1)
"Of this book four hundred copies have been printed... This is number 276. "

NT   0041393   PSC

Tarn, Timothy Graham, 1851-1906.
The supernatural, the essential element in church life, by Rev. T. G. Tarn and lay preaching and nonconformity, by Rev. W. Bishop. Papers read at the annual session of the Baptist Union, on Thursday, April 26th, 1888. London, Alexander & Shepheard, 1888.
20p. 21cm.

1. Baptists--Addresses, essays, lectures. I. Bishop, W   II. Title. III. Title: Lay preach-   ing and nonconformity. IV. Baptist Union   of Great Britain and Ireland.

NT   0041394   KyLoS

Tarn, William Woodthrope, 1869-/957.
Alexander the Great. Cambridge [Eng.] University Press, 1948.
2 v. fold. map. 23 cm.
"Vol. I consists in the main of ... chapters XII and XIII in volume VI of the Cambridge ancient history ... carefully corrected and brought up to date."
CONTENTS.—v. 1. Narrative.—v. 2. Sources and studies.

1. Alexander the Great, 356–323 B. c.

DF234.T3   938.07   48–10280 rev*

NIC NcRS OrPR NWM OKentU MoU MeB
DDO CtY ViU OO PU OU TxU CaBViP MiU CaBVaU AzU MtU
NT   0041395   DLC PHC PLF TU KEmT PU CU MB OC1W PSt

Tarn, William Woodthrope, 1869-/957.
Alexander the Great. Cambridge [Eng.] Univ. Press, 1950.

Contents.-2. Sources and studies.

NT   0041396   MH

938.07
T189a
    Tarn, William Woodthrope, 1869-/957.
    Alexander the Great. Cambridge [Eng.] University Press, 1951-
    2 v. fold. map. 23 cm.
    "Vol. I consists in the main of ... chapters XII and XIII in volume VI of the Cambridge ancient history ... carefully corrected and brought up to date."
    CONTENTS.—v. 1. Narrative.—v. 2. Sources and studies.

NT   0041397   NSyU MH OrU

Tarn, William Woodthorpe, 1869-
... Alexander the Great and the unity of mankind, by W. W. Tarn ...
(*In* British academy, London. Proceedings, 1933. London [1935] 26 cm. [v. 19] p. [123]–166)
At head of title: Raleigh lecture on history.
"Read May 10, 1933."

1. Alexander the Great, 356–323 B. c.

[AS122.L5 vol. 19]   A 35—884
Wisconsin. Univ. Libr.
for Library of Congress   [a57c¹]

NT   0041398   WU MiU OC1 DDO CaBVaU

Tarn, William Woodthorpe, 1869-
Alexander the Great and the unity of mankind, by W. W. Tarn ... London, H. Milford [1933]
46 p., 1 l. 26ᶜᵐ. (The Raleigh lecture on history ... British academy, 1933)
"From the Proceedings of the British academy. Volume XIX."

1. Alexander the Great, B. c. 356–323.

Library of Congress   DF234.25.T3   34–19196
                      938.07

NT   0041399   DLC PHC PSC OC1W OCU OC1 NN

Tarn, William Woodthorpe, 1869-
Antigonos Gonatas, by William Woodthorpe Tarn. Oxford, Clarendon press, 1913.
xi, [1], 501, [1] p. incl. geneal. tables. front. 23½ᶜᵐ.
Bibliographical foot-notes.

1. Antigonous Gonatas, king of Macedonia, B. c. 319?–239. 2. Macedonia—History. 3. Greece—History.

                           A 14—3069
Stanford univ. Library
for Library of Congress   DF237.A6T3

MdBJ NBuC Or OrPR MB
ODW OCU OC1W MiU OO ViU DLC DDO NjP ICU MiU IU NN
NT   0041400   CSt CU NIC MsU OKentU PU PHC PBm NcD CtY

Tarn, William Woodthorpe, 1869-
The Greeks in Bactria & India, by W. W. Tarn ... Cambridge [Eng.] The University press, 1938.
xxiii, 539 p. pl., 3 fold. maps, fold. geneal. tab. 24ᶜᵐ.
Bibliography: p. [xv]–xvii.

1. India—Hist.—Early. 2. Bactria—Hist. 3. Greeks in India. 4. Hellenism. I. Title.

Library of Congress   DS451.T3   38–36951
                            [938.08] 934

OC1W ICU CU KyLoU NN MtU OrPR PU PSC PHC PBm
NT   0041401   DLC OC1 DDO CtY NcD ViU OU OCU OO NNC

Tarn, William Woodthorpe, 1869-
The Greeks in Bactria & India. [2d ed.] Cambridge [Eng.] University Press, 1951.
xxiii, 561 p. plate, 3 fold. maps, geneal. table. 25 cm.
Bibliography: p. [xv]–xviii.

1. India—Hist.—Early. 2. Bactria—Hist. 3. Greeks in India. 4. Hellenism. I. Title.

DS451.T3 1951   [938.08] 934   52–6532

NmU OrPR WaS MsU
NN PLF IU NSyU CSf CLSU KEmT NRU AAP DAU MoU OrU
NT   0041402   DLC CU FMU MiU PPEB ViU CtY DDO NcD NBC

Tarn, William Woodthorpe, 1869-

The **Hellenistic** age; aspects of Hellenistic civilization, treated by J. B. Bury ... E. A. Barber ... Edwyn Bevan ... and W. W. Tarn ... Cambridge, Eng., The University press, 1923.

Tarn, William Woodthorpe, 1869-
Hellenistic civilisation, by W. W. Tarn ... London, E. Arnold & co., 1927.
viii, 312 p. 22½ᶜᵐ.
"List of books": p. 299–303.

1. Civilization, Greek. 2. Hellenism. I. Title.

Library of Congress   DF77.T3   27–25936

WaS
OC1W OCU MiU OC1 OCX ICU MB NN NjP NNJ MeB OrPR Or
NT   0041404   DLC PBm PSC PHC NRCR CtY NcD TU NjNbS

Tarn, William Woodthorpe, 1869-
Hellenistic civilisation, by W. W. Tarn ... 2d ed. London, E. Arnold & co., 1930.
viii, 334 p. 22½ᶜᵐ.
"List of general works": p. 326.

1. Civilization, Greek. 2. Hellenism. I. Title.

Library of Congress   DF77.T3 1930   31–9727
                              913.38

NcD ViU OU OC1W ODW OO IdU
NT   0041405   DLC WaWW TxU NN PBm CaBVaU NBuU MtU CtY

Tarn, William Woodthorpe, 1869-
Hellenistic civilisation, by W. W. Tarn ... 2d ed. *London, E. Arnold & co., [1936]
viii, 334 p. 22½ᶜᵐ.
"List of general works": p. 326.
*2d impression.
"Reprinted 1936."

NT   0041406   ViU DDO MH NNUT

938
T175h
1930r   TARN, WILLIAM WOODTHORPE, 1869-
     Hellenistic civilisation, by W.W. Tarn ... [2d ed.] London, E. Arnold & co. [1947] viii, 334p. 22½ᶜᵐ.

     ."Second edition 1930. Reprinted 1947." "List of general works": p.326.

     1. Civilization, Greek. 2. Hellenism. I. Title.

NT   0041407   TxU PPDrop MH

Tarn, William Woodthorpe, 1869–
Hellenistic civilisation.   3d ed., rev. by the author and
G. T. Griffith.   London, E. Arnold ₍1952₎
xi, 372 p.   maps.   22 cm.
"List of general works": p. 361   Bibliographical footnotes.

1. Civilization, Greek.   2. Hellenism.   I. Title.

DF77.T3 1952   913.38   52–8411

WaWW MtBuM OrPR KEmT CaBVaU
CaBVa LU Wa WaTU CtY MiHM OrU OrAshS OrCS OrPS
KyLoS KyLxCB OrPS WU CU OO PPEB NN NIC CaBVaU MH
NT   0041408   DLC PSt TU PBm DDO WaT DAU MBtS KyU AU

Tarn, William Woodthorpe, 1869–
Hellenistic military & naval developments, by W. W. Tarn
... Cambridge ₍Eng.₎ University press, 1930.
vii, 170 p., 1 l.   19½ᶜᵐ.
"The three lectures here published are the Lee-Knowles lectures in
military history for 1929–30, delivered at Trinity college, Cambridge."

I. Military art and science—Hist.   2. Naval art and science—Hist.
I. Title.

Library of Congress   U33.T3   31–17173
——— Copy 2.   355.09

OC1W ODW OCU ICU MH NN WaS CaBVaU NhU MtBC ViU
NT   0041409   DLC MiU MU CtY PU PHC CtY NcD NIC DDO

Tarn, William Woodthrope, 1869–1957.
The oarage of Greek warships...   [London,
1933]
Cover-title, [52]–74 p.   illus.   25 cm.
Reprinted from the Mariner's mirror, vol. 19,
no. 1, January 1933.

NT   0041410   RPB

Tarn, William Woodthorpe, 1869– *1957.*
Seleucid-Parthian studies, by W. W. Tarn.   London, H.
Milford ₍1930₎
33 p.   25ᶜᵐ.
"From the Proceedings of the British academy, vol. XVI."
Communicated March 12, 1930.
Bibliographical foot-notes.
CONTENTS.—I. The invaders of Bactria.—II. The nomad invasion of
Parthia.—III. The Bactrian satrapies of eastern Tapuria and Traxiane.—
IV. Seleucid administrative subdivisions.
1. Seleucids.   2. Parthia—History.   3. Bactria.   I. British acad-
emy, London.   A 33–439
Title from Univ. of Penn-   ⸗sylvania.   Printed by L. C.

NT   0041411   PU

Tarn, William Woodthorpe, 1869–
Seleucid-Parthian studies, by W. W. Tarn ...
(*In* British academy, London.   Proceedings, 1930.   London ₍1932₎
26ᶜᵐ.   ₍v. 16₎ p. ₍105₎–135)
"Communicated March 12, 1930."
Bibliographical foot-notes.
CONTENTS.—I. The invaders of Bactria.—II. The Nomad invasion of
Parthia.—III. The Bactrian satrapies of eastern Tapuria and Traxiane.—
IV. Seleucid administrative subdivisions.
1. Seleucids.   2. Parthia—History.   3. Bactria.   I. Title.
                                                      A 34–2694
Wisconsin. Univ. Libr.
for Library of Congress   [AS122.L5 vol. 16]

DLC MiU MB
NT   0041412   WU CtY PU PBm MiU MH CaOTP CaBVaU DDO

Tarn, William Woodthorpe.
The treasure of the isle of mist, by W. W. Tarn; with six
illustrations by Somerled Macdonald.   London, P. Allan &
co., 1919.
4 p. l., 163 p.   front., plates.   22½ cm.

I. Title.

PZ8.T176Tr   19—19075

NT   0041413   DLC MB

Tarn, William Woodthorpe.
The treasure of the isle of mist, by W. W. Tarn.   New
York and London, G. P. Putnam's sons, 1920.
v p., 1 l., 192 p.   19ᶜᵐ.

I. Title.

Library of Congress   PZ8.T176Tr 2   20—1903

NcU OEac OC1 NN
NT   0041414   DLC ViU MB PP PWcS PPFr WaSp WaS Or MB

Tarn, William Woodthorpe, 1869–1957.
The treasure of the Isle of Mist, a tale
of the Isle of Skye, by W. W. Tarn.   2d ed.
London, P. Allan ₍1921₎
4 p. l., 163 p.
"A fairy tale" first published 1919 .

NT   0041415   ScU GU

PZ 7
T176   **Tarn, Sir William Woodthorpe,** 1869–1957.
Tr   The treasure of the isle of mist, by
1920   W. W. Tarn.   New York, Putnam's [1926,
              c1920]
              v, 192 p.   21 cm.

NT   0041416   CaBVaU

Tarn, William Woodthorpe, 1869–
The treasure of the isle of mist, by W. W. Tarn; illustrated
by Robert Lawson.   New York, G. P. Putnam's sons ₍ᶜ1934₎
6 p. l., 184 p. incl. illus., plates.   front.   22ᶜᵐ.
Illustrated lining-papers.

I. Title.

Library of Congress   PZ8.T176Tr 16   34–27187

NT   0041417   DLC OO MB NN PPT WaS Or

PZ
8   **Tarn, William Woodthorpe,** 1869–
.T176Fr2   The treasure of the isle of mist, by
1938   W. W. Tarn.   London, Oxford University
              Press, 1938.
              166 p.   19 cm.

NT   0041418   OKentU OC1

Tarn, *France (Dept.)*
Budget des recettes et des dépenses départementales.
Albi.
v.   32 cm.

1. Budget—Tarn, France (Dept.)

HJ9047.A3T32   53–27959 ‡

NT   0041419   DLC

HV
269   Tarn , France (Dept.)
T18   Cahiers des doléances du Tiers-État;
A2   villes, villages & bourgs du diocèse
              de Lavaur.   Albi, G. M. Nouguiès, 1889.
              52 p.   25cm.
              At head of title: Revue du Département
              du Tarn.

NT   0041420   NIC

Tarn, *France (Dept.)* Mémoire sur la vaccine, et rapport sur les vaccinations pratiquées
en 1824, dans l'arrondissement de Gaillac.   Présenté à M. le vicomte de Cazes, préfet du département du Tarn, par Joseph-Jean-Antoine Rigal
f'a.   84 pp.   8°.   Albi, F.-M. Baurens, 1825.

NT   0041421   DNLM

Tarn, *France (Dept.)*
——. Travaux des Conseils d'hygiène publique
et de salubrité du département du Tarn pendant
les années 1851–74.   8°.   Albi, 1857–76.

NT   0041422   DNLM

Tarn,   France (Dept.)
Usages locaux ayant force de loi et
topographie legale (departement du Tarn)
see under   Clausade, Amédée, 1809–1847.

CD1215   **Tarn, France (Dept.) Archives Departementales.**
.f.T2   Inventaire-sommaire des archives départementales...
Tarn... Albi, Impr. G.M. Nouguiès; ₍etc., etc. ₍1873–
v.   31½ cm.   (Half-title: Collection des inventaires-sommaires des archives départementales...publiée
par ordre de son excellence m. le comte de Persigny, ministre de l'intérieur)
Set incomplete.
1. Archives—France—Tarn (Dept.)   2. Tarn, France
(Dept.)—Hist.—Sources.

NT   0041424   ICU

Tarn,   France (Dept.) Archives départementales.
Inventaire-sommaire des Archives départementales antérieures à 1790, rédigé par É. Jolibois,
Archiviste.   Albi,   Impr. G.-M. Nouguiès,
1868?–
v. in 33 cm.   (Collection des inventaires⸗
sommaires des Archives départementales antérieures à 1790)
Contents. –

t. 2. Archives civiles.   Série C, nos. 425–851 [i. e.
1275] - série D. - série E, nos. 1–687. - t. 3.
Archives civiles.   Série E suppl. nos. 688–5438.
Communes. 2 v. - t. 4.   Série G et H.   Archives
ecclésiastiques par Ch. Portal.
1. Tarn, France (Dept.) - History - Sources -
Bibliography.   I. Jolibois, Émile, *1813–*
II. Portal, Charles   Louis Henri Félix Antoine,
1862–

NT   0041426   NjP CU MdBJ

Tarn,   France (Dept.) Archives departementales.
Inventaire sommaire des archives communales
antérieures á 1790...   Ville de Cordes
see under   Cordes, France (Tarn)

Tarn, France (Dept.).   Archives départementales.
Inventaire-sommaire des Archives départementales posté-
rieures à 1789.   Tarn.   Période révolutionnaire, série L.
Albi, Impr. nouvelle, 1926–
v.   33 cm.
Half title, v. 1: Collection des inventaires-sommaires des Archives
départementales postérieures à 1789.
Vol. 2 printed by Impr. albigeoise.
CONTENTS.—Articles 1 à 330, rédigé par C. Thomas, aide-archiviste
⸗paléographe, avec la collaboration de C. Thomas, aide-archiviste
(pour les articles 1 à 129)—t. 2. Articles 331–707, rédigé par C.
Portal, publié par H. Forestier, H. Chanteux et P. Bayaud.—t. 3.

1. ptie. Articles L 708 à 845, rédigé par C. Portal, publié par P.
Bayaud et M. Greslé-Bouignol.   Suivi d'un supplément au répertoire
numérique de la série L, par M. Greslé-Bouignol.

1. Tarn, France (Dept.)—History—Sources—Bibliography.
I. Title.

CD1215.T25T37 1926   68–41029

NT   0041429   DLC CU

Tarn, *France (Dept.) Archives départementales.*
Répertoire numérique de la série Q, rédigé par Ch. Portal, archiviste-paléographe. Albi, Impr. A. Nouguiès, 1919.
48 p. 33 cm.
—— Répertoire numérique. Série Q (supplément) domaines nationaux. Série 1 à 32 Q, domaines, enregistrement et timbre. Séries II C et 33 à 294 Q, registres de formalité. Dressé par Pierre Bayaud, archiviste départemental. Albi, Impr. des orphelins-apprentis, 1938.
61 p. 31 cm.
CD1215.T25A545 Suppl.
1. Tarn, France (Dept.)—Hist.—Sources—Bibl.

CD1215.T25A545   68–41011

NT   0041430   DLC CU

Tarn, *France (Dept.) Archives départementales.*
Répertoire numérique de la série Y (établissements de répression) dressé par Jean Armingaud, sous-archiviste principal. Albi, Impr. coopérative du Sud-Ouest, 1953.
5 p. 32 cm.
At head of title: Archives départementales du Tarn. Posterieures à 1790.

1. Tarn, France (Dept.)—Hist.—Sources—Bibl.

CD1215.T25A554   68–41025

NT   0041431   DLC CU MiU

Tarn, *France (Dept.) Archives départementales.*
Répertoire numérique des archives notariales du Tarn, dû aux travaux successifs de E. Jolibois [et al.], archivistes en chef, et de J. Armingaud, sous-archiviste. Albi, Impr. coopérative du Sud-Ouest, 1951.
123 p. 32 cm.
Cover title.

1. Tarn, France (Dept.)—Hist.—Sources—Bibl.   I. Title.

CD1215.T25A56   68–41010

NT   0041432   DLC CU MdBJ

Tarn, France (Dept.) Comité de vaccine.
Dixième rapport fait au nom du comité, à M. le baron Baude... Albi, Baurens, 1813.
15 p. 4°. [P., v. 857]
Par Jean-Jaques Rigal.

NT   0041433   DNLM

33.17
F8498   Tarn, France (Dept.) Chambre d'agriculture.
L'agriculture tarnaise. [Albi, Tarn] 1936-
1 v. (loose-leaf)
Kept up-to-date by supplementary sheets.
1. France. Département du Tarn. Agriculture. I. France. Département du Tarn. Syndicat de l'   l'enseignement agricole.

NT   0041434   DNAL

Tarn, France (Dep't.) Commission des antiquité[

see

Commission des antiquités de la ville de Castres et du departement du Tarn.

Tarn, *France (Dept.) Conseil général.*
Procès-verbal des délibérations.

Albi.
v. 21 cm.

1. Tarn, France (Dept.)—Pol. & govt.

JS7.F7T25   49–28795*‡

NT   0041436   DLC NN NjP

Tarn, *France (Dept.) Préfecture.*
Rapport du préfet au Conseil général.

Albi.
v. in   22 cm.
Title varies: 1845-50, Rapport du préfet et Délibérations du Conseil.—1858-19   Rapport du préfet au Conseil général et Procès-verbal des délibérations du Conseil (varies slightly)
Issues for 19   bound with Procès-verbal des délibérations du Conseil général.

1. Tarn, France (Dept.)—Pol. & govt.

JS7.F7T22   49–28796 rev*‡

NT   0041437   DLC

Tarn, France (Dept.) Prefecture.
Rapport du préfet au Conseil général et Procès verbal des delibérations du Conseil...
see its   Rapport du préfet au Conseil général.

Tarn, France (Dept.) Prefecture.
Rapport du préfet et Delibérations du Conseil...
see its   Rapport du préfet au Conseil général.

Tarn, France (Dept.) Service Vicinal.
Service vicinal, Département du Tarn: chemins de grande communication; état des anciens chemins dont elles sont formées. Albi, Corbière & Julien, 1894.
195 p.   map.   21 cm.

NT   0041440   NIC

Tarn-et-Garonne, *France (Dept.)* Rapports généraux sur les travaux des Conseils d'hygiène publique et de salubrité du département de Tarn-et-Garonne (juillet 1849 à décembre 1869), présenté à M. le préfet par le Doct. John Lacaze, secrétaire. 2 v. x,-307 pp.; xi, 315 pp. 8°. *Montauban, 1850-70.*

NT   0041441   DNLM

Tarn-et-Garonne, France (Dept.)
Academie de sciences, belles-lettres et arts
see   Academie des sciences, belles-lettres et arts de Tarn-et-Garonne. Montauban.

CD 1217
.C34
T3 Q   Tarn-et-Garonne, France (Dept.) Archives départementales.
Archives communales de Castelsarrasin antérieures à 1789. [Montauban? n.d.]
11 l.   29cm.
Caption title.
Reproduced from typewritten copy.
"Avant-propos" signed Mathieu Méras, Directeur des Services d'archives du Tarn-et-Garonne.
1. Castel-   sarrasin, France - Hist. - Sources -   Bibl. I. Méras, Mathieu.

NT   0041443   MdBJ

TARN-ET-GARONNE, *France (Dept.) Archives depart.*
Archives de Tarn-et-Garonne. Répertoire provisoire des titres des communautés d'habitants dans la série E des Archives de Tarn-et-Garonne dressée par R. Latouche. Montauban, G. Forestié, 1920.

NT   0041444   MH

Tarn-et-Garonne, France (Dept.) Archives départementales.
CD1217
.M56D8   **Dumas de Rauly, Charles.**
Inventaire-sommaire des archives communales et hospitalières de Moissac [antérieures à 1790] Rédigé par Charles Dumas de Rauly et Alfred Gandilhon, archivistes du Département. Montauban, Impr. et lithographie Forestié, 1906-07 [cover 1912]

CD1217
f.V5   *Tarn-et-Garonne, France (Dept.) Archives depart.*
Inventaire-sommaire des archives communales ... de Verdun-sur-Garonne (Tarn-et-Garonne) ... Montauban, Impr. Forestié neveu, 1875-
v. 33cm. (Half-title: Collection des inventaires-sommaires des archives communales ... publiée sous la direction du Ministre de l'intérieur)
Set incomplete.

1. Archives--France--Verdun-sur-Garonne. 2. Verdun-sur-Garonne, France--Hist.--Sources.

NT   0041446   ICU

Tarn-et-Garonne, *France (Dept.) Archives départementales.*
Inventaire sommaire des Archives départementales antérieures à 1790. Tarn-et-Garonne. Archives civiles, série A: fonds d'Armagnac. Rédigé par M. Maisonobe, archiviste. Introd. par Ch. Samaran. Table générale par M. Imbert. Montauban, Impr. du Sud-Ouest, 1910.
xvi, 419 p. 33 cm.
Half-title: Collection des inventaires sommaires des Archives départementales antérieures à 1790.

1. Tarn-et-Garonne, France (Dept.)—Hist.—Sources—Bibl. I. Title.

CD1215.T3A445   68–41028

NT   0041447   DLC

Tarn-et-Garonne, *France (Dept.) Archives départementales.*
Inventaire sommaire des Archives départementales antérieures à 1790. Tarn-et-Garonne. Archives civiles, série C: I. Intendance, élections, Bureau des finances. Rédigé par MM. Gandilhon, Imbert, Canal, Daucet, archivistes. Montauban, Impr. coopérative, 1946.
ix, 336 p. 33 cm.
Half-title: Collection des inventaires sommaires des Archives départementales antérieures à 1790.

1. Tarn-et-Garonne, France (Dept.)—Hist.—Sources—Bibl. I. Title.

CD1215.T3A45   68–41030

NT   0041448   DLC PU

CD 1215
.T3 A48
1894 Q   Tarn-et-Garonne, France (Dept.) Archives départementales.
Inventaire-sommaire des Archives départementales antérieures à 1790. Tarn-et-Garonne. Archives religieuses - Séries G et H. Rédigé par M. Georges Bourbon et M. Charles Dumas de Rauly. Montauban, Imprimerie et lithographie Édouard Forestié, 1894.
540 p. 33cm.
Half-title: Collection des inventaires-sommaires des archives départementales antérieures à 1790.

NT   0041449   MdBJ ICU

CD
1215   Tarn-et-Garonne, France (Dept.) Archives *Départementales.* 1.
.A2   Rapport... [Montauban?]
T3   v. 24 cm.
With this is bound Var, France (Dept.) Archives departementales. Rapport; Var, France (Dept.) Archives communales et hospitalières. Rapport; Vendée, France (Dept.) Archives. Rapport.
Inserted in volume lettered Rapports des archivistes departementaux. Tarn-et-Garonne. Var. Vendée. are Un très ancien inventaire imprimé des archives municipales

de Montauban (1662) (4 p.); Répertoire provisoire des titres des communautés d'habitants dans la série E des archives de Tarn-et-Garonne, dressé par m. R. Latouche 1920 (1 p.l., 29 p.)

NT   0041451   MiU

Tarn-et-Garonne, *France (Dept.) Archives départementales.*
Répertoire numérique de la série E, état civil, et des registres d'état civil conservés aux Archives communales. Dressé par B. Faucher, archiviste du département. Montauban, Impr. coopérative Barrier, 1925.
xxix, 28 p. 32 cm.

1. Tarn-et-Garonne, France (Dept.)—Hist.—Sources—Bibl.

CD1215.T3A533   68–41013

NT 0041452   DLC PU

Tarn-et-Garonne, *France (Dept.) Archives départementales.*
Répertoire numérique de la série L (administration de 1790 à l'an VIII) dressé par M. Latouche, archiviste. [Montauban] 1912.
8 p. 33 cm.
Cover title.

1. Tarn-et-Garonne, France (Dept.)—Hist.—Sources—Bibl.

CD1215.T3A54   68–40993

NT 0041453   DLC

Tarn-et-Garonne, *France (Dept.) Archives départementales.*
Répertoire numérique de la série Q (domaines nationaux) dressé par MM. Maisonobe et Imbert, archivistes. [Montauban] 1910.
16 p. 33 cm.
Cover title.

1. Tarn-et-Garonne, France (Dept.)—Hist.—Sources—Bibl.

CD1215.T3A546   68–41023

NT 0041454   DLC IaU

Tarn-et-Garonne, *France (Dept.) Archives départementales.*
Répertoire numérique de la série T (instruction publique, sciences et arts) dressé par S. Canal, archiviste départemental. Montauban, Impr. coopérative, 1931.
14 p. 33 cm.
Cover title.

1. Tarn-et-Garonne, France (Dept.)—Hist.—Sources—Bibl.

CD1215.T3A55   68–41005

NT 0041455   DLC

Tarn-et-Garonne, *France (Dept.) Archives départementales.*
Répertoire numérique de la série V (cultes) dressé par M. Latouche, archiviste. [Montauban] 1912.
4 p. 33 cm.
Cover title.

1. Tarn-et-Garonne, France (Dept.)—Hist.—Sources—Bibl.

CD1215.T3A553   68–41012

NT 0041456   DLC

Tarn-et-Garonne, *France (Dept.) Archives départementales.*
Répertoire numérique des séries I-IV E (titres féodaux, titres de famille, communautés et municipalités, corporations et confréries) Dressé par René Toujas, sous-archiviste. Introd. de Raymond Daucet. Montauban, Impr. Forestié, 1951.
47 p. 32 cm.

1. Tarn-et-Garonne, France (Dept.)—Hist.—Sources—Bibl.

CD1215.T3A57   68–41014

NT 0041457   DLC

Tarn-et-Garonne, France (Dept.) Comité du tourisme.
Le Tarn-et-Garonne. Guide officiel, édité sous le patronage de la Chambre de commerce de Montauban et de la Commission départementale du tourisme. 2. éd. Toulouse, Editions Inter-publicité [1954]
80 p. illus., map. 21 cm. (Interguide du touriste)
1. Tarn-et-Garonne, France (Department) --Guidebooks, 1954.

NT 0041458   NN

TE72
.T4A4
Tarn-et-Garonne, France (Dept.) Commission chargee de l'etude... du service vicinal.
... Rapport de M. Meuret. Montauban, 1902.

NT 0041459   DLC

Tarn-et-Garonne, *France (Dept.) Commission sur la Caisse des retraites.*
Caisse départementale des retraites du département de Tarn-et-Garonne. Modification des statuts. Rapport de la commission spéciale instituée par le Conseil général dans sa session d'août 1895. Montauban, Impr. administrative et commerciale J. Granié, 1896.
61 p. incl. tables. 22ᶜᵐ.
Signed: H. Dardenne, E. Guibal, F. Cauro.

1. Tarn-et-Garonne, France (Dept.) Caisse des retraites. 2. Old age pensions. I. Title.

CA 15-1279 Unrev'd

Library of Congress   HD7106.F8T3

NT 0041460   DLC

W2
GF7.1
T5C7r
(Dept.)
Tarn-et-Garonne, France, Conseil d'hygiène publique et de salubrité.
Rapport général sur les travaux. [t.] 1-   1849/58-
Montauban.
v.

NT 0041461   DNLM

RA262
.T25
1902
Tarn-et-Garonne, France (Dept.) Conseil general.
... Loi relative à la protection de la sante publique (15 férrier 1902) Organization departe-male. Avis du Conseil d'hygiene...
Montauban, 1902.
43 p.

NT 0041462   DLC

Tarn et Garonne, France (Dept.) Conseil general
Procès verbal des séances. Montauban, 1855-

NT 0041463   NjP

Tarn-et-Garonne, France (Dept.) Conseil general.
...Projet de reseau telephonique departemental..
Montauban, 1900

HE9198
.T3A5

NT 0041464   DLC

Tarn-et-Garonne (department), France. Conseil Général.
...Rapports du préfet, annexe et Procès-verbaux des séances.

Montauban,   8°.

NT 0041465   NN NjP

Tarn-et-Garonne, France (Dept.) Conseil general
Commission sur la Caisse des retraites.

sec

Tarn-et-Garonne, France (Dept.) Commission sur la Caisse des retraites

---

Tarn-et-Garonne, *France (Dept.) Préfecture.*
Rapport de ... préfet ... et Budget supplementaire.
Montauban.
v. 24 cm. annual.
At head of title: Tarn-et-Garonne. Conseil général.

1. Tarn-et-Garonne, France (Dept.)—Pol. & govt.

JS7.F7T415   49–28515*‡

NT 0041467   DLC

Tarn-et-Garonne, *France (Dept.) Préfecture.*
Rapport de ... préfet ... et Rapports des chefs de service.
Montauban.
v. 25 cm. annual.
At head of title: Tarn-et-Garonne. Conseil général.

1. Tarn-et-Garonne, France (Dept.)—Pol. & govt.

JS7.F7T414   49–43836*‡

NT 0041468   DLC

TE72
.T4A3
Tarn-et-Garonne, France (Dept.) Service vicinal.
... Rapport de l'agent voyer en chef.
Montauban, 1-

NT 0041469   DLC

14
T17
Le Tarn-et-Garonne agricole. année
Montauban, Services agricoles de Tarn-et-Garonne.

1. France. Département de Tarn-et-Garonne. Agriculture. 2. Agriculture. Periodicals. I. France. Direction des services agricoles de Tarn-et-Garonne.

NT 0041470   DNAL

Tarn. Nature du sol et population. Agriculture. Mines. Industrie. Communications et commerce. Histoire. Art. Archéologie. Tourisme... Paris: Hachette, 1925. 56 p. illus. (incl. ports.), maps. 12°.
Bibliography, p. 44.

1. Tarn (department), France.
N. Y. P. L.   February 7, 1928

NT 0041471   NN

Tarna, Miika
Kristillinen kansanopisto ja kansankirkko, synodaalikirjoitus Turun arkkihiippakunnan pappeinkokoukseen 1947. Rauma, 1947
168 p.

NT 0041472   MH DLC-P4

DK 411   TARNACKI, JOZEF
.T189   Kwestjonarjusz do badań słownictwa ludowego
         w zakresie kultury materjalnej. Ułożył J.
         Tarnacki.   Ze wstępem Witolda Doroszewskiego.
         ₍Warszawa₎ Nakł. Wydziału Humanistycznego
         Uniwersytetu Warszawskiego, 1933.
            32 p.

            1. Poland--Social life and customs.

NT   0041473   InU

891.85
B473
v.2   Tarnacki, Józef
            ... Studia porównawcze nad geografia wyrazów
         (Polesie-Mazowsze) ₍Études comparées sur la
         géographie des mots₎ Warszawa, Z Zasiłku fun-
         duszu kultury narodowej, 1939.
            2 p.l., 101 p.   illus., maps, fold. diagr.
         25ᶜᵐ. (Biblioteka prac filologicznych. t. II)

            "Literatura": p.₍95₎-97.
            Résumé in French: p. ₍99₎-101.
            1. Linguistic geography - Poland. 2. Polish
         language - Maps.   3. Polish language - Dia-
         lects - Polisia.   4. Polish language - Dia-
         lects - Mazovie.

NT   0041474   NNC IU MH CtY MiU ICU DLC-P4

         Tarnacre, Robert, *pseud.*
                 see
         Cartmell, Robert, 1877–

         Tarnai, Andor, joint ed.
            Batsányi János összes müvei
               see under Batsányi, János, 1763-1845.

         Tárnai, István
            Egyetlen vedő; gyermekszindarab 1 fel-
         vonasban.

NT   0041477   OC1

         Tárnai, István, ed.
            Március 15. Teljesen Kidogozott müsor,
         Második kiadás.
            24 p.
            Hungarian.

NT   0041478   OC1

         Tarnai, János, 1843-1930.
            ... Csemegi Károly emlékezete. A Magyar
         jogászegylet díszülése 1899 október 29.
         Budapest, Franklin-Társulat könyvnyomdája,
         1899.
            21 p. 21½cm. (Magyar jogászegyleti
         értekezések, 162. XIX. köt. 1. füz.)

            Speech by János Tarnai with an introduc-
         tion and epilogue by the president, Béla
         Vavrik.

NT   0041479   MH-L

         Tarnai, János, 1843-1930.
            ... Huszonkét levél az 1842-töl 1854-ig
         terjedő időszakból. Felolvasta 1884.
         nov. 22-én D̃ Tarnai János. Budapest,
         Franklin-Társulat könyvnyomdája, 1885.
            46 p. 23cm. (Magyar jogászegyleti
         értekezések, XX.)

NT   0041480   MH-L

         Tarnai, János, 1843-1930.
            ... A koronaügyészi hivatal. D̃ Tarnai
         János előadása, Hammersberg Jenő és
         Tóth Gerö felszólalásaival ... Budapest,
         Franklin-Társulat könyvnyomdája, 1901.
            29 p. 23cm. (Magyar jogászegyleti
         értekezések, 182. XXI. köt. 2. füz.)

            "A Magyar jogászegylet 1900. évi november
         hó 17-iki teljes ülésén."

NT   0041481   MH-L

         Tarnai, János, *1843-1930.*
            A politikai büntett; büntetőjogi tanulmány.
         Pécs, Wessely és Horváth, 1917.
            54 p. 24cm.

            "Különlenyomat a Büntgyi Szemle V. évfolya-
         mából."
            Bibliographical footnotes.

            1. Criminal law. 2. Political crimes and
         offenses. 3. Comparative law. I. Title.

NT   0041482   IU MH-L

         Tarnai, János, 1843-1930.
            Sajtójogi dolgozatok. Irta Tarnai
         János. Budapest, Franklin-Társulat,
         1913.
            215, ₍1₎ p. 24½cm.

            Bibliographical footnotes.

NT   0041483   MH-L

         Tarnanen, J.,
            Ueber die proteolytischen Enzyme der Milch-
         saeurebakterien.
            Inaug. diss. Helsinki, 1930.

NT   0041484   ICRL CtY

         Tarnani, Ivan   Konstantinovich, *1865-*
            Анатомія телифона (Thelyphonus caudatus (L)) Ana-
         tomie de Thelyphonus caudatus (L). Варшава, Тип. Вар-
         шавскаго учеб. округа, 1904.
            iii, 288 p. illus. 25 cm.
            At head of title: И. К. Тарнани.
            "Приложеніе къ XVI тому 'Записокъ Ново-Александрійскаго
         Института сельскаго хозяйства и лѣсоводства.'"
            Bibliography: p. ₍273₎–279.

            1. Thelyphonus caudatus. 2. Arachnida—Anatomy.   I. Title.
                                        Title romanized: Anatomīa telifona.

         QL458.P3T37   73–294007

NT   0041485   DLC NjP PPAN

         Tarnani, I₍van Konstantinovich₎ 1865–
            ... Insectes nuisibles dans les vergers et dans les pota-
         gers des gouvernements de la Pologne russe et mesures
         à prendre pour les combattre ... Варшава, Типографія
         Варшавскаго учебнаго округа, 1903.
            4 p. l., iv, 138 p. illus. 26ᶜᵐ. (Mémoires de l'Institut agronomique et
         forestier à Nowo-Alexandria (gouv. Lublin) vol. xv ₍suppl.₎)
            Added t.-p. and text in Russian.

            1. Entomology, Economic. 2. Poland. Entomology.
                                                        Agr 5-242

         Library, U. S. Dept. of   Agriculture 423T172.

NT   0041486   DNAL

         Tarnani, Ivan   Konstantinovich, *1865-*
            Насѣкомыя, вредныя для плодоводства и огородниче-
         ства въ губерніяхъ Царства Польскаго и мѣры борьбы
         съ этими насѣкомыми. И. К. Тарнани. Варшава, Тип.
         Варшава, Тип. Варшавскаго учеб. округа, 1903.
            iv, 138 p. illus. 26 cm.

            1. Insects, Injurious and beneficial—Poland. 2. Fruit—Diseases
         and pests—Poland. 3. Vegetables—Diseases and pests—Poland. I.
         Title.
                                        Title romanized: Nasѣkomyia,
                                        vrednyia dlia plodovodstva.

         SB931.T37   70–556962

NT   0041487   DLC

         Tarnassi, Antonio F   M
            La cruz en el árbol. Buenos Aires, Editorial "Ian S.
         Star" ₍1950₎
            215 p. 20 cm.

            I. Title.

         New York. Public Libr.   A 52-2420
         for Library of Congress

NT   0041488   NN TxU

         Tarnassi, Antonio F   M
            Divagaciones de un vigilante ₍relatos humorísticos₎
         Buenos Aires, El Ateneo ₍1947₎
            216 p. 21 cm.

            I. Title.

         New York. Public Libr   A 49-5776*
         for Library of Congress

NT   0041489   NN

         Tarnassi, Antonio F   M
            ... Persecución; relatos policiales del lejano sur. Prólogo de
         Enrique Marciano Iglesias. Buenos Aires ₍Talleres gráficos
         de B. U. Chiesino₎ 1943.
            2 p. L. ₍7₎-156 p., 2 l. illus. 20ᶜᵐ.

            1. Police — Argentine republic — Rio Negro (Ter.) 2. Crime and
         criminals—Argentine republic—Rio Negro (Ter.)   I. Title.
                                                        A 45-1029

         Harvard univ. Library
         for Library of Congress

NT   0041490   MH

         Tarnassi, Antonio F   M
            ... Presillas rojas; recuerdos policiales de la Patagonia.
         Buenos Aires ₍Imprenta Mercatali₎ 1942.
            4 p. L., 11–124 p., 1 l. 18½ᶜᵐ.

            1. Police—Argentine republic—Patagonia. 2. Crime and criminals—
         Argentine republic—Patagonia.   I. Title.
                                                        43-13719

         Library of Congress   HV7917.T3
                                                        351.74

NT   0041491   DLC TxU

         Tarnassi, José, *d. 1906.*

         Sáenz Peña, Roque, *pres. Argentine Republic,* 1851–1914.
            España y Estados Unidos; función dada en el teatro
         de la Victoria el 2 de mayo de 1898 bajo el patrocinio del
         Club español de Buenos Aires, á beneficio de la suscrip-
         ción nacional española; conferencias de los Señores Dr.
         Roque Sáenz Peña, Paul Groussac y Dr. José Tarnassi;
         prólogo del Dr. Severiano Lorente. Buenos Aires, Com-
         pañía sud-americana de billetes de banco, 1898.

         Tarnassi, José, *d.* 1906.
            ... Estudios latinos ... Buenos Aires, "Coni," 1939.
            2 v. front. (port.) facsims. 27½ᶜᵐ. (Facultad de filosofía y letras
         de la Universidad de Buenos Aires. Publicaciones del Instituto de
         literaturas clásicas. Serie especial, vol. I–II)
            "Prólogo" signed: Enrique François.
            "La presente edición reproduce, sin más que ligeras modificaciones
         tipográficas, los volúmenes publicados en vida del doctor Tarnassi,
         todos ellos agotados ya hace tiempo."—v. 1, p. xiii.
            CONTENTS.—I. Los poetas del siglo VI de Roma, estudiados en los
         escritores latinos.—II. Obras varias.

            1. Latin philology—Collected works. 2. Latin literature—Hist. & crit.
         I. François, Enrique, 1891–   ed. II. Title.
                                                        41-23768

         Library of Congress   PA2027.T3
                                                        870.4

NT   0041493   DLC PU TxU CU NIC

Tarnassi, José, d. 1906,-
Los poetas del siglo VI de Roma, estudiados
en los escritores latinos.   Buenos Aires,
J. Peuser, 1903.
xxix p., 1 l., 263 p.   25.5 x 19 cm.
v. 1 of his Estudios latinos.

NT   0041494   NcU

Tarnassi, Paolo.
Comento del passo di Danti dal verso 88-108
dal canto XXV. del Purgatorio, letto nell' adunanza
di Arcadia.   Roma, Tip. delle belle arti, 1859.
31 p.

NT   0041495   PU NIC

F   Tarnassi, Ricardo.
3001   Belgrano de antaño; recuerdos é impresiones.
T375   Buenos Aires, Tall. Gráf. D. Gurfinkel, 1922.
LAC   104p. 19cm.

    1. Belgrano, Argentine Republic (Buenos
Aires) I. Title. Sp.: Martínez Reales
Collection.

NT   0041496   TxU

F   Tarnassi, Ricardo.
3001   Recordar es vivir; continuación de Bel-
T376   grano de antaño.   [Buenos Aires?] Agencia
LAC   General de Librería y Publicaciones, 1923.
    122p. 18cm.

    1. Belgrano, Argentine Republic (Buenos
Aires) I. Title. II. Title: Belgrano de
antaño. Sp.: Martínez Reales Collection.

NT   0041497   TxU

F2809   Tarnassi de Schilken, Fabiola, ed.
.E795
    Estrada, José Manuel, 1842–1894.
        ... Non omnis moriar. Selección de juicios y fragmentos
    de sus escritos y obras completas, realizada por Fabiola Tarnassi
    de Schilken. Buenos Aires, Ediciones, Estrada, 1943.

NT   0041499   MdBP

Tarnat (Benedictine abbey)
Regula. **Regula monasterii Tarnatensis.** 5pp.
    (Mione, J. P., Patrol. s. Lat. v. 66, p. 977.)

NT   0041499   MdBP

Tarnate, Francisco Dalupan y
    see Dalupan y Tarnate, Francisco, 1896–

Tarnauceanu (Marcu), [1888–]. *Etude
sur les modifications de la chronaxie neuro-
musculaire par refroidissement d'un membre
chez l'homme normal. 112 pp. 8°. Paris,
1929. No. 260.*

NT   0041501   DNLM CtY

Tarnaud, Claude.
.La forme réfléchie, carnet de voyage et commentaires.
Illus. de Béatrice de La Sablière. ¡Paris; Le Soleil noir
¡1954;
    89 p. illus. 19 cm.

    I. Title.
                                    A 55–7092
Illinois. Univ. Library
for Library of Congress

NT   0041502   IU

Tarnaud (René). *Étude sur les calculs de la
prostate. 127 pp. 8°. Paris, 1901. No. 400.*

NT   0041503   DNLM

ГS270   *Tarnavskiĭ, Abraham L'vovich.*
N4
    Nedovizii, I   N
        Скоростное волочение низкоуглеродистой стальной
    проволоки. Москва, Гос. научно-техн. изд-во лит-ры по
    черной и цветной металлургии, 1954.

Tarnavskii, E. T.
RC150
.6   Russia. *Glavnoe voenno-meditsinskoe upravlenie.*
.R8   Отчетъ о гриппозной эпидеміи въ русской арміи въ
1891   1889 и 1890 г. По распоряженію главнаго военно-меди-
    цинскаго инспектора, составленъ врачами для командиро-
    ровъ С. П. Верекундовымъ, Е. И. Тарнавскимъ и Д. М.
    Филипповымъ. Подъ руководствомъ и редакціей завѣ-
    дывающаго Санитарно-статистической частью Главнаго
    военно-медицинскаго управленія В. Ф. Шолковскаго. С.-
    Петербургъ, "Владимірская" типо-лит. Л. Мордуховской,
    1891.

Tarnavs'kyĭ, Ostap.
    Слова і мрії; поезії. Зальцбург, 1948.
    48 p. 16 cm.

    I. Title.
                            Title romanized: Slova i mriĭ.
    PG3969.T3S5   72–201295

NT   0041506   DLC

Tarnavs'kyĭ, Ostap.
    Життя; вінок сонетів. ¡Філядельфія, Вид-во "Київ,"
    1952;
    21 p. 21 cm.

    I. Title.
                            Title transliterated: Zhyttìa.
    PG3969.T3Z3   52–38312

NT   0041507   DLC CaBVa

Tarnawa, Julius, Ritter Malczewski von
        see Malczewski von Tarnawa, Julius,
Ritter.

Tarnawski, Aleksander.
    Działalność gospodarcza Jana Zamoyskiego, kanclerza i
hetmana w. kor., 1572-1605. Lwów, Skł. gł.: Kasa im. J.
Mianowskiego, 1935.
    vii, 460 p. port., 7 fold. maps. 25 cm. (Badania z dziejów
społecznych i gospodarczych, nr. 18)
    Summary in French.

    1. Zamojski, Jan, 1541?–1605. I. Title. (Series)

    DK430.2.Z3T3   58–50410

NT   0041509   DLC CSt IU

Tarnawski, Anton.   L666.90700
4301   Kalk, Gyps, Cementkalk und Portland-Cement in Oesterreich-
    Ungarn. ... . vii.[1],272 p. il. 1 pl. Q. Wien: C. Teufen,
    1887.

NT   0041510   ICJ

Tarnawski (Gustave). *De la morve et du
farcin chroniques chez l'homme et de leurs complications. 60 pp. 4°. Paris, 1867, No. 273.*

NT   0041511   DNLM

D765   Tarnawski, M., joint author.
.L56
    Lipka, Czesław.
        Pancernym szlakiem; szlak bojowy wojsk pancernych i
    zmechanizowanych ludowego wojska polskiego. ¡Wyd. 1.
    Warszawa; Wydawn. Ministerstwa Obrony Narodowej
    ¡1953;

W 1   TARNAWSKI, Roman
PO271   O zmianach przetwórczych w mnogiej
ser. 1   kostniakowatości i w twardzieli tchawicy
t. 5   (Tracheopathia osteoplastica et scleroma)
nr. 3   Kraków, Nakł. Polskiej Akademii Umiejęt-
1938   ności, 1938.
        29 p. illus. (Polska Akademia Umiejęt-
    ności. Rozprawy Wydziału Lekarskiego,
    ser. 1, t. 5, nr. 3)
        Cover title
        1. Respiratory system - Diseases
    2. Trachea

    Series: Polska Akademia Umiejętności,
    Kraków. Wydział Lekarski. Rozprawy,
    ser. 1. t. 5. nr. 3

NT   0041514   DNLM

PR   Tarnawski, Władysław, 1886-
97   Historja literatury angielskiej. We
.T4   Lwowie, Nakł. K. S. Jakubowskiego, 1926-
    v. 24 cm.

    Includes bibliographies.
    Contents.- [t.1] Od czasów najdawniejszych
    do Miltona i Drydena.- [t.2.] Od Swifta do
    Burke'a i Burnsa.-

    1. English literature - Hist.

NT   0041515   WU

Tarnawski, Władysław, 1886–
    ... Krysztof Marlowe; jego życie, dzieła i znaczenie w litera-
turze angielskiej. Warszawa, "Bibljoteka polska", 1922.
    2 p. l., 255, ¡1; p. 1 l. 2 pl., 2 port. (incl. front.) facsim. 23ᶜᵐ. ¡On
cover: Bibljoteka historyczno-literacka;
    Summary in English.

    1. Marlowe, Christopher, 1564–1593.

    Library of Congress   PR2674.T3   37–36427
                                            822.32

NT   0041516   DLC CtY CSt NN MH IU PCamA

PR 2881   TARNAWSKI, WŁADYSŁAW, 1886-
.T18   O polskich przekładach dramatów Szek-
    spira. Kraków, Nakł. Akademii Umiejętności,
    1914.
        222 p.

    1. Shakespeare, William--Translations, Po-
    lish--Hist. & crit. I. Title.

NT   0041517   InU NN NcD MiDW MH WU

PR Tarnawski, Władysław, 1886–
2898 Szekspir; książka dla młodzieży i dla
P6T37 dorosłych. Lwów, Wydawn. Zakładu
Narodowego im. Ossolińskich, 1931.
301 p. 24cm.

1. Shakespeare, William, 1564–1616.

NT 0041518   CoU MH

Tarnawski, Władysław, 1886–
Szekspir katolikiem. Shakespeare a Roman Catholic. We
Lwowie, Nakł. Tow. Naukowego; skł. gł.: A. Krawczyński,
1938.
95 p. 26 cm. (Archiwum Towarzystwa Naukowego we Lwowie.
Dział i., t. 9, zesz. 2)
Also paged [375]–469.
Summary in English.

1. Shakespeare, William—Religion and ethics.   (Series: Towarzystwo Naukowe we Lwowie. Wydział i. Filologiczny. Archiwum, t. 9, zesz. 2)

P19.T65 t. 9, zesz. 2   59–59841

NT 0041519   DLC MiD

DA Tarnawski, Władysław, *1886–*
566.4 Z Anglji współczesnej; pięć szkiców.
T37 Lwów, Wydawn. Zakładu Narodowego im. Ossolińskich, 1927.
459 p. 22cm.
Contents.–Charakter Anglików.–"Dynaści"
Tomasza Hardy.–Grupy społeczne w dzisiejszej
beletrystyce angielskiej.–Dwie ostatnie sztuki
Shaw'a.–Kwestja zydowska w Anglji.
1. Gt. Brit. – Soc. life & cust. – 20th cent.
2. Gt. Brit. – Civilization – 20th cent.
I. Title.

NT 0041520   CoU

Tarnawsky, Ostap
see
Tarnavs′kyĭ, Ostap.

Tarneau, J. L.
Du ténia en Algérie et de son endémicité dans
la ville de Bone (province de Constantine) Paris,
J.-B. Baillière, 1860.
87 p. 8°.
Repr. from: Gaz. méd. de l'Algérie,
Alger, 1860, v.

NT 0041522   DNLM

Tarneau, Jean,
Stile & vsage observé av parlement de
Bovrdeavx, tovchant l'exercice de la
ivstice. Avec la forme de ses entrées,
sceances, & audiances. Et vne table
des iovrs des roolles ordinaires de
châque seneschaussée du ressort ...
Bovrdeaux, par G. de la Covrt [n.d.]
4 p.l., 132 p. 17cm.

NT 0041523   MH-L

Tarneaud, Adrien Ernest Jean
see
Tarneaud, Jean, 1888–

Tarneaud, Jean, 1888–
... Le chant, sa construction, sa destruction. Paris, Maloine,
1946.
135 p., 1 l. illus. 21½ᶜᵐ.

1. Voice. 2. Singing.
MT821.T3   Med 47–1483
U. S. Army medical library   [WV908T189c 1946]
for Library of Congress   [2]†

NT 0041525   DNLM PPC PP CLU MH NRU DLC OU

Tarneaud, Jean, [1888–
"Contribution à l'étude de la mastoidite récidivante. 70 pp. 8°. Paris, 1917. No. 71.

NT 0041526   DNLM CtY

Tarneaud, Jean, 1888–
... Laryngite chronique et laryngopathies (leçons cliniques)
Paris [etc.] Librairie Maloine, 1944.
138 p., 1 l. 24½ᶜᵐ.
"Références bibliographiques": p. [135]–138.

1. Larynx—Diseases.
[Full name: Adrien Ernest Jean Tarneaud]
45–17999
Library of Congress   RC794.T3
                   616.22

NT 0041527   DLC DNLM NNC MnU

Tarneaud, Jean, 1888–

Canuyt, Georges, 1888–
... Les maladies du larynx, clinique et thérapeutique, avec la
collaboration de mm. Truffert ... Tarneaud ... et le concours de
Ch. Wild ... Paris, Masson et cⁱᵉ, 1939.

Tarneaud, Jean, 1888–
... Le nodule de la corde vocale; préface de M. le professeur
Sebileau ... Paris, N. Maloine, 1935.
xii, 139 p. illus., diagrs. 22ᶜᵐ.
At head of title: Jean Tarneaud.
"Bibliographie": p. [129]–136.

NT 0041529   ICJ PPC MiU

WV TARNEAUD, Jean, 1888–
500 Précis de thérapeutique vocale.
T189p Paris, Maloine, 1955.
1955 123 p.
1. Larynx 2. Voice - Disorders

NT 0041530   DNLM

                             612.78
Tarneaud, Jean, 1888–   T700
... La stroboscopie du larynx; séméiologie stroboscopique des
maladies du larynx et de la voix ... Paris, N. Maloine, 1937.
4 p. l., [11]–90 p., 1 l. illus., diagrs. 24ᶜᵐ.
At head of title: Jean Tarneaud.
"Rapport présenté au vᵐᵉ congrès de la Société française de phoniatrie, Paris,
19 octobre 1937."
"Travaux du même auteur": 2d–4th prelim. l.
"Bibliographie": p. [87]–90.

NT 0041531   ICJ DNLM

Tarneaud, Jean, 1888–
... Traité pratique de phonologie et de phoniatrie; la voix—
la parole—le chant, avec la collaboration de S. Borel-Maisonny
... 115 figures. Paris, Librairie Maloine, 1941.
2 p. l., xiii, 469, [1] p. illus. (incl. music) diagrs. 24½ᶜᵐ.
At head of title: J. Tarneaud.

1. Voice. 2. Voice culture. 3. Speech. 4. Throat–Diseases.
i. Maisonny, Suzanne (Borel)
[Full name: Adrien Ernest Jean Tarneaud]
45–47549
Library of Congress   RC791.T37
                   616.2

NT 0041532   DLC PPC PU DNLM MnU NNC IU NcU

WV TARNEAUD, Jean, 1888–
500 La voix et la parole; études cliniques
T189v et thérapeutiques [par] J. Tarneud [et]
1950 M. Seeman. Paris, Maloine, 1950.
180 p.
1. Speech - Disorders 2. Voice -
Disorders   I. Seeman, M

NT 0041533   DNLM

Tarnell, Edward V.

National credit office, incorporated.
The paint industry goes to war. [New York] National credit
office, incorporated [ᶜ1942]

DB Tarneller, Josef, 1844–1924.
771 Die Burg-, Hof- und Flurnamen in der
T18 Marktgemeinde Gries bei Bozen.
Innsbruck, Wagner, 1924.
47 p. 24cm. (Schlern-Schriften, 6)

1. Names, Geographical--Italy--Gries.
I. Series.

NT 0041535   NIC CtY

TARNELLER, Josef, *1844–1924.*
Zur namenkunde.i.Tiroler familiennamen. 2.
Deutsche stammwörter. Herausgegeben von
Heimatschutz-verein Meran. Bozen,Kommissionsverlag der buchhandlung Tyrolia,1923.

Title taken from cover.
Pt.i.has special title-page;2.half-title-page.

NT 0041536   MH

D TARNER, GEORGE EDWARD.
06 A concise tabular view of the outlines of
.86 Christian history: showing the course of the
universal church, under its several patriarchates,
&c., and in its two divisions of western and
eastern, from the ascension of the Lord to the
present time (end of 1889): with suggestions for
the promotion of unity in Christendom... London,
H. Frowde[1889?]
fold.table. 146x55cm.fold.to 25 1/2x19 1/2cm.

NT 0041537   ICN

Lb17 [Tarner, George Edward]
I A letter to the vice-chancellors of both
universities, February,1924. Cambridge,
Deighton Bell & co.[ltd.,]1924
Cover-title: 7,[1]p. 20½cm.
Pamphlet

1.Education - England. 2.Education - Aims
and objectives.

NT 0041538   CtY

B
1669
T18
1922

Tarner, George Edward.
Some remarks on the axioms and postulates
of athetic philosophy, with the axioms
and postulates as originally published,
1916.   Cambridge, Deighton, Bell, 1922.
44 p. 20cm.

I. Title: Athetic philosophy.

NT 0041539   NIC CU NjP MH CLSU

Tarner, George Edward.
Suggested legislation on strikes directly affecting the public;
being some remarks prefixed to the accompanying reprint of
"Combinations in restraint of trade."   London: E. Stock, 1911.
15 p.   12°.

Title from cover.

1. Strikes and lockouts, Gt. Br.
N.Y.P.L.   February 1, 1912.

NT 0041540   NN

BX
9
T3
1895

Tarner, George Edward.
Suggestions for the promotion of unity
in Christendom. London, E. Stock, 1895.
vi, 42p. 23cm.

1. Christian union—Addresses, essays, lectures. I. Title. II. Title: Unity in
Christendom.   CCSC/mmb

NT 0041541   CCSC NRCR

Tarner, George Edward.   320.942 P301
Unpopular politics: being non-popular aspects, political and
economic, of some prominent contemporary questions. By George
Edward Tarner. London, E. Stock, 1894.
xi, 60 p. 22cm.
Contents.—1. Introductory.—2. State-provided education.—3. Combinations in
restraint of trade.—4. The progressive transfer of political power to the largest class.

NT 0041542   ICJ MB

Tarner, Tzozeph Mallornt Ouilliam
see
Turner, Joseph Mallord William, 1775-1851.

Tarney-Campbell, Mrs. Sarah E.

Hinsdale, Burke Aaron, 1837-1900.
... Teaching the language-arts; speech, reading, composition,
by B. A. Hinsdale ... with comments by Mrs. Sarah E. Tarney-
Campbell, for the special use of the Indiana teachers' reading
circle. New York, D. Appleton and company, 1897.

Tarnheyden, Edgar Tatarin-
see
Tatarin-Tarnheyden, Edgar, 1882-

Tarnier (Augustin). *Essai* sur l'hémoptysie.
23 pp. 4°. *Paris*, 1896, No. 6, v. 197.

NT 0041546   DNLM PPC

Tarnier (B.-Émile). *Quelques réflexions critiques sur la favus. 47 pp. 4°. *Paris*, 1859,
No. 34, v. 637.

NT 0041547   DNLM

Tarnier, Étienne, 1828-1897.
———. Considérations sur l'accouchement dans
les positions occipito-postérieures et sur la possi-
bilité de transformer ces positions en occipito-
antérieures à l'aide du doigt. 4 pp. 8°. *Paris*,
H. Lauwereyns, 1879.

NT 0041548   DNLM

WQ
T189de
1894

TARNIER, Étienne, 1828-1897
De l'asepsie et de l'antisepsie en
obstétrique, par S. Tarnier. Leçons
recueillies et rédigées par J. Potocki.
Paris, Steinheil, 1894.
xiv, 839 p. illus.
Lectures presented at the Clinique
d'accouchements.
I. Potocki, Julien, ed.

NT 0041549   DNLM PPC ICRL ICU IU-M WaU

WQ
M385d
1860

TARNIER, Étienne, 1828-1897
De la fièvre puerpérale observée à
l'Hospice de la maternité.   Paris,
Baillière, 1858.
207 p.
Bound with Martinenq, L. L. J. F.
de la fièvre puerpérale.   Paris, 1860.

NT 0041550   DNLM PPC

WQ
T189d
1860

TARNIER, Étienne, 1828-1897
Des cas dans lesquels l'extraction du
foetus est nécessaire et des procédés
opératoires relatifs à cette extraction,
par S. Tarnier.   Paris, Baillière,
1860.
viii, 228 p. illus.

NT 0041551   DNLM PPC

B618.81
qT175

Tarnier, Étienne,   1828-1897.
Description de deux nouveaux forceps,
par S. Tarnier. [Paris, Impr. E. Martinet,
1877?]
55, [1] p. illus. 29 cm.

Caption title.
Also published in Annales de gynécologie,
v.7 (1877) 241-264.
Includes bibliographical footnotes.

1.Forceps, Obstetric. I.Title.

NT 0041552   MnU-B

Tarnier, Étienne, 1828-1897.
———. & Brouardel (P.) Inculpation d'avortement; relation médico-légale de l'affaire C ...
et D ... 22 pp. 8°. [*Paris, A. Parent*, 1881.]
Repr. from: Ann. d'hyg., Par., 1881, 3. s., v.

NT 0041553   DNLM

Tarnier, Étienne, 1828-1907.
Cazeaux, Pierre, 1808-1862.
... Obstetrics: the theory and practice; including the diseases
of pregnancy and parturition, obstetrical operations, etc. by
P. Cazeaux ... Remodelled and rearranged, with additions and
revisions, by S. Tarnier ... The 7th American ed. Edited and
rev., based in part upon the 8th French and a recent Italian
ed., with additions, from other recent authorities, a new chapter
upon lacerations of the perineum, and an article on puerperal
insanity, by Robert J. Hess ... With twelve full-page plates,
five being colored, and one hundred and sixty-five wood engravings. Philadelphia, P. Blakiston, son & co., 1884.

WS
100
T189p
1882

TARNIER, Étienne, 1828-1897
Physiologie et hygiène de la première
enfance, considérées surtout au point de
vue de l'alimentation, par S. Tarnier et
J. [i. e. G.] Chantreuil. Paris,
Lauwereyns, 1882.
vii, 250 p. illus.
An extract from Traité de l'art des
accouchements by the same authors.
I. Chantreuil, Gustave

NT 0041555   DNLM

Tarnier (Étienne, 1828-   *Re-
cherches sur l'état puerpéral et sur les maladies
des femmes en couches. 75 pp. 4°. *Paris*, 1857,
No. 50, v. 611.
Name appears as Cl.-Stéphane Tarnier.

NT 0041556   DNLM

Tarnier, Étienne,   [1828-]
———. Réponse de . . . aux critiques dont il a été
l'objet au Congrès médical de Bruxelles à propos
du forceps-scie. 8 pp. 8°. *Paris, Cusset & Cie*,
1875.
Repr. from: Gaz. méd. de Par., 1875, 4. s., iv.

NT 0041557   DNLM

Tarnier, Étienne, 1828-1897, ed.

Cazeaux, Paulin, 1808-1862.
A theoretical and practical treatise on midwifery, including
the diseases of pregnancy and parturition. By P. Cazeaux ...
Rev. and annotated by S. Tarnier ... 5th American from the
7th French ed. By Wm. R. Bullock ... Philadelphia, Lind-
say and Blakiston, 1868.

Tarnier, Étienne, 1828-1897, ed.

Cazeaux, Paulin, 1808-1862.
... The theory and practice of obstetrics; including diseases
of pregnancy and parturition, obstetrical operations, etc. by
P. Cazeaux ... Remodelled and rearranged, with additions
and revisions, by S. Tarnier ... The 8th American ed. Edited and rev. by Robert J. Hess ... With an appendix, by
Paul F. Mundé ... Philadelphia, P. Blakiston, son & co.,
1886.

Tarnier, Étienne, 1828-1897

———. & Chantreuil (Gustave). Traité de
l'art des accouchements. 1. fasc. 384+ pp. 8°.
Paris, H. Lauwereyns, 1878.

NT 0041560   DNLM

Tarnier, Étienne, 1828-1897.   618.2 0201
Traité de l'art des accouchements. Par S. Tarnier, ... et G.
Chantreuil, ...   Tome premier-[quatrième]. Avec ... fi-
gures intercalées dans le texte. Paris, vol. 1, H. Lauwereyns;
vol. 2-4, G. Steinheil, 1882-1901.
4 vol. illus. 24cm.
Vol. 2-4 by S. Tarnier and P. Budin.
"Bibliographie chronologique" at head of chapters and articles, or with special subjects.
Contents.—t. 1ᵉ. [Partie physiologique.] 1882. xii, 956 p. 285 illus.—t. 2ᵉ.
Pathologie de la grossesse. 1886. [4], 586 p. 66 illus.—t. 3ᵉ. Dystocie maternelle.
1898. vi, 771 p. 168 illus.—t. 4ᵉ. Dystocie foetale, accidents de la délivrance, opérations, infections puerpérales. 1901. xix, 754 p. 250 illus.

NT 0041561   ICJ PPC MBCo PBL

WQ
T189t
1901

Film
1083

TARNIER, Étienne, 1828-1897
Traité de l'art des accouchements.
Paris, Steinheil, 1888-1901.
4 v. in illus.
Tomes 1-3 on microfilm.
Tome 1 by S. Tarnier and G.
Chantreuil; tomes 2-4 by S. Tarnier
and P. Budin.
Contents.—t. 1 Grossesse et accouche-
ment physiologiques.—t. 2 Pathologie de
la grossesse.—t. 3 Dystocie maternelle

—t. 4 Dystocie foetale. Accidents de la
délivrance. Opérations. Infections
puerpérales.
I. Budin, Pierre, 1846-1907
II. Chantreuil, Gustave

NT 0041563   DNLM

Tarnier, Etienne, 1828-1897.
Traite theoretique et pratique de l'art des accouchements.
1870.

NT 0041564   Nh

QA464   Tarnier, Étienne Auguste, 1808-1882.
.T2   Éléments de géométrie pratique conformes au programme de l'enseignement secondaire spécial (année préparatoire, sciences) à l'usage des écoles primaires et des divers établissements scolaires, par E.-A. Tarnier ... Paris, Gauthier-Villars, 1872.
xx, 343 p. illus., diagrs. 21½ᶜᵐ.

1. Geometry—Problems, exercises, etc.

NT 0041565   ICU RPB NjP NIC

QA537   Tarnier, Étienne Auguste, 1808-1882.
T3   Éléments de trigonométrie, théorique et
1859   pratique. 3. éd., conforme aux derniers programmes d'enseignement. Paris, L. Hachette, 1859.
184 p. illus., diagrs.

1. Trigonometry - Problems, exercises, etc.

NT 0041566   CU

Tarnier, Etienne Auguste, 1808-1882.
Le langage des nombres (aid-mémoire... A l'usage des divers établissements d'instruction publique des aspirants, des aspirantes aux brevets de capacité, etc. Paris, 1872.
At head of title: Opuscule classique.

NT 0041567   CtY

Tarnier, Etienne Auguste, 1808-1882.
Petite arithmétique et système métrique. 8.éd. Cours moyen. Paris, Hachette et cie., 1878.

NT 0041568   MH

YA 1068   Tarnier, Etienne Auguste, 1808-1882.
Problemes de physique mathematique proposes au baccalaureat es sciences... Paris, 1864.

NT 0041569   DLC

Tarnier, Etienne Auguste, 1808-1882.
Thèse d'astronomie [Solution, par les séries, du problème de Képler, et détermination des coordonnées d'une planète, en supposant très-petites son excentricité et l'inclinaison du plan de son orbite...]... Paris, Imp. de Bachelier, 1845.
50 p. 26 cm. [Thèse de mathématiques. 1845. no. 48]
Thèse - Faculté des sciences de Paris.
1. Orbits.

NT 0041570   CU

Tarnier, Marcelle, joint author.

Tarnier, Maurice.
Claude et Antoinette à la maison forestière, par Maurice et Marcelle Tarnier. Livre de lecture courante. Cours élémentaire. Paris, A. Colin, 1931.

Tarnier, Maurice.
Claude et Antoinette à la maison forestière, par Maurice et Marcelle Tarnier. Livre de lecture courante. Cours élémentaire. Paris, A. Colin, 1931.
iv, 236 p. illus. 20½ᶜᵐ. (On cover: La lecture attrayante)

1. French language—Chrestomathies and readers. I. Tarnier, Marcelle, joint author. II. Title.
      32–13258
Library of Congress   PC2115.T45
Copyright A—Foreign   14429
         448.6

NT 0041572   DLC

Tarnier, S.
see   Tarnier, Etienne, 1828-1897.

Tarnier, Stephane, 1828-1897
see   Tarnier, Etienne, 1828-1897.

Tarnier (Eugène). *De la colique de plomb. 43 pp. 4°. Paris, 1848, No. 204, v. 478.

NT 0041575   DNLM

Tarnizhevskiĭ, V   M
Государственные неналоговые доходы (прочие доходы) Москва, Госфиниздат, 1953.
63 p. 20 cm.

1. Revenue—Russia. I. Title.
Title transliterated: Gosudarstvennye nenalogovye dokhody.

HJ3840.R93T3   54–20577

NT 0041576   DLC

HJ4368   Tarnizhevskiĭ, V. M., joint author.
.A3S6

Solov'ev, L
Лесной доход; учебное пособие для курсов и техникумов системы Наркомфина СССР. Под ред. В. М. Стам. Москва, Госфиниздат, 1945.

Tarnizhevskiĭ, V   M
Налог со зрелищ. Москва, Госфиниздат, 1950.
40 p. forms. 22 cm.

1. Amusements—Taxation—Russia.
Title transliterated: Nalog so zrelishch.

HJ5797.Ta   50–57696

NT 0041578   DLC

HJ3840   Tarnizhevskiĭ, V. M., joint author.
.R93S6

Solov'ev, L
Неналоговые доходы. Допущено в качестве учеб. пособия для курсовой сети и фин. техникумов. Под ред. В. М. Стам. Москва, Госфиниздат, 1946.

Tarnke, Heinrich, 1858-   ed.

Annalen des gesamten versicherungswesens ... Leipzig, Jüstel & Göttel,

---

Tarnmoor, Salvator R., pseud.
see   Melville, Herman, 1819-1891.

PH
3351 ·
.T371   Tarnóczy, Árpád
E5   Éneklő hajnalok; Tarnóczy Árpád versei. Linek Lajos [et al.] rajzaival. [Budapest, Athenaeum [1931?]
160 p. illus., plates, port.

"Kiadatott a Buffalói Hungária Kulturkör tagjainak lelkes segitségével."

NT 0041582   NNC NN DLC-P4 OC1

Tarnóczi, István, 1626-1689.   Aus 82069.1
Rex admirabilis, sive Vita S. Ladislai, regis Hungariæ, historico-politica, ad Christianam eruditionem elogijs theo-politicis illustrata. Authore Stephano Tarnoczi. Viennæ Austriæ, typis J. C. Cosmerovij, 1681.
pp. (8), 495 +. Engraved illus.

NT 0041583   MH

Avery
AA
5570   Tarnóczi, János
T17   A Szent István bazilika éneklő kövei ... A templom története és műemlékei. Budapest, Szt. István Bazilika kiadása, 1937.
124 p. illus. 24 cm.

NT 0041584   NNC

Tarnoczi, Stephanus
see   Tarnóczi, István, 1626-1689.

4X   Tarnóczy, Friedrich von, 1888-
Ger   Die Haftung des Vormundes bei
954   Anlegung von Mündelgeld. München, 1911.
71 p.

NT 0041586   DLC-P4 ICRL MH-L

Tarnóczy, Mme. Gustave de.
Catalogue descriptif et illustré de la collection de bagues de madame Gustave de Tarnóczy. Avec 300 gravures. Par dr. Jean Szendrei ... Paris, A. Lévy, 1889.
lvi, 384 p. illus. 18½ᶜᵐ.

1. Rings. I. Szendrei, János, 1857-

         G S 34–274
Libr., U. S. Geol. Surv.,   Geo. F. Kunz Collection   K090   T17c

NT 0041587   DI-GS MB MdBWA

4NA   Tarnóczy, Tamás
228   Építészeti hangtan. A Mérnöki
        Továbbképző Intézet 1947. és 1948.
        évi tanfolyamainak anyaga. Budapest,
        Mérnöki Továbbképző Intézet Kiadása,
        1948.
            160 p.

        (A Mérnöki Továbbképző Intézet
        kiadványai. Építészet, 34.sz.)

NT   0041588   DLC-P4

621.321 Tarnoff, Norman Harold.
T176l   The light vector. ⟨Paper for⟩ EE-489, 2d
        sem. June, '51, Prof. J. O. Kraehenbuehl.
        ⟨Urbana, University of Illinois, 1951.
            ii, 39, xxivl. diagrs. 28cm.

        On cover: EE-461.
        Blueprint.
        "The light field by A. Gershun as revised and
        abridged by Norman H. Tarnoff": p.ii, 1-22.
        (1st group)
        Appendix B wanting.

NT   0041589   IU

621.321 Tarnoff, Norman Harold.
T176s   A study of the solid angle. ⟨Papers for⟩
        EE-497, fall 1950, Prof. John O. Kraehenbuehl
        advisor. ⟨Urbana, University of Illinois,
        1950⟩
            55, 18l. diagrs. 28cm.

        Cover title: Solid angles. EE-461.
        Blueprint.
        "The unit sphere method of illumination cal-
        culation, by Robert Swern Wiseman, as rev. and
        edited by Norman Harold Tarnoff. January 1951.

        J. O. Kraehenbuehl, professor": p.1-18 (2d
        group)
        Bibliography: leaf at end.

        1. Lighting. I. Kraehenbuehl, John Otto,
        1894-   II. Wiseman, Robert Swern. The
        unit sphere method of illumination calculation.
        III. Title: Solid   angles.

NT   0041591   IU

Tarnogrocki, Friedrich, 1891-
        Behandlungsmethoden des gasödems ... Ber-
        lin, Ebering ⟨1918⟩
            30 p., 1 l.

        Inaug.-diss., Berlin, 1918.
        Lebenslauf.
        "Literatur": p. ⟨29⟩-30.

        1. Edema.

NT   0041592   NNC DNLM

Tarnói, Ladislao.
        El nuevo ideal nacional de Venezuela; vida y obra de
        Marcos Pérez Jiménez. Madrid, Ediciones Verdad, 1954.
            341 p. illus. 25 cm.
            Includes bibliography.

        1. Pérez Jiménez, Marcos, Pres. Venezuela, 1914-   2. Vene-
        zuela—Pol. & govt.—1935-   i. Title.

        F2326.P5T3

NT   0041593   DLC NN IU TxU DPU MU

Tarnói, Ladislao.
        Temas principales de la filosofía del derecho. Caracas,
        Editorial Avila Gráfica; distribuidor, Librería Mundial,
        1952-
            v. 23 cm.
            CONTENTS.—1. Teoría fundamental.

        1. Law—Philosophy. 2. Jurisprudence.   i. Title.

                                                    53-37625 ‡

NT   0041594   DLC

HD4905.5 Tarnói, László, tharnói.
T189   Katonai munkaszázadok; közérdekű munkaszol-
        gálat és honvédelmi munkakötelezettség.
        Budapest, Magyar Munkaszolgálat ⟨1940⟩
            94 p. illus., ports. 24cm.

        1. Service, Compulsory non-military -
        Hungary. 2. Hungary - Army. I. Title.

NT   0041595   CSt-H

---

943   TÁRNOK, Gyula
Ref.358   Magyar reformátusok a Csehszlovákiai
T189ma   kisebbségi sorsban, 1938-1939. Pápa,
1939   Főiskolai Könyvnyomda, 1939.
            91p. 23cm. (A Pápai Református
        Theologiai Akadémia kiadványa, 32)

NT   0041596   MH-AH

PH
3291   Tárnok, László
.M48   A költő Móra Ferenc. Szeged, 1942. ⟨
Z9   15 p. port. 16 cm.

        Portrait on cover.

        1. Móra, Ferenc, 1879-1934. I. Title.

NT   0041597   NNC

Tarnopol, Ioakhim Isaakovich, 1810-1900.
        Notices historiques et caractéristiques sur les
        Israélites d'Odessa. Précedées d'un aperçu
        géneral sur l'état du peuple israélite en Russie.
        Odessa: A. Braun, 1855.
            195 p. (1)

NT   0041598   OCH PP

Tarnopol', Ioakhim Isaakovich, 1810-1900.
        Опытъ современной и осмотрительной реформы въ обла-
        сти юдаизма въ России; размышленія о внутреннемъ и
        внѣшнемъ бытѣ русскихъ евреевъ. Одесса, Въ Тип. Л.
        Нитче, 1868.
            xxxvi, 282 p. 22 cm.

        1. Jews in Russia.   I. Title.
                     Title transliterated: Opyt sovremennoĭ i osmo-
                     tritel'noĭ reformy v oblasti iudaizma.

        DS135.R9T3   55-49989

NT   0041599   DLC

                    Isaakovich,
Tarnopol, Ioakhim∧1810-1900.
        Réflexions sur l'état religieux, politique et social des Israélites
        russes. Essai sur une réforme modérée et progressive, dans le do-
        maine du judaisme en Russie. Résumé de mon ouvrage russe,
        publié en 1868 et suivi d'une étude spéciale sur l'émancipation, par
        Joachim Tarnopol. Odessa: L. Nitzsche, 1871. 191 p. 8°.

        1. Jews in Russia.
        N. Y. P. L.   January 19, 1927

NT   0041600   NN RPB CU PPDrop

Tarnopol, Joachim, 1810-1900
        see Tarnopol, Ioakhim Isaakovich, 1810-
        1900.

Tarnopol (City)
        see Ternopol' (City)

Tarnopolski, Józef Juljusz.
        Prawo ustawowe, umowne i zwyczajowe w zastosowaniu do
        spraw dozorców domowych i służby domowej, zebrał i opraco-
        wał J. J. Tarnopolski ... Przedmową opatrzył Kazimierz
        Ujazdowski ... Warszawa, Nakł. S. Walewskiego, 1935.
            10 p. l., 5–78 p., 1 l. 20⁰.
            On cover: 1936.

        1. Janitors. 2. Master and servant—Poland.   i. Poland. Laws,
        statutes, etc.
                                                    41-39506

NT   0041603   DLC

Tarnopol'skiĭ, G   D
        Щетинно-волосяное и щеточное производство. Под
        ред. З. М. Когана. Москва, Гос. изд-во легкой промыш.,
        1941.
            139 p. illus. 22 cm. (Учебники и учебные пособия для школ
        ФЗУ)
            At head of title: Г. Д. Тарнопольский и А. А. Яровинский.

        1. Bristles. 2. Brooms and brushes.   i. Ĭarovinskiĭ, A. A., joint
        author.
                         Title transliterated: Shchetinno-volosânoe
                         i shchetochnoe proizvodstvo.

        TS2301.B8T3   51-45159

NT   0041604   DLC

Tarnopolsky, Samuel.
        ... Alarma de indios en la frontera sud, novela ... Carátula
        de Equet. 1. ed.—Buenos Aires, 1941. Buenos Aires, S. Rueda
        ⟨1941⟩
            1 p. l., ⟨5⟩–186 p., 2 l. 19½⁰. (*His* Episodios de la conquista del de-
        sierto. 1°)
            "Premiada en el concurso organizado por la agrupación de gente de
        arte y letras 'La Peña.' 1940."

        i. Title.
                                                    42-20177
        Library of Congress   PQ7797.T27E6 t. 1
                                            (863.6) 863.6

NT   0041605   DLC ICU

Tarnopolsky, Samuel.
        Alarma de indios en la frontera sud. ⟨Novela⟩ 2. ed.
        Buenos Aires, Ronal ⟨1952⟩
            190 p. 20 cm. (*His* Episodios de la conquista del desierto)

        i. Title.
        PQ7797.T27A7 1952   863.6   54-25443 ‡

NT   0041606   DLC ICarbS MiU NNC IU

Tarnopolsky, Samuel.
        ... Episodios de la conquista del desierto ... Buenos Aires,
        S. Rueda ⟨1941-
            v. 19½⁰.
            CONTENTS.—v. 1. Alarma de indios en la frontera sud.

        i. Title.
                                                    42-20176
        Library of Congress   PQ7797.T27E6
                                                    863.6

NT   0041607   DLC

Tarnopolsky, Samuel, joint author.

Ruiz Moreno, Aníbal.
        El problema higiénico-social del reumatismo, por los doctores
        Aníbal Ruiz Moreno ... y Samuel Tarnopolsky ... Buenos
        Aires, "El Ateneo," 1940.

G868.8
T176r   Tarnopolsky, Samuel.
       La rastrillada de Salinas Grandes; novela ins-
pirada en la famosa expedición al desierto dirigida por el coronel Pedro Andrés García pocas
semanas después de la Revolución de Mayo. Ilus.
de Melgarejo Muñoz. [Buenos Aires] Ediciones
Feria, 1944.
       162p. illus. 22cm. (His Episodios de la con-
quista del desierto)
       1. García, Pedro Andrés, 1758-1833 – Fiction.
I. Tarnopolsky, Samuel. Episodios de la conquista
del desierto. II.   Title.

NT   0041609   TxU

WE
544
T189r
1951   TARNOPOLSKY, Samuel
       El reumatismo: qué es, y cómo se cura,
un libro de divulgación científica y
educación sanitaria, para instrucción y
aliento de enfermos y predispuestos ...
Buenos Aires, El Ateneo [1951]
       207 p. illus.
       1. Rheumatism

NT   0041610   DNLM

WE
544
T189re
1945   Tarnopolsky, Samuel.
       Reumatología para el médico rural;
conferencias. [Buenos Aires] 1945.
       36 p. ([Buenos Aires] Instituto Agrario
Argentino. Reseñas, año 5, no. 35)
       1. Arthritis, Rheumatoid. 2. Fibrositis.
3. Osteoarthritis. 4. Rheumatic fever.

NT   0041611   DNLM

Tarnor, Pearl G
       Teachers manual for Hasheur Harishon flannel
board material. New,York, United Synagogue
Commission on Jewish Education [195-?]
       ii, 48 p. illus. 28 cm.

NT   0041612   - OCH

Tarnos, José Reigadas
       see   Reigadas Tarnos, José.

Tarnovius, Hermann, *fl.* 1721, *praeses.*
       Dissertatio philologica de rhythmo hebræo-biblico sive
numero oratorio Veteris T: magnam partem ex inter-
punctione prosaica exhibendo ... Rostochii, typis N.
Schwiegerovii, 1721.
       24 p. 19½ᶜᵐ.
       Diss.--Rostock (B. F. Wittenburg, respondent)

       1. Hebrew language--Metrics and rhythmics.   I. Wittenburg, Baltha-
sar Friedrich, fl. 1721.   II. Title.

       Library of Congress   PJ4774.T3

          CA 25-549 Unrev'd

NT   0041614   DLC

Spec.
Arnold   Tarnovius, Hermann, fl. 1721.
PJ 4563   Grammatica Hebraeo-biblica, comprehendens
T 3   etymologiam, syntaxin, eloqventiam atq; poesin,
1722   juxta utramque interpunctionem, prosaicam sc.
et metricam, breviter ac succincte ad captum
accomodata, & ab exceptionibus hactenus relictis
liberata: cum consensu amplissimi collegii
philosophici & praefatione summe reverendi
Domini, Dn. D. Weideneri. Accedunt necessarii
indices Scripturae, rerum & verborum. Lipsiae,
Haeredes Tarnovii; Rostochii, Typis Nicolai

       Schwiegerovii, 1722.
       [8], 248, [16] p. 18 cm.
       On spine: Alphabetum graecum.
       Bound with Alphabetvm Graecum & Hebraicum.
Genevae, 1600.

       1. Hebrew language - Grammar. I. Title.

NT   0041616   MoSW

Tarnovius, Johannes
       see   Tarnow, Johann, 1586-1629.

Tarnovius, Paul
       see   Tarnow, Paul, 1562-1633.

ICELAND
DL
271
F2
T18
1950   Tarnovius, Thomas Jacobsen, b. 1644.
       Ferøers beskrifvelser, av Thomas Tarnovius.
Utgitt av Håkon Hamre. København, E.
Munksgaard, 1950.
       103 p. 3 facsims. 25cm. (Faeroensia,
v. 2)

       Bibliography: p. [94]-95.

       1. Faroe Is   lands. I. Hamre, Håkon,
ed. II. Title.   III. Series.

NT   0041619   IEN PU CU ICN MH CoU CtY IU ICU FU NNC

Tarnovskaia, Praskov'ia Nikolaevna (Kozlova)
       Aperçu sur l'instruction médicale des femmes en Rus-
sie. [St. Petersburg] Impr. R. Golicke [1900]
       cover-title, 18 p., 1 l. pl. 21ᶜᵐ.
       Signed: Pauline Tarnowsky, F.-M.

       1. Woman—Education—Russia. 2. Medicine—Study—Russia.

              E 10-357

       Library, U. S. Bur. of   Education R796.T2

NT   0041620   DHEW

Tarnovskaia, Praskov'ia Nikolaevna (Kozlova)
       ... Étude anthropométrique sur les prostituées et les
voleuses, par le docteur Pauline Tarnowsky. Avec 8 tableaux
anthropométriques et 20 dessins. Paris, Aux bureaux du
Progrès; E. Lecrosnier et Babé, 1889.
       2 p. l., v, 226 p. illus. 22½ cm. (Publication du Progrès médical)

       1. Criminal anthropology. 2. Delinquent women. 3. Prostitution.

       HV6046.T28   38–29638 rev

NT   0041621   DLC NjP DNLM PPC LU ICRL OC1 NN

Tarnovskaia, Praskov'ia Nikolaevna. (Kozlova)
       Les femmes homicides, par le Dʳ Pauline Tarnowsky; avec
40 planches hors texte, contenant 161 figures et 8 tableaux
anthropométriques. Paris, F. Alcan, 1908.
       4 p. l., viii, 591 p. incl. tables. 40 pl. 25½ cm.
       "Bibliographie": p.[575]-591.

       1. Criminal anthropology. 2. Delinquent women—Russia.
   I. Title.

       HV6046.T3   9–19211

NT   0041622   DLC ICRL CU ICJ DNLM MiU NN PU

Tarnovskaia, Praskov'ia Nikolaevna (Kozlova)
       ...Женщины-убийцы. Врача П. Н. Тарновской. Съ 163
рисунками и 8 антропометрическими таблицами. С.-Пе-
тербургъ, "Т-во Художественной печати," 1902.
       2 p. l., vii, 512 p., 1 l. illus., plates. 25½ cm.
       At head of title: Антропологическое изслѣдование.
       "Литературный указатель": p. [499]-512.

       1. Delinquent women—Russia. 2. Criminal anthropology. 3. Mur-
der.   I. Title.   Title transliterated: Zhenshchiny-ubiĭt͡sy.

       HV6046.T29   21–4629 rev

NT   0041623   DLC

Tarnovski, H
       A historical sketch of the Lying-in hospital in
St. Petersburg since its foundation
       see   Tarnovskiĭ, Ippolite Mikhaĭlovich,
1835-

TS225
.G25   *Tarnovskiĭ, Iosif I͡Akovlevich.*
       Ganago, O   **A**
       Безоблойная штамповка на молотах. Свердловск, Гос.
научно-техн. изд-во машиностроит. лит-ры [Урало-Сибир-
ское отд-ние] 1955.

Tarnovskiĭ, Iosif I͡Akovlevich.
       Формоизменение при пластической обработке метал-
лов; ковка и прокатка. Москва, Гос. научно-техни. изд-
во литры по черной и цветной металлургии, 1954.
       534 p. illus. 23 cm.
       Includes bibliography.

       1. Forging. 2. Rolling (Metal-work) 3. Deformations (Me-
chanics)   I. Title.   *Title transliterated:* Formoizmenenie pri
                              plasticheskoĭ obrabotke metallov.

       TS205.T28   55–15462 ‡

NT   0041626   DLC

TS225
U69   *Tarnovskiĭ, Iosif I͡Akovlevich*
       Уральские кузнецы в борьбе за технический прогресс; сбор-
ник статей. [Редакторы: И. Я. Тарновскиĭ, О. А. Ганаго,
П. П. Вшивков] Свердловск, Гос. научно-техн. изд-во
машиностроит. лит-ры [Урало-Сибирское отд-ние] 1955.

WQ
S149k
1874   TARNOVSKIĬ, Ippolit Mikhaĭlovich,
1835-*1899*
       A historical sketch of the Lying-in
Hospital in St. Petersburg since its
foundation. St. Petersburg, 1893.
       37 p. illus.
       Bound with St. Petersburg.
Vospitatel'nyĭ dom. Rodovspomogatel'noe
zavedenie. Klinischer Bericht für die
Jahre 1840-1871. St. Petersburg, 1874.
       Translation of Istoricheskiĭ ocherk

       dĭei͡atel'nosti Rodovspomogatel'nago
zavedeniĭa.
       1. St. Petersburg. Vospitatel'nyĭ dom.
Rodovspomogatel'noe zavedenie

NT   0041629   DNLM MiU PPC IU

Tarnovskiĭ, I[ppolit] M[ikhaĭlovich]) [1833-
99]. Salpingitis puerperalis; pyosalpings. 20
pp. 12°. [St. Petersburg, I. Treĭ, 1882.]
     Repr. from: Vrach, St. Petersb., 1882, iii.
     Bound with: Med. Otchet S.-Peterb. rodovsp. zaved.
     (1877-80), 1883.

NT   0041630   DNLM

RG507
.I46
1893   Tarnovskiĭ, Ippolit Mikhaĭlovich, 1833-1899, ed.
       Leningrad. Vospitatel'nyĭ dom. Rodovspomogatel'noe
zavedenie.
       (Sbornik trudov vracheĭ S.-Peterburgskago rodovspomogatel'nago
zavedeniĭa)
       Сборникъ трудовъ врачей С.-Петербургскаго родов-
спомогательнаго заведения, издаваемый подъ ред. И. М.
Тарновскаго. С.-Петербургъ, Тип. С. Н. Худекова,
1893-

Tarnovskiĭ, Konstantin Avgustovich, 1826–1892.
(Annushka Vlas'eva)
Аннушка Власьева; разсказъ нижегородца, С. Райскаго. С.-Петербургъ, Тип. И. Бочкарева, 1865.
97 p. 18 cm.

I. Title.
PG3361.T25A82 1865

73–221042

NT 0041632   DLC

Tarnovskiĭ, Konstantin Avgustovich, 1826–1892.
(Prishla bĕda—rastvorĭaĭ vorota)
Пришла бѣда—растворяй ворота! Пословица въ 5-ти дѣйствіяхъ. Москва, Тип. В. Давыдова, 1877.
106 p. 27 cm.
"Приложеніе къ журналу Московское обозрѣніе."

I. Title.
PG3361.T25P7 1877

73–216282

NT 0041633   DLC

Tarnoviskiĭ, Mikola, 1895–
see Tarnovs'kyĭ, Mykola Mykolaivych, 1895–

Tarnovskiĭ, N
La scuola russa nella "Scuola 110" di Mosca (di) N. Tarnovskij, P. Glagolev (e) S. Trofimova. (Traduzione di Hanna Mirecka e di Luigi Volpicelli. 1. ed.) Roma, Casa editrice Avio, 1950.
83 p. 20 cm. (I Problemi della pedagogia, v. 3)
"Dalla Ucitelskaja gazeta del 12 ottobre 1947 (i. e. 1946)."

1. Moscow. Shkola no. 110. 2. Education—Russia. I. Title.
LF4435.M75T3

58–29893

NT 0041635   DLC

Tarnovskiĭ, N
La scuola russa nella "Scuola 110" di Mosca (di) N. Tarnovskij, P. Glagolev (e) S. Trofimova. (Traduzione di Hanna Mirecka e di Luigi Volpicelli) 2. ed. Roma, Casa editrice Avio, 1954.
85 p. 20 cm. (I Problemi della pedagogia, v. 3)
"Dalla Ucitelskaja gazeta del 12 ottobre 1947 (i. e. 1946)"

1. Moscow. Shkola no. 110. 2. Education—Russia. I. Title.
LF4435.M75T3 1954

60–22182 ‡

NT 0041636   DLC

Tarnovskiĭ, Nikolaĭ
see
Tarnovs'kyĭ, Mykola Mykolaĭovych, 1895–

Tarnovskiĭ, Vasiliĭ Vasil'evich.

Antonovich, Vladimir Bonifat'evich, 1834–1908.
Историческіе дѣятели юго-западной Россіи въ біографіяхъ и портретахъ. Вып. 1. Составили В. Б. Антоновичъ и В. А. Бецъ по коллекціи Василія Васильевича Тарновскаго. Кіевъ, Тип. Имп. Университета св. Владиміра, 1885.

Tarnovskiĭ, Vasiliĭ Vasil'evich.
Katalog predmetov malorusskoĭ stariny i riedkosteĭ
see under title

Tarnovskiĭ, Veniamin Mikhaĭlovich, 1839–1906.
Anthropological, legal and medical studies on pederasty in Europe, by Prof. Benjamin Tarnowsky ... New York, Priv. print. by Anthropological press (*1933).
xxxiii p., 1 l., 233 p. front., plates, ports. 26ᶜᵐ.

"Of this edition fifteen hundred copies have been privately issued by the Anthropological branch of the Falstaff press for exclusive subscription of adult students of anthropology. The translation is by Paul Gardner ... This copy is ... 1112."
"Bibliography of important works treating with inversion and pederasty": p. 201–233.

1. Sexual perversion. I. Gardner, Paul, tr. II. Title: Pederasty in Europe.
34–34331
Library of Congress   HQ71.T25
—— Copy 2. "This   copy is ... 780."
[159.9734846] 132.7546

NT 0041640   DLC KU NcGU CtY-M

WCA
T189a
1870

TARNOVSKIĬ, Veniamin Mikhaĭlovich, 1839–1906
Aphasie syphilitique. Paris, Delahaye, 1870.
131 p.
Abridged translation of two articles, published in Russian in Revue de médecine militaire, in 1867 and 1868.

NT 0041641   DNLM PPC NN

HQ 10
T17g
1885?

Tarnovskiĭ, Veniamin Mikhaĭlovich, 1839–1906.
Die geschlechtliche Perversität im paralytischen Blödsinn. Päderastie in der progressiven Paralyse der Irren. (Berlin, L. Schumacher, 1885?)
81–152p. 24cm.

Part of the author's Anthropological, legal and medical studies on pederasty in Europe. "Complicirte formen geschlechtlicher Perversität": p. 87–148.
Bibliography: p. 148 (?).
Table of contents, typewritten English translation: ℓ., laid in.

NT 0041642   NcD-MC

Tarnovskiĭ, Veniamin Mikhaĭlovich, 1839–1906.
La famille syphilitique et sa descendance; etude biologique. Clarmont, Diax, 1904.
208 p.

NT 0041643   PPC

HQ71
.T199

Tarnovskiĭ, Veniamin Mikhaĭlovich, 1839–1906.
L'instinct sexuel et ses manifestations morbides au double point de vue de la jurisprudence et de la psychiatrie. Traduction française ... Préf. par le Professeur Lacassagne. Paris, C. Carrington, 1904.
xvi, 304 p.
Includes bibliography.

1. Sexual perversion. 2. Sexual instinct. I. Title.

NT 0041644   ICU OU NcD DNLM CU MiU CtY-M

Tarnovskiĭ, Veniamin Mikhaĭlovich, 1839–1906.
Die krankhaften erscheinungen des geschlechtssinnes. Eine forensisch-psychiatrische studie. Von dr. med. B. Tarnowsky ... Berlin, A. Hirschwald, 1886.
2 p. l., 152 p. 23½ᶜᵐ.
"Literatur": p. 148–152.

1. Sexual perversion. I. Title.
34–24734
Library of Congress   HQ71.T3   [159.973484] 132.754

NT 0041645   DLC ICRL PPC DNLM ICJ MiU MH

RC557
932T

TarnovskiĭY Veniamin *Mikhaĭlovich, 1839–1906.*
Perversiones sexuales; el instinto sexual y sus manifestaciones morbidas; traduccion, introduccion y laminas de la Srta. Hildegart, Epilogo del Dr. Havelock Ellis. Valencia, Biblioteca Cuadernos de Cultura,1932.
78,[2]p. plates. 19cm.

1. Sexual perversion.
Provenance: Hildegart (made)

NT 0041646   CtY-M

Tarnovskiĭ, Veniamin Mikhaĭlovich, 1839–1906.
(Polovaĭa zrĕlost')
Половая зрѣлость, ея теченіе, отклоненія и болѣзни. Общедоступное изложеніе В. М. Тарновскаго. С.-Петербургъ, Тип. М. М. Стасюлевича, 1886.
xviii, 210 p. 28 cm.

1. Generative organs—Diseases. 2. Venereal diseases. I. Title.
RC875.T23

73–201934

NT 0041647   DLC DNLM

Tarnovskiĭ, Veniamin Mikhaĭlovich, 1839–1906.
Prostitution und Abolitionismus; Briefe. Hamburg, L. Voss, 1890.
xi, 222p. tables. 22cm.

Bibliographical footnotes.
Translation of the author's Проституція и аболиціонизмъ.

1. Prostitution. 2. Veneral diseases. I. Title.

NT 0041648   CLSU ICRL NcD-MC DNLM PPC CU MH ICJ

Tarnovskiĭ, Veniamin Mikhaĭlovich, 1839–1906.
Проституція и аболиционизмъ. Докладъ Русскому сифилидологическому и дерматологическому обществу профессора В. М. Тарновскаго ... С.-Петербургъ, Изд. Карла Риккера, 1888.
xv, 261 p. 24½ cm.

1. Prostitution. 2. Prostitution—Russia. 3. Venereal diseases—Russia. I. Title. *Title transliterated: Prostitutsiĭa i abolitsionizm.*
HQ111.T25

20–23999 rev

NT 0041649   DLC DNLM

Tarnovskiĭ, Veniamin Mikhaĭlovich, 1839–1906.
The sexual instinct and its morbid manifestations from the double standpoint of jurisprudence and psychiatry, by Dr. B. Tarnowsky ... Translated by W. C. Costello ... and Alfred Allinson ... Paris, C. Carrington, 1898.
xxiv, 239 p. front. (port.) 22ᶜᵐ.
Bibliography: p. 225–231.

1. Sexual instinct. 2. Sexual perversion. I. Costello, W. C., tr. II. Allinson, Alfred Richard, joint tr. III. Title.
45–27451
Library of Congress   HQ71.T32

NT 0041650   DLC DNLM ICRL NN PPC PU CtY-M

WCA
T189k
1872

TARNOVSKIĬ, Veniamin Mikhaĭlovich, 1839–1906
Vorträge über venerische Krankheiten. Berlin, Hirschwald, 1872.
xvi, 406 p. illus.

Translation of Kurs venericheskikh bolĕzneĭ.
Lectures delivered at the Mediko-khirurgicheskaĭa akademiĭa, 1869–70.

NT 0041651   DNLM OClW-H ViU CtY PPC

Tarnovskij, N
see Tarnovskiĭ, N

833.7
T189   Tarnow, Fanny, 1779-1862.
Auswahl aus Fanny Tarnow's Schriften.
Leipzig, C. Focke, 1830.
v.

NT 0041653   ICarbS MH

Tarnovsky, Nicolas
see
Tarnovs'kyĭ, Mykola Mykolaĭovych, 1895–

4DK
573   Tarnow, Fanny, 1779-1862.
Briefe auf einer Reise nach Petersburg an Freunde geschrieben. Berlin, T. C. F. Enslin, 1819.
292 p.

NT 0041655   DLC-P4 NjP MH

Tarnovs'kyĭ, Mykola Mykolaĭovych, 1895–
Шляхом життя (поезії). Ню Йорк, Культура, 1921.
233 p. port. 21 cm.
At head of title: Микола Тарновський.

I. Title.
Title romanized: Shlîakhom zhyttîa.

PG3948.T3S5   78-288379

NT 0041656   DLC IEdS

Tarnovs'kyĭ, Mykola Mykolaĭovych, 1895–
Вибрані поезії. Київ, Радянський письменник, 1953.
238 p. illus. 17 cm.

Title transliterated: Vybraní poezíĭ.

PG3948.T3A6 1953   56-27340 rev ‡

NT 0041657   DLC

Tarnow, Fanny, 1779-1862.
Die Prophetinn von Caschimir; oder,
Glaubenskraft und Liebesgluth, von Fanny Tarnow.
Nach. Lady Morgen. Wien, C. F. Schade, 1827.
2 v.   14 cm.   (Classische Cabinets-Bibliothek
oder Sammlung auserlesener Werke der deutschen
und Fremd-Literatur, 110)
I. Morgan, Sydney (Owenson) Lady, 1783?-
1859.

NT 0041658   ViU

PT 2534 TARNOW,FANNY,   1779-1862
.T2 T34   Das Testament. Nach Ducange von **Fanny Tarnow**.
Leipzig, C. E. Kollmann, 1835.
2 v.

Adaptation of Le testament de la pauvre
femme, by V.H.J.B. Ducange.

NT 0041659   InU

[Tarnow, Fanny] 1779-1862.
Zwei Jahre in Petersburg; ein roman
aus den papieren eines alten diplomaten.
Leipzig, Brockhaus, 1833.
309 p. 18 cm.

NT 0041660   NjP PPG

PT
2534   Tarnow, Fanny,
T2   1779-1862.
A78   Zwei Jahre in Petersburg. Aus den Papieren
1848   eines alten Diplomaten. 2. Aufl. Leipzig,
F. A. Brockhaus, 1848.
xxxviii, 352 p. 18cm.

A novel.

NT 0041661   NIC NcD

Tarnow, Franziska Christiane Johanne Friedrike,
1797-1862.
see Tarnow, Fanny, 1779-1862.

Tarnow, Fritz.
HD6696
.M38   **Maschke, Walter.**
Eine Auseinandersetzung mit Fritz Tarnow. Mit Beiträ-
gen von Hans Jendretzky [et al.] Berlin, Die Freie Gewerk-
schaft, 1948.

Tarnow, Fritz
Die Gewerkschaften im neuen Staat; Anleitung
für Redner. Hamburg, "Freie Gewerkschaft
G.m.b.H." [19-]
15 p.

NT 0041664   MH-PA

Tarnow, Fritz.
Kapitalistische Wirtschaftsanarchie und Arbeiterklasse;
Referat, gehalten auf dem Leipziger Parteitag der S.P.D.
am 1.Juni 1931. [Berlin, Dietz, 1931]
31 p.

NT 0041665   MH

TARNOW,Fritz.
Warum arm sein? 3.aufl. 8.bis 12.tausend.
Berlin,verlagsgesellschaft des Allgemeinen
deutschen gewerkschaftsbundes m.b.h.,1929.
pp.71.
"Gewerkschaften und wirtschaft,3."

NT 0041666   MH DLC

Tarnow, Johann, 1586-1629.
... Johannis Tarnovii... Exercitationum
biblicarum libri quatuor... Lipsiae, Halleword,
1640.
1250 p.

NT 0041667   PU

Tarnow, Johann, 1586-1629.
Exercitationes Biblicae. Rostochi,--
237p. 4°

NT 0041668   MWA

Tarnow, Johann, 1586-1629.
D. T. O. M. A. Johannis Tarnovii... In aliquot
Psalmos Davidis commentarius:... cum verborum
et rerum indice. Rostoch, 1633.
19.5 cm.

NT 0041669   CtY

TARNOW,Johann,1586-1629.
In prophetam Amos commentarius. 3a ed.
Rostochi,1640.
4°.

NT 0041670   MH-AH

Tarnow, Johann, 1586-1629.
Johannis Tarnovii... in Prophetam Amos
commentarius... Ed. 3... aucta. Rostochi,
Wildii, 1652.
245 p.

NT 0041671   PPLT

BS1560
.T198   Tarnow,Johann,1586-1629.
...Johannis Tarnovii...In prophetam Habacuc
commentarius:in quo textus analysi perspicuâ illustratur,ex fonte hebraeo explicatur,locis S.S.
parallelis confirmatur,à pravis expositionibus
vindicatur... RostochI, J.Hallervordio impensis
suppeditante,typis J.Pedani,1623.
99,[5] p. 19½x15½cm. [With his In prophetam
Micham commentarius. Rostochii,1626]

1.Bible. O.T. Habakkuk--Commentaries.

NT 0041672   ICU MH

BS1560
.T198   Tarnow,Johann,1586-1629.
...Johannis Tarnovii...In prophetam Haggaeum
commentarius:in quo textus analysi perspicua illustratur,ex fonte hebraeo explicatur,locis S.S.
parallelis confirmatur,à pravis expositionibus
vindicatur... RostochI,excudebat J.Pedanus,im-
pensis J.Hallerv[ordi,1624.
[8],77,[6] p. 19½x15½cm. [With his In prophetam Micham commentarius. Rostochii,1626]

1.Bible. O.T. Haggai--Commentaries.

NT 0041673   ICU MH

Tarnow, Johann   1586-1629.
-- In prophetam Hoseam commentarius: in
quo textus analysi perspicua illustratur,
ex fonte Hebraeo explicatur, locis S.S.
parallelibus confirmatur, à pravis expositionibus vindicatur... Rostochii, Literis N. Kilii, Impensis J. Wilden, 1646.
[8] 504 [28] p. 20cm.

With this is bound: His, In prophetam
Joelem commentarius. 1651. [His, In

prophetam Amos commentarius. 1652. His,
In prophetam Obadiam commentarius. 1646.
His, Quaestionum et quae foedera cum
diversae religionis hominibus. 1646.
His, In prophetam Jonam commentarius.
1647.

NT 0041675   NjPT

Tarnow, Johann, 1568-1629.
Johannis Tarnovii... in Prophetam Hoseam
commentarius... Rostochii, Richelii, 1654.
504 p.

NT 0041676   PPLT MH

TARNOW, Johann, *1586-1629.*
In prophetam Joelem commentarius. ultima ed.
Rostochii,1636.

4°.

NT   0041677   MH-AH

Tarnow, Johann, 1568-1629.
Johannis Tarnovil... in Prophetam Joelem.
Rostochi, Wildii, 1651.
206 p.

NT   0041678   PPLT

BS1526 TARNOW, JOHANN,1586-1629.
.F7   ...Johannis Tarnovii...In prophetam Jonam commentarius: in quo textus analysi perspicua illustrat,
ex fonte hebræo explicatur, locis S.S.parallelis confirmatur à pravis expositionibus vindicatur... Editio
secunda ab autore recognita & aucta. RostochI,literis
J.Pedani,impensis J.Hallervordii,1626.
[8],144,[12]p.   19x15½cm. [With Forster,Johann.
Commentarius in prophetam Jeremiam. Witteberge,1672]

1.Bible. O.T. Jonah--Commentaries.

NT   0041679   ICU

TARNOV, Johann, *1586-1629.*
In prophetam,Jonam commentarius.
Rostochi,1634.

2a ed. 4°.

NT   0041680   MH-AH

Tarnow, Johann, 1586-1629.
Johannis Tarnovii... in Prophetam Jonam
commentarius... Ed. 2... aucta. Rostochii,
Richelii, 1647.
144 p.

NT   0041681   PPLT

BS1560 Tarnow,Johann,1586-1629.
.T198   ...Johannis Tarnovii...In prophetam Malachiam
commentarius:in quo textus analysi perspicuâ illustratur,ex fonte hebraeo explicatur,locis S.S.
[parallelis] confirmatur,à pravis expositionibus
vindicatur... RostochI,typis J.Pedani,prostat
apud J.Hallervordium,1624.
100,[8] p.   19½x15½cm. [With his In prophetam
Micham commentarius. Rostochii,1626]

1.Bible. O.T. Malachi--Commentaries.

NT   0041682   ICU MH-AH

BS1560 Tarnow,Johann,1586-1629.
.T198   ...Johannis Tarnovii...In prophetam Micham com-
mentarius:in quo textus analysi perspicuâ illustratur,ex fonte hebraeo explicatur,locis S.S.pa-
rallelis confirmatur,à pravis expositionibus vindicatur... Editio secunda ab autore recognita &
aucta. Rostochii,typis J.Pedani impensis J.Hal-
lerfordij,1626.
[8],220,[16] p.   19½x15½cm.
With this are bound the author's commentaries
on six other minor prophets.

NT   0041683   ICU

TARNOW,Johann, *1586-*
In prophetam Micham commentarius.
Rostochii,1636.

4°.

NT   0041684   MH-AH

Tarnow, Johann, 1568-1629.
Johannis Tarnovii... in Prophetam Micham
commentarius...   Rostochii, Richelii, 1650.
220 p.

NT   0041685   PPLT

BS1526 TARNOW,JOHANN,1586-1629.
.F7   ...Johannis Tarnovii...In prophetam Nahum commen-
tarius:in quo textus analysi perspicuâ illustratur,ex
fonte hebræo explicatur,locis S.S.parallelis confirmatur,à pravis expositionibus vindicatur... RostochI,
J.Hallervordio impensas,typis J.Pedani,1623.
72,[6]p. 19x15½cm. [With Forster,Johann. Commentarius in prophetam Jeremiam. Witteberge,1672]
Imperfect:p.3-6 wanting.

1.Bible. O.T. Nahum--Commentaries.

NT   0041686   ICU MH-AH

BS1526 TARNOW, JOHANN,1586-1629.
.F7   ...Johannis Tarnovii...In prophetam Obadiam com-
mentarius:in quo textus analysi perspicua illustratur,ex fonte hebræo explicatur,locis S.S.παραλλη-
λις confirmatur,à pravis expositionibus vindicatur...
Adjectus et tractatus de foederibus ... Editio secunda ab autore recognita. RostochI,typis J.Pedani,
prostat apud I.Hallervordeum,1631.
43,34,[5]p. 19x15½cm. [With Forster, Johann.
Commentarius in prophetam Jeremiam. Witterberge,1672]
Tractatus de foederibus has special t.-p.and separate paging.

NT   0041687   ICU MH-AH

Tarnow, Johann, 1586-1629.
Johannis Tarnovii... in Prophetam Obadiam
commentarius...   Rostochi, Richelii, 1646.
41 p.

NT   0041688   PPLT

BS1560 Tarnow,Johann,1586-1629.
.T198   ...Johannis Tarnovii...In prophetam Sophoniam
commentarius:in quo textus analysi perspicuâ illustratur,ex fonte hebraeo explicatur,locis S.S.
parallelis confirmatur,à pravis expositionibus
vindicatur... RostochI,typis J.Pedani,impensis
J.Hallervordij,1623.
99,[5] p. 19½x15½cm. [With his In prophetam
Micham commentarius. Rostochii,1626]

1.Bible. O.T. Zephaniah--Commentaries.

NT   0041689   ICU

TARNOW,Johann, *1586-1629.*
In prophetam Sophoniam commentarius.
Stralsundi,1642.

4°.

NT   0041690   MH-AH

BS1560 Tarnow,Johann,1586-1629.
.T198   ...Johannis Tarnovii...In prophetam Zachariam
commentarius:in quo textus analysi perspicuâ illustratur,ex fonte hebraeo explicatur,locis S.S.
parallelis confirmatur,à pravis expositionibus
vindicatur... RostochI,typis exscripsit J.Peda-
nus,sumptibus J.Hallervordi,1625.
[8],394,[16] p. 19½x15½cm. [With his In prophetam Micham commentarius. Rostochii,1626]

1.Bible. O.T. Zechariah--Commentaries.

NT   0041691   ICU

TARNOW,Johann, *1586-*
In prophetam Zachariam commentarius.
Rostochi,1632.

4°.

NT   0041692   MH-AH

Tarnow, Johann, *1586-*
In Prophetas minores commentarius. Rostochii, 1646-47.
2 vols. 4°

NT   0041693   MWA

RARE
BOOK   Tarnow, Johann,   1586-1629.
BS
1560   In prophetas minores commentarius in
T18   qvo textus analysi perspicua illustratur,
exfonte Hebraeo explicatur, Locis S. Scripturae parallelis confirmatur, à pravis
expositionibus vindicatur, & ad usum
deductis Locis Communibus in Scriptura
fundatis applicatur. Cum praefatione Jo.
Benedicti Carpzovii. Francofurti &
Lipsiae, J. A. Pleneri, 1688.
[26],1665   [49]p. front.
1. Bible.   0. T. Minor prophets -
Commentaries.   I. Title. Chronological card.

NT   0041694   MoSCS IaDL NjPT MA MH-AH

BS1560 TARNOW, JOHANN,1586-1629.
.T2   Johannis Tarnovii...In Prophetas minores commentarius, in qvo textus analysi perspicua illustratur, ex
fonte hebræo explicatur,locis S.Scripturæ parallelis
confirmatur,à pravis expositionibus vindicatur... Cum
præfatione Jo.Benedicti Carpzovii... Lipsiæ,apud J.
A.Plenerum,bibliop.Stettin[etc.]1706.
[19],1665,[49]p. 20½x16cm.
Added t.-p.,engr.;head and tail pieces;initials.

1.Bible. O.T. Minor prophets--Commentaries.

NT   0041695   ICU PU NNUT

RARE BOOK Tarnow, *Johann, 1586-1629.*
BS
2615   In Threnos Jeremiae Commentarius...
T3   Rostochi, Literis J. Pedani...Impensis J.
Hallervordii, 1627.
[viii]279[13]p.
Bound with his...in S. Johannis Evangelium
Commentarius...1629.

NT   0041696   MoSCS CtY

Tarnow, Johannes, 1586-1629.
. [In Threnos Jeremiae commentarius: in
quo textus ex fonte hebraeo explicatur,
locis S.S. parallelis confirmatur, à
pravis expositionibus vindicatur, usus
verò in locis communibus ex ipsa scrip-
turâ natis ac probatis indicatur...
Rostochi, Sumptu J. Hallervordii, 1642.
[8], 279 [13] p. 19ᵐ.

NT   0041697   NjPT

Tarnow, Johann, 1586-1629.
... Johannis Tarnovii... In Threnos Jeremiae
commentarius; in quo textus ex fonte Hebraeo
explicatur cum praefatione Joannis Fechtii.
Hamburg, Heilii, pref. 1706.
200 p.

NT   0041698   PU

TARNOW, Johann, 1586-1629.
Quaestionum et quae foedera cum diversae
religionis hominibus, etc. 2a ed. Rostochi, 1631.
4°.

NT 0041699   MH-AH

Tarnow, Johann, 1586-1629.
Quaestionum et quae foedera cum diversae
religionis hominibus and praecipue a Lutheranis cum
Calvinianis salva iniri possint conscientia... ex
Scriptura Sacra, rationibusq inde deductis decisa...
Rostochii, Richelii, 1646.
34 p.

NT 0041700   PPLT

Tarnow, Johann Joachim, respondent.
Disputatio philosophica qua immortalitatis animae
in systemae influxus physici salva sistitur
see under   Pries, Joachim Heinrich,
1714-1763, praeses.

Tarnow, Julius Michael
Rostock im Jahrzehnt 1780/90; Stadt-Karte des
Hospitalmeisters J.M.Tarnow, mit Grundstückseinteilung
und Hausbesitzerverzeichnis. Als Festgabe bei der 700-
Jahr-Feier der Stadt Rostock i.A. des Vereins für
Rostocks Altertümer hrsg.von G.Kohfeldt. Rostock i.M.,
Ausgabe durch G.B. Leopold's Universitäts-Buchhandlung,
1918

25 p. fold. map
1. Rostock, Ger. - Maps.   I.Kohfeldt, Gustav, 1867-
ed.

NT 0041702   MH

Tarnow, Otto-Siegfried, Arzt: Digitalispraeparate. [In Ma-
schinenschrift] 25 S. 4°(2°). — Auszug: Berlin (1920).
Blanke. 2 Bl. 8°
Berlin, Med. Diss. v. 20. Febr. 1920, Ref. Brugsch
[Geb. 9. Sept. 93 Bromberg; Wohnort: Berlin-Westend; Staatsangeh.: Preußen;
Vorbildung: Königstädt. G. Bromberg Reife 12; Studium: Berlin 10 S.; Coll.
13. Febr. 20; Approb. 25. Dez. 19.]   [U 20. 1497

NT 0041703   ICRL

Tarnow, Paul, 1562-1633
Der alte Glaube und Christenthum unserer Vorfahren
... Wie auch Das neue Evangelium, wie solches ... in
einer lateinischen Rede auf der Universität zu
Rostock Anno 1624 vorgestellet, welches fast von
Wort zu Wort verteutschet hierbey mit herausgegeben
wird von Johann Hieronymo Wiegleben. Halle, Schütze,
1699

323, 81 p.
"Das neue Evangelium" has a special t.p. with
title: Rede von dem ne,   uen Evangelio, dass es eine
Ursache alles Unheils   in der Christenheit sey
... 81 p.

NT 0041704   MH

Pam.   Tarnow,   Paul, 1562-1633, praeses.
Coll.
... De ministrorum verbi divini officio:
quod et cuibus partibus illud constet; deque
legitima earum sustinendarum ratione. Ad cujus
theses auxiliante deo trinuno sub praesidio
Pauli Tarnovii ... respondebit publicè ...
Christianus Michael ... Rostochii, Typis
Joachimi Pedani, M. DC. XVIII.
[24] p. 19 cm.

1. Clergy. Religious life. I. Michael,
Christianus,   , respondent

NT 0041705   NcD NcU

T250   Tarnow   Paul ,1562-1633, praeses.
T189mi   ... De ministrorum verbi abdicatione spontanea,
1620   translatione, dimissioneq; cum voluntaria, tum
invita; de immunitatibus & praemijs eorum, qui
fideliter suum munus administrant, poenisq;
caeterorum cum temporarijs, tum aeternis ...
sub praesidio Pauli Tarnovii ... respondebit
M. Matthaeus Calander ... Rostochii, Typis
Joachimi Pedani, Anno 1620.
[44] p. 19cm.

NT 0041706   NcU NcD

624.7   TARNOW, Paul, 1562-1633
W40.9   ...De sacrosancta Trinitate, liber unus:
T5535im   Oppositus Favsti Socini refutationi ...
1650   & huic scripto insertae: qua refellere
conatus est, quae De divinitate Filii &
Spiritus Sancti, Robertus Bellarminus,
T.l.controversiae 2.generalis, libro
primo, & Jacobus Wiekus, Jesuita, pecu-
liari libello, scripserunt. Rostochi
sumptibus Johannis Hallervordij, biblio-
pole, typis

Joachimi Pedani, typographi academiae.
CI Ɔ IƆ CXXV.
10p.l., 1010, [77]p. 19.5cm.
At head of title: "Pavli Tarnovii ..."
Title within ornamental border.
Number 1 in a bound volume of 17th-
century theological works.

NT 0041708   MH-AH

TARNOW, Paul, 1562-1633.
De sacrosancto ministerio, libri tres.
Rostochi, 1623.

(48),1423,(55)p 8°.

NT 0041709   MH-AH

Tarnow, Paul, 1562-1633, praeses.
Examen doctrinae pontificiorum, de oratione
sive precatione, cum in genere, tum etiam in
specie de certa illa forma precum, quam propriam
esse, volunt Sacerdotum & Monachorum, & Horarun
canonicarum nomine appellari solet; quemadmodum,
ea tradita est à Bellarmino lib. I. tote de bonis
opetibus in particulari: T. & ultimo, controversia
tertia & ultima... Rostochii, 1619.
Unpaged, A–F, in fours. 20 cm.
Diss. - (Andreas Virginus, respondent)

NT 0041710   NNUT

RARE BOOK   Tarnow, Paul, 1562-1633.
BS
2615   In Psalmos Poenitentiales septem Commen-
T3   tarius brevis... Rostochi, Literis J.
Pedani...Impensis J. Hallervordii, 1628.
[viii]152[8]p.
Bound with his...in S. Johannis Evangelium
Commentarius...1629.

NT 0041711   MoSCS

566.6   TARNOW, Paul, 1562-1633.
T189qv   ...in S. Johannis Evangelium Comment-
1629   arius: Quo verba & phrases ex graeca,
hellenistica hebraea, & cognatis orientalibus linguis explicantur, cohaerentia
textus & sententiarum in narrationibus
evangelistae, & concionibus Domini nostri
Jesu Christi, analysi logica ostenditur,
eademq; opera in expositiones veterum &
recentium, maximè Johannis Maldonati, in-
quiritur, deque controversiis gravissimis

contra Pontificios, Photinianos novos,
alioque, & de quaestionibus non nullis
curiosis, quae ab interpretibus motae
sunt, judicium exponitur. Inserta Est
Arabicae Paraphrasis A CL.V. M Thoma
Erpenio editae, latina translatio, unà
cum collatione diversitatis lectionum

Continued in next column

Continued from preceding column

in Romano codice Arabico, & interpretationis ejusdem interlinearis, eodem
auctore. Subjuncti Indices Octo Locup-
letissimi omnium, quae toto opere continentur. Rostochi Typis Joachimi Pedani
typographi, Sumptibus Johannis Hallervardii
bibliop. Anno 1629.

8p.l., 1341,[128]p.

At head of title: Pauli Tarnovii, D. &
S. S. Theologiae, in Academia Rostochiensi,
Professoris,
Pages 1100-1341 misnumbered as 2000-4041.

NT 0041715   MH-AH MH MoSCS ICF PPLT

IT4849   **Tarnow, Rudolf.**
T3B8   "Burrkäwers"; plattdütschen Kram von dit un dat, von
1916   Spass un Jernst un süss noch wat. Schwerin, L.
Davids, 1916.
6 v.
Vol.2-6 lack subtitle.
[Bd.1,4 5.Upl.; Bd.2, 4.Upl.; Bd.3, 3.Upl.;
Bd.5, 2.Kriegsband; Bd.6, 2.Upl., 3.Kriegsband

NT 0041716   CU

Tarnow, Rudolf.
"Burrkäwers"; plattdütschen Kram von dit un dat, von
Spass un Jernst un sünss noch wat. Seestadt Wismar,
Hinstorffsche Verlagsbuchhandlung, 1941–
v. 18 cm.

I. Title.

PT4849.T3B8   A F 49–136*

Yale Univ. Library
for Library of Congress   [1]†

NT 0041717   CtY TNJ CU DLC

Tarnow, Rudolf.
Köster Klickermann.   Wismar, Hinstorff,
1921.
273 p. 12°.

NT 0041718   PPG

Tarnow, Rudolf.
Köster Klickermann, von Rudolf Tarnow. 11.-13.
dusend ... Wismar, Hinstorff, 1924.
2 p. l., 273 p. 19ᵐᵐ.
Poems.

I. Title.

Library of Congress   PT4849.T3K6 1924
                                              25-6250

NT 0041719   DLC

Tarnow, Rudolf.
Ringelranken, iernste un spassige gedichte, von Rudolf Tarnow. 1. bis 5. dusend. Wismar i. Meckl., Hinstorff, 1927.
136 p. front. (port.) 18ᵐᵐ.

I. Title.

Library of Congress   PT4849.T3R5 1927
                                              29-597

NT 0041720   DLC OC1

Tarnow, Rudolf.
Rüter-püter, för lütt un grot kinner, von Rudolf Tarnow. 1.–4. dusend. Wismar i. Meckl., Hinstorff, 1924.

142 p. illus. 22½ᶜᵐ.

Poems.

ɪ. Title.

Library of Congress   PT4849.T3R8 1924   25–16099

NT   0041721   DLC

Tarnów, Poland. Sifrija Amamith.
רשימת ספרים. קאטאלאג. טרנוב. בדפוס של י. ענגלבערג.
‎ [W Tarnowie, 1924] תרפ"ד.

106 p. 23 cm.

Added t. p.: Katalog.
A catalog of books; Hebrew, Yiddish, and European languages.

Title transliterated: Reshimat sefarim.

Z938.T3   56–51339

NT   0041722   DLC

Tarnów, Poland. Szkoła Ogrodnicza.
Statut. Tarnów, Nakł. Kuratoryi Szkoły Ogrodniczej, 1883.

14 p. 21 cm.

S539.T3S9   65–59760

NT   0041723   DLC

Tarnów, Poland. Żydowska Biblioteka Ludowa
see
Tarnów, Poland. Sifrija Amamith.

Tarnowski, Casimir 1873–
Die ovariotomie waehrend der schwangerschaft.
Inaug. diss. Leipzig, 1901.
Bibl.

NT   0041725   ICRL CtY DNLM

Tarnowski, Curt Eugen, 1906–
Difteribacillens gruppe- og typeinddeling. København, Munksgaard, 1942.

272 p. illus., diagrs., tables. 26 cm.

Thesis—Københavns universitet.
Summary in English.
Bibliography: p. [247]–272.

1. Diphtheria—Bacteriology. ɪ. Title.

QR201.D5T3   57–51761

NT   0041726   DLC DNLM CtY

TARNOWSKI, Felix.
Die anerkennung als grund der unterbrechung der anspruchsverjährung. Inaug.-diss., Rostock. Berlin, 1904.

8°.

NT   0041727   MH-L ICRL

W 2
A1GG4
[F4
no. 1100
TARNOWSKI, Georg.
Advances in the byochemistry [sic] of the Corynebacterium diphtheria group, with special reference to the pathological physiology of diphtheria in man. [Berlin] Scientific Branch, Field Information Agency, Technical (US) [1947]
136 p. (FIAT report, no. 1100)
Text in German.
1. Diphtheria 2. Diphtheria bacillus
Series: FIAT final report, no. 1100

NT   0041728   DNLM MiU

Tarnowski, Georg, 1878–
Die fiduciarische Abtretung von Forderungen ... gegen die ... Opponenten ... Eugen Ollendorff ... Moritz Henschel ... verteidigen wird Georg Tarnowski ... Breslau, Druck der Breslauer Genossenschafts-Buchdruckerei, 1901.

3 p.l., 62, ² [2] p. 22cm.

Inaug.-Diss. - Breslau.
"Lebenslauf": p. [63]
Bibliographical footnotes.

NT   0041729   MH-L ICRL

Tarnowski, Gertrud Siche-
see **Siche-Tarnowski, Gertrud.**

Tarnowski, Hans.
... Die systematische bedeutung der adaequaten kausalitätstheorie für den aufbau des verbrechensbegriffs, von dr. Hans Tarnowski ... Berlin und Leipzig, W. de Gruyter & co., 1927.

x, 340 p. 22½ᶜᵐ. (Abhandlungen des Kriminalistischen instituts an der Universität Berlin ... 4. folge. 1. bd. 2. hft.)

The author's inaugural dissertation, Berlin.
"Literatur": p. [vii]–x.

1. Proximate cause (Law)—Germany. 2. Criminal law—Germany. ɪ. Title.

     35–24144

Library of Congress   [a44c1]   343.01

NT   0041731   DLC CtY MH

Tarnowski, Heinz, 1922–
Die deutschen Industrie- und Handelskammern und die grossen geistigen, politischen und wirtschaftlichen Strömungen ihrer Zeit. [Mainz? 1951?]

152, xi p. 29 cm.

Inaug.-Diss.—Mainz.
Vita.
Bibliography: p. i–xi.

1. Boards of trade—Germany. ɪ. Title.

HF308.A3T3   56–57837

NT   0041732   DLC

Tarnowski, Jan, 1488-1561.
Dzieła. Krakow, K.J.Turowski, 1858.
3 v. 20cm. (In Biblioteka polska, 1858-59)

CONTENTS: [1]Consilium rationis bellicae.-[2]De bello cum juratissimis christianae fidei hostibus turcis gerendo.-[3]De laudibu; Joannis Tarnovii, by Christophorus Warsevicius.

NT   0041733   CSt

Tarnowski, Jan, 1488–1561.   Slav 5225.6
Consilium rationis bellicae. [Also his " De bello cum juratissimis Christianae fidei hostibus Turcis gerendo disputatio " and " Christophori Warsevicii De laudibus Joannis Tarnovii oratio.] Kraków, 1858.
pp. (2), 47, 35, iii. (Biblioteka polska.)
The Consilium text is in Polish.

||Warszewicki

NT   0041734   MH

Tarnowski, Jan, 1488–1561.
Jana Tarnowskiego Consilium rationis bellicae, drukował Łazarz Andrysowic w Tarnowie, 1558. Z egzemplarza pergaminowego Biblioteki Puławskiej przedrukował homograficznym sposobem A. Piliński. [W. Poznaniu] Nakładem Biblioteki Kórnickiej, 1879.

[79] p. 23ᶜᵐ.

1. Military art and science—Early works to 1800. ɪ. Piliński, Adam, 1810–1887. ɪɪ. Title: Consilium rationis bellicae.

Library of Congress   U101.T21   14–8339

NT   0041735   DLC MH CtY

Law
     Tarnowski, Jan, 1488–1561. O obronie koronnej, i o sprawie i powinności urzędników wojennych.

Poland. *Laws, statutes, etc.*
Ustawy prawa ziemskiego polskiego, dla pamięci lepszej krótko i porządnie z statutów i z konstytucyj zebrane, z przydatkiem: O obronie koronnej, i o sprawie i powinności urzędnikow wojennych, Jego M. Pana Jana Tarnowskiego niekiedy kasztelana krakowskiego etc. etc., temi czasy rycerskiemu stanowi barzo potrzebne. Wyd. Kazimierza Józefa Turowskiego. Kraków, Nakł. Wydawn. Biblioteki Polskiej, 1858.

Law
     Tarnowski, Jan, 1488–1561, ed.

Poland. *Laws, statutes, etc.*
Ustawy prawa ziemskiego polskiego, dla pamięci lepszej krótko i porządnie z statutów i z konstytucyj zebrane, z przydatkiem: O obronie koronnej, i o sprawie i powinności urzędnikow wojennych, Jego M. Pana Jana Tarnowskiego niekiedy kasztelana krakowskiego etc. etc., temi czasy rycerskiemu stanowi barzo potrzebne. Wyd. Kazimierza Józefa Turowskiego. Kraków, Nakł. Wydawn. Biblioteki Polskiej, 1858.

Tarnowski, Jan, 1586–1629
     see Tarnow, Johann, 1586–1629.

Rare Book
Room
DK436   Tarnowski, Jan, hrabia, 1835–1894
.5   Jan Tarnowski z Dzikowa. W Krakowie, [Nakł.
.T372   Zdzisława Tarnowskiego] 1898.
A5   187p. port.,facsim. 27cm.
1898

1. Tarnowski, Jan, hrabia, 1835–1894.

NT   0041739   PSt MH

HD
1294   Tarnowski, Jan, Graf, 1867–
T18   Zur Kritik der Landwirthschaftlichen Taxationsmethoden. Leipzig-Reudnitz, O. Schmidt, 1890.
76 p. 23cm.

Diss.—Leipzig.

1. Agriculture--Taxation.

NT   0041740   NIC ICRL

TARNOWSKI, Jan, hrabia., d. 1928.
Appel d'un Polonais en faveur des peuples liés a la Pologne dans l'histoire et séparés de la Russie dans le courant de cette guerre. [With La Russie et les Ruthenes.] n.p.,n.d.

pp.(4).
Signed "Biarritz,1919. Comte Jean Tarnowski".
Without title-page. Caption title.

NT   0041741   MH

TARNOWSKI, Jan, hrabia, d. 1928.
Le change français et la cause réelle de sa baisse. Biarritz, Grande imprimerie moderne, 1919.

pp. 20.

NT 0041742 MH

TARNOWSKI, Jan, hrabia, d. 1928.
Une erreur qui ne devrait pas se prolonger. n.p., n.d.

pp. (4).
Signed "Comte J. Tarnowski. 1920."
Without title-page. Caption title.

NT 0041743 MH

DK67.5 Tarnowski, Jan, hrabia, d. 1928.
G3T189 ..La menace allemande et le péril russe...
Biarritz, Impr. moderne, 1919.
34 p. 22½ᶜᵐ

At head of title: Comte Jean Tarnowski.
"Errata": p. [2] of cover.

Hoover
Library

1. Russia – Foreign relations – Germany. 2.
Germany – Foreign relations – Russia. 3. European
war, 1914-1918 – Territorial questions – Poland.
I. Title.

NT 0041744 CSt-H MH

TARNOWSKI, Jan, hrabia, d. 1928.
La menace bolcheviste et la Pologne. n.p., n.d.

pp. (2).
Signed "Comte J. Tarnowski. 1920".
Without title-page. Caption title.

NT 0041745 MH

Tarnowski, Jan, hrabia, d. 1928.
Nasze przedstawicielstwo polityczne w Paryżu i w
Petersburgu 1905-1919. Warszawa, Nakł. Księgarni J.
Czerneckiego, 1923

125 p.

1. World War, 1914-19 (5) – Poland 2. Poland –
For. rel.

NT 0041746 MH

TARNOWSKI, Jan, hrabia, d. 1928.
La Pologne; Verdun de l'Europe. [Biarritz,
Grand Imprimerie Moderne, 1920].

pp. (2).
Without title-page. Caption title.

NT 0041747 MH

TARNOWSKI, Jan, hrabia, d. 1928.
La Pologne et la paix mondiale. Biarritz, 1919.

16 p.

NT 0041748 MH-L NN

Tarnowski, Jan, hrabia, d. 1928.
... Projekt nowej ustawy konstytucyjnej (z komentarzem)
Wyd. pośmiertne z przedmową dra Stanisława Tyszkiewicza.
Kraków [etc.] Skład główny: Gebethner i Wolff, 1928.
96 p. 22½ᶜᵐ.
"Bibljografja": p. 96.

1. Poland—Constitutional law.   I. Tyszkiewicz, Stanisław, ed.

41-39597

NT 0041749 DLC

TARNOWSKI, Jan, hrabia, d. 1928.
La question juive en Pologne. n.p., n.d.

(pp. 4).
Signed "Biarritz, 1919. Comte Jean Tarnowski".
Without title-page. Caption title.

NT 0041750 MH

Tarnowski, Jan, hrabia, d. 1928.
Le traité de paix et la Pologne. Biarritz, Impr.
Moderne, 1919

12 p.

NT 0041751 MH

TARNOWSKI, Jan, hrabia, d. 1928.
Le traité de Versailles et la sécurité de
l'Europe. Biarritz, 1919.

(2), 64 p.

NT 0041752 MH

TARNOWSKI, Jan, hrabia, d. 1928.
Ukraine et Galicie. Biarritz, Imprimerie
moderne, 1920.

pp. 7.

NT 0041753 MH

Tarnowski, Jan Feliks, 1779-1842.
Badania historyczne jaki wpływ mieć mogły : mniemania
i literatura ludów wschodnich na ludy zachodnie, szczegól-
niey we względzie poezyi : rzecz czytana na posiedzeniu
Towarzystwa Królewskiego Przyiaciół Nauk, w Warszawie
dnia 24 miesiąca listopada 1819 roku / przez Jana Hrabiego
Tarnowskiego. — W Warszawie : W Druk. Xięży Piiarów,
1819.
205 p. ; 20 cm.
1. Literature, Comparative—Oriental and European. 2. Literature,
Comparative—European. and Oriental.   I. Towarzystwo Królewskie Warszawskie Przyiaciół Nauk.   II. Title.

PN849.O7T3 1819   76-519229

NT 0041754 DLC OU ICU

Tarnowski, Jean, comte
see Tarnowski, Jan, hrabia, d. 1928.

Tarnowski (Julius). *Ueber die Retraktion
der Palmaraponenrose. 22 pp. 8°. *Erlangen,
*E. T. Jacob, [1887].

NT 0041756 DNLM

Tarnowski, Ladislas.   No. I in **M.338.3
Ouverture d'un drame. [A grand orchestre. Partition.]
Wien. Gutmann. 1874. (1), 46, (1) pp. 8°.

F1187 — Overtures.

NT 0041757 MB

PT 2534 TARNOWSKI, LADISLAUS, 1811-1847
.T25 B5   Blutige Fusstapfen; Arme-Sünder-Geschichten.
Braunschweig, G. C. E. Meyer, 1842.
2 v.

NT 0041758 InU

PT 2534 TARNOWSKI, LADISLAUS, 1811-1847
.T25 F49   Der Findling des Henkers; eine Armesünder-
geschichte nach aktenmässigen Quellen bearbeitet. Leipzig, Literarisches Museum, 1844.
199 p.

NT 0041759 InU

PT 2534 TARNOWSKI, LADISLAUS, 1811-1847
.T25 M5   Menschen und Zeiten. In novellistische
Rahmen gefasst. Braunschweig, G. C. E. Meyer,
1840.
3 v.

NT 0041760 InU

PT
2534   Tarnowski, Ladislaus, 1811-1847
.T25   Waldteufel; Gespenstergeschichten und
W3   Geistersagen. Grünberg, Levysohn & Siebert,
1842.
3v. 15cm.

1. Ghost stories, German. I. Title.

NT 0041761 TNJ

Tarnowski, Marceli, tr.

Hagenbach, Arnold.
... Pilot Tex, bohaterzy nocnego ekspresu. Autoryzowany
przekład Marcelego Tarnowskiego. Warszawa, "Świat"
[1935].

Tarnowski, Marceli, tr.

[Clemens, Samuel Langhorne], 1835-1910.
... Przygody Hucka, powieść dla młodzieży. Warszawa,
Nakł. Księgarni J. Przeworskiego, 1934.

Tarnowski, Marceli, tr.

Brion, Marcel.
... Śmierć jest piękna, powieść; autoryzowany przekład z
francuskiego Marcelego Tarnowskiego. Warszawa, Wydawnictwo nowoczesne [1935].

Tarnowski, Marceli, tr.

Pulver, Max, 1889–
... Ucieczka do życia; powieść. Z upoważnienia autora
przełożył z niemieckiego Marceli Tarnowski. Warszawa,
"Świat" [1935].

Tarnowski, Stanisław, *hrabia*, 1837–1917.
   Chopin : as revealed by extracts from his diary ; by Count Stanislas Tarnowski, tr. from Polish by Natalie Janotha, ed. by J. T. Tanqueray, with eight portraits.   London, W. Reeves ₁1905₎
   69, ₁1₎ p. incl. front., 7 port. 18½ᶜᵐ.

   1. Chopin, Fryderyk Franciszek, 1810–1849.   ɪ. Tanqueray, J. T., ed. ɪɪ. Janotha, Natalja, 1856–   tr.   6–39985

   Library of Congress   ML410.C54T2

            OC1
NT   0041766   DLC PP CtY AAP MtU CaBVaU MB OU NN MiU

4ML   Tarnowski, Stanislaw, hrabia, 1837–1917.
13   Chopin i Grottger, dwa szkice.   Kraków, Nakładem Księgarni Spółki Wydawniczej Polskiej, 1892.
         111 p.

NT   0041767   DLC-P4 MH

Tarnowski, Stanisław, hrabia, 1837–1917.
   Henryk Rzewuski ; z odczytów publicznych.   Lwów, Nakł. Księgarni Seyfartha i Czajkowskiego, 1887.
   97 p.   25 cm.
   1. Rzewuski, Henryk, hrabia, 1791–1866.

NT   0041768   NNC MH

Tarnowski, Stanisław, *hrabia*, 1837–1917.
   Historya literatury polskiej ...   W Krakowie, Spółka wydawnicza polska, 1903–07.
   6 v. in 7. 21ᶜᵐ.
   At head of title: St. Tarnowski.
   Vols. 1–5: Wyd. 2. uzupełnione.
   Bibliography at the end of each volume except the last which has the bibliography at the end of part 1.
   Vol. 6 has imprint: W. Krakowie, W drukarni "Czasu" pod zarządem Aleksandra Świerzyńskiego.
   Contents.—t. ɪ. Wiek xvɪ. 1903.—t. ɪɪ. Wiek xvɪɪ. 1903.—t. ɪɪɪ. Wiek xvɪɪɪ. 1904.—t. ɪv. Wiek xɪx, 1800–1830. 1904.—t. v. Wiek xɪx, 1831–1850. 1905.—t. vɪ. część 1. Wiek xɪx, 1850–1863. 1905. część 2. Wiek xɪx, 1863–1900. 1907.
   1. Polish literature—   Hist. & crit.   44–35881
   Library of Congress   PG7012.T3

      ICU MiU IEN KU
Nf   0041769   DLC WU WaU IEdS KU CtY MH OU NcD ICU CSt

PG 7157   TARNOWSKI, STANISŁAW, hrabia, 1837–1917
.K5 Z853   Jan Kochanowski ; studia do historyi literatury polskiej, wiek XVI.   W Krakowie, Nakł. autora, 1888.
            470 p.

            Introduction also in Latin.

            1. Kochanowski, Jan, 1530–1584.

NT   0041770   InU ICU MH

Tarnowski, Stanisław, *hrabia*, 1837–
   ... Józef Szujski jako poeta.   Warszawa, Nakład Gebethnera i Wolffa, 1901.
   2 p. l., 201 p. 21½ᶜᵐ.
   At head of title: St. Tarnowski.

   1. Szujski, Józef, 1835–1883.
                                          17–12529
   Library of Congress   PG7158.S88T3

NT   0041771   DLC OU CSt KU ICU MiDW IU NNC CtY CoU NN

Tarnowski, Stanisław, *hrabia*, 1837–
   Julian Klaczko ...   W Krakowie, Drukarnia "Czasu", 1909.
   2 v. fronts., ports. 23ᶜᵐ.
   At head of title: St. Tarnowski.

   1. Klaczko, Juljan, 1828–1906.
                                          ᴄᴀ 30–263 Unrev'd
   Library of Congress   PG7158.T3J8

NT   0041772   DLC CoU WaU PSt KU OCH NN

PG7158   Tarnowski, Stanisław, hrabia, 1837–1917.
.F8Z8   Komedye Aleksandra hr. Fredry; trzy ódczyty
T2   publiczne. Warszawa, Wyd. Redakcyi Biblioteki Warszawskiéj, 1876.
          92 p.

          1. Fredro, Aleksander, hrabia, 1793–1876.

NT   0041773   ICU

PG 7158   TARNOWSKI, STANISŁAW, hrabia, 1837–1917
.F7 Z853   Komedye Aleksandra Hr.Fredry. O pośmiert-
1896   nych komedyach Fredry. Wyd.2. W Krakowie, Spółka Wydawn. Polska, 1896.
           169 p.

           Part 1 is second edition.

           1. Fredro,Aleksander,hrabia,1793–1876. I. Tc.
           II. Tc.: O pośmier   tnych komedyach Fredry.

NT   0041774   InU

Tarnowski, Stanisław, hrabia, 1837–1917.
   Ksiadz Waleryan Kalinka / St. Tarnowski.
   W Krakowie : Tarnowski, 1887.
   216 p. ; 23 cm.

   "Osobne odbicie z 'Przegladu Polskiego.'"

   1.Kalinka, Walerian, 1826–1886.   I.TITLE.
   SSL NUP SC

NT   0041775   CSt MH

Tarnowski, Stanislaw, hrabia, 1837–1917.
   Ku czci Zygmunta Krasińskiego 1812–1912
   see under title

TARNOWSKI,Stanisław,hrabia,1837–
   Leon XIII;kilka słów z powodu pięcdziesiątej
   rocznicy jego kapłaństwa. Lwów,nakładem autora
   1888.

   pp.(4),58.

NT   0041777   MH

ND   Tarnowski, Stanisław, hrabia, 1837–1917
699   Matejko. W Krakowie, W Księg. Spółki Wydawn.
+H3   Polskiej, 1897.
T3   562 p. illus. 27 cm.

      1. Matejko, Jan Alojzy, 1838–1893

NT   0041778   WU OC1 CoU

943.8 Tarnowski, Stanislaw, hrabia, 1837–
T176   ... Nasze dzieje w XIX wieku. Wydanie 3.,
       uzupełnione ... W Krakowie, Spółka wydawnicza
       polska, 1901.
       4 p. l., 5–165 p. illus., ports., facsims.
       27ᶜᵐ.

       At head of title: St. Tarnowski.

       1. Poland – History – 19th cent.

NT   0041779   NNC NN KU OU

Tarnowski, Stanisław, *hrabia*, 1837–1917.
   Nasze dzieje w ostatnich stu latach. Wyd. 2., uszup. W Krakowie, Spółka Wydawnicza Polska, 1895.
   192 p. illus., ports. 28 cm.

   1. Poland—Hist.—1795–1864. 2. Poland—Hist.—1864–1918.
   ɪ. Title.

   DK434.9.T3 1895   64–58908

NT   0041780   DLC CtY MH IU OU CSt

DK 434.9   Tarnowski, Stanisław, hrabia, 1837–1917.
T3   Nasze dzieje w ostatnich stu latach.
1896   Wyd. 2., uzup. W Krakowie, Spółka Wydawnicza Polska, 1896.
           192 p. illus., ports. 27 cm.

           3d ed. published in 1901 under title: Nasze
           dzieje w XIX ₁i. e. dziewietnastym₎ wieku.

           1. Poland – Hist. – 1795–1864. 2. Poland –
           Hist. – 1864–1918. I. Title.

NT   0041781   OU

Tarnowski, Stanisław, *hrabia, 1837–*   3060.122
   Nasze dzieje w ostatnich stu latach.
   — Chicago. Dyniewicz. 1898. 234 pp. Illus. Portraits. Plates. L.8°.

   E2593 — Poland. Hist. — Poland. Lang. Works in.

NT   0041782   MB

832.63
D   Tarnowski, Stanislaw, hrabia, 1837–1917
T18   O dramatach Schillera. Krakow, Skład
      głowny w spolki wydawniczej Polskiej, 1896.
      395p. 22cm.

      1. Schiller, Johann Christoph Friedrich,
      1759–1805.

NT   0041783   TNJ MH

ML   Tarnowski, Stanisław, hrabia, 1837–1917
2881 O kolędach. W Krakowie, Nakł. Księgarni
P6   Spółki Wydawniczej Polskiej, 1894.
T3   52p. 21cm.

      In Cyrillic characters.

      1. Carols, Polish – Hist. & crit. 2. Christ-
      mas music – Hist. & crit. I. Title

NT   0041784   WU MH KU

Tarnowski, Stanisław, hrabia, 1837–1917.
   O Mickiewiczu : odczyt miany na publicznem posiedzeniu Akademii Umiejętności dnia 14 maja 1898 roku / Stanisław hr. Tarnowski. -- Kraków : Nakł. Akademii Umiejętności, 1898.
   31 p. ; 21 cm.
   Bound in a pamphlet volume.

NT   0041785   MH KU CSt MiU OU

PG   Tarnowski, Stanisław, hrabia, 1837–1917
7158   O "Panu Tadeuszu." Wyd. 2. Do druku przy-
M5   sposobił Stanisław Pigoń. Kraków, Nakł.
P395   Krakowskiej Spółki Wydawn., 1922.
       101 p. 22 cm.

       1. Mickiewicz, Adam, 1798–1855. Pan Tadeusz
       I. Title

NT   0041786   WU ICU MH CSt MiU IU

Tarnowski, Stanisław, hrabia, 1837-1917.
PG7158   O "Panu Tadeuszu" / Stanisław Tarnowski ;
M53   do druku przysposobił Stanisław Pigoń. —
F32   Wyd. 2. — Kraków : Nakł. Krakowskiej Spółki
1923   Wydawniczej, 1923.
         104 p. ; 22 cm. — (Z historji i literatury)

         Xerox copy.

         1. Mickiewicz, Adam, 1798-1855. Pan Tadeusz.
         I. Title(1)

NT   0041787   CtY

Tarnowski, Stanisław, *hrabia*, 1837-1917.
   O Rusi i Rusinach przez St. hr. Tarnowskiego. W Krakowie, Nakł. Księg. Spółki Wydawniczej Polskiej, 1891.
   68 p. 21 cm.
   "Odbitka z 'Krakusa.'"

   1. Ukraine—Hist. 2. Ukraine—Relations (general) with Poland.
3. Poland—Relations (general) with the Ukraine.   I. Title.

DK508.7.T3   65-48214

NT   0041788   DLC ICU CSt

Tarnowski, Stanisław, hrabia, 1837-
   ...Paweł Popiel jako pisarz.   Kraków: Spółka wydawnicza
polska, 1894. 115 p.   8°.
   Repr.: "Przegląd polski," 1894.

1. Popiel, Paweł, d. 1892.
N. Y. P. L.   January 19, 1927

NT   0041789   NN

Tarnowski, Stanisław, *hrabia*, 1837-1917.
   Pisarze poltiyczni xvi wieku; studia do historyi literatury
polskiej. Wyd. Akademii Umiejętności, Wydział Filologiczny. W Krakowie, Nakł. autora, W księg. J. K. Żupań-
skiego & K. J. Heumanna, 1886.
   2 v. 23 cm.
   Includes bibliographies.

   1. Polish literature—Hist. & crit.

PG7012.T33   52-57928

NT   0041790   DLC PSt MH ICU

Tarnowski, Stanisław, hrabia, 1837-1917.
   Rozprawy i sprawozdania. Studia do historyi
literatury polskiej. Wiek XIX
      see his Studia do historyi literatury polskiej.
      Wiek XIX. Rozprawy y sprawozdania.

Tarnowski, Stanisław, hrabia, 1837-1917.
   Studia do historyi literatury polskiej. Pisarze
politiyczni XVI wieku.
      see his Pisarze poltiyczni XVI wieku.

Tarnowski, Stanisław, hrabia, 1837-1917.
   Sienkiewicza "Ogniem i mieczem".   Kraków.
W Drukarni "Czasu" Fr. Kluczyckiego i Sp., 1884.
   63 p.   28 cm.
   At head of title: Z najnowszych powieści
polskich.
   1. Sienkiewicz, Henryk, 1846-1916. Ogniem i
mieczem. I. Title.

NT   0041793   NNC

Tarnowski, Stanislaw, hrabia, 1837-1917.
   Studia do historyi literatury polskiej. Wiek XVI.
Jan Kochanowski
      see his   Jan Kochanowski.

891.8509
T176s   Tarnowski, Stanisław, hrabia, 1837-1917.
        Studia do historyi literatury polskiej; wiek
        XIX: rozprawy i sprawozdania. W Krakowie,
        Nakł. Księg. Spółki Wydawniczej Polskiej,
        1895-96.
        2 v. 22cm.

        No more published?
        Contents.- t.1. O kolędach. O "Konfeder-
        atach" Mickiewicza. O "Księgach pielgrzymstwa"
        Mickiewicza. Ze studyów o Słowackim. "Roczniki
        polskie z lat 1857- 1861" (Paryż 1865).

        "Rachunki" Bolesławity za rok 1867.- t.2.
        Komedye Aleksandra hr. Fredry. O pośmiertnych
        komedyach Fredry. Stefana Garczyńskiego
        "Wacław" i Drobne poezye. Lucyan Siemieński.
        Teofil Lenartowicz.

        1. Polish literature - 19th cent. - Hist. &
        crit. I. T.

NT   0041796   MiDW ICU WU OU CoU PSt CSt KU NjP MiU

TARNOWSKI, Stanislaw, hrabia, *1837-1917.*
   Studia do historyi literatury polskiej. Wiek
   XI^A,Henryk Sienkiewicz. W Krakowie,Sp.wydaw-
   niczej polskiej,1897.

   This work is numbered "Tom.V."

NT   0041797   MH

Tarnowski, St⟨anisław⟩, hrabia, 1837-   Slav 7115.4.801
   Studia do historyi literatury polskiej. Wiek xix. Zygmunt Krasiński. W Krakowie, w księgarni Spółki Wydawniczej polskiej,
1892.
   pp. viii, 695 +. Ports.
   The cover has the date 1893.

   Krasiński

NT   0041798   MH NN NcD CoU WaU

DK
438   Tarnowski,Stanisław,hrabia,1837-1917.
T18   Studya polityczne. W Krakowie, Skł.gł.w
      Księgarni Spółki Wydawniczej Polskiej, 1895.
      2 v.
      MiU copy imperfect: p.vii- of v.1 wanting.
      Articles previously published in various sources
      and speeches.

      1.Poland--Pol.& govt.--1864-1918--Addresses,
      essays,lectures. 2.Europe--Politics--1871-1918--
      Addresses,essays,lectures. I.Title.

NT   0041799   MiU ICU CtY KU

Tarnowski, Stanisław, hrabia, 1837-   Slav 7123.4.801
   Szujskiego młodość. W Krakowie, w księgarni Spółki Wydawniczej polskiej, 1892.
   pp. 232.

   Szujski, Józef, 1835-1883

NT   0041800   MH NNC

Tarnowski, Stanisław, hrabia, 1837-1917, tr.

Klaczko, Juljan, 1828-1906.
   ... Wieczory florenckie; dzieło uwieńczone przez Akademię
francuską; z upoważnienia autora przełożył St. Tarnowski.
Wydanie 5. ⟨Warszawa⟩ F. Hoesick, 1922.

TARNOWSKI,St[anislaw hrabia],1837-
   Wypisy polskie dla klas wyzszych szkół
gimnazyalnych. Wyd.drugie,przerobione. Lwów,
1894-96.

   2 vol.
   Vol.1 is by S.Tarnowski and J.Wójcik;vol.2
is by S.Tarnowski and F.Próchnicki.

NT   0041802   MH IEdS

Slavic   Tarnowski, Stanislaw, hrabia, 1837-1917, comp.
Coll.   Wypisy polskie dla klas wyzszych szkół
425.93   gimnazyalnych; Część pierwsza ulozona przez
T37   St. Tarnowskiego i J. Wójcika. Wyd. 3.
         przerobione. Lwow, Nakladem I. Związkowej
         drukarni, 1903.

           VII, 512 p. 25 cm.
           English translation of title: Polish compend for the higher
         grades of Latin high schools; first part compiled by St.
         Tarnowski and J. Wójcik.

NT   0041803   IEdS

Tarnowski, Stanislaw, hrabia, 1837-1917.
   Wypisy polskie dla klas wyzszych szkół gimnazyalnych... 4. czwarte. Lwow 1909-1911.
   2 v. 23 cm.
   v. 2 by Stanislav Tarnowski and Franciszk
Próchnicki.
   I. Wójcik, J   comp.

NT   0041804   CU

Tarnowski, Stanislaw, hrabia, 1837-1917.
   Wypisy polskie dla klas wyzszych szkół
gimnazyalnych... Lwow, 1906.
   v. 23 cm.
   I. Próchnicki, Franciszk.

NT   0041805   CU

Tarnowski, Stanislaw, hrabia, 1837-1917.
   Z doswiadczen i rozmyslan / St. Tarnowski.
   -- Wyd. 2. -- W Krakowie : Tarnowski : skł.
gł. w Księg. Spolki Wydawniczej Polskiej,
1891.
   422 p. ; 20 cm.

   Originally printed in "Przeglad polski,"
July 1, 1891.
   ISBN 50 centow

   1.Poland--Politics and government--1796-1918.
   2.Poland--Church   history.

NT   0041806   CSt WU MH

Tarnowski, St⟨anisław⟩, hrabia, 1837-*1917.*
   Z wakacyj. W Krakowie, nakładem księgarni J. K. Żupań-
skiego & K. J. Heumanna, 1888.
   2 vol.
   Contents: — 1. Kijów. Moskwa. Wilno.— 2. Prusy królewskie.

   Russia–Descr. 1850–1881

NT   0041807   MH KU

Tarnowski, Stanisław, *hrabia*, 1837-*1917.*
   Zygmunt Krasiński. ⟨Wyd. 2⟩ W Krakowie, Akade
mia umiejętności, 1912.
   2 v. front, ports. 24ᶜᵐ.

   1. Krasiński, Zygmunt, 1812-1859.

                                    CA 18-1533 Unrev'd
   Library of Congress   PG7158.K72T3

NT   0041808   DLC KU CSt IU PSt OU ICU CtY NNC

Tarnowski, Stanisław, hrabia, 1837-1917.
  Zygmunt Krasiński. Studia do historyi
literatury polskiej. Wiek XIX.
    see his Studia do historyi literatury polskiej.
Wiek XIX. Zygmunt Krasiński.

Tarnowski, Władysław, 1841-78
  Achmed (2) Piano-vocal score
  Achmed, oder Der Pilger der Liebe; romantische Oper in
zwei Akten nach Washington Irving's Alhambra Märchen, ge-
dichtet und componirt von L.Tarnowski. Leipzig, Forberg
[18-] Pl.no.2258

  Score (173 p.)
  Title also in Polish; words in German

NT 0041810   MH-L

PG7158
T37K7
  Tarnowski, Władysław, *1841-1878.*
    Krople czary; poezye. Spisał i wydał
Ernest Buława. Drezno, 1865.
    79 p. 18cm.
    Imprint covered by stamp: Lipsk, Paweł
Rhode, 1865.
    Bound with Ginchev Shkip"rĭgov, Tsane.
Dvie topoli. [Tsarigrad, 1872]; Vodovozova,
E.N. S'rbiíà. Plovdiv, 1886; Ch'rnonos a-
shta gospozha. Plovdiv, 1886.

NT 0041811   CSt

Tarnowskiĭ, Benjamin Mikaiĭ, 1836-
    see Tarnovskiĭ, Veniamin Mikhaĭlovich,
    1839-1906.

Tarnowsky, B., 1839-1906
    see Tarnovskiĭ, Veniamin, Mikhaĭlovich,
    1839-1906.

Tarnowsky, Benjamin, 1839-1906
    see Tarnovskiĭ, Veniamin Mikhaĭlovich,
    1839-1906.

Y83724
.JA
  Tarnowsky, George de, 1873-
    A corner of the great battlefield; an
American surgeon in the midst of things.
[Chicago, Ill.? 1918]
    7 p. 22cm.

    Cover title.

NT 0041815   WHi

Tarnowsky, George de, 1873-
  Emergency surgery; the military surgery of the world
war adapted to civil life, by George de Tarnowsky ... illustrated with 324 engravings. Philadelphia and New York,
Lea & Febiger, 1926.
  xvi, [17]-718 p. illus. 24ᶜᵐ.
  Contains bibliographies.

  1. Surgery, Operative. 2. Surgery, Military. I. Title.

  Library of Congress   RD33.T3   26-9428

NT 0041816   DLC PPJ PPcM DNLM ICRL ICJ MiU

Tarnowsky, George de, 1873-
  ... Military surgery of the zone of the advance, by
George de Tarnowsky ... Philadelphia and New York,
Lea & Febiger, 1918.
  iii, 5-330 p. illus., diagr. 15ᶜᵐ. (Medical war manual, no. 7)

  1. Surgery, Military. I. Title.

  Library of Congress   RD151.T3   18-16773

  NN OC1W-H
NT 0041817   DLC PPPCPh PPJ PP DNLM ViU MiU OU ICJ

Tarnowsky, H., 1833-1899
    see Tarnovskiĭ, Ippolit Mikhaĭlovich,
    1833-1899.

Tarnowsky, Ivan, *comp.*
  ... Post war planning for wage earners; a job at all times, a
home our own, a pension for all; illustrated notes specially
compiled for Local 42, International union of marine and ship-
builders of America—C.I.O., by Ivan Tarnowsky ... Preface
by Miss Anne Edelmann. [Washington, 1943]
  cover-title, 1 p. l., 3-52 numb. l. illus., diagrs. 28 x 22ᶜᵐ.
  At head of title: draft #1, June 7, 1943.
  Reproduced from type-written copy.

  1. Economics. I. Industrial union of marine and shipbuilding
workers of America. Local no. 42, Philadelphia. II. Title.

  Library of Congress   HB171.7.T24   43-11194

          330.1

NT 0041819   DLC

Tarnowsky, Ivan, comp.

Townsend, Francis Everett, 1867-
  A ready reference book presenting evidence of our ability as
a nation to achieve and maintain at all times a sound and pros-
perous economy through increasing the circulation of money
by the spending of a uniform and adequate old age pension,
levied and secured on a pay-as-you-go basis: namely, the
Townsend plan; with certain addenda, compiled by Ivan
Tarnowsky, statistician, under the personal supervision of Dr.
Francis E. Townsend ... Chicago, Ill., Townsend national
weekly [ᶜ1941]

Tarnowsky, Pauline
  see
  Tarnovskaíà, Praskov'íà Nikolaevna (Kozlova)

Tarnski, Ivan
  Piesme. U Zagrebu, Tisk. L.Gaja, 1842

  179 p.

NT 0041822   MH

HD5876
.C2C2
  Tarnutzer, Benjamin Charles, ed.

  California employment directory.
  San Francisco.

Tarnutzer, Christian
    see Tarnuzzer, Christian, 1860-

516.6
T17ü
  Tarnutzer, Georg, *1883-*
    **Über die kubischen nullkurven des line-
aren komplexes.** Chur. 1912.
    49p. diagrs.

    Inaug.-diss.--Zürich.
    Lebenslauf.

NT 0041825   IU CtY NjP RPB

Tarnutzer, Georg, 1883-
  Ueber die kubischen nullkurven des linearen komplexe.
  Inaug. diss.   Zurich, 1913

NT 0041826   ICRL

Tarnutzer, Hans Andrea.
  ... Entstehung, organisation und funktion der Eidgenös-
sischen bankenkommission, von dr. Hans Andrea Tarnutzer.
Bern, Stämpfli & cie., 1941.
  vii, 115 p. 23ᶜᵐ. (Abhandlungen zum schweizerischen recht. Neue
folge, begründet von †prof. dr. Max Gmür, hrsg. von dr. Theo Guhl ...
182. hft.)
  Issued also as inaugural dissertation, Bern.
  "Quellenverzeichnis": p. vi-vii.

  1. Switzerland. Eidgenössische bankenkommission. 2. Banking law—
Switzerland. 3. Banks and banking—Switzerland.

  Library of Congress   HG3202.T3   42-16718

          332.100404

NT 0041827   DLC ICRL NNC MH

Tarnutzer (Marie). * Ein Fall von Meningo-
Myelitis lumbalis specifica. 23 pp. 8°. *Basel,*
F. Reinhardt, 1907.

NT 0041828   DNLM CtY

DQ827
T3
  Tarnuzzer, Christian, 1860-
    Aus Rätiens Natur und Alpenwelt, von Chr. Tarnuzzer.
Mit Federzeichnungen von Ch. Conradin. Festgabe an
der Versammlung der Schweizerischen Naturforschenden
Gesellschaft in Tarasp-Schuls-Vulpera, 1916. Zürich,
Art. Institut Orell Füssli, 1916.
    266 p. illus.

    1. Rhaetian Alps. I. Schweizerische Naturforschende
Gesellschaft. II. Title.

NT 0041829   CU

Tarnuzzer, Christian, 1860-
  ... Beiträge zur geologie des Unterengadins. I. teil.
Das gebiet der sedimente. Von dr. Chr. Tarnuzzer. II.
teil. Die kristallinen gesteine. Von prof. dr. U. Grubenmann. Mit 1 geologischen karte in 1 : 50,000, 1 profiltafel
und 25 textfiguren. Bern, In kommission bei A. Francke
(vorm. Schmid & Francke) 1909.
  xii, 248, xii p. col. fold. map, col. fold. profile, diagrs. 31½ᶜᵐ. (Beiträge zur geologischen karte der Schweiz, hrsg. von der Geologischen kommission der Schweiz. naturforschenden gesellschaft, auf kosten der Eidgenossenschaft. n. f., XXIII. lfg., des ganzen werkes 53. lfg.)
  "Benutzte literatur": p. vii-ix.
  1. Geology—Switzerland. 2. Rocks, Sedimentary. 3. Rocks, Crystal-
line and metamorphic. I. Grubenmann, Ulrich, 1850-   joint author.

          G S 13-636

  Library, U. S. Geol.   survey (535) qB2 n. f., lfg. 23

NT 0041830   DI-GS ICJ GU NIC

Tarnuzzer, Christian, *1860-*
    Drei Dezennien der Erdbebenforschung
in der Schweiz.
    (Petermanns Mitt.,Gotha. 58.Jahrg.
Dez. 1912. p.313-316.)

NT 0041831   DAS

Tarnuzzer, Christian, 1860–
Falb und die Erdbeben. Vortrag, gehalten in der Naturforschenden Gesellschaft Graubündens in Chur am 29. Januar 1890. Hamburg, Verlagsanstalt und Druckerei A.-G. (vormals J. F. Richter) 1891.
32 p. 21 cm. (Sammlung gemeinverständlicher wissenschaftlicher Vorträge, n. F., 6. Ser., Heft 139)
1. Earthquakes. 2. Falb, Rudolf, 1838–1903.

NT 0041832 NIC MH CtY

Tarnuzzer, Christian, 1860–
Notice sur quelques gisements métallifères du canton des Grisons, Suisse, par le prof. dr. C. Tarnuzzer, le prof. dr. G. Nussberger et le dr. P. Lorenz … Coire, Impr. H. Fiebig, 1900.
39 p. III col. fold. diagr. 23ᶜᵐ.
Ouvrage rédigé sur la demande du haut gouvernement, et destiné à accompagner la collection de minerals grisons, exposée à Paris en 1900. Contains bibliographies.

1. Mines and mineral resources—Switzerland—Grisons. I. Nussberger, Gustav, 1864– joint author. II. Lorenz, Paul, 1835–1915, joint author.

G S 12–694 Revised
U. S. Geol. survey. Library
for Library of Congress ₍r41b2₎

NT 0041833 DI-GS

L551.22
O702
Tarnuzzer, Christian, 1860–
Die schweizerischen Erdbeben im Jahre 1887. Bearbeitet nach den von der schweiz. Erdbebenkommission gesammmelten₍₎ Berichten … von Christian Tarnutzer … Bern, Stämpfli'sche Buchdruckerei ₍1887₎
47 p. incl. tables. 29½ᶜᵐ.
Inaug.-Diss.—Zürich.
Bibliographical foot-notes.

NT 0041834 ICJ ICRL

Tarnuzzer, Christian, 1860–
Die schweizerischen Erdbeben im Jahre 1887. Nach den von der schweizerischen Erdbebenkommission gesammelten Berichten zusammengestellt von Dr. Christian Tarnutzer... Bern: Stämpfli, 1888. 43 p. incl. tables. 4°.
Cover-title.

I. Earthquakes, Switzerland.
N. Y. P. L. October 7, 1924

NT 0041835 NN

G
3837
.864
TARNUZZER, CHRISTIAN, 1860–
With the Albula railway to the Engadine.
Chur, M. Ebner & Co. ₍1904₎
78p. illus., 1 col.fold.pl. 14x21cm.

NT 0041836 ICN ICJ

Tarnuzzer, Gian Andrea, 1921–
Über die katalytische Dehydratation aliphatischer Säureamide. Zug, 1951.
62 p. diagrs. 24 cm.
Promotionsarbeit—Eidgenössische Technische Hochschule, Zürich.
Vita.
Bibliographical footnotes.

1. Amides.

QD305.A7T25 56–46092

NT 0041837 DLC CtY

Tarnuzzer, Karl Keller-
see Keller-Tarnuzzer, Karl, 1891–

Taro, *pseud.*
see Roth, Johnny, 1915–

Taro (Carolus Amedeus Dalmatius Maria). *1. Febris generatim. II. ₍etc.₎. 10 pp. 4°. Augusta Taurinorum, V. Ghiringhello et H. Bonando, ₍1890₎. ₍P., v. 945.₎*

NT 0041840 DNLM

Taro, Gerda, d. 1937, illus.
Capa, Robert.
Death in the making, by Robert Capa; photographs by Robert Capa and Gerda Taro, captions by Robert Capa, translated by Jay Allen, preface by Jay Allen, arrangement by André Kertesz. New York, Covici-Friede ₍ᶜ1938₎

Tarō, Yashima
see
Yashima, Tarō, *pseud.*

Taro, Zhan
see
Tharaud, Jean, 1877–1952.

Taro, Zherom
see
Tharaud, Jérôme, 1874–1953.

Taro Kanaya
see Kanaya, Taro.

Taro Food Company, Danbury, Conn.
Nature feeding
see under title

… Die tarocchi …
see under [Kristeller, Paul] 1863–1931.

99.76
T172
Tarociński, Edward.
Zarys mechanizacji prac w tartaku.
₍Wyd. 1.₎ Warszawa, Państwowe Wydawn. Rolnicze i Leśne, 1954.
151 p.

1. Sawmill machinery. 2. Sawmills. Work management.

NT 0041848 DNAL

Taron (Esaias). *Heilungsgeschichte eines Fingerwurms. 8 pp. 12°. Kopenhagen, J. R. Thiele. ₍1775₎*

NT 0041849 DNLM

Taron, Stephanos von
see
Stephanus, *of Taron, fl. ca.* 1000.

BX
8637
T37
Tarona, Melavina.
Te atua e te torutahi, na Melavina tarona. Papeete, Tahiti, i nei i te piha neneiraa a te Ekalesia a Iesu Mesia i te Feia Mo'a i te Mau Mahana Hopea Nei, 1922.
22 p. 15cm.

1. Mormons and Mormonism.

NT 0041851 IdPI

Taroncher, Justo Pastor Fustér y.
See
Fustér, Justo Pastor, 1761–1835.

S531
.J8
Tarone, Ernest A., joint author.
Juergenson, Elwood M
Teaching tricks and other aids for teachers of vocational agriculture ₍by₎ Elwood M. Juergenson ₍and₎ Ernest A. Tarone. ₍Danville, Ill., Interstate Printers & Publishers, 1950₎

Tarōnetsʻi, Tʻoros
see
Tʻoros Tarōnetsʻi, fl. 1284–1346.

Tarongí y Cortés, José
see
Taronji y Cortés, José, 1847–1890.

325.345
T176n
Taroni, Clodaco.
La nuova Roma dell'Italia coloniale. Milano, 1908.
141p.

NT 0041856 IU

PQ4424
.A2T2
Taroni, Ercole.
… Cronologia dei fatti storici degli episodi e dei personaggi ricordati nella Divina commedia. Bologna, Tip. L. Parma, 1924.
142, ₍2₎ p. 18½ᶜᵐ.
At head of title: Ercole Taroni.

1. Dante Alighieri—Dictionaries, indexes, etc. 2. Dante Alighieri. Divina commedia.

NT 0041857 ICU DLC-P4

Taroni, Ercole
4PQ
It
3212   Tavole sinottiche della Divina
commedia. Bologna, G. Oberosler,
1921.
       153 p.

NT   0041858   DLC-P4

Taroni, Giovanni Battista.
    Le vittorie della fede in Clodoveo, re di
Francia, opera drammatica da cantarsi in Perugia
nell'Oratorio di S. Filippo Neri, per la festa di
Santa Cecilia... dagl'accademici vnisioni. Parole
del Sig. Gio: Battista Taroni. Posta in musica
dal Sig. Flauio Lanciani... In Perugia, Nella
Stampa vescouale, per gli eredi del Giani, e S.
Amati, 1704.

    Libretto.

NT   0041859   ICN

Taroní (Josephus) [1800-   ]. *De sensibili-
tate. 34 pp., il. 8º. Berolini, formis Brüschckia-
nis. [1823].

NT   0041860   DNLM PPC

Taroni, Luigi, ed.
    I condottieri
       see under   Lomonaco, Francesco, 1772-
1810.

DG551
.B23
1944   Taroni, Luigi, ed.
Balbo, Cesare, conte, 1789-1853.
    Delle speranze d'Italia, sopra la 2. ed. corr. ed accresciuta
dall'autore a cura di Luigi Taroni. Milano, Edizioni Alfa,
1944.

4DG
598   Taroni, Luigi
    I nostri soldati in Africa.
Milano, Edizioni "Aurora" [1935]
       188 p.

NT   0041863   DLC-P4

AY894
.A57   Taroni, Natale, 1892-   comp.
Almanacco delle famiglie; periodico annuale ... utile, istrut-
tivo, dilettevole.
    Milano, Casa editrice Sonzogno della Società anonima A.
Matarelli [19

Taroni, Natale, 1892-
    ... Ippolito Nievo. Milano, Casa editrice Sonzogno [1932]
3 p. l., [9]-187, [1] p. illus. 18ᵐᵐ.
    "Appendice bibliografica": p. [177]-187.

    1. Nievo, Ippolito, 1832-1861.
                               A C 32-91
    Title from Illinois Univ.   Printed by L. C.

NT   0041865   IU CU TU

4DT
547   Taroni, Natale, 1892-
    L'Italia in A. O.; i pionieri,
gli eroi, i conquistatori. Milano,
Sonzogno [1940]
       78 p.

NT   0041866   DLC-P4

Taroni, Natale, 1892-
    ... Rimario italiano.   Firenze, Nerbini
[1943]
    99 p.   (Biblioteca, divulgativa, 13)

NT   0041867   DLC CU CLU

---

de Taroni (Pierre-Gaston-Léon-Jean) [1858-
]. *Contribution à l'étude de l'éléphantiasis
du scrotum, notamment chez les indigènes de la
Nouvelle-Calédonie et des îles environnantes.
51 pp., 1 pl. 4º. Bordeaux, 1887, No. 75.

NT   0041868   DNLM

Taronjí, José
       see
Taronjí y Cortés, José, 1847-1890.

BR
1027
.M3
T3   Taronjí y Cortés, José, 1847-1890
    Algo sobre el estado religioso y social de
la isla de Mallorca; polémica contra las
preocupaciones de clase; capítulos para la
historia del pueblo balear. Palma de
Mallorca, Impr. de P. J. Gelabert, 1877.
    339 p.   23cm.

    1. Majorca - Church history 2. Catholic
Church in Majorca   I. Title

NT   0041870   WU MH PU OCH

TARONJÍ [Y CORTÉS,] José,d.1890.
    Inspiraciónes. Palma de Mallorca,M.Roca,
1882.

NT   0041871   MH

Taronjí y Cortés, José, 1847-1890.
    Una mala causa á todo trance defendida. Refutación del
folleto titulado Una buena causa mal defendida, que don Miguel
Maura, pro., publicó en 29 de diciembre próximo pasado como
contestación al artículo Libros malos y cosas peores, salido á
luz en el Almanaque balear para 1877. Por d. José Taronjí ...
Palma, Imprenta de P. J. Gelabert, 1877.
    36, [1] p. 24ᵐᵐ.

    1. Maura y Montaner, Miguel, 1843-1915. Una buena causa mal
defendida. 2. Catholic church in Majorca. 3. Catholic church—Clergy.
I. Title.
    Library of Congress   BX1586.M3M35   43-47488

NT   0041872   DLC

Taronjí Cortes, José, 1847-1890.
    El sacro monte, pequeño poema descriptivo.
Por D. José Taronjí canónigo de esta insigne
colegiata. Segunda edicion.   Palma de Mallorca
Tipografía Biblioteca popular, 1887.

NT   0041873   NNH

PQ
6637
T176T7   Taronjí y Cortés, José, 1847-1890.
    El trovador mallorquin; poesías escritas
en mallorquin literario, acompañadas de versión castellana, por José Taronjí. Palma
de Mallorca, B. Rotger, 1883.
    x,202 p.

NT   0041874   CLU

Taronts'i, Soghomon, 1904-
    (Ampropits' heto)
Ս·Մպրպ-ց Հ...: Երևան, Հայպետ-Հրատ, 1948:
118 p. 20 cm.
    Poems.

    I. Title.
    PK8548.T34A8   73-219769

NT   0041875   DLC

PK8548
.V3A6
1955
Orien
Armen   Taronts'i, Soghomon, 1904-   ed.
Varowzhan, Daniël, 1884-1915.
Բանաստեղծություններ [գրեց Դանիէլ Վարուժան]
կազմեց և ծանոթագրեց Սողոմոն Տարոնցի: Երևան,
Հայպետհրատ, 1955:

Taronts'i, Soghomon, 1904-
Դավիթ երգը: Երևան, Հայպետհրատ, 1946:
140 p. 21 cm.
    CONTENTS.—Դ Հ-ւրիներ.—Ված ։լերɪ:—Ելեխեց և բամ-ɪ:—
Դ-վիթի երգը:

    I. Sasownts'i Dawit'. II. Title.
                             Title romanized: Davt'i ergĕ.
    PK8548.T34D3   72-243047

NT   0041877   DLC CLU

PK8548
V3
946
Orien
Armen   Taronts'i, Soghomon, 1904-   ed.
Varowzhan, Daniël, 1884-1915.
Երկեր [գրեց Դանիէլ Վարուժան]: կազմեց և խմբագրեց
Սողոմոն Տարոնցի: Երևան, ՀՍՍՌ Պետական Հրատ.,
1946:

TARONY,Girolamo.
    L'amico Paolo Ercole;memorie.
Alessandria,stab.tip.-lit.suc.Gazzotti,e c.,
1896.

NT   0041879   MH

Le tarot de Jarnac; textes de Pierre Boujut [et al.]
avec vingt-deux dessins de Jean-Marie Creuzeau.
[n.p.] La Tour de feu, 1953. 116 p. illus.
23cm.

    130 copies printed. "50 exemplaires hors commerce
destinés aux auteurs et à leurs amis sur Grapho-
Calco, numérotés de 1 à 50 " No. 000025.

    1. Tarot in literature. I. Boujut, Pierre.

NT   0041880   NN

Beinecke
Library
1976
425   ... Le Tarot de la reyne. Première partie.
Histoire de Catherine de Médicis suivie des
Sept pensées de Nostradamus. Illustrations de
H. Steimer. Paris, Eugène Figuière & Cie
[etc., 1911?]
    xiv, [15]-160+ p. illus. 19 cm.
    At head of title: Maguelone.
    Imperfect: all after p. 160 (Les sept pensées
de Nostradamus) wanting.
    Preface by Maurice Lanra dated 1911.
    Original front wrapper.

    Continued in next column

Continued from preceding column

1. Tarot. 2. Catherine de Medicis, consort of Henry II, King of France, 1519-1589. 3. Cary, Melbert Brinckerhoff, 1892-1941 - Ownership. I. Maguelone. II. Steimer, H. III. Lanra, Maurice.

NT 0041882   CtY

Le tarot des bohemiens.

See *under*

ₑEncausse, Gerard Anaclet Vincent, 1865-1916.

...'. Le tarot égyptien; son explication, sa significa-
tion, sa valeur divinatoire
see under Schémahni.

The Tarot of the Bohemians, the most ancient
book in the world...
see
Encausse, Gérard Anaclet Vincent, 1865-1916.
Absolute key to occult science: The Tarot
of the Bohemians...

Tarouca, Amadeo Silva-
see Silva-Tarouca, Amadeo.

BX 2630
V54 T37
1947
   Tarouca, Carlos da Silva, *1883-*
    O cartulário do Mosteiro de Santa
Clara de Vila do Conde; ediçao de 37
cartas régias de Sancho I (a. 1200)
a. Manuel I (a. 1512) Lisboa, 1947.
    119 p.
    Detached from Arqueologia e historia,
v. 4.
    1. Vila do Conde, Portugal. Santa
Clara (Monastery) - Hist. - Sources. 2.
Monasteries   - Portugal - Vila do
Conde. I.   Title.

NT 0041887   CaBVaU

   Tarouca, Carlos da Silva, 1883-   *ed.*
    Crónica de D. Dinis. Ediçao do texto inédito
do Cód
     see under title

DP568
.C7
   Tarouca, Carlos da Silva, 1883-   ed.

   Crónicas dos sete primeiros reis do Portugal. Ed. crítica
pelo académico de número Carlos da Silva Tarouca. Lisboa,
Academia Portuguesa da História, 1952-53.

BV
5730
T7
   TAROUCA, Carlos da Silva, 1883-
    Ecclesia in imperio Romano-Byzantino.
Romae, Universitatis Gregorianae, 1933.

    viii, 190 p. 23 cm. (Institutiones His-
toriae Ecclesiasticae, pars II).

    1. Byzantine empire—Church history. 2.
Church and state in the Byzantine empire.
T. Title. (Series)

NT 0041890   MBtS NNC CU DDO

BR1050
.I4C3
   Tarouca, Carlos *da Silva, 1883-*

   Catholic Church. *Pope.*
    Epistularum Romanorum pontificum ad vicarios per Illyri-
cum aliosque episcopos collectio Thessalonicensis ad fidem
codicis Vat. Lat. 5751 recensuit C. Silva-Tarouca s. I. Romae,
1937.

   Tarouca, Carlos *da Silva, 1883-*

   Exempla scriptvrarvm, edita consilio et opera procvratorvm
Bibliothecae et Tabvlarii vaticani ... Romae, apvd Biblio-
thecam vaticanam, 1929-

   Tarouca, Carlos da Silva, 1883-   *ed.*
    ... Fontes historiae ecclesiasticae medii aevi in usum scho-
larum selegit Carolus Silva-Tarouca ... Romae, apud aedes
Universitatis gregorianae, 1930-
    v. 23½ cm.
    At head of title: Pont. universitas gregoriana.
    CONTENTS.—I. Fontes saecc. v-IX.

    1. Church history—Middle ages—Sources. I. Rome (City) Pon-
tificia università gregoriana. II. Title.

   BR251.T3   270.3   31-33816 rev

      MoU DDO PV PU IU MCW MoU
NT 0041893   DLC PPiPT InStme MH KU GU GDC KU TNJ-R

   Tarouca, Carlos *da Silva, 1883-*
    ... Institutiones historiae ecclesiasticae in usum
auditorum. Romae, apud Aedes Universitatis Gregor-
ianum, 1933.

    v. 22 cm.
    Library has Pars II: Ecclesia in Imperio Romano-
Byzantino (saec. IV-XI)
    At top of title page: Pontificia Universitas
Gregoriana.

    1. Church History - Textbooks - 20th century.

NT 0041894   PLatS MH MnCS

   Tarouca, Carlos da Silva, 1883-
    Inventário das cartas e dos códices manuscritos..
     see under Evora, Portugal. Sé. Cabido.
Arquivo.

   Tarouca, Carlos da Silva, 1883-
    ... Nuovi studi sulle antiche lettere dei papi ... Roma,
Pontificia università gregoriana, 1932-
    v. facsims. 23 cm.
    At head of title: C. Silva-Tarouca.

    1. Letters, Papal—Hist. & crit. I. Title.

   BX863.T3   262.13   33-8852 rev

NT 0041896   DLC CtY

BT1380
.I4
   Tarouca, Carlos *da Silva, 1883-*

   Leo I, *the Great, Saint, Pope, d. 461.*
    S. Leonis Magni epistulae contra Eutychis haeresim.
Ad codicum fidem recensuit C. Silva-Tarouca. De clausula-
rum ratione praefatus est F. di Capua. Romae, Apud aedes
Universitatis Gregorianae, 1934-35.

   Tarouca, Egbert Silva
    see   Silva-Tarouca, Egbert.

   Tarouca, Ernst Silva, *Graf*
   see Silva Tarouca, Ernst Emanuel, *Graf,* 1860-1936.

DP556.6
T5
   Tarouca, Joao Gomes da Silva, conde de,
1671-1738.
    Cartas do conde de Tarouca, embaixador de
Portugal, dirigidas ao cardeal da Cunha.
ₑLisboa? 1927ₑ
    122 p. 2 ports. 17cm. (Archivo de
documentos históricos, 1)

    1. Portugal - Foreign relations. I. Cunha,
Nuno da, 1664-1750.

NT 0041900   GU ICN MH InU CaBVaU

DC801
.M49R6
   Taroux, ——, joint author.

   Romain, Giorgio.
    Meaux, cité de Bossuet. ₑPar Mgr Romain et M. le cha-
noine Taroux. Lyon? 1952ₑ

   Tarozzi, Edoardo.   L617.55 R107
    .... Chirurgia del rene; tecnica operatoria, con appendice di
ricerche sperimentali e di osservazioni cliniche. Città di Castello,
Tip. dell' "Unione arti grafiche", 1911.
    [4], 311 p. incl. I illus., tables. 5 pl. (I fold.) 25½ᶜᵐ.
    At head of title: Dott. Edoardo Tarozzi.
    "Indice bibliografico", at ends of chapters.

NT 0041902   ICJ ICRL

   Tarozzi, Giovanni.
    ... I problemi del lavoro e del proletariato e
la legislazione sociale. Con prefazione del
dott. Filippo Virgilii... Taranto, Tip, dei
fratelli Martucci, 1899.
    xx, 1040 p. 27.5 cm.

NT 0041903   CU

Kd38
927t
   Tarozzi, Giuseppe, 1866-
    Apologia del positivismo. Roma,
A.F.Formiggini,1927.
    92p. 17cm. (Apologie)

NT 0041904   CtY PP

   Tarozzi, Giuseppe, 1866-
    ... Il canto XVIII del Purgatorio, letto da Giuseppe Ta-
rozzi nella sala di Dante in Orsanmichele. Firenze, G. C.
Sansoni ₑ1906ₑ
    43 p. 24½ᶜᵐ. (Lectvra Dantis)
    Title vignette.
    "Letto ... il dì XII di dicembre MCMI."

      9-18165

NT 0041905   DLC CoU PU OCiND

   Tarozzi, Giuseppe, 1866-
    ... Il canto XVIII del Purgatorio, letto da Giuseppe Tarozzi
nella sala di Dante in Orsanmichele. Firenze, G. C. Sansoni
ₑ1925ₑ
    42 p. 25 cm. (Lectvra Dantis)
    Title vignette.
    "Letto ... il dì XII di dicembre MCMI."

NT 0041906   ViU CaBVaU NcU OCU

HM
213
T19
Tarozzi, Giuseppe, 1866–
La coltura intellettuale contemporanea
e il suo avviamento morale.   Civitanova-
Marche, D. Natalucci, 1897.
321 p.   21cm.

1. Italy--Intellectual life. 2. Ethics.
I. Title

NT   0041907   NIC NNC

TAROZZI, Giuseppe, 1866–
Compendio dei principii di psicologia di Wil-
liam James coll'introduzione. Il pensiero di
William James e il tempo nostro.
Milano, Società editrice libraria, 1911.

NT   0041908   MH

Tarozzi, Giuseppe, 1866–
...Coscienza morale e civile, testo di morale
ad uso delle scuole normali. 3.ed. con aggiunte
corr. Bologna ₍1914₎. 322p. 20cm.

NT   0041909   OU

B2773
.I8T3
Tarozzi, Giuseppe, 1866–   ed.

Kant, Immanuel, 1724–1804.
... Critica della ragion pratica; estratti, riassunti, introdu-
zione e note, a cura di Giuseppe Tarozzi. Padova, CEDAM,
Casa editrice dott. A. Milani, 1941.

Tarozzi, Giuseppe, 1866–   370.2 R800
.... L'educazione e la scuola. Testo elementare di pedagogia.
141177 .... Bologna, N. Zanichelli, [1918–1921].
5 vol. 19½cm.
At head of title: Giuseppe Tarozzi.
Contents.—Teoria generale dell'educazione. 2ª edizione. [1920.] xvi, 170 p.—
Sommario di psicologia per gli educatori. [1918.] viii, 200 p.—La scuola e il suo
ordinamento. Seconda edizione, riveduta secondo le disposizioni vigenti. [1921.]
[6], 138, [2] p.—Didattica. 1920. xvi, 470 p.—Cenni integrativi di pedagogia
storica. [1921.] [2], 217, [2] p.

NT   0041911   ICJ

Tarozzi, Giuseppe, 1866–
... L'esistenza e l'anima. Bari, G. Laterza & figli, 1930.
3 p. l., ₍1₎–xvi, 240 p. 20½cm. (*On cover:* Biblioteca di cultura moderna. ₍n. 186₎)

1. Ontology. 2. Reality. 3. Knowledge, Theory of.   I. Title.

Library of Congress   BD314.T3

                                                        31–13870

NT   0041912   DLC NIC OU CU-SB MH OCU NN

Tarozzi, Giuseppe, 1866–
La Filosofia italiana

see under

La Filosofia italiana.

Tarozzi, Giuseppe, 1866–
Gian Giacomo Rousseau. Genova, 1914.
102 p. front. (port.) 18 cm. (Profili,
no. 32)

NT   0041914   CU

Tarozzi, Giuseppe, 1866–
... Gian Giacomo Rousseau. 2 ed. Roma, A. F.
Formiggini, 1926.
2 p.l., ₍7₎–100 p. front. (port.) 16cm.
(Added t.-p.: Profili, n. 32)

Added t.-p. within ornamental border.
"Nota bibliografica": p. 100.

1. Rousseau, Jean Jacques, 1712–1778.

NT   0041915   NNC IU MH

TAROZZI, Giuseppe, 1866–
L'idea di esistenza e la pensabilità del
reale trascendente. Bologna, Coop. tipografica
Azzoguidi, 1927.

pp. 32.
"Estratto dal Rendiconto delle, Sessioni della
R. Accademia delle Scienze dell'Istituto di
Bologna, Classe di Scienze Morali, ser. 31 vol. 1,
1926–27."

NT   0041916   MH

BJ
1500
L8
T19
Tarozzi, Giuseppe, 1866–
Idea di una scienza del bene. Firenze,
F. Lumachi, 1901.
312 p. 22cm.

1. Love. 2. Ethics.

NT   0041917   NIC MH

4BF
619
Tarozzi, Giuseppe, 1866–
L'immaginazione, le sue funzioni
e i suoi limiti. Torino, Edizioni
di "Filosofia" ₍1955₎
8 p.

(Filosofia della scienza, 5)

NT   0041918   DLC-P4 MH

Tarozzi, Giuseppe, 1866–
L'infinito e il divino. ₍Bologna₎ Cappelli ₍1951₎
354 p. 21 cm.

1. Natural theology. 2. Apologetics—20th cent. 3. Infinite.
I. Title.

                                                        A 52–290
Chicago. Univ. Libr.
for Library of Congress

NT   0041919   ICU

Tarozzi, Giuseppe, 1866–
L'Internazionale dei lavoratori e le alleanze.
Ostiglia ₍19--₎

NT   0041920   WU

TAROZZI, Giuseppe, 1866–
Lezioni di filosofia. Torino, F. Casanova,
1896–9⁸

3 vol.
Contents:- i. Preliminari psicologia percet-
tiva. ii.- Logica esperienza, scienza e metodo.-
iii. Morale, psicologia morale.

NT   0041921   MH

Tarozzi, Giuseppe, 1866–
... La libertà umana e la critica del determinismo. Bologna,
Nicolo Zanichelli editore, 1936.
2 p. l., ₍vii₎–xvi, 420 p. 23½cm.
"Bibliografia degli scritti di Giuseppe Tarozzi dal 1887 al giugno del
1936": p. ₍389₎–404.
Bibliographical foot-notes.

1. Liberty. 2. Free will and determinism. 3. Fascism.
                                                        A C 37–2321
New York. Public library
for Library of Congress

NT   0041922   NN OU CU ICU NNC

TAROZZI, Giuseppe, 1866–
"Luce intellettual, piena d'amore"; nota sul
concetto della natura del "Paradiso" di Dante.
Torino, 1888.

pp. 53.

NT   0041923   MH

TAROZZI, Giuseppe, 1866–
Menti e caratteri. Bologna, ditta N. Zanichelli, (C. e G. Zanichelli). 1900.

NT   0041924   MH

TAROZZI, Giuseppe, 1866–
Menti e caratteri. 2a ed. Bologna,
N. Zanichelli, 1910.

Miscellaneous essays.

NT   0041925   MH

PQ
4451
T176n
Tarozzi, Giuseppe, 1866–
Note di estetica sul Paradiso di Dante.
Firenze, F. Le Monnier [1921]
xviii, 91 p.

1. Dante Alighieri. Divina Commedia.
Paradiso. 2. Dante - Criticism & interpretation.   I. Title.

NT   0041926   CLU MH

TAROZZI, Giuseppe, 1866–
Nozioni di psicologia con preliminari
filosofici. Bologna, N. Zanichelli, [1925].

NT   0041927   MH NjP

TAROZZI, Giuseppe, 1866–
Il primo canto del Paradiso; saggio di critica
estetica. [Catania, 1893].

pp. (8).
Revista etnea di Lettere, Arti e Scienza, 1893,
i. 24–31.

NT   0041928   MH NIC

Tarozzi, Giuseppe, 1866–   373-45 5
.... Il problema della scuola media. Milano-Roma-Napoli,
188114 Albrighi, Segati & C., 1922.
8   viii, 148 p. 19½cm. (Biblioteca pedagogica antica e moderna italiana e straniera,
volume XLIII.)
At head of title: G. Tarozzi.

NT   0041929   ICJ NNC

Tarozzi, Giuseppe, 1866-
... Problemi filosofici: conoscenza - morale - estetica - religione. Ad uso dei licei. Bologna, N. Zanichelli [1924]
vi p., 1 l., 142 p. 19 cm.
1. Philosophy.

NT 0041930   CU

Tarozzi, Giuseppe, 1866–
Roberto Ardigò. Roma, A. F. Formíggini, 1928.
99 p. illus. 17 cm. (Profili, n. 100)

1. Ardigò, Roberto, 1828–1920.

B3612.Z7T3   55–47668 ‡

NT 0041931   DLC ICU NNC RPB MH

TAROZZI, Giuseppe, 1866-
Teologia Dantesca, studiata nel Paradiso.
Livorno, R.Giusti, ed., 1906.

(Biblioteca degli studenti.Riassunti, 132, 133)

NT 0041932   MH

Tarozzi, Giuseppe, 1866-
... Teologia dantesca, studiata nel Paradiso;
2. ed. riveduta. Livorno, 1917.
17 cm.

NT 0041933   RPB

Tarozzi, Giuseppe, 1866-
... Trattato di pedagogia e morale ad uso delle scuole normali... Torino, 1894.
2 v. in 1. 19.5 cm.

NT 0041934   CtY

Tarozzi, Giuseppe, 1866-
L'universo galileiano. Torino, Edizioni di filosofia [1950]

14 p. (Filosofia della scienza, 1)

NT 0041935   MH

TAROZZI, Giuseppe, 1866-
La virtù contemporanea. Torino, etc.,
Fratelli Bocca, 1900.

Cover:- Piccola biblio[teca] di scienza moderne, 26.

NT 0041936   MH

Tarozzi, Giuseppe, 1866-
...La vita e il pensiero di Luigi Ferri. Palermo: R. Sandron, 1895. 22 p. 8°.

Repr.: Revista di sociologia. Serie 2, v. 1.

1. Ferri, Luigi, 1826–1895.
N.Y.P.L.   March 3, 1925

NT 0041937   NN

Tarozzi, Raimondus.
Catalogo de' libri medici, anatomici, botanici, chirurgici, filosofici, e mattematici, che per la maggior parte esistevano nella biblioteca del fu celebre signor dottor... esposti in vendita appresso li fratelli Pagliarini mercanti librari a Pasquino... 1743. Roma, 1743.
135 p.

NT 0041938   PPC

Tarozzi, Vincenzo
Industrie per lapace interiore.
ₑPompei, IPSI, 1953₎
205 p.

NT 0041939   OCU

Tarozzi, Vincenzo.
Poesie Latine in onore del Sommo Pontefice Leone XIII. Forlì, G. B. Croppi, 1893.
133 p. 12°.

NT 0041940   NN

Tarozzo, Ferruccio
L'arringa dell'avv. Ferruccio Tarozzo contro il deputato Alberto Calda al Tribunale di Bologna (in difesa di Luigi Tedeschi) Un caso di indegnità e di scorrettezza dell'avvocato. Bologna, Cooperativa tip. Mareggiani, 1915.

38 p. 27½cm.

NT 0041941   MH-L

3781   Tarp, Fred Harald.
S78T   A revision of the family Embiotocidae.
ₑStanford, Calif.₎ 1951.
vi, 178l. plates, mounted diagrs.
Thesis (Ph.D.) - Dept. of Biology. Stanford University, 1951.
Bibliography: l. 166-178.

3.4   ___ ___ Another copy.
T
1.Embiotocidae

NT 0041942   CSt

Tarp, Fred Harald.
A revision of the family Embiotocidae (the surfperches) ₑSacramento₎ 1952.
99 p. illus., diagrs. 23 cm. (California. Bureau of Marine Fisheries. Fish bulletin no. 88)
Bibliography : p. 91–99.

1. Embiotocidae.   I. Title.   (Series)
SH11.C27 no. 8°   597.58   A 53–9017
—— Copy 2.   QL638.E5T36
California. Univ. Libr.
for Library of Congress

NT 0041943   CU DLC NcD DI

Tarp, Kirsten (Gjessing) Gloerfelt-
see
Gloerfelt-Tarp, Kirsten (Gjessing) 1889–

TARP, SVEND ERIK, 1898-

Cirkus, 10 smaa klaverstykker for 2 og 4 haender, op.47. København, Engstrøm & Sødring [1947] 15 p. 31cm.

No. 1, 4, 7-10 from his ballet Den detroniserede dyretaemmer.
No. 1 and 10 for piano, 4 hands.
1. Children's music (Piano). 2. Children's music (Piano 4 hands). 3. Ballets (Piano)—Suites, etc. I. Title. II. Tarp, Svend Erik, 1908- . Den detroniserede dyretaemmer.

NT 0041945   NN

Tarp, Svend Erik, 1898–
ₑConcertino, flute, op. 30₎

Concertino for fløjte og orkester, op. 30. Partitur. København, Edition Dania ₑ1939₎

score (28 p.) 32 cm. (Samfundet til udgivelse af dansk musik. ₑPublikation₎ 3. ser., nr. 68, 1940)

1. Concertos (Flute)—Scores.   (Series)

M1020.T25 op. 30₎   52–56497

NT 0041946   DLC ICN IU CoU NN

M   Tarp, Svend Erik, 1898-
2   ₑConcertino, flute, op. 30; arr.₎
D3818++   Concertino for fløjte og orkester, op. 30.
ser.3   Udg. for fløjte og klaver. København, Edition Dania, 1940.
v.68
score (15 p.) and part. 31cm. (Samfundet til udgivelse af dansk musik. ₑPublikation₎ 3. ser., nr.68)

1. Concertos (Flute)--Solo with piano.

NT 0041947   NIC NcU OU IU

---

sVM   TARP, SVEND ERIK, 1898-
1013   ₑConcerto, violin, op.13, arr.₎ Concertino
T 19c   für Violine und Orchester. Op.13. Ausgabe für Violine und Klavier. København, W.Hansen ₑc1936₎
score (11p.) and part. 30cm. (Wilhelm Hansen edition. Nr.3334)

Caption title: Concertino i een sats for violin og orkester.
Part for violin (3p.) laid in. Cadenza (1p.)

NT 0041948   ICN

M1011   Tarp, Svend Erik, 1898-
T175   ₑConcerto, piano, op. 39, C major; arr.₎
op.39   Concerto, c-dur for piano og orkester, op. 39. Udgave for 2 klaverer. København, Engstrøm & Sødring ₑc1944₎
score (32 p.) 32 cm.
Cover title.

1. Concertos (Piano) - 2₋piano scores.

NT 0041949   CoU PP MH

TARP, SVEND ERIK, 1898-

...Lystspilouverture [op. 36]... København, Edition Dania, 1943. Pl. no. E.D. 82 32 p. 30cm. (Samfundet til Udgivelse af dansk Musik. [Kompositioner] Serie 3⁷⁶)

Score; orchestra.

Overtures. I. Title. II. Ser.

NT 0041950   NN NcU NcD CLU OU ICN

Tarp, Svend Erik, 1898-
Mosaic; 10 lette klaverstykker; 10 leichte klavierstücke; 10 easy pianopieces; op. 31.
Kobenhavn, Hansen, c1939.
11 p. F.

NT 0041951   PP

M35   Tarp, Svend Erik, 1898-
T37M6   [Mosaik]
Mosaik, Miniature-Suite for Orkester. København, W. Hansen, c1942.
score (15 p.) 30cm. (Wilhelm Hansen edition. Nr. 3395)

1. Suites (Orchestra)

NT 0041952   CoU

M1045   Tarp, Svend Erik, 1898-   Preludio festivo,
.T18F6   orchestra.

Tarp, Svend Erik, 1898-
ₑFor frihed og ret. Preludio patetico₎

Preludio patetico. Preludio festivo. For orkester. Partitur. København, J. Thobrither ₑc1952₎

Tarp, Svend Erik, 1898–
₍For frihed og ret. Preludio patetico₎

Preludio patetico. Preludio festivo. For orkester. Partitur. København, J. Thobrither ₍ᶜ1952₎
score (24 p.) 31 cm.
Cover title.
Duration : 5 min., 30 sec.
——— Stemmer. København, J. Thobrither ₍ᶜ1952₎
parts. 31 cm.
Cover title.
M1045.T18F6
1. Orchestral music—Scores. 2. Orchestral music—Parts. I.
Tarp, Svend Erik, 1898– Preludio festivo, orchestra. II. Title. III.
Title: Preludio festivo.

M1045.T18F6   M 53–1537

NT 0041954   DLC

Tarp, Svend Erik, 1898–
..."Pro defunctis," for Orkester... København, Skandinavisk Musikforlag ₍1946₎ Publ.pl.no. S.M.5392. 1 v. 31cm.

Score (8 p.) and parts.
Performance time: 4½ minutes.

410515B. 1. Orchestra—Scores.   2. World war, 1939–1945—Denmark
₍8₎ I. Title.
N. Y. P. L.   April 6, 1948

NT 0041955   NN ICN

Tarp, Svend Erik, 1898–
[Serenade
...Serenade [1930] for fløjte, klarinet,
violin, viola & violoncel. Leipzig, F.
Kistner & C.F.W. Siegel [etc., etc.] 1933.
Pl.no.12333. 1 v. 34cm. (Samfundet
til udgivelse af dansk musik. [Kompositioner]
ser. 3, no. 42)

Parts for flute, clarinet, violin, viola
and violoncello.

1. Chamber music, 20th cent.—Quintets. 2.
Flute in quintets (Flute, clarinet, violin,
viola, violoncello). I. Ser.

NT 0041957   NN CLU MH ViU MiU IU CoU

Tarp, Svend Erik, 1898–
₍Serenade, flute, clarinet & strings₎

Serenade, for fløjte, klarinet, violin, viola & violoncel. København, Edition Dania, 1952.
miniature score (15 p.) 19 cm. (Samfundet til udgivelse af dansk musik. ₍Publikation₎ 3. ser., nr. 42)

1. Quintets (Clarinet, flute, violin, viola, violoncello)   (Series)

M562.T23S5   78–253632

NT 0041958   DLC NcU OU NIC IU

Tarp, Svend Erik, 1898–
₍Serenade, flute & string trio, op. 28b₎

Serenade for fløjte, violin, viola & violoncel ₍op. 28b₎ ₍København₎ Københavns musikforlag ₍1951₎
miniature score (20 p.) 19 cm.
Cover title.
Reproduced from ms.

1. Suites (Flute, violin, viola, violoncello)
M462.T18 op. 28b 1951a   52–27402

NT 0041959   DLC

Tarp, Svend Erik, 1898–
PT8175
.M4TS5
Methling, Finn.
Skyggen; et spil efter H. C. Andersen til 150 års fødselsdagen 2. april 1955. Opført på Odense teater. Musik: Sv. Erik Tarp. København, Nyt nordisk forlag, 1955.

Tarp, Svend Erik, 1898–
Snap-shots, lette smaastykker for klaver; op. 45.
København, Hansen, c1947.
7 p.   F.

NT 0041961   PP

Tarp, Svend Erik, 1898–
₍Suite on old Danish folk-songs, orchestra₎

Suite over danske folkevisemotiver, for orchester. Suite on old Danish folk-songs. Partitur. København, Hansen, ᶜ1936.
score (16 p.) 31 cm.
CONTENTS.—Ravnen, han flyver om aften, om dagen han ikke maa.—Skæmtevise.—Liden Kirstens Dans.—Hr. Ramund.

1. Suites (Orchestra) — Scores. 2. Folk-songs, Danish (Instrumental settings)

M1003.T2S8   52–27013

NT 0041962   DLC

Tarp, Svend Erik, 1898–
₍Symphony, no. 1, op 50, Eb₎

Symfoni i es, op. 50. Partitur. København, Edition Dania ₍1949₎
score (60 p.) 31 cm. (Samfundet til udgivelse af dansk musik. ₍Publikation₎ 3. ser., nr. 108)

1. Symphonies—Scores.   I. Series.

M1001.T22 op. 50   52–29564

NT 0041963   DLC NN NcD ICN NcU O

Tarp, Svend Erik, 1898–
Songs. Selections.
Syv sange til tekster af A. Garff, V.
Bredsdorff og J. V. Jensen. København,
Engstrøm & Sødring [c1940]
Score (7 p.)
Pl. no. E. & S. 77

NT 0041964   MH–Mu

TARP, SVEND ERIK, 1898–
[TE DEUM, OP. 33. VOCAL SCORE, LATIN]
Te Deum, for soli (ad lib.) bl. kor og orkester,
op. 33. Fuldstaendigt klaverudtog med tekst.
København, Edition Dania, 1946. 33 p. 31cm.
(Samfundet til udgivelse af dansk musik. [Kompositioner] ser. 3, nr. 86)

For solo voices (SATB, ad lib.) and chorus (SATB) with keyboard accompaniment.

1. Te Deum. 2. Choral music.   Sacred (Mixed, 4pt.)—Keyboard acc. I. Series.

NT 0041965   NN NIC MB CoU ICN NcU NcD

Tarp, Svend Erik, 1898–
₍Te Deum. Piano-vocal score. Latin₎

Te Deum, for soli (ad. lib.) bl. kor og orkester, op. 33.
2. opl. København, Edition Dania, 1950 ₍ᶜ1946₎
33 p. 31 cm. (Samfundet til udgivelse af dansk musik. ₍Publikation₎ 3. ser., nr. 86)

1. Choruses, Sacred (Mixed voices, 4 parts) with orchestra—Vocal scores with piano. 2. Te Deum laudamus (Music)   (Series)

M2023.T22T415 1950   77–253569
[M2079.L9] [M2072.4]

NT 0041966   DLC MH NcD OU

Tarp, Svend Erik, 1898–
...Thema med Variationer; Carillon. Thème avec variations.
Theme with variations. Piano. ₍Af₎ Sv. Erik Tarp. Op. 43.
København, W. Hansen ₍etc., etc.₎, c1945₎ Publ.pl.no. 26044.
15 p.   30cm.   (Wilhelm Hansen Edition. Nr. 3435.)

1. Piano.
N. Y. P. L.   December 6, 1948

NT 0041967   NN PP MH OOxM CLSU

Tarp, Svend Erik, 1898–
[Sonatas, piano, op. 48]
Tre sonatiner for piano, op. 48.   København,
Engstrøm & Sødring ₍c1947₎
23 p.   31 cm.
Contents. –no. 1. C maj. –no. 2. C min.
–no. 3. D min.
1. Sonatas (Piano)

NT 0041968   CLSU NN CoU

₥781.5 Tarp, Svend Erik, 1898–
T191i [Improvisations, piano, op.21]
Trois improvisations, op.21. Three
improvisations. København, W.Hansen, c1946.
11p. 30cm.

1.Piano music

NT 0041969   CLSU

Tarp, Germany.
Mein Heimatdorf

see under

Huber, Peter.

TARPEL, GUILLAUME.
Reims, cathédrale nationale. Paris, En vente à
l'Office de centralisation d'ouvrages [1939]   31 p.,
135 plates.   27cm.

1. Cathedrals—France—Reims.

NT 0041971   NN IaU NNC NcU

Tarpenning, Walter A.
Social organizations working with rural
people, by Walter A. Tarpenning. Kalamazoo,
Mich., Western State normal school. 1925.
125 pp.

NT 0041972   OU

PR5548 Tarpey, Jessie Toler Kingsley.
.T689   Idylls of the fells. London, R.
I 3   Brimley Johnson, 1901.
206p. illus. 17cm.

Stories.

NT 0041973   NcU

Tarpey, Michael Francis, 1848–   *comp.*
... Levantine grapes commercially known as currants.
Comp. from official sources by Michael F. Tarpey ...
Washington, Govt. print. off., 1913.
39 p. illus. 23½ᶜᵐ. (₍U. S.₎ 63d Cong., 1st sess. Senate. Doc. 178)
Presented by Mr. Fletcher for Mr. Smith of Arizona. Ordered printed, with illustrations, September 3, 1913.

1. Currant grapes. 2. Tariff—U. S.   I. Title.

Library of Congress   HF2651.C9703T3   13–35707

NT 0041974   DLC PPAmP ICJ MiU OO

Tarpey, Michael Francis, 1848–

Fresno magnesite co.
Magnesite, by M. F. Tarpey. To the United States Congress, the "Ways and means committee" of the House of representatives, and the "Committee on finance" of the Senate. [n. p., 1908?]

NT   0041976   NN

Tarpey, W   Kingsley.
Crabbeb age & youth.   London, R. B. Johnson, 1901.
61 p.   sq. 24°.   (Carpet plays)

NT   0041976   NN

Tarpey, W   Kingsley.
O mistress mine; duet. The words from Shakespeare's "Twelfth night." The music by W. Kingsley Tarpey... London [etc.] Boosey & Co., Ltd., cop. 1899. Publ. pl. no. H. 2545.   7 p.   31½cm.

Duet with piano acc.

1. Vocal duos, Secular. I. Shake-   speare, William. Plays. Twelfth
night.   June 19, 1936
N. Y. P. L.

NT   0041977   NN

Tarpinian, Armen.
Le chant et l'ombre.   Paris, L'Arche [1953]
95 p.   20 cm.

500 copies printed. "Quatre cent trente exemplaires sur papier bouffant numérotés de 41 à 470. Exemplaire no 429."

ɪ. Title.

A 53–8652
Illinois. Univ. Library
for Library of Congress

NT   0041978   IU NBuU AU MH PU CtY NN

Tarpininkas...
v.

South Boston, 19   f°, 4°.
v.   illus.

Monthly,   ; weekly, Aug., 1930–
v. 3, nos. 1–7 repeated in numbering.
Title also in English: The Mediator; text in Lithuanian with some articles in English.
Aug., 1930–   official organ of the Amerikos lietuviŋ vaizbos butas, Boston (Lithuanian Chamber of Commerce of the United States).

1. Periodicals—U. S., Lithuanian.   I. Amerikos lietuviŋ vaizbos butas,
Boston.   II. The Mediator.
N. Y. P. L.   October 5, 1931

NT   0041979   NN

CpB
F769t
Tarpley, Collin   S
A eulogy upon the life and character of ex-President James Knox Polk, delivered at the request of the Legislature of the State of Mississippi, February 22, 1850. Jackson, Miss., Fall & Marshall, 1850.
32 p.   22 cm.

1. Polk, James Knox, Pres. U.S., 1795–1849

NT   0041980   NcU

*
TF25
.S68
1846
v.17,
no.8
Tarpley, Collin   S
Four articles on the practicability of a railroad between New Orleans and Jackson, Miss. [Jackson? 1846?]
31 p.   20cm.   (Streeter pamphlets. S.E.R.R.)

1. Railroads—Southeastern States. 2. New Orleans and Jackson Railroad Company. I. Southeastern railroads.

NT   0041981   ViU MH

Tarpley, Donald Greene, joint author.

Eberlein, Harold Donaldson.
Remodelling and adapting the small house, by Harold Donaldson Eberlein and Donald Greene Tarpley; with 127 illustrations and plans. Philadelphia & London, J. B. Lippincott company, 1933.

TN1
.U6
no. 682
Tarpley, Edward
U.S.   Bureau of mines.
... Analyses of Alaska coals. Washington, U. S. Govt. print. off., 1946.

Tarpley, Edward C.
U.S.   Bureau of mines.
... Analyses of Illinois coals. Washington, U. S. Govt. print. off., 1942.

TN1
.U6
no. 652
Tarpley, Edward C.
U. S.   Bureau of mines.
... Analyses of Kentucky coals. Washington, U. S. Govt. print. off., 1944.

TN1
.U6
no. 659
Tarpley, Edward C.
U. S.   Bureau of mines.
... Analyses of Pennsylvania anthracitic coals. Washington, U. S. Govt. print. off., 1944.

TN1
.U6
no. 671
Tarpley, Edward C.
U. S.   Bureau of mines.
... Analyses of Tennessee coals (including Georgia) Washington, U. S. Govt. print. off., 1945.

TN1
.U6
no. 656
Tarpley, Edward C.
U. S.   Bureau of mines.
... Analyses of Virginia coals. Washington, U. S. Govt. print. off., 1944.

Tarpley, Edward C.
U. S.   Bureau of mines.
... Analyses of West Virginia coals. Washington, U. S. Govt. print. off., 1942.

TX340
.R3
1948
Tarpley, Elizabeth, joint author.
FOR OTHER EDITIONS SEE MAIN ENTRY
Rathbone, Lucy.
Fabrics and dress [by] Lucy Rathbone [and] Elizabeth Tarpley; ed. by Alice F. Blood. New rev. ed. Boston, Houghton, Mifflin Co. [1948]

Tarpley, Elizabeth, joint author.

Rathbone, Lucy.
Study guide to problems of fabrics and dress, by Lucy Rathbone ... and Elizabeth Tarpley ... Boston, New York [etc.] Houghton Mifflin company [1937]

Tarpley, George L., compiler.
The principles of English prose as expressed by great writers; collected by George L. Tarpley.   London: Blackie & Son, Ltd., 1925.   ix, 54 p.   16°.   (Blackie's Standard English classics.)

203284A. 1. Style, Literary.
N. Y. P. L.   September 17, 1925

NT   0041992   NN

Tarpley, H   I
An instrument to measure servomechanism performance. [State College, Pa., 1947]
39–43 p.   diagrs.   29cm.   (Pennsylvania. State College. Engineering Experiment Station. Technical paper no. 29]
"Reprinted from the Review of scientific instruments, vol. 18, no. 1, 39–43, January, 1947."
Bibliography: p. 39, 42.

1. Servomechanisms.   I. Ser.

NT   0041993   ViU

Tarpley, Kenneth Jackson, joint author.
Jump over the moon

see under

Tarpley, Vera Chamberlain.

Tarpley, Raymond Edward, 1895–   joint author.
Tykociner, Joseph Tykocinski, 1877–
... Oscillations due to corona discharges on wires subjected to alternating potentials, by J. Tykocinski Tykociner ... Raymond E. Tarpley ... and Ellery B. Paine ... Urbana, University of Illinois [1935]

W 4
L68
v. 52
no. 5
TARPLEY, Thomas Griffin
Dissertatio medica inauguralis de phthisi pulmonali ...
Lugduni Batavorum, Apud Petrum vander Eyk [etc.] 1773.
33 p.   24 cm.
Diss. - Leyden.

NT   0041996   DNLM

Tarpley, Vera Chamberlain.
Father was a housewife, a comedy in three acts, by Vera and Ken Tarpley. Original songs by Vera Tarpley; piano acc. by Barbara Sherman. [Evanston, Ill., Row, Peterson and company, c1952]
119 p.   illus. incl. music, ports., diagr. 21 cm.   (A Row-Peterson play)
Text on p. 2–3 of cover.

NT   0042001   RPB

ML50
T37G6
1953a
WESTERN
Tarpley, Vera *Chamberlain*.
[Golden River. Libretto. English]
Golden River; a western comedy with music, by Vera and Ken Tarpley. Arrangements by Barbara Sherman. Boston, Baker's Plays [c1953]
96p.   illus., music.   26cm.

1. Musical revues, comedies, etc. I. Tarpley, Ken, joint author. II. Sherman, Barbara. III. Title.

NT   0042002   CoFS

Tarpley, Vera Chamberlain.
Jump over the moon, a farce in three acts, by Vera and Ken Tarpley. Boston, Baker's Plays [c1954]
79 p. 19 cm.
I. Tarpley, Kenneth Jackson, joint author.

NT 0042003　RPB NN PU

Tarpley, Vera Chamberlain.
The little dog laughed, a three-act comedy, by Vera and Ken Tarpley. [Evanston, Ill, Row, Peterson and company, c1951]
101 p. illus., diagr. 21 cm. (A Row-Peterson play)
I. Tarpley, Kenneth Jackson, joint author.

NT 0042004　RPB MiD

Tarpley, William Beverly, 1917-
On the mechanism of the catechol-tyrosinase reaction. Spectrophotometric studies. New York, 1951.
78 l. diagrs., tables. 29cm.

Thesis, Columbia university.
Typescript.
Bibliographical footnotes.

NT 0042005　NNC

Tarpley, William Beverly, 1917-
On the mechanism of the catechol-tyrosinase reaction. Spectrophotometric studies. Ann Arbor, University Microfilms, 1951.
([University Microfilms, Ann Arbor, Mich.] Publication no. 6772)
Microfilm copy of typescript. Positive.
Collation of the original: 78 l. diagrs., tables.
Thesis—Columbia University.
Bibliographical footnotes.

1. Tyrosinase. 2. Catechol. 3. Enzymes.

Microfilm AC-1 no. 6772　　　　　Mic A 54-1068

Columbia Univ.　　　　Libraries
for Library of Congress　　([1]†

NT 0042006　NNC DLC

Beinecke
Library
Uzk64
T2
892T
The tarpon. [Boston? 1892]
cover-title, 30 numb. l. front. 13 x 17 cm.
Signed: C. A. D., Boston, 1892.

1. Tarpon. I. D., C. A.

NT 0042007　CtY

Tarpon fishing off the Gulf Coast
see under Louisville and Nashville Railroad Company.

F
394
F822
T376
TXC-ZZ
Tarpon Inn; arcadian haven for joyous week-ends and wonderful vacations. [Freeport, Tex., 193-]
[12] p. illus. 19cm.
Cover title.

1. Tarpon Inn, Freeport, Tex. 2. Summer resorts - Texas - Freeport. 3. Freeport, Tex. - Description.

NT 0042009　TxU

F.2
L47
T191
Tarpon Inn, beautiful Useppa Island, Florida. [n.p., Florida Hotel & Navigation Co., 1918?]
[12] p. illus. (part col.) 21 cm.

Cover title.

1. Useppa Island, Fla. I. Florida Hotel & Navigation Company.

NT 0042010　FU

Tarptautinis geografų kongresas
see
International Geographical Congress.

Tarptautinis geologų kongresas
see
International Geological Congress.

Tarptautine geodezijos ir geofizikos sajunga
see International Union of Geodesy and Geophysics.

Tarptautiné mokslškosios hidrologijos asociacija
see
International Association of Scientific Hydrology.

Tarputschen, von Sauchen
see Saucken-Tarputschen, von.

Tarquin and Tullia
see under [Mainwaring, Arthur] 1668-1712.

Tarquin banished
see under Quarles, John, 1624-1665.

Tarquini, *pseud.*
El anteproyecto de la constitución del estado; herejías de la comisión jurídica asesora y refutación de todas ellas, por el autor "Tarquini" ... Valladolid, Imp. Casa social católica, 1931.
125, [2] p. 18cm.

1. Spain. Comisión jurídica asesora. 2. Church and state in Spain. I. Title.

42-48064

Library of Congress　　　BR1023.T3

NT 0042018　DLC

ND853
.O8T3
folio
Tarquini, Angelo, 1909-

Osswald-Toppi, Margherita, 1897-
Margherita Osswald-Toppi: sechs mehrfarbige Wiedergaben ihrer Werke, mit einer Einführung von Angelo Tarquini. Zürich, Rascher, 1953.

Voci del cuore; composizioni facili e melodiche per harmonium [o] organo. Op. 126 (1953) Torino, Stamperia musicale Filli Amprimo, 1953. 1 v. 31cm.

Fasc. 1.
CONTENTS.--Fasc. 1. Grande largo. Preghiera. Meditazione. Il canto dell'esule.
1. Harmonium. 2. Organ. I. Title.

NT 0042020　NN

TARQUINI, Camillo, *cardinal, 1810-1874.*
Del pase real à las bulas pontificias. Traducida al castellano por un presbitero de Chile Paris, 1853.

NT 0042021　MH

TARQUINI, Camillo, *cardinal, 1810-1874.*
Del pase real a las bulas pontificias; disertacion leida en la Academia de la religion catolica de Roma, 1852. Traducida por un presbitero de la república de Chile, [I.V.Eyzaguirre]. Mexico, L.Abadiano y Valdes, 1854.
pp.24.

NT 0042022　MH

Tarquini, Camillo, *cardinal*, 1810-1874.
Instituciones de derecho eclesiastico publico, por el r. p. Camilo Tarquini ... virtiólo del latin al español, para uso del Seminario conciliar del arzobispado de La Plata, el p. fr. Manuel Murga ... Sucre, Tipografia del cruzado, 1878.
cover-title, 130 p. 20½cm.

1. Ecclesiastical law. I. Murga, Manuel, tr.

44-45175

NT 0042023　DLC InU

BQV
108
T38
Tarquini, Camillo, *Cardinal*, 1810-1874.
Instituciones de derecho público eclesiástico : seguidas de una disertación sobre el pase regio del Syllabus y la Constitución "Pastor Aeternus" del Concilio Baticano / C. Tarquini ; puestas en Español por A. Manjón. -- 2. ed., corr. y mejorada. -- Granada : J. Lopez Guevara, 1890.
xv, 208 p. ; 21 cm.

1. Catholic Church-- Government. 2. Church and state--Catholic Church. I. Catholic Church. Pope. 1846-1878 (Pius IX) Syllabus errorum (8 Dec. 1864) II. Vatican Council. 1869-1870 "Pastor Aeternus."

NT 0042024　CU-L MH-L

Tarquini, Camillo, *cardinal*, 1810-1874.
Iuris ecclesiastici publici institutiones auctore Camillo Tarquini ... Accedit dissertatio eiusdem De regio placet, habita in Academia religionis catholicae, die 2 septembris 1852, nunc primum latine reddita. Romae, ex Typographia polyglotta, S. c. de propaganda fide,
xii, 170 p., 1 l. 24½cm.

1. Ecclesiastical law. 2. Church and state—Catholic church.

NT 0042025　ICU

BV
107
.T19
Tarquini, Camillo, *cardinal*, 1810-1874.
Juris ecclesiastici publici institutiones auctore Camillo Tarquini ... Romae, ex Officina libraria bonarum artium, 1862.
viii, 134 [2] p. 22 cm.

NT 0042026　DCU

Tarquini, Camillo cardinal, 1810-1874.
Juris ecclesiastici publici institutiones.
Romae, Civilitatis Catholicae, 1868.

NT 0042027 PV MH-L

BV
107
.T19
1875

Tarquini, Camillo, cardinal, 1810-1874.
Iuris ecclesiastici publici institutiones,
auctore Camillo Tarquini ... Accedit dissertatio
eiusden De regio placet, habita in Academia religionis catholicae die 2 Septembris 1852, nunc
primum latine reddita. Ed. 4. Romae, ex typographia polyglotta S.C. de Propaganda Fide, 1875.
xii, 170 p., 1 L. 23cm.
Bibliographical footnotes.

1. Canon law - Philosophy. 2. Ecclesiastical
law, Public. 3. Catholic church. Pope, 1846-
1878 (pius IX): Syllabus. I. Title.

NT 0042028 DCU CU OC1StM

Tarquini Camillo, cardinal, 1810-1874.
Juris Ecclesiastici Publici, Romae, 1879.

NT 0042029 OC1StM

Tarquini, Camillo, S.J., Cardinal, 1810-1874.
Juris ecclesiastici publici institutiones.
Accedit dissertatio ejusdem De regio placet habi-
ta in academia religionis Catholicae, 2 Sept.
1852. Nunc primum Latine reddita. Ed. 7.
Romae, ex typographia Polyglotta, S.C. de Prop.
Fide, 1881.

xii, 170p. 23cm.

1. Ecclesiastical law. 2. Bulls, Papal. I. Popes.
1700-1721 (Clemens XI). Nova semper (29 Nov. 1714)
II. Title: De regio placet.

NT 0042030 PLatS

TARQUINI, Camillo, 1810-1874.
Juris ecclesiastici publici institutiones;
accedit dissertatio eiusdem De regio placet,
habita in Academia religionis catholicae die
2 septembris 1852, nunc primum latine reddita.
Ed. 8a. Romae, 1882.

NT 0042031 MH-L

Tarquini, Camillo, 1810-1874.
Iuris ecclesiastici publici institutiones.
Accedit dissertatio eiusdem De Regio Placet
habita in academia religionis Catholicae die
2 Septembris 1852 nunc primum Latine reddita.
Editio Docima. Romae, Ex Typographia Polyglotta, 1885.
167 p.

NT 0042032 OC1JC PLatS

Tarquini, Camillo, 1810-
Iuris ecclesiastici publici institutiones.
De regio placet habita in academia religionis
catholicae die 2 Septembris 1852. Nunc Primum
latine reddita. Editio XI. Romae, Ex Typographia Polyglotta, 1887.
170 p.

NT 0042033 OC1JC

Tarquini, Camillo, cardinal, 1810-
Iuris ecclesiastici publici institutiones
Auct. R. P. Camillo Tarquini, S.J. St.
Eccl. Rom. card. Accedit dissertatio eins-
dien De. Regio Placet, Habita in Academia
Religionis Catholicae. Dis Sept. 2.1852.
Anne prinnum Latine reddita. Editio XIII.
Romae, Ex. Typ. Polygretta, 1890.
170 p.

NT 0042034 OCX

Tarquini, Camillo, *cardinal,* 1810-1874.
Iuris ecclesiastici publici institutions auctore Camillo Tarquini ... Accedit dissertatio eiusdem De regio placet, habita in
Academia religionis catholicae, die 2 septembris 1852, nunc primum latine reddita. Editio 14. Romae, ex Typographia polyglotta, S. c. de propaganda fide, 1892.
xii, 170 p., 1 l. 24½ᵐ.

1. Ecclesiastical law. 2. Church and state—Catholic church.

45-22810

NT 0042035 DLC

Tarquini, Camillo, Cardinal, 1810-1874.
Iuris ecclesiastici publici institutiones.
Nunc primum latine reddita. Ed. 17. Romae,
ex Typographia Polyglotta S.C. de Propaganda
Fide, 1898.
xii, 170 p. 21 cm.

NT 0042036 PLatS

Tarquini, Camillo, S.J., Cardinal, 1810-1874.
Juris ecclesiastici publici institutiones.
Accedit dissertatio ejusdem De regio placet,
habita in Academia religionis Catholicae. Ed. 18.
Romae, ex typographia Polyglotta S.C. de Prop.
Fide, 1901.

xii, 170p. 23cm.

1. Ecclesiastical law. I. Title. II. Title:
De regio placet.

NT 0042037 PLatS

Tarquini, Camillo, cardinal, 1810-1874.
Lettre en réponse à l'écrit de m. Maurice de
Bonald, sur le Concordat de 1801. Rodez, Impr.
de veuve E.Carrère, 1871.

15 p. 23 cm.

NT 0042038 MH

Tarquini, Camillo, cardinal, 1810-1874.
Les principes du droit public de l'Eglise.
Réduits à leur plus simple expression. Préface
et traduction de l'abbé Auguste Onclair.
Bruxelles, 3ème éd., 1876.
164 p.

NT 0042039 RWoU

BT107
T306
1891

Tarquini, Camillo, *cardinal,* 1810-1874.
Les principes du droit public de l'église
réduits à leur plus simple expression par
le R.P. Camille Tarquini ... suivis de la dissertation du même auteur sur le Placet royal,
traduits sur la 12e édition latine par Aug.
Onclair ... Quatrième édition revue et corrigée. Paris, V. Retaux et fils, 1891.

xv, 214 p.
Bibliographical footnotes.
1. Ius Publicum. 2. Public law-Ecclesiastical.
I. Onclair, Augus te. tr. II. Title.

NT 0042040 MBtS MoSU-D

Tarquini, Francesco
... Memoria in svolgimento dei motivi del ricorso presentati avverso la
sentenza della R. Corte di appello
di Roma dei 28 Ottobre 1895 dal Sig.
ing. agronomo Napoleone De Bonis ex
segretario contabile del credito
agrario della Banca generale succursale di Velletri per i reati commessi
dai Signori Palmerini Carlo, Martore
Dante, Falconi Cesare e Barbetta
Dario. ¡Roma? 1896?¿

Continued in next column

Continued from preceding column

30 p. 30cm.
Caption title.
At head of title: Suprema Corte di
cassazione sedente in Roma. Sezione
II. penale.
Signed at end: Avv. Giuseppe
Orano; Avv. Francesco Tarquini, es-
tensore.

NT 0042042 MH-L

Tarquini, G
... Sulla privativa dei servizi pub-
blici affidati ai comuni in rapporto
alla libera concorrenza commerciale.
Roma, Manuzio, 1908.
18 p. 24½cm.

NT 0042043 MH-L

Tarquini, Giovanni.
Possibilità concrete per lo sviluppo del traffico
sulle linee aeree interne. Roma, Assn.
Culturale Aeronautica [1946]
14 p. (Quaderni aeronautici. Ser. Impiego
civile, n. 182)

NT 0042044 DLC

RG128
T17

Tarquini, María Julia
... Radioterapia en los procesos inflamatorios del aparato genital femenino. Tesis
de doctorado por la dra. María Julia Tarquini. Buenos Aires ¡Ferrari¿ 1936.
43, ¡1¿ p. 26½ᵐ.

At head of title: Universidad nacional de
Buenos Aires. Facultad de ciencias médicas.
Año 1936. N.o 5826. •
"Bibliografía": p. 39-41.

1. Generative organs. Female - Diseases.
2. Radiotherapy.

NT 0042045 NNC

Tarquini, Tarquinia Zandonai
see
Zandonai Tarquini, Tarquinia.

Tarquini, Vittoria Bonajuti
see **Bonajuti Tarquini, Vittoria.**

4K
Ital.
952

Tarquinia, Italy. Arte degli Ortolani.
Lo statuto dell'Arte degli ortolani dell'anno
MCCCLXXXIX; A cura di Francesco Guerri.
Roma, Tip. nazionale di G. Bertero, 1909.
69 p. (Fonti de storia cornetana, 2)
I. Guerri, Francesco, 1874- ed.

NT 0042048 DLC-P4 MH

NK4640
.C6 I7
fasc. 25,
etc.
fol.

Tarquinia, Italy. Museo nazionale tarquiniense.
Iacopi, Giulio, 1898-
Museo nazionale tarquiniense. ¡Roma¿ Libreria dello
Stato, 1955-

Tarquinia. fasc. 1–
Roma, Libreria dello stato, 1937–

(Monumenti della pittura antica scoperti in Italia.
Sezione prima: La pittura etrusca)

NT 0042050   OCU

... Tarquinia; la Necropoli e il Museo...
see under   Romanelli, Pietro.

Tarquinia; wandmalereien aus etruskischen Gräben
see under   Pallotino, Massimo.

Tarquinii
see
Tarquinia, *Italy.*

Tarquinio, Mario.
Vias de communicação e meios de transporte no estado da
Bahia; monographia escrita pelo eng. civil Mario Tarquinio...
(In: Instituto geographico e historico da Bahia. Revista. Bahia,
1934. 23½cm. no. 60, p. 305–508.)

"Bibliographia," p. 506–508.

1. Communications—Brazil—Bahia.   2. Transportation—Brazil—Bahia.
N. Y. P. L.   July 19, 1935

NT 0042054   NN

Tarquínio de Sousa, Octávio
see
Sousa, Octávio Tarquínio de, 1889–1959.

Tarquino, Sexto
see
Tarquinius, Sextus.

Tarquis, Pedro.

See

Tarquis Rodríguez, Pedro.

TARQUIS RODRÍGUEZ, PEDRO.
Tradiciones canarias.   Santa Cruz de Tenerife, Impr. Católica,
1952.   276 p.   illus.   23cm.

1. Canary Islands—Hist.

NT 0042058   NN

Tarquis y Rodríguez, Pedro
see
Tarquis Rodríguez, Pedro.

Tarr, Alexander.
*De coffea.   Pestini, J. Beimel, 1836.
21 p., 1 l.   8°.   [P., v. 1328.]
Hungarian text.

NT 0042060   DNLM

Tarr, Andrew.   *7568.159
History of Tremont Lodge, No. 77, of Free and Accepted Masons,
Tremont, Me., from 1854 to 1871.
Portland. Berry. 1874. 19 pp. 8°

H907 — Freemasonry. Maine. Tremont Lodge, Tremont, Me.

NT 0042061   MB

Tarr, Augustus De Kalb.
The American reader of prose and poetry. Designed
for the academies and schools of America ... By Augustus De Kalb Tarr ... Philadelphia, M. Bast, 1857.
504 p. 20ᶜᵐ.

1. Readers and speakers—1800–1870.   I. Title.
                                     CA 17–2911 Unrev'd
Library of Congress   PE1120.TJ5 1857

NT 0042062   DLC PHi

Tarr, Augustus DeKalb.
American reader of prose & poetry, designed for
the academies & schools of America.   Philadelphia,
Boston, 1858.
516 p.

NT 0042063   PU

Tarr, Augustus De Kalb.
The American reader of prose and poetry. Designed
for the academies and schools of America ... By Augustus De Kalb Tarr ... Philadelphia, The author, 1859.
xi, [9]–516 p. 20ᵐᵐ.

1. Readers and speakers—1800–1870.   I. Title.
                                     CA 17–2910 Unrev'd
Library of Congress   PE1120.T35 1859

NT 0042064   DLC

Tarr, Augustus DeKalb.
American reader of prose & poetry, designed for
the academies & schools of America.   Philadelphia,
Tarr, 1860.
516 p.

NT 0042065   PU RPB

Tarr, Charles O., joint author.

Smith, George V   1916–
... Precipitation and reversion of graphite in low-carbon low-
alloy steel in the temperature range 900° to 1300° F., by G. V.
Smith ... R. F. Miller ... and C. O. Tarr ...
(*In* Metals technology. New York, American institute of mining
and metallurgical engineers, inc., 1944. 23ᶜᵐ. v. 11, no. 4, June 1944.
6 p. illus.)

Tarr, Elihu D
Digest of Acts of Assembly relating to the
Kensington District of the Northern Liberties ...
see under   Kensington, Pa. Ordinances, etc.

Tarr, Elihu D.
Memorial of the commissioners of the county of
Philadelphia to the legislature upon the subject of
the laws exempting certain property from taxation;
together with a schedule of exempt property...
Philadelphia, 1851.
51 p.   23 cm.

NT 0042068   RPB PHi PPL

Tarr, Elvira R.
The epistemology of Charles Sanders Peirce and
its relation to education.
218 p.
Thesis (Ph. D.) – N. Y. U., School of Education.
1. Dissertations, Academic – N. Y. U. – 1968.
2. Peirce, Charles Santiago Sanders, 1839–1914.

NT 0042069   NNU

R912.796 Tarr, F   M
T176   Mining districts of the state of Idaho, 1936;
[a map] comp. from the records of the federal
land office, state Mine inspector's reports,
United States geological maps, bulletins and
other sources.   n.p., 1936.

36 x 55 cm.   Folded into cover.
"Property of F.M.Tarr and used by permission

NT 0042070   WaSp

Tarr, Florence.
M2023
.S196 O 2   **Savino, Domenico,** 1882–

O, wondrous star; a Christmas choral fantasy in three epi-
sodes, for mixed voices and piano accompaniment (or organ)
... Music by Domenico Savino, text by Florence Tarr. New
York, Robbins music corporation [1945]

Tarr, Florence.
M1533
.S275W6   **Savino, Domenico,** 1882–
[World of tomorrow. Piano-vocal score]

World of tomorrow, a rhapsodic poem, for mixed voices,
piano solo and soprano or tenor solo ... Music by Domenico
Savino, text by Florence Tarr. New York, Robbins music
corporation [1943]

Tarr, Frederick Courtney, 1896–1939, **joint
author.**

Marden, Charles Carroll, 1867–1932.
A first Spanish grammar, by C. Carroll Marden and F.
Courtney Tarr ... Boston, New York [etc.] Ginn and com-
pany [*1926]

Tarr, Frederick Courtney, 1896–1939.
A graded Spanish review grammar with composition, by
F. Courtney Tarr and Augusto Centeno ... New York, F. S.
Crofts & co., 1933.
xii p., 1 l., 321 p. 19½ cm.

Map on lining-papers.

1. Spanish language—Grammar—1870–   2. Spanish language—
Composition and exercises.   I. Centeno, Augusto, 1901–   joint
author. II. Title.
PC4111.T3   465   33—14964

                OYesA OCIW FU
NT 0042074   DLC MtU OrP IU PHC ViU ICU OCl NcD FTaSU

Tarr, Frederick Courtney, 1896–1939.
A graded Spanish review grammar with composition by F. Courtney Tarr and Augusto Centeno. New York, Crofts, 1936.

NT 0042075   MH

Tarr, Frederick Courtney, 1896–1939. A graded Spanish review grammar with composition.

PC4111
.T313   U. S. *Military academy, West Point. Dept. of modern languages.*
Supplementary material. Third class Spanish. West Point, N. Y., Dept. of modern languages, United States Military academy, 1945.

Tarr, Frederick Courtney, 1896–1939.
Graded Spanish review grammar with composition, by F. Courtney Tarr and Augusto Centeno. N. Y. F. S. Crofts & co., 1942, *1933.
321 p. tables

NT 0042077   OC1ND

Tarr, Frederick Courtney, 1896–1939.
A graded Spanish review grammar with composition, by F. Courtney Tarr and Augusto Centeno.. New York, Appleton-Century-Crofts [195–?, c1933]
xii p., 1 l., 321 p.   19.5 cm.
Map on lining-papers.

NT 0042078   NcD

Tarr, Frederick Courtney, 1896–1939.
Impresiones de España, a course in Spanish composition, by F. Courtney Tarr and Augusto Centeno ... New York, F. S. Crofts & co., 1933.
vii p., 1 l., 171 p.   19¼ᶜᵐ.
Maps on lining papers.
"This book is an amplification of the composition material contained in the authors' A graded Spanish review grammar with composition."—Pref.
1. Spanish language—Composition and exercises.   I. Centeno, Augusto, joint author.   II. Title.
Library of Congress   PC4111.T32   33–17271
————— Copy 2.
Copyright A 64138   (2)   468.242

NT 0042079   DLC ICU IU OC1

Tarr, Frederick Courtney, 1896–1939.   *2950.56.42
Literary and artistic unity in the Lazarillo de. Tormes.
(*In* Modern Language Association of America. Publications. Vol. 42, pp. 404–421. Menasha, Wis. 1927.)
The Lazarillo is by Diego Hurtado de Mendoza.

D6857 — Hurtado de Mendoza, Diego, 1503–1575.

NT 0042080   MB

Tarr, Frederick Courtney, 1896–1939.
Prepositional complementary clauses in Spanish with special reference to the works op (!) Pérez Galdós ... by Frederick Courtney Tarr ... New York, Paris, 1922.
2 p. l., 264 p., 1 l.   25¼ᵐᵐ.
Thesis (PH. D.)—Princeton university, 1921.
Vita.
"Extrait de la Revue hispanique, tome LVI."
Bibliography : p. (261)–264.
1. Spanish language—Clauses. 2. Spanish language—Prepositions. 3. Pérez Galdós, Benito, 1845–1920.
Library of Congress   PC4390.T3 1922   24–14623

NT 0042081   DLC PU NIC NcU OO OCU OU MiU

PQ
6071
T19   Tarr, Frederick Courtney, 1896–1939.
Romanticism in Spain and Spanish romanticism: a critical survey.

(*In* Bulletin of Spanish studies, Liverpool. 24cm. v. 16 (1939) p. 3–37)

1. Spanish literature--Hist. & crit
2. Romanticism--Spain.

NT 0042082   NIC PU RPB OO CtY TNJ

Tarr, Frederick Courtney, 1896–1939.
Shorter Spanish review grammar and composition, by F. Courtney Tarr and Augusto Centeno ... New York, F. S. Crofts & co., 1937.
viii, 208 p.   19¼ cm.

1. Spanish language—Grammar—1870-   2. Spanish language—Composition and exercises.   I. Centeno, Augusto, 1901–   joint author.   II. Title.
PC4111.T34   468.242   37—12244

FTaSU
NT 0042083   DLC OrStbM IdPI WaS WaT PRosC OC1ND OC1

Tarr, Frederick Courtney, 1896–1939.
Shorter Spanish review grammar and composition, by F. Courtney Tarr and Augusto Centeno ... New York, F. S. Crofts, 1942 (c1937)
viii, 208 p.   19¼ cm.

N1 0042084   WaU

PC
4111
T34
1943   Tarr, Frederick Courtney, 1896–1939.
Shorter Spanish review grammar and composition, by F. Courtney Tarr and Augusto Centeno.   New York, F. S. Crofts & Co., 1943.
208 p.

1. Spanish language - Grammar - 1870-
2. Spanish language - Composition and exercises. I. Centeno, Augusto, jt. author.
II. Title.

NT 0042085   NBuU

Tarr, Frederick Courtney, 1896–1939.
Shorter Spanish review grammar and composition, by F. Courtney Tarr and Augusto Centeno ...
New York, F.S. Crofts & co., 1946.

NT 0042086   PPLas

Tarr, Frederick Courtney, 1896–1939.
Substantive clauses governed by a preposition in the novels of Benito Perez Galdos...Baltimore, 1917.

NT 0042087   MdBJ

Tarr, Harry A
Brief review in English four years, with drill exercises. New York city, Colonial book co. [c.1940]

NT 0042088   MH DLC-P4

(Tarr, Henry T   B   )
Qualitative chemical analysis of inorganic substances as practiced in Georgetown college, D. C. / New York, Cincinnati (etc.) American book company, 1894.
61 p.   19 x 26¼ᶜᵐ.
Prepared by H. T. B. Tarr and revised by John W. Fox.   *cf.* Pref.

1. Chemistry, Analytic—Qualitative.   I. Fox, John W., ed.
Library of Congress   QD85.T19   4—23967

NT 0042089   DLC DGU PU-S PPD MiU OC1JC

Tarr, Hugh Lewis Aubrey, 1905-
Brood diseases of the bee.   [Den Haag, W. Junk, 1937]
p. 150–185.   25 cm.   (Tabulae biologicae, v. 14, pt. 2)
"References": p. 184–185.

NT 0042090   OU

RD771
T3   Tarr, Irene.
Analysis of normal and scoliotic spine: with implications for therapeutic exercise. (n.p.) 1947–48.
2 pt.   illus.   27cm.

Extracted from Physiotherapy review, v.27, no.5, and v.28, no.1; Sept.-Oct.1947, Jan.-Feb.1948.

1. Spine - Abnormalities and deformities.

NT 0042091   OrCS

Tarr, Jesse.

Bancroft, Wilder Dwight, 1867–
... Medical aspects of gas warfare; prepared under the direction of Maj. Gen. M. W. Ireland, the surgeon general, by Col. Wilder D. Bancroft ... Maj. H. C. Bradley ... (and others) Washington, Govt. print. off., 1926.

Z250
T25   Tarr, John Charles
A book of alphabets in common use to-day for writing, lettering and printing ... London, I. Pitman (1950)
40 p.

1. Alphabets. 2. Type and type-founding.
3. Printing - Specimens.

NT 0042093   CU CtY

Tarr, John Charles.
Design in typography; an introduction. London, Phoenix House (1951)
31 p. illus. 22 cm.

1. Printing, Practical.   I. Title.
Z246.T37   655.24   53–19185 ‡

NT 0042094   DLC AAP LU NIC NN CSt ICN

Tarr, John Charles.
Good handwriting and how to acquire it. London, Phoenix House (1952)
64 p. illus. 19 cm.

1. Penmanship.   I. Title.
Z43.T25   *652.1   53—18501 ‡

NT 0042095   DLC PU ICN MiD DGU IEN PSt

652.1
T176g
Tarr, John Charles
Good handwriting and how to acquire it.
Philadelphia, Dufour Editions, Saifer, 1953.
68 p. illus. 20cm.

1. Penmanship.   I. T.

NT   0042096   MiDW CtY MB PPT PG1B PSC PP NIC

Tarr, John Charles.
Good handwriting and how to acquire it. ₍2d ed., enl.₎
London, Phoenix House ₍1953₎
68 p. illus. 19 cm.

1. Penmanship.   I. Title.

Z43.T25 1953   *652.1   53–31795 rev ‡

NT   0042097   DLC CaBVa NcD OC1

Tarr, John Charles.
Good handwriting and how to acquire it. ₍3d ed., enl.₎
London, Phoenix House ₍1954₎
80p. illus. 19 cm.

NT   0042098   KEmT OrMonO CaBVa

Tarr, John Charles.
How to plan print, by John Charles Tarr ... London, C.
Lockwood & son, ltd. ₍1938₎
2 p. l., ₍vii₎–x p., 1 l., 175, ₍1₎ p. illus. 22ᶜᵐ.
"First published 1938."
Bibliography: p. ₍171₎–172.

1. Type and type-founding. 2. Type-setting. 3. Printing, Practical.
I. Title.
                                                    39–1728
Library of Congress   Z253.T19
                              ₍5₎   655.24

NT   0042099   DLC NNC

655.2
T192h
1949
Tarr, John Charles
How to plan print. ₍2d ed., rev.₎   London, C. Lockwood ₍1949₎
175p. illus.

1. Type and type-founding. 2. Type-setting.
3. Printing, Practical. I. Title.

NT   0042100   FTaSU TxU MiD ICarbS

Tarr, John Charles.
Lettering; a source book of Roman alphabets. London,
C. Lockwood, 1951.
63 p. 29 cm.

1. Lettering. 2. Alphabets.

NK3620.T2   745.6   52–12560 ‡

NT   0042101   DLC OrP WaS TxU UU KEmT MoSW IU

Z244
.P95
Tarr, John Charles, ed.

Printing theory and practice. 1–
London, Sir I. Pitman, 1946–

Tarr, John Charles.
Printing to-day. With an introd. by Francis Meynell and
a note on modern typography by Bertram Evans. London,
Oxford Univ. Press ₍1945₎
183 p. illus. 22 cm. (The Pageant of progress)

1. Printing, Practical.   I. Title.   (Series)
                                        A 48–8669*
Harvard Univ. Library
for Library of Congress   ₍2₎

NT   0042103   MH NNC

Tarr, John Charles.
Printing to-day. With an introd. by Francis Meynell and
a note on modern typography by Bertram Evans. ₍ Rev. ed.
London₎ Oxford University Press ₍1949₎
184 p. illus. 22 cm. (The Pageant of progress, 17)
Bibliography: p. 179–180.

1. Printing, Practical.   (Series)

Z244.T3 1949   655   50–2270

NT   0042104   NNC MB ScU MiU OrCS Wa WaS
         DLC MoSW OC1 PPD ICU NN NcU OO TxU CU Vi

Tarr, John Charles.
A visit to the workshop of Christophe Plantin in
the city of Antwerp / by Jon C. Tarr; introduction
by R. T. Porte.   Salt Lake City, Porte Pub. Co.,
1936.
88 p. ill. 20 cm. (The Business Printer,
v. 8; no. 7–8)
1. Plantin, Christophe, 1514–1589. I. Antwerp,
Musée Plantin-Moretus.

NT   0042105   CSdS

Tarr, Jon C
see Tarr, John C.

Tarr, Lester W
Fruit jellies ₍by₎ Lester W. Tarr, Philip B.
Myers and George L. Baker.   Newark, Delaware,
University of Delaware Agricultural Experiment
Station, 1923–29.
6 pts.   (various paging)   23 cm.

NT   0042107   DLC

Tarr, Mary Muriel, *sister,* 1905–
... Catholicism in Gothic fiction; a study of the nature and
function of Catholic materials in Gothic fiction in England
(1762–1820) by Sister Mary Muriel Tarr ... Washington,
D. C., The Catholic university of America press, 1946.
vii, 141 p. 23ᶜᵐ.
Thesis (PH. D.)—Catholic university of America.
Bibliography: p. 123–124.

1. English fiction—18th cent.—Hist. & crit. 2. English fiction—19th
cent.—Hist. & crit. 3. Romanticism—England. 4. Catholics in literature.   I. Title.   II. Title: Gothic fiction.
Catholic univ. of America.   Library   A 46–5632
for Library of Congress   PR830.C3T3
                                        823.609

TxU DLC
NT   0042108   DCU IdPI MH ViU NcU MU PV FU TU NcD CoU

Tarr, Raïssa, tr.

Batyrev, Vladimir Mikhaïlovich.
Les finances et le crédit en U. R. S. S. ₍par₎ V. Batyrev et
V. Sitnine. Tr. du russe par Raïssa Tarr. Paris, Presses
universitaires de France, 1948.

891.708
T192nn
Tarr, Raïssa, tr.
Nouvelles soviétiques, traduites du russe
par R. Tarr et G. Cannac. Paris, Plon ₍1950₎
333 p. (Feux croisés; âmes et terres
étrangères)

1. Short stories, Russian--Translations
into French. I. Cannac, G., joint tr.
II. Title.

NT   0042110   MiU

Tarr, Ralph Stockman, 1864–1912.
Acinite trachyte from Crazy mountains Montana.
By Ralph Stockman Tarr, & J.E. Wolff.
(In Harvard Univ. Museum of comparative zoo-
logy. Bulletins. v. 16, no. 12)

NT   0042111   PU

Tarr, Ralph Stockman, 1864–1912.
... An advanced geography, by Ralph S. Tarr ... and
Frank M. McMurry ... with numerous maps and many
illustrations, chiefly photographs of actual scenes. New
York, The Macmillan company; London, Macmillan & co.,
ltd., 1907.
xxii, 2 l l., 478, x p. illus., plates, maps. 21½ x 16½ᶜᵐ. (Tarr and
McMurry geographies)
Half-title: A complete geography.
On cover: Two book series.
1. Geography—Text-books—1870–   I. McMurry, Frank Morton, 1862–
joint author.

Library of Congress   G126.T3   7—13003

NT   0042112   DLC PU DHEW ViU MH

Tarr, Ralph Stockman, 1864–1912.
Advanced geography, by R.S. Tarr and F.M.
McMurry.   New York, Macmillan, 1908.,
v. p.   illus., plate, maps (part. col.)   (Tarr
and McMurry geographies.)
Supplement for Washington.

NT   0042113   WaSp WaE

Tarr, Ralph Stockman, 1864–1912, and F. M. McMurry.
...Advanced geography, by Ralph S. Tarr... and Frank M.
McMurry...   New York: Macmillan Co., 1909.   xxii, 478,
x p.   illus., maps, plates.   8°.
At head of title: Tarr and McMurry geographies.

1. Geography—Textbooks, American,   1909. 2. McMurry, Frank Morton,
1862–.   jt. au.
N. Y. P. L.   July 13, 1926

NT   0042114   NN

Tarr, Ralph Stockman, 1864–1912.
... Advanced geography, Tarr and McMurry. Rev. by
the Text-book committee and approved by the State board
of education. Sacramento, W. W. Shannon, supt. of state
printing ₍1909₎
xxii, ₍2₎, 649, x p. incl. front., illus., pl., maps. 21½ᶜᵐ. (California state
series) $1.00
"California ... a supplement by the State text-book committee, with the
counsel and assistance of Allison Ware, R. E. Holway, Job Wood, jr.,
Mary E. George, R. B. Haydock, Lewis E. Aubury, C. K. Studley, J. B.
Monlux, and Willard S. Johnson": p. ₍543₎–649.
1. Geography—Text-books—1870–   2. California—Descr. & trav.
I. McMurry, Frank Morton, 1862–   joint author. II. California. State
text-book committee.   9—22236
Library of Congress   G126.T32C2 1909

NT   0042115   DLC CLSU

Tarr, Ralph Stockman, 1864–1912.
Advanced geography, by R.S. Tarr and F.M.
McMurry.   1916.

NT   0042116   PP

Tarr, Ralph Stockman, 1864–1912.
   Alaskan glacier studies of the National geographic society in the Yukutat Bay, Prince William Sound and lower Copper River regions, by Ralph Stockman Tarr ... and Lawrence Martin ... based upon the field work in 1909, 1910, 1911 and 1913 by National geographic society expeditions. Washington, The National geographic society, 1914.
   xxvii, 498 p. front., illus., plates, maps (part fold.) 26½ᵐᵐ. $5.00
   Nine folded maps in pocket at end.
      1. Glaciers—Alaska.   I. Martin, Lawrence, 1880–   II. National geographic society, Washington, D. C.

   Library of Congress   QE576.T2
                                                        14—1287?

       OrP IdPI OrSaW OrCS OrPR WaSpG WaWW MtBuM NN MB ICJ
       OOxM MeB OKentU WaTU CaBVaU CaBVa CaBViPA Wa WaS
       PU–BZ DI ODW OU OC1W   MiU OC1C OO DN ViU OrPS
   NT 0042117   DLC PPF MtU MtBC IdU GAT PBm NRCR MoU

G4371   Tarr, Ralph Stockman, 1864–1912. Alaskan
.C3   glacier studies.
1914
.T3   Tarr, Ralph Stockman, 1864–1912.
              ₍Maps to accompany Alaskan glacier studies of the National Geographic Society in the Yukutat Bay, Prince William Sound and lower Copper River regions, by Ralph Stockman Tarr and Lawrence Martin, based upon the field work in 1909, 1910, 1911 and 1913 by National Geographic Society expeditions. Washington, National Geographic Society, 1914₎

F   Tarr, Ralph Stockman, 1864–1912.
119   Artesian well sections at Ithaca, N. Y.
.5   ₍Chicago₎ Printed at the University of
N54   Chicago press ₍1904₎
v.21   69–82 p. illus. 25cm.
no.7
              "Reprinted from the Journal of geology, vol. XII, no. 2, February–March, 1904."

              1. Artesian wells—Ithaca, N. Y. 2. Geology—New York (State)—Cayuga Lake basin. I. Title.

   NT 0042119   NIC MH

Tarr, Ralph Stockman, 1864–1912.
   Asia and Africa, with review of North America. By Ralph S. Tarr and Frank M. McMurry. New England ed. New York, etc., The Macmillan co., 1901.

   "Tarr and McMurry geographies, fifth part."
   "Five book series."

   NT 0042120   MH

G   Tarr, Ralph Stockman, 1864–1912.
126   Asia and Africa, with review of North
T19A8   America, by Ralph S. Tarr, and Frank M. McMurry. With numerous maps and many illustrations, chiefly photographs of actual scenes. New York, Macmillan, 1903.
              ix, 353–557 p. illus., maps. 19cm.
              (Tarr and McMurry geographies. 5th book)

   NT 0042121   NIC WaSp

Tarr, Ralph Stockman, 1864–1912.
   Asia and Africa, with review of North America by Ralph S. Tarr and Frank M. McMurry. New York, etc., Macmillan co., 1905.

   "Tarr and McMurry geographies."
   At head of title: Fifth part.
   Cover: Five book series. New England supplement.

   NT 0042122   MH

Tarr, Ralph Stockman, 1864–1912.

Geography supply bureau, *Ithaca, N. Y.*
   Catalogue, physical geography lantern slides. Ithaca, N. Y., Geography supply bureau ₍1906?₎

Tarr, Ralph Stockman, 1864–1912.
   The central Massachusetts moraine. [New Haven, 1892]
      5 p.   8°.
   "From the American journal of science, vol. xliii., Feb. 1892," p. 141–145.

   NT 0042124   MH OO

Tarr, Ralph Stockman, 1864–1912.
   College physiography, by Ralph Stockman Tarr ... Pub. under the editorial direction of Lawrence Martin ... New York, The Macmillan company, 1914.
   xxii p., 1 l., 837 p. front., illus., maps, diagrs. 22½ᵐ.
   "References to literature": p. xix–xxii and at end of each chapter.

      1. Physical geography. 2. Geology.   I. Martin, Lawrence, 1880–
                                                        14—17141
   Library of Congress   GB55.T15

                   NjP NN MB NRCR
                   ICarbS ODW OC1ND OLak OC1C OC1W DAL MiU OCU OC1 OU
   NT 0042125   DLC PPLas PBm MiU PU MH KEmT OKentU NcRS

Tarr, Ralph Stockman, 1864–1912.   551.02 R400
   College physiography, by Ralph Stockman Tarr ... Pub. under the editorial direction of Lawrence Martin ... New York, The Macmillan company, 1915.
   xxii p., 1 l., 837 p. front., illus., maps, diagrs. 22½ᵐ.
   "References to literature": p. xix–xxii and at end of each chapter.

   NT 0042126   ICJ OU ViU

Tarr, Ralph Stockman, 1864–1912.
   College physiography; published under the editorial direction of Lawrence Martin.   New York, Macmillan, 1918, c1914.
      837 p.

   NT 0042127   PP PPT

Tarr, Ralph Stockman, 1864–1912.
   College physiography, published under the editorial direction of Lawrence Martin. 1920, [c1914]

   NT 0042128   PU

Tarr, Ralph Stockman, 1864–1912.
   College physiography, by Ralph Stockman Tarr ... Pub. under the editorial direction of Lawrence Martin...N. Y., the Macmillan co. c1914 1921.
      837 p.

   NT 0042129   OO

Tarr, Ralph Stockman, 1864–1912.
   College physiography, n.p. 1923.

   NT 0042130   MiHM

Geology   Tarr, Ralph Stockman, 1864–1912.
Library   College physiography. Published under
GB55   the editorial direction of Lawrence Mar-
T3   tin. New York, Macmillan, 1927 [c1914]
1927   xxii, 837 p. illus., maps (part col.)
           22 cm.
              Includes bibliographies.

              1. Physical geography. 2. Geology.

   NT 0042131   CtY MH

TARR, Ralph Stockman, 1864–1912.
   College physiography. Published under the editorial direction of Lawrence Martin. New York, Macmillan Co., 1928.

   pp. xxii, (2), 837. Front., maps, diagrs., and other illustr.
   "References to literature", at end of each chapter.

   NT 0042132   MH

Tarr, Ralph Stockman, 1864–1912.
   ... A complete geography, by Ralph S. Tarr ... and Frank M. McMurry ... with numerous maps and many illustrations, chiefly photographs of actual scenes. New York, The Macmillan company; London, Macmillan & co., ltd., 1902.
   xxii, 464, x p. illus., plates, maps (part double) 21½ᵐ. (Tarr and McMurry geographies)
   On cover: "Two book series."

      1. Geography—Text-books—1870–   I. McMurry, Frank Morton, 1862–   joint author.

   Library of Congress   G126.T21   2–11747

   NT 0042133   DLC DI–GS KEmT PP

Tarr, Ralph Stockman, 1864–1912.
   ... A complete geography, by Ralph S. Tarr ... and Frank M. McMurry ... with numerous maps and many illustrations, chiefly photographs of actual scenes. New York, The Macmillan company; London, Macmillan & co., ltd., 1902.
   xxii p., 1 l., 478, x p. illus., pl., maps. 21½ᵐ. (Tarr and McMurry geographies)
   On cover: "Two book series."

      1. Geography—Text-books—1870–   I. McMurry, Frank Morton, 1862–   joint author.

   Library of Congress   G126.T22   2–17245

   NT 0042134   DLC DHEW OOxM

Tarr, Ralph Stockman, 1864–1912.
   ... A complete geography, by Ralph S. Tarr ... and Frank M. McMurry ... New York, The Macmillan company; London, Macmillan & co., ltd., 1902.
   xix, 557, xi p. illus., plates, maps (part double) 20ᵐ. (Tarr and McMurry geographies)
   Lettered on cover: Two book series.
   Most of the plates and maps printed on both sides.

      1. Geography—Text-books—1870–   I. McMurry, Frank Morton, 1862–   joint author.

   Library of Congress   G126.T19   2–7114

   NT 0042135   DLC DHEW ICJ

Tarr, Ralph Stockman, 1864–1912.
   Complete geography with numerous maps & many illustrations, chiefly photographs of actual scenes. By Ralph Stockman Tarr, & F. M. McMurry. New York, Macmillan, 1904.
      478 p.   (Tarr & McMurry geographies)

   NT 0042136   PU PBa

La Coll
G
126
T22

Tarr, Ralph Stockman, 1864-1912.
    A complete geography, by Ralph S. Tarr
and Frank M. McMurry. With numerous maps
and many illustrations, chiefly photographs
of actual scenes.   New York, London,
Macmillan, 1905 ₍c1902₎
    xxii, 478, x p. illus., maps. 22 cm.
    (Tarr and McMurry geographies)

    On cover: "Louisiana edition."

    1. Geography--Text-books--1870-   I.
McMurry, Frank   Morton, joint author. II
Title. III.   Series.

NT 0042137   LU NcU PPFr

Tarr, Ralph Stockman, 1864-1912.
    ... A complete geography, by Ralph S. Tarr ...
and Frank M. McMurry ... New York, The
Macmillan company; London, Macmillan & co., ltd.,
1906.
    xxii p., 1 l., 478, x p. illus., plates, maps
(part double) 21 cm. (Tarr and McMurry
geographies)

NT 0042138   ViU WaSp

Tarr, Ralph S₍tockman₎, and F. M. McMurry.   910.7-T
  A complete geography.   New York: The Macmillan Co.,
1908. 478 p.   illus., maps (some col'd), pl. 8°. (Tarr
and McMurry geographies.)

1. Geography. 2. McMurry, Frank   Morton, jt. au.
N.Y.P.L.   September 25, 1918.

NT 0042139   NN CaNSWA

Tarr, Ralph Stockman, 1864-1912.
    A course of study in geography to accompany
the Tarr & McMurry geographies
    see under title

Tarr, Ralph Stockman, 1864-1912, comp.
    A descriptive catalog of twelve hundred lantern slide
illustrations of regional, industrial and commercial geography, selected, comp. and ed. by Profesor R. S. Tarr.
Arranged alphabetically by geographical location and
by topics. Ithaca, N. Y., The Geography supply bureau
₍19—₎
    cover-title, 72 p. 23ᵐᵐ.

    1. Lantern slides—Catalogs. 2. Geography—Teaching.   I. Geog-
raphy supply bureau, Ithaca, N. Y.
                                          E 10-1032

Library, U. S. Bur. of   Education G70.T2

NT 0042141   DHEW

F
119
.5
N54
v.21
no.9

Tarr, Ralph Stockman, 1864-1912.
    Drainage features of central New York.
Rochester ₍N. Y.₎ Geological Society of
America, 1905.
    229-242 p. illus., maps (1 fold.)
25cm.

    From the Bulletin of the Geological
Society of America, v. 16 (1905) p. 229-
242.

    1. Drainage   --New York (State)--
Finger Lakes.   2. Geology--New York
(State)--Fin   ger Lakes. I. Title.

NT 0042142   NIC

Tarr, Ralph Stockman, 1864-1912.
    ... The earth as a whole, by Ralph S. Tarr ... and Frank
M. McMurry ... with many colored maps and numerous
illustrations, chiefly photographs of actual scenes. New
York city ed., enlarged to cover grades 4B, 5A, and 5B.
New York, The Macmillan company, 1908.
    ix, 111-307 p. illus. maps. 19ᵐᵐ. (Tarr and McMurry geographies.
₍The five book series₎ 2d pt.)

    1. Geography—Text-books—1870-   I. McMurry, Frank Morton,
1862- joint author.

Library of Congress   G126.T42   8-4602
                           (Copyright 1908 A 198443)

NT 0042143   DLC DHEW

Tarr, Ralph Stockman, 1864-1912.
    ... The earthquakes at Yakutat bay, Alaska, in September,
1899, by Ralph S. Tarr and Lawrence Martin, with a preface
by G. K. Gilbert. Washington, Govt. print. off., 1912.
    135 p. illus., plates (part fold.) maps (part fold.; 1 in pocket) diagrs.
29½ᵐ. (U. S. Geological survey. Professional paper 69)
    Issued also as House doc. 997, 61st Cong. 2d sess.

    1. Earthquakes—Yakutat bay, Alaska.   I. Martin, Lawrence, 1880-
joint author.   G S 12—371

U. S. Geol. survey. Library   (200) B no. 69
  for Library of Congress   QE75.P9 no. 69
—— Copy 2.   QE535.T3

      OrU ODW DAS NN MB ICJ MiU DLC OCl CU CaBVaU OU
NT 0042144   DI-GS CaBViPA PP PU WaS PPAN PBa OrCS OO

TN
23
T2
1893

in
EarthSci

Tarr, Ralph Stockman, 1864-1912.
    Economic geology of the United States, with
briefer mention of foreign mineral products.
₍2d ed.₎ New York, Macmillan ₍c1893₎
    xx, 525 p. illus. (part fold.) 23cm.

    "Literature of economic geology": p. 457-
465.

    1. Geology. 2. Mines and mineral resources
- U. S. I. Title.

NT 0042145   CoU

Tarr, Ralph Stockman, 1864-1912.
    Economic geology of the United States, with briefer men-
tion of foreign mineral products, by Ralph S. Tarr ... New
York and London, Macmillan and co., 1894.
    xx p., 1 l., 509 p. illus., ii pl. (incl. front.) tab. 22½ cm.
    "Literature of economic geology": p. 457-465.
    "List of authors and works referred to in the text": p. 467-470.

    1. Geology—Economic—U. S. 2. Mines and mineral resources—
U. S.

TN23.T2   -553.0973   4-4717

      OC1W OCl OU NcD
NT 0042146   DLC MtBC NIC PU PPD PHC PPFr MdBP MB ODW

Tarr, Ralph Stockman, 1864-1912.
    Economic geology of the United States, with briefer mention
of foreign mineral products, by Ralph S. Tarr ... New York
and London, Macmillan and co., 1895.
    xx p., 1 l., 525 p. illus., ii pl. (incl. front.) fold. tables. 22½ᵐ.

    "Second edition."
    "Literature of economic geology": p. 457-465.
    "List of authors and works referred to in the text": p. 483-486.

    1. Geology. 2. Mines and mineral resources—U. S.

U. S. Geol. survey. Library   403(200) T18el   G S 16-116
  for Library of Congress   ₍TN23.T   ₎

      ICJ MiHM OU
NT 0042147   DI-GS PCW PU-W WaS IdU NcU PU WaU ViU OO

Tarr, Ralph Stockman, 1864-1912.
    Economic geology of the United States, with
briefer mention of foreign mineral products.
New York, Macmillan co., 1898.
    525p. illus.

NT 0042148   ICRL MtBuM

Tarr, Ralph S₍tockman₎, 1864-1912.   **553**
    Economic geology of the United States, with briefer mention
of foreign mineral products.   New York: The Macmillan Company, 1905.   xx p., 1 l., 525 p., 2 pl., 2 tables. 8°.

    1. Geology. 2. Title.
N.Y.P.L.   **May 29, 1911.**

NT 0042149   NN OCU MiU

Tarr, Ralph Stockman, 1864-1912.
    Elementary geology, by Ralph S. Tarr ... New York, The
Macmillan company; London, Macmillan & co., ltd., 1897.
    xxx, 499 p. incl. front., illus., maps. map. 20ᵐ.

    1. Geology.
                                  4—12869

Library of Congress   QE28.T18
                      ₍a39k1₎   -550

      MiHM ICJ MB CaBVaU
NT 0042150   DLC PP PPAN WaE MH OO OU MiU DI-GS WaSp

Tarr, Ralph Stockman, 1864-1912.
    Elementary geology, by Ralph S. Tarr ...
New York, The Macmillan company; London, Macmillan
& co., ltd., 1899. [c1897]
    xxx, 499 p. 20 cm.

NT 0042151   ViU

TARR, Ralph Stockman, 1864-1912.
    Elementary geology. New York, etc., Macmillan
Co., 1900.

NT 0042152   MH

Tarr, Ralph Stockman, 1864-1912.
    Elementary geology, by Ralph S. Tarr ...
New York, Macmillan, 1902.
    499 p.

NT 0042153   NcRS

TARR, Ralph Stockman, 1864-1912.
    Elementary geology. New York, etc., Macmillan
Co., 1903.

NT 0042154   MH

Tarr, Ralph Stockman, 1864-1912.
    Elementary geology. New York, etc., Macmillan
co., 1904.

NT 0042155   MH OCl

Tarr, Ralph Stockman, 1864-1912.
    ... Elementary geography and the earth as a whole, by
Ralph S. Tarr ... and Frank M. McMurry ... with many colored maps and numerous illustrations, chiefly photographs of
actual scenes. New York, The Macmillan company; London,
Macmillan & co., ltd., 1907.
    xv, 279 p. illus., maps. 19 x 15ᵐ. (Tarr and McMurry geographies.
1st book)
    On cover: Two book series.
    Half-title: Home geography and the earth as a whole.
    1. Geography—Text-books—1870-   I. McMurry, Frank Morton,
1862-1936, joint author.
                                  7—15332

Library of Congress   G126.T28

NT 0042156   DLC OrU ViU DHEW MH

Tarr, Ralph Stockman, 1864–1912.
Elementary geology. New York, etc., Macmillan co., 1910.

NT 0042157 MH

Tarr, Ralph Stockman, 1864–1912.
Elementary geology, by Ralph S. Tarr ... New York, The Macmillan company; London, Macmillan & co., ltd., 1912.
xxx, 499 p. incl. front., illus., maps. map. 20°.
"Reprinted ... September, 1912."

NT 0042158 ViU

Tarr, Ralph Stockman, 1864–1912.
Elementary geography. By Ralph S. Tarr and Frank M. McMurry. New York, etc., Macmillan co. 1913.

At head of title: Tarr and McMurry geographies

NT 0042159 MH

Tarr, Ralph Stockman, 1864–1912.
Elementary physical geography, by Ralph S. Tarr ... New York and London, Macmillan and co., 1895.
xxxi, 488 p. incl. front., illus. maps (part double) diagrs. 20½°.
"Reference books": at end of chapters.

1. Physical geography—Text-books—1870–

G S 20—49

U. S. Geol. survey. Library for Library of Congress
503 T18e
[a41d1]

NT 0042160 DI-GS PWcS OCU TU DAU MB OrU MiU

Tarr, Ralph Stockman, 1864–1912.
Elementary physical geography. New York, etc Macmillan co., 1896.

NT 0042161 MH ViU PU-W PP OU ODW

Tarr, Ralph Stockman, 1864–1912.
Elementary physical geography. xxxi,488 p. 267 il. 1 pl. 9 maps. O. New York: Macmillan Co., 1897.
551.02 P500
10888

NT 0042162 ICJ OC1W PPFr OU MH

Tarr, Ralph Stockman, 1864–1912.
Elementary physical geography ... New York, The Macmillan co.; London, Macmillan & co., ltd., 1899.
488 p.

NT 0042163 PHC

Tarr, Ralph Stockman, 1864–1912.
Elementary physical geography by Ralph S. Tarr.. N. Y., The Macmillan co., Lond., Macmillan & co., ltd.
488 p. illus 1900

NT 0042164 OU

Tarr, Ralph Stockman, 1864–1912.
Elementary physical geography. New York, etc., Macmillan co., 1902.

NT 0042165 MH PU

Tarr, Ralph Stockman, 1864–1912.
Elementary physical geography. New York, 1903.

NT 0042166 NjP

Tarr, Ralph Stockman, 1864–1912.
Elementary physical geography, by Ralph S. Tarr ... New York, The Macmillan company; London, Macmillan & co., ltd., 1907.
xxxi, 488 p. incl. front., illus., diagrs. maps (1 double) charts (part double) 20½°.
"Set up and electrotyped October, 1895. Reprinted ... October, 1907." "Reference books" at the end of each chapter.

1. Physical geography—Text-books—1870–

Library of Congress   GB55.T172   8—19201

NT 0042167 DLC ICRL OCU

Tarr, Ralph Stockman, 1864–1912.
Elementary physical geography. New York, 1909.

NT 0042168 NjP

Tarr, Ralph Stockman, 1864–1912.
Elementary physical geography, by Ralph S. Tarr...N. Y., Lond., The Macmillan co. 1912 c1895.

NT 0042169 OC1

Tarr, Ralph Stockman, 1864–1912.
... Europe and other continents, with review of North America, by Ralph S. Tarr ... and Frank M. McMurry ... New York, The Macmillan company; London, Macmillan & co., ltd., 1901.
xx p., 1 l., 574 p. illus., maps (part double) 19°°. (Tarr and McMurry geographies, 3d book)
"References to books, articles, etc.": p. 542–547.

1. Geography—Text-books—1870– 2. Europe—Descr. & trav. I. McMurry, Frank Morton, 1862–1936, joint author. II. Title.

1—31435

Library of Congress   G126.T186
Copyright A 8591   [a37h1 ̄]   -910

NT 0042170 DLC PBm NIC OLak OC1 DHEW OO OU OCU

Tarr, Ralph Stockman, 1864–1912.
Europe and other continents, with review of North America. By Ralph S. Tarr and Frank M. McMurry. New York, etc., Macmillan co., 1902.
"Tarr and McMurry geographies, third book."

NT 0042171 MH MB DNLM WaSp

Tarr, Ralph Stockman, 1864–1912.
Europe and other continents, with review of North America, by Ralph S. Tarr and Frank M. McMurry. New York, Macmillan Co., 1903.
xx, 574 p. illus. 19cm. (Tarr and McMurry geographies, 3d book)
Includes bibliography.

I. McMurry, Frank Morton, 1862–   Joint author. II. Title.
G126 .T186 1903

NT 0042172 ViU

Tarr, Ralph Stockman, 1864–1912.
Europe and other continents with review of North America. By Ralph S. Tarr and Frank M. McMurry. New York, etc., Macmillan co., 1904.
"Tarr and McMurry geographies, third book."

NT 0042173 MH

Tarr, Ralph S[tockman], and F. M. McMurry.
Europe and other continents, with review of North America.
New York: The Macmillan Company, 1905. xx p., 1 l., 574 p., 20 maps. illus., maps. sq. 12°. (Tarr and McMurry geographies. Third book.)
1864-1912
C910.7

1. Geography. 2. Europe. 3. Mc-
N. Y. P. L.   Murry, Frank Morton, jt. au.   June 6, 1911.

NT 0042174 NN

Tarr, Ralph S[tockman], and F. M. McMurry.
Europe and other continents, with review of North America. With numerous maps and many illustrations, chiefly photographs of actual scenes. New York: Macmillan Company, 1906. xx p., 1 l., 574 p., 23 maps. sq. 12°. (Tarr and McMurry geographies. Book 3.)
1864-1912.

Three book series.

1. Geography.—Text-books, 1906.   2. McMurry, Frank Morton, jt. au.
N. Y. P. L.   December 29, 1911.

NT 0042175 NN MH

Tarr, Ralph Stockman, 1864–1912.
Experimental studies of ice with reference to glacier structure and motion, by the late R.S.Tarr and O.D.von Engeln... Leipzig,Gebrüder Borntraeger[1915]
cover-title,p.[81]–139. illus. 30½°°.
Sonderabdruck aus "Zeitschrift für gletscherkunde" bd.IX,1915,hft.2.
Bibliographical foot-notes.
QE576 f.T22 (G1)

1.Glaciers.

NT 0042176 ICU MtBuM NcU

Tarr, Ralph Stockman, 1864–1912.
First book of physical geography, by Ralph S. Tarr ... New York, The Macmillan company; London, Macmillan & co., ltd., 1897.
xxviii, 368 p. incl. front., illus., diagrs. charts (part fold.) 18½°°.

1. Physical geography—Text-books—1870–

6—15710

Library of Congress   GB55.T175 1897

NT 0042177 DLC PPT Or WaSp MtBC OU ODW OC1W MiU MB
ICJ

Tarr, Ralph Stockman, 1864–1912.
First book of physical geography, by Ralph S. Tarr ... New York and London, The Macmillan company, 1898.
xxviii, 13, 368 p. incl. front., illus. plates, maps (part fold.) diagrs. 18½°°.
On cover: Ohio edition.

1. Physical geography—Text-books—1870–

6—18067

Library of Congress   GB55.T175 1898

NT 0042178 DLC OU MH MB

Tarr, Ralph Stockman, 1864-1912.
First book of physical geography. New York, 1899 ₍c1897₎.
368p. illus.

NT 0042179   ICRL OCU

Tarr, Ralph Stockman, 1864-1912.
First book of physical geography. New York, etc., Macmillan co., 1900.

NT 0042180   MH OClWHi

TARR,Ralph,Stockman,1864-1912.
First book of physical geography. New York, etc.,Macmillan Co.,1901.

NT 0042181   MH PU OO OCl

Tarr, Ralph S₍tockman₎, 1864-1912.
First book of physical geography. New York: Macmillan Co., 1902. 1 p.l., vii-xxviii, 368 p., 2 charts, 14 maps, 2 pl. 12°.

1. Geography (Physical).—Compends   and textbooks.
N.Y.P.L.   May 24, 1912.

NT 0042182   NN MH MB

Tarr, Ralph S₍tockman₎, 1864-1912.   **C551**
First book of physical geography. New York: The Macmillan Co., 1911. xxviii, 368 p., 16 maps (9 col'd, 1 folded), 3 pl. 12°.

1. Physical geography.   CENTRAL CIRCULATION.
N.Y.P.L.   December 12, 1911.

NT 0042183   NN OCl

Tarr, Ralph Stockman, 1864-1912.
... General geography: South America and Europe, by R.S. Tarr and F.M. McMurry. Macmillan, 1903.
Illus. map. (Tarr and McMurry geographies, five book series, 4th book)
"References to books, articles, etc." p. 353-58.

NT 0042184   WaSp

Tarr, Ralph Stockman, and McMurry, F. M.
.... General geography, South America and Europe. 1910. (Tarr and McMurry geographies, fourth part)

NT 0042185   OLak

Tarr, Ralph Stockman, 1864-1912.
Geographies. First book: home geography and the earth as a whole. With many colored maps and numerous illustrations chiefly photographs of actual scenes. New York, 1901.
12°.
I. McMurry, Frank Morton.

NT 0042186   MdBP

Tarr, Ralph Stockman, 1864-1912.
Geographies. Second book: North America, with an especially full treatment of the United States and its dependencies. With numerous maps and many illustrations, chiefly photographs of actual scences. New York, 1900.
12°.
I. McMurry, Frank Morton.

NT 0042187   MdBP

Tarr, Ralph Stockman, 1864-1912.
Geographies. Third book: Europe and other continents with review of North America. With numerous maps and many illustrations, chiefly photographs of actual scenes. New York, 1901.
12°.
I. McMurry, Frank Morton.

NT 0042188   MdBP

Tarr, Ralph S₍tockman₎, and F. M. McMurry.   **C910.7**
Geographies. New York: Macmillan & Co., 1908-09. 5 v. illus., maps, port. 12°. (Five book series.)

   v. 1. Home geography.
   v. 2. The earth as a whole.
   v. 3. North America.
   v. 4. Europe, South America, etc.
   v. 5. Asia, Africa, and review of North America.

1. Geography. 2. North America.   3. Europe. 4. South America.
5. Asia. 6. Africa. 7. McMurry,   Frank Morton, jt. au.
N.Y.P.L.   April 12, 1912.

NT 0042189   NN

₍Tarr, Ralph Stockman₎ 1864-1912.
Geography of science, specially prepared from the Tarr and McMurry series of geographies to meet the requirements of the seventh year in the public schools of the city of New York. New York, London, The Macmillan company, 1905.
vi p., 1 l., 249 p. illus. 19 x 15½ᶜᵐ. (On cover: Tarr & McMurry's geographies)
By Ralph S. Tarr and Frank M. McMurry.

1. Physical geography—Textbooks—1870-   I. McMurry, Frank
Morton, 1862-   joint author.

Library of Congress   G126.T188

                          5—36796

NT 0042190   DLC PP DHEW KEmT ICJ

Tarr, Ralph Stockman, 1864-1912, and F. M. McMurry.
Geography of the city of New York. A supplement to Tarr and McMurry's Home geography specially prepared to meet the requirements for grade 4a in the public schools of all boroughs... New York: Macmillan Co., cop. 1903. 111-178 p. illus., maps. 12°.

Cover-title.

1. Geography—Textbooks, Amer.,   1903. 2. New York (city)—
Geography. I. McMurry, Frank   Morton, 1862- , jt. au.
N.Y.P.L.   November 11, 1930

NT 0042191   NN DLC

GEOLOGY
QE
35
T19

Tarr, Ralph Stockman, 1864-1912.
Geological, etc. articles ₍by₎ R. S. Tarr, 1890-1896. ₍v.p.₎ 1890-1896₎.
43 v. in 1. illus., maps. 25cm.

Title from spine.
Contents.--1. List of duplicate marine invertebrates distributed by the United States National Museum.--2. Gypsum Plains district. --3. A preliminary report on the coal fields of the Colorado River.--4. Drainage systems of New Mexico.--5. Erosive agents in the arid regions.--   6. ₍Review of his₎. On the lower car   boniferous limestone

Continued in next column

Continued from preceding column

Texas.--16. Fifth International Congress of Geologists.--17. Russell's visit to St. Elias.--18. The dismal swamp.--Inundated lands of the United States.--19. River valleys. I-₍VI₎--20. The Permian of Texas. --21. The central Massachusetts moraine.-- 22. Reconnoissance of the Guadalupe Mountains.--23. The   cretaceous covering of the Texas Pal   aeozoic.--24. A hint with respect   to the origin of

terraces in glaciated regions.--25. The relation of secular decay of rocks to the formation of sediments.--26. The effect of topography upon thunderstorms.--27. ₍Review of₎ The realm of nature; an outline of physiography, by H.R. Mill.--28. Acmite trachyte from the Crazy Mountains, Montana, by J.E. Wolff   and R.S. Tarr.--29. Notes on the   physical geography of

Texas.--30. Glacial erosion.--31. Discussion on railroad location.--32. The origin of lake basins.--33. Lake Cayuga a rock basin.--34. The origin of drumlins.--35. Laboratory methods of instruction in geology and physical geography.--36. ₍Review of₎ Major James Rennell and the rise of modern English geogra   phy, by C.R. Markham. 37. Geologic   al history of the

Chautauqua grape belt.--38. ₍Review of₎ Geological biology ... by H. S. Williams.-- The teacher's outfit in physical geography.-- 40. Geography in the university.--41. College entrance requirements in science.-- 42. The physical geography of New York State.--43. The Cornell expedition to Greenland.--

     1. Geology--   Collected works.

NT 0042196   NIC MH-A MBH

TARR,Ralph Stockman,1864-1912.
Glacial erosian in Alaska. n.p.,[1907].

NT 0042197   MH NjP

TARR,Ralph S[tockman],1864-1912.
Glacial erosion in the Finger Lake region of central New York. N.Y.,1906.

NT 0042198   MH

TARR,R₍alph S[tockman],1864-1912.
Glacial erosion in the Scottish Highlands. n.p.,[19-].

NT 0042199   MH NjP

F912
Y2T3
Tarr, Ralph Stockman, 1864-1912.
Glaciers and glaciation of Yakutat Bay, Alaska. By Ralph S. Tarr and Lawrence Martin. [New York, 1906]
23 p. illus., fold. map. 24cm.

Cover title.
Paged also: 145-167.
"Reprinted from Bulletin of the American Geographical Society, vol. XXXVIII, March, 1906."
Errata slip inserted.

NT 0042200   CU-BANC CtY NjP MH

F
119
.5
N54
v.21
no.12
Tarr, Ralph Stockman, 1864-1912.
The gorges and waterfalls of central New York. ₍New York₎ 1905.
20 p. illus., map. 25cm.

"Reprinted from Bulletin of the American Geographical Society, April, 1905."

1. Valleys. 2. Geology--New York (State)--Finger Lakes. I. Title.

NT 0042201   NIC MH

F
119
.5
N54
v.21
no.8

Tarr, Ralph Stockman, 1864-1912.
Hanging valleys in the Finger Lake region of central New York. ₍Minneapolis, Geological Publishing Co., 1904₎
₍269₎-291 p. illus., map. 25cm.

"From the American geologist, May, 1904."

1. Glacial epoch--New York (State)--Finger Lakes. 2. Geology--New York (State)--Finger Lakes. I. Title.

NT 0042202   NIC MH

Tarr, Ralph Stockman, 1864-1912.
... Home geography, and the earth as a whole, by Ralph S. Tarr ... and Frank M. McMurry ... With many colored maps and numerous illustrations, chiefly photographs of actual scenes. New York, The Macmillan company; ₍etc., etc.₎ 1900.
xv, 279 p. illus., maps (part double) 19ᶜᵐ. (Tarr and McMurry geographies. ₍1st book₎)
"Books of reference": p. 256-261.

1. Geography--Text-books--1870-   I. McMurry, Frank Morton, 1862-1936, joint author.
               0--2572

Library of Congress   G126.T18
Copyright 1900 A 8987   ₍a37m1₎   -910

NT 0042203   DLC OC1h MH T OU OEac OCU MiU MB OC1

Tarr, Ralph Stockman, 1864-1912.
... Home geography, and the earth as a whole, by Ralph S. Tarr ... and Frank M. McMurry ... with many colored maps and numerous illustrations, chiefly photograph of actual scenes. New York, The Macmillan company, London, Macmillan & co., ltd., 1901.
xv, 279 p. illus., maps (part double) 19 cm. (Tarr and McMurry geographies, 1st book) "Books of reference": p. 256-261.
1. Geography--Textbooks. I. McMurry, Frank Morton, 1862 - joint author.

NT 0042204   DHEW MH OCU

Tarr, Ralph Stockman, 1864-1912.
Home geography and the earth as a whole. By Ralph S. Tarr and Frank M. McMurry. New York, etc. The Macmillan co., 1902.

"Tarr and McMurry geographies, first book."

NT 0042205   MH MtBC PP OU

Tarr, Ralph Stockman, 1864-1912.
... Home geography. Greater New York ed., by Ralph S. Tarr ... and Frank M. McMurry ... New York, The Macmillan company; London, Macmillan & co., ltd., 1903.
xii p., 1 l., 178 p. illus., maps. 19 x 15¼ᶜᵐ. (Tarr and McMurry geographies)
CONTENTS.--pt. 1. Home geography.--pt. 3. The earth as a whole.--pt. 3. The city of New York.

1. Geography--Text-books--1870-   2. New York (City)--Descr. I. McMurry, Frank Morton, 1862- joint author.
              3--24243
Library of Congress   G126.T183

NT 0042206   DLC WaSp DHEW

Tarr, Ralph Stockman, 1864-1912.
Home geography. By Ralph S. Tarr and Frank M. McMurry. New York, etc., Macmillan co., 1904.

"Tarr and McMurry geographies, first part."

NT 0042207   MH PU

Tarr, Ralph Stockman, 1864-
Home geography and the earth as a whole. By Ralph S. Tarr and Frank M. McMurry. New York, etc., Macmillan co., 1905.

"Tarr and McMurry geographies, first book."
Cover: Louisiana ed.
Appended is "Louisiana", by W.E.Taylor, New York, 1905.

NT 0042208   MH OO

Tarr, Ralph S₍t₎ockman, and F. M. McMurry.   C910.7
Home geography and the earth as a whole. New York: The Macmillan Company, 1907. xiii p., 1 l., 279 p., 20 maps. illus. sq. 12°. (Tarr and McMurry geographies. First book.)

1. Geography. 2. McMurry, Frank Morton, jt. au. 3. Title.
N. Y. P. L.   June 6, 1911.

NT 0042209   NN WaSp

Tarr, Ralph Stockman, 1864-1912.
... Home geography, and the earth as a whole, by Ralph S. Tarr... and Frank M. McMurry.... with many colored maps and numerous illustrations, chiefly photographs of actual scenes. N. Y., The Macmillan co. ₍etc., etc.₎ 1909.
xv, 279 p. illus.

NT 0042210   OO

G126
.T18
1910

Tarr, Ralph Stockman, 1864-1912.
Home geography, by Ralph S. Tarr and Frank M. McMurray. New York, Macmillan Co., 1910.
ix, 112 p. illus. 19cm. (Tarr and McMurry geographies. The five book series, 1st pt.)

1. Geography--Text-books--1870-   I. McMurry, Frank Morton, 1862- jt. author.

NT 0042211   ViU

Tarr, Ralph Stockman, and McMurry, F. M.
... Home geography and the earth as a whole. 1915. (Tarr and McMurry geographies, first book)

NT 0042212   OLak

₍Tarr, Ralph Stockman₎ 1864-1912.
... Introductory geography, comp. by the State text-book committee and approved by the State board of education. Sacramento, W. W. Shannon, supt. of state printing ₍1904₎
x, 312 p. illus., maps. 19ᶜᵐ. (California state series)
A new edition of Tarr and McMurray's Home geography and the earth as a whole, with supplement, California, by Jas. A. Barr and Edward Hughes.
"Books of reference": p. 289-294.

1. Geography. I. McMurry, Frank Morton, 1862- joint author. II. California. State text-book committee. III. Barr, James A. IV. Hughes, Edward. V. Title.
            4--14364
Library of Congress   G126.T182

NT 0042213   DLC DHEW

Tarr, Ralph Stockman, 1864-1912.
... Introductory geography, Tarr and McMurry, rev. by the State text-book committee and approved by the State board of education. Sacramento, W. W. Shannon, superintendent of state printing, 1910.
xv, ₍1₎, 350 p. incl. front., illus. plates, maps. 19ᶜᵐ. (California state series)
Plates and maps printed on both sides.
A new edition of the author's Home geography and the earth as a whole.
"California ... a supplement by James A. Barr and Edward Hughes": p. ₍279₎-325.
"Books of reference": p. 327-332.
1. Geography--Text-books--1870-   I. McMurry, Frank Morton, 1862-1936, joint author. II. California. State text-book committee. III. Barr, James A. IV. Hughes, Edward.
            11--10096
Library of Congress   G126.T1824

NT 0042214   DLC

Tarr, Ralph Stockman, 1864-1912.
Introductory geography. ₍By₎ Tarr and McMurry Revised by the State text-book committee and approved by the State board of education. Sacramento [1914, c.1910]

"California state series."
"8th ed., Oct.1914."

NT 0042215   MH

Tarr, Ralph Stockman, 1864-1912.
A laboratory manual of physical geography, by Professor R. S. Tarr and O. D. Von Engeln ... for use in connection with a general course in physical geography in high and secondary schools and in colleges. New York, The Macmillan company, 1910.
xvii, 362 p. incl. illus., pl., maps, tables, diagrs. plates (partly col.) map. 25 x 21½ᶜᵐ.
17 l. of coördinate paper.
            10--15809
Library of Congress   ✳

NT 0042216   PPPL PBm NIC KEmT ICJ

Tarr, Ralph Stockman, 1864-1912.
A laboratory manual for physical and commercial geography, by Ralph S. Tarr ... and O. D. von Engeln ... For use in connection with courses in physical and commercial geography in high schools, normal schools and colleges. New York, The Macmillan company, 1913.
vii, 214 p., 11 l. incl. illus., maps, diagrs. front., pl. 26ᶜᵐ. $0.80
Title also on recto of front.
11 leaves of coordinate paper at end.
1. Physical geography--Laboratory manuals. 2. Geography, Commercial. I. Engeln, Oscar Diedrich von, 1880-
            13--5446
Library of Congress   GB23.T3

NT 0042217   DLC CaBVaU ICJ PU

Tarr, Ralph Stockman, 1864-1912. A laboratory manual of physical and commercial geography.
Engeln, Oscar Diedrich von, 1880-
A guide for laboratory geography teaching, by O. D. von Engeln ... For use in connection with A laboratory manual of physical and commercial geography, by the late Professor R. S. Tarr and O. D. von Engeln, PH. D. New York, The Macmillan company, 1913.

Tarr, Ralph Stockman, 1864-1912.
A laboratory manual for physical and commercial geography, by Ralph S. Tarr ... and O. B. Von Engeln... New York, The Macmillan company, 1914.
vii, 214 p. maps, tables, diagrs. 26 cm.

NT 0042219   DHEW

L551.4
T19l.2

Tarr, Ralph Stockman, 1864-1912.
A laboratory manual for physical and commercial geography, by Ralph S. Tarr and O. D. von Engeln. For use in connection with courses in physical and commercial geography in high schools, normal schools and colleges. New York, Macmillan Co., 1931.
viii, 241p. illus., maps, diagrs. 26cm.

Title also on recto of front.
11 leaves of coordinate paper at end.

NT 0042220   IEN

Tarr, Ralph Stockman, 1864–1912.
List of duplicate marine invertebrates distributed by the United States National museum. Series IV. Educational series no. 2. Prepared by R. S. Tarr under the direction of Richard Rathbun.

(*In* U. S. National museum. Proceedings. Washington, 1884. 23½ᶜᵐ. v. 6, 1883, p. 212–216)

Issued October 5, 1883.

1. Invertebrates.   I. Rathbun, Richard, 1852–1918.   II. U. S. National museum.

S 32–392

Library, Smithsonian   Institution
Library of Congress   [Q11.U55 vol. 6]

NT   0042221   DSI CaBVaU OU

Tarr, Ralph Stockman, 1864–1912.
[Maps to accompany Alaskan glacier studies of the National Geographic Society in the Yukutat Bay, Prince William Sound and lower Copper River regions, by Ralph Stockman Tarr and Lawrence Martin, based upon the field work in 1909, 1910, 1911 and 1913 by National Geographic Society expeditions. Washington, National Geographic Society, 1914]

9 col. maps 48 x 32 cm. or smaller.

Scale ca. 1 : 63,360 or 1 : 126,720.
"Contour interval 100 feet."

Topography by W. B. Lewis, assisted by E. F. Beam and F. E. Williams.

1. Glaciers—Alaska—Maps.   I. Martin, Lawrence, 1880– joint author.   II. Tarr, Ralph Stockman, 1864–1912. Alaskan glacier studies.   III. National Geographic Society, Washington, D. C.

G4371.C3 1914.T3   Map 53–123

NT   0042223   DLC

F
119
.5
N54   **Tarr, Ralph Stockman,** 1864–1912.
v.21   Moraines of the Seneca and Cayuga lake
no.10   valleys.   Rochester [N. Y.] Geological
            Society of America, 1905.
            215-228 p. illus., map.   25cm.

            From the Bulletin of the Geological
            Society of America, v. 16 (1905) p. 215-
            228.

            1. Moraines. 2. Geology--New York
            (State)--Fing   er Lakes. I. Title.

NT   0042224   NIC MH

Tarr, Ralph Stockman, 1864–1912.   *6260a.15.21
The National Geographic Society's Alaskan Expedition of 1909.
(*In* National Geographic Magazine. Vol. 21, pp. 1–54. Illus. Plates. Maps. Washington. 1910.)

M2571 — Alaska. Geog. — National Geographic Society's Alaskan Expedition, 1909.

NT   0042225   MB OLak

Tarr, Ralph Stockman, 1864–1912.
New complete geography...   New York, The Macmillan company, c1912.
410 p.

NT   0042226   WaWW

Tarr, Ralph Stockman, 1864-1912.
New complete geography, by Ralph S. Tarr...and Frank M. McMurry...With many colored maps and numerous illustrations, chiefly photographs of actual scenes. New York, The Macmillan company, 1918
x, 410 p. illus. maps   24 cm
72258

NT   0042227   DNW PPD

Tarr, Ralph Stockman, 1864-1912.
New complete geography. New York, 1920.
410 p.

NT   0042228   DAL OEac

Tarr, Ralph Stockman, 1864–1912.
New geographies, first[–second] book, by Ralph S. Tarr ... and Frank M. McMurry ... with many colored maps and numerous illustrations, chiefly photographs of actual scenes. New York, The Macmillan company, 1910.

2 v. illus., col. plates, maps.   24ᶜᵐ.

"References to descriptions, in prose and poetry, of topics treated in this geography. For teacher and pupil": v. 1, p. 251–252. "References to books and articles": v. 2, p. 415–423.

1. Geography—Text-books—1870–   I. McMurry, Frank Morton,
1862–1936, joint author.

Library of Congress   G126.T5   10—9935
Copyright A 261270,   261397
                                  [a3801]

OC1
NT   0042229   DLC OrP Wa MoU KEmT PP NcRS PU PP MB NN

Tarr, Ralph Stockman, 1864-1912.
New geographies. Second book, pts. 1-2. By Ralph S.Tarr and Frank M.McMurry.   New York, The Macmillan co., 1911.

Cover: With New England supplement.
Each part has supplement, by Philip Emerson, separately paged at end.

NT   0042230   MH WaS MoU

Tarr, Ralph Stockman, 1864–1912, and **F. M. McMurry.**
New geographies...   By Ralph S. Tarr... and Frank M. McMurry... Book   New York: The Macmillan Co., 1912.   v.   diagrs., illus., maps (part col'd).   8°.

"References to books and articles, v. 2, p. 415–423.

1. Geography.—Textbooks (Ameri-   can), 1912. 2. McMurry, Frank
Morton, 1862–   , jt. au.
N. Y. P. L.   October 20, 1920.

NT   0042231   NN MB MH OrSaW

Tarr, Ralph Stockman, 1864-1912.
New geographies. Second book. By Ralph S. Tarr and Frank M.McMurry.   New York, Macmillan co., 1913.

NT   0042232   MH OC1StM

Tarr, Ralph Stockman, 1864-1912.
New geographies, first-second book, by Ralph S. Tarr ... and Frank M. McMurry.. with many colored maps and numerous illus. chiefly photographs of actual scenes. N. Y. The Macmillan co., 1914-15
v

NT   0042233   OLak PP MH

1864-1912
Tarr, Ralph S[tockman], and F. M. McMurry.   C910.7-T
New geographies; first book.   New York: The Macmillan Co., 1916.   illus.

1. Geography. 2. McMurry, Frank   Morton, jt. au.
N. Y. P. L.   January 10, 1918.

NT   0042234   NN OCU

Tarr, Ralph Stockman, 1864-1912.
New geographies. Second book. By Ralph S. Tarr and Frank M.McMurry.   New York, Macmillan co., 1916.

NT   0042235   MH

1864-1912
Tarr, Ralph S[tockman], and F. M. McMurry.   C910.7-T
New geographies; second book.   New York: The Macmillan Co., 1917.   illus.

1. Geography. 2. McMurry, Frank   Morton, jt. au.
N. Y. P. L.   January 10, 1918.

NT   0042236   NN MH OCU

Tarr, Ralph Stockman, 1864-1912.
New geographies - second book, New York, 1918.

NT   0042237   DN

Tarr, Ralph Stockman, 1864-1912.
New geographies. Books I-II. By Ralph S.Tarr and Frank M.McMurry.   New York, Macmillan co., 1919.

Cover of book II: With New England supplement

NT   0042238   MH OO

Tarr, Ralph Stockman, 1864–1912.
New geographies, first[–second] book by Ralph S. Tarr ... and Frank M. McMurry ... with many colored maps and numerous illustrations, chiefly photographs of actual scenes. New York, The Macmillan company, 1920.

2 v. illus. (incl. ports.) col. plates, maps.   24½ᶜᵐ.

1. Geography—Text-books—1870–   I. McMurry, Frank Morton, 1862– joint author.

Library of Congress   G126.T5 1920
                                              20—13871

NT   0042239   DLC PBa PV DHEW KEmT OrU OrP OC1MN

Tarr, Ralph Stockman, 1864-1912.
New geographies, by Ralph S. Tarr and Frank M. McMurry.   New York, Macmillan, 1920-21 [v. 1, 1921]
2 v.   illus. (part col.) maps (part col.)   24 cm.
On cover: Oregon ed.
"The Oregon supplement": (30 p.) at end of v. 2.
1. Geography. Text-books. 1870-1945.
I. McMurry, Frank Morton, 1862-1936, jt. auth.

NT   0042240   OrU

Tarr, Ralph Stockman, 1864-1912.
New geographies, (second) book by Ralph S. Tarr ... and Frank M. McMurry ... with many colored maps and numerous illustrations, chiefly photographs of actual scenes. New York, The Macmillan co., 1922
1 v. illus.(incl.ports.) col.plates, maps.   24½ cm.

1. Geograph-textbooks. I. McMurry, Frank Morton, 1862- joint author.

NT   0042241   DHEW OC1h MiD MH DLC DN

Tarr, Ralph Stockman, 1864-1912.
New geographies, second book, pt.2, by Ralph
S. Tarr, and Frank M. McMurry. New York, Mac-
millan co., 1923.

On cover: With New England supplement.

NT 0042242   MH

1864-1912.
Tarr, Ralph S[tockman], and F. M. McMurry.   J910.7-T
New geographies; second book. New York: The Mac-
millan Co., 1926.   446 p.   illus., maps.   sq. 8°.

1. Geography. 2. McMurry, Frank   Morton, jt. au.
N. Y. P. L.   February 18, 1928

NT 0042243   NN ViU

1864-1912.
Tarr, Ralph S[tockman], and F. M. McMurry.   J910.7-T
New geographies; first book. New York: The Macmillan
Co., 1927.   264 p.   illus., maps (some fold.), col'd pl., port.
8°.

1. Geography. 2. McMurry, Frank   Morton, jt. au.
N. Y. P. L.   February 18, 1928

NT 0042244   NN

Tarr, Ralph Stockman, 1864-1912.
New geographies, first-second book by
Ralph S. Tarr ... and Frank M. McMurry...
with many colored maps and numerous illus.
chiefly photographs of actual scenes. N.Y.,
The McMillan co., 1930.
v.2 contains Ohio supplement.

NT 0042245   OCl

Tarr, Ralph Stockman, 1864-1912.
New physical geography, by Ralph S. Tarr...
Rev. ed.   New York, The Macmillan company,
1903.
689 p.

NT 0042246   PPCCH

Tarr, Ralph Stockman, 1864-1912.
New physical geography, by Ralph S. Tarr ... New York,
The Macmillan company; London, Macmillan & co., ltd., 1904.
xiii p., 1 l., 457 p. front., illus., plates, map. 19ᵐ.
"Reference books": p. 442.

1. Physical geography—Text-books—1870—   I. Title.
3—32580
Library of Congress   GB55.T19

        00 ODW OCX OCl MB ICJ OC1JC
NT 0042247   DLC WaSp MtBuM MtU PU OKentU DHEW Or OU

La Coll
GB
55   Tarr, Ralph Stockman, 1864-1912.
T19   New physical geography, by Ralph S. Tarr.
1905   New York, London, Macmillan, 1905 [c1903]
         xii, 457 p. illus., map. 19 cm.

On cover: "Louisiana edition."
"Reference books": p. 442.

1. Physical geography--Text-books--1870-
I. Title.

NT 0042248   LU PU

Tarr, Ralph Stockman, 1864-1912.
New Physical geography, by Ralph S. Tarr....
N. Y., Lond., The Macmillan co., 1906.
457 p.

NT 0042249   MiU

Tarr, Ralph Stockman, 1864-1912.
New physical geography, by Ralph S.
Tarr...N. Y., Lond., The Macmillan Co.,
1907. [c1903]
xiii p., 1 l., 457 p.

NT 0042250   OCU

Tarr, Ralph Stockman, 1864-1912
New physical geography, by Ralph S. Tarr
...N. Y., The Macmillan co., Lond., Macmillan & co., ltd., 1908.
457 p.

NT 0042251   MiU

Tarr, Ralph Stockman, 1864-1912.
New physical geography. New York, etc.,
Macmillan co., 1909.

NT 0042252   MH PU

GB55
.T19   Tarr, Ralph Stockman, 1864-1912.
1910   New physical geography. New York, Macmillan
         Co., 1910.
         xvi, 457 p. illus., maps. 18cm.
         "Reference books" at end of each chapter;
         p. 442.

1. Physical geography—Text-books—1870—
I. Title.

NT 0042253   MB OC1W NN ViU NcC MoU OKentU

Tarr, Ralph S[tockman], 1864-1912.   551.4
New physical geography. New York: The Macmillan Co.,
1911.   xvi, 457 p., 16 maps, 104 pl.   illus., maps.   12°.

1. Physical geography.   CENTRAL CIRCULATION.
N. Y. P. L.   October 10, 1911.

NT 0042254   NN

Tarr, Ralph Stockman, 1864-1912.
New physical geography, by Ralph S. Tarr ... New York,
The Macmillan company; London, Macmillan & co., ltd., 1912.
xvi p., 1 l., 457 p. front., illus., plates, map. 19ᵐ.
"Reference books": p. 442.

NT 0042255   ViU MH MB

TARR, Ralph Stockman, 1864-1912.
New physical geography. New York, etc.,
Macmillan Co., 1913.

NT 0042256   MH

Tarr, Ralph Stockman, 1864-1912.
New physical geography, by Ralph S. Tarr ... New York,
The Macmillan company; London, Macmillan & co., ltd.,
1914.
xvi,   457 p. front., illus., plates, map. 19 cm.
"Reference books": p. 442.

NT 0042257   ViU

Tarr, Ralph Stockman, 1864-1912.
New physical geography. New York, Macmillan
co., 1915 [c1903]
457p. illus.

NT 0042258   ICRL ViU OCU

Tarr, Ralph Stockman, 1864-1912.
New physical geography, by Ralph S. Tarr.
New York, The Macmillan company; London,
Macmillan & co., ltd., 1917.
xiii p. 1 l., 457 p. front., illus., plates,
maps, 19 cm.
"Reference books"; p. 442
                              Sept. 20, 1920
1. Physical geography-Text-books-1870-
I. Title

NT 0042259   DAL NcU

Tarr, Ralph S[tockman], 1864-1912.   C551.4-T
New physical geography. New York: The Macmillan Co.,
1919.   illus.

References at end of chapters.

1. Physical geography.
N. Y. P. L.   May 21, 1920.

NT 0042260   NN

TARR, Ralph Stockman, 1864-1912.
New physical geography. New York, etc., Macmillan Co., 1920.

NT 0042261   MH OU

Tarr, Ralph Stockman, 1864-1912.
New physical geography. New York, etc.,
Macmillan co., 1922.

NT 0042262   MH OClUr

Tarr, Ralph S[tockmann], 1864-1912.   J551.4-T
New physical geography. New York: The Macmillan Co.,
1923.   457 p.   charts, illus., maps, pl.   12°.
References at end of chapters.

1. Physical geography.
N. Y. P. L.   April 25, 1927

NT 0042263   NN

Tarr, Ralph Stockman, 1864-1912.
New physical geography, by Ralph S. Tarr...
New York, The Macmillan company; London,
Macmillan & co., ltd., 1924.
xvi, 457 p. front., illus., plates, maps.
19 cm.
"Reference books": p. 442.
On verso of t.-p.: L. H. Jenkins, inc., Richmond,
Virginia.
1. Physical geography – Text-books – 1870-

NT 0042264   ViU OLak

Tarr, Ralph Stockman, 1864–1912.
New physical geography, by Ralph S. Tarr ... and O. D. von Engeln ... Rev. ed. New York, The Macmillan company, 1926.
xi, [1], 689 p. incl. front., illus. maps. 24½ᵐ.
Contains "Reference books".

1. Physical geography — Text-books — 1870-
Diedrich von, 1880-   II. Title.   I. Engeln, Oscar
26—15612
Library of Congress   GB55.T19 1926

DHEW NcRS ODW OClh OC1 ICJ
NT 0042265   DLC PWcS PP WaT WaS OrCS OrMonO Or PP

Tarr, Ralph Stockman, 1864–1912.
New physical geography. New York, Macmillan, 1927, c1903.
457 p.

NT 0042266   PP IdU ViU

Tarr, Ralph Stockman, 1864–1912.
New physical geography; by R.S. Tarr and O. D. von Engeln. Rev. ed.   1928, c1903, 1926.

NT 0042267   PP

GB55
.T19   Tarr, Ralph Stockman, 1864-1912.
1929   New physical geography, by Ralph S. Tarr and O. D. von Engeln. Rev. ed. illus. by B. F. Williamson. New York, Macmillan, 1929.
xi, 688 p. illus., maps. 24cm.
Includes bibliographies.

1. Physical geography—Text-books—1870-
I. Engeln, Oscar Diedrich von, 1880-
II. Title.

NT 0042268   MB

GB
55   Tarr, Ralph Stockman, 1864-1912.
.T19   New physical geography, by Ralph S. Tarr and O. D. von Engeln. Rev. ed. New York, The Macmillan Co., 1931
1926   [c1926]
xi, 689 p. illus., maps. 25 cm.
Contains "Reference books."

1. Physical geography—Text-books—1870-1945. I. Engeln, Oscar Diedrich von, 1880-1965. II. Title

NT 0042269   GAT MB WaSp

Tarr, Ralph Stockman, 1864-1912.
New physical geography, by Ralph S. Tarr... and O. D. von Engeln... Rev. ed. N. Y., The Macmillan co., 1932.
689 p. illus.

NT 0042270   OU

GB55
.T19   Tarr, Ralph Stockman, 1864-1912.
1934   New physical geography, by Ralph S. Tarr and O. D. von Engeln. Rev. ed. Illus. by B. F. Williamson. New York, Macmillan Co., 1934.
xi, 688 p. illus., maps. 24cm.
"Reference books" at end of each chapter;
p. 664-666.

1. Physical geography—Text-books—1870-
I. Engeln, Oscar Diedrich von, 1880-
II. Title.

NT 0042271   MB

ar W   Tarr, Ralph Stockman, 1864-1912.
4919   New physical geography, by Ralph S. Tarr ... and O. D. von Engeln ... Rev. ed. New York, The Macmillan company, 1935
[c1926]
xi, 688 p. illus., maps. 24cm.

Contains "Reference books."

NT 0042272   NIC

Tarr, Ralph Stockman, 1864-1912.
New physical geography, by Ralph S. Tarr and O.D. von Engeln. Revised ed. Illustrations by B.F.Williamson. New York, The Macmillan co., 1937.

xi, 688 p. maps, diagrs., illus. 24 cm.

NT 0042273   MH CaBVaU

Tarr, Ralph Stockman, 1864-1912.
... North America; with an especially full treatment of the United States and its dependencies, by Ralph S. Tarr ... and Frank M. McMurry ... with numerous maps and many illustrations, chiefly photographs of actual scenes. New York, The Macmillan company; London, Macmillan & co., ltd., 1900.
xix, 469 p. illus., maps (part fold.) 18¾ᵐ. (Tarr and McMurry geographies. 2d book)
"References to books, articles, etc.": p. 437-444.
1. North America—Descr. & trav. 2. U. S.—Descr. & trav. 3. Geography—Text-books—1870-   I. McMurry, Frank Morton, 1862-1936, joint author. II. Title.
0-3580
Library of Congress   G126.T184
Copyright 1900 A 14876   [n38d1]   -917

NT 0042274   DLC PPT PBm WaE MH DL MiU MB OU OCU

Tarr, Ralph Stockman, 1864-1912, and Frank Morton McMurry.
1862-
North America, with an especially full treatment of the United States and its dependencies.
New York. The Macmillan Co. 1901. xix, 469 pp. Illus. Plates. Maps. [Tarr and McMurray geographies. Second book.] 18 cm.

K8112 — S.r. — Jt. auth. — America, North. Geog.

NT 0042275   MB

Tarr, Ralph Stockman, 1864-1912.
North America, with an especially full treatment of the United States and its dependencies. By Ralph S.Tarr and Frank M.McMurry. New York, etc., The Macmillan co., 1902.

"Tarr and McMurry geographies, second book."
"Three book series."

NT 0042276   MH DI-GS

Tarr, Ralph Stockman, 1864-1912.
... North America, with an especially full treatment of the United States and its dependencies, by Ralph S. Tarr...And Frank M. McMurry...With numerous maps and many illustration, chiefly photographs of actual scenes. New York, The Macmillan co., 1905.
xix, 469 p. illus., maps (part double) 19 cm.
(Tarr and McMurry's geographies. Second book)

NT 0042277   DNW MH

Tarr, Ralph Stockman, 1864-1912.
...North America, with an especially full treatment of the United States and its dependencies, by Ralph S. Tarr...and Frank M. McMurry...with numerous maps and many illustrations, chiefly photographs of actual scenes. New York, The Macmillan company; London, Macmillan company; London, Macmillan & co., ltd. 1906.
xix 469 p. illus., maps (part double, part fold.)
19 cm (Tarr and McMurry geographies. Third part)
Lettered on cover: Five book series.

NT 0042278   DNW

1864-1912.
Tarr, Ralph S[tockman], and F. M. McMurry.   C910.7
North America, with an especially full treatment of the United States and its dependencies.   New York: The Macmillan Company, 1910.   xix, 469 p., 22 maps.   illus., maps.   sq. 12°.
(Tarr and McMurry geographies.   Book 2.)

1. North America. 2. U. S.—Travel   and description. 3. McMurry, Frank Morton, jt. au.   July 15, 1911.
N. Y. P. L.

NT 0042279   NN

TARR,Ralph Stockman,1864-1912.
Notes on the physical geography of Texas.
[Philadelphia,1893].

pp.(45).
"From the Proceedings of the Academy of Natural Sciences,Philadelphia,Aug.29,1893."

NT 0042280   MH

Tarr, Ralph Stockman, 1864-1912.
Oregon supplement [to Tarr and McMurry's New geographies]
see under title

Tarr, Ralph Stockman.
Our earth as a whole as first book of modern geography part II ... revised and adapted for Canadian schools by W. C. Campbell.   Tor., Morang, 1902.
vi, 257 p. illus., maps. 19.5 cm.

NT 0042282   CaNSWA

Tarr, Ralph Stockman, 1864-1912.
Outlines of excursions in physical geography by R.S. Tarr O.D. con Engeln, J.L. Rich.   Ithaca, New York, Taylor and Carpenter, 1909.
160 p.

NT 0042283   OU

TARR,Ralph Stockman,1864-1912.
The peneplain.   [Minneapolis,Minn.,1898].

pp.(20).
American geologist,1898,6.351-370.

NT 0042284   MH OClWHi

Tarr, Ralph Stockman, 1864-1912.
The Permian of Texas.   [New Haven, 1892]
4 p.   8°.
"From the American journal of science, vol. xliii., Jan. 1892," p. 9-12.

NT 0042285   MH

TARR,Ralph Stockman,1864-1912.
The phenomenon of rifting in granite.   [New Haven,1891].

pp.(6). "dcts.
"From the American Journal of Science,vol.xli April,1891,"pp.267-272.

NT 0042286   MH

Tarr, Ralph Stockman, 1864–1912.
The physical geography of New York state, by Ralph
S. Tarr ... (with a chapter on climate by E. T. Turner)
New York, The Macmillan company; London, Macmillan
& co., ltd., 1902.

xiii, 397 p. illus. fold. pl., maps, fold. chart. 23ᶜᵐ.

"In the main the book is a reprint of the articles as published in the Bulletin of the American geographical society."—Pref.

1. Physical geography—New York (State) 2. Glacial epoch. 3. Great
Lakes. 4. New York (State)—Climate. 5. New York (State)—Descr. &
trav. I. Turner, Ebenezer Tousey.

Library of Congress   QE145.T2   2–15196

OKentU MiU ODW OCU OOxM DNW NjP ICJ MB NN
NT   0042287   DLC MtBuM PBm PU PPAN PP CU NIC NNBG OU

Tarr, Ralph Stockman, 1864–1912.
... The physiographic history of Watkins Glen. By
Ralph S. Tarr ...

(In American scenic and historic preservation society. Eleventh annual report, 1906 ... Albany, 1906. 23ᶜᵐ. app. A, p. (127)-141. 3 pl.)

1. Watkins Glen, N. Y.

Library of Congress   E151.A51 vol. 11   9–22097 Revised
——— Copy 2, detached.   F129.W4T19

NT   0042288   DLC OC1

TARR,Ralph Stockman,and MARTIN,Lawrence.
Position of Hubbard glacier front in
1792,and 1794. [New York],1907.

1.8°.

NT   0042289   MH NjP

Morrill
QL   Tarr, Ralph Stockman, 1864-1912.
1   Postglacial and interglacial (?) changes of
H3   level at Cape Ann, Mass., with a note on the
v.42   elevated beaches, J. B. Woodworth. Cambridge,
no.4   Mass.,1903.
       p.179-196. plates. 25cm. (Harvard University. Museum of Comparative Zoology. /
Bulletin, v. 42, no. 4)

      1. Geology - Massachusetts - Cape Ann.
2. Beaches. I. Woodworth, Jay Backus, 1865-
1925. II· Title   (Series)

NT   0042290   MU MB NjP CtY

QL   Tarr, Robert Stockman, 1864-1912.
1   Postglacial and interglacial (?) changes
H331   of level at Cape Ann, Massachusetts. By
v.42   R. S. Tarr. With a note on the elevated
no.4   beaches. By J. B. Woodworth. Cambridge,
      The Museum, 1903.
      [181]-196 p. 13 plates. 25cm. (Bulletin
of the Museum of Comparative Zoölogy, at
Harvard College, v. 42, no. 4. Geological
series, v. 6, no. 4)

      1. Geology   --Massachusetts--Cape
Ann. 2. Beac   hes. I. Woodworth, Jay
Backus, 1862-   1925.

NT   0042291   NIC

Tarr, Ralph S[tockman] 1864-1912.
... A preliminary report on the coal fields of the Colorado River [Texas] By Ralph S. Tarr ... Austin, State
printing office, 1890.

cover-title, [199]-216 p. 25ᶜᵐ.

At head of title: ... Geological survey of Texas ...
"From first annual report, 1889."

1. Coal mines and mining—Texas.

      G S 5–326

NT   0042292   DI-GS CU MiU

551.31   Tarr, Ralph Stockman and Rich, J. L.
T17p   The properties of ice--Experimental
      studies.   Berlin [1912]
      p.225-49, illus.

      Sonderabdruck aus Zeitschrift für
gletscherkunde, v.6, 1912.

NT   0042293   IU NjP

Tarr, Ralph Stockman, 1864–1912.
Questions for First book of physical geography, by Ralph
S. Tarr ... New York, London, The Macmillan company,
1897.

1 p. l., 56 p. 19½ᶜᵐ.

1. Physical geography—Examinations, questions, etc.

Library of Congress   GB55.T176   6–15709

NT   0042294   DLC NN Or ICJ

TARR,Ralph Stockman,1864–1912.
Recent advance of glaciers in the Yakutat
bay Region,Alaska. New York,1907.

1.8°. pp.(30). Map and plates.
"Bulletin of the Geological Society of
America,vol.18,pp.257-286."

NT   0042295   MH

F912   Tarr, Ralph Stockman, 1864-1912.
Y2T34   Recent changes of level in the Yakutat Bay Region. Alaska.
      Rochester, N. Y., The Society [i. e. Geological Society of
      America] 1906.
      29-64 p. illus. maps. 26cm.

      Cover title.
      Extract from the Bulletin of the Geological Society of
      America, v. 17.
      Provenance: George Davidson.

      1. Geology - Alaska - Yakutat Bay Region. 2. Yakutat
Bay Region. Alaska - Altitudes. I. Title.

NT   0042296   CU-BANC MH

Tarr, R[alph] S[tockman] 1864-1912.
... Reconnoissance of the Guadalupe Mountains. By
R. S. Tarr. Austin, H. Hutchings, state printer, 1892.

42 p. 23½ᶜᵐ. (Texas. Geological survey. Bulletin no. 3)

CONTENTS.— pt. I. Reconnoissance section across the Permian of central
Texas.—pt. II. Geology of the Guadalupe Mountains.—pt. III. Economics of
the Guadalupe Mountains.

1. Geology—Texas—Guadalupe Mountains. 2. Guadalupe Mountains.

Library, U. S. Geol.   survey   G S 5-349

OU MiU OC1 MB
NT   0042297   DI-GS MtBuM MU PP PU GU CU OCU TxU ODW

TARR,Ralph Stockman,1864–1912.
Representation of land forms in the physiography laboratory. n.p.,[1909].

By Ralph Stockman Tarr and A.D.von Engeln.

NT   0042298   MH

Tarr, Ralph Stockman, 1864–1912.
Return to Gloucester Harbor for the young codfish hatched
by the U. S. Fish commission. By R. S. Tarr.

(In Bulletin of the United States fish commission for 1884. Washington, 1884. 22½ᶜᵐ. vol. IV, p. 57-58)

1. Fish-culture. 2. [Codfish] 3. Cod fisheries—Massachusetts.

      F 18—219

U. S. Bur. of fish. Library
   for Library of Congress   [a41b1]

NT   0042299   DI OO

Tarr, Ralph Stockman, 1864–1912.

Tyler, Sydney.
San Francisco's great disaster; a full account of the recent
terrible destruction of life and property by earthquake, fire
and volcano in California and at Vesuvius ... by Sydney Tyler
... With an interesting chapter on the causes of this and
other earthquakes,—growing mountains and volcanos, by
Ralph Stockman Tarr ... Philadelphia, P. W. Ziegler co.
[*1906]

NT   0042300   DI OO

Tarr, Ralph Stockman, 1864–1912.
Second expedition to Yakutat Bay, Alaska. [By] Ralph
S. Tarr ... [Philadelphia, 1907]

cover-title, 14 p. illus. (map) 4 pl. 24½ᶜᵐ.

Reprinted from the Bulletin of the Geographical society of Philadelphia,
January 1907.

1. Yakutat Bay, Alaska.

Library of Congress   F912.Y2T2   20–15304

NT   0042301   DLC NjP

F   Tarr, Ralph Stockman, 1864–1912.
119   Some instances of moderate glacial erosion. [Chicago] Printed at the University
.5   of Chicago press [1905]
N54   160-173 p. illus. 25cm.
v.21
no.11   "Reprinted from The Journal of geology,
      vol. XIII, no. 2, February-March 1905."

      1. Glacial epoch. I. Title.

NT   0042302   NIC MH

TARR,Ralph,[Stockman],1864–1912.
Some phenomenons of the glacier margins in the
Yakutat Bay Region,Alaska. n.p.,1908.

NT   0042303   MH

Tarr, Ralph Stockman, 1864–1912.
South America and Europe, by Ralph S.Tarr and
Frank M.McMurry. New York, etc., Macmillan co.
1905.

At head of title: Tarr and McMurry geographies
Fourth part: general geography.
Cover: Five book series.

NT   0042304   MH

Tarr, Ralph Stockman, 1864–1912.
Suggestions for laboratory and field work in high school
geology and questions for use with Tarr's Elementary geology; by Ralph S. Tarr ... New York, The Macmillan company; London, Macmillan & co., ltd., 1897.

2 p. l., 100 p. 19½ᶜᵐ.

1. Geology—Study and teaching.

      5—5372

Library of Congress   QE40.T19

NT   0042305   DLC NN ICJ NjP

Tarr, Ralph Stockman, 1864–1912.
Syllabus for field and laboratory work in dynamic, structural and physiographic geology (Geology 1) at Cornell university, by Ralph S. Tarr. Ithaca, N. Y., A. W. Stephens, 1902.
152 p. 21ᶜᵐ.
Some of the pages blank.

1. Geology—Field work.   2. Geology—Outlines, syllabi, etc.

Library of Congress   QE45.T19   2–29601
                        (Copyright 1902 A 46546)

NT 0042306   DLC NN OU ICJ

Tarr, Ralph Stockman, 1864–1912.
Tarr and McMurry geographies... by Ralph S. Tarr... and Frank M. McMurry... with many colored maps and numerous illus. chiefly photographs of actual scenes. N. Y., Lond., The Macmillan co. 1900–05.
3 v. illus., maps 19cm

NT 0042307   OCU ICJ

Tarr, Ralph Stockman, 1864–1912.
Tarr and McMurry geographies ... by Ralph S. Tarr ... and Frank M. McMurry ... with numerous illustrations, chiefly photographs of actual scenes. London, New York, The Macmillan company, 1901–05.
5 v. illus., maps. 18½ᵐ.
v. 1, 1905; v. 2, 1901; v. 3–5, 1903.
CONTENTS.—v. 1. Home geography.—v. 2. The earth as a whole.—v. 3. North America ... United States and its dependencies.—v. 4. South America and Europe.—v. 5. Asia and Africa, with review of North America.
1. Africa—Descr. & trav.   2. Asia—Descr. & trav.   3. Europe—Descr. & trav.   4. Geography.   5. North America—Descr. & trav.   6. South America—Descr. & trav.   7. U. S.—Descr. & trav.   I. McMurry, Frank Morton, 1862–   joint author.
                                                   A 10–1661

Title from Minneapolis   Pub. Libr. Printed by L. C.

NT 0042308   MnM NN MH OCU OO

Tarr, Ralph S[tockman], and F. M. McMurry.   910.7
Tarr and McMurry geographies; second book: North America, with an especially full treatment of the United States and its dependencies.   New York: The Macmillan Co., 1910.   xix, 469 p., 15 maps (14 col'd).   illus., maps.   12°.   (Three book series.)

1. U. S.—Geography.   2. America,   North.—Geography.   3. Geography.
4. McMurry, Frank Morton, jt. au.
N. Y. P. L.   May 3, 1911.

NT 0042309   NN

Tarr, Ralph Stockman, 1864–1912.   *6260a.15.13
The teaching of geography.
(*In* National Geographic Magazine. Vol. 13, pp. 55–64. Washington, 1902.)

M2814 — Geography. Study and teaching.

NT 0042310   MB

Tarr, Ralph Stockman, 1864–1912.
Use of lantern slides in the teaching of physiography.   Albany, 1904.
(N. Y. State. Univ. Albany. Bulletin, no. 356, secondary education bulletin, no. 28. p. 14–20.)

NT 0042311   PP

Tarr, Ralph Stockton, 1864–1912.
Washington.   New York, Macmillan, 1906.
55 p.   (Tarr & McMurry geographies Supplementary volumes.)
I. McMurry, Frank Morton, ed.

NT 0042312   PPD WaU WaW WaS

TARR, Ralph Stockman, 1864–1912.
Watkins Glen and other gorges of the Finger Lake region of central New York. [New York], 1906.

NT 0042313   MH

Tarr, Ralph Stockman, 1864–1912, joint author.

Williams, Henry Shaler, 1847–1918.
... Watkins Glenn-Catatonk folio, New York, by Henry S. Williams, Ralph S. Tarr, and Edward M. Kindle. Washington, D. C., U. S. Geological survey, 1909.

TARR, Ralph Stockman, 1864–1912.
Wave-formed cuspate forelands.   n.p., [1898]

NT 0042315   MH–Z

Tarr, Ralph Stockman, 1864–1912.
World geographies ... by Ralph S. Tarr ... and Frank M. McMurry ... with many colored maps and numerous illustrations, chiefly photographs of actual scenes.   New York, The Macmillan company, 1912.
2 v. 24½ᵐ.

1. Geography—Text-books—1870–   I. McMurry, Frank Morton, 1862–   joint author.
Library of Congress   G126.T56   12–11137

NT 0042316   DLC OrP CU KEmT OrU

Tarr, Ralph Stockman, 1864–1912.
World geographies. Second book. By Ralph S. Tarr and Frank M. McMurry.   New York, Macmillan co., 1917.

Cover: With geography of the great war.

NT 0042317   MH

Tarr, Ralph Stockman, 1864–1912.
World geographies ... by Ralph S. Tarr ... and Frank M. McMurry ... with many colored maps and numerous illustrations chiefly photographs of actual scenes.   New York, The Macmillan company, 1918.
2 v. illus., maps. 24ᵐ.
"Texas supplement, by E. G. Littlejohn": 51 p. at end of vol. I.
"The geography of the great war, by Frank M. McMurry": 40 p. at end of vol. II.
1. Geography—Text-books—1870–   2. Texas—Hist.   3. European war, 1914—   I. McMurry, Frank Morton, 1862–   joint author.   II. Littlejohn, Elbridge Gerry, 1862–
                                                   18–23264
Library of Congress   G126.T56 1918

NT 0042318   DLC MH DHEW

Tarr, Ralph Stockman, 1864–1912.
World geographies. Books I-II. By Ralph S. Tarr and Frank M. McMurry.   New York, Macmillan co., 1919.

Cover of book I: With Texas supplement, 53 p. at end.
Cover of book II: Texas edition.

NT 0042319   MH

Tarr, Ralph Stockman, 1864–1912.
World geographies ... by Ralph S. Tarr ... and Frank M. McMurry ... with many colored maps and numerous illustrations chiefly photographs of actual scenes.   New York, The Macmillan company, 1920.
2 v. illus., maps. 24ᵐ.
Lettered on cover: Alabama edition.
"Alabama supplement, by P. W. Hodges ...": 8 p. at end of vol. I and 64 p. at end of vol. II.
1. Geography—Text-books—1870–   2. Alabama—Hist.   I. McMurry, Frank Morton, 1862–   joint author.   II. Hodges, Patrick Wayland, 1872–
Library of Congress   G126.T563A2   20–21486

NT 0042320   DLC DHEW

Tarr, Ralph Stockman, 1864–1912.
World geography.   One-volume ed., by Ralph S. Tarr ... and Frank M. McMurry ... with many colored maps and numerous illustrations, chiefly photographs of actual scenes.   New York, The Macmillan company, 1912.
xiv p., 1 l., 536 p. illus., maps. 24½ᵐ.
Appendix III: References to descriptions, in prose and poetry, of topics treated in this geography, for teacher and pupil: p. 500–510.
1. Geography—Text-books—1870–   I. McMurry, Frank Morton, 1862–   joint author.
Library of Congress   G126.T55   12–1413

NT 0042321   DLC NBuG

Tarr, Ralph Stockman, 1864–1912.
... The Yakutat bay region, Alaska. Physiography and glacial geology, by Ralph S. Tarr.   Areal geology, by Ralph S. Tarr and Bert S. Butler ...   Washington, Govt. print. off., 1909.
183 p. illus., xxxvii pl. (incl. maps, part. fold.) 29½ x 23ᵐ.   (U. S. Geological survey.   Professional paper 64)
1. Geology—Alaska—Yakutat bay region.   2. Physical geography—Alaska.   3. Glaciers—Alaska.   4. Petrology—Alaska.   I. Butler, Bert Sylvenus, 1877–
                                                   G S 9—364
U. S. Geol. survey. Library   (200) B no. 64
for Library of Congress   QE75.P9 no. 64
——— Copy 2.   QE84.Y3T3

           ODW MiU DNW ICJ MB OO OCl DLC
NT 0042322   DI–GS WaS OrCS OrU CaBVaU CaBViPA PU OU

Tarr, S   A   J
Leaf curl disease of cotton.   Kew, Surrey, Commonwealth mycological institute, 1951.
55 p.   illus. map.
"References": p.53–55.

1. Mosaic disease.   I. Commonwealth mycological institute, Kew.   II. Title.

NT 0042323   CU NIC IdU TxCM DNAL IU LU TU

Tarr, Sydney Albert John.
The fungi and plant diseases of the Sudan, by S. A. J. Tarr.   Kew, Surrey, Commonwealth Mycological Institute, 1955.
x, 127 p. illus. 25 cm.
Bibliography: p. 111.

1. Fungi, Phytopathogenic—Sudan.   2. Plant diseases—Sudan.
I. Title.
QK610.S8T37   589.2'046509624   74–151732
                                                   MARC

NT 0042324   DLC IdU MH–F NNBG CU LU NIC DNAL NcU TU

Tarr, W
Paysans et parti en U.R.S.S. [Paris, 1955]
47 p.   (Les amis de la liberté, nos.53–55, oct.-nov.- dec., 1955)

NT 0042325   MH

Law

Tarr, Walter L., 1908–　ed.

FOR OTHER EDITIONS
SEE MAIN ENTRY

Ohio. *Laws, statutes, etc.*
Anderson's Ohio school code, annotated; Sections 4830 to 4872 inclusive of the General Code of Ohio and other sections pertaining to schools and colleges. Edited by **Walter L. Tarr** and Harold G. Edwards. Cincinnati, Anderson ₁1950₎

LB2529
.O2
1943

Tarr, Walter L., 1908–　ed.

Anderson (W. H.) company, *Cincinnati.*
Anderson's Ohio school code; sections 4830 to 4863–7 inclusive of the General code of Ohio and other sections pertaining to schools and colleges, with comments by Walter L. Tarr ... and Harold G. Edwards ... Cincinnati, The W. H. Anderson company ₁1943₎

Tarr, William Arthur, 1881–1939.
... The barite deposits of Missouri and the geology of the barite district ... by William Arthur Tarr ... Columbia, Mo., University of Missouri, 1918.

2 p. l., vii–xi, 111 p.   10 pl. (2 fold.; incl. map)   27ᶜᵐ.
Thesis (PH. D.)—University of Chicago, 1916.
"Science series, vol. III, no. 1, the University of Missouri studies."
Bibliography: p. 106–111.

1. Barite. 2. Geology—Missouri.

18–22913

Library of Congress　　　　TN948.B18T3
Univ. of Chicago Libr.

NT 0042328　　ICU PU OrU DLC NIC MoU ViU

Tarr, William Arthur, 1881–1939.
... The barite deposits of Missouri and the geology of the barite district ₁by₎ William Arthur Tarr ... Columbia, Mo., University of Missouri ₁1918₎

2 p. l., vii–xi, 111 p.   10 pl. (2 fold.; incl. map)   27ᶜᵐ. (The University of Missouri studies. vol. III, no. 1. Science series)
Published also as thesis (PH. D.) University of Chicago, 1916.
Bibliography: p. 106–111.

1. Barite. 2. Geology—Missouri.

Library of Congress　　　　TN948.B18T32

18—27342

VtU NcU OU OCU MiU ICJ MB NN
NT 0042329　　DLC WaS PBm PPAmP MoU NIC NcRS MeB UU OO

Tarr, William Arthur, 1881–1939, joint author.

FOR OTHER EDITIONS
SEE MAIN ENTRY

Branson, Edwin Bayer, 1877–
Introduction to geology, by E. B. Branson ... and W. A. Tarr ... 2d ed. New York and London, McGraw-Hill book company, inc., 1941.

Tarr, William Arthur, 1881–1939.
Introductory economic geology, by W. A. Tarr ... 1st ed. New York ₁etc.₎ McGraw-Hill book company, inc., 1930.

ix, 664 p.   illus., diagrs.   24ᶜᵐ.
Contains "Selected readings" and bibliographical foot-notes.

1. Geology, Economic.

Library of Congress　　　　TN260.T3
—— —— Copy 2.
Copyright A 26874　　　　₁5₎

30–22318

553

OU OCU DAL OC1W OC1 CU MiU MB MH WaT Wa Or MtBuM
NT 0042331　　DLC ViU PP PBm PWcS MoU NcD NcC NN ODW

Tarr, William Arthur, 1881–1939.
Introductory economic geology, by W. A. Tarr ... 2d ed. New York and London, McGraw-Hill book company, inc., 1938.

xi, 645 p.   illus., diagrs.   23½ᶜᵐ.
Includes "Selected readings."

1. Geology, Economic.

38–13982

Library of Congress　　　　TN260.T3 1938
—— —— Copy 2.
Copyright A 117742　　　　₁5₎　　　　553

GAT TU OC1 OLak OU OC1W Or
NT 0042332　　DLC PPF PBm NcRS NcD CaBVaU WaE WaT WaS

Tarr, William Arthur, 1881–1939.
... The origin of chert and flint, by William Arthur Tarr ... Columbia, The University of Missouri, 1926.

vi, 54 p.   incl. illus., x pl. on 4 l.   26½ cm. (₁Missouri. University₎ The University of Missouri studies; a quarterly of research ... v. 1, no. 2)
Bibliography: p. 45–46.

1. Chert. 2. Flint.

QE391.C4T3　　　　　　　　　　27—23591
—— Copy 2.　　　　AS36.M82　vol. 1, no. 2

CaBVaU OrSaW
MiU ViU OC1 NSyU MU MoU PSt WaTU WaS OrPR OrU
NT 0042333　　DLC PHC PU NcD FTaSU NIC OU OO OCU OC1W

Tarr, William Arthur, 1881–1939.
... A study of the effects of heat on Missouri granites, by W. A. Tarr ... assisted by L. M. Neuman ... Columbia, Mo., University of Missouri, 1914.

64 p.   incl. plates, tables, diagrs.   22½ᶜᵐ. (The University of Missouri bulletin. v. 15, no. 27.   Engineering experiment station ser. 14)
Bibliography: p. 64.

1. Granite—Missouri.　　ɪ. Neuman, Leo Murry.

14–31795

Library of Congress　　　　TA428.G7T3

NT 0042334　　DLC MoU ViU MiU OU OC1 ICJ

Tarr, William Arthur, 1881–1939.
Tables for the determination of the common minerals and rocks, by W. A. Tarr ... ₁Columbia, Mo., The Herald-statesman publishing co., ₁1914₎

cover-title, 3–18 p.   23ᶜᵐ.
Text on p. 2 of cover.

1. Mineralogy, Determinative. 2. Rocks.　ɪ. Title.

14–11817

Library of Congress　　　　QE367.T2

NT 0042335　　DLC MoU ICJ

Tarr, William Arthur, 1881–1939.
Tables for the determination of the common minerals and rocks, by W. A. Tarr ... Rev. and enl.   Columbia, Mo., For sale by the University co-operative store, 1916.

25, ₁3₎ p.   17ᶜᵐ. $0.40

1. Mineralogy, Determinative.　2. Rocks.　ɪ. Title.

17–3164

Library of Congress　　　　QE367.T2 1916

NT 0042336　　DLC MiU

Tarr, William Arthur, 1881–1939.
Tables for the determination of the common minerals and rocks, by W. A. Tarr ... Rev. and enl.   Columbia, Mo., The Missouri book company, 1921.

32 p.   17ᶜᵐ.

1. Mineralogy, Determinative. 2. Rocks.　ɪ. Title.

21—1209

Library of Congress　　　　QE367.T2 1921

NT 0042337　　DLC Or DI-GS

Tarr, William Arthur, 1881–1939.
Tables for the determination of common minerals and rocks, by W. A. Tarr ... Rev. and enl. Columbia, Mo., Lucas brothers, 1931.

31, ₁1₎ p.   17ᶜᵐ.

1. Mineralogy, Determinative. 2. Rocks.　ɪ. Title.

36–19700

Library of Congress　　　　QE367.T2 1931　　549.1

NT 0042338　　DLC

Tarr, William Arthur, 1881–1939.
... Terminology of the chemical siliceous sediments, by W. A. Tarr. Washington, D. C., National research council, Division of geology and geography. 1936.

2 p. l., 26 p.   28ᶜᵐ.
At head of title: Committee on sedimentation, Subcommittee on nomenclature and classification of sediments.
"Preliminary edition (subject to revision)"
Mimeographed.
Bibliographical foot-notes.
1. Sedimentation and deposition. 2. Rocks, Sedimentary.　ɪ. National research council. Committee on sedimentation. Subcommittee on nomenclature and classification of sediments. ɪɪ. Title. ɪɪɪ. Title: Siliceous sediments, Terminology of the chemical.

G S 37–254

U. S. Geol. survey. Library　　　　213　qT17tc
for Library of Congress　　　　₍QE581.T　₎

NT 0042339　　DI-GS

Tarr, Wilson Edwin.

American management association.
... Efficiency and economy in office procedures, by W. E. Tarr ... W. F. Titus ... Morton P. Francis ... ₁and others₎ New York, N. Y., American management association, *1938.

Tarr & McMurry's geographies
see under Tarr, Ralph Stockman, 1864–1912.

Tarr Homestead Oil Company, Venango Co.,
Pennsylvania.
Description of Property, &c.   Philadelphia, 1865.
11 p.

NT 0042342　　PHi

Tarr Pub. Co., Cleveland.
Cleveland pocket business and street directory
see under title

Tarra, Spanish monk.   About 600 A.D.　　　　*B.122.4
Epistola Tarræ ad Recaredum regem.
(In Patrologiæ cursus completus.   Scriptores Latini.   Series secunda.   Tomus 80, col. 19–20.   Parisiis.   1850.)

K4535 — Reccared I.. King of the Visigoths.　–601.

NT 0042344　　MB

Tarr, Giulio.
Libro di lettura e di premio.   Dialoghi famigliari e scenici ad uso dei fancinlli italiani in iscola ed in famiglia.   Milano, G. Messagi, 1876.
192 p.   12°.
Binder's title: Tarra-Thouar: Dialoghie Teatro.

NT 0042345　　NN

Tarra, Giulio.
Parte seconda delle letture graduate al fanciullo italiano, disposte nell' ordine intellettuale, progressivo, morale e linguistico e ad avviamento al comporre. Letture proposte per la 3a classe elementare... Quinta ristampa, fatta sulla 4a edizione ridotta... Milano: G. B. Messaggi. 1898-99. xviii, 182 p. 12°.

I. Italian language.—Exercises etc.
N. Y. P. L.   September 10, 1912.

NT 0042346   NN

Tarra, Giulio.
The pure oral method, the best for the teaching of all deaf children; translations from the writings, speeches, and correspondence of Giulio Tarra. London, W.H. Allen, 1883.
vol.7-39p. 22cm.

Published by the Society for Training Teachers of the Deaf and Diffusion of the "German" System in the United Kingdom.

NT 0042347   KU-M DNLM

[Tarrab, Isaac]
'... Recherches sur les massifs pulvérulents à paroi inclinée et talus plan. Application de la méthode de Boussinesq ... Paris, 1938.
63, [1] p. incl. tables, diagrs. 24ᵐ.
Thèse—Univ. de Paris.

1. Soils (Engineering) 2. Mechanics, Applied. I. Title.
43-28729
Library of Congress   TA710.T3

NT 0042348   DLC CtY

TARRACA, Gregorio.
Formularium diversorum instrumentorum, contractum et ultimarum voluntatum juxta magis communem stilem notariorum civitatis & regni Valentiae. [Valentiae], 1643.

NT 0042349   MH-L

Ṭarrād, Mīshāl
see
Ṭrād, Mīshāl, 1912-

Tarrade, Adrien, 1844-
Des principaux champignons comestibles et vénéneux de la flore limousine, suivi d'un précis des moyens à employer dans les cas d'empoisonnement par les champignons, par Adrien Tarrade ... 2.éd., revue et augmentée ... Paris, J.-B.Baillière et fils; [etc.,etc.] 1874.
3 p.l.,[3]-138 p. VI col.pl. 19ᶜᵐ.

1.Mushrooms--France--Limousin.

NT 0042351   MiU

Tarrade (Adrien - Clotaire - Florentin - Jean) [1884-]. *Une épidémie de méningite cérébro-spinale à Limoges en 1809. [Bordeaux.] 44 pp. 8°. *Limoges, J. Rippe, 191]

NT 0042352   DNLM

Tarrade (Amédée) [1881-⁻⁻]. *De la ponction lombaire dans le traitement du rheumatisme cérébral et de certains exsudats méningés. 62 pp. 1 tab. 8°. *Paris, 1907, No. 324.

NT 0042353   DNLM

Tarrade (Firmin). *De la tuberculose inoculée par la muqueuse buccale; de l'efficacité des phosphates de chaux dans son traitement. 30 pp. 8°. *Paris, 1897, No. 484.

NT 0042354   DNLM

Tarrade (Jean). *Considérations sur l'hygiène dentaire dans les établissements d'enseignement. 46 pp., 1 l. 8°. *Paris, 1901, No. 451.

NT 0042355   DNLM

Tarrade, Jean.
La résistance et la libération de Civray. Maquis D2 Bayard. Préface de M.R.Bonnet. Civray Vienne, L'auteur [1946]

NT 0042356   MH

282 **Tarradeflot Cornet, Ignazio.**
T688c Cor Iesu praedicandum, seu, Expositio oratoria litaniarum S.S.Cordis Iesu. Romae, Desclée, Lefebvre, 1903.
511p. 23cm.

1.Sacred Heart, Devotion to. I. Title. LC.

NT 0042357   CLSU

Tarradell, Miguel
see
Tarradell i Mateu, Míquel, 1920-

Tarradell i Mateu, Miquel, 1920-
Las actividades arqueológicas en el Protectorado Español en Marruecos. Zaragoza [IV Congreso Internacional de Ciencias Prehistóricas y Protohistóricas] 1953 [i. e. 1954]
37 p. illus. 20 cm.
Summary in English.
Bibliography : p. [26]-27.

1. Morocco (Spanish Zone)—Antiq. I. Title.
DT330.T37   55-22276 rev

NT 0042359   DLC NIC CU TNJ

4DP Tarradell i Mateu, Miquel,1920-
Span. Guía arqueológica del Marruecos
196 Español. Tetuán, Instituto General Franco de Estudios e Investigación Hispano-Árabe, 1953.
43 p.

NT 0042360   DLC-P4 MH-P MH

DT311 Tarradell i Mateu, Miquel,1920-
.T3 Museo Arqueológico de Tetuán; guía sumaria para el visitante, con un apéndice sobre los principales yacimientos arqueológicos del Protectorado. [Madrid, Artes Gráficas Martorell, 1950?]
[28]p. illus. 25cm.
Includes bibliography.

1. Tetuán, Morocco. Museo Arqueológico.

NT 0042361   NNU

Tarradell i Mateu, Miquel,1920-
El paleolítico del Río Martín. Tetuan, Editora Marroquí,1951.
46 p. IX plates,maps(1 fold.),plans. 24cm. (Morocco(Spanish). Servicio de Arqueología. Memorias,12)
At head of title: M.Tarradell - J.Garriga Pujol.
[Published under the auspices of] Instituto General Franco de Estudios e Investigación Hispano-Árabe.

NT 0042362   MH-P

qG332.40982 Tarradellas, Elías D
T176n Un nuevo dinero argentino de circulación internacional: garantía de cheque dinero. Opinan: G.E. Cole [et al. Por] Elías D. Tarradellas. [Buenos Aires, Impr. "Rex", 1952]
149p. illus. 32cm.

Bibliography: p.147-149.

1. Paper money – Argentine Republic. I. Title. II. Title: Garantía de cheque dinero.

NT 0042363   TxU

Tarradellas, José
see
Tarradellas, Josep, 1899-

Tarradellas, Josep, 1899-
... Cataluña en la política española. París [Imprimerie S. P. I., 1946.
1 p. l., 5-31 p. 18ᶜᵐ.
"Texto castellano de la conferencia dada en catalán el día 21 de abril en Tolosa y publicada en 'La Humanitat,' de Perpiñán, del 30 de abril de 1946."

1. Catalonia—Pol. & govt. 2. Spain—Pol. & govt. I. Title.
DP302.S62T28   946.7   47-23416

NT 0042365   DLC

Tarradellas, Josep, 1899-
HJ1249 **Catalonia.** *Departament de finances.*
.C3A5 The financial work of the generalitat of Catalunya; discourse
1938 pronounced by the honourable the councillor of finances, Josep Tarradellas, in the Parliament of Catalunya during the session of the 1ˢᵗ of March 1938. Barcelona, 1938.

Tarradellas, Josep, 1899–
L'obra financera de la Generalitat de Catalunya; discurs pronunciat al Parlament de Catalunya en la seva sessió del 1.ʳ de març del 1938. Barcelona, 1938.

58 p.   28 cm.

Published also in English.

1. Finance, Public—Catalonia.   ɪ. Title.

HJ1429.C3T3   65–59994

NT 0042367   DLC

Tarradellas, Josep, 1899–

Catalonia. *Departament de finances.*
L'œuvre financière de la généralité de Catalogne; discours prononcé par l'honorable conseiller des finances, m. Josep Tarradellas au Parlement de Catalogne au cours de la séance du 1.ᵉʳ mars 1938. Barcelone, 1938.

[Tarradellas, Josep] 1899–
La politique financière de la généralité pendant la Révolution et la Guerre. 19 Juillet – 19 Novembre
see under   Catalonia. Departament de Finances.

W   **Tarradellas, Juan René**
4   Consideraciones radiológicas en el pneumo-
392   pericardias terapéutico. Buenos Aires,
No.4492 Gir ₁1931₎
        61 p. illus. (Buenos Aires. Universidad
        Nacional. Facultad de Ciencias Médicas.
        Tesis. no. 131 ₁i.e. 4492₎)

        Bibliography: p. ₁60₎-61

NT 0042370   DNLM

Tarradellas, Juan René.
... Títulos, trabajos y labor docente, concurso de profesor adjunto de radiología y fisioterapia. Buenos Aires, 1942.

27 p. 28ᶜᵐ.

                                        43–5963
                                   Brief cataloging
Library of Congress   R488.T3A35

NT 0042371   DLC

Tarrades, Abdon
see
Terradas, Abdón.

Tarræus Hebius, pseud.
see Barth, Kaspar von, 1587–1658.

Tarraf, Chams Eldine
Ndm85   ... La restriction au droit de grève en
G5   Angleterre ... Paris,Librairie du Recueil Sirey,
929t   1929.
        2p.ℓ.,[7]-185p.,1ℓ.   25½cm.
        Thèse - Univ. de Paris.
        "Bibliographie": p.[181]-182.

        x.Chams Eldine Tarraf.   1.Strikes and
        lockouts - Gt.Brit.   Card for Law school.

NT 0042374   CtY MH-L

Tarrafa, Franciscus.
See
Tarafa, Francisco, fl. 1550.

Tarragato, Eugenio.
See
Tarragato y Contreras, Eugenio, 1896–

Tarragato y Contreras, Eugenio, 1896–
... La afinidad ... Prólogo de Jerónimo González, introducción de Max Gmur. Madrid, Góngora ₁1923₎

2 p. l., ₁7₎-264, ₁2₎ p. 19ᶜᵐ.

Tesis—Madrid.
At head of title: Universidad central, Facultad de derecho.
"Bibliografía": p. ₁241₎-258.

1. Consanguinity.   2. Marriage law.   3. Canon law.   ɪ. Title.

                                        29–5152 Revised

NT 0042377   DLC

Tarragato y Contreras, Eugenio, 1896–
... La afinidad; estudio histórico y de derecho comparado, por Eugenio Tarragato; prólogo de Jerónimo González; introducción de Max Gmur ... Madrid, Góngora, 1925.

2 p. l., ₁7₎-264, ₁2₎ p. 19½ᶜᵐ. (*Added t.-p.:* Biblioteca de derecho, sociología y política, dirigida por el prof. Quintiliano Saldaña. ₍vol. ɪᴠ₎)

Series title also at head of t-p.
The author's Nuevas doctrinas de derecho de familia. ɪɪ.
Issued also as thesis, Madrid.
"Bibliografía": p. ₁241₎-258.

1. Consanguinity.   2. Marriage law.   3. Marriage (Canon law)
4. Comparative law.   ɪ. Title.

                                        37–8268

NT 0042378   DLC

Tarragato y Contreras, Eugenio, 1896–
... El divorcio en las legislaciones comparadas, por Eugenio Tarragato, prólogo de Quintiliano Saldaña, introducción de Wilhelm Kahl ... Madrid, Centro editorial de Góngora, 1925.

lxxxvii, 240 p., 2 l. 19ᶜᵐ. (*Added t.-p.:* Biblioteca de derecho, sociología y política. ₍vol. ɪɪɪ₎)

At head of title: ... Nuevas doctrinas del derecho de familia ... 1.
"Bibliografía :" p. ₁209₎-232.

1. Divorce. 2. Law, Comparative.   ɪ. Saldaña y García Rubio,
Quintiliano, 1878–   ɪɪ. Title.

                                        27–7820

NT 0042379   DLC

Tarragato y Contreras, Eugenio, 1896–
...Nuevas doctrinas del derecho de familia...por Eugenio Tarragato, prólogo de Quintiliano Saldaña, introducción de Wilhelm Kahl... ₍ᴠ.₎ 1–   Madrid: Centro editorial de Góngora, 1925– .   v.   12°.   (Biblioteca de derecho, sociología y política. v. 3.

Bibliography, v. 1, p. ₁209₎-232.
Contents: ₍ᴠ.₎ 1. El divorcio en las legislaciones comparadas.

1. Divorce—Jurisp. 2. Saldaña y   García Rubio, Quintiliano, 1878–
3. Ser.
N. Y. P. L.   March 24, 1928

NT 0042380   NN MH-L

Tarragato y Contreras, Eugenio, 1896–
...Los sistemas económicos matrimoniales (estudio histórico y de derecho comparado), por Eugenio Tarragato, prólogo de Felipe Clemente de Diego.   Madrid: Editorial Reus (s. a.), 1926.
xix, 116 p.   8°.   (Nuevas doctrinas del derecho de familia. ₍ᴠ.₎ 3.)

Bibliography, p. ₁109₎-111.

ɪ. Property of married persons—   Jurisp.
N. Y. P. L.   February 6, 1928

NT 0042381   NN MH-L CtY

Tarragó, Agustín Prim.
see Prim Tarragó, Agustín.

Tarragó, Agustín Rius y
see Rius y Tarragó, Agustín.

Tarragó, Alejandro, 1907–
... Exploremos el cielo (visión sintética y actual del universo) Ilustraciones de Romera; 3 láminas, 20 fotografías, 60 esquemas. Santiago de Chile, Ediciones Ercilla, 1941.

5 p. l., ₁13₎-182 p., 1 l.   illus., plates (part fold.) diagrs. 22ᶜᵐ.

1. Astronomy.   ɪ. Title.

                                        43–39887
Library of Congress   QB44.T26
                          ₍2₎   523

NT 0042384   DLC DPU

Tarragó, Emeterio.
Conferencia sobre riegos en la provincia de Catamarca, por Emeterio Tarragó...   Buenos Aires, 1908.   24 p.   illus. 8°. (Argentine Republic. Enseñanza Agrícola, Dirección General de. ₁Bol.₎ Serie 2, no. 14.)

1. Irrigation, Arg. Rep.: Catamarca.   2. Series.
N. Y. P. L.   May 6, 1918.

NT 0042385   NN

Tarragó, Ernesto
see
Tarragó M   , **Ernesto.**

M   **Tarrago, Graciano,** 1892–
125   [Guitar works. Selections]
T176g   [Collection of original guitar compositions
         and guitar arrangements in UCLA's Ernie Ball
         Guitar Music Collection. n.p., n.d.]
         25v. in 1

         1. Guitar music. 2. Guitar music, Arranged.

NT 0042387   CLU

M 126*   **Tarragó, Graciano,** 1892–   ed.
T37 M5   Minuetto (Haydn) La alegría del labrador
         (Schumann) Las cuatro notas (F. Sors)
         Barcelona, Editorial Boileau, c1955.
         3 p. 32 cm. (Obras clásicas y modernas)
         Pl. no. 1952.
         Caption title.
         1. Guitar music. 2. Guitar music, Arranged.
         I. Haydn, Joseph, 1732–1809. Minuet, guitar, D
         major. II. Schumann, Robert Alexander, 1810–
         1856. Album für die Jugend. No. 10, Fröh-
         licher Landmann; arr. III. Sors, Fernando,
         1778–1839. Las   cuatro notas.

NT 0042388   OU

Tarragó, José, ed.

Rodríguez, Alonso, *Saint,* 1531–1617.
Magisterio espiritual, ascético y místico, de s. Alonso Rodríguez, s. J., por el José Tarragó ... Barcelona, Librería religiosa, 1935.

Tarragó, Julian Ribera y.
see Ribera y Tarragó, Julian, 1858-1934.

Tarragó, P   Bohigas
see Bohigas, Tarragó, P

Tárrago, Torcuato
see Tárrago y Mateos, Torcuato, d. 1889.

Tarragó M   , Ernesto.
Fugas. Prólogo por Leonardo Pasquel. ¡1. ed. México¡ Ediciones Tonatiuh ¡1955¡
413 p. 18 cm. (Cultura mexicana)

ɪ. Title.

AC75.T27   56-27900 ‡

NT 0042393   DLC PSt NN CU CU-BANC

Tarragó Pleyan, José Alfonso.
Aportación a la bibliografía ilerdense de los siglos XVI al XVIII
see under Spain. Consejo Superior de Investigaciones Científicas. Instituto de Estudios Ilerdenses.

Tarragó Pleyán, José Alfonso.
Buenaventura Corominas y Escaler, impresor, grabador y librero en Lérida: su producción tipográfica (1815-1841) Lérida, Imprenta-Escuela Provincial, 1950.
65 p. illus. facsims. 24 cm.
At head of title: Instituto de Estudios Ilerdenses de la Excma. Diputación Provincial de Lérida. Delegación del Consejo Superior de Investigaciones Científicas.
Correction slip mounted on p. 40.

1. Corominas, Buenaventura, d. 1841.

Z232.C793T3   54-43221

ɪ1ɪ

NT 0042395   DLC

Tarragó Pleyán, José Alfonso.
Ediciones leridanas del Beato fray Diego José de Cádiz
see under Spain. Consejo Superior de Investigaciones Científicas. Instituto de Estudios Ilerdenses.

Tarragó Pleyán, José Alfonso.
Indice de la bibliografía ilerdense; ensayo recopilador de libros, folletos, hojas, artículos de publicaciones periódicas y trabajos manuscritos que tratan de la bibliografía ilerdense. Nota proemial del Dr. Felipe Mateu y Llopis. Lérida, Tip. Selecta, 1949.
78 p. 18 cm.
At head of title: Consejo Superior de Investigaciones Científicas. "Patronato José M.ª Quadrado". Instituto de Estudios Ilerdenses de la Excelentísima Diputación Provincial de Lérida.

1. Lérida, Spain (Province)—Bibl. 2. Bibliography—Bibl.—Spain. ɪ. Title.

Z2704.L4T3   54-43220

NT 0042397   DLC

Tarragó Pleyán, José Alfonso.
Materiales de arqueología de la ciudad de Lérida, por José A. Tarragó Pleyán. Lérida, Imp. Escuela Provincial, 1944–
v. illus. (part col.), plan. 25 cm.
At head of title: Instituto de Estudios Ilerdenses de la Excma. Diputación Provincial de Lérida. Delegación del Consejo Superior de Investigaciones Científicas.
"Se han editado 50 ejemplares como separata del trabajo que con el mismo título ha publicado Revista Ilerda ... en sus números II, fasc. II, pags. 391 a 435 y III, fasc. II, pags. 413 a 438, de 1944."
Bibliographical footnotes.

1. Lérida, Spain—Antiq. ɪ. Title.

DP402.L33T3   68-127798

NT 0042398   DLC

Tarragó Pleyán, José Alfonso.
Reposición del retablo de Santa Lucía (siglo XIV) en la iglesia de San Lorenzo de Lérida. Catalogación histórico-artística y notas sobre los trabajos de restauración.   Lérida, Artes gráficas Ilerda, 1942.
13 p. illus. 22 cm.
At head of title; Ministerio de educación nacional, Dirección general de bellas artes, Servicio de defensa del patrimonio artístico nacional, zona de Levante, Delegación provincial de Lérida.

"100 cop., núm. 16."

NT 0042400   MH

Tárrago y Mateos, Torcuato, *d.* 1889.
... Bodas reales, novela histórica original por D. Torcuato Tárrago. Madrid, M. Martinez, 1875.
255 p. frent. (port.) pl. 17½ᶜᵐ.

ɪ. Title.

22-3394

Library of Congress   PQ6570.T3B7

NT 0042401   DLC 00

Tárrago y Marcos, Torcuato,   -1889.
... La cadena del destino, novela histórica original por Don Trocuato Tárrato. Madrid. Manuel Martinez, 1875.
255 p. front. plates. D. (Biblioteca ilustrada)

NT 0042402   00

Tárrago y Marcos, Torcuato,   -1889.
Carlos, cuarto, el bondadoso, novela histórica originalpor D. Torcuatro Tárrago y Mateos. Madrid, Librerias de Leon Pablo. ɛɛtc.ɛ Barcelona, Librería polariconómica. ɛɛtc.ɛ ɛ1856ɛ
298 p. 1 l. 20 plates.   0

NT 0042403   00

Tárrago y Mateos, Torcuato, d. 1889.
Carlos II, el hechizado. ɪNo hay esperanza: Novela original, por D. Trocuato Tarrago y Mateos. 2. ed. Madrid, Imprenta de D. Peña, 1855.
495, ɛlɛ p. plates. 0

NT 0042404   00

PQ6570 TARRAGO Y MATEOS, TORCUATO, d. 1889.
.T3C4   La caza de las palomas. (Memorias de la corte de
1857   Felipe IV). Novela histórica, original de Don Torcuato Tárrago y Mateos. Madrid, M. Prats, 1857.
571, [5]p. plates. 24cm.
Initials; head and tail-pieces.

1.Felipe IV, king of Spain, 1605-1665—Fiction.

NT 0042405   ICU 00

Tárrago y Mateos, Torcuato, *d.* 1889.   **D.176.37
Los celos de una reina y el amor de una muger. Novela original.
— Madrid. Viuda de D. R. J. Dominguez. 1849. 2 v. 20 cm., in 8s.
The plot is laid in Castile during the reign of John II.

L3912 — T.r. — Castile. Hist. Fict. John II., 1406-1454.

NT 0042406   MB

Tarrago y Mateos, Torcuato, d. 1889.
... Los celos de una reina, y el amor de una mujer ... Mexico, Boix, Besserer y cia., 1852.
267 p. 27 cm.

NT 0042407   CU-BANC

Tárrago y Mateos, Torcuato, d. 1889.
Los celos de una reina; novela historica original por Don T oronato Tárrago. Edicion de lujo... Madrid, Museo literario artístico, 1865.
3 v. plates

NT 0042408   00 DLC-P4

PQ6570 Tárrago y Mateos, Torcuato, d. 1889.
T3D4   El dedo de Dios; segunda parte de Los celos de una reina y el amor de una mujer, novela original.   Mexico, Tip. de M. Villanueva, 1863-64.
4 v.

"Edicion de 'El Pájaro verde'".

NT 0042409   CU

Tárrago y Mateos, Torcuato, d. 1889.
El dedo de Dios, novela historica original de D. Torcuato Tárrago y Mateos ....
Segunda edicion. Madrid, Minuesa y Marés, 1866.
1105 p. plates   0

NT 0042410   00

TÁRRAGO Y MATEOS, Torcuato, d. 1889.
Descansa en paz! Novela original. Madrid, A. de Carlos Hierro. [188-]

On cover:- 5a ed.

NT 0042411   MH

Tárrago y Mateos, Torcuato, d. 1889.
... ¡Descansa en paz! Novela original. Madrid, A. de Cárlos Hierro [189-?]
324 p. 19 cm.
On cover: 2. ed.

NT 0042412   CU 00

TARRAGÓ Y MATEOS, Torcuato, d. 1889.
A doce mil pies   de altura; novela original. Madrid, A. Bacaoya, 1878.

2 vol.

NT 0042413   MH

PQ   Tárrago y Mateos, Torcuato, d. 1889.
6570   Elisenda de Moncada, por D. Torcuato
T3B4+ Tárrago. Barcelona, Sociedad Editorial
    La Maravilla ₁1864₎
     547 p. illus. 27cm.

NT 0042414 NIC

Tárrago y Mateos, Torcuato, d. 1889.
  El ermitaño de Monserrate, por Don Torcuato Tarra-
go y Mateos ... 2. ed., corr. é ilustrada ... Madrid,
N. Cabello, 1852–53.
    2 v. in 1. plates. 23ᶜᵐ.
    Vol. 2 has imprint: Madrid, Estab. tip. de A. Peña, 1853.

    ɪ. Title.

                    14–21736

NT 0042415 DLC

Tarrago y Mateos, Tocuato, d. 1889.
  ... El Gran Capitán; novela histórica ...
Madrid, Gaspar y Roig, 1862.
    715 p. plates. 23 cm.

NT 0042416 CU

Tárrago y Mateos Torcuato, d. 1889.
  Gran Viaje universal Alrededor del mundo
Descrito por una sociedad de Viajeros modernos
Bajo la direccion de. D. Torcuato Tárrago y Mateos.
Australia, Java, Siam, Canton, Pekin, Yeddo,
San Francisco, Patagonia, Zulandia, etc., etc.
Grandiosa obra. Conteniendo noticias detalladas é
interesantes sobre la situacion, costumbres, usos,
trajes y maravillas de la tierra; tragedias, des-
gracias y sucesos portentosos no conocidos hasta el

dia. Obra digna de figurar en las bibliotecas de
todas las Personas Ilustradas Tomo I.   Madrid
Administracion, 1881.
    2 vols. [Imprenta de R. Moreno y R. Rojas.]

NT 0042418 NNH

Tárrago y Mateos, Torcuato,   –1889.
  La leyenda de los reyes, por D. Torcuato Tárrago. Madrid, J. C. Goode y Compañia, 1878.
    287 p. D.

NT 0042419 00

He82 Tárrago y Mateos, Torcuato, d.1889.
t20   ... Lisardo el estudiante, leyenda fantástica,
    por D.Torcuato Tárrago y Mateos. Madrid,
    Administracion,1882.
     252p.,1£. 18cm.
     At head of title: Jesus Graciá, editor.

    I.Graciá, Jesus   ed.   x.Mateos,
    Torcuato Tárrago y

NT 0042420 CtY

4PQ Tárrago y Mateos, Torcuato, d. 1889.
Port   O monge negro; romance historico.
2430 Traducção livre de Julio Baptista.
    Elvas, Typographia Elvense, 1860.
     725 p.

NT 0042421 DLC-P4

PQ   Tárrago y Mateos, Torcuato, d. 1889
6570   O monge negro ou a fome em Madrid; romance
T3   histórico. Lisboa, Typ. Central, 1875.
M67   2v. in 1. 21cm.
    Translation of El monje negro, o el hambre
de Madrid.

NT 0042422 WU

Tarrago y Mateos, Tocuato, d. 1889.
  Monje negro, ó el hambre de Madrid. Novela
histórica ...   Paris, Garnier hermanos, 1865.
    552 p. 22 cm.

NT 0042423 CU

Tárrago y Mateos, Torcuato. –1889
  El mundo por dentro; los grandes secre-
tos de la humanidad desde los tiempos mas
remotos hasta nuestros dias. por Don Torcuato Tárrago y Mateos. ... Madrid, J. M.
Faquineto, 1883–1884.
    4 v. col. Plates. O

NT 0042424 00

Tarrago y Mateos, Tocuato, d. 1889.
  Novias y novios...   Madrid, [1886]

NT 0042425 PPL

Tárrago y Mateos, Torcuato, –1889.
  ...El reloj de la muerte (páginas
lúgubres del reinado de Felipe III) Novela
histórica por D. Torcuato Tárrago y Mateos
... Madrid, J. Muñoz Sanchez ₍18—₎
    2 v col. plates. O.

NT 0042426 00

Tárrago y Mateos, Torcuato, –1889.
  ... El rey fantasma, novela histórica
original de D. Torcuato Tárrago y Mateos
... Madrid, Felipe Gonzalez Rojas, 1891.
    2 v. col. plates O

NT 0042427 00

Tárrago y Mateos, Torcuato, –1889.
  .... Roberto, el diablo, tradicion del
tiempo de las cruzadas, por Don Torcuato
Tárrago y Mateos: Madrid, Administracion,
1883.
    255 p. D.
    At head of title: Jesus Graciá. editor.

NT 0042428 00

4PQ Tárrago y Mateos, Torcuato, d. 1889
Port.   Tempestades da vida. Traducção
726 livre de Julio Baptista. Elvas,
    Typographia Elvense, 1862.
     2 v. in 1.

    (Bibliotheca selecta de Portugal
e Brazil)

NT 0042429 DLC-P4

Tarragon, Adrien de, 1860–
  see Tarragon, Marie Louis Adrien de, 1860–

Tarragon, J   B
  Nouveau traité dv toisé, rendu facile & demontré
par I. B. Tarragon ... A Paris, Chez Laurent
d'Houry, 1685.
    [8], 95 p. fold. plates. 16 cm.
    Title vignette.

NT 0042431 NNC NN

Tarragon, Mariè Louis Adrien de, 1860–
  Historique du 15ᵉ régiment d'infanterie ci-devant Bala-
gny—Rambures—Feuquières—Leuville—Richelieu—Ro-
han—Crillon—La Tour du Pin—Boisgelin—Béarn, l'un
des six Petits vieux, par le lieutenant de Tarragon. Paris, Limoges, H. Charles-Lavauzelle, 1895.
    450 p. 22ᶜᵐ.
    "Principaux ouvrages consultés": p. ₁361₎–364.

    1. France—Army—Infantry—15th regt.

                  22–1180

    Library of Congress   UA703.A7.15th

NT 0042432 DLC NN

Tarragona, Manuel Balcells y
  see Balcells y Tarragona, Manuel.

Tarragona, Spain. Ateneo Tarraconense de la Clase Obrera
  see
Ateneo Tarraconense de la Clase Obrera.

Tarragona, Spain. Biblioteca Provincial.
  Contribución al concocimiento de la Biblioteca
Provincial de Tarragona
    see under   López de Toro, José..

Z   Tarragona, Spain. Biblioteca Pública
6621   Manuscritos de la Biblioteca Pública de
.T3 Tarragona, por Jesús Domínguez Bordona.
    ₍Tarragona₎ Excma. Diputación Provincial de
    Tarragona, 1954.
     30 p. 25cm. (Instituto de Estudios
    Tarraconenses "Ramón Berenguer IV". Sección
    de Arqueología e Historia. Publicación no. 6)

    1. Manuscripts. Spain - Catalogs. 2.
    Manuscripts, Spanish - Catalogs. I.
    Domínguez Bordona,   Jesús. II. Title.

NT 0042436 WU IU MH

                4-serials
  **Tarragona, Spain. Cámara Oficial de
Comercio, Industria y Navegación.
Memoria comercial.**

              v.

NT 0042437 DLC-P4

Tarragona, Spain. Cámara Oficial de Comercio, Industria y Navegación.
Memoria de los trabajos realizados y resúmenes estadísticos.
[Tarragona]
v. 25 cm.

1. Tarragona, Spain—Comm.

HF322.T37   49–57145*‡

NT 0042438   DLC

Tarragona, Spain. Catedral.
[VI [i. e. Sexto] centenario de la consagración de la Catedral de Tarragona, 1331-1931.
[Tarragona, 1931]
57 p. illus. 31cm.

Bibliographical footnotes.

1. Tarragona, Spain. Catedral. I. Title.

NT 0042439   NNC

Tarragona, Spain. Colegio de la Compañia de Iesus. Seminario de Humanas letras.
Torneo poetico
see under Alegre, Felipe.

Tarragona, Spain. Instituto de Estudios Tarraconenses "Ramón Berenguer IV"
see
Instituto de Estudios Tarraconenses "Ramón Berenguer IV," *Tarragona, Spain.* (supplement)

Tarragona, Spain. Junta de Obras del Puerto
see
Junta de Obras del Puerto de Tarragona.

N3480
.A5   **Tarragona, Spain. Museo arqueológico.**
Catálogo del Museo arqueológico de Tarragona, con la clasificación hecha en 1878 por d. Buenaventura Hernández Sanahuja, continuado hasta el presente y precedido de una resena histórica sobre su fundación, vicisitudes y acrecentamientos por d. Angel del Arco y Molinero... Tarragona, Tip. de Adolfo Alegret, 1894.
xxxvip.,2 l.,335p.,2 l. plates. 26cm.

1.Art - Tarragona, Spain. 2.Tarragona, Spain - Antiquities. I.Hernández Sanahuja, Buenaventura. II.Arco y Molinero, Angel del, 1862-1925.

NT 0042444   NNU-W NNC

Tarragona, Spain. Museo arqueológico provincial.
Arco y Molinero, Angel del, 1862-1925.
Estudios de arqueología, por d. Angel del Arco y Molinero ... Tarragona, Est. tip. de F. Arís é hijo, 1894.

DP247
.P77   **Tarragona, Spain (Province)**
(Vol. 11   ... El avance de la provincia de Tarragona, desde
no 1)   el 13 de septiembre de 1923 al 31 diciembre de 1928. Memoria. [Tarragona, Tipografía de J. Pijoán, 1929]
4 p.l., [9]-227, [5] p. ports. 23,5 cm.
([Progreso de España en el periodo 1923-1928. v. 11, no. 1])
At head of title; Gobierno civil de Tarragona.

NT 0042446   DLC

59
T17   Tarragona, Spain (Province) Cámara Oficial Sindical Agraria.
La batalla del grano; trigo, cebada, avena. Tarragona, 1953.
64 p.

1. Cereals. Experimentation. I. Solé Caralt, J

NT 0042447   DNAL

Tarragona, Spain (Province) Colegio oficial de Medicos
see Colegio Oficial de Médicos de la Provincia de Tarragona.

Tarragona, Spain (Province) Comisión de Monumentos Históricos y Artísticos
Jad91   La Comisión de Monumentos Históricos y
946T   Artísticos de la provincia de Tarragona ante las ruínas del monasterio de Poblet, por su presidente Juan Serra y Vilaró. Tarragona[Imp. de Pijoan]1946.
247p. 24cm.
No.240 of an edition of 250 copies.

NT 0042449   CtY

Tarragona, Spain (Province) Escuela Normal.
Introduccion discursos y programa leidos en el acto de la solemne inauguracion de la escuela normal. Tarragona, [1843]

pp.41.18.

NT 0042450   MH

---

*SC5   **Tarragona, Spain (Archdiocese)**
T2722   Constitvtiones Concilii provincialis
602c   tarraconensis iiii. ab illustriss. et reuerendiss. d.d. Ioan. Teres archiep. tarraconen. aeditae mens. ianvar. et febrva. anni MDCII.
Tarracone cum licentia superioris,apud Philippum Robertum.MDCII.
4°. 32p.l.,395(i.e.397)p.,28l.,132,[2],8, [3]p. 19cm.
Title vignette (episcopal arms).
Numbers 366-   367 repeated in paging.

NT 0042451   MH

Tarragona, Spain (Archdiocese)
Constitutiones synodales Archidioecesis Tarraconensis, statutae, et promulgatae in synodo dioecesana, quam in sua metropolitana ecclesia celebravit Josephus Linas ... archiepiscopus tarraconensis assumptus ... anno millesimo septingentesimo quarto, die quarta maij. Barcinonae, 1704.
f°.

NT 0042452   MH-L

Z946.1T17
T17   Tarragona, Spain (Archdiocese)
Constitvtionvm provincialivm Tarraconensivm libri qvinqve. Tarracone, P. Mey, 1580.
[56], 411, [49] p. 20cm.

NT 0042453   MnU NNC MH-L

TARRAGONA, Spain (Archdiocese)
Constitutionum provincialium tarraconensium, libri quinque,quibus sunt in calce voluminis adiectae nonnullae,quae inutiles et superfluae visae sunt ex decreto secundi concilii provincialis celebrati sub illustrissimo d.d. Ioanne Teres,archiepiscopo tarraconensi. Tarracone,1593.

NT 0042454   MH-L

Tarragona Monumenta, ó sea descripcion histórica y artística de todas sus antigüedades y monumentos
see under Albiñana y de Borrás, Juan Francisco, 1802-1868.

DP402
.T3T3   Tarragona, Poblet, Santas Creus.
1. ed. ilustrada, libro de verdadera utilidad para el turista. Tarragona, A. Ventura Altés [192-?]
151p. illus.,fold.plan. 19cm.
(Guías "Tarraco", I)

NT 0042456   NNU-W

TARRAGONA sacrificada en sus intereses y vidas por la independencia de la nacion y libertad de su cautivo monarca Fernando Septimo. Relacion de los sucesos mas memorables ocurridos en esta ciudad durante la ultima guerra defensiva contra la invasion del tirano del siglo XIX, Napoleon Bonaparte. La escribia en año de 1816 una victime escapada del furor de los barbaros, testigo ocular de sus atrocidades en el dia de su entrada e inmediatos. Tarragona. M. Puigrubi, [1816].
pp.(10).82. Table.

NT 0042457   MH

944d   **Tarraire, Jean**
T192f   La France et l'Union française; géographie. Cours moyen des écoles primaires. [Paris] Nathan [1947]
cover-title, 64p. illus.(part col.) maps.
Q

1.France. Descr. & trav. I.Title.

NT 0042458   IaU

Pac.
GB55   **Tarraire, Jean.**
.T37   Geographie a l'usage des écoles primaires des établissements français d'Océanie [par] J. Tarraire et une réunion de professeurs de l'E. F. O. Paris, Fernand Nathan [1954]
64 p. illus. (part col.)

Cover title.

1. Geog-   raphy - Textbooks -
1945-   I. Title.

NT 0042459   HU

Tarral, 1858–
*De l'erythème scarlatiniforme et rubéoliforme
dans le choléra.   Paris, 1886.
    58 p., 1 l.   4°.
    No. 154.

NT   0042460   DNLM

Tarral, Claudius.
    Catalogue de tableaux anciens; oeuvres...par
Jan Stenn, J. Weenix, Berck-Heyde dépendant de la
succession de feu M. Tarral et autre...tableaux
par Asselyn [and others.] ... Vente...Janvier, 1887.
[Paris] F. Albinet, 1887.
    26 p.   12°.
    In: MAX p. v. 11.

NT   0042461   NN

TARRAL, CLAUDIUS.
    Courtes réflexions sur la Galerie des tableaux du Louvre,
et analyse critique du nouveau catalogue, par M. Claudius
Tarral... Paris: Impr. administrative de P. Dupont, 1850.
50 p.   23½cm.

    "Deuxième lettre."

    1. Paris. Musée national du Louvre.

NT   0042462   NN MH

TARRAL, CLAUDIUS.
    Observations sur le classement actuel des tableaux du
Louvre, et analyse critique du nouveau catalogue, par M.
Claudius Tarral... Paris: Impr. administrative de P.
Dupont, 1850.   54 p.   23½cm.

    "Première lettre."

    1. Paris. Musée national du Louvre.

NT   0042463   NN MH RP

Tarral, Claudius, Dr.
    — De traitement des tumeurs érectiles, et
particulièrement du traitement par le caustique.
45 pp. 8°. [Paris], Mignret, [1834].
    Repr. from : Arch. gén. de méd., Par., 1834, 2, s., vi.

NT   0042464   DNLM

Tarral, Claudius, Dr.
    Mémoire sur l'ablation de l'utérus, avec la
description d'une nouvelle méthode opératoire.
Paris, J. B. Baillière, 1829.
    54 p.   16°.

NT   0042465   MB

Tarral (Claudius) Dr. Réflexions et observations
sur les anévrysmes, accompagnées de l'analyse
de l'ouvrage de M. Wardrop. 53 pp. 8°. Paris,
J.-B. Baillière, 1829.
    Repr. from : J. hebd. de méd., Par., 1829, iv.

NT   0042466   DNLM

Tarral (Georges) [1888–   ]. *Contribution à
l'étude de l'incontinence d'urine chez la femme.
50 pp. 8°. Montpellier. 1913. No. 66.

NT   0042467   DNLM CtY

Tarral, Nikolaus, 1872–
    Laut- und formenlehre der mundart des kantons Fal-
kenberg in Lothr. ... Strassburg, Univ.-buchdruckerei
von J. H. E. Heitz (Heitz & Mündel) 1903.
    2 p. l., 117 p., 1 l. 22½cm.
    Inaug.-dis.—Strassburg.
    Lebenslauf.

                                                    5-20681

NT   0042468   DLC PU TxU CU InU

Tarralle, Raymond Marcel, 1914–
    ... Contribution à l'étude des troubles pupillaires dans les
pneumopathies aiguës ... Angers, Siraudeau, 1939.
    38, [1] p. 25 cm. (Nancy. Université. Faculté de médecine. Thèse.
    1939/40. no. 11)

    1. Eye[—Diagnostic significance] 2. Lungs—Diseases—Diagnosis.
    I. [Series]
                                                    Med 47–3049
    U. S. Army Medical Library   [W4N17]
        for Library of Congress   [1]

NT   0042469   DNLM

Tarrant, C   A.
    The Cat climbs, by C. A. Tarrant. London, M. Secker &
Warburg, ltd., 1936.
    347, [1] p. 19cm.

    I. Title.

                                                    37–12728
    Library of Congress   PZ3.T179Cat

NT   0042470   DLC

Tarrant, C   A
    The cat climbs, by C. A. Tarrant.   New York,
Triangle books [c1937]
    4 p. l., 11–307, [1] p.

NT   0042471   WaPS NN ViU

Tarrant, C   A.
    The Cat climbs, by C. A. Tarrant. Philadelphia, London,
J. B. Lippincott company [c1937]
    307, [1] p. illus. (incl. plans) 19½cm.

    I. Title.

                                                    37–12727
    Library of Congress   PZ3.T179Cat 2

NT   0042472   DLC OU

Tarrant, C. A.
    The Cat climbs.   New York, Triangle books,
1938, c1937.
    308 p.   D.

NT   0042473   PP

E446   TARRANT, CARTER.
.T22   The substance of a discourse delivered in the town
Lincoln of Versailles, Woodford county, state of Kentucky, April
        20, 1806. With some additions, and miscelaneous thoughts,
        connected with the subject. By Carter Tarrant... Lex-
        ington, K., Printed by D. Bradford [1806?]
            32 p. 22cm.

            1. Slavery in the U. S.—Controversial literature,
        1806.

NT   0042474   ICU CSmH

Tarrant, Dorothy, 1885–
    The contribution of Plato to free religious thought. Lon-
don, Lindsey Press [1949]
    28 p. 19 cm. (The Essex Hall lecture, 1949)

    1. Plato. 2. Liberalism (Religion) I. Title. (Series)

    B395.T2   184.1   50–23568

NT   0042475   DLC ICU MH NN LU NBuU

Tarrant, Dorothy, 1885–   joint ed.
Bible. *English. Selections. 1934.*
    A golden treasury of the Bible ... selected and edited by
Mortimer Rowe, B. A., with the assistance of Herbert McLach-
lan ... [and] Dorothy Tarrant ... London, The Lindsey press,
1934.

Tarrant, Dorothy, 1885–   ed.
Plato.
    The Hippias major, attributed to Plato; with introductory
essay and commentary by Dorothy Tarrant ... Cambridge
[Eng.] The University press, 1928.

BX
9813   Tarrant, Dorothy, 1885–
.A2   What Unitarians believe. London,
        Lindsey Press [1950]
            17 p. 19 cm.
            No. 5 in bd. vol. with binder's
        title: "Unitarians".

            1. Unitarianism. I. Title

NT   0042478   MH-AH

Tarrant, Eastham.
    The wild riders of the First Kentucky cavalry. A history
of the regiment in the great war of the rebellion, 1861–1865,
telling of its origin and organization; a description of the
material of which it was composed; its rapid and sever
marches, hard service, and fierce conflicts ... A regimental
roster. Prison life, adventures and escapes. By Sergeant
E. Tarrant ... Published by a committee of the regiment.
[Louisville, Press of R. H. Carothers, c1894]
    x, 508 p. front., port. 22 cm.
    1. Kentucky cavalry. 1st regt., 1861–1864. 2. U. S.—Hist.—Civil
war—Regimental histories—Kentucky cavalry—1st. I. Title.

    E509.6 1st   2—13159

NT   0042479   DLC KMK NN ViU NjP DNW NcD WHi KyLx KyHi

Micro-   Tarrant, Eastham.
card   The wild riders of the First Kentucky cavalry. A his-
E509.6   tory of the regiment in the great war of the rebellion,
1st   1861–1865, telling of its origin and organization; a de-
        scription of the material of which it was composed; its
        rapid and severe marches, hard service, and fierce con-
        flicts ... A regimental roster. Prison life, adventures
        and escapes. By Sergeant E. Tarrant ... Pub. by a
        committee of the regiment. [Louisville, Press of R. H.
        Carothers, c1894]
            x, 503 p. front., port. 22cm.
            1. Kentucky cavalry. 1st regt., 1861–1864 2. U. S.—Hist.—Civil war—
        Regimental histories—   Ky. cav.—1st. I. Title.

            Micro-opaque. [Louisville, Ky., Lost Cause
        Press, 1957] 13 cards. 7.5 x 12.5 cm. (Travel
        in the Confederate states)

NT   0042481   OU PSt CaBVaU MsU ICRL

Tarrant, Fred.
    ... Rules for state highway patrol officers
        see under Illinois. Division of Highways.

Tarrant, Fred J   1898–
    A Texan's antic-dotes. San Antonio, Naylor Co. [1954, ᶜ1953]
    121 p. illus. 20 cm.

    I. Title.

    PZ4.T192Te   54–21572 ‡

NT   0042483   DLC TxU NN

[Tarrant, Garland Pratt]
    Farm and gin hand book; tables of amounts for seed cotton and lint cotton at prices by the pound or by the 100 pounds, cotton seed or cotton seed products by the ton of 2000 pounds, convenient for the farmer, the stock man, the miner, the manufacturer, the ginner, the banker, the buyer and the seller; tables adapted to all commodities estimated by the pound, by the hundred pounds, or by the ton of two thousand pounds. [Dallas, Tex., Printed by the Home & state co.] ᶜ1911.
    32 p. incl. tables. 15½ᶜᵐ. $0.25
    1. Cotton—Tables, etc. 2. Cotton seed—Tables and ready-reckoners.

    Library of Congress   HF5716.C6T2   11–31551
    Copyright A 301831

NT   0042484   DLC

---

537   Tarrant, Gerald Thomas Prestoe.
T17e   Electricity, magnetism and modern physics, a textbook for the use of scholarship candidates and university students... London, J.M. Dent [1948]
         xii, 468p. illus. 19cm.   (His Physics, v.II)

         1. Electricity. 2. Magnetism. 3. Physics.

NT   0042485   LU IEN NNC

QC518
.T37   Tarrant, Gerald Thomas Prestoe.
1949
         Electricity, magnetism and modern physics. A textbook for use of scholarship candidates and university students. London, J. M. Dent [1949]
         xii, 468 p. diagrs. 19cm. (His Physics. v. 2) Dent's modern science series.

         1. Electricity. 2. Magnetism. 3. Physics.

NT   0042486   ViU

QC30   Tarrant, Gerald Thomas Prestoe.
T27   Physics, a supplementary textbook for the use of scholarship candidates and university students ... London, J. M. Dent [1938, 1936]
         303 p.   (Dent's modern science series)

         1. Physics - Study and teaching.
         I. T.

NT   0042487   NBuU

Older
N.L.M.
WJ   Tarrant, Harman
700   Functional derangements of the nervous
T192F   system and diseases of the generative organs.
1898   2d ed. Sydney [Printed by McCarron, Stewart, 1898?]
             vi, 264 p. illus. 18 cm.

             1. Genital Diseases, Male. I. Title.

NT   0042488   WU–M

Tarrant, Henry Jefferd.
    Lloyd's bonds: their nature and uses. By Henry Jefferd Tarrant ... London, Stevens and Haynes, 1867.
    18, [2] p. 21ᶜᵐ.

    1. Railroads—Gt. Brit.—Finance. 2. Railroad law—Gt. Brit. 3. Bonds—Gt. Brit.   I. Title.
                                                      38–5307

    Library of Congress   [2]

NT   0042489   DLC CtY

Tarrant, Henry Jefferd, reporter.

North-western Provinces, *India. High court of judicature.*
    ... N.-W. P. High court reports. Reports of cases heard and determined in the High court, N.-W. Provinces, in 1869–1875; ... Allahabad, Printed at the N.-W. P. government press, 1873–76. Rajkot, Reprinted by N. N. Ganatra with the permission of H. E. the governor-general in Council, 1908.

Tarrant, Irving S.

Chicago. Art institute.
    Paintings by Karl Knaths, the Art institute of Chicago, January 22 to February 23, 1942. [Chicago? 1942]

Tarrant, Julian W.
    Master plan studies, Franklin, Virginia [a report to the Town Planning Commission. Richmond, Va., 1952–
    v. maps, diagrs., plans, tables. 28 cm.
    Cover title.
    Contents: no. 1. Basic data. 1952. – no. 2. Transportation. 1953. – no. 3. Public buildings and grounds. 1955.

NT   0042492   NcU Or Vi ICU

Tarrant, Kenneth J
    Micrometrical measures of double stars, 1887. [1889]
    [273]–288 col.   (Astronomische Nachrichten, no. 2998-99)

    From Astronomische Nachrichten, Bd. 121.
    Volume of pamphlets.

    1. Stars, Double.

NT   0042493   NNC

Tarrant, Lydia.
    Canning timetable for fruits...   Burlington, Vt. U. of Vt., 1940.
    2 l. 28 cm.   (Vt. U. College of agriculture. Agricultural extension service. Brieflet no. 566)

NT   0042494   PPD

Tarrant, Lydia.
    Manual for serving community meals. pamp.

NT   0042495   PPD

Tarrant, Lydia.
    Planning lunches for school children [by Lydia Tarrant and Eleanor B. Winters ...] State College, Pa., 1943.
    17 p. illus. (Pennsylvania. State college, State College. School of agriculture. Agricultural extension service. Circular 241)
    Cover-title.
    Issued September 1942, reprinted November 1943.

NT   0042496   PP

Tarrant, Mabel.
    The khaki and the blue...   La Grange, Ill. c1919.
    11 p. 17 cm.

NT   0042497   RPB

Tarrant, Margaret Winifred, 1888–   illus.
    All about the man in the moon
        see under Davidson, Gladys.

Tarrant, Margaret Winifred, 1888–   illus.
    The house that Jack built and Cock Robin
        see under The house that Jack built.
    [supplement]

Tarrant, Margaret Winifred, 1888–   illus.

Rhys, *Mrs.* Grace (Little) 1865–
    In Wheelabout and Cockalone, by Grace Rhys ... With colour drawings by Margaret W. Tarrant; line drawings by Megan Rhys. New York, Frederick A. Stokes company [1918]

Tarrant, Margaret Winifred, 1888–   illus.
    Joan in flowerland; written by Margaret Tarrant & Lewis Dutton; illustrated by Margaret Tarrant. London and New York, F. Warne & co., ltd. [1935]
    59, [1] p. incl. col. front., illus., col. plates. 22ᶜᵐ.
    Illustrated lining-papers.

    I. Dutton, Lewis, joint author. II. Title.   36–1313

    Library of Congress   PZ8.3.T148Jo

NT   0042501   DLC CaBVaU Or PP NN

Tarrant, Margaret Winifred, 1888–   illus.

The Margaret Tarrant Christmas book, a Christmas annual illustrated with reproductions of paintings and drawings by Margaret W. Tarrant. Boston, Hale, Cushman & Flint [ᶜ1940]

Tarrant, Margaret Winifred, 1888–
    The Margaret Tarrant nursery rhyme book. New York, E. P. Dutton [1947]
    [33] p. illus. (part col.) 31 cm.

    1. Nursery rhymes.   I. Title.
                                              A 48–89*

    Illinois. Univ. Librar.
    for Library of Congress   [7]

NT   0042503   IU

Tarrant, Margaret Winifred, 1888– *illus.*
Margaret Tarrant's Christmas garland; pictures by Margaret Tarrant, text compiled by Marian Russell Heath. Boston, Hale, Cushman & Flint ₁1942₎

125 p. incl. mounted col. front., illus., mounted col. plates. 21½ x 18ᶜᵐ.

ɪ. Heath, Marian Russell, comp. ɪɪ. Title: Christmas garland.

42–52198

Library of Congress   PN4305.C5T35

₍3₎   394.268

NT   0042504   DLC OC1 PP WaSp PPFr CPBac OEac OLak OOxM

Tarrant, Margaret Winifred, 1888– *illus.*

Rhymes of old times, illustrated by Margaret **Tarrant.** London & Boston, The Medici society, 1925.

Tarrant, Margaret Winifred, 1888– **illus.**

Stevenson, Robert Louis, 1850–1894.

Songs with music, from 'A child's garden of verses' by R. L. Stevenson; music by Rev. Thomas Crawford, ʙ. ᴅ., drawings by Margaret Tarrant. New York, T. Nelson & sons ₁1936₎

Tarrant, Margaret Winifred, 1888– **illus.**

PE1117 .T25

The Tales the letters tell. Illus. by Margaret W. Tarrant. London, Grant Educational Co., 1944–

Tarrant, Margaret Winifred, 1888–
Three bears. n. p., n. d.
illus.

NT   0042508   WaSp

Tarrant, Margaret Winifred, 1888– **illus**

Kingsley, Charles, 1819–1875.
The water babies, by Charles Kingsley; with coloured illustrations by Margaret W. Tarrant. London, J. M. Dent & sons, ltd.; New York, E. P. Dutton & co. ₁1914₎

Tarrant, Paul, joint author.

QD181 .F1T6

Tompson, Reade Yates, 1918–
... The action of elementary fluorine upon organic compounds: xɪɪ. Vapor phase addition to certain deactivated or condensed aromatic rings, by Reade Y. Tompson, Paul Tarrant and Lucius A. Bigelow. ₁n. p., 1946₎

Tarrant, Percy, illus.

Ewing, *Mrs.* Juliana Horatia (Gatty) 1841–1885.
... Jackanapes and other tales, by J. H. Ewing, illustrated by Percy Tarrant. Philadelphia, David McKay company ₁1927₎

Tarrant, Percy, illus.

PZ3 .S43 Q 67

Scott, *Sir* Walter, *bart.,* 1770–1832.
Quentin Durward, by Sir Walter Scott, with illustrations in color by Percy Tarrant. New York, Dodd, Mead & company, 1944.

Tarrant, Robert F
A guide for forest soil examination in the douglas-fir region. Portland, Ore., U.S. Department of agriculture, Forest service, 1947.

27 p. tables. 21 cm.

NT   0042513   MH–HF

TARRANT, Robert F.
Moisture and the distribution of Lodgepole and Ponderosa Pine (A review of the literature) Portland, 1953.
10p. (U.S. Forest service. Pacific Northwest forest and range experiment station. Research paper no.8)

NT   0042514   WaWW

Tarrant, *Mrs.* **S**₍usan₎ **F**₍rances₎ **(H**₍ale₎**)** 1834– *ed.*
Hon. Daniel Pratt: a biography, with eulogies on his life and character. Ed. by Mrs. S. F. H. Tarrant. Richmond, Va., Whittet & Shepperson, 1904.

173, ₍1₎ p. plates, 2 port. (incl. front.) 19½ᶜᵐ.

"History of Prattville, by S. Mims. ⟨Written in 1877 and 1878⟩": p. ₍20₎–59.

1. Pratt, Daniel, 1799–1873. 2. Prattville, Ala.—Hist. ɪ. Mims, S.

5–17347

NT   0042515   DLC GU ViU NN MB Vi

Tarrant, Thomas Ambrose.
... The humor of the school child. By T. A. Tarrant ... Sydney, W. A. Gullick, government printer, 1918.

29 p. tables, diagrs. 24ᶜᵐ. (New South Wales. The teachers' college, Sydney. Records of the Education society, no 31)

1. Child study. ɪ. Title.

E 18–960

Library, U. S. Bur. of   Education LB1131.T22

NT   0042516   DHEW

Tarrant, Thomas Ambrose.
... The testing of intelligence through school work. In connection with the class work of some of the pupils of Balmain superior public school. By T. A. Tarrant, ʙ. ᴀ. Sydney, W. A. Gullick, government printer, 1913.

35 p. diagrs. 24ᶜᵐ. (... Records of the Education society, no. 15)

At head of title: New South Wales. The Teachers' college, Sydney.

1. Child study. 2. Educational psychology. ɪ. Sydney. Teachers' college.

E 13–1720

Library, U. S. Bur. of   Education LB1131.T2

NT   0042517   DHEW

Tarrant, Thomas Ambrose.
... The transition from phonetic to ordinary script. (Being the result of a series of experiments made with three first year secondary classes in French, at North Sydney intermediate high school.) By T. A. Tarrant ... With an introduction by E. G. Waterhouse ... And an appendix on the transition from phonetic to ordinary spelling. By V. Partington. Sydney, W. A. Gullick, government printer, 1915.

21 p. 24½ᶜᵐ. (New South Wales. The Teachers' college, Sydney. Records of the Education society. no. 24)

1. French language—Study and teaching. 2. French language—Pronunciation. ɪ. Partington, Miss V.

16–21271

Library of Congress   PC2065.T⁷

NT   0042518   DLC

Tarrant, William.
Accounts of the Parliamentary garrisons of Great Chalfield and Malmesbury, 1645–1646
see under   Gt. Brit. Exchequer.

Tarrant, William.
A digest and index of all the ordinances of the Hongkong government
see under   Hongkong. Laws, statutes, etc.

Tarrant, William.
Hongkong, 1839–1844. Canton, Friend of China, 1861.
pt. (Pamphlets: China)
Author's autograph presentation copy.
With this is bound: Faber, Ernst. The famous men of China. 1889; Gardner, Christopher Thomas. The missionary question in China. ₍1894?₎ Morrison, James K. The currency of China. 1895; San tzu ching. Sam–tsz–king. 1892.

NT   0042521   WaU MSaE

Wason DS709 T19

Tarrant, William.
Ningpo to Shanghai in 1857. (Via the borders of An-whui province, Hoo-chow-foo and the Grand Canal) Canton, Printed at the "Friend of China" Office, ₍1862₎
112 p. map. 22cm.

1. China--Descr. & trav. I. Title.

NT   0042522   NIC MSaE

Tarrant, William George, 1853– *comp.*
Daily meditations. Compiled by W. G. Tarrant ... 4th ed., rev. London, P. Green ₍190–?₎

47, ₍1₎ p. 11 x 7ᶜᵐ.

1. Devotional exercises. ɪ. Title.

24–13102

Library of Congress   BV4832.T2

NT   0042523   DLC

TARRANT, William George, 1853–
Faith in Jesus. London, n. d.

1 pam. 11x17 .
(BRIT. & FOREIGN UNIT. ASSOC. [Tracts] New sries, 85).

NT   0042524   MH

Tarrant, William George, 1853–
... Florence Nightingale as a religious thinker, by W. G. Tarrant ... London, British & foreign Unitarian association ₍191–?₎

cover-title, 32 p. 16½ᶜᵐ. (The Unitarian penny library. 137)

1. Nightingale, Florence, 1820–1910.

18–5273

Library of Congress   UH347.N6T3

NT   0042525   DLC

Tarrant, William George, 1853-
Marching with the heroes. [Hymn by] William
George Tarrant, 1853. [Music by] Adam Gibel,
1904.
In- Bayard, L. R. Marching with the heroes.
Los Angeles, c1927. 22 cm. p. 19 music.

NT 0042526 RPB

Tarrant, William George, 1853-
Milton and religious freedom, by W. G. Tarrant ...
London, P. Green, 1908.
cover-title, 28 p. 16½ᶜᵐ. ₁The Unitarian penny library ... no. 73₁

1. Milton, John, 1608-1674.
17-31961

Library of Congress PR3592.R4T3

NT 0042527 DLC ICN MH-AH

Tarrant, William George, 1853-
Milton and religious freedom. (In: Place of
Jesus in modern religion and other essays; by
R.A. Armstrong, Brooks Herford, W.C. Garrett
₁and others₎. London, 1909)

NT 0042528 MH-AH

Tarrant, William George, 1853-
The religion of Oliver Wendell Holmes, by W. G. Tarrant ...
London, The British & foreign Unitarian association, 1902.
cover-title, 16p. 18cm.

1. Holmes, Oliver Wendell, 1809-1894.

Printed by Wesleyan University Library

NT 0042529 CtW

Tarrant, William George, 1853-
... Shakespeare and religion, by W. G. Tarrant, B. A.
₁London₎ British & foreign Unitarian association ₁1916?₎
cover-title, 24 p. 16ᶜᵐ. (Unitarian penny library. 147)

1. Shakespeare, William—Religion and ethics.
17-28254

Library of Congress PR3011.T3

NT 0042530 DLC

BX   Tarrant, William George, b.1853.
9831   The story and significance of the Unitarian
T3   movement. London, P. Green, 1910.
104p. 18cm.

Includes bibliographical references.

1. Unitarianism—History. I. Title.

NT 0042531 CCSC GU MH MiU

Tarrant, William George, 1853-
The story and significance of the Unitarian movement.
₁Reprinted, with additional notes₎ London, Lindsey Press
₁1947₎
68 p. 19 cm.
Includes bibliographical references.

1. Unitarianism—Hist. I. Title.

BX9831.T3 1947   288   48-16765*

NT 0042532 DLC ICU

BX   Tarrant, William George, 1853-
9841   Unitarianism.—New York: Dodge Publishing
T3   Company, n.d.
xvi, 95p.

NT 0042533 MoSCS

TARRANT, WILLIAM GEORGE, 1853-
Unitarianism [by] W.G.Tarrant.   New York: Dodge Pub.
Co. [1912?]   xvi, 95 p.   18cm.

"Authorities," p. 95–[96]

803649A. 1. Unitarian Church—Hist.

NT 0042534 NN CtY-D KMK PPT OC1

Tarrant, William George, 1853-
Unitarianism ₁by₎ W. G. Tarrant. London, Constable
& company ltd., 1912.
3 p. l., ix-xvi, 95, ₁1₎ p. 18½ᶜᵐ. ₁Religions ancient and modern₎
"Authorities": p. 95-₍96₎

1. Title.
12-29380 Revised

NT 0042535 DLC

BX9831 Tarrant, William George, 1853-
T3   Unitarianism.   New York, Dodge ₁1914?₎
1914   xvi, 95, ₁1₎ p.

"Authorities": p.95-₍96₎

1. Unitarianism

NT 0042536 CU

Tarrant and Alten, consulting city planners, Richmond, Va.
Background for planning, prepared by
Tarrant and Alten.   May 1, 1954.
33 p. (Master plan report no. 1)
Prepared for Falls Church, Va., City
Planning Commission.

NT 0042537 PPCPC IU

Avery
AA
9127   Tarrant and Alten, consulting city planners,
F19   Richmond, Va.
Land use plan, Falls Church, Va. Prepared
for the City Planning Commission, by Tarrant
& Alten, consulting city planners, associated.
₁Richmond, Va., 1955₎
32 l. illus., maps, tables. 28cm. (Falls
Church, Va. Master plan report no. 2)

Letter of transmittal signed: Julian Tarrant
and Ivan J. Alten.

NT 0042538 NNC PPCPC

There are no cards for numbers
NT 0042539 to NT 0044000

Tarrant Co., Tex. Commisioners' court
see Texas. Commissioner's court. Tarrant
Co.

Tarrant co., Tex. Free library
see Tarrant county free library.
Fort Worth, Tex.

Tarrant County Baptist Association
see Baptists. Texas. Tarrant County
Association.

Tarrant County Free Library. Fort Worth,
Tex.
Fort Worth, Tex. Carnegie public library.
... Annual report of the Board of trustees of the Carnegie
public library of Fort Worth and the Tarrant county free
library ...
Fort Worth, Tex., 19

W 1   TARRANT County Medical Society
TA61   Bulletin.

Fort Worth, Tex. [1928?]-
v. illus., ports.
W1 TA61
Title: Bulletin of the Tarrant County
Medical Society

NT 0044005 DNLM PPC

Tarrant County Society for Mental Hygiene.
Day care in Tarrant county; a project of the
Research Committee. n.p., 1951.
46 p. map.
Mimeographed.
"Selected references": p. 46.
Cover-title.
1. Day nurseries. 2. Child welfare – Texas.

NT 0044006 TxFTC

Tarrant Hinton, *Eng. (Parish)*
The registers of Tarrant Hinton, Dorset. 1545-1812
... London, Privately printed for the Parish register
society, 1902.
xi, 75 p. 23ᵐᵐ. (Added t.-p.: The Parish register society. ₁Publications₎
XLIV)
"The transcript of this register was made by the late rector, the Rev.
Alfred Stilgoe Newman, in 1895."—Pref.

Subject entries: Registers of births, etc.—Tarrant Hinton, Eng.
8-12685

Library of Congress, no.

NT 0044007 DLC NcD PHi ICN NN OC1

Tarras, Félix.
... De la bronchite ... Paris, Rignoux, imprimeur, 1850.
30 p. 21½ x 17½ᵐᵐ.
At head of title: Faculté de médecine de Paris. N° 160. Thèse pour
le doctorat en médecine ... 19 août 1850, par Félix Tarras.

1. Bronchitis.
36-31024

Library of Congress RC778.T3

NT 0044008 DLC

Tarrás, Juan Francisco.

Film
AC-2
reel 63,
no. 2

Confraternity of Our Lady of the Seven Sorrows.
Patente de la piadosa y devota cofradia, que con el titulo de Nuestra Señora de los Siete Dolores y soledad de la bienaventurada siempre Virgen Maria y santisimo sacramento se halla canónicamente fundada ... ¡Mexico? 1810₁

Tarras, William.
Poems, chiefly in the Scottish dialect. By William Tarras ... Edinburgh, Denham & Dick ₍etc.₎ 1804.
vii, ₍1₎, 151 p. 17¼ᵐ.
Autograph of "John Laidlaw, 1814."
With this copy is bound a collection perhaps by another author, without t-p., but with caption title: "Poems, mostly in the Scottish dialect."

ɪ. Title.
1–1454
Library of Congress   PR5549.T22

NT 0044010   DLC

Tarras-Wahlberg, Bo, 1901–
... On the presence and appearance of histamine in blood and lungs, by B. Tarras-Wahlberg ... Berlin und Leipzig, Walter de Gruyter & co., 1936.
2 p. l., 60 p. diagrs. 23½ᵐ. (Skandinavisches archiv für physiologie ... Supplement zum 73. bd.)
"From the Pharmacological department of the Caroline institute, Stockholm."
"Literature": p. 58–60.
1. Histamine. 2. Blood — Analysis and chemistry. 3. Lungs.
ɪ. Title.
₍Full name: Bo Bosson Tarras-Wahlberg₎
A C 38–1303
Iowa. Univ. Library
   for Library of Congress   ₍2₎

NT 0044011   IaU OU

Tarrasa, Spain.
Llibre dels privilegis de Tarrassa
see under Solery Palet, José.

Tarrasa, Spain. Cámara Oficial de Comercio e Industria.
Memoria comercial, industrial y estadística.
₍Tarrasa₎
v. in   25 cm.

1. Tarrasa, Spain—Econ. condit. ɪ. Title.
HF322.T38   52–18182 rev

NT 0044013   DLC

Tarrasa, Spain. Centre excursionista
see Centre Excursionista de Terrassa.

Fine arts
NA5809
.C3T3   Tarrasa, Spain. Junta Municipal de Museos.
Las iglesias de San Pedro de Tarrasa; antigua sede episcopal de Egara. Tarrasa, 1950.
15p. plates (part col.) fold. plan. 19cm.
"XV centenario de la sede Episcopal de Egara."
Bibliography: p.15.

NT 0044015   NNU-W DDO

Tarrasa, Spain. Museo Textil Biosca
see Museo Provincial Textil. Biosca.

Tarrasch, Fritz.
Der übergang des fürstentums Ansbach an Bayern, von Fritz Tarrasch. München und Berlin, R. Oldenbourg, 1912.
4 p. l., 182 p. 22ᵐ. (Added t-p.: Historische bibliothek, hrsg. von der redaktion der Historischen zeitschrift. 32. bd.)

1. Ansbach—Hist. 2. Bavaria—Hist. 3. Germany—Pol. & govt.—1740–1806.
13–7857
Library of Congress   DD801.B48T3

NT 0044017   DLC PU NN NcD

Tarrasch, Georg.
*Die Aetiologie des Uterusprolapses. Würzburg, F. Röhrl, 1888.
42 p. 8°.

NT 0044018   DNLM

Tarrasch, Siegbert, 1862–1934.
Best games of chess, selected and annotated by Fred Reinfeld. London, Chatto & Windus, 1947.
xxii, 385 p. illus., port. 21 cm.

1. Chess. ɪ. Reinfeld, Fred, 1910–   ed.
GV1451.T26 1947a   794.1   48–2579 rev*

NT 0044019   DLC OrP KEmT OrU TxFTC MiHM

GV1451
.T26
1947   **Tarrasch, Siegbert,** 1862–1934.
Best games of chess, selected and annotated by Fred Reinfeld. Philadelphia, D. McKay Co., 1947.
xxii, 385 p. illus. 22 cm.

1. Chess. ɪ. Reinfeld, Fred, 1910–   ed.
GV1451.T26 1947   794.1   47–11598 rev*

NT 0044020   DLC

SPEC.
COLL.
76A196   Tarrasch, Siegbert, 1862–1934.
Das Champion-Turnier zu Ostende im Jahre 1907 : Sammlung semtlicher Partien mit ausfuhrlichen Anmerkungen, mit Genehmigung des Turnier-Komitees / Hrsg. von Dr. Tarrasch. Leipzig : Veit, 1907.
136 p. : ill. ; 22 cm.
Paper covers.
Gift of Mrs. Paul Arne Hansen.

1. Chess--Tournaments, 1907.
I. Title

NT 0044021   DGU OCl NN NjP DLC-P4

Tarrasch, Siegbert, 1862–1934, ed.
Deutsche schachzeitung, organ für das gesamte schachleben ...
Leipzig, Veit & comp., 18

R-G
794
T192 D Tarrasch, Siegbert, 1862–1934.
Dreihundert Schachpartieen; gespielt und erläutert. Mit dem Bildnis und der Autobiographie des Verfassers. Leipzig, Von Veit, 1895.
500p. port., diagrs. 20cm.

1.Chess. Collections of games I.T1.

NT 0044023   NB MB NjP MH OCl OCU PP

TARRASCH, [Siegbert], 1862–1934.
Dreihundert Schachpartien. Ein unsystematisches Lehrbuch des Schachspiels für geübte Spieler. 2ᵉ, gekürzte und durch neue Partien ergänzte Auflage. Leipzig, Veit & Comp., 1909.
22 cm. Illustr.

NT 0044024   MH OCl

Tarrasch, Siegbert, 1862–1934.
Dreihundert Schachpartien; ein Lehrbuch des Schachspiels für geübte Spieler, von Dr. Tarrasch. Dritte, verbesserte Auflage ... Gouda: G. B. van Goor Zonen, 1925. xvi, 538 p. illus. 21½cm.
Printed in double columns.

635784A. 1. Chess—Games played.

FRANK J. MARSHALL CHESS COLL.
N.Y.P.L.   July 7, 1933

NT 0044025   NN OCl

Tarrasch, Siegbert, 1862–1934.
The game of chess; a systematic text-book for beginners and more experienced players, by Dr. Tarrasch; translated and arranged with some additional matter by G. E. Smith ... and T. G. Bone ... London, Chatto and Windus ₍1935₎.
xvi, 423 p. illus. 21¼ᵐ.

1. Chess. ɪ. Smith, George Ernest, 1893–   tr. ɪɪ. Bone, T. G., joint tr. ɪɪɪ. Title.
Library of Congress   GV1445.T242   35–3376
          ₍3₎   794.1

NT 0044026   DLC WaS IdB OrP IdU NN OClW

Tarrasch, Siegbert, 1862–1934.   6008.302
The game of chess. A systematic text-book for beginners and more experienced players. By Dr. Tarrasch. Translated and arranged with some additional matter by G. E. Smith and T. G. Bone.
— Philadelphia. David McKay Co. 1935. xvi, 423 pp. Illus. 20½ cm., in 8s.

D7813— Bone, T. G., ed. and tr. — Chess. — Smith, G. E., ed. and tr.

NT 0044027   MB OU NN OCl OEac

Tarrasch, Siegbert, 1862–1934.
The game of chess; a systematic text-book for beginners and more experienced players, by Dr. Tarrasch; translated and arranged with some additional matter by G. E. Smith ... and T. G. Bone ... Lond., Chatto and Windus ₍1935₎, Phila. McKay, 1938.
423 p.

NT 0044028   OCX OCl UU PP

Tarrasch, Siegbert, 1862–1934.
　　The game of chess, a systematic text-book for beginners and more experienced players, by Dr. Tarrasch; translated and arranged with some additional matter by G. E. Smith … and T. G. Bone … Philadelphia, David McKay company, 1940.

　　xvi, 423 p. illus. 21 cm.

　　1. Chess. I. Smith, George Ernest, 1893– tr. II. Bone, T. G., joint tr. III. Title.
　　GV1445.T242 19. 794.1 42—13368

NT 0044029　MtBuM MtU　DLC NcRS PU PP NcD NcC MB OU ViU FMU KU

GV
1450
.T25
Tarrasch, Siegbert, 1862–1934.
　　Der gegenwärtige Stand der wichtigsten Eröffnungen : (Spanisch, Vierspringerspiel und Damengambit) mit besonderer Berücksichtigung des Berliner Grossmeisterturniers / von Dr. Tarrasch. Berlin : B. Kagan, c1919.
　　38 p. : ill. ; 22 cm.

　　1. Chess--Openings　I. Title

NT 0044030　DGU MH OC1

TARRASCH, [Siegbert], 1862–1934.
　　Das grosse Schachturnier zu Nürnberg 1896. Sammlung sämtlicher Partien. In 2e Aufl. Berlin und Leipzig, W. de Gruyter & Co., etc., 1921.

　　22 cm. Illustr.

NT 0044031　MH OC1

Tarrasch, Siegbert, 1862–1934, *ed.*
　　Das grossmeisterturnier zu St. Petersburg im jahre 1914. Sammlung sämtlicher partien mit ausführlichen anmerkungen im auftrage des Turnierkomitees, herausgegeben von dr. Tarrasch. Mit einem anhang: Die ergebnisse des turniers für die eröffnungslehre. Nürnberg, Dr. Tarraschs selbstverlag, 1914.
　　xxiv, 192 p. illus., 3 group port. on 2 l. (incl. front.) 21m.

　　1. Chess—Tournaments, 1914. I. International chess tournament. St. Petersburg, 1914. II. Title.
　　　　　　　　　　　　45–42064
　　Library of Congress　GV1455.T3

NT 0044032　DLC OC1 DGU NN

Tarrasch, Siegbert, 1862–1934.
　　Das Grossmeisterturnier zu St. Petersburg im Jahre 1914; Sammlung sämtlicher Partien mit ausführlichen Anmerkungen, im Auftrage des Turnier-Komitees herausgegeben von Dr. Tarrasch. Zweite, verbesserte Auflage. Leipzig: C. Ronniger, 1921. xxiv, 185 p. incl. tables. illus. 21cm.

　　634232A. 1. Chess—Tournaments, 1914. I. Peterburgskoye shakhmatnoye sobraniye.
　　N. Y. P. L.　　　　　　November 17, 1933

NT 0044033　NN OC1

TARRASCH, S[iegbert], 1862–1934.
　　Das internationale Schachturnier des Schachclubs Nürnberg im Juli - August 1896. Sammlung sämtlicher Partien. Herausgegeben von S. Tarrasch und Chr. Schröder. Leipzig, Veit & Comp., 1897.

　　21 cm. Port. and illustr.
　　xx, 294 p.

NT 0044034　MH NjP OC1 NN

Tarrasch, Siegbert, 1862–1934.
　　Internationales Schachturnier zu Baden-Baden vom 15. April bis 14. Mai 1925 veranstaltet durch die Stadtverwaltung Baden-Baden. Sammlung sämtlicher Partien herausgegeben von Dr. Tarrasch. Berlin, Schachverlag B. Kagan, 1925.

　　xv, 127 p. ports., plates, tables. 22.5 cm.

NT 0044035　MH NjP OC1 NN

Tarrasch, Siegbert, 1862–1934.
　　Match for the championship of the world between Emanuel Lasker and Siegbert Tarrasch
　　　　see under　Lasker, Emanuel, 1868–

Tarrasch, Siegbert, 1862–1934.　　　G794-T
　　Die moderne Schachpartie; kritische Studien über mehr als 200 ausgewählte Meisterpartien der letzten zehn Jahre mit besonderer Berücksichtigung der Eröffnungen speziell der spanischen Partie und des Damengambits, von Dr. Tarrasch.　　Nürnberg: Dr. Tarraschs Selbstverlag ₍cop. 1912₎ 455 p. illus. 8°.

　　1. Chess. 2. Title.
　　N. Y. P. L.　　　　　　September 23, 1935

NT 0044037　NN

GV
1445
.T25
1916
Tarrasch, Siegbert, 1862–1934.
　　Die moderne Schachpartie : Kritische Studien über mehr als 200 ausgewählte Meisterpartien der letzten zwölf Jahre mit besonderer Berücksichtigung der Eröffnungen speziell der spanischen Partie und des Damengambits / von Dr. Tarrasch. 2. verb. aufl. Leipzig : C. Ronniger, 1916.
　　455 p. : ill. ; 21 cm.

　　1. Chess　I. Title

NT 0044038　DGU OC1

Tarrasch, Siegbert, 1862–1934.
　　Die moderne schachpartie; kritische studien über mehr als 200 ausgewählte meisterpartien der letzten zwölf Jahre mit besonderer berücksichtigung der eröffnungen, speziell der spanischen partie und des damengambits. 3. verb. aufl. xvi, 455p. Leipzig, C. Ronniger, 1921.

NT 0044039　OC1

Tarrasch, Siegbert, 1862–1934.
　　Die moderne Schachpartie; kritische Studien über mehr als 200 augewählte Meisterpartien der letzten zwanzig Jahre mit besonderer Berücksichtigung der Eröffnungen speziell der spanischen Partie und des Damengambits, von Dr. Tarrasch. 4. verb. Aufl. Leipzig, Hedewig, 1924 [c1923]
　　xv, 431 p. illus. 22 cm.
　　1. Chess.

NT 0044040　NcD NNU-W OC1 MH

Tarrasch, Siegbert, 1862–1934.
　　… Das schachspiel, systematisches lehrbuch für anfänger und geübte. Berlin, Deutsche buch-gemeinschaft g. m. b. h. ₍c1931₎
　　2 p. l., 482, ₍1₎ p. illus. 19m.
　　At head of title: Dr. Tarrasch.

　　1. Chess.
　　Library of Congress　GV1445.T24　　32–10556
　　Copyright A—Foreign　16148
　　　　　　₍2₎　　　　794.1

NT 0044041　DLC IU CtY OC1

Tarrasch, Siegbert, 1862–1934.
　　Das Schachspiel; systematisches Lehrbuch für Anfänger und Geübte. Berlin, C. Habel, 1947 ₍c1931₎
　　482 p. illus. 19 cm.

　　1. Chess. I. Title.
　　GV1445.T24 1947　794.1　　　A F 48–4633*
　　Yale Univ. Library
　　for Library of Congress　₍1₎†

NT 0044042　CtY OC1 DLC IaU

Tarrasch, Siegbert, 1862–1934.
　　Der Schachwettkampf Lasker-Marshall in Frühjahr 1907
　　　　see under　Lasker, Emanuel, 1868–1941.

Tarrasch, Siegbert, 1862–1934.
　　Der Schachwettkampf Lasker-Tarrasch im Lichte Laskerscher Analyse
　　　　see under　Lasker, Emanuel, 1868–1941.

Tarrasch, Siegbert, 1862–1934.
　　Der schachwettkampf Lasker-Tarrasch um die weltmeisterschaft im august-september 1908. Von dr. Tarrasch. Mit einem anhang: Neue untersuchungen über turmendspiele. Leipzig, Veit & comp., 1908.
　　148 p. illus. 20½m.

　　1. Chess. I. Lasker, Emanuel, 1868–1941.
　　　　　　　　　　　42–41578
　　Library of Congress　GV1451.T27

NT 0044045　DLC NjP OC1

Tarrasch, Siegbert, 1862–1934.
　　Der schachwettkampf Lasker-Tarrasch um die weltmeisterschaft (august-september 1908) im lichte Laskerscher analyse. 40p. Wien, C. Ronniger, 1909.

　　Preface signed Georg Marco.

NT 0044046　OC1

Tarrasch, Siegbert, 1862–1934.
　　Der Schachwettkampf Marshall-Tarrasch im Herbst 1905. Mit Erläuterungen hrsg. von Dr. Tarrasch. Leipzig, Veit, 1905. 62 p. illus. 21cm.

　　1. Chess—Games played. I. Marshall, Frank James, 1887–1944.

NT 0044047　NN MH

TARRASCH, SIEGBERT, 1862–1934.
　　Der Schachwettkampf Marshall-Tarrasch im Herbst 1905. Mit Erläuterungen hrsg. von Dr. Tarrasch. [2. Aufl. Berlin, B. Kagan, 192-] 62 p. illus. 21cm.

　　Film reproduction. Positive.

　　1. Chess--Games played. I. Marshall, Frank James, 1877–1944.

NT 0044048　NN

Tarrasch, Siegbert, 1862-1934, and F. J. Marshall.
Der Schachwettkampf Marshall-Tarrasch im Herbst 1905. Mit Erläuterungen herausgegeben von Dr. Tarrasch. ₍Berlin: B. Kagan, 1920?₎ 62 p. illus. 20½cm.

On cover: 2. Auflage.

775261A. 1. Chess—Games played.   I. Marshall, Frank James, 1877–
N.Y.P.L.   October 8, 1935

NT 0044049   NN

Tarrasch, Siegbert, 1862-1934
Der Schachwettkampf Schlechter-Tarrasch auf dem Jubiläums-Kongress des Kölner Schachklubs im Sommer 1911, herausgegeben und erläutert von Dr. Tarrasch; nebst ausgewählten Partien der beiden Hauptturniere, erläutert von Professor Dr. Deichmann... Leipzig: Veit & Comp., 1912. xviii, 136 p. incl. tables. front., illus. 21cm.

635788A. 1. Chess—Games played.   I. Deichmann, Karl.
N.Y.P.L.   August 25, 1933

NT 0044050   NN DGU DLC-P4 OC1

TARRASCH, SIEGBERT, 1862-1934.
Der Schachwettkampf Tarrasch-Mieses im Herbst 1916, mit ausführlichen Erläuterungen hrsg. von Dr. Tarrasch. Nebst einer Abhandlung über die französische und schottische Eröffnung. Leipzig, Veit, 1916. 1921 p. illus., group port. 21cm.

1. Chess--Tournaments, 1916. I. Mieses, Jacques.

NT 0044051   NN OC1

Tarrasch, Siegbert, 1862-1934.
Der schachwettkampf zwischen S. Tarrasch und M. Tschigorin, ende 1893
see under Heyde, Albert.

Tarrasch, Siegbert, 1862-1934, ed.
Stormästarturneringen i S:t Petersburg 1914; en samling av samtliga partier med utförliga abmärkningar, pa turneringskommitténs uppdrag utgiven av Dr Tarrasch; översättning av Eric Uhlin. ₍Orebro₎ Schacks Förlag ₍1955₎ 232p., illus.

NT 0044053   OC1

TARRASCH, SIEGBERT, 1862-1934.
Traité pratique du jeu d'échecs; à l'usage des amateurs et des spécialistes. Traduit de l'allemand par R. Jouan. Paris, Payot, 1952. 463 p. illus. 19cm.

1. Chess.

NT 0044054   NN

TARRASCH, SIEGBERT, 1862-1934.
Die Verteidigung des Damengambits; Kritische Untersuchungen und Tabellen. Gouda, G.B. Van Goor zonen, 1924. 128 p. illus. 22cm.

1. Chess--Gambits, Queen's.

NT 0044055   NN OC1

Tarrasch, Siegbert, 1862-1934.
₍Zashchita ferzevogo gambita...₎ ₍Defense against the queen's gambit; tr. by IA. G. Rokhlin; introduction by P. A. Romanovskii₎ xii, 111 ₍2₎ p. , Kyoyu, 1925.

NT 0044056   OC1

Tarrasch, Siegfried.
Ueber die Complikation der Hauptsymptome des Ileotyphus und der Meningitis cerebrospinalis. Breslau, Proskauer, 1889. 40 p.

NT 0044057   PPC CU DNLM

Tarrasch, Staffi M., 1906-
Die weiblichen angestellten. Das problem ihrer organisation. ... 1931. 59 p. Inaug. Diss. -Heidelberg, 1931. Lebenslauf. Bibliography.

NT 0044058   ICRL CtY PU

Hist.
WZ
294
R526T
1898

Tarrasch, Victor   1874-
Die Anatomie des Richardus. Berlin, E. Ebering, 1898. 49 p. 22 cm.
Inaug.-Diss. - Friedrich-Wilhelms-Universität, Berlin.
Vita.   Richardson Coll.
1. Anatomy - hist. 2. Richardus, Anglicus, 13th century. I. Title.

NT 0044059   WU-M

M1503
.W419S8
1948

Tarrasch, William.
Weill, Kurt, 1900-
₍Street scene. Piano-vocal score. English₎
Street scene, an American opera based on Elmer Rice's play. Book by Elmer Rice, lyrics by Langston Hughes. ₍Piano score ed. by William Tarrasch₎ New York, Chappell ₍1948₎

Tarrasch's Schachzeitung, hrsg. von Tarrasch.
v.1-   1932-
München,

NT 0044061   OC1

Y
185
T 16

TARRATARIA: or, Don Quixote the Second. A romantic, poetical medley, in two cantos. By a traveller of distinction... To which is added a poem, intituled, Christianity against Deism and immortality. By the same author. The work chiefly intended for His Majesty's perusal. London ₍Cooke₎ 1761. 42p.

NT 0044062   ICN OCU CtY

Tarratine club, Bangor, Me.
Constitution, etc. n.d.
15 p.

NT 0044063   PPAmP

Tarrats, José María Fontana
see
Fontana Tarrats, José María, 1911-

W
4
B72
1934/35

Tarraube, Lucien Robert, 1908-
Les boues végéto-minérales de Précnacq-les-Bains (Landes) leurs propriétés biologiques et thérapeutiques. Bordeaux, Impr.-librairie de l'université, 1935. 138 p. illus. (Bordeaux. Université. Faculté de médecine et de pharmacie. Thèse. 1934/35. no. 142)

NT 0044065   DNLM

Tarray, Erika: Wärmeregulation und Schilddrüse. [Maschinenschrift.] 24 S. 4°. — Auszug: Königsberg i. Pr. 1924: Steinbacher. 1 Bl. 8°
Königsberg, Med. Diss. v. 20. Jan. 1925   [U 25.5006]

NT 0044066   ICRL

Tarrazi, Philippe de, *vicomte*, 1865-1956.
اصدق ما كان من تاريخ لبنان وصحة من اخبار السريان،
بقلم فيليب دي طرازي. ₍بيروت، ١٩٤٨.
2 v. ports. 25 cm.
1. Lebanon—Church history.   I. Title.
Title transliterated: Aṣdaq mā kāna 'an ta'rīkh Lubnān.
BR1110.T3   61-20348

NT 0044067   DLC MH

Tarrazi, Philippe de, *vicomte*, 1865-1956.
ارشاد الاعارب الى تنسيق الكتب في المكاتب، بقلم فيليب
دي طرازي. ₍بيروت، الجمهورية اللبنانية، دار الكتب، 1947₎
6, 378 p. 25 cm. ₍منشورات وزارة التربية الوطنية والفنون الجميلة₎
Cover title: Classification décimale des livres arabes, par le vicomte Philippe de Tarrazi. Arabic and French.
1. Classification, Decimal.   I. Title. II. Title: Classification décimale des livres arabes. (Series: Lebanon. Wizārat al-Tarbiyah al-Waṭanīyah wa-al-Funūn al-Jamīlah. al-Manshūrāt)
Title transliterated: Irshād al-a'ārib ilā tansīq al-kutub fī al-makātib.
Z696.D6T37   N E 68-130

NT 0044068   DLC

Tarrazi, Philippe de, *vicomte,* b. 1865-1956.
المخطوطات المصورة والمزوقة عند العرب، بقلم الفيكنت فيليب
دي طرازي. حلب، مطبعة الضاد، 1939؟₎
35 p. 24 cm.
Bibliographical footnotes.
1. Illumination of books and manuscripts, Arabic. I. Title.
Title romanized: al-Makhṭūṭāt al-muṣawwarah wa-al-muzawwaqah 'inda al-'Arab.
ND3238.T3   70-282441

NT 0044069   DLC

Tarrazi, Philippe de, *vicomte,* 1865-1956.
(al-Salāsil al-tārīkhīyah fī asāqifat al-abrashīyāt al-Suryānīyah)
السلاسل التاريخية في اساقفة الابرشيات السريانية، بقلم
فيليب دي طرازي. بيروت، المطبعة الادبية، 1910.
482 p. ports. 21 cm.
Includes bibliographies.
1. Catholic Church. Patriarchate of Antioch (Syrian)—History. 2. Catholic Church. Patriarchate of Antioch (Syrian)—Biography. I. Title.
BX4713.72.T37   74-221213

NT 0044070   DLC

Tarrazi, Philippe de, *vicomte,* 1865-1956.

تاريخ الصحافة العربية، يحتوي على اخبار كل جريدة ومجلة
عربية ظهرت في العالم شرقا وغربا مع رسوم اصحابها والمحررين
فيها وتراجم مشاهيرهم .. بقلم الڤيكونت ڤيليپ دي طرازي.
بيروت، المطبعة الادبية، ١٩١٣-

v. illus., ports. 25 cm.

الجزء الاول: التوطئة. ١٧٩١-١٨٦٩ — الجزء الثاني: ١٨١٢-١٨٦٩
CONTENTS.—

1. Press—Near East.   I. Title.
Title transliterated: Ta'rīkh al-ṣiḥāfah al-'Arabīyah.

PN5359.T3   60-20905

NT   0044071   DLC ICU

Tarrazo, Manuel Barbachano y
       see
  Barbachano y Tarrazo, Manuel.

Tarrazona, Pere Hieroni
      see   Tarazona, Pedro Jéronimo, 16th c.

PC3967 Tarré, Emili.
.T23   Els aucels més útils á la agricultura de
         Catalunya. Barcelona, 1902.
         229 p. illus.

         1. Birds--Catalonia.

NT   0044074   ICU

TARRÉ, Emili.
  Poesíes. 2a serie. Barcelona, Tipografía,
"L'Aveng", 1907.

  pp. 91+

NT   0044075   MH

TARRÉ, Emili.
  El Sahara; poema. Barcelona, Tip. "L'Aveng",
1912.

  pp. 59+

NT   0044076   MH

      Tarré, Francisco del
             see
    Tarré y Draper, Francisco del, 1878–

Tarré, Josep
  ... Converses d'arqueologia: La Catedral de
Barcelona; El trasllat del cor de la Catedral
de Granada. Barcelona, 1930.
  22 p. illus., plans. 24½cm.

  At head of title: Josep Tarré ... Rafael Martorell.
  Contents.--Nota preliminar.--La Catedral de
Barcelona, signed: Josep Tarré.--El Trasllat
del cor de la Catedral de Granada, signed: Rafael Martorell.

NT   0044078   NNC

NK1653 Tarré, Josep.
.S7G8   ...Nocions de liturgia cristiana, per
         Josep Tarré...   Barcelona, Bonavia &
         Durán [1916,
         32p. 19cm. (Minerva; col'lecció
         popular dels coneixements indispensa-
         bles... v.3)
           "Bibliografia": p.[2,
           Bound with Gudiol y Cunill, José.
         L'indumentaria litúrgica. 1918.

           1. Liturgies.

NT   0044079   NNU-W

Tarre, Joseph.
  Sand technology. [East Chicago, Ind.,
Continental Roll & Steel Foundry Co.] 1943.
45p. illus. 28cm.

  Cover title.
  Bibliography: p.45.

  1. Sand, Foundry.

NT   0044080   IU

Tärre M., Francisco.
  Cirugía del tendón (estudio experimental y clínico) Caracas,
Empresa El Cojo, 1940.
  77 p. illus.
  Tesis - Univ. Central de Venezuela.
  "Bibliografía": p. [79]

  I. Venezuela. Universidad Central, Caracas/ Tesis.
1. Tendons (Diseases)

NT   0044081   ICJ DNLM

Tarré y Draper, Francisco del, 1878–
  ... Catálogo básico de los sellos de colonias, ex-colonias y
oficinas españolas en el extranjero. Barcelona, Ediciones
Hymsa [1943]
  3 p. l., 3-196, [1] p. illus. 16ᶜᵐ.
  At head of title: Francisco del Tarré.
  "Segunda edición."

  1. Postage-stamps—Spain. 2. Spain—Colonies—Postage-stamps.
                                              45-15949
  Library of Congress   HE6185.S7T3 1943
                                      [2]   383.22

NT   0044082   DLC

HE6185 Tarré y Draper, Francisco del, 1878-
S82T3   Catálogo de sellos de España y sus varieda-
1947   des. [5. ed.] Barcelona, Ediciones Hymsa
         [1947]
         242 p. illus. 17cm.

           Cover-title: Catálogo especializado de los
         sellos de España.

           1. Postage-stamps - Spain. 2. Postage-
         stamps - Catalogs.

NT   0044083   CU

Tárrega, Francisco, publisher.
  Relacion de las fiestas que el Arçobispo y
Cabildo de Valencia hizieron en la translacion de la
Reliquia del glorioso S. Vincente Ferrer a este
santo Templo. Sacada a luz por su deuocion y
mandamiento, por el Doctor y Canonigo Francisco
Tarrega, y dirigida a los Illustrissimos y Excellentes
señores Condes de Benauente, que Dios guarde.
Con Licencia, Impressa en Valencia, en casa de

Pedro Patricio Mey, junto a S. Martin, 1600.
Vendense en casa de Gabriel Hernandez librero, en
la Corregeria uieja.

NT   0044085   NNH

---

m781.25 Tárrega, Francisco, 1852-1909.
T192a   [Adelita]
           Adelita! mazurka para guitarra.
         Madrid, Union Musical Española [c1942]
         [1]p. 34cm.

           1. Guitar music. I. Title.
    *

NT   0044086   CLSU

Tárrega, Francisco, 1852-1909.
  [Guitar works. Selections]
  [Collection of original guitar compositions and
guitar arrangements in UCLA's Ernie Ball Guitar
Music Collection.   n.p., n.d.]
  77 v. in 4.
  1. Guitar music. 2. Guitar music, Arranged.

NT   0044087   CLU

Mus
M   Tárrega, Francisco, 1852-1909.
126   Doce composiciones para guitarra. Revisión
T3   de Isaias Savio.   Buenos Aires, Ricordi
         Americana [n.d.] Pl. no. B A 11248.
         score (32p.)

         1. Guitar music.

NT   0044088   FTaSU

787.61 Tárrega, Francisco, 1852-1909.
T177es   Estudios y preludios, que sirven de com-
         plemento a la Escuela de la guitarra. Rev.
         y cuidadosamente digitados por Mario Rod-
         riguez Arenas. Buenos Aires, Ricordí
         Americana [n.d.]
         55p.

         1. Guitar - Studies and   exercises.

NT   0044089   PP

---

m781.25 Tárrega, Francisco, 1852-1909.
T192m   [Marieta!]
           Marieta! mazurka para guitarra [and]
         Rosita; polka para guitarra. [Madrid,
         Unión Musical Española, n.d.] Pl.no.
         2095.
           [3]p. 35cm.
           Caption title.
           On cover: Obras escojidas de varios autores.

           1.Mazurkas (Guitar) 2.Polkas (Guitar)
         I.Tárrega, Fran-   cisco, 1852-1909.
         Rosita. II.Ti-   tle. III.Title:
     *   Rosita. LC.   CLSU60

NT   0044090   CLSU

---

m781.25 Tárrega, Francisco, 1852-1909.
T192pO   [Preludes, guitar, no.3-5]
           Preludio no.4, & no.5] para gui-
         tarra. [Madrid, Unión Musical Españo-
         la] c1942.
           [3]p. 36cm.

           Caption title.
           On cover: Obras escojidas de varios
         autores.

           1.Guitar   music.

NT   0044091   CLSU

m781.25 Tárrega, Francisco, 1852-1909.
T192p6   [Prelude, guitar, no.6, B min.]
    Preludio, 6°.   Madrid, Orfeo Tracio
    [n.d.] Pl.no.1053.
    [1]p. 34cm.

    Caption title.
    On cover: Obras escogidas de los mejores
autores españoles.

    1. Guitar music. LC.

NT 0044092   CLSU CLU

m781.25 Tárrega, Francisco, 1852-1909.
T192p7   [Prelude, guitar, no.7, A major]
    Preludio, 7°.   Madrid, Orfeo Tracio
    [n.d.] Pl.no.1054.
    [1]p. 34cm.

    Caption title.
    On cover: Obras escogidas de los mejo-
res autores españoles.

    1. Guitar music. LC.

NT 0044093   CLSU

Tárrega, Francisco Augustín, 1554?-1602.
Mesonero y Romanos, Ramón de, 1803-1882, ed.
    ... Dramaticos contemporaneos a Lope de Vega, coleccion
escogida y ordenada, con un discurso, apuntes biográficas y
críticos de los autores, noticias bibliográficas y catálogos,
por don Ramon de Mesonero Romanos ... Madrid, M. Rivade-
neyra, 1857-58.

Tarrega, Francisco Augustin, 1554?-1602.
    La Enemiga favorable.
        40 p.   (ochoa, E. de, Tesoro teatro españ.
    v. 1, p. 349.)

NT 0044095   MdBP

PQ   Tárrega, Francisco Agustín, 1554?-1602.
6217   La enemiga favorable. [Por] Tarraga.
O16
v.1   (In Moratín, L. F. de. Orígenes del
    teatro español. Paris, 1838. 22cm.
    p. [349]-388)

NT 0044096   NIC NN

Tárrega, Francisco Augustin, 1554?-1602,
    supposed author.
        La fortuna adversa; comedia famosa
    see under title

Tarrega, Francisco Augustin, 1554?-1602.
    El Prado de Valencia. La Sangre leal de los
montañeses de Navarra. La Duquesa constante.
La Enemiga favorable.
    92 p.   (Mesonero Romanos, R. de, Dramat.
contemp. á Lope de Vega, v. 1, p. 31: Bibliot.
de autor. españ.)

NT 0044098   MdBP

PQ6284   Tárrega, Francisco Agustín, 1554?-1602, supposed
.P7S55   author.
Sloman, Albert E
    The sources of Calderón's El príncipe constante; with a
critical edition of its immediate source, La fortuna adversa
del infante don Fernando de Portugal (a play attributed to
Lope de Vega) Oxford. Blackwell. 1950.

Tarrega, Juan Carmelo
    see   Carmelo Tárrega, Juan.

Tárrega y de Arias, Bernabé.
    Ensayo de un compendio de fortificacion para el uso de los
oficiales de infantería, por D. Bernabé Tárrega y de Arias ...
Toledo, Impr. de J. de Cea, 1856.
    2 v. 20½ᵐ. *and atlas of 7 double pl.* 22½ᵐ.
    "Me ha parecido que debía comprender la fortificacion de campaña con
mucha estension, y solo las nociones de la permanente que he conceptuado
necesarias para un oficial de infantería."—Prólogo.
    CONTENTS.—1. pte. De la fortificacion de campaña y de la provisional.—
2. pte. Nociones de la fortificacion permanente.

    1. Fortification.
                                                    29-16142
    Library of Congress   UG401.T25

NT 0044101   DLC

Tarrène, J.
    ... Contribution àl l'étude des thromboses
aortiques dans la fièvre typhoïde.   Toulouse, 1903.
(Inaug. dis.)

NT 0044102   DLC DNLM

W   Tarrène, Maurice
4   Le traitement des ordures ménagères
T74   par l'incinération; l'usine d'incinération
1939   de Toulouse. Toulouse, Impr. toulousaine,
    1939.
        108 p. illus. (Toulouse. Université.
    Faculté mixte de médecine et de pharmacie.
    Thèse. 1939. no. 22)

NT 0044103   DNLM CtY

Tarrible, Jean Dominique Léonard, 1753-1821.
    ... Discours prononcé par Tarrible, orateur du Tribunat, sur
les engagemens qui se forment sans convention. Séance du 19
pluviôse an 12 [Paris, Imprimerie nationale, pluviôse an 12
[1804.]
    18 p. 20½ᵐ.
    Caption title.
    At head of title: Corps législatif.
    No. [17] in a volume of pamphlets lettered: Code civil. Motifs, t. 3.

    1. Quasi contracts—France. 2. Torts—France. i. France. Corps
législatif, 1795-1814.
                                                    42-42349

NT 0044104   DLC

Tarrible, Jean Dominique Léonard, 1753-1821.
    Discours sur le 12e projet de loi, Titre
XI du Code civil, relatif à la majorité,
l'interdiction et au conseil judiciaire.
Corps législatif. Séance du 8 germinal an 11.
[Paris, Impr. nationale, germinal an 11, i.e.
1803]
    22 p. 21cm. [French history pamphlets.
Consulate. v.17, no.3]

    Caption title.

NT 0044105   MnU

Tarrible, Jean Dominique Léonard, 1750-1821.
France. *Tribunat. Section de législation.*
    ... Rapport fait par Tarrible, au nom de la Section de légis-
lation, sur le projet de loi relatif au mandat (Code civil). Séance du 16 ventôse an 12. [Paris, Imprimerie nationale, ventôse an 12 [1804]]

Tarrible, Jean Dominique Léonard, 1753-1821.
    Traite des privilèges et hypothèques suivant
les principes du code civil.   Liège, 1819.
    2 v.

NT 0044107   MH-L

Wason   Tarrida del Mármol, Fernando, 1861-1915.
DP85.8   Les inquisiteurs d'Espagne: Montjuich,
T19   Cuba, Philippines. Paris, P.-V. Stock,
    1897.
        xii, 344 p. 19cm. (Bibliothèque
    sociologique, no 17)

        1. Spain—Pol. & govt.—1886-1931.
    2. Cuba—Hist.—1878-1895. 3. Cuba—Hist.—
    1895-   4. Philippine Islands—Hist.—
    1896-1898. I. Title.

NT 0044108   NIC Wa MH-L

TARRIDA DEL MÁRMOL, Fernando, 1861-1915.
    Problemas trascendentales; estudios de
sociología y ciencia moderna. Paris,
Sociedad de ediciones literarias y artísticas,
1908.

NT 0044109   MH IU

Tarrida del Mármol, Fernando, 1861-1915.
    ...Problemas trascendentales; estudios de sociología y ciencia
moderna. Barcelona: Biblioteca de "La revista blanca," 1930.
202 p. incl. facsim. port. 12°.
    Contents: Fernando Tarrida del Mármol, [by] F. Urales.] Dedicatoria. Cuatro
palabras. Carta-prefacio de Clemencia Royer al autor. Ciencia popular. Sociología
científica. Cosmología. Apéndice: Lista de los autores citados en la obra.

550967A. 1. Science—Essays, etc.   2. Sociology—Essays and
misc. 3. Cosmology.   July 8, 1932
N. Y. P. L.

NT 0044110   NN NNC

Tarrida del Mármol, Juan
    see   Tarrida del Mármol George, Juan.

Tarrida del Mármol George, Juan, tr.
Howard, Harvey James, 1880-
    ... Diez semanas entre los bandidos chinos, traducido del
inglés por Juan Tarrida del Mármol George. Edición ilustrada con veintitrés fotografías. Barcelona. B. Bauzá [1932]

Tarride, Abel Anatole, 1865-
    Le coin du feu; comédie en un acte.   Paris,
Libr. Théatrale, 1904.
    44 p. 12°.

NT 0044113   NN

Tarride, Abel Anatole, 1865-
    Faire fortune. Comédie en trois actes de MM. Abel Tarride
et Fernand Fauré. (Annales politiques et littéraires. Paris,
1921. f°. Tome 77; p. 113-118, 133-138, 153-158.)
    Adapted from George Randolph Chester's Get-rich-quick Wallingford.

1. Drama (French). 2. Title.   3. Fauré, Fernand, 1853-
jt. au. 4. Chester, George Randolph,   1869-   : Get-rich-quick Walling-
ford.   ford.
N. Y. P. L.   November 5, 1921.

NT 0044114   NN

Tarride, Abel Anatole, 1865–
Fin de Vertu. Comédie en un acte.   Paris,
Librairie Théatrale, 1904.
47 p.   12°.

NT 0044115   NN

Hfr
ta90
Tarride, Abel Anatole, 1865–
Papa, comédie en un acte de Abel Tarride
& Henri Piazza. Paris, Librairie théâtrale,
1905.
31p.   19cm.
"Représentée pour la première fois, à
Paris, à la salle des fêtes du Figaro."

NT 0044116   CtY

Hfr
ta90
Tarride, Abel Anatole, 1865–
... Par habitude, comédie en un acte. Paris,
Librairie théâtrale, 1904.
24p.   19½cm. [Bound with his Papa. Paris,
1905]
At head of title: Abel Tarride & François
Vernayre.
"Représentée, pour la première fois, à
Paris, au Théâtre des Mathurins, le 26
septembre 1903."

NT 0044117   CtY NN

Tarride, Abel Anatole, 1865–   joint author.

Croisset, Francis de, 1877–
Le tour de main; comédie en trois actes, de mm. Francis
de Croisset et Abel Tarride, représentée pour la première fois
au Casino municipal de Nice, le 17 mars 1906, et reprise au
théâtre du Gymnase à Paris, le 16 mai 1906 ...

WH
1497
Tarridec, Paul
Contribution à l'étude de quelques alcools
tertiaires di et tétrahydrofuranniques.
[Paris? 1955?]
48 ℓ.
Thèse – Paris.

NT 0044119   CtY MH

Tarrien de Lacouperie, Albert Etienne Jean Baptist
d. 1894.
Formosa notes on Mss., languages and races.
(Including a note on nine Formosan Mss. by E. C.
Baber.) ...   Hertford, S. Austin & Sons, 1887.
2 p. l., 82 p., 1 l.   1 map.   8°.

NT 0044120   NN

Tarrieux (Louis) [1852–   ]. * Des ulcérations de la cornée; pathogénie, mode de guérison. ... 58 pp., 1 l., 4°. *Paris*, 1876, No. 349.

NT 0044121   DNLM

Tarrillon, Amédée.
*Des effets du calorique et du froid, et de leur
traitement.   Paris, 1855.
34 p.   4°.
No. 94, v. 581.

NT 0044122   DNLM

Tarring, *Sir* Charles James, 1845–1923.
Analytical tables of the law of real property, drawn up
chiefly from Stephen's Blackstone, with notes. By Charles
James Tarring ... London, Stevens and Haynes, 1882.
4 p. l., VIII fold. tab. 24½ᵐ.

1. Real property—Gt. Brit.   I. Stephen, Henry John, 1787–1864.
New commentaries on the laws of England.   II. Title.

35–24261

NT 0044123   DLC CtY MH

Tarring, *Sir* Charles James, 1845–1923.
British consular jurisdiction in the East; with topical
indices of cases on appeal from and relating to consular
courts and consuls, also a collection of statutes concerning
consuls, by Charles James Tarring ... London, Stevens and
Haynes, 1887.
x p., 1 l., 132 p. 22 cm.

1. Gt. Brit.—Diplomatic and consular service.   2. Consular jurisdiction.   I. Gt. Brit. Laws, statutes, etc.

JX1784.T3   A 10—1238
Newberry Library
for Library of Congress   [a64b⅓]†

NT 0044124   ICN DLC PU CtY NcD

Tarring, Charles James, 1845–1923.
Chapters on the law relating to the colonies. To which
is appended a topical index of cases decided in the Privy
council, on appeal from the colonies, the Channel Islands
and the Isle of Man, reported in Acton, Knapp, Moore, the
Law journal reports, and the Law reports, to July, 1882.
By Charles James Tarring ... London, Stevens and Haynes,
1882.
xiv p., 1 l., 204 p. 21½ cm.

1. Gt. Brit.—Colonies—Administration.   2. Gt. Brit.—Colonies—
Law. [3. Colonies]

14—20441

NT 0044125   DLC CtY MH

Tarring, Charles James, 1845–1923.
Chapters on the law relating to the colonies. To which
are appended topical indexes of cases decided in the
Privy council on appeal from the colonies, Channel Islands and the Isle of Man and of cases relating to the colonies decided in the English courts ... By Charles James
Tarring ... 2d ed., enl. London, Stevens and Haynes,
1893.
2 p. l., [vii]–xxiii, [1], 478 p. 22ᵐ.

1. Gt. Brit.—Colonies—Administration.   2. Gt. Brit.—Colonies—Law.
I. Gt. Brit. Laws, statutes, etc.

9–34556†

Library of Congress   JV1062.T2

NT 0044126   DLC CaBVaU CtY PU-L DNW OC1W

Tarring, Charles James, 1845–1923.
Chapters on the law relating to the colonies, to which
are appended topical indexes of cases decided in the
Privy council on appeal from the colonies, Channel Islands and the Isle of Man; and of cases relating to the
colonies decided in the English courts otherwise than on
appeal from the colonies. By Charles James Tarring ...
3d ed. London, Stevens and Haynes, 1906.
xxvii, [1], 482 p. 22ᵐ.
P. 8 wrongly numbered 82.

7–27354

NT 0044127   DLC PU-L GU-L

Tarring, Charles James, 1845–1923.
Chapters on the law relating to the colonies, to which
are appended topical indexes of cases decided in the Privy
council, on appeal from the colonies, Channel Islands and
the Isle of Man, and of cases relating to the colonies decided in the English courts, otherwise than on appeal
therefrom, by Sir Charles James Tarring ... 4th ed.
London, Stevens and Haynes, 1913.
xxii, [2], 398 p. 25½ᵐ.

1. Gt. Brit.—Colonies—Administration.   2. Gt. Brit.—Colonies—Law.
[3. Colonies]

14–17947

NT 0044128   DLC CaBVa CtY GU MiU

Tarring, *Sir* Charles James, 1845–1923.
Land provisions of the Taiho rio. By C. J. Tarring ...
(*In* Asiatic society of Japan. Transactions. Yokohama [etc.] 1880
[i. e. 1905] 23ᵐ. v. 8, pt. 2, p. [1]–12)
"Reprinted."

1. Land tenure—Japan—Law.   I. Japan. Laws, statutes, etc.
II. Title: Taiho rio.
A C 38–3220
Chicago. Univ. Library   AS552.A83 vol. 8
for Library of Congress   [AS552.Y8 vol. 8, pt. 2]
[4]   (068.52)

NT 0044129   ICU NcD DLC

Tarring, Charles James, 1845–1923.
A practical elementary Turkish grammar. By Charles
James Tarring ... London, K. Paul, Trench & co., 1886.
viii, 207 p. 18½ᶜᵐ.

1. Turkish language—Grammar.
1–1494
Library of Congress   PL123.T3

NT 0044130   DLC CU CtY

HD9506
T35
Tarring, Leslie Herbert, ed.
In a metal merchant's office; a short guide
to trading in metals, ores, iron and steel and
scrap. 1st ed. Ed. by L.H. Tarring and H. G.
Cordero.   London; Quin Press Ltd., 1943.
240 p.   plate, diagrs.   19 cm.

1. Metal trade. 2. Metals. 3. Ores. 4. Iron
and industry. 5. Scrap. I. Cordero, H. G., jt.
ed. II. Title.

NT 0044131   NN DI

Tarring, Eng. (Deanery)

Chichester, Eng. (Diocese)
Calendar of Sussex marriage licences recorded in the
Peculiar courts of the Dean of Chichester and of the
Archbishop of Canterbury. Deanery of Chichester, Jan-
uary, 1582–3, to December, 1730. Deaneries of Pagham
and Tarring, January, 1579–80, to November, 1730. By
Edwin H. W. Dunkin ... [London, Mitchell, Hughes and
Clarke, printers, 1911]

Tarring, West, *Eng.* (Parish)
The churchwarden's accounts of West Tarring ... Tran-
scribed and edited by the Rev. W. J. Pressey ... [Worthing,
Eng., Printed by B. H. Gadd, 192–?]
2 v. 26 x 20½ᵐ.
Imprint from label on inside of cover, v. 1.
CONTENTS.—v. 1. Churchwardens' accounts, 1515–1579.—v. 2. Church-
wardens' accounts, 1579–1631. The landscot book, 1622–1742.

1. Tarring, West, Eng.—Hist.—Sources.   I. Pressey, William James,
ed.
44–49018
Library of Congress   DA690.T17A2
[2]   942.25

NT 0044133   DLC

Tarrington, Eng. (Yorkshire)
see Terrington, Eng. (Yorkshire)

Tarrio, Ana Rosa.
San Martín, su lucha en verso. ¡Ilustrada con 8 xilografías por Alberto Nicasio¡ Córdoba, 1947.
191 p. illus., port. 28 cm.
"100 ejemplares en papel especial numerados, que llevan la firma autógrafa de la autora." No. 70.

1. San Martín, José de, 1778-1850—Poetry.

A 51-8551

New York. Public Libr.
for Library of Congress   ¡1¡

NT 0044135 NN

Tarrío y Bueno, Toribio.
Sociedad civil de instrucción, mutuo auxilio y beneficencia, Hijos de Riego, *Madrid.*
Disposiciones por que se rige y prácticas en que se ocupa la Sociedad civil de instrucción, mútuo auxilio y beneficencia, Hijos de Riego ... Madrid, 1893.

QB502 **Tarris, Andrew.**
.T2   Anti-Copèrnican, ... Marion, Ind., The Marion Tribune Company, c1911.

NT 0044137 DLC

W 4   TARRIT, André, 1928-
P23   Les accidents hémorragiques du
1955   traitement anticoagulant, d'après
no. 184   l'analyse de 1.500 traitements. Paris, 1955.
80 p. illus. (Paris. ¡Université¡ Faculté de médecine. Thèse, 1955, no. 184)
1. Blood coagulation 2. Hemorrhage

NT 0044138 DNLM

Law   Tarrius, Gervais, joint author.

Laborie, Paul.
Abrégé de législation d'assistance et de protection médico-sociale, d'après les programmes des études préparatoires aux diplômes d'État d'infirmière et assistante sociale. Par Paul Laborie ¡et¡ Gervais Tarrius. ¡Paris. A. Poinat. 1952¡

Tarrius, Gervais.
... Les eaux industrielles internationales et leur réglementation internationale ... par Gervais Tarrius ... Perpignan, Imprimerie Gilles & Trilha, 1935.
4 p. l., ¡7¡-235 p. 24½ᶜᵐ.
Thèse—Univ. de Montpellier.
"Bibliographie": p. ¡229¡-282.

1. Water-rights.   I. Title.
42-40550

Library of Congress   HD1691.T3

NT 0044140 DLC CtY NNC NN

PQ2639 **Tarrius, Gervais.**
.A75A6   Miscellanées (nouvelles et contes) Des larmes et des sourires, des rires et des sanglots. Le Puy ¡Haute-Loire¡ Cahiers du nouvel humanisme ¡1953¡
118 p. 20 cm.
CONTENTS.— Dieu seul pardonne.— Rendez-vous à l'Hôtel des postes.—Marthe, Colette et Nicolas.—Conte (en cinq lettres)—Elle n'avait fait que vœu d'amour.— En sa candeur naïve.— Légende fleurie.

I. Title.
A 53-6544
843.91
Illinois. Univ. Libra
for Library of Congress   ¡1¡

NT 0044141 IU DLC

Tarrius (Jean). *Contribution à l'étude du diagnostic des hallucinations. 80 pp. 8°. Paris, 1919. No. 50.

NT 0044142 DNLM CtY

Tarrius (Pierre). * Le podophyllum peltatum. 43 pp. 4°. *Montpellier, 1882,* No. 317.
École supérieure de pharmacie.

NT 0044143 DNLM

Tarrius (Pierre) [1854-]. * De la gangrène pulmonaire. 64 pp., 2 tab. 4°. *Paris, 1881,* No. 51.

NT 0044144 DNLM

Tarroni, Dino.
L'allevamento dei bovini in provincia di Reggio Emilia./ Reggio Emilia, Comitato Provinciale dell'Agricoltura di Reggio Emilia ¡1950¡
39 p.

NT 0044145 InLP

Tarroni, Evelina.
Cinema e gioventù; studio degli aspetti sociali e dei motivi d'interesse ¡di¡ E. Tarroni e S. Paderni. Roma, Edizione dell'Istituto ¡1952¡
163 p. illus. 18 cm. (Università di Roma. Quaderni dell'Istituto di pedagogia.

1. Moving-pictures and children.   I. Paderni, Sandro, joint author. II. Title.   (Series: Rome (City) Università. Istituto di pedagogia. Quaderni)

A 53-6220

Southern Calif., Univ. of   Library
for Library of Congress   ¡1¡

NT 0044146 CLSU NN CtY

371.335 **Tarroni, Evelina.**
C574q   L'educazione di base e i mezzi audio-
v.4   visivi. Roma, Ministero Pubblica Istruzione, 1952.
16p. 24cm. (Cineteca Scolastica Italiana. Quaderni didattici, 4)

1. Illiteracy - Italy. 2. Audio-visual education. I. Title.

NT 0044147 CLSU

Tarroni, Evelina.
Orientamenti culturali del cinema didattico all'estero. Roma, Cineteca Ministero della P. I., 1953.
15 p. 24 cm. (Cineteca scolastica italiana. Quaderni didattici, 2. ser., n. 3)

1. Moving-pictures in education.   I. Title.   (Series)

A 55-377

Southern Calif., Univ. of.   Library
for Library of Congress   ¡1¡

NT 0044148 CLSU

Tarrot, Louis.
Les écoles et les écoliers à travers les ages. Paris, Laurens, 1893.
3, 339 p. Illus. Portrs. Pls. L. 8°.

NT 0044149 MB

Tarrou, David N
Orthodoxie et libéralisme. Lettre à m. le professeur A. Sabatier. Nîmes, 1888
16 p.

NT 0044150 MH

Tarrou, Maurice, 1891-
... Lait humanisé et allaitement artificiel ... Montpellier, 1925.
25 cm.
Thèse – Univ. de Montpellier.
Bibliographies: p. 30.

NT 0044151 CtY

BTZ   **Tarroux, Ferdinand**
806   Jésus-Dieu et M. Renan philosophe. Paris,
.R391   Librairie catholique internationale de l'Oeuvre
T19   de Saint-Paul, 1887.
xvi, 728 p. 22cm.

1. Renan, Ernest, 1823-1892. Vie de Jésus. 2. Jesus Christ--Biography. I. Title.

NT 0044152 DCU

Tarroux, Ferdinand.
Lettres sur le socialisme, par Ferdinand Tarroux. Paris, Fischbacher, 1894.
2 p. l., ix, 396 p. 18¼ᶜᵐ.

1. Socialism.   I. Title.
16-9931

Library of Congress   HX266.T3

NT 0044153 DLC MH

WO   **TARROW, Arthur Bernard, 1917-**
218   Basic sciences in anesthesiology; a
qT192b   guide for study. Fort Sam Houston,
1950   Brooke General Hospital, 1950.
1 v. (various pagings)
Contains errata slips.
1. Anesthesia - Examinations, questions, etc.

NT 0044154 DNLM

WO   **Tarrow, Arthur Bernard, 1917-**
218   Basic sciences in anesthesiology; ¡a guide
T192   for study). 2d. ed. Texas, Lackland Air Force
1953   Base, 1953.
Variously paged, 27 cm.

Inscribed by author to Paul M. Wood.

1. Anesthesiology. Study & Teaching.
I. U. S. Lackland Air Force Base.

NT 0044155 IParkA

Tarrow, Arthur Bernard, 1917-
Basic sciences in anesthesiology; a guide for study. 2d ed. San Antonio, Tex., Lydette Pub. Co., 1955.
274 p. 27 cm.
Cover title.
Includes bibliography.
1. Anesthetics.

NT 0044156 ViU OrU-M MiU PPJ NNC DNLM ICU

Tarrozo, Thraciano.
Os recursos coloniais na economia nacional.
Lisboa ₍Sociedade astória₎ 1941.
209 p. illus. 23ᵐ.

1. Portugal - Econ. condit. - 1918-
2. Portugal - Colonies. I. Title.

NT 0044157   CSt ICU

Tarrozzi, Giuseppe, 1866-
... Coscienza morale e civile, testo di morale
ad uso delle scuole normali. 3. ed. con aggiunto
e correzioni. Bologna, N. Zanichelli; [etc., etc.,
1914]
xvi, 322 p., 1 l.   20 cm.
1. Conscience.

NT 0044158   CU

TARROZZI, Giuseppe, 1866-
Filosofia morale e nozioni affini, ad
uso dei maestri e del corso, di perfezionamento per i licenziati dalle scuole normali.
Bologna, N. Zanichelli, etc., etc., [1911].

NT 0044159   MH

Tarrozzi, Giuseppe, 1866-
... Nozioni di psicologia, con preliminari
filosofici. Bologna, N. Zanichelli [1925]
1 p. l., [v]-viii, 165 p., 1 l.   21 cm.
1. Psychology.

NT 0044160   CU

Tarruella, Alfredo C.
... Cantos para Hilda. Buenos Aires ₍Talleres gráficos de
E. Valimbri₎ 1931.
3 p. l., 9-99 p., 5 l. incl. plates. 18ᵐ.
At head of title: Alfredo Tarruella.

ɪ. Title.
35-11533
Library of Congress   PQ7797.T3C3   861.6

NT 0044161   DLC

Tarruella, Alfredo C.
La catedral de oro, poesías de Alfredo Tarruella. Buenos
Aires, J. Toia (hijo) 1930.
3 p. l., 9-82 p., 3 l. 18ᵐ.

ɪ. Title.
35-18181
Library of Congress   PQ7797.T3C35   861.6

NT 0044162   DLC

PQ7797 Tarruella, Alfredo C
T3C4   El claro amor.   Buenos Aires, 1948.
58p. 23cm.

NT 0044163   IaU

F
2235.4   Tarruella,Alfredo C
.T22   Las ideas políticas del General San Martín
y su legado histórico. ₍Buenos Aires?₎
Editorial Martín Fierro, 1950.
68 p. illus.

1.San Martin,Jose de,1778-1850. I.Title.

NT 0044164   MiU CU TxHU CLU NNC TxU

Tarruella, Alfredo C.
El pianito de tu casa de Alfredo C. Tarruella. ₍Buenos
Aires, Talleres gráficos de E. Valimbri, 1928₎
56, ₍8₎ p. incl. plates. 16ᵐ.
Poems.

ɪ. Title.
29-28310
Library of Congress   PQ7797.T3P5

NT 0044165   DLC NcU

Tarruella, José
see Tarruella Albarede, José.

G868.8   Tarruella, Víctor María.
T1772m   Miradas rotas.   La Asunción, Instituto Para-
guayo de Cultura Hispánica [1954]
47p. 20cm. (Colección "Poesía", 1)

Poems.

NT 0044167   TxU

WI
460   TARRUELLA ALBAREDE, José
T192i   Ileus renal; oclusión intestinal ₍aguda₎
1943   por cólico nefrético.   Barcelona, Sabadell,
1943.
214 p.
Includes the author's address, Elogio de
la semiología (p. 153-191) and his essay,
El signo del bicarbonato (p. 193-214).
Author's autograph presentation copy.
1. Intestines - Obstruction

NT 0044168   DNLM

W 1
MO555   TARRUELLA ALBAREDE, José
no. 23   Semiologia de les ptosis digestives.
1928   Barcelona, 1928.
62 p. illus. (Monografies mèdiques,
no. 23)
1. Visceroptosis   Series

NT 0044169   DNLM

Tarruella Albarede, José.
Sobre la urobilinuria; monografía premiada por
la Real Academia de medicina y cirugía de Barcelona. Barcelona, L. Tasso, 1897.
147 p., 1 l.   12°.

NT 0044170   DNLM

Film   TARRUELLA ALBAREDE, José
1190   Sobre la urobilinuria.   Barcelona,
no. 2   Tasso, 1897.
147 p.   Film 1190
Film copy.
"Monografía premiada por la Real
Academia de Medicina y Cirugía de
Barcelona."

NT 0044171   DNLM

W 1
MO555   TARRUELLA ALBAREDE, José
no. 24   Tractament de les ptosis digestives.
1929   Barcelona, 1929.
53 p. illus. (Monografies mèdiques,
no. 24)
1. Visceroptosis   Series

NT 0044172   DNLM

QZ
365   TARRUELLA ALBAREDE, José
T192u   Ulcus rodens, su curabilidad médica.
1951   Barcelona, 1951.
181 p.   QZ365 T192u
1. Carcinoma, Basal cell

NT 0044173   DNLM

Tarrugo unmasked, or an Answer to a late
pamphlet intituled, Apollo Mathematicus ...
To which is added by Doctor Pitcairne,
the Theory of the internal diseases of the
eye ...
see under Hepburne, Georgius.

Tarry, Ellen, 1906-
Hezekiah Horton, by Ellen Tarry; pictures by Oliver
Harrington. New York, The Viking press, 1942.
39 p. illus. (part col.) 24 cm.
"First published August 1942."

ɪ. Title.
42—18466
Library of Congress   PZ7.T18He

NT 0044175   DLC Or OrP OCl OO MB PP

Tarry, Ellen, 1906-
Janie Belle, by Ellen Tarry, illustrated by Myrtle Sheldon.
New York, Garden City publishing co., inc., °1940.
₍30₎ p. illus. 26½ x 20ᵐ.
Illustrated title on two leaves.

ɪ. *Sheldon, Myrtle, 1893-   illus. ɪɪ. Title.
40-32986
Library of Congress   PZ7.T18Jan

NT 0044176   DLC IU

Tarry, Ellen, 1906-
My dog Rinty, by Ellen Tarry and Marie Hall Ets, illus-
trated by Alexander and Alexandra Alland. New York, The
Viking press, 1946.
₍48₎ p. incl. front., illus. 24½ x 19½ᵐ.
"First published May 1946."

1. Dogs—Legends and stories.   ɪ. Ets, Marie Hall, joint author.
ɪɪ. Title.
46–4736
Library of Congress   PZ10.3.T1386My

InU ViHaI OO OOxM WaS WaSp
NT 0044177   DLC Or OrP NvU NcGU PWcS MiU PP MsSM OCl

Tarry, Ellen, 1906–
   The runaway elephant. Pictures by Oliver Harrington.
New York, Viking Press, 1950.
   37 p. col. illus. 25 cm.

      I. Harrington, Oliver, illus. II. Title.

     PZ10.3.T1386Ru   50–8863

NT   0044178   DLC OrMonO Or WaS

Tarry, Ellen, 1906–
   The third door; the autobiography of an American Negro
woman. New York, D. McKay Co. [1955]
   304 p. 21 cm.

     I. Title.
     E185.97.T37A3   920.5   55—14466 ‡

   OC1ND OrPS OrU Wa WaE WaS WaSp WaT
   DCU MB OOxM NcR PPLas MCR TxU PRosC PWcS MiU PV OC1
NT   0044179   DLC CaBVa OrCS Or OrLgE PP NcU NcD TU NN

E 185.97
.T19 A3 TARRY,ELLEN,1906–
   The third door; the autobiography of an
American Negro woman. New York, D. McKay Co.
[1955]
   304 p.

   Photocopy. Univ.Microfilms,Ann Arbor,Mich.

NT   0044180   InU

HV
8195
.T3   **Tarry, Frederick T.**
   The police as a career.   Exeter, A.
Wheaton, 1936.
   205 p. port. 19 cm.

   1. Police--Gt. Brit. I. Title.

NT   0044181   OkU

QA471
T36   [**Tarry, Gaston,** d. 1913]
   Équation géométrique des coniques & des
quadriques. [Alger, A. Jourdan, 1885]
   8p.   22cm.

Physical
Sciences
Library   Caption title.
   With his Identité des principes de
dualité et polarité ... 1885.

NT   0044182   RPB

513
T17e   **Tarry, Gaston,** d. 1913.
   Essai sur la géométrie des figures
imaginaires.   Paris [1887]
   21p. diagrs. (Association française
pour l'avancement des sciences fusionnée
avec l'Association scientifique de
France ... Congrès de Toulouse, 1887)

   Caption title.
   Bound with his Novel essai sur la géométrie imaginaire and Géométrie générale.

NT   0044183   IU

Tarry, Gaston, d. 1913.
   Figuration des solutions imaginaires rencontrées
en géométrie ordinaire.   Paris, 1892.
   4p. (Association francaise pour l'avancement
des sciences. Comptes rendus. 1892)
   Bound between pt. 3 and 4 of his: Géométrie
générale.

NT   0044184   IU

513
T17e   **Tarry, Gaston,** d. 1913.
   Géométrie générale.   Paris, [1889]
   28p. diagrs.

   Bound with his Essai sur la géométrie
des figures imaginaires. 1887.

NT   0044185   IU

QA471
T36   **Tarry, Gaston,** d. 1913
   Identité des principes de dualité et
de polarité.   Alger, A. Jourdan, 1885.
   8p.   22cm.

NT   0044186   RPB

513
T17e   **Tarry, Gaston,** d. 1913.
   Nouvel essai sur la géométrie imaginaire.   Paris [1888]
   22p. diagrs.

   Bound with his Essai sur la géométrie
des figures imaginaires. 1887.

NT   0044187   IU

Tarry, G[aston] d. 1913.
   ... Le problème des 36 officiers. Extrait des Comptes
rendus de l'Association française pour l'avancement des
sciences. Congrès de Paris—1900. Paris, Secrétariat de
l'Association [1901?]
   cover-title, 35, [1] p. diagr. 23½cm.

   1. Permutations.

   Library of Congress   QA165.T2   4–26023†

NT   0044188   DLC

QA255
T37
1886   **Tarry, Gaston,** d. 1913
   Représentation géométrique des coniques
et quadriques imaginaires.   Paris, Gauthier-
Villars, 1886.
   31p. diagr. 22cm.

   1. Numbers, Complex.

NT   0044189   RPB IU DCU

513
T17g   **Tarry, Gaston,** d. 1913.
   Sur la théorie des carrés magiques im-
pairs a deux degrés.   Paris, 1896.
   4p. fold. table   (Association française pour l'avancement des sciences.
Comptes rendus.   1896)

   Bound at end of his: Géométrie générale.

NT   0044190   IU

512.81
T17t   **Tarry, Gaston,** d. 1913.
   Tablettes des cotes relatives a la base
20580 des facteurs premiers d'un nombre
inférieur a N et non divisible par 2, 3,
5 ou 7.   Paris, 1906.
   3p. tables.

NT   0044191   IU

Tarry, Harold.
   De la prediction du mouvement des tempêtes
Africaines et des periodes meteorologiques. Alger
1873.
   39 p. 8.

NT   0044192   DAS

Tarry, Harold.
   De la prédiction du mouvement des tempetes, et
des phénomènes qui les accompagnent ...   Roma,
1872.
   Pamphlet.

NT   0044193   CtY

Tarry, Harold
   Exchange de telegrammes meteorologiques entre l'-
Europe et l'Afrique. Paris. 1876.
   35 p. 8.

NT   0044194   DAS

Tarry, H[arold]
   Histoire de l'atmosphere. 1876.
   Paris. 1876.

NT   0044195   DAS

Tarry, Peter Albert.
   Magnetic tape recording, written & comp. by P. A. Tarry...
Birmingham [Eng.] Audigraph [1950]   64 p.   illus.   21cm.

   1. Sound—Recording and repro-   ducing.

NT   0044196   NN

789.92
T177M   **TARRY, Peter Albert.**
   Magnetic tape recording. 4th ed. (rev. &
enl.)
     Birmingham, Eng. Audigraph. 1952.
   70p. diagrs.

NT   0044197   WaS

Tarrytown, N.Y.
   Memorial of Washington Irving/ n.p.,
n.d.
   [4]p. 8°

NT   0044198   MWA

Tarrytown, N.Y. Asbury Methodist Episcopal
Church.
¿One hundredth anniversary of the present church building
of Asbury Methodist Episcopal church, Tarrytown, New York,
April 23, 24 and 25, 1937. One hundred forty-one years of
Methodism in Tarrytown ... Compiled by Elliot Baldwin Hunt,
church historian. ¿Tarrytown, N. Y.: Printed by the Daily
news, 1937¿ 116 p. incl. facsims. illus. (incl. ports.) 23½cm.

At head of title: 1837-1937.

1. Tarrytown, N. Y.—Churches,   Methodist Episcopal—Asbury.
I. Hunt, Elliot Baldwin, comp.
N.Y.P.L.   May 24, 1938

NT 0044199   NN

Tarrytown, N. Y. Charters.
An act creating the charter of the city of
Tarrytown
            see under   New York (State) Laws, statutes,
etc.

Tarrytown, N. Y. First Reformed Church
        see   North Tarrytown, N. Y. First Re-
formed Church.

Tarrytown, N. Y. Hackley school
        see   Hackley school, Tarrytown, N. Y.

Tarrytown, N. Y. Hospital for the care of crippled
    and deformed children
        see   New York (State) Rehabilitation
Hospital, West Haverstraw.

Tarrytown, N. Y. Marymount college

see

Marymount college, *Tarrytown, N. Y.*

Tarrytown, N. Y. Monument committee.
Souvenir of the revolutionary soldiers' monument dedication, at Tarrytown, N. Y., October 19th, 1894. Comp. by
Marcius D. Raymond ... ¿New York, Rogers & Sherwood,
printers¿ 1894.
207, ¿1¿ p., 2 l. front., illus., plates, ports. 26¼ᵐᵐ.
Edition limited to 100 copies.

1. Tarrytown, N. Y. Revolutionary soldiers' monument. 2. Tarrytown, N. Y.—Hist. 3. Tarrytown, N. Y.—Geneal. I. Raymond, Marcius Denison, 1833– II. Title.

                                                              9—10368
        Library of Congress   F129.T19T1

NT 0044205   DLC PHi

Tarrytown, N. Y. St. Faith's House
see St. Faith's House, *Tarrytown, N. Y.*

Tarrytown, N. Y. St. Vincent de Paul Institute
        see   St. Vincent de Paul Institute,
Tarrytown, N. Y.

Tarrytown, N. Y. Second Reformed Church.
Fiftieth anniversary. Rev. Mr. Mabon's
historical address in full.

NT 0044208   PPPrHi

Tarrytown, N.Y. Second reformed church.
A hundred years: The Second Reformed church, Tarrytown,
New York, 1851–1951. ¿Tarrytown, 1951?¿   27 p.   illus.
28cm.

Cover-title.
Text signed: Jack R. Hornady.

1. Tarrytown, N. Y.—Churches.   I. Hornady, Jack ¿R.

NT 0044209   NN

Tarrytown, N.Y. Second reformed church.
The story of the "Town clock church," 1837–1937...The Second Reformed church of Tarrytown...Centennial services, November 21–25, 1937. ¿Tarrytown, 1937¿ 16 p. illus. 23cm.

1. Tarrytown, N. Y.—Churches,   Reformed—Second.
N.Y.P.L.   October 23, 1945

NT 0044210   NN

Tarrytown, N. Y. Sleepy Hollow Cemetery
        see   Sleepy Hollow Cemetry, Tarrytown,
N. Y.

Tarrytown, N. Y. State hospital for the Care of
    Crippled and Deformed Children
        see   New York State Hospital for the Care
of Crippled and Deformed Children, West Haverstraw.

Tarrytown, N. Y. Young men's lyceum. *Library.*
Catalogue of books contained in library of Young men's
lyceum, Tarrytown ... New York, A. Cobb, printer,
1869.
cover-title, 16 p. 19¼ᵐ.

—— Supplementary catalogue of books contained in
library of Young men's lyceum ... Tarrytown, N. Y.,
"Argus" printing office, 1870.
cover-title, 14 p. 19¼ᵐ.

                                                              1–2336–7
        Library of Congress   Z881.T192

NT 0044213   DLC

Business
HQ
2613   Tarrytown and the Tarrytown National Bank and
.T19   Trust Company. Published in commemoration
T3   of the Golden Anniversary of the opening in
        eighteen eighty-two of the Tarrytown National
        Bank. Tarrytown, N. Y., 1932.
        71 p. illus., map (on lining papers)

        1. Banks and banking - Tarrytown, N. Y.
        2. Tarrytown National Bank and Trust Company.

NT 0044214   NNC

CS71   Tarrytown argus, Tarrytown, N.Y.
f.D975 ... Revolutionary sketches of Philipse
1894   manor. The Duytser-Dutcher family.
        ¿Tarrytown,N.Y., Tarrytown argus, 1894¿
        14 numb. l.   34cm.

        Carbon copy.
        "Copied from the Tarrytown argus, Jan.27,
        1894, vol.26, no.13."

NT 0044215   MnHi

BX
6480
A95   **Tarrytown Baptist Church, Austin, Tex.**
T377   Directory. Austin, Tex., 1963.
1963   26p. 15cm.
TXC

NT 0044216   TxU

Tarrytown Daily News.
Sleepy Hollow; a country of beautiful homes. ¿Tarrytown,
N. Y.¿ Tarrytown Daily News ¿191–?¿   45 l.   illus.

Cover-title: In Irving's country.

207123B. 1. Tarrytown, N. Y.—   Hist. 2. Tarrytown, N. Y.—Views.
3. Architecture, Domestic—U. S.—   N. Y—Tarrytown. I. Title.
N. Y. P. L.   November 19, 1942

NT 0044217   NN

Tarrytown Historical Society, Tarrytown, N. Y.
Chronicle. no.1-date; May, 1931-date
Tarrytown, N. Y.   no.   illus., ports.   23cm.

Three times a year (slightly irregular).
Publication suspended June, 1931-Nov.1957.
No. 1, May, 1931, issued by the society under its earlier name:
Tarrytown historical society.

1. Tarrytown, N. Y.--Hist.--Per. and soc. publ. 2. North Tarrytown,
N.Y.--Hist.--Per. and soc. publ. I. Tarrytown historical society,
Tarrytown, N.Y. Chronicle.

NT 0044219   NN MWA

Tarrytown historical society, Tarrytown, N. Y.

North Tarrytown, N. Y. First Reformed church.
First English record book of the Dutch Reformed church
in Sleepy Hollow, formerly the Manor church of Philipsburgh,
now the First Reformed church of Tarrytown ... prepared for
publication by Edgar Mayhew Bacon. ¿Tarrytown, N. Y.¿
Tarrytown historical society, 1931.

Tarrytown historical society, Tarrytown, N. Y.

¿Conklin, Margaret Swancott¿
Historical Tarrytown and North Tarrytown (a guide).
¿Tarrytown, N. Y., The Tarrytown historical society, ᶜ1939¿

Tarrytown historical society, Tarrytown, N.Y.

Raymond, Marcius Denison, 1833–1911.
Washington at Tarrytown. A paper read before the Tarrytown historical society, by Marcius D. Raymond, Tuesday
eve., December 16, 1890. Published by the author by request.
Tarrytown, N. Y. ¿"Tarrytown Argus" print¿ 1893.

Tarrytown tattler.

₍Salem₎

v. in   illus. 29 cm.

Semimonthly (irregular)   —Oct. 1944; monthly, Nov. 1944-
Pub. by the patients of the Oregon State Hospital.

ɪ. Oregon. State Hospital, Salem.

RC445.O7S27   362.2   49–30252*

NT 0044223   DLC Or OrP

Tarrytown, White Plains and Mamaroneck Railway Company.
Franchise documents.   ₍New York₎ 1903.   310 p.   map.
4°.

1. Railways (Interurban), U. S.:   New York:
N. Y. P. L.   October 11, 1922.

NT 0044224   NN

Társadalmi lexikon, szerk. Madzsar, József. Függelékül: A
szociális mozgalmak krónikája, 1750–1928. Budapest, Nép-
szava-Konyvkereskedés ₍1929₎

708 p. illus. (part col.) ports. 25 cm.

1. Encyclopedias and dictionaries, Hungarian.   ɪ. Madzsar,
József, ed.

AG31.T3   52–56998

NT 0044225   DLC MH-L NN NNC

Társadalmi mozgalmak Magyarországon, Agárdi Ferenc...₍és
más₎ tanulmányai. ₍Budapest₎ Anonymus, 1946.   391 p.
25cm. (Századok es tanulságok)

415776B. 1. Hungary—Hist.   2. Hungary—Soc. condit. I. Agárdi,
Ferenc.
N. Y. L.   October 31, 1950

NT 0044226   NN NNC

TÁRSADALMI mozgalmak Magyarországon, Agárdi
Ferenc. [et al.] tanulmányai. [Budapest]
Anonymus, 1946. 391 p. 25cm. (Századok es
tanulságok)

Microfiche (neg.) 8 sheets. 11 x 15cm. (NYPL FSN 10,309)

1. Hungary--Hist. 2. Hungary--   Soc. condit. I. Agárdi,
Ferenc.

NT 0044227   NN

Társadalmi Múzeum
see Budapest. Társadalomegészségügyi Intézet és
Múzeum.

Társadalmi osztályaink az irodalom tükrében. [Budapest]

NT 0044229   MH

Társadalmi szemle.

₍Budapest₎

v. in   23–25 cm. monthly.

Began publication with Jan. 1946 issue. Cf. Union list of serials.
Journal of the Magyar Dolgozók Pártja.

1. Communism—Period.   ɪ. Magyar Dolgozók Pártja.

HX8.T3   55–18230

NN
NT 0044230   DLC MtU NjP NNC MH PPiU MiU CtY FU TxU

**Társadalom- és természettudományi
ismersetterjesztő társulat.
Szobanövényeink ápolása**

see under

Szűcs, Lajos.

Q44   **Társadalom-és Természettudományi Ismeretter-**
.B93   **jesztő Társulat.**

Természet és társadalom. 1.-   évfolyam;
1869-
₍Budapest, etc.₎

QB9   **Társadalom és Természettudományi Ismeretter-**
.C8   **jesztő Társulat. Csillagászati Szakosztály.**

Csillagászati évkönyv.
Budapest, Művelt Nép.

Társadalombiztositás és munkavédelem. 1.-

évf.: 1949 jul.-
₍Budapest₎ Szakszervezetek Országos Tanácsa.

v. illus. 25 cm. monthly.

Title varies : 1949–Sept. 1950, Szociálpolitika.

1. Hungary—Social policy—Period.   ɪ. Szakszervezetek Országos
Tanácsa. ɪɪ. Title: Szociálpolitika.

HN418.H9T3   65–50610

NT 0044234   DLC

Társadalombiztositási közlöny.

₍Budapest, Lapkiadó Vállalat₎

v. 29 cm. monthly.

"A SZOT Társadalombiztositási Főigazgatóság hivatalos lapja."

1. Insurance, Social—Hungary.   I. Szakszervezetek Országos
Tanácsa. Társadalombiztositási Főigazgatóság.

72–623405

NT 0044235   DLC

Társadalomegészségügyi Intézet és Múzeum
see Budapest. Társadalomegészségügyi Intézet és
Múzeum.

Társadalompolitika.

Budapest, M. Kir. Népjóléti és Munkaügyi Minisztérium.

v. 26 cm. monthly.

1. Social sciences—Period.   ɪ. Hungary. Népjóléti és Munkaügyi
Minisztérium.

H8.T26   52–64937 ‡

NT 0044237   DLC NN

Társadalompolitikai közlemények. Szerkeszti: Somogyi Manó. Kötet
ɪ (füzet 2).
= Budapest. 1904. v. 24 cm., in 8s.

L6381 — Periodicals. Hungarian. — ...ungary. Lang. Works in Hungarian. —
Sociology. Periodicals. — Somogyi, Manó, ed.

NT 0044238   MB

H8
.T3   **Társadalomtudomány**; a Magyar társadalomtudományi társulat folyóirata ...

Budapest ₍19
v.   24ᶜᵐ. irregular.

Editors: 19   György Szombatfalvy
and others.
Includes sections "Könyvismertetések",
"Folyóiratok szemléje", and section "Compte
rendu analitique des articles de fond" with
text in French.

NT 0044239   DLC NNC InU IU NN OC1

Társadalomtudományi könyvtár. Budapest, Grill Károly
Könyvkiadóvállalata

kötet 5 (1908): Jászi, Oszkár. Művészet és erkölcs

NT 0044240   MH

Társadalomtudományi Könyvtár, uj sorozat
••••
Budapest, Grill, 19—
v. o.

NT 0044241   OO

Társadalomtudományi Társaság.
Pulszky Ágost emlékezete; a Társadalomtudományi
Társaságnak 1902. április 13-án, Budapesten, a Kereskedelmi
és Iparkamara Dísztermében tartott ünnepélyes ülése.
Budapest, 1902.

107 p. port. 25 cm.

"Pulszky Ágost irodalmi munkássága, összeállították: Pikler Gyula
és Vámbéry Rusztem": p. ₍73₎–74.

1. Pulszky, Ágost, 1846–1901.

HM22.H82P8   65–59632

NT 0044242   DLC NNC

Társadalomtudományi Társaság.
A Társadalomtudományi Társaság Pulszky Ágost
könyvtárának betürendes katalogusa. Budapest,
1903.
111 p.

Continued in next column

Continued from preceding column

1. Catalogs, Library - Hungary. I. Pulszky, Ágost, 1846-1901.

At head of title: Magyar Sociographiai Intézet kiadványai, szám "Az Országos Bibliographiai Központ támogatásával."

NT 0044244 NNC

Társalkodó. Pest, Augustus' 7-dikén, 1833. (Hungarian newspaper)

NT 0044245 PPAmP

Tarschis, Israel.
בכי תמרורים Mourning sermon on the late Rev. Jacob
הנה קטה והי, על מות הרב ר' יעקב ריינהערץ. Reinhertz.
לונדן, 1892/93. London

4 p. 20 cm.
Cover title.

1. Reinhertz, Jacob. I. Title.
Title transliterated: Bekhi tamrurim.
BM755.R35T3 52-47186

NT 0044246 DLC

---

x928.4 Tarschys, Bernhard, 1905 -
T17a Affär i kultur den franska encyklopédins
historia. [Malmö] Bibliofila Klubben
[1950]
17p. illus., ports., facsim. 22cm.
(Kuriositeter i litteraturen, 7)

Cover title.
"Upplaga 475 numrerade ... [n. 51."

1. Encyclopedists. I. Title. II. Bibliofila Klubben, Malmö. (Series)

NT 0044247 IU

TARSCHYS, BERNHARD, 1905-
Chevra kaddischa, Israelitiska sjukhjälps-och begravningssällskapet under 150 år. Stockholm, Judiska litteratursamfundet [1944] 153p. ports. 24cm.

1. Chevra kaddischa, Stockholm. L Judiska litteratursamfundet.

NT 0044248 NN DLC-P4 OU CtY

Tarschys, Bernhard, 1905-
Talis Qualis, studentpoeten; miljö- och idéhistoriska studier. Stockholm, Norstedt, 1949.
vii, 366 p. 25 cm.
Akademisk avhandling—Stockholm.
Extra t. p. with thesis statement, inserted.
"Litteraturförteckning" : p. 336-354.

1. Strandberg, Carl Vilhelm August, 1818-1877.
PT9797.S75Z8 A 52-1613
——— Copy 2. Without extra t. p.
Harvard Univ. Library
for Library of Congress [3]†

DLC
NT 0044249 MH NcD NN NIC CtY MnU NcU ICU WaU TxU

Tarschys, Karin.
Svenska språket och litteraturen; studier över modersmålsundervisningen i högre skolor. Stockholm, Natur och kultur [1955]
416 p. 25 cm. (Stockholm studies in Scandinavian philology, 13)
Akademisk avhandling—Stockholm högskola.
Errata slip inserted.
Bibliography : p. 379-405.

1. Swedish language—Study and teaching. 2. Swedish literature—Study and teaching. I. Title. (Series)

PD5065.T3 56-58248

NIC MnU NcD
NT 0044250 DLC PU NN CU ViU TxU ICU MH CtY CLSU OU

Tarse, Jean.
... M P tegen weerwolf, door Jean Tarse ...
[Brussel, M. R. Warnotte, etc., c1945]
18 p. (Wekelijksche magazine, de honderd mooiste oorlogsverhalen, O.K. nr 29)

NT 0044251 DLC

Tarsey, James Maurice, 1899-
Pain syndromes and their treatment, with special reference to shoulder-arm pain. Springfield, Ill., Thomas [1953]
592 p. illus. 24 cm.

1. Pain. I. Title.

RC73.T27 616.075 53-935 ‡

NT 0044252 DLC

Tarsh, Jack.
Healthy industry ...
see under Automatic Telephone & Electric Co., Ltd.

Tarshis, Mrs. Elizabeth (Kent) 1913- joint author.
Kent, Mrs. Louise (Andrews) 1886-
In good old colony times; a historical picture book, with text by Louise Andrews Kent & Elizabeth Kent Tarshis. Boston, Houghton Mifflin company, 1941.

Tarshis, Elizabeth (Kent) 1913-
Look at America, by Elizabeth Kent Tarshis, illustrated by Harold Haydon. New York, R. M. McBride and company [1942]
[96] p. incl. col. front., col. illus. 24½ᵐ.
"First edition."

1. U. S.—Descr. & trav. I. Title.

Library of Congress E169.T2 42-23238
[18] 917.3

NT 0044255 DLC WaSp Or OO PP OCl

Tarshis, Elizabeth Kent, 1913-
The village that learned to read [by] Elizabeth Kent Tarshis; illustrated by Harold Haydon. Boston, Houghton Mifflin company, 1941.
4 p. l., 158, [2] p. col. front., illus. 25½ x 19½ᵐ.

I. Title.

Library of Congress PZ7.T2Vi 41-8636

OEac OO OCl OOxM DPU OClh OrP OrU WaS CaBViP WaSp Or
NT 0044256 DLC CoAlC MB PWcS NN PP PSt MiU CU OCU

Tarshis, Mrs. Elizabeth (Kent) 1913-
Young sailors of Sidon; a story of long ago Phoenicia, by Elizabeth Kent Tarshis; illustrated by Richard A. Holberg. Boston, L. C. Page & company [1938]
xiii, 162 p. incl. front., illus. 21½ᵐ.
Maps on lining-papers.

1. Children in Phenicia. I. Title.

Library of Congress PZ9.T241Yo 38-35985

NT 0044257 DLC PP NN OCl

308t Tarshis, Irvin Barry, 1914-
T193 The transmission of Haemoproteus lophortyx O'Roke of the valley California quail by hippoboscid flies of the species Stilbometopa impressa (Bigot) and Lynchia hirsuta Ferris and the elucidation of the biology of these ectoparasites. [Berkeley, 1953]
xvii, 250 l. illus., maps, diagrs., tables.

Thesis (Ph.D. in Parasitology) - Univ. of California, June 1953.
Bibliography: p. 242-250.

NT 0044258 CU

Tarshis, Lorie.
The elements of economics, an introduction to the theory of price and employment. Boston, Houghton Mifflin Co. [1947]
xii, 699 p. diagrs. 24ᵐ.
"Under the editorship of Edgar S. Furniss."
"Suggestions for further reading" at end of each part.

1. Economics. I. Furniss, Edgar Stephenson, 1890- ed.
HB171.5.T17 330 47-4536*

OrCS OrU WaWW WaS OrP IdU
ViU ICU LU CU AU NcU NcRS TxU PSt PCW CaBVaU MtU Or
NT 0044259 DLC ICU MH-PA PHC PBL WU NcGU NSyU TU MB

Tarshis, Lorie.
Introduction to international trade and finance. New York, Wiley [1955]
536 p. illus. 24 cm.

1. Commerce. 2. Foreign economic relations. I. Title: International trade and finance.

HF1007.T23 382 55-14305 ‡

OrMonO OU MtU OrCS Wa WaS WaWW WaT MtBC OrP
OCU MB NN TxU OOxM PP PU DS OrU CaBVa CaBVaU CaBViP
NT 0044260 DLC MH-PA CoU NmU MU NBuC OClW AU LU NcD

---

330 Tarshis, Lorie.
T177e Students manual to accompany The elements of economics, an introduction to the theory of price and unemployment [by] Lorie Tarshis [and] Phillip Cartwright. Boston, Houghton Mifflin [1948]
Manual 189p. diagrs., tables. 23cm.

1. Economics. I. Tarshis, Lorie. The elements of economics. II. Cartwright, Phillip, joint author.

NT 0044261 TxU

Tarshis, Maurice Steinmetz.
A study of atypical chronogenic acid-fast bacilli isolated from human sources and blood media for the bacteriologic diagnosis of tuberculosis. A thesis presented to the Department of Bacteriology...University of Oregon Medical School... for the degree of Doctor of Philosophy. September, 1950.
165 p. 21 p. 5 p. (three sections)

NT 0044262 OrU-M

*H
T   Tarshish, Allan, 1907-
8   Board of Delegates of American
Mic   Israelites (1859-1878) 1932.
78   93,xiv l.   28 cm.
    Thesis (Rabbinic)--H.U.C.-J.I.R.
    Typescript.
    -- ---Microfilm (negative).
    Cincinnati, A.J.P.C., 1960. 1 reel. 35
mm.

    1. Board of Delegates of American
Israelites. I. Title

NT   0044263   OCH

Tarshish, Allan, 1907-
    Not by power; the story of the growth of Judaism.   New
York, Bookman Associates ₁1952₎
    277 p.   22 cm.

    1. Jews—Hist.   ɪ. Title.

    DS118.T3   296.09   52—13777 ‡

   IEN OCl MoU CaOTP NcU MB NN OCH PPT
NT   0044264   DLC GU WaTU OrStbM WaS ICJS TxU CoU NcRS

---

*H-D
T   Tarshish, Allan, 1907-
8   The rise of American Judaism (A
Mic   history of American Jewish life from
525   1848 to 1881) [1938]
    xiv, 436, xxvi, cxiv l. 28 cm.
    Thesis--H.U.C.-J.I.R.
    Typescript.
    -- ---Microfilm (negative).
    Cincinnati, A.J.P.C., 1961. 1 reel. 35
mm.

    1. Jews in the United States--
History. 2. Judaism--United States--
History. I. Title

NT   0044265   OCH

Tarshish, Jacob, 1892-
    Half hours with Rabbi Jacob Tarshish; addresses de-
livered over Station WLW, Cincinnati, Ohio. Columbus,
Ohio, F. J. Heer Print. Co. ₁1933₎
    111 p. port. 24 cm.

    1. Sermons, Jewish—U. S. 2. Sermons, American—Jewish authors.
ɪ. Title.

    BM740.T29   64—58303

NT   0044266   DLC OO NN

Tarshish, Jacob, 1892-
    "In your own back yard".   Newark, N.J.
North American accident insurance company, 1937.
    6 p.   28.5 cm.

NT   0044267   PPT

Tarshish, Jacob, 1892–
    ... Judaism and socialism, by Rabbi Jacob Tarshish ...
₁Cincinnati, The Tract commission, 193–?₎
    25 p. 17ᶜᵐ.   (Jewish tracts, no. 13)
    Bibliography: p. 25.

    1. Jews—Pol. & govt. 2. Socialism. ɪ. Title.
                      38–31377
    Library of Congress   BM40.C45 no. 13
                   ₍2₎   (296,082) 296

NT   0044268   DLC CtY ICJS OrStbM OCH ViU

Tarshish, Jacob, 1892–
    Little journeys with The Lamplighter ₍pseud.₎   1st ed.
Columbus, Ohio, F. J. Heer Print. Co., 1936.
    128 p.   port.   24 cm.
    "Second volume" ₍in a series of broadcasts₎

    1. Sermons, Jewish—U. S. 2. Sermons, American—Jewish authors.
ɪ. Title.

    BM740.T3   64–58219

NT   0044269   DLC

TARSHISH, JACOB, 1892-
    Little journeys with the Lamplighter [pseud.] l. ed.
Columbus, O., F.J. Heer print. co., 1935.   128 p.
port.   24cm.

    Film reproduction. Negative.
    Vol. 2 of the author's collection of radio broadcasts.

    1₎ Conduct of life. I. Title.

NT   0044270   NN

Tarshish, Jacob, 1892-
    Prelude to happiness, by The Lamplighter ₍pseud.₎   1st
ed.   Columbus, Ohio, F. J. Heer Print. Co., 1937.
    108 p.   port.   24 cm.
    "Third volume" ₍in a series of broadcasts₎

    1. Sermons, Jewish—U. S. 2. Sermons, American—Jewish authors.
ɪ. Title.

    BM740.T32   64–582!3

NT   0044271   DLC OCH NN

Z6371
.T6T3   Tarshish, Perez.

אישים וספרים ב"תוספות" מאת פרץ תרששׁ, ז"ל. נסדר
על ידי ח. ש. מיהוויצען והוצא לאור על ידי בנו ובנותיו. מו
               ₍New York, 1942₎ 22½ᶜᵐ.

    2 p. l., xxxi p., 1 l., 161 p.; vi p. front. (port.) 22½ᶜᵐ.
    Added t.-p.: The personalities and books referred to in Tosafot,
being a compilation of references to persons and books mentioned
throughout the Tosafot to the entire Talmud, by Perez Tarshish; edited
by Simon A. Neuhausen.
    Paged with Hebrew characters.

    1. Tosafot—Bibl.   ɪ. Neuhausen, Simon Avseyewitz, ed.
                 Title transliterated: Ishim u-sefarim ba-Tosafoth.

    Library of Congress   Z6371.T6T3   44–33408

NT   0044272   DLC

Tarshish silver mining company
    The Tarshish silver mining company. Mines
located in the Tojyabe, or Reese river
mountain range, Union mining district, Nye
county, state of Nevada ... [Prospectus]
New York, W.C.Bryant & co., printers, 1865.
    cover-title, 13p.   fold.map.   23cm.
    Three of the company form letters concern-
ing the mines, its prospectus and its stock
laid in.
    Original wrappers.

NT   0044273   CtY

QB
4   **Tashkend. Astronomicheskaía observatoriía.**
T323   Циркуляр Ташкентской астрономической обсерватории.

    ₍Ташкент, Изд-во Академии наук Узбекской ССР, etc.₎
    v.   22–28 cm.

    Began publication in 1932.   Cf. Летопись периодических изданий
СССР, 1955–1960, № 1189.
    No.   have also title: Astronomical circular.

    1. Astronomy—Observations.   ɪ. Title: Astronomical circular.
                       Title transliterated: Tsirkuliar.

    QB4.T323   54–30318 rev

NT   0044274   DLC LU

I'J7724
5   Tarsi, Ḥayyim, ed. and tr.
T3
Hebr   **Arabian nights.**

אלף לילה ולילה. מעובד לבני הנוער. עברית: חיים תרסי.
תל-אביב, הוצאת "חבל." ₍Tel-Aviv, 195–₎

Tarsi, Ḥayyim, ed. and tr.
    Elef layloh ve-layloh
       see under   Arabian nights. Hebrew.

Tarsia, Antonino
   see   **Tarsia in Curia, Antonino.**

PQ4843
A66   Tarsia, Fernando P
P6   Foglie al vento; raccolte di poesie.
    ₍Salerno, Jovane, 1954₎
    111 p.   22 cm.

    Preface by Giorgio M. Palleschi Altopascio
    "Errata" inserted

NT   0044278   RPB

Tarsia, Galeazzo di, 1470-1530.
    ... Il canzoniere; nuova ed., corretta su tutte le stampe,
con note ed uno studio sull'autore di Francesco Bartelli.
Cosenza, Tipografia L. Vetere già Migliaccio, 1888.
    clxxxiv, 72 p.   19ᶜᵐ.
    Author's presentation copy to E. Pèrcopo.
    "Bibliografia": p. ₍67₎-70.

    ɪ. Bartelli, Francesco, ed.

NT   0044279   MiU CU MH CtY

TARSIA, Galeazzo di, 1470-1530.
    Rime. Raccolte dal Cavalier Basile.
Napoli, presso D.A. Parrino, 1715.

    nar. 24º. pp. 46.+
    (Appended to SCHETTINI, Pirro. Poesie,
1716).

NT   0044280   MH

TARSIA, Galeazzo di, 1470-1530.
    Rime, raccolte dal cavalier Giovambatista
Basile. Padova, 1738.

    (Appended to COSTANZO, Angelo, di. Rime.
pp. 151-185.)

NT   0044281   MH

Tarsia, Galeazzo di, 1470-1530.
    Le rime di Galeazzo di Tarsia ... baron di Belmonte, rac-
colte dal cavalier Giovambatista Basile ... e con ogni dili-
genza ristampate. Padova, G. Comino, 1750.
    (*In* Costanzo, Angelo di. Le rime ... **6.** ed. accresciuta ... Pa-
dova, 1750. 17½ᶜᵐ. p. ₍151₎–191)

    ɪ. Basile, Giovanni Battista, 1575 (ca.)–1632.

                                31–8266
    Library of Congress   PQ4621.C75 1750

NT   0044282   DLC MnU MH

Hd7
900

Tarsia, Galeazzo di, 1490-1530.
Le rime di Galeazzo di Tarsia cosentino,
Signor di Belmonte. In questa nuova edizione
accresciute e' ridotte alla loro vera lezione,
col ritrovamento di un'antichissimo m.s. e con
la giunta di alcune osservazioni, e della
vita dell'autore. Napoli,Stamperia
simoniana,1758.
xlviii,208,[2]p. fold.ports. 19cm.
Dedication signed: Il marchese Spiriti.

NT 0044283   CtY MH MWelC ICN

Tarsia, Galeazzo di, 1470-1530.   *4799·5
Le rime di Galeazzo di Tarsia. Raccolte dal Cavalier Giovambatista
Basile . . .
  (In Costanzo, Angelo di. Rime. Pp. 151-184. Vénezia. M[D]-
CCLIX.)

L.7113 — Basile, Giovambatista. compiler.

NT 0044284   MB

Tarsia, Galeazzo di. 1470-1530.   No. 2 in *4776.6
Le rime di Galeazzo di Tarsia.
In Nozza, Presso la Societe' tipografica. M.DCC,LXXXII. 115-
143 pp. 18½ cm., in 8s.

H1341

NT 0044285   MB

Tarsia, Galeazzo di, 1490-1530.
Rime [a cura di Daniele Ponchiroli. Parigi, Tallone,
1950]
[58] p.

NT 0044286   MH

PQ
4634
T4++
1951

Tarsia, Galeazzo di, 1490-1530.
Rime. [A cura di Daniele Ponchiroli.
Parigi, A. Tallone] 1951.
1 v. (unpaged) 31cm.

I. Ponchiroli, Daniele, ed.

NT 0044287   NIC WU CLU CU-S

Tarsia, Giovanni Domenico, tr.

Lopez [de Sigura], Ruy, *16th cent.*
Il givoco de gli scacchi, di Rui Lopez, Spagnuolo; nuoua-
mente tradotto in lingua italiana, da M. Gio. Domenico
Tarsia ... Venetia, Presso C. Arriuabene, 1584.

[Tarsia, Giovanni Maria]
Esequie del divino Michelagnolo Bvonarroti
celebrate in Firenze dall' Accademia de pittori,
scultori, & architettori
        see under   Giunra, Jacopa, fl. 16th cent.

B851B888
BT1

Tarsia, Giovanni Maria, fl. 16th cent.
Oratione o vero discorso di M. Giovan Maria
Tarsia. Fatto nell' essequie del divino Michelagnolo Bvonarroti. Con alcuni sonetti, e prose
latine e volgari di diuersi, circa il disparere
occorso tra gli scultori, e pittori. In Fiorenza, Appresso Bartolomeo Sermartelli, 1564.
[36] p. 21cm.

Title-vignette.

NT 0044290   NNC CtY MH

Tarsia, Giovanni Maria, fl. 16th cent.
Satira Del Tarsia Sopra La Nobil' Arte De
Pedanti. ... In Fiorenza Per Bartolomeo Sermartelli. MDLXV.
8° ff. (12).

NT 0044291   MWelC

Tarsia, Giovanni Maria, *fl. 16th cent.*
Trattato della natvra de gl'angeli; nel qvale tvtte le
cose attenenti à essa natura angelica si contengono; che
cosi da i filosofi, come da i teologi sono state dette. Del
R. M. Giovan Maria Tarsia ... In Firenze, Nella stamperia di B. Sermartelli, 1576.
12 p. l., 221, [1] p.   16⁵⁄₁₆ᶜᵐ.
Title vignette (printer's device)

1. Angels.

NT 0044292   MiU IU CLU

TARSIA, Michele.
Lettere indiritte al marchese di Villarosa
da diversi uomini illustri, raccolte e pubblicate da Michele Tarsia. Napoli, tip. di
Porcelli, 1844.

The first letter from each correspondent
is followed by a brief sketch of his life and
works.

NT 0044293   MH

Tarsia, Pablo Antonio De.
Ara parentalis didaco Lopez de Haro. A Soto-
mayori Carpiensivm Marchioni, &c. Vita fvncto
epitaphiis, ac symbolis tvmvltvarie erecta,
ornataqve. Per D. Paullum Antonium de Tarsia S.
Theologiae Doctorem, Abbatem Sancti Antonij
Cupersanen & Academicum ociosum Neapolitanum.
Madriti Typis Iuliani de Paredes, año, 1648.
Bound with: Castro, Antonio De. El sermon,
qve de orden del rey nvestro Señor Felipe IIII.

Predico el Reverend.   Padre Fr. Antonio de
Castro, etc. 1644.

NT 0044295   NNH

Z945
fG757
v.9:5

Tarsia, Paolo Antonio di, d.1670.
Historiarum Cupersanensium libri III.
Editio postrema.   Lugduni Batavorum,
sumptibus Petri vander Aa [1723]

76 col. 40cm. (In Graevius, J.G.
Thesavrvs antiqvitatvm et historiarvm
Italiae. v.9, pt.5)

1.Conversano, Italy. Hist.

NT 0044296   MnU

PQ6421
.A1
1790

Tarsia, Paolo Antonio di, d. 1670.
Quevedo y Villegas, Francisco Gómez de, 1580-1645.
Obras. Madrid, A. de Sancha, 1790-94 [v. 1, 1791]

Tarsia, Paolo Antonio di, d. 1670.
Tvmvltos de la civdad y reyno de Napoles; en el año
de 1647. Por Don Pablo Antonio de Tarsia ... Leon de
Francia, C. Bvrgea, 1670.
6 p. l., 195, [26] p. 24ᶜᵐ.
Title vignette.

1. Naples (Kingdom)—Hist. 2. Masaniello, Tommaso Aniello, known as,
1620-1647.
                                              4-33087†

Library of Congress   DG848.13.T19

NT 0044298   DLC CtY NN NIC CU TxU

He67
67

Tarsia, Pablo Antonio di, d. 1670.
Vida de don Francisco de Queuedo y Villegas,
Cauallero del Orden de Santiago, Secretario de
su Magestad, y Señor de la Villa de la Torre
de Iuan Abad. Escrita por el Abad don Pablo...
Madrid, Pablo de Val, 1663.
181 p. 16 cm.

1. Quevedo y Villegas, Francisco Gómez de,
1580-1645.

NT 0044299   CtY NNH MdBP

Tarsia in Curia, Antonino.
Napoli negli anni di guera.   Napoli, Istituto della stampa,
1954. 126 p. 22cm.

1. World war, 1939-1945—Italy—   Naples. [2. World war, 1939-1945
—Free and resistance movements.   Italian. 3. Naples—Hist 1860-   .

NT 0044300   NN

Tarsia in Curia, Antonino.
La verità sulle "Quattro giornate" di Napoli. Napoli,
Stab. tip. G. Genovese, 1950.
144 p. 22 cm.

1. World War, 1939-1945—Italy—Naples. 2. Naples—Hist.
I. Title.
D763.I 82N37   51-39803 ‡

NT 0044301   DLC

BX1733
B6T3

Tarsier, Pedro.
História das perseguições religiosas no
Brasil.   São Paulo, Cultura Moderna [1936]
2 v. in 1. 20ᶜᵐ
Bibliographical references included in
"Notas".

1.Brazil. Inquisition. 2.Catholic Church
in Brazil. I.Title.

NT 0044302   CSt InU RPB

BX
1765
.T25

Tarsier, Pedro
Roma, o jesuitismo e a constituinte; estudo
histórico-crítico.   Porto Alegre [cover 1933]
462 p. 24cm.

Bibliographical footnotes.

1. Catholic Church - Doctrinal and contro-
versial works - Miscallaneous authors 2.
Jesuits - Contro-   versial literature
I. Title

NT 0044303   WU

Tarsis, Veniamin I͡Akovlevich.
Современные иностранные писатели; био-библиогра-
фический справочник. Москва, Гос. изд-во, 1930.
iv, 204 p. 24 cm.
At head of title: В. Тарсис, И. Старцев, С. Урбан.
Title also in French.

1. Fiction—Bibl. I. Star͡sev, Ivan Ivanovich. II. Title.
                                Title transliterated: Sovremennye
                                         inostrannye pisateli.

Z5916.T3   51-54730

NT 0044304   DLC

Tarsis, Veniamin Íakovlevich, tr.

Smolych, Iurii, 1900–
... Театр неизвестного актера; авторизованный перевод с
украинского В. Тарсиса; под редакцией А. П. Рябининой.
Москва, Огиз, Государственное издательство художественной литературы, 1941.

Tarsis y Peralta, Juan de, *conde de Villamediana*
see **Villamediana, Juan de Tarsis y Peralta,** *conde* **de,**
1580–1622.

Tarsis et Zelie
see under   [Le Vayer de Boutigny, Rolland]
1627–1685.

Tarsīsī, 'Adnān
see
Tarcici, Adnan, 1912–

Tarsitani, D.
Nouveau forceps approuvé par l'Académie royale
de médecine de Paris, et destiné à éviter le
decroisement des branches.   Paris, Fortin,
Masson & Cie., 1844.
15 p. 2 pl. 8°. [Also, in: P., v. 1886]

NT 0044309   DNLM

W 6   TARSITANO, Francesco
P3   Nozioni di infortunistica generale per
gli studenti di medicina e di giurisprudenza. Napoli, Idelson, 1954.
44 p.
1. Accident insurance -- Italy

NT 0044310   DNLM

Tarsitano, Francesco.
... Tecnica delle ricerche sull' individualità del sangue. Napoli, Edizioni scientifiche italiane, 1946.
153 p., 1 l. 22ᶜᵐ. (Collana di medicina pratica. n. 2)

1. Blood groups.

                                                          Med 47–791
U. S. Army medical library   [WB359T193t 1946]
for Library of Congress   [2]

NT 0044311   DNLM MnU NNC IU

Tarski, Alfred.

Woodger, Joseph Henry.
The axiomatic method in biology, by J. H. Woodger ...
With appendices by Alfred Tarski and W. F. Floyd. Cam-
bridge [Eng.] The University press, 1937.

Tarski, Alfred.
Cardinal algebras. With an appendix: Cardinal products
of isomorphism types by Bjarni Jónsson and Alfred Tarski.
New York, Oxford Univ. Press, 1949.
xii, 326 p. 23 cm.

Bibliography: p. 313–316.

1. Algebra, Abstract.   I. Jónsson, Bjarni. II. Title.

QA266.T3   512.89   49–8111*

OrPR OrU WaTU
PBm WaU OU ICU TU NIC PPF PSt PSC CaBVaU IdU OrCS
NT 0044313   DLC OO GAT WU CU ViU GU KEmT OCU OC1W

QA482   **Tarski, Alfred.**
.C7
Concerning the degree of equivalence of polygons; two papers
by Alfred Tarski and one paper by Henryk Moese. Trans-
lated by Izaak Wirszup, July 1950. [Chicago, The College,
University of Chicago, °1952.

QA266   Tarski, Alfred
T32   A decision method for elementary algebra and
geometry. Prepared for publication by J.C.C.
McKinsey. Santa Monica, Calif., Rand Corp.,
1948.
iii,60 p. (Rand Corporation [Publications]
R–109)

On cover: U.S. Air Force. Project Rand.
"References": p.59–60.

NT 0044315   CU CtY

---

q510.1   Tarski, Alfred.
T17d   A decision method for elementary algebra and
geometry. Prepared for publication by J. C. C.
McKinsey. August 1, 1948. Santa Monica,
Calif., Rand Corporation [1949]
iii, 60ℓ. 29cm.
On cover: U.S. Air Force. Project Rand.
"This report, although published by the Rand
corporation, was written while the Project was
a part of Douglas Aircraft Co., inc."
"R–109. Copy no.308"
"References": leaves 59–60.

NT 0044316   IU MiU

Tarski, Alfred.
A decision method for elementary algebra and geometry,
by Alfred Tarski; prepared for publication with the assistance of J. C. C. McKinsey. 2d ed., rev. Berkeley, University of California Press, 1951.
iii, 63 p. 28 cm.

Bibliography: p. 59–60.

1. Algebra, Abstract. 2. Geometry. 3. Logic, Symbolic and mathematical.   I. Title.

QA266.T33 1951   512.89   51–8566

MB TU CU TxU
NT 0044317   DLC OrCS OrPR OrU IdPI CaBVaU KEmT DAU

Tarski, Alfred.
A decision method for elementary algebra and geometry,
by Alfred Tarski; prepared for publication with the assistance of J. C. C. McKinsey. 2d ed., rev. Berkeley, University of California Press, 1951.
iii, 63 p. 28 cm.

Bibliography: p. 59–60.
Photocopy (positive)

NT 0044318   CU

QA1   **Tarski, Alfred, joint author.**
.N87
no. 5   Jónsson, Bjarni, 1920–
... Direct decompositions of finite algebraic systems, by
Bjarni Jónsson and Alfred Tarski ... Notre Dame, Ind.,
1947.

QA1   **Tarski, Alfred, joint author.**
.C3
n. s.,
vol. 1,   Chin, Louise Hoy, 1922–
no. 9   Distributive and modular laws in the arithmetic of relation algebras, by Louise H. Chin and Alfred Tarski. Berkeley, University of California Press, 1951.

Tarski, Alfred.
Einführung in die mathematische logik und in die methodologie der mathematik, von Alfred Tarski. Wien, J. Springer,
1937.
x, 166 p. 22ᶜᵐ.
"Literaturangaben": p. 165–166.

1. Mathematics—Philosophy. 2. Arithmetic—Foundations.

                                                          38–10062
Library of Congress   QA9.T3
Copyright A—Foreign   37909
                                    [3]   501.1

OCU
NT 0044321   DLC NcD CtY CU PU PBm CSt NcU NBC ICU

QA9   Tarski, Alfred
T272   Inleiding tot de logica en tot de methodeleer der deductieve
Math.-   wetenschappen. Nederlandse bewerking door E. W. Beth.
Stat.   Amsterdam, N.V. Noord-Hollandsche Uitgevers Maatschappij,
Library   1953.
xix, 259 p.

Translation of Introduction to logic and to the methodology of
deductive sciences.
Includes bibliography.

1. Mathematics - Philosophy.   2. Arithmetic - Foundations.

NT 0044322   CU

QA9   Tarski, Alfred
T282   Introducción a la lógica y a la metodología
Philos-   de las ciencias deductivas. Traducción de
ophy   T.R. Bachiller y J.R. Fuentes. Buenos Aires,
Lib.   Espasa-Calpe Argentina [1951]
237 p.

Bibliography: p.[235]–237.

1. Mathematics - Philosophy.   2. Arithmetic - Foundations.

NT 0044323   CU

Tarski, Alfred.
Introduction to logic and to the methodology of deductive
sciences, by Alfred Tarski. Enl. and rev. ed. New York,
Oxford university press [1941]
xviii, 239 p. 21½ᶜᵐ.
"A partially modified and extended edition of my book 'On mathe-
matical logic and deductive method,' which appeared first in 1936 in
Polish and then in 1937 in an exact German translation (under the title:
Einführung in die mathematische logik und in die methodologie der
mathematik)."—Pref.
"Translated by Olaf Helmer."
"Suggested readings": p. 227–230.
1. Mathematics—Philosophy. 2. Arithmetic—Foundations.
I. Helmer-Hirschberg, Olaf, tr. II. Title.
                                                          41–4214
Library of Congress   QA9.T28 1941
Copyright ——— Copy 2.   [3]   510.1

OC1W WaT MtBC OrCS
CoU GAT NcD TU OOxM OCU OC1 OU OC1W OO ViU MiHM OrU
NT 0044324   DLC PHC CU PSC PBm TxU NN WaWW OrPR PU

Tarski, Alfred.
Introduction to logic and to the methodology of deductive
sciences. [2d ed., rev., tr. by Olaf Helmer] New York,
Oxford Univ. Press [1946]
xviii, 239 p. 22 cm.

"A partially modified and extended edition of my book 'On mathematical logic and deductive method,' which appeared first in 1936 in
Polish and then in 1937 in an exact German translation (under the
title: Einführung in die mathematische Logik und in die Methodologie
der Mathematik)"
"Suggested readings": p. 227–230.
1. Mathematics—Philosophy. 2. Arithmetic—Foundations.
I. Title.
[QA9.T]   510.1   A 49–4565*
Chicago. Univ. Library
for Library of Congress   [3]

ScC1eU MtBC MtU OrCS
IdU Or TU MiD MH MB NNU–W MiU NIC MsSM NcU NIC WaS
NT 0044325   ICU ICCO NBuC MoU PP PBm LU OrPR OrSaW

BC135   Tarski, Alfred
T36   O logice matematycznej i metodzie dedukcyjnej. Lwów,
Książnica Atlas [1935]
167 p. (Biblioteczka matematyczna, 3–5)

1. Logic, Symbolical and mathematical.

NT 0044326   CU

QA9
T193
Tarski, Alfred
O logice matematycznej i metodzie dedukcy-
jnej. Lwów, Książnica-Atlas, ₍1936?₎
167 p. 20cm. (Bibljoteczka matematyczna)

1. Mathematics - Philosophy. 2. Arithmetic - Foundations. I. Title.

NT   0044327   GU

Tarski, Alfred.
מבוא לתורת־ההגיון ולמטודולוגיה של המדעים הדדוקטיביים.
תרגם: יהושע בר־הלל וא. י. י. פוזננסקי. תל־אביב. הסתדרות
הכללית של העובדים העברים בארץ־ישראל. מרכז לתרבות ולחינוך.
₍Tel-Aviv₎ 1954.

207 l. 25 cm.
Cover title.

"תורגם ... לפי המהדורה השניה המתוקנת של הספר."
Introduction to logic and to the methodology of deductive sciences."
1. Mathematics—Philosophy. 2. Arithmetic—Foundations.
Title transliterated: Mavo le-torat-ha-higayon.

QA9.T313 1954   59–57245

NT   0044328   DLC

CA
266
.T3
Tarski, Alfred.
Ordinal algebras; with appendices by
Chen-Chung chang and Bjarni Jónsson.
Amsterdam, North-Holland Pub. Co., 1956.
133 p. 22 cm.
Studies in logic and the foundations of
mathematics.
Bibliography: p. [125]-126.

ALGEBRA, ABSTRACT.
Title. Series.

NT   0044329   MoSW

Tarski, Alfred.
Pojęcie prawdy w językach nauk dedukcyjnych. Warszawa, Nakł. Tow. Naukowego Warszawskiego, 1933.
vii, 116 p. 24 cm. (Prace Towarzystwa Naukowego Warszawskiego III. Nauk Matematyczno-Fizycznych. Prace, nr. 34)
Title also in French.
Bibliography: p. ₍v₎-vii.

1. Truth.   (Series: Towarzystwo Naukowe Warszawskie. Wydział III. Nauk Matematyczno-Fizycznych. Prace, nr. 34)

AS262.W37 no. 34   60–56613

NT   0044330   DLC ICU MH CU NNC MiU GU ICN

Tarski, Alfred.
Undecidable theories, by Alfred Tarski, in collaboration
with Andrzej Mostowski and Raphael M. Robinson. Amsterdam, North-Holland Pub. Co., 1953.
xi, 98 p. 22 cm. (Studies in logic and the foundations of mathematics)
Bibliography: p. 89-91.

1. Metamathematics. I. Title.   (Series)

QA9.T33   54–4341

OKentU
IEN MB ICJ AU TxU TU OU OCU PBm PHC OO PBL IdU OC1W
ICU NBuU OrCS OrU WaS OrStbM OrPR CaBVa CtY PSC PPT
ScU DAU ScC1eU CU IU NIC ViU NN MH CSt NcD NcU IaU
NT   0044331   DLC ICU CNoS OkU TxU OC1W CLU MtU CaBVaU

BC171
T37
Philos-
ophy
Lib.
Tarski, Alfred
Der Wahrheitsbegriff in den formalisierten
Sprachen. Leopoli, 1935.
145 p.

"Seorsum impressum ex Vol. I. Commentariorum
Societatis philosophicae polonorum, Studia
philosophica".
Pages also numbered 262-405.
Bibliography: p.₍1₎-4.

1. Truth.

NT   0044332   CU

Tarski, Alfred.
Der Wahrheitsbegriff in den formalisierten Sprachen.
Leopoli, 1935.

145 p. 22 cm.
"Seorsum impressum ex vol. I Commentariorum Societatis
philosophicae polonorum, Studia philosophica, pp.[261]-
405."
Photostat reproduction (positive)
Another copy.   XVG 6
Photostat reproduction (negative)

NT   0044333   MH IaU

Tarski, Ignacy.
Podstawowe wskaźniki planu żeglugi morskiej. ₍Dla
planistów żeglugi oraz dla studentów wyższych szkół eko-
nomicznych₎ Warszawa, Wydawn. Komunikacyjne, 1952.
127 p. 21 cm.
Includes bibliography.

1. Navigation.   I. Title.

VK145.T3   56–16332 ‡

NT   0044334   DLC

Tarskiĭ, A   Kerdoda-
see Kerdoda-Tarskiĭ, A

Tarsney, John C.
Extravagant pension legislation. Speech
of Hon. John C. Tarsney, of Missouri, in the
house pf representatives, Monday, April 21,
1890. ₍Wash.₎ 18(o
16 p.

Caption title.

NT   0044336   OC1WHi

Tarsney, John C.
Hours of labor. Speech...July 1, 1892.
Wash., 1892.

YA5000   (Congressional speeches, by author)
J 17

NT   0044337   DLC

Tarsney, Timothy Edward, 1849-   ed.
Detroit. *Charters.*
The charter of the city of Detroit, with amendments
thereto, and the acts of the Legislature relating to or af-
fecting the city of Detroit. Comp. under the direction of
Timothy E. Tarsney ... pursuant to resolution of the
Common counsel ₍!₎ Detroit, T. Smith press, 1904.

HS499
.T178
Tarso, Paulo de
Crimes da Franco-Maçonaria Judaica.
₍Praia, Fortimao, 1924₎
167 p.

1. Freemasons and Jews. I. Title.

NT   0044339   CtHC

Tarso, Paulo de.
Crimes da Franco-Maçonaria Judaica.
Guarda, Empresa Veritas,[1928?]
167 p. illus., port. 17 cm.

1.Freemasonry. I.ti.

NT   0044340   OCH

JU83525
+T178
Tarson, T   L
The production-for-use movement, 1932-
1936; an examination of third party
activity. [New Haven, 1953]
90, 10 l. 28 cm.

Reproduced from typewritten copy.
Includes bibliography.

1. Bingham, Alfred Mitchell. 2. U.S. -
Pol. & Govt. -   1933-1945. I. Title.

NT   0044341   WHi

'L5074
A2
)rien
ndo
Tarsono, joint author.

Achmady, S
Kamus praktis, Inggeris-Indonesia Belanda, disusun oleh:
S. Ahmady dan Tarsono. Tjetakan 1. Surabaja, Marhaen
₍1953?₎

Tarsos, *Turkey*
see
Tarsus, *Turkey.*

Tarsot, Louis, 1857-
Le chateau de Fontainebleau par Louis Tar-
cot et Maurice Charlot...Paris, H. Laurens,
₍1889?₎
128 p.

NT   0044344   MiU

Tarsot, Louis, 1857-
Les chateaux de Chantilly et Ecouen. Orné de
10 gravures. Paris, D. Dumoulin et Cie.
32 p.
I. Charlot, Maurice.

NT   0044345   OC1MA

Tarsot, Louis, 1857-   L370.944 P300
Les écoles et les écoliers à travers les âges. Avant-propos de
M. A. Mézières. Ouvrage orné de 130 gravures de L. Libonis.
vi,339 p. 130 il. Q. Paris : H. Laurens, 1893.

NT   0044346   ICJ ICN MH

370.9
T17e
1904
Tarsot, Louis, 1857-
Les écoles et les écoliers à travers les âges.
Avant-propos de A. Mézières. Ouvrage orné
de 84 gravures de L. Libonis, etc. Nouv. éd.
Paris, H. Laurens ₍1904₎
vii, 256p. illus. 26cm.

Bibliographical footnotes.

1. Education—Hist. 2. Learning and scholarship. I. Title.

NT   0044347   IU OU

370.944
T178e
Tarsot, Louis, 1857-
Les écoles et les écoliers a travers les
ages. Avant-propos de M. A. Mézières.
Ouvrage orné de 84 gravures de L. Libonis,
etc. Nouv. éd. Paris, H. Laurens [1905?]
vii,256 p. illus. 25cm.

1. Education - France - Hist. 2. Education -
Hist. I. T.

NT 0044348   MiDW OrU

[Tarsot, Louis] 1857-
Fabliaux et contes du moyen age. Illus. de
A. Robida. Ed. pour la jeunesse; précédée d'une
introd. par L. Tarsot. Paris, H. Laurens [19—?]
iv, 118 p. illus. (part col.)
"These fableaux, or fabliaux ... were collected
and retold in prose, at the end of the eighteenth
century, by ... Legrand d'Aussy ... M.L. Tarsot..
made a choice of some of the best ... and adapted

them for juvenile readers." - Pref., Boston,
1914, ed.

NT 0044350   CLU

Tarsot, Louis, 1857-   ed.
Fabliaux et contes du moyen age; illustrations
de A. Robida. Ed. pour la jeunesse.
[4],iv,118p. il. (part col.) Paris, H. Laurens
[1908]

NT 0044351   OC1 NN

[Tarsot, Louis] 1857-
Fabliaux et contes du moyen âge, ed. with
notes and vocabulary by J. E. Mansion.
viii,9-175p. Boston, New York [etc.] D. C.
Heath & co. [pref. 1913] (Heath's Modern
language series)

NT 0044352   OC1 MtU OrP WaSpG PU OrSaW MH DCU ODW

[Tarsot, Louis] 1857-
... Fabliaux et contes du moyen âge, edited with notes and
vocabulary by J. E. Mansion ... Boston, New York [etc.]
D. C. Heath & co. [1914]
viii, 9-175 p. illus. 17 cm. (Heath's modern language series)
"These fableaux, or fabliaux ... were collected and retold in prose,
at the end of the eighteenth century, by ... Legrand d'Aussy ... M. L.
Tarsot ... made a choice of some of the best ... and adapted them for
juvenile readers. It is M. Tarsot's text, together with his delightful
introduction, which are given here."—Pref.
1. Fables, French. 2. Tales, French. 3. French language—Chrestomathies and readers. I. Le Grand d'Aussy, Pierre Jean Baptiste,
1737-1800. II. Mansion, Jean Edmund, 1870-1942, ed. III. Title.

PQ1319.T3   848.10822   33—23203

NT 0044353   DLC PPT MiU OC1C OOxM ICarbS

TARSOT,Louis,1857-
Fabliaux et contes du moyen âge. Illustrations de A.Robida. Édition pour la jeunesse,
précédée d'une introduction de M.L.Tarsot...
Paris,Librairie Renouard,Henri Laurens,éditeur
...1926...

28 cm. Illustr.(some colored). Publisher's
device on back cover.
Colophon:...Évreux,Imprimerie Ch.Hérissey...

NT 0044354   MH

PQ
1319
.T3
Tarsot, Louis, 1857-
Fabliaux et contes du Moyen Age, précédée
d'une introd. de L. Tarsot. Illus. de A.
Robida. Éd. pour la jeunesse. Paris, H.
Laurens, 1930.
118 p. illus. 29cm. (Les Chefs-
d'oeuvre à l'usage de la jeunesse)

1. Fables, French 2. Tales, French I.
Title

NT 0044355   WU MiD

848.108
T178f
Tarsot, Louis, 1857-
Fabliaux et contes du Moyen Age; adaptation
pour la jeunesse, par M. L. Tarsot. Illus.
de Henry Morin. Paris, Nelson, 1938.
128 p. col. plates. 20cm.

The stories were selected from Le Grand
d'Aussy's collection of tales from 12th and
13th century French manuscripts.

I.T. II.Le Grand d'Aussy, Pierre Jean
Baptiste, 1737- 1800.

NT 0044356   MiDW

TARSOT, Louis,1857-
The Palace of Fontainebleau, by Louis
Tarsot and Maurice Charlot. Paris,
H. Laurens, n.d. 92 p. Illus. D.

1.Fontainebleau, Chateau de I.Charlot,
Maurice, jt.au.

NT 0044357   MoS OC1MA TU

1857-
Tarsot, Louis, and Maurice Charlot.   8115.08.31
The Palace of Fontainebleau.
= Paris. Laurens. [189-?] (3),92 pp. Illus. Plates. 19 cm.

D2789 — Jt. auth. — Fontainebleau, Château de.

NT 0044358   MB

Tarsot, Louis, 1857- , and M. Charlot.
The palace of Fontainebleau, by Louis Tarsot and Maurice
Charlot... Paris: H. Laurens [1900]. 92 p. illus. 12°.

1. Fontainebleau, Palace of.   2. Charlot, Maurice, jt. au.
N. Y. P. L.   June 27, 1921.

NT 0044359   NN InU NNU MnU

Tarsot, Louis, 1857-

The palace of Fontainebleau, by
Louis Tarsot and Maurice Charlot. Paris,
Laurens [1902]
92 p. illus. 19 cm.

1.Fontainebleau,Chateau de. I.
Charlot, Maurice,   jt.auth.

NT 0044360   NjP

Avery
AA
535
F7
T172
Tarsot, Louis, 1857-
The palace of Fontainebleau, by Louis
Tarsot and Maurice Charlot. 14 engravings.
Paris, H. Laurens [1926]
92 p. illus. 20 cm.

1. Fontainebleau, Chateau de. I. Charlot,
Maurice   jt. au. I. Title.

NT 0044361   NNC

1857-
Tarsot, Louis, Les palais nationaux ... At head of title: Bibliotheque d'histoire et d'art. Paris, n. d.   YA 350

NT 0044362   DLC

Tarsot, Louis, 1857-   FA 2235.7
Les palais nationaux; Fontainebleau, Chantilly, Compiegne,
Saint-Germain, Rambouillet, Pau, etc. Par Louis Tarsot et
Maurice Charlot. Paris, Librairie Renouard, H. Laurens, [1889].
6 pt. Vigns. and other illus. (Bibliothèque d'histoire et d'art.)

Architecture–France||Charlot|Series

NT 0044363   MH

Tarsot, Louis, 1857-   ed. and tr.
Robinson Crusoe
see Defoe, Daniel, 1661?-1731.
Robinson Crusoe. French. [1906]

DF
901
.C9T3
Tarsoulē, Athēna N   1887-
Ἄσπρα νησιά [ὑπό] Ἀθηνᾶς Ταρσούλη. Ἀθήναι,
Τυπο-Μυρτίδη [1938]
168 p. illus.
C96567
Title romanized: Aspra nēsia.

1. Cyclades--Descr. & trav. I. Title.

NT 0044365   MoU OCU

Tarsoulē, Athēna N   1887 -
...Ἄσπρα νησια. Δευτερη ἐκδοση.   Ἀθηναι: Τυπο-μυρτιδη, 1939.
165 p. illus., mounted col'd plates.   22 x 18cm.

75258B. I. Cyclades—Descr. and   trav.
N. Y. P. L.   January 29, 1941

NT 0044366   NN OCU MH

---

q914.99
T17d
Tarsoulē, Athēna N   , 1887-
Δωδεκανησα. [Ἀθηνα] Ἐκδοσεις "Ἀλφα"
I. M. Σκαζικη [c1947-50]
3v. illus., plates(part col., 2 double) port.,
maps(1 col.), plans. 31cm.

Contents.- τ.1- Ρόδος, Κάρπαθος, Κάσος, Χάλκη.-
τ.2. Πάτμος, Λέρος, Κάλυμνος, Ἀστυπάλαια.- τ.3.
Κῶς, Νίσυρος, Τῆλος, Σύμη, Καστελλόριχο.
Title transliterated: Dōdekanēsa.

NT 0044367   IU WaU IEN NN MnU MH DLC-P4 OC1

391.0499
T178e
Tarsoulē, Athēna N   1887-
Embroideries and costumes of Dodecanese.
Athens, 1951.
[14]p., 68 col. plates.

In Greek and English.
Second t.p. in Greek.
Inscribed by author.

1.Costume - Dodecanese Islands.
2.Embroidery, Greek.

NT 0044368   MiDA OCU MH

ND603
.A5T3   Tarsoulē, Athena N   1887–   [Helene Altamoura]
      Ἑλένη Ἀλταμούρα. Ἡ πρώτη
      ζωγράφος στήν Ἑλλάδα μετά τό εἰκο-
      σιένα. Ἀθῆναι, ἐκδ. οἶκος Δημη-
      τράκου, 1934.
        42 p. 9 plates. 25cm.

      1. Altamura, Helene, b.1821.

NT   0044369   OCU

---

4 PA   Tarsoulē, Athēna N   1887–
Greek–   Ἑλληνίδες ποιήτριες 1857–1940. Ἀθῆναι,
165   1951–
       v (1)

      Title transliterated: Hellēnides poiētries.

NT   0044370   DLC-P4 CU OCU MH

      Tarsoulē, Athēna N   1887–
      Ἑλληνικές φορεσιές. Costumes grecs. ₍Ἀθῆναι, 1941–
      v. (col. plates, in portfolio) 36 cm.
      Greek and French.
      L. C. copy imperfect: t. p. and last leaf of introduction wanting
      in v. 1?

      1. Costume—Greece, Modern. I. Title.
            Title transliterated: Hellēnikes phoresies.

      GT940.T3   52–15536 rev

NT   0044371   DLC MiDA OrCS OCU

      Tarsoulē, Athēna N   1887–
      Iles blanches. Athènes: Impr. "Rythmos," 1939.   153 p.
      illus., mounted col'd plates.   21½ x 17½cm.

      74801B. 1. Cyclades—Descr. and   trav.
      N. Y. P. L.   October 15, 1940

NT   0044372   NN NNC

---

4 DF   Tarsoulē, Athēna N   1887–
104   Ἡ Καταπολιανή τῆς Πάρου. Ἱ στορία καί θρῦλος.
      Ἀθήνα, 1944.
        60 p.

      Title transliterated: Hē Katapolianē tēs Parou.

NT   0044373   DLC-P4 OCU MH

B.F.
889.3   Tarsoulē, Athēna N   1887–
T193k   Ὁ καπεταν μοναχος; διηγηματα.   Ἀθη-
      να, Πετρος Δημητρακος [19––]
      161p. 19cm.

      I. Title.
          Title transliterated:
         O kapetan monachos.

NT   0044374   IEN

889T178
T

      Tarsoulē, Athēna N   1887–
      Ὁ καπετάν Μοναχός, διηγήματα.
      Ἀθῆναι, Ἐκδοτικός οἶκος Π. Δημητρά-
      κου ₍194–?₎
        161 p.

      Title transliterated: Ho kapetan Monachos.

NT   0044375   NNC

B.F.
L914.95
T193k   Tarsoulē, Athēna N   1887–
      Καστρά καί πολιτειες του μορια.
      Αθηνα, εκδοτικος οικος πετρου
      Δημητρακου [1935]
      260p. illus. (part mounted col.) 30cm.

      1. Peloponnesus. Descr. & trav.
            Title transliterated:
            Kastra kai politoies
            tou Moria.

NT   0044376   IEN MH

      Tarsoulē, Athēna N   1887–
      ΚΕΝΤΗΜΑΤΑ ΚΑΙ ΦΟΡΕΣΙΕΣ ΤΗΣ ΔΩΔΕΚΑΝΗΣΟΥ. Em-
      broideries and costumes of Dodecanese.   Athens,
      1951.
        13 p. 68 plates. 30 cm.

      Greek and English.

NT   0044377   NcGU

---

q956.4
T178k   Tarsoulē, Athēna N   1887–
      Κύπρος ₍ὑπὸ₎ Ἀθηνᾶς Ταρσούλη. Ἀθῆναι, Ἐκδόσεις
      ₍Ἀλφας I. Μ. Σκαζίκη, 1955–
        v. illus., maps (1 col.) plates (part col.) ports.   30 cm.
        Bibliography: v. 1, p. 478–481₎
        CONTENTS.—τ. 1. Γενική μορφή τοῦ νησιοῦ. Τὸ ἱστορικὸ χρονικὸ τῆς
        Κύπρου. Γράμματα, τέχνες. Ἐπαρχία Λευκωσίας. Ἐπαρχία Πάφου.
        Ἐπαρχία Κερυνίας.

      1. Cyprus—Descr. & trav.   2. Cyprus—Antiq.   3. Cyprus—Hist.
      4. Cities and towns—Cyprus.   *Title transliterated:* Kypros.

      DS54.T3   64–51330

      TxU
NT   0044378   DLC WaU NN IU TxU CU DDO MH NNC NjR InU

B.F.
949.5
M457t   Tarsoulē, Athēna N   1887–
      Μαντω Μουρογενους; η ηρωιλη κορη της
      Μυλονος. [Αθηναι, 1931]
      70p. illus. 22cm.

      Contains author's autograph.
      Bibliographical footnotes.

      1. Maurogenous, Mantō, fl. 1790–1812.   2.
      Myconos (Island) Hist. I. Title.
           Title transliterated:
           Mantō Maurogenous.

NT   0044379   IEN

      Tarsoulē, Athēna N   1887–
      Μαργαρίτα Ἀλσανα Μηνιατη, ἡ ζωη της και το ἐργο της ₍ὑπο₎ Ἀθηνας
      Ταρσούλη. Ἀθηναι: Ἐκδοσις "Πορτου," ἀ. ἑ., 1935.   221 p. incl.
      ports. illus. 25cm.
      "Βιβλιογαφια." p. 215–216.
      With autograph of author.

      75586B. 1. Mignaty, Marguerite   (Albana), 1821–1887.
      N. Y. P. L.   January 29, 1941

NT   0044380   NN MH OCU

      Tarsoules, Georgia
        see   Tarsouli, Georgia.

      Tarsouli, Athina
        see   Tarsoulē, Athēna N   1887–

889.114
T178   Tarsouli, Geōrgia.
      Μωραιτικά τραγούδια, Κορώνης καί
      Μεθώνης. Ἀθῆναι, 1944.
        208 p.

      Title transliterated: Mōraitika tra-
      goudia, Korōnēs kai Methōnēs.

NT   0044383   NNC OCU

      Tarsouli, Geōrgia, *ed.*
      Τὰ πρῶτα μου παραμύθια. Συλλογὴ καὶ διασκευὴ Γεωργίας
      Ταρσούλη. Εἰκονογράφηση Ἑλένης Περάκη-Θεοχάρη. Ἀθῆ-
      ναι, N. Ἀλικιώτης ₍1954₎
        ₍82₎ p. illus. (part col.) 21 cm. (Τὰ Βιβλία τῆς Θείας Λένας, 2.
        ₍L. e. 1.₎ σειρά, ἀρ.θ. 3)

      1. Children's stories, Greek.   I. Perakē-Theocharē, Helenē, illus.
      II. Title.   *Title transliterated:* Ta prōta mou paramythia.

      PZ90.G7T32   64–51098

NT   0044384   DLC

      Tarsous, *Turkey*
        see
      Tarsus, *Turkey.*

      Tarsus, Turkey. St. Paul's Institute.
      Prospectus of "St. Paul's Institute," Tarsus, Asia Minor.
      A monument to the memory of the apostle Paul, to be
      erected at his birthplace. New York, W. Knowles, printer,
      1887.
        36 p. 20 cm.

      LG321.T3A6   65–59483

NT   0044386   DLC

      Tarsus, Turkey. Sulu Ziraat Araştırma Enstitüsü.
      Araştırma raporları.
      Tarsus.
        v. illus., tables. 32 cm. annual.
        Began publication in 1955.
        Vols. for 1957–59—   issued in combined form.
        Vols. for 1957–59—   called also "umum sayı"

      1. Irrigation—Turkey.   2. Irrigation farming.   I. Title.

      S616.T8T3   N E 64–1628

NT   0044387   DLC

      Tarsy, James Maurice, 1899–
      Pain syndromes and their treatment, with special refer-
      ence to shoulder-arm pain. Springfield, Ill., Thomas ₍1953₎
        592 p. illus. 24 cm.

      1. Pain.   I. Title.

      RC73.T27   616.075   53–935 rev ‡

      NcU OClW-H NcD DNLM TU MBCo IEdS OrCS OrU-M Wa
NT   0044388   DLC CaBVaU OClW NBuU PPT TxU ICJ ViU OU

Tarsza, Edward
  see
    Grabowski, Michał, 1804-1863.

TN
242
B4T19
  Tart, Louis.
    L'abandon et la déchéance des mines.
  Commentaire des articles 18 à 24 et 27 à
  32 de la loi du 5 juin 1911. Liège,
  Bénard, 1919.
    156 p. 25cm.

    Bibliographical foot-notes.

    1. Mining law--Belgium. I. Title.

NT 0044390   NIC CU MiU-L ICJ MdBJ MnU NNC

951
T17c
  Tart, Louis.
    Chine et Chinois. Liège, Imp. H.,
  Vaillant-Carmanne, 1903.
    78p. 24cm.

    1. China--Hist. 2. China--Social
  conditions.   I. Title.

NT 0044391   LU NIC

DU
114
T17T2
  Tart, Margaret (Scarlett)
    The life of Quong Tart: or, How a foreigner
  succeeded in a British community. Compiled
  and edited by: Mrs. Quong Tart. Sydney, W.
  M. Maclardy, 1911.
    99 p. illus.,ports.

    1. Tart, Quong, 1850-1903.

NT 0044392   CLU

Tart, Mrs. Quong
  see Tart, Margaret (Scarlett)

Tartacover, Savely Grigorïèvitch
    see
    Tartakover, Saveliĭ Grigor'evich, 1887–

Tartacover, Xavier
    see
    Tartakover, Saveliĭ Grigor'evich, 1887–

Tartacovsky, M.
    Contribution à l'étiologie de la peste bovine.
  1896.
    33 p.

NT 0044396   DNAL

Tartafari, Clarice
    Rete d'acciaio; romanzo. Mil.,
  1919.

    289 p.

NT 0044397   PBm

---

fHQ1024
T36
1708
  Tartaglia, Annibale
    Nobilis Annibalis Tartaglia ... Tractatvs de reseruatione
  statutaria fauore filiorum in bonis matris, eiusque testamento, &
  contractibus sine certa solemnitate statutaria non valituris.
  Accedit in fine quaestiuncula commoditatis pensionis in contractum deductae &c.   Romae, Apud Aloysium, & Franciscum de
  Comitibus Impressores Camerales, 1708.
    12 p. ℓ., 591 p. 33cm.

    1. Marriage (Canon law)

NT 0044398   CU NjP

ND
953
.T19
A26
1955
  Tartaglia, Marin.
    Marin Tartaglia. Predgovor Grga Gamulin.
  Zagreb, Zora, 1955.
    59 p. illus.,plates (part.col.)
  (Savremeni umjetnici)

    I. Gamulin, Grga,1910-   , ed.

NT 0044399   MiU NNC CU NN

B2430
.M252
I 87
  Tartaglia, Ferdinando, ed. and tr.
    Marcel, Gabriel, 1887–
    ... Diario e scritti religiosi, a cura di F. Tartaglia. Modena,
  Guanda, 1943.

PQ4843
A7
V44
  Tartaglia, Gino
    Verona mia. Poesie in vernacolo veronese.
  Disegni di Ameglio Trivella. Verona, Centro
  pedagogico didattico [1951]
    149p. illus. 20 cm.

    Errata slip inserted.

NT 0044401   RPB

Tartaglia (Michele). Riflessioni sull' origine
de' vermi del corpo umano, e su' quelle materie,
che sono ai medesimi nocive, dirette al celebre
Valeriano Luigi Brera. 70 pp. 8°. Napoli,
D. Chianese, 1805. [P., v. 1130.]

NT 0044402   DNLM

  Tartaglia, Niccolò, d.1557.
    Opere del famosissimo Nicolo Tartaglia cioè
  Quesiti, Trauagliata inuentione, Noua scientia,
  Ragionamenti sopra Archimede ... In Venetia,
  Al segno del lione, M.DC.VI.

    3 p.ℓ.,72,48,52,284 (i.e.286) p. illus.(incl.diagrs.
  plates (part fold.) 20½ x 16cm.
    Title vignette (device of C.Trajani di Navo); head
  and tail pieces; initials.
    Numbers 122 and 124 repeated in paging.
    "Quesiti", "Trauagliata inuentione" and "Ragionamenti
  sopra Archimede" have half-titles with vignette (port.
  of author)

    Catchword "Delli" at end of Ragionamenti, but work ap-
  pears to be complete.
    "Noua scientia" bound first, followed by "Trauagliata
  inuentione", "Ragionamenti sopra Archimede" and "Quesiti.
    Armorial book-plate: Jacobus Maximilianus co.Collatti.

    1.Science--Early works to 1800.

NT 0044404   MiU TU OkU ICN IU MB MCM

Tartaglia, Niccolò, d.1557.
  L'arithmetique de Nicolas Tartaglia Brescian
  ... Recueillie, & traduite d'italien en françois,
  par Gvillavme Gosselin ... Auec toutes les demonstrations mathematiques: & plusieurs inuentions dudit Gosselin ... A Paris, Chez Gilles
  Beys, 1578.
    2 v. in 1. diagrs. 17cm.
    Title vignette (printer's device); head and tail
  pieces.
    With this is bound Gosselin,Guillaume. De arte magna.
  M. D. LXXVII.

    1.Arithmetic--Before 1846. I.Gosselin,Guillaume,d.
  1590,ed.and tr.

NT 0044405   MiU

Tartaglia, Niccolò, d.1557.
  L'arithmetiqve de Nicolas Tartaglia brescian... Diuisée en
  deux parties... Recueillie & traduite d'italien en françois, par
  Gvillavme Gosselin... Auec toutes les demonstrations mathematiques: & plusieurs inuentions dudit Gosselin, esparses chacune
  en son lieu... Paris: A. Perier, 1613. 2 v. in 1.   diagrs.
  19cm.

1. Arithmetic—Textbooks, 1613.   I. Gosselin, Guillaume, translator.   *Revised*
N. Y. P. L.   August 6, 1934

NT 0044406   NN

Tartaglia, Niccolò, d.1557.
    La Balistique de Nicolas Tartaglia;
  ou, Recueil de tout ce que cet
  auteur a ecrit touchant le mouvement
  des projectiles et les questions qu
  s'y rattachent, compose des deux
  premiers livres de la Science nouvelle
  ... et des trois premiers livres des
  Recherches et inventions nouvelles...
  tr. de l'Italien, aved quelques
  annotations, par Rieffel. Paris,
  J. Correard, 1846.
    316 p. 4 fold.   pl.

NT 0044407   DNW

  Tartaglia, Niccolò, d. 1557.
    López de Arenas, Diego, b. ca. 1579.
    Carpinteria de lo blanco y tratado de alarifes, por Diego
  López de Arenas. 3. ed. que se hace de este libro, con el suple-
  mento que escribió don Santiago Rodriguez de Villafañe, ano-
  tada y glosada por d. Eduardo de Mariátegui ... Madrid, Impr.
  de M. Galiano, 1867.

RARE BOOK
DIVISION
QA
33
T3
  Tartaglia, Niccolò, d. 1557.
    General trattato di numeri et misure. Vinegia,
  Curtio Troiano, 1556-1560.

    6 pts. in 1 v. (277, 186, 51, 63, 90 and 44
  numb. ℓ) illus. 32 cm.
    Leaves printed on both sides.
    Woodcuts: Author's port. (on t.-p. of pts. 1
  and 2), diagrs., figures, initials, printer's
  device.
    No covering title page. Each part has separ-
  ate t.-p.: La prima [...sesta] parte del general
  trattato di numeri et misure...

    Imprint varies: pts. 3-6: Venetia, 1560.
    Each part has a dedication signed by the
  author: Pt. 1: To Richard Wentworth, 23 di
  Marzo, 1556; Pt. 2: To Antonio L'Andriano,
  3 di Aprile, 1556; Pt. 3: To Daniel D'Anna,
  1 di Genaro, 1560, Pt. 4: To Camillo Martinengo [n.d.], Pt. 5: To Sforza Palavicino
  [n.d.], Pt. 6: To Girolamo Martinengo [n.d.].
    Cf. Riccardi, P., I, 505; Smith, D.E., Rara
  Arithmetica, p. 275-8.
    1. Mathematics   Early works to 1800.
  I. Title.

NT 0044410   PPT MNS MH-BA CtY NIC

  Tartaglia, Niccolò, d. 1557
    Stubbs, Henry, 1632-1676.
    Legends no histories; or, A specimen of some animad-
  versions upon The history of the Royal society; wherein
  ... sundry mistakes about the making of salt-petre and
  gun-powder are detected, and rectified: whereunto are
  added two discourses, one of Pietro Sardi, and another of
  Nicolas Tartaglia, relating to that subject; translated out
  of Italian ... Together with the Plus ultra of Mr. Joseph
  Glanvill reduced to a non-plus, &c. By Henry Stubbe ...
  London, 1670.

QA31
.E8767
Rare Bk.
Coll.

Tartaglia, Niccolò, d. 1557, ed. and tr.

Euclides.

Evclide Megarense philosopho, solo introdvttore delle scientie mathematice. Diligentemente rassettato, et alla integrità ridotto, per il degno professore di tal scientie Nicolo Tartalea brisciano. Secondo le dve tradottioni. Con vna ampla espositione dello istesso tradottore di nuono [!] aggiunta. Talmente chiara, che ogni mediocre ingegno, senza la notitia, ouer suffragio di alcun' altra scientia con facilità serà capace a poterlo intendere. Venetia, Appresso Curtio Troiano, 1565.

Tartaglia, Niccolò, d. 1557.

Nova Scientia Inventa Da Nicolo Tartalea. B. ... [Vinegia: S. da Sabio, 1537] 48 l. incl. diagrs. illus. 20½cm. (4°.)

Brunet, V, 660.
Colophon: In Vinegia per Stephano da Sabio. Ad infantia di Nicolo Tartalea brifciano il qual habita a fan Saluador. M D XXXVII.
Engraved, illustrated t.-p.
Caption-title: Inuentione nouamente trouata da Nicolo Tartalea brifciano: vtiliffima p ciafcuno fpeculatiuo Mathematico Bôbardiero ʒ altri intitolata Sciētia noua: diuifa in cinque libri....
Printer's mark on recto of last leaf.
Contains three books only.
Leaf 8 (blank?) wanting.

820181A.   1. Quadrant, 1537.   2. Ballistics, 1537.   January 25, 1937
N. Y. P. L.

CtNowaB

NT   0044413   NN ICJ NNC NIC NjP OkU NSyU DFo InU

Tartaglia, Niccolò, d. 1557.

La noua scientia de Nicolo Tartaglia, con una gionta al terzo libro ... [Colophon: Stampata in Venetia per Nicolo da Bascarini a istantia de l'autore, 1550]

4 p. l., 32 numb. l. illus., diagrs. 20¾ᵐᵐ.

Illustrated t.-p.
First published in Venice, 1537.

1. Mechanics—Early works to 1800.   I. Title.

45-51705

Library of Congress   QC123.T3 1550

NT   0044414   DLC TxU MH CtY-M NcRS MiU

Tartaglia, Niccolò, d. 1557.

La Noua Scientia de Nicolo Tartaglia con vna gionta al terzo Libro. [Woodcut. Three lines] [Colophon: In Vinegia.1558]

Uxq46   4p.l.,32numb.l. illus.(diagrs.) 21½cm.
558t   Signatures: ✳ ⁴A-H4.

The table of contents (verso of t.-p.) calls for five books; there are, however, only three here.

Bound with this is his Regola generale di solevare ogni fondata naue, with colophon:

In Vinegia,Per Curtio Troiano de i Nauò.1562.

It is not clear whether this is a separate book, published four years after the Noua Scientia, or whether both were issued in one volume, the Nauò colophon referring to both works, and the 1558 colophon at the end of the Noua Scientia having been taken over from the earlier edition, perhaps with the same sheets.

MnU ICN NIC

NT   0044416   CtY MiU NNC OkU InU NjP NNC ICU MiU WU

Tartaglia, Niccolò, d. 1557.

La Noua Scientia di Nicolò Tartaglia ... Malignita, Curtio Troiano de i Nauo, 1562.

3 vol in 1.

NT   0044417   InU

Tartaglia, Niccolò, d. 1557.   1583

La Noua Scientia di Nicolò Tartaglia, con vna gionta al terzo Libro. [In Venetia, Appreffo Camillo Caftelli. 1583.] 5 p.l., 34 [i. e. 33] f. incl. diagrs. illus., pl. 20½cm. (4°.)

Brunet, V, 660.
Illustrated t.-p.
With colophon.
Number 4 omitted in foliation, f. 15 wrongly numbered 16.
Comprises books 1-3 only, of the five included in the table of contents. No more published?—cf. *British Museum catalogue*, and Charbonnier, P. J. *Essai sur l'histoire de la balistique*. Paris, 1928. p. 17.
For discussion of this work on the motion of projectiles, cf. Tonni-Bazza, V. *Un matematico del XVI secolo*. (In: *Rivista d'Italia*. Anno 7, v. 1. Roma, 1904. p. 1031-1049.)
With this is bound his: [Quesiti et inventioni diverse. Vinegia, 1562?]

1. Ballistics, 1583.
N. Y. P. L.   Revised May 19, 1937

NT   0044418   NN DFo MNS MB ICJ

15
9522

Tartaglia, Niccolò, d. 1557.

Of sal nitre, and The various compositions of the Gun-powder ...
(In Stubbe, Henry. Legends no histories. London [1670. 8°. p. 110-127)

NT   0044419   DLC

QA
33
T3
T73
f

Tartaglia,Niccolò,d.1557.

La prima [-sesta] parte del general trattato di nvmeri,et misvre di Nicolo Tartaglia,nellaqvale in diecisette libri si dichiara tvtti gli atti operativi,pratiche,et regole necessarie non solamente in tutta l'arte negotiara, & mercantile,ma anchor in ogni altra arte, scientia,ouer disciplina,doue interuenghi il calculo. Vinegia, Per Curtio Troiano de i Nauò, 1556-60.

6pt.in 3v.([6],277l.;[4],186l.;[4],51,[5], 63,[5],90,[4],44l.) illus.,diagrs.,ports. 32cm.

Signatures: ✳ᶜ,A-2Yᵍ,2Zᶜ;✳ᶜ,A-Zᶜ,aa-hhᵍ; Aᵛ,

ᵍA-Hᵍ,Iᶠ,✳ᵛ,³A-Kᶜ,Lᶜ,✳✞✞,ᵍA-Pᶜ,✞✞,ᶠA-Fᶜ,Gᶜ.
First edition,rebound in brown paper boards backed in modern parchment.
Provenance: Biblioteca Riccardi (bookplate)
Imperfect: 2Z1 and 2Z7 in vol.1 supplied in manuscript.

1.Mathematics--Early works to 1800. I. Title: General trattato di numeri,et misure.

NT   0044421   NSyU DFo NNC WU CU MiU NIC

RARE BOOK
DEPARTMENT
MUCKENHOUPT
QA
33
T3
N6
1537

Tartaglia,Niccolò,d.1557.

Qvesiti,et inventioni diverse de Nicolo Tartalea Brisciano ... [Venetia, Per Venturino Ruffinelli, 1546]

[2],132l. illus.,diagrs.,port. 21cm.
Signatures: Aᶜ,B-2Kᵍ.
Bound with the author's Nova scientia. Venice,1537.
Rebound in quarter calf gilt.

1.Military art and science--Early works to 1800. 2.Science--Early works to 1800. 3. Mathematics-- Early works to 1800. I.Title.

DFo CU AzU

NT   0044422   NSyU OrCS NcD NN MH RPB ICN NIC OCU IU

Tartaglia, Niccolò, d. 1557.

Qvesiti et inventioni diverse de Nicolo Tartaglia, di novo restampati con vna gionta al sesto libro, nella quale si mostra duoi modi di redur una città inespugnabile. La divisione et continentia di tvtta l'opra nel seguente foglio si trouara notata. Con privilegio. [Venetia] Appresso de l'avttore, 1554.

4 p. l., 5-128 numb. l. illus., diagrs. 21ᵐᵐ.

Colophon: In Venetia per Nicolo de Bascarini, ad instantia & requisitione, & à proprie spese de Nicolo Tartaglia autore. Nell'anno di nostra salute .MDLIIII.

Signatures: A-II⁴.
Woodcut (portrait of author) on t.-p.; initials.
Dedication "Al clementissimo, et invittissimo Henrico, Ottavo, per la Dio gratia re de Anglia, de Francia, et de Hibernia, etc." (sig. Aᵢᵢᵢ)
Appended (by the same author): Regola generale di solevare ogni fondata naue & nauilii con ragione. [Venetia, 1562]

1. Military art and science—Early works to 1800. 2. Science—Early works to 1800. 3. Mathematics—Early works to 1800. I. Title. II. Title: Regola generale di solevare ogni fondata naue.

25-20108

Library of Congress   U101.T3

PU OC1W ICJ NjP

NT   0044424   DLC MnU NIC NNC TxU InU MH PPAmP PPF MiU

Tartaglia, Niccolò, d. 1557.

[Quesiti et inventioni diverse. Vinegia, 1562?] 94 [i. e. 96] l. incl. diagrs. illus. 22cm. (4°.)

Imperfect: all before f. 5 (including t.-p.) wanting.
Caption-title, f. 5: Il primo libro delli Qvesiti, et inventioni diverse de Nicolo Tartaglia, sopra gli tiri delle artiglierie, et altri svoi varii accidenti.
Numbers 67-68 repeated in foliation; f. 8 and 47 wrongly numbered 7 and 44.
Relates chiefly to ballistics, ordnance and fortification.
For discussion of this work, cf. Tonni-Bazza, V. Un matematico del XVI secolo.
(In: Rivista d'Italia. Anno 7, v. 1. Roma, 1904. p. 1031-1049.)
Bound with his: La Noua Scientia. [In Vinegia. M.D.LVIII.]

✳ KB (1583, Tartaglia)
———— Second copy.   20½cm. (4°.)

Bound with his: La Noua Scientia. [In Venetia, 1583]

1. Ballistics, 1562. 2. Ordnance,   1562. 3. Fortification.
N. Y. P. L.   Revised- May 24, 1937

NT   0044426   NN

Bd.w.
QC
123
T3
1583
Cage

Tartaglia, Niccolò, d.1557.

[Quesiti, et inuentioni diuerse. Venice? 1583?]

5-94 l. B-2A⁴. 4to. illus.
Lacks title-page, preliminary leaves and book 9.
Possibly issued as pt.2 of La noua scientia... [1583] which is bound in same volume.

NT   0044427   DFo

✳IC5
T1788
B555n

Tartaglia, Niccolò, d.1557.

Ragionamenti de Nicolo Tartaglia sopra la sua travagliata inventione. Nelli quali se dechiara uolgarmente quel libro di Archimede siracusano intitolato. De insidentibus aquae, con altre speculatiue pratiche da lui ritrouate sopra le materie, che stano, & chi non stano sopra lacqua, vltimamente se assegna la ragione, et causa naturale di tutte le sottile, et oscure particularità dette, et dechiarate nella detta sua trauagliata inuftione cõ molte altre da quelle

[Venetia]Apresso di lautore.[1551] ...

4°. [48]p. illus.(incl.diagrs.) 21.5cm.
Signatures: A-F⁴.
Colophon: Stampata in Venetia per Nicolo Bascarini à instantia & requisitione & à proprie spese de Nicolo Tartaglia autore. Nel mese di maggio l'anno di nostra salute. 1551.
Woodcut port. of the author on t.-p.
No.4 in a   volume of Tartaglia's works.

NT   0044429   MH CU NNC IaU MiU ICJ TxU DFo

[Tartaglia, Niccolò,] d. 1557.

Regola generale di solevare ogni fondata naue & nauilii con ragione. [Venetia, 1562] 32 l. illus., diagrs. 21ᵐᵐ. [With his Qvesiti et inventioni diverse ... [Venetia, 1554]
Signatures: A-H⁴.
Caption title. Title-page wanting? Colophon: Con li svoi privilegii. In Vinegia, Per Curtio Troiano de i Nauò. M.D.LXII.
The dedication (on E₂ verso) "Al ... signor conte Antonio Landriano," prefixed to the "Primo ragionamento," is dated: In Venetia alli 12. di zugno, 1562, and is preceded by the caption: Primo libro del Archimede De insidentibvs aqvae dechiarata in volgare. The "Secondo ragionamento" is dedicated "Al ... signor Giulio Sauorgnano" and is dated: In Venetia alli 5. marzo. 1551. cf. Riccardi, Bibl. mar. ital., 1898., col. 504.
1. Salvage. 2. Hydro-   statics. 3. Specific gravity. I.
Archimedes. De corporibus   fluitantibus. II. Title.
25-20100 Revised

Library of Congress   U101.T3

MB

NT   0044430   DLC NNC NIC MnU CtY DAS NjP NN MiU InU

Tartaglia, Niccolò, d. 1557.

La seconda parte del general trattato di nvmeri, et misvre, nella qvale in vndici libri si notifica la piv ellevata, et specvlativa parte della pratica arithmetica. Vinegia, 1556.

4, 186 p. fᵒ.

NT   0044431   NIC

Tartaglia, Niccolò, d. 1557.

Sulla soluzione dell'equazione cubica...
see under Olivo, Alberto.

QA
29
.T19
A2
1557a

Tartaglia,Niccolò,d.1557.

... Testamentum d.Nicolai Tartalea doctoris mathematicae q.d.Michaelis de Brixia,de quo rogatus sui ego Rochus de Benedictis q.d.Antonij pubous Venetianae auctᵒ notᵒ sub die supᵗᵃ. Obiʲᵗ die luna hora septima notis xiiij xbris supᵗⁱ [n.p., 19--?]

facsimile: [4] p. 38cm.

Title on p.[4]
At head of title: M D LVII die Veneris decimo ᵭˢ xbris.
Facsimile of manuscript.

NT   0044433   MiU RPB

STC
23689
copy 1

Tartaglia, Niccolò, d. 1557.
Three bookes of colloquies concerning the arte
of shooting in great and small peeces of artillerie
... Written in Italian ... now translated into
English by Cyprian Lucar ... Also the saide Cyprian
Lucar hath annexed ... a treatise named Lucar
Appendix ... to shew ... the properties, office,
and dutie of a gunner ... Imprinted at London for
Iohn Harrison, 1588.
Colophon: ... Printed by Thomas Dawson ...

.·. 4 6 1
.·. , A-R , [S] . (G5, t-p to 'Lucar Appendix'
is a cancel; in this copy cancelland survives;
[S] printed as conjugate leaf with G5; [S] bound
before G5.) Fo. illus., fold. plates, tables.
Slip cancel on sig. C2r.
See Cockle's <u>A bibl. of English military books</u>,
(1900), no. 38.
Harmsworth copy.

NT 0044435   DFo CtY MH CSmH DN ICN TxU

Film
301

Tartaglia, Niccolò, d. 1557.
Three bookes of colloqvies concerning the
arte of shooting in great and small pieces of
artillerie ... Written in Italian ... by
Nicholas Tartaglia ... and now translated
into English by Cyprian Lucar. Also the
saide C. Lucar hath annexed unto the same
three books of Colloquies a treatise named
Lucar appendix ... to shew the office and
duties of a gunner. London, Printed for J.
Harrison, 1588.

Microfilm copy, made by University of
Chicago Library. Negative.
Collation of the original, as determined
from the film: 80, 120 p. illus.

1. Ballisti .cs. 2. Gunnery.
I. Lucar, Cy prian, fl. 1590.

NT 0044437   NIC NNC MiU

QA101
.T22
Rare bk
room

TARTAGLIA,NICCOLÒ,d.1557.
Tvtte l'opere d'arithmetica del famosissimo Nicolò
Tartaglia... In Venetia,1592-93.
2 v.in 1. illus.,diagrs. 21cm.
Title vignettes;head pieces;initials.

1.Arithmetic--Early works to 1800.

NT 0044438   ICU IU

Tartaglia, Nunzio.
Practica m. c. vicariae qvam non solvm ordo
ciuiliter procedendi, libellosq. compilandi, sed etian
super tenore instrumenti criminaliter praesentati,
secundum forma ritus et de periurio breuiter
annotatur. Fructuumque, interesse, appellationum,
nullitatum & hypotecae materia, breuissime
explicatur. Vico Equencse, 1585.

NT 0044439   MH-L

WA
13240

Tartaglia, Paolo,
Sfoghi del cuore e confidenze a Maria; pro-
posti alle anime devote. Omaggio speciale al
Giubileo dell'Immacolata. 2. ed. con correzioni
ed aggiunte. Palermo, Scuola Tip. Boccone del
Povero, 1904.
550 p. illus.

1. Mary, Virgin - Prayer-books and devotions.

NT 0044440   CtY

Tartaglini, Domenico.
Nuova descrizione dell'antichissima città di Cortona,
con l'aggiunta di diversi fatti antichi, ed altri particolari
della medesima; opera, e studio dell'abbate Domenico
Tartaglini Cortonese ... Perugia, Costantini, 1700.
18 p. l., 179 p. front. (port.) 22cm.

1. Cortona—Hist.

14-18625

Library of Congress   DG975.C75T3

Petrarch
M
1621
.3
T19++

Tartaglione, Giulio.
Petrarca, sonetto 212. Melodia in chiave
di sol, con accompag.to di violino obbligato
e pianoforte di Giulio Tartaglione. Firenze, G. Venturini [18--] Pl. no. 263.
3, 15 p. 36cm.
Setting of Petrarch's sonnet, Solea
lontana, for high voice, violin and piano.
Violin obbligato: p. 1-3 (1st set)
1. Songs (High voice) with instr. ensemble. 2. Petrarca, Francesco, 1304-1374--
Musical sett ings.

NT 0044442   NIC

Tartaglione, Raffaele.
Reclamo per gli emigrati del 1820. [Napoli]
1848.
Broadside. 4°.
In: BWL p. v. 1, no. 267.

NT 0044443   NN

Tartaglione, Silvio.
Gli appalti di opere dei comuni. Empoli, Arti grafiche
dei comuni ditta Caparrini [1949]
33 p. 24 cm.

1. Municipal government—Italy. 2. Contracts, Letting of. 3. Public contracts—Italy. I. Title.

A 52-281

Illinois. Univ. Library
for Library of Congress   [3]

NT 0044444   IU

TARTAGLIONE,Tommaso.
La legge di pubblica sicurezza esposta con
annotazioni,richiami e confronti. Grosseto,
F.Perozzo,1890.
8°.

NT 0044445   MH-L

Tartagna, Alessandro
see
Tartagni, Alessandro, 1424-1477.

Typ
525
21.822F

Tartagni, Alessandro, 1424-1477.
Aureum ac diuinum opus excellentissimi. v. j.
monarce Alexandri Tartagni ... sup prima. ff.
veteris sūma cum cura oīumq[ue] industria ex
fidelissimis exēplaribus excerptum et in
pristinum nitorē emendatum. Cum apostillis
doctissimorum doctorum Francisci de curte.
Bernardini de landriano & Antonij francisci ...
Additis etiā additionibus dīī Thome diplouatatij
... in hac vltima impressiōe nouiter editis ...
[Venice,1521]

Continued in next column

Continued from preceding column

f°. 8 pts. illus.(ports.) 44cm.
Title of pt.1 in 21 lines; another issue (?)
has title in 20 lines.
Colophon (pts.1 & 4): Venetijs per Baptistam
de Tortis. Mccccxxj. die. xxv. augusti.
[printer's mark]
Imperfect: pts.1 & 4 only, in 2 vols. A
complete set would contain commentaries for the
Digestum vetus, Digestum novum, Infortiatum, and
Codex, each   in 2 pts.

NT 0044448   MH

Tartagni, Alessandro, 1424-1477.
D. Alex: De Imola Cōmētaria vtili∫∫ima Sup
primā [∫ecundam] codicis partē. vna cū apo-
tillis ... Cum ampli∫∫imo Repertorio noui∫∫ime
edito. [Venice, Philippus Pincius, after 1523]
LXXVII, CXI numb. l. illus. 42.5 x 30 cm.
Vellumized pigskin.
Part 2 has its own t.-p. and foliation.
Titles in red and black, with Pincius' device.
Printed in double column, with side-notes.
Bound with this, his: ... Repertorivm Nouum ac
∫olenne ad omnes eius Lecturas ... [Venice, after
1523]

Woodcut, head of each part, broken at top;
when used 17 Nov. 1523 it was unbroken (cf.
Essling, 2:2, p. 472)
Phillipps coll. no. 456, from Rosenbach 1923.

1. Corpus juris ci~ilis. Codex.

NT 0044450   CSmH

---

xfK349.3742
T37
1527

Tartagni, Alessandro, 1424-1477.
Cōmētaria utilissima... Una cū apostillis
p̄clarissimorū iurecōs. d. Frāci. Curtii papiē.
d. Antonii Frācisci de doctoribus... d. Bernardini de Lādriano... Cum amplissimo repertorio
nouissime edito. [Venetiis, P. Pincius de
Mantuanus, 1527?]
2v.in 1. 45cm.
Vol.2 has special t.p.
Leaves printed on both sides in double
columns.

Printer's device on t.p.
Contents.- [v.1.] Sup prima codicis parte.-
[v.2.] Super secundam codicis partem.

1. Roman law. I. Curtius, Franciscus,
d.1495. II. Bernardini de Landriano.
III. Title: Commentaria utilissima.

NT 0044452   IaU

---

gf
KBD
43
T37
C64
1570

Tartagni, Alessandro, 1424-1477.
Commentaria in primam, & II. Codicis partem;
summo studio & labore, ab innumeris prope mendis
expurgata, cum adnot. ... Francisci Curtii, ...
& aliorum...accesserunt huic omnium postremae
impressioni Legislatorum nomina, ... et Alexandri
Vita per Nicolaum Anto. Grauatium...edita.
Venetiis, apvd Ivntas, 1570.
174 p. 43 cm.
At head of title: Alexandri Tartagni Imolensis.
Known as Lectura super sexta parte Codicis.
1. Corpus juris civilis. Codex. Book 2-6,
title 37. 2. Roman law. I. Title: Commentaria in primam & II. [et secundam]
Codicis partem.

NT 0044453   CU-L CtY-L

Tartagni, Alessandro, 1424-1477.
Alexandri Tartagni Commentaria in I. & II. Codicis
partem, cvm adnot. ... Franc. Cvrtii ... & aliorum ... atque
ipsius Alexandri Vita per Nicolaum Antonium Grauatium
excerpta. Hac postrema editione ... ab erroribus repurgata.
Venetiis, Apvd Ivntas, 1586.
166, 58 l. 42 cm.
Vita wanting.
"Repertorivm ... in omnia Alexandri Tartagni ... Commentaria"
with special t. p.: 58 l. (2d group)
Known as Lectura super sexta parte Codicis.
1. Corpus juris civilis. Codex. Book 2-6, title 37. 2. Roman law.
3. Roman law—Indexes.

74-226800

NT 0044454   DLC CU-L

Tartagni, Alessandro, 1424-1477.
Alexandri Tartagni Commentaria in primam & secundam Infort. part. cvm adnot. Franc. Cvrtii ⟨et al⟩, necnon legislatorum nominibus cuique legi appositis, atque ipsius Alexandri vita per Nicolaum Antonium Grauatium excerpta. Hac postrema ed. summo studio, labore, ac diligentia ab innumeris, quibus singulae scatebant pagellae, erroribus repurgata. Venetiis, Apvd Ivntas, 1586.

295 l. 42 cm.

Colophon dated 1585.
Issued as v. 2 of the author's commentaries on the Corpus juris civilis, 5 v., Venice, 1586. Cf. P. Camerini. Annali dei Giunti, v. 1, pt. 2, 1963, p. 128.

Known as Lectura super prima et secunda parte Infortiati cum apostillia.

1. Roman law.   I. Corpus juris civilis. Digesta. Book 24, title 3—book 38. II. Title: Commentaria in primam & secundam Infortiati partem cum adnotationes.

                                77-231139

NT 0044456   DLC

Tartagni, Alessandro, 1424-1477.
Commentaria. Venic, 1595.
5 v.
Contents: v. 1. In I & II Codicis Partem.
v. 2. Ad frequentiores Pandectarum Tit. v. 3. In I & II Digesti Veteris Partem. v. 4. In I & II Infortiati v. 5. In I & II Digesti Noui Partem.
1. Schulte, T. F. N., 1423 or 4-1477.

NT 0044457   PPB ULC DLC

Tartagni, Alessandro, 1424-1477.
Consilia. Lyons, 1557.
3 v. (vols. 2 & 3 together)

NT 0044458   PPB

Tartagni, Alessandro, 1424-1477.
Consilia. Venice, 1610.
7 parts in 4 volumes.

NT 0044459   PPB

Tartagni, Alessandro, 1424-1477.
Consiliorum Alexandri Volumen Quartum. Clarissimi Iuris Vtriusque Doctoris Alexandri Imolensis Consiliorum pars Quarta, accuratissime nuc demum cum haud vulgari accessione excusa: minime praetermissis quae singulis Consilijs haetenus praefigi consuetum est Summarijs & argumetis. Quibus deniq complurium doctiss. viroru scholia adiecta sunt & in margine posita. Lugduni, Anno, 1532.
100 fo.

NT 0044460   PU-L

---

gf
KBD
41
T37
C65
1536
Tartagni, Alessandro, 1424-1477.
Consiliorvm...Alexandri Imolensis. ⟨Venetiis?⟩ 1536.
v. 43 cm.
-- ---- Repertorivm svper Consiliis Alexandri; Repertorivm sive Index vtilissimvs in septem volumina Consiliorum Alexandri de Tartagnis Imolensis.
Library has v. 2, 4. 6, sup.
1. Corpus juris civilis. Institutiones. 2. Roman law.   I. Title.   II. Title: Repertorivm svper Consiliis Alexandri de Tartagnis Imolensis.

NT 0044461   CU-L

Tartagni, Alessandro, 1424-1477
Consiliorvm Alexandri Tartagni imolensis i. c. celeberrimi lber ⟨⟩ primus   Habes his typis omnivm postremis præter accuratam emendationem, adnotationes repurgatas & expunctas, quæ nouis opinionibus & hæreticis orthodoxam ecclesiam lædebant ... Dvo insvper habes Alexandri responsa restitvta, vnum, quod est xxxiij, lib. 4. multis ab hinc annis prætermissum. Alterum vero est in vij. libri calce, quod inter consilia Lavrentii Calcanei impressum reperitur. Item Alexandri vitam per Nicolavm Antonivm Gravativm i. c. editam. Postremò additamenta doctissima præstantiss. i. c. Marci Antonii Nattæ ... Venetiis, apud Nicolaum Beuilaquam, & socios, MDLXX.
v. in   38ᶜᵐ.

Title vignettes (publisher's device)
—— Index materiarvm qvae in septem Alexandri Imolensis libris continentur, fidelissimvs, ac locvpletissimvs, multis additis hac omnium postrema editione, qvæ maximam ivris prvdentiæ stvdiosis adferent, & commoditatem, & vtilitatem. Venetiis, apud Nicolaum Beuilaquam, & socios, 1570.
⟨102⟩ p. 35ᶜᵐ.
Title vignette (publisher's device)
Prefixed to Consiliorvm ... liber primus.
1. Law—Collected works. 2. Civil law. 3. Canon law. 4. Law reports, digests, etc. I. Natta, Marco Antonio, d. 1616. II. Gravatius, Nicolaus Antonius, 16th cent. III. Title.

                       32-23364

NT 0044463   DLC

Tartagni, Alessandro, 1424-1477.
Consiliorum seu responsorum...liber I ⟨-VII⟩ Francofurti, 1610.
3 pt. in 2.

NT 0044464   NjP

Tartagni, Alessandro, 1424-1477.
Consiliorum, sexta pars. Lyons, 1557.

NT 0044465   PPB

Inc.
+4830.5
with
Inc.
+4829.5
TARTAGNI, ALESSANDRO, 1424-1477.
Consiliorum volumines unus et duo. Venice, Bernardinus Stagninus⟨1488⟩
342 l. 2°. 425x290mm. (with Bolognini, Lodovico. Repertorium aureum. ⟨1488⟩)

2 columns, 67 lines; Haebler, type 10 (93 G) Printer's marks on verso of l. 142 and 342. Hain 7441 = Hain *15257; Stillwell, Inc. in Amer. lib. T22. Goff; T-23

NT 0044466   ICN

Law
Tartagni, Alessandro, 1424-1477.
Alexandri Imolensis in codicem iustinianevm commentariorvm tomvs primvs et secvndvs. Accesserunt haec, Farncisci Curtensis & Bernardini Landriani annotationes. Lvgdvni, 1558.
176 l. 42 cm.

1. Roman law.   I. Curtius, Franciscus, d. 1495. II. Landriano, Bernardino da, III. Title.

NT 0044467   DLC

Tartagni, Alessandro, 1424-1477.

Baldo degli Ubaldi, 1327?-1400.
Baldi Vbaldi Pervsini ivrisconsvlti ... In ⟨Corpus iuris civilis⟩ ... commentaria. Doctiss. hominvm aliis omnibvs hactenvs impre adnotationibus illvstrata. Necnon summarijs, & indice verborum, ac rerum ... cum Pactorum etiam, ac Constituti eiusdem authoris tractatibus ... exornata ... Venetiis, apud Iuntas, 1599.

---

xfK349.375
T36
1541
Tartagni, Alessandro, d.1477.
In prima infortiati... commentariorum. Alexandri Tartagni... Sup infortiato digesti, exactissima uigilantia castigata, ac typis elegãtiusculis denuo excussa. Cui accesserunt annotationes praeclarissimorũ uirorũ dñi Francisci de curte, dñi Bernardini de landriano. ac dñi Francisci de doctoribus. Necnon apostillae ẽt cõpluriũ neotericorũ sub his caracteribus... signatae... Venetiis, 1541.
v. 44cm.

Leaves printed on both sides in double columns.
Contents.- ⟨v.1⟩ Prima pars comment.

1. Roman law. I. Curtius, Franciscus, d.1495. II. Bernardini de Landriano. III. Title. IV. Title: Commentaria in primam infortiati.

NT 0044470   IaU

---

f
PA 6652
.R42J88
T2
(Rare)
Tartagni, Alessandro, 1424-1477.
... In primam et secvndam Codicis partem. Commentariorvm Alexandri Tartagni... in Codicem tomus primus, vnã cũ acutissimis eiusdem disputationibus... &... Francisci de Curte, Bernardini de Landriano Additionibus: quibus accessit & copiosissimum Hieronymi Loreti Repertorium... Lugduni, 1552.
176 l.
Title within architectural woodcut border; initials.
1. Corpus juris civilis. Codex. I. Curtius, Franciscus, 1495d. II. Landriano, Bernardino da, 1552fl. III. Corpus juris civilis. Codex.

NT 0044471   ICU

Tartagni, Alessandro, 1424-1477.
Alexandri Tartagni Imolensis In primam & secundam ff. noui commentaria: collatis netustissimis exemplaribus innumeris mendis perpurgata, additionibus insuper clarissimorum iurisconsultorum illustrata: adiectaq; authoris vita. Augustae Taurinorum, Apud haeredes N. Beuilaquae, 1575.
294 l. 41 cm.

1. Roman law.

                       78-297743

NT 0044472   DLC

---

gf
KBD
42
T37
R46
1570
Tartagni, Alessandro, 1424-1477.
In secundam ff. noui partem commentaria. ⟨Venetiis, apud Iuntas, 1570⟩
p. 193-294. 43 cm.

Bound with author's Repertorivm copiosissimvm in omnia Alexandri Tartagni Imol. ... Commentaria

Title page wanting; caption title.
Imprint from colophon.

1. Corpus juris civilis. Digesta. Books 39-50. 2. Roman law. I. Title. II. Title: Commentaria in secundam Digesti noui partem.

NT 0044473   CU-L

---

xfK349.375
T37
1541
⟨**Tartagni, Alessandro**⟩ d.1477.
Alexander de Imola. In secundam digesti novi, commentariorum... super digesto nouo, exactissima uiglantia castigata, ac typis elegãtiusculis denuo excussa. Cui accesserunt annotationes praeclarissimorũ uiroru dñi Francisci de curte, dñi Bernardini de landriano, ac dñi Francisci de doctoribus. Necnon apostillae et cõpluriũ neotericorũ sub his caracteribus signatae... Venetiis, 1541.
v. 44cm.

Leaves printed on both sides in double columns.
Bound with the author's Reperto ⟨rium⟩ in index locupletissimus materiarum magis singularium... Venetiis, 1541.

1. Roman law. I. Curtius, Franciscus, d.1495. II. Bernardini de Landriano. III. Title: Commentaria, in secundam digesti novi.

NT 0044475   IaU

xfK349.375
T375 ₍Tartagni,₎Alessandro₎ d.1477.
1577   Alexandri Tartagni Imolensis. ₍In secundam
ff. noui partem commentaria. Cum additionibus
Franc. de Curt. Bernardi de Landriano, Thomae
Diploualstii, & Antonii Franc. de Doctoribus.
Venetiis, 1576.
    179-272ℓ. 43cm.
    Imperfect copy, leaves 1-178 wanting.
    Captian title; t.p. wanting.
    Imprint from colphon.
    Running title⋅ De verborium obligationibus.

    Bound with the author's Repertorium copio-
sissimum in omnia Alexandri Tartagni... Venetius,
1577.

    1. Roman law. I. Curtius, Franciscus, d.1495.
II. Bernardini de Landriano. III. Title: In
secundam ff. noui partem commentaria. IV. Title:
Commentaria in secundam ff. noui partem.

NT   0044477   IaU

———

    Tartagni, Alessandro, 1424-1477.
    In sextum codicis librum... commentaria
      see under   Baldo degli Ubaldi, 1327?-1400.
    In Justiniani codicem. 1615.

Tartagni,Alessandro,1424-1477.
    Alexandri Tartagni imolensis,ivrisc.
celeberrimi ₍Commentaria₎ Venetiis, apvd
Ivntas ₍MD XCIII₎-M D XCV.
    6 v.in 3.   42½cm.
    No general title-page; each volume has
special title-page.
    Title of vols.1-5 in red and black;
title of v.1 within engr.ornamental border.
    Printer's device on title-pages of vols.
2-6 and at end of v.5.
    Imprint of v.1   undated; imprints of

vols.2-6 have date 1595. Colophon date of
v.1,1593; colophon dates of vols.2 and 4,
1594.
    Vols.1-4 include under each rubric "Ad-
ditiones" containing the annotations of
Franciscus Curtius and others.
    "Necnon legislatorum nominibus cuique
legi appositis,atque ipsius Alexandri vita
per Nicolaum Antonium Grauatium."
    Contents.--₍v.   1₎ Commentaria in I.

₍: II.Digesti veteris partem.-₍v.2₎ In
primam,& secundam Infortiati partem commentaria.-₍v.3₎ Commentaria in I.& II.Di-
gesti noui partem.-₍v.4₎ Commentaria in
I.& II.Codicis partem.-₍v.5₎ Ad frequentiores Pandectarum titulos,leges,& para-
graphos.-₍v.6₎ Repertorivm copiosissimvm.

NT   0044481   MiU-L

Law   Tartagni, Alessandro, 1424-1477, supposed
      author.

Maino, Giasone dal, 1435-1519.
    Jason de actionibus. ₍Woodcut₎ Domini Jasonis Mayni ...
preclarissima necnon vtilissima Comentaria sup tit. De ac-
tionibus Institu. accurate castigata. Cũ permultis additionibus
eiusdem, iuris prudentie studiosis maximam vtilitatẽ allaturis:
cumq, plurium huiusce tempestatis doctorum apostillis, sum-
marusq, per dominum Baltba Seuerinũ ... illustrata. Repertorio quoq, alphabetico singulares materias complectente locu-
pletata. ₍Lugduni₎ 1540.

Tartagni, Alessandro, 1424-1477.
    Lectura super prima et secunda parte Infortiati,
cum apostillis.   Venice, Bernardinus Stagninus, de
Tridino, 1489-90.
    80 [i. e. 162], 165 numb. l.   41.5 cm.
    Signatures: AA[10], BB-QQ[8], RR-SS[6], TT[8], UU-
XX[6]; AAA-RRR[8], SSS[6], TTT-XXX[8]. AA₁ blank,
AAA₁ blank and lacking, XXX₈ blank.

Continued in next column

Continued from preceding column

    Printed in Gothic type, 2 columns of 78 lines to
the page and head-lines. Capitals supplied in red and
blue.
    Numerous errors in foliation.
    Bound in blind stamped pigskin over wooden
boards, with arms of "Martinus Episcopus Secco-
viensis. 1613." Two clasps.

    Not in Stillwell; not in British Museum; Hain-
Copinger 15301; Panzer III, p. 271, no. 1196 and
p. 284, no. 1277. Goff: T-27.
    Contains marginal manuscript notes.

NT   0044485   CtY-L

Tartagni, Alessandro, 1424-1477.
    Liber primvs ₍-qvartvs₎ consiliorvm
Alexandri Imolensis. His accessere
Caroli Molinaei ... annotationes.
Lvgdvni ₍Blasius Guido₎ 1556-57.
    4 v. in 1. 41½cm.
    Liber 1,4 dated 1556; liber 2-3,
1557.
    Title vignettes.

NT   0044486   MH-L

Law   **Tartagni, Allessandro,** 1424–1477.

Bartolus *de Saxoferrato,* 1314–1357.
    Bartoli de Saxoferrato Prima svper Codice. Continetvr hoc
in volvmine prima pars cõmentariorũ Bartoli de Saxoferrato,
quã (& merito quidẽ) iuris uocitant lucernam, super Codice, ad
uetustissimorum simul ac emẽdatissimorũ exemplariũ fidẽ recognita & emaculata. Et complurium doctissimorum uirorum
additionibus & apostillis illustrata. Summarijs item & con-
cordantijs contrarietatũ Bartoli minime prætermissis. Insuper
& repertorio singularium materiarum in ordinem multo q̃ hactenus commodiorem redacto. Additiones hvivs operis. Alexandri

Imolensis. Andreæ Barbatiæ Siculi. Andreæ de Pomate de
Basignana. Christophori de Nicellis. ₍Colophon: Impressum
Lugduni₎ 1533.

Tartagni, Alessandro, 1424-1477.
    Primvm₍-septimvm₎ volvmen Consiliorvm
Alexandri de Imola. Consiliorvm ivris vt-
rivsqve ... Alexandri Tartagni Imolesis,
Prima₍-septima₎ pars: nouiter ... impressa
... Additis ... summarijs ... per ... Ioan-
nem de Gradibus ... ₍Impressa Lugduni per
Joannem Moylin₎al's de Chambray₎1537.
    7v. in 4. 40cm.
    Device of Jacques Giunta on t.-ps.;
"Édition partagée entre Jac. Giunta et V.

de Portonariis" (H.L. Baudrier, Bibliographie lyonnaise, 6. sér., p.177).
    Imperfect: vol.1 and 6 lack last blank
leaf; t.-p. of v.2 mutilated.
    Colophon of vol.4 dated 1538.

-- Repertorivm Consiliorvm Alexandri de
Imola ... per ... Ioannem de Gradibus, ag-
gregatum ... ₍Impressum Lugduni per Joan-
nẽ Moylin; al's de Chambray₎1537.
    [150]p. 40cm. ₍Bound in front of vol.1
of the above₎
    Device of Jacques Giunta on t.-p.
    Signatures: a-i[8] k[6](k₆ blank)[p.]

NT   0044491   CtY DLC-P4

xfK349.375
T37   ₍Tartagni, Alessandro₎ d.1477.
1541   Reperto ₍rium₎ index locupletissimus materiarum magis singularium, que in commentariis
dñi Alexandri Imoleñ. in ius ciuile continentur, summo & labore, & diligẽtia recognitus,
expunctis superfluis, & iis quae non suo loco
posita erãt, in ordinẽ redactis. Nunc ultimo,
& acuratius in studiosorũ gratiam excussus...
Venetiis, 1541.
    ₍264₎p. 44cm.

Continued in next column

Continued from preceding column

    Pages printed in double columns.
    Bound with vol.2 of the author's In secun-
dum digesti novi... commentariorum. Venetiis,
1541.

    1. Tartagni, Alessandro, d.1477. Commen-
taria. I. Title.

NT   0044493   IaU

gf   Tartagni, Alessandro, 1424-1477.
KBD   Repertorivm copiosissimvm in omnia Alexandri
42   Tartagni Imol... Commentaria. Nouissime
T37   summa diligentia...repurgatum & ad suam demum
R46   integritatem restitutum. Venetiis, apvd
1570   Ivntas, 1570.
    ₍1303₎ p.   43 cm.
    Bound with author's In secundam ff. noui par-
tem commentaria.

    1. Corpus juris civilis. Digesta. Books
39-50. 2. Roman law. I. Title.

NT   0044494   CU-L

xfK349.375
T375   Tartagni, Alessandro, 1424-1477.
1577   Repertorium copiosissimum in omnia Alexandri
Tartagni Imol, iurisc. clarissimi commentaria,
serie alphabetica ita concinne in studiosorum
gratiam dispositum, ut nihil amplius desiderari
queat: hac prostrema editione summa diligentia
ac fide recognitum, ab infinitis erroribus
repurgatum, & ad suam demum integritatem restitutum.   Venetiis, 1577.
    78ℓ. 43cm.
    Leaves printed on both sides in double
columns.

    Printer's device on t.p.
    Bound with the author's In secundam ff.
noui partem commentaria... Venetiis, 1576;
imperfect copy leaves 1-178 wanting.

    1. Tartagni, Alessandro, d.1477. Commen-
taria. I. Title.

NT   0044496   IaU

    Tartagni, Alessandro, de Imola, 1424-1477.
    D. Alex: Repertorivm Nouum ac ſolenne ad omnes
eius Lecturas ... p Dominum Hieronymum Loretum
hyſpanum nunc in lucẽm editum. [Venice, Philippus
Pincius, after 1523]
    134 l.   42.3 x 30 cm. (With his: ... Cõmetaria
Sup primã ₍-ſecundam₎ codicis partẽ. [Venice,
after 1523]
    Title in red and black.
    Printed in double column.
    Pincius's device on t.-p.

    I. Lauretus,   Hieronymus, d. 1571.

NT   0044497   CSmH

    Tartagni, Alessandro, 1424-1477.
    Repertorium Super Consiliis Alexandri. Reper-
torium, sive Index Utilissimus In Septem Volumina
Consiliorum Alexandri de Tartagnis Imolensis, iuris
& pontificij & caesarei consultissimi: denuo magnis
laboribus summaq̃ diligentia recognitum: in quo
materias notabiles dictor consilioru ordine
alphabetico congestas invenies.   Anno, 1532.
    unp.   folio.

NT   0044498   PU-L

Tartagni, Alessandro, 1424–1477.
    Volumina quinq̃ consiliorum Alexandri Imolensis cum
quibuscunq̃ consilijs, ex multis exemplaribus vndecũq̃ col-
lectis, demum per ipsum editis ... Infinitisq̃ antiquorũ ꝛ
recẽtiorum doctorum vtilissimis apostillis ... ₍Tridini, Im-
pẽsis J. de Ferariis, al's de Jolitis, ₍1515₎
    37, cxv, cxci l.   43 cm.
    Preceded by an alphabetical index with special t. p.: Repertorium
omnium principalium ꝛ emergetium questionum ac omnium que cog-
nitu ꝛ notatu digna sunt: Alexandri Tartagni Imolensis super ipsius
cõsiliorum quinq̃ voluminibus nouiter s'm alphabeti ꝛ numerorũ ordine excogitatum.
    I. C. copy imperfect: parts 3-5 wanting.
    1. Roman law. 2. Canon law. 3. Law—Collected works. 4. Glos-
sators.

                             73-202135

NT   0044499   DLC

(Beinecke Library Folio 220)

Tartagni, Giovanni Battista, 1735–ca. 1807, tr.

[Montoya, Joaquín] 1724–ca. 1770.
L'amore scambievole e non mai interrotto tra s. Teresa e la Compagnia di Gesù, dichiarato in tre apologetiche dissertazioni, scritte da d. Giacinto Hoyoman [pseud.] Spagnuolo e ultimamente tradotte in italiano. Lucca, Presso F. Bonsignori, 1794.

Tartagnus, Alexander
see
Tartagni, Alessandro, 1424–1477.

Tartaja, Pepito.
Pepito Tartaja la Satiriada Poema, ó sea patada, en un canto tan solo, ó bien pedrada Precio: 2 reales. Madrid Tigografia de Alfredo Alonso Soldado, 1888. 8 núm.

NT 0044502   NNH

Tartak, Rebeca Krutt
see
Krutt Tartak, Rebeca.

Tartakover, Savelii Grigorevich, 1887–1956.
Am Baum der Schacherkenntnis, von Dr. Tartakower. [Berlin: Kagan, 1921.]   27 p. incl. tables.   illus.   21½cm.

Cover-title.

640219A. 1. Chess, 1921.

NT 0044504   NN DGU OCl MH

Tartakover, Savelii Grigorevich, 1887–1956.
[Autograph letter to Dr. Oskam, with type-written translation prefixed]   [4]p.   [n.p., 1924]

Manuscript.
Appended are a German letter from Richard Réti to Oskam, also with typewritten translation, and an English letter from J. R. Capablanca.

NT 0044505   OCl

Tartakover, Savelii Grigor'evich, 1887–1956.
... Bréviaire des échecs. 122 diagrammes. Paris, Stock (Delamain et Boutelleau) 1934.
2 p. l., [vii]–xii, 318 p., 1 l.   illus.   17½ᶜᵐ.
At head of title: Xavier Tartakower.

1. Chess.
                                                    38-38188
Library of Congress   GV1445.T245
Copyright A—Foreign   26808
                             [2]   794.1

NT 0044506   DLC NN ViU OCl

Tartakover, Savelii Grigor'evich, 1887–1956.
Bréviaire des échecs [par] Xavier Tartakower. Nouv. éd., revue et augm.   Paris, Stock, 1947.
xi, 328 p.   illus.   19 cm.
1. Chess – Collections of games.

NT 0044507   OU

Tartakover, Savelii Grigor'evich, 1887–1956.
A breviary of chess, by S. Tartakower; translated by J. Du Mont.   London, G. Routledge & sons, ltd. [1937]
viii, 267 p.   illus.   19ᶜᵐ.
"First printed 1937."

1. Chess.   I. Du Mont, Julius, tr.
                                                    38-23121
Library of Congress   GV1445.T246
                             [3]   794.1

NT 0044508   DLC NN OCl

                              SG 3647.822.5
Tartakover, Savelii Grigor'evich, 1887–1956.
A breviary of chess. Translated by J. du Mont. Philadelphia, D. McKay Co., 1938.

19 cm.
Printed in Great Britain.

NT 0044509   MH WaS OCl OClW

Tartakover, Savelii Grigor'evich, 1887–1956.
A breviary of chess, by S. Tartakower; translated by J. Du Mont.   London, G. Routledge & sons, ltd. [1942]
vii, 267 p.   illus.   19 cm.

NT 0044510   OCl

Tartakover, Savelii Grigor'evich, 1887–1956.
A breviary of chess, by S. Tartakower; translated by J. Du Mont. London, G. Routledge & sons, ltd. [1946]
viii, 267 p.   illus.   19 cm.
"First printed 1937."

NT 0044511   OrU NcRS

Tartakover, Savelii Grigor'evich, 1887–1956.
A breviary of chess, translated by J. DuMont. London, Routledge & Kegan Paul [1951]
viii, 267 p.   illus.

NT 0044512   MiD

Tartakover, Savelii Grigor'evich, 1887–1956.
A breviary of chess. Translated by J. Du Mont. New York, Van Nostrand, 1955.
267 p.   illus.   19 cm.

1. Chess—Collections of games.
GV1452.T246 1955   794.1   55-244 ‡

NT 0044513   DLC Wa WaS UU MB PP NN

Tartakover, Savelii Grigor'evich, 1887–1956.
A debreceni nemzetközi sakkverseny 1925
see under   International Chess Tournament, Debreczen, 1925.

Tartakover, Savelii Grigorevich, 1887–1956.
Dr. Aljechin Sakkszemlélete
see under   Chalupetzky, Ferenc, ed.

TARTAKOVER, SAVELII Grigor'evich, 1887–
Das entfesselte Schach, ein unsystematisches Lehrbuch der Mittelspielstrategie, zugleich Sammlung und Erläuterung der im Géza Maróczy-Jubiläums-Turnier zu Debrecen 1925 gespielten Meisterpartien.   Kecskemét, Verlag der "Magyar sakkvilág" [c1926]   191 p.   illus., port.   24cm.

1. Chess—Middle games.   2. Chess—Tournaments, 1925.   I. International chess congress, Debreczen,   Hungary, 1925.

NT 0044516   NN NjP OCl

Tartakover, Savelii Grigor'evich, 1887–1956.
500 master games of chess, by S. Tartakower and J. du Mont.   London, G. Bell, 1952.
2 v.   illus.   22 cm.

1. Chess—Collections of games.   I. Title.
GV1452.T3   794.1   52-40950 ‡

NT 0044517   DLC NcD CtY OCl PP MB NN

Tartakover, Savelii Grigor'evich, 1887–1956.
Führende Meister; Schachindividualitäten in ihrem Wirken und Streben, mit Essays, Partien und Diagrammen. Wien [Wiener Schach-Zeitung] 1932–35.
2 v.   illus.   15 cm.   (Bücherei der Wiener Schach-Zeitung, Bd. 3–4)
Vol. 2 has title: Neue Schachsterne.

1. Chess—Biog.   I. Title.   II. Title: Neue Schachsterne.
(Series: Wiener Schach-Zeitung. Bücherei, Bd. 3–4)
GV1438.T3   56–50949 rev

NT 0044518   DLC OCl

GV1455
.I5   Tartakover, Savelii Grigor'evich, 1887–1956.
1928   Das grosse Internationale Schach-
            meisterturnier in Bad Kissingen vom
            11.–25. August 1928.   Sammlung aller
            66 Partien...   Bad Kissingen, O.
            Levin, 1928.
            179p.   plates, ports., diagrs.   24cm.

NT 0044519   NNU-W NjP NN MH

Tartakover, Savelii Grigor'evich, 1887–1956.
Hehapokoba ... [Indiiskaia zashchita...] [the Indian defence; the development of an opening, theory and practice; tr. from the German, by A. N. Lavrov, ed. by V. I. Nenarskov] 103, [2] p. Mockby. 1925.

NT 0044520   OCl

42841   Tartakover, Savelii Grigor'evich, 1887–1956.
.895   Die hypermoderne Schachpartie. Ein Schach-
            lehr- und Lesebuch zugleich eine Sammlung von
            150 schönen Meisterpartien aus den Jahren
            1914-1924. Wien, Wiener Schachzeitung, 1924.
            517 p.   illus.   24 cm.

NT 0044521   NjP MiD OCl

GV   Tartakover, Savelii Grigor'evich, 1887–1956.
1452   Die hypermoderne Schachpartie, von S. G.
.T3119n Tartakover. Ein Schachlehr- und lesebuch
1925   zugleich eine Sammlung von 150 schönen
            Meisterpartien aus den Jahren 1914-1925.
            2., unveränderte Aufl.   Wien, Verlag der
            "Wiener Shachzeitung," 1925.
            517p.   illus., ports.   24cm.

            1. Chess – Collection of games.   I. Title.

NT 0044522   NNU MH NcD

Tartakover, Saveliĭ Grigorevich, 1887-1956.
Ideas modernas en las aperturas de ajedrez;
estudios y análisis profundos de las aperturas
más usadas en los últimos torneos magistrales.
(Traducción de M. V. Podestá) 133,[2]p.
Buenos Aires, "Sol", 1936.

NT   0044523   OCl

Tartakover, Saveliĭ Grigorevich, 1887-
Ideas modernas en las aperturas de ajedrez,
traduccion directa de Adolfo A. Gabarret.
Buenos Aires, Editorial Sopeña argentina,
1941.
141 p. port.

NT   0044524   OCl

42847   Tartakover, Saveliĭ Grigor´evich, 1887-
.895   Indisch (Aus der Werkstätte einer
.2   Eröffnung) Theorie und Praxis, zusammengestellt und erläutert von S.G.Tartakower.
Hrsg.von Bernhard Kagan. Berlin, Kagan,
1924.
60 p. illus. 23 cm.

I.Kagan, Bernard.   ed.

NT   0044525   NjP MH OCl NN

TARTAKOVER, SAVELIĬ Grigorevich,   1887-
Indisch (aus der Werkstätte einer Eröffnung); Theorie
und Praxis. Hrsg. von Bernhard Kagen. Berlin, B.Kagan,
1924. 60 p. illus. 24cm.

Film reproduction. Negative.

Chess--Openings. I. Kagan,   Bernhard, ed.

NT   0044526   NN

Tartakover, Saveliĭ Grigorevich, 1887-
Das internationale Szén-Memorialturnier
zu Budapest, 1929, von S.G.Tartakower.
Kecskemét, Magyar Sakkvilág, 1929.
108 p. illus. 18 cm.

1.Chess - Tournaments, 1929. I.Tartakover,
Saveliĭ Grigorevich, 1887-

NT   0044527   NjP OCl

GV1452   Tartakover, Saveliĭ Grigor´evich, 1887-
.M3
Malmgren, Harald.
Mina bästa partier. Med kommentarer och analyser av
stormästarna S. G. Tartakower, Max Euwe, och Gideon
Ståhlberg. [Örebro, 1953]

Tartakover, Saveliĭ Grigor´evich, 1887-
La moderna partida de ajedrez; traducción y
notas de Miguel Czerniak.   Buenos Aires, Editorial
Sopena Argentina S. R. L. [1952]
3 v. in 1.   illus.   (Nueva biblioteca de ajedrez)

NT   0044529   OCl

Tartakover,   Saveliĭ Grigor´evich, 1887-
Moderne schachstrategie ausgewählt und erläu-
tert... 139p. front.(port.) Breslau, A.
Kramer [1930]

Contains games of O. S. Bernstein.

NT   0044530   OCl NNU-W MH

794.1
T193m
Tartakover, Savelii Grigor´evich, 1887-
My best games of chess, 1931-1954.
Translated and edited by H. Colombek.
Princeton, N. J., D. Van Nostrand [n.d.]
197 p. illus. 22cm.

1. Chess - Collections of games. I. Title.

NT   0044531   FU OCl

Tartakover, Saveliĭ Grigor´evich, 1887-
My best games of chess, 1905-1930. Translated and edited
by H. Golombek. London, G. Bell, 1953.
248 p. illus. 22 cm.

1. Chess—Collections of games.   I. Title.

GV1452.T32   794.1   53-12484 ‡

NT   0044532   DLC NcD OrU UU NNC CtY NN OCl PP MH

GV   Tartakover, Saveliĭ Grigor´evich, 1887-1956.
1452   My best games of chess, 1905-1930. Trans-
.T32   lated and edited by H. Golombek. Princeton,
N.J., Van Nostrand [1953]
xviii,248p. 22cm.

1. Chess. Collections of games. I. Title.

NT   0044533   OrU

Tartakover, Saveliĭ Grigor´evich, 1887-1956.

Neue Schachsterne; 30 Schachindividuali-
täten in ihrem Wirken und Streben. Mit Essays,
Partien und Diagrammen, zusammengestellt und
erläutert von S. G. Tartakower. Wien [Wiener
Schach-Zeitung] 1935.
143 p. illus. 17 cm. (Bücherei der
Wiener Schach-Zeitung, Bd. 4)
Pt. 2 of the author's Führende Meister.

1. Chess. I.   Title.

NT   0044534   NcD OCl

TARTAKOVER, SAVELIĬ Grigorevich,   1887-1956.
Das neuromantische Schach; der Stand der jetzigen
hypermodernen Eröffnungen auf Grund der neuesten
Analysen; Theorie und Praxis. Berlin, B. Kagan [c1927]
130 p. illus. 24cm.

1. Chess--Openings.

NT   0044535   NN NjP OCl

GV   Tartakover, Saveliĭ Grigorevich, 1887-
1452   100 master games of modern chess, by
T33   S. Tartakower and J. du Mont. London,
Bell, 1954.
171p. illus.

Chess--Collections of games.
Du Mont, Jules, 1881-   joint author.
Title.

NT   0044536   UU PP NN NcD

Tartakover, Saveliĭ Grigor´evich, 1887-1956.
100 master games of modern chess, by S. Tartakower and
J. du Mont. New York, Scribner, 1955.
171 p. illus. 22 cm.

1. Chess—Collections of games.   I. Du Mont, Jules, 1881-
joint author. II. Title.

GV1452.T33   794.1   55-14920 ‡

NT   0044537   DLC CaBVa MiU ODW MB MiD

Tartakover, Saveliĭ Grigorevich, 1887-1956.
Das russische Revolutionsgesicht; eine Anthologie zeitge-
nössischer russischer Dichtungen ins Deutsche übertragen und mit
einer Einleitung versehen, von Dr. Savielly Tartakower. Wien:
Interterritorialer Verlag "Renaissance"[, 1923]. 125 p. 8°.
Contents: TARTAKOWER, S. Im Zaubergarten der russischen Poesie. BLOK, A.
Die Zwölf. JESSENIN, S. Verklärung. KLJUJEW, N. Gesang des Sonnenträgers.
Aus der modernen russischen Lyrik. SLJOSKIN. J. Das Unentrinnbare. JUSCHKE-
WITSCH, S. In der Krämerbude. BLOK, A. Die Intellektuellen und die Revolution.
ROSSICA.

199031A. 1. Poetry, Russian—Col-   lections. 2. Fiction, Russian.
3. Title.   January 21, 1926
N. Y. P. L.

NT   0044538   NN

Tartakover, Saveliĭ Grigorevich, 1887-1956.
Schachmethodik; neue grundlagen zur erlernung der mit-
telspielsstrategie, von dr. S. G. Tartakower; mit zahlreichen
beispielen und 145 diagrammen. Berlin, Siedentop & co. verlagsges. m. b. h., 1928.
viii, 175 p. illus. 24½ᶜᵐ.

1. Chess.   I. Title.   29-16679 Revised

Library of Congress   GV1445.T25
Copyright A—Foreign   2386
[r35c2]   794.1

NT   0044539   DLC

Tartakover, Saveliĭ Grigor´evich, 1887-1956.
Schachmethodik; neue grundlagen zur erlernung mittelspieksstrategie, von dr. S. G.
Tartakower; mit zahlreichen beispielen und
145 diagrammen. Berlin, Siedentop & co.,
verlagsges, m.b.h., 1929.

NT   0044540   OCl

Tartakover, Saveliĭ Grigor´evich, 1889-
Sugestiones para la estrategia ajedrecistica;
traducción del alemán por Paulino Alles Monasterio
viii,[1],10-96,[2]p. Buenos Aires, El ajedrez
americano, 1931.

NT   0044541   OCl

Tartakover, Saveliĭ Grigorevich, 1887-1956.
...Sugestiones para la estrategia ajedrecistica traducción directa del alemán de Carlos O.
Mullor. Buenos Aires, Editorial Sopena Argentina
[1941]
60, [1] p. port.

NT   0044542   OCl

Tartakover, Saveliĭ Grigor´evich, 1887-1956.
Tartacover vous parle; choix de ses meilleures parties
d'échecs annotées par lui et constituant un manuel non
systématique de la théorie des débuts, des finales et de la
stratégie générale, 1905-1930. Paris, Stock, 1953.
335 p. illus. 23 cm.

1. Chess—Collections of games.   I. Title.

GV1452.T35   54-21840 ‡

NT   0044543   DLC OCl NN MH

Tartakover, Saveliĭ Grigor'evich, 1887–1956.
... Winke für die schachstrategie, von dr. S. G. Tartakower. Mit 18 diagrammen. Berlin und Leipzig, W. de Gruyter & co., 1927.

60 p. illus. 22 cm. (Veits kleine schachbücherei, hrsg. von dr. F. Palitzsch. bd. 10)

1. Chess.

GV1445.T3

28–24230 rev

NT   0044544   DLC OC1

GV
1450
.2
.Z8
.T3

Tartakover, Saveliĭ Grigor'evich, 1887–
Die Zukunftseröffnung; das Zukertort-Réti-System in neuester Beleuchtung. Theorie und Praxis erläutert von S. G. Tartakover. Wien, 1924.
80p. illus.,ports. 16cm. (Bücherei der "Wiener Schachzeitung," Bd. 1)

1. Chess – Openings. I. Title. II. Title: Das Zukertort-Réti-System in neuester Beleuchtung.

NT   0044545   NNU OC1 MH

Tartakovskaîâ, E
Очерк голландской живописи XVII века. ₍Ленинград₎ Изд-во Ленинградского обл. союза советских художников, 1935.

93 p. illus. 26 cm. (Художественное наследие. Западноевропейское искусство)

1. Painting, Dutch—Hist.
Title transliterated: Ocherk gollandskoĭ zhivopisi XVII veka.

ND646.T3

52–52002 ‡

NT   0044546   DLC

Tartakovskiĭ, Boris Semenovich.
Старшеклассники. ₍Москва₎ Молодая гвардия, 1951.
159 p. illus. 17 cm.

I. Title.

Title romanized: Starsheklassniki.

PZ63.T3

51–37986 rev ‡

NT   0044547   DLC

QA1
.A526
no.160
1952

Tartakovskiĭ, V   A
The sieve method in group theory. Application of the sieve method to the solution of the word problem for certain types of groups. Solution of the word problem for groups with a k-reduced basis for Þ6. Providence, R.I., American Mathematical Society, 1952.
110 p. 23cm. (American Mathematical Society. Translation, no. 60)
Article 1 reprinted from "Matematicheskiĭ sbornik n.g. 25(67), 50 (1949)." Article 2 from "Matematiceskiĭ sbornik n.s. 25(67), 251–274 (1949)." Article 3 from "Izvestiya Akademii Nauk SSSR, Seriya matematiceskaya 13, 483–494 (1949)."
Bibliography: p. 110.
1. Groups, Theory of. I. Title: Sieve method in group theory. II. Ser.

NT   0044548   ViU MH CaBVaU

Tartakovsky (Marie). * Essai critique sur le traitement du lupus érythémateux. 40 pp. 8°. *Genève, E. Chaulmontel*, 1910.

NT   0044549   DNLM

TARTAKOVSKY, Vera.
Etude de l'acidité urinaire chez les tuberculeux. Thèse. Paris, 1912.

NT   0044550   MBCo

Tartakower, Arieh, 1897–
האדם הנודד; על ההגירה ועל העליה בעבר ובימינו. תל-אביב, מ. ניומן, תשי"ד. ₍Tel-Aviv, 1953/54₎
376 p. 22 cm.

1. Emigration and immigration. 2. Population transfers. I. Title.   *Title transliterated:* ha-Adam ha-noded.

JV6080.T3

55–50958 ‡

NT   0044551   DLC

Tartakower, Arieh, 1897–
דאָס ייִדישע עמיגראַציע-פּראָבלעם און דער ייִדישער וועלט-קאָנגרעס. פּאַריז. ₍Paris₎ 1936.
46 p. 23 cm.
At head of title: עקזעקוטיוו-קאָמיטעט פֿון ייִדישן וועלטקאָנגרעס

1. Jews—Migration₍. 2. World Jewish Congress.
Title transliterated: Dos yidishe emigratsye-problem.

JV6348.J4T32

54–54789

NT   0044552   DLC

TARTAKOWER, Arieh, 1897–
Jewish Emigration from Poland in Post-War Years. Reprinted from The Jewish Social Service Quarterly, vol.16, no.3, March 1940, p.273–279.
1.Warsaw Institute for Social Sciences. 2.Jewish Emigrant Aid Society. 3.Immigration and Naturalization. 4.Statistics-Jewish-Poland.

NT·   0044553   NNJ

Tartakower, Arieh, 1897–
The Jewish refugee, by Arieh Tartakower and Kurt R. Grossmann. New York, Institute of Jewish affairs of the American Jewish congress and World Jewish congress, 1944.
xiii p., 1 l., 676 p. 23½ᶜᵐ.
"Errata and addenda": ₍4₎ p. inserted.
Bibliography: p. 597–658.

1. Refugees, Jewish. 2. Jews in Europe. I. Grossmann, Kurt R., joint author. II. Institute of Jewish affairs.

Library of Congress   DS126.T3

44–51443

₍20₎   296

NBuC ICJS OCH
NT   0044554   DLC OrU NNZi PP GU OU MiEM MB PU ICU CU

DS135
G33T18

Tartakower, Arieh, 1897–
The Jewish refugees; a sociological survey, by Arieh Tartakower. New York, Conference on Jewish relations, 1942.
cover-title, 3₎11–348 p. incl.tables. 25ᶜᵐ.
"Reprinted from Jewish social studies, vol. IV, no.4."

1.Jews in Germany. 2.Refugees,Political. I. Conference on Jewish relations, New York. II. Title.

NT   0044555   CSt-H

DS
135
E8T3

Tartakower, Arieh, 1897–
Jews in the "New Europe." ₍New York, Committee on Unity for Palestine, 1945?₎
11 p. 16 cm. (The facts)
Reprinted from the Jewish frontier.

1. Jews in Europe. I. Title

NT   0044556   OCH

Tartakower, Arieh, 1897–
נודדי היהודים בעולם, מאת ד"ר אריה טרטקובר. ₍Jerusalem, 1941₎
8 p. l., 156, ₍1₎ p. 1 l. 16ᶜᵐ. (*Half-title:* הספריה הציונית הקטנה. סדרה א':
ישראל לעמי"ה וזא של דך י. ם.₎
דרישה בבליוגרפית: p. ₍157₎

1. Jews—Migration. I. Mann, Isaac, tr. II. Title.
Title transliterated: Nedude ha-Yehudim ba'olam.

44–21407

Library of Congress   JV6348.J4T3

NT   0044557   DLC

TARTAKOWER, Arieh, 1897–
New Trends in Jewish Sociology. Reprinted from Jewish Social Studies, vol.12, no.2, p.103–118, 1950.

1.Sociology.

NT   0044558   NNJ OSa

Tartakower, Arieh, 1897–
Los refugiados judíos, un estudio sociológico, por Arieh Tartakower. México, D. F., 1943.
1 p. l., 46 p. 22½ᶜᵐ.
"Este estudio se publicó en inglés en los Jewish social studies, vol. IV, no. 4, New York."—p. 46.
A revised English version forms chapter XI of The Jewish refugee, by Arieh Tartakower and K. B. Grossmann, New York, 1944.

1. Refugees, Jewish. 2. Jews—Political and social conditions. 3. Jews—Stat. I. Title.

Library of Congress   DS126.T33

45–15909

₍2₎   296

NT   0044559   DLC

Tartakower, Arieh, 1897–
The Sociological Implications of the Present-Day Aliyah. Reprinted from Jewish Social Studies, Vol.XIII,no.4,pp.291–310. New York, Conference on Jewish Relations, 1951.
1. Israel-Immigration. 2.Israel-Sociology.

NT   0044560   NNJ

Tartakower, Arieh, 1897–
תולדות תנועת העובדים היהודית. ורשה, הועד הפועל של "ברית הנוער" ומרכז "החלוץ" העולמי, תרפ"ם. ₍Warszawa₎ 1929–
v. 20 cm. (₍-2 .מס .₎ יסודות" ספרית)

1. Labor and laboring classes—Jews. (Series: Sifriyah "Yesodot," no. 2–)
Title transliterated: Toldot tenu'at ha-'ovdim ha-yehudit.

HD6305.J3T3

54–46406

NT   0044561   DLC

Tartakower, Arieh, 1897–

יידישע עמיגראציע און יידישע עמיגראציע־פאליטיק. וילנע,
ב. קלעצקין, ﹇Wilno﹈ 1939.

196 p. 24 cm.
Bibliography: p. 193–196.

1. Jews—Migration.   i. Title.
Title transliterated: Yidishe emigratsye un
yidishe emigratsye-politik.

JV6348.J4T34   61–55132

NT   0044562   DLC

Tartakower, Arieh, 1897 –
... Zarys socjologii żydostwa. ﹇Lwów﹈ "Cofim," 1938. 240 p.
24cm.

66767B.   1. Jews—Soc. condit.
N. Y. P. L.   December 26, 1940

NT   0044563   NN ICU

DS135   Tartakower, Arieh, 1897–   joint ed.
.P6S28   **Schiper, Ignacy,** 1884–1943, *ed.*
Żydzi y Polsce odrodzonej; działalność społeczna, gospo-
darcza, oświatowa i kulturalna, pod redakcją d-ra Ignacego
Schipera, d-ra A. Tartakowera, radcy Aleks. Hafftki. Warszawa, Nakł. wydawnictwa "Żydzi w Polsce odrodzonej" ﹇1932–
33﹈

Tartakower, Savelij G
see
Tartakover, Saveliĭ Grigor'evich, 1887–

Tartakower, Xavier
see
Tartakover, Saveliĭ Grigor'evich, 1887–

Tartakowsky Henker, Wladimiro.
... El problema de la migración, los movimientos de la población analizados a través de la historia de la humanidad;
memoria de prueba para optar al grado de licenciado en la
Facultad de ciencias jurídicas y sociales de la Universidad de
Chile. Santiago de Chile, Dirección general de prisiones, imp.,
1941.

198 p. 25½ᶜᵐ.
"Bibliografía": p. ﹇191﹈–193.
1. Emigration and immigration. 2. Migrations of nations. 3. Colonies.
4. Chile—Emig. & immig.   i. Title.

Library of Congress   JV6035.T37   42–25629
                         ﹇3﹈   325

NT   0044567   DLC

Tartalea, Niccolo
    see   Tartaglia, Niccolò, d. 1557.

4PG   **Tartalja, Gvido.**
Croat   **Poema o pruzi.** ﹇U Beogradu, Novo
124   pokolenje﹈ 1946.
        27 p.

NT   0044569   DLC-P4

Tartalja, Gvido.
Pesme. Beograd, Prosveta, 1952. 217 p. 20
cm. (Jugoslovenski savremeni pisci, 19.)

NT   0044570   NN

Tartalja, Guido
Sablazan sa duhovima.

NT   0044571   OCl

W 6   TARTALJA, Hrvoje
P3   Farmaceutska deontologija. Zagreb
﹇Poljoprivredni nakladni zavod﹈ 1954.
53 p.
1. Pharmaceutical ethics

NT   0044572   DNLM CU

RS67   Tartalja, Hrvoje, ed.
.Y82Z357   **600 ﹇i. e. Šest stotina﹈ godina zagrebačkog ljekarništva.**
Uređuje: Hrvoje Tartalja. Zagreb, 1955.

PH3351   .Tartally, Ilona.
.T36E5x   Emberek a végeken / írta Tartally
Ilona. -- Budapest : Palladis R. T.
Kiadása, ﹇194?﹈
319 p. ; 20 cm.

NT   0044574   MB

Tartan, *pseud.*
Philadelphia malignants. Typographed ... By Tartan.
Philadelphia, Weir & co., 1863.
1 p. l., ﹇5﹈–28 p. 18½ᵐ.
A satirical pamphlet, written in Biblical style, dealing with Philadel-
phia politics before and during the civil war.
Autograph letter from Jno. A. McAllister inserted, giving key to the
characters mentioned in the book.

1. Philadelphia—Pol. & govt.—Civil war.   i. Title.
                                     5—36854
Library of Congress   F158.5.T17

NT   0044575   DLC PP PU NIC NcD TU CSmH NjP NN

FILM   Tartan ﹇pseud.﹈
4274   Philadelphia malignants ... By Tartan
PR   ﹇pseud.﹈ Phila., Weir, 1863.
v.2   28 p. (Wright American fiction, v.II,
reel   1851–1875, no. 2428, Research Publications
T2   Microfilm, Reel T-2)

1. Phila. - Pol. & govt. - Civil War.
I. Title.

NT   0044576   CU

Tartan, Beth, *pseud.*
see
Sparks, Elizabeth Hedgecock, 1919–

Tartan. (Minnesota Mining and Manufacturing Co.)
St. Paul. 21st yr.–

NT   0044578   MoS

355.14   T13
      ﹇Tartan samples. s. l., s.n., 1938?﹈
      30 samples.

1. Tartans.

NT   0044579   CaOTP

Tartanson (Ferdinand) [1882–]. * Les
hémorragies et l'hématocèle pelviennes intra-
péritonéales sans grossesse ectopique. 115 pp.
8°. *Lyon.* 1909. No. 126.

NT   0044580   DNLM

Tartar, Eve.
How to design and make your own hats. New York,
Homecrafts Publishers, ©1950.
96 p. illus. 26 cm.

1. Millinery.   i. Title.

TT655.T3   646.54   50–12981

NT   0044581   DLC CaBVa Or Wa WaS WaT NN

646.5   Tartar, Eve.
T17h   How to design and make your own hats.   New
York, Homecrafts Publisher ﹇1951﹈
96p. illus. 26cm.

1. Millinery.   1. Title.

NT   0044582   IU

Tartar, Herman Vance, 1882–   joint author.
Robinson, Reginald Heber, 1886–
... The arsenates of lead, by R. H. Robinson and H. V.
Tartar. Corvallis, Ore., 1915.

Tartar, Herman Vance, 1882–
... Hop investigations. By H. V. Tartar and B. Pilkington ... Corvallis, Ore., Oregon agricultural college
press, 1913.
39 p. incl. vii tab. 23ᶜᵐ. (Oregon. Agricultural experiment station,
Corvallis. Bulletin no. 114)

1. Hops.   i. Pilkington, Bert, 1879–   joint author.
                                    A 15–2637
Title from Oregon Agr.   College. Printed by L. C.

NT   0044584   OrCS OrPR OrU NN

Tartar, Herman Vance, 1883–
A report of chemical investigation on the lime-sulphur spray.
﹇Corvallis, 1914.﹈ 28 p. 8°. (Oregon. Agriculture College.
Research bull. no. 3.)

1. Spraying.
N. Y. P. L.   June 14, 1916.

NT   0044585   NN

Tartar, Herman Vance, 1883–
... The soils of Jackson County, by H. V. Tartar ... &
F. C. Reimer ... Corvallis, Ore., 1920.
62 p. incl. xxx tab. fold. map. 23ᶜᵐ. (Oregon. Agricultural experiment station, Corvallis. Bulletin no. 164)

1. Soils.   i. Reimer, Frank Charles, 1881–   joint author.
                                    A 20–509
Title from Oregon Agr.   College. Printed by L. C.

NT   0044586   OrCS OrU OrPR

Tartar, Herman Vance, 1882–

Reimer, Frank Charles, 1881–
... Sulfur as a fertilizer for alfalfa in southern Oregon, by F. C. Reimer ... and H. V. Tartar ... Corvallis, Ore., 1919.

NT   0044588   Or

TARTAR, NICHOLAS
The early Darter or Tarter clan. Author c1940ɔ
c1ɔ ℓ.

Mimeographed.

NT   0044588   Or

Tartar, Vance, 1911–
... The so-called racial variation in the power of regeneration in *Paramecium* ... Philadelphia, Pa., Press of the Wistar institute of anatomy and biology c1939ɔ

cover-title, p. 181–208. diagrs. 25½ᶜᵐ.

Portion of thesis (PH. D.)—Yale university, 1938.
Thesis note on p. 181.
"Reprinted from the Journal of experimental zoölogy, vol. 81, no. 2, July, 1939."
"Literature cited": p. 208.

1. Paramecium. 2. Regeneration (Biology) 3. Zoology—Variation.
I. Title: Regeneration in *Paramecium*.

Library of Congress   QL368.C5T3   1939   41–6153
       c2ɔ   593.17

NT   0044589   DLC

A tartar.
The letter to the most insolent man alive, answered
     see under title

★
qc378.794   Tartar.   Visalia, Calif., Associated Stu-
VQ   dent Body of Visalia College.
             v. illus. 28cm. annual.

1. Periodicals. I. Visalia College, Visalia, Calif.

NT   0044591   C

Tartar fairy tale, A, literally translated [by Prof. Lesley].
(In Tales for travellers. Vol. 7, pp. 55–60. Boston. 1875.)

G9322 — Kalmucks. Folk-lore. — Lesley, John Peter, tr.

NT   0044592   MB

Tartar republic (A. S. S. R.)
     see
Tatar A. S. S. R.

Tartara, Alessandro, 1847–1924.
... Animadversiones in locos nonnullos Valeri Catulli et Titi Livi.   Romae, 1881.

NT   0044594   CtY

TARTARA, Alessandro, 1847–1924.
Animadversiones in locos nonnullos Valeri Catulli et Titi Livi.   Item emenda-
tiores editae. Romae, 1882.
102 p.

NT   0044595   MH NIC NjP PU OCU

937.04   Tartara, Alessandro, 1847–1924.
T178b   Dalla battaglia della Trebbia a quella
      del Trasimeno.   Questioni di storia
      romana.   Torino, 1882.
      133p.

      Presentation copy.
      Bibliographical foot-notes.

NT   0044596   IU

Tartara, Alessandro, 1847–1924.
De Plavti Bacchidibvs commentatio.   Pisis, 1885.
102 p.
Dal volume 18 degli Annali delle Università toscane (pag. 189–290)

1. Plautus, Titus Maccius.   Bacchides.

NT   0044597   IU MH PBm

Tartara, Alessandro, 1847–1924.
Osservazioni di storia romana all'anno 537/217 sulle legioni, sugli imperii, e sull'istituzione delle provincie consolari. Nota di Alessandro Tartara approvata per la stampa negli Atti dell'Accademia nella seduta del 20 giugno 1880.
(*In* Atti della R. Accademia dei Lincei. Memorie della Classe di scienze morali, storiche e filologiche. Roma, 1880. 29¼ᶜᵐ. ser. 3, vol. v, p. 231–243)
Bibliographical foot-notes.

1. Punic war, 2d, B. C. 218–201.   A C 38–3804
Illinois. Univ. Library
  for Library of Congress   [AS222.R645   ser. 3, vol. 5]
                  c1ɔ   (065)

NT   0044598   IU NcU MoU OU DLC

Tartara, Alessandro, 1847–
I precursori di Cicerone; considerazioni sullo svolgimento dell'eloquenza presso i Romani.
cPisa 1888ɔ   p.c291ɔ–528, 32cm.
Extract from: Pisa, Regia università degli studi. Annali delle Università toscane, pte.1, scienze noologiche. v.18.

NT   0044599   CU

Tartara, Alessandro, 1847–1924.
Tentativo di critica sui luoghi liviani contenenti le disposi-
zioni relative alle provincie e agli eserciti della Repubblica romana. Memoria di A. Tartara approvata per la stampa negli Atti dell'Accademia nella seduta del 20 febbraio 1881.
(*In* Atti della R. Accademia dei Lincei. Memorie della Classe di scienze morali, storiche e filologiche. Roma, 1881. 29¼ᶜᵐ. ser. 3, vol. vi, p. 117–163)
Bibliographical foot-notes.

1. Livius, Titus. 2. Rome—Army—Organization. 3. Rome—Provinces. 4. Punic war, 2d, B. C. 218–201.   A C 38–3810
Illinois. Univ. Library
  for Library of Congress   [AS222.R645   ser. 3, vol. 6]
                  c1ɔ   (065)

NT   0044600   IU MH MsU MoU OU DLC

Tartara, Jules, 1818–
... Nouveau code des bris et naufrages, ou sûreté et sauvetage, par Jules Tartara ... Paris, E. Lacroix, 1874.

3 p. l., xxii, 443 p., 2 l. 18ᶜᵐ. (Bibliothèque des professions industrielles et agricoles. sér. F., n. 3)

1. Shipwrecks. 2. Wreck—France. 3. Salvage—France.   I. Title.
                                29–21315

NT   0044601   DLC NN

Le tartare à Paris, par M. l'abbé A***
     see under   [André, Jean François] b. 1744.

Tartareau (Casimir). *Propositions générales sur les accouchemens.* 23 pp. 4°. *Paris*, 1825, No. 97, v. 193.

NT   0044603   DNLM PPC

Tartarello.   Firenze, Salani c1947ɔ
c15ɔ p. illus. 24 cm. (Librini del cuccù)

NT   0044604   NNC

Tartaren bestormen het hemelsche rijk
     see under   [Hsiao-hsiao-shêng]

Die TARTARENSCHLACHT bei Wahlstadt in
Schlesien, 1241/ In versen dargestellt von
F. S. Löwenberg, 1841.

NT   0044606   MH

RARE BOOK   Tartaretus, Petrus, 15th cent.
B
781   Clarissima singularisqz totius philoso-
T19   phie nec non metaphysice Aristotelis.
E9   [Paris, L. Wolff, 1503]
1501   cxlvi leaves.
         Bound with his Expositio...in summulas
         Petri Hispani [1501]

NT   0044607   MoSCS

        Tartaretus, Petrus, 15th cent.
        Clarissima singularisqz totius philosophie
Gfa84   necnon methaphisice Aristotelis magistri
y509t   Petri Tatareti expositio. [Colophon: [Lyons]
        Impressum /o cura & industria Claudij Dauost
        al's de Troys.Anno xpiane salutis.M.quingen-
        gesimonono[1509].Die.xiij.mensis Julij.]
        1p.ℓ.,cxlvi numb.ℓ.,2ℓ. diagrs. 24cm.
        Signatures: A–I⁸K¹⁰L⁴M–T⁸(T₈ [blank?]
        wanting)
        Imperfect: wormed at the beginning, with
        slight damage to a few leaves.

NT   0044608   CtY

PA   Tartaretus, Petrus, 15th cent.
3049   [Commentarii in Aristotelis philosophiam.
T178e   Latin. 1514]
        Commentarii Petri Tatareti in libros philo-
        sophie naturalis et metaphysice Aristotelis.
        Annotatur in marginibus si quando author, vt
        plerumq; solet, in hisce cōmentarijs ex Scoto
        quippiam desumpserit.   Parisius, Venundantr
        [sic.] in vico diui Jacobi sub intersignio
        Lilii aurei [1514]
        cxviii,[5] ,ℓ.

        Bound with the author's [Expositio super
        logica Aristotelis. Latin] Parisius [1514]
        For variant with bookseller's address dif-
        fering, cf. Bib. Nat. Cat. général des
        livres, v.182, col.843.

        1. Aristoteles. I. Duns, Joannes, Scotus,
        1265?–1308?

NT   0044610   CLU

Tartaretus, Petrus, fl. 1490.
[Commentationes in doctrina Scoti super
Aristotele et Petro Hispano. Wittenberg,
Wolfgang Stoeckel, 1504]
xci, [1], lxxxviii, [4], cvii, [3] l.
woodcuts: illus., diagrs. 33 cm.
Title from colophon.
Colophon: "Commentationū Tattareti viri
preclari in doctrina Scoti super Aristotele et
Petro hyspano finis Impressa4 Albiori in
academia noua ...   per Baccalarium wolfgangum
Stoeckel Monacen-   sem Anno salutis quarto

supra Millesimūquingentesimum. Sexto kalĕdas
Septembris ..."
Printer's device on leaf [1ᵃ] (last group).
In double columns.
Few errors in pagination.
Contents.-[pt. 1] Expositio ... sup textu
logices Aristotelis cum allegatiōnibus passuū
Scoti.-[pt. 2]   Expositio ...

sup summulas Petri hispani cū allegationibūs
passuum Scoti.-[pt. 3] Clarissima singulariso;
totius philosophie necnon metaphysice Aristotelis ... expositio, ac passuum Scoti
allegatio.
No. 1 in a vol. with binder's title:
Opera Petri Tatareti.

1. Aristoteles. Commentaries. 2. Joannes
XXI, Pope, d. 1277. Summulae logicales. 3.
Duns, Joannes, Scotus, 1265?-1308? 4. Logic.
Early works to 1800. I. Tartaretus, Petrus, fl.
1490. Expositio ... super textu logices Aristotelis. II. Tartaretus, Petrus, fl. 1490. Expositio ... super summulas Petri hispani. III. Tartaretus, Petrus,   fl. 1490. Clarissima ...
totius philosophie   necnon metaphysice Aristotelis ... exposi-   tio. IV. Title.

NT   0044614   NcD

Inc.
8155.5 TARTARETUS, PETRUS, 15th cent.
Expositio in Summulas Petri Hispani. Paris, André Bocard, 4 November 1494.
161 of 162 l. 4°. 205x140mm.

First and last leaves blank, first wanting.
With the text.
2 columns, 47 lines of commentary and heading;
Haebler, types 2, 6 (64 G, 94 G) Rubricated.
Ms. notes.
Hain 15333; Stillwell, Inc. in Amer. lib.
T 26.   *Goff T-32*

NT   0044615   ICN

Beinecke
Library Tartaretus, Petrus, 15th cent.
Zi   Expositio in Summulas Petri Hispani.
3215.7 [Freiburg in Breisgau, Kilianus Piscator
(Fischer) 1494]
68 ff. 28 cm. 2°.
Fol. 68 blank.
Imperfect: wormed.
Hain-Copinger 15334; Proctor 3217 (under
Friedrich Riedrer's press); British Museum,
XV cent., v. 3, p. 695; Census T-33.
For fuller description see collation slip
in volume.

1. Incunabula in Yale Library. 2. Freiburg
in Breisgau. Piscator (Fischer), Kilianus.
1494. 3. Stuttgart. Landesbibliothek - Stamp.

NT   0044617   CtY MdBJ DLC

093.8
T19 Tartaretus, Petrus, 15th cent.
1498 Expositio in Summulas Petri Hispani.
Lyons [Lugduni] Jacobus Maillet, 1498.
103 [4] leaves. Quarto. 25.5cm.

Bound with the author's Commentationes in libros totius logicae Aristotelis.
Fully described in this library's
sheet catalog of incunabula.   *Goff T-34*

NT   0044618   MnCS

Tartaretus, Petrus, 15th cent.
Expositio magistri Petri Tatareti in summulas Petri nyspani
cū additiōibus in locis, ppriis.
[Lyons. Wolf. M.cccc. decima octaua January. (1), 95, (1)
ff. Diagrams. Black-letter. Rubricated. Initial spaces. 62
lines to a full page. 25 cm., in 8s.
See Hain 15336.
Contains MS. notes in an old hand.   *Goff T-36*

NT   0044619   MB

FILM Tartaretus, Petrus, 15th cent.
4297 Expositio in summulas Petri Hispani.
AC [Lyon, Nicolaus Wolf] 1500-01.
Roll 196p. 4°.
186 University of Uppsala copy: Collijn no. 1392.

NT   0044620   CU

RARE BOOK Tartaretus, Petrus, 15th cent.
B
78]   Expositio...in Summulas Petri Hispani...
T19   penitus innouata...vna cū toto textu...[n.p.,
E9   1501]
1501   [97] leaves. illus.
Signatures: A-I8, K-L6, M9.
With this are bound his Expositio...super
textu logices Aristotelis [n.d.] and his
Clarissima singularisqz totius philosophie
necnon methaphisice Aristotelis...expositio
[n.d.]

NT   0044621   MoSCS

Tartaretus, Petrus, 15 cent.
Expositio sup summulas Petri Hispani cū
allegationibus passuum Scoti doctoris subtilissimi. [Albiori, 1504.] fo. (*With his* Expositio sup textu logices Aristotelis.) .3261

NT   0044622   MdBP

Tartaretus, Petrus, 15th cent.
Expositio ... in Summulas Petri Hyspani ...
[Lyon: Col., Impressum ... industria Claudij
Dauost als de Troys ... 1509 ...]

NT   0044623   NNNAM

Tartaretus, Petrus, 15th cent.
Expositio magistri petri Tatareti in summulas
Petri Hispani vna cū passibus Scoti vndequaq
in marginib9 sparsis ... Additus est tractatus
insolubiliū eiusdem   obligatoriorū magistri
Martini molenielt ex Liuonia. [Basel, J. Froben,
1514]
87 (i. e. 86) numb. l., 4 l. diagrs. 29 cm.
Woodcut illustration (arms of Basel with two
basilisks) on title page (not in Heitz, Basler
Bûchermarken)

NT   0044624   PU

Tataretus, Petrus, 15th cent.
Expositio ... in sumulas Petri Hispani una cum
passibus Scoti undequaq   in marginibus sparsis ..
Additus est tractatus insolubilium eiusdem & obli-
gatorioru   magistri Martini Molenfelt: ex Liuonia.
Comentarii eiusde   in Isagogas Porphyrii: & libros
logicorum Aristotelis. Comentarii eiusdem in
libros philosophie naturalis & metaphysice Aristotelis. Eiusdem in Aristotelis sex ethicos libros
questiones.   [Venetiis, per Lacar de Soardis,
1514-1515.]
lxxxviii, cviii, cxxvi, xxvi f.
Mss. notes on margins and fly-leaves.

NT   0044625   MdSsW

Tartaretus, Petrus, 15th cent.
Expositio magistri Petri Tatareti in summulas
Petri Hispani vna cu₉ passibus Scoti vndequaq di-
ligetia: summoq studio recognita: a pluribus
mendis que in pɾioɾibus hebetur libɾis emendata
summaq accuratie impɾessa. Additus est tractatus insolubilium eiusdem τ obligatoɾioɾu₉ magistri
Martini Molenfelt: ex Liuonia. Comentarij eiusdem in Isagogas Potphyrii: τ libɾos logicoɾum
Aristotelis. Commentarij eiusdem in libɾos philosophie naturalis τ metaphysice Aristotelis.
Eiusdem in Aristotelis sex ethicos libros questiões. ❋ [Printer's device] [Venetiis, 1520]

lxxxviii, cviii, cxxvi, xxvi numb. l. illus., diagrs.
22ᶜᵐ.
Colophon: Venetijs per Melchiozem Sessam: τ Petrum de
Rauenis socios: anno Dბi 1520. die.2v.mensis junij.
Colophon of first part dated 1518.
Each part except the last has half-title.
Sessa device on t.-p.; other forms at end of each
part and on first half-title. Initials.
A few leaves, including t.-p., trimmed and mended.
1. Aristoteles. 2. Porphyrius. Isagoge. I. Johannes XXI,
pope, d.1277. Summulae logicales. II. Duns, Joannes, Scotus,
1265?-1308. III. Moel   felt, Martin.

NT   0044627   MiU

Tartaretus, Petrus, 15th cent.
Expositio magistri Petri tatareti super
textu logices Aristotelis. [n.p., n.d.]
116 l. (Leaves 115-116 not numerated)
woodcuts.

No colophon.

With this bound His Clarissima singularisque
totius philosophie ...Millesimo CCCCxcviii.
For more information cf. dealer's description
attached to the volume.

NT   0044628   InNd

TARTARETUS, PETRUS, 15TH CENT.
EXPOSITIO MAGISTRI PETRI TATARETI SUPER
TEXTU LOGICES ARISTOTELIS. [PARISIENSIS, N.D.]

NT   0044629   MdBJ

---

787. TARTARETUS, PETRUS. Expositio Super textu logices
Aristotelis.   26 January, 1493
Hain 15340. Claudin: Poitiers, bibliographie XX; recueil de fac-similés 74-87.
Folio. 276 x 191 mm. Capitals and initial strokes supplied in red.
Manuscript foliation in pencil; manuscript notes. Bound in full Niger
morocco by D. Cockerell.   *Goff T-37*

NT   0044630   DLC

AW
1   Tartaretus, Petrus, 15th cent.
R2060: Expositio super Logices Aristote-
133: lis. [Pictavis] Johannes Bouyer &
2   Gulielmus Bouchet, 26 January, 1493.
222 l.

Microfilm.   *Goff T-37*

NT   0044631   CaBVaU AzTeS

Tartaretus, Petrus, 15th cent.
Expositio super textu logices Aristotelis.
[Freiburg I. Preisgau, Kilianus Piscator (Fischer)
1494]
Hain *15337.
B. M.: IB. 14218.
Goff- T-38.

NT   0044632   MdBJ

Tartaretus, Petrus, *15th cent.*
  Expositio magistri Petri Tatereti super
textu logices Aristotelis.   ₍Parisii, A.
Bocerd, 1495?₎
  ₍9₎, 9-110, ₍2₎ ℓ., the first leaf blank.
28 cm.

  Double columns, 63 lines to a column.
Signatures a-k⁸, 1-m⁶, n⁸, o-p.⁶.
Manuscript notes (several hands) in margins.
Date in manuscript on leaf a²: 1494.

  Hain. Repertorium 15338; Brit. Mus. Cat.,
v.234, col. 848.   *Goff-T39*
  Imperfect: leaf a' (title page) and leaf a⁸
wanting.
  Bound with Aristoteles. Clarissima
singularisₐq totius philosophie necnon meta-
phisice Aristotelis; magistri Petri Tatareti
expositio. ₍Parisii, 1494₎

NT   0044634   OkU

TATARETUS,Petrus, *15th cent.*
  Expositio super textu logices Aristotelis.
₍Lugd.?₎,n.pr., ₍cir.1495₎.

  f°. 130 leaves. Wdct.,diagr. 29 cm.(leaf);
Reichling 738.
  Profusely annotated in early hands in Latin &
in German.   *Goff T-40*
  Wormed.

NT   0044635   MH

---

x881   Tartaretus, Petrus, *15th cent.*
A8o.Yta   Expositio super textu logices Aristotelis.
1500   ₍Lyons₎ Nicolaus Wolf, 10 Dec.1500.
    2v. woodcuts: diagrs. 4°. 24.4cm.

    Leaf ₍1₎ª₍ (t.p.): Expositio magistri Petri
    tatareti super textu logices Aristotelis.
      Vol. 1: ₍1₎, CXXVII (i.e. CXXVI), ₍3₎ℓ.;
    v.2: ₍1₎, CXLVI, ₍3₎ℓ.
      Commentary on Porphyrius. Liber primus
    predicabilium: v.1, leaves VIIª-XXII.
      Brit. Mus. Cat .(XV cent.) VIII, p.331

    (IB.42199, 42200); Goff. Third census T-42.
      Error in foliation: LXXI omitted in
    numbering in v.1.
      Capital-spaces, many with guide-letters.
      Imperfect: v.2 (Expositio totius philo-
    sophiae necnon metaphysicae Aristotelis)
    wanting.
      1. Aristoteles. Organon. 2. Porphyrius.
    Isagoge. I. Wolf, Nicolaus, fl.1493-1515.

NT   0044637   IU

FILM   Tartaretus, Petrus, *15th cent.*
4297   Expositio super textu logices Aristotelis.
AC   ₍Lyon, Nicolaus Wolf, c.1500 ₎
Roll   264p.   4°.
186   University of Uppsala copy: Collijn no. 1393.
        Goff T-42

NT   0044638   CU

Tataretus, Peter, 15th cent.
  Expositio magistri Petri Tatereti sup textu
logices Aristotelis cum allegationibus passum
Scoti doctoris subtilissimi.   Albiori ad diuum
Augustinum [1504]
  3 pts.   32 cm.
  Title page in vignette.
  Each pt. has separate t.-p. in vignette.
  With this is bound: Thomas de Vio, Commentaria
subtilissima super tractatum de ente et essentia
sactissimi doctoris Thome de Aquino eiusdem
ordinis. Albertus de Saxonia, Questiones subtilis-
sime in libros de celo et mundo. Andreae,

  Antonius Diuine scietie clarissimi Antonii Andree
questiones. Zimara, Marc Antione, Theoremata.

NT   0044640   NcD MdBP

PA   Tartaretus, Petrus, 15th cent.
3049   ₍Expositio super logica Aristotelis.
T178e   Latin. 1514₎
    Expositio magistri Petri Tatereti sup textu
    logices Aristotelis.   Parisius, Venüdatur in
    vico diui Jacobi ad intersignium Lilii aurei
    [1514]
      cvii,[1] ℓ.

    Incipit: Quaestiones admodum subtiles et
    vtiles cū medulla toti⁹ materie artiū quat-
    tuor librorū sniarū & quotlibeti ... Scoti in

    suis locis quotate magistri Petri Tatereti
    ... super libros logices Porphirii & Aristo-
    telis cū textus clarissima expositiō ...
    feliciter incipiunt.
      Colophon: ... Impress Parrhisijs in Bello-
    uisu expēsis honesti viri bibliopole Francis-
    ci Regnault anno Dñi. 1514. 3. kal. Junij.

    For variant with bookseller's address dif-
    fering, cf. Bib. Nat. Cat. général des
    livres, v.182, col.844.
      With this is bound the author's ₍Commenta-
    rii in Aristotelis philosophiam. Latin₎
    Parisius [1514]
      1. Aristoteles. 2. Porphyrius. I. Duns,
    Joannes, Scotus,   1265?-1308? II.
    Title: Expositio   super logica Aristotelis.

NT   0044643   CLU

Lilly   TATARETUS,PETRUS,15th cent.
PA 3903   ₍Expositio totius philosophiae nec
.A1 T194   non metaphysicae Aristotelis. Colophon,
1499   fol. S 4:₎ Lyons, for Jacques Maillet,
    17 Mar. 1498/99.
      cxxxvii, ₍3₎ ℓ. (total 140 ℓ.)
      diagrs.   4to in eights, 2 sixes (23.7 cm.)
        initial spaces, unfilled

      Title from Goff; printed title begins:
    Clarissima singularisq(ue) totius philo-
    sophie ...

      Pellechet-Polain 10,952; H 15341;
    Goff T-45.
      Includes quotations from works of
    Aristotle in Latin translation.
      Bound in later limp vellum. Marginal
    stains at front and back.

NT   0044645   InU MH MBCo

FILM   Tartaretus, Petrus, *15th cent.*
4297   Expositio totius philosophiae necnon
AC   metaphysicae Aristotelis. [Lyon] Nicolaus
Roll   Wolf, 1500.
186   308p.   4°.
    University of Uppsala copy: Collijn no. 1394.

NT   0044646   CU

Lilly   TATARETUS,PETRUS,15th cent.
PA 3906   ... In Aristotelis philosophiam, naturalem,
.T173   diuinam, & moralem, exactissima commentaria
1581   ... Additae sunt in calce due questiones
    R.P.M. Iacobini Bargii ₍Jacobo Malafossa₎ ...
    Omnia nunc ā mendis expurgata per R.P.F. Sal-
    uatorem Bartol. de Assisio ... Venetiis, Apud
    haeredes Melchioris Sessae, 1581.
      12 p.ℓ.,398 ℓ.   device.   8vo(17.3 cm.)

      At head of title: Petri Tatareti Parisiensis

      BN 182:843; Schwab 1034.
      Collates: a³ b⁴ A-Z⁹ Aa-Zz⁸ Aaa-Ddd⁸.
      Bound in contemporary vellum; in red cloth
    slipcase.

      1. Aristoteles. I. Malafossa,Jacobo. II.
    Bartolucci,Salvatore,   d1603,comp. III.
    Lilly imprint: 1581.

NT   0044648   InU ICU

Lilly   TARTARETUS,PETRUS,15th cent.
PA 3906   ... In Aristotelis philosophiam, natura-
.T173   lem, diuinam, & moralem exactissima commentaria.
1592   Per R.P.F. Liuivm a lege ... repurgata. Addi-
    tae sunt in calce duae questiones R.P.M. Iaco-
    bini Bargij ₍Jacobo Malafossa₎ ... Tertia pars.
    Venetiis, Apud haeredes Melchioris Sessae, 1591
    ₍Colophon: 1592₎
      12 p.ℓ.,398 p.   device.   8vo(15.2 cm.)

      At head of title: Petri Tatareti Parisiensis

      Based on edition by Salvatore Bartolucci₍?₎
    published at Venice. See Riley 416.
      Collates: π³ b⁴ A-Ddd⁶; last two blank.
      Contains also the author's ... Regvlae
    morale. Venetiis, 1591.
      Bound in contemporary vellum; in light
    brown slipcase.

NT   0044650   InU

St. Louis Room
PA   Tartaretus, Petrus, 15th cent.
8585   Petri Tatareti Parisiensis, In gymnasio
.T2   subtilium longē clariss. uniuersæ Aristoteleæ
154   logicæ dissertissima explanatio. Septem
1571   tractibus absolutum opus, ivxta nvmervm
    librorvm, Aristotelis logicam aeqve integrantivm.
    In his excolendis, ₍ristinæ₎que integrati
    restituendis, quantu₍ ₎opere prestiterit F.
    Ioannes Balainius Andrius Conuentualis
    Franciscanus, ex huius editionis ad reliquas
    priores collatione facilē elucebit. Cum indice

    locupletissimo. Venetiis, apud hæredes
    Melchioris Sessæ. M D L X X I.
      16 p.ℓ., 283 numb. ℓ. diagrs. 16 cm.
      Printer's device on t.-p.
      Signatures: *-••⁸, A-Z⁸, Aa-Mm⁸, Nn⁶;
    catchwords; initials.
      In double columns.

      1. Aristoteles. / Logica. 2. Logic. I.
    Balainius, Joannes, d. 1576, O.F.M. II. Title:
    In gymnasio subtilium ... Aristoteleæ logica
    disertissima   explanatio.

NT   0044653   MoSU

MFL.
8182   Tartaretus, Petrus, 15th cent.

    In Porphyrii Isagogen, ac universos logicorum Aristotelis libros
    eruditissima explanationes; per R. P. F. Salvatorem Bartol. de
    Assisio...recognitae atque emendatae... Venetiis, Apud Haeredes
    M. Sessae, 1581.

    Microfilm copy, made in 1970, of the original in the Library at
    ₍es Fontaines, Chantilly, France. Positive.
    Negative film in Pius XII Memorial Library, St. Louis University.
    ₍Manuscripta, microfilms of rare and out-of-print books. List
    84, no.74, Roll 1.₎

NT   0044654   WMM OU PPiD

B   Tartaretus, Petrus, *15th cent.*
765   ...In quartum sententiarū Scoti... dictata siue
D7   (ut dicunt) reportata... Parrhisijs, B. Rembolt.
39   Colophon:... Impressi apud Claudiū Cheuallon,
T3   1520.
1520
Cage   ₍2₎ cclxiiii l. fo.
    W. T. Smedley copy.

NT   0044655   DFo NNUT

Tartaretus, Petrus, 15th cent.
  In quatuor libros Sententiarum et quodlibeta.
Venetiis, Haeredes Galignani, 1583.
  2 v.   *Microfilm.*

NT   0044656   CaBVaU CU NcU NcD

Tartaretus, Petrus, 15th cent.
Petri Tatareti...In Svmmvlas Petri Hispani Exactæ Explicationes./ Per R. P. F. Salvatorem Bartol. ... accuratissime recognitæ, candoriq pristino restitutæ... Venetiis: Apud Hæredes Melchioris Sessæ ⌈Alexander Gryphius Excudebat⌉ 1581. 12 p.l., 207 f., 1 l. 18cm. (8°.)

With colophon dated 1580.
"Petri Tatareti . . . Tractatus de Descensu," f. 185°–192°; "Petri Tatareti . . . Tractatus Insolubilium," f. 192°–197°; "Ervditissimi Magistri Martini Molenfelt . . . Tractatus Obligatoriorum," f. 198–207°.

Imperfect: t.-p. mutilated, last leaf (blank?) wanting; wormed.
With inscription "fue de fr. fran" delsar diolo ala libreria de tulan," and with autographs of Foluca y Henero and Miguel Arias.
With unidentified brand (cf. Sala, Rafael. *Marcas de fuego de las antiguas bibliotecas mexicanas.* Mexico, 1925. p. 12), and stamp of the Convent of San José de Tula, Mexico (cf. Sala, p. 25).

1. Philosophy, Scholastic. 2. Logic. I. John XXI, pope, d. 1277.
Summula. II. Bartolucci, Salvator, 16th cent., ed. III. Moelenfelt,
Martinus. Martinus.
N.Y.P.L. *Card revised*
 April 16, 1943

NT 0044658   NN PU

St. Louis Room
PA
8585
.T2
I52
1571

Tartaretus, Petrus, 15th cent.
Petri Tatareti Parisiensis, ... In triplicem Aristotelis philosophiam; physicam, metaphysicam, et ethicam, castigatissimæ lucubrationes, ... noua nostra editione ... prouia Fratris Ioannis Balainij Andrii Franciscani Conuentualis ope ... Cum indice copiosissimo. Venetiis, Apud hæredes Melchioris Sessæ. MDLXXI.
12 p.l., 400 numb. l. diagrs. 16 cm.
In double columns.
Signatures: *8, **4, A–Z8, Aa–Zz8, Aaa–Ddd8; catchwords; initials; colophon.

1. Aristoteles. I. Balainius, Joannes, d. 1576, O.F.M. II. Title: In triplicem Aristotelis philosophiam; physicam, metaphysicam, et ethicam.

NT 0044660   MoSU

Tartaretus, Petrus, 15th cent.
Petri Tatareti ... In vniversam philosophiam Opera omnia in tres partes distribvta. In qvarvm prima, svmmvlae Petri Hispani commentarijs, & expositionib. acutissimis exacte pertractantur. Opus profecto omnibus sapientiae studio deditis ad integram, & facilem totius philosophici cursus perfectionem assequendam, non vtile minus, quam necessarium. Triplici indice, dubiorum, sophismatum, & rerum memoria dignarum locupletissimo adornatum ... Venetiis.

apud Ioan. Baptistam Combum., 1621.
Microfilm copy, made in 1960 of the original in Vatican. Biblioteca vaticana. Positive.
Negative in Vatican. Biblioteca vaticana.
Collation of the original as determined from the film: 13 p. l., 215, [16], 284 l.
(Series: [Manuscripta, microfilms of rare and out-of-print books. List 19, no. 18])

NT 0044662   MoSU OU WaSpG InU NcU NcD

B
765
D7
 .3
T3
1519
Cage

Tartaretus, Petrus, 15th cent.
...Ioãnis Duns Scoti...Questiones quodlibetales ...Reportate per...Petrum Thartaretum... Parrhisijs, B. Rembolt.
Colophon:... Opera y impesis vidue defuncti Bertholdi Rembolt et Petri Gromors, 1519.

lxviii ⌈2⌉ l. fo.
W. T. Smedley copy.

NT 0044663   DFo NNUT

BQ
6815
.T171
1683

Tartaretus, Petrus, 15th cent.
Lvcidissima commentaria, sive (vt vocant) Reportata, in qvatvor libros Sententiarvm, et Qvodlibeta Ioannis Dvns Scoti svbtilivm principis... insignioribus annotationibus illustra per R.P.F. Bonaventuram Manentum brixianvm, O.F.Min. Conv. Venetiis, apud heredes Simonis Galignani de Karera, 1583.
2 v. 34cm.
1. Duns, Joannes, Scotus, 1265?–1308? 2. Theology--Collected works--15th cent.
I. Manenti, Bo-   naventura, O.F.M. Conv.

NT 0044664   DCU MoSU MH

Tartaretus, Petrus, 15th cent.
D. Petri Tatatareti ... Lvcidissima commentaria siue (vt vocant) reportata, In qvatvor libros sententiarvm et Qvodlibeta Ioannis Duns Scoti svbtilivm principis, in tres priores libros nusquam antehac typis excussa, ab innumeris erroribus expurgata, & Germanae integritati restituta: atque insignioribus Annotationibus illustrata per R.P.F. Bonaventuram Manentum Brixianum ... In studiosorum   quoq; gratiam vnicuique libro   adiectus est Index copiosissimus; qui rerum atq; verborum notabilium dilucidationes continet: necnon omnia ferè doctrinae Scoticae praecipua fundamenta. Accessit etiam alter Index locorum, tum Sacrae Scripturae, ac Sanctorum Patrum: tum Aristotelis, & Averrois, in vnoquoque libro explicatorum ... Venetiis, apud heredes Simonis Galignani de Karera, 1583.

Microfilm copy, made in 1960 of the original in Vatican. Biblioteca vaticans. Positive.
Negative in Vatican. Biblioteca vaticana.
Collation of the original as determined from the film: 2 v.
CONTENTS.- [v.1 on film] Super quarto libro sententiarum Ioan. Duns Scoti ...
- Super Quaes-   tiones Quodlibetales

Ioan. Duns Scoti ... - [v. 2 on film] Super primo libro sententiarum Ioan. Duns Scoti ... - In secvndvm librvm sententiarum.
1. Duns Joannes, Scotus 1265?–1308? Quodlibeta. 2. Petrus Lombardus, Bp. of Paris, 12th cent. Sententiarum libri quatuor. [I. Bonaventuram Manti, O.F.M. Conv.]
(Series: [Manuscr ipta, microfilms of rare and out-of- print books. List 19, no. 17])

NT 0044668   MoSU InU

Tartaretus, Petrus, 15th cent.
Questiões morales Magistri Petri Tatereti in octo capita distincte et ϕ doctissime ab eodeȝ disputate atȝ discusse nec segniter adnotate Nouiter impressum Parrhisiis. [device of de Marnef] Benundantur parrhisiis ... [1509] Colophon, Impresse pari ... pro Gaufrido de Marnef ... Anno dñi millesimo qngētesimo nono. die   o   v tio mēsis marcii ... Opa Guillermi Anabat Impressoris ... [Paris, 1509] sm. 4 to.   Bound in contemporary calf, stamp stamped.
Purchased from Rosenbach (Thomas-Stanford)

Sept. , 1924, item 236 (1)
With this are bound: (2) Tartaretus, Petrus. Questiones super vi libros ethicorum Aristotelis. Paris [after 1496] (3) Paulus Venetus (d. 1428) Tractatus summularum. Venice, 1498.

NT 0044670   CSmH PU

Tartaretus, Petrus, 15th cent.
Questiões morales magistri Petri tatereti in octo capita distincte & q[uam] doctissime ab eodē disputate atq[ue] discusse nec segniter annotate: atq[ue] nouiter emēdate sicut legēti patebit.
Venundantur Parrhisius in ⌈claustro brunelli apud Petrū Gaudoul ad intersignium Diui Cyrici. [1513]
lxvi numb.l.,[4]p. 13.5cm.
Publisher's device on t.-p.; printer's mark of

Continued in next column

Continued from preceding column

Jean Marchant on last page.
Colophon: ... impresse Parisius in bellouisu pro Petro gaudoul morā trahente in clauso brunelli. Anno dñi. 150. 13. die vero. xj. mensis augusti.
Edited by Jodocus Badius Ascensius.

NT 0044672   MH

Inc.
8161.6

TARTARETUS, PETRUS, 15th cent.
Questiones super sex libros Ethicorum Aristotelis. Paris, André Bocard for Anguilbert and Geoffroy de Marnef, 12 May 1098⌈i.e.1498⌉
54 l., the last blank. 4°. 194x125mm.
2 columns, 46 lines; Haebler, types 2*, 3, 6 (63 G, 180 G, 97 G) Initials.
Bocard's device on t.-p.
Edited by Jodocus Badius Ascensius.
Bound by Brugalla.
Reichling (Suppl.) 195; Stillwell, Inc. in Amer. lib. T37.

NT 0044673   ICN MB CtY PU

AW
1
R2060:
123:
1

Tartaretus, Petrus, 15th cent.
Quaestiones super libros Ethicorum Aristotelis. [Parisiis] Johannes Lambert pro Dionysio Roce [after 15 March, 1496]
54 l.
Hain-Copinger 15343.
Microfilm.   Goff T-46

NT 0044674   CaBVaU AzTeS

Lilly
PA 3906
.T173
1592

TARTARETUS, PETRUS, 15th century
... Regvlae morales, in octo capita distincte, & quàmdoctissimè ab eodem disputatae, atq; discusse. Per R.P.F. Livium a Lege Venetum ... repurgata ... Venetiis, Apud haeredes Melchioris Sessae, 1591.
8 p.l., 60 l. 8vo (15.2 cm.)

Bound with his In Aristotelis. Venetiis, 1591.
At head of title: Petri Tatareti Parisiensis ...

Not in Schwab; Riley; Adams, Cambridge; BM; BN, or Graesse.
Collates: +8 A–G8 H4.

1. Ethics. I. Livium a Lege. II. Lilly imprint: 1591.

NT 0044676   InU

St. Louis Room
PA
8585
.T2
I5
1592

Tartaretus, Petrus, 15th cent.
Petri Tatareti Parisiensis ...Regvlæ morales, in octo capita distincte, & quàm doctissimè ab eodem disputatæ, atq; discussæ. Per R. P. F. Livium a lege Venetvm ... nunc recēs summo studio recognitæ, ... quàm diligentissimè repurgata. Cvm indico locvpletissimo. Venetiis, Apud Hæredes Melchioris Sessæ, M. D. XCII.
8 p.l., 60 numb. l. 16 cm. ⌈With his In Aristotelis philosophiam, naturalem, divinam, & moralem exactissima commentaria. Venice, 1592⌉

Signatures: +8, A–G8, H4; catchwords; initials; colophon.
In double columns.

1. Christian ethics--Catholic authors. I. Livius (F.) Venetis. II. Title: Regulae morales.

NT 0044678   MoSU PU

Kress Room

Tartaretus, Petrus. *15th cent.*
   Reportata sup libros ethicorum
Aristotelis, edita a mro nro Tartareto in
Universitate parisiensi p lccicnem Universitatis legente in Collegio Remesi anno
nativiteatis. 1501. ⟨n.p., 1501⟩
37 ℓ. 29 cm.

   Caption title.
   Manuscript: leaves written on both sides
rubricated.

   Bound with Buridan, Jean. Quaestiones
et dubia in Aristotelis politica ... ca.1489.

   1.Economics - Before 1776. I.Aristotle.
Ethica Nicomachea. II.Title.

NT 0044680   MH-BA

Lilly
PA 3906
.T194
1571

TARTARETUS,PETRUS,15th century
   Svbtilivm omnivm facile principis in triplicem Aristotelis philosophiam; Physicam,
Metaphysicam, et Ethicam ... praevia Fratris
Ioannis Balaini ... ope ... Venetiis, Apud
haeredes Melchioris Sessae, 1571.
12 p.ℓ.,400 p. diagrs. 8vo(15 cm.)

   At head of title: Petri Tatareti Parisiensis

   Cosenza,Italian hum., IV, p.3373; Schwab

521; Hoffmann, I, p.373.
   The Summula is not included.
   Collates: *⁸ **⁴ A-Ddd⁸.
   Bound in old vellum, shaken; in red cloth
slipcase.

   1. Aristoteles. I. Ballaini,Joannes,fl.16th
century. II. Lilly imprint: 1571.

NT 0044682   InU WU

Tartari, Ch.
   Allocution prononcée sur la tombe de
M. Edouard-Frédéric Peaudouin, décédé à
Saint-Jean-de-Bournay (Isère) le 6 août
1899, inhumé le 9 août 1899. n.p., n.d.
10 - (1) p.

NT 0044683   MH-L

Tartariae sive magni chami regni typus
   see under [Ortelius, Abraham]
1527-1598.

Wing
Y
144
.968

The TARTARIAN prince; or, The stranger. An
historic tale. London,A.Lemoine⟨1804⟩
36p. front. 14cm. (with Whittington and
his cat. The fortunate history and adventures of
Sir Richard Whittington... ⟨1804⟩)

NT 0044685   ICN CtY

Tartarin, pseud.
   See
Scarfoglio, Edoardo, 1860-1917.

Tartarin (Albert-Ludovic-Charles) [1869-   ].
   * Un cas de dégénérescence myxomateuse géné-
ralisée des nerfs. 38 pp. 4°. *Paris*, 1894,
No. 67.

NT 0044687   DNLM

Tartarin, Albert-Ludovic-Charles, 1869-
   ——. Etudes sur la tuberculose dans les mi-
lieux maritimes en Allemagne et chez les ma-
rins du commerce en France. 62 pp. 12°.
Paris, A. Maloine, 1906.
   Repr. from: Arch. de méd. nav., Par., 1906, lxxxv.

NT 0044688   DNLM

WFA
T194L
1902

TARTARIN, Albert Ludovic Charles,
   1869-
   La lutte antituberculeuse; tuberculose
et sanatoriums... Paris, Naud, 1902.
xv, 156 p. illus.

NT 0044689   DNLM

Tartarin, Albert-Ludovic-Charles, 1869-
   ——. Tuberculose et sanatoriums; préface du
Pr. Landouzy. xv, 156 pp., 1 map. 12°. *Paris,
C. Naud*, 1902.

NT 0044690   DNLM

Tartarin (Ed.) L'âge de la pierre à Saint-
Martin-la-Rivière et environs (Vienne). Description d'un cimetière et de stations préhisto-
riques. 43 pp., 1 plan, 7 pl. 8°. *Paris, O. Doin,
1885.*

NT 0044691   DNLM

Tartarin, Édouard
   ... L'occupation en droit romain et en
droit français ... Paris, Maresco aîné
1872.
iv, ⟨5⟩-236 p. 23cm.
   Thèse - Poitiers.
   Published in 1873 under title: Traité
de l'occupation suivant le droit naturel,
le droit civil et le droit international.
   Bibliographical foot-notes.

NT 0044692   MiU-L MH-L

Tartarin, Édouard.
   Traité de l'occupation suivant le droit naturel, le droit
civil et le droit international ... par Ed. Tartarin ... Paris, Maresco aîné, 1873.
   iv, ⟨5⟩-234 p. 23½ᶜᵐ.
   CONTENTS.—L'exposé des principes généraux.—L'examen complet des
res nullius d'après les textes.—Une étude sur l'occupation des choses in-
corporelles.—Sur les effets de l'occupation militaire.

   1. Occupancy. 2. Possession (Law) 3. Military occupation.

Library of Congress   JX4093.T3   10—20057

NT 0044693   DLC

Tartarin (Émile-Charles-François). * Essai sur
les maladies paludéennes. 76 pp. 4°. *Paris,
1862, No. 28.*

NT 0044694   DNLM

Tartarin (J.-F.) * I. Comment reconnaître si
l'acide succinique a été falsifié avec de l'oxalate
ou du bitartrate de potasse? II. [etc.]. 36 pp.
4°. *Paris, 1838, No. 129, v. 334.*

NT 0044695   DNLM

Tartarin, Jean, 1908-
   ...Contribution à l'étude du syndrome par-
kinsonien d'origine syphilitique ... Lyon, 1932.
   Thèse - Univ. de Lyon.
   "Bibliographie": p. [57]-60.

NT 0044696   CtY

Tartarin tales
   see under Gueulette, Thomas Simon, 1683-
1766.

TARTARINI, Alfonso.
   Fasma (φασμα); sonetti. Prima
centuria. Bologna, P. Virano, 1896.

NT 0044698   MH

[Tartarini, Armando]
   Leopardi; l'anima del poeta. [Roma, Stab.
tip. della Tribuna, 1898]
11 p. ℓ. 8⁻.
   Signed: Armando Tartarini.
   Rivista politica e letteraria, anno II°, vol. IV
face. III, 1°settembre 1898, p. [103]-113.

NT 0044699   MH

TARTARINI, Pietro.
   La Beatrice di Dante e la Bice Portinari.
Torino, 1885.
   pp.54.

NT 0044700   MH NIC RPB

850.9
T17b

Tartarini, Pietro.
   Breve trattato di letteratura italiana.
Livorno, 1915.
   2v.

   Contents:- pte.1. Il discorso letterario.- pte.2. I generi letterari e i componimenti italiani.

NT 0044701   IU

Tartarini, Walter.
   Elementi di topografia e costruzioni stradali, ad uso degli
allievi della Facoltà di architettura. Roma, Edizioni del-
l'Ateneo ⟨1952-
   v. illus., diagrs. 26 cm.
   At head of title: Università degli studi di Roma, Facoltà di architettura.
   CONTENTS.—v. 1. Topografia.

   1. Surveying. 2. Roads—Surveying.
          TA545.T2   A 53-8595
   Michigan. Univ. Libr.
for Library of Congress   ⟨3⟩†

NT 0044702   MiU DLC

914.524
T178s

Tartarino, pseud.?
   S. Pellegrino; note, ricordi e impressione di
Tartarino, con 150 caricature e illustrazioni dal
vero. Milano, Stabilimento di arti grafiche
Alfieri & Lacroix, 1911.
42p.

   1. San Pellegrino, Italy--Social life and customs.

NT 0044703   IU

Tartarinoff, V.
Graphical spring design
see under Machinery (London)

Das tartarische Geseẕ
For libretti see under Gotter, Friedrich
Wilhelm, 1746-1797.
For scores see under Benda, Jiří Antonín,
1722-1795.

Tartarkiewicz, Wladyslaw
see Tatarkiewicz, Wladyslaw, 1886-

Tartaro (Giuseppe). Note cliniche su 5 casi
di pustola da carbonchio ematico. 19 pp. 16°.
Borgo S. Lorenzo. Linon. Forzano, 1899.

NT 0044707 DNLM

6899 **Tartaro, Shelley Barca.**
Zh 1950a The false teeth; one act play.
₍Ithaca, N. Y., 1950₎
₍1₎,16 l. 30cm. (Heermans prize
plays, 1950)

Typewritten.
In folder.

NT 0044708 NIC

Tartarotti (Franciseus). *De fallaci pulmonis
infantum experimento.
In: DE WASSERBERG. Op. min. med. et diss. 8°.
Vindob., 1775, III, 134-16°*

NT 0044709 DNLM

928.5 Tartarotti, Giacomo Antonio, 1708-1737.
T178s Saggio della biblioteca tirolese, o sia, Notizie
istoriche degli scrittori della provincia del Tirolo di Giacopo Tartarotti Roveretano. In Rovereto, Presso Pierantonio Berno, 1733.
99p.

1. Tyrol--Bio-bibl. 2. Italian literature--
Tyrol--Bibl.

NT 0044710 IU ICN CLU

Tartarotti, Giacomo ₍Antonio₎ 1708-1737.
Saggio della biblioteca tirolese, o sia Notizie istoriche
degli scrittori della provincia del Tirolo; di Giacopo Tartarotti, Roveretano e da Domenico Francesco Todeschini
... di giunte e note molto accresciuto. In Venezia, 1777.
viii, 280 p. 22cm.
"Prima parte," first pub. 1733. No more published.

1. Tyrol—Bio-bibl. 2. Italian literature—Tyrol—Bibl. I. Todeschini,
Domenico Francesco.

Library of Congress Z2124.T9T2
4-36912

NT 0044711 DLC IaU

Tartarotti, Girolamo, 1706-1761.
Apologia del congresso notturno delle lammie, o sia Risposta
di Girolamo Tartarotti all' Arte magica dileguata del Sig. march.
Scipione Maffei, ed all' opposizione del Sig. assessore Barto-
lommeo Melchiori. S'aggiunge una lettera del Sig. Clemente
Baroni... Venezia, S. Occhi, 1751. 268 p. 26cm.

290485B. 1. Witchcraft. 2. Magic. 3. Maffei, Francesco Scipione,
marchese, 1675-1755. Arte magica dileguata. 4. Melchiori, Bartolommeo.
N.Y. P. L. December 17, 1945

NT 0044712 NN NjP MB MH NIC

945.322 Tartarotti, Girolamo, 1706-1761.
T178mYt Apologia delle Memorie antiche di
Rovereto. S'aggiunge un'appendice di
documenti non più stampati, con annotazioni del medesimo. Lucca, 1758.
346p.

In reply to "La santità, ed il
martirio del B. Adelpreto Vescovo di
Trento, vindicati dal Baron Leopoldo
Pilati."

NT 0044713 IU

F
272.83 Tartarotti, Girolamo, 1706-1761.
T194 La conclusione dei Fratti Francescani
RARE poemetto. Venezia, n.p., 1765.
BOOK

NT 0044714 WLagF

Tartarotti, Girolamo, Abate, of Rovereto, Tyrol, 1706-1761. *2720.1.25
Hieronymi Tartarotti Roboretani De auctoribus ab Andrea Dandulo
laudatis in Chronico Veneto . . .
(In Muratori. Rerum Italicarum scriptores . . . Vol. 25, col.
i-xxviii. Mediolani. MDCCLI.)
Chronicon Venetum is on shelf-number *2710.1.12.

F9771 — Dandolo, Andrea. 1307-1354.

NT 0044715 MB MdBP

B Tartarotti, Girolamo, 1706-1761.
C345t Hieronymi Tartarotti Roboretani De episcopatu
sabionensi s. Cassiani martyris, deque s. Ingenu-
ini ejusdem urbis episcopi actis, ad Antonium
Roschmannum epistola. Venetiis, typis Jo.
Baptistæ Pasquali, 1750.
cxix p.

1. Cassianus, Saint, martyr. 2. Ingenuinus,
Saint, bp. fl.591. 3. Seben--Church history.

NT 0044716 IU

274.5321 Tartarotti, Girolamo, 1706-1761.
T179d Hieronymi Tartarotti Roboretani De
origine ecclesiæ Tridentinæ et primis
ejus episcopis. Dissertatio. Venetiis, 1743.
95p.

NT 0044717 IU

BR160 Tartarotti, Girolamo, 1706-1761.
.E8H68T2 De versione Rufiniana Historiae ecclesiasticae
Rare Eusebii Caesariensis; dissertatio in qua Vale-
Bk. sianae interpretationis dignitas & praestantia
vindicantur. Tridenti, Apud J. B. Paroni, 1748.
128 p.

1. Eusebius Pamphili, Bp. of Caesarea. Historia ecclesiastica. 2. Rufinus, Tyrannius, Aqui-
leiensis, ca. 345-410. 3. Valois,
Henri de, 1603-1676.

NT 0044718 ICU

Tartarotti, Girolamo, Abate of Rovereto, Tyrol, 1706-1761. **H.92.82
Del congresso notturno delle Lammie libri tre. S'aggiungono due
dissertazioni epistolari sopra l'arte magica . . .
In Rovereto. Giambatista Pasquali. MDCCXLIX. xxxii, 460
pp. 23 cm., in 4s.

L4348 — Witchcraft.

ICU MdBP NIC OClW MdBP OCl
NT 0044719 MB OkU CU PU MnU NjP OCl OClW ICU CtY MH

Tartarotti, Girolamo, Abate, of Rovereto, Tyrol, 1706-1761.
Dialogo della lingua latina, e Annotazioni al Dialogo, delle false
esercitazioni delle scuole d'Aonio Paleario.
(In Raccolta ferrarese di opuscoli scientifici e letterarj . . . Vol.
24, pp. 1-58. Vinegia. MDCCLXXXV.)

F977' — Latin language. Study and teaching. — Palearie, Aonio. 1500?-1570.

NT 0044720 MB

BC66 ₍Tartarotti, Girolamo₎ 1706-1761.
.IGT3 Idea della logica degli scolastici, e de' moderni; ragionamento di Selvaggio Dodoneo
₍pseud.₎ . . . Roveredo, P. Berno, 1731.
₍24₎, 167 p. 22cm.

1. Logic.

NT 0044721 ICU

q471.7 Tartarotti, Girolamo, 1706-1761.
T17i Illustrazione del monumento eretto dalla città
di Trento al suo patrono Caio Valerio Mariano,
opera postuma dell'ab. Girolamo Tartarotti roveretano, supplita nella parte mancante dall'ab.
Bart. Gius. Stoffella dalla Croce. Roveredo,
I. R. Stamperia Marchesani, 1824.
180p. front.(port.)

1. Inscriptions, Latin--Trento. 2. Valerio
Mariano, Caio. I. Stoffella della Croce, Bartolommeo Giuseppe, 1800-1833.

NT 0044722 IU

Tartarotti, Girolamo, Abate, of Rovereto, Tyrol, 1706-1761.
Lettera . . . sopra Giovanni Duns Scoto, in difesa di quanto di lui e
detto nel Poema della conclusione de' Frati . . .
(In Raccolta ferrarese di opuscoli scientifici e letterarj . . . Vol.
17, pp. 65-90. Vinegia. MDCCLXXXV.)
Poema della conclusione . . . is on shelf-number *4776.20.

F9766 — Duns Scotus, Johannes.

NT 0044723 MB

Rare
DG Tartarotti, Girolamo, 1706-1761.
975 Memorie antiche di Rovereto, e de'luoghi
R8T19 convicini, raccolte, e pubblicate da Girolamo
Tartarotti, roveretano. Venezia, M. Cargnio-
ni, 1754.
xii, 202 p. illus. 25cm.

Title vignette.

1. Rovereto, Italy--Antiq. 2. Rovereto,
Italy--Hist.

NT 0044724 NIC MH IU

Tartarotti, Girolamo, 1706-1761.
Orazione funebre e poetici componim.ti
in morte di Girolamo Tartarotti Serbati . . .
see under title

Tartarotti, Girolamo, 1706-61.
— Osservazioni sopra l'opuscolo che ha per
titolo Arte magica dileguata, di un prete dell'
oratorio. Venezia, 1750. sm. 4°. (With *his*
Del congresso notturno delle lammie.)

NT 0044725 MdBP

Tartarotti, Girolamo, Abate, of Rovereto, Tyrol, 1706-1761.
Osservazioni . . . sopra la Sofonisi a di Gio. Giorgio Trissino. [Prefazione di Clementino Vannetti.]
(In Raccolta ferrarese di opuscoli scientifici e letterarj . . . Vol. 14, pp. 63-90. Vinegia. MDCCLXXXIV.)
An edition of the Sofonisba is on shelf-number *4760a.50.46.

F9769 — Vannetti, Clementino, preface 754-1795. — Trissino, Giovanni Giorgio. 1478-1550.

NT 0044726   MB

Tartarotti, Girolamo, Abate, of Rovereto, Tyrol, 1706-1761.
Rime scelte. [Annotazioni del cav. Vannetti.]
Rovereto. Marchesani. MDCCLXXXV. xl, (3), 170, 104, (1), 16 pp. Portrait. 16°.
Contains Stanze del dottor Domenico Tomei . . . in risposta al Poema della conclusione da . . . Tartarotti a lui diretto, catalogued separately.

F9766 — Vannetti, Clementino, ed. 1754-1795.

NT 0044727   MB MH

Tartarotti, Girolamo, Abate of Rovereto, Tyrol, 1706-1761.   **H.92.82
Risposta . . . alla lettera, intorno all'origine, e falsità della dottrina de' Maghi, e delle Streghe, dal sig. conte Gio. Rinaldo Carli.
(In Tartarotti, G. Del congresso notturno delle Lammie. Pp. 351-447. Rovereto. 1749.)

L4346 — Carli, Gian Rinaldo, conte. 1720-1795. — Witchcraft.

NT 0044728   MB

Tartarotti Serbati, Girolamo

See

Tartarotti, Girolamo, 1706-1761.

Tartaruga, Ubald, _pseud._
see
Ehrenfreund, Edmund Otto, 1875-

Tartarus; poéme symphonique (Opus 11) . . .
    see under   [Nicholl, Horace Wadham]
1848-1922.

Tartary, Madeleine, 1903-
Bo67A   Sur les traces de Napoléon. Lettre de S.A.I.
955T   le Prince Napoléon. Préf. de Marcel Dunan.
Paris, J. Peyronnet [1955]
413p. 19cm.

1. Napoléon I, Emperor of the French, 1769-1821

NT 0044732   CtY NN NIC

TF
675   Tartary, Régis.
T2   Construction et exploitation des chemins de fer à voie de 0,60 centimètres; voie, terrassements, ouvrages d'art, machines et matériel roulant, avec étude d'un tracé entre deux points donnés . . . Paris, Baudry et cie, 1891.
245 p.   illus., map.   25cm.

1. Railroads, Narrow-gage.

NT 0044733   MiU CSt ICJ NN

Tartas, David ben
    see   Castro Tartas, David ben, Abraham, fl. 1647-1695. [supplement]

Tartas (Guillaume-Marcellin). *Essai sur les marais. 21 pp. 4°. _Paris,_ 1834, No. 67, v. 271.

NT 0044735   DNLM PPC

Bonaparte
Collection TARTAS, JEAN DE.
No.1339   Onsa hilceco bidia. Ivan de Tartas evscaraz egvina   Orthecen, I. Rovyer [1666]
162+p.   17½cm.

Imperfect: t.-p. mutilated, with loss of part of imprint; loose leaves, closely trimmed, with loss of text; some leaves, including all after p.162, wanting.
In case.   18cm.
Vinson 33.

NT 0044736   ICN

Tartat, Pierre.
Avallon au dix-huitième siècle. Lettre-préf. de Louis Bréhier. Auxerre, L'Universelle, 1951-
v. fold. maps. 25 cm.
CONTENTS.—1. La société et la vie avallonnaises avant 1789.
Bibliographical footnotes.

1. Avallon, France—Hist.
                                                    A 53-158
Harvard Univ.   Library
for Library of Congress   [3]

NT 0044737   MH NN TxU

Tartat, Pierre
Études d'archéologie et d'art moderne en Bourgogne: les églises Saint-Lazare d'Avallon et Saint-Andoche de Saulieu, les stalles de Bar-le-Régulier, le grand animalier Fr. Pompon, etc. Ouvrage illustré de 50 photographies. Avallon (Yonne) Chez l'auteur, 1955.
90 p.   illus.   25cm.

Bibliographical footnotes.

NT 0044738   NNC DLC-P4

Tartat, Pierre.
Variétés bourguignonnes, géographie et histoire. Avallon, Yonne, 1955.
131 p. illus. 19 cm.

1. Avallon, France.   I. Title.

DC801.A947T3   57-27861 ‡

NT 0044739   DLC MH NN NIC

Tartavez (Albert-Jean) [1885-   ]. *Contribution à l'étude des injections réplétives de vaseline iodoformée liquide. 58 pp. 8°. _Lyon,_ 1908, No. 59.

NT 0044740   DNLM

Tartavez (Henri) [1874-   ]. *Le décollement de la plèvre et le refoulement du diaphragme dans les interventions transthoraciques sur la face convexe du foie (abcès, kystes, empyèmes sous-phréniques). 64 pp. 8°. _Lyon,_ 1897, No. 33.

NT 0044741   DNLM

Tartaz, David
    see   Castro Tartas, David ben Abraham, fl. 1647-1695 [supplement]

Tartaz, David de Castro
    see   Castro Tartas, David ben Abraham, fl. 1647-1695. [supplement]

Tarte, André Paul, 1904-
    ... Quelques observations du traitement de l'hypospadias par la méthode de Nové-Josserand ... Nancy, 1931.
Thèse - Univ. de Nancy.
"Bibliographie": p. [41]-43.

NT 0044744   CtY

Tarte, Gustave Auguste Frédéric Xavier
    see   Tarte, Xavier, 1800-1873.

[Tarte, Joseph Israel] 1848-1907.
Le clergé, ses droits, nos devoirs.   1880.
101 p.

NT 0044746   CaBVaU

Tarte, Joseph Israel, 1848-1907.
Judas Iscariote Tarte ...
    see under title

[TARTE, Joseph Israël] 1848-1907.
La pretendue conférence; les perils de la souveraineté des provinces; l'autonomie canadienne est notre sauvegarde. Québec, 1889.
Signed J. Israel Tarte.

NT 0044748   MH CaOTU

Tarte, Joseph Israel, 1848-1907, ed.
Procès Mercier ...
    see under   Mercier, Honoré, 1840-1894, defendant.

Tarte, Josephus Henricus
    ... De collatione bonorum ex jure romano et hodierno ... submittit Josephus Henricus Tarte ... Bruxellis, H. Remy [1822]
30 p. 19½cm.
Diss. - Louvain.

NT 0044750   MH-L

Tarte, Marie Eugène Paul Marcel, 1894–
... De l'occlusion intestinale chez la femme enceinte ... Nancy, 1922.
24.5 cm.
Thèse – Univ. de Nancy.

NT 0044751 CtY

HE
3118
.T19
Tarte, Xavier, 1800–1873.
Grand chemin de fer de jonction directe entre les provinces wallonnes et Les Flanders. Exposé sommaire du but et des avantages du project. Bruxelles, Impr. de Delevigne et Callewaert, 1846.
14 p. fold. map. 28 cm.

1. Railroads–Belgium. 2. Railroads–Early works to 1850.
Full name: Gustave Auguste Frédéric Xavier Tarte

NT 0044752 MiU

Tarte, Xavier i. e. Gustave Auguste Frédéric Xavier, 1800–1873.
Mémoire sur l'utilité et la nécessité de l'établissement d'un chemin de fer de Jemeppe-sur-Sambre à Louvain, en suivant les vallées de l'Orneau et de la Dyle; par M. X. Tarte ... Bruxelles, A. Decq, 1843.
2 p. l., ii p., 1 l., [5]–103 p. fold. map. 28ᶜᵐ.

1. Railroads–Belgium.
11–12688
Library of Congress HE3118.T3

NT 0044753 DLC

Tarteiron
see Tarteyron, Isaac, b. 1769.

Tartelin, Alphonse.
*SC.FR
.59
.T17
Rectifications à propos des quelques réflexions sur les actes du Congrès de Nîmes par le R.P. Prosper de Martigné ... par m. l'abbé Tartelin, du Tiers-Ordre. Richesse, médiocrité ou pauvreté par le T.R.P. Dehon. [Ligugé (Vienne)] Publié par les soins de la Commission des actes du Congrès de Nîmes. 1899.

55p. 18.5cm.
With this are bound 9 broadsides or leaflets

relating to the shrine of St. Antony of Padua, at Brive (Corrèze).

1. Franciscans. Third order–Congresses–Nîmes, 1897.

NT 0044756 MB

Albert James.
Tartenson, * De l'emploi du collodion dans le traitement de certaines maladies inflammatoires des yeux. 63 pp. 4°. Paris, 1872, No. 470.

NT 0044757 DNLM

WJ
T194h
1878
TARTENSON, Albert James.
Hygiène des organes génito-urinaires de l'homme et de la femme; traitement de leurs diverses maladies; physiologie de la génération. Paris, Sagnier, 1878.
339 p. illus. (Médecine pratique)

NT 0044758 DNLM

Albert
Tartenson [James]. Leçons cliniques sur une nouvelle méthode de traitement de la blennorrhée (goutte militaire). 2. éd. 32 pp. 8°. Paris, A. Delahaye, 1875.

NT 0044759 DNLM

WCA
T194s
1882
TARTENSON, Albert James
La sífilis, su historia y tratamiento; método inglés. Obra vertida al castellano por José Ramon de Torres y Martinez. Madrid, Alegre, 1882.
112 p.
Translation of La syphilis, son histoire et son traitement.

NT 0044760 DNLM

WCA
T194s
1880
TARTENSON, Albert James
La syphilis, son histoire et son traitement; méthode anglaise. Paris, Baillière, 1880.
xiv, 238 p. (Médecine pratique)

NT 0044761 DNLM PPC

Tartenson, Albert James.
La syphilis, son histoire et son traitement (méthode anglaise) 2 éd. Paris, Baillière, 1880.
238 p.

NT 0044762 PPC

RB
153
.T370
Tartenson, Albert James
Traité clinique des fièvres larvées : (fièvres de marais) origine, nature, fréquence, danger : élément, de diagnostic : indications thérapeutiques / par le Docteur Albert Tartenson ; precédé d'une préface de Georges Barral. Paris : F. Alcan, 1887.
262 p. ; 23 cm.

NT 0044763 GU DNLM

Tartenson, James
see Tartenson, Albert James.

Tarter, Charles L 1907–
Family of destiny. [1st ed.] New York, Pageant Press [1954]
277 p. 21 cm.

1. Title.
PZ4.T194Fam
54–12344‡

NT 0044765 DLC TxU NcR NN OO

WA
670
qT194s
1927
TARTER, Clyde Sydney, 1900–
A sanitary survey of Middletown, Connecticut, by Clyde S. Tarter [and] N. Stanley Lincoln. [Boston] Harvard Medical School [1927]
78 ℓ. illus.
Typewritten copy.
1. Sanitation – Connecticut
I. Lincoln, Noah Stanley, 1901–

NT 0044766 DNLM

598.2
T17c
1940
Tarter, Delbert Gordon, ed.
Check list of East Texas birds. Sponsored by the East Texas Ornithology Club, Training School [and the] East Texas State Teachers College, Commerce, Tex. 2d ed. Commerce, Tex., 1940.
[4], 19ℓ. 29cm.

Editor's autograph presentation copy.
Bibliography: leaf [4] (first group)

NT 0044767 IU

Tarter, Harry.
Legal resolvents. New York, Merlin Press [1951]
114 p. 21 cm.
Thesis–Columbia University.
Bibliographical footnotes.

1. Law–Philosophy. 2. Law–Interpretation and construction. I. Title.
Columbia Univ. 340.1 A 51–5136
for Library of Congress Libraries
[1]†

NT 0044768 NNC DLC CU-AL

Tarter, John L.
The world's best inspirational poems. [Fort Worth, Tex., Globe printing company, °1933]

Tarterat (Jean) [1900–]. *Contribution à l'étude de l'auto-hémo-lysothérapie (injections de sang lysé) en oto-rhino-laryngologie. 53 pp. 8°. Paris, 1926. No. 246.

NT 0044770 DNLM CtY

Tarteron, Jacques, 1644–1720.
De cometa ann. 1664 et 1665 observationes mathematicae propugnabuntur in aula Coll. Claromontani die Jovis 29 Jan. 1665. Paris, 1665.
sq. 8°
(At head of title: Hieronymus Tarteron.)

NT 0044771 NN

Tarteron, Jacques, 1644–1720, ed. and tr.
Les satyres de Perse et de Juvénal
see Persius Flaccus, Aulus.
Satirae. Latin and French. 1695.

Tarteron, Jacques, 1644–1720, ed. and tr.
Traduction des satyres de Perse, et de Juvénal
see Persius Flaccus, Aulus.
Satirae. Latin and French. 1706 and later.

Tarteron, Jacques, 1644–1720, ed. and tr.
Traduction nouvelle des Satyres de Perse et de Juvénal
see Persius Flaccus, Aulus.
Satirae. Latin and French. 1689. (Also 1698)

Tarteron, Jérôme
see Tarteron, Jacques, 1644–1720.

Case
Y
682
.T 188

TARTESSIUS, MARCUS PAULUS.
Marci Pauli Tartessij...In diuersorū authorū opera praefationes IIII. Eiusdē orationes funebres II. Cremonae, Apud V.Comitem,1559.
24 ℓ. 20cm.

Title within historiated border; initials.

NT 0044776   ICN

Tarteyron, Isaac, b. 1769.
Discours prononcé par Tarteiron, président du Corps législatif, en annonçant la fin de la session. Corps législatif. Séance du 10 germinal an 8. ₍Paris, Impr. nationale, germinal an 8, i.e. 1800₎

3 p. 21cm. ₍French history pamphlets. Consulate. v.3, no.98₎

Caption title.

NT 0044777   MnU

Tarteyron, Isaac, b.1769
Rapport sur une résolution du 12 vendémiaire an 8 relative à la création d'une marine auxiliaire. Séance du 26 vendémiaire an 8. [P, an 8]

26 p.

NT 0044778   MH

Tartib Prawiradihardjo
   see   Prawiradihardjo, Tartib, 1912-

Tartière, Dorothy (Blackman) 1903–
The house near Paris, an American woman's story of traffic in patriots, by Drue Tartière, written with M. R. Werner. New York, Simon and Schuster ₍1946₎
viii p., 2 l., ₍3₎–318 p., 1 l. plates, ports., facsims. 20¾ᵐ.

1. World war, 1939–1945—Personal narratives, American. 2. World war, 1939–1945—France. ᵗ. Werner, Morris Robert, 1897– joint author. II. Title.
Library of Congress *   D811.5.T3   46–25019
     ₍25₎   940.542

    NmLcU TxU MeB NIC OC1 OCU OrU WaE WaS
NT 0044780   DLC CaBVa CaBViP Or OrP MB OU NcC NcGU

Tartière, Dorothy (Blackman) 1903–
The house near Paris; an American woman's story of traffic in patriots, by Drue Tartière, written with M. R. Werner. London, V. Gollancz, 1947.
207 p. plates, ports., facsims. 19 cm.

1. World War, 1939–1945—Personal narratives, American. 2. World War, 1939–1945—France. ᵗ. Werner, Morris Robert, 1897– joint author. II. Title.
   D811.5.T3 1947   940.542   48–20254*

NT 0044781   DLC

Tartière (Émile). *Considérations sur la paralysie atrophique aiguë de l'enfance (symptômes, lésions anatomiques). 40 pp. 4°. *Paris, 1874, No. 66.

NT 0044782   DNLM

Tartière (Émile). De l'aptitude des conscrits au service militaire et de la robustcité humaine, déterminées par les mensurations du poids et de la taille du corps. 20 pp. 8°. *Paris, 1903.

NT 0044783   DNLM

Tartière, Jean Baptiste.
... De tout un peu. Livre de lecture courante a l'usage des élèves des classes du cours moyen ... 8 ed. Paris, n.d.
illus. 18 cm.

NT 0044784   RPB

Tartière (Léon) [1853–]. *Considération sur la diplopie binoculaire. 64 pp. 4°. *Paris, 1879, No. 512.
Last page called 80

NT 0044785   DNLM

864.59
T195C

Tartilan, Sofía
Costumbres populares. Colección de cuadros tomados del natural ... con una carta-prólogo del ... D. Ramón de Mesonero Romanos. Madrid, M. Minuesa, 1880.
xi, 235 p. 19½cm.

1. Spain. Social life and customs. I. Title

NT 0044786   NcD PBm OO MH

DP 232.5
T37
1881

Tartilan, Sofía.
Costumbres populares; colección de cuadros tomados del natural. Con una carta-prólogo del señor D. Ramón de Mesonero Romanos. 3. ed., corr. y aum. Madrid, Tip. de M. Minuesa, 1881.
286 p.

1. Spain - Social life and customs. I. Title.

NT 0044787   CaBVaU

Tartini, Ferdinando.
Memorie, etc., di Tartini notomizzato da Graeberg da Hemsoe. Firenze, 1839.
8vo.

NT 0044788   NN

627.5
T179m
1838a

₍Tartini, Ferdinando₎
Memorie sul bonificamento delle Maremme toscane. Firenze, G. Molini, 1838.
484p. incl.tables.

"Avviso ai lettori" signed: Ferdinando Tartini.

1. Reclamation of land. 2. Maremma. I. Title.

NT 0044789   IU MB NN TxU DNLM

Tartini, Ferdinando.
Notizie e Guida di Firenze e de' suoi contorni. Firenze, 1841.
8vo.

NT 0044790   NN

Tartini, Ferdinardo.
Tavole e prospetti statistici appartenenti alle memorie sul bonificamento delle maremme toscane. Firenze, 1838.
24 pl., 12 tab. F⁶.

NT 0044791   RPB

787.342M
T 179 A Tartini, Giuseppe. 1692-1770.

Adagio cantabile. Transcription pour violoncelle et piano par Hugo Becker. Bruxelles, Bosworth ₍n.d.₎ Pl. no. B. & C⁰ 18132
score (3 p.) and part. 31ᶜᵐ.

NT 0044792   OO PPCI

Tartini, Giuseppe, 1692-1770.
Allegro animosamente. Arrange pour violon et piano par Mischa Elman. Mainz, c1910.

Schott edition.

NT 0044793   PPCI

Tartini, Giuseppe, 1692-1770.
Andante. [By] G. Tartini. Arr. by H. Elkan. [For string orchestra. Score.]
— Philadelphia. Elkan-Vogel Co., Inc. 1933. 7 pp. 31 cm.

E1986 — T.r. For string orchestra. - ₍o₎rchestra. Music. Strings. — Elkan, Henri, ed.

NT 0044794   MB

TARTINI, GIUSEPPE, 1692-1770.
Andante e Presto (dal quartetto in re magg., n.125) Trascrizione per orchestra d'archi di Ettore Bonelli. Padova, G. Zanibon, 1948. score(8 p.) 34cm. (Musica da camera. 3719)

For string orchestra; originally for string quartet. Duration: 6 min.
1.Orchestra, String--   Arr. I.Bonelli, Ettore, ed.

NT 0044795   NN

785.75
T17a

Tartini, Giuseppe, 1692-1770.
Arioso (E minor). Transcribed by George J. Trinkaus. New York, Kay and Kay Music Publ. Corp., c1933.
score (4 p.) (Franklin instrumental ensembles no. 6)

For flute, oboe, clarinet, horn, and bassoon. Bound with Tartini, Giuseppe, 1692-1770. Evening song.

NT 0044796   KEmT

Tartini, Giuseppe, 1692-1770.
...Arioso ₍mi mineur₎... Paris: A. Durand & fils, 1910. Publ. pl. no. D. & F. 7510. 2 parts. 35½cm. (Les vieux maitres du violon. 7.)

Score (including realized basso continuo) and violin part. "Révision par Alfred Moffat."

I. Violin and piano. I. Moffat, Alfred Edward, 1866– ed.
N. Y. P. L.   March 19, 1936

NT 0044797   NN

M
787.1
T195a
And

Tartini, Giuseppe, 1692-1770.
L'arte dell' arco.
L'art de l'archet – Die Kunst der Bogenführung. 50 Variationen über eine Gavotte für die Violine mit Begleitung eines Basso continuo. Fingersatz und Vortragszeichen versehen von Ferd. David. Offenbach, Joh. Andre ₍n.d.₎ Pl. no. 9113.
score (19p.)

Explanations in English, German & French.

NT 0044798   FTaSU IU OO

M
221
.T18
A8
179-
Tartini, Guiseppe, 1692-1770.
  ₁L'arte dell'arco₎
  L'art de l'archet contenant 38 variations
composees sous la plus belle gavotte de
Corelli. Mannheim, J.M.Götz ₁179-?₎
Pl.no.464.
  16 p.   21 x 25 cm.
  Engraved throughout.
  Label mounted at foot of t.p.: Francfort,
Gayl & Hedler.
  1.Variations(Violin and harpischord)--
To 1800. I.Corelli,   Arcangelo,1653-
1713. Sonatas,viol   in & bass,op.5,
no.10,F major. Gav   otte,arranged.

NT 0044799   MiU DLC NPV

Tartini, Giuseppe, 1692-1770.
  L'art de l'archet, ou Cinquante variations
pour violon, accompagné d'une basse continue,
composées par J. Tartini. ... Offenbach, Jean
André [1802]
  15 p.   34 cm.
  Publ. no. 1677.
  Variations on a gavotte by Corelli.
  Title vignette, putto playing violin.
  Lithographed.

NT 0044800   CtY-Mus

Cage
M
42
T179a
1817
Tartini, Giuseppe, 1692-1770.
  [L'arte dell'arco]
  L'art de l'archet ou variations... nouvelle édition,
augmentée d'une lettre de l'auteur adressée à Madame de
Sirmen, son clève ... / composées par Tartini. -- Paris :
Chez Madame Joly [ca. 1817] Pl. no. 58.
  [2], 19 p.

  1. Variations (Violin and piano)--To 1800. I. Title.

NT 0044801   CLU

Tartini, Giuseppe, 1692-1770.
  L'art de l'archet. Die Kunst der Bogenführung. 50 Variationen über eine Gavotte für die Violine mit Begleitung eines Basso
continuo, componirt von J. Tartini. (Zum Gebrauch am Con-
servatorium der Musik in Leipzig mit obligater Pianofortebegleitung, Bogenstrich, Fingersatz und Vortragszeichen versehen von
Ferd. David;... Offenbach a/M.: J. André ₁ca. 1883₎. Publ.
pl. no. 9113. 19 p. f°.

1. Violin and piano. 2. David,	Ferdinand Victor, 1810-73. 3.
Title. 4. Title: Die Kunst der	Bogenführung.
N.Y.P.L.	June 9, 1916.

NT 0044802   NN OkU

Tartini, Giuseppe, 1692-1770.
  L'art de l'archet. Die Kunst der Bogenführung; 50 Variationen üoer eine Gavotte für
die Violine. Offenbach a/M., etc., J. André
[19-]

  31 p.   30.5 cm.
  Score, for violin and piano.
  "Edition André, 259b."

NT 0044803   MH-Mu

Tartini, Giuseppe, 1692-1770.
  L'art de l'archet de Tartini; revu et doigté par Ch. Dorson.
50 variations sur un thème de Corelli...   Paris: R. Deiss₁, 1928₎.
Publ. pl. no. R. 6124 D.   20 p.   f°.

  For violin.

1. Violin--Methods. 2. Corelli,	Arcangelo, 1653-1713. 3. Dorson,
Charles, 1882- , editor. 4. Title.	
N.Y.P.L.	March 14, 1929

NT 0044804   NN

Tartini, Giuseppe, 1692-1770.
  The art of bowing, for violin;ed. by
Ferd.David and newly rev. by E.L.Winn.
Fischer, ©1905.

NT 0044805   OrP

---

sVMT
267
T19a
TARTINI, GIUSEPPE, 1692-1770.
  ₋The art of bowing (L'art de l'archet) for
the violin. 50 variations on a gavotte by Corelli for the violin. Edited and revised by
Leopold Lichtenberg. With piano accompaniment
by Ferdinand David.   New York, Schirmer, c1909.
  19p.   (Schirmer's library of musical classics. vol.922)

  Accompaniment wanting.
  Plate no.: 20092 (1909)

NT 0044806   ICN OrU PPCI OC1 NN MiDW

---

m781.3
T195a
L683
Tartini, Giuseppe, 1692-1770.
  [L'arte dell'arco]
  The art of bowing, for the violin;
fifty variations on a gavotte by Corelli.
Edited and rev. by Leopold Lichtenberg.
New York, G.Schirmer, c1940.
  19p. 30cm. (Schirmer's library of
musical classics, v.922)

  1.Variations (Violin), Arranged. I.
Corelli, Arcangelo, 1653-1713. Sonata,
violin & con-   tinuo, op.5, no.10,
F major. Gavot   te; arr. II.Title.

NT 0044807   CLSU NcU

Brown
MT287
T2A7
Tartini, Giuseppe, 1692-1770.
  Art of bowing; transcribed for viola ₁by
Clemens Meyer₎ New York, Edition Musicus
₁195-?₎
  19 p. 31 cm.
  "Fifty variations on a Gavotte by Corelli."

  1. Viola--Studies and exercises.
  2. Variations (Viola), Arranged.   I. Title.

NT 0044808   MB

Tartini, Giuseppe, 1692-1770.

Crosby, Alpheus Benning, 1832-1877.
  The art of holding the violin & bow as exemplified by
Ole Bull. His pose and method proved to be based on
true anatomical principles, by A. B. Crosby ... London,
W. Reeves ₁1909₎

Tartini, Giuseppe, 1692-1770.
  L'ARTE DEL ARCO/ ou/ L'ART DE L'ARCHET/
Contenant 38. Variations/ Composées sous la
plus Belle Gavotte de Corelly./ PAR/ GIUSEPE
TARTINI/ di Padoüa./ Gravées par Mme Leclair./
Prix 3 ₁fr.₎/ A PARIS/ Chez M. Leclerc, rue du
Roule à la Croix D'or/ Et aux Adresses Ordin-
aires/ Avec Privilège du Roy. ₁n.d.₎
  16 p. 21 x 30 cm.

  Title from cover.
  Printed from copper plates.

NT 0044810   OU

Tartini, Giuseppe, 1692-1770.
  L'arte del arco, ou L'art de l'archet, contenant 38 variations
composées sous la plus belle gavotte de Corelli. Par Giuseppe
Tartini ... Gravées par Mme. Leclair ... Paris, M. Leclerc
₁1780?₎
  16 p. 21 x 30ᵐ.
  Engraved throughout.

  I. Title.

29-6574

Library of Congress   MT267.T172

NT 0044811   DLC OU

Tartini, Giuseppe, 1692-1770.
  ₁L'arte dell'arco₎
  L'arte dell'arco; o siano, Cinquanta variazioni per violino,
e sempre collo stesso basso, composte dal sigʳ Giuseppe Tartini
sopra alla più bella gavotta del Corelli opera v. Napoli, L.
Marescalchi ₁174-?₎
  12 p. 33ᵐ.
  Caption title.
  For violin and unfigured bass.

  1. Variations (Violin and harpsichord)--To 1800.   I. Corelli,
Arcangelo, 1653-1713. Sonatas, violin & bass, op. 5, no. 10, F major.
Gavotte, arranged.

Library of Congress   M221.T   46-31038

NT 0044812   DLC

TARTINI, GIUSEPPE, 1692-1770.
  [L'ARTE DELL' ARCO]
  L'arte dell' arco, o siano cinquanta variazioni per
violino, e sempre collo stesso basso. Composte dal
Sigr. Giuseppe Tartini sopra alla più bella gauotta
del Corelli, opera V. In Napoli, Appresso Luigi
Marescalchi ₁179-?₎ 12 p. 34cm.

  Caption title.

  For violin and unfigured bass.

  1. Violin--Studies and exercises. I. Corelli, Arcangelo, 1653-1713.
Sonatas, violin & continuo,   op. 5.

NT 0044814   NN

---

q
M
219
T2
S66
1906
MUSIC
Tartini, Giuseppe, 1692-1770.
  [Sonatas, violin & continuo. Selections]
  Berühmte Sonaten für Violine mit Klavier-
begleitung. Hrsg. von Friedrich Hermann.
Leipzig, Peters ₁c1906₎
  score (3v.) and part. 31cm.
  "Edition Peters, Nr.1099a-c"
  CONTENTS.--V.1. Sonate F dur. Sonate G dur.
Sonate E moll.--V.2. Teufelstriller-Sonate.--
Sonate G moll.--V.3. Sonate C dur. Sonate D
dur.

NT 0044815   TxU WaU NjP CSt

M219
T36H4
Tartini, Giuseppe, 1692-1770.
  [Sonatas. Selections]
  Berühmte Sonaten für Violine Mit
Klavierbegleitung hrsg. von Friedrich
Hermann. Frankfurt, New York, C. F.
Peters, c1906, 1934.
  score (3 v.) and parts. 30 cm.
(Edition Peters Nr. 1099)
  CONTENTS.--v. 1. No. 1 (F major).
No. 2. (G major). No. 3 (E minor).--v.
2. No. 4 ("The Devil's trill"). No. 5 (G
minor).--v. 3. No. 6 (C major). No. 7 ₁D
major₎.

NT 0044816   OCU CoU IEN

M
219
.T3
H4x
Tartini, Giuseppe, 1692-1770.
  [Sonatas. Violin & piano.
Selections]
  Berühmte Sonaten für Violine Mit
Klavierbegleitung hrsg. von Friedrich
Hermann. Leipzig, C. F. Peters, c1906-
1934.
  score (3 v.) and parts. 30 cm.
(Edition Peters Nr. 1099)
  CONTENTS.--v. 1. No. 1 (F major). No.
2. (G major). No. 3 (E minor).--v. 2.
No. 4 ("The Devil's trill"). No. 5 (G
minor).--v. 3. No. 6 ₁G major). No. 7
(D major).
  1. Sonatas (Violin and piano)--To
1800. I. Title

NT 0044817   WMUW

M1612
.A4C3
case
Tartini, Giuseppe, 1692-1770.

Alay, Mauro d', fl. 1728.
  ₁Cantatas, voice & continuo₎

  Cantate a voce sola, e suonate a violino solo, col basso.
₁Londra, 1728₎

FILM   Tartini, Giuseppe, 1692-1770.
AA371
MT   Caprices, ou Etude du violon dediés aux amateurs,
Music   par Tartini. Vienne, J. Cappi ₍180-?₎ Pl.no.919.
Library   13 p. On film (negative)

        Microfilm. Original owned by Gesellschaft der
      Musikfreunde in Wien.
      Caption title: Adagio, con variazioni.

      1. Violin - Studies and exercises. I. Title.

NT 0044819 CU

787.142M Tartini, Giuseppe, 1692-1770.
T 179 SH ₍Sonatas, violin & continuo. Selections₎

      Célèbres sonates pour violon. Accompagnés
    d'une partie de piano par Friedrich Hermann.
    Leipzig, C.F. Peters, n.d. Pl. no. 8626,
    8649, 8834.
      score (3 v.) and part. 31ᶜᵐ.

      Thematic index in each volume.
    Some t.p.'s in German.
    Contents.--Bd.1. No.2, F major. No.4. • • •

NT 0044820 OU PPCI OrP

M219   Tartini, Giuseppe, 1692-1770.
T19S6p ₍Sonatas, violin & continuo. Selections₎
       Célèbres sonates pour violon. Leipzig,
    Peters ₍19--?₎ Pl. no. 4043-
      score (2 v.) and 2 pts. 32cm.
    Unfigured bass realized for piano.
      Contents.- Cah.1. Op.1, no.2,4,5 ₍F major
    G major, E minor₎ accompagnés d'une partie
    de piano par Henry Holmes.- Cah.2. Trille
    du diable₍et Sonate en sol mineur ₍G minor₎
    accompagnés d'une partie de piano par Fr.
    Hermann.

NT 0044821 CSt MH NBuG MB OCl

---

*M218 Tartini, Giuseppe, 1692-1770.
T3   Célèbres sonates pour violin par J. Tartini.
    Accompagnés d'une partie de piano par Friedrich
    Hermann ... Leipzig, C. F. Peters ₍°1900?₎

     3 vols. 30½cm. (On cover: Edition Peters
    no. 1099)

     Piano score and part for violin.

NT 0044822 NBuG

M218   Tartini, Giuseppe, 1692-1770.
H25   ₍Sonatas, violin & continuo. Selections₎

      Célèbres sonates pour violon, accompagnés
    d'une partie de piano par Friedrich Hermann.
    Leipzig, C.F. Peters ₍°1906?₎ Pl. no.8834.
      score (19 p.) and part. 31cm.

      Bound with: Händel, G.F. Sonatas, violin
    & continuo.- Haydn, J. Sonatas, violin &
    piano.- Schubert, F. Sonatinas, violin &
    piano, op.137.
      Contents.- Le trille du diable (Teufel-
    striller-Sonate) G minor.

      1.Sonatas (Violin and harpsichord) -

NT 0044823 OrCS

787.3 Tartini, Giuseppe, 1692-1770.
T17f
     50 variations sur un thème de Corelli.
    Transcription de Paul Bazelaire. Pour vio-
    loncelle seul. Paris, Salabert ₍1920₎
    26 p. 32cm. (Edition Nationale de
    Musique Classique, no. 5405)

     M.1. Violon-   cello music. M.I.
    Bazelaire, Paul,   1886-

NT 0044824 LU

Film   Tartini, Giuseppe, 1692-1770.
12137   ₍Concertos, violin & string orchestra.
    Selections₎
      Concerti del Signor Giuseppi Tartini, ac-
    commodati per il cembalo da L.Frischmuth.
    Amsterdam, A.Olofsen ₍1755?₎
      2v. (30p.)

      Arr. for harpsichord.
      Contents.- I. Dounias 9, C major (transposed
    to F major)- II. Dounias 63, F major (trans-
    posed to D major)- III. Dounias 32, D major

     Contents (cont.) (transposed to Bb major)-
    IV. Dounias 81, G major (transposed to Eb
    major)
      Microfilm (negative) Cambridge, Fitzwilliam
    Museum, 1968. 1 reel.
      On reel with Richardson, William. Lessons
    for the harpsichord or spinet. London, 1708.-
    Eccles, John. A collection of lessons and

     Contents (cont.) aires for the harpsicord or
    spinett. London, 1702.- Marchand, Louis.
    Works, harpsichord. Selections. Amsterdam,
    ca.1710.- Bononcini, G.B. Divertimenti da
    camera traddotti pel cembalo. Londra, 1722.-
    Froberger, J.J. Works, harpsichord. Selec-
    tions. Amsterdam, ca.1710.

NT 0044827 IaU

Tartini, Giuseppe, 1692-1770.
   ₍Concertos, violin & string orchestra. Selections₎
     ₍Concerti for violin with acc. of 2 violins, viola, and basso.
n. d.₎
       parts. 23 x 30-32 cm.
     18th and 19th century copyists' ms.
     No. 19 has 1st movement only; no. 30 has orchestral acc.
     CONTENTS.—No. 19 bis (Dounias 118) B major.—No. 30 (Dounias
    20) D major.—No. 45 (Dounias 50) E major.—No. 69 (Dounias 119)
    Bb major.—No. 72 (Dounias 66) F major.—No. 75 (Dounias 53) E
    major.—No. 95 (Dounias 36) D major.—No. 96 (Dounias 37) D
    major.—No. 97 (Dounias 35) D major.
     1. Concertos (Violin with string orchestra)—To 1800—Parts.
    2. Concertos (Violin)—To 1800—Parts.

    M1105.T25V59-   63-27936/M

NT 0044828 DLC

Tartini, Giuseppe, 1692-1770.
   ₍Sonatas, violin & continuo. Selections; arr.₎

     Concertino for clarinet and string orchestra; selected and
    arr. from sonatas of Giuseppe Tartini by Gordon Jacob.
    Clarinet and piano. London, New York, Boosey & Hawkes
    ₍1946, °1945₎
      score (16 p.) and part. 31 cm.

     1. Concertos (Clarinet with string orchestra), Arranged—Solo with
    piano. I. Jacob, Gordon Percival Septimus, 1895-   arr.

    M1106.T22J2   47-28564 rev*

NT 0044829 DLC CoU FTaSU INS

M1124 Tartini, Giuseppe, 1692-1770.
T22J2 ₍Sonatas, violin & continuo. Selections; arr.₎
    Concertino for clarinet and string orchestra;
    Selected and arr. from sonatas of Giuseppe
    Tartini by Gordon Jacob. London, Hawkes &
    son; sole selling agents: Boosey & Hawkes
    ₍parts c1947₎ Pl. no. B & H 17047.
      score (16p.) and 8 parts. 31cm.
      Clarinet part c1945, Pl. no. B & H 9028.
      1. Concertos (Clarinet with string orchestra),
    Arranged--Solo with piano. I. Jacob, Gordon
    Percival Septimus,   1895-   arr.

NT 0044830 IU

Tartini, Giuseppe, 1692-1770.
   ₍Concerto, flute & string orchestra, G major (1894)₎
     Concerto à 5. Konzert, G-dur, für Flöte, Streichorchester
    und Continuo, hrsg. von Johannes Brinckmann. ₍Continuo:
    Wilhelm Mohr. 1. Veröffentlichung. Concerto in G major
    for flute, string orchestra, and continuo. 1st publication.
    Hamburg, H. Sikorski ₍c1954₎
      21 p. 32 cm.
      "Edition Sikorski, Nr. 292."
      "Stimmenkopien ... in der Bibliothek der Stockholmer Musikali-
    schen Akademie."
      With realization of the figured bass for harpsichord.
      1. Concertos (Flute with string orchestra)—To 1800—Scores.
    I. Brinckmann, Johannes, 1923-

    M1120.T37 G maj.   (1954)   M 58-580

    OCU
NT 0044831 DLC CaBVaU ViU TxU ICN LU CSt ICU NᵉC

M1105 Tartini, Giuseppe, 1692-1770.
T25   ₍Concerto, violin & string orchestra, Dounias
D.   A major₎
      Concerto, A major for violin and string
    orchestra. Ed. and with foreword by Felix
    Schroeder. London, New York; E. Eulenburg
    ₍n.d.₎ Pl. no. E. E. 6165.
      miniature score (36 p.) 19cm. (Edition
    Eulenburg, no. 1231)

      1. Concertos (Violin with string orchestra)

    - To 1800 - Sco   res.

NT 0044832 CoU

Tartini, Giuseppe, 1692-1770.
    Concerto. A major. Für Violine und
    Klavier; Herausgegeben von Robert Reitz.
    Lpz., c1916.

      Eulenburg edition.

NT 0044833 PPCI

Tartini, Giuseppe, 1692-1770.
    Concerto. A minor. For violin and
    piano harmonized and re-arranged by
    Mario Corti. N.Y., c1929.

      Fischer edition.

NT 0044834 PPCI

Tartini, Giuseppe, 1692-1770.
   ₍Concerto, viola da gamba, D major; arr.₎

     Concerto, D dur, für Violoncello oder Gambe mit Streich-
    orchester und 2 Hörnern. Hrsg. von Rudolf Hindemith.
    Mainz, B. Schott's Söhne ₍°1929₎
      piano-conductor score (18 p.) and part. 32 cm. (Edition Schott,
    No. 1397)
      Acc. originally for string orchestra and 2 horns.

     1. Concertos (Violoncello)—To 1800—Solo with piano.

    M1017.T2H4   M 55-2094

NT 0044835 DLC NN MB CLSU

Tartini, Giuseppe, 1692-1770.
    Concerto. D major. Für Violoncello und
    Pianoforte; herausgegeben von F. Grützmacher.
    Leipzig, Breitkopf, n.d.

NT 0044836 PPCI

Tartini, Giuseppe, 1692-1770.
    Concerto. D minor. Für Violine mit Klavier;
    bearbeitet mit eignen Cadenzen von Emilio Pente.
    Leipzig, c1898.
      Benjamin edition.

NT 0044837 PPCI

W.C.L. Tartini, Giuseppe, 1692-1770.
M785.63 ₍Concerto, violin & string orchestra, D
T195C   minor; arr.₎

      Concerto, d - moll; d - minor, violino &
    piano. ₍Edited by₎ Emilio Pente. Hamburg;
    London, A. J. Benjamin ₍n. d.₎ Pl. no. A. J. B.
    3568.
      score (14 p.) and part. 31 cm. (Elite
    Edition no. 3000)
      Cover title.
      1. Concertos ₍Violin with string orchestra
    To 1800. Solo   with piano. I. Pente,
    Emilio, 1860-   1928, ed.

NT 0044838 NcD OU

Tartini, Giuseppe, 1692–1770.
₍Concerto, violin & string orchestra, Dounias 53, E major; arr.₎

Concerto, E-dur, für Violine und Orchester. Hrsg. von Hermann Scherchen. Ausg-Violine und Klavier. Zürich, Hug ₍1947₎

score (12 p.) and part. 31 cm.

Cover title.
"Klaviersatz von Friedrich Niggli."

1. Concertos (Violin with string orchestra)—To 1800—Solo with piano.   ɪ. Scherchen, Hermann, 1891–   ed.

M1013.T19 D. 53 .S3   48–14710 rev 2*/M

NT   0044839   DLC NN CoU OCU

Tartini, Giuseppe, 1692–1770.
₍Concerto, violin & string orchestra, Dounias 45, D minor; arr.₎

Concerto en ré mineur. Révision et cadences de Émile Chaumont. Paris, Édition M. Senart ₍1930₎

score (12 p.) and part. 35 cm. (Édition nationale ₍de musique classique₎ no. 5413)

Acc. arr. for piano.

1. Concertos (Violin with string orchestra)—To 1800—Solo with piano.   ɪ. Chaumont, Émile, 1878–   ed.

M1106.T22 D. 45 .C5   63–29850/M

NT   0044840   DLC NN

Tartini, Giuseppe, 1692–1770.
₍Concerto, violin & string orchestra, Dounias 81, G major; arr.₎

Concerto, en sol majeur, pour violon avec accomp. d'orchestre ou de piano. Revue et augmenté d'une cadence par Emilio Pente. Éd. avec piano. Mainz, B. Schott's Söhne ₍1920₎

score (13 p.) and part. 34 cm.

1. Concertos (Violin with string orchestra)—To 1800—Solo with piano.   ɪ. Pente, Emilio, 1860–1929, ed.

M1106.T22 D. 81 .P4   63–29842/M

NT   0044841   DLC

Tartini, Giuseppe, 1692–1770.
₍Concerto, violin & string orchestra, Dounias 81, G major; arr.₎

Concerto en sol majeur pour violon avec accompagnement d'orchestre ou de piano. Augmenté d'une cadence, arrangé et instrumenté par Emilio Pente. Mainz, B. Schott's Söhne ₍1929₎

score (27 p.) and part. 34 cm.

For violin and orchestra.

1. Concertos (Violin), Arranged—Scores.   ɪ. Pente, Emilio, 1860–1929, ed.

M1012.T22 D. 81 .P5   63–28744/M

NT   0044842   DLC WaU

M1012 **Tartini, Giuseppe,** 1692–1770.
.T2C7q   ₍Concerto. Violin₎
             Concerto for violnc₍₎ in D-minor.
             ₍Detroit, Luck, 19––?₎
             score(17 p.)   32 cm.

NT   0044843   NjP

787.1 **Tartini, Giuseppe,** 1692–1770.
T17cv

Concerto, G-dur. (E. Pente) Violine und Piano. ₍Mainz, B. Schott's Söhne, °1920₎
        score (13 p.) and part. 31 cm.
(Edition Schott, 877)

Cover title; title page reads: Emilio Pente. Concertos classiques pour violon et

piano ou orchestre.
Edited by Emilio Pente.

1. Concertos (Violin)—Solo with piano.

NT   0044845   LU WaU

Tartini, Giuseppe, 1692–1770.
₍Concerto, viola da gamba, D major; arr.₎

Concerto, harmonisée ₍sic₎ pour violoncelle avec accompagnement de piano, par J. Salmon. Paris, Ricordi, °1921.

score (16 p.) and part. 36 cm.

Cover title.
Acc. originally for string orchestra and 2 horns.

1. Concertos (Violoncello), Arranged—Solo with piano.

M1017.T2 D maj.S3   M 54–1589

NT   0044846   DLC

Tartini, Giuseppe, 1692–1770.
₍Concerto, violin & string orchestra, Dounias 92, A major; arr.₎

Concerto in A major; violino e pianoforte. Wien, Universal-Edition ₍1935₎

score (24 p.) and part. 31 cm. (Universal-Edition, Nr. 10238)

At head of title: G. Tartini—Em. Ondříček.
Prefatory note in English and German.

1. Concertos (Violin with string orchestra)—To 1800—Solo with piano.   ɪ. Ondříček, Emanuel, 1882–   ed.

M1106.T22 D. 92 .O5   63–29841/M

NT   0044847   DLC MB NN

Tartini, Giuseppe, 1692–1770.
₍Concerto, violin & string orchestra, Dounias 115, A minor₎

Concerto in A minor. Concerto in F major. For solo violin and string orchestra. Edited and provided with cadenzas by Gilbert Ross. Northampton, Mass., Smith College ₍1947, i. e. 1948₎

score (38, 47 p.) facsims. (music) 29 cm. (Smith College music archives, no. 9)

"The basso continuo in both concertos has been realized for the keyboard by Ross Lee Finney."

1. Concertos (Violin with string orchestra)—To 1800—Scores.   ɪ. Tartini, Giuseppe, 1692–1770. Concerto, violin & string orchestra, Dounias 67, F major.   ɪɪ. Ross, Gilbert, 1903–   ed.   ɪɪɪ. Finney, Ross Lee, 1906–   (Series)

M2.S653   no. 9   A 48–7874 rev*/M
Newberry Library
for Library of Congress

MeLB OC1W MiU KMK OrP WU ViU
NT   0044848   ICN CaBVaU NSyU PU–FA OOxM MB MH DLC OU

787.35 **Tartini, Giuseppe,** 1692–1770.
T17c   ₍Concerto, viola da gamba, D major; arr.₎
           Concerto in D major for cello and piano (Grΰetzmacher). New York, International Music Co. ₍n. d.₎ Pl. no. 698.
           score (14 p.) and part.

           1. Concertos (Violoncello), Arranged — To 1800 - Solo with piano.

NT   0044849   KEmT

Tartini, Giuseppe, 1692–1770.
₍Concerto, viola da gamba, D major; arr.₎

Concerto in D major for cello and piano (Cruetzmacher ₍sic₎) New York, International Music Co. ₍1944₎

score (19 p.) and part. 31 cm.

Acc. originally for string orchestra and 2 horns.

1. Concertos (Violoncello), Arranged—Solo with piano.   ɪ. Grützmacher, Friedrich Wilhelm Ludwig, 1832–1903, arr.

M1017.T2.D maj.G7 1944   45–15439 rev*

NT   0044850   DLC CLSU NIC OCU OKentU

Tartini, Giuseppe, 1692–1770.
₍Concerto, violin & string orchestra, Dounias 31, D major; arr.₎

Concerto in D major, for violin and orchestra. Edited and provided with cadenzas by Gilbert Ross. Piano reduction by Ross Lee Finney. New York, G. Schirmer, °1953.

score (24 p.) and part. facsim. 30 cm. (Schirmer's library of musical classics, vol. 1765)

For violin and piano.

1. Concertos (Violin with string orchestra)—To 1800—Solo with piano.

M1106.T22 D.31.F5   M 54–2603

NT   0044851   DLC OrP OU CoU OCU NcU

Tartini, Giuseppe, 1692–1770.
₍Concerto, violin & string orchestra, Dounias 45, D minor; arr.₎

Concerto in D minor, for violin and piano. Concert version with original cadenzas by Joseph Szigeti. New York, C. Fischer ₍1943₎

score (13 p.) and part. 31 cm.

Cover title.

1. Concertos (Violin with string orchestra)—To 1800—Solo with piano.   ɪ. Szigeti, Joseph, 1892–   ed.

M1106.T22 D.45 S9   44–30747 rev*/M

NT   0044852   DLC PP MB OrU CLSU IEN

Tartini, Giuseppe, 1692–1770.
₍Concerto, violin and string orchestra, E major₎

Concerto in E-dur, für Violin und Streichorchester. Herausgegeben und bezeichnet von Hermann Scherchen. Leipzig, Gebrüder Hug ₍n.d.₎ Pl. no. G. H. 8883.
        score (12 p.) (Das Kammerorchester, 4)

Notes by Hans Zehntner on insert. (1 p.)
Front cover used as t.p.

NT   0044853   OU

M1105 **Tartini, Giuseppe,** 1692–1770.
T25   ₍Concerto, violin and string orchestra.
D.53   Dounias 53, E major₎
S3   Concerto in E-dur für Violine und Streichorchester. Herausgegeben und bezeichnet von Hermann Scherchen. Zürich, Hug ₍n.d.₎ Plate no. G.H. 8883.
          score (14 p.)   31cm.   (Das Kammerorchester, eine Sammlung unbekannter Meisterwerke aus de Vor- und Frühlassik, IV)
          Cover title.

          1. Concertos   (Violin with string orchestra) - To 1800   - Scores.   (Series)

NT   0044854   CoU NN

M1105 **Tartini, Giuseppe,** 1692–1770.
.T25   ₍Concerto, violin & string orchestra.
D.52   Dounias 52, E major₎
1930   Concerto in E-dur; für Violine und Streichorchester. Hrsg. und bezeichnet von Hermann Scherchen. Zürich, Hug ₍193–?₎; stamped: sole agents: C. F. Peters, New York₎
          score (14 p.) 31 cm. (Das Kammerorchestor; eine Sammlung unbekannter
No. 4   Meisterwerke aus der Vor-und Frühk-
in M   lassik; 4)
*M1001
.S24K3   ————₍Anot   her copy₎

          1. Concertos (Violin with string orchestra)—To 1800—Scores.

NT   0044856   MB

TARTINI, GIUSEPPE, 1692–1770.
[CONCERTO, VIOLIN, DOUNIAS 53]
Concerto in E-dur für Violine und Streichorchester. Hrsg. und bezeichnet von Hermann Scherchen. Leipzig, Hug [194–?] Pl. no. G.H. 8883. score (12 p.) 31cm. (Das Kammerorchester 4)

For violin and string orchestra.
Stamped on t.p.: Sole agents C.F. Peters corp., New York.

1. Concertos (Violin)——To 1800   2. Violin and orchestra—— To 1800. ɪ. Scherchen,   Hermann, 1891–   ed.

NT   0044857   NN

Tartini, Giuseppe, 1692–1770(2)

Concerto in E-dur für Violine und Streichorchester. Hrsg. und bezeichnet von H. Scherchen. Leipzig, Hug [195–?]

Score (12 p.)

NT   0044858   MH–Mu

qM785.6
T195cF
Tartini, Giuseppe, 1692-1770.
[Concerto, orchestra, F major; arr.]
Concerto in fa magg. N. 58 per
archi, 2 oboi e 2 corni. Libera
elaborazione di Ettore Bonelli.
Padova, G. Zanibon, 1948.
score (12 p.) 34 cm. (Musica da
camera, 3713)
Cover title.
No. 1 of "Due concerti con strumenti
di flato" in A. Capri's thematic
index, p. 530.
For 2 oboes, 2 horns with string
orchestra.
1. Concerti grossi—Scores.
I. Bonelli, Ettore, ed.

NT 0044859   ICarbS NN ICN

M
785.6
T179cv
D.86
Tartini, Giuseppe, 1692-1770.
[Concerto, violin & string orchestra,
Dounias 86, G minor; arr.]
Concerto in G minor, for violin and
strings with continuo. Edited by Max
Rostal. London, Novello [Pref. 1941] Pl.
no. 16938.
score (27 p.) and part. (Novello edition)

For violin and piano.
Duration: about 20 min.

NT 0044860   WaU

Tartini, Giuseppe, 1692-1770.
[Concerto, violin & string orchestra, Dounias 86, G minor]
Concerto in G minor, for violin and strings with continuo.
Edited by Max Rostal. Score. London, Novello [1952]
42 p. 28 cm.

Duration : about 20 min.
With realization of figured bass for organ or piano.

1. Concertos (Violin with string orchestra)—To 1800—Scores.

M1105.T25 D.86 R6   M 58–435

NT 0044861   DLC OrCS IaU

Tartini, Giuseppe, 1692-1770.
[Concertos. Violin.   A maj.]
Concerto in la maggiore per violino e orchestra d'archi, di
Giuseppe Tartini; liberamente armonizzato ed istrumentato da
Mario Corti . . .   Milano [etc.] G. Ricordi & c. [1926?]   Publ.
pl. no. 120066. 44 p.   20cm.

Miniature score (including realized basso continuo).
See: Dounias. Die Violinkonzerte Giuseppe Tartinis.   p. 282, no. 93.

1. Concertos—Violin—Full score   —To 1800. 2. Violin and orchestra—
To 1800. I. Corti, Mario, 1883–
N. Y. P. L.   December 21, 1937

NT 0044862   NN IaU ICN CLU PP

Tartini, Giuseppe, 1692-1770.
[Concerto, violin & string orchestra, Dounias 93, A major; arr.]
Concerto, in la maggiore, per violino e orchestra d'archi.
Liberamente armonizzato ed istrumentato da Mario Corti.
Riduzione per violino con accompagnamento di pianoforte.
Milano, New York, G. Ricordi [1926]
score (17 p.) and part. 32 cm.

1. Concertos (Violin with string orchestra)—To 1800—Solo with
piano.   I. Corti, Mario, 1882–1957. ed.

M1106.T22 D. 93 .C7   63–29840/M

NT 0044863   DLC

Tartini, Giuseppe, 1692-1770.
[Concerto, violin & string orchestra, Dounias 92, A major; arr.]
Concerto, in la maggiore, per violino, orchestra d'archi e
cembalo, rifatto e instrumentato sull'autografo per uso di
Mrs. E. S. Coolidge da Mario Corti (estate 1924) 1924.
score ([8] l.) 45 cm. MS.
Arranger's holograph, in ink.
On t. p.: Copiato nell'Archivio tartiniano della Veneranda Arca di
S. Antonio di Padova per gentile concessione della Presidenza.
For violino and piano.
Published Milano, G. Ricordi, °1926.
Gift of Elizabeth Sprague Coolidge, Nov. 20, 1924.
1. Concertos (Violin with string orchestra)—To 1800—Solo with
piano.   I. Corti, Mario,   1882–   arr. II. Corti, Mario, 1882–
MSS.
ML29c.C84   M 55–1665

NT 0044864   DLC

Tartini, Giuseppe, 1692-1770.
[Concerto, viola da gamba & string orchestra, A major; arr.]
Concerto, in La maggiore, per violoncello solo con orchestra
d'archi, ed organo ad lib. [Elaborazione di Oreste Ravanello; riduzione violoncellistica e cadenze di Luigi Silva]
Riduzione per violoncello solo e pianoforte. Padova, G.
Zanibon, 1938.
score (19 p.) and part. 35 cm. (Edizioni Zanibon, n. 3168)
No. 87 of the "Concerti" in A. Capri's thematic index.
1. Concertos (Violoncello with string orchestra)—To 1800—Solo
with piano.   I. Ravanello, Oreste, 1871–1938, arr. II. Silva, Luigi.

M1106.T22R3   M 55–350

CoU ICN
NT 0044865   DLC OrCS NcD CSt OU OkU MH MU ICarbS

M
1106
.T18
C7
C83
Tartini, Giuseppe, 1692-1770.
. . . Concerto in re maggiore per violino e
orchestra d'archi liberamente armonizzato ed
instrumentato da Mario Corti; riduzione per
violino con accompagnamento di pianoforte.
Milano [etc.] G. Ricordi e c. [19––]
1 p. l., 18 p. and part.   32 cm.
Publisher's plate no.; E.R. 622.
Score and part.
1. Concertos (Violin with string orchestra)--
To 1800--Solo with   piano. I. Corti, Mario,
1882-

NT 0044866   MiU

Tartini, Giuseppe, 1692-1770.
[Concertos. Violin. (Boivin lib. 1) no. 3]
Concerto in re maggiore per violino e orchestra d'archi, di
Giuseppe Tartini; liberamente armonizzato ed istrumentato da
Mario Corti . . .   Milano [etc.] G. Ricordi & c. [1926?] Publ.
pl. no. 120068.   41 p.   20cm.

Miniature score (including realized basso continuo).
See: Dounias. Die Violinkonzerte Giuseppe Tartinis. p. 258, no. 29.
The second movement is the Adagio from another concerto.

1. Concertos—Violin—Full score   —To 1800. 2. Violin and orchestra
—To 1800. I. Corti, Mario, 1883–
N. Y. P. L.   December 14, 1937

NT 0044867   NN ICN

M787
T17c45
Tartini, Giuseppe, 1692-1770.
[Concerto, violin & string orchestra, no.
45, D minor]
Concerto in re minore. [Edited by] E.
Pente. Hamburg, H. Thiemer, 1898.
parts. 28cm.

Caption title.

1. Concertos (Violin with string orchestra)
—To 1800—Parts.

NT 0044868   IU

Tartini, Giuseppe, 1692-1770.
[Sonata, violin & continuo, G major; arr.]
Concerto in sol, per orchestra d'archi, organo ad lib., da
una sonata. Trascrizione di G. Francesco Malipiero. Parti-
tura. Milano, New York, G. Ricordi, 1939.
score (20 p.) 32 cm. (Edizione Ricordi, 2018)
No. 12 of "60 sonate" in A. Capri's thematic index.
For string orchestra, with organ ad lib.

1. String-orchestra music, Arranged—Scores.

M1160.T2M3   M 53–1128

NT 0044869   DLC

Tartini, Giuseppe, 1692-1770.
[Concerto, violin, Dounias 28, D major; arr.]
Concerto n. 57 per violino principale, archi, 2 trombe, 2
corni e timpani. Elaborazione e cadenze di Ettore Bonelli.
Padova, G. Zanibon, °1953.
score (24 p.) 35 cm.
Rearr. for violin and orchestra.
Duration : 20 min.

1. Concertos (Violin), Arranged—Scores.   I. Bonelli, Ettore, ed.

M1012.T22 D. 28 .B7   63–28743/M

NT 0044870   DLC NIC CoU IaU MH NN OU NNU ICU NSyU

TARTINI, GIUSEPPE, 1692-1770.
[CONCERTO, VIOLA DA GAMBA. D MAJ.]
Concerto per viola da gamba.   score ([33] l.).   22cm.

Photostatic reproduction of ms.

1. Concertos (Violoncello)--To 1800. 2. Violoncello and orchestra--To
1800. 3. Viola da gamba and   orchestra

NT 0044871   NN

Tartini, Giuseppe, 1692-1770.
[Concerto, violin & string orchestra, Dounias 45, D minor; arr.]
Concerto, ré mineur, cadence de César Thomson. Violin
et piano, révision, Marcel Lejeune. Bruxelles, Schott
Frères [1947]
score (12 p.) and part. 31 cm.

1. Concertos (Violin with string orchestra)—To 1800—Solo with
piano.

M1106.T22 D.45 L4   48–21156 rev*/M

NT 0044872   DLC

M 1013
.T195
D.81
Tartini, Giuseppe, 1692-1770.
[Concerto, violin & string orchestra, Dounias
81, G major; arr.]
Concerto, sol majeur (G dur) Mainz, B.
Schott's Söhne [c1920] Pl. no. 30132.
score (13 p.) and part. 31 cm. (Edition
Schott No. 877)
At head of title: Emilio Pente; Concertos
classique pour violon et piano ou orchestre à
cordes d'après la basse chifrée.

NT 0044873   MdBP NcU NN

M1040
.S5
case
Tartini, Giuseppe, 1692-1770.
Select harmony. Fourth collection. Six concertos in seven
parts for two violins and other instruments, compos'd by
Mr Handel, Tartini, and Veracini. London, I. Walsh [1741]
Pub. no. 682.

M
1113
T195 +
D.45
P4
Tartini, Giuseppe, 1692-1770.
[Concerto, violin & string orchestra,
Dounias 45, D minor; arr.]
D-moll Concert für Violine, mit Beglei-
tung des Streichorchesters, bearb. mit
eignen Cadenzen, hrsg. und Joseph Joachim
gewidmet von Emilio Pente. Neue Ausgabe.
Klavierauszug mit Solostimme. Hamburg,
A. J. Benjamin [c1898]
score (14 p.) and part. 35 cm.
Cover title.
1. Concertos   (Violin with string
orchestra)--To   1800--Solo with piano.

NT 0044875   CtY-Mus NBuG

Tartini, Giuseppe, 1692-1770.
De' principj dell'armonia musicale contenuta nel diatonico
genere, dissertazione di Giuseppe Tartini. Padova, Stamperia
del Seminario, 1767.
6 p. l., 120 p. 24½cm.
Title vignette; initials; head-piece.

1. Harmony. 2. Music—Acoustics and physics.

7—13081
Library of Congress   ML3815.A2T19

ICU ICN OrU
NT 0044876   DLC MiU WaU OU IaU CSt TxDN PPiD CtY NPV

Tartini, Giuseppe, 1692–1770.

De' principj dell' armonia musicale contenuta nel diatonico genere, dissertazione. Padova, Nella stamperia del Seminario, 1767. Microcard edition (4 cards)

. 1. Harmony. 2. Music—Acoustics and physics. I. Title.

NT 0044877   ViU OO OrU OU NNC ICRL

___

MFL. 8230   Tartini, Giuseppe, 1692–1770.
De' principj dell'armonia musicale ... Padova, Nella stamp. del Seminario, 1767. Microfilm copy, made in 1968, of the original in the Biblioteca Vaticana. Positive. ₍Manuscripta, microfilms of rare and out-of-print books. List 77, no.25₎

NT 0044878   WMM NSyU OU

___

787.142M
T 179 S   Tartini, Giuseppe, 1692–1770.
G min.   ₍Sonata, violin & continuo, G minor ("Il
TK   trillo del diavolo")₎

The devil's trill (Le trille du diable) for violin and piano. ₍Newly transcribed by Fritz Kreisler₎ New York, Charles Foley ₍ᶜ1932₎
score (15 p.) and part.   30ᵐ.

At head of title: Fritz Kreisler.

NT 0044879   OO

___

Tartini, Giuseppe, 1692–1770.
₍Sonatas, violin & continuo. Selections₎

XII ₍i. e. Dodici₎ solos for a violin with a thorough bass for the harpsicord or violoncello. London, I. Walsh ₍1746₎
score (57 p.) 32 cm.

₍Op. 1₎ in A. Bachmann's thematic index (Les grands violinistes du passé, p. 320–330).
Includes the composer's Pastorale in A major for violin and continuo.

1. Sonatas (Violin and harpsichord)—To 1800. I. Tartini, Giuseppe, 1692–1770. Pastorale, violin & continuo, A major. 1746.
M219.T2W3   46-31603

NT 0044880   DLC ViU

___

Tartini, Giuseppe, 1692–1770.
₍Sonatas, violin & continuo. Selections₎

XII ₍i. e. Dodici₎ sonate a violino e basso. Opera terza. Paris, Le Clerc ₍1747₎
score (55 p.) 35 cm.

Op. 2 in A. Bachmann's thematic index (Les grands violinistes du passé, p. 331–339).

1. Sonatas (Violin and harpsichord)—To 1800.
M219.T2I43   62-43804

NT 0044881   DLC

___

Tartini, Giuseppe, 1692–1770.
₍Sonatas, violin & continuo. Selections₎

XII ₍i. e. Dodici₎ sonate et una pastorale, a violino, e violoncello, o cembalo. Opera prima. Amsterdam, J. J. Hummel ₍ca. 1760₎ Pl. no. 576.
score (57 p.) 34 cm.

In A. Bachmann's thematic index (Les grands violinistes du passé, p. 320–330).
Reprinted from the plates of the 1st ed., published by G. F. Witvogel in Amsterdam, 1732.
1. Sonatas (Violin and harpsichord)—To 1800.   I. Tartini, Giuseppe, 1692–1770. Pastorale, violin & continuo, A major. 1760.
M219.T2H8   46-30319

NT 0044882   DLC

___

Tartini, Giuseppe, 1692–1770.
₍Sonatas, violin & continuo. Selections₎

. Douze sonates pour le violon. Œuvre 1. Nouv. éd. Paris, Imprimerie du Conservatoire de musique ₍ca. 1797₎ Pl. no. 137.
score (2 v. in 1 (52+ p.)) 32 cm.
L. C. copy incomplete; all after p. 52 wanting.
₍Op. 1₎ in A. Bachmann's thematic index (Les grands violinistes du passé, p. 320–330).

1. Sonatas (Violin and harpsichord)—To 1800.
M219.T2 I 5   M 57-2276

NT 0044883   DLC

___

Tartini, Giuseppe, 1692–1770.
₍Sonatas. Violin & piano. Op. 1, no. 2, 4–5₎
…3 Sonaten: F dur, G dur ₍und₎ E moll… (Holmes.) ₍Leipzig: C. F. Peters, ca. 1889₎ Publ. pl. no. 7597. 1 v. 31cm. (Édition Peters. No. 1099a.)
Score (31 p.) including realized basso continuo. Violin part.
From his: Sonate a violino e violoncello o cimbalo. Opera prima. Amsterdam: M. C. le Cene ₍1734₎
Cover-title; t.-p. reads: Célèbres sonates pour violon par J. Tartini. Cah. 1, Opus 1, no. 2, 4, 5, accompagnés d'une partie de piano par Henry Holmes…

1. Violin and piano—To 1880.   2. Sonatas—Violin and piano—To
1800. I. Holmes, Henry, 1839–1905.
N. Y. P. L.   January 27, 1941

NT 0044884   NN NIC

___

fM152
T23S6   Tartini, Giuseppe, 1692–1770.
₍Sonate a quattro. Selections₎
Due sonate a quattro per due violini, viola e violoncello. Rev. di Michelangelo Abbado.   Milano, S.Zerboni ₍1942₎
score (21p.) and 4 pts.in 1v. 31cm.

Contents.- G major.- D major.

1. String quartets - To 1800 - Scores and parts.

NT 0044885   IaU OrU IU CLSU

___

Tartini, Giuseppe, 1692–1770.
[Fugue, violin & piano, arr.]
Fuge. Arr. by Fritz Kreisler.   New York, C. Fischer, c1913.
score (7 p.) and 1 part.   (Classical Masterpieces, 4)
Pl. no. 4.
1. Violin and piano music, Arranged.
I. Kreisler, Fritz, 1875–1962, arr.

NT 0044886   FTaSU

___

Mus ·
M
269
T37   Tartini, Giuseppi, 1692–1770.
G73   Grave. ₍Transcribed by₎ M. Mule. Paris, A. Leduc, ₍1937. Pl. no. A.L. 19,542.
score (3p.) and part. (Les classiques du saxophone ₍par₎ Marcel Mule, no. 17)
Caption title.

1. Saxophone and piano music, Arranged - Scores and parts. I. Mule, Marcel, arr. II. Series: Mule, Marcel. Les classiques du saxophone, no. 17.

NT 0044887   FTaSU

___

Tartini, Giuseppe, 1692–1770.
…Konzert A dur. Nach dem im Besitze der fürstlichen Musikaliensammlung zu Schwerin befindlichen Manuskript… Leipzig: E. Eulenburg ₍cop. 1916₎. Publ. pl. no. E. E. 4154. 2 parts. f°.

Violin and piano in score and violin part.
At head of title: Konzerte aus alter Zeit für Violine mit Orchester, zum ersten Male hrsg. und nach den Manuskripten für Violine und Klavier bearbeitet…von Robert Reitz… no. 2.

1. Concertos.—Violin and piano.   2. Reitz, Robert, editor.
N. Y. P. L.   April 16, 1924.

NT 0044888   NN

___

785.673.GM
T 179   Tartini, Giuseppe, 1692–1770.
₍Concerto, viola da gamba, string quartet & 2 horns; arr.₎

Konzert, D dur, für Violoncell und Pianoforte. Eingerichtet und hrsg. von Friedrich Grutzmacher. Leipzig, Breitkopf & Härtel ₍n.d.₎ Pl. no. V.A.3096.
score (19 p.) and part.   33ᵐ.

Originally for viola da gamba with accompaniment of quartet and 2 horns.

NT 0044889   OO PP

___

Tartini, Giuseppe, 1692–1770.
₍Concerto, violin & string orchestra, Dounias 52, E major; arr.₎

Konzert, E dur, für Violine und Pianoforte, oder Streichorchester. Hrsg. und mit Schlusskadenz versehen von Clemens Meyer. Leipzig, F. E. C. Leuckart ₍1922₎
score (15 p.) and part. 35 cm.

1. Concertos (Violin with string orchestra)—To 1800—Solo with piano.
M1013.T19 D.52.M.   52-59050 rev

NT 0044890   DLC

___

Tartini, Giuseppe, 1692–1770.
₍Concerto, viola da gamba & string orchestra, A major₎

Konzert in A-dur für Violoncello und Streichorchester. Hrsg. und bearb. von Rolf van Leyden; Kadenzen von Richard Krotschak. Partitur und Klavierauszug. Leipzig, Musikwissenschaftlicher Verlag ₍1937₎
score (29 p.) 31 cm.
No. 87 of the "Concerti" in A. Capri's thematic index.
The unfigured bass is realized for harpsichord.
"Kadenz-Vorschläge von Richard Krotschak": leaf inserted.
Includes piano reduction.

Duration: about 15 min.
"Die handschriftliche Partitur … befindet sich im 'Archivio Musicale della Cappella Antoniana' in Padua. (Bibl. Ant. Autogr. Nr. 87)"

1. Concertos (Viola da gamba with string orchestra)—To 1800—Scores. I. Leyden, Rolf van, ed. II. Krotschak, Richard.
M1105.T25L3   M 55-362

NT 0044892   DLC NN

___

Tartini, Giuseppe, 1692–1770.
…Larghetto. (G moll.) (Tartini.) ₍Arranged by₎ Franz Ries. ₍Boston;₎ O. Ditson & Co.₍, 1882?₎ Publ. pl. no. 49116. 2 parts. f°.

At head of title: Chef d'œuvres pour le violon avec l'accompaniment ₍sic₎ de piano…

1. Violin and piano. 2. Ries, Franz.   1846-
N. Y. P. L.   February 6, 1928

NT 0044893   NN

___

Tartini, Giuseppe, 1692–1770.
₍Sonatas. Violin & piano. (Devil's trill) Larghetto₎
…Larghetto, tiré d'une sonate pour violon…   Moscou: P. Jurgenson ₍etc., etc., 1910₎   Publ. pl. no. 33581. 1 v. 34½cm.

Score (5 p.) and viola part.
At head of title: Répertoire de morceaux de concert transcrits pour alto (viola) avec piano par Jules Conus…no. 6.

1. Viola and piano—To 1800.   I. Konyus, Yulii Eduardovich,
1869-   , arr.

NT 0044894   NN PPCI

785.75 Tartini, Giuseppe, 1692-1770.
T17slvL 〔Sonata, violin & continuo, G minor. Largo;
      arr.〕
      Largo from Violin sonata in G minor 〔by〕 G.
Tartini. Transcribed for woodwind by George J.
Trinkaus.   New York, M. Witmark & Sons, c1933
    score (7 p.) (The Witmark instrumental li-
brary)

    For flute, oboe, clarinet, horn, and bassoon.
    1. Wind quintets (Bassoon, clarinet, flute,
horn, oboe), Arranged.

    1. Wind quintets (Bassoon, clarinet, flute,
horn, oboe) Arranged. I. Tartini, Giuseppe,
1692-1770, Evening song. II. Title.

NT 0044896   KEmT OrP

Tartini, Giuseppe, 1692-1770.
    A letter from the late Signor Tartini to Signora Maddalena
Lombardini, (now Signora Sirmen.) Published as an im-
portant lesson to performers on the violin. Translated by Dr.
Burney. London, Printed for R. Bremner by G. Bigg, 1779.

    2 p. l., 7 〔i. e. 11〕 p. illus. (music) 26ᶜᵐ.
    Added t.-p.: Lettera del defonto Signor Giuseppe Tartini ...
    Italian and English on opposite pages.

    1. Violin—Instruction and study.   I. Burney, Charles, 1726-1814, tr.
                                            18-17819
    Library of Congress   ML410.T18A42 1779
                                  〔a45b1〕

NT 0044897   DLC OOxM ScU NcGU NBC PP

Tartini, Giuseppe, 1692-1770.
    A letter from the late Signor Tartini to Signora **Maddalena**
Lombardini (now Signora Sirmen) Published as an impor-
tant lesson to performers on the violin. Translated by Dr.
Burney ... London, W. Reeves, 1913.

    25 p. front. (port.) illus. (music) 21 x 16¼ᶜᵐ.
    Added t.-p.: Lettera del defonto Signor Giuseppe Tartini ...
    Italian and English on opposite pages.

    1. Violin—Instruction and study.   I. Sirmen, Maddalena Laura
(Lombardini) b. 1735. II. Burney, Charles, 1726-1814, tr.
                                         44-48001
    Library of Congress   ML410.T18A42 1913

NT 0044898   DLC NcD KMK AAP NcU CU ViU IaU CtY

Tartini, Giuseppe, 1692-1770.   (3)
    Letters
    Lettere, trascritte dalle autografe dell'Archivio di
Pirano. Con pref. di A.Hortis. np 〔1884?〕

    p.〔209〕-229
    Reprinted from Archeografo triestino, nuova ser., vol.X

NT 0044899   MH-Mu

MT80 Tartini, Giuseppe, 1692-1770.
T29   〔Traité des agrémens de la musique〕
MUSIC Libro de regole, ed esempi necessari per ben
suonare
    〔24〕 ℓ.

    Manuscript copy, probably dating from the 2d
half of the 18th century, of Tartini's treatise.
Cf. D.D. Boyden, The missing Italian manuscript
of Tartini's Traité des agrémens, Music quarterly, v.46 (1960) p.315-328.
    Photocopy (positive) of the MS. in the Music
Library, University of California, Berkeley.
    〔24〕 ℓ.on 〔48〕 p.

    1. Embellishment (Music) 2. Violin - Instruc-
tion and study - To 1800
    x Entry. Libro de regole, ed esempi necessari
per ben suonare 〔to Entry. Uniform title〕

NT 0044901   CU

Tartini, Giuseppe, 1692-1770.
    Nel giorno della inaugurazione del monumento a
Giuseppe Tartini in Pirano
    see under   Comitato provinciale pel
centenario Tartini.

Tartini, Giuseppe, 1692-1770.   (2)
    Sonatas, violin & continuo. Selections
    Nuova raccolta di 11 sonate o un minuetto variato, per
violino con acc. di pianoforto. Interpretazione o revisione tecnica di Emilio Pente. Parte di pianoforte secondo il
basso originale di Maffeo Zanon. Leipzig, Schmidl, c1911

    Score (11 v.in 3) & 1 pt. (Edition Schmidl, 4312-4822)
    Vol.12, Minuetto variato, lacking
    Contents: - 1. A min. (C.〔II〕 56). - 2. G maj.). - 3. G
maj. (Op.6/6). - 4. E min. (C.〔II〕 57). - 5. G maj. (Op.6/
1). - 6. D maj. (Op.7/1). - 7. A maj. (C.〔II〕 21). - 8.
A maj. (Op.6/4). - 9. ⌢ maj. (Op.7/4). - 10. F maj.
- 11. G min. (C.〔II〕 33).

NT 0044903   MH-Mu

Film TARTINI, GIUSEPPE ,1692-1770
ML   Oservazioni d'oppossizione uno e due del
98 circolo come imagine esemplare delle frazione
manoscritto donato da' Sig. Fratelli Vata nel,
1881. 〔Pirano, Yugoslavia,n.d.〕

    Negative film reproduction.
    Original in City Archives,Pirano,Yugo-
slavia.
    Collation of original as determined from
film: unpaged manuscript. music.

NT 0044904   InU

Tartini, Giuseppe, 1692-1770.
    ...Pastorale per violino e basso. Realizzazione per violino e
pianoforte di Ottorino Respighi.   Milano 〔etc.〕 G. Ricordi e
c., c1921. Publ. pl. no. E.R. 267. 1 v. 32ᶜᵐ. (Edizione
Ricordi.)

    Score (11 p.) including realized basso continuo. Violin part.
    From his: XII sonate e 1 pastorale a v. e vcl. o cemb. Op. 1. Amst.: Hummel
〔176-?〕-- cf. Eitner. Quellen-Lexikon; Bachmann. Les grands violinistes du passé.
p. 329.

    1. Violin and piano—To 1800.   I. Respighi, Ottorino, 1879-1936, arr.
N. Y. P. L.   January 29, 1941

NT 0044905   NN IaU MiU

Tartini, Giuseppe, 1692-1770.
    〔Sonata a quattro, string quartet, D major〕

    Quartet no. 1 in D major for two violins, viola, and cello.
(Pente) New York, International Music Co. 〔1947〕
    score (4 p.) and   parts. 31 cm.
    No. 〔8〕 of the "Opere varie" in A. Capri's thematic index.

    1. String quartets—To 1800—Scores and parts.
    M452.T215 D maj. 1947   50-36248 rev

NT 0044906   DLC CaBVa MH OKentU NIC

Tartini, Giuseppe, 1692-1770.
    Quartet no. 1. (Sonata) D major. Leipzig,
n.d.
    Leuckart edition.

NT 0044907   PPCI

Tartini, Giuseppe, 1692-1770.
    Quartet no. 2. (Symphonia) A major.
Leipzig, n.d.
    Leuckart.

NT 0044908   PPCI

M 52
.T215S6 Tartini, Giuseppe, 1692-1770.
    〔Sonata a quattro, string quartet, D major〕
    Quartett, D-Dur (sonata a quattro) für zwei
Violinen, Viola und Violoncello, hrsg. von
Emilio Pente. München, Leuckart 〔n.d.〕 Pl.
no. F.E.C.L. 5113.
    score(5 p.) and 4 parts. 31cm. (Alte
Musik für verschiedene Instrumente, Nr.33)
    Cover title.
    1. String quartets - To 1800 - Scores and
parts. I. Ser. X: His Quartett, D-Dur.

NT 0044909   MiDW

M   TARTINI, GIUSEPPE, 1692-1770.
452   〔Sonata a quattro, string quartet, D major〕
.T215 Quartett I, sonata a quattro in D dur. 〔Hrsg.
D maj. von Emilio Pente. München, F.E.C. Leuckart,
n.d.〕 Pl. no. F.E.C.L. 5113.
    score (3-5 p.) and 4 parts. 31cm.
(Leuckartiana; alte Musik für verschiedene
Instrumente, Nr. 33)

    1. String quartets--To 1800--Scores and parts.

NT 0044910   NhD

Tartini, Giuseppe, 1672-1770.
    Quatre pieces de concert pour piano d'apres
Tartini et Veracini
    see under   Philipp, Isidore Edmond, 1863-
1958.

M351
.T2P2 Tartini, Giuseppe, 1692-1770.
no.1-2 〔Sonatas,nos. 1, 2, G major〕
n.d.
    4 〔i. e. quattro〕 sonate a tre per 2
violini e violoncello 〔ed. par〕 Emilio
Pente. Torino, M. Capra 〔n. d.〕 Pl. no.
M. 65 C.
    score (5 p.) and 3 parts. 30cm.
    Score and parts: vl. I, vl. II, cello.

    1. Trio-sonatas. 2. String trios (2 violins,
violoncello)—To   1800—Scores and parts.

NT 0044912   ViU

M351
.T2P2 Tartini, Giuseppe, 1692-1770.
no.3-4 〔Sonatas,nos. 3, 4, D major〕
n.d.
    4 〔i. e. quattro〕 sonate a tre per 2
violini e violoncello 〔ed. par〕 Emilio
Pente. Torino, M. Capra 〔n. d.〕 Pl. no.
M.66 C.
    score (5 p.) and 3 parts. 30cm.
    Score and parts: vl. I, vl. II, cello.

    1. Trio-sonatas. 2. String trios (2 violins,
violoncello)—To   1800—Scores and parts.

NT 0044913   ViU

Tartini, Giuseppe, 1692-1770.
    ...Quattro sonate a tre per due violini e violoncello, raccolte
ed accuramente rivedute e diteggiate da Emilio Pente. fasc. 1-
    〔Torino:〕 Marcello Capra 〔, ca. 1900〕. Publ. pl.
no. M. 65   C.   parts.   f°.

    Score and 3 parts.
    At head of title: Edizione Marcello Capra, N. 65...

    1. Trios—Two violins and violoncello.   2. Pente, Emilio, 1800- ,
editor.
N. Y. P. L.   July 1, 1927

NT 0044914   NN

M
2 9 Tartini,Giuseppe,1692-1770.
.T18
T13   ... Quattro sonate per violino e violoncello
o cembalo dalle dodici edite nel 1735,rivedute
da Riccardo Tagliacozzo con accompagnamento di
pianoforte,dal basso numerato di Felice Boghen
... Milano 〔etc.〕, G.Ricordi, ᶜ1921.
    1 p.l.,36 p.and part. 32 cm.
    Publisher's plate no.: E.R.127.
    Score (piano and violin) and part.
    1.Sonatas(Violin   and harpsichord)--To
1800. I.Tagliacozzo   Riccardo,1878- II.
Boghen,Felice,1875-

NT 0044915   MiU

m781.3   Tartini, Giuseppe, 1692-1770.
T195s0-1   [Sonatas, violin & continuo. Selections]
15 [i.e. Quindici] sonate per violino e
pianoforte. Interpretazione e revisione
tecnica di Emilio Pente. Parte di pianoforte (secondo il basso orginale (vol.I e
II) di Maffeo Zanon; (vol.III) di Carlo
Angelelli). Leipzig, C.Schmidl, c1911.
   score (3v.) and part (3v. bound with score) 31cm.
(Universal-edition, nr.4994)

    At head of title: Sonate per violino dei grandi maestri
italiani antichi.
On cover: Altitalienische Meister. Old Italian masters.

    1.Sonatas (Violin and piano) - To 1800.

NT   0044917   CLSU CtY

V   TARTINI, GIUSEPPE, 1692-1770.
22   Risposta di Giuseppe Tartini alla critica
.86351   del di lui Trattato di musica di Mons. Le
Serre di Ginevra. In Venezia, Appresso A.
Decastro, 1767.
74,[1]p. illus. 20cm.

    A reply to passages in Jean Adam Serre's
Observations sur les principes de l'harmonie.

NT   0044918   ICN MiU NRU-Mus

Tartini, Giuseppe, 1692-1770.
   Scienza universale delle ragioni e filio
poesioni, espressa ed esignata col numera,
contenuta e dimostrata nel ceechio. [Trieste,
n.p.]
   Negative film reproduction.
   Original in Biblioteca Civica di Trieste.
   Collation of original as determined from film:
[269 p.] illus.
   1. Music - Acoustics and physics.

NT   0044919   InU

Tartini, Giuseppe, 1692-1770.
   ⌈Concertos, violin & string orchestra. Selections⌉
   Sei concerti, a cinque é sei stromenti, a violino principale,
violino primo di ripieno, violino secondo, alto viola, organo e
violoncello. Opera prima, libro primo. Amsterdam, M. C.
le Cene ⌈1728⌉ Pl. no. 536.
    parts. 26 x 32 cm.
    Photocopy (positive)
    Dounias 85, 55, 60, 15, 58, and 80, respectively.
    CONTENTS.—G minor.—E minor.—F major.—D major.—F ma-
jor.—A major.
    1. Concertos (Violin with string orchestra)—To 1800—Parts.

M1105.T25 D.85   1728a   M 53-1054

NT   0044920   DLC CU

Tartini, Giuseppe, 1692-1770.
   ⌈Concerti grossi, op. 1⌉
   Sei concerti a cinque é sei stromenti; a
violino principale, violino primo di ripieno,
violino secondo, alto viola, organo e violoncello. Op. 1. Amsterdam, M. C. Le Cene
⌈1730⌉ Pub. no. 536.
   6 pts. 31cm.
    Parts: vl. principiae; vl. 1st, 2nd repieno;
viola; figured bass for violoncello and for organ.
    1. Concerti gros — si-To 1800.

NT   0044921   ViU MNF

Tartini, Giuseppe, 1692-1770.
   ⌈Concerto, violin & string orchestra, Dounias 111, A minor⌉
   Sei concerti a cinque stromenti, a violino principale, vio-
lino primo e secondo, alto viola, organo e violoncello, delli
signori Giuseppe Tartini e Gasparo Visconti. Opera prima,
libro terzo. Amsterdam, M. C. Le Cene ⌈1728⌉ Pl. no. 537.
    parts. 28 x 33 cm.
    Photocopy (positive)
    The figured bass is unrealized.
    The 1st concerto is by Tartini; the 2d to 6th, by Visconti. Cf.
Dounias. Die Violinkonzerte Tartinis, p. 56-58.
    1. Concertos (Violin with string orchestra)—To 1800—Parts.   I.
Visconti, Gasparo, fl.   1703. Concertos, violin & string orchestra. Selections.

    M1105.T25 D.111   1728a p   M 53-1055

NT   0044922   DLC

Tartini, Giuseppe, 1692-1770.
   ⌈Concertos, violin & string orchestra. Selections⌉
   Sei concerti a cinque stromenti, a violino principale, vio-
lino primo e secondo, alto viola, organo e violoncello, opera
1, libra 2. Amsterdam, M. C. Le Cène ⌈ca. 1730⌉ Pl. no.
548.
    parts. 30 cm.
    CONTENTS.—Dounias 111, A minor.—Dounias 91, A major.—
Dounias 59, F major.—Dounias 71, G major.—Dounias 88, A major.—
Dounias 18, D major.
    1. Concertos (Violin with string orchestra)—To 1800—Parts.

M1105.T25V554   66-50001/M

NT   0044923   DLC

Tartini, Giuseppe, 1692-1770.
   ⌈Concertos, violin & string orchestra. Selections⌉
   VI ⌈i. e. Sei⌉ concerti a otto stromenti, a violino principale,
violino primo, violino secondo, violino primo di repieno, violino secondo de repieno, alto viola, organo, e violoncello
obligato, opera 2. Amsterdam, G. F. Witvogel ⌈ca. 1745⌉
Pub. no. 26.
    parts. 33 cm.
    CONTENTS.—Dounias 73, G major.—Dounias 2, C major.—Dounias
124, B minor.—Dounias 62, F major.—Dounias 3, C major.—Dounias
46, E major.
    1. Concertos (Violin with string orchestra)—To 1800—Parts.

M1105.T25V559   66-50000/M

NT   0044924   DLC

Tartini, Giuseppe, 1692-1770.
   ⌈Sonatas, violin & continuo. Selections⌉
   Sei sonate a violino e violoncello o cimbalo.   **Opera**
seconda. Paris, Le Clerc ⌈1746⌉
    score (55 p.) 35 cm.
    Includes no. 33, 21, 22, 57, and 13 of "60 sonate" in A. Capri's
thematic index.

    1. Sonatas (Violin and harpsichord)—To 1800.

M219.T2L42   62-43805

NT   0044925   DLC

Tartini, Giuseppe, 1692-1770.
   ⌈Sonatas. Violin & piano. Op. 2⌉
   Sei sonate a violino e violoncello o cimbalo. Opera seconda di
Giuseppe Tartini... A Paris, Chez Mr. Le Clerc ⌈1762?⌉ 25 p.
34cm.

    Score: violin and figured bass.
    With autograph of Alfred Moffat, and notes in his hand, including the themes of
opus 2 to show comparative order of the Le Clerc and Walsh editions, and also the
themes of opus 3 (published at Rome 1745? as opus 2).

312184B.   1. Violin and violoncello—   To 1800.   2. Violin and piano—1o
1800.
N. Y. P. L.   October 17, 1945

NT   0044926   NN

Tartini, Giuseppe, 1692-1770.
   ⌈Sonatas, violin & continuo. Selections⌉
   Sei sonate a violino e violoncello o cimbalo.   **Opera 6.**
Paris, Le Clerc ⌈1748?⌉
    score (27 p.) 35 cm.
    First ed.
    Op. 6 in A. Bachmann's thematic index (Les grands violinistes
du passé, p. 344-349;) includes no. 12, 34, 26, 27, and 41 of "60
sonate", in A. Capri's thematic index.

    1. Sonatas (Violin and harpsichord)—To 1800.

M219.T2L46   62-43801

NT   0044927   DLC NN

787.1   Tartini, Giuseppe, 1692-1770.
T17s05
    Sei sonate (op. 5) per violino e
pianoforte. Elaborazione dal basso
centinuo di Ettore Bonelli. Padova,
G. Zanibon, 1951.
    score (71 p.) and part. 34 cm.

    1. Sonatas (Violin and piano)--To 1800.
I. Bonelli, Ettore.

NT   0044928   LU NIC MH

M   Tartini, Giuseppe, 1692-1770.
219   ... Sei sonate per violino con accompagna-
.T18   mento di pianoforte, revisione e realizzazione
P78   dell'accompagnamento di pianoforte a cura di
Enrico Polo ... Milano ⌈etc.⌉ G.Ricordi &
c. 1942.
    1 p.ℓ.,59 p.and part.   32cm.
    Publisher's plate no.: E.R.177.
    Score and part.
    1.Sonatas (Violin and harpsichord)--To 1800.
    I.Polo,Enrico,1868-

NT   0044929   MiU

M219   Tartini, Giuseppe, 1692-1770.
.T19S4   ⌈Sonatas, violin & continuo. Selections⌉
6 ⌈i. e. Sei⌉ sonate per violino e pianoforte.
6 sonatas for violin and piano. Enrico Polo
⌈elaboratore⌉ Milano, New York, G. Ricordi,
1953 ⌈c1921.
    score (59 p.) and part.
    Includes op.1, no.1, 3-5, and 10; and op.2,
no.12.
    1. Sonatas (Violin and piano)   2. Sonatas
(Violin and harpsichord)

NT   0044930   ICU MH

Tartini, Giuseppe, 1692-1770.
   Sinfonia pastorale; für 2 Violinen (Solo und Tutti),
Viola, Violoncello (Kontrabass) und Klavier. ⌈Für den
praktischen Gebrauch bearb. von A. Schering⌉ Leipzig,
C. F. Kahnt ⌈1926⌉
    score (19 p.) and   parts. 30 cm.   (Perlen alter Kammer-
musik ...)
    Concerto grosso.
    Edited from an 18th century ms. score in the possession of the editor.
    The bass is realized for piano.
   ———— Another issue.
    score (19 p.)   34 cm.   (Perlen alter Kammermusik)
                                  M1040.T2S582
    1. Concerti grossi—To   1800—Scores and parts.   I. Sche-
ring, Arnold, 1877-1941.   ed. II. Title.   (Series)
M1040.T2S58   51-45024 rev

NT   0044931   DLC NIC ICarbS NN ViU

M785.74   Tartini, Guiseppe, 1692-1770.
T195a
    Sinfonie, oder; Streichquartett in A.
Hrsg. von Hans Erdmann. Kassel, Bärenreiter
[1950] Pl.no. Bärenreiter-Ausg. 311.
score(9p.)and 4 parts. 29cm. (Hortus
musicus, 53)

NT   0044932   IEN CLSU IU LU MH ICN CSt NcU NcD ICU

M   Tartini, Giuseppe, 1692-1770.
219   ⌈Sonatas, violin & continuo. Selections⌉
T19   Six solos for a violin, with a thorough
W4++   bass for the harpsichord. London, P.
Welcker ⌈174-?⌉
33 p.   22cm.

    The bass is figured.

    1. Sonatas   (Violin and harpsi-
chord)--To   1800.

NT   0044933   NIC ViWC

Tartini, Giuseppe, 1692-1770.
   ⌈Sonatas, violin & continuo. Selections⌉
   Six solos for a violin with a thorough bass for the harpsichord or violoncello, opera seconda. London, I. Walsh
⌈1746⌉
    score (35 p.) 33 cm.
    Includes no. 33, 57, and 22 of "60 sonate" in A. Capri's thematic
index.

    1. Sonatas (Violin and harpsichord)—To 1800.

M219.T2W32   76-209157

NT   0044934   DLC

Tartini, Giuseppe, 1692-1770.
[Sonatas, violin, op.2]
Six solos for a violin with a thorough bass
for the harpsichord or violoncello, compos'd
by Giuseppe Tartini. Opera seconda. London,
Printed for I.Walsh[ca.1755]
35p. 32cm.
With figured bass.
Engraved throughout.

NT 0044935   CtY-Mus

Tartini, Giuseppe, 1692-1770.
Six solos for a violin with a thorough bass for
the harpsichord. Compos'd by Sigʳ. Giuseppe
Tartini. [Score] London, printed by Longman
and Broderip [178-?]
1 p.l., 33 p.   30 cm.

NT 0044936   NRU-Mus

qM787.1 Tartini, Giuseppe, 1692-1770.
T17si   Six sonates pour violon. Accompagnement
1921   de piano, d'après la basse de l'auteur,
doigter, nuances et coups d'archet par H.
Leonard. Nouvelle éd. rev. et doigtée par
Issay Barmas.   Bruxelles, Schott frères
[1921?] Pl. no. S.F.1107.
score (6v.) and part. 35cm.

Contents.- no.1. En la mineur.- no.2. En
sol mineur.-

NT 0044937   IU

Tartini, Giuseppe, 1692-1770.
Sonata. A minor. For violin and piano.
Paris, c1921.
Ricordi edition.

NT 0044938   PPCI

D895 Tartini, Giuseppe, 1692-1770.
[Sonata a quattro, string quartet, D major.
Larghetto]
Sonate à quatre: Larghetto [et] Andante
assai. [Société de l'] Édition de musique
sacrée 1145 [194-]
2 s. 12 in. 78 rpm.

Quatuor "In cimbalis bene sonantibus."
The Andante assai here recorded is not from
the Quartet in D major, and has not been
identified.

1. String   quartets - To 1800. I.
Tartini, Giu-   seppe, 1692-1770./ Andante assai,   string quartet.

NT 0044939   CU

Tartini, Giuseppe, 1692-1770.
[Trio-sonata, violins & continuo, op. 8, no. 6, D major]
Sonata a tre, per due violini e basso continuo, op. VIII/6.
Hrsg. von Erich Schenk. Klavier und Stimmen. Wien,
Österreichischer Bundesverlag [°1954]
score (7 p.) and   parts. 32 cm. (Hausmusik, 167)
Cover title.
The figured bass is realized for organ or harpsichord. Part for
violoncello included.
1. Trio-sonatas.   I. Schenk, Erich, 1902- ed.   (Series)
M312.4.T2 op.8, no.6.S3   M 55-1427

NT 0044940   DLC CoU ICU

Tartini, Giuseppe, 1692-1770.
Sonata. C major. Harmonisée pour violon
avec piano, par J. Salmon. Paris, c1921.
Ricordi edition.

NT 0044941   PPCI

Tartini, Giuseppe, 1692-1770.
Sonata. C minor. Harmonisée pour violon
avec piano, par J. Salmon.   Paris, c1921.
Ricordi edition.

NT 0044942   PPCI

Tartini, Giuseppe, 1692-1770.
Sonata. G minor. (Devil's trill) Ausgabe
für Violine mit Pianofortebegleitung von Fritz
Kreisler. Leipzig, c1905.
Eulenberg edition.

NT 0044943   PPCI

Tartini, Giuseppe, 1692-1770.
Sonata. G minor. (Devil's trill) For violin
and piano. Edited and provided with an original
cadenza by Leopold Auer. New York, c1919.
Fischer edition.

NT 0044944   PPCI

Tartini, Giuseppe, 1692-1770.
Sonata. G minor. (Devil's trill) For violin
and piano; edited by Joseph Joachim. Berlin,
c1905.
Simrock edition.

NT 0044945   PPCI

Tartini, Giuseppe, 1692-1770.
Sonata. G minor. (Devil's trill) Pour violon
et piano, par Emile Sauret. Leipzig, n.d.
Peters edition.

NT 0044946   PPCI

Tartini, Giuseppe, 1692-1770.
Sonata. Op. 1, No. 10. For
violin and piano; edited by Leopold Auer.
New York, c1919.
Fischer edition.

NT 0044947   PPCI

Tartini, Giuseppe, 1692-1770.
Sonata. G minor. Op. 1, No. 10. Für
Violine und Klavier; bearbeitet von D. Alard und
Fritz Meyer. Mainz, n.d.
Schott edition.

NT 0044948   PPCI

Tartini, Giuseppe, 1692-1770.
Sonata. G minor. Op. 1, No. 10. Pour
violon et piano; harmonisée par J. Salmon.
Paris, c1921.
Ricordi edition.

NT 0044949   PPCI

Tartini, Giuseppe, 1692-1770.
Sonata. Op. 2, No. 1. Pour piano
et violon. Nouvelle édition revue et doigtée par
Ed. Nedaud. Paris, n.d.
Costallat edition.

NT 0044950   PPCI

Tartini, Giuseppe, 1692-1770.
Sonata. G minor. Pour violon avec piano.
Accompagnement de piano, d'apres la basse de
l'auteur, doigter, nuances et coups d'archet par
H. Leonard. Paris, n.d.
Schott edition.

NT 0044951   PPCI

Tartini, Giuseppe, 1692-1770.
Sonata. G minor. Pour violon et piano, par
H. Leonard. Nouvelle edition revue et doigter
par Issay Barmas. Brussels, n.d.
Schott edition.

NT 0044952   PPCI

Tartini, Giuseppe. 1692-1770.   No. I in **M.432.42.1
Sonata in A. Für Violine & Klavier. Nach der Original-Ausgabe
... bearbeitet von Alfred Moffat.
= Mainz. Schott. 1909. 11 pp. [Kammer-Sonaten für Violine &
Klavier des 17ten & 18ten Jahrhunderts. No. I.] 33½ cm.

H8664 — Sonatas. Violin and pianoforte. — Violin. Music.

NT 0044953   MB

787.2   Tartini, Giuseppe, 1692-1770.
T17s
Sonata in C minor, op. 1, no. 10.
Transcriptions for viola and piano by
Watson Forbes and Alan Richardson.
[London] Oxford University Press [°1954]
score (11 p.) and part. 32 cm.

Duration: 9 minutes.
Cover title.
1. Sonatas (Viola and piano), Arranged.

NT 0044954   LU

Tartini, Giuseppe, 1692-1770.
[Trio-sonata, violins & continuo, D major]

Sonata in D major for two violins and piano, with cello
ad lib. (H. Dameck) New York, International Music Co.
[1943]
score (8 p.) and   parts. 31 cm.
No. 49 of the "Sonate a tre" in A. Capri's thematic index.

1. Trio-sonatas.   I. Dameck, Hjalmar von, 1864-1927, ed.

M312.4.T2 D maj.   45-18090 rev*

NT 0044955   DLC CtY OKentU

Tartini, Giuseppe, 1692-1770.
[Sonatas. Violin & piano, op. 1, no. 10]
...Sonata in G minor for violin and piano. Edited by Leopold
Auer.   New York: C. Fischer [c1919] Publ. no. 21204b.
1 v.   30½cm.   (Carl Fischer's music library. no. 850.)

Score (9 p.) including realized basso continuo. Violin part.
From his: Sonate a violino e violoncello o cimbalo. Opera prima. Amsterdam:
M C. le Cene [1734]

1. Violin and piano—To 1800.   2. Sonatas—Violin and piano—
To 1800. I. Auer, Leopold, 1845-   1930, ed.
N. Y. P. L.   January 27, 1941

NT 0044956   NN OrPS OO NBuG ICU CLSU CSt

M219   Tartini, Giuseppe, 1692-1770.
.T32   [Sonata, violin & continuo, op.1,
op.1   no.10, G minor; arr.]
no.10   Sonata in G minor, for violin and
pianoforte. London, Novello & Co.
[c1900]
score (12 p.) and part. 30 cm. (A
modern school for the violin, no.14)
"...the tenth of a set of "XII.
solos for a violin with a thorough bass
for the harpsichord or violoncello,
compos'd by Giuseppe Tartini," published
in London by Walsh.

NT 0044957   OCU

sVM   TARTINI, GIUSEPPE, 1692-1770.
219   ₍Sonata, violin; G major₎   Sonata in Sol
T 19sG   maggiore per violino e pianoforte.   Nuova edizione liberamente riveduta da Mario Corti.
Milano, A. & G. Carisch & c. ₍c1921₎
7p.   31cm.

Piano part (12p.) laid in.
Plate no.: C. 13786.

NT   0044958   ICN

Tartini, Giuseppe, 1692–1770.
₍Sonata, violin & continuo, F major; arr.₎

Sonata no. 2 in F major for viola and piano.   (Alard-
Dessauer)   New York, International Music Co. ₍1947₎
score (8 p.) and part.   31 cm.
"Sonata 2" ₍op. 1₎ in A. Bachmann's "Catalogue thématique" (Les
grands violonistes du passé, p. 321)
Score (violin and piano) and part for viola.

1. Sonatas (Viola and piano), Arranged.

M228.T   50–36222 rev

NT   0044959   DLC OrP IEN OKentU CtY-Mus

M
223   Tartini, Giuseppe, 1692-1770.
.T18   ... Sonata per violino e basso, realizzazione
S6   per violino e pianoforte di Ottorino **Respighi.**
R43   Milano ₍etc.₎, G. Ricordi & c., ₍1921.
1 p.ℓ., 13 p. and part.   32cm.
Publisher's plate no.: E. R. 268.
Score and part.

1. Sonatas (Violin and piano), Arranged.
I. Respighi, Ottorino, 1879-1936, arr. ⁄

NT   0044960   MiU CLSU

Tartini, Giuseppe, 1692-1770.
Sonatas.   For the violin; with bass accompani-
ment, arranged for the pianoforte by
G. F. Malipiero.
(In Annunzio, G. d' Classici della musica
italiana.   Vol. 32.   c1919)

NT   0044961   PPCI

Tartini, Giuseppe, 1692–1770.
₍Sonatas. Violin & piano. Op. 1, no. 1₎
Sonate ₍A dur₎ von Giuseppe Tartini... Bearbeitung von A.
Moffat.   Berlin: N. Simrock G.m.b.H. ₍1899₎   Publ. pl. no.
11231.   2 parts in 1 v.   34cm.   (Meister-Schule der alten
Zeit: Sammlung klassischer Violin-Sonaten. 18.)

Score (including realized basso continuo) and violin part.   Amsterdam:
From his: Sonate a violino e violoncello o cimbalo. Opera prima.   Amsterdam:
M. C. Le Cene ₍1734₎
Caption-title.

1. Violin and piano.   2. Sonatas—   Violin and piano.   I. Moffat, Alfred
Edward, 1866–   , ed.
N. Y. P. L.   March 4, 1936

NT   0044962   NN

Tartini, Giuseppe, 1692–1770.
... Sonate, A-moll...   Mainz: B. Schott's Söhne ₍etc., etc.,
1910₎   Publ. pl. no. 28583.   2 parts in 1 v.   31cm.   (Kammer-
Sonaten des 17ten und 18ten Jahrhunderts. 1.)

Score (including realized basso continuo) and violin part.
"Arrangement von Alfred Moffat."
"Edition Schott... No. 801."

1. Violin and piano.   2. Sonatas—   Violin and piano.   I. Moffat, Alfred
Edward, 1866–
N. Y. P. L.   March 4, 1936

NT   0044963   NN

M787.1   Tartini, Giuseppe, 1692-1770.
T17s   ₍Sonatas, violin & continuo.   Selections₎
Sonate à violin solo è basso del sigʳ
Giuseppe Tartini.
₍58₎p.   22x29cm.

Contemporary (?) ms.
With signature of Charles Wesley and bookplate of William F. Hill.
Contents.— ₍Sonata 1ª, A major₎—Sonata
seconda ₍G minor₎—Sonata 3ª ₍B minor₎—Sonata
4ª ₍A major₎—Sonata 5 ₍D major₎—Sonata 6 ₍E
major₎—Sonata 7ª   ₍C major₎—Sonata 9
₍i.e. 8, F major₎   Sonata 9ª ₍G major₎.

NT   0044964   IU

---

qM787.1   Tartini, Giuseppe, 1692-1770.
T17so   ₍Sonatas, violin & continuo.   Selections₎
Sonate a violino e basso.   ₍n.p.₎, 17—?₎
₍13₎p.   32cm.

Title from caption, p. ₍3₎
In manuscript.
Sonata no. 3 has attached leaf (unnumbered) of
18 variations.

NT   0044965   IU

Tartini, Giuseppe, 1692-1770.
₍Sonatas, violin & continuo.   Selections₎

Sonate a violino e basso, opera seconda.   Roma, A. C.
Scul ₍1745₎
score (63 p.)   24 x 36 cm.
First ed.
Op. 2 in A. Bachmann's thematic index (Les grands violonistes du
passé, p. 331–339).

1. Sonatas (Violin and harpsichord)—To 1800.

M219.T2S4   70–209158

NT   0044966   DLC NRU-Mus IU

M
219   Tartini, Giuseppe, 1692-1770.
T18   Sonate a violino e basso ... di Giuseppe
op.2   Tartini. Opera seconda. Roma ₍1745?₎
59 ℓ.   31½ x 36ᶜᵐ.
Photostat reproduction (negative) made by
the Library of Congress.
Collation of original on basis of facsimile:
1 p.ℓ., 63 p.

1. Sonatas (Violin and harpsichord)--To 1800.

NT   0044967   MiU

Tartini, Giuseppe, 1692-1770.
Sonate a violino e basso.   Op. 2.   Roma,
1769?

NT   0044968   MBCM

Tartini, Giuseppe, 1692-1770.
₍Sonatas, violin & continuo.   Selections₎

Sonate a violino e violoncello o cimbalo, opera prima.
Amsterdam, H. Chalon ₍ca. 1738₎   Pl. no. 576.
score (57 p.)   33 cm.
Reprinted from the plates of the 1st ed., published by G. F. Witvogel in Amsterdam, 1732.
In A. Bachmann's thematic index (Les grands violonistes du
passé, p. 320–330)
Includes the composer's Pastorale in A major, for violin and continuo.

1. Sonatas (Violin and harpsichord)—To 1800.   I. Tartini, Giuseppe, 1692-1770. Pastorale, violin & continuo, A major. 1738.

M219.T2C5   73–209159

NT   0044969   DLC MB NRU-Mus

Tartini, Giuseppe, 1692-1770.
₍Sonatas, violin & continuo.   Selections₎

Sonate a violino e violoncello e cimbalo.   **Opera prima.**
Paris, Le Clerc ₍1740₎
score (57 p.)   35 cm.
In A. Bachmann's thematic index (Les grands violonistes du
passé, p. 320–330).
Includes the composer's Pastorale in A major for violin and continuo.

1. Sonatas (Violin and harpsichord)—To 1800.   I. Tartini, Giuseppe, 1692-1770. Pastorale, violin & continuo, A major, 1740.

M219.T2L4   62–43806

NT   0044970   DLC

TARTINI, Giuseppe, 1692-1770.
Sonate a violino solo col basso.   Opera,
VII.   Paris, also Lyon, ₍1745₎

4º. pp.27.

NT   0044971   MH-Mu

Tartini, Giuseppe, 1692–1770.
₍Sonatas, violin & continuo.   Selections₎

Sonate a violino solo col basso.   Opera 7.   2d ed.   Paris,
Maupetit ₍1745?₎
score (27 p.)   35 cm.
Includes no. 1–3 and 5 of op. 7 in A. Bachmann's thematic index
(Les grands violonistes du passé, p. 349–353); includes no. 18, 56,
and 23 of "60 sonate" in A. Capri's thematic index.

1. Sonatas (Violin and harpsichord)—To 1800.

M219.T2M47   62–43800

NT   0044972   DLC

M312   Tartini, Giuseppe, 1692-1770.
.4   ₍Trio-sonata, violins & continuo, D major₎
.T19S6   Sonate D-dur, für zwei Violinen und Klavier
(Violoncello ad libitum) Berlin, Bote & Bock
₍19—₎
score (9 p.) and 3 parts.

1. Trio-sonatas.

NT   0044973   ICU

Tartini, Giuseppe, 1692–1770.

...Sonate 18. Révision et annotations par Éd. Nadaud et Kaiser.
Paris: Éditions M. Senart & cie., c1920.   Publ. pl. no. M. S. &
cie. 5266.   1 v.   34cm.   (On cover: Édition nationale de
musique classique.)

Score (6 p.) including realized basso continuo.   Violin part.

1. Violin and piano—To 1800.   2. Sonatas—Violin and piano—
To 1800.   I. Nadaud, Édouard Louis,   1862–1928, ed.   II. Kaiser, Henri
Charles, 1861–1921.   January 27, 1941
N. Y. P. L

NT   0044974   NN ICN

Tartini, Giuseppe, 1692-1770
Sonate e violino solo col basso.   Opera VII.   Paris,
₍1745₎

Score (27 p.)

NT   0044975   MH-Mu

---

sVM   TARTINI, GIUSEPPE, 1692-1770.
219   ₍Sonata, violin; E major₎   Sonate (en Mi)
T 19sE   pour piano et violon.   Réalisation de la basse
continué par Paul Vidal.   Révision et annotations
de la partie de violon par Ed. Nadaud.   Paris,
M. Senart & cie, c1917.
12p.   34½cm.   (Édition nationale)

Violin part (4p.) laid in.
Plate no.: M.S. & cie. 5208.

NT   0044976   ICN

TARTINI, GIUSEPPE, 1692-1770.

Sonate für Violine [G moll];   Clavierbegleitung
versehen von Robert Franz.   Leipzig, F. E. C. Leuckart
[188-]   Pl. no. F. E. C. L. 4017.   score (7 p.) and part.   35cm.

No. 33 of the "60 sonate a violino e basso in parte autografe" of
A. Capri's Catalogo tematico.

1. Violin and piano--Arr.   I. Franz, Robert, 1815-1892, arr. ⁄

NT   0044977   NN

Tartini, Giuseppe, 1692–1770.
⟨Sonatas. Violin & piano. (Devil's trill) Arr. for vln & orch.⟩
... Sonate, G. moll ("Der Teufelstriller"), von Giuseppe Tartini; für Violine mit Streichorchester (oder Streichquintett) bearbeitet von Hugo Kauder... Wien: Universal-Edition A. G., cop. 1923.   Publ. pl. no. U. E. 7183.   34 p.   27½cm.

Score.
Composed, 1730, for violin with figured bass; published posthumously.

1. Violin and orchestra—Arr.
Arr. for violin and orch.   3. Violin—
'Hugo, 1888– , arranger.
         2. Sonatas—Violin and piano—
Sextets, String—Arr. I. Kauder,
         August 14, 1934

NT   0044978   NN IaU

Tartini, Giuseppe, 1692–1770.
[Sonata, violin & violoncello, G minor.
Bachmann, op. 1, no. 10. Arr. violin & piano]
... Sonate, g moll - sol min. Didone abandonnata, op. 1, no. 10. Bearbeitet von D. Alard und Fritz Meyer. Klavierbegleitung zur violin-ausgabe C2739. Einzelausgabe.   Leipzig [etc.] B. Schott's söhne [191–?]
8 [2] p.   34 cm.
Publ. no. Edition Schott C2740.
Score, violin and piano.
Originally for violin and cello or cembalo.
--- Sonate X. ... Violine.

Violin part. In pocket in back cover of the above.

NT   0044980   CtY-Mus

Tartini, Giuseppe, 1692–1770.
⟨Sonatas. Violin & piano. Op. 3, no. 4⟩
...Sonate...H-moll.   Mainz, B. Schott's Söhne ⟨etc., etc.,⟩ 1912⟩ Publ. pl. no. 29418.   1 v.   32cm.   (Kammer-Sonaten des 17ten und 18ten Jahrhunderts... 21.)

Score (12 p., violin and piano ⟨realized basso continuo⟩) and violin part.
From his 12 sonatas published in Paris as Op. 3 (ca. 1735) and in Rome (1745?) as Op. 2. Adagio from his Sonata Op. 6, no. 1, included as middle movement.
"Edition Schott...No. ...821."
"Arrangement von Alfred Moffat."

1. Violin and piano—To 1800.
ed.
N. Y. P. L.
    I. Moffat, Alfred Edward, 1866–   CARNEGIE CORP. OF NEW YORK.
         Card revised
         November 15, 1945

NT   0044981   NN

Tartini, Giuseppe, 1672–1770.
⟨Sonatas. Violin and piano. Op. 1, no. 8.⟩
...Sonate in c moll...   Berlin: N. Simrock G.m.b.H.⟨-⟩, etc., etc.,⟩ 1921.   Publ. pl. no. 14205.   2 parts in 1 v.   34cm.
(Alte Sonaten für Violine und Klavier. 5.)

Score (including realized basso continuo) and violin part.
From his: 12 Sonate à violino e vcl. o cemb. Op. 1. Amsterdam: M. C. le cene, 1734.— cf. Eitner. Quellen-Lexikon.
"Ausgabe von Paul Klengel."

1. Violin and piano. 2. Sonatas—
K., 1854– , editor.
N. Y. P. L.
   Violin and piano. I. Klengel, Paul
         November 28, 1934

NT   0044982   NN

M 219
.T2S32

Tartini, Giuseppe, 1692–1770.
... Sonate (La mineur) harmonisée pour violon avec accompagnement de piano par J. Salmon.
Paris, Société Anonyme des Éditions Ricordi, ᶜ1921.   Publ.no.R.729.
fol.

Cover title.
Score(13p.) and part.
Composer's name at head of title.

NT   0044983   DLC

Tartini, Giuseppe, 1692–1770.
⟨Sonatas. Violin & piano. Op. 1, no. 12⟩
... Sonate 11. Révision et annotations par Éd. Nadaud et Kaiser. Paris: Éditions M. Senart & cie., ᶜ1920.   Publ. pl. no. M. S. & cie. 5264.   1 v.   34½cm.   (On cover: Édition nationale de musique classique.)

Score (9 p.) including realized basso continuo. Violin part.
From his: Sonate a violino e violoncello o cimbalo. Opera prima.   Amsterdam: M. C. le Cene ⟨1734⟩

1. Violin and piano—To 1800.
1800. I. Nadaud, Édouard Louis,
Charles, 1861–1921.
N. Y. P. L.
    2. Sonatas—Violin and piano—To
1862–1928, ed. II. Kaiser, Henri
         January 31, 1941

NT   0044984   NN ICN MB PU IaU

M
2
.R13
no.131-
136

Tartini, Giuseppe, 1692–1770.
⟨Sonatas, violin & continuo. Selections⟩
Sonate per violino con accompagnamento di basso elaborato per pianoforte a cura di G. Francesco Malipiero. Revisione tecnica violinistica di Mario Corti. Sonatas for the violin with bass accompaniment, arranged for the pianoforte. Milano, Istituto editoriale italiano ⟨ᶜ1919⟩
score (3 v.) and part. 25 cm.   (Raccolta nazionale delle musiche italiane. 1.ser.: Le musiche antiche, quaderno n.131/132-135/136)
"The eight sonatas ... are taken from a manuscript of the Biblioteca Marciana of Venice."

NT   0044985   MiU ICN NIC

M
223
.T18
S62
F18

Tartini, Giuseppe, 1692–1770.
... Sonate per violino solo e basso edita per la prima volta; revisione violinistica di G.B. Faini, elaborazione del basso per pianoforte di F. Boghen. Milano ⟨etc.⟩, G. Ricordi e c., 1927.
1 p.ℓ., 11 p. and part.   32 cm.
Publisher's plate no.: E.R.793.
Score and part.
1. Sonatas (Violin and piano), Arranged. I. Faini, Giovanni Battista. 1857– . II. Boghen, Felice, 1875–

NT   0044986   MiU

M785.7273
T185sD

Tartini, Giuseppe, 1692–1770.
[Sonata, violin & continuo, D major; arr.]
Sonate pour deux violoncelles et piano. Réalisation par Paul Bazelaire. Paris, A. Leduc [c1951, c1942]
score (15 p.) and part. 34 cm.
Part is for 1st violoncello.
Figured bass realized for piano.
Arrangement of Sonata, op. 1, no. 6 in v. 7 of his Works, ed. by E. Farina, pub. 1972 by Carisch, Milano; based on the 1734 ed. pub. by M. Ch. Le Cène in Amsterdam.
1. Trio-sonatas (Violoncellos (2), continuo), Arranged. I. Bezelaire, Paul, ed.

NT   0044987   ICarbS

M 219
.T2S36

Tartini, Giuseppe, 1692–1770.
... Sonate (Sol mineur) harmonisée pour violon avec accompagnement de piano par J. Salmon.
Paris, Société Anonyme des Éditions Ricordi, ᶜ1921.   Publ.no.R.731.
fol.

Cover title.
Score(15p.) and part.
Composer's name at head of title.

NT   0044988   DLC

Tartini, Giuseppe, 1692–1770.
...Sonate 13. Révision et annotations par Éd. Nadaud et Kaiser.
Paris: Éditions M. Senart & cie., ᶜ1920.   Publ. pl. no. M. S. & cie. 5265.   1 v.   34cm.   (On cover: Édition nationale de musique classique.)

Score (7 p.) including realized basso continuo. Violin part.

1. Violin and piano—To 1800.
1800. I. Nadaud, Édouard Louis,
Charles, 1861–1921.
N. Y. P. L.
    2. Sonatas—Violin and piano—To
1862–1928, ed. II. Kaiser, Henri
         January 24, 1941

NT   0044989   NN ICN

Tartini, Giuseppe, 1692–1770
⟨Sonata, violin & continuo, G major⟩
⟨Sonate 3 of⟩ Six sonates pour violon, accompagnement de piano, d'après la basse de l'auteur, doigter, nuances et coups d'archet par H. Leonard. Schott, n.d.
score (9 p.) & part.

1. Sonatas (Violin & piano)

NT   0044990   OrP

M
219
T17s
1921

Tartini, Giuseppe, 1692–1770.
[Sonata, violin & continuo, G major]
Sonate (Ut majeur) harmonisée pour violon / avec accompagnement de piano par J. Salmon.
Paris, Société Anonyme des Éditions Ricordi, c1921.
score (15 p.) and part.

1. Sonatas (Violin and continuo) - To 1800.

NT   0044991   CLU DLC

---

sVM
219
T 19s21

TARTINI, GIUSEPPE, 1692–1770.
⟨Sonata, violin; no.21, B minor⟩ Sonate 21. Révision et annotations par Ed. Nadaud et Kaiser. Paris, M. Senart & cie., c1920.
8p.   34½cm.   (Édition nationale)

Violin part (4p.) laid in.
Plate no.: M.S. & cie. 5267.

NT   0044992   ICN

---

sVM
219
T 19s25

TARTINI, GIUSEPPE, 1692–1770.
⟨Sonata, violin; no.25, D major⟩ Sonate 25. Révision et annotations par Ed. Nadaud et Kaiser.   Paris, M. Senart & cie., c1920.
4p.   34½cm.   (Édition nationale)

Violin part (3p.) laid in.
Plate no.: M.S. & cie. 5269.

NT   0044993   ICN NN

M
219
T19++
C major

Tartini, Giuseppe, 1692–1787.
⟨Sonata, violin & continuo, C major⟩
Sonaten C dur, D dur. ⟨Mit Klavierbegleitung hrsg. von Friedrich⟩ Hermann. ⟨Leipzig, C. F. Peters, 19--⟩ Pl. no. 8649.
score (19 p.) and part.   31cm.   (His Berühmte Sonaten für Violine, Bd. 3)
Edition Peters, Nr. 1099c.
Cover title.
1. Sonatas (Violin and harpsichord)--To 1800. Scores and parts.   I. Tartini, Giuseppe, 1692–1787. Sonata, violin and piano, D major.

NT   0044994   NIC

Tartini, Giuseppe, 1692–1770.
⟨Sonatas, violin & continuo. Selections⟩

Sonates a violon seul avec la basse continue. Œuvre 4. Paris, Mme. la veuve Boivin ⟨1747⟩
score (27 cm.) 35 cm.
First ed.

1. Sonatas (Violin and harpsichord)—To 1800.

M219.T2B64   62–43803

NT   0044995   DLC

Tartini, Giuseppe, 1692–1770.
⟨Sonatas, violin & continuo. Selections⟩

Sonates à violon seul avec la basse continue. Œuvre 5. Paris, Mme. la veuve Boivin ⟨1747⟩
score (29 p.) 35 cm.

First ed.
Op. 5 in A. Bachmann's thematic index (Les grands violinistes du passé, p. 339-344)

1. Sonatas (Violin and harpsichord)—To 1800.

M219.T2B65   62–43802

NT   0044996   DLC

M
2079
L82T19+

Tartini, Giuseppe, 1692–1770.
⌐Stabat Mater¬

Stabat Mater, a 4 voix mixtes alternant
avec le chant grégorien.   St. Leu-la-Forêt
(Seine & Oise) Procure générale de musique
⌐1948¬
score (11 p.)   29cm.

1. Stabat Mater   dolorosa (Music)

NT 0044997   NIC

Tartini, Giuseppe, 1692–1770.

Il Tartini a Giuseppe Valeriano Vannetti;
dodici lettere inedite con appendice la
famiglia Vannetti ⌐per¬ Ferdinando Pasini.
Capodistria, C. Priora, 1906.
27 p.   25cm.

"Estratto dalle Pagine Istriane, IV."

1. Vannetti family. I. Vannetti, Giuseppe
Valeriano Antonio, 1719–1764. II. Pasini, Ferdinando, 1876–   ed.

NT 0044998   ViU

ML30
.3e2
.D3
case

Tartini, Giuseppe, 1692–1770.

Dallapiccola, Luigi, 1904–
⌐Tartiniana¬

Tartiniana; divertimento per violino e orchestra. Par-
titura. Milano, Edizioni Suvini Zerboni ⌐1952¬

FILM
9962
M
Music
Library

Tartini, Giuseppe, 1692–1770.
[L'arte dell' arco]

Tartini's celebrated art of bowing for the violin, consisting of
50 variations on a subject taken from Corelli's solos, with an
accompaniment for a bass.   London, R. Cocks & Co. [183–?]
Pl. no. 13170.
score (13 p.)   On film (Negative)

Microfilm.   Original in Royal College of Music, London.
For violin and unfigured bass; the variations are in score format;
the continuo part for the bass is printed at the foot of each recto
page.

NT 0045000   CU

M
787.1
T195so
Pe

Tartini, Giuseppe, 1692–1770.
⌐Sonatas, violin & continuo. Selections¬
Teufels- und G moll- Sonate. Trille du
Diable et sonate en sol mineur. Mit Klavier-
begleitung hrsg. von Friedrich Hermann.
Leipzig, Peters ⌐n.d.¬   Pl. no. 8834.
score (19p.) and 1 part.   (Edition Peters
Nr.1099b)
Cover title.
Contains two sonatas in G minor, the first
called the Devil's trill.
1. Sonatas (Violin & piano) – To 1800. I.
Hermann, Friedrich, 1828–1907, ed.

NT 0045001   FTaSU CLSU RPB

M
219
T19++
G minor

Tartini, Giuseppe, 1692–1787.
⌐Sonata, violin & continuo, G minor¬
Teufelstriller-Sonate. G moll-Sonate. ⌐Mit
Klavierbegleitung hrsg. von Friedrich Hermann.
⌐Frankfurt, New York, C. F. Peters, c1934¬
score (19 p.) and part.   31cm. (His
Berühmte Sonaten für Violine, Bd.2)

Edition Peters, Nr. 1099b.
Cover title.

1. Sonatas   (Violin and harpsichord)–
To 1800. I. Ti   tle.

NT 0045002   NIC

Tartini, Giuseppe, 1692–1770.
Traité des agrémens de la musique, contenant l'origine de la
petite note, sa valeur, la manière de la placer, toutes les différentes espèces de cadences, la manière de les employer, le
tremblement et le mordant, l'usage, qu'on en peut faire, les
modes ou agrémens naturels, les modes artificiels qui vont à
l'infini, lan manière de former un point d'orgue ... composé par
le célèbre Giuzeppe Tartini ... et traduit par le sig.ʳ P. Denis.
Paris, Chez l'auteur ⌐1782¬
1 p. l., 94 p. 23cm.
Engraved throughout.
Apparently never published in the original. A "Trattato delle appog-
giature ... per il violino" is given by Lichtenthal in his Dizionario ...
della musica as being in   manuscript.
1. Embellishment (Music)
1. Denis, Pierre, fl. 1780, tr.   2. Violin–Instruction and study.
Library of Congress   MT80.A2T2   8–17369

NT 0045003   DLC CtY PPiU ICN

Tartini, Giuseppe, 1692–1770.
Traité des agrémens de la musique. Paris,
Chez L'auteur ⌐1782¬
94p.

Microcard edition.

NT 0045004   ICRL NNC OU CoU OrU OO ViU CaBVaU

⌐Tartini, Giuseppe¬ 1692–1770.
Trattato di musica secondo la vera scienza dell' armonia.
Padova, Nella stamperia del Seminario, appresso G. Manfrè,
1754.
4 p. l., 175, ⌐1¬ p. fold. pl. 24½cm.
Title vignette.
Tartini is given as author in the preface, written by Decio Agostino
Trento, who published the work.

1. Music–Acoustics and physics.   I. Title.

Library of Congress   ML3805.A2T2   4–9433

MdBP NmU IU
InU MiU ICN MB NIC FMU MNS IEN FMU   PLatS MH
NPV ICU OClW NjP NcU MB MdBP CU CLU-C WaU CSt PPiU
NT 0045005   DLC DAU MdBP KyU CtY CSt WU InU NPV CU

781.64
T195T

Tartini, Giuseppe, 1692–1770.
Treatise on ornamentation ... Tr, and ed.
by Sol Babitz ⌐Chicago, Journal of Research
in Music Education, 195–¬
p. 75–102 music 23 cm.

Detached from the Journal of Research in
Music Education.
Caption title.
1. Embellishment (Music) I. Title. II. Babitz,
Sol,   ed. and tr.

NT 0045006   NcD

Tartini, Giuseppe, 1692–1770

Le trille du diable; sonate pour violon,
l'accompagnement de piano par Robert Volkmann.
Leipzig, F. Kistner, n.d. Pl.no.2070.
2 pts.

Pt.1. Violin-piano score. Pt.2. Violin
part (in pocket of pt.1)

NT 0045007   OC1

787.142M
T 179 S
G min.
TV

Tartini, Giuseppe, 1692–1770.
⌐Sonata, violin & continuo, G minor ("Il
trillo del diavolo")¬

Le trille du diable. Sonate pour le violon,
composée en 1730. Arrangée pour être execu-
tée dans les concerts. Avec accompagnement
de piano ... par Henri Vieuxtemps. Offenbach s/M, J. André, n.d. Pl. no. 7498.
score (15 p.) and part.   35cm.

Title from violin part.

NT 0045008   OO

---

sVM
219
T 19s

TARTINI, GIUSEPPE, 1692–1770.
⌐Sonata, violin: G minor¬ ...Le trille du
diable, sonate... Mayence,B.Schott⌐1864¬
11p.   (Les maîtres classiques du violon.
no.3)

Violin part (5p.) laid in.
Plate no.: 17184.

NT 0045009   ICN

M219
.T19S6

Tartini, Giuseppe, 1692–1770.
⌐Sonatas, violin & continuo. Selections¬
Trille du diable et Sonate en sol minour,
accompagnés d'une partie de piano par Fr.
Hermann. Leipzig, C. F. Peters ⌐187–¬
score and part.   (Edition Peters, No.1099b)
For violin and piano.

1. Sonatas (Violin and piano)

NT 0045010   ICU

Tartini, Giuseppe, 1692–1770   8052.856
Le trille du diable: sonate pour le violon composée en 1730 ... / arrangée pour être exécutée dans les concerts avec accompagnement de piano ou d'un second violon, alto et violoncelle par Henri
Vieuxtemps. [Violon principale et piano. Partition et partie de
violon.]
Offenbach a/M. André. [188–?] 2 v. 34½ cm.

K3579 — Sonatas. Violin and pianofo... — Violin. Music. — T.r. — Vieuxtemps, Henri, ed. 1820–1881.

NT 0045011   MB

Tartini, Giuseppe, 1692–1770.
⌐Sonata, violin & continuo, G minor¬

Le trille du diable. Teufelstrillersonate. Neu hrsg., bezeichnet und mit einer Cadenz versehen von Fritz Kreisler.
⌐190–?¬
score (16 p.) 34 cm.
Fritz Kreisler's ms. realization for violin and piano. On t. p.:
Meinem lieber Freunde Dr. B. Pollack herzlichst zugeeignet.
Published Leipzig, E. Eulenberg ⌐1905¬
"Orgelstimme" ⌐ad lib.¬ (⌐?¬ p.) laid in.
Gift of Fritz Kreisler, Jan. 19, 1955.
1. Sonatas (Violin and harpsichord)—To 1800. I. Kreisler, Fritz,
1875–   arr. II. Title. III. Title: Teufelstrillersonate.

ML96.K782   M 59–1933

NT 0045012   DLC

Tartini, Giuseppe, 1692–1770.
⌐Sonata, violin & continuo, G minor¬

Le trille du diable, for violin, edited and fingered by Leopold Lichtenberg, the piano accompaniment by Robert Volkmann. With a biographical sketch of the author by Richard
Aldrich. New York, G. Schirmer, °1901.
score (12 p. port.) and part. 30 cm. Masterpieces for the violin,
v. 23)
Schirmer's library of musical classics, v. 522.
No. 35 of the "60 sonate" in A. Capri's thematic index.
1. Sonatas (Violin and harpsichord)—To 1800. I. Title.

M219.T2L45   3–3938 rev*

NT 0045013   DLC MB NN PP

Tartini, Giuseppe, 1692–1770.
⌐Sonatas. Violin & piano. (Devil's trill)¬
... Trille du diable et Sonate en sol mineur. Teufels- und G
moll-Sonate. (Hermann.) ⌐Leipzig: C. F. Peters, ca. 1902¬
Publ. pl. no. 8834. 1 v. 31cm.   (Edition Peters. No. 1099b.)

Score (19 p.) including realized basso continuo. Violin part.
Cover-title; t.-p. reads: Célèbres sonates pour violin par J. Tartini accompagnés
d'une partie de piano par Friedrich Hermann ...

1. Violin and piano—To 1800.   2. Sonatas—Violin and piano—To
1800. I. Hermann, Friedrich, 1828–   1907. II. Title.
N. Y. P. L.   January 31, 1941

NT 0045014   NN PU-FA ICN

---

sVM
219
T 19s
E 88

TARTINI, GIUSEPPE, 1692–1770.
⌐Sonata, violin: G minor¬ ...Le trille du diable (Teufelstriller-sonate). Mit neuer cadenz...
Leipzig,E.Eulenburg,c1905.
15p. 34½cm. (Fritz Kreisler. Freie be-
arbeitungen älterer werke der violin-litteratur.
Ausgabe für violine mit pianoforte-begleitung)

Violin part (6p.) laid in.
Edited by Fritz Kreisler.
Plate no.: E.E. 2636.

NT 0045015   ICN CLSU

sVM TARTINI, GIUSEPPE, 1692-1770.
219   ⌐Sonata, violin; G minor⌐ Le trille du dia-
T 19s ble. (The devil's trill) New York,G.Schirmer
S 33   ⌐c1905⌐
       15p. 35cm. (Free arrangements of works
       from earlier violin literature arranged and edited
       by Fritz Kreisler. no.6)

       Also known as The devil's sonata.
       Violin part (9p.) laid in.
       Plate no.: 24418.

NT 0045016   ICN OC1

Tartini, Giuseppe, 1692-1770.
    Le trille du diable. Teufelstriller-Sonate, von Giuseppe Tar-
tini, für Violine mit Streichorchester und Orgel bearbeitet und
herausgegeben von Fritz Kreisler. Mainz: B. Schott's Söhne⌐,
cop. 1928⌐ Publ. pl. no. 32254. 15 p. f°.
    Score.
    Composed, 1730, for violin with figured bass; published posthumously.
    "Mit Genehmigung der Verlagshandlung Ernst Eulenburg, Leipzig."

1. Violin and basso continuo. 2. Con-   certos—Violin and string orchestra.
3. Violin—Sonatas. I. Kreisler,   Fritz, 1875-   , arranger. II. Title.
N. Y. P. L.   March 16, 1932

NT 0045017   NN

Tartini, Giuseppe, 1692-1770.
    ⌐Sonata, violin & continuo, G minor⌐

    Il trillo del diavolo; sonata. ⌐n. d.⌐
        score (19 p.) 34 cm.
    Copyist's ms., in ink, with emendations in C. M. T. Loeffler's hand
throughout.
    Unfigured bass realized for piano by Loeffler or César Thomson.

1. Sonatas (Violin and harpsichord)—To 1800.   I. Loeffler,
Charles Martin Tornov, 1861-1935. II. Title.

ML96.L61   63-34065/M

NT 0045018   DLC

M   Tartini,Giuseppe,1692-1770.
219   ... Il trillo del diavolo. Sonata ...
.T18   Milano ⌐etc.⌐ G.Ricordi & c⌐ ⌐19--?⌐
T8   1 p.₤.,12 p.and part. 34ᶜᵐ. (I maestri
19--   classici del violino. Collezione di pezzi
       scelti ... per Delfino Alard)
       Publisher's plate no.: 34313.
       Score (Violin and piano) and part.

       1.Sonatas (Violin and piano). I.Title.

NT 0045019   MiU

Tartini, Giuseppe, 1692-1770.
    ⌐Sonatas, violin & continuo. Selections⌐

    XII solos for a violin with a thorough bass for the harpsi-
cord or violoncello. London, I. Walsh ⌐1750?⌐
    score (57 p.) 32 cm.
    Following no. 12 is the composer's Pastorale in A major, also for
violin and continuo.
    Sonatas 1-12 and the Pastorale ⌐op. 1⌐ in A. Bachmann's "Cata-
logue thématique" (Les grands violonistes du passé, p. 320-330)
    1. Sonatas (Violin and harpsichord)—To 1800. I. Tartini, Giu-
seppe, 1692-1770. Pastorale, violin & continuo, A major.

M219.T2S69 1750   46-31603 rev*

NT 0045020   DLC ViU ViWC NN

Tartini, Giuseppe, 1692-1770.
    ⌐Trio-sonatas, flute, violin & continuo. Selections⌐

    Twelve sonatas in three parts, for a German flute and
violin, or two violins, with a bass for the violoncello or
harpsichord. Opera terza. London, I. Walsh ⌐175-?⌐ Pub.
no. XXIV.
        parts. 36 cm.
    The continuo part is figured.
    No. 28, 30, 16, 46, 40, 12, 47, 43, 14, 27, 44, and 48, respectively, of the
"Sonate a tre" in A. Capri's thematic index.

    1. Trio-sonatas.

M322.T2T79   46-29551 rev*

NT 0045021   DLC NN

Tartini, Giuseppe, 1692-1770.
    Two solos for the violin ⌐with a thorough bass.
Score⌐ Compos'd by Sigʳ. Tartini. London,
Longman Lukey & Co. ⌐1775?⌐
    1 p.l., 9 p. 33.5 cm.
    Cover-title.

NT 0045022   NRU-Mus

Tartini, Giuseppe, 1692-1770.
    ⌐Trio-sonatas, violins & continuo. Selections⌐

    2 sonatas for two violins and cello (E. Pente) New York,
International Music Co. ⌐1943⌐ Pl. no. 648.
        score (6 p.) and   parts. 31 cm.
    No. 2 and no. 44, respectively, of the "Sonate a tre" in A. Capri's
thematic index.

    1. Trio-sonatas.   I. Pente, Emilio, 1860-1929, ed.

M351.T2T77   45-17657 rev*

NT 0045023   DLC CaBVaU NN

M219   Tartini, Giuseppe, 1692-1770.
.T315   ⌐Sonatas, violin & piano⌐
1902
         Two sonatas for violin with piano
       accompaniment. No. 1 in E minor; 2 in G
       major. Edited and fingered by Leopold
       Lichtenberg. New York, G. Schirmer, ᶜ1902.
         score (19 p.) and part. 31cm. (Schirmer's
       library of musical classics. v. 725. Master-
       pieces for the violin, v. 31)

         1. Sonatas (Violin and piano)—To 1800.

NT 0045024   ViU MiDW OCU SdU OC1W NN PP MeB

Tartini, Giuseppe, 1692-1770.
    [Trio-sonatas, violins & bass. Selections, arr.]
    Two trio sonatas in D major [for] two violins and
cello. New York, Edition Musicus [n. d.]
    3 pts. 30.5 cm.
    Cover title.

NT 0045025   OOxM

Tartini, Giuseppe, 1692-1770.
    ⌐Trio-sonatas, violins & bass. Selections, arr.⌐

    Two trio sonatas in D major ⌐for⌐ two violins and viola.
⌐Viola part transcribed by Charles H. Edwards⌐ New York,
Edition Musicus ⌐1948, ᶜ1947⌐
        parts. 31 cm.
    Cover title.

    1. String trios (2 violins, viola), Arranged.   I. Edwards, Charles
H., 1882-   arr.

M353.T   48-21062*

NT 0045026   DLC OrU WaU

Tartini, Giuseppe, 1692-1770.
    ⌐L'arte dell'arco. Selections⌐

    Variationen über ein Thema von Corelli. Tartini-Corelli
variations. ⌐19--⌐
    score ⌐4⌐ p.) 36 cm.
    Fritz Kreisler's ms. realization of the figured bass. For violin and
piano.
    Contains an unpublished variation, intended originally to follow
variation III in Kreisler's published version (Mainz, B. Schott's
Söhne ⌐1910⌐)
    Gift of Fritz Kreisler, Jan. 19, 1955.
    1. Variations (Violin and piano)—To 1800.   I. Corelli, Arcangelo,
1653-1713. Sonata, violin & continuo, op. 5, no. 10, F major. Gavotte.
II. Kreisler, Fritz, 1875-   arr. III. Title. IV. Title: Tartini-Corelli
variations.

ML96.K782   M 59-1930

NT 0045027   DLC

M787.1 Tartini, Giuseppe, 1692-1770.
T195v   [L'arte dell'arco. Selections]
        Variationen über ein Thema von Corelli.
        [Transcribed by] Fritz Kreisler. New York,
        C.Fischer [1910]
          score (6p.) and part. 31cm.

          I. Corelli, Arcangelo, 1653-1713. Sonata,
        violin & continuo, op.5, no.10, F major.
        Gavotte. II. Kreisler, Fritz, 1875-   arr.
        III. Title.

NT 0045028   IEN OrP ICN OO

M787.1 Tartini, Giuseppe, 1692-1770.
T195a   ⌐L'arte dell' arco. Selections; arr.⌐
Music   Variationen über ein Thema von Corelli.
lib.   Violine & Klavier. Mainz, B. Schott ⌐1938⌐
          score (4p.) and part. 32cm. (Fritz Kreis-
        ler's⌐ Klassische Manuskripte, Violine & Kla-
        vier, n.9)

          Cover title.

          I. Corelli, Arcangelo, 1653-1713. Sonata,
        violin & continuo, op.5, no.10, F major. Ga-
        votte. II. Kreisler, Fritz, 1875-1962,
        arr.

NT 0045029   NcU

•M221 Tartini, Giuseppe, 1692-1770.
T25   Variations on a gavotte by Arcangelo Corelli.
       (Piano accompaniment by H. Léonard) Ed. by
       Sam Franko. New York, G. Schirmer, o1927.

         score(15p.) and part(8p.) 30 1/2cm.
       (Schirmer's library of musical classics, vol.
       1513)

         I. Title.
         II. Corelli, Arcangelo, 1653-1713.
         1. Variations (Violin and piano)

NT 0045030   NBuG OO

Tartini, Giuseppe, 1692-1770.
    ⌐L'arte dell'arco. Selections; arr.⌐

    Variations on a theme by Corelli ⌐by⌐ Tartini-Kreisler.
⌐19--⌐
    score ⌐5⌐ p.) 27 x 37 cm.
    Fritz Kreisler's ms. transcription for violin and string orchestra of
his version of the Tartini work for violin and piano published Mainz,
B. Schott's Söhne ⌐1910⌐
    Gift of Fritz Kreisler, Jan. 19, 1955.
    1. Variations (Violin with string orchestra). Arranged—Scores.
I. Corelli, Arcangelo, 1653-1713. Sonata, violin & continuo, op. 5, no.
10, F major. Gavotte. II. Kreisler, Fritz, 1875-   arr. III. Title.

ML96.K782   M 59-2016

NT 0045031   DLC

Tartini, Giuseppe, 1692-1770.

    Variations on a theme by Corelli. Tran-
scribed by J. Stutschewsky ⌐for⌐ cello and
piano. New York, International Music Co.,
1945.
    score (4 p.) and part. 31ᶜᵐ.

    Caption title.

NT 0045032   OO

MUSIC   Tartini, Giuseppe, 1692-1770.
M   ⌐L'arte dell'arco. Selections⌐
221   Variations on a theme of Corelli for
T19A7 violin and piano. ⌐Figured bass real-
1937   ized by⌐ Fritz Kreisler. New York, C.
       Foley ⌐c1937⌐ Pl.no.29027.
         score (6p.) and part. 31cm.

         √1.Variations (Violin and piano) – To 1800.√⌐I.Corelli,
       Arcangelo, 1653-1713. Sonata, violin & continuo, op.5,
       no.10, F major.   Gavotte.√II.Kreisler, Fritz,
       1875-1962, arr. √III.Title.

NT 0045033   CLSU

Tartini, Giuseppe ⌐1692-1770·
    Variations pour le violon sur une
gavotte of Corelli. Accompagnement de
piano par Hubert Léonard. Mainz, n.d.

    Schott edition.

NT 0045034   PPCI

Oberlin
787.142M
T 179 ALB

Tartini, Giuseppe, 1692-1770.
[L'arte dell'arco. Selections]

Variations sur une gavotte de Corelli.
1653. [Par] Tartini-Léonard; revu et doigté
par Issay Barmas. [Bruxelles, Schott Freres,
n.d.] Pl. no. S.F.1164.
score (11 p.) and part. 35cm.

Caption title.

NT 0045035 00

---

f785.6
T19v.C

Tartini, Giuseppe, 1692-1770
...Violin concerto (A minor) with
piano (or string orchestra and
cembalo) accompaniment. Harmonized
and re-arranged by Mario Corti.
New York, Fischer [c1919]
2v. F. (Carl Fischer's music library,
no.914)
Contents: [v.1.] Score for violin and
piano]- [v.2.] Violin.

NT 0045036 IaU

785.671.6M
T 179 Tartini, Giuseppe, 1692-1770.
[Concerto, violin & string orchestra,
Dounias , A minor; arr.]

Violin concerto (A minor) with piano (or
string orchestra and cembalo) accompaniment;
harmonized and re-arranged by Mario Corti.
New York, C. Fischer [c1929]
score (21 p.) and part. 31cm. (Carl
Fischer's music library, no. 914)

With piano acc.

NT 0045037 00 MdBP

TARTINI, GIUSEPPE, 1692-1770.
[SONATA A QUATTRO, STRING QUARTET, D MAJ.]
Zwei Quartette (Due quartetti) für zwei Violinen,
Viola und Violoncell. Erstmals nach dem Autograph
hrsg. und bezeichnet von Emilio Pente. Leipzig,
F. E. C. Leuckart [1898] score (2 v. in 1) 34cm.

CONTENTS. --Nr. 1. Quartett in D dur (Sonata a quattro)--Nr. 2.
Quartett in A dur (Sinfonia a quattro)

1. Chamber music, 18th cent. --Quartets. 2. Violin in quartets (2 violins,
viola, violoncello)--To 1800. 3. Symphonies--To 1800. I. Pente,
Emilio, 1860-1929, ed. II. Tartini, Giuseppe, 1692-1770. Sonata a
quattro, string quartet, A maj.

NT 0045039 NN MH

M452
.T56
no.1-2
19—

Tartini, Giuseppe, 1692-1770.
[Quartets, string]

Zwei Quartette (Due quartetti) für zwei
Violinen, Viola und Violoncell. Erstmals
nach dem Autograph hrsg. und bezeichnet von
Emilio Pente. Leipzig, F. E. C. Leuckart
[19—.] Pl. no. F.E.C.L. 5113.
score (5 p.) and 4 parts. 34cm.
2 copies each of score and parts for Quartet no. 2.
CONTENTS.--Nr. 1. Quartett in D dur (Sonata a
quattro)--Nr. 2. Qua rtett in A dur (Sinfonia
a quattro)
1. string quarte ts—To 1800—Scores
and parts.

NT 0045040 ViU

Tartini, Giuseppe, 1692-1770.
[Sonatas. Violin & piano. Op. 2, no. 6]
...2 Sonaten: C dur...D dur... (Hermann.) [Leipzig:
C. F. Peters, 1900] Publ. pl. no. 8649. 1 v. 31cm. (Edition Peters. No. 1099c.)

Score (19 p.) including realized basso continuo. Violin part.
From his: Sonate a violino e basso... Opera seconda. Romae [1745?]—*cf. Brit.
mus. Cat. of printed music (1487-1800); Breitkopf. Cat. Suppl. 7, 1772.*
Cover-title; t.p. reads: Célèbres sonates pour violon par J. Tartini accompagnés
d'une partie de piano par Friedrich Hermann...

1. Violin and piano—To 1800.   2. Sonatas—Violin and piano—
To 1800. I. Hermann, Friedrich,   1828-1907.
N.Y.P.L.   January 27, 1941

NT 0045041 NN

MUSIC
M
219
T2
op.1,
no.4

Tartini, Giuseppe, 1692-1770.
[Sonata, violin & continuo, op.1, no.4,
G major]
2 [i.e.Zwei] Sonaten, G, g moll. Bearb.
von Gustav Jensen. Mainz, B.Schott's
Söhne [c1911]
score (19p.) and part. 31cm. (Edition
Schott, no. 796)

1.Sonatas (Violin and harpsichord) - To
1800. I.Tartini, Giuseppe, 1692-1770.
Sonata, violin & continuo, op.1,
no.10, G minor.

NT 0045042 CLSU

Tartini, Giuseppe Maria.
Catalogi IV: quorum II ... ad collectionem
scriptorum rerum Italicarum Muratorii, Tartinii,
et Mittarelli. 1853.

NT 0045043 MdBP

QB42
-B7
1721
Physical
Sciences
Library
✱

Tartini, Giuseppe Maria,
Novarum, ac veterum philosophicarum hypothe-
sium usus, et veritas ... a Josepho Maria
Tartini, dicata ... Florentiae, Typis Regiae
Celsitud, apud Tartinium & Franchium, 1729.
23p. 29cm.

Engraved title-vignette.
(In Briga, Melchior della, 1686-1749.
[Novae ac veteris philosophiae harmonia ...
1721-1729])

NT 0045044 RPB

Tartini, Giuseppe Maria, comp.
Rerum italicarum scriptores ab anno aerae
christianae
see under Muratori, Lodovico Antonio,
1672-1750.

Tartini Salvatici, Ferdinando, 1797-1858.
De la nécessité d'introduire dans les écoles
primaires de Toscane la méthode de Bell et
Lancaster
see under Nesti, Philippe.

Kress
Room

Tartini Salvatici, Ferdinando, 1797-1858
Dell' utilità di estendere all' estero il
commercio dei vini Toscani e del modo di
migliorarne la manifattura; memoria letta
nell' adunanza dell' I.E.R. Accademia dei
georgofili dei 2. maggio 1824 ... Firenze,
Presso G. Piatti, 1825.
42 p. 21.5 cm.

1.Wine - Tuscany. I.Title.

NT 0045047 MH-BA

Tartinville, A., ,1847-
Cours d'arithmétique ... Paris, Nony & cie,
1889.
515p.

NT 0045048 MiU

Tartinville, A., 1847-
Théorie des équations et des inéquations du
premier et du second degré a une inconnue ...
Paris, 1886.
214 p. diagrs. 25 cm.

NT 0045049 RPB

Tartinville, A, 1847-
Théorie des équations et des inéquations
du premier et du second degré à une inconnue,
à l'usage des aspirants au baccalauréat es-
sciences et au baccalauréat de l'enseignement
spécial, des candidats aux écoles du gouvernement et des élèves des écoles normales...
2. ed. revue et augmentée. Paris, Nony & cie,
1891.
224 p.

NT 0045050 MiU

Tartinville, A. , 1847-   L512.82 P001
Théorie des équations et des inéquations du premier et du second degré à une inconnue, à l'usage des aspirants aux baccalau-
réats d'ordre scientifique, des candidats aux écoles du gouvernement et des élèves des écoles normales, par A. Tartinville ... .
Troisième édition. Paris, Nony & cie, 1902.
[4], 226 p. 25½cm.

NT 0045051 ICJ

Tartinville, Georges, 1905-
... Contribution à l'étude de quelques ascites...
Paris, 1930.
Thèse - Univ. de Paris.
"Bibliographie": p. 59-63.

NT 0045052 CtY

Tartinville, J.
Comptage de l'énergie électrique en courants alternatifs,
par J. Tartinville ... Paris, Dunod, 1930.
vii, 154 p. illus., diagrs. 25cm.
"Bibliographie": p. [149]

1. Electric measurements. 2. Electric meters. 3. Electric currents,
Alternating.

		30-10510
Library of Congress	TK275.T3	
Copyright A—Foreign	5989	
	[2]	621.37

NT 0045053 DLC NN

Tartivel (F.-P.-Aimé). *De l'hypochondrie.
46 pp., 4°. Paris, 1866, No. 524, v. 533.

NT 0045054 DNLM

Tartler, Alexander, 1905-
On a certain class of orthogonal polynomials ... [by] Alex-
ander Tartler ... Philadelphia, 1935.
1 p. l., p. 627-644. 24½cm.
Thesis (PH. D.)—University of Pennsylvania, 1933.
"Reprint from the American journal of mathematics, vol. LVII, no. 3."

1. Functions, Orthogonal.

		36-6906
Library of Congress	QA404.5.T3 1933	
Univ. of Pennsylvania	Libr.	
———— Copy 2.	[2]	517.35

NT 0045055 PU DLC PSC OC1 OCU OU

Tartler, Georg.
Der einfluss der musik auf die milchergiebigkeit der kühe,
von diplomlandwirt und tierzuchtinspektor Georg Tartler.
Halle, Akademischer verlag, 1936.
57 p. incl. tables. pl. 23cm.

1. Music, Physical effect of. 2. Milk. 3. Cows. I. Title.

		40-17218
Library of Congress	ML3838.T19E35	
	[2]	780.13

NT 0045056 DLC MWalA

Tartler, Georg.
  ... Die hygienische Eroberung der Tropen
durch die weisse Rasse ... Halle (Saale) 1934.
  Inaug.- diss.- Halle-Wittenberg.
  Lebenslauf.
  "Schriftenberzeichnis": p. 24.

NT   0045057   CtY

K
T3
1791
[Tartler, Johann]
  Das Recht des Eigenthums der sächsischen
Nation in Siebenbürgen, auf dem ihr vor mehr
als 600 Jahren von ungrishcen Königen ver-
liehenen Grund und Boden ... und denen auf
dem Landtag in Klausenburg versammelten Landes-
ständen vorgelegt von den Repräsentanten der
Nation, im Jahre 1791. Wien, Bey J.G.
Mössle, 1791.
  4 p.l.,114 p. front. 18cm.
  Ascribed to J.Tartler. Cf.Deutsches Anonymen-
Lexikon.
  Imperfect copy: p.111-114 torn, with some

loss of text.
  Text partly in Latin.
  Frontispiece engraved by C.G.Schütz.

  1.Feudal law - Transylvania. I.Schütz,
Christian Georg I, 1718-1791, engraver.
II.Title. NUC SC

NT   0045059   CSt

Tartler (Otto Peter) [1901-   ]. *Ueber den
Antagonismus und Synergismus zwischen
einigen Analeptica und Medinal. [Giessen.]
14 pp. 8°. [Leipzig, Breitkopf & Hartell]
1929.
*Also in Arch. f. exper. Path. u. Pharmakol., Leipz., 1929,
cxliii.*

NT   0045060   DNLM ICRL DLC OC1W MH

Bonaparte
Collection
No.344
TARTO-MA kele kässi ramat...   **Riga**, G.C. Frölich,
1788.
  4.pt.in 1v. 17 1/2cm.

  Imperfect: all before p.[7](including general t.-p.),p.183-184(1st group), p.193-196, 205-
206(2d group) and all after p.12 (last group)
wanting. Title supplied in ms. on flyleaf.
  Each part has special t.-p.
  "Palwusse ramat" and "Lutterusse Katekismus"
have imprint: Riga, J.C.D. Müller, 1790.
  Blank leaves are inserted in place of missing
pages.

  "Zenoppus" signed: J.C.F.M.

  Contents.--[pt.1] Ewangeliumi nink Epistli.
[The suffering, death and resurrection of Our
Lord Jesus Christ. The coming of the Holy Ghost.
The destruction of Jerusalem]--[pt.2] Laulu-
Wastse laulu.--[pt.3] Palwusse ramat.--[pt.4]
Lutterusse Katekismus.

NT   0045062   ICN

Bonaparte
Collection
No.840
TARTO-MA-KELE kässiramat...   Tarto-linan,H.Laak-
manni man,1859.
  3v.in 1. 19cm.

  "Tarto-ma-kele laulo-ramat", and "Lühhikenne
tarto-ma-kele palwusse ramat" have special title-
pages and separate paging.
  The liturgical Epistles and Gospels, and the
history of the Passion, forming the contents of
v.1, were translated into Estonian by J.Rossih-
nius.--cf. Darlow & Moule 3530, note.

  Contents.--[v.1] Ewangeliumi nink Epistli.
Meije Issanda Jesusse Kristusse ellokäük. Pühha
waimo tulleminne apostlide päle. Jerusalemi-
lina ärrahäetaminne.--[v.2] Laulo-ramat.--[v.3]
Lühhikenne palwusse-ramat. Kirriko palwusse
Önsa Lutterusse Wäikenne katekismus.

NT   0045064   ICN

Bonaparte
Collection
No.301
TARTO PIIBLI-SELTS.
  Tarto piibli-seltsi kolmas arwo-andmisse
kirri Tarto-ma piibli abbi-koggodustele. Tar-
tun,Schünmann,1822.
  32p. 19cm.

NT   0045065   ICN

Tartois (Etienne-Lucien) [1888-   ]. *Nouveau procédé de blépharoplastie sans pédicule.
36 pp. 8°. Paris, 1918. No. 92.

NT   0045066   DNLM CtY NNC

Tartolin
  see
Tartu.

Tartoma
  see
Tartu.

Tartoué, Pierre.
  The art of portrait painting. New York: P. Tartoué [1920?].
201   illus. (incl. ports.)   12°.

514341A.   1. Portrait painting, French.
N. Y. P. L.   February 18, 1931

NT   0045069   NN

Tartour, Felix Étouil, dit
  see   Étouil, Felix, dit Tartour, 1897-

Tartour, Jules.
  ... Le charbon et la collaboration franco-britannique ...
Paris, Librairie sociale et économique, 1940.
  196 p.   24cm.
  Thèse—Univ. de Paris.
  "Bibliographie": p. [193]-194.

  1. Coal trade. 2. Coal trade—France. 3. Coal trade—Gt. Brit.
I. Title.
  Library of Congress   HD9540.5.T3
                                     42-28693

NT   0045071   DLC CtY

Tartra, A   E   1775-1840.
  De l'opération de la cataracte. Paris,
Impr. de L. P. Dubray, 1812.
  86 p.   24cm.

  At head of title: Concours pour la chaire
de médecine opératoire.
  Thesis - Faculté de médecine de Paris.

  1. Cataract.

NT   0045072   NNC-M NBuG DNLM PPC PPPH

QD
181
N1 T17
TARTRA,A   E   ,1775-1840
  Traite' de l'empoisonnement par l'acide
nitrique, par A. E. Tratra, médecin ...
Paris, Chez Méquignon l'aîné, an X, 1802.
  8vo viij, 302 p. 20 cm.

  Autograph of Edwin V. Hill.
  Halfbound in contemporary mottled calf and
tan speckled boards, and with tan paper at
corners, red leather label on spine, spine
lettered and stamped in gilt.
  1. Nitric acid--   Physiological effect.
  A. Ex libris: Hill,Edwin V.

NT   0045073   MBCo KyU

2578
272
L 65
Tartre, Père de.
  Lettre du Père de Tartre, Missionaire de la
Cie. de Jesus, à M. de Tartre son père.
  Lettres édifiantes et curieuses, Vol. 17, p. 5.

NT   0045074   DCU-H

Tartrou (Michel-Jacques-Joseph). *Contribution à l'étude de l'action de l'éther en injections
intramusculaires dans la coqueluche. 69 pp.
8°. Paris, 1921. No. 130.

NT   0045075   DNLM CtY

Tartschoff, Todja.
  The vision and other poems. Translated by James Kirkup and
Leopold Sirombo. [1. ed.] London, Newman & Harris [1953]
37 p. 18cm.

  I. Kirkup, James, 1918-   , tr.   II. Sirombo, Leopold, tr. III. Title.
IV. Sirombo, Leopold.

NT   0045076   NN

---

q977.235
T17h
Tartt, Jas. T., & co.
  History of Gibson county, Indiana, with illustrations descriptive of its scenery, and biographical sketches of some of its prominent men
and pioneers. By Jas. T. Tartt & co. Edwards-
ville, Ill., 1884.
  244p. plates(part fold.) ports., map.

  1. Gibson co., Indiana--Hist. 2. Gibson co.,
Indiana--Biog.

NT   0045077   IU InU MWA CtY OC

Tartt, William Macdowall, supposed author.

  America, an epistle in verse: with other poems ...
London, Longman, Hurst, Rees, Orme, and Brown; [etc.,
etc.] 1820.

Tartt, William MacDowall.
  Essays on some modern works, chiefly biographical.
By W. M. Tartt ... London, Tinsley brothers, 1876.
  2 v. 20½cm.
  CONTENTS.—v. 1. The dukes of Urbino. Edward Baines. Francesco
Sforza. Social life in past centuries. Harford's Michael Angelo. Decade of Italian women. Peden the prophet. Filippo Strozzi. Lord Macaulay as a translator. The pope and the friar. Whittington and his cat. Autobiography of Mrs. Piozzi. Early years of Pitt. Later years of Pitt. Last
years of Pitt.—v. 2. Washington Irving. Irving at Sunnyside. Reliques of
Miss Knight. Marc Isambard Brunel. Colossal vestiges. Lady Morgan.
Lord Stanhope. "Pictor Ignotus." Miss Berry. Windham. Our merchant
princes. Lucrezia Borgia. America by an American.
  1. Biography. 2. English literature—Hist. & crit.

  Library of Congress   CT104.T3
                                    3-2655

NT   0045079   DLC CtY NcD ICN PP NjP

Tartt, William MacDowall.
  Memoirs connected with the life and writings of Pandolfo-
Collenuccio, da Pesaro; with other memoirs of the fifteenth
century, the whole tr., comp., or written by W. M. Tartt ...
[Cheltenham?] 1868.
  vi p., 1 l., 329, [1] p., 1 l. front. (port.) illus. 23cm.
  "Edition of only 50 copies."
  Appended: "Explanations suggested by a review of 'Memoirs' ...":
1 p. l., 5 p.

  1. Collenuccio, Pandolfo, 1444-1504.

  Library of Congress   PQ4619.C8T3
                                   17—10972

NT   0045080   DLC CtY NN

Tartter, Eugen, 1905-
  Ueber Haemophilie ... Bergzabern (Pfalz)
1930.
  Inaug.- diss.- Heidelberg.
  Lebenslauf.
  "Literatur": p. [27]

NT   0045081   CtY

Tartu.
Tartu linna   aasta eelarwe. ₍Tartus, 19
   v. 30ᶜᵐ.

1. Budget—Tartu.

                               31–17850

Library of Congress   HJ9055.2.T3B2   352.109474

NT   0045082   DLC

Tartu. Academia Gustaviana
   see   Tartu. Ülikool.

Tartu. Astronomical and Geophysical Observatory
   see
Tartu. Astronoomia Observatoorium.

Tartu. Astronomicheskaïa observatoriïa
   see
Tartu. Astronoomia Observatoorium.

Tartu. Astronoomia Observatoorium.
   Beobachtungen
   see its
   Publikatsioonid.

Tartu. Astronoomia Observatoorium.
   Beobachtungen des Halleyschen Cometen ...
     see under   Struve, Wilhelm, 1793–1864.

Tartu. Astronoomia Observatoorium.
   Catalogus 795 stellarum duplicium, ex diversorum astronomorum observationibus conges-
tus in Specula Dorpatensi. Dorpati, Ex officina academica J. C. Schuenmanni, 1822.
   20 p. 24cm. in 28cm.

   "Ex volumine III. observationum Dorpaten-
sium."
   With manuscript notes.
   Volume of pamphlets.

NT   0045088   NNC

Tartu. Astronoomia Observatoorium.
   Étoiles doubles
     see under   Struve, Wilhelm, 1793–1864.

Tartu. Astronoomia Observatoorium.
   Наблюденія (*transliterated:* Nablïûdeniïa)
   see its
   Publikatsioonid.

Tartu. Astronoomia Observatoorium.
   Publications
   see its
   Publikatsioonid.

Tartu. Astronoomia Observatoorium.
   Publikatsioonid. Публикации.

   Tartu (Dorpat, Jurjew) 18 –19
      v. in   illus., diagrs., tables. 22–34 cm. irregular.
   Part of illustrative matter folded.
   Began publication in 1814 under title: Observationes astronomicas.
Cf. Union list of serials.
   Title varies: 18 –99, Beobachtungen (vols. for 18 have
also title: Наблюденія)—   Труды. Publikationen.—19
Publications.
   Issued under earlier names of the university and observatory:
18   Kaiserliche Universitäts-Sternwarte zu Jurjew (vormals

   Dorpat) (varies slightly);   Astronomicheskaïa observatoriïa
Imperatorskogo ïûr'evskogo universiteta (varies slightly); 19
Observatoire astronomique de l'Université de Tartu (Dorpat)
   Issued 18 –19   in German, 19   in English, 1952–   in
Russian (with summaries in English, 1957–)

   1. Astronomy—Collected works.

QB1.T25   46–43925 rev*

     MoKL RPB NNC InU PHC PU PSC CLSU ICJ
NT   0045093   DLC IU CU NjP LU MBdAF NN AzU CtY OU

Tartu. Astronoomia Observatoorium.
   Stellarum duplicium et multiplicium mensurae...
     see under   Struve, Wilhelm, 1793–1864.

QB6
.S9

     Tartu.   Astronoomia Observatoorium.

   Struve, Wilhelm, 1793–1864.
   Stellarum fixarum imprimis duplicium et multiplicium posi-
tiones mediae pro epocha 1830,0, deductae ex observationibus
meridianis annis 1822 ad 1843 in Specula dorpatensi institutis.
Auctore F. G. W. Struve ... Editae jussu et expensis Academiæ
caesareae petropolitanae. Petropoli, ex Typographia academica, 1852.

Tartu. Astronoomia Observatoorium.
   Tables donnant les mesures micrométriques
de plus de 500 étoiles doubles et multiples
observées à Dorpat, par M. F. G. W. Struve,
et classées par constellations, par Ch. Dien.
Paris, Chez Ch. Dien; et Bachelier, libraire,
1843.
   ₍10₎, 18 p. 4 double maps. 31cm.

NT   0045096   NNC

Tartu. Astronoomia Observatoorium.
   Tartu tähetorni kalender.

   Tartu, Eesti Riiklik Kirjastus.
     v. illus., diagrs. 26 cm. annual.
   Began publication in 1924. Cf. Tartu. Astronoomia Observa-
toorium. Publikatsioonid, v. 33, no. 5-6.
   Cover title: 19   Tähetorni kalender.

   1. Astronomy — Societies, etc.   I. Title.   II. Title: Tähetorni
kalender.

QB1.T32   64–44519

NT   0045097   DLC CU

QB
4
T255

   Tartu. Astronoomia Observatoorium.
     Teated. no.1-   19 -
     Tartu, 19 -
       v. illus. 21-27 cm.
   Largely reprints.
   Some issued under earlier names of the
university and observatory: Kaiserliche Uni-
versitäts-Sternwarte zu Jurjew (vormals
Dorpat); Astronomicheskaïa observatoriïa Im-
peratorskogo ïûr'evskogo universiteta; Ob-
servatoire astronomique de l'Université de
Tartu (Dorpat)
   Some have also title: Soobshchenïïa.

     1. Astronomy--Collected works. I. Tartu.
Astronoomia Observatoorium. Soobshchenïïa.

NT   0045099   LU TxU ICU CtY-D

Tartu. Astronoomia Observatoorium.
   Труды (*transliterated:* Trudy)
   see its
   Publikatsioonid.

Science
526
D73
   Tartu. Astronoomia Observatoorium.
   Vorläufiger Bericht von der russischen Grad-
messung mit allerhöchster Genehmigung auf
Veranstaltung der Kaiserlichen Universität zu
Dorpat während der Jahre 1821 bis 1827 in den
Ostseeprovinzen des Reichs, ausgeführt von Dr.
W. Struve. Denkschrift der Philosophen Facul-
tät zur Feier des am 12ten December 1827 zu
begehenden fünfundzwanzigjährlichen Jubel-
festes des Kaiserlichen Universität zu Dorpat.
Dorpat, J. C. Schünmann ₍1827₎
   iv, 24 p. fold. plate. 34cm.

NT   0045101   NNC

Tartu. Baltischer moorverein
   see
Baltischer moorverein, *Tartu.*

Tartu. Baltischer samenbauverband
     see   Baltischer samenbauverband, Tartu.

Tartu. Derptskiĭ universitet
   see
Tartu. Ülikool.

Tartu. Eesti Kirjanduse Selts
   see
Eesti Kirjanduse Selts.

20
E₅83
   Tartu. Eesti Põllumajanduse Akadeemia.
   Üliõpilaste teaduslike tööde kogumik.
   Agronoomia-alased tööd. Sbornik nauchnykh
   trudov studentov. Trudy po agronomii.
   Tartu.

   Includes Russian summaries.

NT   0045106   DNAL DLC

Tartu. Eesti Rahva Muuseum.
   Aastaraamat
   see
Tartu. Etnograafia Muuseum.
   Aastaraamat.

Tartu. Eesti rahva muuseum.
   ... Eesti rahvariiete album. Album estnischer volkstrach-
ten. Tartu ₍Trükk. H. Laakmanni graafiline kunstiasutus₎
1927.
   ₍6₎ p. x col. pl. 25½ᶜᵐ.

   At head of title: Eesti rahva muuseum.
   "Joonist. hra A. Mõtus" (Illustrations by A. Mõtus)

   1. Costume—Estonia.   I. Mõtus, A., illus.   II. Title.

                         CA 32–522 Unrev'd

Library of Congress   GT1330.E7T3   391.09474

NT   0045108   DLC NBC DSI MH

Tartu. Eesti rahva muuseum.
... Eesti rahvaröivad; 250 tekstijoonisega, 32 mitmevärvilise vasesügavtrükis ja 36 ühevärvilise ofsett-trükis tahvliga ning 5 mustrilehega, kirjutanud Helmi Kurrik. Toimetanud F. Linnus. Tartu, Sihtasutis Eesti rahva muuseum i kirjastus ₁1938₎
xxii p., 1 l., 221 p., 1 l. illus., LXVIII pl. (part col.) on 38 l. *and* portfolio of 5 fold. pl 30ᶜᵐ.
At head of title: Eesti rahva muuseum.
Résumé in French (16 p.) with t.-p.: Musée national estonien. Costumes nationaux estoniens ... 2. éd. Tartu ₁1938₎
1. Costume—Esthonia.   I. Kurrik, Helmi.   II. Linnus, Ferdinand, ed. III. Title.

New York. Public library   A 41-3761
for Library of Congress   GT1330.E7T32

NT   0045109   NN InU CLU CLSU WaS DLC OCU

Tartu. Eesti rahva muuseum.
... Eesti vanem mesindus ...
see under   Linnus, Ferdinand.

Tartu. Eesti rahva muuseum.
Estonian national museum, Eesti rahva muuseum. Tartu, Postimehe trükk, 1926.
14 p.

NT   0045111   PU

Tartu. Eesti rahva muuseum.
... Führer durch die ethnographischen sammlungen, von dr. I. Manninen. Tartu ₁Typogr. J. Mällo₎ 1928.
154 p., 1 l. illus., fold. map. 17ᶜᵐ.
At head of title: Eesti rahva muuseum. Estnisches nationalmuseum.

I. Manninen, Ilmari.

Library of Congress   AM101.T265 1928   32-14404
                      [069.54572] 572.074

NT   0045112   DLC MH

Tartu. Eesti rahva muuseum.
Musée national estonien. Eesti rahva muuseum. Tartu ₁"Postimehe" trükk₎ 1929.
14 p. 21¾ᶜᵐ.
Signed: F. L. ₁i. e. Ferdinand Leinbock₎

                     32-14403
Library of Congress   AM101.T266A5 1929   069.09474

NT   0045113   DLC DSI

Tartu. Eesti Rahva Muuseum.
... Rahvateadus likud küsimuskavad; questionnaire ethnographique. Tartu, 1932.
v. illus. 18 cm.
At head of title: Eesti rahva museum.

NT   0045114   DSI

Tartu. Eesti Rahva Muuseum
see also
Tartu. Fr. R. Kreutzwaldi nimeline Kirjandusmuuseum.

Tartu. Eesti Rahva Muuseum. Arhiivraamatukogu.
Z168
.E7A65
   Antik, Richard.
     Eesti raamatu 400 ₁i. e. nelisada₎ aastat; ülevaade eesti raamatu arengust ja juubelinäitus Arhiivraamatukogus 29. IX.-13. X. 1935. Toimetanud ja korraldanud R. Antik. Tartus, Sihtasutis Eesti Rahva Muuseum, 1935.

Tartu. Eesti Rahvaluule Arhiiv.
Rahvapärimuste selgitaja. 1-   Okt. 1936-
₁Tartu₎
   v. illus. 24 cm.

NT   0045117   OU

Tartu. Eesti Rahvaluule Arhiiv.
Toimetused. Commentationes. 1-
Tallinn, 1935 -

   Vols.   issued by Folkloristlik Osakond of the Riiklik Kirjandusmuuseum.

NT   0045118   CtY FU

Tartu. Eesti tervishoiu muuseum.
The aims and tasks of the Estonian museum of hygiene. Tartu, Estonia, Eesti tervishoiu muuseum, 1927.
cover-title, 3 (1) p. 20 cm.

NT   0045119   DL

WA
28
qT195
   TARTU. Eesti Tervishoiu Muuseum
     ₁Collection of publications₎

     The Library has a collection of miscellaneous publications of this organization kept as received. These publications are not listed or bound separately.

NT   0045120   DNLM

WA
28
T195e
1935
   TARTU. Eesti Tervishoiu Muuseum
     Eesti Tervishoiu Muuseum 1924-1934; 10 a. tegevuse ülevaade. The Estonian Museum of Hygiene; a survey of 10 years' work. Tartu, 1935.
     69 p. illus. (Its Väljaanne, 85)
     Summary in English.
     Series

NT   0045121   DNLM DL

Tartu. Eesti tervishoiu muuseum.
Miscellaneous printed matter.

   4 pieces.

NT   0045122   DL

W 1
TA612
   TARTU. Eesti Tervishoiu Muuseum
     Report of the Estonian Museum of Hygiene.
     Tartu [192-]-
     v.

NT   0045123   DNLM DL

W 1
TA616
   TARTU. Eesti Tervishoiu Muuseum
     Väljanne.

     A file of this publication is kept as received but not bound. Issues in the Library may be found on the shelves under the above call number.

NT   0045124   DNLM DL

Tartu. Entomoloogia Katsejaam
see **Tartu. Ülikool.** *Entomoloogia Katsejaam.*

Tartu. Estnisches Nationalmuseum
see
Tartu. Eesti rahva muuseum.

Tartu. Ėstonskaíà sel'skokhozíàĭstvennaíà akademiíà
see
Tartu. Eesti Põllumajanduse Akadeemia.

Tartu. Ėstonskiĭ narodnyĭ muzeĭ
see
Tartu. Etnograafia Muuseum.

Tartu. Etnograafia Muuseum.
Aastaraamat. 1.-
Tallinn ₁etc.₎ Eesti Riiklik Kirjastus ₁etc.₎ 1925-
     v. in   illus., col. plates, ports., maps, diagrs., plans. 24 cm.
Vols. 16-   have added t. p. in Russian.
Vols. 1-15 issued by Eesti Rahva Muuseum.
Some vols. have summaries in German, some in English, French and German, some in English, German and Russian.

1. Ethnology—Estonia.

AM101.T2742   32-7758 rev*

NT   0045129   DLC NN InU CU CtY MH PU

TARTU. Etnograafia Muuseum.
Aastaraamat. 1-
Tartu. Sihtasutis "Eesti rahva muuseumi" Kirjastus, etc. 1925-
    15 v. on 2 reels. illus., ports., maps.
Microfilm.
Annual.
At head of title of v.15: Eesti NSV teaduste Akadeemia. Академия наук Эстонской ССР.

NT   0045130   NN InU

4NK
174
   Tartu. Etnograafia Muuseum
     Eesti rahvakunst XIX sajandil; rahvaröivastes, tööriistades ja tarbeesemetes; näituse juht. ₁Koostajad: V. Kalits, et al.₎ Tartu, 1955.
     46 p.

NT   0045131   DLC-P4 MH

Tartu. Etnograafia Muuseum.
Ежегодник (*transliterated:* Ezhegodnik)
see its
Aastaraamat.

Tartu. Etnograafia Muuseum
see also
Tartu. Eesti Rahva Muuseum.

Tartu. Ėtnograficheskiĭ muzeĭ
see
Tartu. Etnograafia Muuseum.

Tartu. F.R. Kreutzwald-Literaturmuseum
    see
    Tartu. Fr. R. Kreutzwaldi nimeline Kirjandus-
        muuseum.

Tartu. Fr. R. Kreutzwaldi nimeline Kirjandus-
        muuseum.
            Eesti luule antaloogia
                see under title

PH665   Tartu. Fr. R. Kreutzwaldi nimeline Kirjandus-
.K68Z54   muuseum.

        Eesti NSV Teaduste Akadeemia. *Keele ja Kirjanduse Insti-*
        tuut.
            Ф. Р. Крейцвальд в портретах и иллюстрациях. ₍Редак-
        ционная коллегия: Э. Я. Сыгель и др.₎ Таллин, Эстонское
        гос. изд-во, 1953.

PH665   Tartu. Fr. R. Kreutzwaldi nimeline
.K68Z58   Kirjandusmuuseum.

        Fr. R. Kreutzwald, 1803–1882; elu ja tegevus sõnas ja pildis.
        ₍Toimetuskolleegium: E. Sõgel, et. al. Koostand M. Lepik
        ja L. Raud₎ Tallinn, Eesti Riiklik Kirjastus, 1953.

Tartu. Fr. R. Kreutzwaldi nimeline Kirjandus-
        muuseum.
            Riikliku Kirjandusmuuseumi aastaraamat
                see under title   [supplement]

Tartu. Fr. R. Kreutzwaldi nimeline
        Kirjandusmuuseum.
            Valimik eesti vanasõnu
                see under   Normann, Erna.

Tartu. Fr. R. Kreutzwaldi nimeline Kirjandusmuuseum
    see also
    Tartu. Eesti Rahva Muuseum.

Tartu. Fr. R. Kreutzwaldi nimeline Kirjandus-
        muuseum. Folkloristlik Osakond.
            Toimetused. Commentationes
                see under   Tartu. Eesti Rahvaluule
    Arhiiv.

Tartu. Gelehrte estnische gesellschaft
            see Tartu. Ülikool. Õpetatud eesti
    selts.

HJ9055
.2
.T3A3   **Tartu.** *Gorodskaĭa uprava.*
            Отчетъ объ исполненіи смѣты доходовъ.

        Юрьевъ, Г. Лаакманъ.
            v. in   33 cm. annual.

        1. Finance—Tartu.
        Title transliterated: Otchet ob ispolnenii smĕty dokhodov.

        HJ9055.2.T3A3   49–32359*

Tartu. Gosudarstvennyĭ literaturnyĭ muzeĭ
    see
    Tartu. Fr. R. Kreutzwaldi nimeline Kirjandusmuuseum.

Tartu. Gosudarstvennyĭ teatr "Vanemuĭne"
    see
    Tartu. Riiklik Teater "Vanemuine."

Tartu. Imperatorskaĭa meteorologicheskaĭa observa-
        toriĭa
    see
    Tartu. Ülikool. *Meteoroloogia observatoorium.*

Tartu. Imperatorskiĭ ĭŭr'evskiĭ universitet
    see
    Tartu. Ülikool.

Tartu. ĭŬr'evskiĭ universitet
    see
    Tartu. Ülikool.

Tartu. Kirjandusmuuseum
    see
    Tartu. Fr. R. Kreutzwaldi nimeline Kirjandusmuuseum.

Tartu. Kreutzwaldi nimeline Kirjandusmuuseum
    see
    Tartu. Fr. R. Kreutzwaldi nimeline Kirjandusmuuseum.

Tartu. Kunstiinstituut
    see also
    Tallinn. Eesti NSV Riiklik Kunstiinstituut.

Tartu. Kunstiühing "Pallas"
    see
    Kunstiühing "Pallas," *Tartu.*

Tartu. Landes-universität
    see
    Tartu. Ülikool.

Tartu. Literaturnyĭ muzeĭ
    see
    Tartu. Fr. R. Kreutzwaldi nimeline Kirjandusmuuseum.

Tartu. Livländische gemeinnützige und ökonomische
        sozietät
    see
    Livländische gemeinnützige und ökonomische sozietät.

Tartu. Loomatervishoiu ja piimahügieeni
        instituut
    see
    Tartu. Ülikool. Loomatervishoiu ja piimahüg-
        ieeni instituut.

Tartu. Meditsiiniline Kliinik
    see
    Tartu. Ülikool. *Meditsiiniline Kliinik.*

Tartu. Meteoroloogia observatoorium
    see
    Tartu. Ülikool. *Meteoroloogia observatoorium.*

Tartu. Musée national estonien
    see
    Tartu. Eesti rahva muuseum.

Tartu. Observatoire astronomique
    see
    Tartu. Astronoomia Observatoorium.

Tartu. Patoloogia-instituut
    see
    Tartu. Ülikool. Patoloogia-instituut.

Tartu. Postimees
        see Postimees.

Tartu. Realschule.
        Die Dorpster Realschule in dem ersten
        Decennium ihres Bestehens
            see under   ₍Ripke, Johannes₎ ed.

Tartu. Riiklik Etnograafiline Muuseum
    see
    Tartu. Etnograafia Muuseum.

Tartu. Riiklik Kirjandusmuuseum
    see
    Tartu. Fr. R. Kreutzwaldi nimeline Kirjandusmuuseum.

        TARTU. Riiklik Teater "Vanemuine."
        Vanemuine, 1865–1925. Tartus, "Vanemuise"
        kirjastus, 1925. 224 p. illus., ports. 24cm.

    1. Theatres—Estonia—Tartu.

Tartu. Riiklik Ülikool
see
Tartu. Ülikool.

Tartu. Sternwarte
see
Tartu. Astronoomia Observatoorium.

Tartu. Tähetorn
see
Tartu. Astronoomia Observatoorium.

Tartu. Ülikool.
  ... Acta et commentationes Imp. universitatis jurievensis (olim dorpatensis) [v.] 1–25, no. 6. Юрьевъ, Типографія К. Маттисена, 1893–1917.
  25 v. in 34. illus., plates, ports., maps, facsims., tables, diagrs. 25ᶜᵐ.
  Issued in parts forming annual volumes.
  Part of the illustrative material is folded.
  Title varies slightly.
  At head of title: Ученыя записки Императорскаго юрьевского университета.
  Chiefly in Russian.
  Superseded by its Acta et commentationes Universitatis tartuensis (dorpatensis) [Ser.] A–C; and Voronezh, Russia . Universitet. Acta Universitatis voronegiensis.

  AS262.T22A2   46–43956

NT   0045171   DLC MH NN WaU CU TxU

Tartu. Ülikool.
  ... Acta et commentationes Universitatis tartuensis (dorpatensis) A : Mathematica, physica, medica. [v.] 1–
Tartu, 1921–
  v. in   illus., plates, maps, tables, diagrs. 24ᶜᵐ. irregular.
  Supersedes in part its Acta et commentationes Imp. universitatis jurievensis (olim dorpatensis)
  Part of the illustrative material is folded.
  Title varies slightly.
  At head of title: Eesti vabariigi Tartu ülikooli toimetused.
  Articles chiefly in German, some in Estonian, etc. The Estonian and Russian articles are accompanied by summaries in German, French or English.
  1. Science—Societies, etc.

  AS262.T22A22   508   46–43953

     CU TU ICU DNLM ICJ N NN OU WvU
NT   0045172   DLC ViU CtY MH IaU MBdAF PPF PU PHC NcD

Tartu. Ülikool.
  ... Acta et commentationes Universitatis tartuensis (dorpatensis) B : Humaniora. [v.] 1–
Tartu, 1921–
  v. in   illus., plates, ports., maps, tables, diagrs. 24ᶜᵐ. irregular.
  Supersedes in part its Acta et commentationes Imp. universitatis jurievensis (olim dorpatensis)
  Part of the illustrative material is folded.
  Title varies slightly.
  At head of title: Eesti vabariigi Tartu ülikooli toimetused.
  Articles chiefly in German, some in Estonian, etc. The Estonian and Russian articles are accompanied by summaries in German, French or English.

  AS262.T22A23   082   46–43955

     ICJ
NT   0045173   DLC CU N PU PHC KyU NcD OClW NN DI-GS

Tartu. Ülikool.
  ... Acta et commentationes Universitatis tartuensis (dorpatensis) C : Annales. [v.] 1–
Tartu, 1929 [i. e. 1921]–
  v. in   illus., plates, ports., maps, tables. 23½ᶜᵐ. irregular.
  Supersedes in part its Acta et commentationes Imp. universitatis jurievensis (olim dorpatensis)
  At head of title: Eesti vabariigi Tartu ülikooli toimetused.
  Chiefly in Estonian.

  AS262.T22A24   082   46–43954

NT   0045174   DLC NcD PU PHC N PPF NN KU NhD WvU

Tartu. Ülikool.
  Album academicum der Kaiserlichen universität Dorpat. Bearbeitet von A. Hasselblatt and dr. G. Otto ... Dorpat, C. Mattiesen, 1889.
  viii, 1007 p. 23ᶜᵐ.
  On spine: 1802–1889.

  I. Hasselblatt, Arnold, 1852–   ed. II. Otto, Gustav Adolf Friedrich,
  1843–   joint ed.
  Library of Congress   LF4225.A4   15–1564 Revised

NT   0045175   DLC CLU

Tartu. Ülikool.
  Album academicum der Kaiserlichen Universität Dorpat. Zur Jubel-Feier ihres fünfzigjährigen Bestehens, am 12. December 1852. Dorpat: H. Laakmann, 1852.   iv, 134, xxx p.   4°.

  1. Dorpat.   Universität.—Registers.
  N. Y. P. L.   November 28, 1924

NT   0045176   NN

Tartu. Ülikool.
  Apophoreta Tartuensia. Acta Universitati Tartuensi
  see under   Olvet-Jensen, Jaan, ed.

Tartu. Ülikool.
  Beschreibung der festlichkeiten bei der jubelfeier der Kaiserlichen universität Dorpat am 12. und 13. december 1852. [St. Petersburg, Buchdr. der Kaiserl. akademie der wissenschaften, 1853]
  21 p. 22½ᶜᵐ.
  Caption title.
  "St. Petersb. zeitung 1853, no. ... 1, 2, 3, 4 u. 5."

                    46–36911
  Library of Congress   LF4220.A3

NT   0045178   DLC

Tartu. Ülikool.
  [Библіографическіе матеріалы по исторіи Дерптскаго-Юрьевскаго университета. [Юрьевъ, Типографія К. Маттисена, 1899]
  11 p. 24½ᶜᵐ.
  Title taken from introduction, p. [1] (t.-p. wanting?)
  "Печатается какъ рукопись.
  Preface signed: Редакціонная коммиссія для изданія матеріаловъ по исторіи Императорскаго Юрьевскаго (Дерптскаго) университета.

  1. Dorpat.   Universitet—Bibl.   I. Title.
                    41–41380
  Library of Congress   Z5055.R9D68

NT   0045179   DLC

Tartu. Ülikool.
  Біографическій словарь профессоровъ и преподавателей Императорскаго Юрьевскаго, бывшаго Дерптскаго, университета за сто лѣтъ его существованія (1802–1902). Подъ ред. Г. В. Левицкаго. Юрьевъ, Тип. К. Маттисена, 1902.
  2 v. 26 cm.

  I. Levitskiĭ, Grigoriĭ Vasilʹevich, 1852–1918, ed. II. Title.
        Title romanized : Biograficheskiĭ slovarʹ professorov i prepodavateleĭ Imperatorskago I͡Urʹevskago, byvshago Derptskago, universiteta.

  LF4294.A2B56   5–39262

NT   0045180   DLC WU

   W
   19. 5   TARTU. Ülikool
   GE7
   D7D7   Catalogs, announcements of courses, requirements for admission and other publications relating to the academic program will be found under the above call number. Included also are similar publications of individual schools or departments of instruction of the institution.

NT   0045181   DNLM

Tartu. Ülikool.
  Dante pidu, 14. Sept. 1921
  see under title

Tartu. Ülikool.
  Der kaiserlichen universitaet Dorpat zu ihrem fünfzigjaehrigen jubelfeste am 12. dec. 1852. widmet ...
  see under   Naturforscher-Verein zu Riga.

Tartu. Ülikool.
  [Dissertationen] 1825–

NT   0045184   ICJ

Tartu. Ülikool.
  [Dissertationen. v. 1–   ] Dorpat,[etc.]
1887–
  v. in   26 cm.
  1. Dissertations, Academic.

NT   0045185   CU ICJ

Tartu. Ülikool.
  Доклады Комиссіи, избранной Совѣтомъ Императорскаго Юрьевскаго университета для составленія проекта мотивированныхъ отвѣтовъ на вопросы, предложенные господиномъ Министромъ народнаго просвѣщенія, относительно желательнаго устройства университетовъ. Юрьевъ, Тип. Шнакенбурга, 1901.
  158 p. 26 cm.
  "На правахъ рукописи.

  I. Russia Ministerstvo narodnogo prosveshcheniia.
                 Title transliterated: Doklady Komissii.
  LF4211.B8   74–220427

NT   0045186   DLC

   LF4226
   .S4T3   Tartu. Ülikool.
         Документы по дѣлу объ увольненіи и. о. ассистента Геологическаго кабинета при Юрьевскомъ университетѣ Д. П. Севастьянова. Юрьевъ, Тип. К. Маттисена, 1907.
         iv, 46, 82 p. 24 cm.

  1. Sevastʹi͡anov, Dmitriĭ Petrovich.   I. Title.
                Title transliterated: Dokumenty po dĕlu ob uvolʹnenii ... D. P. Sevastʹi͡anova.
  LF4226.S4T3   56–48035

NT   0045187   DLC

Tartu. Ülikool.
  Eesti Vabariigi Tartu Ülikool, 1919–1929. Tartu, 1929.
  xvi, 432 p. illus., ports. 24 cm. (Its Acta et commentationes Universitatis Tartuensis (Dorpatensis) C: 10)

  1. Tartu. Ülikool—History.   I. Title. II. Series: Tartu. Ülikool. Acta et commentationes Universitatis Tartuensis (Dorpatensis) C: Annales, 10.
  AS262.T22A24 no. 10   72–177551
  [LF4224]

NT   0045188   DLC

   AS262   Tartu. Ülikool.
   D 63   Eesti Vabariigi Tartu ülikooli ettelugemiste kava. Tartus, 19
         v.   22.5 cm.
         Program of lectures of the Tartu university of the Esthonian Republic.

NT   0045189   DLC NN DNLM PU

Tartu. Ülikool.
    Eesti vabariigi Tartu ülikooli toimetused
      see its

    Acta et commentationes Universitatis tartuensis (dorpatensis) A : Mathematica, physica, medica.
    Acta et commentationes Universitatis tartuensis (dorpatensis) B : Humaniora.
    Acta et commentationes Universitatis tartuensis (dorpatensis) C : Annales.

Tartu. Ülikool.
    Eesti Wabariigi Tartu ülikooli isiklik koosseis ... République Estonienne. État du personnel du l'Université de Tartu (Dorpat)
    Tartu, 19
      v. 22½ᵐ.

192 –23 have title in Esthonian only.
1922– illustrated t.-p.

                                CA 27–479 Unrev'd
Library of Congress   AS262.D64

NT   0045191   DLC NN DSI ICJ MiU

Tartu. Ülikool.
    Die ehrenlegion der 14,000 Immatriculierten
      see under Hasselblatt, Arnold, 1852–

Tartu. Ülikool.
    ... Ettelugemiste kava
      see its Eesti Vabariigi Tartu ülikooli ettelugemiste kava.

LF 4229.5
.T2   TARTU--Ülikool.
    Facultäts-Schriften der Kaiserlichen Universität Dorpat, dargebracht zur Feier ihres 50-jährigen Bestehens, am 12. December 1852.
    Dorpat, 1852,
      5 v. in 1. tables.

    Each volume has separate t.-p.

    I. Title.

NT   0045194   InU

Tartu. Ülikool.
    Festrede zur Jahresfeier der Stiftung der Universität Dorpat
      see under Meyer, Leo, 1830–1910.

Tartu. Ülikool.
    Festrede₍ₙ₎ zur jahresfeier der stiftung der Universität Dorpat .../ nebst den mittheilungen über die preisaufgaben sowie dem universitäts-jahresbericht ... Hrsg. von der Kaiserlichen universität Dorpat.
    Dorpat, 18
      v. 25½–27½ᵐ.

            ₍30b1₎   CA 7–5937 Unrev'd
Library of Congress   LF4211.C5

NT   0045196   DLC DNLM CU

Tartu. Ülikool.
    Indices scholarum per semestre prius et alterum a.1862. Dorpati,1862.

    4°.

NT   0045197   MH

LF 4229.5
.T25   TARTU--ÜLIKOOL
    Die Kaiserliche Universität Dorpat während der ersten fünfzig Jahre ihres Bestehens und Wirkens. Denkschrift zum Jubelfeste am 12ten und 13ten Dec. 1852. Dorpat, gedr. bei J.C. Schünmann's Wittwe und C. Mattiesen, 1852.
      168 p.

NT   0045198   InU MH

Tartu. Ülikool.
    Die Kaiserliche universität zu Dorpat. Fünfundzwanzig jahre nach ihrer gründung. Dorpat ₍Gedruckt bei J. C. Schünmann₎ 1827.
    3 p. l., xxxiv, 60 p. xix pl. (incl. plans) 49½ᵐ.
    Engraved t.-p.

                          9–8677 Revised
Library of Congress   LF4220.A2

NT   0045199   DLC

Tartu. Ülikool.
    Die landwirtschaftlichen Versuchsstationen der Universität Tartu. Tartu, 1937. 64 p. illus. (incl. ports.) 23cm.
    Bibliographical footnotes.
    "Publikationen der phytopathologischen Versuchsstation," p. 52–55.

1. Agriculture—Experiment   stations—Esthonia—Tartu.
N. Y. P. L.   May 4, 1938

NT   0045200   NN DNAL

Tartu. Ülikool.
    Личный составъ.
    Юрьевъ (Дерптъ)
      no. in   v. 27 cm. annual.
    Issued by the university under its earlier names: 18( )–02. Imperatorskiĭ Derptskiĭ universitet; 1893–19 'Imperatorskiĭ fürevskiĭ universitet.

             Title transliterated: Lichnyĭ sostav.
    LF4211.C92   51–34320

NT   0045201   DLC

Tartu. Ülikool.
    Loi concernant l'Université de la République Estonienne à Tartu. Éd. inofficielle. Tartu, 1925. 45 p. 21cm.
    Cover title.

NT   0045202   NN

Q171
.M315   Tartu. Ülikool.
    Материалы двадцать второй научной студенческой конференции: Биология, география, геология. Тарту, 19

Microfilm
11384
PA
    Tartu . Ülikool.
    Paucker, Karl Heinrich von, 1820–1883.
    Meletematum lexistoricorum specimen conscripsit C. Paucker ... inclytae Universitatis litterarum lugdunensis batavae sacris secularibus tertiis concelebrandis Caes. universitatis litt. dorpatensis iussu et auctoritate editum. Dorpati, typis H. Laakmanni, 1875.

Tartu. Ülikool.
    Das mineralogische Cabinet der Kaiserlichen Universität
      see under Grewingk, Constantin Caspar Andreas, 1819–1887.

Tartu. Ülikool.
    ₍Obzor di︠e︡i︠a︡tel'nosti Imperatorskago Derptskago universiteta₎ Обзоръ дѣятельности Императорскаго Дерптскаго университета; на память о 1802–1865 годахъ. Дерптъ, Тип. К. Матисена, 1866.
    172 p. 27 cm.

    1. Tartu. Ülikool—History. I. Title.

    LF4290.A6   72–226427

NT   0045206   DLC

Tartu. Ülikool.
    Ordinis medicorum in Universitate Caesarea Dorpatensi annales
      see under Köhler, Hermann Johann von, 1792–1860.

LF
4211
qD715pe   Tartu. Ülikool.
    Personal, nebst Beilage.
    Dorpat ₍18—?₎-
      v.

NT   0045208   DNLM

Tartu. Ülikool.
    Practicum juridicum
      see under Bröcker, Erdmann Gustav von.

LF 4221   TARTU--Ülikool.
.A7   Statut der kaiserlichen Universität Dorpat.
    Dorpat, 1820.
      137 p.

    Title and text in Russian and German.

NT   0045210   InU

378.4741
T195
E   Tartu. Ülikool.
    Tartu Ülikooli ajaloo allikaid. Quellen zur Geschichte der Universität Tartu (Dorpat) Im Auftrage der Universität Tartu hrsg. und mit einer Einleitung versehen von Juhan Vasar. Tartu, 1932–
      v. 24cm. (Eesti Vabariigi Tartu Ülikooli toimetused. Acta et commentationes Universitatis Tartuensis (Dorpatensis) C. Annales, 14)

NT   0045211   IEN

Tartu. Ülikool.
    Tartu ülikool soñas ja pildis, 1919–1932. Tartu, E. v. Tartu ülikool, 1932.
    174 p. illus., diagrs. 27ᵐ.
    Foreword signed: J. Kõpp.
    Errata slip attached to back cover.

                          42–32681

Library of Congress   LF4222.A4

    ICRL
NT   0045212   DLC CU CSt PPF DSI ICJ NN MiU ICF DNLM

Tartu. Ülikool.
    Tartu ülikooli nõukogu kodukord (U. S. 23) ₍Tartus, 1927₎
    7 p. 21cm.
    Film reproduction. Negative.

NT   0045213   NN

AS
262
T17t
Tartu. Ülikool.
Teaduslikud tööd pühendatud Tartu Riikliku
Ülikooli 150. aastaṗievale, 1802-1952. [Redaktsiooni-kollegium: E. Martinson et al.]
Tallinn, Eesti Riiklik kirjastus, 1952.
483 p. illus.

Added title in Russian. Articles in Estonian
or Russian, with summaries in Russian or Estonian.

NT   0045214   CLU CtY

Tartu. Ülikool.
Tentamen generis tamaricum species accuratius
difiniendi
    see under   Bunge, Alexander von, 1803-
1890.

Tartu. Ülikool.
Toimetised. Ученые записки.
Tartu, 19

no. in   v. illus., ports., maps. 22 cm.
Began publication in 1941. Cf. Serial publications of the Soviet
Union, 1939-1957.
Publication suspended 1942-45.
Estonian or Russian.
Tables of contents also in English and German; summaries in
English and German.

AS262.T22A25   61-26211

NT   0045216   DLC MiU MBCo NN NNM CtY NcD CSt NjR NN

Tartu. Ülikool.
Toimetused
  see its
Acta et commentationes Universitatis tartuensis (dorpatensis) A : Mathematica, physica, medica.
Acta et commentationes Universitatis tartuensis (dorpatensis) B : Humaniora.
Acta et commentationes Universitatis tartuensis (dorpatensis) C : Annales.

Tartu. Ülikool.
Ученые записки (*transliterated:* Uchenye zapiski)
see its
Toimetised.

Tartu. Ülikool. Ученыя записки Императорскаго юрьевскаго университета (*transliterated:* Uchenyĭa zapiski Imperatorskago i͡ur'evskago universiteta)
see its Acta et commentationes Imp. universitatis jurievensis.

Tartu. Ülikool.
        L378.47
        TaE1
L'Université de la République Esthonienne à Tartu et l'Union des étudiants d'Esthonie. Tartu, Imprimerie "Postimees", 1923.
34, [2] p. 26ᶜᵐ.
On cover: Édition du Bureau des affaires étrangères de l'Union des étudiants d'Esthonie.

NT   0045220   ICJ

Tartu. Ülikool.
Verzeichniss der Vorlesungen
    see its   Eesti Vabariigi Tartu Ülikooli
ettelugemiste kava.

Tartu. Ülikool.
Vorschriften für die Studierenden der Kaiserl. Universität
Dorpat... Dorpat: J. C. Schünmann, 1832. 60 p. 12°.

1. Student life—Russia, 1832.
N. Y. P. L.   February 4, 1925

NT   0045222   NN

Tartu. Ülikool.
Vorschriften für die studirenden der Kaiserlichen universität Dorpat. Dorpat, Druck von Schnakenburg's anstalt, 1880.
69 p. 21½ᶜᵐ.

                    46-36913
Library of Congress   LF4211.A7 1880

NT   0045223   DLC DNLM

Tartu. Ülikool.
Vorschriften für die studirenden der Kaiserlichen universität Dorpat. Dorpat, Schnakenburg's buchdruckerei, 1886.
76 p. 22ᶜᵐ.

                    46-36910
Library of Congress   LF4211.A7 1886

NT   0045224   DLC

Tartu. Ülikool.
Vorschriften für die Studirenden.   Jerjew,
C. Mattiesen, 1893.
32 p.   8°.

NT   0045225   DNLM

LF4212
.5
.A74   Tartu. Ülikool.
Заключенія факультетовъ, выработанныя, по порученію Правленія, докладъ профессора Срезневскаго, докладъ Библіотечной коммиссіи и мнѣнія отдѣльныхъ членовъ Совѣта Императорскаго Юрьевскаго университета по вопросамъ, предложеннымъ господиномъ министромъ народнаго просвѣщенія относительно желательнаго устройства университетовъ. ҊЮрьевъ, 1901҉
1 v. (various pagings)   tables.   25 cm.
"На правахъ рукописи."
1. Universities and colleges.   I. Title.
Title transliterated: Zaklîûchenîi͡a fakul'tetov ... po voprosam ... otnositel'no zhelatel'nago ustroĭstva universitetov.

LF4212.5.A74   63-57528

NT   0045226   DLC

Tartu. Ülikool.
Zur jebelfeier der Kaiserlichen universität Dorpat, am 12 und 13 Dezember 1852. Festschrift der medizinischen facultät. Die monogene fortpflanzung.   Dorpat, Gedruckt bei J.C. Schünmann's Wittwe und C. Mattiesen [1852]
150 p.   27.5 cm.

NT   0045227   PPAN

Tartu. Ülikool.
Das zweite Jubelfest der Kaiserlichen Universität Dorpat, fünfzig Jahre nach ihrer Gründung gefeiert am 12.und 13.December 1852. Dorpat, Gedruckt bei Schürmann & Mattiesen, 1853
xxxiv, 94 p.   tables

NT   0045228   MH

Tartu. Ülikool
  see also
Voronezh, Russia (City) Universitet.

        Tartu. Ülikool. Akadeemiline Emakeele Selts.
AP95
.E4E38
Eesti keel. 1.–19. aastakäik; 1922–40. Tartu.

Tartu. Ülikool. Akadeemiline Emakeele Selts
  see also
Emakeele Selts.

Tartu. Ülikool. Arstiteaduskond.
Festschrift der medizinischen Facultät. Die monogene fortpflanzung ...
    see   Tartu. Ülikool.
Zur Jubelfeier der Kaiserlichen Universität Dorpat ...

Tartu. Ülikool. Arstiteaduskond.
Verzeichniss der von der medicinischen Facultät zu Dorpat seit ihrer Gründung (1802-1892) veröffentlichen Schriften ...
    see under   Grünfeld, Abraham, 1866-

Tartu. Ülikool. *Arstiteaduskond. Meditsiiniline Kliinik*
  see
Tartu. Ülikool. *Meditsiiniline Kliinik.*

Tartu. Ülikool. *Astronomicheskai͡a observatorii͡a*
  see
Tartu. Astronoomia Observatoorium.

Tartu. Ülikool. Augenklinik
    see   Tartu. Ülikool. Silmakliinik.

Tartu. Ülikool. *Bibliothek*
  see
Tartu. Ülikool. *Teaduslik Raamatukogu.*

Tartu. Ülikool. *Bogoslovskiĭ fakul'tet*
  see
Tartu. Ülikool. *Usuteaduskond.*

Tartu. Ülikool. *Botaanika Aed.*
... Acta Horti botanici Universitatis imperialis Jurjevensis. ... Trudy Botanicheskago sada Imperatorskago iur'evskago universiteta. ... Iur'ev, Pechatano v tipo. K. Mattisena, 1900-1914.
Library has vol. 1-15, pt. 1, 1900-1914. illus., plates, ports., maps. 25½ᶜᵐ.
Director: N. I. Kuznetsov.
No more published?

NT   0045239   ICJ PPAN MiU

Tartu. Ülikool. *Botaanika Aed.*
Die officinellen und technisch wichtigen pflanzen des Botanischen gartens der Veterinär-schule zu Dorpat. Dorpat, Druck von Schuenmanns wittwe und C. Mattiesen, 1861.
v, [1], 38 p. 21½ᶜᵐ.

1. Botany, Economic.
                      11-13840
Library of Congress   SB60.D7A3

NT   0045240   DLC

Tartu. Ülikool. Botaanika Instituut.
Acta Instituti et Horti botanici Universitatis Tartuensis (Dorpatensis) v. 1-6; 1926-1937/38.
v. illus., plates, diagrs. 24 cm.
QK1.T3

NT   0045241   DSI DLC MH-G PPAN PU-BZ

Tartu. Ülikool. Botaanika-instituut.
Taimefüsioloogia laboratoorium.
Kaho, Hugo, 1885–
... Das verhalten der eiweissstoffe gesunder und abbaukranker kartoffelknollen gegen salze, von Hugo Kaho. Tartu ₍K. Mattiesens buchdr. ant.-ges.₎ 1935 ₍i. e. 1936₎

Tartu. Ülikool. Botanicheskii s'ad
 see Tartu. Ülikool. Botaanika Aed.

Tartu. Ülikool. Botanischer Garten
 see Tartu. Ülikool. Botaanika Aed.

Tartu. Ülikool. *Chair of Systematic Botany and Geobotany*
 see
Tartu. Ülikool. *Matemaatika-Loodusteaduskond.*

Tartu. Ülikool. Chirurgische Klinik
 see Tartu. Ülikool. Kirurgiakliinik.

Tartu. Ülikool. Eesti Rahvaluule Arhiiv
 see Tartu. Eesti Rahvaluule Arhiiv.

Tartu. Ülikool. *Eesti veekogude uurimiskomisjon.*
Väljaanne.
Tartus.
 v. illus. 23 cm.

1. Baltic Sea.

GC571.T3   55–22177 ‡

NT 0045248 DLC

Tartu. Ülikool. Emakeele Selts
 see
Tartu. Ülikool. Akadeemiline Emakeele Selts.

Tartu. Ülikool. *Entomoloogia Katsejaam.*
Teadaanded.
Tartu, 19
 no. illus. 24–27 cm.
 No. have title also in German.
 Each number summarized, usually in German.
 Reprints from various scientific journals.

1. Insects, Injurious and beneficial—Estonia.

SB599.T35   55–52126 ‡

NT 0045250 DLC DSI PPAN

TARTU. Ülikool. Estonia.
Album Estonorum. Hrsg. vom Philisterverbande der Estonia. 4. Aufl. Tallinn, Estländische Druckerei, 1939. 455 p. 21cm.

 —— Nachtrag zum Album Estonorum von 1939. Bovenden. 1961.
36 p. 21cm.

1. College societies--Esthonia--Tartu Ülikool. 2. Students, Foreign--
Assoc. and org.--Esthonia--   Tartu. 3. Germans in
Esthonia--Tartu. I. Title.

NT 0045252 NN CtY

Tartu. Ülikool. *Faculty of Mathematics and Natural Science*
 see
Tartu. Ülikool. *Matemaatika-Loodusteaduskond.*

Tartu. Ülikool. Farmakoloogia Instituut.
Arbeiten des pharmakologischen Institútes zu Dorpat. Hrsg. von R. Kobert. Pts. 1–13. Stuttgart, F. Enke, 1888–96.
8 .

NT 0045254 DNLM PPC OU MiU

QP509
.K6

Tartu. Ülikool. Farmakoloogia-Instituut.
Arbeiten. (Indexes)
Kobert, Rudolf, 1854–1918, *ed.*
Görbersdorfer Veröffentlichungen. Stuttgart, F. Enke, 1898.

RM
41
T19

Tartu. Ülikool. Farmakoloogia-Instituut.
Historische Studien aus dem Pharmakologischen Institut der Kaiserlichen Universität Dorpat. Hrsg. von Rudolf Kobert. Halle, a. S., Tausch & Grosse, 1889-96.
5 v. 26cm.

1. Pharmacology--Hist. I. Kobert, Rudolf, 1854-1918, ed.

 WU NcD-MC DNLM UU ICJ NN
NT 0045256 NIC InU PPC WaU OClW CtY-M CU-M MiU PPC

PA5000
.R4

Tartu. Ülikool. Filosoofiateaduskond.

Revue byzantine... Византійское обозрѣніе, издаваемое при Историко-филологическомъ факультетѣ Императорскаго Юрьевскаго университета. t. 1– 1915–
Юрьевъ ₍1915–

Tartu. Ülikool. *Fiziko-matematicheskiĭ fakulʹtet*
 see
Tartu. Ülikool. *Matemaatika-loodusteaduskond.*

Tartu. Ülikool. Frauenklinik
 see Tartu. Ülikool. Naistekliinik.

QC989
.R6T3

Tartu. Ülikool. Füüsika instituut.
Tartu. Ülikool. *Meteoroloogia observatoorium.*
Meteorologische beobachtungen angestellt in Dorpat. ₍1.₎– jahrg.; 1866– Dorpat, 1868–19

Tartu. Ülikool. *Füüsika-kabinett*
 see
Tartu. Ülikool. *Füüsika instituut.*

Tartu. Ülikool. Gelehrte estnische gesellschaft
 see
Tartu. Ülikool. Õpetatud eesti selts.

Tartu. Ülikool. Geograafia Instituut.
Publicationes Instituti universitatis Tartuensis geographici. Tartu, published 1925-39?

NT 0045263 DLC OUCA

Tartu. Ülikool. Geoloogia instituut.
...Toimetused; Publications of the Geological institution of the University of Tartu, no. Tartu, 1924-39.
 v. illus., plates. 24 cm.
 No more published?

NT 0045264 DSI DI-GS KyU MoU

Tartu. Ülikool. *Historisch-philologische fakultät*
 see
Tartu. Ülikool. *Filosoofiateaduskond.*

Tartu. Ülikool. Hortus botanicus
 see Tartu. Ülikool. Botaanika Aed.

Tartu. Ülikool. Institut de physique
 see Tartu. Ülikool. Füüsika Instituut.

Tartu. Ülikool. Institut zootomique.
Bulletin biologique. n.p., 1907.

NT 0045268 PPAN

Tartu. Ülikool. Institutum Botanicum
 see Tartu. Ülikool. Botaanika Instituut.

Tartu. Ülikool. Institutum Geographicum
 see Tartu. Ülikool. Geograafia Instituut.

Tartu. Ülikool. *Istoriko-filologicheskiĭ fakulʹtet*
 see
Tartu. Ülikool. *Filosoofiateaduskond.*

Tartu. Ülikool. *I͡Uridicheskiĭ fakulʹtet*
 see
Tartu. Ülikool. *Õigusteaduskond.*

Tartu. Ülikool. *Juristische fakultät*
 see
Tartu. Ülikool. *Õigusteaduskond.*

Tartu. Ülikool. Juuditeaduse Seminar.
Tartu ülikooli Juuditeaduse seminari ettekanded... Scholae
Seminarii litterarum Judaearum Universitatis Tartuensis.
[nr.] 1

Tartu, 1935   23cm.
no.
Title also in Hebrew.

1. No subject.
N. Y. P. L.   November 30, 1937

NT   0045274   NN DLC MH

Tartu. Ülikool. Kirurgiakliinik.
Annalen der Chirurgischen Abtheilung des Clinicum der Kaiser-
¹¹⁹¹²² lichen Universität Dorpat ... . Dorpat, C. A. Kluge, 1837–1839.
Library has vol. 1–2. plates, fold. table. 23ᶜᵐ.
Editor: Nicolaus Pirogoff.

NT   0045275   ICJ

Tartu. Ülikool. Kirurgiakliinik.
Arbeiten der chirurgischen Universitätsklinik
Dorpat. Hrsg. von W. Koch. Leipzig, Vogel,
1896–

NT   0045276   PPC OClW-H DNLM

W 1
DO741   Tartu. Ülikool. Kirurgiakliinik.
Mittheilungen.
1856–
Dorpat.
v.
Editor: 1856–   G. von Oettingen.
I. Oettingen, Georg Philipp von,
1824–   ed.

NT   0045277   DNLM

WX
qD715u   Tartu. Ülikool. Kirurgiakliinik.
1843   Uebersicht der im zweiten Semester
1841 und im Jahre 1842 in dem Chirurgischen Klinikum der Kaiserlichen Universität zu Dorpat behandelten Krankheiten
und verrichteten Operationen, von Georg
F. B. Adelmann. Dorpat, Laakmann,
1843.
18 p.
I. Adelmann, Georg Franz Blasius,
1811–1888

NT   0045278   DNLM

Tartu. Ülikool. Litterarum societas esthonica
see
Tartu. Ülikool. Õpetatud eesti selts.

Tartu. Ülikool. Loodusuurijate Selts.
Annales
see
Loodusuurijate Selts.
Aastaraamat.

Tartu. Ülikool. Loodusuurijate Selts.
Aruanded
see
Loodusuurijate Selts.
Aastaraamat.

Q4
.E3   Tartu. Ülikool. Loodusuurijate selts.
Eesti loodus. 1.–   a.-k.; 15. veeb. 1933–
Tartu [1933–

Q60
.T264   Tartu. Ülikool. Loodusuurijate selts.
Eesti loodusteaduse arhiiv ... Acta ad res naturae estonicae
perscrutandas ... I ser.: Geologica, chemica et physica. v.
1–
Tartu (Dorpat) 1854–19

Q60
.T265   Tartu. Ülikool. Loodusuurijate selts.
Eesti loodusteaduse arhiiv ... Acta ad res naturae estonicae
perscrutandas ... II ser.: Biologica. v. 1–
Tartu (Dorpat, Jurjew) 1859–19

Tartu. Ülikool. Loodusuurijate selts. Kirjatööd
see its Schriften.

[Tartu. Ülikool. Loodusuurijate selts]
Lepidoptera baltica. Schmetterlings-verzeichniss der Ostseeprovinzen nach dem catalog Staudinger-Rebel. [Jurjew
(Dorpat) Druck von C. Mattiesen, 1902.
xl, [4], 79 p. 25ᶜᵐ. (On cover: Archiv für die naturkunde Liv-, Ehst-
und Kurlands. Hrsg. von der Naturforscher-gesellschaft bei der Universität Jurjew (Dorpat) 2. ser. Biologische naturkunde. Bd. XII,
lfg. 1)
1. Lepidoptera—Baltic provinces. [1. Baltic provinces—Entomology]
I. Staudinger, Otto, 1830–1900. Catalog der lepidopteren des palaearcti-
schen faunengebietes. 3. aufl. II. Title.
Q60.T265 bd. 12, lfg. 1   Agr 3–196 rev †

U. S. Dept. of agr. Library   511J97
for Library of Congress   [r46b2]†

NT   0045286   DNAL DLC

Tartu. Ülikool. Loodusuurijate Selts.
Протоколы (transliterated: Protokoly)
see
Loodusuurijate Selts.
Aastaraamat.

Tartu. Ülikool. Loodusuurijate selts.
... Schriften. [v.]
Jurjew [etc.] 1884–19
v. in   illus., plates, maps, tables, diagrs. 23½–28½ᶜᵐ. irregular.
Part of the illustrative matter is folded.
Vols. 1–   1884–19 issued under the society's earlier name:
Naturforscher-gesellschaft bei der Universität Jurjew (varies slightly)
Vols. 10–23 have also title: Труды Общества естествоиспытателей
при Императорскомъ юрьевскомъ университетѣ; v. 24 has also title:
Tartu ülikooli juures oleva Loodusuurijate seltsi kirjatööd.
Text of v. 1–9, 24 in German; of v. 10–23 in Russian.
Vol. 10 published in Moscow.
Ceased publication with v. 24, 1925. cf. Union list of serials.
1. Biology—Societies, etc.
Q60.T27   46–43926

NT   0045288   DLC ICJ PPAmP PU PPAN NN

Tartu. Ülikool. Loodusuurijate Selts.
Sitzungsberichte
see
Loodusuurijate Selts.
Aastaraamat.

Tartu. Ülikool. Loodusuurijate selts.
Списокъ изданій и Обшія именной указатель статей,
помѣщенныхъ въ томахъ III (1869) по XIV (1905) включ.
Протоколовъ общества. Verzeichnis der Editionen und
General-Namenregister zu den Bänden III (1869) bis XIV
(1905) incl. der Sitzungsberichte der Naturforscher-Gesell-
schaft. Jurjew, Druck von C. Mattiesen, 1906.
[cl]–clv p. 24 cm.
Title from cover.
Separate from the society's Sitzungsberichte, v. 14, pt. 2.
1. Natural history—Bibl.   2. Natural history—Russia—Bibl. 3.
Indexes.   Title transliterated: Spisok izdanïi.
Z7403.T3   9–7356 rev*

NT   0045290   DLC DI-GS

Tartu. Ülikool. Loodusuurijate selts. Труды (transliterated: Trudy)
see its Schriften.

Tartu. Ülikool. Loodusuurijate Selts
see also
Loodusuurijate Selts.

Tartu. Ülikool. Loodusuurijate Selts. Raamatukogu.
... Katalog der bibliothek der Naturforscher-gesellschaft bei der Universität Jurjew (Dorpat), redigiert
von der Bibliothek-kommission ... Jurjew (Dorpat) Naturforscher-gesellschaft, 1908–10.
2 v. 24ᶜᵐ.
Russian and German.

1. Libraries. Catalogues.
                                           Agr 12–275
Library, U. S. Dept. of   Agriculture 240.5D73

NT   0045293   DNAL PPAmP

Xq17
T17   Tartu. Ülikool. Loodusuurijate selts.
939   Raamatukogu.
... Loodusuurijate seltsi raamatukogu kataloog
... Catalogue of the library of the Society of
naturalists. (Headquarters at Tartu university)
Tartu, 1939–
v. 24cm.
Contents: v.1. Perioodika.

NT   0045294   CtY MiU NcU CU NIC

SH 343
.E7 T2   Tartu. Ülikool. Loodusuurijate Selts.
Seenkommission.
Seenkommission des Dorpater Naturforscher-
vereins, Dorpat. Dorpat, Druck von H. Laakmann,
1910.
7 p.
At head of title: Im Hauptgebäude.
Catalog of fisheries exhibits.

NT   0045295   InU

Tartu. Ülikool. Loomatervishoiu ja
piimahügieeni instituut.
Ridala, Vassil.
... Inquiries into the pathogenic effects produced by *Brucella
abortus* in the udder and certain other organs of the cow, by
Vassil Ridala, M. D. VET. Illustrated by twenty-six plates with
fifty figures and one scheme in the text. Tartu [Printed by
K. Mattiesen, ltd.] 1936 [i. e. 1937]

QB154
.S41   Tartu. Ülikool. Matemaatika-loodusteaduskond.
Schwarz, Ludwig, 1822–1894.
Eine studie auf dem gebiete der practischen astronomie, von
professor dr. L. Schwarz. Dorpat, Druck von C. Mattiesen,
1889.

Tartu. Ülikool. *Matemaatika-Loodusteaduskond. Chair of
Systematic Botany and Geobotany*
see
Tartu. Ülikool. *Matemaatika-Loodusteaduskond.*

Tartu. Ülikool. *Matemaatika-Loodusteaduskond. Taimesüstemaatika ja Geobotaanika Kateeder*
see
Tartu. Ülikool. *Matemaatika-Loodusteaduskond.*

Tartu. Ülikool. Meditsiimline Kliinik.
  Annales scholae clinicae medicae dorpatensis
annorum 1818, 1819, & 1820.   Dorpati, 1821.
  227 p.

NT   0045300   DNLM

Tartu. Ülikool. Meditsiimline Kliinik.
  Historischer Bericht über die Leistungen des
medicinischen Klinikums
       see under   Struve, Ludwig August, 1795-
1828, ed.

Tartu. Ülikool. Medizinische Fakultät
    see   Tartu. Ülikool. Arstiteaduskond.

M06.1
474.2
T195e

Tartu. Ülikool. Meteoroloogia Observatoorium.
  Eesti meteoroloogia aastaraamat ...   The
meteorological year book of Estonia.   Vol. 1-
1921-   Tartus, O./U.K. Mattieseni Trükikoda,
1922-
      v. illus., maps, tables.   27 cm.
  Annual.
  Title varies: v. 1-3; 1921-23, Meteoroloogia
aastaraamat Eesti vabariigi kohta.
  Vols. 1-13; 1921-33, have alternate title in
German: Meteorologisches Jahrbuch für Eesti.

NT   0045303   DAS

Tartu. Ülikool. Meteoroloogia Observatoorium.
  Merejää vaatlused.   Tartus, 1920-1932.
  29 cm.

NT   0045304   DAS

Tartu. Ülikool. *Meteoroloogia observatoorium.*
  Meteorologische beobachtungen angestellt in Dorpat. [1.]-
jahrg.; 1866-   Dorpat, 1868-19
      v. in   tables, diagrs. 25ᶜᵐ.
  Report for 1866 issued in jahrg. 5, published in 1871.
  Jahrg. 1-30, 1866-95, called also bd. [1]-6.
  Vols. for -1873, "von der direction des Physikalischen cabinetes."
  Title varies slightly.
  Vols. for 1893-19 have also title: Наблюдения.
  Vols. for 1866-75 issued also in ser. I, v. 4, 6-7 of the Archiv für
die naturkunde Liv-, Ehst- und Kurlands (later Eesti loodusteaduse
arhiiv)

  "Zehnjährige mittelwerthe (1866 bis 1875)" and "Zwanzigjährige
mittelwerthe ... 1866 bis 1885" issued as supplements to bd. 2 and 4,
respectively. Issued also in ser. I, v. 8 and 9 of the above Archiv.

  1. Meteorology—Baltic provinces. 2. Meteorology—Period.
I. Tartu. Ülikool. Füüsika instituut. II. Title.
  QC989.R6T3   46-43903

NT   0045306   DLC CU DAS ICJ MBdAF

Tartu. Ülikool. Meteoroloogia Observatorium.
  Meteoroloogilised vaatlused
       see its   Meteorologische Beobachtungen.

Tartu. Ülikool. Meteoroloogia Observa-
    torium
  [Sbornik Trudii] 1, 1906-
  German: Sammlung von Arbeiten Ausgeführt von
  Studenten am Meteorologischen Observ. der K.
  Universität zu Jurjew (Dorpat)...
  Spine: Tartu. Ülikool. Meteoroloogia Observ.
  Sbornik Trudii

NT   0045308   MBdAF

Tartu. Ülikool. Meteoroloogia Obser-
    vatoorium.
  ... Scientific papers of the meteorological
observatory of the University of Tartu, no. 1-
Tartu, 1936-
      1 v. tables, diagrs.   24 cm.
  At head of title: Tartu Ülikooli meteoroloogia
observatoriumi. Teaduslikud väljaanded.

  Contents.-
    Kirde, K.   Meteorological elements character-
ized by frequency-curves, 1936.

NT   0045309   DSI

QC874
.W4

Tartu. Ülikool. Meteoroloogia observatoorium.

  Weihrauch, Karl Filipovich, 1841-1890.
  ... Ueber die berechnung meteorologischer jahresmittel von
prof. dr. K. Weihrauch ...   Dorpat, Druck von C. Mattiesen,
1886.

99.9
T172

Tartu. Ülikool. Metsandulik uurimisinsti-
    tuut.
  Metsandualikud uurimused. v.1-

  Tartu, 1939-

  1. Forestry. Research.   2. Estonia.
Forestry.

NT   0045311   DNAL

Tartu. Ülikool. Naistekliinik.
  Berichte und Arbeiten aus der Universitäts-
Frauenklinik zu Dorpat
       see under   Küstner, Otto Ernst, 1849-
1931, ed.

Tartu. Ülikool. Naturalists' society
    see
Tartu. Ülikool. Loodusuurijate selts.

Tartu. Ülikool. Naturforscher-gesellschaft
    see
Tartu. Ülikool. Loodusuurijate selts.

Tartu. Ülikool. *Nauchnaia biblioteka*
    see
Tartu. Ülikool. *Teaduslik Raamatukogu.*

Tartu. Ülikool. *Observatoire astronomique*
    see
Tartu. *Astronoomia Observatoorium.*

Tartu. Ülikool. Obshchestvo estestvoispytatelei
    see
Tartu. Ülikool. Loodusuurijate selts.

Law

Tartu. Ülikool. Õigusteaduskond.

Loening, Edgar, 1843-1919.

FOR OTHER EDITIONS
SEE MAIN ENTRY

  Die haftung des staats aus rechtswidrigen handlungen seiner
beamten nach deutschem privat- und staatsrecht. Eine festschrift, von dr. Edgar Loening ... Dorpat, 1879.

Tartu. Ülikool. *Õigusteaduskond.*
  Zeitschrift für Rechtswissenschaft. 1.-11. Jahrg. Dorpat, C. Mattiesen [etc.] 1869 [i. e. 1868]-92.
      11 v. 21 cm.

  1. Law—Period.—Baltic States. I. Title.

                                              57-56853

NT   0045319   DLC

Tartu. Ülikool. Õpetatud eesti selts.
  Aastaraamat. Annales Litterarum societatis esthonicae.
1861-
Tartu (Dorpat, Jurjew) 1861-19
      v. in   illus., plates, ports., maps, plans, tables, diagrs. 18½ x
24½ᶜᵐ.
  Reports for 1839-60 issued in Das Inland.
  Part of the illustrative material is folded.
  Title varies: 1861-1923, Sitzungsberichte der Gelehrten estnischen ge-
sellschaft zu Dorpat (varies slightly)
    1924-35, Aastaraamat. Sitzungsberichte ...
    1936-   Aastaraamat. Annales ... (added t.-p. has subtitle: Sit-
zungsberichte)
  Articles chiefly in German, some in French, etc.
  INDEXES:
    1861-76, in 1877.
  AS262.T215   067.4   46-43951

NT   0045320   DLC CU NN NNC PU OCl ICN

Tartu. Ülikool. Õpetatud Eesti Selts.
  Das älteste Wittschopbuch der Stadt Reval.
  1888
       see under   Tallinn.

Tartu. Ülikool. Õpetatud eesti selts. Annales
see its Aastaraamat.

Tartu. Ülikool. Õpetatud eesti selts. Commentationes
see its Toimetused.

Z2533
.E23

Tartu. Ülikool. Õpetatud eesti selts.

  Eesti filoloogia ja ajaloo aastaülevaade. Jahresbericht der
estnischen philologie und geschichte. [v.] 1-
1918-
Tartu (Dorpat) 1922-

PH651
.E7

Tartu. Ülikool. Õpetatud eesti selts.

  Estländische Literärische Gesellschaft.
  Ehstnische Volkslieder. [Reval, Gedr. bei Lindfors Erben,
1863]

A42d
57

Tartu. Ülikool. Õpetatud Eesti Selts.
  Eritoimetused. Sonderabhandlungen. 1-
Tartu, 1931-
      27 cm.

  I. Tartu. Ülikool. Õpetatud Eesti Selts.
Sonderabhandlungen.

NT   0045326   CtY DLC

Tartu. Ülikool. Õpetatud Eesti Selts.
Erneuerte statuten. Verzeichniss dermit-
gleider. Verzeichniss der gelehrten vereine
etc., mit welchem die gesellschaft schriften-
austausch unterhält. Verzeichniss der von der
gesselschaft herausgegebenen schriften. Dorpat
E. J. Karow, 1863.
pp. 31.
"Verzeichniss der von der Gesellschaft herausgegebenen schriften", pp. 20-31.
"Schriften der Gelehrten estnischen gesellschaft, 1."

NT 0045327 MH

Tartu. Ülikool. Õpetatud Eesti Selts.
Fest-Album der Gelehrten Estnischen Gesellschaft zu
deren fünfzigjährigem Jubiläum. Dorpat, 1888.
35 p. illus. 23 cm.
Twelve unnumbered leaves, containing the illus., precede the t. p.
Excerpts from the society's annual reports, 1840-83, and ports. of
presidents, compiled by F. Amelung.

I. Amelung, Friedrich, 1842-1909, comp. II. Title.

AS262.T225A6 72-202001

NT 0045328 DLC

Tartu. Utikool. Õpetatud eesti selts.
Festschrift der bei der Kaiserlichen Universität
Dorpat bestehenden Gelehrten estnischen Gesellschaft zur Feier ihres fünfzigjährigen Bestehens
see under title

Tartu. Ülikool. Õpetatud Eesti Selts.
Jahresbericht der estnischen philologie und geschichte, hrsg.
von der Gelehrten estnischen gesellschaft bei der Universität Dorpat ... bd. 1– 1918–
Dorpat, 1922–

PH648
.G5
1861
Tartu. Ülikool. Õpetatud eesti selts.
Kalevipoeg.
Kalewipoeg, eine estnische sage, zusammengestellt von F. R.
Kreutzwald, verdeutsch von C. Reinthal und dr. Bertram
[pseud.] Herausgegeben von der Gelehrten estnischen gesell-
schaft in Dorpat. Dorpat, Druck von H. Laakmann, 1861.

Tartu. Ülikool. Õpetatud eesti selts.
Kaleviste mailt
see under title

Tartu. Ülikool. Õpetatud eesti selts.
Kirjad.
Tartu, 19
v. illus. (incl. maps, plans) diagrs. 25ᵐ.
Publication began in 1932.

AS262.T225K5 43-40905 rev

NT 0045333 DLC CU

AS 262
.T22 T6
TARTU--Ülikool--Õpetatud Eesti Selts
Liber saecularis; Litterarum Societas Estho-
nica, 1838-1938. Tartu, 1938.
2 v. illus. (Tartu--Õpetatud Eesti Selts.
Toimetused, v. 30) DLC: AS262.D7

1. Finno-Ugrian philology--Collections. 2.
Estonia--Addresses, essays, lectures. I. Title.

NT 0045334 InU DLC

Tartu. Ülikool. Õpetatud Eesti Selts.
Oeffentliche versammlung der Gelehrten estnischen gesellschaft zur feier ihres 25-jährigen bestehens am 18.
januar 1863. [Dorpat, 1863]
16 p. 22ᶜᵐ.
Separate issue of "Sitzungsberichte," 1863, p. 1-16.

8-21466

Library of Congress AS262.D71

NT 0045335 DLC

067
TAR
Tartu. Ülikool--Õpetatud eesti selts.
Schriften der gelehrten estnischen Gesell-
schaft. no. 1-7. Dorpat, 1863-69.
7 no. 23 cm.

NT 0045336 IU DLC PU ICN NN

Tartu. Ülikool. Õpetatud eesti selts. Sitzungsberichte
see its Aastaraamat.

Tartu. Ülikool. Õpetatud eesti selts.
Toimetused. Commentationes Litterarum societatis esthonicae. [v.] 1–
Tartu (Dorpat, Jurjew) [etc.] 1846 [i. e. 1840]–19
v. in illus. (incl. music) plates, ports., maps, plans, facsims.,
tables, diagrs. 21⅓-25ᶜᵐ. irregular.
Part of the illustrative material is folded.
Title varies: v. 1-23, 1840-1925, Verhandlungen der Gelehrten estnischen
gesellschaft zu Dorpat (varies slightly)
v. 24-28, 1927-36, Toimetused ... Verhandlungen ...
v. 29– 1988– Toimetused. Commentationes ... (v. 29-30
have subtitle: Verhandlungen)
Articles chiefly in German, some in Estonian, etc.
INDEXES:
Vols. 1-13, 1840-88, in v. 13.
Vols. 1-20, 1840-1900. 1 v.
AS262.T225T6 067.4 46-43952

NT 0045338 DLC MH ICN PU ICRL ICU NNC

Tartu. Ülikool. Õpetatud eesti selts. Verhandlungen
see its Toimetused.

Tartu. Ülikool. Õpetatud eesti selts. Bibliothek
see
Tartu. Ülikool. Õpetatud eesti selts. Raamatukogu.

Tartu. Ülikool. Õpetatud eesti selts. Raamatukogu.
Chronologisches verzeichniss aller in der Bibliothek der Gelehrten estnischen gesellschaft sich befindenden estnischen
druckschriften. Zusammengestellt von Andr. Joh. Schwabe.
Dorpat, Druck von E. J. Karow, 1867.
iiii, 92 p. 21ᵐᵐ. (On cover: Schriften der Gelehrten estnischen gesellschaft. No. 5)

1. Estonian literature--Bibl. I. Schwabe, Andreas Johann, 1810-
1878.
1-19552 Revised 2
Library of Congress Z2533.T3

NT 0045341 DLC NN

Tartu. Ülikool. Patoloogia Instituut.
Arbeiten. Dorpat, 1888-1890.
v.

NT 0045342 MiU

Tartu. Ülikool. Patoloogia-instituut.
Ridala, Vassil.
... Inquiries into the pathogenic effects produced by Brucella
abortus in the udder and certain other organs of the cow, by
Vassil Ridala, M. D. VET. Illustrated by twenty-six plates with
fifty figures and one scheme in the text. Tartu [Printed by
K. Mattiesen, ltd.] 1936 [i. e. 1937]

Tartu. Ülikool. Pearaamatukogu
see
Tartu. Ülikool. Teaduslik Raamatukogu.

Tartu. Ülikool. Pharmakologisches Institut
see Tartu. Ülikool. Farmakoloogia-
Instituut.

Tartu. Ülikool. Physikalisches cabinet
see
Tartu. Ülikool. Füüsika instituut.

Tartu. Ülikool. Physiko-mathematische fakultät
see
Tartu. Ülikool. Matemaatika-loodusteaduskond.

Tartu. Ülikool. Raamatukogu
see
Tartu. Ülikool. Teaduslik Raamatukogu.

Tartu. Ülikool. Seminarium Litterarum
Judaearum
see Tartu. Ülikool. Juuditeaduse
Seminar.

Tartu. Ülikool. Silmakliinik.
Mitteilungen aus der Augenklinik in Jurjew.
Hft. 1-2 ... Berlin, S. Karger, 1904-1905.
2 v. illustrated.
"Herausgegeben von professor dr. Th. von
Ewetzky".
No more published?

NT 0045350 PU-UH-Des PPC PL

Tartu. Ülikool. Societas rebus naturae investigandis
see
Tartu. Ülikool. Loodusuurijate selts.

Tartu. Ülikool. *Sternwarte*
see
Tartu. Astronoomia Observatoorium.

Tartu. Ülikool. *Tähetorn*
see
Tartu. Astronoomia Observatoorium.

Tartu. Ülikool. <u>Taimefüsioloogia laboratorium</u>

see

Tartu. Ülikool. <u>Botaanika-instituut</u>. <u>Taimefüs-</u>
<u>ioloogia laboratoorium</u>.

Tartu. Ülikool. Taimehaiguste-
kabinett.

Lepik, Elmar, 1898–
... Fungi estonici exsiccati. *Uredinaceae* edidit E. Lepik.
Tartu [K. Mattieseni trükikoda o.-ü.] 1934–

Tartu. Ülikool. *Taimesüstemaatika ja Geobotaanika Katee-*
der
see
Tartu. Ülikool. *Matemaatika-Loodusteaduskond.*

Tartu. Ülikool. *Teaduslik Raamatukogu.*
E. V. Tartu Ülikooli Raamatukogu dublettide nimestik.
Catalogue des doubles de la Bibliothèque de l'Université de
Tartu, Estonie. Tartu, 1926.
167 p. 21 cm.
CONTENTS.—Raamatud. Livres.—Ajakirjad. Publications périodi-
ques.—Lisa. Supplément.

Z940.3.T22   28–2100 rev*

NT 0045357   DLC ICJ MiU NN

4Z   Teaduslik
787 Tartu. Ülikool.∧Raamatukogu.
Eesti raamatute üldnimestik, 1937
-1939, koostanud Tartu Riikliku Ülikooli
Pearaamatukogu. Tartu, "Teaduslik Kir-
jandus", 1941.
559 p.

NT 0045358   DLC-P4

AS   Teaduslik
262 Tartu. Ülikool.∧Raamatukogu.
T19A2 Tartu Ülikooli raamatukogude ajakirjade
ser.C nimestik; / koostanud Friedrich Puksoo juhen-
v.23 dusel Eduard Vigel. Catalogue des périodiques étrangers, recus par les bibliothèques
de l'Université de Tartu; dressé sous la
direction de Friedrich Puksoo, par Eduard
Vigel. Tartu, 1940.
676 p. 24cm. (Acta et commentationes
Universitatis Tartuensis (Dorpatensis) C.
Annales. 23)

1. Periodicals--Bibl.--Catalogs. I. Puksov,
Friedrich. II. Vigel, Eduard. III. Series:
Tartu. Ülikool. Acta et commentationes Uni-
versitatis Tartuensis (Dorpatensis) C: Annales.
XXIII.

NT 0045360   NIC IU DNAL DSI NNC

Tartu. Ülikool. *Theologische fakultät*
see
Tartu. Ülikool. *Usuteaduskond.*

Tartu. Ülikool. *Uchebnyĭ okrug*
see
Rizhskiĭ uchebnyĭ okrug.

PG3350 Tartu. Ülikool. Ucheno-literaturnoe obshchestvo.
.Z8P3 (Pami͡ati A. S. Pushkina)
1899 Памяти А. С. Пушкина; торжественное засѣданіе Учено
-литературнаго Общества при Императорскомъ Юрьевскомъ университетѣ 23 мая 1899 г. Юрьевъ, Тип. К.
Маттисена, 1899.

LH5 Tartu. Ülikool. Üliõpilaskond.
.T3U4 Üliõpilasleht.
[Tartu, Tartu Üliõpilaskonna Edustus]

Tartu. Ülikool. Üliõpilaskond.
L'Université de la République Esthonienne à
Tartu et l'Union des étudiants d'Esthonie
see under   Tartu. Ülikool.

Tartu. Ülikool. Usuteaduskond.
Beiträge zu den theologischen Wissenschaften von den Professoren der Theologie zu Dorpat. Erstes Bändchen.
Hamburg, F. Perthes, 1832.
384 p. 20cm.

Contents: Ueber die Entstehung, die Be-
standtheile und das Alter der Bücher Esra
und Nehemia, von Dr. Kleinert.- Verthei-
digung der lutherischen Abendmahlslehre

gegen die reformirte und katholische, von
Dr. Sartorius.- Die lutherische Lehre von
der gegenseitigen Mittheilung der Eigenschaften der beiden Naturen in Christo,
vertheidigt von Dr. Sartorius.

NT 0045367   NjPT

Tartu. Ülikool. Usuteaduskond.
Gutachten über die von der deutschen gelegten
fragen, den kirchlichen lehrconsensus betreffend.
n.t.p.
31 p.

NT 0045368   PPLT

Tartu. Ülikool. *Veekogude uurimise komisjon*
see
Tartu. Ülikool. *Eesti veekogude uurimiskomisjon.*

Tartu. Ülikool. *Versuchsstation für Angewandte Entomo-*
logie
see **Tartu. Ülikool.** *Entomoloogia Katsejaam.*

Tartu. Ülikool. *Zooloogia instituut ja muuseum.*
Tartu ülikooli Zooloogia-instituudi ja-muuseumi tööd.
Acta Instituti et musei zoologici Universitatis tartuensis. n° 1–
Tartu, 1929–
v. illus., pl., diagrs. 24cm.
Text in Estonian, German, French or English.
Reprints from various scientific periodicals.

1. Zoology—Societies, etc.   I. Title: Acta Instituti et musei zoologici Universitatis tartuensis.

Library of Congress   QL1.T3
                                                    CA 33—173 Unrev'd
                                            [a1]   590.62474

NT 0045371   DLC DSI

Tartu. Universität
see
Tartu. Ülikool.

Tartu. Vanemuine
see
Tartu. Riiklik Teater "Vanemuine."

Tartu. Versuchsstation für Angewandte Entomologie
see **Tartu. Ülikool.** *Entomoloogia Katsejaam.*

Tartu. Veterinär-schule
see **Tartu. Veterinarnyĭ institut.**

Tartu. Veterinarnyĭ institut.
Альбомъ имматрикулированныхъ въ Дерптскомъ, нынѣ
Юрьевскомъ ветеринарномъ институтѣ, 1848–1898. Со-
ставили и издали И. Вальдманъ и Я. Неготинъ. Юрьевъ,
Печатано въ тип. К. Матисена, 1898.
368 p. 25 cm.

I. Waldmann, Ivan Osipovich, 1856–   ed.
                    Title transliterated: Al'bom immatrikulirovannykh.

SF779.T3A37   48–42199*

NT 0045376   DLC

Tartu. Veterinarnyĭ institut.
Пятидесятилѣтнія юбилей Юрьевскаго ветеринарнаго
института 14 января 1898 г., подъ ред. К. Гаппиха и Я.
Неготина. Юрьевъ, 1898.
115 p. port. 21 cm.

I. Gappikh, Karl Karlovich, 1863–   ed.
                    Title transliterated: Pi͡atidesi͡atili͡etniĭ i͡ubileĭ.

SF779.T3A38   48–42198*

NT 0045377   DLC

Tartu. Veterinarnyĭ institut.
Die wirksamkeit der klinik der Dorpatschen veterinairschule
in den jahren 1860 and 1861, unter der leitung von professor
P. Jessen und professor-adjunct A. Unterberger. Mit rück-
blicken in die frühere zeit. Dorpat, Gedruckt bei E. J. Karow,
1862.
4 p. l., 111 p., 1 l. 22½cm.
Edited by P. Jessen.

1. Veterinary medicine--Russia.   I. *Jessen, Peter, 1801–1875, ed.
II. Unterberger, Aleksandr Semenovich, 1827–1875. III. Title.

                                                    44–28233
Library of Congress   SF779.D7A4

NT 0045378   DLC

Tartu. Tartu linna-uurimise toimkonna korraldatud ja toimetatud. Tartu, Tartu linna väljaanne, 1927.
4 v. in 1. illus., maps.
Includes suppl. containing maps, plans, statistics, etc., and a French and a German summary.

NT 0045379 InU

G2129
.T3T3
1927
Map
Tartu: kaardid, plaanid, tabelid. Tartu: cartes, plans, tableaux statistiques. Tartu, 1927.
8 fold. col. maps, 9-17 tables. 28 cm.

Cover title.
At head of title: Lisa-- Supplément.
1. Tartu aps. 2. Tartu-- Stat.

NT 0045380 DLC

TARTU KREDIITKASSA KELDRI OHVRITE MÄLESTAMISE JÄÄDVUSTAMISE KOMITEE.
14. jaanuari 1919. a. kümnendaks aastapäevaks, mälestamiskabeli pühitsemise puhul Tartu "tapakeldris." [2. taiendatud väljaanne. Tartus, 1922]
43 p. illus., ports. 19cm.

Microfiche (Negative). 1 sheet. 11 x 15cm. (NYPL FSN 1201)

1. Esthonia--Hist.--Revolution, 1918-1920. i.[Title] Neljateistkümnenda...

NT 0045381 NN

Law
Tartu Õigusteadlaste Selts.
Õigus, juriidiline ajakari. [1.]- aastakäik;
okt. 1920-
[Tartu] Tartu Õigusteadlaste Selts.

Tartu Riiklik Ülikool
see
Tartu. Ülikool.

Tartu State University
see
Tartu. Ülikool.

Tartu ülikool sõnas ja pildis, 1919-1932
see under Tartu. Ülikool.

Tartu Ülikooli entomoloogia katsejaama teadaanded

see

Tartu. Ülikool. Entomoloogia katsejaama. Teadaanded.

Tartu Üliõpilaskond
see
Tartu. Ülikool. Üliõpilaskond.

4K
940
Tartufari, Alfredo
La moratoria, esposta. Roma, Fratelli Pallotta, 1895.
506 p.

NT 0045388 DLC-P4

Tartufari, Assuero.
Degli effetti del possesso. Torino, Unione tipografico-editrice, 1886-88.
3 v. in 4. 23 cm.
Bibliographical footnotes.

1. Possession (Law)—Italy. 2. Possession (Roman law)
I. Title.
54-47803

NT 0045389 DLC MH-L

Tartufari, Assuero.
Del possesso considerato nella sua nozione in quanto riguarda soggetti ed oggetti. Ed. postuma, pubblicata a cura dell'avv. Luigi Tartufari. Torino, Unione tip.-editrice, 1898.
611 p. 23 cm.

1. Possession (Law)—Italy.
51-45905

NT 0045390 DLC

Tartufari, Assuero.
Del possesso qual titolo di diritti, per Assuero Tartufari ... Torino [etc.] Fratelli Bocca, 1878.
2 v. 24cm. (On cover: Nuova collezione di opere giuridiche, n. 24, 25)
Paged continuously.
Cover of v. 2 dated 1879.

1. Possession (Law)—Italy. I. Title: Possesso qual titolo di diritti, Del.
12-12412 Revised

NT 0045391 DLC

4K
Ital.-242
Tartufari, Assuero.
Del pubblico ministero in reggimento libero e civile; brevi considerazioni. Torino, Unione Tipografico-Editrice, 1868.
237 p.

NT 0045392 DLC-P4

Tartufari, Assuero
... Dell'acquisizione del possesso per disposizione di legge. Napoli, L. Vallardi, 1881.
1 p.l., 85 p. 24½cm.
Bibliographical footnotes.

NT 0045393 MH-L

4K Ital.-
628
Tartufari, Assuero.
Della acquisizione e della perdita del possesso. Milano, L. Vallardi, 1887-88.
2 v.

NT 0045394 DLC-P4 MH-L

Tartufari, Assuero.
Risposta alla lettera del senatore Giuseppe Musio. Modena, C. Vincenzi, 1869.
(4) 94 p.
In answer to Musio's criticism of Tartufari's work, "Del pubblico ministero in reggimento libero e civile".

NT 0045395 MH

Tartufari, Assuero
Risposta dell'avvocato Assuero Tartufari alla lettera del senatore Giuseppe Musio ... Modena, C. Vincenzi, 1869.
2 p.l., 94 p. 24½cm.

NT 0045396 MH-L

TARTUFARI, Assuero.
"Lo straniero nel diritto civile italiano" di Sebastiano Gianzana. [Bologna], n. d.
14 x (1) p.
"Estratto dall' Archivio giuridico."

NT 0045397 MH-L

PQ
4843
A7A4
Tartufari, Clarice, 1870-1933.
L'arbero della morte. Roma, E. Voghera, 1912.
130p. 15 x 7cm. (Piccola collezione "Margherita")

NT 0045398 MU

Ed66
ta71
Tartufari, Clarice, 1870-
... Il dio nero, romanzo ... Firenze, R. Bemporad & figlio, 1921.
3p.l., 301p., 1l. 19cm. ([Collezione letteraria economica])

NT 0045399 CtY NN NNC MH NPV PU NjP

Tartufari, Clarice, 1870-
... Il dio nero; romanzo... [Firenze] Bemporad, 1928.
2 p.l., 301 p., 1 l. 19 cm. (Collezione letteraria economica)

NT 0045400 NPV NNC OC1W-H

Tartufari, Clarice, 1870-1933.
Il giardino incantato; novelle. Roma: Armani & Stein, 1912. 2 p.l., (1)8-337 p., 1 l. 12°.

1. Fiction (Italian). 2. Title.
N. Y. P. L. June 28, 1912.

NT 0045401 NN

Tartufari, Clarice, 1870-
... Il gomitolo d'oro, romanzo. Milano, Trevisini, 1924.
202 p., 1 l. illus. 18½cm. (Collana di romanzi e novelle per la gioventù serenissima)

NT 0045402 NNC PP

Tartufari, Clarice, *1870–*
Imperatrice dei cinque re. Romanzo.
— Foligno. Campitelli. [1931.] 279 pp. 18 cm., in 8s.   **2799B.662**

NT 0045403   MB IU

Tartufari, Clarice, 1870–
... Lampade nel sacrario, romanzo. Foligno, F. Campitelli
[1929]
2 p. l., [8]–292 p., 1 l. 19½ᶜᵐ.

ɪ. Title.
Library of Congress   PQ4843.A7L3 1929   29–21019

NT 0045404   DLC OrP WaS PU PP NN

Tartufari, Clarice, 1870–1933.
Logica; commedia in 4 atti.   Roma, Soc.
Editrice Dante Alighieri, 1900.
64 p.   8°.

NT 0045405   NN

Tartufari, Clarice, *1870–*
Il mare e la vela. Romanzo.   **2799B.474**
— Firenze. Bemporad. [1924.] viii, 286 pp. 21 cm., in 8s.

NT 0045406   MB CtY NNC MU

Tartufari, Clarice, *1870–*
Il miracolo.   Roma: G. Romagna e C., 1909.   361 p.   12°.

NT 0045407   NN

853.91
T195m.2   Tartufari, Clarice, 1870–
Il miracolo; romanzo. [2. ed.]   Roma,
G. Romagna, 1909.
361 p. 19ᶜᵐ.

NT 0045408   IEN

Tartufari, Clarice, 1870–
... Il miracolo, romanzo, preceduto da uno studio di
Adriano Tilgher. Roma, A. Stock, 1925.
1 p. l., 5–258 p. 20ᶜᵐ.

ɪ. Title.
Library of Congress   PQ4843.A7M5 1925   28–7447

NT 0045409   DLC CU

Tartufari, Clarice, 1870–
... La nave degli eroi, romanzo. Foligno, F. Campitelli
[*1927]
1 p. l., [7]–408 p., 1 l. 19½ᶜᵐ.

ɪ. Title.
Library of Congress   PQ4843.A7N3 1927   27–23988

NT 0045410   DLC WaS PPT CtY NN MB OClND

D855T17
V5   Tartufari, Clarice, 1870–
Rete d'acciaio, romanzo di Clarice Tartufari.
Milano, Treves, 1919.
3 p. l., 289 p. 19ᶜᵐ.

NT 0045411   NNC MB

Tartufari, Clarice, *1870–1933*
Le ultime lettere di Jacopo Ortis. Commedia in tre atti.
(Nuova antologia.   Roma, 1924.   8°.   1924, July 16, p. 114–
129, Aug. 1, p. 213–225, Aug. 16, p. 309–321.)

1. Drama, Italian. 2. Title.
N. Y. P. L.   October 29, 1924

NT 0045412   NN

Tartufari, Clarice, 1870–*1933.*
... L'uomo senza volto, romanzo. Roma, Tosi [1941]
3 p. l., 9–290, [1] p., 1 l. 20ᶜᵐ.   (On cover: "Esperia," n. 3)

ɪ. Title.
PQ4843.A7U6   853.91   A F 46–1265
Illinois. Univ. Library
for Library of Congress   [4]†

NT 0045413   IU NjP CtY DLC

Tartùfari, Filippo.
Un bottegaro poeta a Torino.   Torino, Rattero
[1952]   235 p.   port.,facsim.   19cm.

"Libri di Clarice Tartùfari," p. 232.

1. Tartùfari, Clarice, 1861–1933.

NT 0045414   NN RPB

Tartufari, Filippo.
... Du' risate e un sospiro, sonetti romaneschi. Illustrazioni
del pittore Felice Vellan. [Torino, Fiorini [1946]
150 p., 4 l. illus. 17ᶜᵐ.

"Alcune considerazioni sull' ortografia e sull' ortoepia del dialetto romanesco" (p. [7]–12) signed: Giovanni Gargiulo.

1. Italian language—Dialects—Texts. 2. Italian language—Dialects—
Rome.   ɪ. Title.
PQ4843.A73D8   A F 47–3660
Yale univ. Library
for Library of Congress   [2]†

NT 0045415   CtY IU NjP DLC

Tartùfari, Filippo.
Er Cappio ar Collo, sonetti Romaneschi.
Prefazione di Vittorio Clemente su "Spiriti e
forme della poesia Romanesca".   Torino,
G. B. Petrini.
151 p.

NT 0045416   DLC

Tartùfari, Filippo
Un gomitolo d'oro. [Versi in dialetto
romanesco]   Torino, Rattero [1955]
vii, 134 p. illus. 21 cm.

NT 0045417   RPB

PQ
4843   Tartufari, Filippo.
.A75   Pietro Micca ('Na scampagnata a Superga);
P5   sonetti romaneschi. Schizzi del pittore
Felice Vellan, presentazione di Nino Costa.
Torino, Associazione Torinese "Pietro Micca",
1942.
30 p. illus. (Edizioni "Pietro Micca",
n. 6)

1. Micca, Pietro, 1677–1706. 2. Italian
language - Dialects - Rome.

NT 0045418   DGU

Tartùfari, Filippo
Quadretti senza cornice.   Torino,
L. Rattero [1955]
190 p. illus. 22 cm.

NT 0045419   RPB

PQ4843
.A73T3   Tartufari, Filippo.
La Tampa, del circolo degli artisti di
Torino. Con illustrazioni di Felice Vellan.
Cicalata proemiale de Arrigo Frusta; a cura
del socio Livio Suppo. Torino, F. Casanova
[1948]
29 l. illus. 22cm.

NT 0045420   MiDW

PQ4843
.A76   Tartufari, Filippo
T56   Torino bella: le piazze. Sonetti romaneschi.
1953   [2.ed.] Torino, Ed. Rattero [1953]
47 p. illus. 35 cm.

NT 0045421   RPB

Tartufari, Luigi, 1864–1931.

Italy.   *Laws, statutes, etc.*
Il Codice di commercio, commentato da Ascoli prof. Prospero—Asquini Alberto ... Azzariti Gaetano ... [e. a.] Coordinato dai professori Leone Bolaffio ... Alfredo Rocco ... Cesare
Vivante ... 6. ed. interamente rifatta ... Torino, Unione tipografico-editrice torinese, 1933–

LAW   Tartufari, Luigi, 1864–1931, ed.

Italy. *Laws, statutes, etc.*
Il Codice di commercio italiano, commentato coi lavori
preparatori, con la dottrina e con la giurisprudenza. Verona,
Drucker & Tedeschi, 1883–97.

Tartufari, Luigi, *1864–*
Dei contratti a favore di terzi, di Luigi Tartufari. Verona,
D. Tedeschi e figlio, 1889.
2 p. l., [3]–416 p., 1 l. 25ᶜᵐ. (On cover: Biblioteca giuridica nazionale,
vol. ɪ)

1. Third parties (Law) 2. Third parties (Law)—Italy. 3. Contracts.
4. Contracts—Italy.   ɪ. Title.
                                              13–19810

NT 0045424   DLC

4K   Tartufari, Luigi, 1864-1931.
It   Della rappresentanza nella
1526   conclusione dei contratti in diritto
      civile e commerciale. Torino,
      Unione tipografico-editrice, 1892.
      598 p.

NT   0045425   DLC-P4 MH-L

TARTUFARI, Luigi, 1864-1931.
Della vendita e del riporto. 5a ed. Torino,
1925.

   4o.
"Il codice di commercio ... coordinato da
Leone Bolaffio e Cesare Vivante", 5a ed., 3.

NT   0045426   MH-L

TARTUFARI, Luigi, 1864-1931.
  Della vendita e del riporto. Art.59 a 75 cod.
com. 6a ed. ... a cura del Prof.Enrico Soprano.
Torino,1936.

   8o.
"Il codice di commercio ... coordinato dai
Professori Leone Bolaffio,Alfredo Rocco,Cesare
Vivante",6a ed.,3.

NT   0045427   MH-L

Le **Tartufe** révolutionnaire. Imité de l'anglais, par
Madame * * * * ... Paris, À la librairie, rue Saint André-
des-Arcs, an VIII, 1800.
   2 v. fronts. 17ᵐᵐ.

I. * * * *, Madame, pseud.

                               12-13169
Library of Congress   PQ2067.T15 1800

NT   0045428   DLC

Tartuferi (Ferruccio). Contributo anatomico
sperimentale alla conoscenza del tratto ottico e
degli organi centrali dell' apparato della visione.
62 pp., 2 pl. 8°. *Torino, Celanza & Comp.*, 1881.

NT   0045429   DNLM

Tartuferi, Ferruccio
 ——. Le eminenze bigemine anteriori ed il
tratto ottico della talpa europea. Nota di anatomia microscopica. 47 pp., 1 pl. 8°. *Reggio-
Emilia, S. Calderini*, 1878.

NT   0045430   DNLM

Tartuferi, Ferruccio
  Studio di un microftalmo per cheratite intra-
uterina a contributo della patologia dell'occhio
embrionale ... Torino, Celanza, 1884.
   19 p. plate.

"Estratto dal volume d'Atti della R. Accademia
di medicina di Torino pubblicato in omaggio del
senatore prof. Casimiro Sperino celebrandosene
il giubileo dottorale nel 1884."
   1. Eye - Diseases - defects. 2. Cornea -
Diseases.

NT   0045431   NNC

Tartuferi (Ferruccio). Sull' anatomia microscopica e sulla morfologia cellulare delle eminenze bigemine dell' uomo e degli altri mam-
miferi. 14 pp. 8°. *Milano, frat. Rechiedei*,
1877.

NT   0045432   DNLM

Le Tartuffe; avec de nouvelles notices historiques
   see under   [Molière, Jean Baptiste
Poquelin], 1622-1673.

Le Tartuffe des comédiens
   see under   [Molière, Jean Baptiste
Poquelin] 1622-1673.

Le Tartuffe; ou, L'imposteur, comédie en cinq
actes. 1667
   see under   [Molière, Jean Baptiste Poquelin]
1622-1673.

O Tartufo de 1808, ou O retrato do imperador dos
Francezes, e dos seus infames sequazes.
Author a honra portugueza. Lisboa, Na
Impressao regia, 1808.
   11 p.   23 cm. [Binder's title: Epoca
franceza, 1808-1813. III]
   In verse.

NT   0045436   CtY

Tartumaa; maadeteadusline, majandusline ja
    ajalooline kirjeldus
   see under   Rumma, J.

Tarturro, Giuseppe.
   ...Una famiglia dell'Esopo italiano nei
codici e negli incunabuli fiorentini e
romani, con la trascrizione di un Esopo
Palatino, ancora inedito, d'altra famiglia. Bari, G.Laterza & figli, 1907.
   54 p.

   Bibliographical foot-notes.

NT   0045438   NjP

---

al-Tartusi ibn abi Randaka, Abubekr Muhammad
ibn al-Walid
   see   Muhammad ibn Walid, al-Turtushi,
called Ibn al-Rundakah, ca., 1059-ca. 1126.

Tartuskiĭ gosudarstvennyĭ universitet
   see
Tartu. Ülikool.

Tartuskiĭ universitet
   see
Tartu. Ülikool.

Tartusskaĭa meteorologicheskaĭa observatoriĭa
   see
Tartu. Ülikool. *Meteoroloogia Observatoorium.*

Tārū, Jīrūm
   see
Tharaud, Jérôme, 1874-1953.

Taru Datta
   see
Dutt, Toru, 1856-1877.

Taruc, Luis, 1913–
  Born of the people. With a foreword by Paul Robeson.
New York, International Publishers [1953]
  286 p. illus. 21 cm.

1. Hukbong Mapagpalaya ng Bayan (Philippine Islands)   I. Title.

DS686.2.T3A3   991.4   53–10412 ‡

      TNJ
      OU NcD ViU TxU NN OrU IU IaU NBu NNU OO OrCS OrU
NT   0045445   DLC FU HU ICU TU CoU UU OYesA MoU WaU

Taruffi, Cesare, 1821-1902.
 ——. Caso di cyclope dirrhinus nella specie
umana. Osservazione. 7 pp. 8°. *Bologna,
Gamberini & Parmeggiani*, 1896.
Repr. from: Rendic. Accad. d. sc. d. Ist. di Bologna,
1896.

NT   0045446   DNLM

Taruffi, Cesare, 1821–
 ——. Caso di perineo-melus in un maiale. 11
pp., 2 pl. roy. 8°. *Bologna, tip. Gamberini &
Parmeggiani*, 1885.
Repr. from: Mem. d. r. Accad. d. sc. d. Ist. di Bologna,
1884, 4. s. vi.

NT   0045447   DNLM

Taruffi, Cesare, 1821-1902.
 ——. Caso di pleuro-gastro-schisi con cripto-
mele. 12 pp. 8°. *Bologna, Gamberini & Parmeggiani*, 1896.
Repr. from: Rendic. Accad. d. sc. d. Ist. di Bologna,
1896.

NT   0045448   DNLM

QZ   TARUFFI, Cesare, 1821-1902
T196c   Compendio di anatomia patologica
1870   generale, tratto dalle lezioni orali.
      Bologna, Regia tip., 1870.
      842 p. illus.

NT   0045449   DNLM

Taruffi, Cesare, 1821–
 ——. Del teratomi sacrali. 60 pp., 1 pl. 8°.
Bologna, tip. Gamberini & Parmeggiani, 1881.
Repr. from: Mem. d. r. Accad. d. sc. d. Ist. di Bologna,
1880, 4. s. ii.

NT   0045450   DNLM

Taruffi, Cesare, 1821–
  Del marchese Cosimo Ridolfi e del suo
istituto agrario di Meleto; brevi cenni. Firenze,
G. Barbèra, 1887.
   port. 1. 8°.

NT   0045451   MH

Taruffi (Cesare) [1821-   ]. Della legislazione italiana intorno le lesioni personali, esaminate sotto il rapporto medico-legale. 129 pp., 1 l. 4°. *Bologna, tipog. governativa della volpe e del sassi,* 1857.
— *Repr. from:* Mem. Soc. med.-chir. di Bologna, 1857, vi.

NT   0045452   DNLM DLC-P4

GN
T196d
1879
    TARUFFI, Cesare, 1821-1902
      Della macrosomia, memoria.   Milano, Rechiedei, 1879.
      193 p. illus.
      Reprinted from Annali universali di medicina, v. 247, 1879.

NT   0045453   DNLM

GN
T196de
1878
    TARUFFI, Cesare, 1821-1902
      Della microsomia, memoria. Bologna, Fava e Garagnani, 1878.
      122 p. illus.
      Reprinted from Rivista clinica, ser. 2, anno 8, 1878.

NT   0045454   DNLM

WE
725
T196d
1890
    TARUFFI, Cesare, 1821-1902
      Della rachischisi; studio critico. Bologna, Regia, 1890.
      109 p. illus.
      Also published as part of v. 6 of the author's Storia della teratologia.

NT   0045455   DNLM

Taruffi, Cesare, 1821-
— Delle anomalie dell'osso malare. Memoria letta nella sessione 29 gennaio 1880. 21 pp., 1 pl. 4°. *Bologna, tip. Gamberini & Parmeggiani,* 1880.
— *Repr. from:* Mem. Accad. d. sc. d. Ist. di Bologna, 1880, 4, s., i.

NT   0045456   DNLM

Taruffi, Cesare, 1821-
— Delle azioni meccaniche rispetto alla teratologia. 18 pp. 8°. *Milano, frat. Rechiedei,* 1880.
— *Repr. from:* Ann. univ. di med., Milano, 1880, cclii.

NT   0045457   DNLM

WE
T196d
1873
    TARUFFI, Cesare, 1821-1902
      Delle ernie congenite del capo, memoria. Bologna, Fava e Garagnani, 1873.
      122 p. illus.
      Reprinted from Rivista clinica, 1873.

NT   0045458   DNLM NN

Taruffi, Cesare, 1821-
— Due casi nella specie umana del genere Synocphalus dilecanus (Diphallus Gurlt). 9 pp. 4°. *Bologna, tip. Gamberini & Parmeggiani,* 1880. *Repr. from:* Mem. d. r. Accad. d. sc. d. Ist. di Bologna, 1880-2, 4, s., ix.

NT   0045459   DNLM

Taruffi, Cesare, 1821-
    Elenco delle pubblicazioni del Prof. Cesare Taruffi, 1846-1899. [Bologna, Tip. Gamberini e Parmeggiani, 1899]

cover-title, 8 p. 22cm.

Mainly contributions to medical periodicals.

Library of Congress, no.   Z8859.5.T2.

NT   0045460   DLC

Taruffi, Cesare, 1821-1902.
    Ermafroditismo ed agenosoma.   Bologna, Gamberini, 1902.

NT   0045461   PPC

Taruffi, Cesare, 1821-
— Frammenti storici sulla terza dentizione. 8 pp. 8°. *Bologna, tip. Gamberini & Parmeggiani,* 1880.
— *Repr. from:* Bull. d. sc. med. di Bologna, 1880, 6, s., vi.

NT   0045462   DNLM

Taruffi, Cesare, 1821-
— Il gigante Chawang-In-Sing. 11 pp. 8°. *Bologna, tip. Gamberini & Parmeggiani,* 1880.
— *Repr. from:* Bull. d. sc. med. di Bologna, 1880, 6, s., vi.

NT   0045463   DNLM

WJA
T196h
1903
    TARUFFI, Cesare, 1821-1902
      Hermaphrodismus und Zeugungsunfähigkeit; eine systematische Darstellung der Missbildungen der menschlichen Geschlechtsorgane. Autorisierte deutsche Ausgabe von R. Teuscher. Berlin, Bardsdorf, 1903.
      vii, 417 p. illus.

NT   0045464   DNLM PPC MiU

612.608
T179h2
    TARUFFI, Cesare, 1821-
      Hermaphrodismus und Zeugungsunfähigkeit; eine systematische Darstellung der Missbildungen der menschlichen Geschlechtsorgane, autorisierte deutsche Ausgabe von Dr. med. R. Teuscher, mit 40 Abbildungen. 2. Aufl. Berlin, H. Barsdorf, 1908.
      vii, 417 p. front., plates.

NT   0045465   WaU ICJ CLSU WU-M

Taruffi, Cesare, 1821-
— Intorno ad un idiota cretinoide. 22 pp., 2 pl. roy. 8°. *Bologna, tip. Gamberini & Parmeggiani,* 1884.
— *Repr. from:* Mem. d. r. Accad. d. sc. d. Ist. di Bologna, 1883, 4, s., v.

NT   0045466   DNLM

Taruffi, Cesare, 1821-
— Intorno ad un nuovo gruppo di mostri appartenente al genere dicephalus diibrachius (Förster). 11 pp., 1 pl. roy. 8°. *Bologna, tip. Gamberini & Parmeggiani,* 1882.
— *Repr. from:* Mem. d. r. Accad. d. sc. d. Ist. di Bologna, 1880-81, 4, s., ii.

NT   0045467   DNLM

Taruffi, Cesare, 1821-
— Intorno al genere ileopago (Ileadelphus di St. Geoffroy Saint-Hilaire). 35 pp. 8°. *Bologna, tip. Gamberini & Parmeggiani,* 1882.
— *Repr. from:* Bull. d. sc. med. di Bologna, 1881, 6, s., viii.

NT   0045468   DNLM

Taruffi, Cesare, 1821-
— Intorno alla macrosomia. 41 pp. 4°. *Bologna, tip. Gamberini & Parmeggiani,* 1888.
— *Repr. from:* Mem. d. r. Accad. d. sc. d. Ist. di Bologna, 1887-8, 6, s., viii.

NT   0045469   DNLM

QSB
T196i
1877
    TARUFFI, Cesare, 1821-1902
      Introduzione alla storia della teratologia in Italia. Bologna, Regia tip., 1877.
      89, 52 p.

NT   0045470   DNLM

Taruffi, Cesare, 1821-
— Nota intorno ai derodimi (Dicephalus dibrachius Förster). 7 pp. 8°. [*Modena, tipi Vincenzi,* 1882.]
— *Repr. from:* Spallanzani, Modena, 1882, 2. s., xi.

NT   0045471   DNLM

Taruffi, Cesare, 1821-
— Nota storica sulla polimelia delle rane. 12 pp. 8°. [*Milano,* 1880.]
— *Repr. from:* Atti d. Soc. ital. di sc. nat., xxiii.

NT   0045472   DNLM

Taruffi, Cesare, 1821-
— Nuovo caso di degenerazione colloide del fegato. 10 pp., 1 pl. 4°. *Bologna, tip. Gamberini & Parmeggiani,* 1887.
— *Repr. from:* Mem. d. r. Accad. d. sc. d. Ist. di Bologna, 1887, 4, s., viii.

NT   0045473   DNLM

Taruffi, Cesare, 1821-
    Storia della teratologie. Bologna, Regia tipografia, 1881-1894.
    8 v. illus.

    1. Deformities. I. Title.

NT   0045474   WaU ICJ DNLM PPC MBCo MiU

Taruffi, Cesare, 1821-
— Storia di un caso di pseudo-rachite fetale. 21 pp., 2 pl. roy. 8°. *Bologna, tip. Gamberini & Parmeggiani,* 1885.
— *Repr. from:* Mem. d. r. Accad. d. sc. d. Ist. di Bologna, 1885, 4, s., vi.

NT   0045475   DNLM

Taruffi, Cesare, 1821-1902.
    Studj fatti e da farsi intorno al cretinismo.   Milano: Tipografia Fratelli Rechiedei, 1883.   49 p.   8°.

With numerous bibliographical footnotes.

1. Cretinism.
N. Y. P.   July 15, 1912.

NT   0045476   NN DNLM

Taruffi, Cesare, 1821-
— Studi antomatici ed antropometrici sul cretinismo della valle d'Aosta. 28 pp., 2 tab., 1 pl. roy. 8°. *Bologna, tip. Gamberini & Parmeggiani,* 1882.
— *Repr. from:* Mem. d. r. Accad. d. sc. d. Ist. di Bologna, 1882, 4, s., iv.

NT   0045477   DNLM

Taruffi, Cesare, 1821-
— Sulle anomalie delle vene azigos od emiazigos. 12 pp., 1 pl. roy. 8°. *Bologna, tip. Gamberini & Parmeggiani,* 1882.
— *Repr. from:* Mem. d. r. Accad. d. sc. d. Ist. di Bologna, 1880-81, 4, s., ii.

NT   0045478   DNLM

WG   TARUFFI, Cesare, 1821-1902
qT196s   Sulle malattie congenite e sulle ano-
1875   malie del cuore. Bologna, Gamberini
       e Parmeggiani, 1875.
       323 p.   WG qT196s

NT   0045479   DNLM

Taruffi, Dino.
    ... L'altipiano di Benguella (Angola) ed il suo avvenire
agricolo (Dalla "Relazione della missione agricola italiana inviata in Angola" dal Sindacato italiano per imprese
nell'Africa Occidentale) Firenze, Instituto agricolo coloniale italiano, 1916.
    48 p. 12 pl. (incl. 2 maps) 25ᶜᵐ. (Istituto agricolo coloniale italiano.
Relazioni e monografie agrario-coloniali, n. 8)
    "Estratto da 'L'Agricoltura coloniale' anno x, fasc 8-9, settembre 1916."

    1. Agriculture—Africa—Benguella. ₍1. Benguella, Africa—Agriculture₎
                                                   Agr 19-974

    Library, U. S. Dept. of   Agriculture 16 Is7 no. 8

NT   0045480   DNAL

Taruffi, Dino.
    ... I concetti informatori del colonizzamento agricolo;
sistemi seguiti nei principali paesi europei ed extra-euro-
pei ad immigrazione bianca. Firenze, Istituto agricolo
coloniale italiano, 1915.
    1 p. l., ₍vi₎-vii, 268 p. 24½ᶜᵐ. (Istituto agricolo coloniale italiano.
Relazioni e monografie agrario-coloniali, n. 5)

    1. Agricultural colonies. ₍1. Colonization, Agricultural₎
                                                   Agr 19-975

    Library, U. S. Dept. of   Agriculture 16Is7 no. 5

NT   0045481   DNAL DLC-P4

Taruffi, Dino.
    La questione agraria e l'emigrazione in Calabria; note
statistiche ed economiche dei dottori D. Taruffi, L. de
Nobili e C. Lori, con prefazione di Pasquale Villari, carta
ipsometrica a colori dell' Istituto geografico militare e 34
tavole fuori testo. Firenze, G. Barbèra, 1908.
    2 p. l., ₍viii₎-xliv, 907 p. incl. tables. plates, fold. map, diagrs. 25ᶜᵐ.
    CONTENTS.—Prefazione.—Introduzione.—Taruffi, D. Descrizione geo-
grafica e geologica.—Nobili, L. de. Cenni demografici.—Taruffi, D. L'am-
biente generale agrario.—Taruffi, D. Proprieta, mano d'opera e rapporti
reciproci.—Lori, C. Le banche, il credito e l'agricoltura.—Taruffi, D. La
tecnica agricola.—Taruffi, D. Le industrie.—Nobili, L. de. L'emigrazione.
    1. Agriculture—Calabria. 2. Calabria—Econ. condit. 3. Calabria—
Emig. & immig. 4. Agricultural credit—Calabria. ₍1. Nobili, Leonello de.
II. Lori, Cesare. III. Villari,   Pasquale, 1827-
                                                   10-9275
    Library of Congress   11C307.C3T2

NT   0045482   DLC CtY MBU NIC ICJ MH

DG   Taruffi, Giovanni Andrea
975   Antica fondazione della città di Bologna degnis-
.B64   sima madre de' studj; con le misure della linea
T19   circondaria delle di lei mura,strade,piazze,e
        vicoli ... Con la descrizione del Fiume Reno,
        et altri Fiumi,e canali del nostro contado,con
        altre cose non a tutti note,nel presente libro
        descritte. Bologna, Stamperla di B.Borghi,
        1738.
        125 p. 23 cm.

        1.Bologna--   Descr.

NT   0045483   MiU DNLM NNC NIC IU

DG975   Taruffi, Giovanni Andrea
B59T3   Breve compendio di diverse misure delle strade, vicoli, e
        piazze; descrizione delle chiese, palazzi ed altro della città di
        Bologna, e suo contado, per dieci miglia, fatica fatta ... da
        Gianandrea Taruffi, perito.   Bologna, Stamperla dell'Angelo
        custode negli Orefici, 1731.
        83 p.

        1. Bologna (City) - Streets. 2. Bologna (City) - Descr.

NT   0045484   CU

Taruffi, Giovanni Andrea.
    Breve compendio di diverse misure delle
strade, vicoli, e piazze, descrizione delle
chiese, palazzi, ed altro della città di
Bologna, e suo contado, per dieci miglia;
fatica fatta. Bologna, Angelo Custode
negli Orefici, 1731.
    Microfilm copy, made in 1966, of the original
in Vatican. Biblioteca vaticana. Positive.
Negative film in Vatican. Biblioteca
vaticana.

    Collation of the original, as determined
from the film: 83, [1] p.

    1. Bologna--Description. (Series:
[Manuscripta, microfilms of rare and out-
of-print books. List 58, no. 17])

NT   0045486   MoSU

Avery
AA
2515   Taruffi, Giovanni Andrea
T17   Breve discorso intorno ad alcuni avvertimenti
        concernenti l'architettura e le regole per ben
        fabbricare; con altre notizie necessarie da
        sapersi ed il modo sicuro per levare il fumo
        alli camini. Da fabbricarsi di nuovo, come
        pure per quelli, che sono già fatti. Il tutto
        raccolto da varij autori da Gio: Andrea Taruffi
        ... In Bologna, Nelle Stampe de' Peri nelle
        Calzolarie, 1724.
        56 p. 14cm.

NT   0045487   NNC

Taruffi, Giuseppe Antonio, 1722–1786.
    Montgolfierii machina volans; carmen elegiacum. ₍E
secessu Tusculano, 1784₎
    xii p. 22 cm.

    1. Montgolfier, Jacques Étienne, 1745–1799. 2. Montgolfier, Joseph
Michel, 1740–1810. I. Title.

    TL617.T3   54–46498

NT   0045488   DLC CoCA MB MH CSmH CoD

WQ   TARUFFI, Pompeo
T196o   L'ostetricia pratica; vademecum per
1905   i medici. Roma, Amministrazione del
        policlinico ₍1905₎
        417 p. illus.

NT   0045489   DNLM

Taruffi, Riccardo.   4779a.88
    Michelangiolo poeta. Discorso letto la sera del di 11 settembre,
1875, nella sala del Circolo filologico di Firenze.
= Firenze. Tipografia della Gazzetta d'Italia. 1875. 38 pp. 12°.

    E₃₅₁₂ — Buonarroti, Michelangelo.

NT   0045490   MB CaOTU

Taruffius, Joseph
    see Taruffi, Giuseppe Antonio, 1722-
1786.

Tarugi (B.) Contributo alla conoscenza della
morbilità dell' asse spinale secondo i criteri
della morfologia. Tesi di dottorato. 31 pp.
8°. Padova, P. Prosperini, [1904].

NT   0045492   DNLM

Tarugi, P   ed.
    L'assistenza sociale di fabbrica. Milano, U.N.S.A.S.,
Scuola per assistenti sociali, 1952

NT   0045493   MH

Pamphlet   Tarugo, Tirso
Mexico   A ver si pegaba; pero no pegó, porque ya
1822   dá basca gobierno español. [Mexico,1822]
T17   Attacks a political paper entitled Recono-
        cimiento de nuestra independencia por España.

        1. Reconocimiento de nuestra independencia
        por España. I. Ti⟨tle⟩

NT   0045494   CtY

Tarulata Datta
    see Dutt, Toru, 1856-1877.

Tarulis, Albert N
    Wirtschaftliche Rückständigkeit europäischer Agrarlän-
der und ihr Zusammenhang mit dem Industrialisierungsgrad.
Frankfurt am Main, 1947.
    95 p. 21 cm.
    "Literaturverzeichnis": p. 91-95.

    1. Agriculture—Economic aspects—Europe.
    HD1917.T36   49-24190*

NT   0045496   DLC OU CtY MH MB CLU CSt NNC MoU IU

Tarulis, Petr., pseud.
    see Petrenas, Juozas, 1899-

Tarumianz, Mesrop, 1885-
    Sarkome und carcinome der kiefer. ₍Berlin,
Blanke, 1910₎
    86 p. plates.

    Inaug.-diss., Berlin.
    "Literaturverzeichnis": p. ₍87-89₎

    1. Jaws - Cancer.

NT   0045498   NNC-M DLC DNLM ICRL

Tarumov, A   N
    Электромонтер электрических станций и подстанций.
Москва, Изд-во Министерства коммунального хозяйства
РСФСР, 1947.
    81, ₍1₎ p. diagrs. 21 cm.
    Errata slip inserted.
    "Использованная литература": p. ₍82₎

    1. Electric engineering—Handbooks, manuals, etc. I. Title.
                                  Title transliterated: Elektromonter elek-
                                  tricheskikh stantsii.
    TK151.T37   48-26055*

NT   0045499   DLC

Tarus, İlhan, 1907-
    Ahiler. Ankara, Ulus Basımevi, 1947.
    51 p. 20 cm. (T. C. Çalışma Bakanlığı yayınları, sayı: 7)

    1. Class distinction—Turkey. 2. Turkey—Soc. life & cust. I.
Title. (Series: Turkey. Çalışma Vekâlcti. Çalışma Bakanlığı
yayınları, sayı 7)
    HN613.T3   59-30127

NT   0045500   DLC NNC MH UU

Tarus, İlhan, 1907-
Apartman. İstanbul, Varlık yayınları [1950]
111 p. port. (Türk hikâyecileri: 9)

NT 0045501 NNC ICU

Tarus, İlhan, 1907-
Ceza hâkimi, dram 3 perde 4 tablo. Ankara, Ulusal
Matbaa, 1940.
80 p. 20 cm. (Cümhuriyet Halk Partisi. Yeni seri temsil yayını, no. 7)

ı. Title.

PL248.T8C4 58-50365

NT 0045502 DLC MH MiU NNC

TARUS, İLHAN, 1907-
Ekin iti (hikâyeler). Ankara, Bukot matbaası, 1953.
128 p. 17cm. (Kaynak yayını. Yeni seri: [no.] 6)

1. Turkish literature--Fiction. I. Kaynak yayını.

NT 0045503 NN

Tarus, Ilhan, 1907-
Hifzissıhha Enstitüsü'nü tanıtıyoruz. Yazanlar İlhan
Tarus [and] Cevad Baykal. Ankara, Alâeddin Kıral Basi-
mevi, 1940.

30 p. (Millî Müesseselerimiz, 2)

NT 0045504 MH

Tarus, Ilhan, 1907-
Köle Hanı. [Istanbul] Yeditepe yayınları
[1954]
87 p. illus.

NT 0045505 CLU

TARUS, ILHAN, 1907-
Yeşilkaya savcısı; roman. İstanbul, Varlık yayınevi
[1955] 222 p. 17cm. (Varlık büyük kitapları. 11)

1. Turkish literature--Fiction. I. Varlık büyük cep kitapları.

NT 0045506 NN

Taruschio, Leopoldo, *Don.* **FR49.S4t
I Fraticelli del Piceno nello spirito della Divina Commedia.
— (*Cut from* Fra Crispino, periodico popolare. Anno 7, pp. 47-51,
77-81, 115-119. Grottammare. 1921.)
Relates to the Spiritual Franciscans.

E3640 — Spiritual Franciscans. — Franciscans in Italy. Piceno.
Dante Alighieri. La divina commedia. Sources and parallels.

NT 0045507 MB

FILM Taruschio, Leopoldo.
808 Nuova stilistica; ovvere, Dell'elemento
T178n musicale in letteratura. Macerata (Italia)
1936 Tipografia A. Slavi, 1936.

Microfilm copy (positive)
Collation of the original: 87p.
First published in 1914.

NT 0045508 IU

Taruschio, Leopoldo, ed.
PQ4562
.A35T4 Acquaticci, Giulio, 1603–1688.
1941 ... Il tempio pellegrino. La penitente d'Egitto. Firenze,
A. Salani [1941]

NT 0045510 DLC

Tarusov, Boris Nikolaevich.
Основы биологического действия радиоактивных излу-
чений. Москва, Медгиз, 1955.
137, [3] p. illus. 21 cm.
Bibliography: p. 134–[138]

1. Radiobiology. ı. Title.
Title transliterated: Osnovy biologicheskogo
deĭstviĭa radioaktivnykh izluchenĭĭ.

QH652.T3 56–32941

NT 0045510 DLC

WN TARUSOV, Boris Nikolaevich
610 Principles of biological action of
qT221o radioactive radiation. [n. p. , 1954?]
1954 116 p. illus.
Translation of Osnovy biologicheskogo
deĭstviĭa radioaktivnykh izluchenĭĭ.
1. Radiation - Effects

NT 0045511 DNLM

Tarussio, Ugo.
HA1360
.A2 Ellena, Vittorio, 1841–1892.
ser. 2, La statistica di alcune industrie italiane. Per Vittorio
vol. 13 Ellena. [Roma, Tipografia Eredi Botta, 1880]

Tarutin, Aleksandr.
(Stikhotvorenĭĭa).
Стихотворения. С.-Петербургъ [Типо-лит. М. Ф. Пай-
кина] 1899.
184, v p. 22 cm.
At head of title: Александръ Тарутинъ.
Poema.

PG3470.T34S8 1899 74–214684

NT 0045513 DLC

Tarutino, Russia. Deutsche Zeitung Bessarabiens
see Deutsche Zeitung Bessarabiens, *Tarutino, Russia.*

Taruvāgrahāram Gaṇapati Śāstrī
see
Gaṇapati Śāstrī, Taruvāgrahāram, *mahāmahopādhyāya,*
1860–1926.

Tarvainen, Olavi, 1909-
Conformitas Christi-ajatus Lutherin
teologiassa... Turku [Turun sanomalehti
ja kirjapaino osakeyhtiö] 1943.
136 p., 25ᵐ.

Thesis - Helsinki.
"Kirjallisuutta": p. [129]-134.

NT 0045516 NjPT CtY NNUT

Tarvainen, Olavi, 1909-
...Herännyt ennen heränneitä. Tutkielma Mikael Argicolan
kristillisyysdennäkemyksestä. Turku, Aura [1944] 91 p.
21cm.
"Lähdeviittaukset," p. 79–90.

1. Agricola, Mikael, bp., c. 1510– 1557.
N. Y. F. L. May 6, 1949

NT 0045517 NN MH

4BX Tarvainen, Olavi, 1909-
Luth Paavo Ruotsalainen als luther-
17 ischer Christ. Helsinki, Komis-
sionsverlag Akateeminen Kirjakauppa [1944]
78 p.
(Schriften der Luther-Agricola
Gesellschaft in Finnland, 6)

ICU NNUT
NT 0045518 DLC-P4 CSt NN NcD NjPT NjP MH-AH CtY-D

BT Tarvainen, Olavi, 1909-
130 Salattu Jumala (Deus absconditus);
.T37 raamattuteologinen tutkimus.
Helsinki, 1955.
149 p. 24 cm. (Suomalaisen
teologisen kirjallisuusseuran
julkaisuja, 61)
1.God--Attributes. 2.God--Biblical
teaching. I.T. (S:Suomalaisen
teologinen kirjallisuusseuran
julkaisuja, 61)

NT 0045519 MH-AH DLC-P4

Tarvainen, Olavi, 1909-
...Savolainen sielunpaimen; muistelmia
rovasti H. G. Th. Brofeldtista. Porvoo,
Helsinki, W. Söderström [1951] 86 p.
port. 19cm.

Bibliography, p. 85-86.

1.Brofeldt, Henrik Gustaf Theodor, 1837-

NT 0045520 NN DLC-P4

Tarvel, Peeter, 1894- ed.
DK511
.E8E4 Eesti biograafiline leksikon. Toimetus: A. R. Cederberg,
peatoimetaj [et al.] Tartus, K.-Ü Loodus, 1926–29.

Tarvel, Peeter, 1894-
Jones, Charles Sheridan, 1876-
... George Washington; inglise keelest tõlkinud O. Truu,
täiendustega varustanud prof. P. Treiberg. Tartu, Eesti
kirjanduse seltsi kirjastus, 1931.

Tarvel, Peeter, 1894-
Villecourt, Louis.
... L'Université de Tartu, 1919–1932. Tartu [“Postimehe”
trükk] 1932.

TARVER,B. E.
Speech on the Public debt bill,delivered in
the House of Representatives of the State of
Texas,December 18th,1855. Austin,"State Times"
Office,1856.

23 cm. pp.28.

NT 0045524 MH

[Tarver, E   R   ]
ᵛ Laredo, the gateway between the United States and Mexico. An illustrated description of the future city of the great South west. Laredo, Texas, Daily times print [1889]

28 pp. illus. 8°.

Issued by Laredo immigration society.

F394.L2T2

1-11960—M 1

NT 0045525   DLC CU TxU

TARVER, Edward J.
    A guide to the study of the history of architecture.
══   London. Pettitt & co. 1888. (3), ii, 47 pp. Plans.

NT 0045526   MB RP

Tarver, Francis Batten Cristal, b. 1828 or 9.
    French stumbling-blocks and English stepping-stones, to which is added a list of nearly 3,000 colloquialisms which cannot be rendered literally from English into French, by Francis Tarver... London: J. Murray, 1897.   viii, 212 p.   16°.

157362A. 1. French language—Con-   versation and phrasebooks, English.
N. Y. P. L.   January 7, 1925

NT 0045527   NN CtY OO

TARVER, Francis Batten Cristal, b. 1828 or 9.   268
    French stumbling-blocks and English stepping-stones.
—   N. Y. Appleton & co. 1897. viii, 212 pp. Sm. 8°.

NT 0045528   MB

Tarver, Francis Batten Cristal, b. 1828 or 9,
    joint author.   FOR OTHER EDITIONS
                         SEE MAIN ENTRY
Oliphant, Margaret Oliphant (Wilson) 1828–1897.
    Molière, by Mrs. Oliphant and F. Tarver. M. A. Edinburgh and London, W. Blackwood and sons, 1879.

Tarver, Harold, 1908–
    Studies on sulfur metabolism with special reference to the conversion of methionine to cystine, by Harold Tarver ... [Berkeley, Calif., 1939]
        1 p.l., 69 numb. l.   29 cm.
        Thesis (Ph. D.) – Univ. of California, May 1939.
        "References": p. 63–69.
        1. Sulphur in the body. 2. Metabolism. 3. Cystin. 4. Methionine.

NT 0045530   CU

T371.971
T179e   Tarver, Harold McBride, 1870–
    An epoch signalized by race emigration; the race loses by quitting the South.   San Antonio, 1920.
    20p. 21cm.

    1. Negroes – Southern States. 2. U.S. – Race question. I. Title.

NT 0045531   TxU

Tarver, Harold McBride, 1870–
    The negro in the history of the United States from the beginning of English settlements in America, 1607, to the present time, with the Constitution of the United States and illustrations, by H. M. Tarver ... Austin, Tex., The State printing company, 1905.
    2 p. l., [31]–186, [2] p. illus. (incl. ports.) 20½ᵐ.

    1. Negroes. I. Title.

                                    6–3119 Revised
Library of Congress   E185.T2

NT 0045532   DLC MoU TxU

Tzz
371.971   Tarver, Harold McBride, 1870–
T179w   The whiteman's primary, an open letter to D.A. McAskill.   [San Antonio? 1922?]
    [8]p. 21cm.

    Cover title.

    1. San Antonio – Pol. & govt. 2. McAskill, D.A.
    3. Negroes – Politics and suffrage. I. Title.

NT 0045533   TxU

Tarver, Henry.
    Colloquial French.   London, Williams, 1885.
    319 p.

NT 0045534   PPD

Hf32
175j   Tarver, Henry
    The Eton first French reading book, being a new ed. of "Tarver's new method", by H. & F.Tarver, rev. with considerable alterations and additions, by F.Tarver. 4th ed. rev. Eton,R.I.Drake,1885.
    11,251p. 18cm.

NT 0045535   CtY

Hf21
487at   Tarver, Henry
    The Eton French accidence and first French exercise book, with vocabularies. Eton,E.P.Williams,1865.
    x,262p. 18cm.
    "By far the greater portion of the exercises is on the verbs." Pref.

NT 0045536   CtY

Tarver, Henri.
    ...Second French reader with grammatical & explanatory notes by Henry Tarver... 6th ed. London, Hachette, 1887.
    180 p. 18 ᶜᵐ.

    1.French language–Chrestomathies and readers.

NT 0045537   NjP MH

Tarver, James L
    [The little colonel]
    The little colonel, overture. [New York] Belwin [1950]
    condensed score (8 p.) and   parts. 27 cm. (Famous band series, no. 192)
    Cover title.

    1. Overtures (Band)—Scores (reduced) and parts. I. Title.

    M1204.T   51–39926

NT 0045538   DLC

Tarver, James L
    Western plains, overture. New York, Belwin [1949]
    score (30 p.), condensed score (12 p.) and   parts. 31 cm. (Belwin domestic edition for the concert band, no. 189)
    Cover title.

    1. Overtures (Band)—Scores (reduced) and parts. I. Title.

    M1204.T22W5   50–15336

NT 0045539   DLC

Tarver, John Charles, 1790–1851.
    Choix en prose et en vers... suivi de la phraséologie expliquée et comparée, et précédé de remarques sur la construction des vers français. 3.ed., soigneusement corrigée. Londres, J.Souter, 1834.

NT 0045540   MH

Tarver, John Charles, 1790–1851.   4689.5
    Dictionnaire des verbes français. Or, dictionary of French verbs, shewing their different regimen. 2d edition, carefully revised and improved. To which has been prefixed a concise French grammar . . .
    London. Longman, Rees, & Co. 1829. 56, 306 pp. 18 cm., in 12s.

L7100 — Verbs. French. — France. Lang. Grammar. — France. Lang. Dict.

NT 0045541   MB

Tarver, John Charles, 1790–1851, ed.

Wanostrocht, Nicolas.
    A grammar of the French language, with practical exercises. By N. Wanostrocht, LL. D. Rev. and enl. by J. C. Tarver ... 22d ed. London, Longman and co.; [etc., etc.] 1851.

NT 0045543   MH

TARVER, John Charles, 1790–1851.
    The royal phraseological English-French, French-English dictionary. [Pt. I.] London, 1845.

    1.8°.
    I. English-French.

NT 0045543   MH

Tarver, John Charles, 1790–1851.
    ... The royal phraseological English-French, French-English dictionary. By J. Ch. Tarver ... 3d ed. London, Dulau & co.; [etc., etc.] 1854–58.
    2 v. 26½ᵐ.
    Title vignette: coat of arms.
    Vol. 2 has added half-title: Le dictionnaire phraséologique royal ...

    1. English language—Dictionaries—French. 2. French language—Dictionaries—English.

                                    10–26212†
Library of Congress   PC2640.T35

NT 0045544   DLC

'Tarver, John Charles, 1790–1851. Royal phraseological English-French, French-English dictionary. 4 ed. London, 1862–67.
2 v. r. 8°.   R.24

NT 0045545   MdBP NjP DN

PC2640   Tarver, John Charles, 1790–1851.
.T35   ... The royal phraseological English-French, French-English dictionary. By J. Ch. Tarver ... 4th ed. London, Dulau
1867   & co.; [etc., etc.] 1867–
    3 v. 26½ᵐ.
    Title vignette: coat of arms.
    Vol. 2 has added half-title: Le dictionnaire phraséologique royal ...
    Contents.– [1] French-English part.

NT 0045546   FMU PPFr

Tarver, John Charles, 1854–1926, tr.

Hanotaux, Gabriel, 1853–
    Contemporary France, by Gabriel Hanotaux ... with portraits ... Westminster, A. Constable & co., ltd., 1903–09.

Tarver, John Charles, 1854-1924.
Debateable claims: essays on secondary
education.
275 p. D. Westminister Constable. 1893.

NT 0045548   OCl

Tarver, John Charles, 1854-1926.
Debateable claims; essays on secondary education, by
John Charles Tarver ... Westminster, A. Constable &
co., 1898.
xxxi, 274, [1] p. 19½ᶜᵐ.

1. Secondary education—Gt. Brit.

E 11-649

Library, U. S. Bur. of   Education LA635.T2

NT 0045549   DHEW CtY AAP MiU ICJ NN

PQ2247
.T3
1895x
Tarver, John Charles, 1854-
Gustave Flaubert as seen in his works and
correspondence / by John Charles Tarver. --
New York : Appleton, 1895.
xvi, 368 p., [1] leaf of plates : ill. ;
24 cm.

1. Flaubert, Gustave, 1821-1880.
I. Title.

NT 0045550   MB CtY NcD OClW OU NIC

Tarver, John Charles, 1854-1926.
Gustave Flaubert as seen in his works and correspondence,
by John Charles Tarver. Westminster, A. Constable and
company, 1895.
3 p. l., [ix]-xvi p. 1 l., 368 p. front. (port.) pl. 23 cm.

1. Flaubert, Gustave, 1821-1880.

PQ2247.T3   12—23785

LU
NT 0045551   DLC WaSp NmU PU IaAS NN OCl CU MiU IEN

Tarver, John Charles, 1854-
Gustave Flaubert as seen in his works and correspond-
ence, by John Charles Tarver. New York, D.
Appleton, 1905.
3 p. l., [ix]-xvi p., 1 l., 368 p. front. (port.) pl. 23ᶜᵐ.
Inscribed: P.M. March 22 with A. notes, Nov. 46.

NT 0045552   TxU

[Tarver, John Charles] 1854-1926.
James; or, Virtue rewarded. New York, Stone & Kimball,
1896.
viii, 285 p., 1 l. 19½ᶜᵐ.

I. Title.
45-82982
Library of Congress   PR5548.T52J3

NT 0045553   DLC NN NNC ICN OClW IEdS

828
T196mu [Tarver, John Charles] 1854-1926.
Muggleton College; its rise and fall. Westminster, A. Constable, 1894.
167p. 18cm.

NT 0045554   IU ICU ViU CtY PU

TARVER, John Charles, 1854-, attributed author.
Muggleton College; its rise and fall;
[a skit]. Westminster, A. Constable & Co.,
1896.
nar.16°.
"2d ed."
Sometimes attributed to J.C. Tarver.

NT 0045555   MH

Tarver, John Charles, 1854-
Some observations of a foster parent; by John Charles
Tarver ... Westminster, A. Constable & co., 1897.
xx, 282 p. 20ᶜᵐ.
On various questions relating to education.

1. Education.
3—10505
Library of Congress   LB775.T2

NT 0045556   DLC CtY PSC PP PU PPPL ICJ MB DHEW

937.07
T43btF TARVER, John Charles, 1854-
... Tibère. Avec huit gravures hors-
texte. Paris, Payot, 1934.
347p.   8 pl. on 4 l. (incl. ports) 22cm.
(Bibliothèque historique)
"Premier tirage, janvier 1934."
1. Tiberius, emperor of Rome, B.C.42-
A.D.37. 2. Rome. Hist. 14-37.

NT 0045557   MnU

Tarver, John Charles, 1854-1926.
Tiberius, the tyrant; by J. C. Tarver ... New York,
Dutton, 1902.
v, 449, [1] p. front. (port.) 22 cm.

NT 0045558   NcD ViU KyU OO OCl OCH NjP MH MB

Tarver, John Charles, 1854-1926.
Tiberius, the tyrant; by J. C. Tarver ... Westminster, A.
Constable and co., ltd., 1902.
v, 449, [1] p. front. (port.) 23 cm.

1. Tiberius, emperor of Rome, B. C. 42-A. D. 37. 2. Rome—Hist.—
Tiberius, 14-37.
3—1342
Library of Congress   DG282.T19

OOxM MiU OClW GASU FMU NIC PBm
NT 0045559   DLC PPL PHC PSC CaBVaU NjP NN OU OCU

Tarver, John Charles, 1854-1926.
Tiberius, the tyrant. Westminster,
Constable, 1903.
450 p.

NT 0045560   OClW

Tarver, Malcolm Connor, 1885-
U. S. Congress. House. Committee on education.
Amend act to incorporate Howard university. Hearing be-
fore the Committee on education, House of representatives,
Sixty-ninth Congress, first session on H. R. 8466 (H. R. 393)
a bill to amend an act to incorporate Howard university in
the District of Columbia. Reprinted in connection with
H. R. 279, Seventieth Congress, first session. Supplemented
by a statement of Hon. Malcolm C. Tarver. Washington,
U. S. Govt. print. off., 1928.

Tarver, Malcolm Connor, 1885-
U. S. Congress. House. Committee on appropriations.
... Department of labor, Federal security agency, and related
independent offices appropriation bill, fiscal year 1942 ... Re-
port. ⟨To accompany H. R. 4926⟩ ... [Washington, U. S.
Govt. print. off., 1941]

Tarver, Malcolm Connor, 1885-
HD9006
.A5
1945 f U. S. Congress. House. Committee on appropriations.
... Investigation of the War food administration under House
resolution 50 ... Report. ⟨Pursuant to H. Res. 50⟩ [Wash-
ington, U. S. Govt. print. off., 1945]

Tarver, Malcolm Connor, 1885-
U. S. Congress. House. Committee on the judiciary.
... Make it a crime to advocate or promote the overthrow
of the government of the United States ... Report. ⟨To accompany H. R. 8378⟩ ... [Washington, U. S. Govt. print. off.,
1933]

Tarver, Malcolm Connor, 1885-
U. S. Congress. House. Committee on the judiciary.
... Prison industries board ... Report. ⟨To accompany
H. R. 5153⟩ ... [Washington, U. S. Govt. print. off., 1933]

Lmg62
T725
929t Tarver, Matthew Arthur Joseph
Trent college, 1868-1927; a rough sketch, by
M.A.J.Tarver. London, G.Bell & sons,ltd.,1929.
x,143p. front.,plates,ports. 19½
1.Trent college.

NT 0045566   CtY NjR OCl

Tarver, Micajah.
The moral uses of plants. By M. Tarver ... St. Louis,
C. Witter, 1855.
19, [1] p. 2 col. pl. (incl. front.) 27½ᶜᵐ.

1. Flowers. I. Title.
4—13568
Library of Congress   QK81.T19

NT 0045567   DLC

Tarver, Micajah, ed.
The Western journal and civilian, devoted to agriculture, manufactures, mechanic arts, internal improvement, commerce,
public policy, and polite literature ... v. 1-14, v. 15, no. 1-
4; Jan. 1848-Mar. 1856. St. Louis, Charles & Hammond,
printers [etc.] 1848-56.

BT821
.T2 TARVER, SAMUEL.
Course and culmination of empire according to
prophecy. By Samuel Tarver... Louisville,Ky.,
Printed by J.P.Morton & co.,1866.
240 p. illus. 19½cm.

1.Eschatology.

NT 0045569   ICU DLC

Tarver, Samuel.
A theological poem. Louisville, Ky.,
Morton & Griswold, 1852.
304 p.   20 cm.
Preface by Samuel Tarver, Denmark, Tenn.,
1851.

NT 0045570   T

Tarver, Samuel.
A theological vision.   Louisville, 1852.
304 p.   D.

NT 0045571   RPB

Tarvia and pitch filler
see under   [Barrett company (West Virginia)]

Tarvia-lithic. The ready-to-lay pavement.
n.p., Barrett co., 1931.
31 p.   illus.   O.
1. Pavements.

NT 0045573   NcD

796.357 Tarvin, A   H
T17c   A century of baseball, 1839-1939 ...   [Louis-
ville, Ky., The Standard printing co., inc.,
c1938]
128p. illus.(incl.ports.)

Illustrated t.-p. and cover.

1. Base-ball--Hist. I. Title.

NT 0045574   IU NN FU OC1 MH ICU OrPU

Tarvin, Donald, 1905–
The methane fermentation of organic acids, by Donald
Tarvin ... Urbana, Ill., 1933.
8 p. 23ᶜᵐ.
Abstract of thesis (PH. D.)—University of Illinois, 1933.
Vita.
Bibliography: p. 7.

1. Acids, Organic. 2. Fermentation. 3. Methane.
Library of Congress   QD305.A2T18 1933   34–1422
Univ. of Illinois Libr.
———— Copy 2.   [2]   547.7

NT 0045575   IU DLC OU

TARVISIUM, Italy

See TREVISO.

PH355   Tarvo, Liisa.
.K78Z54
Krohn, Aune.
Matkamiehiä ja muukalaisia; muuan kirjeenvaihto, 1933–
1938. Julkaissut Aune Krohn. Porvoo, W. Söderström
[1943]

BR
123   Tarvydas, Jonas.
.T89   Trumpi skaitymeliai. Sutaise Jonas
Tarvydas. [n.p.] "Darbininko" spauda,
1923.
151 p. 20 cm.
Stamped on t.p.: Dievas tevyne.
Alka. R. F. D. 2. Putnam, Conn.

1. Christianity--Addresses, essays,
lectures. 2. Lithuanian collection.
I. Title

NT 0045578   OKentU

Tarwater, Nan.
The 4-H club girl makes a costume
see under   Louisiana. State University and
Agricultural and Mechanical College. Division of
Agricultural Extension.

Tarwé, Gérard.
...Feux nouveaux. Illus. de G. Delancre.   Tournai [etc.]
Casterman, 1948. 181 p. illus. 18cm. (Collection Fleur
rouge)

535143B. I. Drama, French. I. Title.
N. Y. P. L.   February 16, 1951

NT 0045580   NN PU

Tarweld, Mathilde, pseud.
see Bourdon, Mathilde (Lippens) 1817–
1888.

W 4   TARY, Paul, 1924-
L99   Traitement de la maladie de Bouillaud
1950/51   par le gentisate de sodium. Lyon,
no. 45   Annequin, 1950.
79 p. (Lyons. [Université] Faculté
mixte de médecine et de pharmacie.
Thèse, 1950/51, no. 45)
1. Gentian 2. Rheumatic fever

NT 0045582   DNLM

Tarybine lietuviu literatura ir kritika
see under Lietuvos TSR Mokslu akademija,
Vilna. Lietuviu Kalbos ir literaturos institutas.

[vault]   Taryf der goude en zilvere specien met hunne eval-
HG   uatien volgens de leste placcaeten, tot gerief van't pub-
3854   lic, inponden schellingen grooten wisselgeld en courant,
T32   als ook in guldens stuyvers oorden, zoo in wissel-geld als
courant, beginnende van een tot duyzent; geëxamineert
en goedgekeurt in haere K.K. en A. majesteyts privéen
raede. Brugge, J. De Busscher, boekdrukker en
boekverkooper, 1774
48 p. illus., tables. 15cm.

NT 0045584   PPT

Taryf der goude en zilvere specien met hunne
evaluatien volgens de laetste placaeten, tot
gerief van het publik, in ponden, schellingen,
grooten wissel-geld en courant, als ook in guldens, stuyvers, deniers, zoo in wissel-geld als
courant, beginnende van een, tot duyzend; geëxamineert en goedgekeurt in Zyne K.K.en A.Majes-
toyts privéen raede. Brugge, J.de Busscher,
1783.
48 [i.e.54] p.incl.illus., tables. 16.5 cm.
Text in French and Dutch.

NT 0045585   MH-BA

---

al-Taryuman, ʿAbdallāh
see
Turmeda, Anselmo, 1352-1432?

SF287   Tarzana, Calif. School of applied horsemanship.
.A5
American association of animal lovers.
The art of horse management. pt. 1–
[Tarzana, Calif.] School of applied horsemanship [1945–

Tarzī, Fuʾād.
(al-Mārkslyah barakah rajʿiyah)
الماركسية حركة رجعية : نقد للفلسفة المادية وتطبيقها
الاجتماعي من الوجهة العلمية والنفسية والاقتصادية
والفلسفية / فؤاد طرزي. ـــ الطبعة 1. ـــ بغداد : مكتبة
الشرق، 1948.
64 p. : 22 cm. (سلسلة المطبوعات القومية الحرة)
Bibliography: p. 61–62.
1. Communism—Addresses, essays, lectures.   I. Title. II. Series: Silsilat al-maṭbūʿāt al-qawmīyah al-ḥurrah.

HX431.1 TT37   75–587822

NT 0045588   DLC

PK2200   Tarzī, Khān Maḥbūb.
.T3G8   گل بانو. مصنفہ خان محبوب طرزی. [کراچی] قیّوم یکدپو
[Orien   [195-?]
Urd
241 p. 18 cm.
In Urdu.
Text partially vocalised.
A novel.

I. Title.
                            Title transliterated: Gul bānū.

PK2200.T3G8   S A 64-5370

NT 0045589   DLC

Tarzī, Khān Maḥbūb.
نواب قدسیہ محل، تاریخی اودھ کا ایک ورق.
مصنفہ خان محجوب طرزی. [کراچی، اودھ کتاب گھر]
319 p. 19 cm.
In Urdu.
Text partially vocalized.

I. Title.
                            Title transliterated: Navāb Qudsīyah maḥal.

PK2200.T3N3   S A 65-4659

NT 0045590   DLC

Tarzī, Khān Maḥbūb.
(Paighām-i ajal)
پیغام اجل : ایک جاسوسی ناول / خان محبوب طرزی. ـــ لاہور :
خالد یکدپو، [-19]
256 p. : 19 cm.
In Urdu.

I. Title.
PK2200.T3P3   75-986786

NT 0045591   DLC

Tarzī, Khān Maḥbūb.
(Pānch hazār sāl qabl)
پانچ ہزار سال قبل / خان محبوب طرزی. ـــ لاہور : خالد یکدپو،
[-19]
160 p. : 18 cm.
In Urdu.

I. Title.
PK2200.T3P35   75-986788

NT 0045592   DLC

Ṭarzī, Khān Maḥbūb.
(Ṣanam kadah)
صنم کده :،ناول / خان محبوب طرزی. — کراچی : رحمت پبلشنگ
ایجنسی، [19 –].
396 p. ; 19 cm.
In Urdu.

I. Title.

PK2200.T3S19   75-986787

NT 0045593   DLC

Ṭarzī, Khān Maḥbūb.
صنوبر؛ ایک روماٹی ناول. [مصنف] خان محبوب طرزی. [کراچی،
سلیم برادرز، 195–]
192 p. (p. 191-192 advertisement) 19 cm.
In Urdu.

I. Title.
                                 Title romanized: Ṣanobar.

PK2200.T3S2   S A 68-10696

NT 0045594   DLC

Ṭarzī, Khān Maḥbūb.
(Shabāb-i qurṭabah)
شباب قرطبہ : ایک اسلامی تاریخی ناول / خان محبوب طرزی. —
لاہور : خالد بکڈپو، [19 –].
512 p. ; 19 cm.
In Urdu.

I. Title.

PK2200.T3S5   75-986790

NT 0045595   DLC

Ṭarzī, Khān Maḥbūb.
(Sunahrī reshah)
سنہری ریشہ : ایک حیرت انگیز جاسوسی ناول / خان محبوب طرزی.
— کراچی : اودھ کتاب گھر، 1955.
272 p. ; 19 cm.
In Urdu.

I. Title.

PK2200.T3S8   76-985989

NT 0045596   DLC

Ṭarzī, Maḥmūd.
(Az har dahan sukhanī va az har chaman samanī)
از هر دهن سخنی و از هر چمن سمنی، مؤلفش محمود
طرزی. کابل، کتبخانهٔ مطبعهٔ عنایت [3 or 1952]. 1331.
268, 4 p. ports. 18 cm.
Short prose sketches.

I. Title.

PK6561.T284A9   74-220370

NT 0045597   DLC

Ṭarzī Afshār, fl. 1616-1650.
[Dīvān]
دیوان طرزئ افشار : برگذار نادر ادبی، با یك مقدمهٔ جامعی
راجع بشرح حال شاعر مبتکر و شامل تحقیقات کامله دائر بطرز
وی و شیوهٔ خاص اشعار آبدار شیرین و افکار عالیه و متین
وی / بقلم مصحح و مدون، تمدن. — رضائیه : کتابخانهٔ تمدن،
[1930 or 1931]
24, 208 p., [1] leaf of plates : port. ; 22 cm.
I. Tamaddun, M.
                            Title romanized: Dīvān-i Ṭarzī Afshār.

PK6550.T35A6 1931   77-970644

NT 0045598   DLC

Tarzia, Bruno.
A comparative analytical chart of the forms
of poetry. Rev., corr., & enl. [n. p.] c1935.
1 fold. chart. 24 cm.

NT 0045599   OKentU

TARZIA, BRUNO.
A comparative analytical chart of the forms of poetry. [Rev., corr.
and enl.] [Bayonne? N. J., 1939, c1933] 1 fold. chart. 25cm.

Cover-title.

I. Prosody, English.

NT 0045600   NN

Tarzia, Miguel.
... Carducci; la vida, el hombre, la técnica de su creación
poética. Buenos Aires [Talleres gráficos de Porter hnos.]
1936.
231 p., 2 l. 18½ᵐᵐ.

1. Carducci, Giosuè, 1835-1907.
                                                    38-23100
Library of Congress   PQ4686.T3
                               [2]   928.5

NT 0045601   DLC DPU WU IU IaU OU

Tarzia, Miguel.
... Ensueño y acciòn; Virgilio, Juan Jaurés, Florencio Sánchez, y otros ensayos. Chivilcoy, 1934.
6 p. l., [11]-65, [143] p. 23½ᵐᵐ.
"Algunas opiniones autorizadas sobre el autor": p. [140]-[141]
"Bibliografía": p. [142]-[143]
CONTENTS.—Virgilio.—Juan Jaurés.—Florencio Sánchez.—Glosas y
notas kantianas—La fuerza espiritual más pura del cosmos.—En el
centenario de la muerte de Hegel.—La danza.—Rivadavia.—Un perso-
naje del Greco : Pascal.—Una incitación a la juventud.—Algo sobre los
griegos y nuestro tiempo.—En el día de la patria.—El libro.

I. Title.
                                                    35-23083
Library of Congress   AC75.T3   081

NT 0045602   DLC NcU

Tarzia, Miguel.
... El romero visionario. Buenos Aires [Talleres gráficos de
Porter hnos.] 1938.
113 p., 4 l. 20½ᵐᵐ.
Poems.

I. Title.
                                                    39-23720
Library of Congress   PQ7797.T32R7
                               [2]   861.6

NT 0045603   DLC DPU

Italy
T17
18
1775
Tarzo, Italy. Laws, statutes, etc.
Statuta Tartii recentioribus sanctionibus
adiectis. [Venice] ex typographia ducali
Pinelliana, 1775.
1 p. l., 122 p. 27 cm.

Title vignette (coat of arms of Venice)
Latin and Italian on opposite pages.

NT 0045604   CtY-L CLU NN MH PU

TARZO, Italy. Laws, statutes, etc.
Gli statuti di Tarzo latini et volgari con
le loro tavole. Coneglieno, M. Claseri,
1620.

NT 0045605   MH

TD 897   Tarzwell, Clarence Matthew, 1907–
T57   Application of biological research in the con-
         trol of industrial wastes, by Clarence M. Tarz-
         well and Peter Doudoroff. [Cincinnati, 1952?]
         18 l. illus. 27 cm.
            At head of title: Federal Security Agency,
         Public Health Service, Environmental Health Cen-
         ter, Cincinnati, Ohio.
            "Reprinted from Proceedings of the National
         Technical Task Committee on Industrial Wastes,
         1952 Meeting held at Cincinnati, Ohio, June 3-4,
         1952."

NT 0045606   OU DI

SH1   Tarzwell, Clarence Matthew, 1907–   joint
.M5   author.
no. 1   Hubbs, Carl Leavitt, 1894–
            ... Methods for the improvement of Michigan trout
         streams, by Carl L. Hubbs, John R. Greeley and Clarence
         M. Tarzwell ... Ann Arbor, Mich., University of Michigan
         press, 1932.

Tarzwell, Clarence Mathew, 1907–
   Observations on the nighttime resting and biting habits of
anopheline mosquitoes in DDT-treated and untreated buildings, by Clarence M. Tarzwell and Frank W. Fisk ... [Wash-
ington, U. S. Govt. print. off., 1947]
12 p. incl. tables, diagrs. 23ᶜᵐ. ([U. S. Public health service] Public health reports. Reprint no. 2768)
Running title: Habits of anopheline mosquitoes.
"Reference": p. 12.

1. Mosquitoes—Extermination. 2. DDT (Insecticide)   I. Fisk,
Frank Wilbur, joint author. II. Title: Habits of anopheline mosquitoes.

RC116.T25   614.43   Med 47-1479

NT 0045608   DLC PP

Tarzwell, Clarence Matthew, 1907–
   The resistance of construction materials to penetration by
rats [by] C. M. Tarzwell [and others. Washington, U. S.
Govt. Print. Off., 1953]
iv, 16 p. illus., tables. 26 cm. (Public Health Service publication
no. 277. Public health monograph no. 11)

1. Ratproof construction.   (Series: U. S. Public Health Service.
Publication no. 277. Series: U. S. Public Health Service. Public
health monograph, no. 11)

RA641.R2T3   *693.84   53-61412

NT 0045609   DLC AAP MoU TU DNLM PPWM PPD PP ViU

Z6673   Tarzwell, Clarence Mathew, 1907–   joint
.U515   author.
no. 13   Ingram, William Marcus, 1913–
            Selected bibliography of publications relating to undesir-
         able effects upon aquatic life by algicides, insecticides [and]
         weedicides [by] William Marcus Ingram and Clarence M.
         Tarzwell. Cincinnati, U. S. Dept. of Health, Education,
         and Welfare, Public Health Service, 1954.

TD425   Tarzwell, Clarence Mathew, 1907–
T25   Some important biological effects of pollution
         often disregarded in stream surveys. [By]
         Clarence M. Tarzwell and Arden R. Gaufin.
         [Cincinnati, U.S. Dept. of Health, Education and
         Welfare, Public Health Service, Environmental
         Health Center, 1953]
            [1], 38, [4] l. illus., diagrs. 27 cm.
            "Reproduced from Proceedings of the 8th
         Industrial Waste Conference, May 4, 5 and 6, 1953]
            Bibliography: p. 25-38.
            1. Water — Pollution. I. Gaufin, Arden Rupert,
         1912–   jt. aut.   II. Title: Biological
effects of   pollution.

NT 0045611   DI OU

Tarzwell, Clarence Matthew, 1907–
I   Studies in stream improvement ... ₍n. p., 1935–
9   38₎
.T196   4 pts. in 1 v.
           Cover-title.
           Thesis (Ph. D.)--University of Michigan, 1936.
           Consists of four reprints from Transactions of
           the 21st American game conference, 1935, Transac-
           tions of the North American wildlife conference,
           1936 and 1938, and Transactions of the American
           fisheries society, v. 66, 1936.
           CONTENTS.--1. Progress in lake and stream
           improvement.--2. Lake and stream improvement

           in Michigan.--3. Experimental evidence on the
           value of trout stream improvement in Michigan.--
           4. An evaluation of the methods and results of
           stream improvement in the Southwest.

NT   0045613   MiU MiD

Tas,   pseud.
       De Taschiade, of, Wie wil 800 gulden cadeau
hebben? Blijspel met zang in één bedrijf. Vrij
naar Tas door M. M. van Leeuwen Jr.
Kampen, L. van Hulst, 1880.
       48 p.   12°.

NT   0045614   NN

Tas, Adam, 1668–1722.
       The diary of Adam Tas (1705–1706) ed. by Leo Fouché
... with an enquiry into the complaints of the colonists against
the governor, Willem Adriaan van der Stel. English translation by A. C. Paterson ... With two maps. London, New
York ₍etc.₎ Longmans, Green and co., 1914.
       xlvii, 367, ₍1₎ p.   2 maps (1 fold.; incl. front.)   23½ᶜᵐ.
       Added t.-p. in Dutch.   Dutch and English on opposite pages.
       1. Cape of Good Hope—Hist.   2. Cape of Good Hope—Soc. life & cust.
3. Stel, Willem Adriaan van der, 1664–1723.   I. Fouché, Leo, 1880–
ed.   II. Paterson, Alfred Croom, tr.
                                                    17–20728
       Library of Congress   DT843.T2
                                   ₍a41b1₎

       CLSU
NT   0045615   DLC MB PPFr WaS IEN CU NjP NN OClW TxU

Tas, Adam, 1668–1722.
Law
       Spilhaus, Margaret Whiting.
       The first South Africans and the laws which governed
them; to which is appended The diary of Adam Tas. Cape
Town, Juta ₍1949₎

Tas, J
       Viertalig textiel-woordenboek voor de handel. Neder-
lands, Duits, Engels, Frans, met alfabetische registers en
enkele tableaux. 1. druk. Doetinchem, Uitg. Mij. "Misset,"
1951.
       242 p.   illus.   28 cm.

       1. Textile industry and fabrics—Dictionaries—Polyglot.   2. Dutch
language—Dictionaries—Polyglot.   I. Title.
       TS1309.T3   A 51–10198
       Illinois. Univ. Library
       for Library of Congress   ₍1₎†

NT   0045617   IU NN DLC

Tas, J
       Viertalig textiel-woordenboek voor de handel. Neder-
lands, Duits, Engels, Frans, met alfabetische registers en
enkele tableaux. Tekeningen en ruiten en bindingen door
Caspar Jansen. 2. verb. druk. Doetinchem, Misset, 1953.
       243 p.   illus.   28 cm.

       1. Textile industry and fabrics—Dictionaries—Polyglot.   2. Dutch
language—Dictionaries—Polyglot.   I. Title.
       TS1309.T3   1953   54–31897

NT   0045618   DLC NN

Tas, J
       Viertalig textiel-woordenboek voor de handel. Neder-
lands, Duits, Engels, Frans, met alfabetische registers en
enkele tableaux. Tekeningen van ruiten en bindingen door
Caspar Jansen. 2. verb. druk. Doetinchem, Misset, 1953.
       243 p.   illus.   28 cm.

       1. Textile industry and fabrics—Dictionaries—Polyglot.   2. Dutch
language—Dictionaries—Polyglot.   I. Title.

       TS1309.T3   1953   54–31897

NT   0045618   DLC NN

Tas, Kas, pseud.
       see   Kas Tas, pseud.

Tas, Leonard, 1889–
       Vegetatieve vermenigvuldiging bij *Hevea brasiliensis*,
door L. Tas.   Batavia, G. Kolff & co., 1921.
       2 p. l., 33 p.   front., illus., plates.   22½ᶜᵐ.

       1. India-rubber.   ₍1. Hevea brasiliensis₎
                                                    Agr 23–692
       Library, U. S. Dept. of   Agriculture   77T18

NT   0045620   DNAL

Tas, Sal, 1905–
       ...Analyse van een charme.   Amsterdam, G. A. van Oorschot,
1948.   210 p.   illus.   21cm.

       481111B.   1. Drama—Hist. and crit.,   20th cent.   2. Drama—Technique.
N. Y. P. L.   July 15, 1949

NT   0045621   NN OU

WASON   Tas, Sal, 1905–
PT   Een critische periode / S. Tas.
5864   Amsterdam : De Bezige Bij, ₍1946₎
P45   118 p. ; 20 cm. (Periscoop-reeks ; 3.
Z94   deel)

              1. Perron, Edgar du, 1899–1940--
       Criticism and interpretation.
              2. Braak, Menno ter, 1902–1940
       Criticism and interpretation.   I. Title

NT   0045622   NIC MH

Tas, Sal, 1905–
       ... De illusie van de ondergang; wereldtragedie en wereld-
beschouwing.   Amsterdam, De Bezige bij, 1946.
       2 p. l., 7–310 p., 1 l.   19½ cm.

       1. History—Philosophy.   2. Civilization—Philosophy.   3. Pessimism.
4. Christianity—Psychology.   I. Title.
       D16.9.T33   901   A F 47–1316

NT   0045623   DLC CtY ICU CU NNCU-G MH

JC   Tas, Sal, 1905–
259   Intellect en macht.   Haarlem, Uni-
T19   versum-Editie ₍192-?₎
             319 p.   20cm.

             1. Political science.   I. Title.

NT   0045624   NIC

TAS, Sal, 1905–
       Intellect en macht.   Haarlem, Universum-editie
[194-?]   319 p.   20cm.

       1. Political science, 1918–

NT   0045625   NN

Tas, Sal, 1905–
       Johan Brouwer, outsider en bezieler.   Den Haag, H. P.
Leopold, 1946.
       35 p.   port.   22 cm.

       1. Brouwer, Johannes, 1898–1943.
       DP63.7.B7T3   55–34527

NT   0045626   DLC NN

Tas, Sal, 1905–
       De koude vrede.   Amsterdam, G. A. van Oorschot, 1954.
       320 p.   21 cm.

       1. World politics—1945–   I. Title.
       D843.T3   56–30375 ‡

NT   0045627   DLC NN NNC

Tas, Sal, 1905–
       Leiderschap en intellect, of De mach der intellec-
tuelen.   's-Gravenhage, Stols, 1946
       45 p.   (De vrije bladen, jg. 18, schrift 5, Mei 1946)

NT   0045628   MH

[Tas, Sal] 1905–
       Naar een nieuwe wereldoorlog
       see under title

Tas, Sal, 1905–
       Nederland-Indonesië, een analyse en een politiek.   Am-
sterdam, L. J. Veen ₍1945₎
       40 p.   20 cm.

       1. Indonesia—Politics and government—20th century.   I. Title.
       DS644.T3   48–15292

NT   0045630   DLC CU CtY NN ICU

Tas, Sal, 1905–
       ... De politieke crisis van Nederland.   Amsterdam, J. M.
Meulenhoff ₍1945₎
       1 p. l., 30 p.   24 cm.   (On cover: Tijd- en strijdragen)

       1. Political parties—Netherlands.   2. Netherlands—Politics and
government—1945–   I. Title.
       JN5981.T3   A F 47–5316

NT   0045631   DLC MH NN

Tas, Sal, 1905–
De tweede wereldvrede, door S. Tas. 's-Gravenhage, H. P. Leopold, 1945.
365 p. 22 cm.

1. Reconstruction (1939–1951) 2. World politics—1933–1945. 3. Netherlands — Politics and government — 1940–1945. I. Title.

D825.T35   A F 47–5470

NT   0045632   DLC PU IU

Le Tas des blagues; journal des prisonniers du Camp de Schneidemühl.
₍Schneidemühl, Eichstädtsche buchdruckerei W. Pein₎ 191
v. illus. 38ᶜᵐ. 3 no. a month.
René Lévy, editor.

1. European war, 1914–1918—Period. 2. European war, 1914–1918—Prisoners and prisons, German—Schneidemühl.

Library of Congress   D627.G3A17   CA 29–114 Unrev'd

NT   0045633   DLC

Tasa Coal Company.
Comparing coals.   Zelienople, Pa., 1953.
28 p. illus., ports. 28 cm.
On cover: Coal is coal, or is it?
Bibliography: p. 26.

NT   0045634   OCU

Tasaki, Hanama.
Long the imperial way. Tokyo, Itagaki-Shoten ₍ᶜ1949₎
523 p. 19 cm.

I. Title.
PZ3.T18Lo   49–54537*

NT   0045635   DLC HU NN OKentU

Tasaki, Hanama.
Long the imperial way. 田崎花馬₍著 東京₎ 月曜書房 ₍昭和25 i.e. 1950₎
285 p. 19 cm.
On spine: 皇道は遙かなり
In Japanese.
Fiction.

1. World War, 1939–1945—Fiction. I. Title. II. Title: Kōdō wa haruka nari.

PL839.A735L6   75–798255

NT   0045636   DLC

Tasaki, Hanama.
Long the imperial way. Boston, Houghton Mifflin, 1950
₍ᶜ1949₎
372 p. 22 cm.

1. World War, 1939–1945—Fiction. I. Title.

PZ3.T18Lo 2   50–3997

OrSaW WaE WaS WaT WaSpG OCU
NcGU TxU MH ViU MB TxCM GU PPPrHi GAT OrP Or IdU
NT   0045637   DLC PPD PPA PSt PPL OCl CaBVa MtBC IdB

Tasaki, Hanama.
The mountains remain. Boston, Houghton Mifflin, 1952.
408 p. 22 cm.

I. Title.

PZ3.T18Mo   52–5256 ‡

NT   0045638   DLC CaBVa IdB Or OrCS OrP MtU WaE WaS

Tasaki, Hanama.
The mountains remain. London, V. Gollancz, 1953.
408 p. 22 cm.

NT   0045639   OrU

Tasaki, Ichiji, 1910–
Nervous transmission. Springfield, Ill., Thomas ₍1953₎
164 p. illus. 25 cm.

1. Nerves. 2. Nodes of Ranvier. I. Title.

QP363.T3   612.822   53—2360 ‡

OrU
ICJ DNLM TxU IEN OrU-M ICJ CaBVaU ViU PU-Med WaWW
NT   0045640   DLC RPB MiU OOxM OU PSt TU NcU OClW NcD

Tasaki, Masashi
see
Tazaki, Masashi, 1898–

Tasan. No. 1–   1930–   Merzifon.
v. in
Published by "Merzifon Halkevi".
No. 25– also called ₍New Series₎ no. 1–
1. Community centers - Turkey - Period.
I. Merzifon, Turkey. Halkevi.

NT   0045642   CLU

... Tasas e impuestos sobre la industria minera en Bolivia ...
see under   ₍Banco minero de Bolivia, La Paz. Sección estadística y estudios económicos₎

Tasat Gelar Sutan Bagindo
see   Bagindo, Tasat Gelar Sutan.
₍supplement₎

Tasawa, Yutaka
see
Tazawa, Yutaka, 1902–

BP189
.A15
Orien
Arab

al-Taṣawwuf 'inda al-'Arab.
'Abd al-Nūr, Jabbūr.

التصوف عند العرب ₍تأليف₎ جبور عبد النور. ₍بيروت₎
₍1938₎

Tasborough, John, *defendant.*
The tryal and conviction of John Tasborough and Ann Price for subornation of perjury, in endeavouring to perswade Mʳ. Stephen Dugdale to retract and deny his evidence about the horrid Popish plot : with an intention to stifle the further prosecution and discovery of the same. At the King's bench bar at Westminster, Tuesday the third day of February, 16⁷⁹₈₀. before the Right Honourable Sir William Scroggs, knight, lord chief justice, and the rest of the judges of that court. London, R. Pawlett, 16⁸⁰.
2 p. l., 59 p. 30½ᶜᵐ.
No. 14 in a volume lettered : Tryals, vol. I.
1. Popish plot, 1678. 2. Dugdale, Stephen, 1640?–1683. I. Price, Ann, defendant. II. Gt. Brit. Court of King's bench.
42–26930

CSmH MH CLL WaU-L
NT   0045647   DLC GU TxU NN PU CLU-C MnU DFo OCl CtY

D754
.R9C3

Tasca, Angelo, 1892–   ed.
Cahiers du communisme.
Les Cahiers du bolchevisme pendant la campagne 1939–1940: Molotov, Dimitrov, Thorez, Marty. Avant-propos de A. Rossi ₍pseud.₎ Paris, D. Wapler ₍1952, *1951₎

Tasca, Angelo, 1892–
A Communist Party in action; an account of the organization and operations in France, by A. Rossi ₍pseud.₎ Translated and edited, with an introd., by Willmoore Kendall. New Haven, Yale University Press, 1949.
xxiv, 301 p. 25 cm.
"A somewhat abridged English translation of A. Rossi's Physiologie du Parti communiste français."
Bibliographical references included in "Notes" (p. ₍269₎–289)

1. Parti communiste. 2. Communism—France. I. Title.

JN3007.C6T313   329.944   49—11815°

OrPR OrU WaS OrCS OrStbM
ICU ViU CPFT MiU IU NcD NcGU DS MH MB CaBVaU Or MtBC
NT   0045649   DLC NNCU-G OCl OU OClU OC1C OClW PP TxU

Tasca, Angelo, 1892–
Les communistes français pendant la drôle de guerre; une page d'histoire, par A. Rossi ₍pseud.₎ Paris, Iles d'or, 1951.
365 p. facsims. 29 cm.
Includes bibliographical references.

1. Communism—France. 2. World War, 1939–1945—France. I. Title.

DC396.T34   335.4   51–25537 rev

CaBVaU OrPR OrCS OrU
CtY TU TNJ PHC NN GU ViU NNCFR KyU NBuU CU-S CSt-H
NT   0045650   DLC DAU MeB MoSU OU NBC ICU OU NcD IaU

Tasca, Angelo, 1892–
I consigli di fabbrica e la rivoluzione mondiale; relazione letta all' assemblea della Sezione socialista torinese la sera del 13 aprile 1920. Torino: Alleanza coop. torinese, 1921. 58 p. 12°.
(Pagine socialiste. no. 1.)

1. Employee representation, Italy. 2. Series.
N. Y. P. L.   November 6, 1922.

NT   0045651   NN

944.08
R831c

Tasca, Angelo, 1892–
Crise française, crise mondiale. ₍t. 1₎
Physiologie du Parti communiste française.
Paris, Self, 1948.
xxxvi, 465p. 22cm.
₍At head of title: A. Rossi.₎
No more published.

1. France. Pol. & govt. 1914–1940.
2. France. Pol. & govt. 1940–1945. I. Title.

NT   0045652   IEN

Tasca, Angelo, 1892–
  Deux ans d'alliance germano-soviétique, août 1939–juin 1941 ₍par₎ A. Rossi ₍pseud.₎   Paris, A. Fayard ₍1949₎
    225 p.   group port., facsims.   19 cm.
    Bibliographical footnotes.

    1. Germany—For. rel.—Russia.   2. Russia—For. rel.—Germany.   3. World War, 1939–1945—Diplomatic history.   I. Title.

    D754.R9T3   940.5324   49–27469 rev*

       NN TxU MeB MoSW KyU OrU CaBVaU
NT   0045653   DLC IaU MH–IR NNUN NNC PU NcD OU ICJ NcU

Tasca, Angelo, 1892–
  Due anni di alleanza germano-sovietica, agosto 1939–giugno 1941.   Ed. riv. con appendice di documenti inediti. ₍Traduzione dal francese di Aldo Garosci₎   Firenze, La Nuova Italia ₍1951₎
    xvi, 208 p.   group ports., facsims.   (Documenti della crisi contemporanea, 7)
    Bibliographical footnotes.
    1. Germany—For. rel.—Russia.   2. Russia—For. rel.—Germany.   3. World War, 1939–1945—Diplomatic history.   I. Title.
    D754.R9T315 1951   940.5324   52–20679

NT   0045654   DLC MH NN

Tasca, Angelo, 1892–
  La guerre des papillons; quatre ans de politique communiste (1940–1944) par A. Rossi ₍pseud.₎   Paris, Iles d'or ₍1954₎
    332 p.   48 facsims.   21 cm.   (*His* Sous l'occupation, 1)
    Bibliographical footnotes.

    1. Communism—France.   2. France—Pol. & govt.—1940–1945.   I. Title.
                                    A 55–4897
    Rochester. Univ. Libr.   DC397.T3
    for Library of Congress   ₍3₎

       DLC PU ViU IU CaBVaU OrCS MH OrU
       MiU InU InNd CLU MH CaOTU NjP TU OrU FU MoSU TNJ MB
NT   0045655   NRU MH NIC GU TxU IaU NcD OOxM NN CtY

Tasca, Angelo, 1892–
  In Francia nella bufera.   ₍Parma, Guanda, 1953₎
    259 p.   19 cm.   (Collana clandestina, 7)
    Bibliographical footnotes.

    1. World War, 1939–1945—Underground movements—France.   2. Communism—France.   I. Title.   (Series)
                                   A 55–234
    Wisconsin. Univ. Libr.
    for Library of Congress   ₍3₎

NT   0045656   WU DLC MH NN

Tasca, Angelo, 1892–
  El nacimiento del fascismo; Italia de 1918 a 1922 ₍por₎ A. Rossi ₍pseud.₎   Versión española y nota preliminar de Guillermo Díaz.   Buenos Aires, Editorial La Vanguardia, 1941.
    585 p.   18 cm.

    1. Italy—Hist.—1914–1945.   2. Fascism—Italy.   I. Title.

    DG571.T359   945.09   42–3795 rev*

NT   0045657   DLC

Tasca, Angelo, 1892–
  La naissance du fascisme; l'Italie de 1918 à 1922 ₍par₎ A. Rossi ₍pseud.₎   Paris, Gallimard ₍1938₎
    296 p.   20 cm.

    1. Italy—Hist.—1914–1945.   2. Fascism—Italy.   I. Title.

    DG571.T35   945.09   40–1677 rev*

NT   0045658   DLC NBC NN CoU TxU

Tasca, Angelo, 1892–
  La naissance du fascisme; l'Italie de 1918 à 1922.   2. éd.   Paris, Gallimard ₍c1938₎
    296 p.   21 cm.
    At head of title: A. Rossi.
    Half title: La naissance du fascisme (l'Italie de l'Armistice à la Marche sur Rome.)
    1. Italy – Hist. – 1914–1945.   2. Mussolini, Benito, 1883–1945.   3. Fascism – Italy.   4. Partito nazionale fascista.   I. Title.

NT   0045659   CSt-H

Tasca, Angelo, 1892–
  ... La naissance du fascisme; l'Italie de 1918 à 1922.   Cinquième édition.   Paris, Gallimard ₍1938₎
    4 p. l., ₍11₎–296 p., 1 l.   21ᶜᵐ.
    At head of title: A. Rossi.
    Half-title: La naissance du fascisme (L'Italie de l'armistice à la marche sur Rome.)

    1. Fascism—Italy.   2. Italy—History—1914–   I. Title.
                                   A C 38–3017
    New York. Public library
    for Library of Congress   ₍2₎

NT   0045660   NN OU CU

Tasca, Angelo, 1892–
  Nascita e avvento del fascismo; l'Italia dal 1918 al 1922 ₍di₎ Angelo Tasca (A. Rossi)   Firenze, La Nuova Italia ₍1950₎
    lxxvii, 582 p.   illus., ports.   20 cm.   (Documenti della crisi contemporanea, 5)
    Includes bibliographical references.

    1. Italy—Hist.—1914–1945.   2. Fascism—Italy.   I. Title.

    DG571.T357   52–27162

       NNC TxU CaBVaU
NT   0045661   DLC MiU OClW MB CtY NcD NIC NN RPB IEN

Tasca, Angelo, 1892–
  Le pacte germano-soviétique; l'histoire et le mythe, par A. Rossi ₍pseud.₎   Paris? Éditions liberté de la culture, 1954₎   114 p.   18 cm.   (Cahiers des Amis de la liberté)
    Bibliographical footnotes.

    1. Russo-German treaty, 1939.   I. Amis de la liberté.

NT   0045662   NN NjP MH TxU

Tasca, Angelo, 1892–
  Le pacte germano-soviétique: l'histoire et le mythe, par A. Rossi ₍pseud.₎   Paris₎ Preuves ₍1954₎
    114 p.   19 cm.   (Essais et témoignages)
    "L'étude ... constitue la version, revue et considérablement augmentée, d'un essai paru dans 'Preuves' (nos 36 et 37), en réponse au livre La vérité sur 1939."   Bibliographical footnotes.

    1. World War, 1939–1945—Diplomatic history.   2. Germany—For. rel.—Russia.   3. Russia—For. rel.—Germany.   I. Title.
    D751.T3   65–55276

NT   0045663   DLC MH OU NIC KyU InU PSt

Tasca, Angelo, 1892–
  Physiologie du Parti communiste français, par A. Rossi ₍pseud.₎   Paris, Éditions Self, 1948.
    xxxvi, 465 p.   22 cm.   (*His* Crise française, crise mondiale, 1)
    Bibliographical footnotes.

    1. Parti communiste.   2. Communism—France.   I. Title.

    JN3007.C6T3   329.944   49–25513 rev*

       ViU NjP NNUN OU IU MoSU KyU GU MU OrU OrPR CaBVaU
NT   0045664   DLC KyU CaQML OCl PBm WU NcD CtY   TxU ICU

HX291
.P6
     Tasca, Angelo, 1892–

    ... La **politica** delle classi medie e il planismo, con prefazione di Angelo Tasca su: L'umanismo socialista e la **lotta** contro la crisi.   Paris, Partito socialista italiano ₍1938₎

Tasca, Angelo, 1892–
  The rise of Italian fascism, 1918–1922, by A. Rossi ₍pseud.₎   With a pref. by Herman Finer.   Translated by Peter and Dorothy Wait.   London, Methuen ₍1938₎
    xvi, 376 p.   map.   22 cm.
    "Translated from La naissance du fascisme, l'Italie de 1918 à 1922."

    1. Italy—Hist.—1914–1945.   2. Fascism—Italy.   I. Title.

    DG571.T353   945.09   39–7992 rev*

       WU ViU MeB OrPS
NT   0045666   DLC CU CtY IU NN OU ViU TxU NNC NcD PPD

Tasca, Angelo, 1892–
  Den Russisk-Tyske allianse, august 1939–juni 1941 ₍av₎ A. Rossi ₍pseud.   Oversatt av Ingrid Scheflo.   Oslo₎ Fram forlag ₍1954₎
    148 p.   23 cm.
    Translation of Deux ans d'alliance germano-soviétique.   Bibliographical references included in "Noter" (p. 133–148)

    1. Germany—For. rel.—Russia.   2. Russia—For. rel.—Germany.   3. World War, 1939–1945—Diplomatic history.   I. Title.
                                   A 55–6095
    Wisconsin. Univ. Libr.
    for Library of Congress   ₍3₎

NT   0045667   WU DS

Tasca, Angelo, 1892–
  The Russo-German alliance, August 1939–June 1941 ₍by₎ A. Rossi ₍pseud.   Translated by John and Micheline Cullen₎   London, Chapman & Hall, 1950.
    xiii, 218 p.   23 cm.
    Translation of Deux ans d'alliance germano-soviétique.   Bibliographical footnotes.

    1. Germany—For. rel.—Russia.   2. Russia—For. rel.—Germany.   3. World War, 1939–1945—Diplomatic history.   I. Title.
    D754.R9T313 1950   940.5324   51–231 rev

       CaBVaU ScCleU OrPR OrU MtU
NT   0045668   DLC NBuU TxU GAT OCl OO IEN MH ViU TU

Tasca, Angelo, 1892–
  The Russo-German alliance, August 1939–June 1941 ₍by₎ A. Rossi ₍pseud.   Translated by John and Micheline Cullen₎   Boston, Beacon Press, 1951.
    xiii, 218 p.   22 cm.
    Translation of Deux ans d'alliance germano-soviétique.   Bibliographical footnotes.

    1. Germany—For. rel.—Russia.   2. Russia—For. rel.—Germany.   3. World War, 1939–1945—Diplomatic history.   I. Title.
    D754.R9T313 1951   940.5324   51–5123 rev

       OClJC TxU UU MtU OrLgE OrCS
NT   0045669   DLC IU MB NN NNC NcU DGU DGW KU KEmT MiU

Tasca, Angelo, 1892–

  Sous l'occupation.   Paris, Les Iles d'or [1954]

    facsims.
  Contents: [1] La guerre des papillons.

NT   0045670   MH

Tasca, Angelo, 1892–
Zwei Jahre deutsche-sowjetisches Bündnis ¡von¡ A. Rossi ¡pseud. Aus dem Italienischen von Hans Naumann. Köln¡ Verlag für Politik und Wirtschaft ¡1954¡
209 p. illus. 21 cm.

1. Germany—For. rel.—Russia. 2. Russia—For. rel.—Germany. 3. World War, 1939–1945—Diplomatic history.

D754.R9T314   61–33888 ‡

NT 0045671   DLC MdU MiU TxU NN InU KU TU

Tasca, F   A
Personaggi noti ed ignoti nella storia e nella cronaca di Pavia. In appendice: Elenco dei podestà ... Pavia, Industria grafica M. Ponzio ¡1951¡
vii, 302 p. 25 cm.

1. Pavia—Biog. I. Title.

DG975.P3T38   52–34703

NT 0045672   DLC NN

Tască, Gheorghe, 1875–   L333.5 Q702
.... Considérations sur les lois relatives à la propriété rurale en Roumanie, Angleterre et Irlande (étude de droit comparé), par Georges Tasca. ... . Paris, V. Giard & E. Brière, 1907.
[4], 352 p. 25⁴ᵐ.
Thèse – Univ. de Paris.

NT 0045673   ICJ

HB
179
.T17
Tască, Gheorghe, 1875–
Liberalism, corporatism, intervenţionism. Bucureşti [Tip. Bucovina] 1938.
170, 41, iv p.
MiU copy imperfect: p. 1–41 (2d group) wanting.

1. Economics. 2. Marxist economics. 3. Romania—Econ. condit. 4. Industry and state. I. Title.

NT 0045674   MiU

Tasca, Gheorghe, 1875–   L333.0498 Roo1
Les nouvelles réformes agraires en Roumanie, par Georges Tasca.
.... Paris, V. Giard & E. Brière, 1910.
212 p. 26ᵐ.

NT 0045675   ICJ

Tască, Gheorghe, 1875–
... Politica socială a României (legislaţia muncitorească) de G. Tască ... Bucureşti [Tiparul Românesc] s. a., 1940.
2 p. l., 7–386 p. 25¼ x 20ᵐ. (Biblioteca monetară, economică şi financiară, tipărită cu cheltuiala Băncii naţionale a României. Seria 1ª. Realităţile economiei naţionale)
"Tabla bibliografică": p. 373–379.

1. Labor laws and legislation—Rumania. 2. Insurance, Industrial—Rumania. 3. Insurance, State and compulsory—Rumania. I. Title.

Library of Congress   HD7921.8.A58   42–28441
                                 [2]   42–28441

NT 0045676   DLC CtY

Tască, Gheorghe, 1875–
... La position de la Roumanie après la conférence de Munich. Conférence faite ... sous les auspices de la Société "Louis Barthou" le 17 novembre 1938 ... Bucarest: Imprimerie "Satelit," s. a. r. ¡1938?¡ 22 p. 23cm.
"Extrait de la revue: 'Revista cursurilor şi conferinţelor universitare,' no. 9 et 10 novembre – decembre 1938."

1. Rumania—For. rel., 1938.   I. Société franco-roumaine "Louis Barthou," Paris.
N. Y. P. L.   April 17, 1944

NT 0045677   NN

MANN
HD
582
T19
Tasca, Gheorghe, 1875–
La question agraire; commentaire critique de la législation rurale en Roumanie, Angleterre, Irlande, Russie et Allemagne (étude de droit comparé) Paris, V. Giard & E. Brière, 1907.
v. 25 cm.

Contents: 1. Roumanie, Angleterre et Irlande.

1. Agricultural laws and legislation - Europe. 2. Land tenure -   Europe - Law. I. Title.

NT 0045678   MH

Law
Taşcă, Gheorghe, 1875–

Revista de drept comercial şi studii economice; doctrină, adnotări, note, jurisprudenţă română şi străină. v. 1– ian. 1934– Bucureşti.

G570.92
Am32Yt
Tasca, Giordano Bruno.
... Florentino Ameghino; ensayo sobre su vida y su obra; prólogo de Adolfo Arnoldi. Buenos Aires, Editorial Claridad [193–?] 78p., 1t. 16cm.
"Bibliografía completa de Florentino Ameghino": p. 53–78.

1. Ameghino, Florentino, 1854–1911. 2. Ameghino, Florentino, 1854–1911 - Bibl.

NT 0045680   TxU

WB
63350
Tasca, Giordano Bruno
Orígenes del socialismo crítico; el manifiesto y sus autores. Buenos Aires [19—?] 182 p. 18 cm. (Colección Claridad, Manuales de cultura socialista)

POOR
CONDITION
1. Socialism (Works published 1919–1938) 2. Marx, Karl, 1818–1883. Das kommunistische Manifest.

NT 0045681   CtY

TASCA, Giovanni Angelo.
Due poesie in morte di Napoleone, [one by Manzoni, the other by Lamartine. Asti, Tip. cooperativa], 1919.
20 cm. pp. 18.

NT 0045682   MH

Tasca, Gio[vanni] Pietro.
Relatione del viaggio d'Alessandria d'Egitto: con il negotiati, chi Mons. di Breves seco ne' regni di Tunisi, e d'Algieri; l'anno 1606. [1606?]
[87] p. 27 cm.
Holograph.

1. France. Foreign relations. Tunis. 2. France. Foreign relations. Algeria. 3. Brèves, François Savary de, 1560–   1628. I. Title.

NT 0045683   MnU

Tasca, Giuseppe Bongiorno
see Bongiorno Tasca, Giuseppe.

Tasca, Henry Joseph, 1912–
The reciprocal trade policy of the United States; a study in trade philosophy ¡by¡ Henry Joseph Tasca ... Philadelphia, 1938.
xiv, 371 p. incl. tables. 23ᵐ.
Thesis (PH. D.)—University of Pennsylvania, 1937. Published also without thesis note. Bibliography: p. 337–366.

1. U. S.—Commercial treaties. 2. Tariff—U. S. 3. Reciprocity. I. Title.

Library of Congress   HF1731.T3 1937   38–8367
Univ. of Pennsylvania   Libr.
———— Copy 2.   [2]   337.0973

DLC
NT 0045685   PU PSC PU-W PHC PBm CU OCU OC1 OC1W OU

Tasca, Henry Joseph, 1912–
The reciprocal trade policy of the United States; a study in trade philosophy, by Henry J. Tasca, PH. D. Philadelphia, University of Pennsylvania press; London, H. Milford, Oxford university press, 1938.
xiv, 371 p. incl. tables. 23¼ᵐ.
Issued also as thesis (PH. D.) University of Pennsylvania. Bibliography: p. 337–366.

1. U. S.—Commercial treaties. 2. Tariff—U. S. 3. Reciprocity. I. Title.

Library of Congress   HF1731.T3 1938   38–6909
———— Copy 2.
Copyright A 114621   [10]   337.0973

CU NcRS OU AAP ViU WaS
NT 0045686   DLC NcD PU PPT PU-W NN NIC MB MH-PA NcU

4HC
623
Tasca, Henry Joseph, 1912–
Strengthening the Korean economy, report to the President. ¡Pusan, Korea
1953¡
105 l.

NT 0045687   DLC-P4

Tasca, Henry Joseph, 1912–
... World trading systems; a study of American and British commercial policies, by Henry J. Tasca. Paris, International institute of intellectual co-operation, League of nations, 1939.
5 p. l., 172 p., 1 l. 25ᵐ.
At head of title: International studies conference.

1. U. S.—Commercial policy. 2. Gt. Brit.—Commercial policy. I. International studies conference. 12th, Bergen, Norway, 1939. II. International institute of intellectual co-operation. III. League of nations. IV. Title.
(L. of N. author file Biv; topic file C: Commercial policy. Great Britain, United States)

Library of Congress   HF3031.T3   40–8688
———— Copy 2.   337.0973

MH IdU MH-PA WaWW MtBC OrU OrP OrPR
OU ODW OO OC1 OC1W ViU NIC ScU TU PU NNC CaBVa NN
NT 0045688   DLC PPT PHC OrU PSC PBm NcD CtY NcU CU

[TASCA, OTTAVIO]
Brindisi d'un imparziale a quanti figurarono nel Teatro alla Scala durante la stagione carnevalesca del 1842-43. Scherzo poetico di O. T. Milano, G. Chiusi, 1843. 38 p. 20cm.

1. Dancing—Poetry. I. T., O.   II. Title.

NT 0045689   NN

TASCA, Ottavio.
Inni cristiani. Bergamo, 1866.

NT 0045690   MH

TASCA, Ottavio, compiler.
Preghiere del soldato. 5a ed. Bergamo, 1868.¡
32°. pp. 31.   Pam.
The same. 9a ed. Bergamo, 1870.
32°. pp. 31.

NT 0045691   MH

TASCA, Ottavio.
Il settimo centenario della Lega lombarda, il 7 Aprile 1867. Versi.   Bergamo. Bolis. 1868. 13 pp. 8°.

NT   0045692   MB

Tasca, Ottavio.
Sullo stato dell'antica chiesa del Piemonte; considerazioni cavate dalla storia.   Bergamo, dalla tip. Frat. Bolis, 1865.

NT   0045693   MH

M
1503
T182a
Tasca, Pier Antonio, 1864-1934.
[A Santa Lucia. Piano-vocal score. German & Italian]
A Santa Lucia. Melodramma in due atti, dalle scene popolari napolitane di Goffredo Cognetti. Versi di Enrico Golisciani. Riduzione per canto e pianoforte di Joh. Doebber. [Berlin] E. Bote [c1893]
131 p.

I. Golisciani, Enrico. II. Title.

NT   0045694   CLU CU MB NN

Tasca, Radu
Calauza cerdatorului Bibliei, pentru toti doritorii a studia Sf. Scriptura Editura "Farul Mentuirei", 1926.

109 p.

NT   0045695   OC1

Tasca, Radu
Poezii religioase.
n.d.

45 p.

NT   0045696   OC1

TASCA, SUSANA.
Utopia; novela.   Buenos Aires, 1953.   194 p.   21cm.

1. Fiction, Argentine. I. Title.

NT   0045697   NN MB

Tascabile del cinema. 1-
Milano, Sedit [1955-
v. illus. 17 cm.

1. Moving-pictures.
A 56-5184
Southern Calif., Univ. of.   Library
for Library of Congress   [2]

NT   0045698   CLSU

TASCABILE del cinema.
Milano, Sedit.
Film reproduction. Positive.

1. Moving pictures--Biog. 2. Cinema--Biog. 3. Cinema--Stars.

NT   0045699   NN

Tascanus, Franz Louis Leopold.
... Die grosse not der Deutschen, ihre ursachen und wege zu wirklichem wiederaufstieg. Hannover, Akropolis-verlag, 1928.
76 p. diagr. 23cm.
CONTENTS.—Allgemeines.—Die reformen in der staatsführung.—Das neue reichsbanner.—Die neue regierungsform.—Der reichssparzwang.—Der steuerabbau.—Die reichskrankenkasse.—Der beamtenabbau.—Die reformen von recht und gesetz.—Das geschäftsunkostenkonto der firmen und die preisgestaltung.—Die familie.—Das wohnungsproblem.—Das arbeitslosenproblem.—Das schulwesen.—Das arbeitsdienstjahr.—Vom übermässig betriebenen sport.—Vom unnützen lotteriebetrieb.—Die wehrmacht des deutschen volkes.—Das verkehrsproblem.—Vom lebensunwerten leben.
1. Germany—Economic policy. 2. Germany—Pol. & govt.—1918-
3. Germany—Soc. condit.   I. Title.
29-2804
Library of Congress   HC286.3.T3

NT   0045700   DLC MH

Tasch, Alcuin William, O.S.B., 1892-
Formal organization of the Benedictine Society of Westmoreland County and the St. Vincent College, Latrobe, Pennsylvania.   [Latrobe,Pa., St. Vincent College] 1950.
v, 123 l. 28 cm.
Mimeographed.
Bibliography: p. 122-123.

NT   0045701   PLatS

LC6999
Tasch, Alcuin William, Reverend, 1892-
Religious constitutions and institutional control. 1953.
274 l.

Thesis--Univ. of Chicago.

1. Catholic Church in the U.S.--Education.
2. Universities and colleges--U.S.--Administration.   I. Title.

NT   0045702   ICU

Tasch, Friedrich Wilhelm, 1916-
Die verfassungsrechtlichen Verhältnisse in der freien Reichsstadt Schweinfurt gegen Ende ihrer Reichsunmittelbarkeit. München, 1952.
xi, 125 l. plate, fold. map. 29 cm.
Typescript (carbon)
Inaug.-Diss.—Munich.
Vita.
Bibliography : leaves v-xi.

1. Schweinfurt, Ger.—Pol. & govt. 2. Law—Schweinfurt, Ger.—Hist. & crit.
54-41680

NT   0045703   DLC

TASCH, Fritz,1894-
Die aenderung der Umwelt unserer landwirtschaft und die aopassung an diese abenderung. Auszug aus der Dissertation, Giessen. n.p., [1921].
f°. pp.(4). iii, 36 (14)
Manifold copy.
"Lebenslauf", at end.

NT   0045704   MH ICRL DLC

Tasch, Heinrich, 1887-
Der anteil der ausländischen wanderarbeiter an der landwirtschaftlichen erzeugung im herzogtum Braunschweig und die betriebswirtschaftlichen folgen eines teilweisen ausfalles dieser arbeiter ... Giessen, Druck von J. H. Meyer, 1919.
3 p. l., 61, [1] p., 1 l. 23½cm.
Diss.—Giessen.
Lebenslauf.
"Verzeichnis der benutzten literatur" : page after p. 61.
1. Agricultural laborers. [1. Agriculture—Labor] 2. Agriculture—Brunswick. [2. Brunswick, Ger.—Agriculture]
Agr 29-626
Library, U. S. Dept. of   Agriculture 283T19

NT   0045705   DNAL PU CtY ICRL DLC

TASCH, LEOPOLD.
Allgemeine Fachkunde. [Wien] Österreichischer Gewerbeverlag [c1952] 302 p. (p. 293-302 advertisements) illus. 24cm.   (Austria. Wirtschaftsförderungsinstitut, Vienna. Fachkunde für Friseure. [Bd. 1])
Austria. Wirtschaftsförderungsinstitut, Vienna. Schriftenreihe: Das österreichische Gewerbebuch.

1. Hair dressing. I. Series.

NT   0045706   NN DLC-P4

FILM
562
T18c
Tasch, Paul.
Causes and paleoecological significance of dwarfed fossil marine invertebrates / by Paul Tasch. 1952.
viii, 246 leaves : ill.
Thesis--Iowa University.
Bibliography: leaves 186-209.
Microfilm (negative) of typescript.
Iowa City: University of Iowa Microfilm Service, 1976. -- 1 reel; 35mm.

NT   0045707   IU

759.5
M62t
Tasch, Paul
Michelangelo's creation frescoes, a contribution to the history of science. Wichita, University of Wichita, 1912.
24 p. (Wichita. University. Bulletin v. 33, no. 3; University studies no. 40)

1. Michael Angelo Buonarroti. I. Series.

NT   0045708

Tasch, Ruth Jacobson, 1912-
The role of the father in the family ... Ann Arbor, University Microfilms, 1950 [i. e. 1951]
([University Microfilms, Ann Arbor, Mich.] Publication no. 2358)
Microfilm copy of typescript. Positive.
Title supplied by publisher ; original title : The role of the father in the family. Fathers' expressed attitudes and opinions with regard to their role in family life and the responsibilities, satisfactions, and perplexities which fatherhood entails.
Collation of the original : iv, 229 l. tables.
Thesis—Columbia University.
Abstracted in Microfilm abstracts, v. 11 (1951) no. 2, p. 457-458.
Bibliography : leaves 183-189.
1. Fathers. 2. Parent and child. 3. Family. I. Title.
Microfilm AC-1   no. 2358   Mic A 51-102
Michigan. Univ. Libr.
for Library of Congress   [1]†

NT   0045709   MiU DLC NNC DCU OrU NcRS

Tasch, Ruth Jacobson
The role of the father in the family; father's expressed attitudes and opinions with regard to their role in family life and the responsibilities, satisfactions and perplexities which fatherhood entails. 1952.
[319]-361 p. tables.
Reprinted from the Journal of experimental education, vol. XX, no. 4, June 1952.
Issued also as thesis, Columbia university.
"References": p. 359-361.

NT   0045710   NNC

RD1
.C45
Tasch, Wilhelm, ed.
Central-blatt für technische hilfsmittel der heilkunde.
Berlin [18

8
67
.T3

Taschdjian, Edgar.
Dialectic realism : a series of
lectures / by Edgar Taschdjian. --
[s. l. : s. n.], 1940 (Peking : San
Yu Press)
195, vii p.
"Printed for private circulation."
Author's presentation copy to
Cornelius Benjamin.
#Science--Philosophy.
#Philosophy, Modern.
(A)Dialectic realism : a series of
lectures.

NT   0045712   MoU CU

Taschdjian, Edgar.
The hunger problem. [n.p.] 1949.
[208]-251 p. O. (Chicago, Illinois-
Loyola university - Department of biological
sciences - Contributions, no. 3)

NT   0045713   CaBViP

AC
831

Tasche, Franz Wilhelm, 1900-
Zur frage der beeinflussung der alimentären
glykämischen reaktion durch das carcinom ...
Charlottenburg, [1934?]   87 p.
Inaug. Diss. - Berlin, [1934]
Lebenslauf.
Bibliography.

NT   0045714   ICRL CtY

Tasche, Friedrich, Ref.: Fremdwirkende Spezifikation, ihr
Umfang und Wesen. Lage i. L. 1920: Welchert. VIII,
82 S. 8° ¶ Auch b. Vandenhoeck & Ruprecht, Göttingen.
Göttingen, R.- u. staatswiss. Diss. v. 16. Juli 1920, Ref.
Oertmann
[Geb. 28. Febr. 96 Ahmsen, Lippe-Detmold; Wohnort: Lage i. Lippe; Staats-
angeh.: Lippe; Vorbildung: G. Herford Reife 14; Studium: Münster 4, Göttingen
2 S.; Rig. 4. März 20.]   [U 20. 409

NT   0045715   ICRL

554.3
T117b

Tasche, Hans
Bilder auf der Reise zur Naturforscherver-
sammlung in Königsberg, im Herbst 1860. Mit
besonderer Berücksichtigung der Bernstein-
ablagerung an der samländischen Ostseeküste,
des Steinsalzvorkommens bei Stassfurt; nebst
einigen anderen wichtigen geologischen und
socialen Fragen. Gissen, Heinemann, 1861.
viii, 207p. illus. 22cm.

1. Nature study. 2. Geology - Field work.
I. Title.

NT   0045716   TNJ

Tasche, Leslie William, 1898–
Factors bearing upon the etiology of femoral hernia ... by
Leslie William Tasche ... [Chicago, 1932]
cover-title, 34 p. incl. illus., tables, diagrs. 25ᶜᵐ.
Thesis (PH. D.)—University of Minnesota, 1930.
Vita.
"Reprinted from the Archives of surgery, October, 1932, vol. 25."
Bibliography: p. 31–34.

1. Hernia.   I. Title: Femoral hernia. Etiology of.

Library of Congress   RD621.T2 1930   34–33325
Univ. of Minnesota Libr.
—— Copy 2.   [2]   616.34

NT   0045717   MnU DLC

Tasche, Leslie William 1898-
Factors bearing upon the etiology of
femoral hernia. 1930
Thesis (P.h.D.) - Univ. of Minnesota.

Abridgment of thesis.
Reprinted from the Archives of surgery, Oct 1932
25 pp 749-782.

NT   0045718   OU

Tasche, Lisa.
Hurra, wir zwingen das glück; erlebnisse—gestalten—bilder
aus dem weiblichen arbeitsdienst, von Lisa Tasche; mit 20
zeichnungen von Heinz Gerster. Berlin, Verlag für kultur-
politik [1935]
281, [1] p. illus. 21½ᶜᵐ.

"Arbeitsdienst ist Nationalsozialismus der tat."—p. [6]

1. Woman—Employment—Germany. 2. Women in Germany. 3. Nationalsozialistische deutsche arbeiter-partei.   I. Title.   II. Title: Arbeitsdienst.
     36–24084
Library of Congress   HD6149.T3
Copyright A—Foreign   32516
     [2]   331.40943

NT   0045719   DLC

Tasche, Max.
... Morphologie des Illerquellgebietes. Mit 3 tafeln und 1
textfigur. Von dr. Max Tasche. Herausgegeben im auftrage
des vorstandes des Vereins für geographie und statistik in
Frankfurt a. M., von dr. Max Hannemann. Frankfurt am
Main, 1934.
112 p. 1 illus., III pl. (1 fold.; incl. map) 24ᶜᵐ. (Frankfurter geo-
graphische hefte. 8. jahrg., 1934, hft. 1)
Issued also as author's thesis, Frankfurt a. M.
"Literaturverzeichnis": p. 110–112.

1. Physical geography — Bavaria.   2. Physical geography—Iller river
and valley.
     A C 36–2971
Title from John Crerar   Libr.
Library of Congress   [G13.F8 8. jahrg., 1934, hft. 1]

NT   0045720   ICJ MoU MiU OCU

Tasché, Sophie (Hofmann)
Dichtung und Wahrheit. Erzählungen von
Sophien
     see under   Sophie, *pseud.*

Tasché, Toni Hawick-
see Hawick, Toni (Tasché)

Taschek, Richard Ferdinand, 1915–

Lithium, proton-neutron reaction. De-
classified: June 25, 1946. Oak Ridge,
Tenn., Technical Information Division,
Oak Ridge Directed Operations [1946]
5 p. diagrs. 27cm.
At head of title: United States Atomic Energy
Commission. MDDC -229.

1. Neutrons. 2. Protons. I. U. S. Atomic
Energy Commission. II. Title.

NT   0045723   ViU

Taschek, Richard Ferdinand, 1915–

Observations of naphthalene scintillations
due to tritum beta rays, by R. F. Taschek
[and] H. T. Gittings. Oak Ridge, Tenn.,
Technical Information Branch, Tennessee AEC,
1949.
3 p. diagr. 27cm
At head of title: United States Atomic Energy
Commission. AECD - 2273 (LADC-552)
"Declassified: September 2, 1949."
Bibliography: p. 3.
1. Beta rays. 2. Atomic energy. 3.
Naphthalene and Gittings, H. T.,
joint author. II. U. S. Atomic Energy
Commission. III. Title. naphthalene scintillations
due to tritium beta rays.

NT   0045724   ViU

Taschek, Richard Ferdinand, 1915–
Preliminary results on the cross section of
the reaction T3 (d,n) He4 between 1.0 Mev
and 2.5 Mev deuteron energy
     see under title

Taschek, Richard Ferdinand, 1915–

Reaction constants for Li^7 (p,n)Be^7, by
Richard Taschek [and] Arthur Hemmendinger. Oak
Ridge, Tenn., Technical Information Division,
Oak Ridge Directed Operations [1948]
25 p. diagrs. 27cm.
At head of title: United States Atomic Energy Com-
mission, AECD - 1820, LADC - 469.
"Declassified: March 17, 1948."
bibliography: p. 16.
I. Hemmendinger, Arthur, jt. author. II. Title.
III. Ser.

NT   0045726   ViU

Taschek, Richard Ferdinand, 1915–

Relative sensitivities of some organic
compounds for scintillation counters. Oak
Ridge, Tenn., Technical Information Branch,
Tennessee AEC, 1949.
3 p. diagrs. 27cm.
At head of title: United States Atomic Energy
Commission. AECD - 2353 (LADC - 571)
"Declassified: October 21, 1948."
Bibliography: p. 3.
1. Chemistry, Analytic. I. U. S. Atomic Energy
Commission. II. Title.

NT   0045727   ViU

Taschen Kalender für Damen
     see   Taschen-Kalender auf das Jahn...
1843.

Taschen- und address-handbuch von Fürth im
königreich Baiern...
     see under   Eger, Johann Gottfried.

Taschenatlas der ganzen Welt.
     FOR OTHER EDITIONS
     SEE MAIN ENTRY
Perthes, Justus, *firm, publishers, Gotha.*
Taschenatlas der ganzen Welt. 81. neubearb. Aufl. Mit
Index und statistischem Text. [Redaktion: Hans-Richard
Fischer. Kartographie: Erich Oschmann] Gotha, 1952.

Taschen-atlas der Schweiz, politisch, statistisch
     see under   Kümmerly & Frey.

Taschen-atlas ueber alle theile der erde nach
dem neuesten zustande in 24 illuminarten
karten in kupferstich
     see under   Perthes Justus, firm,
publishers, Gotha.

Taschenatlas von Deutschland
     see under   Haack (Hermann) Geographisch-
Kartographische Anstalt, Gotha, VEB.

Taschenausgabe der Gesetze des Norddeutschen Bundes.

Band 1.   Berlin: O. Müller, 1868.   v. p.   16°.
Contents: Verfassung des Norddeutschen Bundes vom 26. Juli 1867...
vi, 90 p.
Gesetz über das Passwesen vom 12. Oktober 1867 über die Freizügigkeit
vom 7. November 1867 und über die Verpflichtung zum Kriegsdienste vom 9.
November 1867.   22 p.
Militairgesetze eingeführt durch Verordnung vom 7. November 1867...
iv, 115 p.
Gesetz über das Postwesen. Reglement...   2 p.l., 87 p.

Continued in next column

Continued from preceding column

Gesetz betreffend die Nationalität der Kauffahrteischiffe und die Führung der Bundesflagge vom 25. Oktober 1867.   2 p.l., 37(1) p.
Gesetz betreffend die vertragsmässigen Zinsen vom 14. November 1867.
4 p.
Gesetz betreffend die Erhebung einer Abgabe von Salz vom 12. Oktober 1867.   24 p.

1. Statutes, Germany.
N. Y. P. L.   May 27, 1916.

NT   0045735   NN PSt

Taschenberg, E. P.
     see   Taschenberg, Ernst Ludwig, 1818–1898.

MANN
Thesis
QL   Taschenberg, E mil   Frederick, 1916–
498   Studies on the control of grape berry moth,
1945   Polychrosis viteana, (Clemens) in Chautauqua
T197   County. ₍Ithaca, N. Y.₎ 1945.
       ii, 232 l. illus. 27 cm.

Thesis --- ----- Archival copy.
1945   Thesis (Ph. D.) - Cornell Univ., Jan. 1945.
T197   1. Grape berry moth. ₍I. Title₎

NT   0045737   NIC

Taschenberg, Ernst Ludwig, 1818–1898.   FOR OTHER EDITIONS
Brehm, Alfred Edmund, 1829–1884.   SEE MAIN ENTRY
Brehms thierleben, allgemeine kunde des thierreichs. Grosse ausg. 2. umgearb. und verm. aufl. ... Leipzig, Verlag des Bibliographischen instituts, 1876–79.

QK314
.T3   Taschenberg, Ernst Ludwig, 1818–1898.
     Deutschlands Pflanzengattungen oder charakte-
ristische Merkmale der in Deutschland wildwachsen-
den Gattungen der Phanerogamen, einiger Kryptoga-
men und der überall angepflanzten ausländischen
Bäume und Sträucher besonders zum Schulgebrauche,
zusammengestellt von Dr. E. L. Taschenberg.
Merseburg, Nulandt, 1845.
     xii, 147 p. 18 cm.

9115 Pritzel.

1. Botany - Germany.   i. t.

NT   0045739   NNBG

Taschenberg, Ernst Ludwig, 1818–1898.
     Die der landwirthschaft schädlichen insekten und wür-
mer. Von Dr. E. L. Taschenberg. Eine durch das
Königlich preussische landes-oekonomie-collegium mit
dem ersten preise gekrönte schrift ... Auch unter dem
titel: "Naturgeschichte der wirbellosen thiere, die in
Deutschland sowie in den provinzen Preussen und Posen
den feld-, wiesen- und weide-culturpflanzen schädlich werden." Leipzig, E. Kummer, 1865.
     xii, 288 p. illus., vii col. pl. 24ᶜᵐ.
     Slip pasted over imprint reads: Bremen, M. Heinsius.
     "Nachweis der wichtigsten literatur, welche bei der benennung und lebensweise der thiere benutzt wurde": p. (256)–274.
1. Entomology,   Economic.

Library, U. S. Dept. of   Agriculture 423T18L   Agr 4–233

NT   0045740   DNAL PLF

Taschenberg, Ernst Ludwig, 1818–1898.
     Entomologie für gärtner und gartenfreunde oder Natur-
geschichte der dem gartenbau schädlichen insekten, würmer
etc., so wie ihrer natürlichen feinde, nebst angabe der gegen
erstere anzuwendenden schutzmittel, von dr. E. L. Taschenberg ... Leipzig, E. Kummer, 1871.
     vi, 585, ₍1₎ p. illus. 22 cm.

1. Entomology, Economic.

                           Agr 9—113

U. S. Dept. of Agr. Libr.   423T18E
for Library of Congress   ₍a48b₎

NT   0045741   DNAL CLSU MdBP

Taschenberg, Ernst Ludwig, 1818–1898.
     Forstwirthschaftliche insekten-kunde oder Naturge-
schichte der den deutschen forsten schädlichen insekten,
angabe der gegenmittel nebst hinweis auf die wichtigsten
waldbeschützer unter den thieren. Von prof. dr. E. L.
Taschenberg. Leipzig, E. Kummer, 1874.
     vi p., 1 l., 548 p. illus. 22½ᶜᵐ.
     Slip pasted over imprint reads: Bremen, Verlag von M. Heinsius.

1. Trees. Pests.
                           Agr 10–1511
Library, U. S. Dept. of   Agriculture 423T18F

NT   0045742   DNAL DSI IU NcRS

QK
10   Taschenberg, Ernst Ludwig, 1818–1898
T3   Handbuch der botanischen
Morrill   Kunstsprache, systematisch
     bearbeitet von Ernst Taschenberg.
     Halle, E. Anton, 1843.
     184 p. plates. 21 cm.

     1. Botany—Terminology. I. Title.

NT   0045743   MU

Taschenberg, Ernst Ludwig, 1818–1898.
     Die hymenopteren Deutschlands nach ihren
gattungen und theilweise nach ihren arten als
wegweiser für angehende hymenopterologen und
gleichzeitig als verzeichnis der Halle'schen
hymenopterenfauna, analytisch zusammengestellt
von dr. E. L. Taschenberg ... Leipzig, E. Kummer,
1866.
     vi, 277, ₍1₎ p. illus. 21ᶜᵐ.
     Imprint covered by label: Bremen, M. Heinsius.

     1. Hymenoptera—Germany.

NT   0045744   MiU CaBVaU PPAN IU NcD MH NNM CU NcRS

Taschenberg, Ernst Ludwig, 1818–1898.
Brehm, Alfred Edmund, 1829–1884.
Illustrirtes thierleben. Eine allgemeine kunde des thier-
reichs, von A. E. Brehm. Mit abbildungen, ausgeführt
unter leitung von R. Kretschmer ... Hildburghausen,
Bibliographisches institut, 1864–69.

Taschenberg, Ernst Ludwig, 1818–1898.
     Die insekten nach ihrem schaden und nutzen, von Prof.
Dr. E. Taschenberg ... Leipzig, G. Freytag, 1882.
     3 p., 1, 300 p. illus. 18⁴ᵐᵐ. (*Added t.-p.:* Das wissen der gegenwart, deutsche universal-bibliothek für gebildete. IV bd.)

1. Entomology, Economic.
                           Agr 3–1187
Library, U. S. Dept. of   Agriculture 423T18

NT   0045746   DNAL MU PPG CU

Taschenberg, Ernst Ludwig, 1818–1898.
     Die insekten nach ihrem schaden und nutzen,
von prof. dr. E. Taschenberg ... Leipzig,
G. Freytag; [etc., etc.] 1883.
     3 p.l., 300 p. illus. 19.5 cm. (Added t.-
p.: Das wissen der gegenwart ... Bd. 4)

NT   0045747   CU MH

SB931   Taschenberg, Ernst Ludwig, 1818–1898.
T3   Die Insekten nach ihren Schaden und Nutzen.
1906   2., verm. und verb. Aufl. Hrsg. von dessen
Sohne dr. Otto Taschenberg ... Leipzig, G.
Freytag, 1906.
     312 p. illus. (Das Wissen der Gegenwart,
Deutsche-Universal-Bibliothek für Gebildete,
IV. Bd.)

     1. Insects, Injurious and beneficial.
I. Taschenberg, Otto, 1854–1922, ed.

NT   0045748   CU NIC

Taschenberg, Ernst Ludwig, 1818–1898.
     Die Insekten, Tausendfüssler und Spinnen.
Leipzig, 1877.
     25.5 cm.   In Brehm, A. E. Thierleben, v. 9]

NT   0045749   CtY

Taschenberg, Ernst Ludwig, 1818–1898
     Die insekten, tausendfüssler und
spinnen, von dr. E. P. Taschenberg......
Leipzig, 1880.
     711 p.

NT   0045750   OU

Taschenberg, Ernst Ludwig, 1818–1898.
     Die insekten, tausendfuessler und spinner.
Leipzig, Verlag des Bibliogr. insts. 1884.
     711 p. (In Brehm, A. E. Thierleben ...
v. 9)

NT   0045751   PU

Taschenberg, Ernst Ludwig, 1818–1898.
     Die insekten, tausendfüsser und spin-
nen. Neubearb. von professor dr. E.L.
Taschenberg. Mit 287 abbildungen im text
und 21 tafeln, von Emil Schmidt und Heinrich Morin. Leipzig und Wien, Bibliographisches institut, 1892.
     xxxii, 764, ₍3₎ p. illus., pl. (part
col.), fold. col. map. 26 cm. (Added
t.-p.: Brehms Tierleben ... 3. gänzlich
neubearb. aufl., hrsg. von prof. dr. Pech-
uel-Loesche ₍9. bd.₎)
     1. Insects. 2. Myriapoda. 3. Arachnida.
I. Title.

NT   0045752   IaAS

Taschenberg, Ernst Ludwig, 1818–1898.
     Die insekten, von Ernst Taschenberg. Vollkommen neu
bearb. von Carl W. Neumann ... Leipzig, P. Reclam jun.
₍1929₎
     2 p. 1., 544 p. illus., plates (part col.) 19¼ᶜᵐ. (Added t.-p.: Brehms
Tierleben ... Jubiläums-ausgabe ... hrsg. von Carl W. Neumann ...
bd. 7)

     1. Insects. ₍1. Entomology₎   i. Neumann, Carl Wilhelm, 1871–
ed.
                           Agr 29–1168
Library, U. S. Dept. of   Agriculture 423T18 I

NT   0045753   DNAL TU OU

Taschenberg, Ernst Ludwig, 1818–1898.
     Naturgeschichte der wirbellosen thiere die in
Deutschland sowie in den provinzen Preussen und
Posen dem feld-, wiesen- und weide cultur-
pflanzen schädlich werden. Von dr. E. L. Tas-
chenberg ... Leipzig, E. Kummer, 1865.
     xii, 288 p. illus., 7 col. pl. 25 cm.
     1. Insects, Injurious and beneficial. 2. Zoology,
Economic.

NT   0045754   CU MH

Taschenberg, E₍rnst₎ L₍udwig₎ 1818–1898.
     Praktische insekten-kunde oder Naturgeschichte aller
derjenigen insekten, mit welchen wir in Deutschland nach
den bisherigen erfahrungen in nähere berührung kommen können, nebst angabe der bekämpfungsmittel gegen
die schädlichen unter ihnen, von Prof. Dr. E. L. Taschenberg ... Bremen, M. Heinsius, 1879–80.
     5 v. in 2. illus. 23ᶜᵐ.
     Each part has both general and special t.-p.
     CONTENTS.—1. Einführung in die insektenkunde. 1879.—2. Die käfer
und hautflügler. 1879.—3. Die schmetterlinge. 1880.—4. Die zweiflügler,
netzflügler und kaukerfe. 1880.—5. Die schnabelkerfe, flügellosen para-
siten und als anhang einiges ungeziefer, welches nicht zu den insekten
gehört. 1880.
     1. Germany. Entomol-   ogy.
                           Agr 5–537
Library, U. S. Dept. of   Agriculture 422T18P.

NT   0045755   DNAL MB CtY ICJ NIC CLSU

Taschenberg, Ernst Ludwig, 1818–1898.
Reblaus und blutlaus. Erläuternder text zu der
"Wandtafel zur darstellung der reblaus und der
blutlaus". Stuttgart, 1878.
29 p. 8°.

NT   0045756   MH-A

Taschenberg, Ernst Ludwig, 1818–1898.
Die schlupfwespen familie Cryptides (Cryptus)
mit besonderer berucksichtigung der deutschen
arten. 1865.
142 p.

NT   0045757   PPAN

SB808   Taschenberg, Ernst Ludwig, 1818–1898.
F8T3   Schutz der Obstbäume und deren Früchte gegen feindliche
Thiere; im Auftrag des Deutschen Pomologen-Vereins. Ravensburg,
E. Ulmer, 1874.
xi, 152 p. illus., port. (Der Obstschutz, hrsg. vom Deutschen
Pomologen-Verein, 1.Abt.)

1. Fruit - Diseases and pests.

NT   0045758   CU CU-A

Taschenberg, Ernst Ludwig, 1818–1898.
Schutz der obstbäume gegen feindliche tiere. Im auftrag des Deutschen pomologen-vereins bearb. von prof.
dr. E. L. Taschenberg. 3., bedeutend verm. aufl. von dr.
Otto Taschenberg ... Stuttgart, E. Ulmer, 1901.
x, 341 p. illus. 21½ᶜᵐ. (Added t.-p.: Schutz der obstbäume gegen
feindliche tiere und gegen krankheiten. 1. bd. ...)

1. Fruit—Diseases and pests. ₍1. Fruit pests₎

                        Agr 16–89
Library, U. S. Dept. of   Agriculture   464.06Sch8 vol. 1

NT   0045759   DNAL CU KMK CU-A

Taschenberg, Ernst Ludwig, 1818–1898.
Brehm, Alfred Edmund, 1829–1884.
La vida de los animales, por el dr. A. E. Brehm. Conoci-
miento general del reino animal. Traducción directa de la
segunda edición alemana, por don Cárlos Fernandez de Castro-
verde ... 1. ed. española. Barcelona, A. Riudor y c.ᵃ, 1880–83.

Taschenberg, Ernst Ludwig, 1818–1898.
Wandtafel zur darstellung der reblaus und der
blutlaus. Stuttgart [1878]
28 x 21 7/8 in., folder in 4° cover.

NT   0045761   MH-A

QL463   Taschenberg, Ernst Ludwig, 1818–1898.
T3   Was da kriecht und fliegt! Bilder aus dem
Insekten-Leben mit besonderer Berücksichti-
gung ihrer Verwandelungsgeschichte.
Berlin, G. Boffelmann, 1861.
vii, 652 p. illus.

1. Insects.

NT   0045762   CU PPAN

Taschenberg, Ernst Ludwig, 1818–1898.
Was da kriecht und fliegt! Bilder aus dem
Insektenleben, mit besonderer Berücksichtigung
der Verwandlungsgeschichte. 2. neu bearb. Aufl.
Berlin, Wiegandt, Hempel & Parey, 1878.
656 p. illus. 23 cm.
1. Insects - Development. I. Title.

NT   0045763   NcRS

Taschenberg, Ernst Otto Wilhelm
see
Taschenberg, Otto, 1854–

Taschenberg, Ernst Wolfgang, 1886–
Bibliotheca zoologica ₍1₎ Verzeichniss der schriften über
zoologie, welche in den periodischen werken enthalten
und vom jahre 1846–1860 selbständig erschienen sind.
Mit einschluss der allgemein-naturgeschichtlichen, periodischen und palaeontologischen schriften. Bearb.
von J. Victor Carus ... und Wilhelm Engelmann ...
Leipzig, W. Engelmann, 1861.

Taschenberg, Ernst Wolfgang, 1886–
*Ueber einige atypische Fälle der übertragbaren
Genickstarre. [Munich.] Berlin, J. Springer,
1911.
32 p. 8°.

NT   0045766   DNLM

Taschenberg, Joannes Ludovicus, 1757–
*De usu evacuantium medicamentorum in
febribus acutis. Jenae, lit. Maukianis.[1784]
24 p., 1 l. 8°.

NT   0045767   DNLM

Taschenberg, Otto, 1854–1922.
Anatomie, histiologie und systematik der *Cylicozoa*
Leuckart, einer ordnung der *Hydrozoa* ... Halis Saxo-
num, formis Gebauerio-Schwetschkeanis, 1877.
2 p. l., 101, ₍3₎ p. 22ᶜᵐ.
Inaug.-diss.—Halle.
Vita.
"Verzeichnis der benutzten literatur": p. ₍98₎–101.

1. Cylicozoa.
                  ₍Full name: Ernst Otto Wilhelm Taschenberg₎
                             6–9227 Revised
Library of Congress   QL377.H9T2

NT   0045768   DLC

rQL391   Taschenberg, Otto, 1854–1922.
T7T3   Beiträge zur Kenntniss ectoparasitischer
mariner Trematoden. Halle, Schmidt, 1879.
51p. 2 plates. 30cm.

1. Trematoda.

NT   0045769   IaU MH

Taschenberg, Otto, 1854–1922.
Bibliotheca zoologica ₍1₎ Verzeichniss der schriften über
zoologie, welche in den periodischen werken enthalten und
vom jahre 1846–1860 selbständig erschienen sind. Mit einschluss der allgemein-naturgeschichtlichen, periodischen und
paleontologischen schriften. Bearb. von J. Victor Carus ...
und Wilhelm Engelmann ... Leipzig, W. Engelmann, 1861.

Taschenberg, Otto, 1854–1922.
...Bilder aus dem Tierleben, von Dr. Otto Taschenberg...
Leipzig: G. Freytag ₍etc., etc.₎ 1885. 232 p. illus. 18½cm.
(Das Wissen der Gegenwart; deutsche Universal-Bibliothek für
Gebildete. Bd. 41.)

80520B. 1. Zoology. I. Ser.
N. Y. P. L.   November 8, 1940

NT   0045771   NN DLC-P4 PPG CU CtY MH OU OC1W

Taschenberg, Otto, 1854–1922.
Die bisherigen publicationen Rudolf Leuckart.
(In Festschrift zum siebenzigsten geburtstage
Rudolf Leuckarts)

NT   0045772   PPAN

Taschenberg, Otto, 1854–1922.
Die exotischen käfer in wort und bild ...
see under   Heyne, Alexander.

TASCHENBERG, Otto, 1854–1922.
Die flöhe. Die arten der insectenordnung
suctoria nach ihrem chitinskelet monographische dargestellt. Halle, M. Niemeyer,
1880.
4°.pp.120, [2], 4 pls.

NT   0045774   MH-Z CtY RPB

C43   Taschenberg, Otto, 1854–1922.
H15ZzH   Geschichte der zoologie und der zoolo-
gischen sammlungen an der universität
Halle, 1694–1894, von Dr. Otto Taschenberg ... Halle, 1894.
176p. ports., map.

NT   0045775   IU

RA1255   Taschenberg,   Otto, 1854–1922.
T27   Die giftigen tiere. Ein lehrbuch für
1909   zoologen, mediziner und pharmazeuten, von
dr. Otto Taschenberg ... Mit 68 abbildungen.
Stuttgart, Ferdinand Enke, 1909.
xv,325p. illus. 23cm.

1. Animal poisons. I. Title.

NT   0045776   NBuG ICJ NjP MiU DNLM PU PPAN PPPCPh

Taschenberg, Otto, 1854–1922.
Historische entwickelung der lehre von der
parthenogenesis. Halle, Niemeyer, 1892.
82 p.
"Litteratur", p. [62]–89.

NT   0045777   MtBC

Taschenberg, Otto, 1854–1922.
Die Insekten nach ihrem Schaden und Nutzen
see under   Taschenberg, Ernst Ludwig,
1818–1898.

Taschenberg, Otto, 1854–1922.
Die lehre von der urzeugung sonst und jetzt. Ein bei-
trag zur historischen entwicklung derselben, von dr. Otto
Taschenberg ... Halle, M. Niemeyer, 1882.
111 p. 22½ᶜᵐ.
"Literatur über urzeugung": p. ₍75₎–111.

1. Generation, Spontaneous. 2. Biology—Hist.
                  ₍Full name: Ernst Otto Wilhelm Taschenberg₎
                           6–21516 Revised
Library of Congress   QH325.T19

NT   0045779   DLC CU ICJ

Taschenberg, Otto, 1854-1922.
... Die mallophagen mit besonderer berücksichtigung der von dr. Meyer gesammelten arten systematisch bearb. von dr. O. Taschenberg ... Eingegangen bei der Akademie den 9. december 1881. Halle, Druck von E. Blochmann & sohn in Dresden, 1882.
244 p. vii pl. 32½ᵐᵐ. (Nova acta der Ksl. Leop.-Carol.-deutschen akademie der naturforscher, bd. xliv. nr. 1)
1. Bird-lice. ¡1. Mallophaga¿
¡*Full name:* Ernst Otto Wilhelm Taschenberg¿
Agr 6-946 Revised

Library, U. S. Dept. of   Agriculture 432T18
Library of Congress   [Q49.H162 bd. 44, nr. 1]

NT   0045780   DNAL OU

Taschenberg, Otto, 1854-1922, ed.
Die **Natur.** Zeitung zur verbreitung naturwissenschaft-licher kenntnis und naturanschauung für leser aller stände ... 1.-23. bd., jan. 1852-dez. 1874; 24.-50. bd., 51. bd., no. 1-13 (neue folge 1.-28. bd.) jan. 1875-mar. 1902. Halle, G. Schwetschke. 1852-1902.

Q
159   **Taschenberg, Otto,** 1854-1922
R425   Repetitorium der Zoologie für Studierende
1890   der Medicin, Pharmacie und der Naturwissen-
T.4   schaften. 2. verb. und verm. Aufl. Breslau.
        Preuss & Jünger, 1901.
        xi, 453 p. illus. (Repetitorium der
        medicinischen Hilfswissenschaften: Chemie.
        Physik, Botanik und Zoologie, T. 4)

NT   0045782   DNLM

Taschenberg, Otto, 1854-1922.
... Repetitorium der zoologie für studierende der medizin, pharmacie und naturwissenschaften, von dr. Otto Taschenberg ... 3. neu bearb. aufl. ... Breslau, Preuss & Junger, 1921.
xii, 276 p. illus. 22 cm. (Preuss & Jüngers Repetitorien der medizin und naturwissenschaften. Bd. 2)
1. Zoology - 1901-

NT   0045783   CU

Taschenberg, Otto, 1854-1922
Die verwandlungen der tiere, von Dr. Otto Taschenberg ... Leipzig, G. Freytag, 1882.
2 p. L, 268 p. illus. 18½ᵐᵐ. (*Added t.-p.:* Das wissen der gegenwart, deutsche universal-bibliothek für gebildete. vii. bd.)

1. Metamorphosis (Zoology)

Agr 3-1188

Library, U. S. Dept. of   Agriculture 411T18V

NT   0045784   DNAL NcD CU MU PPC ICJ CtY ICJ

*Z1023
.T37   Taschenbibliographien für Büchersammler, heraus-
        gegeben von Max Sander. Bd. 1-5. Stuttgart,
        J. Hoffmann [1924-27]
        5 v. plates. 20cm.
        "Unter dem Patronat der Schweizer Bibliophil-
        engesellschaft."
        Bd. 1 has title repeated in French: Bibliogra-
        phies de poche pour collectionneurs.
        CONTENTS.—Bd. 1. Sander, M. Die illustri-
        erten französischen Bucher des 19. Jahrhunderts.

—Bd. 2. Brieger, L. Ein Jahrhundert deutscher Erstausgaben; die wichtigsten Erst- und Originai-ausgaben von etwa 1750 bis etwa 1880.—Bd. 3. Sander, M. Die illustrierten französischen Bücher des 18. Jahrhunderts.—Bd. 4. Rumann, A. Die illustrierten deutschen Bücher des 19. Jahr-hunderts.—Bd. 5. Rümann, A. Die illustrierten

deutschen Bücher des 18. Jahrhunderts.

1. Illustrated books—Bibl. 2. French litera-
ture—Bibl. 3. German literature—Bibl.
I. Société suisse des bibliophiles, Bern. II.
Sander, Max, ed. III. Brieger, Lothar, 1879-
IV. Rümann, Arthur, 1888-

NT   0045787   MB OO OC1W ICN NcD

Taschenbibliothek der naturwissenschaften.
Dresden, 1829.
8°

NT   0045788   NN

Taschen-bibliothek der wichtigsten und interessantesten reisen durch Aegypten ...
see under Jäck, Joachim Heinrich, 1777-1847, ed.

Taschen-Bibliothek der wichtigsten und interessantesten Reisen durch Griechenland
see under Jäck, Joachim Heinrich, 1777-1847, ed.

Taschen-Bibliothek der wichtigsten und inters-santesten Reisen durch Ost- West- und Sud-Indien
see under Jaeck, Joachim Heinrich 1777-1847.

Taschen-Bibliothek der wichtigsten und interessantesten Reisen durch Palästina
see under Jäck, Joachim Heinrich, 1777-1847, ed.

Taschen-bibliothek der wichtigsten und interessantesten reisen in die Türkei
see under Jäck, Joachim Heinrich, 1777-1847, ed.

Taschen-Bibliothek der wichtigsten und interessantesten See- und Land-Reisen
see under Jaeck, Joachim Heinrich, 1777-1847, ed.

Taschen- Bibliothek; unterhaltender Lecture für die elegante Welt. Wien

NT   0045795   MH

Taschen-Brockhaus zum zeitgeschehen. Mit rund 900 abbil-dungen, schaubildern und karten im text und auf 24 einfar-bigen und bunten tafelseiten sowie 38 übersichten und einer bunten karte Europas. Leipzig, F. A. Brockhaus, 1940.
2 p. L, 284 p. illus., plates (1 col.) maps (1 fold., in pocket) diagrs. 214ᵐᵐ.

1. European war, 1939- —Dictionaries. 2. Encyclopedias and dictionaries, German.   i. Brockhaus, firm, publishers, Leipzig.

Library of Congress   D740.T3   41-13003
                          ¡2¿   940.5303

RPB
NT   0045796   DLC PU NcU CSt-H ICU MH CtY NN IU NcD

Taschen-Brockhaus zum zeitgeschehen. Mit über 800 ab-bildungen, schaubildern und karten im text und auf 28 ein-farbigen und bunten tafelseiten sowie 61 übersichten und je einer bunten Europa- und weltkarte. 2., erweiterte aufl. Leipzig, P. A. Brockhaus, 1942.
376 p. illus., plates (1 col.) ports., maps (part fold. in pocket) diagrs. 21 cm.

1. World war, 1939-1945—Dictionaries. 2. Encyclopedias and dictionaries, German.   i. Brockhaus, firm, publishers, Leipzig.

D740.T3 1942   940.5303   A F 47-5327
No. Carolina. Univ. Libr.
for Library of Congress   ¡2¿†

NT   0045797   NcU NNC CLU MH NN DLC

PT 1136   **TASCHENBUCH AUF DAS JAHR**
.T122   Jahrgang   ¡n. p.¿
         v.

         Vol. 2 ed. by J. W. Petzold.
         Contents:

         v.2. Rebecca, die schöne Jüdin von Wileika,
         von J. W. Petzold; Jacob und Johanna, von S.

NT   0045798   InU

PT19   **Taschenbuch auf das jahr** 1803-1804. Dem edeln und
.T19   schönen, der frohen laune und der philosophie des lebens
Rare bk gewidmet, vom hofrath C. F. Pockels ... Hannover, Bei
room   den gebrüdern Hahn ¡1803?-04?¿
         2 v. front., plates. 13ᵐᵐ.
         No more published.

         1. German literature—Collections. 2. Gift-books (Annuals, etc.)

NT   0045799   ICU IEN NjP

Taschenbuch auf das Jahr 1804. Herausgegeben von Wieland und Goethe. Tubingen, in der Cotta'schen Buchhandlung [1803]
3 p. l., 3-152 p. front., 4 plates. 12.5 cm.
First edition.
Colophon: Jena, gedruckt bey Frommann und Wesselhöft.
Plates accompanied by guard-sheets (not included in the pagination and signatures) with descriptive letter-press.
Signatures: 2 l. unsigned, 1-9⁸, 10⁴.

NT   0045800   CtY CU PBm MdBJ WaU

Taschenbuch auf das Jahr 1807
see under Kotzebue, August Friedrich Ferdinand von, 1761-1819.

Taschenbuech.auf das Jahr 1819 [-20]. Neue Folge, erster [bis zweiter] Jahrgang. Leipzig, Brockhaus, 1819 [-20]
13 cm.

NT   0045802   CU

Taschenbuch auf das Jahr ... für Natur- und Gartenfreunde
see also Taschenkalender ... für natur-und gartenfreunde.

Avery
AB
T17   Taschenbuch auf das Jahr ... für Natur- und
       Gartenfreunde.
       1795-
       Tübingen, Cotta [1794?-
       v. plates (part fold.) 11cm.

       Vol. for 1795: "Zweite Auflage."

NT 0045804   NNC

SB406
.T34   Taschenbuch auf das Jahr 1801 für Natur- und
        Gartenfreunde. Tübingen, Gotta [1800?]
        [2] 202 p. front. (plan) 11 fold. plates.
        12 cm.
        Page [1]-[16]:"Taschenkalender auf das Jahr
        1801 für Natur- und Gartenfreunde."

        1. Gardening. i.t.: Taschenkalender auf das
        Jahr 1801 für Natur- und Gartenfreunde.

NT 0045805   NNBG

        Taschenbuch auf der Reise von St. Petersburg
        bis Moskwa nebst einem Anhange über die
        landesüblichen Reisearten und ihren Kostenbelauf
        see under [Glushkov, Ivan]

PT19   **Taschenbuch** aus Italien und Griechenland auf das jahr
.T207   1829-1830. Hrsg. von Wilhelm Waiblinger. 1.-2. buch.
Rare bk ... Berlin, Bei G. Reimer [1829?-30?]
room   2 v. fronts. 16ᵐ.
        CONTENTS.—1. buch. Rom.—2. bd. Neapel und Rom.

        1. German literature—Collections. 2. Gift-books (Annuals, etc.)

NT 0045807   ICU InU

9-NASZ
Taschenbuch auserlesener Mährchen von Göthe, dem Fürsten
Pückler, Friedrich Rückert und dem Herausgeber Dr. Friedr.
Förster.
Jahrg. 1

Berlin: J. G. Hasselberg, 1838   17½cm.
v. plates.

1. Fairy tales, German—Collections.   I. Förster, Friedrich Christoph,
1791–1868, editor. II. Goethe, Johann   Wolfgang von. III. [Pueckler-
Muskau, Hermann Ludwig Heinrich,   Fürst von,] 1785–1871. IV. Rückert,
Friedrich, 1788–1866.   Friedrich, 1788–1866.
N.Y.P.L.   September 10, 1934

NT 0045808   NN

Taschenbuch Berlin in Zahlen
  see Berlin in Zahlen.

... Taschenbuch britisches heer ...
  see under Germany. Heer. Generalstab.

Taschenbuch der alten und neuen Masken. 1793.
[Frankfurt und Leipzig, 1793?] [Wien,
Hermes-Druckerei, für den Amalthea-Verlag
Zürich-Leipzig-Wien, 1920]
    1 p.l., 54, 64 p. plates (part. double,
part. col.) 10.5 cm. in case 11.5 cm.
    Facsimile reprint.
    Illustrated t.p.: "Manheim" in lower left
corner.
    Added title-page: Taschenbuch für das
Karnaval. Frankfurt und Leipzig.
    A limited edition of 750 numbers of which
this is no. 648.

    The "Taschenbuch" is on heavier paper than
the above, gilt edges, in silk binding.
    A limited edition of 750 numbers of which
this is no. XVI.
    I. Payer von Thurn, Rudolf, Ritter, 1867-
II. Taschenbuch für das Karnaval. III. Goethe,
Johann Wolfgang von, 1749-1832. Römischer
Carneval. 1920.

NT 0045812   CtY ICU IEN MWiCA

Taschenbuch der Arbeiter in den graphischen und papierverarbeitenden Betrieben.

    Wien, Gewerkschaft der Arbeiter in den graphischen und
papierverarbeitenden Betrieben.
    v. 14 cm.

    1. Labor and laboring classes—Yearbooks. 2. Labor and laboring
classes—Austria. I. Gewerkschaft der Arbeiter in den graphischen
und papierverarbeitenden Betrieben.

HD8405.T35   48-31916*

NT 0045813   DLC NN IaAS MCM GAT

Taschenbuch der Chirurgie für angehende
praktische Aerzte und Wundärzte
    see under Ebermaier, Johann Erdwin
Christoph, 1769-1825.

Taschenbuch der deutschen Kriegsflotte
    see Taschenbuch der deutschen und der
fremden Kriegsflotten.

⁕⁕⁕⁕ Taschenbuch der deutschen und der fremden Kriegsflotten. Mit
teilweiser Benutzung amtlichen Materials. Continued from no. 1.
[1900]. il. pl. D. München 1900-.
    Edited by B. Weyer.
    No. 1 published under the title: Taschenbuch der deutschen Kriegsflotte.

NT 0045816   ICJ

Taschenbuch der eleganten und bürgerlichen
Kochkunst
    see under Juch, Karl Wilhelm, 1774-1821.

Taschenbuch der evangelischen Kirchen in **Deutschland**.
1955-
Stuttgart, Evangelisches Verlagswerk.
    v. fold. maps. 15 cm.
    First published in 3 parts. 1955-58: Bd. 1: Zentrale Stellen der
Evangelischen Kirche und ihre Werke mit Landesstellen. Bd. 2: Die
Landeskirchen in der Bundesrepublik Deutschland (ohne Berlin)
Bd. 3: Die Landeskirchen in der Deutschen Demokratischen Repub-
lik und in Berlin.
    Beginning in 1962 issued in one volume, called "Zusammengefasste
Ausgabe."
    Includes also rev. edition (1959) of pt. 1.
    1. Evangelische Kirche in Deutschland—Direct.

BX8020.A1T3   60-30113 rev

NT 0045818   DLC MoSCS CBGTU NN ICMcC MH-AH

Taschenbuch der Feinmechanik.

Berlin-Nikolassee, F. & M. Harrwitz [etc.]
    v. illus., diagrs. 10 cm.
    Began publication with 1901 issue. Cf. Hinrichs' Fünfjahrs-
Katalog, 1896-1900.
    Title varies: Taschenbuch für Präzisionsmechani-
ker, Optiker, Elektromechaniker und Glasinstrumentenmacher.
    Editor: F. Harrwitz and others.

    1. Instrument manufacture—Handbooks, manuals, etc. 2. Technol-
ogy—Handbooks, manuals, etc. I. Harrwitz, Fritz, 1859- ed.

T49.T3   64-43857

NT 0045819   DLC CU MiU NN PPF

Taschenbuch der Finanz- und Steuerstatistik in Rheinland-
Pfalz. 1.-   Jahrg.; 1953-
Bad Ems.
    v. tables. 21 cm.
    Vols. for 1953- issued by Statistisches Landesamt Rheinland-
Pfalz.

    1. Finance, Public—Rhineland-Palatinate. I. Rhineland-Palati-
nate. Statistisches Landesamt.

HJ1150.R45A3   63-41934

NT 0045820   DLC

Taschenbuch der Finanzstatistik in Preussen
    see under Germany. Finanzausgleichsamt.

Taschenbuch der Fleischwarenstellung einschliesslich Konservierung
    see under Grüttner, Felix, 1884-

W 1   TASCHENBUCH der Fortschritte der
TA672   physikalisch-diätetischen Heilmethoden.
        1. -   Jahrg.; 1901-
        Leipzig.
             v.
        Title varies slightly.
        Ed. by F. Schilling.
        1. Therapeutics - Physiological -
        Period. I. Schilling, F   ed.

NT 0045823   DNLM

DF12   **Taschenbuch** der geschichte des griechischen volkes in all-
.T2   gemeinen umrissen von der ältesten bis zur neueren zeit.
Rare bk Nebst der jetzigen griechischen konstitution und andern
room   aktenstücken als anhang. 1. jahrg. ... Heidelberg, Bei
        C. F. Winter, 1823.
        vi, 162, 107 p. front., plates. 16ᵐ.
        Continued as Taschenbuch für freunde der geschichte des griechischen volkes
        älterer und neuerer zeit.

        1. Greece—Hist. 2. Greece, Modern—Hist. 3. Gift-books (Annuals, etc.)

NT 0045824   ICU

Taschenbuch der Giesserei-Praxis.

Berlin, Fachverlag Schiele & Schön.
    v. illus. 17 cm.

    1. Founding.

TS230.T18   55-16756 ‡

NT 0045825   DLC IU NN

PT19   Taschenbuch der grazien...
.T215   Mannheim,
Rare bk   v. fronts.,plates. 12½ᶜᵐ.
room

     Includes music.
     1820 has imprint:Mannheim,F.Kaufmann.

NT   0045826   ICU

Lilly
PT 1799   TASCHENBUCH DER GRAZIEN, 1820. MIT KUPFERN.
.A1 T19   Mannheim, Schwan und Goetz ₍1820₎
1820   7 p.ℓ.,200,₍4₎p.   front.,plates.
     12.1 cm.

     "Inhalt," ₍4₎p. at end.
     In decorated pink boards, all edges gilt;
     in a library case.

NT   0045827   InU

Taschenbuch der handelsflotten
     see under   Gröner, Erich.

Taschenbuch der handelskorrespondenz
     see   Simon, Ludwig.
     Manual of mercantile correspondence.

Taschenbuch der Heere. Ausg. 1939–
München, J. F. Lehmann.
     v. illus. 18 cm.
     At head of title, 1939–   : Kurt Passow.

     1. Armies.   I. Passow, Kurt.

     UA15.T3   355   49–30384*

NT   0045830   DLC MH NN CtY NcD NjR CU NNC CaOTP DAL

Taschenbuch der höhern Magie für Freunde wahrer
Weisheit und höherer Kenntnisse. Hrsg. von
einigen ehemaligen Mitgliedern der afrikanischen
Bauherrn-Loge. Altenburg, Petersen, 1804.
164 p.

NT   0045831   PPC

Taschenbuch der homöopathie zum familien-gebrauch.
New York, Philadelphia, Boericke & Tafel ₍1873₎
     233 p. 14½ᶜᵐ.

     1. Homeopathy—Popular works.

     Library of Congress   RX76.T21   7–13672†

NT   0045832   DLC

Taschenbuch der homöopathie zum
familien gerbrauch. N.Y. Phila.
Boericke and Tafel 1889.

     233 p.

NT   0045833   MiU OU

Taschenbuch der homoopathie zum familien-gebrauch. Ohila, Boericke & Tafel 1912.

     233 p.   3 aufl.

NT   0045834   MiU

Taschenbuch der in Deutschland geschützten
Pflanzen
     see under   Germany. Reichsstelle für
Naturschutz.

Taschenbuch der Krankenpflege
     see under   Fessler, Julius, 1862-1937.

Taschenbuch der Kriegsflotten
see
Weyers Flottentaschenbuch.

Lilly
PT 1799   TASCHENBUCH DER LAUNE UND DES SCHERZES.
.A6 T197   Dreihundert Nummern aus dem Raritäten-Kabi-
1806   nette eines Einsiedlers.   Leipzig, Heinrich
     Gräff, 1806.
     2 p.ℓ.,₍3₎-166 p.   16.7 cm.

     Not in Holzmann-Bohatta.
     In original grey printed wrappers.

NT   0045838   InU

Taschenbuch der leichten artillerie ...

     Berlin, Verlag "Offene worte" ₍19

     v. illus., diagrs. 19ᶜᵐ.
     Editor: 19   L. H. von Ondarza.

     1. Germany—Army—Artillery, Field and mountain. 2. Germany—
Army—Artillery—Drill and tactics.   I. Ondarza, Leon Herbert von,
1903–   ed.   43–18054

     Library of Congress   UF405.G3T3
     ₍2₎   358.1

NT   0045839   DLC DLC-P4 DNW

PT19   **Taschenbuch** der liebe für 1806. Hrsg. von Ernst Müller
.T219   ... Leipzig, Im Industrie-comptoir ₍1806₎
Rare bk   ₍18₎, 162 p. front.,plates. 11½ᶜᵐ.
room   No more published.

     1. German literature—Collections. 2. Gift-books (Annuals, etc.) 3. Almanacs.

NT   0045840   ICU

Taschenbuch der Liebe und Freundschaft gewidmet
1834
     see   Taschenbuch für das jahr 1834
der liebe und freundschaft gewidmet.

Taschenbuch der Luftfahrt. 1954–
München, J. F. Lehmann.
     v. illus. 20 cm. annual.
     Supersedes Handbuch der Luftfahrt.
     Vol. for 1955/57 issued as "Ergänzungsband" to 1954.

     1. Aeronautics—Yearbooks.

     TL503.T28   55–16942 rev

NT   0045842   DLC

Taschenbuch der Luftflotten. 1.–9. Jahrg.; 1914–34. München, J. F. Lehmann.
     9 v. in 11. illus. 18 cm. annual (irregular)
     Publication suspended 1916–22, 1930, 1932–33.
     Issues for 1927–31 have no. vol. numbering but constitute v. 6–8.
     Supersedes Jahrbuch der Luftfahrt.
     Issues for 1927–31 have also titles in English and French.
     Superseded by Handbuch der Luftfahrt.

     1. Aeronautics—Yearbooks.   I. Title : Pocket almanac of aero-
nautics. II. Title : Almanach des flottes aériennes.

     TL503.T3   26–1991 rev*

NT   0045843   DLC CSt-H DNW IU CoD ICJ NjP MiU DAL

---

b   Taschenbuch der Luftflotten. 4. Jahrg.,
     1924/25. Hrsg. von Dr.-Ing. Werner von
Hitler   Langsdorff. München, J. F. Lehmanns
coll.   Verlag ₍c1925₎

     536 p. illus. tables.

     Dedication by publisher.

NT   0045844   DLC MH-BA

---

b   Taschenbuch der Luftflotten. Jahrgang 1931.
     Abteilung: Militär-Luftfahrt. Hrsg.
Hitler   vom Dr.-Ing. Werner v. Langsdorff.
Library   München, J. F. Lehmanns Verlag, 1931.

     214 p. illus. tables.
     DLC Rare Book Room
     Dedication by publisher: "Möchte im
nächsten Jahrgang auch wieder von einer
deutschen Luftflotte berichten."

NT   0045845   DLC WaS

Taschenbuch der medizinisch-klinischen Diagnostik.

München ₍etc.₎ J. F. Bergmann ₍etc.₎
     v. illus. (part col.) 21 cm.
     At head of title: Müller-Seifert.
     First edition, 1886, prepared by O. Seifert and F. Müller and several
subsequent issues edited by them.
     Editor: F. Müller.—194   H. Frh. von Kress.

     1. Diagnosis.   I. Seifert, Otto, 1853-1933. II. Müller, Friedrich
von, 1858-1941. III. Kress, Hans, Freiherr von, 1902–   ed.

     RC71.A185   616.075   50–23016 rev

     PPC IU-M CtY ICRL NNNPSan PPPH MH MBCo MnU NBuU DNLM
NT   0045846   DLC ICU ICJ CU OClW-H WaU NNC ViU PU

Taschenbuch der neuesten ärztlichen Erfahrungen
aus allen Zweigen der Arzeneiwissenschaft
     see under   Meyer, Gustav, fl. 1842.

U   TASCHENBUCH der neuesten Kriegsbegebenheiten für
0   gebildete Leser aller Stände. 1.–2.Jahrg.
.863   Leipzig, G.J.Göschen,1809-10.
     2v. illus.(part col.,part fold.)ports. 13cm.

     Vol.1 has title: Kriegs-Kalender für gebilde-
te Leser aller Stände.

NT   0045848   ICN CtY

Taschenbuch der Panzer. ₍l.₎–   **Jahrg.; 1943–1954—**

München, J. F. Lehmann.
    v. illus. 20 cm.
    Vols. 1–   are cumulative from 1943.
    Vols. 1–   by F. M. v. Senger und Etterlin.

    1. Tanks (Military science)   I. Senger und Etterlin, Ferdinand Maria von.

UG446.5.T38   54–41226 rev 2

NT   0045849   DLC NN LNU

Taschenbuch der Papierprüfung; Hilfs- und Nachschlagebuch für die Prüfung von Papier, Zellstoff und Holzschliff. Herausgeber: Karl Frank. 2. erw. Aufl. Darmstadt, E. Roether, 1954.
    174 p. illus., tables. 22 cm.

    1. Paper making and trade—Handbooks, manuals, etc.   I. Frank, Karl, ed.

                A 56–308

Washington. Univ.,   Seattle. Library
for Library of Congress   ₍s₎

NT   0045850   WaU

Taschenbuch der Reisen, oder unterhaltende
Darstellung der Entdeckungen des 18ten
Jahrhunderts
    see under   Zimmermann, Eberhard August
Wilhelm von, 1743–1815, editor.

Taschenbuch der Rheinschiffahrt. Manuel de la navigation rhénane. 1949–
Basel, Verlag Schiffahrt und Weltverkehr.
    v. illus., maps (part fold.) 17 cm.

    1. Rhine River—Navigation.

HE669.5.R5T28   386.309434   50–22714

NT   0045852   DLC DS MiU

    Taschenbuch der Sagen und Legenden,
*GC8   herausgegeben von Amalie v Helwig geb. v.
L1937   Imhof und Fr. Baron de la Motte Fouqué.
812t   ₍1.₎–2. Jahrg.
    Berlin in der Realschulbuchhandlung.[1812]–
17.
    2v. fronts.,15 plates. 14.5–15.5cm.,in case
17cm.
    Engraved title-pages; plates engr. after
Peter von Cornelius & others.
    Original engraved illustrated boards; edges
gilt; in cloth   case.
    Imperfect: in   v.1, 5 plates wanting;
p.121-2 slight-   ly mutilated.

NT   0045853   MH-A NIC

PN905 Taschenbuch der sagen u. legenden, hrsg. von Amalie v. Hel-
.T2   wig geb. v. Imhof und Fr. baron de la Motte Fouqué ...
    Berlin, In der Realschulbuchhandlung, 1817.
    2 v. fronts., plates. 16ᶜᵐ.
    No more published.

    1. Legends.

NT   0045854   ICU NIC PU

Taschenbuch der spiele; eine anweisung zum
taroc, l'hombre, whist, schach und anderen spielen. Neue ausg. [2],104p. Brandenburg, A.
Müller, 1839.

    Bound with this is Gesellschafts-spiele und
räthsel. Brandenburg, 1839.

NT   0045855   OCl

Taschenbuch der Tanks ...
    see under   Heigl, Fritz, 1885–

Taschenbuch der teutschen Vorzeit
    see under   Mereau, Friedrich Ernst Karl,
1765–1825.

W 1   **TASCHENBUCH** der Therapie.
TA674   Ausg. 1.–   ; 1905–
    Leipzig.
      v.   W1 TA674
    Issued 1939-58 with title: Taschen-
jahrbuch der Therapie.
    1939, Teil 1 issued as 35. Ausg.,
Teil 2 issued as 41. Ausg.
    1. Therapeutics - yearbooks I. Title:
Taschenjahrbuch der Therapie

NT   0045858   DNLM DLC

                   615.13
                   Q802
    Taschenbuch der Therapie; mit besonderer Berücksichtigung
der Therapie an den Berliner, Wiener u. a. deutschen Kliniken,
herausgegeben von Dr. M. T. Schnirer ... Vierte vermehrte
und verbesserte Ausgabe. Würzburg, A. Stuber (C. Kabitzsch)
1908.
    15, 387 p. 14½ᶜᵐ.

NT   0045859   ICJ

RM27   Taschenbuch der Therapie, mit besonderer
915S   Berücksichtigung der Therapie an den Berliner,
    Wiener u. a. deutschen Kliniken. 11. Ausg.
Würzburg, C. Kabitzsch, 1915.
    485, [55]p. incl. advertisements. 15cm.

    1. Therapeutics - Handbooks, manuals, etc.

NT   0045860   CtY-M

Taschenbuch der therapie. Hrsg. von medizinalrat dr. M. T.
Schnirer. Unter mitwirkung von privatdozent dr. Adolf
Heidenhain ... privatdozent dr. Felix Mandl ... professor
dr. Hermann Marschik ... ₍u. a.₎ 29. ausg. ... Leipzig,
C. Kabitzsch, 1933.
    2 v. 15½ᶜᵐ.
    Vol. 2 has only cover-title.
    Advertising matter interspersed in v. 1.

    1. Therapeutics.   I. Schnirer, Moritz Tobias, 1861–   ed.

                A C 33–728

Title from Univ. of Minn.   Printed by L. C.

NT   0045861   MnU

Taschenbuch der Therapie. Leipzig, C. Kabitzsch,
1938.
    2v. illus.

NT   0045862   ICRL

Taschenbuch der Therapie
    see also   Medizinal-Index und
therapeutisches Vademecum.

Taschenbuch der Untersuchungs-Methoden und
Therapie für Dermatologen und Urologen
    see under   Notthafft, Albrecht Freiherr
von, ed.

Taschenbuch der Verwaltungsbeamte
    see   Die Bundesrepublik.

W 1   **TASCHENBUCH** der Wasserheilkunde.
TA676   1.–2. Bdchn. ; 1841. Kempten.
    2 v.
    No more published?

NT   0045866   DNLM

Taschenbuch der Weltorganisationen. ₍l.₎–   Aufl.;
1952–
München ₍etc.₎, Isar Verlag ₍etc.₎.
    v. 19–30 cm.
    Title varies: 1952, Internationale Abkürzungen die nicht im Lexikon stehen.—1954, Das ABC der Weltorganisationen.
    Editor: 1952–   W. Grosse.
    (L.C. has v.1-3, 1952-55 in 3 v.)

    1. Associations, institutions, etc.—Abbreviations.   I. Grosse,
Will, ed.

AS8.T3   A 53–206 rev

Illinois. Univ. Library
for Library of Congress   ₍r56b1₎†

NT   0045867   DLC DS NNC IU

341.1   *Taschenbuch der Weltorganisationen.*
G911   **Das ABC der Welt-Organisationen:**
1954   **Anschriften, Abkürzungen, Kommentare.**
    Ein aktueller Führer durch die interna-
tionale Zusammenarbeit. Ausgabe 1954.
Wiesbaden, Brandstetter ₍1954₎
    79 p. 25 x 11 cm.

    Previously published under title: In-
ternationale Abkürzungen.
    1. Interna-   tional agencies.
    2. Abbreviations.   I. Title.

NT   0045868   LU NNU

Taschenbuch der Werkzeugmaschinen und Werkzeuge.

Berlin, Schiele & Schön.
    v. illus., diagrs. 16 cm.
    Began publication with issue for 1954.
    Compiler: 19   A. Linek.

    1. Machine-tools.   I. Linek, August, comp.

TJ1185.A1T3   56–39579

NT   0045869   DLC NN

Taschenbuch des ärztlichen Fortbildungs-
Unterrichtes im Deutschen Reiche. Ostern
1895. Zusammengestellt nach einer Umfrage
bei den medizinischen Facultäten im Deutschen
Reiche.   Leipzig, G. Thieme, 1895.
57 p.   16°.

NT 0045870   DNLM

Taschenbuch des bücherfreundes für 1909-11. [1.-3.
jahrg. Hrsg. von G. A. E. Bogeng. Nikolassee bei
Berlin, M. Harrwitz [1909-11]
3 v. forms. 22½ x 12ᶜᵐ.
In two parts: (1) Accession note-book for book collectors. (2) Beilage
zum Taschenbuch des bücherfreundes: Jahrbuch für bücher-kunde und lieb-
haberei, 1.-3. jahrg., 1909-11.

1. Book collecting.   I. Bogeng, Gustav Adolf Erich, 1881-   ed.
9-21285 Revised
Library of Congress   Z1007.T19

NT 0045871   DLC ICJ

Taschenbuch des bücherfreundes. Supplement.

Jahrbuch für bücher-kunde und -liebhaberei; hrsg von
G. A. E. Bogeng. 1.-4. jahrg. Nikolassee-Berlin, M.
Harrwitz, 1909-12.

TASCHENBUCH des deutschen Buchhandels. 1950.
Leipzig.   225 p.   18cm.
Published by Börsenverein der deutschen Buchhändler.
Edited by P. Heilmann.
No more published?

1. Booksellers and book trade--Germany. I. Börsenverein der deutschen
Buchhändler. II. Heilmann, Paul, ed. III. Heilmann, Paul.

NT 0045873   NN CtY

WB   Taschenbuch des Feldarztes. München,
100   Lehmann, 19 -
T197   v. illus.
1900

NT 0045874   DNLM

Taschenbuch des feldarztes.
Muenchen, 1914
RC971
T35

NT 0045875   DLC DNW ICJ

RD151
T18
Taschenbuch des feldarztes ... München, Lehmann,
1915.
3 v. illus., fold. table. 17½ᶜᵐ.

Contents.--I. th. Kriegs-chirurgie, von Alfred
Schönwerth. 4. verm. und verb. aufl., unveränderte neudruck.--II. th. Übertragbare, innere
krankheiten, usw. 2. verm. und verb. aufl.--III.
th. Kriegs-orthopädie, von F. Lange und J. Trumpp.

1. Surgery, Military. 2. Medicine, Military.
3. Orthopedia. I. Schönwerth, Alfred, 1865-
II. Lange, Fritz,   1864-   III. Trumpp
Joseph, 1867-

NT 0045876   NNC

Taschenbuch des Feldarztes. ... München, J. F. Lehmann,
1915-1918.
Library has v. 2-9. illus., col. plates. 18ᶜᵐ.
Ceased publication with v. 9.

NT 0045877   ICJ

423
D485   Taschenbuch des Forstschutzes gegen Tiere.
[Neuwied a. Rh] Euting, 1952-
1 v. (loose-leaf)

Kept up-to-date by Formblätter which are
inserted.

1. Entomology, Economic. Germany.
2. Germany. Forestry. I. Forstschutzstelle
Südwest.   Forstschutzstelle

NT 0045878   DNAL

Taschenbuch des gewerblichen rechtsschutzes
see under   Germany. Reichspatentamt.

Taschenbuch des Grenz-und Auslanddeutschtums. Ber-
lin
In Verbindung mit A. Hillen Ziegfeld und Heinz
Hendriock hrsg. von K.C. von Loesch

NT 0045880   MH

Lilly
PN 2616   TASCHENBUCH DES KAISERL. KÖNIGL. PRIVIL.
.V66 M51   Leopoldstädter Theaters, für das Jahr 1824.
1824   herausgegeben zum Besten der hinterlassenen
Familie des Schauspielers Ziegelhauser von
Carl Meisl. Eilfter Jahrgang.   Wien, J. P.
Sollinger, 1824.
3 p.ℓ.,[v]-vi,[1]ℓ.,247 p.   front.(port.)
13.1 cm.

Goedeke VIII, p. 81, no. 161δ.
Added engraved title page.
In pink   boards.

NT 0045881   InU

Lilly
PN 2616   TASCHENBUCH DES KAISERL. KÖNIGL. PRIVIL.
.V66 M51   Leopoldstädter Theaters, für das Jahr 1826.
1826   Herausgegeben zum Besten der hinterlassenen
Familie des Schauspielers Ziegelhauser, von
Carl Meisl. Dreyzehnter Jahrgang.   Wien,
Felix Stöckholzer v. Hirschfeld, 1826.
12 p.ℓ.,[23]-225,[2]p.   front.(port.),
fold.music,ports.   13.7 cm.

Goedeke VIII, p. 81, no. 161δ.
Added engraved title page.
In grey silk   stamped in black, all
edges gilt.

NT 0045882   InU

Taschenbuch des Metallhandels 1952. Bearbeiter Herbert
Wegner, unter Mitwirkung von W. Hammersen. Berlin,
Metall-Verlag [1952]
306 p. (p. 268-306 advertisements) tables. 15 cm.

1. Metals. 2. Metal trade. 3. Metal trade—Germany.   I. Wegner, Herbert, 1905-
A 53-1116
Illinois. Univ. Library
for Library of Congress   [3]

NT 0045883   IU NN

Taschenbuch des müllers, VIII. ausgabe, 1927
see under   Mühlenbau und industrie a.-g.

Taschenbuch des NS.-Reichskriegerbundes...
see under
Nationalsozialistischer Reichskriegerbund.

Taschenbuch des öffentlichen Lebens.
Bonn, Europress.
v. 15 cm.

1. Germany (Federal Republic, 1949-   )—Direct.
DD15.5.T38   52-38676 ‡

NT 0045886   DLC CLU PP CSt-H IEN NN DNAL DNLM TxU LU

Taschenbuch des Patentwesens; Sammlung der den
Geschäftskreis des kaiserlichen Patentamts und
den gewerblichen Rechtsschutz berührenden
Gesetze und ergänzenden Anordnungen, nebst
Liste der Patentanwälte
see under   Germany. Reichspatentamt.

Das **Taschenbuch** des Polizeibeamten. Bd. 1-
Berlin, Deutsche Polizeibuchhandlung und Verlag [1931]-
v. 19 cm.

1. Police—Handbooks, manuals, etc. 2. Police—Germany—Handbooks, manuals, etc.
HV8031.T373   49-38973 rev*

NT 0045888   DLC

47.8
T18   **Taschenbuch** des Rassegeflügelzüchters.
Bochum, Allgemeine Geflügel-Zeitung.

1. Poultry. Breeding. I. Allgemeine Geflügel-
Zeitung.

NT 0045889   DNAL

Taschenbuch des ungarischen Aussenhandels
see
Magyar külkereskedelmi zsebkönyv.

Taschenbuch des verständigen gärtners. Aus dem
französischen übersetzt von J. F. Lippold ... Nebst be-
deutenden zusätzen und verbesserungen von den bekann-
ten kunst- und handels-gärtnern, gebrüder Baumann ...
Stuttgart und Tübingen, In der J. G. Cotta'schen buchhandlung, 1824.
2 v. 29 pl. 19ᵗᵉᵐ.

1. Gardening. [1. Horticulture]   I. Lippold, Johann Friedrich, tr.
II. Baumann, Gebrüder.
Agr 16-998
Library, U. S. Dept. of   Agriculture 90T18

NT 0045891   DNAL CU

Taschenbuch des Wiener Theaters. 1 Jahr.
Wien, gedruckt bey Johann Thomas Edlen v.
Trattnern, 1777.
iv, 192 p.   fold. music.   16 cm.
Editor: Karl von Schelheim.
No more published.
1. Theater - Vienna.

NT 0045892   CLSU

Taschenbuch des Wissenswerten; interessante und wichtige
Tatsachen aus allen Gebieten. Heidelberg, C. Winter ₁1950₁
320 p. illus. (part col.) map. 16 cm.
"Berichtigungen und Ergänzungen": leaf inserted.

1. Encyclopedias and dictionaries, German.

AG27.T3   52-15259

NT 0045893   DLC

PT19   **Taschenbuch** dramatischer originalien. Hrsg. von dr.
.T225   Franck. 1.-5. jahrg.; n. f., 1. jahrg. ... Leipzig, F. A.
Rare bk   Brockhaus, 1837-42.
room   6 v. plates (part col.) ports. 18ᶜᵐ.
No more published.

1. German drama—Collections.

NT 0045894   ICU CtY InU IU

Taschenbuch dramatischer Originalien. 1-5; n
n. F., 1. Leipzig, 1837-81.
Editor: Dr. Franck.

NT 0045895   WU ULC

Taschenbuch dramatischer originalien, hrsg.
von ... Franck. Leipzig, Brockhaus, 1838.
v. 2.

NT 0045896   PU

Taschenbuch dramatischer Originalien. Leipzig
Jg. 3-4; 1839-40
Hrsg. von Dr. Franck

I. Franck, ——, ed.

NT 0045897   MH

832.08   Taschenbuch dramatischer Originalien.
T197   1.-5.Jahr⁻., 1837-1841; n.F.,1.-Jahrg.,
18₁2-
Leipzig, F.A.Brockhaus
v. ports. 18cm. annual.

Editor: 183 - , Dr.Franck

1.German drama (Collections) LC StL

NT 0045898   CLSU

Taschenbuch für 1798-1803. Berlin, F. Vieweg
der ältere; [etc., etc., 1797-1802]
5 v. illus., plates, port. 12-14 cm.
1801-03 have imprint: Braunschweig, F.
Vieweg.
None issued for 1800.
1798 contains the first publication of
Goethe's Hermann und Dorothea.
1801 "Herausgegeben von Friedrich Gentz,
Jean Paul und Johann Heinrich Voss."

1. German literature - Collections.
2. Gift books (Annuals, etc.)

NT 0045900   ICU CU

Lilly   TASCHENBUCH FÜR 1802. Braunschweig, Fried-
PT 1799   rich Vieweg ₑ1802ₑ
.A1 T19   10 p.ℓ.,ₑ3₁-192 p.,ₑ1₁ℓ.   plates,vig-
1802   nettes. 13.2 cm.

Title vignette.
Publisher's ads ₑ1₁ℓ. at end.
Includes Johann Gottfried Herder's Eloise.
Bound in red sheep, wallet style.

NT 0045901   InU

PT19   Taschenbuch für   1803...
.T227   Berlin[etc.,   1803?]
Rare bk   v. fronts.,illus.,plates,port. 12-14ᵐ.
room
O3 have imprint:Braunschweig,Bei F.
Vieweg.
Each vol.contains gift plate.
have blank leaves for "Tabellen."
None issued for 1800.

NT 0045902   ICU IEN NIC

PT19   **Taschenbuch** für 1814. Hrsg. von Friedrich Rassmann.
.T23   1. jahrg. Düsseldorf, Bei J. H. C. Schreiner ₑ1814ₑ
Rare bk   ₑ8₁, 205, ₑ3₁ p. front. (port.) 12ᵐ.
room   No more published.

1. German literature—Collections. 2. Gift-books (Annuals, etc.)

NT 0045903   ICU

---

838   Taschenbuch für 1818. Offenbach bey Brede.
T1918   96p. illus. 11cm.

No more published.

NT 0045904   IEN

Taschenbuch für alchemisten, theosophen und weisen-
steinsforscher, die es sind und werden wollen ... Leipzig, C. G. Hilscher, 1790.
7 p. l., 342 p. 16½ᶜᵐ.

1. Alchemy.

                                                17-16703
Library of Congress   QD25.T3

NT 0045905   DLC WU

Taschenbuch für angehende practische Aerzte
see under   Consbruch, George Wilhelm
Christoph, 1764-1837.

Taschenbuch für aufklärer und nichtaufklärer auf
das jahr 17   . Berlin, F. Unger
v. illus. 14 cm.

NT 0045907   OCU

W 1   TASCHENBUCH für Augenärzte.
TA692   1. -   Aufl. ; 1903-
Berlin ₑetc. ₑ
v. port.
Cover title, 1903.
On cover, 1904-05: Medicinische
Special-Taschenbücher; 1906-07,
Spezialärztliche Taschenbücher.
Ed. by L. Jankau.
Issues for 1903—04—05 include section
Personalien, issued 1906—07—   as 2.
T.

1. Ophthalmologists - Germany -
Direct. 2. Ophthalmology - Handbooks
✓I. Jankau. Ludwig, 1865-   ed.

NT 0045909   DNLM

Taschenbuch für Augenärzte samt Augen-
ärzte-Verzeichnis, etc. Hrsg. von L. Jankau.
2. Aug. x, 235 pp. 12°. *München, Seitz &
Schauer.* 1904.

NT 0045910   DNLM

Taschenbuch für beamte der öffentlichen banken.
Berlin, Beamtenpresse g. m. b. h. ₑ19
v. 14ᵐ.

1. Banks and banking—Year-books. 2. Banks and banking—Germany.
                                                45-33796
Library of Congress   HG3044.T3
                    ₑ2₁   332.1058

NT 0045911   DLC MH-BA

Taschenbuch für beamte der sozialverwaltungen und
körperschaften des öffentlichen rechts
see
Taschenbuch für sozialverwaltungen und körperaschaften des
öfftl. rechts.

Taschenbuch für bibliothekare, bibliophilen,
bibliographen, 1926.   Halle (Saale),
Schmidt & Erdel ₑ1926ₑ
2 p.l., ₑiii₁-v, ₑ1₁ p., 1 l., 342 p. 16ᶜᵐ.

Contains sections, "Bibliothekarische, bibliophile und verwandte vereinigungen, institute,
usw." and "Bibliotheks- und buchwissenschaft-
liche periodica."
No more published.

NT 0045913   NNC NN

Taschenbuch für Bodenseebesucher ...
see under   [Mayer, Willy]

Taschenbuch für brennstoffwirtschaft und feuerungstechnik
... für bergleute, feuerungstechniker, konstrukteure und
brennstoffverbraucher ... 1926-
Halle (Saale) W. Knapp, 1926-
v. illus., diagrs. 16½ᵐ.
Editor: 1926-   Hubert Hermanns.

1. Fuel. 2. Furnaces. I. Hermanns, Hubert, 1884-   ed.
                                                27-7415
Library of Congress   TP318.T25

NT 0045915   DLC

Taschenbuch für briefmarken-sammler, 1889.
Leipzig, 1889.

NT 0045916   PPL

...**Taschenbuch** für Buchbindereibesitzer nebst Kalkulations-
tabellen.
192

Berlin: W. R. Saling & Co.₁ 192   16cm.
v.
192   are Jahrg.
At head of title: 1930   Saling's Taschenbücher für das graphische Gewerbe.

I. Bookbinding.
N. Y. P. L.   February 10, 1934

NT 0045917   NN DLC

Taschenbuch für bücherfreunde.   Leipzig.
v.   illus., ports.   15-16.5 cm.
Annual.
Editor: Rudolf Greinz.

NT 0045918   ICU

Taschenbuch für bücherfreunde.

Taschenbuch für büchersammler. 1925–
1.–   jahrg. München, Verlag der Münchner drucke
₁1925₁–

Taschenbuch für büchersammler. 1925–
1.–   jahrg. München, Verlag der Münchner drucke
₁1925₁–
v. illus., plates, ports., facsims. 18¾ᶜᵐ.
Title varies: 1925, Taschenbuch für bücherfreunde.
1927–   Taschenbuch für büchersammler.
Editor: 1925–   Albert Schramm.

1. Bibliography — Year-books.   2. Book collecting — Year-books.
I. Schramm, Albert, 1880– ed.   II. Taschenbuch für bücherfreunde.

Library of Congress   Z1007.T21

29–14603

NT 0045920   DLC WaSp ICJ NN MiD

Taschenbuch für Chemiker und Apotheker auf das
Jahr 1827
see under   Trommodorff, Johann
Bartholomäus, 1770-1837.

W 1   **TASCHENBUCH** für Chirurgen und Orthopäden.
TA695   1. -   Aufl. ; 1904-05—
Berlin ₁etc.₁
v.
On cover: 1904-05, Medicinische
Special-Taschenbücher; 1906-07, Spe-
zialärztliche₁Taschenbücher.
Ed. by L.₁ Jankau.
Includes section Personalien, 1904-05—
06-07; issued as 2. T., 1910-
1. Surgeons - Germany - Direct.

2. Surgery - Handbooks₁ I.₁ Jankau,
Ludwig, 1865-   ed.

NT 0045923   DNLM

Taschenbuch für Damen auf das Jahr ...
Herausgegeben von Huber, Lafontaine,
Ofeffel, Sulzer. Mit Kupfern. Tübingen,
J. G. Cotta'schen Buchhandlung, 1798-
v.   plates.   8 vo. in half sheets.
Title and editors vary.
Library has volumes for: Voo. for 1798,
3d ed.; vol. for 1799, 2d ed.
Gift of the Bernardo Mendel estate.

NT 0045924   InU KyU NjP ICU NNU-W OU IU

Taschenbuch für Damen auf das Jahr 1800.   2879.29
Tübingen. Cotta. [1800.]   1 v.   11½ cm., in 8s.
Editors: 1800, Huber, Lafontaine, Pfeffel und andern.

M3804 — Huber, Ludwig Ferdi   nand, ed., 1764–1804. — Lafontaine, August Heinrich Julius, ed., 17₅. -1831. — Pfeffel, Gottlieb Conrad, ed.,
1736-1800. — Women. Periodicals. — Periodicals. German.

NT 0045925   MB IU

Taschenbuch für damen auf das jahr 1803 ...
Tübingen, J. G. Cotta [1803]
1 v.   front., plates.   12 cm.
Edited by Huber, Lafontaine, Pfeffel and
others.
1. German literature (Collections) I. Huber,
Ludwig Ferdinand, 1764-1804, ed.

NT 0045926   CU

PT
1105   Taschenbuch für Damen auf das Jahr 1807.
T3   Hrsg. von Huber, Lafontaine, Pfeffel und
1807   andern. Tübingen, J. G. Cotta ₁1807?₁
x, 242, lxxii p. music.

Contents.- Gedichte.- Prosaische Aufsätze.

1. German poetry - Collections and selections.
2. German literature - Collections and selections.

NT 0045927   WaU

Lilly
PT 1799   TASCHENBUCH FÜR DAMEN AUF DAS JAHR 1810.
.A1 T197   Mit Beiträgen von Goethe, Lafontaine, Pfeffel,
1810   Jean Paul Richter und andern. Mit Kupfern.
Tübingen, J. G. Cotta'sche Buchhandlung ₁1810₁.
10 p.ℓ.,₁iii-xxxii,288 p.   front.,
plates.   11.3 cm.

In decorated boards, all edges gilt; in
a marbled library case.

NT 0045928   InU

Y
.1141 Taschenbuch für Damen aus das Jahr 1814. Tü-
.A2T15 bingen, Cotta [1814]
1814   x, 282 p. plates. 11cm.

1. Almanacs, German. 2. Gift-books (Annuals,
etc.)

NT 0045929   MB

Taschenbuch für damen auf das jahr
1817-1818
Mit Beiträgen von Goethe, Lafontaine,
Pfeffel, Jean Paul Richter, Schiller und andern.
Mit kupfer, Tübingen. J. G. Cotta.

3 v.

NT 0045930   OU

Y
9544 TASCHENBUCH für Damen. Auf das Jahr 1829.
.862   Stuttgart, J.G.Cotta,1829.
1v. illus. 15cm.

"Einladung nach der Insel Palmaria. Von
August Grafen von Platen" (verse): p.₁414₁-418.

NT 0045931   ICN

Taschenbuch für Damen. Auf das Jahr 1829.
Mit 10 englischen Kupfern. Stuttgart,
Cotta, 1829.
xxxiii, 428 p.   14 cm.
H. Heine. Gedichte, p. 65-72.

NT 0045932   OCH

665.7
T181   **Taschenbuch** für das Gas- und Wasserfach. 1954–
Engin   München, R. Oldenbourg.
Lib'ty   v. 19 cm. annual.
Issued in parts.
Pt. 1, Jahrbuch Gas und Wasser mit Werkverzeichnis, called v. 65–
supersedes Jahrbuch für das Gas- u. Wasserfach and continues its vol.
numbering.
Issued 1955/56–   by Deutscher Verein von Gas- und
Wasserfachmännern and Verband der Deutschen Gas- und Wasser-
werke.
1. Gas manufacture and works—Yearbooks. 2. Gas manufacture
and works — Germany — Direct. 3. Water-supply — Yearbooks. 4.
Water-supply—Germany—Direct.   I. Deutscher Verein von Gas-
und Wasserfachmännern. II. Verband der Deutschen Gas- und Was-
serwerke.

TP700.T3   56–26578

NT 0045933   DLC TxU NSyU

Taschenbuch für das jahr   ; hrsg. von
Johann Georg Jacobi.   Hamburg.
v.   front., plates.   15.5 cm.
Contains music.

NT 0045934   ICU CU CtY NjP OU

Lilly
AY 859
.H199 J16   Taschenbuch für das Jahr 1802. Herausgegeben von Johann Georg Jacobi. Hamburg,
bey Friedrich Perthes [1802]
1 p.ℓ.,vi,214,[1]ℓ. plates,front.,
music. 14.9 cm.

2 p. (fold.) music tipped on to fly leaves
at end.
First edition: Imprint from Wilpert and
Gühring; Kohring p. 107; Goedeke VIII,59,no.49.
Bound in marbled boards, gilded edges.

NT 0045935   InU

PT19   Taschenbuch für das jahr
.T246   Münster[18
Rare bk   v. front.(port.)plates(part fold.) 12½ᵐ.
room
Contains music.
Edited by Karl Reinhard.

NT 0045936   ICU

Taschenbuch für das jahr... der liebe und freundschaft gewidmet
gewidmet... Bremen, Friedrich Wilmans,
v. plates. 8vo in half sheets
Title, editors, and place vary.

Gift of the Bernardo Mendel estate.

--Additional copies with minor variations.

NT 0045937   InU IU NBuG MdBJ

830.8   **Taschenbuch** für das Jahr 1801-[41]; der
T1972   Liebe und Freundschaft gewidmet. Frankfurt am Main, Wilmans.
41v. illus. 12cm.

Editors: 1801-13, U.Spazier; 1814-33,
J.S. Schütze; 1834-41, J.S. Schütze und
L.Storch.

1.German literature - Yearbooks. 2.Ger-
man literature -   Collections. LC

NT 0045938   CLSU PU NjP ICU CU

S830.8
S39t
  Taschenbuch für das Jahr 1820. Frankfurt, Gebrudern Wilmans [18- ?]
[56],258- p. illus. 13cm.

  Edited by Stephen Schütze.

1. German literature - Collections.
I. Title.

NT 0045939   TNJ ICU

X47Y
.SCH8
Cutter
  Taschenbuch für das jahr 1822-27, 1829,
1838, der liebe und freundschaft gewidmet.
Frankfurt am Main, 1822-38.
8v. illus. TT.
Edited by Stephen Schütze.
1. German literature - 19th century
I. Title

NT 0045940   WU

830.8
T197
  **Taschenbuch für das k.k. privilegirte
Theater in der Leopoldstadt auf das
Jahr ...**
Wien, F.Ludwig [1813?]-
v. illus. 14cm. annual.

1.German literature - Collections. ⱽLC.

NT 0045941   CLSU

  Taschenbuch für das karnaval [1793]
see   Taschenbuch der alten und neuen
Masken 1793.

  Taschenbuch für das schoene geschlecht ...
1812.   Augsburg [1812?]

NT 0045943   NjP

  Taschenbuch für das wissenschaftliche Leben; Vademecum
deutscher Lehr- und Forschungsstätten. [1.]-
1953-
Bonn [etc.] Festland Verlag [etc.]
v. 16-25 cm.
  Title varies: 1953-57, Vademecum deutscher Forschungsstätten.
  Vols. for 1953-   issued by the Stifterverband für die Deutsche
Wissenschaft (1953-57, "unter Beratung der Deutschen Forschungs-
gemeinschaft")
  Compiler: 1953-   F. E. Nord.
  1. Germany—Learned institutions and societies—Direct. 2. Research—Germany. i. Nord, Ferdinand Ernst, 1896— ii. Stifterverband für die Deutsche Wissenschaft.

AS178.T3   58-26815 rev

DNAL
NT 0045944   DLC IU OU ICU IaU NN MH CtY TxU NcRS

  Taschenbuch für den artilleristen
see under   Rheinmetall-Borsig ag.

  Taschenbuch für den bautechnischen Eisenbahndienst
see   Elsners Taschenbuch für den bautechnischen Eisenbahndienst.

  Taschenbuch für den Bergbau. Hrsg. von einem Autoren-
kollektiv unter Mitwirkung des Zentralvorstandes der IG
Bergbau. Leipzig, Fachbuchverlag, 1953.
  239 p. illus. 18 cm.

  1. Mining engineering—Handbooks, manuals, etc. 2. Mineral industries—Germany.
TN151.T2   57-21432 ‡

NT 0045947   DLC IU

  Taschenbuch für den Betriebswirt.
Berlin, Deutscher Betriebswirte-Verlag.
  v. 16 cm.

  1. Germany—Indus.—Yearbooks.
HC281.T3   55-16990 ‡

NT 0045948   DLC

  Taschenbuch für den einzelhandels-kaufmann
see
  Taschenjahrbuch für den einzelhandelskaufmann.

TE3
T3
  Taschenbuch für den gesamten strassen - und
wegebau ... 20. jahrg. 1929-
Berlin, Bock & Co., G.m.b.H. [1929-   ]
1 v. illus. 16 cm.
Editor: 1929-   H.C. Stueck.

NT 0045950   DLC

  Taschenbuch für den Gross- und Aussenhandel.
Köln, C. Röhrig.
  v. 17 cm.

  1. Wholesale trade—Germany—Yearbooks. 2. Germany—Comm.—
Yearbooks.
HF5349.G3T27   55-16711 ‡

NT 0045951   DLC

  Taschenbuch für den Holzfachmann [1952] bearb. und zusammengestellt von H. Bellmann und H. H. Fickler, unter
Mitarbeit von F. Bender. Hamburg-Blankenese, Kröger,
1952.
  340 p. illus., tables. 15 cm.

  1. Wood. 2. Woodwork. i. Bellmann, Heinz. ii. Fickler, Hans
Heinrich.
                            A 53-1900
Illinois. Univ. Library
for Library of Congress   [1]

NT 0045952   IU DNAL

389.8
T18
  Taschenbuch für den Nahrungsmittelgrosshandel.
  Berlin.

  1. Food industry and trade. Germany.

NT 0045953   DNAL

90.04
T18
  Taschenbuch für den Obstbau.
  Holzminden, Trowitzsch.
Edited by Schmitz-Hübsch, H.

  1. Germany. Pomology. 2. Calendars.
I. Schmitz-Hubsch, Hans.

NT 0045954   DNAL InLP

  Taschenbuch für den pionier-unter-offizier.
Auf dienstliche veranlassung bearbeitet.
Berlin, A. Bath, 1904.
v. p. illus. 15.5 cm.

NT 0045955   DNW

  Taschenbuch fuer den Polizei-Beamten...
see under   Rahn, Dietrich, 1914-

  Taschenbuch fuer den Sprengmeister...
see under   Weichelt, Friedrich.

  Taschenbuch für den Textilfachmann; hrsg. von einem Kollektiv unter Leitung von Alexander Grote. Leipzig, Fachbuchverlag, 1954.
  viii, 465 p. illus. (part col.) 17 cm.

  1. Textile industry and fabrics—Handbooks, manuals, etc.
  i. Grote, Alexander, ed.
TS1445.T24   A 55-4561
Georgia. Inst. of Tech.   Library
for Library of Congress   [3]†

NT 0045958   GAT NN DLC

HC337
P7T19
  Taschenbuch für den Verkehr mit dem Generalgou-
vernement 1943.   Berlin, W. Jaspert [1943]
  196 p.   15ᶜᵐ.

  1.Poland -Economic conditions - 1918-
2.World War, 1939-1945 - Economic aspects -
Poland.

NT 0045959   CSt-H

  Taschenbuch für den Winterkrieg; gekürzte Ausg. vom 1.
Sept. 1942.   Berlin, E. Zander [1942]
  254 p. illus. 15 cm.

  1. Winter warfare.
U167.5.W5T3 1942   49-40842*

NT 0045960   DLC DAL

  Taschenbuch für den winterkrieg; gekürzte ausg.
vom 1. september 1942. Nachdruck mit
eingearbeiteten ergänzungen nach dem stande
vom 1. november 1942.   Berlin, E. Zander
[1942?]
  270 p. illus. (incl. plans) diagrs.
15.cm.
  1. Germany. Heer - Field service.
2. Military art and science. 3. Germany.
Heer - Officers' handbooks. I. Title:
Winterkrieg.

NT 0045961   NcD DLC

Taschenbuch für den winterkrieg; gekürzte ausg. vom 1. september 1942. Nachdruck mit eingearbeiteten ergänzungen nach dem stande vom 1. november 1942. Berlin, E. Zander ₍1943₎.

270 p. illus. (incl. plans) diagrs. 15ᶜᵐ.

1. Germany. Heer—Field service. 2. Military art and science. 3. Germany. Heer—Officers' handbooks. I. Title: Winterkrieg.

U175.G4T3   A F 47–626

Duke univ. Library
for Library of Congress   ₍4₎†

NT 0045962   TNJ NNC TxDaM OC1 ICU FU ICRL AAuP KyU DLC
           NcD NjR DNLM CtY NN MH CoD UU IU CSt CoU

Taschenbuch für den wirtschaftlichen und verwaltungstechnischen Krankenanstalts-Betrieb. Ein Auskunfts- und Nachschlagebuch über Bau, Einrichtung, wirtschaftlichen Betrieb, Organisation und Verwaltung der Krankenhäuse, Hoepitäler, Lazarette, Kliniken, Irrenund Pflegeanstalten, Heilstätten, Sanatorien, etc. 291 pp. 12°. Leipzig, F. Leineweber, 1910.

NT 0045963   DNLM

Taschenbuch fuer denker und denkerinnen auf das jahr 1799. Frankfurt am Main, 1799.
     v. 1.

NT 0045964   PU

W1   **Taschenbuch für deutsche Wundärzte.** 1789-90. Altenburg.
TA695H   2 v. in 1.
      Superseded by Medicinisch-chirurgische Aufsätze, Krankengeschichten und Nachrichten.

NT 0045965   DNLM

Taschenbuch für Dichter und Dichterfreunde. Leipzig, Dyck, 1774.
     152 p.

NT 0045966   PPG

PT
1155   **Taschenbuch für Dichter und Dichterfreunde.**
.T37   Leipzig, Duckischen Buchhandlung, 1774.
      2v. in 1 16cm.

      1. German poetry – Collections.

NT 0045967   TNJ CU

Taschenbuch für Dichter und Dichterfreunde. Abtl. 1-12. Leipzig, Dyck, 1774-1880.
     12 v. in 7. 8°.

NT 0045968   NN NjP

PT19   **TASCHENBUCH** für dichter und dichterfreunde. 1.-12.
.T2468   und lezte abth. Leipzig, In der Dyckischen buchRare bk   handlung,1774-81.
room   12 v.in   16½cm.
      Title vignettes.
      Edited by C.H.Schmid and J.G.Dyck.
      "Enthält gedichte von Ramler,Götz...Hölty etc.welche nicht in ihren werken stehen."--Köhring. Bibliog.der almanache.
      1.German poetry--Collections. 2.Gift-books(Annuals, etc.)

NT 0045969   ICU InU MH NjP NcD NcU

Taschenbuch für dichter und dichterfreunde. Leipzig, 1774-1781.
     12 v. in 2. 18 cm.
     V. 1-6 ed. by Christian Heinrich Schmid and Johann Gottfried Dyk. v. 7-12 ed. by Dyk.
     No more published.

NT 0045970   CU NjP

PT19   **Taschenbuch** für dichter und ihre freunde; hrsg. von J. C.
.T247   Giesecken ... Magdeburg, Beym herausgeber, 1792-93.
Rare bk   2 v. 16½ᶜᵐ.
room

      1. German poetry—Collections. 2. Gift-books (Annuals, etc.)

NT 0045971   ICU

Taschenbuch für die Badegäste von Tepliz
     see under   Reuss, Franz Ambrosius, 1761-1830.

Taschenbuch für die Besucher der
    Textilmeister
      see under   Bocholt.
    Textilmeisterschule.

Taschenbuch für die Farben- und Lackindustrie sowie für dén einschlägigen Handel, hrsg. von Hans Wolff, W. Schlick, und Hans Wagner. 5. Aufl. Stuttgart, Wissenschaftliche Verlagsgesellschaft, 1929.

381 p. illus. 16 cm.
Bibliography : p. 323–326.

1. Paint. 2. Varnish and varnishing. I. Wolff, Hans, 1879– ed.

TP935.T3 1929   42–34174 rev*

NT 0045974   DLC

Taschenbuch für die farben- und lackindustrie sowie für den einschlägigen handel. 8. auflage. Herausgegeben unter mitarbeit von Otto Merz ... Joh. Scheiber ... Erich Stock ... Hans Wagner ... ₍und₎ Fritz Zimmer ... von Erich Stock ... Mit 12 abbildungen und einer tabellarischen übersicht über die öllackanalyse. Stuttgart, Wissenschaftliche verlagsgesellschaft m. b. h., 1937.

xvi, 556 p. incl. illus., tables, diagrs. 16½ᶜᵐ.
Advertisements, on colored leaves, inserted.
"Anlage", folded sheet, in pocket.

1. Paint. I. Title.

New York. Public library   A C 37–2899
for Library of Congress   ₍2₎

NT 0045975   NN

Taschenbuch für die farben- und lackindustrie sowie für den einschlägigen handel. 9. auflage. Herausgegeben unter mitarbeit von Otto Merz., Joh. Scheiber... Erich Stock ... Hans Wagner ... [und] Fritz Zimmer... von Erich Stock... Mit 132 abbildungen und einer tabellarischen übersicht über die öllackanalyse. Stuttgart, Wissenschaftliche verlagsgesellschaft m. b. h., 1940.
     xx, 711 p. incl. illus., tables, diagrs. 16.5 cm.
     Advertisements, on colored leaves, inserted.

     "Anlage", folded sheet S, attached at end.
     1. Paint. 2. Pigments. 3. Varnish and varnishing.

NT 0045977   CU

Taschenbuch für die Farben- und Lackindustrie sowie für den einschlägigen Handel. 11. Aufl., hrsg. unter Mitarbeit von Otto Merz ₍et al.₎ von Erich Stock. Mit 141 Abbildungen, einer tabellarischen Übersicht über die Öllackanalyse und einer Farbstofftabelle. Stuttgart, Wissenschaftliche Verlagsgesellschaft, 1947.

xx, 778 p. illus. 17 cm.
"Anlage" (2 fold. sheets) in pocket.

1. Paint. 2. Varnish and varnishing. I. Stock, Erich, 1889-

TP935.T3 1947   667.6   49–13484 rev*

NT 0045978   DLC NN OU

Taschenbuch für die Farben- und Lackindustrie sowie für den einschlägigen Handel. 12. verb. und verm. Aufl., hrsg. unter Mitarbeit von Hellmut Gnamm ₍et al.₎ von Erich Stock. Stuttgart, Wissenschaftliche Verlagsgesellschaft, 1950.

xxxi, 1010 p. illus. 17 cm.
"Anlage" (2 fold. sheets) in pocket.

1. Paint. 2. Varnish and varnishing. I. Stock, Erich, 1889- ed.

TP935.T3 1950   667.6   51–33705

NT 0045979   DLC ICJ NN

Taschenbuch für die Farben- und Lackindustrie sowie für den einschlägigen Handel. 13., verb. und verm. Aufl., hrsg. unter Mitarbeit von Hellmut Gnamm ₍et al.₎ von Erich Stock. Stuttgart, Wissenschaftliche Verlagsgesellschaft, 1954.

xxxii, 1006 p. illus. 17 cm.

1. Paint. 2. Varnish and varnishing. I. Stock, Erich, 1889- ed.

TP935.T3 1954   55–15184

NT 0045980   DLC CU MiDW

Taschenbuch fuer die gesammte mineralogie mit hinsicht auf die neuesten entdeckungen. Jahrgang 1-18. Frankfurt-a-M., 1807-24.
     18 vols. 8 vo.

NT 0045981   NN MA NjR

Taschenbuch für die gesammte mineralogie . . . Repertorium. 1.–3. quinquennium; jahre 1807–21. Frankfurt am Main, J. C. Hermann, 1811–22.

3 v. in 1. 18ᶜᵐ.
Title varies: 1807-16, Repertorium . . . 1817-21, Allgemeines repertorium der mineralogie. Von Karl Caesar ritter v. Leonhard.

       2–143—M 2

NT 0045982   DLC

Taschenbuch für die gesammte mineralogie, mit hinsicht auf die neuesten entdeckungen, hrsg. von Karl Caesar ritter von Leonhard. 20. Jahrg., II. Band. Frankfurt am Main, J.C. Hermann,1826.
602 p. fold. pl. 18 cm.

1. Mineralogy-Period. I. Leonhard, Karl Cäsar von, 1779-1862, ed.

NT 0045983   MH-GS

Taschenbuch für die gesammte mineralogie, mit hinsicht auf die neuesten entdeckungen, hrsg. von Karl Caesar ritter von Leonhard. 1.–23. jahrg. ; 1807–29. Frankfurt am Main, J. C. Hermann ₍etc.₎ 1807–27; Heidelberg, J. C. B. Mohr, 1828–29.

   23 v. fold. pl. (part col.) port., fold. maps. 18ᶜᵐ.

   The vols. for 1813–20 were issued in 2 pts. each (1.–2. abth.) 1821–22, in 3 pts.; 1823–24, in 4 pts.; 1825–29, in 2 pts. (1.–2. bd.) Each part has special t.-p.: 1818–24, Mineralogisches taschenbuch; 1825–29, Zeitschrift für mineralogie.
Continued as Jahrbuch für mineralogie.

—— Repertorium. 1.–3. quinquennium; jahre 1807–21. Frankfurt am Main, J. C. Hermann, 1811–22.

   3 v. in 1. 18ᶜᵐ.

   Title varies: 1807–16, Repertorium ... 1817–21, Allgemeines repertorium der mineralogie. Von Karl Caesar ritter v. Leonhard.

   1. Mineralogy—Period.   I. Leonhard, Karl Cäsar von, 1779–1862, ed.

                2–142–3 Revised

Library of Congress   QE1.N4

NT 0045985   DLC DI-GS CSt MiU OU

Micro-3
QE
1
.N4

Taschenbuch für die gesammte mineralogie, mit hinsicht auf die neuesten entdeckungen, hrsg. von Karl Caesar ritter von Leonhard. 1.–23 jahrg.; 1807–29. Frankfurt am Main, J. C. Hermann ₍etc₎ 1807–27. Heidelberg, J. C. B. Mohr, 1828–29.
23 v. fold. pl. (part col.) port., fold. maps. 18 cm.
The vols. for 1813–20 were issued in 2 pts. each (1.–2. abth.) 1821–22, in 3 pts.; 1823–24, in 4 pts.; 1825–29, in 2 pts. (1.–2. bd.) Each part has special t.-p.: 1818–24, Mineralogisches taschenbuch; 1825–29, Zeitschrift für mineralogie.
Continued as Jahrbuch für mineralogie.
Microfiche . Tumba, Sweden,
International Documentation Centre, 1967. 316 sheets 9 x 12 cm.

1. Mineralogy—Periodicals. I. Leonhard, Karl Cäsar von, 1779–1862. ed.

NT 0045987   OKentU

DB 541
.T2

TASCHENBUCH FÜR DIE GESCHICHTE MÄHRENS UND Schlesiens.   Jahrgang
182
Brünn
    v.

Ed. by Gregor Wolny.

1. Moravia—Hist.—Period. 2. Silesia, Austrian—Hist.—Period. I. Volný, Řehoř Tomáš,1793–1871,ed.

NT 0045988   InU

Taschenbuch für die gesundheit auf das jahr 1801
    see under   Hildebrandt, Friedrich i.e. Georg Friedrich.

PT
1110
J4T3.8

Taschenbuch für die Kinder Israels; oder, Almanach für unsre Leute. Mit Kupfern und Musik. Berlin, J.W. Schmidt, 1804.
364 p. illus., music. 14 cm.
H.u.C. copy imperfect: p.3–4 mutilated with loss of text.

NT 0045990   OCH

Taschenbuch für die Krankenpflege in der Familie, im Hospital, im Gemeinde- und Armendienst, sowie im Kriege. Bearbeitet von Dr. Ed. Brehme ... Prof. Dr. P. Fürbringer ... ₍u. a.₎ Herausgegeben im Auftrage der unter dem Protektorat Ihrer Königlichen Hoheit der Frau Grossherzogin von Sachsen stehenden Pflegerinnen-Anstalt in Weimar vom Geh. Medizinal-Rath Dr. L. Pfeiffer ... Weimar, H. Böhlau, 1883.
xii, 286, [4] p. illus., diagrs. XII (i.e. 6) pl. 17½ᶜᵐ.
The plates have illustrations on both sides.

NT 0045991   ICJ ICRL

Taschenbuch für die Kriegsmarine.

Hannover, A. Sponholtz.
   v. illus. (part col.) maps. 12 cm.
Vols. for   "herausgegeben im Auftrage des Oberkommandos der Kriegsmarine von Korvettenkapitän der Reserve Fritz Otto Busch."

   1. Germany. Kriegsmarine—Yearbooks.   I. Busch, Fritz Otto, 1890- ed.

V10.T3   359   49–35573*‡
          1.

CoU TNJ NNC AAP PMA NN OC1
MH CoD NjR UU NNC KyU MnU PPG PHi MoU CoU FU ICU
NT 0045992   DLC DCaE CSt TU MdAN MiU TxDaM NcD CtY MH

Taschenbuch für die Margarine-Industrie (2. Aufl. des Addressbuchs für die Margarine-Industrie, Talgschmelzen, Speisefett-Fabriken und Oel-Raffinerien)
    see under   Margarineverband e. V. , Berlin.

DC220
.T24
Rare bk
room

Taschenbuch für die neuste geschichte. 1.- jahrg. ₍1794-   ₎Nürnberg,1794-
   v. fronts.,plates(part col.,part fold.incl. music) fold.maps. 12cm.
Title-pages and plates,engr.
Edited by E.L.Posselt.
Comprises "Krieg der fränkischen nation gegen die coalirten mächte Europens. 1.- jahrg.₎1792-

   1.France--Hist.--Revolution--1792-1799.

NT 0045994   ICU MWiW-C InU CSt NjP DLC

Gimbel
DC
220.6
T19

Taschenbuch für die neuste Geschichte, hrsg. von D. Ernst Ludwig Posselt. Dritter Jahrgang ... Nürnberg, in der Bauer- und Mannischen Buchhandlung, 1796.
xvi, 268 p. illus. 12cm.
Partial contents: Uiber die Luftbälle, als Werkzeuge des Krieges, p.₍197₎-206 (with a folded engraving of 3 balloons; deals with the campaign of 1794: France against the Coalition)

    I. Posselt, Er℔   Ludwig

NT 0045995   CoCA

Taschenbuch für die schaubühne.   Gotha [177 ?]-
   v.   1776–

NT 0045996   NjP

Lilly
PN 2643
.T 197
1782

TASCHENBUCH FÜR DIE SCHAUBÜHNE, AUF DAS JAHR 1782. Mit Kupfern. Gotha, Carl Wilhelm Ettinger ₍1782₎
3 p.ℓ.,285,₍5₎p.   plates.   16mo (10.5 cm)

"Inhalt," ₍5₎p. at end.
Introduction typesigned Reichard.
In full brown leather, all edges red.

NT 0045997   InU

Lilly
AY 859
.N485 T19
1799

TASCHENBUCH FÜR DIE SCHWÄBISCHE GESCHICHTE von G. A. Neuhofer. Zweyter Jahrgang enthaltend Schwabens Schicksale im Spanischen Erbfolgekriege. Augsburg, Johann Georg Rollwagen ₍1799₎
17 p.ℓ.,184 p.   front.,plates. 11.3 cm.

Added engraved t.p.: Deutsch und französischer Calender für das Jahr 1799.
In brown decorated boards; spine damaged.

NT 0045998   InU

---

²⁰⁰⁹¹ Taschenbuch für die Stein- und Zement-Industrie .... Berlin, Gebrüder Borntraeger, 1902–1904.
   Vol. 1, 3, 1902, 1904. illus., plates. 16ᶜᵐ.
   Edited by A. Eisentraeger.

NT 0045999   ICJ DI-GS

Taschenbuch für die Textilindustrie. Berlin, Fachverlag Schiele & Schön.
   v. illus. 16 cm.

   1. Textile industry and fabrics.

TS1445.T25   55–17146 ‡

NT 0046001   DLC NN

Taschenbuch für die Textilindustrie, 1952. ₍Für die Redaktion verantwortlich: Richard Hünlich₎ Berlin, Schiele und Schön ₍1952₎
   396 p. illus., diagrs. 16 cm.

   1. Textile industry and fabrics.   I. Hünlich, Richard, ed.

                A 53–1984

Georgia Inst. of Tech.   Library
for Library of Congress   ₍3₎

NT 0046002   GAT

Lilly
DD 18
.T18 H82

TASCHENBUCH FÜR DIE VATERLÄNDISCHE GESCHICHTE. jahrg.1-₍ ₎,1811-14; n.F.2,jahrg.1-10,1820-29; n.F.3,jahrg.1-20,1830-49;
   Berlin, G. Reimer.
   jahrg. fronts.,plates. 15 cm.
annual.

Köhring, Bibliographie der Almanache, p. 122, nos. 912-13; ULS V,4155.
Suspended 1815-19.
Neue Folge 2 has no series designation.
Imprint var-   ies.

Edited from 1811-29 by Josef freiherr von Hormayr zu Hortenburg and Alajos Mednyánszky, continued until 1850 by Hormayr.
Bound in quarter red morocco and marbled boards.

NT 0046004   InU ICU CSt PLatS

HV763
.T2

Taschenbuch für die wohlfahrtspflege... hrsg. vom Deutschen archiv für jugendwohlfahrt... Berlin₍192
   v. 16½ᶜᵐ.

   2.jahrgang des Taschenbuchs für wohlfahrtspflegerinnen 1925.

NT 0046005   ICU

PT19
.T248
Rare bk
room

Taschenbuch für edle frauen u.mädchen... Carlsruhe₍etc.₎
   v. front.,plates. 12½ᶜᵐ.

1801-   have title:Taschenbuch auf das jahr...für edle weiber und mädchen.
Contains music.
Edited by Wilhelmine Müller.

NT 0046006   ICU

830.8 Taschenbuch für edle teutsche frauen, mit kupfern,
T1813 1802. Leipzig, H. Müller [1802]
1802 342p. front.(port.) plates.

    1. German literature (Collections) 2. Gift-
books (Annuals, etc.)

NT 0046007 IU PU

Taschenbuch für eisenbahntechnischen Dienst. 1.– Ausg.;
1950–
Frankfurt am Main, A. Tetzlaff.
    v. illus. 15 cm.

    1. Railroads—Handbooks, manuals, etc.
    TF151.T38   53–35759

NT 0046008 DLC

Taschenbuch für Energiestatistik.
Wien, Bohmann Verlag.
    v. 17 cm. annual.
    "Herausgegeben vom Bundesministerium für Handel, Gewerbe und
Industrie."

    1. Power resources—Austria—Statistics. I. Austria. Bundes-
ministerium für Handel, Gewerbe und Industrie.
    HD9502.A9T36   333.7   76–645211
                                     MARC–S

NT 0046009 DLC

Taschenbuch für energiewirtschaft.
Berlin, Franckh [19
    v. diagrs. 15ᶜᵐ.

    1. Mechanical engineering—Handbooks, manuals, etc. 2. Power (Me-
chanics) 3. Engineering societies. 4. Engineering law—Germany.
                                 45–34047
    Library of Congress   TJ151.T84
                         [2]   621.102

NT 0046010 DLC MCM

Taschenbuch für erfinderbetreuer
    see under Dapper, Josef.

Taschenbuch für Exlibris-Sammler
    see under Schramm, Albert, 1880– ed.

Taschenbuch für Familiengeschichtsforschung, von
Friedrich Wecken. Mit einem Geleitwort von
Ludwig Finckh. 4. umgearb. und erw. Aufl.
Leipzig, Degener, 1930.
    xii, 173 p. 16 cm.
    1. Genealogy. 2. Germany – Geneal.
    I. Wecken, Friedrich, 1875– ed.

NT 0046013 CSt

CS Taschenbuch für Familiengeschichtsforschung,
18 von Friedrich Wecken. Mit einem Geleitwort
T36 von Ludwig Finckh. 4. umgearbeitete und
1930 erweiterte Aufl. Leipzig,Degener,1930.
    173p. illus. 16cm.

    __Kalender, 1930. (in pocket)
    75p. 16cm.

    1. Genealogy. 2. Germany _ Geneal.
    I. Wecken, Friedrich, 1875– ed.

NT 0046014 MU

CS Taschenbuch für Familiengeschichtsforschung,
18 von Friedrich Wecken. Mit einem Geleitwort
T36 von Ludwig Finckh. 5. Aufl. Leipzig,
    Degener, 1937.
    244 p. illus. 16cm.
    "Alle Jahreskalender auf einem Blatt, von Dr. Deliarius
(Joh. Ed. Böttcher)": fold. leaf of tables (in pocket)
accompanied by leaf with a movable frame containing key
text for use with one of the tables. Verso of this leaf
contains "Vorwort," "Gebrauchsregel," etc.
Includes bibliographies.

NT 0046015 WU

Taschenbuch für Familiengeschichtsforschung, von Friedrich
Wecken. Mit einem Geleitwort von Ludwig Finckh. 6.
Aufl. Marktschellenberg, Degener, 1941.
    301 p. illus. 16 cm.
    "Alle Jahreskalender auf einem Blatt, von Dr. Deliarius (Joh. Ed.
Böttcher)": fold. leaf of tables (in pocket) accompanied by leaf with
a movable frame containing key text for use with one of the tables.
Verso of this leaf contains "Vorwort," "Gebrauchsregel," etc.
Includes bibliographies.

    1. Genealogy. 2. Germany—Geneal. I. Wecken, Friedrich, 1875–
ed. II. Böttcher, Johannes Eduard, 1847–1919.
    CS18.T36 1941   929.1   49–30901*

NT 0046016 DLC WU CtY NN

Taschenbuch für Familiengeschichtsforschung, begründet
von Friedrich Wecken. Neubearb. von Johannes Krausse.
7. Aufl. Schellenberg bei Berchtesgaden, Degener, 1951.
    321 p. illus. 16 cm.

    1. Genealogy. 2. Germany—Geneal. I. Wecken, Friedrich, 1875–
ed. II. Krausse, Johannes, ed.
    CS18.T36 1951   929.1   52–21947

NT 0046017 DLC MH NN

Taschenbuch für Fleischbeschauer. Hrsg.
von H. Schmutterer. 29 pp., 50 l. 12°. München, C. Gerber, 1903.

NT 0046018 DNLM

Taschenbuch für Forst- und Holzwirte.
    Berlin, Deutscher Zentralverlag.
    v. illus., maps. 15 cm. annual.
    Began publication in 1947?
    "Herausgegeben unter Mitwirkung von Forst- und Holzfachleuten,"
19

    1. Forests and forestry—Yearbooks. 2. Forests and forestry—Ger-
many, Eastern.
    SD1.T2   634.90943   52–20248 ‡

NT 0046019 DLC CtY MnU

Taschenbuch für Forst- und Jagdfreunde
    see Sylvan, Jahrbuch für Forstmänner,
jäger und jagdfreunde...

99.83 Taschenbuch für Forstwirtschaft.
T182
    Berlin, Deutscher Bauernverlag,

    1. Germany. Forestry. 2. Forestry.
Handbooks, manuals, etc. 3. Forestry.
Year-books.

NT 0046021 DNAL IaU

W 1 TASCHENBUCH für Frauenärzte. 3. Aufl.;
TA696 [1909?]-10 Eberswalde [Deutschland]
    2 v.
    Continues Taschenbuch für Frauenärzte
und Geburtshelfer.
    Ed. by L. Jankau.
    Continued by Taschenbuch für Frauen-
heilkunde und Geburtshilfe.
    Contents. —

    2. T. Personalien.
        1. Gynecology - Germany - Direct.

    2. Obstetrics - Germany - Direct.
    I. Jankau, Ludwig, 1865– ed.

NT 0046023 DNLM

W 1 TASCHENBUCH für Frauenärzte und Ge-
TA696 burtshelfer. 1.–2. Ausg.; 1904/05-06/07.
    Leipzig [etc.]
    2 v.
    On cover, 1904/05: Medicinische
special-Taschenbücher; 1906/07:
Spezialärztliche Taschenbücher.
    Ed. by L. Jankau.
    Continued by Taschenbuch für Fraue-
närzte.
    Includes section: Personalien.

    1. Gynecology - Germany - Direct.
    2. Gynecology - Handbooks 3. Obstetrics
Germany - Direct. 4. Obstetrics
    I. Jankau, Ludwig, 1865– ed.

NT 0046025 DNLM

Taschenbuch für Frauenheilkunde und Gebrutshilfe
    see under Jankaw, Ludwig, 1865– ed.

Taschenbuch für Frauenzimmer von Bildung auf
das Jahr 1799. Stuttgart, J. F. Steinkopf.
    1 v. plates, music. 11 cm.
    Editor: 1799– C. L. Neuffer.
    1. German literature – 18th cent. 2. German
literature – Yearbooks. I. Neuffer, Christian
Ludwig, 1769-1839, ed.

NT 0046027 CU

Taschenbuch für Freimaurer auf das Jahr
1798
Göthen: J. A. Aue [, 1798   15½cm.
    v. plates (part col'd, incl. music), ports.
    1798   added t.-p.: Jahrbuch der Maurerey, Bd. 1.

    1. Freemasons—Yearbooks. I. Jahr-   buch der Maurerey.
N. Y. P. L.   January 11, 1934

NT 0046028 NN MH CtY

HS Taschenbuch für Freimaurer auf das Jahr
365 1798-1805. Göthen, August Aue [1798-
T19 1805]
    7 v. illus. 15cm.

    Extra t.-p. reads: Jahrbuch der
Maurerey.

NT 0046029 NIC

PT19 Taschenbuch für freunde altdeutscher zeit und kunst auf
.T25 das jahr 1816. Köln, Gedruckt bei M. Du Mont-Schau-
Rare bk berg [1815]
room   xiv, 389, [1] p. plates. 17½ᶜᵐ.
    Edited by Eberhard von Groote.

    1. German literature—Collections. 2. Gift-books (Annuals, etc.)

NT 0046030 ICU MH PPG

838
T1971   Taschenbuch für Freunde der Declamation.
                                                    Bd.
         Leipzig.

NT 0046031   IEN

550
T181   Taschenbuch für Freunde der Geologie.
         1.-   Jahrg.; 1845-   Stuttgart, E.
        Schweizerbart'sche Verlagsbuchhandlung.
             v. illus., plates(part col.) 20cm.
        annual.

NT 0046032   IU

Taschenbuch für Freunde des Fischfanges
        see Neuestes vollständiges und unentbehr-
    liches Taschenbuch für Freunde des Fischfanges.

Taschenbuech für Freunde des Guten und Schönen
        zur Unterhaltung und Belehrung. Mit Kupfern
        und Musik.   Kreuznach, Kehr, 1805.
        20 cm.

NT 0046034   CU

Taschenbuch für freunde des scherzes und der
        satire
        see under   Falk, Johannes Daniel, 1768-
    1826, ed.

838
T1981   Taschenbuch für Freunde höherer Bildung.
         1827. Wien.
        [18],252,[4]p. ports. 14cm.

        No more published.

NT 0046036   IEN

PT19   Taschenbuch für freunde höherer bildung, enthaltend:
.T26   eine auswahl gelungener denksprüche und poet-
Rare bk   ischer gedanken aus den werken der vorzüglichsten
            schriftsteller ... Wien, Pfautsch [1829,
        [18], 252, [4] p. front., ports.
        No more published?
        "Verzeichniss der geburts- und todestage jener
        gefeyerten dichter und heroen": p. [7-14], first
        group of paging.

            1. Quotations, German. 2. Gift books, annuals,
        etc.

NT 0046037   ICU

PT19   Taschenbuch für freunde und freundinnen des schönen und
.T27   nützlichen, besonders für edle gattinnen und mütter und
Rare bk   solche die es werden wollen.   Auf das jahr 1805-1807.
room   Hrsg. von M. Friedrich Herrmann ... Leipzig, Bei J. C.
        Hinrichs, 1805-07.
        3 v. fronts., plates. 11-12cm.
            1807 has title: Taschenbuch für freunde des schönen und nützlichen, and also
        appeared with new title-page for 1808. cf. Goedeke, v. 8, p. 63.

            1. German literature—Collections. 2. Gift-books (Annuals, etc.)

NT 0046038   ICU

Lilly
PT 1799   TASCHENBUCH FÜR FREUNDINNEN ROMANTISCHER
.A1 T197   Lectüre, auf das Jahr 1807. Mit 6 Kupfern.
1807   Wien, Joseph Grämmer [1807]
        1 p.ℓ.,58,[10]p.   9.8 cm.

            Includes three stories by an anonymous
        author: Die Brüder; Das Burgverliess; Hel-
        dengrösse und Menschlichkeit.
            Various statistical information, [10]p.
        at end.
            Lacks plates.
            In laven-   der wrappers, all edges
        gilt.

NT 0046039   InU

Taschenbuch für froshinn und liebe auf das
        Jahr 1826 von C. Kuffner. Wien, Fr.
        W. Pfautsch, [1826]
            [18] iv, 332 p. [7] leaves of plates.
        illus., fold. music. 13.2 cm.
            Goedeke VIII, p. 117; only 2 v. published.
            In pink boards, stamped in blind and gold,
        all edges gilt; in an open library case.
            1. Almanacs, German. I. Kuffner,
        Christoph, 1780-1846.

NT 0046040   InU

Taschenbuch für Gabelsberger Stenographen.
18
        Dresden: G. Dietze [, 18   16°.
             v. plates.
        Publ. by the Koenigliches stenographisches Institut in Dresden.
        Text partly in shorthand.

    1. Shorthand—Per. and soc. publ.
N. Y. P. L.   May 13, 1926

NT 0046041   NN

tSB406
T3   Taschenbuch für Gartenbesitzer und für
        Blumenfreunde.   Leipzig, Sommer [1811]
        xxxii,256 p. col.front. 13cm.

            1. Floriculture - Germany.

NT 0046042   CU

SB453   Taschenbuch für gartenfreunde, hrsg. von C.C.L.
.T32   Hirschfeld...
        Altona, Gedruckt bey J.D.A. Eckhardt, 178 -
             v. plates. 12x10cm.

            1. Gardening.

NT 0046043   ICU MiU

Taschenbuch für gartenfreunde. 2. verb.
aufl. Leipzig, O. Leiner, 1884.

        308.

NT 0046044   MiU

Taschenbuch für gasanstalten, kokereien, schwelereien und
        teerdestillationen. 1926-
        Halle (Saale) W. Knapp, 1926-
             v. illus., diagrs. 16½cm.
        Editor: 1926-   Heinrich Winter.

            1. Gas manufacture and works. 2. Coke. 3. Coal-tar products.
        I. Winter, Heinrich, ed.
        Library of Congress   TP751.T3   27-7414

NT 0046045   DLC

Taschenbuch für gemeindebeamte.
        Berlin, Verlag Beamtenpresse gmbh. [19
             v. 14cm.
        Editors: 19   Karl Vogt, Helmut Bartsch.

            1. Municipal government—Year-books. 2. Municipal government—
        Germany. I. Vogt, Karl, ed. II. Bartsch, Helmut, ed.
        Library of Congress   JS5303.T3   46-29905
                                [2]   352.043

NT 0046046   DLC MH MiU CU NN

Taschenbuch für geologen, palaontologen und
        mineralogen. 1901
                    See
        Kalender für geologen, palaontologen und mineralo-
    gen

DD1   Taschenbuch für geschichte und alterthum in Süd-
.T2   deutschland. Hrsg. von dr. Heinrich Schreiber...
        Freiburg im Breisgau, 1839-46.
        5 v. plates. 17cm.

NT 0046048   ICU

Taschenbuch für geschichte und alterthum in
        Süddeutschland. Hrsg. von dr. Heinrich
        Schreiber ... Jahrg. 5.-   Freiburg im
        Breisgau, Emmerling, 1846-
        1 v. plate. 18 cm.
            1. Germany - Antiq. I. Schreiber, Heinrich
        i.e. Johann Heinrich, 1793-1872, ed.

NT 0046049   CU

Lilly
AY 859   TASCHENBUCH FÜR GESCHICHTE UND UNTERHALTUNG
.N485 T19 auf das Jahr 1800. Herausgegeben von G. A.
1800   Neuhofer. Dritter Jahrgang. Augsburg,
        Johann Georg Rollwagen, 1800.
            17 p.ℓ.,190 p. front.,plates. 11.3 cm.

            Köhring, Bibliographie der Almanache,
        p. 123, no. 917 does not list an 1800 issue.
            Added engraved t.p.: Deutsch und franzö-
        sischer Calender ... Enthaltend die Fortset-
        zung der Geschichte des gegenwärtigen Krieges.
            In decora-   ted boards.

NT 0046050   InU

Lilly
AY 859   TASCHENBUCH FÜR GESCHICHTE UND UNTERHALTUNG
.N485 T19 auf das Jahr 1802. Herausgegeben von G. A.
1802   Neuhofer. Fünfter Jahrgang. Augsburg,
        Joh. Georg Rollwagen [1802]
            21 p.ℓ.,184 p. front.,plates. 11 cm.

            Added engraved title page.
            Includes a German and a French calendar
        on light blue paper.
            In decorated boards, all edges gilt.

NT 0046051   InU

Case
-A   TASCHENBUCH für gesellschaftliche unterhaltung.
1   1794.
.86   Mannheim, 1795.
            1v. plates(part fold.,part col.,incl.music)
        11cm.

NT 0046052   ICN

Taschenbuch für grabennymphen auf das jahr 1787.
[Wien, P. Knepler, 1909]

3 p. l., 5–84 p. 12 pl. 11ᶜᵐ.

In portfolio.
Reprint of the original edition of 1786? with engr. t.-p. in facsim.
"Dieses buch wurde in einer einmaligen numerierten auflage von 750 exemplaren gedruckt, davon nr. 1–50 in glanzleder. Dieses exemplar erhielt die nummer 251."
G. Gugitz, in his Kulturgeschichtliches begleitwort zum neudruck des "Taschenbuch" ... attributes the authorship to Joseph Richter.

————Kulturgeschichtliches begleitwort zum neudruck des "Taschenbuch für grabennymphen auf das jahr 1787" von Gustav Gugitz. Wien, P. Knepler [1909]

21 p. 11ᶜᵐ.

In same portfolio with the "Taschenbuch."

1. Erotic literature. 2. Prostitution—Vienna.   I. Richter, Joseph, 1749–1813, supposed author. II. Gugitz, Gustav.

10–16164–5

Library of Congress   HQ461.T3

NT 0046054   DLC NjP

Taschenbuch für Gymnasiasten und Realschüler. Enthaltend Tabellen, Jahreszahlen und Formeln aus der Welt-, Kirchen-, Litteratur- und Kunstgeschichte, der Mathematik, Astronomie, Physik, Chemie, Naturkunde und Geographie, nebst einer Uebersicht der Maass-, Gewichts- und Münz-Systeme und Chronologie. Achte verbesserte und vermehrte Auflage. Dresden: W. Violet, 1900.   iv, 224 p. incl. tables (1 geneal.). 15½cm.

992979A.   1. Ready reference.
N. Y. P. L.   September 22, 1939

NT 0046055   NN

PT19
.T285
Rare bk
room
Taschenbuch für häusliche und gesellschaftliche freuden [auf das jahr 1796–1802] Frankfurt am Main; [etc., etc.] 1796–1802.

7 v. fronts. (ports.) plates. 12½ᶜᵐ.

Contains music.
Added title-pages engr. (1796–1800: Almanach und taschenbuch ...)
Editors: 1796–99, Carl Lang.—1800–02, Ludwig Lang.
1796–99 have imprint: Heilbronn am Neckar, Beim verfasser.

1. German literature—Collections. 2. Gift-books (Annuals, etc.) 3. Almanacs.

NT 0046056   ICU

Taschenbuch für Heizung und Lüftung.

München, R. Oldenbourg.

v. 19 cm.

Began publication in 1898. Cf. Deutsches Bücherverzeichnis, 1895–98.
Title varies: 19   Hermann Recknagels Kalender für Gesundheits- und Wärme-Technik.
At head of title, 19   Recknagel-Sprenger.
Founded and for some years edited by H. Recknagel.

1. Heating—Yearbooks.   I. Recknagel, Hermann, 1860–1919.

TH7201.T3   697.058   46–36682 rev*

NT 0046057   DLC OCl IU NN

Taschenbuch für Heizung, Lüftung und Klimatechnik
     see   Taschenbuch für Heizung und Lüftung.

Taschenbuch für hütten- und giessereileute ... 1926–
Halle-Saale, W. Knapp, 1926–

v. illus., diagrs. 16½ᶜᵐ.

Editor : 1926–   Hubert Hermanns.

1. Metallurgy—Handbooks, manuals, etc. 2. Iron—Metallurgy. 3. Steel—Metallurgy. 4. Iron industry and trade. 5. Steel industry and trade.   I. Hermanns, Hubert, 1884–   ed.

27–7680

Library of Congress   TN671.T3

NT 0046059   DLC

Taschenbuch fuer junge Menschen
     see under   Suhrkamp, Peter, 1891–1959.

Taschenbuch für Keramiker.
19

Berlin[, 1926   16°.
v. illus.

1926   published by the Keramische Rundschau (later Keramische Rundschau und Kunst-Keramik).

1. Pottery—Directories. 2. Pottery   —Handbooks. 3. Keramische Rundschau und Kunst-Keramik.
N. Y. P. L.   May 2, 1930

NT 0046061   NN MiD OU IU

Taschenbuch für Keramiker, 1931. Band [I]–II. Berlin, Keramische Rundschau G.m.b.H. [1931]

2 vol. illus., diagrs. 16ᶜᵐ.

"Strassenplan von Berlin" on lining paper of vol. 2.
"Fachliteratur für Keramik, Glas, Email": Bd. I, p. 222–242.
Includes advertising matter.
Contents.—I. Textband.—II. Alphabetischer Führer durch die Keramik, Glas- und Emailindustrie, mit Bezugsquellen.

NT 0046062   ICJ

Taschenbuch für Kinder
     see under   [Splittegarb, Karl Friedrich]
1753–1802.

Taschenbuch für kinderärzte
     see under   Jankaw, Ludwig, 1865–   ed

HV763
.T23
TASCHENBUCH für kindergärtnerinnen, hortnerinnen und jugendleiterinnen/hrsg. vom Deutschen archiv für jugendwohlfahrt. /Berlin, F.A.Herbig, 1927.
78,[1]p.incl.forms. 16½ cm.
"Literaturangaben und zeitschriftenliste":p.68–75.

1.Children--Care and hygiene.

NT 0046065   ICU

Taschenbuch für Krankenpflege
     see under   Pfeiffer, Ludwig, 1842–1921, ed.

Taschenbuch für Krankenpflege für Aerzte, Pflegerinnen, Pfleger und für die Familie
     see under   Pfeiffer, Ludwig, 1842–1921, ed

W 1
TA698
TASCHENBUCH für Krankenpflegerinnen.
1. -   Jahrg. ; 1879–
Weimar.
v.
Issued by the Pflegerinnen-Anstalt in Weimar.
I. Weimar.   Pflegerinnen-Anstalt

NT 0046068   DNLM

Taschenbuch für Krieger und Freunde des Kriegerstandes. Darmstadt, C.W. Leske, 1829–
v. illus.
"Aus dem Allgemeinen Militär-Almanach abgedruckt".
1. Germany – History – Military.

NT 0046069   InU

Taschenbuch für Kriminalisten. 1.–   **Jahrg.;**
1951–
Lübeck, Verlag Polizei-Rundschau.
v. illus. 15 cm. annual.

1. Police—Yearbooks. 2. Police—Handbooks, manuals, etc. I. Polizei-Rundschau.

HV7551.T35   52–16900

NT 0046070   DLC CtY

PT19
.T286
Rare bk
room
Taschenbuch für kunst und laune auf das jahr 1801–[1804] Köln, Bei Haas und sohn [1801?–03?]

3 v. front., plates. 13–14ᶜᵐ.

Contains music.
Edited by K. G. Cramer.–
None published for 1803.
No more published.

1. German literature—Collections. 2. Gift-books (Annuals, etc.) 3. Almanacs.

NT 0046071   ICU CU-BANC CU

Taschenbuch für kunst und laune, no. 12. 1804.
Köln, 1803.
1 v. plates (part fold.)   14 cm.

NT 0046072   CU

Taschenbuch für Lackierbetriebe.

Hannover, C. R. Vincentz.

v. illus. 15 cm. annual.

Began publication with vol. for 1939 ; publication suspended 1945–49. Cf. Deutsches Bücherverzeichnis, 1936–40–1941–50.
Title varies: Jahrbuch für Lackierbetriebe.
"Gemeinschaftsarbeit des Mitarbeiterstabes des 'Industrie-Lackier-Betrieb.'"

1. Lacquer and lacquering—Yearbooks.   I. Industrie-Lackier-Betrieb. II. Title: Jahrbuch für Lackierbetriebe.

TP939.J3   47–40012

NT 0046073   DLC DBS ICJ NN

Taschenbuch für landwirtschaftliche Genossenschaften.
Auflage

Darmstadt, 19   16°.
v.
Published by Reichsverband der deutschen landwirtschaftlichen Genossenschaften.

1. Agriculture.—Assoc. and organi-   zations, Germany.
N. Y. P. L.   October 27, 1923.

NT 0046074   NN DNAL OrCS MH

---

tPN3169
G3T3
1795
Taschenbuch für Liebhaber des Privat-theaters. Leipzig, Sommersche Buchhandlung [1795]
7,216 p. front. 13cm.

"Schauspiele für Liebhabertheater":
p.[101]–216 p.

1. Amateur theatricals. 2. German drama - 18th cent.

NT 0046075   CU InU

Taschenbuch für mathematiker und physiker
see under   Auerbach, Felix, ed.

Taschenbuch für medicin-studirende. Inhalt. Gesetzliche bestimmungen. Promotionsordnungen sämmtlicher deutschen universitäten. Arzneimittel, mit angabe ihrer dosirung, form, anwendnng ₍!₎ und ihres preises etc. Breslau, Preuss & Jünger ₍1890₎

3 p. l. ₍3₎–196 p. 14ᵐ.

"Bade- und curorte, irrenanstalten, nervenanstalten, sanatorien": p. 188–195.

1. Medicine—Study and teaching—Germany. 2. Materia medica. 3. Health resorts, watering-places, etc.

Library of Congress   R785.A2T3   41-35880

NT   0046077   DLC

Taschenbuch für Metallarbeiter. 1953–
₍Gütersloh₎ C. Bertelsmann.
v. illus. 15 cm.

1. Metal-work—Handbooks, manuals, etc.

TS210.T37   53-35758

NT   0046078   DLC IU

Taschenbuch für Nervenärzte
see under   Jankaw, Ludwig, 1865–   ed.

Taschenbuch für Officiere der leichten Infanterie ..
see under   [Minutoli, Johann Heinrich Carl],
Freiherr von, 1772-1846.

Taschenbuch für Ohren-, Nasen-, und Halsärzte
see under   Jankaw, Ludwig, 1865–   ed.

Taschenbuch für Parfümerie und Kosmetik
see under   Davidsohn, Isser, 1875–

Taschenbuch für Präzisionsmechaniker, Optiker, Elektromechaniker und Glasinstrumentenmacher
see
Taschenbuch der Feinmechanik.

Taschenbuch für pressluft-betrieb...

See under:

Frankfurter maschinenbau, a.g.

Taschenbuch für preussische Militair-Aerzte
see under   Schubert, A., physician.

JN3961 •
.5
.T3   **Taschenbuch für reichs- und länderverwaltungsbeamte sowie für wehrmachtsbeamte.**

Berlin, Verlag Beamtenpresse gmbh. ₍19
v. 14ᵐ.
Editor : 19   Karl Vogt.

1. Germany — Officials and employees — Year-books. 2. Germany. Wehrmacht.   I. Vogt, Karl, ed.
                                    46–29904
Library of Congress   JNS961.5.T3
                                    351.1

NT   0046086   DLC

Taschenbuch für reichsjustizbeamte.
Berlin, Verlag Beamtenpresse gmbh. ₍19
v. 14 cm.
Editor :   Karl Vogt.

1. Germany—Officials and employees—Year-books. 2. Law—Year-books.   I. Vogt, Karl, ed.
                                    47–40046

NT   0046087   DLC

Taschenbuch für reichspostbeamte.

Berlin, Verlag Beamtenpresse gmbh. ₍19
v. 14ᵐ.
Editors : 19   Karl Vogt, Otto Dan.

1. Postal service—Germany.   I. Vogt, Karl, ed.   II. Dan, Otto, ed.
                                    46–29935
Library of Congress   HE6993.T3
                                    ₍2₎   383.4943

NT   0046088   DLC

Taschenbuch für reichssteuerbeamte.

Berlin, Verlag Beamtenpresse gmbh. ₍19
v. 14ᵐ.
Editors : 19   Karl Vogt, Wilhelm Müller.

1. Taxation—Germany.   I. Vogt, Karl, ed.   II. Müller, Wilhelm, of Stuttgart, ed.
                                    46–29936
Library of Congress   HJ3484.A4T3
                                    ₍2₎   336.2

NT   0046089   DLC MH

Taschenbuch für reichszollbeamte.

Berlin, Verlag Beamtenpresse gmbh. ₍19
v. 14ᵐ.
Editor : 19   Karl Vogt.

1. Customs administration—Germany.   I. Vogt, Karl, ed.
                                    46–30834
Library of Congress   HJ6921.T3
                                    ₍2₎   336.262

NT   0046090   DLC

₃14.39   Taschenbuch für Reisende durch Deutschland,
T18   enthaltend: die Gasthöfe, Entfernungen der
           Städte, Reisestrassen, Wagenspuren, Münzen,
           Maasse und Gewichte, Messen, Jahr-, Vieh-
           und Wollmärkte, Freimaurer-Logen, Bäder &c.
           &c. in Deutschland.   Berlin, Kunst- und
           Industrie-Comptoir, 1818.
           623p.   13cm.

           Added t.p.: Adressbuch der Gasthöfe in den
           Residenz-, Haupt- und vorzüglichsten Provinzial-
           städten Deutsch-   lands.

.T3   NT   0046091   IU

Taschenbuch für reisende im Berner Oberlande ...
Aarau, 1829.
276 p.

NT   0046092   PBm

Lilly
PT 1799   TASCHENBUCH FÜR ROMANTISCHE LECKTÜRE. 1798
.A1 T197   mit Nachbildungen merkwürdiger Natur Scenen.
1798   Heilbronn, Industrie Comtoir; Frankfurt am
       Mayn, Guilhaumann ₍1798₎.
           2 p.ℓ.,₍128₎ p.   front.,plates(part fold.)
       16mo   in halfsheets(12 cm)

       Not in Köhring or Goedeke.
       Several pages missing at end.
       In soft grey boards, with a pictorial
       plaque inset in upper cover; all edges gilt.

NT   0046093   InU

Taschenbuch für Schauspieler und Schauspielfreunde.
       -₍5.₎ Jahrg.;   –1823.
Wien, Tendler und von Manstein.
v. 11–14 cm.
Publication began with issue for 1816; none for 1818–20, inclusive.
Editor : –1823, Lembert, *pseud.*
Vols. for 18   pub. in Stuttgart by Metzler.

1. Theater—Germany. 2. Theater—Yearbooks.   I. Tremler, Wenzel, 1779–1851, ed.
PN2640.T28   47–42999*

NT   0046094   DLC

---

792   **Taschenbuch für Schauspieler und**
T197   **Schauspielliebhaber. [1.Theil,1779]**
       Offenbach am Mayn, Weiss, 1779.
       1v. illus. 16cm.

       Editor: Ulrich Weiss.
       No more published?

       1.Theater - Germany. ✓LC

NT   0046095   CLSU

W 1
TA702   TASCHEN-BUCH für Scheidekünstler und
       Apotheker./ 1. -50. Jahrg.; 1780-1829.
       Weimar, Hoffmann.
           50 v.   illus.
           Some vols. have title: Almanach oder
       Taschen-Buch für Scheidekünstler und
       Apotheker.
           41. -50.Jahrg., 1820-1829, issued also
       as J. B. Trommsdorff's Taschen-Buch
       für Chemiker und Apotheker, 1.-10. Jahrg.

       Indexes:
           Vols. 1-24, 1780-1803. 4 v. in 1.
           Vols. 25-31, 1804-10, in ₍v. 31₎
           Vols. 32-37, 1811-16, in v. 37.
           1. Pharmacy - Period. 2. Chemistry
       - Pharmaceutical - Period. I. Tromms-
       dorff, Johann Bartholomäus, 1770-1837.
       Taschen-Buch für Chemiker und

       Apotheker   Title: Almanach oder
       Taschen-Buch für Scheidekünstler und
       Apotheker   Title: Taschen-Buch
       für Chemiker und Apotheker

NT   0046098   DNLM

Taschenbuch für schweizerische Wehrmänner
see also   Taschenkalender für schweizerische Wehrmänner.

Taschenbuch für schweizerische Wehrmänner.
1954–
Frauenfeld, Huber.
(l)v. illus. 15 cm.
Supersedes Taschenkalender für schweizerische Wehrmänner.

1. Switzerland. Armee—Yearbooks.

U10.T3   55–31229

NT   0046100   DLC

378.439   Taschenbuch für siebenbürgisch-sächsische
Ak1t   Hochschüler ⌐1914–15⌐ Hermannstadt,
Gedruckt und in Kommission bei W. Krafft
⌐1914⌐
iv, 321p. 17cm.
"Kalendarium: August – Dezember 1914
(S. 18–27) * Januar – Juli 1915 (S. 4–17)"
inserted after p.iv.
"Vorwort" signed: Der Schriftleitungs-
ausschuss der "Akademischen Blätter" als
Herausgeber.

NT   0046101   IU

**Taschenbuch für sozialverwaltungen und körperschaften des
öfftl. rechts.**
Berlin, Beamtenpresse gmbh. ⌐19
v. 14ᶜᵐ.
On cover, 19   : Taschenbuch für beamte der sozialverwaltungen
und körperschaften des öffentlichen rechts.
Editors: 19   Karl Vogt, Wilhelm Lasch.

1. Insurance, State and compulsory—Germany. 2. Labor laws and
legislation—Germany.   i. Vogt, Karl, ed.   ii. Lasch, Wilhelm, ed.

                         46–29933

Library of Congress   HD7178.T3

                         331.2544

NT   0046102   DLC

Taschenbuch für Stenographie-Schüler...
19
Darmstadt: Stenographisches Institut⌐, 19   24°.
v. illus.

1. Shorthand—Per. and soc. publ.
N.Y.P.L.   May 13, 1926

NT   0046103   NN

968.805
T197   **Taschenbuch für Südwestafrika.**
       Jahrg.;
Berlin, W.Weicher.

1. Africa, Southwest. Registers.

NT   0046104   IEN

Taschenbuch fur tabaksraucher
see under   [Pope, Johann Heinrich Moritz
von] 1776–1854.

Taschenbuch für Theater-Freunde auf das Jahr 1800. Von
Karl Albrecht ⌐pseud.⌐ Berlin, C. G. Schöne, 1799.
xii, 210 p. front. 12 cm.
Contains "Geschichte der deutschen Bühnen in Berlin."
No more published?
L. C. copy imperfect: front. wanting.

1. Theater—Germany. 2. Theater—Yearbooks.   i. Heidemann,
Theophil Albrecht, b. 1778, ed.

PN2640.T34   47–43001*

NT   0046106   DLC NjP

Taschenbuch fuer Theetrinker
see under   Berard.

                            667.4 F2
⁷⁹³⁰⁰ Taschenbuch für Tinten-Liebhaber, oder Gründlicher Unterricht
aller Arten Tinten zu machen, nebst einer Geschichte der Tinten
und des abstringirenden Pflanzenstoffs. Leipzig, Schwickertscher
Verlag, 1795.
viii, 172, [2] p. 17 x 10ᶜᵐ.

NT   0046108   ICJ

Taschenbuch für Truppenärzte des Ersatzheeres
see under   Neuber,   ed.

Taschenbuch für Verwaltungsbeamte
see
Die Bundesrepublik.

Taschenbuch für weisen und frohen lebens-genuss,
1800
see under   Lindemann, A. [pseud.]
[supplement]

Taschenbuch für zivil-ärzte
see
Ärztliches taschenbuch, der Wiener medizinisches wochen-
schrift.

Taschenbuch für Zöglinge des Buchhandels
see under   [Hilsenberg, Ludwig] 1814–
1843.

Taschenbuch fürs Theater. 1795–
Hamburg.
v. illus., ports. 12–16 cm.
No issue for 1797.
Editor: 1798/99–18   Schmieder.
Vols. for 1795–96 pub. in Mannheim; 1798/99–   in Mainz and
Hamburg.

1. Theater—Germany. 2. Theater—Yearbooks.   i. Schmieder, Heinrich Gottlieb, 1763–1828, ed.

PN2640.T36   47–43003*

NT   0046114   DLC

W 1   TASCHENBUCH nebst Spezialisten-Verzeichni⌐
TA701   und Taschen-Kalender für Ohren-, Nasen-
Rachen-, und Halsärzte. 6.–8. Jahrg.;
1901–03. München.
3 v.
Continues Vademecum nebst Spezi-
alisten-Verzeichnis und Taschenkalender
für Ohren-, Nasen-, Rachen-, und
Halsärzte.
Ed. by L. Jankau.
Continued by Taschenbuch für Ohren-,
Nasen-, und Halsärzte.

Includes section: Personalien.
1. Otorhinolaryngology - Direct.
2. Otorhinolaryngology - Handbooks
I. Jankau, Ludwig, 1865–   ed.

NT   0046116   DNLM

838
T1917   Taschenbuch ohne Titel. 1822–1832.
Leipzig.

No more published.
Issued in 1820, 1830 and 1832 only.
Vol. for 1822 issued also under title:
Manuscript aus Odessa.

NT   0046117   IEN

Taschenbuch sämmtlicher syphilitischen Krank-
heitsformen
see under   Müller,   of Stuttgart.

Taschenbuch USA-Heer, bestimmt

see

Germany. Heer. Generalstab.

Taschenbuch vom K.K. priv. Theater in der
Leopoldstadt. Wien, 1814–
v. plates.
Each vol. has special title page, with
varying title.
Founded by Gottfried Ziegelhausen; 1.–2.
Jahrg. have title: Theatralisches Taschenbuch
zur geselligen Unterhaltung vom K.K. priv.
Theater in der Leopoldstadt. cf. Goedecke,
VII, 298.
1. Almanacs, German - Austria. 2. Vienna -
Theater in der Leopoldstadt.

NT   0046120   ICU

       Taschenbuch von der Donau ...
H12.26t   Ulm,In der Stettin'schen Buchhandlung
front.,plates. 14cm.
Edited by Ludwig Neuffer.
Engraved title-page.
Ceased publication with 1825.

NT   0046121   CtY NjP

---

*GC8   Taschenbuch von der Donau auf das Jahr 1825,
H6716   herausgegeben von Ludwig Neuffer.
A824n   Ulm,in der Stettin'schen Buchhandlung.[1824]
2p.l.,[iii]-xxiv,357,[3]p. front.,plates.
13cm.
Frontispiece, t.-p., & plates engr. after
designs by Karl von Heideloff.
Includes first printings of 2 poems by
Hölderlin, "Einladung" & "Trost" (p.201-202 &
222).
Imperfect: p.235-236 wanting.

NT   0046122   MH

Taschenbuch von der Donau auf das jahr 1824.
Herausgegeben von Ludwig Neuffer. Ulm,
In der Stettinischen buchhandlung [1824]
1 p.l., xii, 373 [1] p., 2 l. front., plates.
14 cm.
Title vignette.
1. German literature (Selections: Extracts,
etc.) I. Neuffer, Ludwig,   ed.

NT   0046123   CU

Taschenbuch von der Donau. Auf das Jahr ...
Herausgegeben von Ludwig Neuffer. Ulm,
in der Stettin'schen Buchhandlung, 1824–25.
2 v. fronts., plates. 13,9 cm.
Only 2 vols. published; Köhring, Bibliographie
der Almanache, p. 114, no. 835.
With title vignettes.
Vol. 1 in yellow, vol. 2 in green decorated
boards, all edges gilt; in library cases.

NT   0046124   InU CtY

PT19   Taschenbuch von J.G.Jacobi und seinen freunden
.T32   für...
Rare bk   Königsberg und Leipzig
room   v. front.,plates. 12½ᵐ.

           Contains music.

NT 0046125   ICU CU NjP NNC

830.8   Taschenbuch von J. G. Jacobi und seinen freunden
T1815   für 1796. Mit kupfern von Penzel. Königs-
1796   berg [etc.] F. Nicolovius [1795?]
           242p. front., plates(2 fold.)

           Contains music.

           1. German literature--18th cent. 2. Gift-books
           (Annuals, etc.) I. Jacobi, Johann Georg, 1740-
           1814.

NT 0046126   IU

Lilly
PT 1169   TASCHENBUCH VON J. G. JACOBI UND SEINEN
.T19 J16   Freunden ... Mit Kupfern ... Königsberg und
           Leipzig, Nicolovius, 1795-96; Basel, Flick,
           1796.
               3v. fronts.,fold.music,plates. 16mo in
           halfsheets(11.5-12.5 cm)

           Köhring, Bibliographie der Almanache,
           p. 127, no. 949.
           Not published in 1797.
           Vols. 1-2 in decorated boards, vol. 3 in
           brown mottled   calf; vol. 3 in a library
           case.

NT 0046127   InU CU

830.8   Taschenbuch von J. G. Jacobi und seinen
T1815   Freunden für 1798. Mit Kupfern von Küfner.
1798   Basel, S. Flick [1797?]
           [20],166p. plates, music. 13cm.

           I. Jacobi, Johann Georg, 1740-1814.

NT 0046128   IU

4DQ-   Taschen-Buch zu Schweizer-Reisen, mit Hinwei-
68   sung auf alle Sehens- und Merkwürdigkeiten der
           Schweiz, eines Theiles von Savoyen und einiger
           anderer Orte angrenzender Länder und mit
           Angabe der Wirthshäuser, Entfernungen, Mün-
           zen, Postwagen, Schiffe, Führer u. 2., ganz
           umgearb. und stark verm. Aufl. Glarus,
           F. Schmid, 1833.
           394 p.

NT 0046129   DLC-P4

Taschenbuch zum geselligen Vergnügen.

Leipzig, G. J. Göschen.
    v. illus., music. 12 cm.
Pub. for the years 1791-1833, inclusive.
Title varies: Taschenbuch zum geselligen Vergnügen (engr. t.-p.,
    : Almanach und Taschenbuch zum geselligen Vergnügen)--18
W. G. Becker's Taschenbuch zum geselligen Vergnügen (half-title, 18   :
Taschenbuch zum geselligen Vergnügen)
Editors: W. G. Becker.--18   Friedrich Kind.
Vols. for   pub. by Roch und Weigel.

    I. Becker, Wilhelm Gottlieb, 1753-1813, ed. II. *Kind, Friedrich,
1768-1843, ed.
    AY17.T3   47-43050*

           Taschenbuch zum geselligen vergnügen. Auf das
           jahr 1817. Leipzig, C.H.F. Hartmann.
               v. illus. 13 cm.

NT 0046131   OCU

Lilly
PT 1169   TASCHENBUCH ZUM GESELLIGEN VERGNÜGEN AUF
.T1925   das Jahr ... Leipzig, Joh. Fr. Gleditsch,
           1819-1829.
               v. fronts.(part ports.),music(part
           fold.),plates(part fold.),ports. 8vo in
           half-sheets(11.4-12.4 cm)

               Until 1818, Gleditsch had published G.W.
           Becker's Taschenbuch zum geselligen Vergnü-
           gen; following a dispute, the editor of
           Becker's Taschenbuch changed publisher. Gle-
           ditsch continued to publish a Taschenbuch zum
           geselligen Vergnügen, and, in defiance of a
           court order, used the same Jahrgang numeration
           previously in use for Becker's Taschenbuch.
           Goedeke VIII, p. 46-49.
               Vols. 1-5 (1819-23) have additional pub-
           lisher: Carl Gerold in Wien; vols. 9-11 (1827-
           29) published in Leipzig by Leopold Voss.

               Vols. 1-7 edited by Amadeus Wendt; vols.
           8-11 edited by Ferdinand Philippi.
               Several vols. with Paul Hirsch's bookplate
               Gift from the Bernardo Mendel estate.
               Binding and size vary.

           1.Almanacs,German. I.Wendt,Amadeus,1783-
           1836,ed.   II.Philippi,Ferdinand,1795-1852,
           ed.

NT 0046134   InU PPG PU

           Taschenbuch zum geselligen Vergnügen auf das
               Jahr 1823. Leipzig, Gleditsch, 1823.
               (Heinsius)

NT 0046135   IU ICU InU PU CaBVaU MdBJ

GT
3020   Taschenbuch zum Nutzen und Vergnügen für Tabaksraucher
T19   und ihre Freunde. Regensburg, Montag und Weiss,
           1800.
           178 p. fold. front. 19 cm.

           Engraved frontispiece, signed: Mayr Sc., Ratisbon [i.e. Regens-
           burg]

           I. Smoking. 2. Tobacco.

NT 0046136   Vi InU CU MH NcD NN

           Taschenbuch zum nutzen und vergnügen fur
               wald und jagdfreunde

               See

           Sylvan. Jahrbuch fur forstmänner

Zm   Taschenbuch zum Nutzen und Vergnügen fürs Jahr
Z55   ·8·
           Göttingen,Bey Johann Christian Dieterich.
               plates. 10cm. annual.
           [1786 bound with Goettinger Taschen Calender,
           1786. [Göttingen,1785?] 10cm.]

           First published 1776.
           Ceased publication with 1893.

NT 0046138   CtY ICU OCU PU

AY860   Taschenbuch zum Nutzen und Vergnügen fürs Jahr
.O6   1787. Mit Kupfern von Chodowiecky, nebst den
1787   neuesten Frauenzimmer- und Manns-Kleidungen,
Rare   in Kupfer. Göttingen, J.C. Dieterich
Bk   [n.d.]
           272 p. illus. 10 cm. [With: Göttinger Ta-
           schen Calender vom Jahr 1787]

           1. Almanacs. 2. Calendars. I. Chodowiecki,
           Daniel Nikolaus, 1726-1801, illus.

NT 0046139   ICU

           Taschenbuch zum praktischen Gebrauch für
               Flugtechniker und luftschiffer
               see under Moedebeck, Hermann W.L.,
           1857-1910.

           Taschenbuch zunächt für katholische geistliche
               und solche, die es werden sollen; dann für
               jeden gebildeten, zur belehrung und erbauung
               im geiste und in der wahrheit. Augsburg, J.
               Wolff, 1822.

               vi, 360 p. 18 cm.

NT 0046141   PLatS

AY 858   Taschenbuch zur Beförderung der
.P3T2   Vaterlandsliebe. Auf das Jahr 1801.
(Rare)   Schnepfenthal, Buchhandlung der
           Erziehungsanstalt, 1801.
           [32] 310 p. plates.
           Compiled by Christian Gotthelf
           Salzmann. Cf. Deutsches
           Anonymen-Lexikon, v.4, p. 154, no.
           4732.

           1. Calendars. 2. Patriotism--Germany.
           I. Salzmann, Christian Gotthelf,
           1744-1811.

NT 0046142   ICU

           Taschenbuch zur beforderung des allgemeinen
               und hauslichen glucks

               See

           Almanach zur beförderung des allgemeinen und
               hauslichen glucks

           Taschenbuch zur belustigung für jedermann. Frankfurt
               und Leipzig [Wienbrack] 1781.
               208 p. incl. front. 17ᵐ.

           1. Anecdotes. 2. German wit and humor.

                                                            34-10506

           Library of Congress   PN6263.T3   837.6

NT 0046144   DLC

           Taschenbuch zur verbreitung geographischer kenntnisse.
               Eine übersicht des neuesten und wissenswürdigsten
               im gebiete der gesammten länder- und völkerkunde.
               Hrsg. von Johann Gottfried Sommer. 1.- jahrg.;
               1823-
               Prag, J. G. Calve, 1823-
               v. plates (part fold.) ports. fold. maps. 14½-16ᵐ.
           Vols. 1-5 include in subtitle: Zugleich als fortlaufende ergänzung zu
           Zimmermanns Taschenbuch der reisen.

           1. Geography—Year-books. 2. Discoveries (in geography) I. Som-
           mer, Johann Gottfried, 1782 or 3-1848, ed.

                                                            16-8660

           Library of Congress   G1.T3

           MiU MnHi
NT 0046145   DLC CSmH FTaSU WaU DNLM CtY MB ViU NN

HG
136   **Taschenbücher** für Geld, Bank und Börse. v. 1-
.T3   Frankfurt am Main, F. Knapp, 19 -

           1. Finance-Collections.

NT 0046146   DAU

Taschenbücherei Druck und Papier.

see *under*

Deutsche Arbeitsfront. <u>Fachamt Druck und
Papier.</u>

Taschenbüchlein des musikers
see under [Merseburger, Carl Wilhelm]
1816-1885.

Taschenbüchlein für auswanderer und reisende
nach den Vereinigten Staaten von Nord-Amerika
see under Bauer, F. A.

TASCHENBÜCHLEIN für Jugend auf das Jahr
1
Zürich: L. v. Leer junger[,   1   12cm.
v.   plates (part col'd).

1. Annuals, Literary, Juvenile.

NT 0046150   NN

Taschen-Encyklopädie der medicinischen Klinik ...
see under Frank, Martell, 1810-1886.

Taschen-Encyclopädie der practischen Chirurgie,
Geburtshülfe, Augen- und Ohrenheilkunde ...
see under Frank, Martell, 1810-1886.

Taschenfachbuch für Kraftfahrzeughandwerk und -Handel;
Handbuch für die tägliche Praxis.
Berlin, Krafthand Verlag W. Schulz.
v. 16 cm.
Vol. for   "herausgegeben von Hauptschriftleiter Walter E.
Schuls im Einvernehmen mit dem Reichsinnungsverband des Kraft-
fahrzeughandwerks und der Fachgruppe Kraftfahrzeuge, Kraftstoffe,
Garagen der Wirtschaftsgruppe Einzelhandel."

1. Automobiles—Handbooks, manuals, etc.   I. Schuls, Walter,
1894-
TL151.T3   49-30272*‡

NT 0046153   DLC

Taschenfuehrer durch Konstantinopel (Istanbul)...   Konstantinopel: A. Plathner, 1929.   44 p.   map, plan.   16°.

447074A. 1. Constantinople—   Guidebooks, 1929.
N. Y. P. L.   August 5, 1931

NT 0046154   NN

Taschenhandbuch der Forstwirtschaft
see under Müller, Rudolf, forester, ed.

Taschen-Jahrbuch der Deutschen Nationalsozialisten
auf das Jahr
see under   Nationalsozialistische Deutsche
Arbeiter-Partei.

Taschenjahrbuch der Therapie
see   Taschenbuch der therapie.

Taschenjahrbuch für den einzelhandelskaufmann. [1.-]
jahrg.; 1937–
Berlin, Verlag der Deutschen arbeitsfront [1936–
v. illus., diagrs. 15½ᵐ.
Issues for 1937– published by the Fachamt Der deutsche handel of
the Deutsche arbeitsfront called in 1937: Reichsbetriebsgemeinschaft
handel; in 1938–   : Reichsdienststelle Der deutsche handel) (19
in cooperation with the Wirtschaftsgruppe Einzelhandel of the Reichsgruppe Handel)
Title varies: 1937–   Taschenbuch für den einzelhandels-kaufmann.
19   Taschenjahrbuch für den einzelhandelskaufmann.
1. Retail trade—Year-books. 2. Retail trade—Germany. I. Deutsche arbeitsfront. Fachamt Der deutsche handel. II. Reichsgruppe Handel. Wirtschaftsgruppe Einzelhandel.
46–29911
Library of Congress   HF5349.G3T3
[2]   658.87058

NT 0046158   DLC MH-BA

Taschen-jahrbuch für den grossdeutschen buchhandel.
Berlin [etc.] O. Elsner [19
v. illus. (incl. diagrs.) 16ᵐ.
Publication began with issue for 1937.
Editor: 19   Ludwig Warmuth.

1. Book industries and trade—Germany. I. Warmuth, Ludwig, ed.

Z319.T35   47–36560

NT 0046159   DLC NN

TASCHEN-JAHRBUCH für den grossdeutschen Buch-
handel.
Berlin, O. Elsner.   v.   illus.   16cm.
Film reproduction. Negative.

Began publication 1937.
Editor: –1942, L. Warmuth.
Ceased publication.
1. Booksellers and book trade—Germany—Yearbooks. I. Warmuth,
Ludwig, ed. II. Warmuth,   Ludwig.

NT 0046160   NN

Taschenjahrbuch für den nichttechnischen Eisenbahndienst
see Elsners Taschenjahrbuch für den nichttechnischen Eisenbahndienst.

Taschen-jahrbuch für den strassenbau
see
Elsners taschen-jahrbuch für den strassenbau.

Taschenjahrbuch für die deutsche bekleidungsindustrie.
1.–   jahrg.; 1941–
Berlin [etc.] Otto Elsner verlagsgesellschaft, 1941–
v. illus., diagrs. 16ᵐ.
On cover, 1941–   : Elsners taschen-jahrbuch der bekleidungsindustrie (on spine, 1941–   : Bekleidungsindustrie)
Issues for 1941–   published by the "Wirtschaftsgruppe
Bekleidungsindustrie in zusammenarbeit mit dem Fachamt Bekleidung
und leder in der DAF."

1. Clothing trade—Year-books. 2. Clothing trade—Germany. I.
Reichsgruppe Industrie. Wirtschaftsgruppe Bekleidungsindustrie. II.
Deutsche arbeitsfront. Fachamt Bekleidung und leder.
46–29910
Library of Congress   HD9940.G3T3
[2]   338.47687

NT 0046163   DLC

Taschen-Jahrbuch für Fernmeldetechnik
see
Elsners Taschenbuch für den fernmelde- und signaltech-
nischen Eisenbahndienst.

Taschenjahrbuch ... für Österreichs jugend. 1.–   jahrg.;
1925/26–
Wien, Österreichischer bundesverlag für unterricht, wissenschaft und kunst, 1925–
v. illus., plates. 16ᵐ.
Vol. 1 has folded chart in pocket inside back cover.
Editor: 1925/26–   Ernst Kunzfeld.

1. Almanacs, German—Austria. I. Kunzfeld, Ernst, ed.

33–16250
Library of Congress   AY804.T3
[2]   529.43

NT 0046165   DLC

Taschenkalender, mit Daten aus der Musikgeschichte.
Schwerin, Musikverlag Schimanke.
v. 15 cm.

1. Music calendars.

ML21.T35   52–42312 ‡

NT 0046166   DLC

AY804   **Taschen-Kalender** auf das gemeine Jahr nach der
.T2   Geburt Jesu Christi 1822. Wien, Rollinger
1822   [1821?]
Rare Bk   1 v. (unpaged)

1. Almanacs, German—Austria.

NT 0046167   ICU

Taschen-kalender auf das jahr 1817, mit sechs fabeln von
Lafontaine, deutsch und französisch, und 12 dazu ge-
hörigen kupfern. [Berlin] Hrsg. von der Königl. preuss.
kalender-deputation [1817]
16 l., 36 p. 12 pl. 75 x 43ᵐᵐ.
Added t.-p. in French. The almanac is in German and French in parallel
columns; the Fables in French and German on opposite pages.
German translation of the Fables by J. W. L. Gleim.

I. La Fontaine, Jean, 1621–1695. II. Gleim, Johann Wilhelm Ludwig,
1719–1803.
CA 9–2841 Unrev'd

NT 0046168   DLC

Lilly   TASCHEN-KALENDER AUF DAS JAHR ... 1843.
AY 859   Wien, Franz J. Mechtler [1843]
.T197   [66?]p.   front.   9.1 cm.
1843
Added engr. t.p.: Taschen Kalender für
Damen.
T.p. and calendar pages in red and black.
Mirror mounted inside upper cover.
In blindstamped purple boards, all edges
silver.

NT 0046169   InU

AY804   Taschen-Kalender auf das Jahr nach der Geburt
.T2   Jesu Christi 1826. Wien, F. T. Hofer [1825?]
1826   1 v. (unpaged)
Rare Bk

1. Almanacs, German—Austria.

NT 0046170   ICU

Taschenkalender der Bautätigen. 1940–
Berlin, Berliner Buch- und Zeitschriften-Verlag E. O.
Erdmenger.
v. illus., diagrs. 16 cm.
Vols. for 1940– "herausgegeben im Auftrage des Generalbe-
vollmächtigten für die Regelung der Bauwirtschaft von Ingenieur
Franz Erdmenger."

1. Building—Yearbooks. 2. Building—Germany. i. Erdmenger,
Franz, ed.

TH3.T3   690.58   49–30273*

NT   0046171   DLC

Taschenkalender der K. P. D.
see under   Kommunistische Partei
Deutschlands.

HV8208
.G4T3   Taschenkalender der kasernierten volks-
polizei

Berlin, Verlag des Ministerium des innern.

v. illus.

1. Police—Germany (Russian zone). 2. A18
(Russian zone)—Police. 3. Germany (Democratic Republic, 1949–) Ministerium des
innern.

NT   0046173   DS

Taschen-kalender für advokaten.
Reichenberg, Gebrüder Stiepel ges. m. b. h. [19
v. 12°.

1. Law—Year-books. 2. Lawyers—Czechoslovak republic.

43–20065

NT   0046174   DLC

Film
S584   TASCHEN-KALENDER für Aerzte der
schweizerischen Eidgenossenschaft.
1.-12. Jahrg.; 1864-75. Bern.
12 v.
Film copy.
No more published?

NT   0046175   DNLM

Taschen-Kalender für Aerzte der schweizerischen Eidgenossenschaft. 2. Theil. 48, 36
pp. 16°. Bern, M. Flals, [1871?].

NT   0046176   DNLM

Taschenkalender für Aquarien - & Terrarienfreunde
1934. Bilder, 16.   Braunschweig, Wenzel.

NT   0046177   PPG

Taschenkalender für Bautechniker.
Berlin, Verlag Technik.
v. illus. 15 cm.

1. Building—Handbooks, manuals, etc.

TH151.T35   59–27734 ‡

NT   0046178   DLC

Taschenkalender für Buchführung und Beratung in der
Landwirtschaft.

Berlin.
v. 16 cm.
Vol. for   "herausgegeben vom Reichsverband für Landwirtschaftliche Buchführung und Betreuung e. V."

1. Agriculture—Yearbooks. 2. Agriculture—Germany. 3. Almanacs, German. i. Reichsverband für Landwirtschaftliche Buchführung und Betreuung.

S414.T3   49–127*‡

NT   0046179   DLC

Taschen-Kalender für Damen
see   Taschen-Kalender auf das Jahr ...
1843.

355.43
T182

Taschenkalender für das deutsche Reichsheer.
Jahrg.

Berlin, G. Bath,
v. 15cm. annual.

"Begründet von W. Freiherr von Fircks."
Editor: K. v. Oertzen.

NT   0046181   NNC DNW

Lilly
AY 859
.V66 T 197   TASCHEN-KALENDER FÜR DAS JAHR NACH DER
1890   Geburt Jesu Christi 1890.   Wien, Jg. Lien-
hart [1890.
64 p.   10.9 cm.

T.p. and calendar pages in red and
black.
In decorative pink boards, in a marbled
library case.

NT   0046182   InU

Lilly
AY 859
.T197   TASCHEN-KALENDER FÜR DAS SCHALTJAHR 1844.
1844   Wien, Franz Riedl's sel. Witwe und Sohn [1844.
[32]p.   front.,plates(part.col.)
10.2 cm.

T.p. and calendar pages in red and black.
In decorative grey boards, all edges gilt;
spine broken.

NT   0046183   InU

Taschenkalender für den Bergbau auf Braunkohle, Erz,
Salz, Erdöl.
Düsseldorf, K. Marklein.
v. illus. 15 cm. annual.
Began publication with vol. for 1958 under title: Taschenbuch
für den Braunkohlenbergbau.

1. Mining engineering—Handbooks, manuals, etc.

TN151.T203   67–33436

NT   0046184   DLC

99.8
T18   Taschenkalender für den Forstwirt.

Wien

NT   0046185   DNAL

Taschen-kalender für den Reichsarbeitsdienst. jahrg. [1.,–
1934–
Berlin, Hollerbaum & Schmidt [1933?–
v. illus., plates. 15°".
Various editions.
Title varies slightly.
Editor: 1934–   Paul Beintker.

1. Service, Compulsory non-military—Germany. i. Beintker, Paul,
1889–   ed. ii. Reichsarbeitsdienst.

44–881

Library of Congress   HD4875.G4T3
[2]   331.9

NT   0046186   DLC

Taschen-Kalender für die Aerzte des Deutschen Reiches. Hrsg. von Lorenz. v. 1–5,
1888–92. 12°. Berlin.
After 1889, title: **Taschen-Kalender** für die Aerzte.

NT   0046187   DNLM

GV204   Taschenkalender für die Deutsche turnerschaft für
.G3T2   ...1894–
Braunschweig, G.Westermann, 1894–
v.   front.(v.3)illus.,port.,maps. 15½°".

Editor:1894–   H.Brendicke.

1.Deutsche turnerschaft.

NT   0046188   ICU

99.83
T183   Taschenkalender für die Forstwirtschaft.

Berlin

1. Germany. Forestry. 2. Calendars.
I. Sabetzki, Eckhard,   ed.

NT   0046189   DNAL

18
T18   Taschenkalender für die Landbuch-
Gemeinschaft.

Hannover.

1. Almanacs. 2. Germany. Agriculture.
I. Landbuch-Gemeinschaft.

NT   0046190   DNAL

Taschenkalender für die Rheinschiffahrt.

Mainz, J. Diemer.
7. 17 cm.

1. Shipping—Rhine River.

HE669.5.R5T3   57–50842 ‡

NT   0046191   DLC

W 1
TA752   TASCHENKALENDER für Fleischbeschauer
und Trichinenschauer 1.-11. Jahrg.;
1901-11.   Berlin.
11 v. illus.
Title varies: 1901-03? Taschenkalender für Fleischbeschauer.
Ed. by A. Johne.
No connection with later publication
of same title, issued 1928–
Supplements accompany some issues.

NT   0046192   DNLM

W 1
TA753
TASCHENKALENDER für Fleischbeschauer und Trichinenschauer.
1. -　　　Jahrg. ; 1928-
Hannover.
v.
Publication suspended 1945-49.
Editor: 1928-　　Paul Heine.
No connection with earlier publication of same title, issued 1901-11.
1. Meat inspection - Germany
2. Trichina I. Heine, Paul

1. Meat inspection - Germany
2. Trichina I. Johne, Heinrich Albert

NT　0046194　DNLM DNAL

280.28
T18
Taschenkalender für Genossenschaftsbauern.

(Berlin)

1. Agriculture, Cooperative. Germany.
2. Germany. Agriculture. 3. Calendars.

NT　0046195　DNAL

Taschenkalender für Grubenbeamte. 1951.
Düsseldorf, K. Marklein-Verlag.

NT　0046196　IU

90.3
T18
Taschenkalender für Kleingärtner und
Kleintierzüchter.
Berlin, Deutscher Bauernverlag

1. Gardening. 2. Domestic animals.

NT　0046197　DNAL

Taschenkalender für Lehrer und Erzieher.

Berlin, Volk und Wissen.
v. illus. 15 cm. annual.
"Herausgegeben von der Gewerkschaft Unterricht und Erziehung."
Includes directives to teachers in Eastern Germany.

1. Education—Germany—1945-　　I. Gewerkschaft Unterricht
und Erziehung.
L101.G3G4　　　54-24596 ‡

NT　0046198　DLC

Taschenkalender für Musikvereine...
Jahrg.
Luzern: Keller & Co. A.-G., 19　　　16°.
v. plates.
1926　　title in German and French; French title reads: Agenda pour
sociétés de musique...

1. Music—Almanacs, yearbooks, etc.　2. Music—Assoc., etc.—Switzerland.
N. Y. P. L.　　　　June 29, 1926

NT　0046199　NN

Lilly
AY 859
.T19 C 84
TASCHENKALENDER ... FÜR NATUR- UND GARTEN-
freunde ... Tübingen, Cottaische Buchhand-
lung, 1795-1806.
11v. fronts.(part fold.),plates(part
col.,part fold.) 11 cm.
Köhring p. 157 f.
Title alternates between "Taschenkalender"
and "Taschenbuch".
Library has vols. for 1795, 1797-1806.
Imperfect vols. for 1797 and 1806.
In decorated boards.

NT　0046200　InU

Taschenkalender ... für natur und gartenfreunde...
see also Taschenbuch auf das jahr ...
für natur- und gartenfreunde.

Taschen-Kalender für Pflanzen-Sammler. Ausgabe A mit 500
Pflanzen. Leipzig, O. Leiner, [1878].
iv, 124 p. 15½ᶜᵐ.

NT　0046202　ICJ

Taschen-Kalender für Pflanzen-Sammler. Ausgabe B mit 800
Pflanzen. Leipzig, O. Leiner, [1880].
iv, [24], 180 p. 14½ᶜᵐ.
20 p. blank for notes.
Advertisements, p. 167-180.

NT　0046203　ICJ

Taschen-Kalender für Pflanzen-Sammler. Ausgabe A, mit 500
Pflanzen. Leipzig, O. Leiner, [1880].
iv, 124 p. 17ᶜᵐ.
Advertisements, p. 113-124.

NT　0046204　ICJ

Taschenkalender für rechtsanwälte, notare und patentanwälte ...
Berlin (etc.) Deutscher rechtsverlag g. m. b. h. (19
v. 15ᶜᵐ. annual.
Title varies: -1939, Taschenkalender für rechtsanwälte und
notare.
1940- Taschenkalendar für rechtsanwälte, notare und patentanwälte.
19 "Herausgegeben vom reichsgruppenwalter Rechtsanwälte des NS-Rechtswahrerbundes."
"Der 'Taschenkalender ...' ist aus dem vor etwa 60 jahren zum erstenn-
mal erschienenen 'Jahrbuch für deutsche rechtsanwälte und notare' ent-
standen." Vorwort, 1941.
1. Lawyers—Germany—Year-books. I. Nationalsozialistischer
rechtswahrerbund. Reichs-　　gruppe Rechtsanwälte.
43-48279

NT　0046205　DLC

Taschenkalender für rechtsanwälte und notare
see
Taschenkalender für rechtsanwälte, notare und patentanwälte.

Taschenkalender für schweizerische Wehrmänner.

Frauenfeld, Huber.
v. 15 cm. annual.
Superseded in 1954 by Taschenbuch für schweizerische Wehrmänner. Cf. Schweizer Buch, 1954.

1. Switzerland. Armee—Yearbooks.
U10.T32　　　55-35961 ‡

NT　0046207　DLC DN

Taschenkalender für schweizerische Wehrmänner
see also Taschenbuch für schweizerische
Wehrmänner.

41.8
T18
Taschen-Kalender für Tierzüchter.

Hannover,

1. Veterinary medicine, Germany.

NT　0046209　DNAL

Taschenkalender für Verwaltungsbeamte
see
Die Bundesrepublik.

W1
TA754
Taschenkalender für Zahnärzte und Spezialärzte für Zahn-
u. Mundkrankheiten. Jahrg. 1; 1902. Burg.
1 v.
No more published?

NT　0046211　DNLM

529.5
T181
1797
Taschenkalender zur belehrenden unterhaltung
für die jugend und ihre freunde/ Auf das jahr
1797. Bayreuth, J. A. Lübecks erben [1796]
320p. col.front., col.illus., col.plates.

Introduction signed: Ellrodt.

1. Almanacs, German. I. Ellrodt, Theodor
Christian, 1767-1804 ed

NT　0046212　IU

381
W5
n1797
Taschenkalender zur belehrenden Unterhaltung
für die Jugend und ihre Freunde auf das Jahr
1798. Von Theodor Christian Ellrodt ...
Bayreuth, J.A.Lübecks Erben[1797]
17p.ℓ.,[3]-288p. front.,illus.,col.plates.
10½cm.
"Benjamin Franklins Pfeife": p.195-201.

NT　0046213　CtY

Taschen-Kommersbuch; eine Sammlung der schönsten
Studenten-, Volks- und Vaterlandslieder. 15.Aufl. Lahr,
Schauenburg [1899]

NT　0046214　MH

Taschen-konversations-lexikon ...
see under [Kürschner, Joseph] 1853-1902.

Taschenlexikon politischer Begriffe
see under Mojonnier, Arthur, 1901- ed.

... Taschen-liederbuch für das deutsche volk. Eine ausgewählte sammlung der beliebtesten und bekanntesten
volks-, studenten-, soldaten-, jäger-, wander-, liebes-,
trink-, und gesellschafts-lieder. 1. amerikanische, um
100 lieder und 48 seiten verm. ausg. New York, J.
Wieck (186-)
xviii, 494 p. 13ᶜᵐ.
At head of title: Freut euch des lebens.
Without music.

1. German poetry (Collections) 2. German ballads and songs.
19-8531
Library of Congress　　PT1173.T3

NT　0046217　DLC NN

Taschen-liederbuch für das deutsche volk;
eine ausgewählte sammlung der beliebtesten und
bekanntesten volks-, studenten-, jäger-, solda-
ten-, liebes-, trink-, wander-, opern- und
gesellschaftslieder. 25. verm. aufl. Plauen,
A. Schröter [186-]
xii,400p.

Advertising, p.393-400.

NT　0046218　OC1

RA831.04
T197   Taschen-Liederbuch für das deutsche Volk.
Eine ausgewählte Sammlung der belieb-
testen und bekanntesten Volks-, Studenten-,
Jäger-, Soldaten-, Liebes-, Trink-,
Wander-, Opern- und Gesellschaftslieder.
Amerik. Stereotyp Ausg. nach d. 19
deutschen Aufl. Cincinnati, A. E.
Wilde [1885?]
482p.14cm.

1. Songs, German.   I. Wilde, A. E.
publisher, Cincinnati   (RA cat. only)
    [ah]

NT   0046219   OC

Taschenliederbuch für Trompete, Cornet à Piston oder Posthorn.
Eine Sammlung von über 100 Gebirgs und Volksliedern, Opern-
narien, Ländlern, Märschen etc., leicht spielbar arrangirt von F.
v. P... München: J. Seiling [pref. 1892]. Publ. pl. no. 108.
2 p.l., 63 p.   ob. 24°.

1. Trumpet. 2. Cornet. 3. Folk-   songs (German). 4. P., F. von.
N Y P L.   November 1, 1920.

NT   0046220   NN

S599
.G3H4   Taschenmacher, Willibald, 1902–
Herzog, Heinrich, *of the Reichsfinanzministerium.*
Bodenbewertung; die Bewertung der mineralischen Acker-
böden Deutschlands, von Heinrich Herzog. Die morphologi-
schen Merkmale in der Praxis der Bodenbewertung, von W.
Taschenmacher. Berlin, P. Parey, 1932.

DD
491   Taschenmacher, Willibald, 1902–
W41   Die Böden des Südergebirges. Münster/
S75   Westfalen, Im Selbstverlag der Geographischen
no.6   Kommission [für Westfalen] 1955.
135 p. fold. map. 21cm. (Spieker;
landeskundliche Beiträge und Berichte, 6)

1. Soils--Germany--Südergebirge. 2. Soils--
Westphalia. I.   Title.

NT   0046222   NIC CU MH NN

Taschenmacher, Willibald, 1902–
Entwicklung der bodenkartierung landwirtschaftlicher be-
triebe und die möglichkeiten ihrer praktischen leistung. Mit
dem beispiel der bodenaufnahme des rittergutes Krzyzanki.
Von dr. W. Taschenmacher ... Danzig, Zu beziehen bei Max
Weg in Leipzig, 1930.
78 p. fold. tab., diagrs. 23ᶜᵐ.
"Literatur": p. 76.

1. Farms. [1. Farm management] 2. [Soil maps] 3. [Rittergut Krzy-
zanki]
Agr 31–865
Library, U. S. Dept. of   Agriculture 56T18

NT   0046223   DNAL

Taschenmacher, Willibald, 1902–
Der faktor bodentypus und seine bedeutung für die land-
wirtschaftliche praxis.
Landw. Jahrb. bd. 67, p. 763–778.   Berlin, 1928.

1. Soils. [1. Soil types]
[*Full name:* Willibald Adolph Sebastian Taschenmacher]
Agr 29–1289
Library, U. S. Dept. of   Agriculture 18L23 bd. 67
5   [2]

NT   0046224   DNAL

Taschenmacher, Willibald, 1902–
... Grundriss einer deutschen feldbodenkunde; entstehung,
merkmale und eigenschaften der böden Deutschlands, ihre
untersuchung, kartierung und abschätzung im felde und ihre
eignung für den anbau landwirtschaftlicher kulturpflanzen,
von dr. Willi Taschenmacher ... Mit 5 abbildungen. Stuttgart, Verlagsbuchhandlung Eugen Ulmer [1937]
178 p. incl. illus. (map) tables, diagr. 21ᶜᵐ. (Schriften über neuzeit-
lichen landbau; hrsg. von E. Klapp, hft. 8)

1. Soils--Germany.
G S 39–86
U. S. Geol. survey. Library   941 (530) T18g
for Library of Congress   [S599.G   ]

NT   0046225   DI-GS MH

Taschen-Notiz-Kalender und Merkbuch für Einigungssteno-
graphen.
Jahrg.

Berlin, 19   16°.
no.
Editor : 19   , F. Schrey.

1. Shorthand--Almanacs.
N. Y. P. L.   August 11, 1928

NT   0046226   NN

Taschen-Pharmakopöe
see under   Pharmacopoea Germanica. 3d ed.

Taschen-rezeptierbuch der dynamischen Oligoplexe
und Präparate
see under   Madaus (Dr.) und Companie.

TASCHEN-RHEIN-PANORAMA von Mainz bis Cöln,
Mainz, n. d.

NT   0046229   MH

Taschen-Rhein-panorama von Mainz bis Cöln.
Mainz. Halenza. [184–?] Size, 58 x 7¾ inches. Scale, none
The title is repeated in French and English

NT   0046230   MB MH

GV1542
.H6   Der taschenspieler; oder, Neue sammlung von
vol.21,   karten-, rechen-, magischen, mechanischen
no. 5   und andern kunststücken. Berlin, Trowitzsch
Houdini Coll.   und sohn [n. d.]
36 p. 16,5 cm.
Houdini pamphlets: magic and tricks, v. 21,
no. 5.
Illustrated t.-p.

NT   0046231   DLC

...Eine Taschenspieler-Vorstellung in Krähwinkel. Ritter
Toggenburg, oder: Liebe, Hass, Rache, Reue, Romantik, Selbst-
mord und moralisches Bewusstsein...   Wien: Wallishausser,
1883. 14 p. 22½cm. (Wiener Theater-Repertoir. Lief. 375.)
Cover-title.

1. Drama, German. I. Ritter   Toggenburg.
N. Y. P. L.   October 6, 1938

NT   0046232   NN

Taschen-Welt-Atlas der Luftwaffe. 1942
see under   Germany. Luftwaffe. Führungs-
stab.

Taschen-Weltatlas der Luftwaffe. 1944
see under   Germany. Luftwaffe. Wehr-
betreuung.

Taschen-wörterbuch des flugmotorenbaues und
der verwandten gebiete
see under   [Michaelis, Ernst]

Taschenwörterbuch der dänischen und deutschen
Sprache
see under   Mohr, F.A.
and see also   Langenscheidts Taschenwörterbuch der dänischen und deutschen Sprache.

Taschenwörterbuch der deutschen sprache
see under   [Harnisch, Johann Christian]
1761-1814.

Taschenwörterbuch der französischen und deutschen Sprache; mit Angabe der Aussprache nach dem phonetischen
System der methode Toussaint-Langenscheidt, Zusammengestellt von Jacob Schellens. Berlin-Schöneberg, Langenscheidt [1911]
2 v. 16 cm. (Methode Toussaint-Langenscheidt)
Fonalexica Langenscheidt ...   Langenscheidts Taschenwörterbücher ...
Added t. p. in French.
CONTENTS.--1. T. Französisch-Deutsch.--2. T. Deutsch-Französisch.
1. French language--Dictionaries--German. 2. German language--
Dictionaries--French. I. Schellens, Jacob.
PC2645.G3T3 1911   11–22389 rev*

NT   0046238   DLC ICF PP PV OCl MiU MiD

Taschenwörterbuch der französischen und
deutschen Sprache, mit Angabe der Aussprache
nach dem phonetischen System der Methode
Toussaint-Langenscheidt. 3. revidierte Aufl.
Berlin-Schöneberg, Langenscheidtsche Verlagsbuchhandlung [c1911]
2 v. 16 cm.
Added t. p. in French.
On cover: Langenscheidts Taschenwörterbuch.

NT   0046239   PLatS

Taschenwörterbuch der französischen und deutschen
Sprache; mit Angabe der Aussprache nach dem
phonetischen System der methode Toussaint-
Langenscheidt. Zusammengestellt von Jacob
Schellens. 8.rev.Aufl. Berlin-Schöneberg,
Langenscheidt [1911]
2v. in 1. 16cm. (Methode Toussaint-
Langenscheidt)
Fonalexica Langenscheidt ... Langenscheidts
Taschenwörterbücher ...
Added t.p. in   French.
CONTENTS.-   1.T.Französisch-Deutsch.-
2.T.Deutsch-   Französisch.

NT   0046240   CLSU

PC 2645
.G3 T2   TASCHENWÖRTERBUCH DER FRANZÖSISCHEN UND DEUT-
schen Sprache. Mit Angabe der Aussprache nach
dem phonetischen System der Methode Toussaint-
Langenscheidt. Zusammengestellt von Jacob
Schellens. 12. revidierte Aufl. Berlin-
Schöneberg, Langenscheidt [1911]
2 v.

Added t.-p. in French.
Contents: v.1. Französisch-Deutsch. v.2.
Deutsch-Französisch.

NT   0046241   InU

PC 2645
G3 S42
1911   [Taschenwörterbuch der französischen
und deutschen Sprache : mit Angabe der
Aussprache nach dem phonetischen System
der Methode Toussaint-Langenscheidt.
Berlin-Schöneberg : Langenscheidt,
1911.
2 v. in 1 ; 16 cm. (Fonolexika
Langenscheidt)
Langenscheidts Taschenwörterbücher
CONTENTS.--1. t. Französisch-
Deutsche. 12, rev. Aufl.--2. t.
Deutsch-Französisch. 11. rev. Aufl.
1. French language--Dictionaries--
German 2. German language--
Dictionaries--French I. Title

NT   0046242   OU IU

Taschenwörterbuch der französischen und
deutschen Sprache
see also under   Villatte, Césaire,
1816–1895.
and see also   Langenscheidts Taschenwörterbuch der französischen und deutschen
Sprache.

PA445   Taschenwörterbuch der griechischen und deutschen
G5L35   Sprache.   Berlin- Schöneberg, Langenscheidt
[pref. 1903]
v.   (Langenscheidts Taschenwörterbücher)

At head of title: Methode Toussaint- Langenscheidt.

Contents. - 1. Griechisch- Deutsch, von H. Menge.

1. Greek language - Dictionaries - German.   I. Menge,
Hermann, 1841-1939.

NT   0046244   CU IU MH

483
lG98t   ... Taschenwörterbuch der griechischen
und deutschen sprache. Teil II Deutsch-
griechisch ...   Berlin-Schöneberg [1905]
546p.   (Half-title: Langenscheidts
taschenwörterbücher)

At head of title: Methode Toussaint-
Langenscheidt.
Title in red and black.
Series title on cover.

NT   0046245   IU

Taschenwörterbuch der griechischen und deutschen Sprache.
Berlin-Schöneberg, Langenscheidt [*1910–11]
2 v. 16 cm. (Methode Toussaint-Langenscheidt)
Fonolexika Langenscheidt; Langenscheidts Taschenwörterbücher.
Contents.—1. T. Griechisch-Deutsch, von H. Menge. 2. erweiterte
Bearbeitung.—2. T. Deutsch-Griechisch, von O. Güthling.

1. Greek language—Dictionaries—German. 2. German language—
Dictionaries—Greek.   I. Menge, Hermann, 1841–1939.   II. Güthling,
Otto, 1853–1931.
PA445.G3L32   61–56894

NT   0046246   DLC NN OC1

... Taschenwörterbuch der griechischen und deutschen
sprache ... zusammengestellt von professor dr. Hermann
Menge ... Berlin-Schöneberg, Langenscheidt [*1910–*13]
3 v. 16ᵐ. (Methode Toussaint-Langenscheidt)
Teil 1: 26. bis 35. tausend. Half-title: Fonolexika Langenscheidt.
Contents.—t. 1. Griechisch-deutsch, zusammengestellt von H.
Menge.—2. Deutsch-griechisch, zusammengestellt von O. Güthling.
1. Greek language—Dictionaries—German. 2. German language—Dictionaries—Greek.   I. Güthling, Otto, 1853– II. Title.   III.
Ser.   IV. Ser.   [Full name: August Hermann Menge]

NT   0046247   ViU

Taschenwörterbuch der griechischen und deutschen
Sprache
see also   Langenscheidts Taschenwörterbuch der griechischen und deutschen Sprache.

Taschenwörterbuch der italienischen und deutschen Sprache,
mit Angabe der Aussprache nach dem phonetischen System
der Methode Toussaint-Langenscheidt. Zusammengestellt
von Gustavo Sacerdote. Berlin-Schöneberg, Langenscheidt
[1905]
v. 16 cm. (Methode Toussaint-Langenscheidt)
Langenscheidts Taschenwörterbucher ...
Added t. p. in Italian.
Contents.—1. T. Italienisch-Deutsch.
1. Italian language—Dictionaries—German. 2. German language—
Dictionaries—Italian.   I. Sacerdote, Gustavo, 1867–1948.
PC1645.G3T23   52–55588

NT   0046249   DLC

Taschenwörterbuch der italienischen und deutschen Sprache,
mit Angabe der Aussprache nach dem phonetischen System der Methode Toussaint-Langenscheidt. Zusammengestellt von Gustavo Sacerdote. Revidierte Ausg. Berlin-
Schöneberg, Langenscheidt [1910]
2 v. 16 cm. (Methode Toussaint-Langenscheidt)
Langenscheidts Taschenwörterbucher ...
Added t. p. in Italian.
"Das deutsche Zeitwort, Schema der Konjugation und Wörterbuch
der Zeitwörter, verfasst von Prof. Dr. Dan. Sanders, revidiert und
bearbeitet von Dr. Julius Dumcke," with special t. p.: v. 2, 40 p. at
end.
Contents.—T. 1. Italienisch-Deutsch.—T. 2. Deutsch-Italienisch.
1. Italian language—Dictionaries—German. 2. German language—
Dictionaries—Italian.   I. Sacerdote, Gustavo, 1867–1948.
PC1645.G3T24   453.3   11–1751 rev 2*

     WaSpG
NT   0046250   DLC CU-I MH CU ViU CSt CaBVaU OWorP

Tachenwörterbuch der italienischen und deutschen
Sprache
see also   Langenscheidts Taschenwörterbuch der italienischen und deutschen Sprache.

Taschenwörterbuch der katalanischen und
deutschen Sprache
see under   Vogel, Eberhard, 1861-

Taschenwörterbuch der lateinischen und deutschen Sprache,
zusammengestellt von Hermann Menge. Berlin-Schöneberg,
Langenscheidt [*1910]
2 v. 16 cm. (Methode Toussaint-Langenscheidt)
Langenscheidts Taschenwörterbücher.
Contents.—T. 1. Lateinisch-Deutsch.—T. 2. Deutsch-Latein.

1. Latin language—Dictionaries—German. 2. German language—
Dictionaries—Latin.   I. Menge, Hermann, 1841–1939.   Series.
PA2365.G5L27 1910   11–1748 rev*

NT   0046253   DLC CU OC1 WaU PBm NmU

Taschenwörterbuch der lateinischen und deutschen
Sprache. 2.erweiterte Bearbeitung. Berlin, Langenscheidt
[1910]
(Methode Toussaint-Langenscheidt)
Contents: -1. Lateinisch-deutsch

NT   0046254   MH

Taschenwörterbuch der lateinischen und deutschen Sprache,
zusammengestellt von Hermann Menge. Berlin-Schöneberg,
Langenscheidt [1915]
2 v. 16 cm. (Methode Toussaint-Langenscheidt)
Langenscheidts taschenwörterbücher.
Half title: Fonolexika Langenscheidt.
Vol. 1: 2., erweiterte Bearbeitung.
Contents.—1. t. Lateinisch-Deutsch.—2. t. Deutsch-Lateinisch.
1. Latin language—Dictionaries—German. 2. German language—
Dictionaries—Latin.   I. Menge, Hermann, 1841–1939.
PA2365.G5L27 1915   473.3   36–6020 rev*

NT   0046255   DLC ViU NcU

Taschenwörterbuch der lateinischen und
deutschen Sprache
see also   Langenscheidts Taschenwörterbuch der lateinischen und deutschen Sprache.

Taschenwörterbuch der medizinischen
Fachausdrücke

see under

Gillert, Karl Ernst, ed.

Taschenwörterbuch der neugriechischen Umgangs-
und Schriftsprache
see under   Mitsotakis, Johannis K
1840?–1905.
and see also Langenscheidts Taschenwörterbuch der neugriechischen und deutschen Sprache.

Taschenwörterbuch der niederländischen und
deutschen Sprache
see under   Leviticus, Felix, 1862-
and see also   Langenscheidts Taschenwörterbuch der niederländischen und deutschen
Sprache.

Taschenwörterbuch der polnischen und deutschen Sprache;
mit Angabe der Aussprache nach dem phonetischen System
der Methode Toussaint-Sangenscheidt, bearb. von Albert
Zipper und Emil Urich. 1. Aufl. Berlin-Schöneberg, Lan-
genscheidt [1919–21; v. 1, 1921, *1920]
2 v. 16 cm. (Methode Toussaint-Langenscheidt)
Langenscheidts Taschenwörterbücher.
Added t. p. in Polish.
Contents.—Bd. 1. Polnisch-Deutsch.—Bd. 2. Deutsch-Polnisch.
1. German language—Dictionaries—Polish. 2. Polish language—
Dictionaries—German.   I. Zipper, Albert, 1855-   II. Urich,
Emil, ed.
PG6645.G5T3   23–688 rev*

NT   0046260   DLC NNC CaBVaU OU NjP ViU

Taschenwörterbuch der Polnischen und Deutschen
Sprache. Mit Angabe der Aussprache nach dem
phonetischen System der Methode Toussaint-
Langenscheidt. 2. Aufl. Berlin, Langenscheidtsche Verlagsbuchhandlung [1921]
v.
Title also in Polish.
Contents: t. 1. Polnisch-Deutsch.
1. Polish language - - Dictionaries - - German.
2. German language - - Dictionaries --Polish.

NT   0046261   InU

Taschenwörterbuch der polnischen und deutschen
Sprache
see also   Langenscheidts Taschenwörterbuch der polnischen und deutschen Sprache.

Taschenwörterbuch der portugiesischen und
deutschen Sprache
see under   Ey, Louise, 1854–1936.
and see also Langenscheidts Taschenwörterbuch der portugiesischen und deutschen Sprache.

Taschenwörterbuch der romanischen und deutscher
sprache mit angabe der aussprache nach dem
phonetischen system der methode Toussaint-
Langenscheidt ...   Berlin, Langenscheidt,
c1911.
508 p.

NT   0046264   PSC

Taschenwörterbuch der russischen, deutschen,
englischen und französischen sprache ...
Deutscher theil ...
see under   Fuchs, Paul.

491.73 **Taschenwörterbuch der russischen und deutschen Sprache,**
T181   mit Angabe der Aussprache nach dem phonetischen System
der Methode Toussaint-Langenscheidt, von Karl Blattner.
Berlin-Schöneberg, Langenscheidt [*1910-11]

    2 v. 16 cm. (Methode Toussaint-Langenscheidt)

    Langenscheidts Taschenwörterbücher.
    Added t-p. in Russian.

    [1. German language — Dictionaries — Russian. [2. Russian lan-
guage—Dictionaries—German. [I. Blattner, Karl, 1862-   ed.

    PG2643.G5L27 1910   10-12975 rev*

NT   0046266   DLC CaBVaU OrU MB DAS NcU NBuG IU

    Taschenwörterbuch der russischen und deutschen **Sprache,**
mit Angabe der Aussprache nach dem phonetischen System
der Methode Toussaint-Langenscheidt, von Karl Blattner.
Berlin-Schöneberg, Langenscheidt [*1911]

    2 v. 16 cm. (Methode Toussaint-Langenscheidt)

    Langenscheidts Taschenwörterbücher.
    Added t-p. in Russian.

NT   0046267   ViU OU

    Taschenwörterbuch der russischen und deutschen
    Sprache
        see also   Langenscheidts Taschenwörter-
buch der russischen und deutschen Sprache.

    Taschenwörterbuch der schwedischen und deutschen **Sprache,**
mit Angabe der Aussprache nach dem phonetischen System
der Methode Toussaint-Langenscheidt, von Ernst Wrede.
Berlin-Schöneberg, Langenscheidt [*1909-12]

    2 v. 16 cm. (Methode Toussaint-Langenscheidt)

    Langenscheidts Taschenwörterbücher für Reise, Lektüre, Konver-
sation und den Schulgebrauch.
    Added t. p. in Swedish.

    CONTENTS.—T. 1. Schwedisch-Deutsch.—T. 2. Deutsch-Schwedisch.
3. Aufl.

    1. Swedish language — Dictionaries — German. 2. German lan-
guage—Dictionaries—Swedish. I. Wrede, Ernst.

    PD5645.G3T3   10-7665 rev 2*

NT   0046269   DLC CCl CtY NcU

    Taschenwörterbuch der schwedischen und deutschen **Sprache,**
mit Angabe der Aussprache nach dem phonetischen **System**
der Methode Toussaint-Langenscheidt, von Ernst Wrede.
Berlin-Schöneberg, Langenscheidt [1916?-20? *1909-12]

    2 v. 16 cm. (Methode Toussaint-Langenscheidt)

    Langenscheidts Taschenwörterbücher für Reise, Lektüre, Konversa-
tion und den Schulgebrauch.
    Added t. p. in Swedish.

    CONTENTS.—T. 1. Schwedisch-Deutsch. 3. Aufl.—T. 2. Deutsch-
Schwedisch. 6.-10. Aufl.

    1. Swedish language — Dictionaries — German. 2. German lan-
guage—Dictionaries—Swedish. I. Wrede, Ernst.

    PD5645.G3T32   35-28602 rev*

NT   0046270   DLC CU

    Taschenwörterbuch der schwedischen und deutschen **Sprache,**
mit Angabe der Aussprache nach dem phonetischen **System**
der Methode Toussaint-Langenscheidt, von Ernst **Wrede.**
Berlin-Schöneberg, Langenscheidt [1916?-20? *1911-12]

    2 v. 16 cm. (Methode Toussaint-Langenscheidt)

    Langenscheidts Taschenwörterbücher für Reise, Lektüre, Konversa-
tion und den Schulgebrauch.
    Added t. p. in Swedish.

    CONTENTS.—T. 1. Schwedisch-Deutsch. 7. Aufl.—T. 2. Deutsch-
Schwedisch. 26.-30. Tausend.

NT   0046271   ViU

[PD5645   Taschenwörterbuch der schwedischen u. deutschen Sprache.
G3T3   6. Aufl.   Leipzig, O. Holtze, 1923.
1923   2 v. (Holtze's Wörterbücher)
    14cm.
    Vol. 1 has added t. p. in Swedish: Svensk och tysk handordbok.

    Contents. - 1. delen. Svensk-tysk. - 2. T. Deutsch-Schwedisch.

    1. Swedish language - Dictionaries - German. 2. German
language - Dictionaries - Swedish. I. Title: Svensk och tysk
handordbok.

NT   0046272   CU

    Taschenwörterbuch der schwedischen und deut-
    schen Sprache
        see also   Langenscheidts Taschenwörter-
buch der schwedischen und deutschen Sprache.

PC4645   Taschenwörterbuch der spanischen und deutschen Sprache. Mit
G3L3   Angabe der Aussprache nach dem phonetischen System der
1927   Methode Toussaint- Langenscheidt.   Neubearbeitung von Eberhard
Vogel.   Berlin- Schöneberg, Langenscheidtsche Verlagsbuch-
handlung [c1927]
    2 v.   (Langenscheidts Taschenwörterbücher für Reise, Lektüre,
Konversation und den Schulgebrauch)

    At head of title, v. 1: Methode Toussaint- Langenscheidt.
    Added t. p. in Spanish.
    Vol. 2 has title: Langenscheidts Taschenwörterbuch ...
    Subtitle varies slightly.
    Contents. - 1. T. Spanisch- Deutsch. 15. Aufl. - 2. T. Deutsch-
Spanisch. 16. Aufl.

NT   0046274   CU

    Taschenwörterbuch der spanischen und deutschen
    Sprache
        see also under   Paz y Melia, Antonio,
1842-1927.
        and see also   Langenscheidts Taschenwörter-
buch der spanischen und deutschen Sprache.

    Taschenwörterbuch; Deutsch-Aserbeidschanisch, Aser-
beidschanisch-Deutsch. Berlin, O. Stollberg [1943?]
    220 p. 15 cm.

    1. German language – Dictionaries – Azerbaijani. 2. Azerbaijani
language—Dictionaries—German.

    PL313.T3   53-54553

NT   0046276   DLC PU ICU IU

PL 313   TASCHENWÖRTERBUCH: DEUTSCH-ASERBEIDSCHANISCH;
.T197   Aserbeidschanisch-Deutsch. Cib lygeti. [Edi-
ted by Kaukasische Mittelstelle, Aserbeidscha-
nische Abtlg.] Berlin, Verl. Otto Stollberg
[1941]
    220 p.

    1. German language--Dictionaries--Azerbaijani.
2. Azerbaijani language--Dictionaries--German.
I. Title: Cib lygeti.

NT   0046277   InU

    Taschenwörterbuch: deutsch-englisch, englisch-deutsch.
Stuttgart, Deutsche Verlags-Anstalt, 1945.
    viii, 359 p. 17 cm.

    1. German language — Dictionaries — English. 2. English lan-
guage—Dictionaries—German.
    PF3640.T35   A F 48–1587*

    Yale Univ. Library
    for Library of Congress   [1]†

NT   0046278   CtY ICU NcD ICRL DLC

    Taschenwörterbuch zum Corpus juris civilis,
    und anderen römischen rechtsquellen. Mit
einer übersicht über juristen, leges und
senatus consulta, nebst 2 verwandtschaftstafeln.
Berlin, H. W. Müller, 1907.
    2 p. l., 172 p.   diagrs.   19 cm.

NT   0046279   CtY-L MH

    Taschenwörterbuch zum Corpus juris civilis, den Institu-
tionen des Gajus und anderen römischen rechtsquellen. Mit
einer übersicht über juristen, leges und Senatus consulta,
nebst 2 verwandtschaftstafeln. 2. verb. aufl. Berlin, H. W.
Müller, 1911.

    2 p. l., 172 p. diagrs. 19cm.

    1. Roman law - Dictionaries. 2. Corpus juris civilis—Dictionaries.
3. Gaius – Dictionaries. 4. Latin language—Dictionaries—German. 5.
Roman law—Sources.

                                12–19432

NT   0046280   DLC

    Taschenwörterbuch zum Corpus juris civilis, den Institu-
tionen des Gajus und anderen römischen Rechtsquellen. Mit
einer Übersicht über Juristen, leges und Senatus consulta
nebst 2 Verwandtschaftstafeln. 4. u. 5. Aufl. München,
H. W. Müller, 1923.

    172 p. 19 cm.

    Imprint covered by label: München, J. Schweitzer, 1923.

    1. Roman law—Dictionaries. 2. Latin language—Dictionaries—
German.

                                58–54646

NT   0046281   DLC

Ex   **Tascher, Ferdinand, comte de, 1779-1858**
1509   Oraison funèbre de Maurice de Tascher...et
.18   d'Eugène de Tascher...tous deux morts dans la
.895   retraite de Moscow...par leur frère, le baron
Ferdinand de Tascher... À Paris, 1814.
    150 p.   21 cm.

    "Recueil de lettres de famille, " p.[87]-150.

NT   0046282   NjP MH

    Tascher, Harold, 1900-
    American foreign policy relative to the selection of the
trans-isthmian canal route, by Harold Tascher ... Urbana,
Ill., 1933.
    11 p. 22½ᵐ.

    Abstract of thesis (PH. D.)—University of Illinois, 1933.
    Vita.
    Bibliography: p. 10.

    1. U. S.—For. rel.—Colombia. 2. Colombia—For. rel.—U. S.
3. Panama canal.   I. Title.

    Library of Congress   E183.8.C7T28   33-31727
    Univ. of Illinois Libr.
    ———— Copy 2.   [3]   827.730986

NT   0046283   IU DLC OU DNW MiU NIC DPU

    Tascher, Harold, 1900-
    Maggie and Montana; the story of Maggie Smith Hatha-
way. [1st ed.] New York, Exposition Press [1954]
    134 p. illus. 21 cm.

    1. Hathaway, Maggie (Smith) 1867-   I. Title.

    F731.H3T3   923.273   54-5559 ‡

    MtBuM NN TxU PP PBm
NT   0046284   DLC MtHi MtU MtBC CaBVaU WaT WaSpG WaU

Tascher, Jean Samuel Ferdinand, comte de, b.1779
De la propriété des fabriques catholiques en France.
P; 1837

    23 p.

NT   0046285   MH

    Tascher, Julia M.
    Arbutus and dandelions. A novel. By Julia M. Tascher.
New York, Press of J. J. Little & co., 1883.
    400 p. 19¼ᵐ.

                               8–25559†

    Library of Congress   PZ3.T181A
                      (Copyright 1883: 7255)

NT   0046286   DLC

Tascher, Julia M.

FILM
4274
PR
v.3
reel
T-3

Arbutus and dandelions. A novel. By Julia M. Tascher. New York, Press of J. J. Little & co., 1883.

400 p. 19½ᶜᵐ.

(Wright American Fiction, v. III, 1876-1900, no. 5371, Research Publications, Inc. Microfilm, Reel T-3)

NT 0046287   CU NNC

Historical
Library

Microform
Room

Tasher, Lucy Lucile, 1904–

The Missouri Democrat and the Civil War. 1934.

ii, 199 l. 31 cm.

Typescript (carbon copy)
Thesis—University of Chicago.
Bibliography: leaves 192-199.
Microfilm of typescript. Chicago [n. d.]
1 reel. 35 mm.

1. Daily Missouri democrat, St. Louis. 2. United States—History—Civil War. I. Title.

PN4899.S27D37 1934b   74-152037
                MARC

NT 0046288   DLC

Tascher, Maurice Charles Marie de, 1786-1813.

... Journal de campagne d'un cousin de l'impératrice (1806-1813) par Maurice de Tascher, avec une gravure hors texte et trois cartes dans le texte. Paris, Librairie Plon, les petit-fils de Plon et Nourrit [1933]

3 p.l., x, 324 p. front. (port.) illus. (maps, 1 double) 18.5 cm. (Les Témoins de l'épopée. 2)

NT 0046289   CtY NcU FTaSU

Tascher, Maurice *Charles Marie de, 1786-1813.*

Notes de campagnes, ₍par₎ Maurice de Tascher, sous-lieutenant au 8e régiment de hussards, puis capitaine au 12e régiment de chasseurs, mort à l'âge de vingt-sept ans lors de la retraite de Moscou (1806-1813). ₍Chateauroux: Société d'imprimerie, d'édition et des journaux du Berry, 1932.₎ 342 p. front. (port.), plans, pl. 19cm.

693811A. 1. Napoleonic wars, 1806–   1813.
N. Y. P. L.   March 29, 1934

NT 0046290   NN

Tascher, Robert, 1908–

Grundfragen der Buchhaltung und Bilanzierung von Kreditgenossenschaften ... Bückeburg, 1934.

Inaug.- diss.- Frankfurt am Main.

NT 0046291   CtY

Tascher, Wendell Russel, 1898–

Experiments on the control of seed-borne diseases by X rays ...

(*In* U. S. Dept. of agriculture. Journal of agricultural research. v. 46, no. 10, May 15, 1933, p. 909-915. 23½ᶜᵐ. Washington, 1933)

Contribution from Missouri Agricultural experiment station (Mo.—11)
Contribution from the Department of field crops, Agricultural experiment station, University of Missouri, Journal series no. 344.
Adapted from thesis (PH. D.) University of Missouri ₍1932₎
Thesis note in foot-note on p. 909.
Published June 22, 1933.
"Literature cited": p. 914-915.

1. Seeds. ₍1. Seed infection₎ 2. X-rays ₍for control of plant diseases₎
                       Agr 33-630

Library, U. S. Dept. of   Agriculture 1Ag84J   vol. 46, no. 10
Library of Congress   [S21.A75   vol. 46, no. 10]
                       ₍4*₎

NT 0046292   DNAL OU OCl

Tascher, Wendell Russel, 1898–

Experiments with X ray treatments on the seeds of certain crop plants, by Wendell Russel Tascher ... ₍Columbia, Mo.₎ 1929.

Film copy of type-written manuscript. Made in 1942 by University microfilms (Publication no. 469) Positive.
Collation of the original: 2 p. l., 38 numb. l. incl. tables. 2 diagr.
Thesis (PH. D.)—University of Missouri, 1929.
Abstracted in Microfilm abstracts, v. 4 (1942) no. 2, p. 8.
Vita.
"Literature cited": leaves 17-18, 29-30, 37.

1. Plants, Effect of X-rays on. 2. Seeds.
                       A 43-303

Michigan. Univ. Library
for Library of Congress   Film AC-1   no. 469
                      ₍2₎†

NT 0046293   MiU DLC

Tascher, Wendell Russell, 1898–   joint author.
Stewardship of the land

see under

Niederfrank, Evlon Joy, 1904–

Tascher de la Pagerie, Joséphine.

See

Josephine, empress consort of Napoleon I, 1763-1314.

944.05
P699p

Tascher la Pagerie, Pierre-Claude-Louis-Robert, comte de, 1787-1861.

Le Prince Eugène; réfutation des Mémoires du Duc de Raguse, en ce qui concerne le Prince Eugène. Paris, Typographie Panckoucke, 1857. 30p. 24cm.

"Extrait du Moniteur Universel du 5 Mars 1857."
Bibliographical footnotes.
Bound with: Planat de la Faye, Nicolas Louis; Le Prince Eugène   en 1814. Paris, 1857.

NT 0046296   NcU

DC
277
.1
T19
1893

Tascher de la Pagerie, Stéphanie, comtesse de.
Mon séjour aux Tuileries. Paris, P. Ollendorff, 1893-95.
3 v. 19cm.

Contents.—₍1. sér.₎ 1852-1858. 5₍ém₎—2.sér. 1859-1865. 4. éd.—3. sér. 1866-1871. 2. éd.

1. Tuileries—Hist. 2. France—Pol. & govt.—1852-1870. I. Title.

NT 0046297   NIC MB NjP PPL NNF MH-L

Tascheraw, Robert
   see Taschereau, Robert, 1896–

BT770
Q5T3

Taschereau, Elzéar Alexandre, cardinal, 1820-1898
Discipline du Diocese de Quebec, par Monseigneur E.-A. Taschereau... Quebec, Chez P.-G. Delisle, imprimeur—editeur, 1879.

252 p. 22cm.

1. Quebec (Diocese) 2. Canon law—Canada.

NT 0046299   MBtS

Taschereau, Elzéar Alexandre, *cardinal,* 1820-1898.

Mandement de Mgr. E.-A. Taschereau, archevêque de Québec, promulguant la bulle Inter varias sollicitudines, qui érige canoniquement l'Université Laval, 13 septembre 1876. Québec, Typ. de P.-G. Delisle, 1876.

48 p. 30 cm.
cover-title: Documents relatifs à l'érection canonique de l'Université Laval.
"Sanctissimi in Christo patris et domini nostri domini Pii divina providentia pape Noni litterae apostolicae quibus Universitas lavallensis ... canonice erigitur, (with French translation)": p. ₍19₎-39.
"Lettre de S. E. le cardinal A. Franchi ... à Mgr. l'archevêque de Québec pour l'établissement d'une succursale de l'Université Laval à Montréal 9 mars 1876": p. ₍41₎-48.

1. Quebec (City)   Université Laval.   I. Catholic
church. Pope, 1846-1878   (Pius IX) Inter varias sollicitudines. II. Franchi,   Alessandro, cardinal, 1810-1878.
Library of Congress   LE3.L82T2   7—15991

NT 0046300   DLC CaOTP

Taschereau, Elzéar Alexandre, cardinal, 1820-1898.

Quebec (*Archdiocese*)
Mandemens, lettres pastorales et circulaires des évêques de Québec; publiés par mgr H. Têtu et l'abbé C.-O. Gagnon. (Nouvelle série) Son éminence le cardinal Taschereau ... Québec, Imprimerie générale A. Coté et cⁱᵉ, 1889-90.

---

q977.3
T18m

[Taschereau, Elzéar Alexandre, cardinal]
Mission du Séminaire de Quebec chez les Tamarois ou Illinois, sur les bords du Mississippi. E. A. T. Ptre.   n.p. 1849
42 numb. l.

Typewritten copy, on one side of leaf only.
Has marginal notes.
"Copié en mars 1919 par Rosario Benoit. Copie faite d'après le texte suivi du manuscrit."

NT 0046302   IU

Taschereau, Elzéar Alexandre, *cardinal,* 1820-1898.

... Pastoral letter of His Grace E.-A. Taschereau, archbishop of Quebec, concerning the solemn depositing of the mortal remains of Bishop François de Laval de Montmorency into the chapel of the seminary, 30th April 1878. ₍Quebec, 1878₎

11 p. 23ᵐᵐ.

At head of title: (No. 77.)

1. Laval de Montmorency, François Xavier de, bp. of Quebec, 1623-1708.
I. Title.   12-18983

Library of Congress   F1030.L28

NT 0046303   DLC

Taschereau, Elzear Alexandre, cardinal, 1820-1898.
   see also   Québec (Archdiocese) Archbishop, 1871-1898 (Taschereau)

Taschereau, Gabriel Elzéar, *1745-1809*

Würtele, Frederic Christian, 1842–   ed.
... Blockade of Quebec in 1775-1776 by the American revolutionists (les Bastonnais) Pub. by the Literary and historical society of Quebec and ed. by Fred. C. Würtele ... Quebec, The Daily telegraph job printing house. 1905-06.

Taschereau, Gabriel Elzéar, 1745-1809, joint author.
Journal de MM. Baby
see under   Baby, François, 1733-1820.

Taschereau, Gabriel Elzéar, *1745-1809.*   No. 7 in *4472.7.Ser.7

Rôle général de la milice canadienne de Québec passée en revue le 11 septembre, 1775 . . . Aussi Nouveau rôle de la milice canadienne qui a fait le service pendant le blocus de Québec depuis le 14 novembre 1775, et qui le continuera [sic] jusqu' au jour où il plaira à Son Excellence le Général Carleton d'en ordonner autrement.

(*In* Literary and Historical Society of Quebec. Historical documents. Ser. 7, pp. 269-307. Quebec. 1905.)

D6874 — Quebec, Province. Militia.

NT 0046307   MB CaOTP

₍**Taschereau,** *Sir* **Henri Elzéar**₎ 1836-1911.

Branche aînée de la famille Taschereau en Canada. ₍Ottawa, 1906₎

33 p. 22ᶜᵐ.

1. Taschereau family (Thomas Jacques Taschereau, 1680-1749)
                           3—8731

Library of Congress   CS90.T3

NT 0046308   DLC

Taschereau, Henri Elzéar, 1836–1911.
Bref Examen de quelques-unes des questions qui peuvent se soulever sur l'onus probandi sous les articles 1053 et 1054 du Code civil [Quebec] n.p. [1910?]
12 p. 4°.
n.t.-p.
Printed on one side of leaf only.

NT 0046309   MH-L

Taschereau, Sir Henri Elzéar, 1836–1911, ed.

Quebec (*Province*) *Laws, statutes, etc.*
Le Code de procédure civile du Bas Canada tel qu'en force le 1ᵉʳ août 1876, comprenant les autorités citées par les codificateurs dans le projet soumis à la Législature et des annotations compilées par Henri Elzéar Taschereau ... suivi d'un index. Québec, Impr. de A. Coté et cⁱᵉ, 1876.

Taschereau, Sir Henri Elzéar, 1836–1911.
Criminal law consolidation and amendment acts, 1869, 32-33 Vict.
see under   Canada. Laws, statutes, etc.

Taschereau, Sir Henri Elzéar, 1836–1911.
The criminal statute law of the Dominion of Canada
see under   Canada. Laws, statutes, etc.

Taschereau, Henri Thomas, 1841–

Canada. *Commissioner appointed in the matter of the alleged combination of paper manufacturers.*
... Report of commissioner and other documents in connection with the royal commission in re the alleged combination of paper manufacturers and dealers. Printed by order of Parliament. Ottawa, Printed by S. E. Dawson, 1902.

Taschereau, J. Ernest M.
Petit code militaire à l'usage des officiers, sous-officiers et soldats canadiens-français de la milice active du Canada ... Qué., Coté, 1884.
202 p. 14.5 cm.

NT 0046314   CaNSWA

Taschereau, Jules Antoine, 1801–1874.
Bibliographie de Molière. [Paris, 1828]

pp.(20). Facsimile plate.
Cut from his "Histoire de la vie et des ouvrages de Moliere" 2e éd., 1828, pp.415–436.

NT 0046315   MH

Taschereau, Jules Antoine, 1801–1874.
Catalogue des livres composant la bibliothèque de feu m. Jules Taschereau ... Ouvrages concernant l'histoire de la Touraine; ouvrages des écrivains tourangeaux ou qui ont été publiés en Touraine. Paris, Se distribue à la librairie A. Labitte, 1875.
xxvii, 300 p. 22½ᶜᵐ.
"La vente aura lieu le ... 1ᵉʳ avril 1875, et les onze jours suivants."

1. Touraine—Bibl.—Catalogs.
45-31321
Library of Congress   Z999.L12   1. avr. 1875

NT 0046316   DLC KU NIC NN MnU MH

Taschereau, Jules Antoine, 1801–1874.

Paris. Bibliothèque nationale. *Département des manuscrits.*
... Catalogue général des manuscrits français ... Paris, 1868–19

Taschereau, Jules Antoine, 1801–1874, ed.

Grimm, Friedrich Melchior, *freiherr von,* 1723–1807.
Correspondance littéraire, philosophique et critique de Grimm et de Diderot, depuis 1753 jusqu'en 1790. Nouv. éd., revue et mise dans un meilleur ordre, avec des notes et des éclairissemens, et où se trouvent rétablies pour la première fois les phrases supprimées par la censure impériale ... Paris, Furne [etc.] 1829–31.

Taschereau, Jules Antoine, 1801–1874.
Détails et révélations sur le duel de Dulong... Paris: Paulin, 1834. x, 39 p. facsim. 12°.
Facts relating to the duel between député Dulong and général Bugeaud.

545411A. 1. Dulong, François Charles, 1792–1834. 2. Bugeaud de la Piconnerie, Thomas Robert, duc d'Isly, 1784–1849. 3. Dueling.
N.Y.P.L. September 3, 1931

NT 0046319   NN

Taschereau, Jules Antoine, 1801–1874.
Histoire de la vie et des ouvrages de Molière, par J. Taschereau ... Paris, Ponthieu, 1825.
vi, 448 p. front. (port.) facsim. 21ᶜᵐ.
Title vignette.

1. Molière, Jean Baptiste Poquelin, 1622–1673. i. Title.
12-11666
Library of Congress   PQ1852.T3

NT 0046320   DLC CtY NjP InU KU TU WaU

Taschereau, Jules Antoine, 1801–1874.
Histoire de la vie et des ouvrages de Moliere. Bruxelles, 1828.
v. 2.

NT 0046321   PHC

PQ. 1852 .T197 1828
Taschereau, Jules Antoine, 1801–1874.
Histoire de la vie et des ouvrages de Molière, par Jules Taschereau. 2.éd.,rev.et augm. Paris, Brissot-Thivars, 1828.
vij,352 (i.e.452) p. front.(port.) 21cm.
"Bibliographie de Molière": p.415–436.

1.Molière,Jean Baptiste Poquelin,1622–1673.

NT 0046322   MiU PU CaBVaU AU ViU CtY NcU OCl IU NjP

TASCHEREAU, JULES ANTOINE, 1801–1874.
Histoire de la vie et des ouvrages de Molière ...
Deuxième édition, revue et augmentée.
Paris,Brissot-Thivars,libraire.M DCCC XXVIII.
vij,452p. pl.(facsims.) 26cm.
Title vignette.
Signatures: [-]⁴,1-28⁸,29².
Three-quarter red mor.

NT 0046323   PPRF MH

Taschereau, Jules Antoine, 1801–1874.
Histoire de la vie et des ouvrages de P. Corneille; par M. Jules Taschereau.
Paris, 1829.

NT 0046324   PPL PHC

Taschereau, Jules Antoine, 1801–1874.
Histoire de la vie et des ouvrages de P.Corneille ... Paris, A.Mesnier, 1829.
vii,418p. front.(port.)geneal.tab. 22cm.

NT 0046325   CLSU NN MH

Taschereau, Jules Antoine, 1801–1874.
Histoire de la vie et des ouvrages de Molière. Bruxelles, Mons, 1835.
2 v. front. (port), facsim. 16 cm.

NT 0046326   CaBVaU

PQ1852 .T3 1844
Taschereau, Jules Antoine, 1801–1874.
Histoire de la vie et des ouvrages de Molière, par M. J. Taschereau ... 3. éd. Paris, J. Hetzel, 1844.
2 p. l., iv, 346 p. front. (port.) facsim. 18ᶜᵐ.
"Bibliographie de Molière": p.[277]–300.

1. Molière, Jean Baptiste Poquelin, 1622–1673.
S D 19-278
U. S. Dept. of state. Libr.
for Library of Congress

NcU MiU
NT 0046327   DS DLC CU PPC DAU CSt NN CtY MdBP InU

TASCHEREAU, J[ules], 1801–1874.
Histoire de la vie et des ouvrages de Molière 4e ed., illustree par Gerard Seguin. Paris, Marescq et cie, etc., 1851.
f°.pp.64. Illustr.
"Bibliographie de Molière", pp.51–60.
Cover Serves as title-page.

NT 0046328   MH

Taschereau, Jules Antoine. 1801–74. Histoire de la vie et des ouvrages de P. Corneille. Paris, 1855. 16° —1148

NT 0046329   MdBP

Taschereau, Jules Antoine, 1801–1874.
Histoire de la vie et des ouvrages de P. Corneille, par M. J. Taschereau. 2. éd., augm. ... Paris, P. Jannet, 1855.
viij, 400 p. incl. geneal. tables. 15½ cm. [Bibliothèque elzevirienne. v. 101]
"Bibliographie de Corneille": p. [389]–420.

1. Corneille, Pierre, 1606–1684.
CA 11—2749 Unrev'd
Library of Congress   PQ1103.B5 vol. 101

OClW NcD OU AU TU PU OCl CU FU IaU PHC
NT 0046330   DLC CaBVaU WaSpG OrU CtY MU NN IaU NjP

Taschereau, Jules Antoine, 1801–1874.
Histoire de la vie et des ouvrages de Moliere 5th ed. Par. 1863.
252 p.

NT 0046331   OCU

PQ1772
.T18H4
Taschereau, Jules Antoine, ,1801-1874.
Histoire de la vie et des ouvrages de P. Corneille, par M. J. Taschereau. 2.éd., augm. Paris, P. Jannet, 1865.
440 p. incl. geneal tables. (Bibliothéque elzevirienne, v.10)
"Bibliographie de Corneille" : p.c389╕420.

I. Corneille, Pierre, 1606-1684. H. Series.

NT 0046332 NBuU

PQ
1772
T3
1869
Taschereau, Jules Antoine, 1801-1874.
Histoire de la vie et des ouvrages de P. Corneille, par J. Taschereau. 3. éd., augmenté. Paris, Firmin Didot, 1869.
2 v. in 1. 18 cm.

1. Corneille, Pierre, 1606-1684.

NT 0046333 CU-S NIC MiU

Taschereau, Jules Antoine, 1801-1874.
Lettre à M. le marquis de Fortia d'Urban en reponse à ses dissertation sur Moliere et sur sa femme. Paris,1824.

pp.16.
Answered by Fortia d'Urban in his "Supplement aux diverses éditions des oeuvres de Moliere", 1825 .

NT 0046334 MH CtY

Taschereau, Jules Antoine, 1801-1874, ed.

Corneille, Pierre, 1606-1684.
Oeuvres complètes de P. Corneille. Nouvelle éd. rev. et annotée par M. J. Taschereau. Paris, P. Jannet, 1857.

Taschereau, Jules Antoine, 1801-1874. 3666.48
Procès relatif à la publication du catalogue intitulé Livres du boudoir de Marie Antoinette, prétendue contrefaçon imputée aux éditeurs sur la plainte de M. J. Taschereau. Réquisitoire de M. Hémar. Plaidoyer de Mᵉ Gallien. Jugement en faveur de M. Gay, éditeur et de M. Louis Lacour, auteur de la publication.
— Paris, 1864. 48 pp. 16°.

E2807 — Lacour de la Pijardière, Lᵤ .. de. — Marie Antoinete Josèphe Jeanne de Lorraine, queen of France. — Literary property.

NT 0046336 MB

Taschereau, Jules Antoine, 1801-1874, ed.

Revue rétrospective; ou, Archives secrètes du dernier gouvernement ₁1830-1848₎ recueil non périodique. no. 1-33; mars-nov. 1848. Paris, Paulin, 1848.

Taschereau, Jules Antoine, 1801-1874, ed.

Revue rétrospective, ou Bibliothèque historique, contenant des mémoires et documents authentiques inédits et originaux, pour servir à l'histoire proprement dite, à la biographie, à l'histoire de la littérature et des arts ... t. 1-5, 1833-34; 2. sér., t. 1-12, 1835-37; 3. sér., t. 1-3, 1838. Paris, Impr. de H. Fournier aîné, 1833-38.

Taschereau, Jules Antoine, 1801-1874.

₁Molière, Jean Baptiste Poquelin₎ 1622-1673.
Le Tartuffe; avec de nouvelles notices historiques, critiques et littéraires, par m. Étienne. Paris, C. L. F. Panckoucke, 1824.

HG
8018
I59
v.23
no.19
Taschereau, Louis Alexandre, 1867-1952 .
The challenge of Canada's new frontiers.
New York, Association of Life Insurance Presidents, 1927.
7 p. 23cm.

At head of title: Betterment of life insurance service.
"Delivered at the twenty-first annual convention of the Association of Life Insurance Presidents at New York, December 8, 1927."

NT 0046340 NIC MH NcD PHC MiU

F
5467
T38
Taschereau, Louis Alexandre, 1867-1952
L'habitant de Québec ; L noblesse canadienne-française : conférences prononcées à Toronto devant l'Empire Club et le Women's Canadian Club le 27 avril 1922 / par L.-A. Taschereau. -- ₍Montreal : s.n., 1922?₎ 62 p. : port.

"Ces deux discours ont été prononcés en anglais. Le texte que nous publions maintenant n'est qu'une traduction aussi fidèle que possible."

NT 0046341 CaOTU CaBVaU

Taschereau, Louis Alexandre, 1867-1952
The lottery issue; text of speeches
see under Quebec (Province) Legislature. Legislative Assembly.

Taschereau, Louis Alexandre, 1867-1952.
La question des loteries
see Quebec (Province) Legislature. Legislative Assembly.
The lottery issue ...

AC25
.xT3
Taschereau, Marguerite.
Études : prix d'action intellectuelle, 1920. Ottawa : Bibliothèque de l'Action française, 1921.
97 p. : ill. ; 19 cm.

NT 0046344 NjP RWoU MWAC

Taschereau, Marguerite
Études... ₍Montreal₎ L'Action française ₍1921₎.
97p. (Bibliothèque de l'Action française)
"Prix d'Action intellectuelle, 1920."
Contents:
L'attention.- L'eau.- La sérénité.- L'amitié.- En lisant Ernest Hello.- L'art.- L'architecture.- Rodin.- Ames d'artistes.- Priere d'apres guerre.

NT 0046345 CaOTU

Taschereau, Marguerite.

Les pierres de mon champ. Pref. par M. A. Lamarche. Montreal, L. Carrier, 1928.

133 p. 18 cm.

NT 0046346 CaBVaU

Taschereau, Robert, 1896-

F1084
.A5
1946 c
Canada. *Royal commission to investigate disclosures of secret and confidential information to unauthorized persons.*
Documents relatifs aux délibérations de la Commission royale établie par Arrêté en Conseil C. P. 411 du 5 février 1946. Le 13 mars 1946. Ottawa, E. Cloutier, imprimeur du roi, 1946.

F1034
.A5
1946 a
Taschereau, Robert, 1896-

Canada. *Royal commission to investigate disclosures of secret and confidential information to unauthorized persons.*
Documents relatifs aux délibérations de la Commission royale établie par Arrêté en conseil C. P. 411 du 5 février 1946 y compris les premier et second rapports intérimaires de la Commission royale. Ottawa, E. Cloutier, imprimeur du roi, 1946.

F1034
.A5
1946 b
Taschereau, Robert, 1896-

Canada. *Royal commission to investigate disclosures of secret and confidential information to unauthorized persons.*
Documents relating to the proceedings of the Royal commission established by Order in council P. C. 411 of February 5th, 1946. March 13th, 1946. Ottawa, E. Cloutier, printer to the King, 1946.

F1034
.A5
1946
Taschereau, Robert, 1896-

Canada. *Royal commission to investigate disclosures of secret and confidential information to unauthorized persons.*
Documents relating to the proceedings of the Royal commission established by Order in council P. C. 411 of February 5, 1946, including the first and second interim reports of the Royal commission. Ottawa, E. Cloutier, printer to the King, 1946.

Taschereau, Robert, 1896-

Canada. *Royal commission to investigate disclosures of secret and confidential information to unauthorized persons.*
Le rapport de la Commission royale, nommée sous le régime de l'arrêté en conseil C. P. 411 du 5 février 1946 pour enquêter sur les faits intéressant et les circonstances entourant la communication, par des fonctionnaires publics et autres personnes occupant des postes de confiance, de renseignements secrets et confidentiels aux agents d'une puissance étrangère. Le 27 juin 1946. L'honorable juge Robert Taschereau, l'honorable juge R. L. Kellock, commissaires ... Ottawa, E. Cloutier, imprimeur du roi, 1946.

Taschereau, Robert, 1896-

Canada. *Royal commission to investigate disclosures of secret and confidential information to unauthorized persons.*
The report of the Royal commission appointed under Order in Council P. C. 411 of February 5, 1946 to investigate the facts relating to and the circumstances surrounding the communication, by public officials and other persons in positions of trust, of secret and confidential information to agents of a foreign power. June 27, 1946. Honourable Mr. Justice Robert Taschereau, Honourable Mr. Justice R. L. Kellock, commissioners ... Ottawa, E. Cloutier, printer to the King, 1946.

Taschereau, Robert, 1896-

Canada. *Royal Commission to Investigate Disclosures of Secret and Confidential Information to Unauthorized Persons.*
Russisk Spionage i Canada; "Den blaa Rapport." Uddrag Af Rapport fra den Kongelige Canadiske Undersøgelseskommission. ₍Oversat fra Engelsk af Erik Krog-Meyer₎ København, Schultz, 1947.

Taschereau, Robert, 1896-
... Théorie du cas fortuit et de la force majeure dans les obligations ... Montréal, C. Theoret, 1901.
vii,164 p. 22½ᶜᵐ.
These--Université Laval. Faculté de droit de Montréal.

NT 0046354 MiU-L

Taschereau, Robert, 1896–

F1034
A5
1946 d

Canada. *Royal commission to investigate disclosures of secret and confidential information to unauthorized persons.*
Third interim report of the Royal commission established by Order in Council P. C. 411 of February 5, 1946. March 29, 1946. Ottawa, E. Cloutier, printer to the King, 1946.

Taschereau, Robert, 1896–

Canada. *Royal commission to investigate disclosures of secret and confidential information to unauthorized persons.*
Troisième rapport intérimaire de la Commission royale établie par Arrêté en Conseil C. P. 411 du 5 février 1946. Le 29 mars 1946. Ottawa, E. Cloutier, imprimeur du roi, 1946.

French
Rev.
DC
141
F87+
v.541

Taschereau de Fargues, Paul Auguste Jacques, 1757-1832.
Il en est tems encore. [Paris?] an 4, i.e. 1796]
35 p.   22cm.

Dated: 15 ventôse an 4.
In favor of the assignats.

1. France--History--Revolution--Finance, confiscations, etc.

NT 0046357   NIC MH-BA PPAmP

French
Rev.
DC
141
F87+
v.330

Taschereau de Fargues, Paul Auguste Jacques, 1757-1832.
P. A. Taschereau-Fargues à Maximilien Robespierre aux enfers.   Paris, an 3 [i.e. 1795]
31 p. 22cm.

In his own defense.

1. France--History--Revolution--Poetry.

NT 0046358   NIC

French Rev.
DC
141
F87+
v.228

Taschereau de Fargues, Paul Auguste Jacques, 1757-1832.
Plan de finances pour percevoir les tributs en un seul jour.   [Paris, 1795]
29 p.   22cm.

Dated: 17 floréal an 3.
Includes his letter "Aux représentans du peuple" p. 23-29.

1. Franc   e--Hist.--Revo-
lution--Fin   ance. Confiscations, etc.

NT 0046359   NIC

Taschereau-Fortier, Mme. Marie Caroline Alexandra (Bouchette) 1874–
L'Aiglon Blanc de Illinois.   Montréal, Beauchemin [1938]
125 p.   pl.

NT 0046360   CaOTU

Taschereau-Fortier, Mme. Marie Caroline Alexandra (Bouchette) 1874–
L'auberge Bonacina (un drame au temps de Papineau) roman.   Montréal, Beauchemin, 1945.
185 p.

NT 0046361   CaOTU

Taschereau-Fortier, Mme. Marie Caroline Alexandra (Bouchette) 1874–
La cache aux canots (histoire d'un Indien) préface du C. H. Lefebve.   Montréal, Editions de l'A.C.F. [1939]
132 p.   (Romans historiques)

NT 0046362   CaOTU

819.33 T132.2
Taschereau-Fortier, Marie Caroline Alexander (Bouchette), 1874–
La cache aux canots. (Histoire d'un Indien)
Préface du R.P.C.-H. Lefebvre, [3,éd.]
Montréal, Editions Beauchemin, 1946.
158 p. illus.

1. Fiction, Canadian: French. I. Title.
Ref. from Fortier, Marie Caroline Alexandra (Bouchette) Taschereau- Ref. from Maxine, pseud.

NT 0046363   CaOTP

Taschereau-Fortier, Mme. Marie Caroline Alexandra (Bouchette) 1874–
Champlain, 1608; illus. de J.-Arthur Lemay.   Montreal, Lévesque, 1933.
29 pages, illustrated.   (Rimes historiques

With this is bound the author's Dollard des Ormeaux, 1660; Frontenac, 1672-1689.
Signed by the author.

NT 0046364   CaBVa

Taschereau-Fortier, Mme. Marie Caroline Alexandra (Bouchette) 1874–
Dollard des Ormeaux, 1660.   Illus. de J.-Arthur Lemay.   Montreal, Lévesque, 1933.
29 pages, illustrated.   (Rimes historiques

Bound with the author's Champlain, 1608.
Signed by the author.

NT 0046365   CaBVa

Taschereau-Fortier, Mme. Marie Caroline Alexandra (Bouchette) 1874–
Fanfan d'Estrées; (Un protégé de Pierre Lemoyne d'Iberville)   Montréal, Éditions Beauchemin, 1948.
131 p.   illus., map.

NT 0046366   CaOTU

Taschereau-Fortier, Marie Caroline Alexandra (Bouchette) 1874–
...Fées de la terre canadienne.   Montréal: Librairie d'Action canadienne-française ltée., 1928.
209 p.   illus.   8°.

440244A. 1. Folk lore, Indian-   American--Canada. 2. Folk
lore--Canada. 3. Title.
N. Y. P. L.   December 17, 1929

NT 0046367   NN

Taschereau-Fortier, Marie Caroline Alexandra (Bouchette) 1874–
Frontenac, 1672-1689.   Illus. de J.-Arthur Lemay.   Montreal, Lévesque, 1933.
29 pages, illustrated.   (Rimes historiques)

Bound with the author's Champlain, 1608.
Signed by the author.

NT 0046368   CaBVa

819.33
T132

†Taschereau-Fortier, Marie Caroline Alexandra (Bouchette) 1874–
La Huronne [par] Maxine [pseud.] Illus. de L. Roisin.   Paris, Editions Casterman [n.d.]
158 p. illus.   (Ma bibliothèque)

1. Fiction, Canadian: French. I. Title.
Ref. from Fortier, Marie Caroline Alexandra (Bouchette) Taschereau-. Ref. from Maxine, pseud.

NT 0046369   CaOTP

---

f1926
TA8134j

Harris
Collection

Taschereau-Fortier, Marie Caroline Alexandra (Bouchette) 1874–
Jacques Cartier, 1534. Illus. de J.-Arthur Lemay.   Montréal, Editions Albert Lévesque, 1933.
29 p., 1 ℓ. illus. 15 cm.
At head of title: Maxine [pseud.]
On cover: Rimes historiques.
Printed in red.

1. Cartier, Jacques, 1491-1557--Poetry.
2.French-Canadian poetry

NT 0046370   RPB

WC
23018

[Taschereau-Fortier, Marie Caroline Alexandra (Bouchette)] 1874–
Jean "La Tourte"; histoire d'un marin.
Illustrations de F. Clément. [Montréal, Granger, n.d.]
134 p. illus.   (Bibliothèque de la jeunesse canadienne)
Author's pseud. Maxine, at head of title.

I. Title (1)

NT 0046371   CtY KyU

Taschereau-Fortier, Mme. Marie Caroline Alexandra (Bouchette) 1874–
Miche, un petit gars de Coutances.
Montréal, Beauchemin, 1941.
155 p.   illus.

NT 0046372   CaOTU OC1

[Taschereau-Fortier, Mme. Marie Caroline Alexandra (Bouchette] 1874–
... Moment de vertige; roman canadien (pour adultes). Montréal, Librairie d'Action canadienne-française ltée.,1931.
2 p. ℓ.,[7]-290 p., 1 ℓ. 19½ cm. ([Les romans])
Author's pseudonym, Maxine, at head of title.

NT 0046373   CtY

Taschereau-Fortier, Marie Caroline Alexandra (Bouchette), 1874–
L'ogre de Niagara; illustrations d'Arline Généreux. Montréal: A. Lévesque, 1933. 110 p. illus. 21cm.

Contents.--L'ogre de Niagara.--La sirène des Mille-Isles.--Le sorcier du Saguenay.--Les sept géants des montagnes Rocheuses.--La légende de la mer Bleue.--Le géant des marches de pierre.

696650A. 1. Legends, Canadian--   French. 2. Giants--Folk lore--
Canada. 3. Indians, N. A.--Canada   --Fiction. I. Title.
N. Y. P. L.   April 20, 1934

NT 0046374   NN

[Taschereau-Fortier, Mme. Marie Caroline Alexandra (Bouchette)] 1874–
Les orphelins de Grand Pré. Montréal, Lévesque, 1932.

161, [1] p. illus. 23cm. (On cover: Les récompenses)

At head of title: Maxine [pseud.]

NT 0046375   CaBVaU

Taschereau-Fortier, Mme. Marie Caroline
Alexandra (Bouchette) 1874-
L'ogre de Niagara; illustrations d'Arline
Généreux. [Ed. 5] Montréal, Éditions de
l'A.C.F. [1938]
111 p. illus. (Contes et récits)

NT 0046376 CaOTU

[Taschereau-Fortier, Mme. Marie Caroline
Alexandra (Bouchette)] 1874-
Hfs ... Les orphelins de Grand Pré. Montréal,
ta355 Librairie d'Action canadienne-française, limitée,
1931.
144p. illus. 20½cm. (["Les récompenses"])
Author's pseudonym, Maxine, at head of title.

NT 0046377 CtY

PZ Taschereau-Fortier, Mme. Marie Caroline
25 Alexandra (Bouchette) 1874-
.T38 Les orphelins de Grand Pré [par] Maxine.
Or Montreal, Editions Albert Lévesque, 1935
LA.COL. [c1931]
163 p. illus. 25cm.

NT 0046378 LNU

[Taschereau-Fortier, Marie Caroline Alexandra (Bouchette)]
...Le pêcheur d'éperlan. (3. éd.) Montréal, Granger frères
[1943] 143 p. illus. 23cm.

Author's pseud., Maxine, at head of title.

355802B. 1. No subject. I. Title.
N.Y.L. January 10, 1947

NT 0046379 NN

Taschereau-Fortier, Mme. Marie Caroline Alexandra
(Bouchette) 1874-
... Le petit page de Frontenac. Illustrations
de M. Jean-Paul Lemieux ... Montréal, Librairie
d'Action canadienne-française, ltée, 1950.
3 p. l., [9]-168 p. incl. plates. 24.5cm.
At head of title: Maxine [pseud.]

NT 0046380 CaBVaU

Taschereau-Fortier, Mme. Marie Caroline
Alexandra (Bouchette) 1874-
"Quand passe la plume rouge ..." Illus.
de Jacques Bédard et Madeleine Lorrain.
Montréal, Éditions Beauchemin, 1951.
132 p. illus.

NT 0046381 CaOTU

Taschereau-Fortier, Mme. Marie Caroline
Alexandra (Bouchette) 1874-
Le saut du Gouffre. Montréal, Beauchemin
[1940]
123 p.

NT 0046382 CaOTU

Taschereau-Fortier, Mme. Caroline Alexandra
(Bouchette) 1874-
Stowaways (a tale of old French Canada)
Montreal, Beauchemin, 1943.
145 p. illus.

NT 0046383 CaBVa

Taschereau-Fortier, Mme. Caroline Alexandra
(Bouchette) 1874-
Le talisman; (Odyssée du jeune Pierre
Sabourin) Montréal, Beauchemin, 1948.
190 p. illus.

NT 0046384 CaOTU

Taschereau-Fortier, Mme. Caroline Alexandra
(Bouchette) 1874-
Le tambour du regiment; illustrations de
Maud Devlin. [Montréal] Levesque [1935]
143 p. illus. (Romans Historiques)

NT 0046385 CaOTU

Taschereau-Fortier, Mme. Marie Caroline
Alexandra (Bouchette) 1874-
Unknown faries of Canada. Toronto,
Macmillan, 1926.
[vii] 90 p. illus.

NT 0046386 CaOTU TxU

Taschereau-Fortier, Mme. Marie Caroline
Alexandra (Bouchette) 1874-
Le vendeur de paniers. Montréal,
Lévesque, 1936.
105 p. (Contes et récits)

NT 0046387 CaOTU

Tascheret, Oscar.
Dr. Oscar Tascheret, senador nacional por San Juan; su
actuación en el Parlamento Argentino, 1946-1949. [Buenos
Aires, 1949]
242 p. 28 cm.
Cover title: Labor parlamentaria del senador nacional por la provincia de San Juan, Dr. Oscar Tascheret.

1. Argentine Republic—Pol. & govt.—1910- 2. Argentine Republic. Congreso. Cámara de Senadores.

F2846.T26 923.282 51–18561

NT 0046388 DLC CU

Taschini, Giuseppe.
Le feste della Santissima Vergine, celebrate
con ossequiosi sonetti dall'abate Giuseppe Taschini.
Parma, Li fratelli Gozzi, 1797.
128 p., 1 l. 12.5 cm.
1. Mary, Virgin- Poetry.

NT 0046389 CtY

Taschini, Giuseppe.
Le lodi di Maria eroicamente cantate ...
1799.

NT 0046390 NIC

Taschkent
see
Tashkend.

Taschköprüzäde
see
Tāshkubrīzādah, Aḥmad ibn Muṣṭafā, 1495-1561.

Taschkoff, L. W.
Bulgarisches gefaengnisswesen...
Inaug. Diss. Wuerzburg, 1892

NT 0046393 ICRL

Taschlitzki, N I
see
Tashliṭskiĭ, N I

Taschner, Christian Friedrich.
Dissertatio inauguralis medico-botanica de
duabus novis trichomanum speciebus de earum
nec non aliarum hujus generis plantarum structura
... auctor Christianus Fridericus Taschner ...
Jenae, Schlotter [1843?]
2 p.l., 35 [1] p. 2 pl. 26 cm.
Inaug.- diss.- Jena.
1. Trichomanes.

NT 0046395 CU MBH

Tasci, Cecili Cebrià
see Cyprianus, Saint, bp. of
Carthage.

Tasciotti (Emilio). Contributo alla cura delle
artrosinoviti tubercolari con le iniezioni iodo-
iodurate (metodo Durante). 17 pp. 8°. Fondi,
A. Pansera. 1902.

NT 0046397 DNLM

Tasco, Manuel
see
Tosco, Manuel

Tascón, Alfredo M
La pulpitis dental y sus diversos tratamientos.
Bogota, El republicano, 1915.
35 p.
Colegio dental de Bogotá, D.D.S. diss. 1915.

NT 0046399 PU-D

Tascón, Antonio Matilla
see Matilla Tascón, Antonio.

Tascón, Jorge H.

Tascón, Leonardo.
Diccionario de provincialismos y barbarismos del valle del
Cauca, por Leonardo Tascón ... Edición hecha bajo la dirección de Tulio Enrique Tascón y Jorge H. Tascón. Bogotá,
Editorial Santafé [1935?]

Tascón, Jorge H.
El hospital, Buga, Departamento del Valle del Cauca, julio
de 1918. La Paz [1918] 18 p. illus. (incl. port.) 8°.
Cover-title.
At head of title: Jorge H. Tascón — Rafael Renjifo O.

1. Hospitals.—History: Colombia: Cauca. 2. Renjifo O., Rafael.
N.Y.P.L. October 25, 1921.

NT 0046402 NN

Tascón, Jorge H.

Tascón, Leonardo.
Quechuismos usados en Colombia, por Leonardo Tascón ...
Edición hecha bajo la dirección de Tulio Enrique Tascón y
Jorge H. Tascón. [Bogotá] Editorial Santafé [1934?]

786 sb Tascón, Leonardo.
T197　Diccionario de provincialismos y barbarismos
di　del valle del Cauca, por Leonardo Tascón ... Ed.
hecha bajo la dirección de Tulio Enrique Tascón y
Jorge H. Tascón. Bogotá, Editorial Santafé
c1934?3
x, c11-291 p. 24cm.

NT 0046404　CU

Tascón, Leonardo.
Diccionario de provincialismos y barbarismos del valle del
Cauca, por Leonardo Tascón ... Edición hecha bajo la direc-
ción de Tulio Enrique Tascón y Jorge H. Tascón. Bogotá,
Editorial Santafé c1935?1

x, c11-291 p. 23½cm.

1. Spanish language—Provincialisms—Cauca valley.　I. Tascón,
Tulio Enrique, 1888–　II. Tascón, Jorge H.　III. Title.

37-15099

Library of Congress　　PC4880.C3T3
c3j　　　　467.9

NT 0046405　DLC OrU CLSU FMU MH DS

Tascón, Leonardo.
Quechuismos usados en Colombia, por Leonardo Tascón ...
Edición hecha bajo la dirección de Tulio Enrique Tascón y
Jorge H. Tascón. ¡Bogotá, Editorial Santafé c1934?1

153 p., 2 l. 20cm.

1. Spanish language — Provincialisms — Colombia. 2. Spanish language—Foreign words and phrases—Kechua.　I. Tascón, Tulio Enrique, 1888–　II. Tascón, Jorge H.　III. Title.

35—12003

Library of Congress　　PC4886.T3
ca40c1j　　　467.9

NN CLSU
NT 0046406　DLC NBuU KU CU NcD CtY NcU MH OCl OCU

F　　Táscon, Tulio Enrique, 1888–
2274　Biografía del general José María Cabal,
.C18T28　procer de la independencia. Bogotá, "La
Luz," 1909.
128 p.　illus.

1. Cabal, José María, 1769–1816.
2. Colombia - Hist. - War of Independence,
1810–1822. I. T.

NT 0046407　NBuU MH

Tascón, Tulio Enrique, 1888–
La conquista de Buga (historia del descubrimiento y colo-
nización española de la provincia de Buga) por Tulio Enrique
Tascón ... Buga, Tipografía Colombia, 1924.

2 p. l., iii p., 1 l., 176, c1j p., 2 l. 20½cm.

1. Buga, Colombia (City)　2. Buga, Colombia (Province)　3. Colombia—Hist.—To 1810.

43-27692

Library of Congress　　F2291.B8T27 1924

NT 0046408　DLC DPU TNJ TxU

Tascón, Tulio Enrique, 1888–　ed.
Colombia. *Constitution.*
FOR OTHER EDITIONS
SEE MAIN ENTRY
Derecho constitucional colombiano; comentarios a la Consti-
tución nacional, por Tulio Enrique Tascón ... 3. ed., corr. y
aumentada con el comentario a las reformas de 1936 y años
posteriores. Bogotá, Colombia, Librería editorial La Gran
Colombia c1944j

Tascón, Tulio Enrique, 1888–　ed.
Derecho contencioso-administrativo colombiano; comentarios
al nuevo código de la materia (Ley 167 de 1941) por Tulio
Enrique Tascón ... Bogotá, Librería colombiana c1942.

314 p. 24cm.

1. Administrative law—Colombia. 2. Administrative courts—Colombia. 3. Administrative responsibility—Colombia.　I. Colombia (Republic of Colombia, 1886–　) Laws, statutes, etc.

43-46694

Library of Congress　　JL2831.T3
c3j　　　　354.86

NT 0046410　DLC

Tascon, Tulio Enrique, 1888–
Derecho contencioso-administrativo colombiano; comentarios al código de la materia.
4. ed. corr. y aumentada con el comentario a
las últimas reformas constitucionales ;
legales y con las doctrinas del Consejo ue
Estado. Bogota, Minerva, 1954.
432 p.

"Código de lo contencioso-administrativo":
p. c343a-404.

NT 0046411　NNC MH-L

Tascon, Tulio Enrique, 1888–

Tascón, Leonardo.
Diccionario de provincialismos y barbarismos del valle del
Cauca, por Leonardo Tascón ... Edición hecha bajo la direc-
ción de Tulio Enrique Tascón y Jorge H. Tascón. Bogotá,
Editorial Santafé c1935?1

Tascón, Tulio Enrique, 1888–
El general Murgueitio, su biografía y documentos inéditos para la historia de su tiempo.
Bogota, Casa Editorial de Arboleda & Valencia,
1915.
141 p.　port.　17 cm.
1. Murgueitio, Pedro José, 1789–1860.
2. Colombia - Hist. - War of Independence, 1810–
1822.

NT 0046413　IaU

Tascón, Tulio Enrique, 1888–
Historia de Buga en la colonia, por Tulio Enrique Tascón ...
Bogotá, Editorial Minerva, s. a., 1939.

1 p. l., c5j-416 p. 19½cm.

1. Buga, Colombia (City)　2. Colombia—Hist.—To 1810.

40-17452

Library of Congress　　F2291.B8T3
c2j　　　　986

NT 0046414　DLC CU KU TNJ CSt IaU FU FMU

Tascón, Tulio Enrique, 1888–
Historia de la conquista de Buga, por Tulio Enrique Tascón
... 2. ed., aum. y corr. Bogotá, Editorial Minerva, s. a. c1938j

1 p. l., c5j-278 p. 19½cm.

1. Buga, Colombia (City)　2. Buga, Colombia (Province)　3. Colombia—Hist.—To 1810.

40-20553

Library of Congress　　F2291.B8T35
c2j　　　　986

NT 0046415　DLC KU TNJ TxU NBuU FMU

G342.86　Tascón, Tulio Enrique, 1888–
T181h　Historia del derecho-constitucional colombiano, por Tulio Enrique Tascón ... cBo-
gotá, Impreso en "Cátedra ltda.," 1951j
2p.l.,9-220p. port. 25cm. (On cover:
Ediciones "Cátedra". I: Derecho, no.1)

Reproduced from type-written copy.

1. Colombia - Constitutional history.

NT 0046416　TxU

K　　Tascon, Tulio Enrique, 1888–
.T35
1953　Historia del derecho constitucional
colombiano. Lecciones de historia politica
dictadas en el externado de derecho y en la
Universidad Libre. Bogotá, Editorial Minerva
1953.
265 p.　25cm.

1. Colombia—Constitutional law—Hist.

NT 0046417　ViU InU MiU-L

Tascón, Tulio Enrique, 1888–
Nueva biografía del general José María Cabal, por Tulio
Enrique Tascón. Bogotá, Editorial Minerva, 1930.

374 p. plates, ports. 19½cm.

1. *Cabal, José María, 1769–1816. 2. Colombia—Hist.—War of independence, 1810–1822.　I. Title.

34-11025

Library of Congress　　F2274.C18
c2j　　　　923.58 1

NT 0046418　DLC TNJ NcU

Tascón, Tulio Enrique, 1888–

Tascón, Leonardo.
Quechuismos usados en Colombia, por Leonardo Tascón ...
Edición hecha bajo la dirección de Tulio Enrique Tascón y
Jorge H. Tascón. ¡Bogotá, Editorial Santafé c1934?1

Tascone, Giacomo.
Tempo vero e tempo medio fusi orarii. Tavole di riduzione
per convertire in modo speditivo il tempo vero in tempo medio
dell' Europa centrale per le provincie d' Italia.　Torino: Società
meteorologica italiana, 1911.　2 p.l., (1)8-64 p.　4°.

1. Time (Standard), Italy.
N. Y. P. L.　　　　　May 16, 1913.

NT 0046420　NN

Tascone, Giacomo Luigi.
Riassunto delle osservazioni meteorologiche
prese all'Osservatorio Simbruino nell'anno 1916.
1917.

NT 0046421　DAS

Soc　Tasea, Angelo, 1892- 1960
DC　Les communistes français pendant la drôle
396　de guerre; une page d'histoire, par A.
T34　Rossi cpseud.j　Paris, Iles d'or, 1951.
365p.　facsims.

Includes bibliographical references.

1. Communism - France. 2. World War,
1939–1945 - France. I. Title.

NT 0046422　FTaSU

Tasdemir, Cebbar.
... Comparaison des principes fondamentaux de la succession
en droit musulman et en doit c1j romain ... Paris, G. Saffroy,
1939.

3 p. l., cIxj–xiv, 198 p., 1 l. 25cm.

Thèse—Univ. de Paris.
"Bibliographie": p. c195j

1. Inheritance and succession (Roman law) 2. Inheritance and succession (Mohammedan law)

A 41–2051 Revised

New York. Public library
for Library of Congress　　cr43c2j†

NT 0046423　NN CtY CU DLC

Tašean, Yakôbos
see
Tashian, Hakovbos, 1866–1933.

Tasei, Sajū, 1886–
(Gensei hihan, Fashizumu to kyōiku)
最正批判ファシズムと教育　田制佐重著　東京
南光社　c昭和7 i. e. 1932j
4, 8, 235 p. 23 cm.

1. Socialism. 2. Fascism. 3. Education and state—Japan.　I.
Title. II. Title: Fashizumu to kyōiku.

HX414.T37　　　　74–815885

NT 0046425　DLC

Tasei, Sajū, 1886–
(Monogatari Nihon kagaku shi)
物語日本科學史 田制佐重著 東京 啓文社
(昭和15 i.e. 1940)
3, 17, 472 p. 23 cm.

1. Science—History—Japan.   I. Title.
Q127.J3T35   73-817074

NT 0046426   DLC

Tasei, Sajū, 1886–
(Risō ni ikeru daikyōikuka no seikatsu)
理想に生ける大教育家の生活 田制佐重 (著)
東京 文教書院 1922.
15, 7, 481, 110 p. ports. 20 cm.

1. Pestalozzi, Johann Heinrich, 1782–1827.   2. Froebel, Friedrich
Wilhelm August, 1782–1852. 3. Educators—Biography.   I. Title. II.
Title: Daikyōikuka no seikatsu.
LB627.T37   73-817472

NT 0046427   DLC

Tasei, Sajū, 1886–
(Shakai shisō tokuhon)
社會思想讀本 田制佐重著 (東京) 文教書院
(昭和2 i.e. 1927)
2, 6, 261, 5 p. 23 cm.

1. Socialism. 2. Sociology—History.   I. Title.
HX414.T38   74-818047

NT 0046428   DLC

Tasei, Sajū, 1886–
(Shinkō kyōiku undō no tembō)
新興教育運動の展望 田制佐重著 (東京) 日
東書院 (昭和6 i.e. 1931)
2, 4, 617 p. 19 cm.

1. Educational innovations. 2. Education—Philosophy.   I. Title.
LA128.T37   73-816613

NT 0046429   DLC

Tasende, Martín Héctor.
... Conferencias ... Montevideo, Escuela tipográfica Talleres Don Bosco, 1934.
132 p. port. 19¼ᶜᵐ. (On cover: Biblioteca uruguaya de autores
católicos)
At head of title: Martín H. Tasende.
CONTENTS.—A los que sufren.—El pobre, amor verdadero.—Amor
inteligente.—La limosna material.—La limosna intelectual.—La limosna
en el orden moral.—La limosna del perdón.—El padre de los pobres, san
Vicente de Paúl.—Las hijas de la caridad (Hermanas vicentinas)

1. Catholic church—Addresses, essays, lectures.
                                          36-32996
Library of Congress   BX890.T33
                                              204

NT 0046430   DLC TxU

Tasende, Martín Héctor.
... Formación del sentido religioso; prólogo del excmo. mons.
dr. don Antonio M.a Barbieri ... Montevideo, Editorial Mosca
hermanos, 1938.
viii p., 1 l., 132 p. plates. 19ᶜᵐ.
"Ensayos de pedagogía catequística."

1. Catechetics—Catholic church.   I. Title.
                                          41-31870
Library of Congress   BX925.T35
                          (2)   268

NT 0046431   DLC DPU

895.482
Iy25
no.18
Tager, Suat
Kendini tanı. İstanbul, Millî Eğitim Basımevi, 1950.
98 p. (İyi yaşama serisi: 18)

1. Psychology. 2. Character.

NT 0046432   NNC

PL248
.T28H3
1954
Tager, Suat, 1919–
Haraç mezat; şiirler. Ankara, Seçilmiş Hikâyeler Dergisi Kitapları (1954)
79 p. (Seçilmiş Hikâyeler Dergisi Kitapları,
19)

NT 0046433   ICU MH InU

Taserye, Pierre, supposed author.
Le bon payeur et le sergent boiteux et borgne
see under title

Taserye, Pierre. 16 cent. Le Pelerin passant,
monologue. 8 pp. 1 pl. (Fournier, E., Théât. français
avant la renaissance, p. 275.)

NT 0046435   MdBP

Taserye, Pierre.   *6679a.143
Le pèlerin passant, monologue seul . . . [En vers.]
[Paris.] Techener. [1835?] 16 pp. 17 cm.
One of an edition of 76 copies.

NT 0046436   MB

*FC8
L5626
838r
(A)
v.3
Taserye, Pierre.
Le pelerin passant, monologue seul, composé
par maistre Pierre Taserye.
[Paris]Se vend place du Louure,Chez Techener,
libraire.[1837]
16p. 19cm. (Pt.58 in v.3 of A. J. V. Le Roux
de Lincy's Recueil de farces, moralités et
sermons joyeux, 1837[1858])
"Soixante et seize exemplaires. N° [unnum-
bered]." This copy is on vergé d'Hollande.
In verse.

Another copy. 18.5cm.
This copy is unnumbered.
Ms. revisions (by Le Roux de Lincy?)
throughout, probably from collation with the
original ms.

NT 0046438   MH

S268
.M3T3
Tasev, Ivan.
Урбанистичко решаванье на стопанските дворови во
СРЗ. (Скопје) Задружен живот, 1950.
70 p. illus. 21 cm.

1. Agriculture, Cooperative. Macedonia.   I. Title.
            Title transliterated: Urbanističko rešavanje
            na stopanskite dvorovi vo SRZ.
S268.M3T3   52-21673 ‡

NT 0046439   DLC

Tasev, Khristo.
Наследствено право на НРБ. (София) Наука и изку-
ство (1953)
167 p. diagrs. 25 cm. (Университетска литература)

1. Inheritance and succession—Bulgaria—Compends.   I. Title.
            Title transliterated: Nasledstveno pravo na NRB.

                                          63-55349

NT 0046440   DLC

BF 1680
.T2
(Rare)
Tasqresti, Giovanni Battista.
La vera e falsa astrologia; con
l'aggiunta della vera, e della falsa
chiromanzia. In Roma, A spese di G.
Corvo Libraro, 1683.
508 p. illus.

1. Astrology—Early works. 2.
Palmistry—Early works to 1850. I.
Title.

NT 0046441   ICU

Tash, David, 1928–1948.
דוד טש (מור־שלום) אחד מלמד תא. תל־אביב. עם עובד.
(Tel-Aviv, 1951/52) תשי״ב.
176 p. ports. 22 cm. (מבורה)
Includes material by and about the author.

Bibliography: p. 176.   *Title transliterated:* David Tash.
PJ5053.T27Z52   57-53203

NT 0046442   DLC

Tash, Eli.
Financial transactions of the Jews
of Angevin England (12th cent)...by Eli Tash...
Cincinnati, 1931.
144 l.

NT 0046443   OCU

Tash, Lowell Homer, 1910–   joint author.

Black, William Henry, 1888–
... Effects of phosphorus supplements on cattle grazing on
range deficient in this mineral, by W. H. Black ... L. H. Tash
... J. M. Jones ... and R. J. Kleberg, jr. ... (Washington, U. S.
Govt. print. off., 1943)

Tashauzskaía ikhtiologicheskaía stantsiía
see
Murgabskaía gidrobiologicheskaía stantsiía.

Tashca, George
see
Tașcă, Gheorghe, 1875–

Tʻashchian, B
(Arshakowni Hayastani hazarameay pʻarhkʻ8)
Արշակունի Հայաստանի հազարամեայ փառքը (Երեվ) Բ.
Թաշճեան (Բարհկ) ԳաՖրէ, Sոպuш bn-Uenp, 1950.
557 p. illus. 24 cm.
Includes bibliographical references.

1. Armenia—History—To 428.   I. Title.
DS181.T37   74-229094

NT 0046447   DLC

Tasher, Lucy Lucile, 1904–
The Missouri Democrat and the Civil War. 1934.
11, 199 l. 31 cm.

Typescript (carbon copy)
Thesis—University of Chicago.
Bibliography: leaves 192–199.

1. Daily Missouri democrat, St. Louis. 2. United States—History—
Civil War.   I. Title.
PN4899.S27D37 1934b   74-152037
                                              MARC

NT 0046448   DLC

Tasher, Lucy Lucile, 1904–
... The Missouri democrat and the civil war ... by Lucy
Lucile Tasher ... Chicago, Ill., 1936.
1 p. l., 11 p. 24ᶜᵐ.
Part of thesis (PH. D.)—University of Chicago, 1934.
Photolithographed.
"Private edition, distributed by the University of Chicago libraries."

1. Daily Missouri democrat, St. Louis. 2. U. S.—Hist.—Civil war.
I. Title.

Library of Congress	PN4899.827D37 1934	37–4659
Univ. of Chicago Libr.		
—— Copy 2.	⟨2⟩	071.7866

NT 0046449   ICU NcD DLC OrU IdU NcU OU OCU MiU

TashGU
see
Tashkend. Universitet.

Tashi, Yoritomo-, *pseud.*
see
Blanchard, *Mme.*

Tashian, Hakovbos, 1866–1933.
Ագաթանգեղոս ու Գէորգայ Ասորի Եպիսկոպոսի եւ
ուսումնասիրութիւն Ագաթանգելեայ գրոց։ Վիեննա, Մխիթարեան Տպարան, 1891։
11, 159 p. 18 cm. (Ազգային մատենադարան, 3)
Includes bibliographies.

1. Agat'angeghos. Patmut'iwn. 2. George, Bp. of the Arabs,
d. 724. I. Title. II. Series: Azgayin matenadaran, 3.
Title romanized: Agat'angeghos arh Gēorgay
Asori Episkoposin.

DS181.A634T37   73–215240

NT 0046452   DLC CLU

Tashian, Hakovbos, 1866–1933.
Անեակի ձ եայ Հնագրութեան վրայ. ուսումնասիրութիւն Հայոց գրուենեան արուեստի։ Վիեննա, Մխիթարեան Տպ., 1898։
11, 208 p. illus. facsims. 18 cm. (Ազգային մատենադարան, 28)
Includes bibliographical references.

1. Paleography, Armenian. 2. Armenian alphabet. I. Title.
(Series: Azgayin matenadaran, 28)   *Title romanized:* Aknark mē
hay hnagrowt'ean vray.

Z115.A7T3   75–247872

NT 0046453   DLC NNC

Tashian, Hakovbos, 1866–1933.
⟨Arshakowni dramner⟩
Արշակունի դրամներ։ Վիեննա, Մխիթարեան Տպարան,
1917–60։
2 v. (7, 381 p.) illus. 19 cm. (Ազգային մատենադարան, 80, ⟨.
192)
Vol. 2 has added t. p.: Die Arsaciden-Münzen, von J. Dashian.
Previously published in part in Հանդէս ամսօրեայ, 1904–5.
Includes bibliographical references.
CONTENTS: մասն 1. Յոյնարնագիր Արշակունի Թագաւորի,
Հատատուս զարքիասովլ պատմութեան—մասն 2. Գաւառային տեսա-
կներ, ապիքիները։
1. Coins, Armenian. 2. Coins, Parthian. I. Petrowicz, Alexan-
der von. II. Title. III. Title: Die Arsaciden-Münzen. IV. Series:
Azgayin matenadaran, 80 ⟨etc.⟩

CJ1397.T37 1917   72–204723

NT 0046454   DLC

Tashian, Hakovbos, 1866–1933.
⟨Barbakhōsakan ditoghowt'iwnner hayerēn gitakan lezowi masin⟩
Բառախոսական դիտողութիւններ հայերէն գիտական լե-
զուի մասին։ Վիեննա, Մխիթարեան Տպարան, 1926։
8, 224 p. 18 cm. (Ազգային մատենադարան, 116)
Հարաքոյր լոյս տեսած "Հանդէս ամսօրեայ" ուսումնական մէջ,
1925–26 ⟨ $

Indexes in Armenian and Western languages.
Includes bibliographical references.

1. Geology—Terminology. 2. Chemistry—Terminology. 3. Armenian language—Lexicology. I. Title. II. Series: Azgayin matenadaran, 116.

QE7.T37   73–201548

NT 0046455   DLC CLU

Tashian, Hakovbos, 1866–1933, ed.

Oswald, Felix, 1866–1958.
Երկրաբանութիւն Հայաստանի ⟨զբ ⟩ Ֆելիքս Օսվալդ։
Թարգմանեց եւ ժամանակակերպուեաց Նախագոյս Թաշեան
Տաշեան։ Վիեննա, Մխիթարեան Տպարան, 1933։

Tashian, Hakovbos, 1866–1933.
Հայեր եւ Ուրարտանեաց. մատենագիտական ուսումնա-
սիրութիւն։ Վիեննա, Մխիթարեան Տպարան, 1934։
6, 343 p. 21 cm. (Ազգային մատենադարան, ⟨. 137)
Added t. p.: Die Hettiter und Urartier; eine bibliographische
Studie, von Jakobus Dashian.
Հատածաբար մաս առ մաս լոյս տեսած էր Հանդէս ամսօրեայ
ուսումնակիրոյի մէջ, 1931–34 ⟨ι
Includes bibliographical references.

1. Hittites—Bibliography. 2. Urartu—Bibliography.   I. Title.
II. Series: Azgayin matenadaran, h. 137.
     Title romanized Hat'er ew Owrartiank'.

Z3008.H6T38 1934   72–218410

NT 0046457   DLC

Tashian, Hakovbos, 1866–1933.
Հայ ազգի ռարդրարութեիւ գերմանական վավերագիրներ-
րու Համեմատ։ Մաս 1. Վիեննա, Մխիթարեան Տպարան,
1921։
7, 241, 10 p. 19 cm. (Ազգային մատենադարան, ⟨. 136)
Added t. p.: Die Deportation der Armenier nach den deutschen
Aktenstücken, von Jacobus Dashian.
No more published.
Based on Deutschland und Armenien, 1914–1918; Sammlung diplo-
matischer Aktenstücke, edited by J. Lepsius.
Includes bibliographical references.
1. Armenian massacres, 1915–1923. I. Lepsius, Johannes, 1858–
1926, comp. Deutschland und Armenien, 1914–1918; Sammlung di-
plomatischer Aktenstücke. II. Title. III. Series: Azgayin matenadaran, h. 136.
     Title roman-   ized: Hay azgi taragrowt'iwnē ger-
     manakan vaweragirnerow hamemat.
DS195.5.T36   72–204674

NT 0046458   DLC

Tashian, Hakovbos, 1866–1933.
⟨Hay bnakch'owt'iwnē Sew Tsovēn minch'ew Karin⟩
Հայ բնակչութիւնը Սեւ Ծովէն մինչեւ Կարին· պատմական
-ազգագրական Համեմատ անէսարի մը։ Վիեննա, Մխիթարեան Տպարան, 1921։
84, 12 p. 18 cm. (Ազգային մատենադարան, 90)
Includes bibliographical references.

1. Armenians in Trabzon, Turkey (Province) 2. Armenians in
Rize, Turkey (Province) 3. Armenians in Erzurum, Turkey (Province) I. Title. II. Series: Azgayin matenadaran, 90.

DS51.T7T37   73–201550

NT 0046459   DLC CLU NNC

Tashian, Hakovbos, 1866–1933.
Մատենագրական մանր ուսումնասիրութիւն. Հեռագո-
տութիւնը եւ բացեք։ Վիեննա, Մխիթարեան Տպարան,
1895–1901։
2 v. 19 cm. (Ազգային մատենադարան, 16, 37)
Based on articles originally published in Հանդէս ամսօրեայ.
Includes bibliographical references.
CONTENTS: մասն 1. Մեկնաբան, Գրոց, Աստղիկ, Դաբիեան, եւ
Անեկատաղէ— Մխիթար եւ իոր Դանասունիւն, Ագաթանգ եւ
իոր Ոզերաբանէ։ աո Թովմաբինեան, Ընթացքցիին Ագարաս եւ
Ֆիլիստեան քաս նարզին աղկատարդ։—մասն 2. Գառունեան ատա-
տիս, Ֆիֆիրիֆ։
1. Christian literature, Early—Translations into Armenian—History and criticism. I. Title. II. Series: Azgayin matenadaran, 16,
37.
     Title romanized: Matenagrakan
     manr owsowmnasirowt'iwnk'.
BR67.T33   75–587012

NT 0046460   DLC CLU

Tashian, Hakovbos, 1866–1933.
Ուսումն դասական Հայերէն լեզուէ· Հայկաբանութիւն,
զոր յօրինեաց Գէորգէէ Սանխեան։ Լրացուցական Հանդերձ
լաւելուածով։ Առաջին զպրութիւն։ Ստեֆ եւ դասեմ,
զրմց Ց. Տաշեան։ Ի Վիեննա, ի Մխիթարեան Տպ.,
1920։
8, 724 p. 29 cm. (Մատենադարան Արտահե Ընկերութեան, 16)
Vol. 1 was drafted by Spenian, rewritten by Tashian for publication; no more published.
1. Armenian language, Classical. I. Spenian, K'erovbē, 1817–
1886. II. Title.
     Title romanized: Owsowmn dasakan hayerēn lezowi.
PK8013.T3   73–255905

NT 0046461   DLC CLU

Tashian, Hakovbos, 1866–1933.
Ուսումնասիրութիւնք Սառսիվ-կանխախիւններ, Վաբուց Աֆֆ-
զատանքերի։ Վիեննա, Մխիթարեան Տպարան, 1892։
4, 270 p. 18 cm. (Ազգային մատենադարան, 5)
Includes bibliographical references.
Based on a set of articles which originally appeared in Հանդէս
ամսօրեայ, 1891–92.

1. Callisthenes, Pseudo- Historia Alexandri Magni. Armenian.
I. Title. II. Series: Azgayin matenadaran, 5.
     Title romanized : Owsowmnasirowt'iwnk' Stoyn-
     Kalist'eneay Varowts' Aghek'sandri.

PA3946.C3Z8   72–204648

NT 0046462   DLC CLU

Tashian, Hakovbos, 1866–1933, comp.
(Owsowmnasirowt'iwnk' hayerēn p'okharheal barhits')
Ուսումնասիրութիւնք Հայերէն փոխառեալ բառից /
Թարգմանեց Բագուրթու Տաշեան.—Վիեննա : Մխիթարեան
Տպարան, 1894.
145 p. ; 20 cm. — (Ազգային մատենադարան ; 15)

CONTENTS: Հիւստիան. Հ. Սեմական փոխառեալ բառք Հին
Հայերէն մէջ.—Թոութեան, Գ. Յունական փոխառեալ բառք Հայերէն մէջ—Թութեսան։ Հիւստիան, Զ. Հայական յատուկ աեաստք.—
Bound with Tēr-Movsēsian, P. Das armenische Bauernhaus. Armenian. Vienna, 1894.

1. Armenian language—Foreign words and phrases—Semitic.
2. Armenian language—Foreign words and phrases—Greek. 3.
Names, Personal—Armenian. I. Hübschmann, Heinrich, 1848–
1908. Die semitischen Lehnwörter im Altarmenischen. Armenian.
1894. II. Brockelmann, Carl, 1868–1956. Die griechischen Fremd-
wörter im Armenischen. Armenian. 1894. III. Hübschmann, Heinrich, 1848–1908. Die altarmenischen Personennamen. Armenian.
1894. IV. Title. V. Series: Azgayin matenadaran ; 15.

PK8084.S4T3 1894   75–587473

NT 0046464   DLC NNC

Tashian, Hakovbos, 1866–1933, ed.

Gat'rchian, Hovsēp', 1820–1882.
Սրբազան Պատարագամատոյց Հայոց։ Թարգմանե-
թիւնց Կատարաց Բանիւց, Ասորոց եւ Լատինացոց,
Հատերէն Բնանժբ, Ասարքակիռսեց եւ ժամանա-
թեամբց. Հրատարակեաց Հակոբէէ յատիունակէ ի
Ուղորում Տաշեան։ Վիեննա, Մխիթարեան Տպ., 1897։

Tashian, Hakovbos, 1866–1933.

Vienna. Mkhit'ariants' Vank'. Matenadaran.
Ցուցակ Հայերէն ձեռագրաց Մխիթա-
րեանց ի Վիեննա, Catalog der armenischen Handschriften
in der Mechitharisten-Bibliothek in Wien. Վիեննա, Մխիթարեան Տպ., Mechitharisten-Buchdruckerei. 1895–

Tashian, Hakovbos, 1866–1933.
(Ts'owts'ak hayerēn dzerhagrats' Kayserakan Matenadaranin i
Vienna)
Ցուցակ Հայերէն ձեռագրաց Կայսերական Մատենադարա-
նին ի Վիեննա = Catalog der armenischen Handschriften
in der K. K. Hofbibliothek zu Wien / կազմեց Յակոբոս
Տաշեան.—Վիեննա : Մխիթարեան Տպարան, 1891.
49 p. ; 32 cm. — (Մայր ցուցակ Հայերէն ձեռագրաց ; ⟨. 1,
Աստատր, տետր 1 (⟨. e. 1⟩)
Summary in German.
1. Manuscripts, Armenian—Vienna—Catalogs. 2. Vienna. Na-
tionalbibliothek. I. Vienna. Nationalbibliothek. II. Title. III.
Title: Catalog der armenischen Handschriften in der K. K. Hof-
bibliothek zu Wien. IV. Series: Mayr ts'owts'ak hayerēn dzerhagrats' ;
h. 1.
Z6605.ATM4 vol. 1   13–26530
[Z6621.V62]

NT 0046467   DLC NNC

Tashian, Hakovbos, 1866–1933.
(Vardapetowt'iwn Arhak'elots' anvawerakan kanonats' matenē)
Վարդապետութիւն Առաքելոց անվաւերական կանոնաց
մատենէ, Բուոյթ Բակարայ աո Կոզրատոս, եւ Կանոնք
Թադէի.—Ճանունեթիւն եւ ընաբերգ։ Վիեննա, Մխիթարեան
Տպարան, 1896։
9, 442 p. 20 cm. (Ազգային մատենադարան, 20)
Includes bibliographical references.

1. Canon law, Eastern. I. Armenian Church. Kanonagirk'
Hayots'. Kanonk' arhak'elakan. 1896. II. Armenian Church. Ka-
nonagirk' Hayots'. Kanonk' Arhak'eloyn T'adēosi. 1896. III. Title.
IV. Series: Azgayin matenadaran, 20.

     73–205275

NT 0046468   DLC CLU

Tashian, Hakovbos, 1866–1933.
(Zhoghovatsoyk' arhakats' Vardanay)
Ժողովածոյք առակաց Վարդանայ, հրիթք պատահքեան հայոց Միքիչապետական մատենադարաններ բան հպանել։ Մարր. սկզբնառութիւն եւ գաղումբ, գրեց Հակոբոս Տաշեան. Վիեննա, Մխիթարեան Տպարան, 1900։
11, 198 p. 18 cm. (Ազգային մատենադարան, 36)
Includes bibliographical references.
1. Vardan Aygekts'i, 12th cent. 2. Marr, Nikolaĭ ÍAkovlevich, 1864–1934. Sborniki pritch Vardana. I. Marr, Nikolaĭ ÍAkovlevich, 1864–1934. Sborniki pritch Vardana. II. Title. III. Series: Azgayin matenadaran, 36.
PK8547.V35Z9
75–549922

NT 0046469 DLC NNC

W 1 TASHIMA, I Sam, 1914–
UN7844 Surgical treatment of lesions and
v.9 diseases of the adrenal glands. Des
no.2 Moines, 1955.
1955 44 p. ₍U. S.₎ Veterans Administration.
Center, Des Moines. Surgical staff meet-
ings, v. 9, no. 2)
Bibliography: p. 36–44.
1. Adrenal glands - Neoplasms
Series

NT 0046470 DNLM

Tashiro, Akitaro, 1867–
Über bau und pigmentierung der aderhautsar-
kome. Halle, 1902.
Inaug.- diss.- Halle.

NT 0046471 ICRL DNLM MH

Tashiro, Fujio, 1910–
(Shakai-fukushigaku gaisetsu) 社会福祉学概説
田代不二男著 東京 光生館 ₍昭和30 i. e. 1955₎
3, 196 p. 19 cm.
Bibliography: p. 188–189.
1. Social service. I. Title.
HV31.T32
76–824001

NT 0046472 DLC

Tashiro, Haruo, 1917–
The biology and attempted control of
Tabanidae in New York. ₍Ithaca, N. Y.₎
1950.
v, 239 l. illus., plates. 27cm.
Thesis (Ph.D.)—Cornell Univ., June 1950.
Typewritten.
Biography.
Bibliography: leaves 231–239.

NT 0046473 NIC

Tashiro, Kanenobu, 1899–
出版新體制の話 田代金宣著 東京
日本電報通信社 昭和17₍1942₎
312 p. 19 cm.
Appendices (p. 206–312): 出版新體制關係法規.—出版關
係法規.
For locations see Union Catalogs
in Orientalia Division
1. Publishers and publishing—Japan. 2. Booksellers and book-
selling—Japan. 3. Liberty of the press. I. Title.
Title romanized: Shuppan shintaisei no hanashi.
Z452.T3
J 58–4023 ‡

NT 0046474 DLC

Tashiro, Kōji, 1900–
標準語のアクセント教本 田代晃二著 大阪
創元社 昭和28₍1953₎
7, 350, 6 p. 19 cm.
1. Japanese language—Accents and accentuation. I. Title.
II. Title: Akusento kyōhon.
Title romanized: Hyōjungo no akusento kyōhon.
PL544.T3
J 67–578

NT 0046475 DLC

Tashiro, Kōji, 1909–
言葉の使い方 田代晃二著 ₍大阪₎ 創元社
₍1951₎
274 p. 19 cm.
1. Oral communication. 2. Public speaking. I. Title.
Title romanized: Kotoba no tsukaikata.
PN4129.J3T33 1951
77–815102

NT 0046476 DLC

Tashiro, Minoru.
Tōa Kenkyūjo, Tokyo.
(Futsuryō Indoshina ni okeru dochakumin gyōsei)
佛領印度支那に於ける土着民行政 ₍撰常者
田代稔 東京₎ 東亞研究所 昭和18₍1943₎
1. Title.

Tashiro, Motoya, 1919–
社會教育學 田代元彌著 ₍東京₎ 岩崎書店
₍1951₎
2, 4, 146 p. 22 cm.
Colophon inserted.
Bibliography: p. 134–135.
1. Educational sociology. I. Title.
Title romanized: Shakai-kyōikugaku.
LC191.T35
77–808623

NT 0046478 DLC

Tashiro, Shiro.
Carbon dioxide production from nerve fibres when rest-
ing and when stimulated ... by Shiro Tashiro ... ₍Bos-
ton, 1913₎
1 p. l., p. ₍107₎–145, 1 l. illus., diagrs. 24ᶜᵐ.
Thesis (PH. D.)—University of Chicago, 1912.
"Reprinted from the American journal of physiology. vol. XXXII—
June 2, 1913—no. II."
1. Nerves. I. Title: Carbon dioxide production from nerve fibres.
Library of Congress QP331.T3
14–9955
Univ. of Chicago Libr.

NT 0046479 ICU DLC PPAN OU NIC MiU

Tashiro, Shiro.
A chemical sign of life, by Shiro Tashiro ... Chicago,
Ill., The University of Chicago press ₍1917₎
ix, 142 p. illus. 19½ᶜᵐ. (Half-title: The University of Chicago science
series) $1.00
"An attempt to apply facts discovered during the study of the nerves, to
living processes in general."—Pref.
1. Life (Biology) 2. Nerves. 3. Biological chemistry. I. Title.
Library of Congress QH345.T3
17–8224

PPAN OC1 OO OCU MiU OU MB IdU OrCS WaWW OrPR MtBC
NT 0046480 DLC CU NN NjP ICJ OkU PPT DNLM PBm PPF

Tashiro, Shiro, joint ed.
Kawamura, Rinya, 1879–
Studies on tsutsugamushi disease (Japanese blood
fever) by Rinya Kawamura ... English translation (authorized by Dr. Kawamura) edited by N. C. Foot ... and
Shiro Tashiro ... ₍Cincinnati, Spokesman printing company, ⁰1926₎

Tashiro, Shiro
III. Quantitative studies on the Pettenkofer
reaction of different lipids and of blood filtrate.
By Shiro Tashiro, L. H. Schmidt and Esther Bogen
Tietz. XVI. A preliminary report on the relation
of blood phospholipids to experimental gastric
ulcer, by Shiro Tashiro and L. H. Schmidt, XVII.
The effect of the administration of bile salts on
Pettenkofer positive substances and lipid phosphorus
content of blood. (Preliminary report) by Shiro
Tashiro and L. H. Schmidt. [Cincinnati, 1931]
3 pts.
Univ. of Cincinnati 1932, Ph.D.
3 articles, U. of C/ Med. Bull., v. 6, Dec.1931

NT 0046482 DLC

Tashiro, Tsuramoto, 1678–1748.
Yamamoto, Tsunetomo, 1659–1719.
₍Hagakure₎
校註葉隠 / ₍山本常朝談話 ; 田代陣基筆錄₎ ;
栗原荒野編著.— 訂正3版. — 東京：内外書房,
昭和19₍1944₎

Tashiro, Yasusada, 1856–1928.
(Okinawa ketsujō kō)
沖繩結繩考 田代安定著 長谷部言人校訂
₍丹波市町（奈良縣）₎ 養德社 ₍昭和20 i. e. 1945₎
13, 3, 227 p. illus. 21 cm.
Caption title: 沖繩縣諸島結繩記標考
1. Knots and splices. 2. Okinawa (Prefecture)—Social life and customs. I. Hasebe, Kotondo, 1882– ed. II. Title.
GR950.K6T37 1945
73–816730

NT 0046484 DLC

Tashiro, Yasusada, 1856–1928.
(Taiwan kōdōju oyobi shison shokuju yōkan)
臺灣行道樹及市村植樹要鑑 ₍田代安定編成
臺北₎ 臺灣總督府營林局 ₍大正9 i. e. 1920₎
2 v. illus. 26 cm.
Cover title.
1. Tree planting—Formosa. 2. Trees in cities. I. Formosa
(Government-General of Taiwan, 1895–1945). Eirinkyoku. II. Title.
SB484.F6T37
73–816353

NT 0046485 DLC

Tashjian, James H
The Armenian American in World War II. With an
appendix on the part played in the Korean conflict and
prefatory statements by Louis F. Johnson ₍and others₎
Boston, Hairenik Association, 1952.
511 p. illus. 26 cm.
1. World War, 1939–1945—Biog. 2. World War, 1939–1945—U. S.
3. Armenians in the U. S.—Biog. I. Title.
D769.88.A7T3
940.541273
53–37019 ‡

NT 0046486 DLC WaWW CU DI MB NN NNC TU

Tashjian, James H
The Armenians of the United States and Canada; a brief
study. Boston, Armenian Youth Federation ₍1947₎
62 p. illus., ports. 21 cm.
Bibliography: p. 60–62.
1. Armenians in the U. S. 2. Armenians in Canada.
E184.A7T3
325.2566
48–16081*

NT 0046487 DLC MH CU

E184
.A7T3 Tashjian, James H
The Armenians of the United States and Canada;
a brief study. Boston [Hairenik Press, 1947]
[3], 62 p. incl. illus., ports. 21cm.
"A publication of the Armenian Youth Federa-
tion, Boston, Mass."
1. Armenians in the U. S. 2. Armenians in
Canada. I. Armenian Youth Federation.
II. Title.

NT 0046488 MB

Tashjian, Neshan D S
... Miootian gam hamerashkhootian khendir ...
Boston, Dbaran "Hairenik", 1909.
144 [2] p. 18 cm.

NT 0046489 CU

Tashjian, Nouvart.
    Library of Congress classification in a public
library. [St. Paul, Minn., 1917]
    3 numbered leaves. 30 cm.
    Typewritten mss.
    1. Classification – Books.

NT   0046490   CU

Tashjian, Nouvart, comp.

New York university. *Washington square library.*
    List of doctors' and masters' theses in education, New York
university, 1890–June 1936, compiled under the direction of
Nouvart Tashjian, chief of Catalogue department, Washington square library, New York university. New York city,
Rho chapter, Phi delta kappa, School of education, New York
university, 1937.

Tashjian, Nouvart.
    The Priscilla Armenian needlepoint lace book, containing full directions for making edgings, insertions, round
doilies, square and triangular insets, also a great number
of finished pieces and lace flower pendants for luncheon
cloths and scarfs, by Nouvart Tashjian. Boston, Mass.,
The Priscilla publishing company, '1923.
    36 p. illus. 27ᶜᵐ.

    1. Lace and lace making.   I. Priscilla publishing company, Boston.
    II. Title.
                                        23–15992
    Library of Congress   TT805.T3

NT   0046492   DLC

X247
+1
v.1
    Tashjian, Nouvart
    What the Library of Congress Card division
service has meant in the long career of a
cataloguer ... [New York? 1937]
    1p.ℓ.,9 numb.ℓ. 28cm.
    Carbon copy of typewritten manuscript.

NT   0046493   CtY NNC

Tashjian, Vahan.
    The Easter story; a play in one act.   Boston, Baker's plays
[c1953]   18 p.   19cm.

    1. Easter—Drama.

NT   0046494   NN RPB

Tashjian, Vahan.
    The linden tree...   Boston [etc., c1949]   22 p.   19cm.
(Baker's royalty plays)

    1. Drama, Radio, American.

NT   0046495   NN RPB

Tashkarov, Petr Mikhaĭlovych, 1902– comp.

Papernyĭ, Lev Lazarevich.
    ... В. И. Ленин в борьбе с фракционностью в В. К. П. (б.).
Изд. 2. Москва, Ленинград, Государственное издательство,
1927.

Dr. Tashkarov, Petr Mikhaĭlovych, 1902 – comp.
.L45

Lenin, Vladimir Il'ich, 1870–1924.
    ... О Китае; составил и снабдил примечаниями П. М.
Ташкаров. Москва, Ленинград, Государственное издательство, 1926.

Tashkarov, Petr Mikhaĭlovich, 1902– comp.

Lenin, Vladimir Il'ich, 1870–1924.
    В. И. Ленин о характере нашей революции и социалистическом строительстве в СССР; составил П. Ташкаров. Москва, Ленинград, Государственное издательство, 1928.

HD1491
.R9L89
    Tashkarov, Petr Mikhaĭlovich, 1902–

Lenin, Vladimir Il'ich, 1870–1924.
    Ленин о колхозах и о борьбе с кулаком; вводная статья
П. Ташкарова; под общей ред. К. А. Попова. Москва,
Гос. изд-во, 1930.

Tashkend. Antifashistskiĭ miting narodov Uzbekistana,
    Turkmenii, Tadzhikistana, Kazakhstana, Kirgizii, 1943
  see Antifashistskiĭ miting narodov Uzbekistana, Turkmenii, Tadzhikistana, Kazakhstana, Kirgizii, *Tashkend*,
  1943.

Tashkend. Astronomicheskaíà observatoriíà.
    Astronomical circular
    see its
    Циркуляр (*transliterated:* TSirkuliar)

Tashkend. Astronomicheskaíà observatoriíà.
    Бюллетень. Bulletin. т. 1–
    Aug. 25, 1933–
    [Ташкент]
    no. in   /v. 28 cm.

    1. Astronomy—Period.   *Title transliterated:* Biulleten'.
    QB1.T332   54–30315

NT   0046502   DLC InU PPAmP

Tashkend. [Astronomicheskaíà observatoriíà]
    Publications de l'Observatoire astronomique et physique de Tachkent. n° 1–   Tachkent, Impr. de
l'État-major du Turkestan, 1899–19
    v.   fold. plates. 27½ x 22½ᶜᵐ. and atlas. 35 x 46ᶜᵐ.
    Imprint varies: no. 1, impr. F*** F. et G. Kamenski, 1899; no. 2, text,
Impr. V. M. Iline, 1900.
    Atlas, in 2 parts, accompanies publications nos. 2 and 3, and has imprint:
Lithographie de la section topographique de l'État-major du Turkestan,
1900–01.
    On verso of t.-p. of no. 1: Publié avec les fonds donnés par le gouverneur-général par intérim du Tourkestan, le général-lieutenant N. A. Ivanoff.
    Published also in Russian.
    1. Astronomy—Obser-   vations.   I. Title.
                                    .9–651 Revised
    Library of Congress   QB4.T33

      MiU NjP ICJ MBdAF
NT   0046503   DLC CtY NN PBL PHC ODW PPAmP MdBJ PU OU

Periodical
shelves
T27
    Tashkend. Astronomicheskaíà observatoriíà.
    Циркуляр Ташкентской астрономической обсерватории.

    [Ташкент, Изд-во Академии наук Узбекской ССР, etc.]
    v. 22–28 cm.
    Began publication in 1952. Cf. Летопись периодических изданий
CCCP, 1955–1960, № 1189.
    No.   have also title: Astronomical circular.
    No. 348–   called also no.1–
    1. Astronomy—Observations.   I. Title: Astronomical circular.
                            Title transliterated: TSirkuliar.
    QB4.T323   54–30318 rev

NT   0046504   DLC OU InU MCSA

Tashkend. Astronomicheskaíà observatoriíà.
    Записки. вып. 1–3. Москва, 1885–89.
    3 v. in 1. illus. fold. maps, tables. 28 cm.
    Issued by the observatory under its earlier name: Tashkentskaíà
astronomicheskaíà i fizicheskaíà observatoriíà.

    1. Astronomy—Observations.   *Title transliterated:* Zapiski.
    QB4.T322   54–55398

NT   0046505   DLC

Tashkend. Bûro pressy Srednego Vostoka
  see Bûro pressy Srednego Vostoka, *Tashkend.*

Tashkend. Botanicheskiĭ institut Uzbekistanskogo
    filiala Akademii nauk SSSR
  see
  Akademiíà nauk SSSR. *Uzbekistanskiĭ filial, Tashkend.
  Botanicheskiĭ institut.*

Tashkend. Botanicheskiĭ sad
  see
  Akademiíà nauk Uzbekskoĭ SSR, *Tashkend. Botanicheskiĭ
  sad.*

Tashkend. Dānishgāh-i Dawlatī-i Tāshkand
  see
  Tashkend. Universitet.

Tashkend. Experiment Investigation Institute of the
    Water Economy of Middle Asia
  see
  Tashkend. Sredne-Aziatskiĭ opytno-issledovatel'skiĭ institut vodnogo khozíàĭstva.

Tashkend. Experiment Research Institute of the Water
    Economy of Middle Asia
  see
  Tashkend. Sredne-Aziatskiĭ opytno-issledovatel'skiĭ institut vodnogo khozíàĭstva.

Tashkend. Fiziko-tekhnicheskiĭ institut Akademii nauk
    Uzbekskoĭ SSR
  see
  Akademiíà nauk Uzbekskoĭ SSR, *Tashkend. Fiziko-tekhnicheskiĭ institut.*

Tashkend. Geofizicheskaíà observatoriíà.
    Труды. Ленинград, Гидрометеорологическое изд-во, 194
    (v. in   illus. maps. 26 cm.
    Began publication in 1940; publication suspended 1941–48. Cf.
    Serial publications of the Soviet Union, 1939–1957.
    Vol.   called also v.

    1. Geophysics—Societies, etc. 2. Meteorology—Societies, etc.
                            Title transliterated: Trudy.
    QC801.T3A3   59–54448

NT   0046513   DLC

Tashkend. Gosudarstvennaíà publichnaíà
    biblioteka.

Tashkend. Universitet. *Fundamental'naíà biblioteka.*
    Указатель докторских и кандидатских диссертаций,
защищенных в Узбекистане в 1936–1951 гг. Общественные науки, естественные науки, математика. [Ответственные редакторы: Д. Ф. Железняков и М. С. Виридарский]
Ташкент, Изд-во САГУ, 1954.

Tashkend. Gosudarstvennaĭa publichnaĭa biblioteka.
Узбекистан; библиографический указатель литературы.
1953/55–
Ташкент, Гос. изд-во Узбекской ССР.
v. 22 cm.

1. Uzbekistan—Bibl.   *Title transliterated:* Uzbekistan.

Z3413.U9T3   60–18012 rev

NT   0046515   DLC

Tashkend. *Gosudarstvennyĭ pedagogicheskiĭ institut.*
Ученые записки.
Ташкент, 19
v. in illus. 22 cm.
Began publication in 1947. Cf. Летопись периодических изданий
СССР, 1955–60.
Russian or Uzbek.

Title transliterated: Uchenye zapiski.

AS581.T273   67–35624

NT   0046516   DLC NIC

**Tashkend. Institut ėkonomiki Akademii nauk Uzbekskoĭ
SSR**
see Akademiĭa nauk Uzbekskoĭ SSR, *Tashkend. Institut
ėkonomiki.*

**Tashkend. Institut fizyka, literatury i istorii Uzbeki-
stanskogo filiala Akademii nauk SSSR**
see
Akademiĭa nauk SSSR. *Uzbekistanskiĭ filial, Tashkend.
Institut fizyka, literatury i istorii.*

**Tashkend. Institut inzhenerov irrigatsii i mekhanizatsii
sel'skogo khozĭaĭstva**
see
Tashkend. Institut irrigatsii i mekhanizatsii sel'skogo
khozĭaĭstva.

**Tashkend. Institut inzhenerov zhelezno-dorozhnogo trans-
porta.**
Труды
Москва, Гос. трансп. жел-дор. изд-во, 19½
v. in illus. 23 cm.
Began publication in 1948. Cf. Летопись периодических изданий
СССР, 1950–1964, № 1229.

1. Railroads—Collected works.   *Title transliterated:* Trudy.

TF7.T33   60–33322

NT   0046520   DLC

Tashkend. Institut irrigatsii
see
Tashkend. Sredne-Aziatskiĭ nauchno-issledovatel'skiĭ institut irrigatsii.

**Tashkend. Institut irrigatsii i mekhanizatsii sel'skogo
khozĭaĭstva.**
Труды.
Ташкент, 19
v. illus. 23 cm.
Began publication in 1955. Cf. Летопись периодических изданий
СССР, 1957, № 677.

1. Agricultural machinery — Collected works. 2. Irrigation — Collected works.   *Title transliterated:* Trudy.

TJ1480.A1T32   61–42250

NT   0046522   DLC

Tashkend. Institut irrigatsionnykh sooruzhenii
see
Tashkend. Sredne-Aziatskiĭ nauchno-issledovatel'skiĭ institut irrigatsii.

Tashkend. Institut iskusstvoznaniĭa Uzbekskoĭ SSR
see
Tashkend. Nauchno-issledovatel'skiĭ institut iskusstvoznaniĭa Uzbekskoĭ SSR.

**Tashkend. Institut istorii i arkheologii Akademii nauk
Uzbekskoĭ SSR**
see Akademiĭa nauk Uzbekskoĭ SSR, *Tashkend. Institut istorii i arkheologii.*

Tashkend. Institut khimii Akademii nauk Uzbekskoĭ SSR
see
Akademiĭa nauk Uzbekskoĭ SSR, *Tashkend. Institut khimii.*

**Tashkend. Institut khimii rastitel'nykh veshchestv Aka-
demii nauk Uzbekskoĭ SSR**
see
Akademiĭa nauk Uzbekskoĭ SSR, *Tashkend. Institut
khimii rastitel'nykh veshchestv.*

Tashkend. Institut khlopkovoĭ prmyshlennosti
see   Tashkend. Vsesoĭuznyĭ nauchno-
issledovatel'skiĭ institut khlopkovodstua.

Tashkend. Institut kurortologii i fizioterapii
see
Tashkend. Uzbekskiĭ gosudarstvennyĭ nauchno-issledovatel'skiĭ institut kurortologii i fizioterapii.

**Tashkend. Institut matematiki Akademii nauk Uzbekskoĭ
SSR**
see
Akademiĭa nauk Uzbekskoĭ SSR, *Tashkend. Institut
matematiki.*

Tashkend. Institut matematiki i mekhaniki
see Akademiĭa nauk Uzbekskoĭ SSR, *Tashkend. Institut
matematiki i mekhaniki.*

Tashkend. Institut po khlopkovodstvu
see Tashkend. Vsesoĭuznyĭ nauchno-issledovatel'skiĭ institut khlopkovodstva.

Tashkend. Institut pochvovedeniĭa i geobotaniki
see
Tashkend. Universitet. *Institut pochvovedeniĭa i geobotaniki.*

**Tashkend. Institut sel'skogo khozĭaĭstva Akademii nauk
Uzbekskoĭ SSR**
see
Akademiĭa nauk Uzbekskoĭ SSR, *Tashkend. Institut sel'-
skogo khozĭaĭstva.*

Tashkend. Institut vodnogo khozĭaĭstva
see
Tashkend. Sredne-Aziatskiĭ opytno-issledovatel'skiĭ institut vodnogo khozĭaĭstva.

**Tashkend. Institut vostokovedeniĭa Akademii nauk Uzbek-
skoĭ SSR**
see Akademiĭa nauk Uzbekskoĭ SSR, *Tashkend. Institut vostokovedeniĭa.*

**Tashkend. Institut zoologii i parazitologii Akademii nauk
Uzbekskoĭ SSR**
see
Akademiĭa nauk Uzbekskoĭ SSR, *Tashkend. Institut
zoologii i parazitologii.*

Tashkend. Karantinnaĭa laboratoriĭa NKZ UzSSR
see
Uzbekistan. *Narodnyĭ komissariat zemledeliĭa. Karantinnaĭa
laboratoriĭa.*

Tashkend. Meteorological Institute.
Meteorological data of stations of Middle Asia.
1924. Tashkent, 1930.
34.5 cm.

NT   0046539   DAS

Tashkend. Muzeĭ istorii Uzbekskoĭ SSR
see
Akademiĭa nauk Uzbekskoĭ SSR, *Tashkend. Muzeĭ istorii
Uzbekskoĭ SSR.*

HB9
.T33
Tashkend. Institut narodnogo khozĭaĭstva.
Научные записки.
Ташкент, 19
v. diagrs., tables. 22–27 cm.
Vols issued by Tashkentskiĭ finansovo-ėkonomicheskiĭ in-
stitut.
Some vols. have title: Nauchnye trudy.

1. Economics—Societies, etc. i. Tashkend. Finansovo-ėkonomicheskiĭ institut. Nauchnye zapiski. *Insert from ed. 2*
    Title transliterated: Nauchnye zapiski.

HB9.T33   57–52960 rev

NT   0046541   DLC

Tashkend. Nauchno-issledovatel'skiĭ geologicheskiĭ
Institut
Popov, Vladimir Ivanovich, 1883–
... История депрессий и поднятия западного Тянь-
Шаня ... Ташкент, Издательство Комитета наук УзбССР,
1938.

Tashkend. Nauchno-issledovatel'skiĭ institut iskusstvoznaniia Uzbekskoĭ SSR.
Музыкальная культура Советского Узбекистана; очерки. ¡Редакторы: С. Б. Бабаев, Т. С. Вызго, Г. П. Яковлев¡ Ташкент, Гос. изд-во Узбекской ССР, 1955.
287 p. 21 cm. (Искусство Советского Узбекистана)
"Нотные примеры": p. ¡215¡–287.

1. Music—Uzbekistan—Hist. & crit.   i. Babaev, S. B., ed.   ii. Title.
Title transliterated: Muzykal'naia kul'tura sovetskogo Uzbekistana.

ML309.U9T4   57–19862 rev

NT   0046543   DLC NN OrU

Tashkend. Nauchno-issledovatel'skiĭ institut iskusstvoznaniia Uzbekskoĭ SSR.
Akademiia nauk Uzbekskoĭ SSR, *Tashkend. Institut istorii i arkheologii.*
Народное декоративное искусство Советского Узбекистана: Текстиль. Ташкент, Изд-во Академии наук Узбекской ССР, 1954.

Tashkend. Nauchno-issledovatel'skiĭ institut iskusstvoznaniia Uzbekskoĭ SSR.
Народное декоративное искусство Советского Узбекистана. ¡Под общей ред. Г. П. Яковлева¡ Москва, Гос. изд-во изобразительного искусства, 1955.
153 p. 35 cm.

1. Folk art—Uzbekistan.   i. Iakovlev, G. P., ed.   ii. Title.
Title transliterated: Narodnoe dekorativnoe iskusstvo Sovetskogo Uzbekistana.

NK1075.T3   56–42167 rev 2 ‡

NT   0046545   DLC KU CSt

ML300 .U9 I 8

Tashkend. Nauchno-issledovatel'skiĭ institut iskusstvoznaniia Uzbekskoĭ SSR.
(Istoriia uzbekskoĭ sovetskoĭ muzyki)
История узбекской советской музыки / ¡ред. коллегия Т. С. Вызго ... et al.¡ — Ташкент : Изд-во лит. и искусства, 19

Tashkend. Nauchno-issledovatel'skiĭ institut khlopkovodstva
see Tashkend. Vsesoiuznyĭ nauchno-issledovatel'skiĭ institut khlopkovodstva.

Tashkend. Nauchno-issledovatel'skiĭ institut po khlopkovodstvu
see Tashkend. Vsesoiuznyĭ nauchno-issledovatel'skiĭ institut khlopkovodstva.

Tashkend. Nauchno-issledovatel'skiĭ institut po khlopkovodstvu, khlopkovoĭ promyshlennosti i irrigafsii
see Tashkend. Vsesoiuznyĭ nauchno-issledovatel'skiĭ institut khlopkovodstva.

Tashkend. Observatoire astronomique et physique
see
Tashkend. Astronomicheskaia observatoriia.

Tashkend. Opytno-issledovatel'skiĭ institut vodnogo khoziaĭstva
see Tashkend. Sredne-Aziatskiĭ nauchno-issledovatel'skiĭ institut irrigafsii.

Tashkend. Opytno-issledovatel'skiĭ institut vodnogo khoziaĭstva
see
Tashkend. Sredne-Aziatskiĭ opytno-issledovatel'skiĭ institut vodnogo khoziaĭstva.

Tashkend. Pedagogicheskiĭ institut
see
Tashkend. Gosudarstvennyĭ pedagogicheskiĭ institut.

Tashkend. Publichnaia biblioteka
see
Tashkend. Gosudarstvennaia publichnaia biblioteka.

Tashkend. Rabochee soveshchanie po itogam izucheniia chetvertichnogo perioda, *1948*
see
Vsesoiuznoe rabochee soveshchanie po itogam izucheniia chetvertichnogo perioda, *Tashkend, 1948.*

Tashkend. Respublikanskaia publichnaia biblioteka
see
Tashkend. Gosudarstvennaia publichnaia biblioteka.

Tashkend. Scientific Society
see Tashkend. Universitet. Turkestanskoe nauchnoe obshchestvo.

Tashkend. Sredazkolkhozfsentr
see Sredne-Aziatskiĭ soiuz sel'skokhoziaĭstvennykh kollektivov, *Tashkend.*

TC555 .P4

Tashkend. Sredne-Aziatskiĭ gosudarstvennyĭ institut po proektirovaniiu vodokhoziaĭstvennykh i gidrotekhnicheskikh sooruzheniĭ.
Peplov, É   É
Стандарт секторных щитов системы инж. Пеплова. Модель М–3–31. Ташкент, 1931–

Tashkend. Sredne-Aziatskiĭ gosudarstvennyĭ universitet
see Tashkend. Universitet.

Tashkend. Sredne-Aziatskiĭ kommunisticheskiĭ universitet.
Kommunisticheskaia mysl'
see under title

Tashkend. Sredne-Aziatskiĭ nauchno-issledovatel'skiĭ institut irrigafsii.
Труды.
Ташкент, 19
no. illus. 22–26 cm.
Began publication with no. 2, in 1932. Cf. Периодическая печать СССР, 1917–1949; журналы ... по сельскому хозяйству, № 787.
Nq   have also a distinctive title.

1. Irrigation—Societies, etc. 2. Irrigation—Soviet Central Asia.
Title transliterated: Trudy.

TC909.T33   52–43329 rev

NT   0046562   DLC

Tashkend. Sredne-Aziatskiĭ nauchno-issledovatel'skiĭ institut irrigafsionnykh sooruzheniĭ
see
Tashkend. Sredne-Aziatskiĭ nauchno-issledovatel'skiĭ institut irrigafsii.

Tashkend. Sredne-Aziatskiĭ opytno-issledovatel'skiĭ institut vodnogo khoziaĭstva
see Tashkend. Sredne-Aziatskiĭ nauchno-issledovatel'skiĭ institut irrigafsii.

Tashkend. Sredne-Aziatskiĭ opytno-issledovatel'skiĭ institut vodnogo khoziaĭstva.
Труды.
Ташкент, 19
no. in ¡ ¡ v. 26 cm.
Published 1927–31. Cf. Периодическая печать СССР, 1917–1949; журналы ... по сельскому хозяйству, № 1214–19.
All issues divided into sub-series: А–Г, Ж–З, each with its own numbering.
Each issue has also a distinctive title.
Name of agency varies slightly.
No. 1.   have added title pages in English;
no.   have summaries in English.
1. Water-supply—Societies, etc. 2. Water-supply—Soviet Central Asia.   *Title transliterated:* Trudy.

TC1.T33   58–32869

NT   0046565   DLC

Tashkend. Sredneaziatskiĭ industrial'nyĭ institut.
... Труды Среднеазиатского индустриального института. вып. 1–   Ташкент, САИИ, 1938–
v. illus. diagrs. 25 cm.
At head of title, 1938–   : НКТП ГУУЗ. Среднеазиатский индустриальный институт.

1. Industrial arts—Societies, etc. 2. Technology—Societies, etc.
Title transliterated: Trudy.

Library of Congress   T4.T17   43–45787

NT   0046566   DLC

Tashkend. Sredneaziatskiĭ nauchno-issledovatel'skiĭ institut po khlopkovodstvu
see Tashkend. Vsesoiuznyĭ nauchno-issledovatel'skiĭ institut khlopkovodstva.

Tashkend. Tashkentskaia astronomicheskaia i fizicheskaia observatoriia
see
Tashkend. Astronomicheskaia observatoriia.

Tashkend. Tekstil'nyĭ institut.
Научные труды.
Ташкент, 19
v. in illus. 22–27 cm.
Began in 1933. Cf. Letopis' periodicheskikh izdaniĭ SSSR, 1958.
Title varies: Сборник научно-исследовательских работ.

1. Textile industry and fabrics—Collected works. i. Tashkend. Tekstil'nyĭ institut. Sbornik nauchno-issledovatel'skikh rabot.
Title romanized: Nauchnye trudy.

TS1300.T118   64–33048

NT   0046569   DLC MoKL

TS1300 .T118

Tashkend. Tekstil'nyi institut. Sbornik nauchno-issledovatel'skikh rabot.
Tashkend. Tekstil'nyĭ institut.
Научные труды.
Ташкент, 19

Tashkend. Tovarishchestvo turkestanskikh sadovladel'-
 fsev
  see
Tovarishchestvo turkestanskikh sadovladel'fsev, *Tashkend.*

Tashkend. Tovarnaîa birzha.

Uzbek S. S. R. *Mezhduvedomstvennoe bûro standartizafsii.*
Торговый стандарт на узбекистанские сухофрукты (Уз.
ОСТ №№ 12-33) Ташкент, 1930.

Tashkend. Trest po shelkovodstvu
  see Uzbekshelktrest, *Tashkend.*

Tashkend. TŜentral'nyï nauchno-issledovatel'skiï institut
 khlopkovoï promyshlennosti
  see Tashkend. Vsesofûznyï nauchno-issledovatel'skiï institut khlopkovodstva.

Tashkend. Turkestanskafâ vystavka plodovodstva, ogorod-
 nichestva, pchelovodstva i ptifŝevodstva, *1912.*
Туркестанская выставка плодоводства огородничества,
пчеловодства и птицеводства 1912 года в гор. Ташкентѣ;
сборникъ статей. Ташкентъ, Тип. при Канц. Турк. ген.-
губ., 1913.

iv, 174 p. illus. 25 cm.

1. Agriculture—Turkestan.
    Title transliterated: Turkestanskafâ vystavka.

S557.T8 1912c   67–58847

NT   0046575   DLC

Tashkend. Turkestanskiï kruzhok lîûbiteleï arkheologii
  see
Turkestanskiï kruzhok lîûbiteleï arkheologii, *Tashkend.*

Tashkend. Turkestanskoe nauchnoe obshchestvo
  see Tashkend. Universitet. Turkestanskoe nauchnoe
obshchestvo.

Tashkend. Universitatis Ásiae Mediae
  see
Tashkend. Universitet.

Tashkend. Université d'État
  see Tashkend. Universitet.

Tashkend. Universitet.
Founded 1918 as Tashkentskiï narodnyï universitet; in 1919 name
changed to Turkestanskiï universitet; present form of name (since
1923): Sredne-aziâtskiï gosudarstvennyï universitet.

Tashkend. Universitet.
Биологические науки. кн. 1
Ташкент, 1945

v. illus. 20–26 cm. (*Its* Труды. Новая серия)

Publication suspended 1946–49.
One issue of 1952 called erroneously v. 2.
Title varies: v. 1, Биология.
Vols. 2-   have also a distinctive title.

1. Biology—Societies, etc.   i. Title: Biologifâ.   II. Title
    Title transliterated: Biologicheskie nauki.

QH301.T353   58–34176

NT   0046581   DLC MiU

Tashkend. Universitet.
Биология (*transliterated:* Biologifâ)
  see its
Биологические науки (*transliterated:* Biologicheskie
nauki)

Tashkend. Universitet,
Bulletin de l'Université de l'Asie centrale ... Бюллетень
Средне-азиатского государственного университета. вып.
1/6-   ; 1923/24–
Ташкент-Taschkent, 1923/24–

v. illus., plates, ports., maps, tables, diagrs. 25 cm. (t. 1/6:
21½ cm.)

Title in French, Turko-Tataric and Russian.
Summaries in English, French or German.
Editors: 1923/24–   (v. 1/6-   ) P. A. Baranov (with
V. G. Mukhin, 1923/24–1926)

Descriptive sketch of the university, in Turko-Tataric (15 p.)
appended to v. 10.

1. Science—Societies, etc.   2. Asia, Central.   i. Mukhin, Vladimir
Grigorievich, 1885–   ii. Baranov, Pavel Aleksandrovich, 1892–
joint ed. iii. Title. iv.   Title: Бюллетень Среднеазиатского
государственного уни-   верситета.

Q60.T33   37—37865

NT   0046584   DLC OrCS ICJ GU

Tashkent. Universitet.
Catalogue of the publications of the Univ. of
Central Asia press. 1-   1922.29–
Tashkent, 1930–
  v.

NT   0046585   OU

Tashkend. Universitet.
Экономические науки. кн. 1–
Ташкент, 1955–

v. 22–26 cm. (*Its* Научные труды. Новая серия)

Vols. 1-   issued by the university under its variant name:
Среднеазиатский государственный университет имени В. И. Ленина.

1. Russia—Econ. condit.—Period.   i. Title.
    Title romanized: Ekonomicheskie nauki.

HC331.H1T38   68–129982

NT   0046586   DLC

Tashkend. Universitet.
Филологические науки. кн. 1–
Ташкент, 1952

v. illus. 20–27 cm. (*Its* Труды. Новая серия)

Vols.   have also a distinctive title.
Vols.   in Uzbek have added title pages in Russian.

1. Philology—Period.   i. Title.
    Title transliterated: Filologicheskie nauki.

P9.T33   58–33481

NT   0046587   DLC IU

Tashkend. Universitet.
Физико-математические науки. кн. 1⌐
Ташкент ₍etc.₎ Изд-во Академии наук УзССР ₍etc.₎ 1945–57

v. illus. 22–26 cm. (*Its* Труды. Новая серия)

Title varies: v. 7-   Математические науки.
     s title.

1. Mathematics—Societies, etc.   2. Physics—Societies, etc.   i.
Title.   *Title transliterated:* Fiziko-matematicheskie nauki.
Matematicheskie nauki.   II. Title .

QA1.T33   58–34175

NT   0046588   DLC MiU

Tashkend. Universitet.
Географические науки. кн. 2-
Ташкент, 1951–

v. illus. 22–26 cm. (*Its* Труды. Новая серия)

Vol. 7 incorrectly numbered 6.
Vol. 1 issued as Геолого-географические науки, which divided
into 2 publications: above and Геологические науки. Vol. 1 classified
with the latter.
Vols.   have also a distinctive title.

1. Geography—Societies, etc.   2. Asia, Central—Descr. & trav.
i. Title.   *Title transliterated:* Geograficheskie nauki.

G23.T33   58–33609

NT   0046589   DLC

Tashkend. Universitet.
Геологические науки. кн. 1-
Ереван ₍etc.₎ Изд-во Ереванского университета ₍etc.₎ 1949–57

v. illus. 25 cm. (*Its* Труды. Новая серия)

Title varies: v. 1–2, Геолого-географические науки.
Vols. 1-   have also a distinctive title.

1. Geology—Societies, etc.   2. Geology—Soviet Central Asia.   i.
Title.   *Title transliterated:* Geologicheskie nauki.

QE1.T382   58–34174

NT   0046590   DLC MiU

Tashkend. Universitet.
Геолого-географические науки (*transliterated:* Geologo-
geograficheskie nauki)
  see its
Геологические науки (*transliterataed:* Geologicheskie
nauki)

Tashkend. Universitet.
Гуманитарные науки. кн. 1–
Ташкент, 1945

v. illus. 22–26 cm. (*Its* Труды. Новая серия)

Vols.   have also a distinctive title.

1. Humanities—Period.   i. Title.
    Title transliterated: Gumanitarnye nauki.

AS581.T275   58–33463

NT   0046592   DLC MiU

Tashkend. Universitet.
Исторические науки.
Ташкент, 19

v. illus. 22–26 cm. (*Its* Труды. Новая серия)

Vols.   have also a distinctive title.
(LC set incomplete: v.1-6, 8-9, 12,15-
wanting.)

1. Asia—Hist.—Period.   2. History—Period.   i. Title.
    Title transliterated: Istoricheskie nauki.

DS1.T32   58–53486

NT   0046593   DLC

Tashkend. Universitet.
Химические науки. кн. 1–
Ереван ₍etc.₎ Изд-во Ереванского университета ₍etc.₎ 1945–

v. in   illus. 26 cm. (*Its* Труды. Новая серия)

Vol. 1 has title: Химия.

1. Chemistry—Societies, etc.   i. Title.
    Title transliterated: Khimicheskie nauki.

QD1.T3   59–50278

NT   0046594   DLC MiU DNAL

Tashkend. Universitet.
Химия (*transliterated:* Khimiiā)
see its
Химические науки (*transliterated:* Khimicheskie nauki)

Tashkend. Universitet.
Математические науки (*transliterated:* Matematicheskie nauki)
see its
Физико-математические науки (*transliterated:* Fiziko-matematicheskie nauki)

Tashkend. Universitet.
Сборник научных трудов аспирантов. вып. 1-
Ташкент, Изд-во САГУ, 1952-

no. illus. 25 cm.

No. 1-   issued by the university under its variant name : Sredneaziatskiĭ gosudarstvennyĭ universitet.

1. Dissertations, Academic—Uzbekistan.
    Title romanized: Sbornik nauchnykh trudov aspirantov.

AS581.T27S2   72-298369

NT 0046597   DLC

Tashkend. Universitet.
Сборник студенческих работ.
Ташкент, 19

v. in   26 cm.

Began publication in 1949. Cf. Serial publications of the Soviet Union, 1939-1957.
Issued by Ministerstvo vysshego obrazovaniĭā SSSR.

(L.C. set incomplete: v. 5 wanting.)

1. Russia (1923-   U. S. S. R.) Ministerstvo vysshego obrazovaniĭa.   *Title transliterated:* Sbornik studencheskikh rabot.

AS581.T2753   59-49666

NT 0046598   DLC

Tashkend. Universitet.
Систематический указатель к изданиям с 1922-1950 г.г. ₁составленный Библиографическим отделом Фундаментальной библиотеки университета. Составитель О. В. Маслова₁ Ташкент, Изд-во САГУ, 1952.

118 p. 20 cm. (Среднеазиатский государственный университет. Материалы к библиографии, вып. 2)

1. Tashkend. Universitet—Bibl. I. Maslova, O. V. II. Tashkend. Universitet. Fundamental'naĭā biblioteka. III. Title.   *Title transliterated:* Sistematicheskiĭ ukazatel' k izdaniĭām.

Z5055.R9T18   57-42643

NT 0046599   DLC

Tashkend. Universitet.
Средне-Азиатский государственный университет; к десятилетнему юбилею Октябрьской революции. Ташкент, 1927.

61 p. illus. 22 cm.

Title transliterated: Sredne-Aziatskiĭ gosudarstvennyĭ universitet.

LF4425.T356A45   50-48087

NT 0046600   DLC

Tashkend. Universitet.
Travaux
see its
Труды (*transliterated:* Trudy)

Tashkend. Universitet.
Труды. Серия VIII-a: Зоология. Acta. Series VIII-a: Zoologia. вып. 1-54. Ташкент, 1927-38.

54 no. in 3 v. illus., maps. 26 cm.
No. 30-49 "Dedicated to the twenty-fifth anniversary of ... professor A. L. Brodsky. xxv."
"Список научных трудов проф. А. Л. Бродского": p. 20-22 (preceding no. 30)
Series VII-d, no. 6, issued with no. 30-49 of Series VIII-a, bound after no. 40 of the latter. *LC set incomplete: no 32-45,*
No. 3 in English with summary in Russian. *27-38 wanting*
Summaries in English or German.
1. Zoology—Collected works. 2. Brodskiĭ, Abram L'vovich, 1883-
I. Title. II. Title: Acta. Series VIII-a: Zoologia.
    Title transliterated: Trudy. Seriĭā VIII-a: Zoologiĭā.

QL1.T325   62-40740

NT 0046602   DLC PU

Tashkend. Universitet.
Востоковедческие науки.
Ташкент, 19

(₁v. 26 cm. (*Its* Труды. Новая серия)

1. Oriental studies—Societies, etc. I. Title.
    Title transliterated: Vostokovedcheskie nauki.

DS1.T323   59-49594

NT 0046603   DLC

Tashkend. Universitet. Botanicheskiĭ institut

Определитель растений окрестностей Ташкента; иллюстрированное руководство к определению дикорастущих сосудистых споровых и цветковых растений. Составили: Введенский, А. И. ₁и др.₁. Ташкент, 1923-24.

Tashkend. Universitet. Fundamental'naiā biblioteka.

Tashkend. Universitet.
Систематический указатель к изданиям с 1922-1950 г.г. ₁составленный Библиографическим отделом Фундаментальной библиотеки университета. Составитель О. В. Маслова₁ Ташкент, Изд-во САГУ, 1952.

Tashkend. Universitet. *Fundamental'naĭā biblioteka.*
Указатель докторских и кандидатских диссертаций, защищенных в Узбекистане в 1936-1951 гг. Общественные науки, естественные науки, математика. ₁Ответственные редакторы: Д. Ф. Железняков и М. С. Виридарский₁ Ташкент, Изд-во САГУ, 1954.

174 p. 23 cm. (Среднеазиатский государственный университет. Материалы к библиографии, вып. 4)
At head of title: Среднеазиатский государственный университет. Фундаментальная библиотека САГУ и Государственная публичная библиотека УзССР. *Mikhail Sergeyevich*
1. Dissertations, Academic—Uzbekistan—Bibl. I. Zhelezniākov, D. F., ed. II. Viridarskiĭ, M. S., ed. III. Tashkend. Gosudarstvennaĭā publichnaĭā biblioteka. IV. Title.
    Title transliterated: Ukazatel' doktorskikh i kandidatskikh dissertaĭsiĭ zashchishchennykh v Uzbekistane.

Z5055.U9T3   57-44297

NT 0046606   DLC

Tashkend. Universitet. *Institut pochvovedeniĭā i geobotaniki.*
Bulletin ... Известия. вып. 1-
Ташкент, 1925-

v. plates, maps, diagrs. 25 cm.

Summaries in German or French.

1. Soils—Societies, etc. 2. Botany—Societies, etc.

S590.T32   48-34655

NT 0046607   DLC

Tashkend. Universitet. *Institut pochvovedeniĭā i geobotaniki.*
... Труды ... Казакстанская серия. Transactions. Kazakstanian series.
Ташкент, 19

v. plates. 25 cm.   Additions on Shelflist

Summary in English.
(Tashkend— Learned Institutions and societies)

science —
1. Soils—Societies, etc. 2. Botany—Societies, etc.
    Title transliterated: Trudy.

S590.T3   47-44583

NT 0046608   DLC

Tashkend. Universitet. Pamirskaia ekspeditsiĭa.
... Results of the Pamir expedition of the Middle Asiatic state university. fasc. 1-10.
Taschkent, Editio Universitatis Asiae mediae, 1936-

(Acta Universitatis Asiae Mediae. Ser. VIII-d, fasc. 5; ser. VIII-a, fasc. 22-25; ser. VIII-b, fasc. 30-32; ser. X, fasc. 3; ser. XII-a, fasc. 15.

NT 0046609   PU

Tashkend. Universitet. Turkestanskoe nauchnoe obshchestvo. Transactions
see its Труды (*transliterated:* Trudy)

Tashkend. Universitet. Turkestanskoe nauchnoe obshchestvo.
Труды. Transactions. т. 1-2; 1923-25. Ташкент.

2 v. illus., fold. map. 26 cm.

No more published?
Vol. 1 has imprint: Ташкент, Туркестанский гос. изд-во.

(Tashkend — Learned Institutions and Societies

1. Natural history—Societies. 2. Natural history—Turkestan.
    Title transliterated: Trudy.

QH7.T25   50-52234

NT 0046611   DLC

Tashkend. University of Central Asia
see **Tashkend. Universitet.**

Tashkend. Uzbekistanskaĭā karantinaĭā laboratoriĭa NKZ UzSSR
see UzbekSSR. Narodnyĭ komissariat zemledeliĭā. Karantinnaĭā laboratoriĭa.

Tashkend. Uzbekistanskiĭ filial Akademii nauk SSSR
see
Akademiĭā nauk SSSR. *Uzbekistanskiĭ filial, Tashkend.*

Tashkend. Uzbekistanskoe otdelenie Vsesoĭūznogo mineralogicheskogo obshchestva
see **Vsesoĭūznoe mineralogicheskoe obshchestvo.** *Uzbekistanskoe otdelenie, Tashkend.*

Tashkend. Uzbekshelktrest
see **Uzbekshelktrest,** *Tashkend.*

Tashkend. Uzbekskaĭā respublikanskaĭā kontora Gosudarstvennogo banka SSSR
see
Gosudarstvennyĭ bank SSSR. *Uzbekskaĭā respublikanskaĭā kontora, Tashkend.*

Tashkend. Uzbekskiĭ gosudarstvennyĭ nauchno-issledovatel'skiĭ institut.
... Ilmii fikr. n° 1-
₁maj/ijyn, 1930-
Samarqand, Taşkent, 1930-

v. illus. 25ᶜᵐ.

At head of title; 1930-   : Özbek devlet ilmii tekşiriş instityti.
Published also in Russian.

I. Title.
                                43-20669
Library of Congress   AS581.T28

NT 0046618   DLC

Tashkend. Uzbekskiĭ gosudarstvennyĭ nauchno-issledovatel'skiĭ institut.
... Научная мысль. Ilmii fikr. вып. 1–
май/июнь ₁1930₎– Самарканд–
Ташкент, 1930–
₍1₎ v. illus., tables. 25ᶜᵐ.
At head of title, 1930– ₍: Узбекский государственный научно-
исследовательский институт. Özbek dävlät ilmii tekşiriş instityti.
Published also in Uzbeg.
i. Title. *Title transliterated:* Nauchnaĭa mysl'.

43–32640
Library of Congress AS581.T3 Ldj Myai

NT 0046619 DLC

Tashkend. Uzbekskiĭ gosudarstvennyĭ nauchno-issledovatel'skiĭ institut kurortologii i fizioterapii.
Гипертоническая болезнь и лечение ее физическими
методами. ₍Ответственные редакторы В. М. Файбушевич
и Я. К. Муминов₎ Ташкент, Изд-во Академии наук
Узбекской ССР, 1955.
306, ₍5₎ p. illus. 27 cm. (*Its* Труды т. 13)
At head of title: Министерство здравоохранения Узбекской ССР.
Includes bibliographies.
1. Hypertension. i. Faĭbushevich, Veniamin Mikhaĭlovich, ed.
ii. Muminov, Ĭ. A., ed. iii. Title. (Series: Tashkend. Uzbekskiĭ
gosudarstvennyĭ nauchno-issledovatel'skiĭ institut kurortologii i fizioterapii. Trudy, t. 13)
Title transliterated: Gipertonicheskaĭa
bolezn' i lechenie ee.

RA791.T3A2 t. 13 66–93987

NT 0046620 DLC

Tashkend. Uzbekskiĭ gosudarstvennyĭ trest po shelkovodstvu
see Uzbekshelktrest, *Tashkend.*

Tashkend. Vsesoĭuznoe rabochee soveshchanie po itogam
izucheniĭa chetvertichnogo perioda, 1948
see
Vsesoĭuznoe rabochee soveshchanie po itogam izucheniĭa
chetvertichnogo perioda, *Tashkend, 1948.*

Tashkend. Vsesoĭuznyĭ nauchno-issledovatel'-
skiĭ institut khlopkovodstva.
Moscow. Vsesoĭuznyĭ nauchno-issledovatel'skiĭ institut kor-
mov.
Люцерна. ₍Авторы: бригада научных сотрудников
Всесоюзного научно-исследовательского института кор-
мов и Всесоюзного института по хлопководству₎ Москва, Гос. изд-во сельхоз. лит-ры, 1950.

Tashkend. Vsesoĭuznyĭ nauchno-issledovatel'skiĭ institut
khlopkovodstva.
Научный бюллетень.
Ташкент, 193
₍no. 1₎ v. illus. 23 cm.
Began publication in 1930. Cf. Периодическая печать СССР,
1917–1949; журналы ... по сельскому хозяйству, № 1227.
No₍2?–25₎ issued by the Institute under its earlier name: Vse-
soĭuznyĭ nauchno-issledovatel'skiĭ institut po khlopku.
Text also in Uzbek; summaries in English and Uzbek.
L. C. copy imperfectly bound: no.25 precedes 24.
1. Cotton growing—Period. *Title transliterated:* Nauchnyĭ bĭulleten'.

SB245.T3 60–34257

NT 0046624 DLC OrCS

Tashkend. Vsesoĭuznyĭ nauchno-issledovatel'skiĭ institut
khlopkovodstva.
За высокий урожай; агротехнические мероприятия по
повышению урожайности хлопчатника в 1932 году. Москва, Объединение гос. издательств, Среднеазиатское
отд-ние, 1932.
247 p. 27 cm.
Table of contents and errata (16 p., laid in)
1. Cotton growing—Russia. i. Title.
Title transliterated: Za vysokiĭ urozhaĭ.

SB251.R9T3 51–45706

NT 0046625 DLC

Tashkend. Vsesoĭuznyĭ nauchno-issledovatel'skiĭ institut
po khlopkovodstvu
see Tashkend. Vsesoĭuznyĭ nauchno-issledovatel'skiĭ institut khlopkovodstva.

Tashkend. Vsesoĭuznyĭ nauchno-issledovatel'skiĭ institut po
khlopkovodstvu, khlopkovoĭ promyshlennosti i irrigatsii
see Tashkend. Vsesoĭuznyĭ nauchno-issledovatel'skiĭ institut khlopkovodstva.

Tashkend. Vsesoĭuznyĭ nauchno-issledovatel'skiĭ institut
po khlopku
see
Tashkend. Vsesoĭuznyĭ nauchno-issledovatel'skiĭ institut
khlopkovodstva.

Tashkend. Vsesoĭuznyĭ tsentral'nyĭ nauchno-issledovatel'-
skiĭ institut khlopkovoĭ promyshlennosti
see Tashkend. Vsesoĭuznyĭ nauchno-issledovatel'skiĭ institut khlopkovodstva.

Tashkend (*District*) *Okruzhnaĭa posevnaĭa komissiĭa.*
План весенней посевной кампании по Ташкентскому
округу на 1930 год. Ташкент, 1930.
88 p. 30 cm.

1. Agriculture—Russia—Tashkend (District) i. Title.
Title transliterated: Plan vesennei posevnoĭ
kampanii po Tashkentskomu okrugu.

S471.R92T3 59–55437

NT 0046630 DLC

Tashkend (*District*) Okruzhnoe upravlenie
stroitel'nogo kontrolĭa.
Tashkend (*District*) *Upravlenie okruzhnogo inzhenera.*
Ведомость справочных цен на строительные материалы
и рабочую силу.
Ташкент.

Tashkend (*District*) *Posevnaĭa komissiĭa*
see Tashkend (*District*) *Okruzhnaĭa posevnaĭa komissiĭa.*

Tashkend (*District*) *Upravlenie okruzhnogo inzhenera.*
Ведомость справочных цен на строительные материалы
и рабочую силу.
Ташкент.
₍ ₎ v. 35 cm.
Issued by Tashkendskoe okruzhnoe upravlenie stroitel'nogo kontrolĭa.
"Издание официальное."
1. Building materials—Prices. 2. Building—Tashkend (District)
i. Tashkend (District) Okruzhnoe upravlenie stroitel'nogo kontrolĭa.
ii. Title.
Title transliterated: Vedomost' spravoch-
nykh tsen na stroitel'nye materialy.

TH86.T3A3 55–45863

NT 0046633 DLC

Tashkent
see
Tashkend.

Taskenspillerkunster eller den aff-
lørede heksemester; en samling af mor-
somme og underholdende taskenspiller-
og kortkunster og pudsige smaating, som
enhver kan udføre. København, J.
Strandberg [ ]
30 p.

NT 0046635 DLC-P4

Taskent, Hikmet.
Afroditin adasindan siirler. [Ankara, Yeni
Matbaa, 1945]
39 p.

NT 0046636 CLU

915.86 Tashkent. ₍Foreign Languages Publishing
T197 House₎ ₍n.d.₎
1v. (unpaged, chiefly illus.) 16cm.

1. Tashkent - Description - Views.

NT 0046637 NcU

Tashkentskaĭa astronomicheskaĭa i fizicheskaĭa observatoriĭa, *Tashkend*
see
Tashkend. Astronomicheskaĭa observatoriĭa.

Tashkentskaĭa geofizicheskaĭa observatoriĭa
see
Tashkend. Geofizicheskaĭa observatoriĭa.

Tashkentskaĭa okruzhnaĭa posevnaĭa komissiĭa
see Tashkend (*District*) *Okruzhnaĭa posevnaĭa komissiĭa.*

Tashkentskaĭa tovarnaĭa birzha
see Tashkend. *Tovarnaĭa birzha.*

Tashkentskiĭ gosudarstvennyĭ pedagogicheskiĭ institut
see
Tashkend. Gosudarstvennyĭ pedagogicheskiĭ institut.

Tashkentskiĭ gosudarstvennyĭ universitet
see
Tashkend. Universitet.

Tashkentskiĭ institut inzhenerov irrigatsii i mekhanizatsii
sel'skogo khozĭaĭstva
see
Tashkend. Institut irrigatsii i mekhanizatsii sel'skogo
khozĭaĭstva.

Tashkentskiĭ institut inzhenerov zheleznodorozhnogo trans-
porta
see
Tashkend. Institut inzhenerov zheleznodorozhnogo trans-
porta.

Tashkentskiĭ narodnyĭ universitet
see Tashkend. Universitet.

Tashkentskiy okrug, *Russia*
see Tashkend (District)

Tashkentskoe okruzhnoe upravlenie stroitel'nogo kontrolîa
see Tashkend (District) *Okruzhnoe upravlenie stroitel'-
nogo kontrolîa.*

Tashkentskiĭ tekstil'nyĭ institut
see
Tashkend. Tekstil'nyĭ institut.

Ṭashköprüzäde, Aḥmed ibn Muṣṭafā
see
Ṭāshkubrīzādah, Aḥmad ibn Muṣṭafā, 1495–1561.

Tashkovski, Dragan
see
Taškovski, Dragan.

Ṭāshkubrīzādah, Aḥmad ibn Muṣṭafā, 1495–1561.
Eš-šaqā'iq en-no'mānijje, von Ṭašköprüzäde, enthaltend
die biographien der türkischen und im osmanischen reiche
wirkenden gelehrten, derwisch-scheib's und ärzte von der
regierung sultān 'Oṭmān's bis zu der Sülaimân's des Grossen.
Mit zusaetzen, verbesserungen und anmerkungen aus dem
arabischen uebersetzt, von O. Rescher. Konstantinopel-
Galata, Buch- und steindruckerei Phoenix, 1927.
2 p. l., ₍II₎–iv, 361, ₍1₎ p. 28½ cm.

1. Turkey — Biog. — Dictionaries. 2. Scholars, Turkish.
I. Rescher, Oskar, 1883– tr. II. Title.

AZ760.T315   46–37323 rev

NT 0046652   DLC MH CU CtY ICU MB NN OCl

Ṭāshkubrīzādah, Aḥmad ibn Muṣṭafā, 1495–1561.
كتاب مفتاح السعاده ومصباح السياده فى موضوعات العلوم،
لاحمد بن مصطفى المعروف بطاش كبرى زاده. الطبعة الاولى·
حيدراباد دكن، مطبعة دائرة المعارف النظامية ₍١٢٢٨₎–١٢٥٦·
₍1911–37₎
3 v. 26 cm.
حيدراباد الدكن، مطبعة دائرة المعارف العثمانية : Vol. 3 has imprint
CONTENTS.—الجزء الاول: بيان العلوم الخطية. — علوم تتعلق بالالفاظ. —
علوم باحثة عما فى الاذهان. العلم المتعلق بالاعيان. الحكمة العملية— العلوم
الشرعية — الجزء الثانى: العلوم الشرعية (تابع) — الجزء الثالث: علوم الباطن·

1. Encyclopedias and dictionaries—Early works to 1600. I. Title:
Miftāḥ al-sa'ādah wa-miṣbāḥ al-siyādah.
Title transliterated: Kitāb miftāḥ al-sa'ādah.

AE3.T3 1911   N E 61–144

NT 0046654   DLC

Ṭāshkubrīzādah, Aḥmad ibn Muṣṭafā, 1495–1561.
كتاب مفتاح السعاده ومصباح السياده فى موضوعات العلوم·
لاحمد بن مصطفى المعروف بطاش كبرى زاده. الطبعة الاولى·
حيدراباد دكن، مطبعة دائرة المعارف النظامية ₍١٢٢٨₎–١٢٥٦·
₍1911–37₎
3 v. 26 cm.
الجزء الاول: بيان العلوم الخطية. علوم تتعلق بالالفاظ. —CONTENTS
علوم باحثة عما فى الاذهان. العلم المتعلق بالاعيان. الحكمة العملية— العلوم
الشرعية — الجزء الثانى: العلوم الشرعية (تابع) — الجزء الثالث: علوم الباطن·

1. Encyclopedias and dictionaries—Early works to 1600. I. Title:
Miftāḥ al-sa'ādah wa-miṣbāḥ al-siyādah.
Title transliterated: Kitāb miftāḥ al-sa'ādah.

AE3.T3 1911   N E 61–144

NT 0046656   DLC

Ṭāshkubrīzādah, Aḥmad ibn Muṣṭafā, 1495–1561.
طبقات الفقهاء، لمولانا طاش كبرى زاده، عن نسخة مخطوطة
وجدت فى مكتبة الامير غازى العامة فى الموصل. نشر هذا الكتاب
بعد تنقيحه وتعليق حواشيه وتصديره أحمد نيلة. الطبعة 1.
الموصل، مطبعة نينوى، ١٩٥٤ ₍1954₎
136 p. 22 cm.

1. Islamic law—Biog. I. Title.
Title transliterated: Ṭabaqāt al-fuqahā'.

N E 66–336

NT 0046657   DLC

Ṭāshkuprī-zādah, Aḥmad ibn Muṣṭafā
see
Ṭāshkubrīzādah, Aḥmad ibn Muṣṭafā, 1495–1561.

Tashlin, Frank.
The bear that wasn't, by Frank Tashlin.
London, J. Murray [1946]
[60] p. illus. 26 cm.
"First edition".

NT 0046659   PU

Tashlin, Frank.
The bear that wasn't, by Frank Tashlin. New York, E. P.
Dutton & co., inc., 1946.
₍55₎ p. illus. 26ᶜᵐ.
"First edition."

1. Bears—Legends and stories. I. Title.

                             46–1683
Library of Congress ⊚   PZ10.3.T139Be

        WaS WaSp
NT 0046660   DLC NcD NcRS ViU PWcS PP NIC PPL OrP OCl

Tashlin, Frank.
The 'possum that didn't; story and illustrations by Frank
Tashlin. New York, Farrar, Straus ₍1950₎
₍61₎ p. illus. 26 cm.
SUMMARY: When littering busybodies from the city decide that
a smiling, upside-down possum in the forest is frowning, they try to
entertain him at movies and nightclubs in the city.

₍1. Opossums—Fiction₎ I. Title.

PZ7.T21114Po   [E]   50–9357

NT 0046661   DLC WaE

Tashlin, Frank.
The world that isn't. New York, Simon and Schuster,
1951.
unpaged. illus. 23 cm.

1. American wit and humor, Pictorial. I. Title.

NC1429.T18A55   741.5   51–14037 ‡

NT 0046662   DLC WaE WaT WaS MH NN

Tashlifäkiĭ, N   I
Bearbeitbarkeit des Stahls; Einfluss der mechanischen
Eigenschaften und der Wärmeleitfähigkeit. ₍Übersetzung
aus dem Russischen: N. Michailoff₎ Berlin, Verlag Technik, 1954.
94 p. illus. 21 cm. (Schriftenreihe des Verlages Technik, Bd.
178)
Translation of Влияние механических свойств и теплопроводности сталей на их обрабатываемость (transliterated: Vliîanie mekhanicheskikh svoĭstv i teploprovodnosti staleĭ na ikh obrabatyvaemost')

1. Steel. 2. Metal-work. I. Title.

TS320.T315   57–58555 ‡

NT 0046663   DLC

Tashlifäkiĭ, N   I
Влияние механических свойств и теплопроводности сталей на их обрабатываемость. Москва, Гос. научно-техи.
изд-во машиностроит. лит-ры, 1952.
84, ₍4₎ p. illus. 22 cm. (Центральный научно-исследовательский
институт технологии и машиностроения. Научно-техническая ин-
формация, 14)
Bibliography: p. 84–₍85₎
1. Steel. 2. Metal-work. I. Title. (Series: Moscow. Tsentral'nyĭ nauchno-issledovatel'skiĭ institut tekhnologii i mashinostroe-
niîa. Nauchno-tekhnicheskaîa informatsiîa, 14)
Title transliterated: Vliîanie mekhanicheskikh svoĭstv
i teploprovodnosti staleĭ na ikh obrabatyvaemost'.

TS320.T3   54–17602

NT 0046664   DLC

Tashmukhammedov, Musa, 1905–
see Aĭbek, *pseud.*

Tashnagtzagants Society
see
Hay Heghap'okhakan Dashnakts'owt'iwn.

Tashnagtzagantz society
see Armenian revolutionary
federation.

Tashrak, pseud.
see Zevin, Israel Joseph, 1872–1926.

Tasi, Diego.   **FR30.T:8
Ruota simbolica e profetica di Saint' Anselmo Vescovo di Marsico,
con altre figure . . . corredate di commenti e d'altre profezie. 2a
edizione . . .
Torino. Foa. 1870. 258, (1) pp. Illus. Plate. 18.5 cm., in 8s.

E3568 — T.r. — Popes. — Joachim,   Cistercian Abbot of Fiore,
1133–1202. — Prophecy.

NT 0046669   MB

PQ
4733   Tasi, Nane.
T178P2   Passatempi de Tasi Nane. — Venezia : Stab.
tip. Fratelli Visentini editori, 1894.
74 p.

Poems.

NT 0046670   CLU NNC

854.7W
I15

Tasi, Nane.
Strena, de Tasi Nane, ano 1896. Venezia,
Ferrari, 1895.
63 p.

Poems.

1. Italian language - Dialects - Venice.
I. Title.

NT 0046671   NNC

Tasić, Antonije.
Osnovi osiguranja; znatno skraćeni kurs. 2. izd. Beograd,
1952.
109 p. 20 cm. (Izdanja "Finansija," sv. 3)

1. Insurance.   I. Title.

HG8051.T3 1952   55–19838 ‡

NT 0046672   DLC

Tasić, Đorđe, 1892–
La conscience juridique internationale, par Georges Tas-
sitch ...
(*In* Hague. Academy of international law. Recueil des cours,
1938, III. Paris, 1938. 24½ cm. v. 65, p. ₍305₎–₍393₎, port.)
"Notice biographique. Principales publications": p. ₍307₎
"Bibliographie": p. ₍391₎–392.

1. International cooperation. 2. ₍Internationalism₎   A 40—694
Carnegie Endow. for Int.   Peace. Library
for Library of Congress   JX1295.A3A24 vol. 65
        [JX74.H3 vol. 65]
        ₍a50c¼₎   (341.082)

NT 0046673   NNCE NcD OCU

Tasić, Đorđe, 1892–
... Одговорност државе по принципу једнакости терета ...
Београд, Штампарија "Мироточиви" В. Карацина, 1921.
245 p. 23ᶜᵐ.
"Оштампано из 'Архива за правне и друштвене науке'."

1. State, The. 2. Yugoslavia—Constitutional law. 3. Administrative
law—Yugoslavia.   I. Title.
        41–87040

NT 0046674   DLC

Tasić, Đorđe, 1892–
Правне расправе. Београд, Г. Кон, 1921.
88 p. 20 cm.
Includes bibliographies.

1. Public law—Yugoslavia—Addresses, essays, lectures.   I. Title.
      Title transliterated: Pravne rasprave.

        56–55160

NT 0046675   DLC

Tasić, Đorđe, 1892–
Проблем оправдања државе. Београд, Држ. штампарија
Краљевине Срба, Хрвата и Словенаца, 1920.
90 p. 24 cm.
Doktorska teza—Belgrad.

1. State, The.   I. Title.
      Title transliterated: Problem opravdanja države.

JC273.T35   54–49187 ‡

NT 0046676   DLC CSt

Tasić, Djordje, 1892–
Socijalna ideologija i nacionalizam Antuna Radića.
Beograd, Izd.zadruga Politika i društvo [1939]

35 p.   (Biblioteka Politika i društvo, 30)

NT 0046677   MH

Tasić, Đorđe, 1892–
... Три расправе из јавног права. Београд, Издавачка
књижарница Г. Кона, 1931.
71 p. 23ᶜᵐ
"Литература": p. 71.

1. Administrative law. 2. Constitutional law. 3. Law—Philosophy.
I. Title.
        41–87041

NT 0046678   DLC

Tasić, Đorđe, 1892–
Увод у правне науке (енциклопедија права) предавања
д-р Ђорђа Тасића. Београд, Штампарија Главног савеза
српских земљорадничких задруга, 1933.
332 p. 24½ᶜᵐ.
Bibliography: p. ₍316₎–322.

1. Law—Hist. & crit. 2. Law—Philosophy. 3. Jurisprudence.
I. Title.
        41–87042
        340.1

NT 0046679   DLC

Law

Tasić, Đorđe, 1892–
Увод у правне науке. 3. изд., попр. и доп. Београд,
1941.
234 p. 24 cm.

1. Law—Hist. & crit. 2. Law—Philosophy. 3. Jurisprudence.   I.
Title.   *Title transliterated:* Uvod u pravne nauke.
        53–56586 ‡

NT 0046680   DLC

Tasić, Gjordje
    see Tasić, Đorđe, 1892–

QA37
.T3

Tasić, Milan.
Виша математика : диференцијални рачун, интегрални
рачун, диференцијалне једначине. Београд, Изд. Графич-
ког ин-та "Народна мисао," 1930.
446 p. illus. 23 cm.

1. Mathematics.   *Title transliterated:* Viša matematika.

QA37.T3   54–45456 ‡

NT 0046682   DLC

Tasić, Milos, 1900–
... Tumeurs cérébrales et radiothérapie ...
Lyon, 1925.
25 cm.
Thèse - Univ. de Lyon.
At head of title: Travail du laboratoire médical
du professeur Cluzet et du service du docteur
Froment ...
Bibliographie: p. 115–118.

NT 0046683   CtY

Tasić, Vandel, 1899–
(О сунчању и лековитим водама)
О сунчању и лековитим водама; предавања, одржана
на Коларчевом народном универзитету. Београд, 1952.
44 p. 20 cm. (Библиотека Коларчевог народног универзитета,
бр. 12)

1. Sun-baths. 2. Health resorts, watering-places, etc.   I. Title.

RM843.T37   75–581444

NT 0046684   DLC

T113
St8
1927

Tasić, Vandel, 1899
... Les stations hydro-minérales du royaume
des Serbes, Croates et Slovènes ...
Strasbourg, 1927. 22ᶜᵐ.
Thèse - Univ. de Strasbourg.
"Bibliographie": pp. ₍130₎–133.

NT 0046685   CtY ICRL

Tasin, Nicolas
...La dictadura del proletariado según Marx, Engels, Kaut-
sky, Bernstein, Axelrod, Lenin, Trotzky y Bauer. Madrid:
Biblioteca nueva ₍1920₎. 240 p. 12°.

1. Socialism. 2. Bolshevism.   3. Marx, Karl, 1818–83. 4. Engels,
Friedrich, 1820–95. 5. Kautsky,   Karl, 1854– . 6. Bernstein,
Eduard, 1850– . 7. Akselrod,   Pavel Borisovich, 1850– . 8. Len-
in, Nikolai, 1870– . 9. Trotzky,   Leon, 1880– . 10. Bauer, Otto.
N. Y. P. L.   May 24, 1921.

NT 0046686   NN

Tasin, Nicolas

Lenin, Vladimir Ilʹich, 1870–1924.
... El estado y la revolución proletaria, semblanza del autor,
por N. Tasin. Madrid, Biblioteca nueva ₍1920?₎

Tasin, Nicolas.
Heroes y martires de la Revolucion Rusa
precursores (excluída la Gran Revolución
Socialista de 1917) ₍La Habana, Tosco é
Hijos, n.d.₎
159p. 23cm.

1.Revolutionists, Russian. I.Title.

NT 0046688   CLSU

Tasin, Nicolas   S947-T
Héroes y mártires de la revolución rusa; episodios de la lucha
revolucionaria desde 1825, hasta nuestros días. Madrid: Biblioteca
Nueva ₍19—?₎. 233 p. 12°.

1. Russia.—History. 2. Title.
N. Y. P. L.   October 21, 1921.

NT 0046689   NN

Tasin, Nicolas, tr.

Kropotkin, Petr Alekseevich, *kni͡azʹ*, 1842–1921.
... Origen y evolución de la moral, traducción directa del
ruso por Nicolás Tasin. Buenos Aires, Editorial Americalee
₍1945₎

Tasin, Nicolas
A prodigal daughter: a play...by N. Tassin ₍pseud.₎ (Translated from the Russian by: Walter Ross.) ₍New York?
c1936₎ 96 f. 29cm.

Typescript.

        Russian Historical Archives.
1. Drama, Russian. I. Ross,   Walter, tr. II. Title.
N. Y. P. L.   March 29, 1945

NT 0046691   NN

Tasin, Nicolas
...La revolución rusa; sus orígenes, caída del zarismo. la revolución de marzo, el bolchevismo, sus doctrinas, sus hombres, su acción. Madrid: Biblioteca nueva ₍1919₎. 3 p.l., 9–309 p., 1 l. 12°.

"Texto íntegro de la constitución rusa, aprobado en enero de 1918 por el III Congreso panruso de los Soviets," p. 289–309.

1. Russia.—History: Revolution, 1917– . 2. Bolshevism.
N. Y. P. L. April 9, 1920.

NT 0046692 NN

Tasiro, K
Ueber die gruppenspezifischen substanzen in den menschlichen speicheldrusen. Jena, Fischer, 1938.
p. 111–118. tab. 8°.
Rep. Zeitsch. f. immunitätsforsch. June 11, 1938.

NT 0046693 PU-D

Tasis, conde de Oñate y Villamediana, Inigo Vélez de Guevara
see Oñate y Villamediana, Iñigo Vélez de Guevara Tasis, conde de, 1597-1658.

Tasis, Rafael
see Tasis i Marca, Rafael.

Tasis i Marca, Rafael, *ed.*
Antologia de la poesia catalana de Ramon Llull a Jacint Verdaguer (segles XIII a XIX) Selecció, pròleg i notes biogràfiques de Rafael Tasis. Barcelona ₍Editorial Selecta, 1949₎
275 p. facsim. 14 cm. (Biblioteca Selecta, 58)

1. Catalan poetry (Collections) I. Title.

PC3929.T3
50-35161

NT 0046696 DLC NcU CtY OU NN PBm CU

Tasis i Marca, Rafael.
La Bíblia valenciana. ₍Novel·la. 1. ed.₎ Barcelona, Albertí ₍1955₎
170 p. 16 cm. (Nova col·lecció lletres, no. 11)

I. Title.

PC3941.T3B5
56-19031

NT 0046697 DLC IU NN

Tasis i Marca, Rafael.
Històries de coneguts; figures i moments de la nostra història. Paris, E. Ragasol, 1945.
187 p. 22 cm. (Col·lecció Poesia i prosa catalana, 2)

1. Catalonia—Hist. 2. Catalonia—Biog. I. Title. (Series)

DP302.C62T29
50-26451

NT 0046698 DLC

Tasis i Marca, Rafael.
... La literatura catalana moderna. Barcelona, Comissariat de propaganda de la generalitat de Catalunya, 1937.
81 p., 1 l. 17½ᶜᵐ. (Aspectes de la actividad catalana. 1)

1. Catalan literature—Hist. & crit. I. Title.
40-15114

Library of Congress DP302.C57A8 t. 1
₍2₎ (914.67) 849.909

NT 0046699 DLC

Tasis i Marca, Rafael.
La novel·la catalana. ₍Barcelona₎ Sagitari, 1954.
105 p. 18 cm. (Col·lecció Assaig)

1. Catalan fiction—Hist. & crit. I. Title.

PC3917.T3
56-34970 ‡

NT 0046700 DLC CU

Tasis i Marca, Rafael.
Les pedres parlen, fulls d'historia de Catalunya ₍per₎ Rafael Tasis i Marca. Dibuixos: Xirinius. ₍Barcelona₎ Comissariat de propaganda de la generalitat de Catalunya, 1938.
64 p., 1 l. illus. 19 x 17ᶜᵐ.

1. Catalonia—Hist. 2. Catalonia—Historic houses, etc. I. Catalonia. Comissariat de propaganda. II. Title.
44-16808

Library of Congress DP302.C62T3
₍2₎ 946.7

NT 0046701 DLC

Tasis i Marca, Rafael.
... La revolución en los ayuntamientos ... Paris ₍Association hispanophile de France₎ 1937.
35 p. 19ᶜᵐ. (Antecedentes y documentos. 3)

48-30758
Brief cataloging

Library of Congress DP252.A6 no. 3

NT 0046702 DLC GU MH NN

Tasis i Marca, Rafael.
... La révolution dans les municipalités ... Paris [Association hispanophile de France]
38 p., 1 l. 20.5 cm. (Antécédents et documents [3])

NT 0046703 CtY

Tasis i Marca, Rafael.
Sol ponent. ₍1. ed.₎ Barcelona, Club de Divulgació Literària ₍1953₎
165 p. 17 cm. (Col·lecció Lletres, volum núm. 4)

I. Title.

PC3941.T3S6
56-19848 ‡

NT 0046704 DLC NN

Tasis i Marca, Rafael.
La vida del rei En Pere III. Pròleg de Ferran Soldevila. ₍1. ed.₎ Barcelona, Editorial Aedos ₍1954₎
425 p. illus. 23 cm. (Biblioteca biogràfica catalana, 5)
Includes bibliography.

1. Pedro IV, King of Aragon, 1319?–1387.

DP130.7.T3
54-41896 ‡

NT 0046705 DLC

Tasis i Marca, Rafael
Una visió de conjunt de la novela catalana. Barcelona, "La Revista", 1935.
154 p. (Publicacions de "La Revista")
1. Catalan fiction - Hist. & crit.

NT 0046706 ICU MH NcU

Tasistro, Louis Fitzgerald, 1808-1868.
Etiquette of Washington: setting forth the rules to be observed in social intercourse ... By L. F. Tasistro ... Washington city, W. H. & O. H. Morrison, 1866.
30 p. 15½ᶜᵐ.

1. Etiquette—Washington, D. C.
9—30580

Library of Congress BJ1858.T3

NT 0046707 DLC NIC OCl

Tasistro, Louis Fitzgerald, 1808-1868.
The Expositor. A weekly journal of foreign and domestic intelligence, literature, science, and the fine arts. v. 1; Dec. 8, 1838–June 15, 1839. New-York, 1838–39.

B812T182
Q5
1842 **Tasistro, Louis Fitzgerald,** 1808-1868.
Fitzhenry, or, A marriage in high life. A story of the heart, in fifteen chapters. Founded on events in the life of a fashionable English lady of high rank. Boston, 1842.
40 p. 29cm.

From The Boston Notion. Extra series, vol. I, nos. 1, 2, 3, January 1842.

NT 0046709 NNC CtY

Za **[Tasistro, Louis Fitzgerald]** 1808-1868
T182 Fitzhenry; or, A marriage in high life./ A story
847f of the heart. Founded on events in the life of a fashionable English lady of high rank. Boston, F. Gleason, 1847.
1p. ℓ., [7]-100p. 22 1/2cm.
In double columns.

NT 0046710 CtY

Tasistro, Louis Fitzgerald, 1808-1868, &c.
FOR OTHER EDITIONS
SEE MAIN ENTRY
Paris, Louis Philippe Albert d'Orléans, *comte de,* 1838-1894.
History of the civil war in America. By the Comte de Paris Published by special arrangement with the author ... Philadelphia, Porter & Coates ₍ᶜ1875–88₎

Tasistro, Louis Fitzgerald, 1808-1868.
Morrison's stranger's guide for Washington city; with etiquette to be observed in calling upon the President, officers of the government, foreign ministers, etc., by L. F. Tasistro ... Entirely re-written, and brought down to the present time. Washington, D. C., W. H. & O. H. Morrison, 1866.

Tasistro, Louis Fitzgerald, 1808-1868.
Random shots and southern breezes, containing critical remarks on the southern states and southern institutions, with semi-serious observations on men and manners. By Louis Fitzgerald Tasistro ... New-York, Harper & brothers, 1842.
2 v. 18½ᶜᵐ.

1. Southern states—Descr. & trav. 2. Southern states—Soc. life & cust. I. Title.
15-10681

Library of Congress 36b1.
F213.T19

OClW OU MB NN MiU
NT 0046713 DLC TxHU OC AAP FMU PPL CtY ViU NcD CU

Tasistro, Louis Fitzgerald, 1808-1868.

Random shots and Southern breezes, containing critical remarks on the Southern States and Southern institutions, with semi-serious observations on men and manners. New-York, Harper, 1842.

Microcard edition (7 cards) (Travels in the Old South III, 246) microprinted by the Lost Cause Press, Louisville, 1961.
1. Southern States—Descr. & trav. 2. Southern States—Soc. life & cust. I. Title. II. Ser.

NT 0046714   ViU OOxM MoU CSt MsU

Micro Film D50 reel 455 no.1

Tasistro, Louis Fitzgerald
Random shots and southern breezes, containing critical remarks on the southern states and southern institutions, with semi-serious observations on men and manners. By Louis Fitzgerald Tasistro ... New-York, Harper & brothers, 1842.
(On American culture series, reel 455, no.1)
Microfilm (positive). 35mm. Ann Arbor, Mich., University Microfilms, 1971.
Collation of the original: 2v.
1. Southern states - Descr. & trav. 2. Southern states - Soc. life & cust. I. Title.

NT 0046715   PSt

Tasistro, Louis Fitzgerald, 1808-1868
Random shots and southern breezes, containing critical remarks on the southern states and southern institutions, with semi-serious observations on men and manners ... 2d ed. New York, Harper & brothers, 1847.

2v.in 1.   19cm.

NT 0046716   CLSU

Tasistro, Louis Fitzgerald, 1808-1868
Woman: her character, her position, and her treatment, from the earliest days down to the present times. Being the substance of a lecture delivered before the Baltimore Addison lyceum, by Louis Fitzgerald Tasistro ... Baltimore, J. Murphy & co., ornamental printers, 1850.
vi, [7]-50 p. 23cm.   YA. 17714
Pub. by request of the society.
Cop 2 In 040 C45
1. Woman—History and condition of women.

9-5371†

Library of Congress   HQ1306.T22

NT 0046717   DLC NcGU ICJ

---

al-Tasjīl 'alá Faransā fī quṭr Tūnis wa-al-Jazā'ir.

al-Sharīf, Ṣāliḥ.
(al-Tasjīl 'alá Faransā fī quṭr Tūnis wa-al-Jazā'ir)
التسجيل على فرنسا في قطر تونس والجزائر ، بيان توحش
فرنسا في القطر التونسي الجزائري والاستنجاد اليه ، بقلم صالح
الشريف التونسي . [Berlin? 1916?]

Task, Harry.
The life of the party, by Harry Task. [Columbus, O., °1928]
94 p. 22 x 10cm.

1. Entertaining. 2. Amusements. I. Title.

Library of Congress   GV1471.T3

28-22683

NT 0046719   DLC

Task; a magazine for architects and planners. [no. 1]- [New York, etc.], 1941-
nos. in   v. illus., maps, diagrs. 23½-28cm.
Subtitle varies (no. 3 lacks subtitle)

1. Architecture—Period. 2. Cities and towns—Planning—Period. 3. Regional planning—Period.

46-39145

Library of Congress   NA1.T15
[2]   720.5

NT 0046720   DLC MWelC OrU MB CU CaOTU MoSW

The task and the method of Quakerism
see under Friends, Society of. International conference, 9th, Geneva, 1939.

Task force. v. 1-
May 1954-   Ormond Beach, Fla. [etc.]
13 v. in   27 cm.   Monthly.
"Official publication of Defenders of the American Constitution".
1. U.S. Pol. & govt. 1945-   Period.
I. Defenders of the American Constitution.

NT 0046722   OrU

Task Force from Philco, DuMont, RCA and General Electric.
The impact of TV expansion [prepared for the Radio-Television Manufactures Association Television Committee by the Task Force appointed November 1, 1951, W.H. Chaffee, Chairman. n.p. [1952?]
43 p. illus.

NT 0046723   OC1

Task Force 68 (U. S. Navy)
see U. S. Navy. Task Force 68.

The TASK of the Christian church; a world survey. London, World dominion press [1926]
viii, 141 p. 25.5 cm.
Pref. signed by Thomas Cochrane, editor.
And. H.

NT 0046725   MH WaS CtY ODW

Taskaev, Ivan.
Первый тракторный. Саратов, Гос. изд-во, Нижне-Волжское краевое отд-ние, 1930.
57 p. illus. 23 cm.

1. Stalingradskiĭ traktornyĭ zavod imeni F. Dzerzhinskogo. I. Title.   Title transliterated: Pervyĭ traktornyĭ.

TL86.S8T3

53-56677

NT 0046726   DLC

Taskeen, Qamar, 1922-
ہزاروں لڑکیاں ، ناول ، ایک اداس نوجوان کی داستان
محبت. ۔ مصنفہ قمر تسکین . لاهور، شعاع ادب،
1955
192 p. 19 cm.
In Urdu.
Text partially vocalized.

I. Title.   Title transliterated: Hazāroṃ laṛkiyāṃ.

PK2200.T37H39

S A 65-4075

NT 0046727   DLC

Tasker, A.
Ruth: a poem. By A. Tasker. London, T. Danks [189-]
1 p. l., 45 p. 15½cm.

1. Ruth—Poetry. I. Title.

27-22874

Library of Congress   PR5548.T54R8

NT 0046728   DLC

F 91151 .862

TASKER, A   E
Early history of Lincoln County from the early writings of old pioneers, historians and later writers. Compiled by A. E. Tasker together with a collection of biographical sketches of early Lincoln County pioneers. [Lake Benton, Minn.,] Lake Benton News Print, 1936.
352p. 23cm.
Additional biographical information

tipped in.
Pencilled notes and corrections in margins.

NT 0046730   ICN MnHi MiD ICU

Tasker, Albert P.
Grand army of the republic. Dept. of the Potomac.
Address of the department commander. Headquarters Department of the Potomac, Grand army republic, Washington, D. C., February 5, 1906. To the thirty eighth annual encampment. [Washington, 1906]

Tasker, Arthur H
Earth saga, a poetic novel, by Arthur H. and Litha M. Tasker. [1st ed.] Portland, Me., Bond Wheelwright Co., 1954.
261 p. 24 cm.
"A Cumberland Press book."

I. Tasker, Litha M., joint author. II. Title.

PS3539.A7E3   811.5   52-11677 ‡

NT 0046732   DLC NN OrU LU WaS WaWW IdB OrSaW IdU

Tasker, Arthur Newman, 1878-
U. S. Surgeon-general's office.
The medical department of the U. S. army in the world war; prepared under the direction of Maj. Gen. M. W. Ireland ... vol. IX: Communicable and other diseases, by Lieut.-Col. Joseph F. Siler ... Washington, U. S. Govt. print. off., 1928.

Tasker, Benjamin.
... Complaint being made to Me, Levin Gale, Esq; Chief Justice of the Provincial Court of Maryland, by Benjamin Tasker, Charles Carrol, and Daniel Dulany, of Annapolis, Esqrs; That Seven Men Servants ran away from them, and others their Partners from their Iron-Works at Potapsco River, the 24th Day of June last ...
see under Maryland (Colony) Provincial Court.

Tasker, Benjamin, appellant.
Maryland. Benjamin Tasker, esq; appellant
see under Ryder, Sir Dudley, 1691-1756.

Tasker, Dain L[oren] 1872-
Principles of osteopathy, by Dain L. Tasker ... Los Angeles, Cal., Baumgardt publishing co., 1903.
1 p. l., [7]-352, [7] p. front., illus., diagr. 23½cm.   3-11482

NT 0046736   DLC MB

Tasker, Dain Loren, 1872-   615.87 Q502
Principles of osteopathy. By Dain L. Tasker, ... Second edition revised and enlarged, illustrated. Los Angeles, Cal., Baumgardt Publishing Co., 1905.
392, [8] p. incl. front., illus. 23½cm.

NT 0046737   ICJ

Tasker, Dain Loren, 1872–
Principles of osteopathy, by Dain L. Tasker ... 3d ed.,
rev. ... Los Angeles, Cal., Bireley & Elson printing co.
[1913]
1 p. l., [7]–531, [7] p. front., illus. 23½ cm.

1. Osteopathy.

RZ341.T19 1913   13—18043

NT 0046738   DLC DNLM ICJ

RZ
341
.T19
1916
    Tasker, Dain Loren, 1872–
    Principles of osteopathy / by Dain L.
Tasker. 4th ed. illus. Los Angeles,
Calif. ; Bireley & Elson, [c1916]
531, [7] p. : front., ill. ; 24 cm.
Bibliography: p. 529–531.
Includes index.

1. Osteopathy I. Title

NT 0046739   MiEM

RZ.
341
.T19
1925
    Tasker, Dain Loren, 1872–
    Principles of osteopathy, by Dain L.
Tasker. 5th ed., rev. Los Angeles,
Cal., Bireley & Elson [c1925]
589 p. illus. 24 cm.
Includes bibliography.

1. Osteopathy. I. Title

NT 0046740   MiEM PPPH ICJ DNLM

TASKER, David.
Musings of leisure hours; [poems]
Dundee, 1865.

NT 0046741   MH

PR
6039
.A854
A6
1907
    Tasker, David
    Readings, recitations, and sketches.
Dundee, Printed by John Pellow, 1907.
120p. front.(port.)

NT 0046742   ScU

W
.15
    [Tasker, E.   , compiler]
    CATALOGUE of a private library, containing
an exceedingly valuable collection of fine-art
and illustrated books, illuminated manuscripts,
original drawings, etc., etc. to be sold by auction March 3d, and following eve'gs... Geo. A.
Leavitt & co., auctioneers... [New York, 1880]
109p.

669 entries.
Priced in ms.
Inserted: ms. letter from Isaac N. Demmon.

NT 0046743   ICN OC1RC

DA
690
I34T3
    Tasker, George E
    Ilford past and present, including an
account of Aldborough Hatch, Barkingside,
Chadwell, Hainault Forest; Seven Kings; and a
history of events connected with the parish
of Ilford, by Geo. E. Tasker. Ilford, S. W.
Hayden, [1901]

160 p. front., illus. 22 cm.

1. Ilford, England. I. Title.   rw

NT 0046744   IEdS MH

Tasker, George Pease, 1872–
Synthetic studies in the Pentateuch (major) by G. P. Tasker
... New York, N. Y., Bible study by mail, [1911.
25 pt. 20½ᶜᵐ.

CONTENTS.—Foreword to the student.—Introduction to a study of the
tabernacle.—Introduction to Leviticus.—Introduction to Deuteronomy.—
Lessons I–XXI.

1. Bible. O. T. Pentateuch—Study—Text-books. 2. Bible—Study—
Text-books—O. T. Pentateuch. I. Title.
                   42–45221

Library of Congress   BS1225.T35

NT 0046745   DLC

Tasker, George Pease, 1872–
What about the second coming. By G. P. Tasker
... [Bangalore, 1938]
52 p. 20 cm.

NT 0046746   NRCR

Tasker, H. A., ed.

Tasker, Joseph Louis, d. 1848.
Travels in Europe and the East. Letters written to
his relatives at home. By the late J. L. Tasker ... York,
J. L. Foster, 1864.

Tasker, H   McK
An introduction to the history of Australia, by H. McK.
Tasker ... and R. J. N. Tasker ... Melbourne, F. W. Cheshire
pty. ltd., 1938.
256 p. incl. front., illus. (incl. ports., maps, facsims.) 18½ᶜᵐ.

1. Australia — Hist. 2. Australia — Disc. & explor. I. Tasker,
R. J. N., joint author.
Library of Congress   DU98.1.T3
                              44–29055
               [2]   904

NT 0046748   DLC CtY OO OC1 ViU

QC
537.53
T 184
    TASKER, H   S
    ...Some properties and uses of X-ray inten-
sifying screens, by H. S. Tasker... London,
The Royal photographic society of Great Britain,
1945]
p.76–91. illus. 24cm.

Caption title.
Analyzed from Photographic Journal, sec.B.,
Scientific and technical photography, vol.85B, no.
4, July-August, 1945.
"References"   p.91.
PU 49–3064

NT 0046749   PU-EI

Tasker, John.
Sufficient reasons for a religious, conscientious,
and peaceable separation from the communion of
the Church of England. London, 1751.
22 cm.

NT 0046750   RPB

BT1101
.T2
    TASKER, JOHN GREENWOOD, 1853–
    Spiritual religion; a study of the relation of facts
to faith; being the thirty-first Fernley lecture delivered in Newcastle-on-Tyne, August, 1901, by John G. Tasker
... London, C. H. Kelly, 1901.
xii, 179 p. 22½cm.

1. Apologetics.

NT 0046751   ICU CBPac MH OO

Tasker, Joseph.
Case & claims of the holders of treasury bonds
or exchequer bills of Spain ... London, R dgway
1842.
60 p.

NT 0046752   PU

Tasker, Joseph.
Letter to the proprietors of the Sun fire & life
companies, a short correspondence with the
directors & a few remarks upon the select-vestry
system. London, Wilson, 1833.
35 p.

NT 0046753   PU

Tasker, Joseph Louis, d. 1848.
Travels in Europe and the East. Letters written to
his relatives at home. By the late J. L. Tasker ... York,
J. L. Foster, 1864.
viii, [9]–174 p., 1 l. 22ᶜᵐ.
Preface signed: H. A. Tasker.

1. Europe—Descr. & trav. 2. East—Descr. & trav. I. Tasker, H. A.,
ed.
                               20–3542
Library of Congress   D975.T3

NT 0046754   DLC

Tasker, Lawrence Hermon.
... The United Empire loyalist settlement at Long
Point, Lake Erie. By L. H. Tasker ... Toronto, W.
Briggs, 1900.
1 p. l., [vii]–viii, [9]–128 p. front. (plan) plates. 25½ᶜᵐ. (Ontario histor-
ical society. Paper and records, vol. II)

1. Long Point, Ont.—Hist. 2. United empire loyalists.
                               8–31585
Library of Congress   F1056.O58
——— Copy 2.   Library of Congress   F1059.L8T2

NT 0046755   DLC CaBVaU MB NN MoU CU MiU OC1 OC1WHi

Tasker, Rev. Levi B.
Record of marriages and baptisms in Sandwich
N.H. ... n.p., n.d.

NT 0046756   Nh

Tasker, Litha M., joint author.

Tasker, Arthur H
Earth saga, a poetic novel, by Arthur H. and Litha M
Tasker. [1st ed.] Portland, Me., Bond Wheelwright Co.
1954.

Tasker, R. J. N., joint author.

Tasker, H   McK
An introduction to the history of Australia, by H. McK
Tasker ... and R. J. N. Tasker ... Melbourne, F. W. Cheshir
pty. ltd., 1938.

BT
153.W7
T198b
    Tasker, Randolph Vincent Greenwood, 1895–
    The Biblical doctrine of the wrath of God.
London, Tyndale Press [1951]
48p. 22cm. (Tyndale Press monographs)

"The Tyndale Lecture in Biblical Theology for
1951...delivered...July 11, 1951 at a meeting
convened by the Tyndale Fellowship for Biblical
Research."
Bibliographical footnotes.

1. God—Wrath. I. Title.   (Series—2)

    IEG KyLxCB
NT 0046759   ICMcC CtY-D KyU NjP NjPT NNJ RPB ICU CU

Tasker, Randolph Vincent Greenwood, 1895–
ed.

Augustinus, Aurelius, *Saint, bp. of Hippo.*
The city of God (De civitate Dei) ... ₍by₎ Saint Augustine.
London, J. M. Dent & sons ltd.; New York, E. P. Dutton & co.
inc. ₍1945₎

BS3775 Tasker, Randolph Vincent Greenwood, 1895–
.T2 The gospel in the Epistle to the Hebrews.
London, Tyndale Press ₍1950₎
64 p.

 1. Bible. N.T. Hebrews—Criticism, interpretation, etc.

NT 0046761 ICU PPWe

Tasker, Randolph Vincent Greenwood, 1895–

 The Gospel in the Epistle to the
Hebrews. ₍1st ed.₎ London, Tyndale
press ₍1950₎
64 p., 22ᶜᵐ. ₍The Tyndale New
Testament lecture. 1949₎

NT 0046762 NjPT ICMcC NcD RPB

WV10 Tasker, Randolph Vincent Greenwood, 1895–
T182n The narrow way. ₍1st ed.₎ Chicago, Inter-
varsity Christian fellowship ₍1952₎
96 p. 19 cm.

 1. Sermons, English. I. Inter-varsity
Christian fellowship, Chicago. II. Title.

NT 0046763 CtY-D

Tasker, Randolph Vincent Greenwood, 1895–
 The narrow way. ₍1st ed.₎ London, Inter-
varsity Fellowship, ₍1952₎

96 p.

NT 0046764 PPEB NcD

Tasker, Randolph Vincent Greenwood, 1895–
 The nature and purpose of the Gospels ₍by₎ R. V. G. Tasker
... London, S. C. M. press ltd. ₍1944₎
111, ₍1₎ p. 19ᶜᵐ.
"First published, 1944."
"Select bibliography": p. ₍112₎

 1. Bible. N. T. Gospels—Criticism, interpretation, etc. I. Title.
45–5369

Library of Congress BS2555.T28 1944
 ₍5₎ ⁎226

NT 0046765 DLC WaTU WaS MH MCE PPWe NjPT ICU PPLT

Tasker, Randolph Vincent Greenwood, 1895–
 The nature and purpose of the Gospels, by
R. V. G. Tasker ... New York, Harper &
brothers. [1944]
x p., 1 l., 137 p. 19 cm.
First published, 1944.

NT 0046766 PHC NRCR

Tasker, Randolph Vincent Greenwood, 1895–
 The nature and purpose of the Gospels, by R. V. G. Tasker
... New York and London, Harper & brothers publishers ₍1944₎
x p., 1 l., 137 p. 19½ᶜᵐ.
Bibliographical foot-notes.

 1. Bible. N. T. Gospels—Criticism, interpretation, etc. I. Title.
46–12739

Library of Congress BS2555.T28 1944 a
 ₍2₎ 226

NT 0046767 DLC MB NN OO OC1

Tasker, Randolph Vincent Greenwood, 1895–
 The nature and purpose of the Gospels, by R. V. G. Tasker
... New York and London, Harper & brothers publishers ₍1945₎
x p., 1 l., 137 p. 19½ᶜᵐ.
Bibliographical foot-notes.

NT 0046768 ViU

Tasker, Randolph Vincent Greenwood, 1895–
 The Old Testament in the New Testament ₍by₎ R. V. G.
Tasker ... London, S. C. M. press ltd., 1946.
151 p. 19ᶜᵐ.
"First published January 1946."
"The first five chapters ... are based on lectures given to teachers at
the Easter school of Christian education at Selly Oak,
Birmingham, in April 1945 ... In many ways this book is a sequel to
The nature and purpose of the Gospels, published in 1944."—Pref.

 1. Bible. N. T.—Relation to O. T. I. Title.

BS2387.T3 225 47–1341

NT 0046769 DLC CtY CLSU INS PPDrop PPWe MCE NjPT

Tasker, Randolph Vincent Greenwood, 1895–
 The Old Testament in the New Testament ₍by₎ R. V. G.
Tasker ... Philadelphia, The Westminster press ₍1947₎
176 p. 19½ᶜᵐ.
"The first five chapters ... are based on lectures given to teachers
at the Easter school of the Institute of Christian education at Selly Oak,
Birmingham, in April 1945 ... In many ways this book is a sequel to
The nature and purpose of the Gospels, published in 1944."—Pref.

 1. Bible. N. T.—Relation to O. T. I. Title.

BS2387.T3 1947 225 47–18414

  KyU TxU
NT 0046770 DLC OrP WaTU WaWW ICJS PPLY PP KyLxCB

Tasker, Randolph Vincent Greenwood, 1895–
 The Old Testament in the New Testament. ₍2d fully rev.
ed.₎ London, SCM Press ₍1954₎
159 p. 19 cm.

 1. Bible. N. T.—Relation to O. T. I. Title.

BS2387.T3 1954 225 55–46 ‡

NT 0046771 DLC CaBVaU PP CLSU

BS2387 Tasker, Randolph Vincent Greenwood, 1895–
T3 Our Lord's use of the Old Testament. ₍London,
The Bookroom, Westminster Chapel₎ 1953.
18 p. 23 cm. (The Campbell Morgan Bible
lectureship. 5th, 1953)

 1. Bible. N. T. Gospels—Relation to O.T.
2. Jesus Christ—Teachings. I. Title. II.
Series.

NT 0046772 IaDuU-S MH-AH

Tasker, Sir Robert Inigo, 1868–

London. *County council. Advisory committee on the amendment of the London building act, 1930.*
 ... Report of the Advisory committee on the amendment of
the London building act, 1930. 1935 ... ₍London, London
County council, 1935₎

Tasker, Robert Joyce, *1903–*
 Grimhaven.
— New York. Knopf. 1928. (4), 241 pp. 22 cm. 5578.274
 The book was written while the author was serving a sentence in San
Quentin Prison.

           5578.274R

D2424 — T.r. — Prisons and prison discipline. — San Quentin Prison.

NT 0046774 MB NcC

Tasker, Robert Joyce, 1903–
 Grimhaven ₍by₎ Robert Joyce Tasker. New York & London,
A. A. Knopf, 1928.
3 p. l., 3–241 p., 1 l. 22½ᶜᵐ.
 An account of prison life, written while the author was serving in the
San Quentin prison.

 1. California. State prison, San Quentin. 2. Crime and criminals.
I. Title.
           28—23009

Library of Congress HV9475.C8S78
—— Copy 2.
Copyright A 1054702 ₍a37m1₎ 365.979462

  MU CU-I KEmT
  OrSaW WaTU OrP IdU WaSp OrPR WaS ICU TxU DLU NcD
NT 0046775 DLC OU CU ViU WaU MH-L MB NN MiU OC1 Or

HV9475 Tasker, Robert Joyce, 1903–
.C3P78 Grimhaven ₍by₎ Robert Joyce Tasker. New
1929 York & London, A. A. Knopf, 1929
3 p. l., 3–241 p., 1 l. 22½ᶜᵐ.
           author₎
 An account of prison life, written while the₎
was serving in the San Quentin prison.

 1. California. State prison, San Quentin.
2. Crime and crimi- nals. I. Title.

NT 0046776 ViU OrU MB

Thesis Tasker, Roy Carleton, 1896–
1934 The morphology and transformation of the
T199 gonopodium of the viviparous top-minnow Platypoecilus maculatus. ₍Ithaca, N. Y.₎ 1934.
87 l. 13 plates. 28 cm.

 Thesis (Ph. D.) - Cornell Univ., June 1934.

 1. Cyprinodontes. 2. Platypoecilus maculatus.
3. Generative organs. I. Title.

NT 0046777 NIC

Tasker, Roy Carleton, 1896–
 The morphology and transformation of the gonopodium of
the viviparous top-minnow *Platypoecilus maculatus* ... by Roy
Carleton Tasker ... ₍Ithaca, N. Y., 1934₎
₍3₎ p. 23ᶜᵐ.
Abstract of thesis (PH. D.)—Cornell university, 1934.

 1. Platypoecilus maculatus. 2. Fins.
           35–3629

Library of Congress QL638.C95T3 1934
Cornell Univ. Libr.
———— Copy 2. ₍2₎ 597.5

NT 0046778 NIC OU DLC

Tasker, Stephen P. M.
 Steve patrols more territory. Wynnewood, Pa.,
n.p., 1936.
111 p. illus. O.

NT 0046779 PP

Tasker, Stephen P. M.
Under fur and feather.   Wynnewood, Pa.,
1929.
29 p. illus. O.

NT 0046780   PP

Tasker, Stephen P. M.
Valuable ... books from the library of
S.P.M. Tasker ... sold ... March ... 1890 ...
T. Birch's Sons, auctioneers.   Philadelphia,
T. Birch's Sons, 1890.
63 p. 8°. (Catalogue No. 639)

NT 0046781   NN

Tasker, Thomas T.
Patent for regulating the Temperatures of
Hot water heating apparatus. Dec. 5, 1854.
4 p. pl. 1 8°.
Reissued May 1866.

NT 0046782   PBL

Tasker, Thomas T
Thomas T. Tasker's self-regulating water
furnace. Reprint from Journal of the Franklin
Institute.   Philadelphia, 1855.
3 p.

NT 0046783   PHi

Tasker, Thomas T
September 1876. Ayrshire cattle, imported
and home bred ... Thomas T. Tasker, Sr. ...
Philadelphia, 1876.

NT 0046784   PPL

Tasker (*Rev.* WILLIAM) of *Edinburgh*
Elijah's translation : a sermon, preached in Chalmers'
Territorial church, West Port, on June 6, 1847, being the
Sabbath immediately following the death of Thomas
Chalmers, D.D. *Edinburgh: J. Johnstone,* 1847. 16
pp. 8°.
In : AN (Chalmers)

NT 0046785   NN

Tasker, Rev. William, of Edinburgh.
Territorial savings banks, annuities, friendly
societies and life assurance: Their adaptation to
the ... working classes.   Edinburgh, Johnstone &
Hunter, 1852.
15 p.   16°.
In: *C p. v. 1316.

NT 0046786   NN

Tasker, William, Rev. of Edinburgh.
The territorial visitor's manual.   Edinburgh,
Johnstone, 1849.
146 p.   16 cm.

NT 0046787   MH-AH

Tasker, William, Rev. of Edinburgh.
The territorial visitor's manual. 4th ed. rev.
and enl.   Edinburgh, Johnstone, Hunter, 1874.
166 p.

NT 0046788   OO

Tasker, William, 1740-1800.
*EC75   Annus mirabilis; or, The eventful year
W1654   eighty-two. An historical poem. By the Rev. W.
Zz797p19 Tasker ...
Exeter:Printed by B.Thorn and son.And sold by
R.Baldwin,Pater-noster row,and R.Dodsley,Pall-
Mall,London.[1783] Price two shillings and six-
pence. <Entered at Stationers-hall.>
4°. 1p.ℓ.,ii,[5]-44p. 25.5cm.
Preface dated: Devon, Jan. 1, 1783.
Includes references to the war in America.

No.2 in a volume with Horace Walpole's arms
on covers, his ms. table of contents inside
front cover, and lettered on spine: Poems. Geo.
3. Vol. 19.

NT 0046790   MH

Tasker, William, 1740-1800.
Arviragus, a tragedy. (Never performed.) By the Rev.
Wm. Tasker, A. B. Exeter, Printed for the author, by R. Trew-
man and son [1796]
xi, [1], 68 p. 17¼ᶜᵐ.
[Longe, F. Collection of plays. v. 323, no. 1]

I. Title.

28-3230

Library of Congress   PR1241.L6 vol. 323

NT 0046791   DLC CSmH

Tasker, William, 1740-1800.
Arviragus. n. p., 1796.
(In Three centuries of drama: English,
1751-1800)

Microprint.

1. Arviragus--Drama. I. Title.

NT 0046792   MoU

[Tasker, William] 1740-1800.
779   A congratulatory ode to the Honourable
T182   Augustus Keppel, admiral of the blue .. 2d ed.,
by the author of the Ode to the warlike genius
of Great Britain. London, For the author,
printed at Laidler's office, and sold by
Dodsley[etc.]1779.
[20]p. 26½x20½cm.

NT 0046793   CtY ICU

Rare
PR   [Tasker, William] 1740-1800.
5548   An elegy on the death of David
T54   Garrick, esq. By the author of the Ode
E3+   to the warlike genius of Great Britain.
London, Author, 1779.
[9] p. 26cm.

1. Garrick,   David, 1717-1779.
I. Title.

NT 0046794   NIC PP DFo CtY

[Tasker, William] 1740-1800.
An elegy on the death of David Garrick, esq. .... 2d ed.,
with additions, by the author of the Ode to the warlike
genius of Great Britain. London, For the author, Printed
at Laidler's office, and sold by Dodsley [etc.] 1779.
[9] p. 27ᶜᵐ.
No. 4 in a volume of poems lettered: Sanitas. &c. 1772.

1. Garrick, David, 1717-1779.   I. Title.

19-4843

Library of Congress   PN2598.G3S3

NT 0046795   DLC CtY MiU MH CSmH

Rare
PR   Tasker, William, 1740-1800.
5548   An Ode to the memory of the Right
T54   Reverend Thomas Wilson, late Lord Bishop
O2+   of Sodor and Man. [London?] Author,
1780.
14, [1] p. 26cm.

Publisher's catalogue: p. [15]
Presentation copy, inscribed "E. Rack,
presented by the   author," probably by
the recipient.

1. Wilson, Thomas, Bp. of Sodor and Man,
1663-1755. I.   Title.

NT 0046797   NIC CtY

[Tasker, William] 1740-1800.
An ode to the warlike genius of
Great Britain. London, For the author,
printed and sold at Laidler's office
[etc.] 1778.
21 p. 24½ ᶜᵐ.

NT 0046798   NjP DFo CtY

Tasker, William, 1740-1800.
An ode to the warlike genius of Great
Britain...The 2d. ed. with considerable
additions, by the Rev. W. Tasker, A. B.
London, for the author, Printed and sold
at Laidler's office, and by Dodsley [etc.]
1778.

NT 0046799   DFo NN

Case
Y   TASKER, WILLIAM, 1740-1800.
185   Poems. An ode on the warlike genius of Great
.T 172 Britain. The 3d edition with additions. An ode
to curiosity, a Batheaston amusement. The 2d
edition. A poetical encomium on trade, addressed
to the mercantile city of Bristol. And, An epi-
taph intended for the Reverend Mr. Eccles.
London, For the author, 1779.
[4], 52p. 24½cm.

Imperfect? p.7-8 (sig. C 2) cut out, cancelled?

NT 0046800   ICN DFo

Tasker, William, 1740-1800.
Selected odes of Pindar and Horace; ... some
original poems ... 2. ed.   Exeter, 1790.
3 v.

NT 0046801   NjP

Taskin, George A   1893-
Geographic studies in Soviet universities and teachers'
colleges. New York, Research Program on the U. S. S. R.,
1954.
40 p. 28 cm. ([East European Fund] Mimeographed series, no.
64)

Text in Russian.
Bibliography: p. 38-40.

1. Geography—Study and teaching (Higher)   I. Title.
(Series)

DK1.E35 no. 64   54-4453

NT 0046802   DLC NN NNC

TASKIN, Jacques, 1885-
Contribution à l'etude des images radiologiques normales chez le chien. Thèse.
Paris, Editions de la Revue de pathologie comparée et d'hygiene generale, 1925.
1. 8°. pp.61-. Illustr.
At head of title-page: Ecole nationale
vétérinaire d'Alfort.
"Bibliographie", p.61.

NT 0046803   MH CtY DNLM

619.7   Taskin, Jaques, 1888–
T181   Les images radiologiques normales et
anormales chez le chien.   Paris, Éditions
de la Revue de pathologie comparée et d'hygiène generale, 1932.
111, ₍1₎p. illus. 25cm. (Collection des
travaux de pathologie comparée)

Cover title.
In 2 pts.; pt.1 with special t.p.: Contribution à l'etude des images radiologiques normales chez le chien.
Bibliography: p.53; ₍112–

NT   0046804   IU

Taskin, Nikolai Aleksandrovich.
Dictionnaire des travaux publics et du batiment.
t. 2. [Paris] Éditions OCIA [194   ]
1 v.
Contents. – T. 2 Deutsch-Französisch-Russisch.
1. Building - Dictionaires - Polyglot. 2. French
language - Dictionaries - Polyglot. 3. German
language - Dictionaries - Polyglot. 4. Russian
language - Dictionaries - Polyglot.

NT   0046805   CU

Taskin, Nikolai Aleksandrovich.
Wörterbuch des Bauwesens...von N. Taskin... Teil
₍Paris₎ Éditions Ocia   v.   21cm.

Title-page and preface in German, French and Russian.
CONTENTS.   Teil 2. Deutsch-
Französisch-Russisch.

1. Building—Dictionaries,   Polyglot, 1944.
N. Y. P. L.   September 21, 1948

NT   0046806   NN DS IU

338.0496
T182
   Taşkin, Ridvan H
Ziraatte maliyet muhasebesi. 1. basim.
Ankara, Zerbamat, 1944.
xv, 235 p.

1. Turkey - Econ. cond. 2. Agriculture -
Turkey.

NT   0046807   NNC NN

Taşkın, Rifat, ed.

Turkey. *Laws, statutes, etc.*
Askerî ceza kanunu; şerh. ₍1944 senesine kadar yapılan
değişikliklere göre. Hazırlıyan₎ Rifat Taşkın. 7. basım.
Ankara, 1944.

Taşkın, Rifat.
Millî müdafaa hukuku ve devletler harp hukuku. Ankara,
1943.
242 p. 25 cm.
Includes legislation.

1. Military law—Turkey. 2. War (International law)   I. Title.
                        60–58463

NT   0046809   DLC

Taşkın yıllığı. sayı 1–   1955–
Ankara, DSİ Matbaası ₍etc.₎
v. illus., maps, charts, diagrs., tables. 31 cm. *genel*
Vols. for 1955-19 issued by Devlet Su İşleri Umum Müdürlüğü,
Etüd ve Plân Dairesi Reisliği.
₍Called 1955-58, Devlet Su İşleri Umum
Müdürlüğü₎
1. Floods—Turkey.   I. Turkey. Devlet Su İşleri Umum Mü-
dürlüğü. Etüd ve Plân Dairesi Reisliği. *genel*

GB1325.T3   59–53824

NT   0046810   DLC

Taskinen, K
Beiträge zur Kenntnis der Ermüdung des
Muskels ...   Leipzig, 1909.
2 p.l., 54 p. illus., 2 fold. pl.   22.5 cm.
Akademische Abhandlung - Helsingfors.
"Diese Arbeit erscheint im 'Skandinavischen
Archiv für Physiologie', Bd. XXIII, 1909".

NT   0046811   CtY DNLM ICRL

Ţāšköprîzāde, Aḥmad ibn Muṣṭafā
see
Ţāshkubrîzādah, Aḥmad ibn Muṣṭafā, 1495–1561.

Taşköprülüzade, Ahmet Efendi
see
Ţāshkubrîzādah, Aḥmad ibn Muṣṭafā, 1495–1561.

₍Taskine, E   de₎
L'industrie houillère dans le bassin du Donetz, déve-
loppement et situation actuelle   St.-Pétersbourg, Impr.
de M. Stassuléwitch, 1900.
24, v p., 1 l., ₍2₎, 147 p. 3 diagr. 21ᶜᵐ.
Contains: Charbonnages du bassin du Donetz. St. Petersbourg, 1900.
Signed: E. de Taskine.
On cover: Paris. Exposition universelle, 1900.

1. Coal mines and mining—Russia.   I. Paris. Exposition universelle,
1900.
                       G S 17–239

Library, U. S. Geological   Survey 463(570) T18i

NT   0046814   DI-GS

DR
701   **Taškovski, Dragan.**
M13S623   Богомилското движење. Скопје, Изд. на Научниот ин-
v.1   ститут за националната историја на македонскот народ,
1949.
75 p. 20 cm. (Научна историска библиотека, бр. 1)

1. Bogomiles.   I. Title.   (Series: Naučna istoriska biblioteka,
br. 1)   *Title transliterated:* Bogomilskoto dviženje.
DR701.M13S532   vol. 1   52–42276
        3

NT   0046815   DLC CSt DDO MH CLU

Taškovski, Dragan.
Карпошевото воcтание. Скопје ₍Култура₎ 1951.
32 p. illus. 20 cm.
At head of title: Научен институт за национална историја на
македонскиот народ.
Bibliographical footnotes.

1. Macedonia—Hist.—1453–   2. Turkey—Hist.—Suleiman II,
1687–1691.   I. Title.   *Title transliterated:* Karpoševoto vostanie.

DR701.M4T3   65–78849

NT   0046816   DLC MH

Taškovski, Dragan.
Марксизмот и религијата. Скопје, Главни одбор на
Народниот фронт на Македонија, 1949.
58 p. 21 cm. (Идеолошко-воспитна библиотека, бр. 3)

1. Church and state in Yugoslavia.   I. Title.
       Title transliterated: Marksizmot i religijata.

BR966.T3   52–30443

NT   0046817   DLC

Taškovski, Dragan, *comp.*
За религијата; зборник на статии и писма. Скопје, Кул-
тура, 1952.
156 p. 20 cm.
At head of title: Маркс, Енгелс, Ленин.

1. Christianity—Controversial literature.   I. Marx, Karl, 1818–
1883.   II. Title.   *Title transliterated:* Za religijata.

BL2780.T28   56–16202 ‡

NT   0046818   DLC

The **Tasks** of economic history; papers presented at the ...
annual meeting of the Economic history association ...
1st–   1941–
₍New York₎ Published for the Economic history association
by New York university press, 1941–
v. diagrs. 26ᶜᵐ.
Title varies slightly.
"A supplemental issue of the Journal of economic history."

1. Economic conditions—Societies.   I. Economic history association.   II. The Journal of economic history. Supplement.
                    43–16404 Revised

Library of Congress   HC10.T3
             ₍r45d2₎   330.627

   OCU
NT   0046819   DLC DAU NcU CtY ICJ NNC ICU NIC ViU PU

Tasks of the Slavic philology and the Ukrainian slavistics.
Augsburg, Assoc. of the Friends of UFAS, 1948.   28 p.
illus. 21cm. (Slavistica. nr. 1)
Added t.-p. in Ukrainian; text in Ukrainian.
Ukrainian title: Завдання слов'янської філології я українська
славістика.

587260B. 1. Slavonic philology.   I. Ser.

NT   0046820   NN

Tăslăuanu, Octavian C
Trei luni pe câmpul de război. Text abridged and
adapted for advanced students. Vocabulary and expressions
by Alexander Burz, Traian Ocneanu ₍and₎ Leon Vasu. Presidio of Monterey, Army Language School ₍195–?₎
91 p. 21 cm.

1. European War, 1914–1918—Campaigns—Eastern. 2. European
War, 1914–1918—Personal narratives, Austrian.   I. U. S. Army
Language School, Monterey, Calif.   II. Title.

D556.T332   52–61765 ‡

NT   0046821   DLC

Tăslăuanu, Octavian C.
... Trois mois de campagne en Galicie; carnet de route
d'un Transylvain, officier dans l'armée austro-hongroise.
Paris, Neuchatel, Attinger frères ₍1918₎
259 p. fold. map. 19¼ᶜᵐ.
London edition (Skeffington & son) has title: With the Austrian army
in Galicia ...

1. European war, 1914– —Campaigns—Eastern. 2. European war,
1914– —Personal narratives.   I. Title.
                      19–6599

Library of Congress   D556.T33

NT   0046822   DLC MU NcD DNW TxU NjP NN

Tăslăuanu, Octavian C.
With the Austrian army in Galicia, by Octavian C.
Tăslăuanu. London, Skeffington & son, lᵈ. ₍1918₎
255 p. front. (fold. map) 19¼ᶜᵐ.
Paris edition (Attinger frères) has title: Trois mois de campagne en
Galicie.

1. European war, 1914– —Campaigns—Eastern. 2. European war,
1914– —Personal narratives, Austrian.   I. Title.
                      19–6598

Library of Congress   D556.T32

NT   0046823   DLC MH NN ICJ CtY NcD DNW IU

Taslé,
 Catalogue des mollusques observés dans le département du Morbihan. Par M. Taslé, père ... Vannes, Impr. de J.-M. Galles, 1864.
 cover-title, 34 p. 25ᶜᵐ.
 Extrait du Bulletin de la Société polymathique du Morbihan, année 1864.

 1. Mollusks—France—Morbihan (Dept.)

 Library of Congress   QL425.F8T19

          6-24185†

NT 0046824   DLC

4PG   **Tasler, Matej.**
Slovak   Nákaza; hra z posledných rokov
36   slovenskej histórie v 3 dejstvách.
        ₍Vyd. 1. V Liptovskom sv. Mikuláši₎
        Tranoscius [1947]
          57 p.

NT 0046825   DLC-P4

 Tasley, England (parish)
 The register of Tasley
        see under   Shropshire Parish Register
 Society.

 Tasley, England (Parish)
 Tasley registers
        see under   Shropshire Parish Register
 Society.

 Taşlıcalı Yahya bey
  see
 Yahya, *d.* 1582.

895.482
T184   **Taşlıklıoğlu, Zafer**
        Eski Yunancada ilk adımlar. Istanbul,
        Üçler Basımevi, 1948.
          vi, 230 p. (Istanbul Universitesi yayınları,
        no. 362. Klâsik Filoloji Enstitüsü, 3)

          1. Greek language - Grammar.

NT 0046829   NNC

BL
820   **Taşlıklıoğlu, Zafer.**
.A7   Tanrı Apollon ve Anadolu ile münasebeti, yazan
T18   Z.Taşlıklıoğlu. Istanbul, Ibrahim Horoz Basımevi,
        1954.
          84 p.   21 cm.

          Bibliography: p.₍82₎-84.

          1.Apollo.

NT 0046830   MiU

 Taslim, Md.
 ... Stem-rot of berseem caused by *Rhizoctonia solani* Kühn,
 by Md. Taslim ... Calcutta, Government of India central
 publication branch, 1928.
   1 p. l., 8 p. II pl. (1 col.) 24½ᶜᵐ. (Pusa. Agricultural research
 institute. Bulletin no. 180)

   1. Berseem—₍Stem-rot₎

          Agr 29-324
 Library, U. S. Dept. of   Agriculture 22P97 no. 180

NT 0046831   DNAL

 Taslitt, Israel I
  Hello, cousin Tillie; a skittish skit for Purim.
 n. d.
   3 p.

NT 0046832   PPT

 Taslitt, Israel I
  The homentosh Mikado; the Persian version of
 Gilbert & Sullivan. Book and lyrics by Israel I.
 Taslitt. 5th ed. rev. Based on the book of Esther.
 Clebeland, Ohio, Reniarc assoc., n. d.
   14 p. (3 p. notes)

NT 0046833   PPT

 Taslitt, Israel I
  A TV director in the 21st century is hurled back
 by a time machine, and that's ... How TV came
 to Persia. Another Pur-Impish play, in five
 scenes. Cleveland, Ohio, Reniarc, c1954.
   11 p.

NT 0046834   PPT

 Taslitzky, Boris.
  L'âge mûr, par Taslitzky et Guillevic. Paris, Cercle d'art
 ₍1955₎
   ₍76₎ p. 29 plates. 28 cm.
   Drawings and verse.

   I. Guillevic, Eugène, 1907-

          A 56-6561

 Harvard Univ. Library
 for Library of Congress   ₍1₎

NT 0046835   MH IEN NN

TASLITZKY, BORIS.
  111 dessins faits à Buchenwald, 1944-1945
présentés par Julien Cain. Paris, Bibliothèque
française [1946, c1945] 11 l. 111 plates (5 col.). 25cm.

  Issued in portfolio.
  Plate captions in French, Russian and English.

  1. Buchenwald, Weimar, Germany (Concentration camp) 2. World war,
1939-1945--Prisoners and prisons, German. I. Cain, Julien, 1887-
i. [Title] Cent onze.

NT 0046837   NN MnU MoU MH CU OU IEN

 Taslitzky, Boris.
  Deux peintres et un poète retour d'Algérie: Boris Taslitzky, Mireille Miailhe et Jacques Dubois. Introd. de
 Jeanne Modigliani. Paris, Éditions Cercle d'art ₍1952₎
   27 p. 60 plates. 27 cm.

   I. Glodek-Miailhe, Mireille. II. Dubois, Jacques, poet. III. Title.

          A 53-5325
 Harvard Univ. Library
 for Library of Congress   ₍1₎

NT 0046838   MH

 Tasma, *pseud.*
  see
 Couvreur, *Mme.* Jessie Catherine (Huybers) ca. 1850-
 1897.

wason   **Tasmaja, Jaja.**
Pamphlet   Kimia anorganik praktikum, analisa kuali-
Q   tatif. Djakarta, Technipres ₍1951₎
21   95 p. illus. 21 cm.

NT 0046840   NIC

Iq   **Tasman,** pseud.
T183   A little aversion, by Tasman ₍pseud₎ With
910   coloured illustrations by J.A.Symington. London,
         The Religious tract society, 1910.
           2p.₍.₎, 3-256p. col.front.,col.plates. 20½ᶜᵐ
         (The Girl's library)
           Title-page illus. in colors.
           "Preface" signed: "L".

           I.Title. II. L.   x.Ser.ᴬ

NT 0046841   CtY

PR 6039
A85   **Tasman**
I5   A little aversion, by Tasman. London,
1911   the Religious Tract Society [1911]
           256 p. col. illus. 20 cm.

NT 0046842   CaBVaU

 Tasman, Abel
  Snelheidsmetingen bij ringopening van
 phtaliedderivaten ... Leiden, 1927.
  Proefschrift - Leiden.

NT 0046843   CtY

 Tasman, Abel Janszoon, 1603?-1659.
  Abel Janszoon Tasman & the discovery of New Zealand.
 Wellington, Dept. of internal affairs, 1942.
   66 p. illus. (incl. maps, facsims.) 26ᶜᵐ.
   "This edition of part of Tasman's Journal, with the introductory
 essay & poem, has been produced by the government of New Zealand to
 commemorate the tercentennial of the first discovery of the country,
 1642-1942."
   CONTENTS.—Landfall in unknown seas, by Allen Curnow.—The place
 of Tasman's voyage in history, by J. C. Beaglehole.—Tasman's Journal
 or description, newly translated by M. F. Vigeveno.—Notes.
   1. New Zealand—Disc. & explor. I. *Curnow, Allen, 1911-
 Landfall in unknown seas. II. Beaglehole, John Cawte. The place of
 Tasman's voyage in history. III. Vigeveno, M. F., tr. IV. Title: The discovery of New Zealand.
          A 43-3349
 Harvard univ. Library
 for Library of Congress   DU410.T3
                  ₍5₎†   993.1

 CtY PU MB NjP DLC
NT 0046844   MH ScU CU CU-S NIC RPJCB ICU CaBVaU NNC

fG160   **Tasman, Abel Janszoon,** 1603?-1659.
H27   An Account of a Voyage made towards the South Terra-incog-
v.1   nita; taken from the Journal of Captain Abel Johnson Tasman,
x   who not only discovered a New Passage by Sea to the South of
         Nova Hollandria, Vandieman's Land, &c. and sailed round a
         vast Tract of Land and Sea, but also made very useful Observations
         concerning the Variation of the Magnetical Needle in Parts of the
         World, almost Antipodas to us, with several other curious Remarks
         concerning those Places and its Inhabitants: Published in Low-
         Dutch by Dirk Rembrantse, and since done into English from Dr.
         Hook's Collections.
           (In Harris, John. Navigantium atque Itinerantium Bibliotheca
         ...London, 1705. 40cm. v. 1, p. 608-610)
           1. Scientific exped   itions.

NT 0046845   CU-BANC

 Tasman, Abel Janszoon, 1603?-1659.

  An account of several late voyages & discoveries to the
 South and North ... By Sir John Narborough, Captain
 Jasmen Tasman, Captain John Wood, and Frederick Marten
 ... London, Printed for S. Smith and B. Walford, 1694.

 Tasman, Abel Janszoon, 1603?-1659.

  An Account of several late voyages and discoveries: I. John
 Narbrough's voyage to the South-Sea by the command of
 King Charles the Second ... II. Captain J. Tasman's discoveries on the coast of the south terra incognita. III. Captain J. Wood's attempt to discover a northeast passage to
 China. IV. F. Marten's observations made in Greenland and
 other northern countries ... London, D. Brown ₍etc.₎ 1711.

G8200 **Tasman, Abel Janszoon,** d. 1659.
1644   Carten dese landen zin ontdeckt bij de
.T3   compangie ondeckers behaluen het norder deelt
      van Noua Guina ende het West Eynde van Java
      dit Warck aldus bij mallecanderen geuoecht ut
      verscheijden schriften als mede ut eijgen
      beuinding jib Abel Jansen Tasman.   Sydney,
      S. T. Leigh ₁1947₎
      col. map.   73x94cm.

      Scale given on bar scale on which 100 geo-
      graphical miles measure 6.8cm.

      Facsimile by James Emery from original in
      The Mitchell Library Sydney.
      Cylindrical projection with the coast lines
      appearing as if the map were on Mercator's
      projection.
      Inset of Java and Sumatra.
      No. 125.
      ---- The Tasman map of 1644. ₍Prepared by
      Phyllis Mander Jones, Mitchell librarian and

      F. R. Dabinett₎ ₍Sydney₎ Trustees of the
      Public Library of New South Wales, 1948.
      31p.   4 maps (part col.)   24cm.

      1. Australia--1644.   I. Emery, James.   II.
      Jones, Phyllis Mander.

NT   0046850   IU

      Tasman, Abel Janszoon, 1603?-1659.
      The discovery of Tasmania, 1642. Selections from Doctor
      J. E. Heeres' translation of Tasman's journal Aug.-Dec. 1642.
      ₍Hobart, Tasmania, H. H. Pimblett, government printer, 1942₎
      2 p. l., 43 p., 1 l.   illus. (ports.) 2 fold. maps, facsim. 24½ᵐ.
      "Published by the authority and under the direction of the Honourable
      John Lewis Madden ... and edited by John Reynolds."—Verso of 2d pre-
      lim. leaf.
      1. Australasia—Disc. & explor. 2. Tasmania—Hist.   I. Heeres, Jan
      Ernst, 1858-1932, tr. II. Reynolds, John, of Tasmania, ed. III. Title.
                                                                A 43-2892
      Harvard univ. Library
      for Library of Congress   DU98.T25
                                     ₍3₎†   904.6

NT   0046851   MH CaBVa PSt PU ViU DLC NjP

DS **Tasman, Abel Janszoon, d. 1659.**
618   ... Journaal lastbrief en kaarten.
T2   [1844-1896?]
      4 pams. in 1 v.   fold. plates (incl. maps,
      facsim., diagrs.)   22 cm.
      Binder's title for volume made up of
      articles extracted from various publica-
      tions.
      CONTENTS.--Journal van de reis naar het
      Zuidland.--Instructie of lastbrief voor
      Abel Jansen Tasman in 1644. Medegedeeld
      door Jacob Swart.--On an old manuscript

      chart of Tasmania. By A. Mault.--Notes on
      an early chart showing the tracks of Tas-
      man's voyages in 1642 and 1644 [by A. Mault]

NT   0046853   MiU

      Tasman, Abel Janszoon, 1603?-1659.
      Abel Janszoon Tasman's journal of his discovery of Van
      Diemens land and New Zealand in 1642, with documents relat-
      ing to his exploration of Australia in 1644, being ... facsimiles
      of the original manuscript ... with an English translation ...
      to which are added Life and labours of Abel Janszoon Tas-
      man by J. E. Heeres ... and Observations made with the com-
      pass on Tasman's voyage by Dr. W. van Bemmelen ... Am-
      sterdam, F. Muller & co., 1898.
      5 p. l., ₍195₎ p. (facsims.) 1 l., 59 p., 1 l., 163 p., 1 l., 21 p. illus.,
      5 fold. maps in pocket. 45ᶜᵐ.
      Translated by J. de Hoop Scheffer and C. Stoffel. cf. Pref.
      1. Australasia—Disc. & explor.   I. Heeres, Jan Ernst, 1858-   II.
      Bemmelen, W. van, 1868-   III. Scheffer, Johannes de Hoop,
      1849-   tr.   IV. Stoffel,   Cornelis, 1845-1908, joint tr.
      Library of Congress   DU98.T19   5—8032

ICJ MB
NT   0046854   DLC NIC NBU MdBP CU CtY PPL PHi NjP MiU

      Tasman, Abel Janszoon, 1603?-1659.
      Tasman's kaart van zijn australische ontdekkingen, 1644,
      "de Bonaparte-kaart," gereproduceerd op de ware grootte in
      goud en kleuren naar het origineel in de Mitchell library, Syd-
      ney (N. S. W.) Met toestemming de autoriteiten door dr.
      F. C. Wieder. 's-Gravenhage, M. Nijhoff, 1942.
      xi, 140 p. incl. illus., maps (part fold.) 33ᶜᵐ. and map. 94 x 78ᶜᵐ.
      The large map is issued in a case.
      "Literatuur": p. 130-132.
      1. Australasia—Descr. & trav.—Maps. 2. Australasia—Disc. & explor.
      I. Wieder, Frederik Caspar, 1874—
                                                                46-34739

NT   0046855   DLC ICU NNA NN MH

      Tasman, Abel Janszoon, 1603?-1659.
      Kort verhael uyt het journael van den kommander
      A.J. Tasman int. ontdekken van't onbekende Suit-
      lant.   Amsterdam, 1674.

NT   0046856   DLC

      Tasman, Abel Janszoon, 1603-1659.
      Records relating to Tasman's voyage.
      (In McNab, Robert, comp. Historical records
      of New Zealand. 1914.   v. 2, p. 1-43)

NT   0046857   CaBViPA

      Tasman, Abel Janszoon, 1602 or 03-1659.
      Abel Janszoon Tasmans Reise längs der Küste von Kaiser-
      Wilhelms-Land im Jahre 1643. Von ... Otto Reche ...   (Geo-
      graphische Gesellschaft in Hamburg. Mitteil. Hamburg, 1918.
      8°.   Bd. 31, p. 183-203.   diagr., maps.)

      1. Pacific ocean.—Exploration, 1643.   2. Kaiser Wilhelmsland.—History.
      3. Reche, Otto, 1879-   , editor.
      N. Y. P. L.   November 19, 1923.

NT   0046858   NN

G160   **Tasman, Abel Janszoon,** 1603?-1659.
A43   Abel Jansen Tasmans Reise nach den Südländern.
v. 12
x   (In Allgemeine Historie der Reisen zu Wasser und Lande.
      25cm. v. 12 (1754) p. 217-222)

      1. Australia - Discovery and exploration.

NT   0046859   CU-BANC

      Tasman, Abel Janszoon, 1603?-1659.
      De reizen van Abel Janszoon Tasman en Franchoys Jacob-
      szoon Visscher ter nadere ontdekking van het Zuidland in
      1642/3 en 1644, uitg. door R. Posthumus Meyjes, met 10 kaar-
      ten en 68 schetskaarten, landverkenningen en platen. 's-Gra-
      venhage, M. Nijhoff, 1919.
      xxxii p., 1 l., xcvii, ₍1₎, 299, ₍1₎ p. front., illus., maps (part fold.) 25ᶜᵐ.
      (Half-title: Werken uitg. door de Linschoten-vereeniging. XVII)
      "Carto- en bibliographie: Lijst van aangehaalde werken": p. ₍259₎-276.
      1. Australasia—Disc. & explor. 2. Visscher, Frans Jacobszoon.
      I. Meyjes, R. Posthumus, ed.   21—8044
      Library of Congress ·   DU98.T2 1919

         TxU MiU MH OCl
NT   0046860   DLC CaBViPA CaBVaU KyLoU WU ViU RPJCB

      Tasman, Abel Janszoon, 1603?-1659.
      Relation d'un voyage aux Terres australes inconnues. Tirée
      du Journal du capitaine Abel Jansen Tasman.
      (In Coreal, Francisco. Voyages de François Coreal aux Indes occi-
      dentales ... traduits de l'espagnol. nouv. éd. Paris, 1722. 16½ᶜᵐ. v. 2,
      p. 319-337)

      1. Australasia—Disc. & explor.
                                                                2-72 rev.
      Library of Congress   F2221.C80

NT   0046861   DLC

      Tasman, Abel Janszoon, d. 1659.
      Relation d'une voyage aux terres australes inconnues,
      tirée du journal du capitaine Abel Jansen Tasman.
      (In Coreal, Francisco. Relation des voyages ... aux Indes Occidentales.
      Bruxelles, 1736. 17ᶜᵐ. t. 2, p. 319-337)
      Caption title.
      The journal extends from Aug. 14, 1642, to June 15, 1643.
      The present translation appears to have been made from the English
      version pub. in "An account of several late voyages & discoveries to the
      South and North," London, 1694.
      1. Australasia—Disc. & explor.
                                                                8-37384
      Library of Congress   F2221.C82 vol. 2

NT   0046862   DLC

      Tasman, Abel Janszoon, 1603?-1659.
      A relation of a voyage made towards the South
      Terra Incognita.
      plate.   (In account of several late voyages and
      discoveries, 1711, p. 129-140)

NT   0046863   MH-A

      Tasman, Abel Janszoon, 1603?-1659.
      The Tasman map of 1644. Historical note and
      description of the manuscript map in the Mitchell
      Library, Sydney. [Sydney] Trustees of the
      Public Library of New South Wales, 1948.
      31 p.   maps (part col.)   24 cm.
      "Selected bibliography": p. 31.

NT   0046864   PSt

      Tasman, Abel Janszoon, d. 1659. ₍1603?-₎
      Voyage d'Abel Tasman.   L'an M.DC.XLII.
      (In Thevenot, M. Relations de divers voyages. Paris, 1696. 35½ᵐ.
      t. 2 ₍no. 16₎ 4 p.)

G159
.T5
1696
₍6₎l. 2. no 16
Office   1. New Zealand—Disc. & explor.
                                                         CA 8-1457 Unrev'd
      Library of Congress   G159.T41

NT   0046865   DLC

      Tasman, Abel Janszoon, 1603?-1659.
      The voyage of Captain Abel Jansen Tasman for the dis-
      covery of southern countries, by direction of the Dutch East
      India company. ₍Taken from his original journal.₎
      (In Pinkerton, John, ed. A general collection of the best and most
      interesting voyages and travels ... London, 1808-14. 27¼ x 21ᶜᵐ.
      v. 11 (1812) p. 439-463)

      1. Australasia—Disc. & explor.
                                                         CA 8—2081 Unrev'd
      Library of Congress   G161.P65 vol. 11

NT   0046866   DLC PU

15742   **Tasman, H. J., ed.**
HN   **Sociaal** weekblad. 1.-25₎ jaarg.; 1. Jan. 1887-30 Sept.
      1911. Haarlem, H. D. Tjeenk Willink ₍etc., 1887-1911₎

      Tasman, H. J., ed.
      Sociale kroniek ... 1.-   jaarg.;
      Oct. 1911-
      Haarlem, H. D. Tjeenk Willink & zoon ₍1911-

TN
2
A45
no.15   Tasman, Mehlika Izgi.
Adana strüktür sondajlari mikro-fauna'sinin
etüdü. Foraminifera from test wells in Adana,
Turkey. Ankara, 1949.
42 p. illus. 28cm. (Maden Tetkik ve
in   Arama Enstitüsü yayinlarindan. Seri B, no.15)
Earth Sci   1. Geology - Turkey. 2. Foraminifera, Fossil
- Turkey. I. Title. (Series: Ankara. Maden
Tetkik ve Arama Enstitüsü. Maden
Tetkik ve Arama Enstitüsü yayinlarindan. Seri B, no.15)

NT   0046869   CoU NN

Tasman Empire Airways, Ltd.
Annual report and accounts. 19 -
Auckland, N.Z.
Vols. for 19   -1964 issued under earlier
name: Tasman Empire Airways Ltd.
Title varies: 19   -1964, Report and Accounts.

NT   0046870   MiU

Tasmania, Francis Russell Nixon, *Bp. of*
see
Nixon, Francis Russell, *Bp.*

Tasmania. Blue book.

Tasmania. *Statistical and registration dept.*
Statistics of the state of Tasmania.

Hobart Town, 18   -1924.

Tasmania.
..."The case for Tasmania" presented to Sir Nicholas Lockyer
...special representative of the commonwealth government appointed to inquire into the financial position of Tasmania, by the
Hon. A. G. Ogilvie...and the Hon. Tasman Shields...for and
on behalf of the government of Tasmania... Tasmania: J.
Vail, 1926. iv, 67 p. incl. tables. chart. 8°.

At head of title: 1926.

1. Finance—Tasmania.
N. Y. P. L.   January 12, 1927

NT   0046873   NN

JS
8173
A3
T2
HRC
GRA   Tasmania.
The case for Tasmania, 1930; statement of a
claim for an increased special grant from the
Commonwealth. Prepared by a committee appointed
by the Government of Tasmania to be placed
before the Commonwealth Parliamentary Joint
Committee of Public Accounts. Tasmania, J.
Vail, Govt. Pr., 1930.
74p. 25cm.

1. Tasmania - Politics and government.
I. Title.

NT   0046874   TxU MH DLC-P4 NcD

Tasmania.

HJ795
.A1B5   Binns, K   J
Federal financial relations in Canada and Australia; re-
port prepared for the Government of Tasmania. Hobart,
H. H. Pimblett, Govt. Printer, 1948.

Tasmania.
Industrial products of Tasmania transmitted to the
Crystal Palace at Sydenham for exhibition there.
Hobart, 1859
15 p.

NT   0046876   MH PPAmP

Tasmania.
Leading facts connected with federation
see under   Just, Thomas Cook.

Tasmania.
The official handbook of Tasmania
see under   Just, Thomas Cook, comp.

Tasmania.

HJ795
.A6B5
1947a   Binns, K   J   FOR OTHER EDITIONS
SEE MAIN ENTRY
Social credit in Alberta; report prepared for the Government of Tasmania. Hobart, H. H. Pimblett, Govt. Printer,
1947.

Tasmania.
Standing orders for the regulation of the proba-
tion system of convict labour in Van Diemen's Land.
Hobart, 1841.
23 p.

NT   0046880   CSt

Tasmania.
Statistical returns of Van Diemen's Land from
1824 to 1839.
Hobart Town, 1839.
15, 60 p.

NT   0046881   CSt

Tasmania.
Tasmania, the island state of the commonwealth. Its pro-
ductions, agricultural, pastoral, mineral, trade, and commerce...
Hobart: J. Vail, 1910. 46 p., 1 l., 1 map. illus. 12°.

1. Tasmania.—Description.
N. Y. P. L.   March 31, 1914.

NT   0046882   NN

Tasmania.
Tasmanian contributions to the Universal exhibition of
industry at Paris. 1855. [Hobart Town, H. & C. Best,
1855]
cover-title, 48, [2] p. 31ᶜᵐ.

1. Paris. Exposition universelle, 1855—Tasmania.

Library of Congress   T800.G1T2   5-30804†

NT   0046883   DLC PPAmP PP

Tasmania.
Tasmanian timbers, their qualities and uses; explanatory notes on the exhibit of native woods in
the artisans section of the International exhibition, shown by the Tasmanian government. Hobart,
1894
15 p.
"Corrigenda," inserted before p. 3.

NT   0046884   MH-A

Tasmania.

Australia. *War service homes commission.*
... War service homes act—Arrangement between the war
service homes commissioner and the government of Tasmania
... [Melbourne] Printed and pub. for the government of the
commonwealth of Australia by A. J. Mullett, government
printer for the state of Victoria [1924]

HC641
.A25   Tasmania. Agent-general in London.
Report.

[Hobart, 19
v. 34½cm.

1. Tasmania—Comm. 2. Shipping—
Tasmania. 3. Tasmania—Econ. condit.

NT   0046886   DLC

Tasmania. Agricultural and Stock Dept.
see   Tasmania Dept. of Agriculture.

Tasmania. Agricultural Bank
see   Agricultural Bank of Tasmania.

Tasmania. *Agricultural Dept.*
see   **Tasmania.** *Dept. of Agriculture.*

Tasmania. *Apprenticeship Commission.*
Report.

Hobart, H. H. Pimblett, Govt. Printer.
v. 35 cm. annual.

1. Apprentices—Tasmania.

HD4885.A83A3   331.86   50-54869 ‡

NT   0046890   DLC DS

Tasmania. *Auditor-General.*   L336.946 1
... Annual report of the Auditor-General ... accompanied by
the statement of public accounts prepared by the Treasurer
... Hobart, Govt. Printer, 1924–.
tables. 33ᶜᵐ.

At head of title: ... Parliament of Tasmania.
Report year ends June 30.

NT   0046891   ICJ CU

S342.94
qT192   Tasmania. Attorney-General's Office.
Australasian federation. Hobart, 1891.
14 p. 32 cm.

Caption title.
Letter signed by A. Inglis Clark.

1. Federal government. 2. Australia. Constitutional
history. I. Clark, Andrew Inglis, 1848- II. Title.

NT   0046892   N

Tasmania. *Board of commissioners of state sinking fund.*
... The state sinking fund : report ...

₍Hobart,
    v. tables. 34½ᶜᵐ.
    Report year ends June 30.
    –1927/28 have title: Public debts sinking fund : report ...

    1. Debts, Public—Tasmania.   ɪ. Title. ɪɪ. Title : Public debts sinking
fund : report.

                                       34–33718
    Library of Congress   HJ94.D15
                      ₍2₎   336.3309946

NT   0046893   DLC DS

Tasmania. Board of education

     See

Tasmania. Education dept.

HV802
.T3A3   **Tasmania.** <u>Charitable grants and children of</u>
     <u>the state dept.</u>
    ... Boarding-out destitute children : report
...
  ₍Hobart, 1875–
    v. 34cm.—

    1. Children—Charities, protection, etc.—
Tasmania.

NT   0046895   DLC

Tasmania. *Charitable grants and children of the state dept.*
  Report.

₍Hobart, 18 –19₎
    v. tables. 34ᶜᵐ.
    Mimeographed, 1929/30–
    Report year irregular. 1904/05 covers period from January 1, 1904
to June 30, 1905.
    Beginning with 1923/24 includes also the reports of the Infirmary,
New Town ; Home for invalids, Launceston ; Ashley home for boys, Deloraine ; Kennerley boys' home, Hobart ; Northern Tasmanian home for
boys, Launceston ; Girls' industrial school, Hobart ; St. Joseph's orphanage for girls, Hobart and Girls' home, Launceston.

    Title varies: 18 –1883, Administrator of charitable grants : Report.
    1884–1894, Out-door relief : Report.
    1895–1922/23, Charitable grants department : Report.
    1923/24–   Charitable grants and children of the state depart-
ment : Report.

    1. Charities—Tasmania. ɪ. New Town, Tasmania. Infirmary. ɪɪ.
Launceston, Tasmania. Home for invalids. ɪɪɪ. Deloraine, Tasmania.
Ashley home for boys. ɪᴠ. Hobart. Kennerley boys' home. ᴠ. Launceston, Tasmania. Northern Tasmanian home for boys. ᴠɪ. Hobart. Girls'
industrial school. ᴠɪɪ. St. Joseph's orphanage for girls, Hobart. ᴠɪɪɪ.
Launceston, Tasmania. Girls' home. ɪx. Title. x. Title : Out-door relief : Report.

                                 34–38414
    Library of Congress   HV501.A3
                    ₍3₎   360.9946

NT   0046897   DLC CU

Tasmania. *Chief Geologist*
  see
Tasmania. *Geological Survey.*

Tasmania. *Chief secretary's dept.*
  ... General election for House of assembly, April 30,
1909. Report on the system of proportional representation used in accordance with "The electoral act, 1907,"
by P. C. Douglas ... E. L. Piesse ... W. A. B. Birchall ...
Hobart, J. Vail, government printer, 1909.

    25 p. 8 fold. tab. 34ᶜᵐ.
    At head of title: Tasmania.
    Report made to the chief secretary.

    1. Tasmania. Parliament. House—Elections. ɪ. Douglas, P. C.

                         9–34553†
    Library of Congress   JQ5194.A5 1909

NT   0046899   DLC NN

Tasmania. Chief Secretary's Dept.
  Tasmania wages boards. Determinations of
specific boards, 1912–1918. [Hobart, J. Vail,
govt. printer, Tasmania, 1912–19]
  [40] l. 8 p. [37] l.   34 cm.
    1. Wages - Minimum wage - Tasmania.

NT   0046900   CU

ʹTasmania. Chief secretary's dept. Statistical
  and registration dept.

     See

Tasmania. Statistical and registration dept.

HG2051
.A82T323 **Tasmania.** Closer Settlement Board.
  Agricultural Bank of Tasmania.
    Reports of the Board of Management and of the Closer
Settlement Board.

    Hobart, H. H. Pimblett, Govt. Printer.

Tasmania. Colonial secretary's office.
Tasmania. *Statistical and registration dept.*
  Statistics of the state of Tasmania.

    Hobart Town, 18 –1924.

Tasmania. *Commissioner for railways.*
  ... Report on the working of the government railways ...
Hobart,
    v. in   tables (part fold.) 33ᶜᵐ.   annual.
    At head of title,   : ... Tasmania.
    Report year ends June 30.

    1. Railroads—Tasmania.

    HE3521.A32   46–44510

NT   0046904   DLC CaBVaU MH-BA MiU

Tasmania. *Commissioner for railways*
  see also
Tasmania. *Railway dept.*

Tasmania. *Commissioner of Police*
  see
Tasmania. *Police Dept.*

Tasmania. Commissioner of taxes.
  ... Report for the year

  Hobart, 19 -
    v. tables. 34½cm.
    Issued as Tasmania Parliament documents.
    Report year ends June 30.

NT   0046907   MH-L IU

Tasmania. Commissioners of State   Sinking
  Fund, Board of
    see   Tasmania. Board of Commissioners
of State Sinking Fund.

Tasmania. *Commissioners on Valuation of Property,* **L336.946 N500**
                                Hobart Town and Launceston.
108861 ... . Valuation of property, Hobart Town and Launceston.
Report of the Commissioners. Laid upon the table by the Attorney-General, and ordered by the House to be printed, August
10, 1875. [Hobart Town, Tasmania, J. Barnard, gov't printer,
1875.]
    102 p. 34½ᶜᵐ.   (Tasmania. House of Assembly. [Reports.] 1875. no. 46.)

NT   0046909   ICJ CtY MB NjP PPAmP

Tasmania. *Commissioners to the Intercolonial exhibition
  of Australasia, 1866–1867.*
    Catalogue of the contributions made by Tasmania to
the Intercolonial exhibition of Australia at Melbourne, in
1866. Tasmania, J. Barnard, government printer, 1866.
    26 p. 21 x 16½ᶜᵐ.

    1. Melbourne. Intercolonial exposition of Australasia, 1866–1867—Tas-
mania.

                                5–27954†
    Library of Congress   T730.1.F3T2

NT   0046910   DLC

Tasmania. *Commissioners to the Melbourne interna-
  tional exhibition, 1880–1881.*
    ... Catalogue of the exhibits in the Tasmanian court.
Hobart Town, J. Barnard, 1880.
    67 p. fold. map. 21ᶜᵐ.
    At head of title: Melbourne international exhibition, 1880.
    Catalogue to accompany an index cabinet of the minerals and rocks of
Tasmania ... by T. C. Just: p. 25–67.

    1. Melbourne. International exhibition, 1880–1881—Tasmania. 2. Mines
and mineral resources—Tasmania. ɪ. Just, Thomas C.

                                6–2421†
    Library of Congress   T731.G1T2

NT   0046911   DLC NN

308
Z
Box 837
  Tasmania. Committee appointed to inquire
    into Tasmanian disabilities under Federation.
    Report. Hobart, J. Vail, government printer,
    1925.
    45 p.

    1. Finance, Public - Tasmania. 2. Tasmania
- Pol. & govt.

NT   0046912   NNC NN TxU

Tasmania. *Controller of Prisons*
  see **Tasmania.** *Gaols Dept.*

Tasmania.   Council of agriculture.

Lea, Arthur M.
  Insect and fungus pests of the orchard and farm. (3d
ed.) By Arthur M. Lea ... government entomologist.
Issued by the Council of agriculture, Tasmania. Hobart,
Tasmania, J. Vail, government printer, 1908.

Tasmania. Council of education

     See

Tasmania. Education dept.

Tasmania. Courts

Ratcliffe, John Vincent, *ed.*
Income tax decisions of Australasia; being a compendium of reported and numerous unreported legal decisions (excepting the decisions in the New South Wales Court of review), on appeals arising under the income tax assessment acts of the Commonwealth and the states of Australia and the Dominion of New Zealand and containing the text of the sections of the various acts upon which the cases were decided, with exhaustive indexes, by John Vincent Ratcliffe ... and John York McGrath ... Sydney [etc.] The Law book company of Australasia limited, 1928.

Tasmania. Courts.

Ratcliffe, John Vincent, *ed.*
Income tax decisions of Australasia, 1928–1930, with exhaustive indexes, by John Vincent Ratcliffe ... and John York McGrath ... Sydney [etc.] The Law book company of Australasia limited, 1931.

Tasmania. Dept. of Agriculture.
The Agricultural gazette of Tasmania
see under title [supplement]

S393
A39
Tasmania. Dept. of Agriculture.
Bulletin. New ser. [i.e. ser.2]

[Hobart] 1904-
nos. in   v.   illus.

Successively issued by:
Agricultural and Stock Dept.
Dept. of Agriculture.

NT   0046919   CU KMK OrCS

630.8
T18b
Tasmania--Dept. of Agriculture.
Bulletin no.
n.s. no.1-   1928-
Hobart.
no. illus., diagrs., tables. 25cm.
irregular.
Each bulletin has also a distinctive title.
Issued   by the department under an earlier name: Agricultural and Stock Dept.
Some no. also in rev. editions.
Some no. accompanied by supplements.

NT   0046920   IU CU-A CU CaBVaU

23
T18L
Tasmania. Dept. of Agriculture.
Leaflet no. 1-
[n.p., 19--? -

1. Tasmania. Agriculture. I. Tasmania.
Dept. of agriculture. Vegetable growing.
Leaflet.

NT   0046921   DNAL

Tasmania. *Dept. of Agriculture.*
Ministerial statement of the Minister for Agriculture and minister administering the Agricultural Bank.

Hobart, H. H. Pimblett, Govt. Printer.
v. 34 cm. annual.

1. Agriculture—Tasmania. 2. Agriculture—Economic aspects—Tasmania. I. Agricultural Bank of Tasmania.

S393.A32   630.6194   50–56038 ‡

NT   0046922   DLC

43.9
T18
Tasmania. Dept. of Agriculture.
The official Australian pure-bred dairy cattle production recording scheme; annual report.
[Hobart]

1. Cattle, Dairy. Performance records and registration.

NT   0046923   DNAL

434
T18
Tasmania. Dept. of Agriculture.
Orchard mite investigations; progress report.
1948/49-
[Hobart?] 1949-

1. Acarina. 2. Miticides.

NT   0046924   DNAL

fSB722
T2A3
Agric.
Library
Tasmania. Dept. of Agriculture.
Plant disease survey of Tasmania for the three year period 1943, 1944, 1945. [Hobart? 1946?]
30 p. map. 36cm.

Cover title.

1. Plant diseases - Tasmania.

NT   0046925   CU DNAL

Tasmania. *Dept. of Agriculture.*
Report.

Hobart, H. H. Pimblett, Govt. Printer [etc.]
v. 34 cm. annual.
Reports for   issued by the Dept. under a variant name: Agricultural and Stock Dept.

1. Agriculture — Tasmania. 2. Agriculture — Economic aspects—Tasmania.

S393.A3   338.1   50–56173 ‡

NT   0046926   DLC OrCS NbU DS

S
393
A28
Tasmania. Dept. of Agriculture.
Research bulletin. no. 1-
Nov. 1952-
[Hobart].
v.

Title varies: no. 1, Research series bulletin.

1. Agriculture--Tasmania. I. Title.

NT   0046927   KMK IU DNAL

Tasmania. Dept. of Agriculture.
Research series bulletin
see its   Research bulletin.

S17
.T3
Tasmania. Dept. of Agriculture.

Tasmanian journal of agriculture.

Hobart.

Tasmania. *Dept. of Agriculture.*
War service land settlement : progress report.

Hobart, H. H. Pimblett, Govt. printer.
v. 35 cm.
At head of title, 19   : Parliament of Tasmania.

1. Veterans—Employment—Tasmania. 2. Land settlement—Tasmania. I. Title.

54–20282 rev ‡

NT   0046930   DLC DNAL

Tasmania. Dept. of Health Services
see   Tasmania. Dept. of Public Health.

Tasmania. *Dept. of Industrial Development.*
Industrial development ; report of the director
see its
Report of the director.

Tasmania. *Dept. of Industrial Development.*
Report of the director.
[Hobart, Govt. Printer]
v. 34 cm. annual.
At head of title, 19   : Industrial development.
Report year ends June 30.

1. Tasmania—Indus.

HC641.A35   55–30483

NT   0046933   DLC DS

Tasmania. *Dept. of Labour and Industry.*
Annual report.
Hobart.
v. 34 cm.

1. Labor and laboring classes—Tasmania.

HD8901.A32   331.06194   48–33859*

NT   0046934   DLC MH IU CU MiD OrU

TASMANIA - Dept. of labour and industry]
The industrial pattern in Tasmania. n.p. [19?-].
5 leaves.
Typewritten.
Sent by Industrial registrar, E.J. Ogilvie, 14 Aug. 1947.
Caption title.

NT   0046935   MH

Tasmania. Dept. of Labour and Industry.

Report on factories, wages boards, shops, etc.
1st-   1915/16-
Hobart, J. Vail, Government Printer.
v. 33 cm. annual.

Supersedes Chief inspector of factories. Annual report.
1. Labor and laboring classes - Tasmania.
2. Factory inspection - Tasmania.

NT   0046936   CaBVaU

Tasmania. *Dept. of Labour and Industry*
see also **Tasmania.** *Industrial Dept.*

Div. of Maps

Tasmania. Dept. of Land and Surveys.

Tasmania. *State Economic Planning Authority.*
Regional planning atlas. Economic resources of Tasmania. ₍2d ed.₎ Hobart, Printed by Davies Bros., 1947.

Tasmania. *Dept. of lands and surveys.*
Report.

Hobart, Tasmania,
v. tables. 33½ᶜᵐ.
Report year irregular.

1. Tasmania—Public lands.

                         34–33719
Library of Congress   HD1091.A25
                ₍2₎   336.109946

NT   0046939   DLC CU MiU

Tasmania. Dept. of Land and Surveys.
   ... Tasmanian forest plantation scheme...
Hobart, J. Vail, govt. print., 1923.
28 p. plates, fold. diagrs. 23 cm.
At head of title: Tasmania.
Pub. by authority of the Hon. Ernest F. Blyth, Minister for lands.
1. Forestations. 2. Forests and forestry - Tasmania. 3. Agricultural colonies. - Tasmania. 3. Children. - Charities, protection, etc. - Tasmania.

NT   0046940   CU MH-A

Tasmania. *Dept. of land and surveys.*
Tasmanian forestry. Timber products and sawmilling industry, a description of timber trees indigenous to Tasmania, their commercial value and process of manufacture, with methods adopted by the government to foster the industry. Comp. by J. Compton Penny, chief forest officer, under the superintendence of E. A. Counsel ... surveyor-general and secretary for lands. Pub. by authority of the Hon. Alexander Hean, commissioner of crown lands for the state of Tasmania. 1st ed. Hobart, J. Vail, government printer, 1905.
vi, 69 p. 16 pl. (1 fold.) fold. map, fold. tab. 25½ᶜᵐ.
"Regulations under 'The crown lands act, 1903'": p. 48–69.
1. Forests and forestry — Tasmania. 2. Timber—Tasmania.
I. Penny, John Compton.
                                7–7304
   Library of Congress   SD243.T2

NT   0046941   DLC ICJ

Tasmania. *Dept. of land and surveys.*
Tasmanian forestry. Timber products and sawmilling industry, a description of timber trees indigenous to Tasmania, their commercial value and process of manufacture, with methods adopted by the government to foster the industry. Comp. by J. Compton Penny, chief forest officer, under the superintendence of E. A. Counsel ... surveyor-general and secretary for lands. Pub. by authority of the Hon. Alexander Hean, commissioner of crown lands for the state of Tasmania. 2d ed. Hobart, J. Vail, government printer, 1910.
vi, 98 p. double front. (ports.) illus., fold. map, fold. tab. 25½ᶜᵐ.
"Regulations under 'The crown lands act, 1903'": p. ₍70₎–98.
1. Tasmania. Forestry. I. Penny, John Compton.
                          Agr 12–763
   Library, U. S. Dept. of   Agriculture 99P384

   MnSU ICJ MH
NT   0046942   DNAL CaBVaU WaS NcD InU ICJ MH MH-A CU

Tasmania. *Dept. of Lands and Surveys. Mapping Branch.*
Australia 1:63,360, State aerial survey: Tasmania. Hobart, 1954–
col. maps 48 x 70 cm.
Scale 1:63,360.
Issued in quadrangles 15 minutes of latitude by 30 minutes of longitude.
"Projection: Transverse Mercator."
Relief shown by contours and spot heights.
"Complies with National Mapping Standards."
In margins: Index to adjoining sheets.
1. Tasmania—Maps, Topographic. I. Title.

G9060s 63.T3   Map 67–524
            ₍1₎

NT   0046943   DLC

---

q912.946 Tasmania. *Dept. of Lands and Surveys. Mapping Branch.*
T18h   Hobart and suburbs; aerial survey maps. Hobart, Printed by Davies Bros. ₍1948₎
       46p. 26 col maps(part fold) 36cm.

"Drawn by the Mapping Branch of the Lands and Surveys Department, from aerial photos taken in connection with the Aerial Survey of Tasmania."

1. Hobart, Tasmania--Maps.

NT   0046944   IU NN

Tasmania. *Dept. of Lands and Surveys. Mapping Branch.*
Hobart and suburbs, aerial survey maps. ₍Rev. 2d ed. Hobart, 1954₎
44 p. col. maps. 36 cm.
Scale of maps 1:7,920; 10 chains to 1 inch.
"Published by authority, Eric Reec, Minister for Lands and Works."

1. Hobart—Maps. I. Title.

G2754.H6T32 1954   Map 68–589

NT   0046945   DLC NNC

G2791   Tasmania. Dept. of Lands and Surveys. Mapping
.G3T3   Branch.
1955   **Tasmania.** *Directorate of Industrial Development.*
Map   Regional planning atlas; economic resources of Tasmania. 3d ed. Hobart, Printed by Davies Bros. ₍1955?₎

Tasmania. *Dept. of Lands and Surveys. Mapping Branch.*
Tasmania 1:15,840: Section map. Hobart, 1949–
col. maps on sheets 50 x 78 cm.
Scale 1:15,840; 20 chains to 1 inch.
"Projection—Transverse Mercator."
Relief shown by contours and spot heights.
Includes indexes to adjoining sheets.

1. Tasmania—Maps, Topographic.

G9060s 15.T3   Map 67–515

NT   0046947   DLC

Tasmania. *Department of Lands and Works.*   333.0946 I
   .... Crown lands guide, ... Published by the authority of
112339 the ... Minister of Lands and Works. Hobart, Tasmania, Gov't Printer, 1898.
   Library has 1898. plates, maps. 22ᶜᵐ.
   At head of title: Tasmania.

NT   0046948   ICJ PPAmP

Tasmania. Dept. of Lands and Works.
                          Crown lands
guide. 1909. Hobart. 1909. 8°. pp. xi, 182. Map and other illustr.

NT   0046949   MH-A PP

Tasmania. *Dept. of lands and works.*
   ... Crown lands guide, 1914. Published by the authority of the Hon. James Belton, minister of lands and works. Hobart, J. Vail, government printer, 1914.
xii, 202 p. incl. front., illus. fold. map. 21½ᶜᵐ.
At head of title: Tasmania.
"Tenth edition."

1. Tasmania—Public lands. 2. Tasmania—Economic conditions. I. Title.
                           Agr 20—1698
U. S. Dept. of agr. Library   271.5L232
   for Library of Congress   HD1091.D3 1914

NT   0046950   DNAL

AD1091   Tasmania. Dept. of Lands and Works.
.A3   Ministerial statement... delivered in the Houses of Assembly... 1922–   Hobart, 1922–
       1 v. tables. 33.5 cm.

NT   0046951   DLC

Tasmania. Dept. of Lands and Works.
Tasmanian timbers: their qualities and uses. With tables showing the botanical and local names, specific gravities, weights, strengths, and cost of various timbers; and the regulations controlling the cutting of timber on crown lands. Pub. by authority of the honourable Carmichael Lyne, minister of lands and works for the state of Tasmania. Comp. by A. O. Green, esq., Public works dept. Issued by E. A. Counsel ... surveyor-general and secretary for lands. 2d ed. Hobart, Tasmania, J. Vail, government printer, 1903.
63 p. front, plates, tables (1 fold.) 21½ᶜᵐ.
1. Tasmania. Forestry. 2. Timber.
                           Agr 3–1109
   Library, U. S. Dept. of   Agriculture 99G822.

NT   0046952   DNAL ICJ MH-A

Tasmania. Dept. of lands and works. Council of agriculture

           See

Tasmania. Council of agriculture.

Tasmania. Dept. of mines

           See

Tasmania. Mines dept.

Tasmania. Dept. of mines. Geological survey

           See

Tasmania. Geological survey.

Tasmania. *Dept. of public health.*
Annual report.
Tasmania, 19
v. 34ᶜᵐ.
19   have title: Annual report of the Department of public health ... by the chief health officer ...

1. Tasmania—Sanit. aff.
                          9–8248†
   Library of Congress   RA372.T2A3

NT   0046956   DLC IU TxU PP DI DNLM ICJ

Tasmania. Dept. of public health. Office of chief inspector of factories

           See

Tasmania. Office of chief inspector of factories.

Tasmania. *Dept. of Public Works.*
Report.
Hobart.
v. 35 cm. annual.

1. Tasmania—Public works.

     HD4401.A32   351.8   49–44178*

NT   0046958   DLC DS

HJ94
.R1   **Tasmania. Dept. of the Treasury.**
     The budget speech and financial statement.
1949/50;

     Hobart, Govt. printer, 1949–
       v. annual.

     1. Budget – Tasmania.   2. Tasmania – Budget.
     3. Finance – Tasmania.   4. Tasmania – Finance.
     I. Serials – Australia – Annuals, etc.

NT   0046959   DS IU NN

HJ94
C2   **Tasmania. Dept. of the Treasury.**
     Comparative statement of revenue and expendi-
ture... 1875–   [Hobart Town? 1877–]
     1 v.   34.5 cm.

NT   0046960   DLC

HJ94
.C245   **Tasmania. Dept. of the treasury.**
     ... Consolidated revenue. Account current,
and assets and liabilities ...

     [Hobart, 18
       v.   tables.   34½cm.

     1. Finance--Tasmania.   I. Title.

NT   0046961   DLC

Tasmania. *Dept. of the treasury.*
     ... Consolidated revenue ... Explanatory statement ...

     [Hobart, 1874–19
       v. tables. 34½ᶜᵐ.
     1872–1875—   **have title: Treasurer's balances.**

     1. Finance—Tasmania.   I. Title.   II. Title: Treasurer's balances.

     Library of Congress   35–23627
     ——— 2d set.   HJ94.C25
                                336.946

NT   0046962   DLC

HJ94
.B15   **Tasmania. Dept. of the treasury.**
     Estimate of the probable expenditure
chargeable on the consolidated revenue fund
of the government of Tasmania ... ⟨Draft⟩

     Tasmania, 19
       v.   tables.   27½cm.

     1. Budget--Tasmania.   I. Title.

NT   0046963   DLC

HJ94
.C215   **Tasmania. Dept. of the treasury.**
     ... Finance. Account current ...

     [Hobart, 18
       v.   tables.   34½cm.

     1. Finance--Tasmania.

NT   0046964   DLC

HJ94
.S155   **Tasmania. Dept. of the treasury.**
     ... Finance. Comparative statement, land
fund ...

     [Hobart, 18
       v.   tables.   34½cm.

     1. Finance--Tasmania.   I. Title: Land
fund. Comparative statement.

NT   0046965   DLC

HJ94
.C24   **Jasmania. Dept. of the Treasury.**
     ... Financial statement...
     Hobart, Tasmania, 19-
       1 v.   tables (part. fold.)   33 cm.

NT   0046966   DLC

HJ94
.C22   **Tasmania. Dept. of the treasury.**
     ... General revenue. Account current,
and assets and liabilities ...

     [Hobart, 18
       v.   tables.   34½cm.

     1. Finance--Tasmania.   I. Title.

NT   0046967   DLC

HJ94
.S15   **Tasmania. Dept. of the treasury.**
     ... Land fund. Account current, and
assets and liabilities ...

     [Hobart, 18
       v.   tables.   34½cm.

     1. Finance--Tasmania.   I. Title.

NT   0046968   DLC

Tasmania. *Dept. of the treasury.*
     ... Loans by the state to local bodies, &c. ...

     [Hobart, 1916–
       v. tables (part fold.) 34½ᵐ.

     1. Finance—Tasmania.   I. Title.

     Library of Congress   34–33720
                   HJ94.S13
                  [2]   336.946

NT   0046969   DLC

HJ94
.A14   **Tasmania. Dept. of the treasury.**
     ... Statement of public accounts prepared
by the treasurer ...

     Hobart [18]-19
       v.   tables (part fold.)   33½cm.

     1. Finance--Tasmania.   I. Tasmania.
Audit. dept.   II. Title.

NT   0046970   DLC

330.9946   **Tasmania. Dept. of the treasury.**
T199   ... Statement presented to the Commonwealth
no.3,   grants commission on behalf of the government
     of Tasmania, by the... treasurer.   [Hobart,

       v.   tables.   32ᵐ.   (S.T.E. no.
     At head of title: Tasmania...
     On cover: [no.8] Revised.

     1.Finance - Tasmania.   I.Australia.Common-
wealth grants commission.

NT   0046971   CSt

HJ94
.B14   **Tasmania. Dept. of the treasury.**
     ... Supplementary estimates ...

     [Hobart, 185
       v.   tables.   34cm.

     1. Budget--Tasmania.   I. Title.

NT   0046972   DLC

HJ94
.S16   **Tasmania. Dept. of the treasury.**
     ... Supplementary estimates ... Land fund
...
     [Hobart, 18
       v.   tables.   34½cm.

     1. Finance--Tasmania.   I. Title.

NT   0046973   DLC

Tasmania. *Directorate of Industrial Development.*
     Regional planning atlas; economic resources of Tasmania.
3d ed.   Hobart, Printed by Davies Bros. [1955?]
     [65] p.   illus., col. maps.   50 cm.
     Scale of maps 1 : 1,013,700 or 16 miles to 1 inch.
     "Maps drawn and reproduced by the Department of Lands and
Surveys, Mapping Branch."
     Second ed. issued in 1947 by State Economic Planning Authority.

     1. Natural resources — Tasmania — Maps.   2. Tasmania — Econ.
condit.—Maps.   I. Tasmania. Dept. of Lands and Surveys. Mapping Branch.   II. Tasmania. State Economic Planning Authority.
Regional planning atlas.   III. Title.

     G2791.G3T3   1955   Map 68–1031

     MH

NT   0046974   DLC CaBVaU NNC NN MiDW NjP WU IU CaBVaU

---

q
HJ
1743   **Tasmania. Economic Case for Tasmania Committee.**
A552   Petrol taxation: an addendum to the report of
1935   the Economic Case for Tasmania Committee on the
HRC   financial relations of the Commonwealth and
GRA   States...   Hobart, W.E. Shimmins, Govt. Printer.
     1935.
     17p.   34cm.

     1. Finance Public - Tasmania.   2. Petroleum -
Taxation - Tasmania

NT   0046975   TxU

Tasmania. *Economic Planning Authority*
     see **Tasmania.** *State Economic Planning Authority.*

Tasmania. *Education dept.*
     The centenary of Tasmania: notes on its discovery,
colonisation, history, and progress.   Hobart, J. Vail, government printer, 1903.
     32 p.   21½ᶜᵐ.
     Herbert Nicholls, minister of education.
     Prepared by S. O. Lovell, inspector of schools.—Pref. note.

     1. Tasmania—Hist.   I. Lovell, S. O.
                                         8–28326

     Library of Congress   DU470.A2

NT   0046977   DLC

Tasmania. Education Department.
     ... The course of instruction (A) [and] (B)
for the primary schools.   Hobart, John Vail,
government printer, 1929.
     2 v.   18 cm.

NT   0046978   PPT

Tasmania. *Education Dept.*
     Course of study for modern schools.   [Hobart] 1947.
     196 p.   25 cm.
     Includes bibliographies.

     1. Education—Tasmania—Curricula.

     LB1629.5.T3   1947   373.946   49–57369*

NT   0046979   DLC

Tasmania. Education Department.
... Courses of study for high schools.
Hobart, Walter, E. Shimmins, govt. printer,
1936.
83 p. 25 cm.

NT 0046980 PPT

Tasmania. *Education Dept.*
Curriculum for primary schools. ₍Hobart₎ 1948.
160 p. 25 cm.

1. Education—Tasmania—Curricula.
LB1564.T3A5 1948 372.9946 49–57366*

NT 0046981 DLC

372.89 Tasmania--Education Dept.
T28c Curriculum for primary schools. History
and geography. ₍Hobart?₎ 1951.
24p. 25cm.

"Supplement to 'Educational record.'"

1. History--Study and teaching. 2.
Geography--Study and teaching. 3. Education-
Tasmania--Curricula.

NT 0046982 IU

Tasmania. Education dept.

Tasmania. *Laws, statutes, etc.*
... The Education act, 1885, and amendment acts with
regulations of October, 1908. Hobart, J. Vail, government printer, 1908.

L767 Tasmania. Education Dept.
.A3 The educational record. Tasmania, 1905–
v. 27.5 cm. monthly.
Official gazette of the Education Dept. of
Tasmania".

NT 0046984 DLC NN MnU

L91 Tasmania. Education Dept. The educational
.T3 record. Supplement.

Tasmanian education.

₍Hobart₎

Tasmania. *Education dept.*
... Regulations, 1894. Hobart, Tasmania, W. Grahame, jun., government printer, 1894.
21 p. 33ᶜᵐ.
At head of title: Tasmania. Education department.

1. Education—Tasmania.
E 15–2098
Library, U. S. Bur. of Education L767.B2 1894

NT 0046986 DHEW

Tasmania. Education Department.
Regulations.

Issue 1914. ₍Hobart: J. Vail, 1914.₎ 30 p. 4°.
Suppl.: Educational Record. 1913, Dec.

1. Schools.—Regulations, Australia: Tasmania.
N. Y. P. L. November 27, 1916.

NT 0046987 NN

Tasmania. *Education dept.*
Report.
₍Tasmania, 18 –19
v. 34½ᶜᵐ.

1. Education—Tasmania.
9–8541
Library of Congress L767.A2

NT 0046988 DLC PPT DHEW CSt

Tasmania. Education Dept.

Neale, William Lewis, 1853–
Tasmania. Report on the system of primary educa-
tion in Tasmania: by W. L. Neale ... Hobart, Tasmania,
J. Vail, government printer, 1904.

Tasmania. *Education dept.*
The Tasmanian area school. Compiled by officers of the
Education department, Tasmania. ₍Hobart₎ Tasmania, H. H.
Pimblett, government printer, 1942.
3 p. l., ₍5₎–65, ₍1₎ p. incl. illus. (maps) tables. front., plates. 19ᶜᵐ.

1. Rural schools—Tasmania. 2. Schools—Centralization—Tasmania.
3. Education—Tasmania.
43–5348
Library of Congress LB1567.T18 1942
₍2₎ 379.173

NT 0046990 DLC CtY NBC NN

L91 Tasmania. Education Dept.
.T3
Tasmanian education.

₍Hobart₎

Z7164 Tasmania. Electoral dept.
.R4P6
Piesse, Edmund Leolin, 1880–
... Bibliography of proportional representation in Tas-
mania, by E. L. Piesse ... Hobart, J. Vail, government printer,
1913.

JF1075 Tasmania. Electoral dept.
.T3P5 FOR OTHER EDITIONS
1913 Piesse, Edmund Leolin, 1880– SEE MAIN ENTRY
... The theory of the quota in proportional representation.
II, by E. L. Piesse ... (Papers and proceedings of the Royal
society of Tasmania, 1913) Hobart, J. Vail, government
printer, 1913.

Tasmania. Factories, Office of chief inspector
of

See

Tasmania. Office of chief inspector of factories.

Tasmania. *Finance Committee*
see Tasmania. *State Finance Committee.*

Tasmania. *Fire Brigades Commission.*
Annual report. 1st– 1946/47–
Hobart.
v. tables. 34 cm.
Report year ends June 30.

1. Fire-departments—Tasmania.
TH9598.T3A32 352.3 48–19978*

NT 0046996 DLC DS

Tasmania. *Fisheries dept.*
Great international fisheries exhibition, South Kensington, London, 1883. Catalogue of the exhibits in the
Tasmanian court. Forwarded by the Commissioners of
fisheries of Tasmania ... London, Printed by William
Clowes and sons, limited, 1883.
14 p. 21½ᶜᵐ.

1. Fishes—Tasmania. 2. London. International fisheries exhibition,
1883—Tasmania. I. Title.
15–4138
Library of Congress SH343.L8T2

NT 0046997 DLC

---

q634.9 Tasmania--Forestry Commission.
T1831b Bulletin. no.1–
Hobart, Tasmania, Gov't Printer, 1933–
v. illus. 30cm.

Includes reprinted no.

NT 0046998 IU

Tasmania. *Forestry Commission.*
Report. 1946/47–
Hobart.
v. in illus. 34 cm. annual.
Report year ends June 30.
Supersedes Report of the Forestry Dept.

1. Forests and forestry—Tasmania.
SD111.T3A32 57–20233

NT 0046999 DLC CU NcRS

SD557 Tasmania. Forestry Commission.
T3 Standard volume table for Eucalyptus obliqua, second growth,
Forestry from southern forests. Hobart, 1953.
Library 91 p. tables.

1. Forests and forestry - Mensuration. 2. Forests and forestry -
Tables, etc. I. Title.

NT 0047000 CU

Tasmania. *Forestry Commission*
see also
Tasmania. *Forestry Dept.*

Tasmania. *Forestry Commission. Mapping Branch.*
₍Forest classification, density, and potential, Tasmania₎
Compiled from air photographs by the Mapping Branch of
the Forestry Commission. Hobart, 1948–
maps 45 x 65 cm.
Scale 1 : 31,680; 40 chains to 1 inch.
Blue line print.
Indexes to adjoining sheets in margins.

1. Forests and forestry—Tasmania—Maps.
G9061s .K2 31 .T3 Map 65–506

NT 0047002 DLC

Tasmania. Forestry Dept.
... A brief note on the principles of state forest policy, by S.W. Steane... Published under the authority of the ... minister of forests. Tasmania, W.E. Shimmins, govt. printer, 1935.
54 p. incl. front., plates. 21 cm.
At head of title: Tasmania.
1. Forests and forestry - Tasmania. I. Steane, S W

NT 0047003 CU

99.69
T18C Tasmania. Forestry Dept.
Comments on the Kessell report. ⌈n.p., 1945⌉
12 l.

For full report see Report on the forests and forestry administration of Tasmania, by S.L. Kessell (99.69 K48R)

NT 0047004 DNAL

Tasmania. Forestry Dept.
... Forestry handbook, compiled and issued by the acting Conservator of forests... Hobart, John Vail, govt. printer, 1928.
73 p. incl. plates, tables, diagrs. fold. maps. 24 cm.
At head of title: Tasmania.
"Compiled in connection with the Empire forestry conference of 1928". - p. [3]
1. Forests and forestry - Tasmania.

NT 0047005 CU

99.4
T18 Tasmania. Forestry Dept.
Handbook of forest assessment. Tasmania, W.E. Shimmins, 1937.
43 p.
1. Forestry mensuration. 2. Forest surveys. I. Lane, D A

NT 0047006 DNAL

Tasmania. *Forestry Dept.*
Report. 19 -45/46. Hobart.
v. in illus. 34 cm. annual.
Report year ends June 30.
Began publication with 1920 report. Cf. List of the serial publications of foreign governments.
Superseded by the Report of the Forestry Commission.

1. Forests and forestry—Tasmania.

SD111.T3A3 634.909946 34-33949 rev*

NT 0047007 DLC CU DNAL DS

99.28
T18S
1952 Tasmania. Forestry Dept.
Statement for the sixth British Commonwealth Forestry Conference. Ottawa, 1952.
30 l.
1. Tasmania. Forestry. I. British Commonwealth Forestry Conference. 6th, Ottawa, 1952.

NT 0047008 DNAL

Tasmania. *Forestry Dept.*
see also
Tasmania. *Forestry Commission.*

Tasmania. Freemasons
see Freemasons. Tasmania.

Tasmania. *Gaols Dept.*
Report of the controller of prisons.
⌈Hobart?⌉
v. 34 cm. annual.
At head of title, : Parliament of Tasmania.
Report year ends June 30.

1. Prisons—Tasmania.

HV8475.A3 365.994 51-33428 ‡

NT 0047011 DLC DS IU

Tasmania. Geological Survey.
... Bulletin...
see Tasmania. Geological Survey.
... Geological survey bulletin

Tasmania. *Geological survey.*
... The coal resources of Tasmania, by the Geological survey of Tasmania ... Issued under the authority of the Hon. J. B. Hayes ... minister for mines for Tasmania. Hobart, J. Vail, government printer, 1922.
xiv, 273 p. pl., tables. 24½cm. *and* XXXVI fold. pl. in separate envelope (incl. col. maps, plans, diagrs.) (*Its* Mineral resources no. 7)
At head of title: Tasmania. Department of mines.
Bibliographical references.

1. Coal—Tasmania. I. Title.

G S 24-103

Library, U. S. Geological Survey (880) M2 no. 7

NT 0047013 DI-GS NN ViU

Tasmania. *Geological survey.*
... Geological survey bulletin. no. 1–
Hobart, 1907–
v. illus., plates (part fold.) maps (part fold.) plans (part fold.) diagrs. (part fold.) 21½cm.
At head of title: Tasmania. Department of mines.
CONTENTS.
1. The Mangana goldfield, by W. H. Twelvetrees. 1907.—2. The Mathinna goldfield. pt. III, by W. H. Twelvetrees. 1907.—3. The Mount Farrell mining field, by L. K. Ward. 1908.—4. The Lisle goldfield, by W. H. Twelvetrees. 1909.—5. Gunn's plains, Alma, and other mining fields, North-west coast, by W. H. Twelvetrees. 1909.—6. The tin field of North Dundas, by L. K. Ward. 1909.—7. Geological examination of the Zeehan field, preliminary statement, by W. H. Twelvetrees and L. K. Ward. 1909.

8. The ore-bodies of the Zeehan field, by W. H. Twelvetrees and L. K. Ward. 1910; Geological map and mine plans to accompany Geological survey bulletin, no. 8. 1910.—9. The Scamander mineral district, by W. H. Twelvetrees. 1911.—10. The Mount Balfour mining field, by L. K. Ward. 1911.—11. The Tasmanite shale fields of the Mersey district, by W. H. Twelvetrees. 1911.—12. The X river tin field, by L. K. Ward. 1911.—13. The Preolenna coal field and the geology of the Wynyard district, by L. Hills. 1913.—14. The Middlesex and Mount Claude mining field, by W. H. Twelvetrees. 1913.—15. The Stanley river tin field, by L. L. Waterhouse. 1914. Maps and sections to accompany same.—16. The Jukes-Darwin mining field, by L. Hills. 1914. Maps and sections to accompany same

17. The Bald hill osmiridium field, by W. H. Twelvetrees. 1914.—18. Geological reconnaissance of the country between cape Sorell and point Hibbs, by L. Hills. 1914.—19. The zinc-lead sulphide deposits of the Read-Rosebery district: pt. I. Mount Read group, by L. Hills. 1915.—20. The Catamaran and Strathblane coal fields and coal and limestone at Ida bay (southern Tasmania), by W. H. Twelvetrees. 1915.—21. The South Heemskirk tin field, by L. L. Waterhouse. 1916.—22. Catalogue of publications issued by the Government of Tasmania, relating to the mines, minerals, and geology of the state, to 31st December, 1914, comp. by W. H. Twelvetrees ... 1915.—23. The zinc-lead sulphide deposits of the Read-Rosebery district: pt. II. Rosebery group, by L. Hills. 1915.

24. Reconnaissance of country between Recherche bay and New river, Southern Tasmania, by W. H. Twelvetrees. 1915.—25. The Gladstone mineral district, by W. H. Twelvetrees. 1916.—26. The tin field of North Dundas, by H. Conder. 1918.—27. The Bangor mineral district, by W. H. Twelvetrees. 1918.—28. The North Pieman and Huskisson and Sterling valley mining fields, by A. M. Reid. 1918.—29. The mining fields of Moina, Mt. Claude, and Lorinna, by A. M. Reid. 1919.—30. The Mount Pelion mineral district, by A. M. Reid. 1919.—31. The zinc-lead sulphide deposits of the Read-Rosebery district: pt. III. Metallurgy and general review, by L. Hills. 1919.—32. Osmiridium in Tasmania, by A. M. Reid. 1921.—33. The silver-lead deposits of the Waratah district, by P. B. Nye. 1923. (Text and plates)—34. The Mount Bischoff tin field, by A. McIntosh Reid. 1923.

35. The sub-basaltic tin deposits of the Ringarooma valley, by P. B. Nye. 1925.—36. The Dundas mineral field, by A. M. Reid. 1925.—37. The Golconda gold mining district, by A. McI. Reid. 1926.—38. Blue Tier tin field, by A. McIntosh Reid and Q. J. Henderson. 1928.—39. The osmiridium deposits of the Adamsfield district, by P. B. Nye. 1929.—40. Avoca mineral district, by A. McIntosh Reid and Q. J. Henderson. 1929.—41. The Smithton district, by P. B. Nye, K. J. Finucane and F. Blake. 1934.—42. Lefroy and Back creek goldfields, by E. Broadhurst. 1935.—43. Mathinna and Tower hill goldfields, by K. J. Finucane, with an appendix by P. B. Nye. 1935.—44. The geology and mineral deposits of Tasmania, by P. B. Nye and F. Blake. 1938.
1. Geology—Tasmania. I. Title.

G S 13-158 (rev. '39)

U. S. Geol. survey. Library (880) B6
for Library of Congress QE346.A3

OrU MtBuM
NT 0047018 DI-GS TxU ICJ PPAN PPF NcU KU NIC DLC

Tasmania. *Geological survey.*
... Geological survey record. no. 1–5. Hobart, Tasmania, 1913–19.
5 v. plates. 21½ cm.
At head of title: Tasmania. Dept. of mines.
No more published.
CONTENTS.—1. Marine fossils from the Tasmanite spore beds of the Mersey river, by W. S. Dun.—2. Stichtite, a new Tasmanian mineral; notes by various authors, collected and ed. by W. H. Twelvetrees.—3. Darwin glass, a new variety of the tektites, by Loftus Hills.—4. A monograph of *Nothotherium tasmanicum* (genus-Owen: sp. nov.) by H. H. Scott.—5. On the occurrence of tetradium in the Gordon river limestone, Tasmania, by Frederick Chapman.

1. Geology—Tasmania.

G S 13-435

U. S. Geol. Survey. Libr.
for Library of Congress ⌈a48r35d1⌉†

DLC
NT 0047019 DI-GS NNC INS ICJ NN KU CtY IU PPAN CU

Tasmania. *Geological survey.*
Geological survey report no. 1–
Hobart, Tasmania, 1910–
v. plates, fold. maps. 21½cm.
At head of title: Tasmania. Dept. of mines.

1. Geology—Tasmania.

G S 15-303

Library, U. S. Geological Survey (880) G

NT 0047020 DLC ICJ OrU INS IU KU

Tasmania. *Geological survey.*
... Mineral resources. no. 1–
Hobart, 1916–
v. fold. maps. 22cm.

1. Mines and mineral resources—Tasmania.

G S 16-448 rev

U. S. Geol. survey. Library
for Library of Congress ⌈r46b2⌉†

NT 0047021 DI-GS CU ViU PPF PPAN ICJ TxU DLC

Tasmania. *Geological survey.*
On coal at Mount Rex. (One map) ⌈Hobart? J. Vail, government printer⌉ 1905.
7 p. double map. 21½ cm.
Caption title.
Signed: W. H. Twelvetrees, government geologist.

1. Coal—Tasmania.

G S 14-99 rev

U. S. Geol. Survey. Libr.
for Library of Congress ⌈r60b⌉

NT 0047022 DI-GS MtBuM

Tasmania. *Geological survey.*
Report of the ore deposits (other than those of tin) of north Dundas. ⟨Four plans.⟩ ⌈Hobart? J. Vail, government printer⌉ 1902.
66 p. 3 fold. plans, fold. tab., fold. diagr. 21½ cm.
Caption title.
Signed: George A. Waller, assistant government geologist.

1. Mines and mineral resources—Tasmania.

G S 14-106 rev

U. S. Geol. Survey. Libr.
for Library of Congress ⌈r60b⌉

NT 0047023 DI-GS PPF

Tasmania. *Geological survey.*
Report on coal near George Town, and slate near Badger Head. ⟨Two maps.⟩ ⌈Hobart? J. Vail, government printer⌉ 1904.
10 p. 2 double maps. 20½ cm.
Caption title.
Signed: W. H. Twelvetrees, government geologist.

1. Coal—Tasmania. 2. Slate—Tasmania.

G S 14-92 rev

U. S. Geol. Survey. Libr.
for Library of Congress ⌈r60b⌉

NT 0047024 DI-GS MtBuM PPF

Tasmania. *Geological survey.*
Report on coal seams at Thornedale, near Thompson's marshes, and the Jubilee colliery, near St. Marys. [Hobart? J. Vail, government printer] 1901.
8 p. fold. map. 22½ cm.
Caption title.
Signed: W. H. Twelvetrees, government geologist.

1. Coal—Tasmania.

G S 14–94 rev

U. S. Geol. Survey. Libr. for Library of Congress [r60b2]

NT 0047025 DI-GS

Tasmania. Geological Survey.
Report on country on the east shore of Lake Sorell, and on a discovery of coal near Oatlands. Launceston, 1902.
10 p.

NT 0047026 PPF

Tasmania. *Geological survey.*
Report on Cox's Bight tin-field. ⟨With one map.⟩ [Hobart? J. Vail, government printer] 1906.
18 p. double map. 21½ cm.
Caption title.
Signed: W. H. Twelvetrees, government geologist.

1. Tin ores—Tasmania.

G S 14–97 rev

U. S. Geol. Survey. Libr. for Library of Congress [r60b2]

NT 0047027 DI-GS MtBuM NN

Tasmania. *Geological survey.*
Report on deep sinking at the Moonlight-cum-wonder gold mine, Beaconsfield. ⟨One plan.⟩ [Hobart? J. Vail, government printer, 1902]
12 p. fold. plan. 21½ cm.
Caption title.
Signed: W. H. Twelvetrees, government geologist.

1. Gold mines and mining—Tasmania—Beaconsfield.

G S 14–108 rev

U. S. Geol. Survey. Libr. for Library of Congress [r60b2]

NT 0047028 DI-GS

Tasmania. *Geological survey.*
Report on deposits of clay at George's Bay and elsewhere. [Hobart? J. Vail, government printer] 1904.
10 p. 21 cm.
Caption title.
Signed: W. H. Twelvetrees, government geologist.

1. Clay—Tasmania.

G S 14–85 rev

U. S. Geol. Survey. Libr. for Library of Congress [r60b2]

NT 0047029 DI-GS MtBuM PPF

Tasmania. *Geological survey.*
Report on deposits of opal at Bothwell, and an alleged discovery of gold at Hunterston, on the Shannon. [Hobart? J. Vail, government printer] 1902.
8 p. 22½ cm.
Caption title.
Signed: W. H. Twelvetrees, government geologist.

1. Opals. 2. Gold—Tasmania—Hunterston.

G S 14–104 rev

U. S. Geol. Survey. Libr. for Library of Congress [r60b2]

NT 0047030 DI-GS PPF

Tasmania. *Geological survey.*
Report on Findon's copper sections, Mount Darwin. [Hobart? J. Vail, government printer] 1903.
14 p. 21½ cm.
Caption title.
Signed: George A. Waller, assistant government geologist.

1. Copper mines and mining—Tasmania—Darwin, Mount.

G S 14–112 rev

U. S. Geol. Survey. Libr. for Library of Congress [r60b2]

NT 0047031 DI-GS MtBuM

Tasmania. *Geological survey.*
Report on gold and coal at Port Cygnet. [Hobart? J. Vail, government printer] 1902.
8 p. 22 cm.
Caption title.
Signed: W. H. Twelvetrees, government geologist.

1. Gold—Tasmania—Port Cygnet. 2. Coal—Tasmania—Port Cygnet.

G S 14–105 rev

U. S. Geol. Survey. Libr. for Library of Congress [r60b2]

NT 0047032 DI-GS PPF

Tasmania. *Geological survey.*
Report on gold at Port Cygnet and Wheatley's Bay, Huon River. [Hobart? J. Vail, government printer] 1907.
12 p. 21½ cm.
Caption title.
Signed: W. H. Twelvetrees, government geologist.

1. Gold ores—Tasmania.

G S 14–116 rev

U. S. Geol. Survey. Libr. for Library of Congress [r60b2]

NT 0047033 DI-GS PPF

Tasmania. *Geological survey.*
Report on kerosene shale and coal seams in the parish of Preolenna. ⟨One map.⟩ [Hobart? J. Vail, government printer] 1903.
16 p. fold. map. 22 cm.
Caption title.

1. Coal—Tasmania—Preolenna.

G S 14–83 rev

U. S. Geol. Survey. Libr. for Library of Congress [r60b2]

NT 0047034 DI-GS MtBuM

Tasmania. *Geological survey.*
Report on mineral fields between Waratah and Long Plains. (With one map) [Hobart, J. Vail, government printer] 1903.
38 p. double map. 21½ cm.
Caption title.
Signed: W. H. Twelvetrees, government geologist.

1. Mines and mineral resources—Tasmania.

G S 14–89 rev

U. S. Geol. Survey. Libr. for Library of Congress [r60b2]

NT 0047035 DI-GS PPF MtBuM

Tasmania. *Geological survey.*
Report on north-west coast mineral deposits. ⟨Six maps.⟩ [Hobart? J. Vail, government printer] 1905.
51 p. 6 maps (part fold.) 21 cm.
Caption title.
Signed: W. H. Twelvetrees, government geologist.

1. Mines and mineral resources—Tasmania.

G S 14–95 rev

U. S. Geol. Survey. Libr. for Library of Congress [r60b2]

NT 0047036 DI-GS MtBuM NN PPF

Tasmania. *Geological survey.*
Report on some discoveries of copper ore in the vicinity of Point Hibbs. [Hobart? J. Vail, government printer] 1902.
7 p. 22 cm.
Caption title.
Signed: George A. Waller, assistant government geologist.

1. Copper ores—Tasmania—Point Hibbs.

G S 14–100 rev

U. S. Geol. Survey. Libr. for Library of Congress [r60c2]

NT 0047037 DI-GS PPF

Tasmania. Geological Survey.
Report on some Wolfram sections near Pieman Heads. 1901. Report on deposits of opat at Bothwell... Report on the coal field in Recherche Bay. 1902. W.H. Twelvetrees.
3 p.

NT 0047038 PPFr

Tasmania. *Geological survey.*
Report on the Bell Mount and Middlesex district. [Hobart? J. Vail, government printer] 1907.
32 p. 21½ cm.
Caption title.
Signed: W. H. Twelvetrees, government geologist.
"Note by Mr. W. F. Petterd on examination of altered spodumene from the Shepherd and Murphy lode": p. 31-32.

1. Mines and mineral resources—Tasmania.

G S 14–117 rev

U. S. Geol. Survey. Libr. for Library of Congress [r60b2]

NT 0047039 DI-GS

Tasmania. *Geological survey.*
Report on the coal field in the neighbourhood of Recherche Bay. By W. H. Twelvetrees, government geologist. [Hobart, J. Vail, government printer, 1902]
16 p. fold. map. 21½ cm.

1. Coal—Tasmania—Recherche Bay region.

G S 14–111 rev

U. S. Geol. Survey. Libr. for Library of Congress [r60b2]

NT 0047040 DI-GS

Tasmania. *Geological survey.*
Report on the Den Hill gold deposits. [Hobart? J. Vail, government printer] 1902.
7 p. 22½ cm.
Caption title.
Signed: W. H. Twelvetrees, government geologist.

1. Gold ores—Tasmania.

G S 14–110 rev

U. S. Geol. Survey. Libr. for Library of Congress [r60b2]

NT 0047041 DI-GS MtBuM PPF PPL

Tasmania. *Geological survey.*
Report on the Dial Range and some other mineral districts on the northwest coast of Tasmania. [Hobart? J. Vail, government printer] 1903.
27 p. 21½ cm.
Caption title.
Signed: W. H. Twelvetrees.

1. Mines and mineral resources—Tasmania.

G S 14–114 rev

U. S. Geol. Survey. Libr. for Library of Congress [r60b2]

NT 0047042 DI-GS MtBuM

Tasmania. *Geological survey.*
Report on the iron and zinc-lead ore deposits of the Comstock district. ⟨Two plans.⟩ ₍Hobart? J. Vail, government printer₎ 1903.

34 p. fold. plan, diagr. 21½ cm.

Caption title.
Signed: George A. Waller, assistant government geologist.

1. Mines and mineral resources—Tasmania.

G S 14–113 rev

U. S. Geol. Survey. Libr.
for Library of Congress   ₍r60b¾₎

NT 0047043   DI-GS MtBuM PPF

Tasmania. *Geological survey.*
Report on the Mathinna goldfield … ₍Hobart? J. Vail, government printer₎ 1906–07.

3 v. plans. 22ᶜᵐ.

Caption title.
Signed: W. H. Twelvetrees, government geologist.
Pt. 3 is entitled: The Mathinna goldfield. Geological survey bulletin, no. 2.

1. Gold mines and mining—Tasmania—Mathinna. ɪ. Twelvetrees, William H., 1848– ɪɪ. Tasmania. Government geologist.

G S 14–96

Library, U. S. Geol.   survey (880) M62

NT 0047044   DI-GS, PPF

Tasmania. *Geological survey.*
Report on the mineral resources of the districts of Beaconsfield and Salisbury. ⟨Four maps.⟩ ₍Hobart? J. Vail, government printer₎ 1903.

62 p. fold. map, 2 fold. plans, fold. profile. 21 cm.

Caption title.
Signed: W. H. Twelvetrees, government geologist.

1. Mines and mineral resources—Tasmania.

G S 14–115 rev

U. S. Geol. Survey. Libr.
for Library of Congress   ₍r60b¾₎

NT 0047045   DI-GS MtBuM

Tasmania. *Geological survey.*
Report on the Mt. Farrell mining district. ₍Hobart? J. Vail, government printer₎ 1904.

16 p. 21½ cm.

Caption title.
Signed: George A. Waller, geological surveyor.

1. Mines and mining—Tasmania—Farrell, Mount.

G S 14–87 rev

U. S. Geol. Survey. Libr.
for Library of Congress   ₍r60b¾₎

NT 0047046   DI-GS MtBuM PPF

Tasmania. *Geological survey.*
Report on the Mount Victoria goldfield. ⟨Two maps.⟩ ₍Hobart? J. Vail, government printer₎ 1904.

30 p. 2 fold. maps. 21½ cm.

Caption title.
Signed: W. H. Twelvetrees, government geologist.

1. Gold mines and mining—Tasmania.

G S 14–90 rev

U. S. Geol. Survey. Libr.
for Library of Congress   ₍r60b¾₎

NT 0047047   DI-GS MtBuM

Tasmania. Geological Survey.
Report on the occurrence of coal near Catamaran river, Rehcerche Bay.   Launceston, 1902.

7 p.

NT 0047048   PPF

Tasmania. *Geological survey.*
Report on the Primrose Mine, Rosebery. ₍Hobart? J. Vail, government printer₎ 1903.

4 p. 22½ cm.

Caption title.
Signed: G. A. Waller, assistant government geologist.

1. Primrose Mine.

G S 14–93 rev

U. S. Geol. Survey. Libr.
for Library of Congress   ₍r60c¾₎

NT 0047049   DI-GS MtBuM

Tasmania. *Geological survey.*
Report on the prospects of the Stanley River tinfield. ⟨One plan.⟩ ₍Hobart? J. Vail, government printer₎ 1904.

19 p. fold. map. 21½ cm.

Caption title.
Signed: G. A. Waller, geological surveyor.

1. Tin ores—Tasmania.

G S 14–84 rev

U. S. Geol. Survey. Libr.
for Library of Congress   ₍r60b¾₎

NT 0047050   DI-GS MtBuM

Tasmania. *Geological survey.*
Report on the recent discovery of cannel coal in the parish of Preolenna and upon the New Victory copper mine, near Arthur river. By George A. Waller, assistant government geologist. ₍Hobart? J. Vail, government printer, 1901₎

16 p. fold. profile. 22½ cm.

1. Coal—Tasmania—Preolenna. 2. Copper mines and mining—Tasmania.

G S 14–107 rev

U. S. Geol. Survey. Libr.
for Library of Congress   ₍r60b¾₎

NT 0047051   DI-GS

Tasmania. *Geological survey.*
Report on the Renison Bell tin-field. ₍Hobart? J. Vail, government printer₎ 1906.

12 p. 21½ cm.

Caption title.
Signed: W. H. Twelvetrees, government geologist.

1. Tin ores—Tasmania.

G S 14–98 rev

U. S. Geol. Survey. Libr.
for Library of Congress   ₍r60b¾₎

NT 0047052   DI-GS MtBuM NN

Tasmania. *Geological survey.*
Report on the Sandfly coal mines. ₍Hobart? J. Vail, government printer₎ 1903.

12 p. 21½ cm.

Caption title.
Signed: W. H. Twelvetrees, government geologist.

1. Coal mines and mining—Tasmania.

G S 14–91 rev

U. S. Geol. Survey. Libr.
for Library of Congress   ₍r60b¾₎

NT 0047053   DI-GS MtBuM

Tasmania. *Geological survey.*
Report on the South Mount Victoria mining field. ₍Hobart? J. Vail, government printer₎ 1904.

22 p. 21 cm.

Caption title.
Signed: W. H. Twelvetrees, government geologist.

1. Gold mines and mining—Tasmania. 2. Mines and mineral resources—Tasmania—Mount Victoria.

G S 14–88 rev

U. S. Geol. Survey. Libr.
for Library of Congress   ₍r60b¾₎

NT 0047054   DI-GS MtBuM

Tasmania. *Geological survey.*
Report on the tin ore deposits of Mount Heemskirk. ⟨Four plans.⟩ ₍Hobart? J. Vail, government printer, 1902₎

46 p. 4 maps (3 fold.) 21½ cm.

Caption title.
Signed: George A. Waller, assistant government geologist.

1. Tin ores—Tasmania—Heemskirk, Mount.

G S 14–103 rev

U. S. Geol. Survey. Libr.
for Library of Congress   ₍r60b¾₎

NT 0047055   DI-GS MtBuM PPF

Tasmania. *Geological survey.*
Report on the tin mines of the Blue Tier, county of Dorset. ₍Hobart? J. Vail, government printer₎ 1901.

33 p. fold. map, 2 fold. diagr. 22½ cm.

Caption title.
Signed: W. H. Twelvetrees, government geologist.

1. Tin mines and mining—Tasmania—Blue Tier.

G S 14–102 rev

U. S. Geol. Survey. Libr.
for Library of Congress   ₍r60b¾₎

NT 0047056   DI-GS

Tasmania. *Geological survey.*
Report on the tin-mining district of Ben Lomond. ₍Hobart? J. Vail, government printer₎ 1901.

41 p. fold. map, 3 fold. diagrs. 21½ cm.

Caption title.
Signed: George A. Waller, assistant government geologist.

1. Tin mines and mineral resources—Tasmania.

G S 14–101 rev

U. S. Geol. Survey. Libr.
for Library of Congress   ₍r60b¾₎

NT 0047057   DI-GS CSt PPF

Tasmania. *Geological survey.*
Report on the Western silver mine, Zeehan. ⟨Two plans.⟩ ₍Hobart? J. Vail, government printer₎ 1902.

18 p. 2 fold. plans. 22 cm.

Caption title.
Signed: George A. Waller, assistant government geologist.

1. Silver mines and mining—Tasmania—Zeehan.

G S 14–109 rev

U. S. Geol. Survey. Libr.
for Library of Congress   ₍r60b¾₎

NT 0047058   DI-GS MtBuM

Tasmania. *Geological survey.*
Report on the Zeehan silver-lead mining field. ⟨With map and two plates.⟩ ₍Hobart? J. Vail, government printer₎ 1904.

101 p. fold. map, fold. diagr. 21 cm.

Caption title.
Signed: George Waller, geological surveyor.

1. Lead mines and mining—Tasmania—Zeehan. 2. Silver mines and mining—Tasmania—Zeehan.

G S 14–86 rev

U. S. Geol. Survey. Libr.
for Library of Congress   ₍60b¾₎

NT 0047059   DI-GS MtBuM

Tasmania. *Geological survey.*
Report upon the present position of the Tasmania mine, Beaconsfield. ₍Hobart? J. Vail, government printer₎ 1903.

8 p. 22 cm.

Caption title.
Signed: W. H. Twelvetrees, government geologist.

1. Gold mines and mining—Tasmania—Beaconsfield.

G S 14–82 rev

U. S. Geol. Survey. Libr.
for Library of Congress   ₍r60b¾₎

NT 0047060   DI-GS MtBuM

Tasmania. *Geological survey.*
... Tungsten and molybdenum ...
Hobart, J. Vail, government printer, 1916–

v. fold. maps, plans. 21½–22ᶜᵐ. (*Its Mineral resources, no. 1*)

At head of title: Tasmania. Dept. of mines ...

CONTENTS.—pt. 1. North-eastern and eastern Tasmania, by L. Hills. 1916.—pt. 2. Middlesex and Mt. Claude districts, by L. Hills. 1916.—pt. 3. King island, by L. L. Waterhouse. 1916.

1. Tungsten ores—Tasmania. 2. Molybdenum ores—Tasmania.

          G S 16–424 Revised 3

U. S. Geol. survey. Library
for Library of Congress   TN490.T9T3
        ₍r45b2₎†

NT 0047061   DI-GS DLC NN ICJ ViU

Tasmania. *Geological survey.*
...The underground water resources of the Jericho-Richmond-Bridgewater area, by P. B. Nye ... Hobart, Tasmania, John Vail, government printer, 1922.

viii, 98 p. v fold. pl. (incl. maps) tables. 21½ᶜᵐ. (Underground water-supply paper no. 2)

At head of title: Tasmania. Department of mines.

1. Water-supply—Tasmania. I. Nye, Percival Bartlett, 1893–
II. Title.

          G S 22–369 Revised

Library, U. S. Geological   Survey (886) U

NT 0047062   DI-GS TxU ViU

Tasmania. *Geological survey.*
... The underground water resources of the midlands, by P. B. Nye ... Hobart, J. Vail, government printer, 1921.

x, 142 p. vii pl. (incl. 6 fold. maps, diagr.) tables, diagrs. 21½ cm. (Tasmania. Government geologist. Underground water supply paper no. 1)

At head of title: Tasmania. Department of mines.

1. Water, Underground—Tasmania. 2. Water-supply—Tasmania.
I. Title.

          G S 21–333 rev

U. S. Geol. Survey. Libr.
for Library of Congress   ₍r00d2₎

NT 0047063   DI-GS TxU ViU

Tasmania. *Geological survey.*
... Underground water supply paper no. 1–

Hobart, John Vail, government printer, 1921–

v. plates, tables, diagrs. (part fold.) 21½ᶜᵐ.

At head of title: Tasmania. Department of mines.

CONTENTS.—no. 1. The underground water resources of the Midlands, by P. B. Nye. 1921.—no. 2. The underground water resources of the Jericho-Richmond-Bridgewater area, by P. B. Nye. 1922.—no. 3. The underground water resources of the Richmond-Bridgewater-Sandford district, by P. B. Nye. 1924.—no. 4. The Campbell Town-Conara-St. Marys district, by P. B. Nye. 1926.

1. Water-supply—Tasmania. I. Nye, Percival Bartlett, 1893–
II. Title.

          G S 21–332 Revised

Library, U. S. Geological   Survey (880) U

NT 0047064   DI-GS DLC KU AzU ViU TxU CU

Tasmania. *Geological Survey.*
Volunteer Gold Mining Company: report of the Government Geologist on the deep shaft. Presented to both Houses of Parliament by His Excellency's command.
= [Hobart Town. 1899.] 7 pp. [No. 63.] F°.

E0066 — Tasmania. Mines. — Volunteer Gold Mining Co. — Gold. Mining, etc.

NT 0047065   MB

Tasmania. *Geological Surveyor*
   see
Tasmania. *Geological Survey.*

Tasmania. *Government Geologist*
   see
Tasmania. *Geological Survey.*

Tasmania. *Government insurance office.*
Annual report.

₍Hobart, 1921–
   v. tables. 35½ᶜᵐ.

Report year ends June 30.

1. Insurance, Fire—Tasmania. 2. Insurance, Marine—Tasmania.
3. Insurance, Accident—Tasmania.

          34–33721

Library of Congress   HG8734.T3A3
      ₍2₎   368.9946

NT 0047068   DLC DS

Tasmania. Govt. meteorologist.
Rainfall.
1905–07.

NT 0047069   DAS

Tasmania. Government printing dept.

See

Tasmania. Printing office.

Tasmania. Government statistician

See

Tasmania. Statistical and registration dept.

919.46 **Tasmania. Government Tourist Bureau.**
T187c   Complete guide to Tasmania.
1918   Tasmania, 1918.
        186p. illus., fold.map.

Advertising matter interspersed.

NT 0047072   IU

Tasmania. Government Tourist Bureau.
Complete guide to Tasmania. [Hobart] John Vail, Govt. Print., 1922.
vii, 186 p. illus., fold. map. 23 cm.
1. Tasmania. Descr. and trav. Guidebooks.
I. Title.

NT 0047073   OrU

Tasmania. Government Tourist Bureau.
Complete guide to Tasmania giving routes, roads, fares, timetables and tours. Issued by the Tasmanian Government Tourist Department...

1915. Tasmania: J. Vail, 1915.   vii(i), 205 p.   illus., fold. map. 8°.
1916. ib., 1916.   vii(i), 244 p.   illus., fold. map. 8°.

1. Tasmania.—Guidebooks.
N. Y. P. L.   January 25, 1921

NT 0047074   NN

Tasmania. *Government tourist bureau.*
North-western Tasmania illustrated, the gateway to the Garden Island. Devonport and Burnie, Tasmania, Harris & company limited ₍1915?₎
42 p. illus. 16 x 23ᶜᵐ.
Advertising matter interspersed.

1. Tasmania—Descr. & trav.—Guide-books. I. Title.

          CA 17–414 Unrev'd

Library of Congress   DU455.T3

NT 0047075   DLC

DU   **Tasmania. Government Torist Bureau.**
480   Port Arthur, Tasmania. [Hobart?] W.E.
P68   Shimmins, govt. pr. [1935?]
HRC.   folder (8p.) illus. (part col.) map.
GRA   25x9cm.

1. Port Arthur, Tasmania – Description.

NT 0047076   TxU

Tasmania. Government Tourist Bureau.
Tasmania, Australia's playground. [Hobart: Govt. Tourist Dept., 1928?] 40 p. illus. sq. 8°.

Cover-title.
Advertising matter throughout.

412059A. 1. Tasmania—Descr. and   trav.   May 31, 1929
N. Y. P. L.

NT 0047077   NN

919.46   **Tasmania. Government Tourist Bureau.**
T199t   Tasmania, holiday island. [Hobart, Cox Kay, 19--]
        32p. illus. 25cm.

Cover title.

1. Tasmania. Descr. & trav. I. Title.

NT 0047078   IEN

Tasmania. Government Tourist Bureau.
Tasmania, the wonderland. Issued by the Tasmanian government tourist bureau. Hobart, n. d.
illus. (part col.) ₎9 cm.
"Second edition".
1. Tasmania. Descr. & travel.

NT 0047079   NcD

Tasmania. Government Tourist Dept.
see **Tasmania. Government Tourist Bureau.**

Tasmania. Governor.
Laws and ordinances of Governor and council of Van Diemen's land, 1826–30
      see under   **Tasmania. Laws, statutes, etc.**

Ndb78   **Tasmania. Governor, 1945–1951 (Sir Thomas Hugh Binney)**
T8   Regulations(with index) for conducting the
947T   survey of land in Tasmania under the Crown Lands Act, 1935 and the Land Surveyors Act, 1909. Hobart, Tasmania, H.H. Pimblett, Govt. printer, 1947.
       xi, 76 p. illus. 26 cm.

1. Tasmania – Public lands. 2. Surveying – Public lands – Tasmania.

NT 0047082   CtY

Tasmania. Hobart rat extermination committee.
Rat extermination. Report for 1900. [Hobart:] J. Vail
₍1900₎.   6 p.   f°.

1. Rat.—Extermination of, Aus-   tralia: Tasmania: Hobart.
N. Y. P. L.   July 27. 1911.

NT 0047083   NN

q331.833
T183   Tasmania—Housing Dept.
      Report of the Director of Housing.

      Hobart, 1955/56–
        v.   34cm.   annual.

      Report year ends June 30.

NT   0047084   IU

TK1522
.T3T3
1925   **Tasmania. Hydro-electric department.**

      Tait publishing co. pty. ltd.
        The hydro-electric power of Tasmania; a description of
the Great lake hydro-electric development, and of the Tasmanian electricity supply system. Melbourne ₍etc.₎ Published under authority, Hydro-electric department of Tasmania, Tait publishing co. ltd., 1925

TK1522
.T3A3   Tasmania. Hydro-electric dept.
      Report.

      Hobart, 19
        v.   plates, tables, diagrs. (part fold.)
33½cm.

      Report year ends June 30.

NT   0047086   DLC TxU DNAL DI NN

      Tasmania. *Industrial Dept.*
      see also **Tasmania.** *Dept. of Labour and Industry.*

      Tasmania. *Industry, Dept. of Labour and*
      see **Tasmania.** *Dept. of Labour and Industry.*

      Tasmania. *Labour and Industry, Dept. of*
      see **Tasmania.** *Dept. of Labour and Industry.*

      Tasmania. Land and surveys, Dept.

           See

      Tasmania. Dept. of land and surveys.

HD1206
.T3A3   Tasmania. Lands title and registry of deeds
      dept.
      ... Recorder of titles and registrar of
deeds: report ...

      [Hobart,
        v.   tables.   34½cm.

      1. Land titles—Registration and transfer—
Tasmania.   I. Title.

NT   0047091   DLC

      Tasmania. *Laws, statutes, etc.*
      ... An act for the regulation of the civil service of the
colony of Tasmania, for providing retiring allowances to
the members thereof, and for other purposes ... ₍Hobart?
J. Vail, government printer, 1901₎

      ₍589₎-602 p.   34ᶜᵐ.

      At head of title: Tasmania. 1900. Anno sexagesimo quarto Victoriæ
reginæ, no. 69.

      1. Civil service—Tasmania.

                            9–15428

      Library of Congress   JQ5145.D4   1901

NT   0047092   DLC

      Tasmania. *Laws, statutes, etc.*
      ... An act to amend "The Education act, 1885." ⟨29
October, 1898.⟩ ₍Hobart, W. Grahame, government
printer, 1898₎

      p. ₍385₎-387.   33ᶜᵐ.

      Caption title.
      At head of title: Tasmania. 1898. Anno sexagesimo-secundo Victoriæ
reginæ, no. 37.

      1. Educational law and legislation—Tasmania.

                            10–152†

      Library of Congress   LB2787.T3   1898

NT   0047093   DLC

HD
7385
A3
1936
HRC
GRA   Tasmania. Laws, statutes, etc.
      ... An act to amend the Homes Act 1935
₍Hobart₎ Walter E. Shimmins, govt. printer
₍1936₎

      1₎.   25cm.

      At head of title: Tasmania. 1936. Anno
Primo. Edwardi VIII. Regis. No.43.
      Short title: Homes act 1936.

      1. Housing – Tasmania.   I. Title: Homes
Act 1936.

NT   0047094   TxU

---

q
HD
7385
A3
1935
HRC
GRA   Tasmania. Laws, statutes, etc.
      ... An act to consolidate certain enact-
ments relating to the provision of homes and
advances for homes for persons of limited
means. ₍Hobart, Walter E. Shimmins, govt.
printer, 1935₎

      ₍19₎p.   29cm.

      At head of title: Tasmania. 1935. Anno
Vicesimo Sexto. Georgii V. Regis. No.98.
      Marginal ms. notes.
      Short title: Homes act, 1935.

NT   0047095   TxU

      Tasmania. *Laws, statutes, etc.*
      ... An act to further amend "The Education act, 1885,"
to amend "The Education act, 1898," and for other purposes. ⟨20 November, 1905.⟩ ₍Hobart, J. Vail, government printer, 1905₎

      p. ₍409₎-414.   28½ x 22½ᶜᵐ.

      Caption title.
      At head of title: Tasmania. 1905. Anno quinto Edwardi VII. regis,
no. 32.

      1. Educational law and legislation—Tasmania.

                            10–151†

      Library of Congress   LB2787.T3   1905

NT   0047096   DLC

      Tasmania. *Laws, statutes, etc.*
      ... An act to make more adequate provision for public edu-
cation. ⟨5 December, 1885⟩ ₍Hobart, W. T. Strutt, government printer, 1885₎

      p. ₍73₎-82.   33ᶜᵐ.

      Caption title.
      At head of title: Tasmania. 1885. Anno quadragesimo-nono Victoriæ
reginæ, no. 15.

      1. Educational law and legislation—Tasmania.

                            10–150

      Library of Congress   LB2787.T3   1885

NT   0047097   DLC

      Tasmania. Laws, statutes, etc.
      ₍Acts.₎

      ₍Hobart?₎

NT   0047098   NN

      Tasmania. *Laws, statutes, etc.*
      Acts of Council, 1833–1851. ₍Hobart, J. Barnard, Govt.
printer, Van Diemen's Land, 1833?–1851?₎

      126 no. in 1 v.   34 cm.

      Title from label on spine.
      Contains acts of Parliament, enacted during the reigns of William
IV and Victoria, which were extended to the colony by the act of
Council.

                            67–122735

NT   0047099   DLC

Tasmania. Laws, statutes, etc.
      Acts of the governor and council of Tasmania
[1855–56]. Hobart Town, 1856.

      Vol.3, pt.18.   f°.

NT   0047100   MH-L

      Tasmania. *Laws, statutes, etc.*
      The acts of the lieutenant-governor and Council of Van
Diemen's Land ... Van Diemen's Land, Hobart Town,
J. Barnard, government printer,

        v.   33ᶜᵐ.

                            8–30638

NT   0047101   DLC MH-L

      Tasmania. *Laws, statutes, etc.*
      The acts of the Parliament of Tasmania. v. 1–
Session of Parliament 20° Victoriæ (1856–7)–
Hobart, Tasmania, T. G. Prior, acting government printer,
1857–19

        v.   fold. maps.   28–33½ cm.

      Cover-title.
      Imprint varies.

                            21—6862

NT   0047102   DLC NcD CaBVaU CLU WaU-L

Tasmania. Laws, statutes, etc.
      ...Acts to amend the mines and works regulation
act, 1915...
      (Hobart, 1926–
        v.   29 cm.
      Library has:
      Dec., 1926
      Jan., 1929
      Jan., 1930
      Oct., 1930   to amend the mining act, 1929
      Dec., 1931

NT   0047103   DI-GS

      Tasmania.   Laws, statutes, etc.

      Australian legislative digest. Summary of principal bills in-
troduced into, and acts passed by, the parliaments of Australia ... 19   Published under the
authority of the premier of New South Wales ... Sydney,
19

Z7164
.R4P6   Tasmania. Laws, statutes, etc.

      Piesse, Edmund Leolin, 1880–
      ... Bibliography of proportional representation in Tas-
mania, by E. L. Piesse ... Hobart, J. Vail, government printer,
1913.

KTA [Tasmania. Laws, statutes, etc.]
T28   The casual workers and unemployed persons
HRC   homes act, 1936.   [Tasmania, W.E. Shimmins,
GRA   govt. pr., 1936?]
       397-409p. 25cm.

       Running title: 1 Ed. VIII & Geo. VI, no.57.

       1. Home ownership - Tasmania. I. Title.

NT 0047106   TxU

W   TASMANIA. Laws, statutes, etc.
32   [Collection of publications]
KA8
T2L4   The Library has a collection of
       miscellaneous publications of this
       organization kept as received. These
       publications are not listed or bound
       separately.   W32KA8 T2L4

NT 0047107   DNLM

Tasmania. *Laws, statutes, etc.*
   Copies of the laws and ordinances passed by the Governor
and Council of the Colony of Van Diemen's Land, 1826–
1830. [London, 1831]
   91 p. 35 cm.
   At head of title: Van Diemen's Land.
   "Ordered, by the House of Commons, to be printed, 11 March 1831."

   I. Title.
                                          67–118672

NT 0047108   DLC

Tasmania. Laws, statutes, etc.
   "The diseased animals importation act".
   (1898)
   4 p.

NT 0047109   DNAL

Tasmania. *Laws, statutes, etc.*
   ... The Education act, 1885, and amendment acts with
regulations of October, 1908. Hobart, J. Vail, government printer, 1908.
   2 p. l., 93 p. 21 cm.
   "A reprint of the education acts ... represents the law at this date."

   1. School law—Tasmania.   I. Tasmania. Education dept.
                                          E 9-476
   Library, U. S. Bur. of   Education   LB2787.T2 1908

NT 0047110   DHEW ICJ

LB2787 Tasmania. Laws, statutes, etc.
T3   The Education act, 1885 and amendment acts,
1915   with regulations of 1915.   Hobart, J. Rail, 1915.
         67 p.   27.5 cm.

NT 0047111   DLC IU

Tasmania. Laws, statutes, etc.
   ... The education act, 1885, and amendment
acts with regulations of 1925.   Hobart, John Vail,
government printed, 1926.
   181 p.   21.5 cm.

NT 0047112   PPT

Tasmania. Laws, statutes, etc.
   The forestry act, 1920. [An act to establish a
Forestry department, and to provide for the better manage-
ment and protection of forests, and for other purposes.
Hobart. 1920.] 4°.   (11° Georgii v. No. 60.)

NT 0047113   MH-A

Tasmania. Laws, statutes, etc.
—— Forestry regulations under "The Crown lands act,
1911." Hobart. 1920. 16°. pp. iv, 42.
"Reprinted from *Tasmanian government gazette*, March 30, 1920."

NT 0047114   MH-A

Tasmania. Laws, statutes, etc.
Ratcliffe, John Vincent, *ed.*
   Income tax decisions of Australasia; being a compendium
of reported and numerous unreported legal decisions (excepting the decisions in the New South Wales Court of review), on
appeals arising under the income tax assessment acts of the
Commonwealth and the states of Australia and the Dominion
of New Zealand and containing the text of the sections of the
various acts upon which the cases were decided, with exhaustive
indexes, by John Vincent Ratcliffe ... and John York McGrath
... Sydney [etc.] The Law book company of Australasia limited, 1928.

TASMANIA - Laws,statutes,etc.
   Laws and ordinances of Governor and Council
of Van Diemen's Land, 1826-30. [London,1831].

   Fol.

NT 0047116   MH-L

Tasmania. Laws, statutes, etc.
   ...The mines and works regulation act, 1915 and
regulations, Hobart, J. Vail, government printer,
1916.
   72 p.   21½ cm.

NT 0047117   DI-GS

4K   Tasmania. Laws, statutes, etc.
2344   The Mining act, 1917, 7 Georgii V.
       no. 62, with regulations thereunder.
       Hobart, J. Vail, Govt. printer, 1918.
       203 p.

NT 0047118   DLC-P4

Tasmania. Laws, statutes, etc.
   ...The mining act, 1929. (Hobart, 1929) p. 763-83 5.
29 cm. (20 mo Georgii V regis no. 71)

NT 0047119   DI-GS

Tasmania. Laws, statutes, etc.
   Nurses' registration act, 1927, with regulations and syllabus of
study. — [Hobart] : Dept. of Public Health, 1929.
   42 p. ; 21 cm.
   Cover title.

   1. Nurses and nursing—Legal status, laws, etc.—Tasmania.   I. Tasmania.
Dept. of Public Health. Regulations under The nurses' registration act, 1927.
1929. II. Title.
                            344'.946'041   75-321255
                                                    MARC

NT 0047120   DLC

Tasmania. Laws, statutes, etc.
   Proclamations, government orders, and notices
issued by Lieutenant-Governor of Van Diemen's
Land, 1837
   see under   Tasmania. Lieutenant-Governor
1824-1836 (Sir George Arthur)

Tasmania. *Laws, statutes, etc.*
   The public general acts of Tasmania (reprint) classified and
annotated, 1826-1936 ... Cross-referenced throughout to: Halsbury's Laws of England. Halsbury's Statutes of England.
English and empire digest. Encyclopaedia of forms and prec-
edents. Sydney, N. S. W., Butterworth & co. (Australia) ltd.;
Toronto, Butterworth & co. (Canada) ltd.; etc., etc., 1936-39[?]
   7 v. 25 cm.
   "It is the intention of the publishers ... to keep the Reprint up-to-date
by means of annual cumulative annotations."—Publisher's announcement, v. 1.
   Editorial board: Andrew Inglis Clark, and others. Managing editor:
J. H. Keating. Consultant editor: J. R. Rule.
   Vol. 7: Tables of acts   and general index.
   I. Clark, Andrew Inglis,   1882-   II. Keating, John Henry,
   1872-   III. Rule, James   Roland, 1873-   IV. Title.
                                          36-25122 Revised

NT 0047122   DLC WaU-L NcD OU CtY

Tasmania. Laws, statutes, etc.
   Regulations for the guidance of authorised
surveyors. Hobart, William Grahame, Govt.
printer, 1899.
   43 p. illus.

   At head of title: Tasmania.

NT 0047123   NNC

Tasmania. Laws, statutes, etc.
   Regulations under "The Crown lands act,
1903" and "The Crown lands act, 1905."
Hobart, Tasmania, John Vail, 1906.
   vii, 114 p. forms.

   1. Tasmania - Public lands. 2. Crown lands
- Tasmania.

NT 0047124   NNC

Tasmania. Laws, statutes, etc.
   Regulations (with index) for conducting the
survey of land in Tasmania under the Crown Lands
Act, 1935 and the Land Surveyors Act, 1909
   see under   Tasmania. Governor, 1945-1951
(Sir Thomas Hugh Binney)

Tasmania. Laws, Statutes, etc.
   Rules and regulations of the port of Hobart Town
   see under   Hobart. Marine Board.

K3409   Tasmania. Laws, statutes, etc.
F5   ... The Sea fisheries regulations, 1950.
1950   [Hobart? H. H. Pimblett, Government printer, n.d.]
       32 p. forms.   25 cm.
       Caption title.
       "Extract from Tasmanian government gazette,
       July 5, 1950, p. 1966."

       1. Fishery law and legislation - Tasmania.
       I. Title.

NT 0047127   DI

Tasmania. Laws, statutes, etc.
   Statutes of Tasmania. Vol.6,pt.1,1901-12.
Hobart,1915.

   8 vo.

NT 0047128   MH-L

Tasmania. *Laws, statutes, etc.*
Statutes of Tasmania from 7th George 4th (1826) to ₍52nd Victoria (1888)₎ Alphabetically arranged, with notes, by Frederick Stops ... Pub. by authority. Hobart, Tasmania, W. T. Strutt, government printer, 1883-90.

5 v. 25½ᶜᵐ.
Paged continuously.

ɪ. Stops, Frederick, ed.

21-5445

NT 0047129   DLC IU

Tasmania. *Laws, statutes, etc.*
Statutes of Tasmania from 7th George 4th (1826) to 64th Victoria (1901) Arranged, with notes by Frederick Stops ... Pub. by authority. Tasmania, J. Vail, government printer, Hobart, 1902-05.

5 v. 25ᶜᵐ.
Paged continuously.
Contents.—ɪ. "Admiralty, Lands," to "Cruelty to animals."—ɪɪ. "Dead bodies, Exhumation of," to "Lunatics and insane persons."—ɪɪɪ. "Mandamus" to "Rural voting."—ɪᴠ. "Sale of goods" to "Youthful offenders, destitute and neglected children." Index. Chronological table. Acts of Federal council. Proclamation notifying separation of Tasmania from New South Wales. Governor's and lieutenant-governor's commissions and instructions.—ᴠ. Local and personal ₍acts₎

ɪ. Stops, Frederick, eᵈ

7—8909

NT 0047130   DLC CtY PU-L MH-L WaU-L PBa

Tasmania. *Laws, statutes, etc.*
Statutory rules, with tables and historical and explanatory note on the publication and enumeration of subordinate legislation. 1954-
Hobart, Govt. Printer, Tasmania.

v. 25 cm. annual.

57-21491

NT 0047131   DLC NNC

Tasmania. *Laws, statutes, etc.*
Tasmania. Copy of the electoral act 1901. No. 57. London: Eyre and Spottiswoode, 1902. 36 p. f°. (H. of C. pap. 73.)

In: †† SEH p. v. 33, no. 4.

1. Elections.—Jurisprudence, Australia: Tasmania, 1901.
N. Y. P. L.   January 8, 1913.

NT 0047132   NN

Tasmania. *Laws, statutes, etc.* (*Indexes*)
Index to the Statutes of Tasmania and acts of the Federal council of Australasia in force on June 1, 1897. From 7 George ɪᴠ. (1826), to 60 Victoria, both inclusive. By John Kidston Reid, clerk of the House of assembly. Hobart, Tasmania, W. Grahame, jun., government printer, 1897.

36 p. 22ᶜᵐ.
Index to the Statutes in force February 4, 1889, edited by Frederick Stops, 5 v., 1883-90, and to sessional parts issued later. *cf.* Pref.
"Revised edition."—₍p. 3₎
Addendum slip inserted.
1. Law—Tasmania—Indexes. 2. Law — Australasia — Indexes. ɪ. Australasia. Laws, statutes, etc. (Indexes) ɪɪ. Reid, John Kidston, 1863-1926. ɪɪɪ. Title.

21-5444 Revised

NT 0047133   DLC

Tasmania. *Laws, statutes, etc.* (*Indexes*)
Index to the Statutes of Tasmania in force on June 1 1907, from 7 George ɪᴠ., 1826, to 6 Edwardi ᴠɪɪ. (Both inclusive) by John Kidston Reid, clerk of the House of assembly. ₍3d ed.₎ Hobart, Tasmania, J. Vail, government printer, 1907.

40 p. 22½ᶜᵐ.
Interleaved.
Index to the Statutes ₍1826-1901₎ edited by Frederick Stops, 5 vols., 1902-05, and to sessional parts issued later. *cf.* Pref.
1. Law—Indexes. ɪ. Reid, John Kidston, 1863-   ɪɪ. Title.

21-5443

NT 0047134   DLC

Tasmania. *Laws, statutes, etc.* (*Indexes*)
Index to the statutes of Tasmania in force on July 1, 1928 from 8 Geo. ɪᴠ. to 18 Geo. ᴠ., 1827-1927 (both inclusive) by John Kidston Reid, clerk of the House of assembly. 6th ed., rev. and enl. by Henry McPherson, clerk of the House of assembly. Hobart, Tasmania, J. Vail, government printer, 1928.

64, ₍2₎ p. 25ᶜᵐ.
Interleaved.
"Acts passed since the publication of this edition. Anno 19° Georgii v. (1928)": ₍2₎ p. at end.
1. Law—Tasmania—Indexes. ɪ. Reid, John Kidston, 1863-1926. ɪɪ. McPherson, Henry, ed. ɪɪɪ. Title.

30-21563

NT 0047135   DLC CtY

Tasmania. *Laws, statutes, etc.* (*Indexes*)
Index to the Statutes of Tasmania in force on June 1, 1914, from 7 George ɪᴠ. to 4 George ᴠ., 1826-1913 (both inclusive) by John Kidston Reid, clerk of the House of assembly. 4th ed. Hobart, Tasmania, J. Vail, government printer, 1914.

47 p. 22½ᶜᵐ.
Interleaved.
Index to the Statutes ₍1826-1901₎ edited by Frederick Stops, 5 vols., 1902-05, and to sessional parts issued later. *cf.* Pref.
1. Law—Indexes. ɪ. Reid, John Kidston, 1863-   ɪɪ. Title.

21-5442

NT 0047136   DLC

Tasmania. *Laws, statutes, etc.* (*Indexes*)
Index to the Statutes of Tasmania in force on July 1, 1921, from 7 Geo. ɪᴠ. to 11 Geo. ᴠ., 1826-1920 (both inclusive) by John Kidston Reid, clerk of the House of assembly. 5th ed. Hobart, Tasmania, J. Vail, government printer, 1921.

59 p. 22ᶜᵐ.
Interleaved.

*1. Law—Indexes. ɪ. Reid, John Kidston, 1863-   ɪɪ. Title.

22-17487

NT 0047137   DLC MH-L

Tasmania. Legislative council

See

Tasmania. Parliament. Legislative council.

Tasmania. *Library Board.*
Report of the State Library of Tasmania. 1st- Jan./June 1944-
Hobart, H. H. Pimblett, Govt. Printer.

v. 34 cm. annual.

ɪ. Tasmania. State Library, Hobart.

Z871.H72   027.5946   50-57954 rev

NT 0047139   DLC

DU460   Tasmania. Lieutenant0Governor 1824-1836.
T19   (Sir George Arthur)
                By His Excellency Colonel George Arthur...
             Proclamation [June 23, 1836-   Hobart Town,
             J. Ross [1836]

NT 0047140   DLC

Beinecke   Tasmania. Lieutenant-Governor, 1824-1836 (Sir
Library   George Arthur)
1974   Proclamations, government orders, and
+61   notices, issued by His Excellency Colonel
             George Arthur, lieutenant governor of Van
             Diemen's Land, 1835. Hobart Town ₍Tasmania₎
             Printed by James Ross, 1836.
                186, 14 p. incl. fold. tables. 30 cm.

             I. Arthur, Sir George, bart., 1784-1854.

NT 0047141   CtY

Tasmania. Lieutenant-Governor, 1824-1836 (Sir George Arthur)
Proclamations, government orders, and notices issued by Lieutenant-Governor of Van Diemen's Land, 1837. Hobart Town, 1838.

Fol.

I. Tasmania. Laws, statutes, etc. II. Arthur, Sir George, bart., 1784-1854.

NT 0047142   MH

Tasmania. *Meat board*
see **Tasmania.** *State meat board.*

Tasmania. Mental Health Services Commission.
Report.
₍Hobart₎ Govt. Printer.

v. 30 cm.
Report year ends June 30.
Presented to both Houses of Parliament.

1. Community mental health services—Tasmania—Periodicals.

RA790.7.T37T36a   362.2'2'09946   73-640237

NT 0047144   DLC

Tasmania. Meteorological observer.
Meteorological observations.
1882-87; 1890-93; 1898-1901.

NT 0047145   DAS

Tasmania. Meteorological observer.
Monthly record of results of meteorological observations. Jan.-Sept. 1891.

NT 0047146   DAS

Tasmania. *Milk Board.*
Report. 1st-   1948-
Hobart, H. H. Pimblett, Govt. Printer.

v. 35 cm.
Report year ends June 30.
First report covers period Mar. 5-June 30, 1948.

1. Milk trade—Tasmania.

HD9282.A8T3   51-20842

NT 0047147   DLC IU

Tasmania. *Miners' Pensions Board.*
Report. 1944/45-
Hobart.

v. in   35 cm. annual.
Issued in the parliamentary series as Printed papers.
Report year ends June 30.
First report covers period Nov. 1944-June 1945.

1. Coal-miners—Tasmania. 2. Old age pensions—Tasmania.

HD7116.M6T3   51-20978

NT 0047148   DLC

Tasmania. Mines Dept.

Geological sketch map of Tasmania, based on map by R. M. Johnston, government statistician, and revised by the Geological survey of Tasmania. Hobart. 1914. 17½ x 21½ (in 8° cover.)

NT 0047149   MH-A

TN122
.T3A35   Tasmania. Mines dept.
              ...Mines department circular...
          Hobart, 19
              v.   21cm.

NT   0047150   DLC

Tasmania. Mines Dept.
    The mineral industry of Tasmania. Compiled by J. Harcourt-
Smith...geological surveyor for Tasmania, by order of the Hon-
orable Alfred T. Pillinger, minister of mines. 1897.   Hobart,
Tasmania: W. Grahame, jun., 1897.   18 p.   8°.

1. Minerals, Australia: Tasmania.   2. Harcourt-Smith, J., compiler.
N. Y. P. L.   December 16, 1921.

NT   0047151   NN

Tasmania. Mines Dept.
    The mineral resources of Tasmania
        see its   The progress of the mineral
    industry of Tasmania...

TN122   Tasmania. Mines Dept.
T3A3   Ministerial statement... delivered in the
          House of assembly... 1920-1921, 1923-
          Hobart, 1920-23.
              3 v.   tables.   33.5 cm.

NT   0047153   DLC

Tasmania. *Mines dept.*
    The progress of the mineral industry of Tasmania for

Hobart, 18 -19
    v. 22ᶜᵐ. quarterly.
    18 -1897, annual.
Title varies: 18   The mineral resources of Tasmania.
    18   The mineral industry of Tasmania.
    1898-   The progress of the mineral industry of Tasmania.
    18   report compiled by the geological surveyor; 1898-Sept. 1907,
by the government geologist; Dec. 1907-   by secretary for mines.

    1. Mines and mineral resources—Tasmania.   I. Title.
                                                    G S 14-118
U. S. Geol. survey. Library   (880) B4
for Library of Congress   TN122.T3A27
                              (a38b1)
                                                    622.09946

NT   0047154   DI-GS MB DLC

Tasmania. *Mines Dept.*
    Report.

Hobart.
    v. illus., fold. maps. 34 cm.
    Report year irregular.

    1. Geology—Tasmania. 2. Mines and mineral resources—Tasmania.
    TN122.T3A25   G S 12-254 rev*
U. S. Geol. Survey. Libr.
for Library of Congress   (r48b1)†

NT   0047155   DI-GS MB PPF ICJ PSt CU DLC

Tasmania. *Mines dept.*
    ... Report on the investigation of the tin-bearing ores
of the Renison Bell district, by Joseph H. Levings, government mining engineer. (Hobart) John Vail, government printer, 1921.
    15 p. tables. 21ᶜᵐ.

    Issued under the authority of the Honourable Sir Neil Elliott Lewis ...
minister of mines for Tasmania.

    1. Mines and mineral resources—Tasmania. 2. Tin mines and mining—
Tasmania. I. Levings, Joseph H. II. Title: Tin-bearing ores ...
                                                    G S 21-199
    Library, U. S. Geological   Survey (880) M11

NT   0047156   DI-GS NN

Tasmania. Mines Dept.

Underground water supply paper.
Hobart, Dept. of Mines

Tasmania. *Mines Dept. Geological Survey*
    see
Tasmania. *Geological Survey.*

        Tasmania. Mining Board.
Law
    The **Tasmanian** State reports. 1905–
Hobart.

Tasmania. *Mining Geologist*
    see
Tasmania. *Geological Survey.*

919.46   Tasmania—Nomenclature Board.
T183d   Decision list.

          Hobart.
              no. 17–34cm.

NT   0047161   IU

HD   Tasmania. Office of Chief Inspector of
3787   Factories.
T3A3   Annual report. 1st- [2d.]
              Report year ends June 30.

NT   0047162   DLC MiD DL

Tasmania. Office of Commissioners of Public
    Debts Sinking Fund
        see   Tasmania. Board of Commissioners
    of State Sinking Fund.

Tasmania. Office of Public Service Commissioner.

    The Tasmania Public Service Board was established in 1905. In
1918 the Board was abolished and replaced by the Office of Public
Service Commissioner. In 1973 the name Public Service Board was
resumed.
    Works by these bodies are found under the following headings
according to the name used at the time of publication:

    Tasmania. Public Service Board.
    Tasmania. Office of Public Service Commissioner.

Tasmania. *Office of public service commissioner.*
    Report.

(Hobart, 1907–
    v. tables. 33½ᶜᵐ.

Report year ends June 30.
1906/07 covers period from January 1, 1906 to June 30, 1907.
Issued by the Public service board, 1906/07-1918/19; by the Office of
public service commissioner, 1919/20–

    1. Civil service—Tasmania. 2. Tasmania—Officials and employees.
I. Tasmania. Public service board.
                                                    34-33722
    Library of Congress   JQ5145.A3

NT   0047165   DLC

HD9539   Tasmania. Parliament.
.A6A885
          Australian Aluminium Production Commission.
              Annual report. 1st-   1945/46–
          Hobart.

Tasmania. Parliament.

Nowell, Edwin Cradock, 1831–
    A history of the relations between the two houses of Parlia-
ment in Tasmania and South Australia, in regard to amendments to bills containing provisions relating to the public
revenue or expenditure. By Edwin Cradock Nowell ... Hobart, Tasmania, W. T. Strutt, government printer, 1890.

Tasmania. *Parliament.*
    Journals and printed papers. v. 1–
1884–
    (Hobart)
        v. illus., maps (part fold.) 34 cm.
    Supersedes Journals of the House of Assembly and Journals of the
Legislative Council.
    INDEXES:
        Papers.
            1856-91. 1 v.
            1856-99. 1 v.
            1856-1921. 1 v.
            1856-1941. 1 v.
        Includes index to papers in the Journals of the House of Assembly
and in the Journals of   the Legislative Council.
    1. Tasmania—Pol. &   govt.
    J926.L3   55-16301

NT   0047168   DLC CaBVaU ICU

Tasmania. Parliament.
    The Parliament of Tasmania 1856-1943
        see under   Thompson, Leonard, Albert.

25.3   Tasmania. Parliament.
51512a   Parliamentary handbook, showing the practice
          of the English house of commons, in cases not
          specially provided for by the standing orders of the
          legislative council, Tasmania.   Tasmania,
          T. W. Strutt, government printer, 1887.
              viii, 218 p.   16°.

NT   0047170   DLC

Tasmania. Parliament.
    Printed papers
        see its
    Journals and printed papers.

Tasmania. Parliament.
    Report on parliamentary elections.   Hobart,
D. E. Wilkinson [etc.] Govt. Printer.
    v.   33 cm.
    Title varies: Report on general election.

NT   0047172   IU

Tasmania. *Parliament. House of Assembly.*
    Journals, with appendices. v. 1-45; 1856-1883. Hobart.
        45 v. 34 cm.

    Superseded by Journals and printed papers of Parliament.
    Index to papers included in the indexes to the Journals and printed
papers of Parliament.

    1. Tasmania—Pol. & govt.

    J926.K3   55-45536

NT   0047173   DLC CSt PPAN ICU

Parliament.
Tasmania. House of Assembly.
Standing rules and orders prepared and adopted
by the house of assembly and approved by the
governor.
Hobart Town, 1857.
xviii, 90 p.

NT   0047174   CSt

Otv57   Tasmania. Parliament. House of Assembly.
913T   Standing rules and orders of the House of
Assembly. [Hobart?] J. Vail, Govt. Printer,
1913.
xxiv, 79 p. 17 cm.

"Agreed to by the House, 19th December, 1912.
Approved by His Excellency by Governor, 21st
December, 1912."

NT   0047175   CtY

Tasmania. *Parliament. House of Assembly. Sesquicenten-
nial Committee.*
Report for the period ended, 30th June, 1954. Tabled
in the House of Assembly on 8th September, 1954. By
Charles Henry Hand. [Hobart] L. G. Shea, Govt. printer,
1954.
8 p. 34 cm.
Cover title.
At head of title: No. 67.

1. Tasmania—Centennial celebrations, etc.   I. Hand, Charles
Henry.

DU479.A55   394'.4   77–249769
                                           MARC

NT   0047176   DLC

Parliament.
Tasmania. Legislative council.
Centenary of the first elective Legislative council of Tasmania
and jubilee of the Commonwealth of Australia. [Hobart] 1951.
23 p. port. 21cm.

Cover title.

NT   0047177   NN

Tasmania. *Parliament. Legislative Council.*
Journals, with papers. v. 1–35; 1856–1883. Hobart.
35 v. 34 cm.
Superseded by Journals and printed papers of Parliament.
Index to papers included in the indexes to the Journals and printed
papers of Parliament.
L. C. set incomplete: v. 2 wanting.

1. Tasmania—Pol. & govt.

J926.J3   55–45529

NT   0047178   DLC PPAN

Tasmania. *Parliament. Legislative council.*
... Standing rules and orders, and forms of proceeding,
of the Legislative council. [Hobart Town] J. Barnard,
government printer, 1875.
xvi, 90 p. 16ᶜᵐ.
At head of title: Tasmania.

                          CA 10–4348 Unrev'd
Library of Congress   JQ5162.A3   1875

NT   0047179   DLC NjP

J926   Tasmania. Parliament. Legislative council.
.A2   Votes and proceedings... with various papers
connected therewith.

NT   0047180   DLC

Tasmania. *Parliament. Library.*
Catalogue of the Parliamentary library of Tasmania.
Arranged in two parts: I.—Classes and subjects. II.—
Names of authors. 1899. John Kidston Reid ... libra-
rian. Hobart, J. Vail, government printer, 1899.
230 p., 1 l. 22ᶜᵐ.

1. Reid, John Kidston.

                                      13–11202
Library of Congress   Z975.H7   1899

NT   0047181   DLC

Tasmania. *Parliament. Library.*
... Classified catalogue of books in the Parliamentary
library. 1st May, 1867. Hobart Town, J. Barnard, government printer, 1867.
49 p. 21ᶜᵐ.

                                      13–11201
Library of Congress   Z975.H7

NT   0047182   DLC

Tasmania. *Parliament. Library.*
A classified catalogue of the Parliamentary library of Tasmania, arranged alphabetically according to authors and subjects,
1876; together with the rules for the regulation of the Parliamentary library. [Hobart: J. Barnard, 1876] 27 p. 34½cm.

Caption-title.
Printed in double columns.

1. Bibliography—Catalogues—   Libraries, Govt.—Australia—Tasmania.   mania.
N. Y. P. L.   May 14, 1942

NT   0047183   NN PPAmP DNLM

Tasmania. *Parliament. Library.*
A classified catalogue of the Parliamentary library of
Tasmania, arranged alphabetically in two parts: I. Subjects. II. Names of authors or persons referred to. Together with the rules for the regulation of the Parliamentary library. 1882. Fred. A. Packer, clerk of the
House of assembly and librarian. Hobart, W. T. Strutt,
government printer, 1882.
101 p. 22ᶜᵐ.

1. Packer, Frederick Augustus.

                                      13–9101
Library of Congress   Z975.H7   1882

NT   0047184   DLC

Tasmania. *Parliament. Library.*
Report.
[Hobart]
v. 34½ᶜᵐ.
1875/76: Report from the Joint committee, transmitting the librarian's
report.
Report for 1875/76 has a classified catalogue of the library annexed.

                                CA 13–760 Unrev'd
Library of Congress   Z871.H6

NT   0047185   DLC

Tasmania. Parliament. Mental Deficiency Board.
... Report for 1922–23. Presented to both houses of Parlia-
ment ... [Hobart, Govt. Printer, 1923]
11 p. 33½ᶜᵐ.
Caption title.
At head of title: 1923. Parliament of Tasmania. Mental Deficiency Board.
Report year ends June 30.
No more published?

NT   0047186   ICJ ICRL

Tasmania. *Parliament. National park board.* Reports. 1917–
18—1919–20. [Hobart. 1918–20.] f°.

NT   0047187   MH–A

Tasmania. *Parliament.* Select committee to inquire into
and report upon the *monetary system.*
... Monetary system: report of select committee, with minutes
of proceedings. [Hobart, 1935] 28 p. 34cm. (Tasmania.
Parliament. Journals and printed papers. v. 113, 1935, no. 25.)
Caption-title.

1. Money—Australia—Tasmania.   2. Banks and banking—Australia—
Tasmania.   I. Ser.
N. Y. P. L.   June 30, 1938

NT   0047188   NN TxU

Tasmania. *Parliament. Standing Committee on Public
Works.*
General report.
[Hobart]
v. 35 cm.
Report year ends June 30.

1. Tasmania—Public works.

HD4401.A33   351.8   50–39935 ‡

NT   0047189   DLC

HE368   Tasmania. Parliament. Standing committee
.A3   on public works.
Northern outlet road: Berriedale to Granton.
[Hobart] L. G. Shea, Govt. printer, 1955.
10 p.

1. Roads – Tasmania.   2. Tasmania – Roads.

NT   0047190   DS

Tasmania. Parliamentary library, Hobart

           See

Tasmania. Parliament. Library.

---

q351.5   **Tasmania. Parliamentary Retiring Allowances**
T182   **Trust.**
Report, 1955–
Hobart.
v. tables. 34cm. annual.
Report year ends June 30.

NT   0047192   IU

Tasmania. *Police dept.*
Report.
[Hobart, 1900–
v. tables. 34ᶜᵐ.
A report upon the centralized police forces of Tasmania.
Report year irregular. 1904/05 covers period from January 1, 1904–
June 30, 1905.
1923/24 not issued in printed form.
1925/26–1927/28 published in combined number.

1. Police—Tasmania.

                                       34–33723
Library of Congress   HV7880.A3
                    [2]   351.7409946

NT   0047193   DLC

Tasmania. Postmaster-General's Department.
  ...Report for

₍Hobart,   4°.

1. Postal service, Tasmania.   2. Telegraphy.—History, Tas-
N. Y. P. L.   mania.
                                               July 5, 1922.

NT 0047194   NN

75.9
T18   **Tasmania. Potato Marketing Board.**
      Annual report and balance sheet.

      Burnie, Tas.

      1. Potatoes. Marketing. Societies.
      2. Potato industry and trade. Tasmania.

NT 0047195   DNAL

Tasmania. *Printing office.*
  Annual report.
  Hobart, 1915–
    v. 34ᶜᵐ.
  1913/14: First annual report of the Government printing department ...

    1. Printing, Public—Tasmania. 2. Tasmania—Government publications.
                                               16–25292
    Library of Congress   Z232.T2T2

NT 0047196   DLC ICJ

Tasmania. Printing Office.
  Statement of accounts. 1926–

NT 0047197   PP

Tasmania. *Prisons, Controller of*
  see **Tasmania.** *Gaols Dept.*

Tasmania. Public Debts Sinking Fund, Office
  of Commissioners of
        see **Tasmania.** Board of Commissioners of
State Sinking Fund.

Tasmania. Public health, Dept. of

        See

Tasmania. Dept. of public health.

Tasmania. Public Service Board.
    The Tasmania Public Service Board was established in 1905. In
1918 the Board was abolished and replaced by the Office of Public
Service Commissioner. In 1973 the name Public Service Board was
resumed.
    Works by these bodies are found under the following headings
according to the name used at the time of publication:

    Tasmania. Public Service Board.
    Tasmania. Office of Public Service Commissioner.

Tasmania,. Public Service Board.
    Report
        see under   Office of Public Service
Commissioner.

Tasmania. *Public trust office.*
  Report.
  ₍Hobart, 1913–
    v. tables. 35ᶜᵐ.
  Report year ends June 30.
  1912/13 covers period from December 17, 1912 to June 30, 1913.
  Title varies: 1912/13, Balance-sheet.
    19   1919/20, 1. Statement of receipts and expenditures. 2. Profit
          and loss account. 3. Balance sheet.
  1920/21–   Report.

    1. Trusts and trustees—Tasmania.

                                               34–35435

    Library of Congress   HG4490.T3A3   332.14

NT 0047203   DLC

Tasmania. *Public Works, Dept. of*
  see **Tasmania.** *Dept. of Public Works.*

4DU   Tasmania. Railway Dept.
71   Complete guide to Tasmania. With
      article on "Tasmania as a health re-
      sort," by J. S. C. Elkington. Tas-
      mania, J. Vail, Govt. printer, 1906.
      112 p.

NT 0047205   DLC-P4 PP

Tasmania. *Railway dept.*
  ... Illustrated guide to Tasmania, the holiday resort of
  Australia. Launceston, Tasmania, Printed at the
  "Examiner" and "Weekly courier" offices ₍1903?₎
    60 p. illus., fold. map. 22½ x 29ᶜᵐ.
  At head of title: Tasmanian government railways.
  Addenda, dated 1903: 1 leaf, inserted in front.

    1. Tasmania—Descr. & trav.—Guide-books.   i. Title.
                                               17–2901
    Library of Congress   DU455.A5 1903

NT 0047206   DLC CtY

Tasmania. Railway Dept.
    ...Tasmanian government railways: Statement comparing
the rates in operation on the Tasmanian railways with those in the
other colonies... ₍Hobart? 1896.₎   27 p. incl. tables.   f°.

    At head of title: 1896. Session II. Parliament of Tasmania.

    1. Railways.—Rates, Australia·   Tasmania.
N. Y. P. L.   December 14, 1921.

NT 0047207   NN

Tasmania. *Railway dept.*
  see also
Tasmania. *Commissioner for railways.*

Tasmania. *Railways, Commissioner for*
    see
Tasmania. *Commissioner for railways.*

q333.34 Tasmania--Recorder of Titles and Registrar of
T183   Deeds.
        Report.

      Hobart.
        v. 34cm. annual.

      Report year ends June 30.

NT 0047210   IU

Tasmania. Registration dept.

    See

Tasmania. Statistical and registration dept.

₁332.14 Tasmania--Royal commission appointed to enquire
T1841p into the administration of the Public trust
        office.
          Public trust office: report of Royal commis-
        sion appointed to enquire into the administration
        of the Public trust office by the Honourable Al-
        bert George Ogilvie ... and by the public trustee.
        Presented to both houses of Parliament by His
        Excellency's command.   Hobart, J. Vail, govern-
        ment printer, 1927.
          39p.
          At head of title: ₍no.31)

NT 0047212   IU

4HJ   Tasmania. Royal Commission on the
391   Public Debts Sinking Funds of
      Tasmania.
      Report of the commissioners with
      evidence taken and other documents.
      Hobart, J. Vail, Govt. printer, 1915.
        72 p.

NT 0047213   DLC-P4

**Tasmania. Royal Commissioner on Forestry Administra-
tion.**
    Report. Hobart, H. H. Pimblett, Govt. printer, 1946.
      2 v. 34 cm.
    At head of title: v. 1, Session 1945–46. (No. 39) ; v. 2, (No. 1)
  Judge Richard Clarence Kirby, Royal Commissioner.
    Report presented to Sir Thomas Hugh Binney, Governor of Tas-
  mania, on Feb. 28 and May 25, 1946.
    "Report of the Royal Commissioner upon alleged irregularities
  connected with the administration of the Forestry Department."

    1. Tasmania. Forestry Dept.   i. Kirby, Sir Richard Clarence,
  1904–
    SD666.T37A48   73–296391
                                               MARC

NT 0047214   DLC

    Tasmania. Royal Visit State Directorate.
WD   Her Majesty the Queen and H.R.H. the
11439   Duke of Edinburgh; royal visit to Tas-
      mania, 1954. Hobart, Oldham, Beddome &
      Meredith ₍1954?]
      ₍32] p. illus. 25 cm.

      1. Elizabeth II, Queen of Great Britain,
      1926–   2. Visits of state – Tasmania.

NT 0047215   CtY

Tasmania. *Rural Fires Board.*
  Report.

  Hobart, Govt. Printer.
    v. 34 cm. annual.
  Report year ends June 30.

    1. Fire-departments—Tasmania.

    TH9598.T3A34   53–36498

NT 0047216   DLC IU

Tasmania. *Rural Industries Board.*
  Report.
  Hobart.
    v. tables. 34 cm. annual.
  Report year ends June 30.
  Reports for 1945/46 and 1946/47 issued together as 2d report.

    1. Agriculture—Economic aspects—Tasmania.

    HD2181.A33   338.1   48–27677*

NT 0047217   DLC

SH349
.T32

Tasmania. <u>Salmon</u> <u>and</u> <u>freshwater</u> <u>fisheries</u>
<u>commissioners.</u>
Report.

Tasmania, 19

v.　　　tables, diagr.　33^{cm}.

Report year ends June 30.
19　　　　　　issued in combined
number.
1. Salmon-fisheries--Tasmania. 2.
Fish-culture--　　　　Tasmania.

NT　0047218　DLC IU MnU CU

Tasmania. *Schools Board.*
Manual.

Hobart.

v. illus. 22 cm. annual.

1. Education—Tasmania.

L767.A35　　　370.9946　　　50-27097

NT　0047219　CLU

Tasmania.　Secretary for Mine
see　Tasmania.　Mines Dept.

Tasmania.　*Shale oil investigation committee.*
... Report of Tasmanian shale oil investigation committee ...
Hobart, W. E. Shimmins, government printer, 1933.

v, 214 p. incl. tables. 2 fold. maps, fold. tables. 21½^{cm}. (Tasmania.
Geological survey. Mineral resources no. 8, vol. ii)
At head of title: Tasmania. Department of mines.
Hon. Claude James, chairman.

1. Oil shales. i. James, Claude Ernest. ii. Title.
　　　　　　　　　　　　　　G S 34-62
Library, U. S. Geological　　Survey　(880) M2　no. 8. vol. ii
　　　　　　　　　　　　　　[TN871.T　　]

NT　0047221　DI-GS MiU

Tasmania. *Social Services Dept.*
Report.

[Hobart]

v. 34 cm. annual.

Report year ends June 30.

1. Public welfare—Tasmania.

HV501.A33　　　360.994　　　48-37764*

NT　0047222　DLC DL IU

TASMANIA. Southern Tasmanian volunteers. City
guards.
Rules and regulations of the City guards, Southern
Tasmanian volunteers.　[Hobart?] Tasmania, J.
Barnard, govt. printer, 1863.　21 p.　21cm.

Electrostatic reproduction.

i. Militia--Australia--Tasmania.　i. 1863.

NT　0047223　NN

Tasmania. *State Economic Planning Authority.*
Regional planning; economic resources of Tasmania.
Hobart, H. H. Pimblett, Govt. Printer, 1945.

[4] l., 24 (i. e. 27) col. maps. 50 cm.

Cover title.
Each map preceded by leaf (34 cm.) of text.
Scale of maps 1 : 1,013,760 or 16 miles to 1 inch.

1. Natural resources — Tasmania — Maps. 2. Tasmania—Econ.
condit.—Maps.
G2791.G3T3　1945　　　　Map 54-1143

NT　0047224　DLC CU MnU

Tasmania. *State Economic Planning Authority.*
Regional planning atlas. Economic resources of Tasmania. [2d ed.] Hobart, Printed by Davies Bros., 1947.

[8] p., 25 (i. e. 28) col. maps. 50 cm.

Text and illus. on versos of maps 1-24.
"Maps drawn and reproduced by the Dept. of Lands and Surveys,
Mapping Branch."

1. Natural resources — Tasmania — Maps. 2. Tasmania — Econ.
condit.—Maps.
G2791.G3T3　1947·　　　　Map 49—755*

NT　0047225　DLC OU CaBVaU DNAL MH NN

G2791
.G3T3
1955
Map

Tasmania.　State Economic Planning Authority.
Regional planning atlas.
Tasmania. *Directorate of Industrial Development.*
Regional planning atlas; economic resources of Tasmania.
3d ed. Hobart, Printed by Davies Bros. [1955?]

Tasmania.　State Finance Committee.
... Economic trends in Tasmania, 1931-32
to 1935-36
see under　Mauldon, Frank Richard
Edward, 1891-

Tasmania.　State Finance Committee.
Employment and its seasonality in Tasmania
see under　Exley, H　　J

HJ1743
A3
Documents
Dept.

Tasmania.　State Finance Committee.
Statement presented to the Commonwealth Grants Commission
on behalf of the Government of Tasmania.

Hobart.

v.　　　33cm.

NT　0047229　CU PU-W

Tasmania. *State Finance Committee.*
Statement presented to the Commonwealth Grants Commission on behalf of the Government of Tasmania.　Hobart,
H. H. Pimblett, Govt. printer [1947]

7 p. 34 cm.

1. Finance, Public—Tasmania.

HJ1743.A55　　　　54-33586 ‡

NT　0047230　DLC

Tasmania. State
　　　　　Finance committee.
Studies of the Tasmanian economy. no. [1]–

Hobart, 1936–　　　　　28 – 34cm.

Nos. 1, 5, issued without series title or numbering.

no. 1. Statement presented to the Commonwealth grants commission.　1936.
no. 2. Economic trends in Tasmania, 1931/32 – 1935/36.　1936.
no. 3. Statement presented to the Commonwealth grants commission.　[1937]

no. 4. The Tasmanian economy, 1936/37.　1937.
no. 5. Statement presented to the Commonwealth grants commission.　Rev. [1939]
no. 6. The Tasmanian economy, 1937/38.　1938.
no. 7. Exley, H. J. Employment and its seasonality in Tasmania, by H. J. Exley and
　F. R. E. Mauldon.　1938.

no. 9. The Tasmanian economy, 1938/39.　1939.

NT　0047232　NN

Tasmania.　State Finance Committee.
The Tasmanian economy.
Hobart.
v.　diagr. (Studies in Tasmanian economy)

NT　0047233　CU

Tasmania.　State Finance Committee.
... The Tasmanian economy in 1937-38
see under　Mauldon, Frank Richard
Edward, 1891-

Tasmania.　State Library, *Hobart*
see　**Hobart.　State Library of Tasmania.**

Tasmania. *State meat board.*
Report.
[Hobart, 19

v. tables. 33^{cm}. annual.

Caption title.
Report year ends June 30.

1. Lamb (Meat) 2. Meat industry and trade—Tasmania.
HD9436.A83T33　　　338.476649　　47–1731
　　　　　　　　　　　　　　　　Brief cataloging

NT　0047236　DLC

Tasmania.　State Sinking Fund, Board of
Commissioners of
see　Tasmania.　Board of Commissioners
of State Sinking Fund.

Tasmania.　Statistical and Registration Dept.

In Nov. 1924 the Statistical and Registration Dept. of Tasmania
became the Tasmania Branch of the Commonwealth Bureau of Census and Statistics of Australia.　In 1957 the name of the branch
was changed to Tasmanian Office.　In 1974 the Commonwealth Bureau of Census and Statistics was renamed Australian Bureau of
Statistics.　The Tasmanian Office of the earlier Bureau continued
as an office of the Bureau of Statistics.
Works by these bodies published before the change of name of the
Bureau in 1974 are found under:

Tasmania.　Statistical and Registration Dept.
Australia.　Bureau of Census and Statistics.　Tasmania Branch,
Hobart.

Australia.　Bureau of Census and Statistics.　Tasmanian Office.

Works published after that change of name are found under:

Australia.　Bureau of Statistics.　Tasmanian Office.

Tasmania. *Statistical and registration dept.*
Agricultural and live stock statistics.
[Hobart?]

v. 34½^{cm}.

1. Agriculture — Tasmania — Stat. 2. Stock and stock-breeding — Tasmania.

　　　　　　　　　　　　　　　　9-9078
Library of Congress　　　HD2181.A3

NT　0047240　DLC DNAL

271.5
St2B

Tasmania. Statistical and Registration Dept.
Beefarming statistics, Tasmania. 1949/50-

Hobart, 1950-

1. Tasmania.　Apiculture. 2. Apiculture.
Statistics.

NT　0047241　DNAL

Tasmania. *Statistical and Registration Dept.*
Census, 1901. ₍Hobart, 1901₎
8 pts. in 1 v. (489 p.) 34 cm.

1. Tasmania—Census, 1901.

HA3111.A5 1901   58–54402

NT   0047242   DLC NN

Tasmania. Statistical **and Registration Dept.**
Census of the colony of Tasmania, 1891. Parts I – VIII.
With introductory report by the registrar-general. Hobart:
W. Grahame, 1893. lxxxvi p. incl. tables. col'd diagrs. f°.

1. Tasmania.—Census, 1891.
N. Y. P. L.   November 16, 1921.

NT   0047243   NN

Tasmania. Statistical **and Registration Dept.**
General report on the ninth census of Tasmania. By R. M.
Johnston...registrar-general and government statistician of Tasmania. Hobart: J. Vail, 1903. cxii p.   diagr., form, maps.
4°.

1. Tasmania.—Census.
N. Y. P. L.   March 1, 1923.

NT   0047244   NN

DU450
.T32   **Tasmania, Statistical and registration dept.**
Handbook of Tasmania, 1892–93.
Hobart, Tasmania, 1892–94
2 v.   8°

NT   0047245   DLC NcD DNLM

DU
455   **Tasmania. Statistical and Registration Dept.**
T3   Handbook of Tasmania, issued by the government of Tasmania. Hobart, J. Vail, government printer, 1908.
xx, 400 p. illus., maps (part col.) plates.
23 cm.

On verso of t.-p.: Also issued separately
ᶦn 5 sections.

1. Tasmania.

NT   0047246   CU-S PP

Tasmania. Statistical and Registration Dept.
Handbook of Tasmania, issued by the government of Tasmania ...   (2d ed.) Hobart, J. Vail, government printer, 1914.
xx, 499 p. incl. front., illus., plates. col. pl., 2 fold. maps. 22½ᶜᵐ.
On verso of t.-p.: Also issued separately in 5 sections.

1. Tasmania.
Agr 20–1524

Library, U. S. Dept. of   Agriculture 271.5T18H

NT   0047247   DNAL TxU NcD DLC NN ICJ

Tasmania. Statistical and Registration Dept.
Handbook of Tasmania, issued by the government of Tasmania ...   (2d ed.) Hobart, J. Vail, government printer, 1914.
xx, 499 p. incl. front., illus., plates. col. pl., 2 fold. maps. 22½ᶜᵐ.
On verso of t.-p.: Also issued separately in 5 sections.
———. Addenda to the Handbook of Tasmania. (Second edition, 19₁4.) ... Tasmania, 1919.
51 p. incl. tables. 21½ᶜᵐ.
1. Tasmania.
Agr 20–1524

Library, U. S. Dept. of

NT   0047248   DNAL ICJ

271.5
St2N   **Tasmania. Statistical and Registration Dept.**
**Number of farms, farm population, employment
and machinery used, Tasmania. 1954–**
₍Hobart₎ 1954–

1. Tasmania. Agriculture. Statistics.

NT   0047249   DNAL

Tasmania.   Statistical and registration dept.

Australia. *Bureau of census and statistics. Tasmania branch, Hobart.*
The pocket year book of Tasmania ...

Hobart ₍19

271.5
St2Po   **Tasmania. Statistical and Registration Dept.**
Potato statistics. 1949/50–
[Hobart] 1951–

1. Potatoes. Statistics. 2. Potatoes.
Tasmania.

NT   0047251   DNAL

271.5
St2Pro   **Tasmania. Statistical and Registration Dept.**
Production of meat in Tasmania.
Hobart,

1. Meat. Statistics. 2. Meat industry
and trade. Tasmania.

NT   0047252   DNAL

271.5
.St2Pr   **Tasmania. Statistical and Registration Dept.**
Production statistics [1950–51]
Hobart

1. Tasmania. Statistics.

NT   0047253   DNAL

Tasmania. *Statistical and registration dept.*
... Progress of the colony in the period from 1871 to 1880.
Comp. in the office of the government statistician. Hobart,
W. T. Strutt, government printer, 1882.
9 p. 33ᶜᵐ.
At head of title: Tasmania.

1. Tasmania—Stat.   ɪ. Title.
ᴄᴀ 10—4879 Unrev'd

Library of Congress   HA3115.A5 1880

NT   0047254   DLC DNLM

Tasmania. Statistical and Registration Dept.
Report of the statistician on friendly societies
see under   Australia. Bureau of Census
and Statistics. Tasmania Branch, Hobart.

Tasmania. Statistical **and Registration Dept.**
Reference list of various books & memoirs on scientific and
social and economic subjects, written and published since the year
1873, by R. M. Johnston... registrar-general and government
statistician... Hobart: "The Mercury" Off., 1893. 10 p.
8°.

1. Natural history.—Bibliography.   2. Economics.—Bibliography.
N. Y. P. L.   December 29, 1921.

NT   0047256   NN

Tasmania . **Statistical and Registration Dept.**
Statistical summary for the years 1900, 1907–8, 1908–9, 1909–10,
& 1910–11.   Tasmania: J. Vail, 1911.   broadside.   f°.
——— ——— A second copy.

1. Tasmania.—Statistics, 1900–11.
N. Y. P. L.   March 28, 1912.

NT   0047257   NN

Tasmania. *Statistical and registration aept.*
Statistical tables relating to the colony of Tasmania.
₍Hobart town? James Barnard, government printer, Tasmania, 1870?₎
7 p. 34ᵐᵐ.
Comp. from official records in the government statistician's office, Hobart Town.
E. C. Nowell, government statistician.

1. Tasmania—Stat.   ɪ. Nowell, Edwin Cradock, 1831–
11–17510

Library of Congress   HA3115.A5 1870

NT   0047258   DLC

70.9
T18   **Tasmania. Statistical and Registration Dept.**
Statistics of hop production.
Hobart,

1. Hops. Statistics. 2. Hops. Tasmania.

NT   0047259   DNAL

Tasmania. *Statistical and registration dept.*
Statistics of the state of Tasmania.

Hobart Town, 18 –19
v.   tables (part fold.) diagrs. 33–34ᵐᵐ.
Compiled in the Colonial secretary's office from official records, 18   ;
in the office of the government statistician from official records, 18   –19
Title varies slightly. (18   Statistics of Tasmania.—18   –1900,
Statistics of the colony of Tasmania)
Government statistician: E. C. Nowell, 18   –1882.—R. M. Johnston,
1882–19
"Nominal list of officers in the service of the colonial government on
31st December 1865" ...: 1865. n. 104–110.

"Establishments and institutions maintained or assisted by government":
18   –1874, pt. ɪᴠ; 1875, pt. v.
"Blue book": 1876–19   pt. ɪ.
1910/11 includes also "Statistical summary relating to Tasmania, 1816 to
1910/11."

1. Tasmania—Stat. 2. Tasmania—Registers.   ɪ. Tasmania. Colonial
secretary's office. ɪɪ. Tasmania. Blue book. ɪɪɪ. Title.
6—11771

Library of Congress   HA3113

NT   0047261   DLC CSt ICJ PPAN DNLM

HA3115   **Tasmania. Statistical and Registration Dept.**
.A5   Tasmania. Statistical summary for the years
1914   1902, 1909–10, 1911–12 & 192–13... Hobart,
J. Vail [1914?]
broadside.   69 x 43.5 cm.

NT   0047262   DLC

Tasmania. Statistical and Registration Dept.
Tasmanian agricultural statistics.
Hobart,
Figures are provisional; revised later in its
Production – agriculture and live stock (271.5 St2Ag

NT 0047263   DNAL

Tasmania. Statistical and Registration Dept.
Tasmanian official record. 1890. By R. M. Johnston...government statistician and registrar-general of Tasmania... Tasmania: W. T. Strutt, 1890.   ix, 439 p. incl. tables.   charts, maps.   8°.

35001A. 1. Tasmania. 2. Tas-   mania.—Registers. 3. Tasmania.—
Statistics.   April 7, 1922.
N. Y. P. L.

NT 0047264   NN DLC

Tasamania. Statistical and Registration Dept.
Tasmanian official record. 1890-92. Hobart, 1890-92.
3 v. col. fold. map. 26 cm. annual.
Superseded bu Handbook of Tasmania.

1. Tasmania. I. Title.

NT 0047265   MH-L NcD

271.5
St2W   Tasmania. Statistical and Registration Dept.
Wool production statistics, Tasmania.

(Hobart) 1953/54–

1. Wool. Statistics. 2. Wool trade and
industry. Tasmania. 3. Wool trade and
industry. Statistics.

NT 0047266   DNAL

Tasmania. Statistican
see Tasmania. Statistical and
Registration. Dept.

Tasmania. *Superannuation Fund Board.*
Report.
(Hobart)
v. tables. 34 cm. annual.
Report year ends June 30.

1. Civil service pensions—Tasmania.

JQ5149.P4A32   351.5   48-37176*

NT 0047268   DLC

Tasmania. Superintendent of Vaccinations.
—— Report of the superintendent of vaccinations for the year 1879. 1 l. fol. [*Hobart Town*, 1880.]

NT 0047269   DNLM

Tasmania. Supreme court.

Hore, Leslie Fraser Standish, 1870–
Digest of cases decided in Tasmania, 1856–1896. By
L. F. S. Hore ... Pub. by the Southern law society of
Tasmania. Hobart, Tasmania, Cox & co., printers, 1897.

Tasmania. *Supreme court.*
Reports of cases determined in the Supreme court of
Tasmania by Herbert Nicholls ... and W. J. T. Stops ...
1897–1904. Melbourne, C. F. Maxwell (G. Partridge &
co.) 1906–07.
2 v. 24½ᶜᵐ.
To bridge "the gap between the end of Mr. Hore's Digest (1856–1896)
and 1905, when the issue of a regular series of reports was begun."

1. Law reports, digests, etc.—Tasmania.   I. Nicholls, Sir Herbert,
1868–   ed. II. Stops, William Joshua Tilley, joint ed.

6–36408

CaBVaU ViU-L
NT 0047271   DLC PPB PU-L CtY ICU GU-L CU-AL WAU-L

Law   Tasmania. Supreme Court.

The *Tasmanian* State reports. 1905–
Hobart.

Tasmania. Surveys, Dept. of land and

See

Tasmania. Dept. of land and surveys.

Tasmania. Tasmanian shale oil
investigation committee

see

Tasmania. Shale oil investigation
committee.

Tasmania. *Tourist and Immigration Dept.*
Report.
(Hobart)
v. 34 cm. annual.
Report year ends June 30.

1. Tasmania—Emig. & immig. 2. Tourist trade—Tasmania.

JV9230.A32   48-33753*

NT 0047275   DLC IU

Tasmania. *Tourist and Immigration Dept.*
Tasmania today. (Hobart) 1952.
47 p. illus. 24 cm.

1. Tasmania.

DU455.A53   919.46   54-16759 ‡

NT 0047276   DLC

Tasmania. *Tourist and Immigration Dept.*
Tasmania today. (Hobart, 1954?)
49 p. illus. 24 cm.

1. Tasmania.

DU455.A53 1954   919.46   56-32412 ‡

NT 0047277   DLC

Tasmania. Tourist Dept.
see Tasmania. Government Tourist
Bureau.

Tasmania. *Transport Commission.*
Report on the operations, business, and affairs of the
Transport Department.
Hobart, H. H. Pimblett, Govt. Printer.
v. 34 cm. annual.
Report year ends June 30.

1. Transportation—Tasmania. 2. Tasmania. Transport Dept.

HE110.A3   385   51-18698 ‡

NT 0047279   DLC NN MiU-L

Tasmania. Treasury
see Tasmania. Dept. of the Treasury.

Tasmania. University, *Hobart.*
... Employment relations and the basic wage; lectures
and papers published in connection with the Pitt Cobbett
foundation, 1925. (Hobart, Tasmania, Printed by Davies
brothers ltd., at "The Mercury" office, 1925)
46 p. 22ᶜᵐ.
At head of title: The University of Tasmania.
"Such of the contents as are not acknowledged are the work of J. B.
Brigden, Pitt Cobbett lecturer and professor of economics in the University of Tasmania."—Pref.
Most of the contents of this publication are reprinted from the Mercury. cf. Pref.
1. Wages—Minimum wage. 2. Labor and laboring classes—1914–
3. Labor and laboring classes—Australia. 4. Wages—Australia. I. Brigden, James Bristock. II. Title. III. Title: Pitt Cobbett
foundation, 1925.

Library of Congress   HD4918.T3
                                            26-11024

NT 0047281   DLC NN

Tasmania. University, Hobart. *Dept. of Economics and
Commerce.*
...Research monograph.
no. 1

Hobart, 1938
v. illus.   34cm.

CONTENTS.

no. 1. MAULDON, F. R. E. Mechanisation in Australian industries. 1938.

NT 0047282   NN NcD

550
T183s   Tasmania. University, Hobart--Dept. of Geology.
Symposia. 1–
Nov. 1955–
Hobart.
v. illus., maps(part col., part fold.)
tables(part col., part fold.) 26cm.

Some vols. are rev. editions.
Each issue has also a distinctive title.

NT 0047283   IU CtW

Tasmania, University, Hobart. Dept. of Tutorial Classes.
Annual report of the Committee for Tutorial Classes...
19

(Hobart, 19
no.   33cm.

19   , reproduced from typewritten copy.
At head of title: The University of Tasmania.
1923–   published with Workers' Educational Association of Tasmania.
Annual report. (See entry under that title.)

1. University extension—Tasmania.
N. Y. P. L.   November 21, 1932

NT 0047284   NN

Tasmania. University, Hobart. Dept. of Tutorial
Classes.
Literature and the Australian wage-earner. (Hobart,) 1927.
5 p. 8°.

1. Books and reading.
N. Y. P. L.   September 11, 1928

NT 0047285   NN

Tasmania. **University**, *Hobart. Geology Dept.*
    see
Tasmania. **University**, *Hobart. Dept. of Geology.*

Tasmania. University, *Hobart.*   Pitt Cobbett Foundation.
    Lectures and papers...
192

   (Hobart, 192   8°.
    no.

NT 0047287   NN

Tasmania. **University**, *Hobart. Tutorial Classes,*
   Dept. of
    see   Tasmania. **University**, *Hobart.*
Dept. of Tutorial Classes.

Tasmania. **University**, *Hobart. Zeehan school*
  of mines and metallurgy

     See

Zeehan school of mines and metallurgy, Zeehan,
Tasmania.

Tasmania (Diocese) Bishop.
   Transportation; copy of a communication upon
the subject of transportation addressed to Earl
Grey.
   Launceston, 1847.
    24 p.

NT 0047290   CSt

...**Tasmania** and its mineral wealth. Issued as a special edition
of the Australian mining standard. July 1, 1898...   Melbourne,
1898.   92 p. illus. (incl. plans, ports.)   2. ed.   f°.
   Cover-title.

  1. Mines and mining, Tasmania.   2. Tin.—Mines and mining, Tas-
nania. 3. Australian mining standard.   mania.
N. Y. P. L.   September 20, 1923.

NT 0047291   NN

Tasmania and its resources.
   Launceston, n.d.
    56 p.

NT 0047292   CSt

Tasmania, 1854-1954
    see under   The Mercury, Hobart, Austra-
lia.

919.46
 T1992   **Tasmania** for the tourist and the settler.
     Hobart, Tasmania, W.E. Shimmins, Govt.
     printer, 1933.
     44p. illus. 19cm.

    1. Tasmania. Descr. & trav.

NT 0047294   IEN

---

*T730
.1
.D6M5   ... **Tasmania**, its early history and progress.
1867   Extracted from the special Exhibition edition of
    the Hobart Town Mercury ... [Melbourne, Blundell
    & co., printers, 1867]
      (In Melbourne. Intercolonial exhibition of
    Australasia, 1866-1867. Official record. Mel-
    bourne, 1867. 22 1/2cm. [pt. 2] p. 461-518)
      At head of title: Intercolonial exhibition,
    1866-67.

    1. Tasmania—   Hist.

NT 0047295   MB CSt

Tasmania Methodist Assembly.
   A century of Tasmanian Methodism, 1820-1920
    see under   Dugan, C   C

Tasmanian official record
    see under   Tasamania. Statistical and
Registration Dept.

Tasmania, the isle of scenic beauty. [Mentone,
Nucolorvue productions, n.d.] 16 l. illus.
18cm.

   1. Tasmania—Views.

NT 0047298   NN

Tasmania, Western Australia, Fiji, Samoa, Tonga, Hawaiian
Islands directory.
 1

 [n. p., 1   8°.
   no.

  1. Tasmania.—Directories. 2. West-   ern Australia.—Directories.
3. Fiji islands.—Directories. 4. Sa-   moa.—Directories. 5. Tonga islands.
—Directories. 6. Hawaii.—Direc-   tories.
N. Y. P. L.   September 13, 1922.

NT 0047299   NN

The Tasmanian almanac
    see   Walch's Tasmanian almanac.

The Tasmanian cyclopedia: an historical,
   industrial and commercial review; biographical
   facts showing the progress of Tasmania.
   Hobart, Service Pub. Co., 1931.
    420 p. illus., ports. 29 cm.
    Cover title: The cyclopedia of Tasmania.
    1. Tasmania. 2. Tasmania. Biography.
  I. Title: The cyclopedia of Tasmania.

NT 0047301   NcD

Tasmanian education.

  [Hobart]
    v. in   illus. 25-28 cm. bimonthly.
   Issued by the Education Dept. of Tasmania.
   "Supplement to the Educational record."

   1. Education—Tasmania——Period.   I. Tasmania. Education
Dept. II. Tasmania. Education Dept. The educational record. Sup-
plement.
  L91.T3   54-32847

NT 0047302   DLC CaBVaU ICU

The **Tasmanian** farmer.
  v.

   Launceston, Tasmania: Telegraph printery pty. ltd., 193
    v. illus. (incl. ports.)   28cm.
   Monthly.
   Official organ of the Tasmanian producers' organisation, the National utility
poultry breeders' association, and other organizations.

   1. Agriculture—Per. and soc.   publ.   May 13, 1941
N. Y. P. L.

NT 0047303   NN

45
T18   **Tasmanian Farmers'**, Stockowners' and
     Orchardists' Association.
     Recommendations of the executive: "Improving
     the Tasmanian wool clip".   Hobart, 1947.
     [3] p.

NT 0047304   DNAL

The **Tasmanian** fruitgrower and farmer...
  v.

   Franklin, Tasmania: Huon Newspaper Co., 19   4°.
  v.
   Monthly.
   Numbering continuous.
   Official organ of the Port Huon Fruitgrowers' Co-operative Association.

   1. Fruit—Per. and soc. publ.   June 14, 1927
N. Y. P. L.

NT 0047305   NN

Tasmanian field naturalists' club, *Hobart.*
   ... Annual report.

   Hobart,
    v. 23ᶜᵐ.
   Caption title.
   At head of title: Tasmanian field naturalists' club.

   1. Natural history—Societies.

                               CA 13-255 Unrev'd

   Library of Congress   QH1.T18

NT 0047306   DLC

Tasmanian field naturalists' club, *Hobart.*
   ... Easter camp-out.
   Hobart,
    v. illus. 22ᶜᵐ.
   Cover-title.
   At head of title: Tasmanian field naturalists' club.
    Reprinted from "The Tasmanian mail."
   List of camp members.

   1. Natural history—Tasmania.

                               CA 11-278 Unrev'd

   Library of Congress   QH1.T2

NT 0047307   DLC PPAN MH-A

Tasmanian field naturalists' club, Hobart.

   Rodway, Leonard.
    ... Ferns of Tasmania, by L. Rodway ... Hobart, Printed
   at "The Mercury" office [1905]

J8
f. B86   **Tasmanian** government gazette.
     Hobart,
      v. 34 1/2 cm.

    Title varies: The Hobart gazette.

NT 0047309   ICU

DU
450
T3843
MAIN

Tasmanian Historical Research Association.
Papers and proceedings. v.1–
1954–
Hobart.
v. in   illus. 25cm.
quarterly.

1. Tasmania – History – Periodicals.

NT 0047310   TxU

Tasmanian journal.

Morton, Alexander.
Register of papers published in the Tasmanian journal and the Papers and proceedings of the Royal society of Tasmania, from the year 1841 to 1885. Comp. by Alexander Morton ... Tasmania, W. T. Strutt, government printer, 1887.

Tasmanian journal of agriculture.
Hobart.
v. in   illus. 25 cm. quarterly.
Began publication with Nov. 1929 issue. Cf. Union list of serials.
Vols.   called new ser.
Published by the Dept. of Agriculture.

1. Agriculture—Period. 2. Agriculture—Tasmania—Period. I. Tasmania. Dept. of Agriculture.

S17.T3   56–36135

NT 0047312   DLC OrCS PPAN IU ICJ CU-A ICRL PSt

The **Tasmanian** journal of natural science, agriculture, statistics, &c. v. 1–3. Hobart, Tasmania, J. Barnard, gov't printer; [etc., etc.] 1842–49.
3 v. plates, maps, tables. 23ᶜᵐ.
Published also in London by J. Murray.
Vol. 1–2 comprise 11 parts consecutively numbered; v. 3 comprises 6 parts. No more published.
Contains the substance of the transactions of the Tasmanian society, which was founded by Sir John Franklin in 1838.
Index to the three volumes is included in "Register of papers published in the Tasmanian journal and the Papers and proceedings of the Royal society of Tasmania ... 1841 to 1885. Comp. by Alexander Morton."

1. Natural history—Period. 2. Tasmania. I. Tasmanian society, Hobart.
13–3382

Library of Congress   QH1.T22

NT 0047313   DLC NN ICRL PPAmP PPAN ICJ

The **Tasmanian** law reports
see
The **Tasmanian State** reports.

Tasmanian letters, 1824–1852
see under Richards, Jack, ed.

The **Tasmanian** messenger. No. 5. V. VI, May, 1865.
Hobart Town, 1878.
v. p.

NT 0047316   CSt

QH1
T23

The **Tasmanian** naturalist; the journal of the Tasmanian field naturalists club. v. 2, no. 3; Oct. 1910.   Tasmania, 1910.
1 v.

NT 0047317   DLC ICJ DSI PPAN DI-GS

Tasmanian Presbyterian magazine. V. I–II.
Hobart Town, 1878.
v. p.

NT 0047318   CSt

Tasmanian public library, *Hobart*.
Catalogue of books in the Tasmanian public library, Hobart Town, 1870. Mr. Samuel Hannaford, librarian. Hobart Town, J. Barnard, government printer, 1871.
113 p. 21½ᶜᵐ.

I. Hannaford, Samuel, 1828–1874.
13–9102

Library of Congress   Z975.H73

NT 0047319   DLC

Tasmanian public library, *Hobart*.
Report.
[Hobart, 1872–
v. 34ᶜᵐ.

CA 13–758 Unrev'd
Library of Congress   Z871.H7

NT 0047320   DLC NN

Tasmanian Shale Oil Investigation Committee
see   Tasmania. Shale Oil Investigation Committee.

Tasmanian society, *Hobart*.

The **Tasmanian** journal of natural science, agriculture, statistics, &c. v. 1–3. Hobart, Tasmania, J. Barnard, gov't printer; [etc., etc.] 1842–49.

The **Tasmanian State** reports. 1905–
Hobart.
v. 24 cm. annual.
Reports for 1905–40 called v. 1–35.
Reports for 1926–27, 1942–43, 1945–46 are combined issues.
Title varies: 1905–40, The Tasmanian law reports; cases determined in the Supreme Court of Tasmania and by the Mining Board (subtitle varies)—1941–53, The State reports, Tasmania.
Editors: 1905–17, W. J. T. Stops (with H. Nicholls, 1905–08)—1918–28, P. L. Griffiths.—1929–35, 1937–40, R. C. Wright.—1936, 1941, 1947–51, J. R. Rex (with F. D. Cumbrae-Stewart, 1951)—1942–43—1945–46, 1952—   F. D. Cumbrae-Stewart.
Earlier reports in Tasmania. Supreme Court. Reports of cases determined in the Supreme Court of Tasmania, 1897–1904.

1. Law reports, digests, etc.—Tasmania. I. Stops, William Joshua Tilley, ed. II. Nicholls, Sir Herbert, 1868– ed. III. Griffiths, Philip Lewis, ed. IV. Wright, Reginald Charles, 1905– ed. V. Rex, John Richmond, 1907– ed. VI. Cumbrae-Stewart, F. D., ed. VII. Tasmania. Supreme Court. VIII. Tasmania. Mining Board.

7–24278 rev 3*

NNC-L PU-L CU-AL
NT 0047324   DLC GU-L CaBVaU PPB CU TxU ViU-L IU CtY

Tasmanian telephone directory ...
–
19 .   [N.p.n.pub.]1948–
[v.sq.0.

NT 0047325   CaBViP

AC901
.V5

Tasmaniana: A description of the island of Tasmania and its resources... Launceston, T.C. Just [1876]
56 p. (Victorian pamphlets, 1:9)

NT 0047326   DLC

Tasmania's national park; a week-end visit. [Hobart? 1919.] 8°. pp. 5.

NT 0047327   MH-A

Tasnádi-Kubacska, András.
Franz Baron Nopcsa. Budapest, Verlag des Ungarischen Naturwissenschaftlichen Museums, 1945.
295 p. plates, ports., map, facsim. 25 cm. (Leben und Briefe ungarischer Naturforscher, 1)
Bibliography : p. 9–10.

1. Nopcsa, Ferencz, Báró, 1877–1933. (Series)

QE22.N6T3   925.5   49–42658*

NT 0047328   DLC MiU

Tasnádi-Kubacska, András.
Die Grundlagen der Literatur über Ungarns Vertebratenpaläontologie. [Ins Deutsche übertragen von Géza Ferenczy] Budapest, Königliche Ungarische Universitäts-Druckerei, 1928–
(Hefte des Collegium Hungaricum in Wien, 4)

NT 0047329   MiU

Tasnádi-Kubacksa, András,   *2. i.*
Leben und Briefe ungarischer Naturforscher ...
see under title

Tasnádi-Kubacska, András.
... Paleobiológiai vizsgálatok Magyarországból. Andras Kubacska: Palaobiologische untersuchungen aus Ungarn. Budapestini, Editio instituti regii hungarici geologici, 1932.
19, 65, [1] p., 8 l. incl. illus., tables. VIII pl. 30½ᶜᵐ. [Hungary. Földtani intézet] Geologica hungarica, ser. palaeontologica 10)
Eight leaves at end are double.
Text in Hungarian and German.
Bibliographies interspersed.

1. Paleontology—Hungary. I. Title. II. Title: Palaobiologische untersuchungen aus Ungarn.
G S 33–40

Library, U. S. Geological Survey (534) qG36 ser. pal. no. 10

NT 0047331   DI-GS ICU CU

Tasnádi Nagy, András
see   Nagy, András, tasnádi.

Tasnádi Nagy, László
see   Nagy, László, tasnádi, 1880–1914.

PG 5038
.T3 L6

TAŠNER, ALOIS, 1875–
Loutkář za mřížemi Gestapa: Kus Loutkářské historie; ve vězeních Gestape v létech 1942–1945. Napsal Alois Tašner. V Náchodě, Nákl. vlastním, V generalni komisi knihkupectvi Fr. Novotný, 1946.
62 p. illus.
Contents: [pt.1] Moje loutkářské vzpomínky. [pt.2] Koblížek na útěku.

I. Title. II. Title: Koblížek na útěku.

NT 0047334   InU

Tasner, Dénes.

Magyar tudományos akadémia, *Budapest.*
Halaink és haltenyésztésünk. Vitéz pályamunkák
MDCCCLXVII-re. Közrebocsátja a M. Tudom. akadémia.
Pest, Kiadja Emich Gusztáv, 1868.

Law

TASNER, Joža, ed.

Yugoslavia. *Laws, statutes, etc.*
Zakon o likvidaciji agrarne reforme na velikim posedima,
sa komentarom i potrebnim zakonima agrarne reforme.
Priredili: Joža Tašner i Albin Radikon. Beograd, Štamparija "Skerlić," 1931.

Tasnier, L.
... Levensbeelden; vertaald door Commandant
C. Sevens ... Voorwoord van Theodoor Sevens.
Brussel, A. Dewit, 1920.
122 p.   18.5 cm.
At head of title: Majoor L. Tasnier...
1. Belgium - Hist. - German occupation,
1914-1918 - Personal narratives.   I. Sevens,
C., tr. II. Title.

NT 0047337   CSt-H

Tasnier, L.
... Silhouettes du front belge & Notes d'un
combattant.   Bruxelles, Veuve F. Larcier, 1919.
3 p.l., 154, [2] p., 1 l.   19 cm.
At head of title: Le major L. Tasnier...
1. Belgium - Hist. - German occupation, 1914-
1918 - Personal narratives.   I. Title.

NT 0047338   CSt-H

Tasnier, Maurice Albert Émile, 1876–
L'armée belge dans la guerre mondiale, par le lieutenant-
colonel breveté d'État-major Tasnier ... et le major d'artillerie breveté d'état-major R. van Overstraeten ... Bruxelles,
H. Bertels, 1923.
4 p. l., 406 p., 1 l. illus., plates (part mounted col.) ports., maps.
32cm.

1. Belgium—Army. 2. European war, 1914–1918—Campaigns—Belgium. I. Overstraeten, Raoul François Casimir van, 1885–   joint
author. II. Title.

Library of Congress   D541.T3   27-17236

NT 0047339   DLC NN

Tasnier, Maurice Albert Emile, 1876–
... Nouveaux récits de guerre.   Bruxelles,
A. Dewit, 1923.
363 p.   incl. front. illus. (incl. ports.,
maps, facsims.)   18.5 cm.
At head of title: M. & L. Tasnier.
On cover: 3e édition, revue et augmentée.
1. Belgium - Hist. - German occupation, 1914-
1918 - Personal narratives.   I. Tasnier, L.

NT 0047340   CSt-H NN

Tasnier, Maurice Albert Emile, 1876–
... Récits de guerre.   Bruxelles, A. Dewit,
1920.
190 p.   illus. (incl. ports., maps)   18.5 cm.
At head of title: M. & L. Tasnier.
"Préface" signed: Th. Henusse...

NT 0047341   CSt-H

Tasnīm al-Ḥaqq Kākākhel.
د پښتو قواعد ٬تاليف د تسنيم الحق كاكاخيل ٬دى تقويم
الحق كاكاخيل. پښاور، اداره اشاعت سرحد ٬ګلدارش 1963،
8, 216 p. 19 cm.
Binder's title: Da Pukhto qawā'id ¡by¿ Sayyid Muḥammad Tasnī-
mul Ḥaq au Sayyid Muḥammad Taqvīmul Ḥaq.

1. Pushto language—Grammar. I. Taqwīm al-Ḥaqq Kākākhel,
joint author. II. Title.
                               Title transliterated: Da Pushto qawā'id.

PK6723.T3   S A 66-545
                                          PL 480: P-Pushto-115

NT 0047342   DLC NSyU

Tasniya Isarasena
see Isarasena, Tasniya, 1922–

Taşo, P
Mon frère l'Abbé Paul.   Istanbul, Imp.
Rizzo, 1939.
66 p. illus.   20cm.
Cover title.

BX1595
T199

1. Taşo, Paul N., 1874-1934.   2. Catholic
Church in Turkey.   I. Title.

NT 0047344   CSt-H

Tasof (Ralica) [1893–   ]. *Etude sur la
gangrène diabétique par artérite et son traitement. 69 pp. 8°. Paris. 1924. No. 368.

NT 0047345   DNLM CtY

Tasolampros, L
Ὁ Κάρολος Μάρξ ἐναντίον τῶν
σλαβων... Ἀθήνα, 1949.
62 p.   22cm.

HB501
.M5T3

1. Marx, Karl, 1818-1883. I.
Title.

NT 0047346   OCU DLC-P4

Tasolampros, L.
Πολιτικα σαραντα χρονων 1909-1949.
Ἀθήνα, 1949.   163 p. port. 22cm.
Cover-title: Πολιτικα σαραντα ἐτῶν
1909-1949.
Title transliterated: Politika saranta
chronōn 1909-1949.

1. Greece, Modern   —Politics, 1909-
1949.

NT 0047347   NN OCU DLC-P4

Tasolampros, L.
Πολιτικα σφαλματα 5 Μαρτιου ἑως 15
Ἀπριλιου 1950. Ἀθηναι [1950] 75 p.
23cm.
Title transliterated: Politika
sphalmata 5 Martiou heōs 15 Apriliou 1950.

1. Greece, Modern   —Politics.

NT 0047348   NN DLC-P4 OCU MH

Tasovac, Siniša.
О жени; циклус предавања, одржаних на Коларчевом
народном универзитету. 2., доп. изд. Београд, Коларчев
народни универзитет, 1953.
85 p. illus. 21 cm. (Дописни народни универзитет, број 7)
At head of title: Синиша Тасовац, Босиљка Милошевић, Петар
Костић.

1. Gynecology.   I. Title.   *Title transliterated:* O ženi.

RG121.T2 1953   59-26067 ‡

NT 0047349   DLC

Taspinar, Adnan Halet.
Technisches Wörterbuch: Deutsch-Türkisch für Maschinenbau und Elektrotechnik, von Adnan Halet Taspinar... Istanbul ¡Universum matbaasi¿ 1937. 138 p.   17cm.
Added t.-p. in Turkish.

934164A. 1. Industrial arts—   Dictionaries, German—Turkish.
I. Title.
N. Y. P. L.   April 4, 1938

NT 0047350   NN NjP

Taşpınar, Adnan Halet.
Turkey. *İnhisarlar Umum Müdürlüğü.*
Tobacco affairs. ¡Articles by Adnan Halet Taşpınar et al.
İstanbul, 1939¿

SB278
.T8A52

Taşpınar.
No. 1-   1932-
Afyon.
v. in

AP
95
T8T18

Published by: Afyon Halkevi.
"Sayı" 1-   also called "Cilt" 1-

1. Community centers - Turkey - Period.
I. Afyon, Turkey. Halkevi.

NT 0047352   CLU

TASRIF,S
Djepang sekarang. Djakarta, Bulan-Bintang
¡1952¿
138 p. illus., ports.

DS 811
.T212

1. Japan--Descr.--1945-   I. Title.

NT 0047353   InU NIC CtY

Tasrif, S
Tiga laporan perdjalanan djurnalistik, oleh S. Tasrif,
Mochtar Lubis ¡dan¿ Rosihan Anwar. ¡Djakarta, Kemen-
terian Penerangan R. I., 1953¿
96 p. ports. 23 cm.
Cover title: Kebarat dari rumah.
CONTENTS.—Kisah dari dua kota.—Panorama dari Tudjuh Bukit.—
Tjatatan dari pinggir Nil.

1. Europe—Descr. and trav.—1945-   2. Egypt—Descr. and
trav.—1945-   I. Lubis, Mochtar, 1919–   II. Anwar, Rosihan, Hadji. III. Title. IV. Title: Kebarat dari rumah.

D910.T37   S A 68-6839

NT 0047354   DLC

Tasriphi
see al-Zanjānī, 'Abd al-Wahhāb ibn
Ibrāhim, fl. 1257.

Tass, Antal, ed.
Stella csillagászati egyesület, *Budapest.*
... Almanachja. ¡1-¿   évfolyam; 1925–
Budapest, Kir. Magyar egyetemi nyomda, 1924–

Tass, Antal.
Die Sternkunde in Ungarn. [n.p., n.d.]
299-311p. 26cm.

1. Astronomy - Hist. - Hungary. I. Title.

NT 0047357   CSdS

Tass, Antal.
Változó csillagok photometrikus megfigyelései. Ógyalla, 1918; Budapest, 1925.
327 p. illus. 30cm. (A Konkoly-Alapitványú Budapest' Magy. Kir. csillagvizsgáló-Intézet Nagyobb kiadványai. II. kötet)
Added title-pages in German and English.

1. Stars, variable. I. Ser.

NT 0047358   ViU ODW RPB CtY

Tassa, pseud.
see Christiansen, Ingrid.

TASSA, ALEKSANDER.
Höbelinik Legendid. Tallinnas, "Warrak" 1921. 105 p. 26cm.

Electrostatic reproduction by The New York Public Library.

1. Fiction, Esthonian.   I. Title.

NT 0047360   NN DLC-P4

Tassa, Aleksander.
Nõiasõrmus; fantastilised novellid. ₁Tartus₁ "Odamehe" kirjastus, 1919. 160 p. 19cm.

Film reproduction. Negative.

1. Fiction, Esthonian.

NT 0047361   NN DLC-P4

Tassa, Aleksander.
Puulõikekunstist; materjale ja allikaid Eesti puulõikekest xix sajandil. Tallinn, Ilukirjandus ja Kunst, 1948.
85 p. illus. 28 cm.

1. Wood-engravers, Estonian. 2. Wood-engravings, Estonian. I. Title.
NE1171.E8T3   54–19720 ‡

NT 0047362   DLC NN

4K   Tassa, K
4601   Riigikohtu poolt lahendatud küsimusi tsiviilõiguse alal. 1920. a. - 1937. a. [   ] 1937.
        160 p.

NT 0047363   DLC-P4

Z615.1
qT183
1613   TASSA de' medicinali. Vltamente stabilita dell' eccellentiss. Collegio de' medici, & honor.ᵈᵃ Compagnia de' speciali. Bologna, Appresso V. Benacci, 1613.
        16 p. illus. 27cm.

Title vignette (coat of arms)
1. Materia medica. Early works to 1800. 2. Drugs. Prices and sale. I. Bologna. Università. Collegio della medicina. II. Bologna. Compagnia de' speciali.

NT 0047364   MnU

Tassa de medicinali semplici, composti, e spagirici, disposta con l'ordine dell' alfabetto, e pubblicata dall' ... Collegio di medicina ed ... compagnia degli speciali della città di Bologna l'anno m. deci. 40pp. fol. *Bologna, dall' erede di V. Benacci, 1701.*
Pages 25-26 and 31-32 wanting.

NT 0047365   DNLM

Tassa delle robbe medicinali tanto semplici quanto composte ad uso di questa illustrissima città di Modana
see under   Modena. Ordinances, local laws, etc.

Tassa sulle polveri piriche
see under   [Colombo, Luigi]

Tassaert, Nicolas Francois Octave
see   Tassaert, Octave, 1800-1874.

---

*Tassaert, Octave, 1800-1874.
...Octave Tassaert; notice sur sa vie et catalogue de son œuvre
see under   Prost, Bernard, 1849-1905.

Tassaert, Philip James.
A catalogue of a collection of loose prints... drawings... housefhold furniture... and numerous other effects of the late P.J. Tassert, dec. ... sold by auction by Mr. Christie... December... 1803. [London,] Christie, 1803.
13 p. 8°.
In: MNH p.v.2.

NT 0047370   NN

Tassain, Édouard, joint author.
Maguéro, Édouard, 1856–   FOR OTHER EDITIONS SEE MAIN ENTRY
Répertoire fiscal du commerce et de l'industrie. 2. éd., par Édouard Maguéro ... Édouard Tassain ... et Étienne Molas ... Paris. Aux bureaux de la "Revue des impôts". 1928.

Tassain, Édouard, joint ed.
Maguéro, Édouard, 1856–   ed.
Traité alphabétique des droits d'enregistrement, de timbre et d'hypothèques. 3. éd. Nouveau recueil de législation, de doctrine et de jurisprudence, par Édouard Maguéro ... Édouard Tassain et Étienne Molas ... avec la collaboration ... de mm. Arnaud ... Bérenger ₁et autres₁ ... Paris, Bureaux de la "Revue de l'enregistrement", 1928-30.

Tassain (Georges) [1877-   ]. * Valeur pronostique des idées hypocondriaques de négation dans quelques maladies mentales. 93 pp. 8°. *Paris. 1902.* No. 123.

NT 0047373   DNLM

Tassaly, Jean André, 1904–
. ... À propos d'un cas d'abcès amibien du foie, traité par injections d'émétine dans la poche... Paris, 1930.
Thèse – Univ. de Paris.
"Bibliographie: 1 l. at end.

NT 0047374   CtY

Tassani.
L'Alfiere; commedia inedita del signor Tassani. Venezia, 1801.
PG 1231   64 p. 17½cm. (Il teatro moderno
.A7 T4   applaudito. t. LV [pt. 2])
t. 55

NT 0047375   MdBJ MB

Tassani, Alessandro.
——. Cura di mare agli scrofolosi della provincia di Como nel 1884. 23 pp. 12°. *Como, F. O. tirelli, 1885.*
Repr. from: Almanacco prov. di Como, 1885.

NT 0047376   DNLM

Tassani (Alessandro). Invasione del colèra nella provincia di Como durante il 1855, e modo

di sua diffusione. 34 pp., 1 tab. 12°. *Como, C. & F. Ostinelli, 1856.*
Repr. from: Riv. comense, 1856.

NT 0047377   DNLM

Tassani, Alessandro.
——. Invasione e modo di diffusione del colèra asiatico nella provincia di Como durante il 1867. 48 pp. 8°. *Como, figli di C. A. Ostinelli, 1868.*
Repr. from: Manuale prov., 1868.

NT 0047378   DNLM

614.0945 Tassani, Alessandro F
T18c   Cenni topografici statistico-medici sulla città di Como, del medico provinciale dott. Alessandro Tassani ... Como, C. e F. Ostinelli, tipografi provinciali, 1861.
        83p.,1l.

"Altri lavori ed opuscoli dello stesso autore": 1 leaf at end.

1. Hygiene, Public--Como, Italy. 2. Como, Italy--Statistics, Vital.

NT 0047379   IU

614.0945 Tassani, Alessandro F
T18s   Saggio di topografia statistico-medica della provincia di Cremona del dott. Alessandro F. Tassani. Milano, Tipografia di G. Chiusi, 1847.
        134p. incl.tables.

"Estratto dalla Gazzetta medica di Milano. Tomo sesto."

1. Hygiene, Public--Cremona (Province) 2. Cremona (Province)--Statistics, Vital.

NT 0047380   IU

Tassani, Sandro.
Memoria defensionale per Stoppa Adolfo. Dell'applicabilità del R. Decreto di amnistia 24 ottobre 1896, n. 464 in causa di contrabbando. Como, Tipografia cooperativa comense, 1896.

cover-title, 13 p., 1 l. 31cm.
At head of title: Avanti la Eccellentissima Corte di cassazione in Roma.
Signed at end: Avv. Sandro Tassani; Avv.   Alfredo Tassani.

NT 0047381   MH-L

Tassano, Manuel.
... Revelaciones históricas del valle de Punilla, Sierras de Córdoba, 1585–1930. Buenos Aires, J. Lajouane & cía., 1931.
198, ₍2₎ p. illus., fold. map, facsims. 23ᶜᵐ.

1. Punilla valley, Argentine republic. I. Title.

Library of Congress　　F2886.T26　　31-30040
　　　　　　　　　　　　　₍2₎　　982

NT 0047382　DLC TxU IU CU NcU DPU

Tassara, Antonio.
In notariorvm excessvs, errores, atque peccata, Compendium: naturalibus theologicis, legalibusq₎ rationibus exornatum, Antonio Tassara auctore. Mvltis nvper additis capitulis, insuperq₎ & copioso ac opulentissimo repertorio ad principales materias reperiendas. Venetiis ₍Apud B. Cæsanum₎ 1550.
112 l. 16 cm.

1. Notaries (Roman law) I. Title.

67-43423

NT 0047383　DLC IU MH

TASSARA, Atilio.
El proyecto de código penal peruano de 1916.
Lima, "La Opinión nacional", 1920.

pp. 33. 8°.
Tésis --- Universidad mayor de San Marcos.

NT 0047384　MH-L

Tassara, Gabriel García y
see
García y Tassara, Gabriel, 1817–1875.

ITA　Tassara, Giuseppe
958　Progetto per l'istituzione di una cassa
TAS　nazionale per la pensione ai lavoratori.
　　Genova, Bacigalupi, 1894.

8, ₍7₎ p. incl. tables. 28cm.

Preface signed: Giuseppe Tassara ...

NT 0047386　MH-L

Tassara, Juan Marconi
see Marconi Tassara, Juan.

　Tassara Baillet, Glicerio, ed.
F1401
.M86
Mundo americano ₍revista quincenal de índole cultural e
informativa₎ t. 1–　　9. dic. 1938–
₍Lima, Perú, 1938–

Tassard, Joseph, 1865–
La cardiopathie latente chez l'enfant.
Lyon, A. Rey, 1894.
57p., ℓ. 26cm.

1. Heart diseases. 2. Infant. 3. Pediatrics.
I. Title.

NT 0047389　NcD-MC DNLM

Tassart, Charles Louis.
L'industrie de la teinture; avec 55 figures
intercalées dans le texte. Paris, J. B. Baillière
et fils, 1890.
(1) 305 p. illus. sm. 8°. [Bibliothèque
des connaissances utiles]

NT 0047390　MB NN

Tassart, Charles Louis,
Les matières colorantes et la chimie de la
teinture... Paris, J. C. Baillière et fils, 1890.
vii, 296 p. illus. 18 cm. (Bibliothèque
des connaissances utiles)
1. Dyes and dyeing.

NT 0047391　CU PPF

₍Tassart, François₎
Recollections of Guy de Maupassant, by his valet François, tr.
from the French by Mina Round. London, John Lane; New
York, John Lane company, 1912.
xv, 324 p. front. (port.) plates. 23ᶜᵐ. $3.00

1. Maupassant, Guy de, 1850–1893. I. Round, Mina, tr.
　　　　　　　　　　　　　　　　　12-18185 rev.
Library of Congress　　PQ2353.T32

OC1 NmLcU NmU FU CU CSt MB
NT 0047392　DLC NNU KEmT PP PU NIC NN ViU MH OKentU

₍Tassart,₎ François.　　　　　　　　　　FB-M
Souvenirs sur Guy de Maupassant, par François, son valet de
chambre. Paris: Plon-Nourrit et Cie., 1911. iii, 314 p. 12°.

1. Maupassant, Guy de.
N. Y. P. L.　　　　　　　　　　September 13, 1912.

NT 0047393　NN WU MU IaU NcD

[Tassart, François]
Souvenirs sur Guy de Maupassant, par
François, son valet de chambre (1883–1893)
2. éd. Paris, Plon-Nourrit et cie, 1911.
3 p. l., 314 p., 1 l. 18 cm.

NT 0047394　CU NjP CtY ICU MiEM

840.81　Tassart, François.
M452zTa　Souvenirs sur Guy de Maupassant, par François, son valet de chambre (1883–1893) 3. éd.
Paris, Plon-Nourrit, 1911.
314p. 20cm.

1. Maupassant, Guy de, 1850–1893.

NT 0047395　NcU RPB PBm CaBVaU

PQ　Tassart, François.
2353　Souvenirs sur Guy de Maupassant, par
T3　François, son valet de chambre (1883–1893)
1911　5. éd. Paris, Plon-Nourrit, 1911.
314 p. 19cm. (Librairie Plon)

1. Maupassant, Guy de, 1850–1893.
I. Title.

NT 0047396　CoU NcD TU

[TASSART, FRANCOIS]
Souvenirs sur Guy de Maupassant, par François, son valet
de chambre (1883–1893). Sixième édition. Paris: Plon,
1911. 314 p. 18½cm.

Preface signed: François Tassart.

597874A. 1. Maupassant, Guv de. 1850–1893. I. Title.

NT 0047397　NN OU OCU PHC TxHU

PQ2353
T3　Tassart, François.
Souvenirs sur Guy de Maupassant, par
François ₍Tassart₎ son valet de chambre
(1883–1893) 7. éd. Paris, Plon-Nourrit,
1911.
314 p. 18 cm.

1. Maupassant, Guy de, 1850–1893. I. Title.

NT 0047398　MeB MH OrSaW

Tassart, Juan Carlos.
El descenso de la mortalidad por tuberculosis en la República Argentina. Prólogo del Prof. Dr. Ramón Carrillo.
Buenos Aires, 1951.
57 p. illus. 27 cm.

1. Tuberculosis—Argentine Republic. 2. Argentine Republic—Statistics, Medical. 3. Mortality. I. Title.

RC315.A7T3　　　　　　60-24665 ‡

NT 0047399　DLC DPAHO

Tassart, L　　C.
Exploitation du pétrole. Historique—extraction—procédés de sondage—géographie et géologie—recherches des
gîtes—exploitation des gisements—chimie—théories de la
formation du pétrole, par L.-C. Tassart ... Paris, H. Dunod et E. Pinat, 1908.
xiv p., 1 l., 726 p. illus., xvii fold. pl. (incl maps, plans) diagrs. 28ᶜᵐ.

1. Petroleum.　　　　　　　　　G S 8-32

Library, U. S. Geol.　　　　　survey 467 qT18

NT 0047400　DI-GS CU NIC DI OC1 ICJ NN

Zc91
M32
880tag
Tassé, Elie
The North-West; the province of Manitoba
and North-West Territories - their extent -
salubrity of the climate - fertility of the
soil - products - regulations concerning
lands - prices of cereals and farm implements
- salaries and wages - travelling routes by
land and water, etc. ... Ottawa, Printed
at "Le Canada" Office, 1880.
46, [2] p. 22 cm.
Original wrappers.

NT 0047401　CtY MnHi CaBVaU ICN

Tassé, Elie.
Le Nord-Ouest. La province de Manitoba et les territoires du Nord-Ouest,
leur étendue, salubrité du climat,
fertilité du sol, produits en général,
réglements concernant les terres, prix
des denrées et des instruments de ferme,
salaires, voies de communication, etc.,
etc., etc. Ottawa, Impr. du "Canada",
1880.
56 p. 22cm.

1. Manitoba. Descr. & travel. 2. Northwest, Canadian. Descr. & travel. 3.
Canada. Emig. and immig. I. Title.

NT 0047403　MnU

F
1060.9 TASSÉ, ÉLIE.
.T21   Le Nord-ouest; la province de Manitoba et
les territoires du Nord-ouest; leur
étendue, salubrité du climat, fertilité
du sol, produits en général, réglements
concernant les terres, prix des denrées
et des instruments de ferme, salaires, voies
de communication, etc.,etc.,etc., par Élie
Tassé. Ottawa, Imprimerie du Canada, 1880.
72p. 23cm.
1. Manitoba--Descr. & trav. 2. Northwest,
Canadian--Descr.   & trav. 3. Canada--
Emig. & immig.   I. Title.

NT   0047404   NhD CtY WaU MH CaNSWA CaBViPA MnU

Tassé, Élie.
Le Nord-ouest; la province de Manitoba et les territoires
du Nord-ouest; leur étendue, salubrité du climat, fertilité du
sol, produits en général, réglements concernant les terres,
chemins de fer, prix des denrées et des instruments de ferme,
salaires, voies de communication, etc., etc., etc., par Élie Tassé.
2. éd., rev. et augm. Ottawa, Imprimerie du Canada, 1882.
91 p. 22½ᵐ.

1. Manitoba—Descr. & trav. 2. Northwest, Canadian—Descr. & trav.
3. Canada—Emig. & immig.
                                                    2–315
Library of Congress   F1060.9.T21

NT   0047405   DLC CaBViPA CtY N

Tasse, Gustave Marie Joseph.
La randonnée du 9ᵉ Zouaves. Paris, Berger-Levrault,
1943.
274 p. illus., maps. 20 cm.

1. France. Armée. 9. régiment de zouaves. 2. World War, 1939–
1945—Regimental histories—France—9. régiment de zouaves.   I.
Title.
D761.38.T3 1943   A F 48–1353*
New York. Public Libr.
for Library of Congress   (2)

NT   0047406   NN CtY DLC

Tasse, Gustave Marie Joseph.
... La randonnée du 9ᵉ Zouaves, 1939–1940 ... Croquis de
Charle Brouty. Alger, L. Chaix (1941)
cover-title, 250 p., 2 l. illus., plates. 20½ᵐ.
At head of title: Lᵗ-colonel Tasse.

1. World war, 1939–   —Regimental histories—France—Infantry—
Zouaves—9th regt. I. Title.
                                                    44–23624
Library of Congress   D761.9.F7T3
(2)   940.541265

NT   0047407   DLC MH

Tasse, Heinz, 1908–
Die Rechtsbeziehungen zwischen mehreren
Sicherungsverpflichteten nach Befriedigung
des Gläubigers durch einen von ihnen ...
von Heinz Tasse ... Dessau, G. Zichäus,
1931.
85 p. 21cm.

Inaug.-Diss. - Halle-Wittenberg.
"Lebenslauf": p.85.
"Schrifttum": p.(75)-84.

NT   0047408   MH-L ICRL

Tassé, Henriette (Lionais) 1870–
De tout un peu.   Montreal, Impr.
par Marchands, 1923.

120 p.   20cm.

NT   0047409   MnU RWoU CaOTU MH

301.412 T13
Tassé, Mme Henriette (Lionais), 1870 –
La femme et la civilisation. Montréal
(Thérien Frères) 1927.
109 p. illus.

1. Woman--History and condition of women.
2. Civilization--History.
I. Title.

NT   0047410   CaOTP CaBVaU RWoU MH CaOTU

Tasse, Henriette (Lionais) 1870 –
——Les Salons français.—Quarante gravures et portraits. *Montréal, 1930.* 376 p.
Du XVIIème siècle jusqu'à nos jours; leur influence, grâce aux femmes,
sur les lettres et la culture françaises. Série de tableaux depuis la marquise de Rambouillet jusqu'à Mmes de Caillavet et Juliette Adam.

NT   0047411   RWoU CaOTU

Tassé, *Mme.* **Henriette (Lionais)** 1870–
... Les salons français; préface de Firmin Roz ...   Avignon,
Maison Aubanel père (*1939–
v. front., ports. 22½ᵐ.
At head of title: Madame Henriette Tassé.
Bibliographical foot-notes.

1. Salons. 2. Paris—Soc. life & cust. 3. Paris—Intellectual life.
                                                    40–11046
Library of Congress   DC33.T3
Copyright A—Foreign   42966
(2)   914.436

NT   0047412   DLC

DC33.6
T2
Tassé, Mme. Henriette (Lionais) 1870–
Salons français du dix-neuvième siècle;
pref. de Firmin Roz. Ouvrage orne de 16
hors-texte.   Montréal (Impr. Saint-Joseph)
1952.

243 p.
Bibl. footnotes.

1. Salons. 2. Paris - Social life and customs.
3. Paris - Intellectual life. I. T.

NT   0047413   NBuU ICU NNC CaOTU

808.8
T183 Tassé, Henriette (Lionais) 1870–
La vie et le rêve.   Montréal
(Impr. au "Devoir") 1915.

cover title, 144 p.   19cm.

1. Quotations, French. I. Title.

NT   0047414   MnU RWoU

Tassé, *Mme.* **Henriette (Lionais)** 1870–
... La vie humoristique d'Hector Berthelot; préface de m.
Victor Morin. Montréal, A. Lévesque, 1934.
8 p. l., (19)–239 p., 4 l. front., illus., port. 19½ᵐ. (*On cover:* Figures
canadiennes)
At head of t.-p.: Henriette Tassé; at head of cover-title: Henriette
Lionais-Tassé.
"Bibliographie": p. 229.

1. Berthelot, Hector, 1842–1895.
                                                    40–15738
Library of Congress   PQ3919.B38T3
(2)   928.4

NT   0047415   DLC NN

CD 71   Tasse, Johann Adolf, 1585–1654.
.T21   Joannis Adolfi Tassii... Chronologiae
(Rare) compendium, descriptum ex recensione
Henrici Siveri..., cujus sciagraphia
opusculi accessit. Hamburgi, Typis
Rebenlinianis, 1691.
(12) 115 p. tables.
Printer's device.

1. Chronology. 2. Calendar. I.
Sivers, Heinrich, 1626–1691, ed. II.
Title: Chronologiae compendium.

NT   0047416   ICU

Tasse,Johann Adolf,1585-1654.
Joannis Adolfi Tassii ... Trigonometriae ca-
nonicae compendium,in usum gymnasij hamburgen-
sis editum,ex recensione Henrici Siveri ...
Hamburgi, sumtibus Zachariae Hertelii; typis
Georgii Rebenlini, anno 1676.
6 p.ℓ.,48 p. diagr. 21½cm.
Title vignette; tail-pieces.

1.Trigonometry--Early works to 1800. I.Siver,Hen-
rich,1626-1691, ed.

NT   0047417   MiU

Tassé, Joseph, 1848–1895.
Au Temiskaming: lettres de voyage, par Joseph Tassé
... Montréal, Imprimerie générale, 1887.
cover-title, 1 p. l., 19 p. 21ᵐ.
"Reproduit de la Minerve."

Subject entries: Temiscaming, Lake.
                                                    8–9744
Library of Congress, no.   F1054.T3T2.

NT   0047418   DLC

Tassé, Joseph, 1848–1895.
Aux Canadiens-Français emigrés; discours, par M.
Joseph Tassé, M. P., prononcé à la Convention franco-
canadienne du Massachusetts, tenue à Lowell, le 4 octobre
1882. (Ottawa? 1883?)
14 p. 21½ᵐ.
Caption title.
Owing to an imperfect impression, the first three letters of the word
"discours" are wanting in this copy.

1. Canada—Nationality. 2. Canada—Annexation. 3. French-Canadians
in Massachusetts.
                                                    CA 23–154 Unrev'd

NT   0047419   DLC CtY

Tassé, Joseph (1848-1895)
Aux Canadiens français émigrés; discours
prononcé à la Convention Franco-Canadienne
du Massachusetts, tenue à Lowell, le 4
octobre 1882.
14p.   Ottawa,Impr.du Canada,1883.

NT   0047420   CaOTU RWoU

Tassé, Joseph, 1848–1895.
Canada : Riel et les Métis du Nord-Ouest.
(*In* Revue française de l'étranger et des colonies. Paris, 1886. 25ᵐ.
v. 3, p. (427)–434)
"M. Tassé, membre du Parlement, a prononcé le 19 février 1886, au
Cercle Lafontaine d'Ottawa, un discours où il cherche à justifier l'exécution
de Riel ... Nous en extrayons les passages qui ont un trait plus spécialement
à la question des Métis du Nord-Ouest et des sauvages ..."

1. Riel rebellion, 1885. 2. Northwest, Canadian—Hist. 3. Manitoba—
Hist.   10–31430
Library of Congress   G1.R45 vol. 3
——— Copy 2, detached.   F1060.9.T22

NT   0047421   DLC

Tasse, Joseph, 1848–1895.
The Canadians of the West. Translated by Charlotte
Storm (between 1939 and 1941)
95 l. 30 cm.
Typescript (carbon copy)
Translation of Les canadiens de l'Ouest.
"Work Projects Administration # 3888, O. P. 165-1-98-11."

1. French-Canadians — Biography. 2. French-Canadians in the
United States. 3. Northwest, Canadian—Biography. I. Title.
E184.F85T23   70–237945
                                                    MARC

NT   0047422   DLC

TASSÉ (Joseph)—Les Canadiens de l'Ouest.—Vital Guérin.—*Montréal, 1871.*
12 p.

NT 0047423 RWoU

TASSÉ (Joseph)—Les Canadiens de l'Ouest.—F.-X. Aubry.—*Montréal, 1871.*
34 p.

NT 0047424 RWoU

Tassé, Joseph, 1848–1895.
Les Canadiens de l'Ouest, par Joseph Tassé ... Montréal, Cie. d'imprimerie canadienne, 1878.
2 v. 6 pl., 15 port. 23ᶜᵐ.
Biographical sketches of noted French-Canadians of the middle and western states of the United States and of the western part of Canada.

1. French Canadians—Biog. 2. French Canadians in the U. S. 3. Northwest, Canadian—Biog.

Library of Congress E184.F85T2
6—9055

CtY OC1 MH CaNSWA CaBViPA CaBVaU WaSpG
NT 0047425 DLC TxU NjP CtY ICN NBu MnHi OU WaSp OO

Micro-film
E
82
Tassé, Joseph, 1848–1895.
Les Canadiens de l'Ouest, par Joseph Tassé ... Montreal, Cie. d'imprimerie canadienne, 1878.
2 v. 6 pl., 15 port. 23ᶜᵐ.

Film

NT 0047426 ICU

920.071
T212C
Tassé, Joseph, 1848–1895.
Les Canadiens de l'Ouest, par Joseph Tassé. [2. éd.] Montréal, Cie. d'imprimerie canadienne, 1878.
2 v. 6 pl. 15 port. 23 cm.
Biographical sketches of noted French-Canadians of the middle and western states of the United States and of the western part of Canada.
1. French-Canadians. Biog. 2. French-Canadians in the U. S. 3. Northwest, Canadian. Biog. I. Title.

NT 0047427 NcD WaU RWoU

E
184
F85T3
1882
Tassé, Joseph, 1848–1895
Les Canadiens de l'Ouest. 4. ed. Montréal, Berthiaume & Sabourin, 1882.
2 v. illus.

1. French-Canadians – Biography 2. French-Canadians in the U.S. 3. Northwest, Canadian – Biography I. Title CaOTU

NT 0047428 CaOTU CtY CaBVaU CaBViPA

920.071
T212
Tassé, Joseph, 1848–1895.
Les Canadiens de l'Ouest. 5.ed. Montreal, Imprimerie générale, 1886. [°1878]
2 v. plates, ports. 23 cm.

1. French Canadians. Biog. 2. Western states. Hist.

NT 0047429 N CtY IaHi CU CaBViP WaU RWoU CaBVaU

TASSÉ, Joseph, 1848–1895.
Les canadiens de l'Oeust; Charles de Langlade.

Newspaper cuttings from l'Opinion publique. 7 oct. 1875 – 20 jan. 1876.

NT 0047430 MH

Tasse, Joseph, 1848–1895.
Le chemin de fer Canadien du Pacifique, par Joseph Tasse. Montréal, E. Senécal, 1872.
62 p., 1 l. 23ᶜᵐ.

1. Canadian Pacific railway.

Library of Congress HE2810.C2T2
7–6520†

NT 0047431 DLC

TASSÉ (Joseph).—*Ottawa, Montréal, de 1875 à 1881.* (61 lettres).
Correspondance suivie et intéressante entre ces deux amis; échange de vues; demande de documents, de renseignements concernant son ouvrage: "Les Canadiens de l'Ouest", etc., etc.

NT 0047432 RWoU

Tassé, Joseph, 1848–1895, ed.
Discours de Sir Georges Cartier
see under Cartier, Sir George Etienne, 1814–1873.

TASSÉ (Joseph)—Eloge funèbre de Mgr Guigues, évêque d'Ottawa.—*Montréal, 1874.* 12 p.
Prononcé devant l'Institut canadien-français d'Ottawa, séance du 18 février 1874.

NT 0047434 RWoU

Tassé, Joseph, 1848–1895.
La France et le Canada français
see under title

TASSÉ, Joseph, 1848–1895.
The French question. Montreal, Imprimerie generale, 1888.

pp.87.
"The letters are an answer to a series of charges made by The mail against the French Canadian race".- [pref.]

NT 0047436 MH CaNSWA MnU

4DA
210
Tassé, Joseph, 1848–1895.
Lord Beaconsfield et Sir John Macdonald, un parallèle. Ottawa, Impr. du "Canada", 1880.
41 p.

NT 0047437 DLC-P4

Tassé, Joseph, 1848–1895.
Memoir of Charles de Langlade. By Joseph Tasse ... ⟨Tr. from the French by Mrs. Sarah Fairchild Dean.⟩
(*In* Wisconsin. State historical society. Report and collections ... 1873–1876. Madison, 1876. 23ᶜᵐ. v. 7, p. [123]–187)

1. Langlade, Charles Michel de, 1729–1800. i. Conover, Mrs. Sarah Fairchild Dean.

Library of Congress F576.W81 vol.7
20–12315

NT 0047438 DLC MdBP

Tassé, Joseph (1848–1895)
Official report of the speech delivered on French domiation, House of Commons, Session 1882.
23p. Ottawa, MacLean(pr.),1882.

NT 0047439 CaOTU

971.42
T212
Tassé, Joseph, 1848–1895.
The Ottawa River canal system; speech delivered – in the House of Commons, on the 20th April, 1885. Montreal, Imprimerie générale, 1886.
22 p. 23 cm.

1. Ottawa River. I. Title.

NT 0047440 N

942.08
B355Bta
Tassé, Joseph, 1848–1895.
Un parallèle: Lord Beaconsfield et Sir John Macdonald. Ottawa, Impr. du Canada, 1880.
41p. ports. 22cm.

1. Beaconsfield, Benjamin Disraeli, 1st earl of, 1804–1881. 2. Macdonald, Sir John Alexander, 1815–1891. I. Title.

NT 0047441 TxU CaBViP

F
1054.5
.H8
W9
T2
Tassé, Joseph, 1848–1945.
Philemon Wright; ou, Colonisation et commerce de bois, par Joseph Tassé. Montréal, Des presses à vapeur de la Minerve, 1871.
iv,77 p. 19½ᶜᵐ.

1.Hull,Quebec—Hist. 2.Wright,Philemon,1760–1839.

NT 0047442 MiU CaBVaU MH CaNSWA CaOTU

Tassé, Joseph, 1848–1895.
"La question Riel; discours de M. Tassé...prononcé devant le "Cercle Lafontaine" d'Ottawa, le 19 février 1886. [Ottawa? 1886?] 13 p. 4°.

Cover-title.

1. Indians, N. A.—Canada—Wars— 1885—Riel rebellion.
N. Y. P. L. November 30, 1928

NT 0047443 NN MnHi CtY MH CaBViPA

Micro-film
Tassé, Joseph, 1848–1895.
La question Riel [discours de M. Tassé, M.P., prononcé devant le "Cercle Lafontaine" d'Ottawa, le 19 février 1886. [s.l. : s.n., 1886?]
13 p.
Microfilm. New Haven : Research Publications, [196-?] — 1 reel ; 35 mm. — (History of the Canadian Northwest ; reel 20)

1. Riel, Louis David, 1844–1885. 2. Riel Rebellion, 1885. I. Title

NT 0047444 OOxM

F
1C33
.T22

Tassé, Joseph, 1848-1895.
... Le 38ᵐᵉ fauteuil; ou, Souvenirs parlementaires ... Montréal, E. Senécal & fils,
1891.

3 p.l., 290 p., l l. 5 port. 23ᶜᵐ.
CONTENTS.--Joseph Alfred Mousseau.--Louis François
Roderick Masson.--Charles Joseph Coursol.--Joseph
Royal.--Désiré Girouard.
1. Mousseau, Joseph Alfred, 1838-1886. 2. Masson,
Louis François Rodrigue, 1833-1903. 3. Coursol,
Charles Joseph, 1819-1888. 4. Royal, Joseph, 1837-1902.
5. Girouard, Désiré, 1836-1911. 6. Canada. Parliament--
Biog. I. Title.

NT   0047445   MiU CaBViP CaBVaU MH MnU CaNSWA CtY

Tassé, Joseph, 1848-1895.
La vallée de l'Outaouais : sa condition géographique
ses ressources agricoles et industrielles ; ses exploitations
forestières ; ses richesses minérales ; ses avantages pour
la colonisation et l'immigration ; ses canaux et ses chemins
de fer, par Joseph Tassé ... Montreal, E. Senécal, 1873.
58 p. 24ᶜᵐ.

1. Ottawa Valley--Econ. condit. I. Title.

22-24398

Library of Congress   HC117.O8T3

NT   0047446   DLC NN

Tassé, Joseph, 1848-1895.
Voltaire, mme. de Pompadour et quelques
arpents de neige, par Joseph Tassé. Levis,
P.-G. Roy, 1898.
103 p. 16.5 cm. (Half title: Bibliothèque
canadienne)
Bibliographical foot-notes.
1. Voltaire, François Marie Arouet de, 1694-
1778. 2. Pompadour, Jeanne Antoinette (Poisson)
marquise de, 1721-1764.

NT   0047447   MiU CaBVaU MiI RWoU CaOTU

Law
Eng
T2122res

Tassé, Roger.
Responsabilité stricte sous le droit
civil de la province de Quebec et la "common
law". Montreal, 1954.
ii, 94p.

At head of title: Institut de droit comparé
de l'Université de Toronto.
Typewritten.
Bibliography: p. 83-84.

NT   0047448   CaOTU

TASSÉ, Stanislas.
La liberté de la presse. Solution de
divers cas. Montreal, 1887.

pp.15.

NT   0047449   MH

Le Tasse. Supplemento.
Raccolta delle leggi, decreti e regolamenti
sulle diverse imposte
see under Italy. Laws, statutes, etc.

La Tasse de café sans sucre. n.p., n.d.
14 p.

NT   0047451   PPAmP

Tassel (Alfred). *De l'hygiène des femmes
grosses. 20 pp. 4°. Paris, 1853, No. 330, v.
265.

NT   0047452   DNLM

Tassel, G., joint author.

TR705
.T49

Thévenard, P
Le cinéma scientifique français (par) P. Thévenard (et)
G. Tassel. Illus. de 105 photos. hors texte. Préf. de Jean
Painlevé. Paris, La Jeune Parque (1948)

Tassel, Leonhard von
see Dassel, Leonhard von.

Tassel (P.-Alexandre). *Recherches historiques
sur la nature des altérations séniles des artères.
47 pp. 4°. Paris, 1856, No. 268, v. 507.

NT   0047455   DNLM

TASSEL, Robert.
Réaction contre les clauses d'irresponsa-
bilité dans les contrats de transport maritime.
Rennes, 1925.

4°.
Thèse --- Rennes.

NT   0047456   MH-L CtY

Tassel, Valentine Van
see Van Tassel, Valentine.

Tasselli, Pietro.
Nel cinquantenario delle mistiche nozze
di Don Evaristo Previdi. Mantova, Tipografia
A.L.C.E., 1954.

19 p.

NT   0047458   DCU

Tassels on the boots...
see under [Coombs, Robert]

Tasserie (Georgina-Marie). *Contribution
l'étude de la tuberculose au Maroc. 66 p
1 l. 8°. Paris, 1921. No. 106.

NT   0047460   DNLM CtY

Tasseron, Fijtje Hendrika (van Griethuysen)
see Tasseron-van Griethuysen, Fijtje Hendrika.

CS829
.G745
1951

Tasseron, Johannes Anthony, joint author.

Tasseron-van Griethuysen, Fijtje Hendrika.
Genealogie van Griethuysen, door F. H. van Griethuysen
& J. A. Tasseron. Rotterdam, H. de Bot (1951)

Tasseron-van Griethuysen, Fijtje Hendrika.
Genealogie van Griethuysen, door F. H. van Griethuysen
& J. A. Tasseron. Rotterdam, H. de Bot (1951)
140 p. illus., coats of arms. 21 cm.
"Schematisch overzicht Utrechtse tak": leaf laid in.
Bibliography : p. 106-129.
———— Wijzigingen en aanvullingen April 1954. Zeist,
1954.
141-163 p. 21 cm.   CS829.G745 1951 Suppl.
1. Griethuysen family.   I. Tasseron, Johannes Anthony, joint
author.

CS829.G745   1951   54-15073 rev

NT   0047463   DLC NN

MT220
T212

Tasset, Aline.
La main et l'ame au piano. D'après Schiffmacher: L'intelligence dans le mécanisme -
les qualités du son révélées par les gestes
et les états successifs de la sonorité dans
l'étude. Paris, C. Delagrave (18--)
88 p. music. 20ᶜᵐ.
Includes Notes manuscrites de Schiffmacher.

1. Piano - Instruction and study. 2. Schiffmacher, Joseph,   1827-1888. I. Title.

NT   0047464   CSt

TASSET, Mme. Aline.
La main et l'ame au piano d'apres
Schiffmacher. Paris, Ch. Delagrave, [1908]

sm.4°.

NT   0047465   MH-Mu

Tasset, André, tr.
Le paradis perdu ...
see under Milton, J[ohn], 1608-1674.

Tasset, André, tr.

Milne, William Charles, 1815-1863.
La vie réelle en Chine, par le révérend William C. Milne
... tr. par André Tasset, avec une introduction et des notes par
M. G. Pauthier ... 2. éd. rev., cor. et augm. du plan de Chang-
Haï. Paris, L. Hachette et cⁱᵉ, 1860.

Tasset, Charles.
————. De la fiebre amarilla en el Perú. Consideraciones prácticas sobre su naturaleza y su
curacion. 23 pp. sm. 4°. Lima, A. Alfaro y
Ca., 1869.

NT   0047468   DNLM

Tasset, Charles.
————. Nouvelles considérations pratiques sur le
typhus, la fièvre jaune, les fièvres intermittentes
pernicieuses paludéennes et la verrue péruvienne.
64 pp. 8°. Paris, A. Delahaye, 1872.

NT   0047469   DNLM

Tasset (Charles). *Sur quelques points de la
physiologie du sens de l'ouie. 22 pp. 4°. Paris, 1836. No. 274, v. 302.

NT   0047470   DNLM PPC

Tasset, Émile, 1838-1879.
Catalogue de l'exposition de gravures des
anciens maîtres liégeois, organisée en 1869
see under Liège. Musée communal.

Tasset, Émile, 1838–1879.
Catalogue raisonné de l'œuvre du graveur Richard Collin, d'origine luxembourgeoise (XVII° siècle). Par Émile Tasset...
Partie 1—   Luxembourg: V. Buck, 1876—   v.
port.   4°.

1. Collin, Richard, 1627–1697.
N. Y. P. L.   September 15, 1926

NT   0047472   NN

Tasset, J.
Traité pratique de maréchalerie à l'usage des maréchaux, vétérinaires, officiers montés, hommes de cheval etc.   Paris: Librairie J. B. Baillière et fils, 1912.   2 p.l., (1)8–480 p.   illus. 12°.

1. Horseshoeing.
N. Y. P. L.   Sentember 6, 1912.

NT   0047473   NN CtY

Tasset, Jacobus Henricus.
De volkenrechtelijke uitzonderingen van art. 8, Wetboek van strafrecht ...   Amsterdam, J. H. de Wit, 1892.
4 p. l., 311, vii p., 1 l.   24½ᶜᵐ.

Proefschrift—Amsterdam.

1. International law and relations. 2. Law—Netherlands.

28–30003

NT   0047474   DLC PU-L

Tasset-Nissolle, Élisabeth.
... Conquérantes. Paris, Éditions "Je sers" ₁1936₎
3 p. l., ₉9₎–250 p., 2 l. illus. (plan) port. 19ᶜᵐ.
CONTENTS.—Élisabeth Fry.—Florence Barclay.—Joséphine Butler.— Catherine Booth.—Emmeline Pankhurst.—Katherine Mansfield.—Renée de Benoît.

1. Woman—Biog. 2. Gt. Brit.—Biog.   I. Title.
                                                          36–14262
Library of Congress   CT3234.T3
Copyright A—Foreign   31691
                                  ₂₎   920.7

NT   0047475   DLC PHC

Tassey, John
The supreme and exclusive authority of the Lord Jesus Christ, in religious matters, maintained, and the rights, liberties, and privileges of the children of God established from the sacred scriptures, in opposition to the assumed powers of ecclesiastics. In two parts. By John Tassey ... To which is added, a small treatise on the Lord's supper, by the late celebrated John Brown ... Pittsburgh [Pa.] Printed by D. & M. MacLean, for the author, 1826.
xi, [15]–299 p.   19 cm. Boards. Uncut.

The treatise on the Lord's supper has separate t.-p.: An apology for the more frequent administration of the Lord's supper. By John Brown ... Pittsburgh, Printed by D. and M. MacLean, 1826. (p. [267]–295) Anal.

1. Church polity. 2. Jesus Christ.

NT   0047477   CSmH OO OClWHi PPPrHi PHi

854T184 **Tassi, Alessandro.**
Oh   L'hvmilta trionfante del miracolosissimo S. Carlo Borromeo. Espressione divota per il giorno di sva festa. ₍Ode₎   Milano, Ramelati ₍17––₎
          15p. 23cm.

1. Carlo Borromeo, Saint, 1538-1584--Poetry.

NT   0047478   IU

Tassi, Antonio.
La cuestión del Pacífico, divulgación de antecedentes históricos, el Perú en la historia y en la guerra ₍conferencia₎ Buenos Aires, Imp. Tragant ₍pref. 1920₎
81 p.   18 cm.

1. Chile—Hist.—War with Peru, 1879–1882. 2. Tacna-Arica question.   I. Title.
F3097.T3   50–51774

NT   0047479   DLC NN ICU TxU MH

Tassi, Attilio. Sulla flora della provincia Senese e Maremma toscana. Siena. 1862. 8°. pp. 63. Plate.
"Estratto dalla Guida di Siena pubblicata in occasione del x. Congresso degli scienziati italiani."

NT   0047480   MH-A

Tassi, Auguste.
Guide du correcteur; or, Complement des grammaires & des lexiques... 10me ed... Paris, n. d.
124 p.

NT   0047481   PBm

F
244.7   **Tassi, Eleonora.**
T 213   Dal Rosaio Francescano. Padova, Messaggero di S. Antonio Basilica del Santo, 1941.
          159 p.

NT   0047482   WLagF

Tassi, Emidio.
——. Delle osteopatie epifisarie nella tenera età e dell' abuso delle loro resezioni. 22 pp. 8°.
Roma, M. Armanis, 1882.
Repr. from: Gazz. med. di Roma, 1882. viii.

NT   0047483   DNLM

Tassi, Emidio.
——. Sopra due forme di osteomielite infettiva, malarica e spontanea. 8 pp. 8°. Napoli, G. Jovene, 1884.
Repr. from: Riv. clin. e terap., Napoli, 1884, vi.

NT   0047484   DNLM

WE   **TASSI,** Emidio.
T213s   Studi di anatomia patologica e clinici sulle malattie delle ossa. Roma, Tip. romana, 1877.
1877   103 p. illus.
           Author's autograph presentation copy.

NT   0047485   DNLM

Adelmann
R   **Tassi,** Emilio.
111   Sulle resezioni sottoperiostali memorie.
M67   Roma, C. Bartoli, 1872.
           31 p. 23cm.

No. 15 in a vol. lettered: Miscellanea.

1. Periosteum. 2. Bones--Surgery.

NT   0047486   NIC DNLM

Tassi, Flaminio, ed.

Siena. *Università. Istituto botanico.*
... Bullettino del Laboratorio ed Orto botanico ...

Siena, 18

Tassi, Flamino.
Degli effetti anestesici del cloridrato di cocaina sui fiori di alcune piante.   Siena, 1885.
15 p.   8°.
"Estratto dal Bollettino della Soc. tra i cult. delle scienze med".

NT   0047488   MH-A

Tassi (Flaminio). Quadri statistici delle infermerie del manicomio di Siena nell' anno 1876, 1877, 1878. 6 l.; 14 pp.; 7 l. 4°. Siena, G. Bartellini, 1877–9.

NT   0047489   DNLM

Tassi, Flaminio.
——. 'Relazione sanitaria sui bambini poveri' scrofolosi di Siena inviati all' Ospizio marino di porto S. Stefano nell' estate del 1877. 31 pp. 8°. Siena, A. Mucci, 1878.

NT   0047490   DNLM

Tassi, Flaminio.
——. Rivista delle principali malattie accidentali osservate negli alienati. 58 pp., 1 l. 8°. Milano, frat. Rechiedei, 1878.
Repr. from: Arch. ital. per le mal. nerv., Milano, 1878, xv.

NT   0047491   DNLM

Tassi, Flaminio.
Sui movimenti delle foglie della *Salvia argentea* Linn. Con quadri grafici pel Dott. Flaminio Tassi. Siena, Tip. all' insegna dell' Ancora, 1885.
8 p. VIII fold. diagr. 31ᶜᵐ.
"Estratto dagli Atti della R. Accademia dei fisiocritici.—serie III.— volume IV."

1. Plants, Irritability and movements of. 2. Salvia argentea.
                                                        5–36035†
Library of Congress   QK791.T21

NT   0047492   DLC

Tassi, Francesco, ed.

Giamboni, Bono, *fl.* 1264.
Della miseria dell' uomo, Giardino di consolazione, Introduzione alle virtù, di Bono Giamboni; aggiuntavi, La scala dei claustrali, testi inediti, tranne il terzo trattato, pub. ed illustrati con note dal dottor Francesco Tassi. Firenze, G. Piatti, 1836.

Tassi, Francesco, ed.

Orosius, Paulus.
Delle storie contra i pagani di Paolo Orosio libri VII; volgarizzamento di Bono Giamboni; pubblicato ed illustrato con note dal dott. Francesco Tassi. Firenze, T. Baracchi, 1849.

Tassi, Francesco Maria, conte, 1710-1782, ed.
Girone il cortese, romanzo cavalleresco di Rustico o Rusticiano da Pisa
see under [Guiron le Courtois]

N
6921   **Tassi, Francesco Maria,** *conte,* 1710–1782.
.B48   Vite de' pittori, scultori e architetti bergamaschi, scritte dal conte cavalier Francesco Maria Tassi. Opera postuma ... Bergamo, Dalla Stamperia Locatelli, 1793.
T22
           2 v. front. (port.) 26 x 20½ᶜᵐ.
           Includes additions by Girolamo and Carlo Marenzi. *cf.* v. 1, p. XXVI– XXVII.
           "Trattato scientifico di fortificazione sopra la storia particolare di Bergamo; opera postuma del nobile signor Ferdinando Caccia": v. 2, p. ₍159₎–283.

           1. Artists, Italian—Bergamo.   I. Marenzi, Girolamo. II. Marenzi, Carlo. III. Caccia, Ferdinando, 1689–1778. IV. Title.
                                                        43–47203
           Library of Congress

NT   0047496   DLC MiDA ICU CtY CU MiU

1927   **Tassi, Francesco Maria,** conte, 1710–1782
T184v   **Vite de'pittori, scultori e architetti bergamaschi.**   Bergamo, 1797.
2v. front.(port.)

NT   0047497   IU MB

Tassi, Francesco, ed.   FOR OTHER EDITIONS
                            SEE MAIN ENTRY
Cellini, Benvenuto, 1500–1571.
Vita di Benvenuto Cellini, orefice e scultore fiorentino, scritta da lui medesimo, restituita alla lezione originale sul manoscritto Poirot ora Laurenziano ed arricchita d'illustrazioni e documenti inediti dal dottor Francesco Tassi ... Firenze, Presso G. Piatti, 1829.

Tassi, Hercole
    see   Tasso, Ercole, 16th cent.

Tassi, Ildefonso, 1914–
Ludovico Barbo (1381–1443)   Roma, Storia e letteratura, 1952.
xvi, 179 p.   26 cm.   (Uomini e dottrine, 1)
Bibliographical footnotes.

1. Barbo, Ludovico, Bp., 1382–1443.   2. Benedictines.   Congregazione di S. Giustina.   ₍2. Benedictines.   Congregations.   S. Giustina₎
                                     A 53–5780
Catholic Univ. of   America.   Library
for Library of Congress   ₍2₎

NT   0047500   DCU DGU ICU CtY-D DLC NN InStme KAS

Tassi, Jan Baptist de
    see   Taxis, Johann Baptista de, 1530–1610.

Tassi, Lorenzo.
Tavole sinottiche della lingua francese... Piacenza, 1870.

NT   0047502   PPL

Tassi, Lorenzo.
Vocabolario della lingua Italiana con relazioni di sinonimi e figure rettoriche ₍compilato sui dizionarii del Tramater e del Trinchera₎ sul dizionario etimologico dell' Abate Marchi e sul prontuario del Carena per opera del Lorenzo Tassi. Milano, Francesco Pagnoni, 1866.

xxxvii, 124 p.   14 cm.
1. Italian lagnuage – Dictionaries. I. Marchi, Mar
∾ Aurelio. II Title.

NT   0047503   PLatS

Tassi, Luigi.
Guida per l'ispezione delle carni.   Presentazione del prof. Nai.   2. ed. riv. e aggiornata.   Milano, Istituto editoriale cisalpino ₍1955₎
331 p.   21 cm.
"Contiene in ordine alfabetico per ogni malattia o lesione la linea di condotta consigliata per la destinazione delle carni, nonchè le voci della parte generale e legislativa sulla vigilanza sanitaria delle stesse. Annesso il Regolamento 20 Dicembre 1928 no. 3298."
Errata leaf inserted.

1. Meat inspection—Italy.   I. Title.
                                   A 56–4605
Iowa.   State Coll.   Libr.
for Library of Congress   ₍3₎

NT   0047504   IaAS

Tassi, Luigi, O.F.M.
    see   Luigi Tassi da Fabriano, Father, 1832

Tassi, Luigi, 1832 –
    see   Luigi Tassi da Fabriano, Father, 1832-

Tassi, Niccolò.
L'amore soldato.

For a musico-dramatic work based on this see Sacchini, Antonio Maria Gasparo, 1730–1786.   L'amore soldato.

M1500
.C128A5   **Tassi, Niccolò.**   L'amor soldato.
Case   **Calegari, Luigi Antonio,** 1780 (ca.)–1849.
    ₍L'amor soldato.   Italian₎
    L'amor soldato ₍di₎ Calegari.   ₍181–?₎

W 1
AR595   **TASSI, Umberto.**
v. 34   Alterazioni della laringe in seguito a
1923   lesione dei nervi laringei, ricerche
          sperimentali.   Napoli, La Nuovissima, 1923.
          159 p.   illus.   ₍Naples.   Università. Clinica otorinolaringologica.   Pubblicazioni, v. 5₎
          Issued as supplement to Archivio italiano di otologia, rinologia e laringologia, v. 34, 1923, and bound with that volume.

NT   0047509   DNLM

Tassie, James, 1735–1799.
Account of the present state and arrangement of Mr. James Tassie's collection
    see under   Rapse, Rudolf, Erich,
1737–1799. [supplement]

Tassie, James, 1735–1799.
A catalogue of impressions in sulphur, of antique and modern gems, from which pastes are made and sold, by J. Tassie ...   London, Printed for I. Murray, 1775.
1 p. l., v–vii p., 1 l., 99 p.   20¼ᶜᵐ.
Engr. t.-p., with vignette.

1. Gems—Catalogs.
                                 12–11901
Library of Congress   NK5520.T25

NT   0047511   DLC PMA NN

Tassie, William.
Descriptive catalogue of a collection of devices and mottos English, French, and Italian, from engraved seals, formed in composition paste and sold by William Tassie...   London, Printed by William Bulmer and Co., 1816.
4 p.l., 43 p.   18 cm.

NT   0047512   MH CJ RPB

Tassie, James, 1735–1799.

Raspe, Rudolf Erich, 1737–1794.
A descriptive catalogue of a general collection of ancient and modern engraved gems, cameos as well as intaglios, taken from the most celebrated cabinets in Europe; and cast in coloured pastes, white enamel, and sulphur, by James Tassie ... arranged and described by R. E. Raspe; and illustrated with copper-plates. To which is prefixed, an introduction on the various uses of this collection, the origin of the art of engraving on hard stones, and the progress of pastes ... London, J. Tassie ₍etc.₎ 1791.

Tassie, William.
Descriptive catalogue of devices & mottos, in various languages, parts I & 2.   London, J. Barfield, 1820.
48–76 p.

NT   0047514   PPF NN

Tassier, Suzanne.
La Belgique et l'entrée en guerre des États-Unis, 1914–1917.   Bruxelles, Renaissance du livre ₍1951₎
171 p.   illus.   19 cm.   ("Notre passé," 6. sér., ₍6₎)

1. European War, 1914–1918—Belgium.   2. European War, 1914–1918—Public opinion.   I. Title.

D615.T3   55–58580 ‡

   ViU OCU OrU
NT   0047515   DLC IU DS OCl MiU NN UU ICU CSt-H ICN

Tassier, Susanne.
Collection "Notre passé"
    see under title

Tassier, Suzanne.
... Les démocrates belges de 1789; étude sur le vonckisme et la révolution brabançonne ...   Bruxelles, M. Lamertin, 1930.
479 p.   pl., 2 port. (incl. front.)   25¼ᵐ.
"Mémoire couronné par l'Académie royale de Belgique."
Issued also in series Académie royale de Belgique.   Classe des lettres et des sciences morales et politiques.   Mémoires.   Collection in-8° ₍2. sér.₎ t. XXIII, fasc. 2.
"Principaux documents et travaux consultés": p. ₍449₎–457.

1. Belgium—Hist.—Revolution, 1789–1790.   2. Vonckists.   3. Brabant—Hist.   I. Title.

Library of Congress   DH618.T3   40–20049
                                         949.3

NT   0047517   DLC WaU MiU

Tassier, Suzanne.
Les démocrates belges de 1789.   Étude sur le Vonckisme et la révolution brabançonne, par Suzanne Tassier ... ₍Bruxelles, M. Lamertin, 1930₎
479 p.   front., pl., port.   25¼ᶜᵐ.   (On cover: Académie royale de Belgique.   Classe des lettres et des sciences morales et politiques.   Mémoires.   Collection in-8° ₍2. sér.₎ t. XXVIII, fasc. 2)
"Mémoire couronné le 8 avril 1929."
"Principaux documents et travaux consultés": p. ₍449₎–457.

1. Belgium—History—Revolution, 1789–1790.   2. Vonck, Jean François, 1743?–1792.   I. Title.   A C 33–2937
Title from Yale Univ.
Library of Congress   ₍A8242.B325   vol. 28, pt. 2₎

NT   0047518   CtY PPAmP PBm PU NcD MH ICN OrU OCl NN

Tassier, Suzanne.
Figures révolutionnaires, XVIIIe siècle.   Bruxelles, Renaissance du livre ₍1942₎
113 p.   ports.   19 cm.   (Collection "Notre passé," 1. sér., v. 6)

1. Revolutionists.   2. Belgium—Biog.   I. Title.

DH613.A1T3   949.3   50–20265 rev

NT   0047519   DLC IU NcD CSt CtY NN NcU WU ViU

DH   **Tassier, Suzanne.**
613   Figures révolutionnaires, XVIIIe siècle.
A1   ₍2. éd.₎ Bruxelles, Renaissance du livre
T3   ₍c1954₎
1954   111 p.   ports.   19 cm.   (Collection "Notre passé,")

     1. Revolutionists.   2. Belgium – Biog.   I. Title.

NT   0047520   CU-S OrU

Tassier, Suzanne.

Z733   ...Un grand centre historique américain: la
L5H7T21 Hoover library... Bruxelles, Imprimerie médicale et scientifique (soc.an.) 1940.
cover-title, p. [68]-80. il. 24½^{cm}.
"Extrait de la Revue de l'Université de
Bruxelles, n°s 1 et 2, octobre-novembre-décembre
1939-janvier 1940.".

1. Leland Stanford junior university. Hoover
library on war,   revolution and peace.
I. Title.

NT   0047521   CSt-H NNC

Tassier, Suzanne.
... Histoire de la Belgique sous l'occupation française en
1792 et 1793. Bruxelles, Falk fils, G. van Campenhout, succ^r,
1934.
382 p. 25½^{cm}.
"Cet ouvrage présenté à l'Université de Bruxelles, a valu à l'auteur
le grade d'agrégé de l'enseignement supérieur."
"Principaux documents et travaux consultés": p. [343]-361.

1. Belgium—Hist.—1648-1794.
                              35-10240
Library of Congress   DH619.T35
                             [2]   949.3

NT   0047522   DLC WaU FTaSU CSt OU VtU NjP MiU ICU

Tassier, Suzanne.
... L'histoire de la guerre mondiale, pour un Musée de la
guerre mondiale et un Office de documentation contemporaine
... Bruxelles, Office de publicité, s. c., 1944.
1 p. l., 70 p., 1 l. front. 18¼^{cm}. (Actualités sociales. Nouv. sér. [3])
At head of title: Université libre de Bruxelles. Institut de sociologie
Solvay.
Bibliographical foot-notes.
1. European war, 1914-1918—Museums. 2. Vincennes, France. Bibliothèque de documentation internationale contemporaine et musée de la
grande guerre. 3. Stanford university. Library. Hoover library on
war, revolution and peace.

D503.T3   A F 47-4985
Illinois. Univ. Library
for Library of Congress   [2]†

NT   0047523   IU TxU NcD NN CSt DLC

Tassier, Suzanne.
... Idées et profils du xviiie siècle ...   Bruxelles, Office de
publicité, 1944.
77, [1] p. port. 18¼^{cm}. (Collection nationale. 5. sér., n° 52)

1. Belgium—Hist.—18th cent. 2. Belgium—Intellectual life.
) DH612.T3   A F 47-4732
Stanford univ. Library
for Library of Congress   [2]†

NT   0047524   CSt ICU NN DLC

Tassigny, Bernard de Lattre de
   see Lattre de Tassigny, Bernard de, 1928-1951.

Tassigny, Guy.
Le jour de la colère. Paris, OCIA éditions [1951]
216 p. 19 cm.

1. Judgment Day. I. Title.
BT881.T25   236.9   51-31296

NT   0047526   DLC

Tassigny, Guy.
... Les merdophages. [Paris] OCIA [1946]
223 p., 1 l. 19^{cm}.

I. Title.
PQ2639.A76M4   47-21550

NT   0047527   DLC

Tassigny, Guy.
... Le paquebot des jours perdus (dans les griffes de la Ge-
stapo) [Paris, OCIA, 1945]
298 p., 1 l. 18¼^{cm}.

1. World war, 1939-1945—Prisoners and prisons, German. 2. World
war, 1939-1945—Personal narratives, French. I. Title.
                            46-21880
Library of Congress   D805.G3T3
                         [2]   940.547243

NT   0047528   DLC CSt NN IU NcD CtY

Tassigny (Jean) [1888-]. *Traitement
abortif de l'amygdalite phlegmoneuse par les
injections intraveineuses de collargol. 39 pp.
8°. Paris. 1920. No. 11.

NT   0047529   DNLM CtY

Tassigny, Jean Joseph Marie Gabriel de Lattre de
   see Lattre de Tassigny, Jean Joseph Marie Gabriel de,
1889-1952.

Tassigny (Paul) [1874-]. *Contribution
à l'étude clinique des amyotrophies paraly-
tiques de cause articulaire. 80 pp. 8°. *Paris,*
1900, No. 545.
  ——. The same. 58 pp., 1 l. 8°. *Paris, G.
Steinheil,* 1900.

NT   0047531   DNLM

TASSILLY, Eugène, 1867-
L'atmosphere terrestre. Paris,1899.

NT   0047532   MH-C DNLM DAS

Tassilly, Eugène, 1867-
Caoutchouc et gutta-percha, par E. Tassilly ... avec 56
figures dans le texte. Paris, O. Doin et fils, 1911.
xviii, 395 p. illus. 19¼^{cm}. (*Half-title:* Encyclopédie scientifique, pub.
sous la direction du Dr Toulouse ... Bibliothèque des industries chimiques,
directeur: Juvénal Derôme)
"Index bibliographique": p. [381]-386.

1. India-rubber. 2. Gutta-percha.
                              11-6045
Library of Congress   TS1890.T2

NT   0047533   DLC MH-A ICJ MB NN OAkU

Tassilly, Eugène, 1867-
Étude des propriétés physiques des alliages métalli-
ques, par E. Tassilly ...   Paris, A. Joanin et c^{ie}, 1904.
2 p. l., 200 p., 1 l. illus., diagrs. 25^{cm}.
"Bibliographie": p. [199]-200.

1. Alloys. 2. Metallography.
                              5-19392
Library of Congress   TA490.T21

NT   0047534   DLC DNLM ICJ

Tassilly (Eugène) [1867-]. *Sur le dosage
de la caffeïne. 56 pp. 4°. *Paris,* 1897, No. 2.
  École de pharmacie.

NT   0047535   DNLM

Tassilly, Eugene, 1867-
Use of cold in the pharmaceutic products industry.   (In:
International Congress of Refrigeration, II. Vienna, 1910. Reports and proceedings. English edition. Vienna, 1911. 4°.
p. 745-749.)

1. Pharmacy.
N. Y. P. L.   October 14, 1912.

NT   0047536   NN

Tassilo
   see under [Boguslawski, Karl Andreas von]
1759-1817.

Tassin,
Plan d'un ouvrage à présenter aux États-
généraux. Par M. Tassin, secrétaire de
l'Assemblée du département de Bar-sur-Aube.
[1789?]
16 p. 20cm. in 22cm.

Date from manuscript note on title-page.
Volume of pamphlets.

NT   0047538   NNC

Tassin, A. Why our glasses don't fit. p.203-7.
[8°. [n. p., 191?]

NT   0047539   DNLM

Tassin (Albert). *Des lésions infectieuses du
rein (d'ordre chirurgical). Diagnostic différentiel. [Paris.] 68 pp. 8°. *Dijon,* 1906, No. 134.

NT   0047540   DNLM

Tassin, Algernon de Viver, 1869-
Baccalaureate hymn.
(In Harvard college - Class of 1892.
Baccalaureate sermon [etc.] Cambridge, Mass.,
1892. 23 cm. p. [13])

NT   0047541   RPB

Tassin, Algernon de Vivier, 1869-
A child's story of American literature, by Algernon Tassin
and Arthur Bartlett Maurice; with decorations by Maurice
Day and others. New York, The Macmillan company, 1923.
viii p., 1 l., 353 p. front., illus., ports. 20^{cm}.

1. American literature—Hist. & crit. I. Maurice, Arthur Bartlett,
1873- joint author. II. Title.
                              23-15293
Library of Congress   PS96.T3

           OLak OEac OC1 NN WaSp
NT   0047542   DLC PP PWcS DHEW DAU WaS Or OrP OC1h MB

Amer Lit   Tassin, Algernon de Vivier, 1869-
810   A class-day conspiracy; a comedy
T213   in one act, by Algernon Tassin.
tC   As originally performed at the Grand
Opera House, Boston, Mass. June 6th,
1894. Boston, W.H.Baker, [c1895]
18p. diagrs. 19cm. (On cover:
Baker's edition of plays)

NT   0047543   CLSU MH PU NN OC1 RPB

Tassin, Algernon de Vivier, 1669-
　　The craft of the tortoise; a play in four acts, by Algernon Tassin. New York, Boni & Liveright, 1919.
　　xxviii p., 3 l., 3-157 p.　19½ᶜᵐ.

　　1. Title.
　　Library of Congress　　　　PS3539.A73C7 1919
　　　　　　　　　　　　　　　　　　　19—18735

NT　0047544　　DLC PP PU OU WaS WaSpG NN MB OC1

Tassin, Algernon de Vivier, 1869-
　　The craft of the tortoise; a play in four acts, by Algernon Tassin. N.Y. Duffield, 1921.
　　157 p.

NT　0047545　　OEac CSt ViU RPB

Tassin, Algernon de Vivier, 1869-　　　　4596.159
　　Julius Caesar.
　　(In Matthews, J. B., and A. H. Thorndike, editors. Shaksperian studies. Pp. 253-287. New York. 1916.)

K0480 — Shakespeare, William. Julius Caesar.

NT　0047546　　MB

Tassin, Algernon de Vivier, 1869-
　　The magazine in America. ₍Parts 1-10₎
1v.
　　Articles extracted from the Bookman.

NT　0047547　　ICRL

Tassin, Algernon de Viver, 1869-
　　The magazine in America, by Algernon Tassin... New York, Dodd [c1915]
　　374 p.

NT　0047548　　NcRS OC1RC OCB

Tassin, Algernon de Vivier, 1867-
　　The magazine in America, by Algernon Tassin ... New York, Dodd, Mead and company, 1916.
　　5 p. l., 374 p. front.　21½ᶜᵐ.　$2.00
　　"These papers, for the most part published in the Bookman, present an informal history of the magazine movement in the United States, from its beginning down to the close of the nineteenth century."—Pref.

　　1. American periodicals—Hist.　1. Title.
　　Library of Congress　　　PN4877.T3
　　　　　　　　　　　　　　　　　16—13360

　　IdB
　　CU-I TU OrMonO WaSp WaWW NjP ICJ NN MB MWA OrP IdU
　　OFH OOxM OEac MiU OCU OC1 ViU OO PPLas PPT PU KEmT
NT　0047549　　DLC WaT Or PRosC WaS MtU WaTU NcD MB OU

＊
PS1918
.A633　Tassin, Algernon de Vivier, 1869-
1911
　　Miss Bisland's "The Japanese letters of Lafcadio Hearn" ₍book review₎
　　(In The Bookman. New York. 25½cm. v. XXXII. no. 5 (Jan. 1911) p. 491-493)

　　1. Hearn, Lafcadio, 1850-1904. 2. Wetmore, Elizabeth (Bisland) 1861-1929—The Japanese letters of Lafcadio Hearn.

NT　0047550　　ViU

Tassin, Algernon de Vivier, 1869-
　　The oral study of literature, by Algernon Tassin ... New York, A. A. Knopf, 1923.
　　5 p. l., 431 p.　19¼ᶜᵐ.

　　1. English literature—Study and teaching. 2. English literature (Collections)　I. Title.
　　Library of Congress　　　PR33.T3
　　　　　　　　　　　　　　　　　23—8894

　　OC1
NT　0047551　　DLC OC1W OkU KEmT UU NcU OC1Ur OC1U NN

PR
33
T3　　Tassin, Algernon de Viver, 1869-
1925　　　The oral study of literature. 2d ed., rev. and enl. New York, Knopf ₍c1925₎
　　　473 p.

　　1. English literature - Collections and selections. 2. English literature - Study and teaching. I. Title.

NT　0047552　　WaU OO

Tassin, Algernon de Vivier, 1869-　　820.8-T
　　The oral study of literature.　New York: Alfred A. Knopf, 1929.　483 p.　3. ed., rev. and expanded.　12°.

　　1. Title. 2. English literature—Collections and selections.
　　N.Y.P.L.　　　　　　　　　　　January 6, 1931

NT　0047553　　NN MiU

PR
33
T21　　Tassin, Algernon de Vivier, 1869-
1930　　　The oral study of literature. 4th ed., rev. and expanded.　New York, F. S. Crofts, 1930.
　　　483 p.　19cm.

　　1. English literature—Study and teaching.
　　2. English literature (Collections)
　　I. Title.

NT　0047554　　NIC PPWe OO NNC ODW

Tassin, Algernon de Vivier, 1869-
　　The oral study of literature, by Algernon Tassin ...　5th ed., rev. and expanded.　New York, F. S. Crofts & co., 1939.
　　6 p. l., 497 p.　19¼ᶜᵐ.

　　1. English literature—Study and teaching. 2. English literature (Collections)　I. Title.
　　Library of Congress　　　PR33.T3 1939
　　　　　　　　　　　　　　　　　39—17767
　　―――― Copy 2.
　　Copyright A 131282　　₍3₎　　　　　808

NT　0047555　　DLC NcGU NcU OrU OrStbM NNC ViU

808.8　Tassin, Algernon de Vivier, 1869-
T185o5　　The oral study of literature, by Algernon Tassin ... 5th ed., rev. and expanded.　New York, F. S. Crofts & co., 1941₍°1939₎
　　6 p. l., 497 p.　19¼ᶜᵐ.

NT　0047556　　LU

Tassin, Algernon de Vivier, 1869-
　　The rainbow string, by Algernon Tassin, illustrated by Anna Richards Brewster.　New York, The Macmillan company, 1921.
　　6 p. l., 114 p. incl. illus., plates. col. front. 19ᶜᵐ.
　　Illustrated lining-papers.

　　1. Title.
　　Library of Congress　　　PZ8.T185Ra
　　　　　　　　　　　　　　　　　21—19155

NT　0047557　　DLC OKentU PBa WaS WaSp NN MB OC1h

Tassin, Algernon ₍de Vivier₎, 1869-　　　J-T
　　The rainbow string; illustrated by Anna Richards Brewster. New York: The Macmillan Co., 1929.　114 p.　col'd front., illus.　₍new ed.₎　8°.

　　1. Fairy tales. 2. Title.
　　N.Y.P.L.　　　　　　　　　October 21, 1929

NT　0047558　　NN

Tassin, Algernon de Vivier, 1869-
　　Rust; a play in four acts, by Algernon Tassin. New York, Broadway publishing co. ₍1911₎
　　172 (i. e. 166) p. 20ᶜᵐ.

　　1. Title.
　　　　　　　　　　　　11—11668 Revised
　　Library of Congress　　　PS3539.A73R8 1911

NT　0047559　　DLC PU PHC WaU MU OU ViU OC1 MiU NN

Tassin, Algernon de Vivier, 1869-
　　Story of American literature, by Algernon Tassin and Arthur Bartlett Maurice; with decorations by Maurice Day and others.　New York, The Macmillan company, 1927.
　　viii p., 1 l., 353 p. front., illus., ports. 20ᶜᵐ.
　　Published 1923 under title: A child's story of American literature.

　　1. American literature—Hist. & crit.　1. Maurice, Arthur Bartlett, 1873-　joint author. II. Title. III. Title: A child's story of American literature.
　　Providence.　Public library　　　　　A 27—272
　　　for Library of Congress　　　₍PS96.T

NT　0047560　　DLC RP PPT PP PU ViU MH OC1h OC1

Tassin, Algernon de Vivier, 1869-
　　McKay, Frederic Edward, ed.
　　Vignettes : real and ideal; stories by American authors, ed. by Frederic Edward McKay. Boston, De Wolfe, Fiske & co. ₍1890₎

TASSIN, Algernon de Vivier, 1869-
　　Voices. n.p., n. d.

NT　0047562　　MH

DG
738.14　Tassin, Charles.
G53T3　　Giannoti, sa vie, son temps et ses doctrines; étude sur un publiciste florentin du XVI° siècle.　Paris, C. Douniol, 1869.
　　387p. 23cm.

　　1. Giannotti, Donato, 1492-1573.

NT　0047563　　MU ICN

Tassin, Charles. Le Marquis d'Argenson.
28 pp.　(Correspondant, n. s. v. 97, 1883, p. 332.)

NT　0047564　　MdBP

Tassin (Édouard). * De l'hérédité physiologique et pathologique. 42 pp.　4°. Paris, 1863, No. 164.

NT　0047565　　DNLM

Tassin, Eugène, *joint author.*
[Denayrouze, Louis] 1848–1910.
... La revanche fantastique. Paris, E. Dentu, 1873.

TASSIN, J. B. Chart of Choo-Keang or Canton River and the different passages leading to Macao roads. Calcutta, 1840. 79 x 104 cm. Folded in l.8° covers.
"Drawn from Hosburgh's chart of the Canton River combined with Daniell Ross & Philip Maughan's chart of the different passages leading to Macao Roads."

NT   0047567   MSaE

Tassin, J. B.
—— Chart of the coasts of China. Calcutta [1840?] 74 x 120 cm. Folded in 4° covers.
"Drawn and lithographed from Hosburgh's charts of the eastern coast of China and of the eastern passages to China."

NT   0047568   MSaE

RARE BOOK DEPT.
XfE   Tassin, J   B
.835   Maps of the rivers Hoogly, Bhagruttee, Jellin-
.T18M   ghee, Ganges, and Jumna, from Calcutta to the Himalaya range, compiled from the most accurate surveys: by J.B. Tassin[n]
[Calcutta?] 1835. Price 16 Rs.

cover-title,1f.,col.table,vii fold.col.maps. 25x34cm.(obl.fol.)
Three-quarters green morocco, pale green linen boards; printed paper label on front cover.

Imperfect: paper label on cover slightly mutilated.
Ex libris: Horatio Brooks, Brig Nabob, Capt. G.W. Putnam, 1835 (inscription); Daniel Webster (bookplate)

NT   0047570   MB

TASSIN, L. F.
Rapport sur les dunes du golfe de Gascogne.
Mont-de-Marsan. Delaroy jeune. 1ᵉ année [1792.] 54 pp.

NT   0047571   MB

WZ   TASSIN, Léonard, d. 1687
250   Les administrations anatomiques ...
T213a   Sedan, François Chayer, 1676.
1676   [6], 226 p. 17 cm.
"Myologie": p. 137–226.
Published in Paris in 1678 and later under title: Les administrations anatomiques et la myologie.

NT   0047572   DNLM

QM   Tassin, Léonard, d. 1687.
151   Les administrations anatomiques, et la
T21   myologie ... À Paris, Chez Michel Vaugon, 1678.
314 p. 15cm.

1. Muscles. 2. Anatomy, Human——Early works to 1800. 3. Dissection.

NT   0047573   NIC

WZ   TASSIN, Léonard, d. 1687
250   Les administrations anatomiques, et
T213a   la myologie ... 3. ed. Paris, Michel
1688   Vaugon, 1688.
[8], 314 (i. e. 304) p. 16 cm.
Previously issued by the same press in 1678.
With this is bound the author's La chirurgie militaire. Paris, 1688.

NT   0047574   DNLM

WZ   TASSIN, Léonard, d. 1687
250   Les administrations anatomiques, et la
T213a   myologie ... Derniere ed. Lyon, La
1696   Veuve de Jean-Bapt. Guillimin, 1696.
[8], 304 p. 16 cm.
Reprint (page for page, except for the preliminary matter) of the 3d ed. published in Paris in 1688.
With this is bound the author's La chirurgie militaire, Lyon, 1696, which was issued with it.

NT   0047575   DNLM

WZ   TASSIN, Léonard, d. 1687
260   De behandeling van de ontleedkonst,
T213aDu   benevens de verhandeling der spieren in 't
1732   generaal en in 't byzonder ... Uit het Fransch in 't Nederduitsch vertaalt, door Pieter Samson ... Amsterdam, By de Erven van J. Ratelband, en Compagnie, 1732.
[14], 260p. front. 16 cm.
Translation of Administrations anatomiques.

With this is bound: Saint-Yves, Charles de. Nieuwe verhandeling over de ziektens der oogen. Leyden, 1739.
I. Samson, Pieter. tr.

NT   0047577   DNLM

WZ   TASSIN, Léonard, d. 1687
250   La chirurgie militaire; ou, L'art de
T213a   guarir les playes d'arquebusades ...
1688   Paris, Michel Vaugon, 1688.
57 p. 16 cm.
Previously published in Nijmegen in 1673.
Bound with the author's Les administrations anatomiques. Paris, 1688.

NT   0047578   DNLM ICJ

WZ   TASSIN, Léonard, d. 1687
250   La chirurgie militaire; ou, L'art de
T213a   guerir les playes d'arquebusades ...
1696   Lyon, La Veuve de Jean-Bapt. Guillimin 1696.
57, [1] p. 16 cm.
Page-for-page reprint of the edition published in Paris in 1688.
Bound with the author's Les administrations anatomiques, Lyon, 1696, with which it was issued.

NT   0047579   DNLM

Tassin, Léonard, d.1687.
17th cent.   Kurtze Kriegs-Wund-Artzney, oder die Kunst, Schuss-und Kugel-Wunden zu heylen ... Nürnberg, J. D. Tauber, 1676.
32p. plates. 16cm. [With ADERLASS-BÜCHLEIN Nürnberg, 1665]
Includes a chapter on gangrene.

1. Surgery, Military. 2. Gunshot wounds.
3. Gangrene.

NT   0047580   CtY-M

Tassin, Louis, 1894–
... Remarques sur la pathogénie et le traitement de l'érythromélalgie... Lyon, 1922.
25 cm.
Thèse – Univ. de Lyon.

NT   0047581   CtY

Tassin, Louis-Alphonse.
*Dissertation sur l'hygiène des femmes enceintes. Paris, 1835.
22 p. 4°. [No. 93, v. 284]

NT   0047582   DNLM

Tassin (Marie-Jules-Maurice) [1894–   ]. *Les épanchements pleuraux au cours du pneumothorax thérapeutique. 83 pp. 8°. Paris, 1923. No. 388.

NT   0047583   DNLM CtY

Tassin, Marie Tassin de
see
Tassin de Tassin, Marie, 1889–

Tassin, Mrs. Miriam T., *joint tr.*

France. *Direction générale des douanes.*
... The import and export schedule of France ... Washington, Govt. print. off., 1920.

Tassin (N.) *Sur l'asthme.* 1 p. l., 24 pp. 4°. *Strasbourg, 1827, v. 56.*

NT   0047586   DNLM

Tassin, N. [pseud.]
see Tasin, Nicolas.

G1315   TASSIN, NICOLAS.
1655   Carte generale de la geographie royalle, par le sr.
Rare bk   Tasin, geographe dv Roy. Paris, Chez N. Berey, 1655.
room   [1],40,[3]p. 84 maps, diagrs. 18x24cm.
Title within scroll border in colors; maps of the provinces of France and Spain preceded by special t.-p.

1. Atlases.

NT   0047588   ICU

GA   Tassin, Nicolas.
864   Cartes generalles de toutes les prouinces de
.1633   France et d'Espaigne, reüeues et corrigées, par
T22   S.ᴿ T., geographe ordinaire du Roy. [Paris?]
1633.
[2] l., 68 maps. 15 x 20 cm.
Imperfect: lacks map 1.
Error in binding: map 44 bound upside down.

1. France——Maps. 2. Spain——Maps.

NT   0047589   MiU

Tassin, Nicolas.
Les cartes générales de tovtes les prouinces de France, royaumes et prouinces de l'Europe. Reueües corrigées & augmentées ...
1640. 1 p. l., 100 maps, pl. fol. [Paris, N. Berey, 1640–1643]
4023
NOTE.—Engraved title-page and plate. Double page plate follows t. p.; the center figure is an equestrian statue of Louis XIII, beneath which his courtiers are represented as homagers. Near the lower right hand corner is the following: N. Picart fecit. A Paris, chez N. Berey au bout du neuf proche les Augustins, avec priuilège du roy. Imprint date is 1640; maps are dated 1625–1643

NT   0047590   DLC

Ex   Tassin, Nicolas.
1561
.895   Description de tovs les cantons, villes, bovrgs, villages, et avtres particvlaritez dv pays des Svisses, auec vne brieue forme de leur republique... À Paris, Chez M. Vanlochom, 1635.
63 p. plates, fold. map. 18½ x 23½ cm.
Plates preceded by special half-title with author's name, Sr. Tassin.
Title and text in French and Latin.

NT   0047591   NjP DLC

Beinecke Library 1973 +68 2
Tassin, Nicolas.
Description de tovs les cantons, villes, bovrgs, villages, et avtres particvlaritez dv pays des Svisses, auec vne brieue forme de leur Republique. Descriptio cantonvm, vrbivm, pagorum, & aliorum memorabilium quae in Heluetia reperiuntur: unâ cum breui forma rei Heluetiorum Publicae. A Paris, Chez Sebastien Cramoisy, Imprimeur ordinaire du Roy, ruë sainct Iacques, aux Cicognes, 1639.
63, [1] p. 1 plate, 35 maps. 19 x 25 cm.

Bound with v.2 of his Les plans et profils de tovtes les principales villes ... de France ... A Paris, 1638.
Signatures: A-H⁴

1. Switzerland - Maps. 2. Cities and towns - Switzerland. I. Title (1)

NT 0047593 CtY

GA 862 T3 1631 Cage
Tassin, Nicolas.
... Les plans et profilz de toutes les principalles villes et lieux considerables de France, ensemble les cartes generalles de chascune prouince et les particuliéres de chasque gouuernement d'icelles ... [n.p., 1631?]

2 v. V.1: 39 [1] p. A^5, B-E^4. 216 plates; v.2: [4] 3-44 p. A^5, B-E^4, F^2. 228 plates. (V.1 & 2: original A1 cancelled by 2 conjugate leaves; v.1: plates 51 & 52 of "Champagne"

lacking; v.2: A1 & 2 misbound after F2, title-page and table of contents to "Bourgogne" bound in their place; plates 2 & 3 of "Oranges" misbound after plate 25 of "Languedoc".)
Plates include a title-page and a table of contents leaf to each province.
Earl of Ilchester copy.

NT 0047595 DFo

DC14 .T23 Rare bk
Tassin, Nicolas.
Les plans et profils de toutes les principales villes et lieux considérables de France; ensemble les cartes générales de chacune province: et les particulières de chaque gouvernement d'icelle. Paris, 1634.
2 v. in 1. plates, maps, plans. 16x21cm.
Imperfect: t.-p. wanting, title supplied from Brit. Mus. Cat.; mutilated copy.

1. France--Descr. & trav.--Maps. 2. Cities and towns--France.

NT 0047596 ICU DLC MnU MH MdBP

Tassin, Nicolas.
Les plans et profils de tovtes les principales villes et lievx considérables de France; enfemble les cartes générales de chacune prouince: & les particulières de chaque gouuernement d'icelle . . . 2 v. obl. 8°. Paris, I. Messager, 1636. 2949
Note.—Collation: v. 1, 39 pp., [15] l., 156 maps, 48 p. l.; v. 2, 44 pp., [20] l., 181 maps, 31 pl.
Engraved title-page to v. 1, wanting.
Maps, views and titles of 1634 edition, with the following additions:
v. 1. Lorraine. no. 26. Govvernement de La Motte.
" " " " 27. La Motte.
" 2. Beavlce. " 1. Govvernement de Bourges.
" " " " 2. Bovrges.

NT 0047597 DLC

DC 14 .T22 1638
Tassin, Nicolas.
Les plans et profils de tovtes les principales villes et lievx considérables de France. Ensemble les cartes générales de chacune prouince: & les particulières de chaque gouuernement d'icelles. Par le sieur Tassin ... Paris, S.Cramoisy, 1638.
2 v.in 1. plates,maps,plans (1 fold.) 18 x 24½cm.
Armorial book-plate: Henry Barrett Lenard.

1.France--Maps. 2.Cities and towns--France.

NT 0047598 MiU NjP PP CtY DLC CU PMA

Tassin, René Prosper, O.S.B., 1697-1777.
Gelehrtengeschichte der Congregation von St. Maur, Benedictiner Ordens, worinnen man das Leben und die Arbeiten der Schriftsteller antrift, die seit ihrem Ursprung von 1618, bis auf gegenwärtige Zeit hervor gebracht... Aus dem französischen ins teutsche übersetzt. Frankfurt, August Lebrecht Stettin, 1773.

2v. 20cm.

NT 0047599 PLatS PPLT

Z 7840 .B3 T3 1773
Tassin, René Prosper, 1697-1777.
Dom Renatus Prosper Tassins ... Gelehrtengeschichte der Congregation von St. Maur, Benedictiner Ordens, worinnen man das Leben und die Arbeiten der Schriftsteller antrift, die sie seit ihrem Ursprung von 1618 bis auf gegenwärtige Zeit hervor gebracht: nebst den Aufschriften, der Anzeigen, dem Inhalt, den verschiedenen Ausgaben ihrer Schriften, und den Urtheilen, welche die Gelehrten darüber gefället: [s]amt der Beschreibung vieler hand- schriftlicher Werke, die

von Benedictinern eben dieser Gesellschaft verfertiget worden. Aus dem Französischen ins Teutsche [von Anton Rudolph] übersetzt ... Frankfurt und Leipzig, A. L. Stettin, 1773-74.
2 v. 19½cm.

"Vorrede" by Johann Georg Meusel.

NT 0047601 MdBJ MnCS CtY

[Tassin, René Prosper] 1697-1777.
Histoire littéraire de la Congrégation de Saint-Maur, ordre de S. Benoît, où l'on trouve la vie & les travaux des auteurs qu'elle a produits, depuis son origine en 1618, jusqu'à présent: avec les titres, l'énumération, l'analyse, les diférentes éditions des livres qu'ils ont donnés au public, & le jugement que les savans en ont porté: ensemble la notice de beaucoup d'ouvrages manuscrits, composés par des Bénédictins du même corps. Bruxelles, Paris, Chez Humblot, 1770.
xxviii, 800, [28] p. 26½ x 20cm.
Cancels of the following pages are bound at end of volume: p. 313-314, 321-328, 529-530, 347-350, 537-538, 541-542, 581-584, 701-702, 737-738.
1. Benedictines. Congrégation de Saint Maur—Bio-bibl. I. Title.
24—7057
Library of Congress Z7840.B3T3

NT 0047602 CoU WaSpG DLC UU NNC NjP CU-L ICU CtY MoSU KAS MB

Tassin, René Prosper, 1697-1777. Histoire litteraire de la Congregation de St-Maur.
Wilhelm, Henry, b. 1821.
... Nouveau supplément à l'Histoire littéraire de la Congrégation de Saint-Maur; notes de Henry Wilhelm, pub. et complétées par Dom Ursmer Berlière, o. s. b., avec la collaboration de D. Antoine Dubourg, o. s. b., et de A. M. P. Ingold ...
Paris, A. Picard et fils, 1908-

Tassin, René Prosper, 1697-1777. Histoire litteraire de la Congregation de St.-Maur.
Robert, Ulysse Léonard Léon, 1845-1903.
Supplément à l'Histoire littéraire de la Congrégation de Saint-Maur, par Ulysse Robert ... Paris, A. Picard, 1881.

Z113 .T67
Tassin, René Prosper, 1697-1777.
[Toustain, Charles François] 1700-1754.
Nouveau traité de diplomatique, où l'on examine les fondemens de cet art; on établit des règles sur le discernement des titres, et l'on expose historiquement les caractères des bulles pontificales et des diplômes donnés en chaque siècle; avec des éclaircissemens sur un nombre considérable de points d'histoire, de chronologie, de critique & de discipline ... Par deux religieux bénédictins de la Congrégation de S. Maur ... Paris, G. Desprez [etc.] 1750-65.

Tassin, Victorien.
Le château des diables; ou, Les souterrains du Caillou-qui-biquo, essai romantique. [4],269,[2]p. Valenciennes, J. Giard; [etc., etc.] 1868.

Contains the author's autograph.

NT 0047606 OCl

Tassin, Wirt de Vivier, 1869-1915.
The Casas Grandes meteorite. By Wirt Tassin ...
(*In* U. S. National museum. Proceedings. Washington, 1903. 23½cm. v. 25, p. 69-74. pl. I-IV)
Issued September 2, 1902.

1. Meteorites. I. Title.
S 33—672
Smithsonian Inst. Library for Library of Congress [Q11.U55 vol. 25]

NT 0047607 DSI PPAN PPT CaBVaU OU OCU OCl

Tassin, Wirt de Vivier, 1869-1915.
Catalogue of the series [in the U. S. National museum] illustrating the properties of minerals. By Wirt Tassin ...
(*In* U. S. National museum. Annual report. 1897. Washington, 1899. 23½cm. pt. I, p. 647-688)
Half-title.
Running title: Properties of minerals.

1. Mineralogy—Catalogs and collections. I. Title: Properties of minerals.
14-19893 Revised
Library of Congress Q11.U5 1897
——— Copy 2.
——— Separate. QE386.U5

NT 0047608 DLC PPT KMK MiU OClMN OU OCl NN

Tassin, Wirt de Vivier, 1869-1915.
Classification of the mineral collections in the U. S. National museum. By Wirt Tassin ...
(*In* U. S. National museum. Annual report. 1897. Washington, 1899. 23½cm. pt. I, p. 747-810)
Half-title.
Running title: Classification of minerals.

1. Mineralogy—Classification. 2. U. S. National museum—Collections. I. Title: Classification of minerals.
14-19896 Revised
Library of Congress Q11.U5 1897
——— Copy 2.
——— Separate. QE388.T3

NT 0047609 DLC PPT WaS OClMN OO MiU OU NN

Tassin, Wirt de Vivier, 1869-1915.
... Classification of the mineral collections in the U. S. National museum. By Wirt Tassin ... Washington, Govt. print. off., 1899.
1 p. l., p. 747-810. 24½cm.
At head of title: Smithsonian institution ...
"From the Report of the U. S. National museum for 1897."

1. Mineralogy.
G S 5-513 Revised
Library, U. S. Geological Survey 106 T19

NT 0047610 DI-GS

Tassin, Wirt de Vivier, 1869-1915, joint author
Merrill, George Perkins, 1854-1929.
Contributions to the study of the Canyon Diablo meteorites, by George P. Merrill and Wirt Tassin.
(*In* Smithsonian institution. Smithsonian miscellaneous collections. Washington, 1908. 24½cm. vol. L (Quarterly issue, vol. IV) p. 203-215. illus., pl. XVIII-XXI)

Tassin, Wirt de Vivier, 1869–1915.
Descriptive catalogue of the collections of gems in the
United States National museum. By Wirt Tassin ...
(*In* U. S. National museum. Annual report. 1900. Washington, 1902.
23½ᶜᵐ. p. 473–670. illus., 9 pl., diagrs.)
Half-title.
Running title: Catalogue of gems.
Bibliography: p. 649–670.
CONTENTS.—Definition and properties of gem minerals.—Description of
minerals used as gems.—Comparative tables of the colors and distinguish-
ing characters of the better known gems.—Index of names of gems.—The
cutting of gem stones.—Imitations, sophistications, and artificial formation
of gems.—Gems of the Bible.—Mystical properties of gems.—Catalogue of
the Isaac Lea collection of gems.
1. Gems. 2. Precious stones. 3. U. S. National museum—Collections.
ɪ. Title: Catalogue of gems.

Library of Congress   Q11.U5 1900
                                            14–19910 Revised

  00
NT 0047612   DLC MB ViU NIC KMK WaS PPT MiU OC1MN OU

Tassin, Wirt de Vivier, 1869–1915.
... Descriptive catalogue of the collections of gems in
the United States National museum. By Wirt Tassin ...
Washington, Govt. print. off., 1902.
1 p. l., p. 473–670. illus., 9 pl. 25ᶜᵐ.
Running title: Catalogue of gems.
At head of title: Smithsonian institution. United States National
museum.
Reprinted "from the Report of the United States National museum for
1900."
Bibliography: p. 649–670.

  CONTENTS.—Definition and properties of gem minerals.—Description of
minerals used as gems.—Comparative tables of the colors and distinguish-
ing characters of the better-known gems.—Index of names of gems.—The
cutting of gem stones.—Imitations, sophistications, and artificial formation
of gems.—Gems of the Bible.—Mystical properties of gems.—Catalogue of
the Isaac Lea collection of gems.

  1. Gems. 2. Precious stones. 3. U. S. National museum—Collections.
ɪ. Title: Catalogue of gems.
                                            5–36465 Revised
Library of Congress   QE392.T21
———— Copy 2.   TN980.T2

NT 0047614   DLC MtBuM

Tassin, Wirt de Vivier, 1869–1915.
Descriptive catalogue of the meteorite collection in the
United States National museum, to January 1, 1902. By
Wirt Tassin ...
(*In* U. S. National museum. Annual report. 1900. Washington,
1902. 23½ᶜᵐ. p. 671–698. 4 pl. (incl. front.))
Half-title.

  1. Meteorites. 2. U. S. National museum—Collections.
                                            14–19911
Library of Congress   Q11.U5 1900
———— Copy 2.
———— Separate.   QE395.T21

NT 0047615   DLC WaS

Tassin, Wirt de Vivier, 1869–1915.
... Directions for collecting minerals. By Wirt Tassin ...
Washington, Govt. print. off., 1895.
6 p. illus. 24½ᶜᵐ. (Pt. ʜ of Bulletin of the United States National
museum, no. 39)
At head of title: Smithsonian institution. United States National
museum.

  ɪ. Mineralogy—Collecting of specimens.
                                            S 13–147
Smithsonian inst. Library   Q11.U6
for Library of Congress   Q11.U6 no. 39

     ViU MiU OU ICJ MB OO OCU OC1MN OrP CaBVaU
NT 0047616   DSI MdBP MU WaS MoU PHC PU PBa PPAN PP

Tassin, Wirt de Vivier, 1869–1915.
The mineralogical collections in the U. S. National museum. By Wirt Tassin ...
(*In* U. S. National museum. Annual report. 1895. Washington, 1897.
23½ᶜᵐ. p. 995–1000. plan)

  1. Mineralogy—Catalogs and collections. 2. U. S. National museum—
Collections.
                                            16–6378
Library of Congress   Q11.U5 1895

NT 0047617   DLC WaS PPT OO OC1MN MiU NN OU

Tassin, Wirt de Vivier, 1869–1915.
... The mineralogical collections in the U. S. National
museum. By Wirt Tassin, assistant curator, Department
of minerals ... Washington, Govt. print. off., 1897.
1 p. l., p. 995–1000. plan. 24½ᶜᵐ.
At head of title: Smithsonian institution. United States National museum.
"From the report of the U. S. National museum for 1895."

  1. Mineralogy—Catalogs and collections. 2. U. S. National museum—
Collections.
                                            9–19295 Revised
Library of Congress   QE386.U6

NT 0047618   DLC

Tassin, Wirt de Vivier, 1869–1915.
The Mount Vernon meteorite. By Wirt Tassin ...
(*In* U. S. National museum. Proceedings. Washington, 1905.
23½ᶜᵐ. v. 28, p. 213–217. illus., pl. ɪɪɪ–ɪᴠ)
Issued February 23, 1905.

  1. Meteorites.   ɪ. Title.
                                            S 33–782
Library, Smithsonian   Institution
Library of Congress   [Q11.U55 vol. 28]

NT 0047619   DSI PPAN NN OU

Tassin, Wirt de Vivier, 1869–1915.
Note on an occurrence of graphitic iron in a
meteorite.   Washington, Govt. Prtg. Off., 1906.
1 p. l., 573–574.   8°.   (Smithsonian
Institution)
    From: Proceedings of the U. S. Nat. Museum,
v. 31, no. 1497)

NT 0047620   NN PPAN

Tassin, Wirt de Vivier, 1869–1915.
Note on an occurrence of graphitic iron in a meteorite. By
Wirt Tassin.
(*In* U. S. National museum. Proceedings. Washington, 1907.
23½ cm. v. 31, p. 573–574. illus.)
Issued November 14, 1906.

  1. Meteorites.
                                            S 34–93
Smithsonian Institution.   Library
for Library of Congress   Q11.U55 vol. 31

NT 0047621   DSI OC1 OU

Tassin, Wirt de Vivier, 1869–1915.
Merrill, George Perkins, 1854–1929.
Notes on the composition and structure of the Henderson-
ville, North Carolina, meteorite. By George P. Merrill, with
chemical analyses by Wirt Tassin.
(*In* U. S. National museum. Proceedings. Washington, 1907.
23½ᶜᵐ. v. 32, p. 79–82. illus., pl. ᴠɪɪɪ–ɪx)

Tassin, Wirt de Vivier, 1869–1915.
On meteoric chromites. By Wirt Tassin.
(*In* U. S. National museum. Proceedings. Washington, 1908.
23½ cm. v. 34, p. 685–690)
Issued September 15, 1908.

  1. Chromite. 2. Meteorites.
[Q11.U55 vol. 34]   S 34—224
Smithsonian Institution.   Library
for Library of Congress   [a56d½]

NT 0047623   DSI NN PPAN MiU OU OC1

Tassin, Wirt de Vivier, 1869–1915.
Merrill, George Perkins, 1854–1929.
On the meteorite from Rich mountain, Jackson county,
North Carolina. By George P. Merrill, with chemical analyses
by Wirt Tassin.
(*In* U. S. National museum. Proceedings. Washington, 1907.
23½ᶜᵐ. v. 32, p. 241–244. pl. xvɪ)

Tassin, Wirt de Vivier, 1869–1915.
On the occurrence of calcium sulphide (oldhamite) in the
Allegan meteorite. By Wirt Tassin.
(*In* U. S. National museum. Proceedings. Washington, 1908.
23½ᶜᵐ. v. 34, p. 433–434)
Issued August 19, 1908.

  1. Meteorites.
                                            S 34–218
Library, Smithsonian   Institution
Library of Congress   [Q11.U55 vol. 34]

NT 0047625   DSi NN PPAN MiU OU

Tassin, Wirt de Vivier, 1869–1915.
The Persimmon creek meteorite. By Wirt Tassin ...
(*In* U. S. National museum. Proceedings. Washington, 1904.
23½ᶜᵐ. v. 27, p. 955–959. illus., pl. xLɪx–L)
Issued June 27, 1904.

  1. Meteorites.   ɪ. Title.
                                            S 33–770
Library, Smithsonian   Institution
Library of Congress   [Q11.U55 vol. 27]

NT 0047626   DSI NN DLC PPAN OCU OU

Tassin de Tassin, Marie, 1889–
    ...Alphonse XIII et le cardinal Segura...   Rouen, Maugard
[1939]   78 p.   23cm.
At head of title: ...Deux grandes figures d'exilés.
No. 195 of 500 copies printed.

  1. Alphonso XIII, king of Spain   1886–1941. 2. Segura y Saenz,
Pedro, abp., 1880–   February 6, 1948.
N. Y. P. L.

NT 0047627   NN

Tassin de Tassin, Marie, 1889–
Blanche de Rosemai, par Armie [pseud.] Illustrations de
Manon Iessel. Paris, Gautier-Languereau, 1955.
128 p. illus. 18 cm. (Bibliothèque de Suzette)

  ɪ. Title.

PZ23.T28B4   56–16732 ‡

NT 0047628   DLC

Tassin de Tassin, Marie, 1889–
María Cristina de Habsburgo, Reina de España, por
Armie [pseud.] Con un prólogo de Blanca de los Ríos, y un
epílogo del conde de Rodríguez San Pedro. Barcelona,
Ediciones María Rosa Urraca Pastor [1945]
268 p. port. 17 cm. (Colección Biografías y memorias)

  1. María Cristina, consort of Alfonso xɪɪ, King of Spain, 1858–1929.
                  Full name: Marie Louise Pauline Angèla Tassin de Tassin.
                                            A 51–4313 rev
New York. Public Libr.
for Library of Congress   [r56c⅝]

NT 0047629   NN ViU

Tassin de Tassin, Marie, 1889–
La vraie gloire du roi charmant; toute la vie d'Alphonse
xɪɪɪ (suite de poèmes) [par] Armie [pseud.] Paris, P. de
Ronsard [1948]
102 p. 20 cm.

  1. Alfonso xɪɪɪ, King of Spain, 1886–1941—Poetry. ɪ. Title.
                                  Full name: Marie Louise Pauline
                                            Angèla Tassin de Tassin.
PQ2639.A77V7   A 49–2718 rev*
Illinois. Univ. Library
for Library of Congress   [r57b⅝]†

NT 0047630   IU DLC

Tassinari (A. F.) Spedale di S. Verdiana in Castelfiorentino. Relazione al consiglio sulla nuova costruzione di uno spedale secondo il pro-

getto particolareggiato dell' architetto Luigi Fusi. 8 pp. 8°. *Castelfiorentino, A. Profeti,* 1891.

NT   0047631   DNLM

Tassinari (Alessandro). Raccolta delle cose pubblicate alla memoria dell' consigliere prof. Valeriano Luigi Brera. 55 pp. 8°. *Venezia, G. B. Merlo,* 1840. [P.. ~ 1121.]

NT   0047632   DNLM

Tassinari, Catherine Danyell
see
Danyell Tassinari, Catherine, 1863–

Tassinari, Giovanna.
Brush up your Italian (Perfezionate il vostro italiano) By Giovanna Tassinari. With thirty drawings by P. R. Ward. London and Toronto, J. M. Dent and sons ltd. [1931]

2 p. l., ix–xiv, 109, [1] p. illus. 19ᶜᵐ. (*Half-title:* [The "Brush up" language books] General editor: W. G. Hartog ...)

Maps on lining-papers.
English and Italian on opposite pages.

1. Italian language—Conversation and phrase books.   I. Title.

Library of Congress   PC1121.T3   32–16546 Revised
                             [r35d2]   458.242

           LU CaBVaU OC1
NT   0047634   DLC PPLas OrU OrP NcC OC1W MB PLF KAS MB

458.2   Tassinari, Giovanna.
T18b   Brush up your Italian (Perfezionate il vostro
          italiano) ... With thirty drawings by P. R. Ward.
          [2.ed.]   Philadelphia, David McKay company
          [1937]
             109p. illus.   (Half-title: [The "Brush up" lan-
          guage series] General editor: W. G. Hartog ...)
          Maps on lining-papers.
          English and Italian on opposite pages.

             1. Italian language--Conversation and phrase
          books. I. Title.

NT   0047635   IU ICU OCU IdB OrP WaS ViU

PC1121   Tassinari, Giovanna.
.T3   Brush up your Italian (Perfezionate il
1949   vostro italiano) by Giovanna Tassinari. With
          thirty drawings by P. R. Ward. [4th ed.]
          New York, D. McKay [pref. 1949]
             xiv, 115 p. illus., maps (on lining-
          papers) 19 cm. (The "Brush up" language
          series)

          English and Italian on opposite pages.

             1. Italian lan-   guage - Conversation and
          phrase books.   I. Title.

NT   0047636   OWoC IaU MB CaBViP CaBVa

Hb50   Tassinari, Giovanna
T18   Brush up your Italian (Perfezionate il
1952   vostro italiano) with drawings by P. R.
          Ward. London, J. M. Dent [1952]
             ix, 115p. illus., maps on lining-papers.
          19cm. (The "Brush up" language books)

             1. Italian language - Conversation and
          phrase books. I. Ser.

NT   0047637   CtY

Tassinari, Giuseppe, 1891–
Appunti di economia e politica agraria, dalle lezioni tenute dal prof. Giuseppe Tassinari nella R. Università di Bologna. Vol. 1. Economia agraria. Roma, Ramo editoriale degli agricoltori [1942]

630 p. diagrs. 25 cm.

No more published.

1. Agriculture—Economic aspects.   I. Title.

HD1411.T26   338.1   44–33185 rev*

NT   0047638   DLC DNAL

Tassinari, Giuseppe, 1891–
... Autarchia e bonifica. Bologna, N. Zanichelli, 1940.

3 p. l., [3]–271 p. 21ᶜᵐ.

"Una serie di articoli, comparsi quasi tutti sul 'Corriere della sera'."— Premessa.

1. Italy—Economic policy. 2. Italy—Commercial policy. 3. Reclamation of land—Italy. I. Title.

                                                      44–50886
Library of Congress   HC305.T32

                                                      330.945

NT   0047639   DLC NcD MH NN

Tassinari, Giuseppe, 1891–
... Die bodenverbesserung und siedlung 10 jahre nach dem Mussolini-gesetz. Faenza, Gebrüder Lega, 1939.

3 p. l., 11–179 p., 1 l. incl. tables. 40 pl. on 20 l., fold. map. 21½ᶜᵐ.

Plates 3–6 duplicated.
Issued also in French and English.

1. Reclamation of land—Italy. 2. Italy—Public works.   I. Title.

Library of Congress   HD1683.I 8T33   40–25104
Copyright A—Foreign   45721
                              [2]   627.50945

NT   0047640   DLC CLU

Tassinari, Giuseppe, 1891–
... La bonifica integrale nel decennale della legge Mussolini. Roma [Bologna, Editrice Arti grafiche "Aldina", xvii [1939]

2 p. l., 7–394 p., 4 l., 7–212 p., 1 l. incl. plates, tables. plates, maps (part fold.; 1 in pocket) 29½ᶜᵐ.

Issued also in English.

1. Reclamation of land—Italy. 2. Italy—Public works.   I. Title.
                                                      45–34838
Library of Congress   HD1683.I 8T36

                                                      631.6

NT   0047641   DLC NN NNC

Tassinari, Giuseppe, 1891–
... La bonification intégrale dix ans après la loi Mussolini; traduction française de Fernand Hayward. Faenza, Lega frères [1939]

3 p. l., 11–171 p., 1 l. plates, fold. map. 21½ᶜᵐ.

Issued also in German and English.

1. Reclamation of land—Italy. 2. Italy—Public works.
I. Hayward, Fernand, 1888–   tr. II. Title.

Library of Congress   HD1683.I 8T8   40–25147
Copyright A—Foreign   45586
                              [2]   631.60945

NT   0047642   DLC CLU

Tassinari, Giuseppe, 1891–
... La colonizzazione del latifondo siciliano ... Firenze, Tipografia Mariano Ricci, 1940.

12 p., 1 l. 25½ᶜᵐ.

"Conferenza tenuta nell' adunanza inaugurale della Reale accademia dei georgofili il 7 gennaio 1940–xviii e pubblicata negli 'Atti', sesta serie, vol. vi."

1. Agricultural colonies—Sicily. 2. Land tenure—Sicily.   I. Title.
                                                      44–33658
Library of Congress   HD1516.I 8T3

NT   0047643   DLC

Tassinari, Giuseppe, 1891–
... La distribuzione del reddito nell' agricoltura italiana. Piacenza, Federazione italiana dei consorzi agrari, 1931.

298 p., 1 l. incl. tables, diagrs. 24½ᶜᵐ.

1. Agriculture—Italy. 2. Agriculture—Economic aspects.   I. Title.

Library of Congress   HD1970.T3   31–29728
                              [2]   338.10945

NT   0047644   DLC NN CU MU

Tassinari, Giuseppe, 1891–
Economia agraria; lezioni. Roma, Ramo editoriale degli agricoltori [1952]

302 p. 18 cm. (Manuali di agricoltura, 5)

First published as v. 1 of the author's Appunti di economia e politica agraria.

1. Agriculture—Economic aspects.

HD1411.T26 1952   55–43000 ‡

NT   0047645   DLC NNU

338.1   Tassinari, Giuseppe, 1891–
T18eSPg   Economía agraria; traducción de la segunda
          edición italiana por Gaspar González y González
          y Andrés Suárez y Suárez.   Madrid [Artes Grá-
          ficas Helénica] 1954.
             xxiii, 275p. diagrs., tables. 22cm.

             Translation of v.1 of the author's Appunti di
          economia e politica agraria.

             1. Agriculture--Economic aspects--Italy. I.
          Title.

NT   0047646   IU

HC   Tassinari, Giuseppe, 1891–
305   L'Économie fasciste. Traduit de l'italien
T314   par Ch. Belin. Roma, "Laboremus", 1937.
             189p. 18cm.

             1. Italy - Economic policy 2. Fascism -
          Italy I. Title

NT   0047647   WU FMU CSt-H DNAL MH

Tassinari, Giuseppe, 1891–
... Faschistische wirtschaftslehre (deutsch von Ernst Hohenemser) Roma, "Laboremus", 1937.

4 p. l., 11–187 p., 1 l. 18½ᶜᵐ.

1. Italy—Economic policy. 2. Fascism—Italy.   I. Hohenemser, Ernst, 1870–   tr. II. Title.
                                                      45–45903
Library of Congress   HC305.T334

                                                      330.945

NT   0047648   DLC

Tassinari, Giuseppe, 1891–
... Fascist economy; translation by Eduardo Cope. Roma, "Laboremus", 1937.

3 p. l., 9–159, [1] p. 18ᶜᵐ.

1. Fascism—Italy. 2. Italy—Economic policy.   I. Cope, Eduardo, tr. II. Title.
                                                      38–14434
Library of Congress   HC305.T33

                                                      330.945

         PPAmP PSC
         OC1FC NjP NN OO OC1 PU-PSW IdU WAWW PU PPT PV PHi
NT   0047649   DLC NcD OYesA NBuU NIC OU CtY NcU OCU

Tassinari, Giuseppe, 1891–
Manuale dell' agronomo. 2. ed. Roma, Ramo editoriale degli agricoltori, 1944 ¡i. e. 1945¡
6 p. l., 2139 p., 1 l. illus. (incl. plans) col. pl., diagrs. 16ᵐ.

1. Agriculture.
S493.T3 1945

47–17439

NT 0047650 DLC MH CU NNC

33.19
T18
Ed.3
Tassinari, Giuseppe, 1891–
Manuale dell'agronomo. 3. ed. Roma, Ramo editoriale degli agricoltori [1951]
2442 p.

1. Agriculture. Handbooks, manuals, etc. 2. Italy. Agriculture. 3. Agriculture. Economic aspects. Italy.

NT 0047651 DNAL DLC-P4

Tassinari, Giuseppe, 1891–
...Per lo sviluppo dell 'economia rurale della nostra montagna; con prefazione del Prof. Arrigo Serpieri. Bologna: N. Zanichelli ¡1921¡. xiv, 122 p. incl. tables. 12°. (L'Italia nuova. Serie B, no. 26.)

Bibliographical footnotes.

1. Agriculture, Italy. 2. Serpieri, Arrigo. 3. Series.   June 12, 1922.
N. Y. P. L.

NT 0047652 NN

Tassinari, Giuseppe, 1891–
...Problemi della agricoltura italiana.   Roma: Confederazione nazionale fascista degli agricoltori ¡1933¡   viii, 164 p. 25cm.

"Ho riunito...i discorsi e le relazioni fatte dal novembre 1930 ad oggi, come commissario prima e come presidente poi della Confederazione nazionale fascista degli agricoltori." — p. vii.

877779A. 1. Agriculture—Italy.   2. Agriculture—Economics—Italy.
I. Confederazione fascista degli   agricoltori.
N. Y. P. L.   April 26, 1937.

NT 0047653 NN DNAL OCl DLC-P4

Tassinari, Giuseppe, 1891–
... Saggio intorno alla distribuzione del reddito nell' agricoltura italiana. Piacenza, Federazione italiana dei consorzi agrari, 1926.
2 p. l., ¡7¡–179 p. 25ᵐ.
At head of title : G. Tassinari.

1. Agriculture—Italy. ¡1. Italy—Agriculture¡ 2. Agriculture — Economic aspects—Italy. ¡2. Profits in agriculture¡
                                            Agr 28–296 Revised
U. S. Dept. of agr. Library   281T19
for Library of Congress   HD1970.T33
                                 ¡r43c2¡†

NT 0047654 DNAL DLC

Law   Tassinari, Giuseppe, 1891–

Confederazione fascista degli agricoltori. *Commissione di studi giuridici.*
Schema di norme per il riordinamento della proprietà fondiaria. Milano, Bestetti e Tumminelli ¡1930?¡

Tassinari, Giuseppe, 1891–
... Scritti di economia corporativa ... Seconda edizione. Bologna, Nicola Zanichelli editore, 1937.
2 p. l., ¡7¡–252 p., 1 l. incl. tables. 21ᵐ.
On verso of t.-p. : N° 1100.
A collection of previously published addresses and articles, with introduction : Premesse di economia corporativa.

1. Italy—Economic conditions—1918–   2. Italy—Economic policy.
3. Agriculture—Italy. 4. Agriculture—Economic aspects.   I. Title.
                                            A C 38–2010
New York. Public library
for Library of Congress   ¡3¡

NT 0047656 NN

Tassinari, Giuseppe, 1891–
... Ten years of integral land-reclamation under the Mussolini act.   Faenza, Italy, Fratelli Lega ¡1939¡
3 p. l., 11–165, ¡1¡ p. plates, fold. map. 21½ᵐ.
Issued also in German and French.

1. Reclamation of land—Italy. 2. Italy—Public works. 3. Agriculture—Italy. I. Title.
                                            40–30979
Library of Congress   HD1683.I 8T29
———— Copy 2.   ¡10¡   631.60945

CU-S WaU DAU PP PPT PU CtY
OOxM NN ViU MH NjP ODW OCU OClW TU IdU WaSp OrU Wa
NT 0047657 DLC PHC WaU NcD CU OCl OU OO OClC OClND

A
630.6
R66s
no.23
Tassinari, Giuseppe, 1891–
Le vicende del reddito dell'agricoltura dal 1925 al 1932.   Roma [Fratelli Lega] 1935.
365p. tables, graphs. 26½cm.   (Rome. Istituto nazionale di economia agraria. Studi e monografie. no.23.)

1. Income. 2. Agriculture--Italy--Economic aspects.

NT 0047658 LU NNC KU

Tassinari, Guido, joint ed.
La resistenza nella letteratura

see under

Marchetti, Aristide, ed.

Tassinari, Ottorino.
Ordinamento democratico di uno Stato collettivista. Libro 5. Agricoltura.   Bologna, Cooperativa tip. Azzoguidi, 1945 ¡i. e. 1947¡
vii, 191 p. 24 cm.
No more published.
Includes bibliographies.

1. Agriculture—Economic aspects—Italy.

HD1970.T35   56–25960

NT 0047660 DLC

Tassinari, Renato, 1899–
... Sulle vie dello sport. ¡Milano¡ Rizzoli & c., 1940.
2 p. l., ¡7¡–190 p., 3 l. plates, ports. 19½ᵐ.

1. Sports. I. Title.   44–44882
Library of Congress   GV181.T3
                                ¡2¡   796

NT 0047661 DLC

Tassinari, Renato, 1899–
945.091
B582
no.15
La vera libertà dei popoli. Venezia, Edizioni Erre, 1945.
12 p. 12 cm. (Bibliotechina d'attualità, 15)

"Da 'La Stampa' del 1 ottobre 1944."
1. Italy. Hist. Allied occupation, 1943-1947. 2. Fascism. Italy. I. Title.

NT 0047662 NcD

TASSINARI, VASCO.
...È arrivato il milione; commedia brillantissima... Roma, Libreria editrice salesiana, 1951. 46 p. 17cm. (Collana teatrale maschile. n. 64)

1. Drama, Italian. I. Title.

NT 0047663 NN RPB

Tassinari, Vasco.
...Nella tormenta; commedia drammatica... Colle Don Bosco, Asti, Libreria Dottrina cristiana [1948]
85 p. 17cm. (Teatro maschile. n. 18)

1. Drama, Italian.

NT 0047664 NN

Tassinari, Vasco.
L'oro, questo nemico; tre atti. ¡Torino¡ Libreria Dottrina cristiana ¡1948¡
67 p. illus. 17 cm. (Teatro maschile, 10)

I. Title.
                                            A 52–3446
New York. Public Libr.
for Library of Congress   ¡2¡

NT 0047665 NN

Tassinari (Vincenzo). Brevissimi cenni su Corsoole Reale, le sue acque minerali, il suo clima. 14 pp. 8°. *Bologna, Soc. tip. Azzoguidi,* 1888.

NT 0047666 DNLM

BX
1547
V55T18
Tassini, Dionisio.
La questione storico-giuridica del patriarcato di Venezia (Aquileja)   Genova, G. Bacchi Palazzi, 1906.
280 p.

Bibliographical footnotes.

1. Catholic Church. Patriarchate of Venice. 2. Aquileia (Patriarchate) I. Title.

NT 0047667 CLU CtY

DG
671.4
T21a
Tassini, Giuseppe, 1827-1899.
Alcune delle più clamorose condanne capitali eseguite in Venezia sotto la repubblica. Memorie patrie. Venezia, Tip. di G.Cecchini, 1866.
318p. 24cm.
Notes at end of each case.

1. Crime and criminals - Venice. 2. Justice, Administration of - Venice.

NT 0047668 NRU DLC-P4

Tassini, Giuseppe, 1827–1899.
... Alcune delle più clamorose condanne capitali eseguite in Venezia sotto la repubblica. 2. ed., cor. ed ampliata dall' autore. Venezia, M. Fontana, 1892.
291 p. 25½ᵐ.
Notes at end of each case.
"Elenco generale dei giustiziati in Venezia dal principio alla fine della repubblica": p. ¡257¡–291.

1. Crime and criminals—Italy—Venice. 2. Justice, Administration of—Venice.
                                            15–21683
Library of Congress   DG671.4.T3

NT 0047669 DLC

Tassini, Giuseppe, 1827–1899.
Alcuni palazzi ed antichi edificii di Venezia, storicamente illustrati con annotazioni per Giuseppe dott. Tassini. Venezia, Tipografia M. Fontana, 1879.
2 p. l., 7–296 p. 24ᵐ.

1. Venice—Palaces. 2. Venice—Historic houses, etc.
                                            21–19014
——— Library of Congress ———   DG674.T35

NT 0047670 DLC

Tassini, Giuseppe, 1827-1899.
   Alcuni palazzi ed antichi edifici di Venezia, storicamente illustrati con annotazioni per Giuseppe dott. Tassini.   Venezia, Tipografia M. Fontana, 1879.
   2 p. l., 7-296 p.   24 cm.
   Photocopy (positive)

NT   0047671   CU

DG
675
T21c
   Tassini, Giuseppe, 1827-1899.
   Curiosità veneziane, ovvero Origini delle denominazioni stradali di Venezia.   Venezia, Gio.Cecchini, 1863.
   2v.in 1. 24cm.

   1. Venice - Antiq.   2. Venice - Descr. - Gazetteers.   I. Title.

NT   0047672   NRU CtY

DG
675
T21c
1872
   Tassini, Giuseppe, 1827-1899.
   Curiosità veneziane; ovvero Origini delle denominazioni stradali di Venezia. 2.ed. corretta ed aumentata dall'autore. Venezia, Grimaldo E.C., 1872.
   805p. 26cm.

   1. Venice - Antiq.   2. Venice - Descr. - Gazetteers.   I. Title.

NT   0047673   NRU OKentU

DG
675
T21c
1882
   Tassini, Giuseppe, 1827-1899.
   Curiosità veneziane, ovvero Origini delle denominazioni stradali di Venezia. 3.ed., corretta e riv.dall'autore. Venezia, M.Fontana, 1882.
   690p. 18cm.

   1. Venice - Antiq.   2. Venice - Descr. - Gazetteers.   I. Title.

NT   0047674   NRU

DG
675
T21c
1886
   Tassini, Giuseppe, 1827-1899.
   Curiosità veneziane. 4.ed. ₍Venezia, Tip.dell'Ancora₎ 1886.
   869p. 24cm.

   1. Venice - Antiq.   2. Venice - Descr. - Gazetteers.   I. Title.

NT   0047675   NRU

Tassini, Giuseppe, 1827-1899.
   Curiosità veneziane, ovvero Origini delle denominazioni stradali di Venezia del Dott. Giuseppe Tassini. 4. ed. Venezia ₍Alzetta e Merlo, 1887₎
   2 p. l., 869 p., 1 l. 24ᶜᵐ.
   Alphabetical arrangement under streets, localities, institutions, etc.

   1. Venice—Antiq. 2. Venice—Descr.—Dictionaries.
                          3—4566
   Library of Congress   DG675.T2

NT   0047676   DLC CtY IdU NNC VtMiM

DG675
T2
1915
   Tassini, Giuseppe, 1827-1899
   Curiosità veneziane. Con prefazione e cenni biografici dell'autore di Elio Zorzi. 5th ed. Venice, Giusto Fuga, 1915.
   xii, 771 p.   22 cm.

   Alphabetical arrangement under streets, localities, insitutions, etc.
   1.Venice—Antiq. 2.Venice—Descr.—Gazetteers. 3.Architecture--Venice. I.Zorzi,Elio, 1892- ,ed. II.Title.

NT   0047677   RPB

DG675
T2
1933
   Tassini, Giuseppe, 1827-1899.
   Curiosità veneziane. 6.ed.   Venezia, Edizione Scarabellin, 1933.
   xxxix, 831 p.

   Photocopy (positive) made by Micro Photo, Cleveland.

   1. Venice (City) - Antiq.   2. Venice (City) - Descr. - Gazetteers.

NT   0047678   CU IU NN

Tassini, Giuseppe, 1827-1899.
   Edifici di Venezia distrutti o vôlti ad uso diverso da quello a cui furono in origine destinati, per Giuseppe d'. Tassini. Venezia, Reale tip. G. Cecchini, 1885.
   3 p. l., ₍9₎-134 p. 24½ᶜᵐ.

   1. Venice—Historic houses, etc. 2. Venice—Churches.   I. Title.
                          20-22494
   Library of Congress   DG674.T3

NT   0047679   DLC NN CU

Tassini, Giuseppe, 1827-1899.
   Feste, spettacoli, divertimenti e piaceri degli antichi Veneziani, per Giuseppe dott. Tassini. 2. ed. Venezia, Stab. tip.-lit. success. M. Fontana, 1891.
   186 p., 1 l. 20½ᶜᵐ.

   1. Venice—Festivals, etc. 2. Venice—Amusements.   I. Title.
                          20-22489
   Library of Congress   DG675.6.T3 1891

NT   0047680   DLC MH

TASSINI, Giuseppe, 1827-1899.
   Iscrizioni dell' ex chiesa e monastero del S. Sepolcro in Venezia, annotate per cura di Giuseppe Dott. Tassini. [Venezio, M. Visentini, 1879]

   pp. (28).
   Without title-page. Caption title.
   Cut from "Archivio Veneto", 1879, pp. [274]-300.   FA 2211.7

NT   0047681   MH

CN
1015
.V4
T21i
   Tassini, Giuseppe, 1827-1899.
   Iscrizioni della chiesa e convento di S. Salvatore di Venezia; illustrate. Venezia, S.Luca, 1895.
   95p. 26cm.

   1. Epitaphs - Venice.   I. Title.

NT   0047682   NRU

Tassini, Giuseppe, 1827-1899.
   Lido; cenni storici per Giuseppe d.r Tassini. 2. ed. Venezia, Tipografia Società di m. s. fra comp. ed imp. tip., 1889.
   31 p. 20ᶜᵐ.
   No. ₍8₎ in a volume lettered: Miscellanea veneta.

   1. Lido, Italy—Hist.
                          32-15216
   Library of Congress   DG671.2.M5   945.3

NT   0047683   DLC

PQ4623
F628
   Tassini, Giuseppe, 1827-1899.
   Veronica Franco, celebre poetessa e cortigiana del secolo XVI. 2.ed., corr. ed ampliata dall' autore coll'aggiunta di quattro testamenti inediti.   Venezia, M.Fontana, 1888.
   97p. port. 17cm.

   1. Franco, Veronica, 1546-1591.

NT   0047684   IaU NRU ICN

Tassini, Giuseppe, 1827-1899.
   Veronica Franco, celebre poetessa e cortigiana del secolo XVI. Ed. 2 enl.   Ven. Fontana, 1889.
   97 p.

NT   0047685   PU

Law
   Tassino, Mario, comp.

   Uruguay. *Laws, statutes, etc.*
   Sociedades anónimas: bancos limitadas, cooperativas, mutualistas; recopilación. Leyes, decretos, resoluciones, antecedentes. 3. ed. Montevideo, Florensa & Lafon, 1948.

Law
   Tassino, Mario, comp.

   Uruguay. *Laws, statutes, etc.*
   ... Sociedades anónimas, limitadas, cooperativas, mutualistas. Recopilación leyes, decretos, resoluciones, antecedentes, 1825 hasta 1941. República o. del Uruguay. 2. ed. ampliada hasta el 31 de diciembre de 1943. Montevideo ₍Editorial Florensa & Lafon₎ 1944.

PQ4843
A775
S4
   Tassino, Silvio.
   Sìsifo.   [Genevo] Edmondo Del Mastro [1953]
   76 p. front. (illus.) 21 cm.

NT   0047688   RPB NN

Tassis, Auguste
   see   Tassis, S   Auguste.

Tassis, Jan Baptist de
   see   Taxis, Johann Baptista von, 1530-1610.

Tassis, Johan Baptista de
   see   Taxis, Johann Baptista von, 1530-1610.

B
G7712t
Tassis, Maria Aurelia.
La vita di s. Grata vergine regina nella Germania, poi principessa di Bergamo, e protettrice della medesima città; descritta da donna Maria Aurelia Tassis ... Padova, Stamperia di G. Comino, Per G. Baldano, 1723.
147p. front.(port.)

1. Grata, Saint. d.ca.305?

NT 0047691 IU CtY

TASSIS, Pietro.
Attinenze e riscontri della letteratura italiana colle letterature greca e latina.- Versione e breve illustrazione storica dei 21-29 della iiia Olinthiaca di Demostene. Urbino, 1893.

pp.26.

NT 0047692 MH

TASSIS, Pietro.
Peccati e pene nell'Inferno dantesco. Nuove ricerche. Treviso, 1886.

pp.32-. Dn 149.8

The same. 2a ed. Milano, 1888.
pp. 29.
For addition, see his Principale allegoria della Divina Commedia. (Call-no.: Dn 144.12.2)
Dn 144.12
The same. 3a ed. Macerata, 1894.
1.8°. pp.27+.

NT 0047693 NIC

Tassis, Pietro.
Plutarco ed il Pericle de Plutarco; ricerche. Milano, Tipografia A. Guerra, 1888.
67 p. 20 cm.
1. Plutarchus.

NT 0047694 NIC MH

[TASSIS, Pietro]
Principale allegoria della Divina Commedia. [Urbino, 1893]

pp.3.
"Breve aggiunta ai Peccati e pene nell' Inferno dantesco."

NT 0047695 MH NIC

Tassis, S Auguste.
Guide du correcteur; ou, Complément des grammaires et des lexiques donnant la solution des principales difficultés pour l'emploi des lettres majuscules et minuscules dans l'écriture et l'impression ... par Auguste Tassis ... 10. éd., cor. d'après [!] les modifications adoptées par l'Académie. Paris, Librairie de Paris, Firmin-Didot et cie [n.d.]
vi, [7]-124 p. 18½cm.
On cover: 11.éd.
6.éd., rev. et aug / m., 1862.
1. French language—Capitalization. 2. Proof-reading. I. Title.

NT 0047696 ViU

Bonaparte
Collection Tassis, S Auguste.
No. 3275
Guide du correcteur et du compositeur, donnant la solution des principales difficultés pour l'emploi des lettres majuscules et minuscules dans l'écriture et l'impression ... 4e éd.... augm. Par.1856. S.

NT 0047697 ICN

Tassis, S Auguste.
Guide du correcteur; ou, Complément des grammaires et des lexiques, donnant la solution des principales difficultés pour l'emploi des lettres majuscules et minuscule dans l'écriture et l'impression ... par Auguste Tassis ... 10. éd., corrigée d'après les modifications adoptées par l'Académie. Paris, Firmin-Didot et cie [186-?]
vi p., 1 l., [9]-124 p. 18½cm.

1. Proof-reading. 2. Printing, Practical.

NT 0047698 MiU IU

Tassis, S Auguste.
Guide du correcteur et du compositeur, donnant la solution des principales difficultés pour l'emploi des lettres majuscules et minuscules dans l'écriture et l'impression ... par S.-A. Tassis, correcteur à l'imprimerie de MM. Firmin Didot frères. 6. éd., rev. et augm. Paris, F. Didot frères [1862]
106, [2] p. 18½cm.

1. French language—Capitalization. 2. Proof-reading. I. Title.
27-20541

Library of Congress Z254.T21 1862

NT 0047699 DLC ICU

655.25
N1
Tassis, S Auguste.
Guide du correcteur, ou Complément des grammaires et des lexiques, donnant la solution des principales difficultés pour l'emploi des lettres majuscules et minuscules dans l'écriture et l'impression ... Par Auguste Tassis ... Dixième édition, corrigée d'après les modifications adoptées par l'Académie. Paris, Firmin-Didot et cie, [187-?].
vi, [2, 9]-124 p. 19cm.

NT 0047700 ICJ ViU

Wing
Z
41
.864
no.1
TASSIS, S Auguste.
Guide du correcteur; ou, Complément des grammaires et des lexiques, donnant la solution des principales difficultés pour l'emploi des lettres majuscules et minuscules dans l'écriture et l'impression ... Par Auguste Tassis ... Neuvième édition, corrigée d'après les modifications adoptés par l'Académie. Paris, Librairie de Firmin-Didot et Cie [188-?]
124p. 18cm.

NT 0047701 ICN

Tassis, S Auguste. 2689.32
Guide du correcteur, ou complément des grammaires et des lexiques ... 10e édition, corrigée d'après les modifications adoptées par l'Académie.
Paris. Firmin-Didot & cie. [1896?] 124 pp. 18°.
Contents. — Protocole pour la correction des épreuves, extrait du Manuel typographique de Brun.—De l'emploi des lettres majuscules et minuscules. — Règles diverses. — Relevé général des mots qui offrent des difficultés pour l'emploi des lettres majuscules et minuscules. — Liste des substantifs simple et composé qui offrent des difficultés pour la formation du pluriel.— Liste des mots offrant quelque difficulté pour l'orthographe.
Brun's Manuel . . . is on shelf-number 2119.8.

G1454 — France. Lang. Gram. — T.r. — Proof-reading. — France. Lang. Spell.

NT 0047702 MB

Tassis, S Auguste.
Traité pratique de la ponctuation, contenant plus de 800 exemples en vers et en prose ... Par S.-A. Tassis ... Paris, Firmin Didot frères, fils et cie, 1859.
130 p., 1 l. 18½cm.

1. French language—Punctuation.
10-34793

Library of Congress PC2450.T3

NT 0047703 DLC

Wing
Z
41
.864
no.3
TASSIS, S Auguste.
Traité pratique de la ponctuation, contenant plus de 800 exemples en vers et en prose, dans lequel sont exposés les véritables règles de la ponctuation, règles puisées dans la logique et confirmées par des citations variées et choisies; ouvrage donnant la solution des principales difficultés omises par les grammairiens, et dans lequel se trouvent relevées les erreurs et les

méprises auxquelles ces omissions donnent lieu dans l'écriture et l'impression; par S.-A. Tassis ... Troisième édition. Paris, Librairie de Firmin Didot Frères, Fils et Cie, 1873.
130p. 18cm.

NT 0047705 ICN

Tassis, S Auguste.
Traité pratique de la ponctuation, contenant plus de 800 exemples en vers et en prose ... Par S.-A. Tassis ... Paris, Firmin Didot et cie, 1882. 4 éd.
130 p. 18½cm.
On covers 3. éd.

NT 0047706 ViU

Tassis y Peralta, Juan de, *conde de Villamediana*
see Villamediana, Juan de Tarsis y Peralta, *conde de,* 1580-1622.

Tassis y Villarroel, Juan de Vera
see Vera Tassis y Villarroel, Juan de, d. 17th cent.

Tassistro, Pietro.
Duetto per violino e viola, composto ... da Pietro Tassistro ... Milano, G. Ricordi [181-?]
2 pts. 34cm.
No. 5 in each of two volumes lettered: Duetti per violino e viola. Rolla.
Publisher's plate no.: 2433.

1. Sonatas (Violin and viola)
46-29829

Library of Congress M286.R64D83 no. 5

NT 0047709 DLC

Tassitch, Georges
see Tasić, Đorđe, 1892-

Tassitch, Miloch
see Tasić, Miloš, 1900-

Tassitch, Vandjel
see Tasić, Vandel, 1899-

Tassius, Albert.
Pyelitis in graviditate.   Frankfurt a. M.: W. Vogel, 1912.
55 p.   8°.

Dissertation, Erlangen.
Bibliography, p. 53-55.

1. Pyelitis. 2. Kidney.—Diseases.   3. Pregnancy.—Complications.
N. Y. P. L.   February 24, 1914.

NT 0047713   NN NIC DNLM ICRL

Tassius, Johann Adolf
see   **Tasse, Johann Adolf, 1585-1654.**

W 4   TASSIUS, Rudolf, 1921–
F82   Die Entwicklung des Krankenhauswesens
1949   in Frankfurt a. M.   Frankfurt, a. M.,
              1949.
                 70 ℓ.
                 Inaug. -Diss. - Frankfurt.
                 Typewritten copy.
                 1. Hospitals - Germany.

NT 0047715   DNLM

Tassius (Victor). "Indicationen und Erfahrungen über einige antiseptische Verbände, welche
gegenwärtig in der Chirurgie zur Anwendung
kommen. 38 pp. 8°. München, C. Wolf u. Sohn,
1884.

NT 0047716   DNLM

Tassler, Milford Charles, 1921–
Film coefficients for mass transfer during liquid atomiza-
tion. Urbana, 1952.
4 p. 23 cm.

Abstract of thesis—University of Illinois.
Vita.
Bibliography : p. 4.

1. Gases—Absorption and adsorption. 2. Film coefficients (Physics)
I. Title.
QC182.T26   A 53–3430
Illinois. Univ. Library
for Library of Congress   [3]†

NT 0047717   IU NIC DLC

Tassman, Isaac Samuel, 1892–
The eye manifestations of internal diseases, by I. S. Tassman
... with 201 illustrations, including 19 in color. St. Louis, The
C. V. Mosby company, 1942.
3 p. l., 5–542 p. illus., col. plates, diagrs. 25ᶜᵐ.
"References" at end of each chapter except one.

1. Diagnosis. 2. Eye.   I. Title.
                                                            42–14399
Library of Congress   RC73.5.T3
                                      [3]   616.0753

NT 0047718   DLC PU PPHa PPC CaBVaU OrU-M ICJ OU OC1M

Tassman, Isaac Samuel, 1892–
The eye manifestations of internal diseases ... 2d ed. St.
Louis, Mosby, 1946.
614 p. illus. (part col.) 25ᶜᵐ.

1. Diagnosis. [1. Eye—Diseases—Diagnosis] 2. Eye. [2. Eye—Diagnostic significance]   I. Title.
RC73.5.T3 1946   616.0753   Med 47–119
© 7Nov46; C. V. Mosby company; A8824.

U. S. Army medical library   [WW14ST213e 1946]
for Library of Congress   [7]†

CaBVaU DLC
NT 0047719   DNLM NcD OrU-M PPPCPh PU-V NcU NBuU CtY-M

Tassman, Isaac Samuel, 1892–
The eye manifestations of internal diseases ... 2d ed. St.
Louis, Mosby, 1946. [i.e. 1947]
614 p. illus. (part col.) 25ᶜᵐ.

"Reprinted February, 1947."

NT 0047720   ViU

Tassman, Isaac Samuel, 1892–
The eye manifestations of internal diseases; medical ophthalmology. 3d ed. St. Louis, Mosby, 1951.
672 p. illus. (part col.) 25 cm.
Includes bibliographies.

1. Diagnosis. 2. Eye.   I. Title.
RC73.5.T3 1951   616.0753   51–2024
[U. S. Army Med. Libr.: 1. Eye—Diseases—Diagnosis. 2. Eye—
Diagnostic significance. WW475 T213e]

ICJ ICU
NT 0047721   DLC OC1W-H CU DNLM CaBVaU OrU-M IdPI ViU

Tasso Australasiatticus, pseud.
see Burn, David.

Tasso, A
Una parola in confidenza. [no.] 1. [Napoli,
1848]
f°. Broadside.
In: BWL p. v. 1, no. 214.

NT 0047723   NN

TASSO, ANTONIO.
La questione degli stretti (i Dardanelli) Milano,
L. Trevisini [1955] 336 p. 21cm.

Bibliographical footnotes.

1. Dardanelles—Political and economic aspects.

NT 0047724   NN

Tasso, Bernardo, 1493–1569.
L'amadigi del S. Bernardo Tasso ... Vinegia, G. Gio-
lito de' Ferrari, 1560.
4 p. l., 612, [2] p. illus. (incl. port.) 24½ᶜᵐ.
Title vignette (device of G. Giolito de' Ferrari) ; initials ; head-pieces.
Dedication by Lodovico Dolce.
Book-plate of Sylvester lord Glenbervie.

I. Dolce, Lodovico, 1508–1568, ed. II. Title.
                                                            17–7394
Library of Congress   PQ4634.T6A6

NT 0047725   DLC MH DFo NN MWelC NIC NN

Tasso, Bernardo, 1493–1569.
L'Amadigi Del S. Bernardo Tasso ... Nuouamente ristampato, & dalla prima impressione da molti errori espurgato.
Venetia: Appresso Fabio & Agostino Zoppini Fratelli, 1581.
4 p.l., 731(1) p. 22cm. (4°.)

"Ai Lettori. Lodovico Dolce," prelim. l. 2–4.
With autograph of Giovanni Barbi.

1. Poetry, Italian. I. Dolce,   Lodovico, 1508–1568, ed.
N. Y. L.   Card revised
                                                  January 11, 1943

NT 0047726   NN CtY PBm NNC NjP ICN MH-H OU

Tasso, Bernardo. 1493-1569.
L'Amadigi. Nuouamente ristampato, & dalla
prima impressione da molti errori espurgato.
Venetia, 1582.

NT 0047727   WU

Tasso, Bernardo, 1493-1569.   Ital 7770.5
L'Amadigi del S. Bernardo Tasso. Nuouamente ristampato &
dalla prima impressione da molti errori espurgato. Venetia, appresso Fabio & Agostino Zoppini fratelli, 1583.
4°. pp. (8), 731 +.
With printer's mark on title-page.

Print. spec.

NT 0047728   MH PU ICN MH-H InU DFo CLSU MNS

Hd28   **Tasso, Bernardo, 1493-1569.**
753   L'Amadigi ... colla vita dell'autore e varie
              illustrazioni dell'opera ... Bergamo,P.
              Lancellotti,1755.
                 4v. front.(port.) 16cm.
                 "La vita di Bernardo Tasso scritta da
              Pierantonio Serassi": t.1,p.1-xxxvii(2d count)

NT 0047729   CtY CU NcD INS MB PBm MNAt

Tasso, Bernardo, 1493-1569.
L'Amadigi. Tomo 1-8. Venezia,
G. Antonelli, 1836-37.
8 v. in 4. port. 48°.

NT 0047730   NN

Tasso, Bernardo, 1493–1569.
L'Amadigi di Gaula di Bernardo Tasso. Venezia, G. Antonelli, 1836.
2 p. l. [1]-lxviii col., [2] p., 1148 col. port. 24½ᶜᵐ. (In Parnaso italiano, v. 3)
"Vita di Bernardo Tasso scritta da Pierantonio Serassi": col. [lx]-
xxvi.

I. Serassi, Pietro Antonio, 1721-1791. II. Title.
                                                            2-11977 Revised
Library of Congress   PQ4207.P3 1832 vol. 3

NT 0047731   DLC

PQ4634   TASSO,BERNARDO,1493-1569.
.T6A17   ...Il codice autografo di rime e prose di **Bernardo
              Tasso**,appendice al Libro terzo degli amori. **Firenze,**
              Stab.grafico C.A.Materassi,1902.
                 36 p. 21½cm.
                 At head of title:Domenico Tordi.
                 "Note[bibliografiche]":p.32-34.

NT 0047732   ICU MH

---

858   Tasso,Bernardo,1493-1569.
T20   Delle lettere di m.Bernardo Tasso,accres-
A35   ciute,corrette,e illustrate ... Con la vita
V93   dell' autore scritta dal sig.Anton-Federigo
              Seghezzi ... Padova, Presso G.Comino, 1733-
              1751.
                 3 v.in 2. front.(port.) 18½cm.
                 Title vignettes (v.1,3,printer's marks)
                 Arms of the Volpi family at end of v.1 and 2.
                 Dedication signed: Gaetano Volpi.
                 Vol.2 has title: Delle lettere ... molto corretto,
              e accresciute. Si è aggiunto anche in fine il Ragio-
              namento della poesia,dello stesso autore

                 Vol.3 has title: Delle lettere ... accresciute,
              corrette,e illustrate ... contenente le famigliari,
              per la maggior parte ora la prima volta stampate,e
              alcune di Torquato suo figliuolo pur esse finora
              inedite. Si premette il Parere dell' abate Pieranto-
              nio Serassi intorno alla patria de' suddetti.
                 "Edizioni delle opere di Bernardo Tasso": v.1,
              p.lxv-lxxi.
                 I.Seghezzi,Anton Federigo,d.1745. II.Serassi,
              Pietro Antonio,1721-1791. III.Volpi,Gaetano Cristo-
              foro,1689-1761,ed.

              NIC CLSU InU IaU ICarbS NcD PU
NT 0047734   MiU CtY MH ICU PU ICN IU InU PBm IEN

Rare Book
Collection
PQ4634
.T6
A17
1560

Tasso, Bernardo, 1493-1569.
Delle rime di Messer Bernardo Tasso.
Libro quarto. In Vinegia, Appresso Gabriel
Giolito de' Ferrari, M.D.LX.
11 p. l., 1-304; 3-67, ⸤1⸥; 3-120 p. 14 cm.

Printer's device on t.-p.
Initials. Head and tail pieces.

NT   0047735   NcU

Tasso, Bernardo, 1493-1569.
Li dve libri delle lettere... intitolati à Monsig.
D'Aras; alli quali nouamente s'è aggiunto il terzo
libro. In Venezia, appresso V. Valgrisi & B.
Constantini, 1557.
3 v. in 1 (585, [6] p.) 16 cm.

NT   0047736   NjP CaBVaU PU MH ICN

PQ
4201
C7
ser.2
v.57

Tasso, Bernardo, 1493-1569.
Il floridante. Introduzione e note di
Michele Catalano. Con tre tavole. Torino,
Unione Tipografico-Editrice Torinese [n.d.]
xxvii, 317 p. port. facsim. 18 cm.
(Collezione di classici italiani. 2. ser.,
v.57)
"Nota bibliografica": p. [xxviii]
I. Catalano, Michele, 1884- ed.
II. Title. (Series)

NT   0047737   NBuU

Case
Y
712
.T 155

TASSO, BERNARDO, 1493-1569.
Il floridante del Signor Bernardo Tasso..
Con gli argomenti à ciascun canto del Signor
Antonio Constantini. Nuouamente stampato.
In Bologna, Per Gio.Rossi, 1587.
⸤7⸥,158,⸤1⸥p. 16cm.

Three eds. of this unfinished poem were
pub. in 1587: Mantua,Fr.Ossana; Bologna,A.
Benacci; and Bologna, G.Rossi.-cf.Brunet,Haym
The first 8 cantos from his Amadigi.
Signatures: A-I⁸, K-L⁴.

NT   0047738   ICN PU MnU CtY

Tasso, Bernardo, 1493-1569.
... Il Floridante. Introduzione e note di Michele Catalano.
Con tre tavole. Torino, Unione tipografico-editrice torinese
⸤1931⸥
xxvii, ⸤1⸥, 317 p., 1 l. III pl. (port., facsims.) on 2 l. 18ᶜᵐ. (Added
t.-p.: Collezione di classici italiani ... 2. ser., diretta da Gustavo
Balsamo-Crivelli. vol. LVII)
"Nota bibliografica": p. [xxviii]

1. Catalano, Michele, 1884- ed. II. Title.   38-9465

Library of Congress   PQ4201.C7 2. ser., vol. 57
      (850.82) 851.3'

NT   0047739   DLC CU PU OrU CtY ICU IU IEN

---

*IC5
T1852
549l

Tasso, Bernardo, 1493-1569.
Le lettere di m. Bernardo Tasso. Intitolate
à monsig.ᵒʳ d'Aras...
In Vinegia,Nella bottega d'Erasmo di Vincenzo
Valgrisi:M.D.XLIX.
8°. 16p.l.,477,[3]p. 17.5cm.
Printer's mark on t.-p. & verso of last leaf.
Imperfect: p.301-302,309-310 wanting.
In ms. on verso of last leaf: Io Bernardo
Tassi scrissi di man: propria.

NT   0047740   MH ICN ICU

---

*IC5
T1852
549lb

Tasso, Bernardo, 1493-1569.
Le lettere di m. Bernardo Tasso. Intitolate
à monsig.ᵒʳ d'Aras ...
In Vinegia Appresso Vincenzo Valgrisi.MDLII.
8°. 458(i.e.488),[8]p. 15.5cm.
Printer's mark on t.-p.
Page 488 misnumbered 458.
Presented to the Harvard college library by
Thomas Hollis, 8 Dec. 1764.

NT   0047741   MH ICN IU RPB

Rare
PQ
4634
T6A2
1551

Tasso, Bernardo, 1493-1569.
Le lettere ... In Vinegia, Appresso
Vincenzo Valgrisi, 1551-60.
2 v. 17cm.

Title-page of vol. 2 reads: Delle
lettere ... nvovamente posto in lvce ...
In Vinegia, Appresso Gabriel Giolito
de' Ferrari, 1560.

NT   0047742   NIC

853T18
C1553

Tasso, Bernardo, 1493-1569.
Le lettere di m. Bernardo Tasso. Intitolate a
monsig. d'Aras ... In Vinegia, Appresso Vincenz
Valgrisi, 1553.
488, ⸤8⸥p. 15cm.

Signatures: A-Z⁸, Aa-Hh⁸.
Device of printer on t.-p.
Italic type; initials.
In manuscript on t.-p: Manilij Scipionis.

NT   0047743   IU ICU MH MWelC IaU

Case
E
5
.T 1835

TASSO, BERNARDO, 1493-1569.
Le lettere di M. Bernardo Tasso. Di nuouo
ristampate, riuedute e corrette. Venetia,I.
Sansouino,1570.
⸤7⸥,284 l. 15cm.

Title vignette.
Imperfect: last leaf mutilated.
Armorial bookplate: C.W.G.V.N.

NT   0047744   ICN DFo CSt ICU

SPECIAL COLLECTIONS
B851T1851
S6
1574

Tasso, Bernardo, 1493-1569.
Le lettere di M. Bernardo Tasso, vtili non
solamente alle persone priuate, ma anco a
secretarij de principi, per le materie che ui
si trattano, & per la maniera dello scriuere.
Lequali per giudicio de gli intendenti sono
le piu belle & correnti dell'altre. Di nuouo
ristampate, riuedute & corrette con molta
diligenza. Venetia, Appresso Gio. Antonio
Bertano, 1574.
⸤7⸥, 284 l. 16cm.

Printer's mark on title page.

NT   0047745   NNC PPLT MH INS RPB

Spec.
PQ 4634
.T6 Z5
1578

TASSO, BERNARDO, 1493-1569
Le lettere di M. Bernardo Tasso, vtili non
solamente alle persone priuate, ma anco a
secretarij de prencipi, per le materie che vi si
trattano, & per la maniera dello scriuere. Le
quali per giudicio de gli intendenti sono le
piu belle & correnti dell' altri. Di nuouo
ristampate, riuedute & corrette con molta
diligenza. Venetia, Appresso G. de Picchi, &
fratelli, 1578.
7 p.l., 284 numb. l.

NT   0047746   InU ICN TU IU

---

*IC5
T1852
549ln

Tasso, Bernardo, 1493-1569.
Le lettere di m. Bernardo Tasso. Vtili non
solamente alle persone priuate, ma anco a
secretarii de principi, per le materie che
vi si trattano, & per la maniera dello
scriuere. Le quali per giudicio de li
intendenti sono le piu belle, & correnti dell'altri. Di
nuouo ristampate, riuedute & corrette con
molta diligenza.
In Venetia.Appresso Domenico Caualcalupo.
MDLXXX.

8°. 7p.l.,248(i.e.284)numb.l. 15.5cm.
Printer's mark on t.-p.
Leaf 284 misnumbered 248.

NT   0047748   MH OU

---

*IC5
T1852
549lo

Tasso, Bernardo, 1493-1569.
Le lettere di m. Bernardo Tasso. Vtili non
solamente alle persone priuate, ma anco à
secretarij de prencipi, per le materie che vi
si trattano, & per la maniera dello scriuere.
Le quali per giudicio de gli intendenti sono
le più belle, & correnti dell'altri. Di nuouo
ristampate, riuedute & corrette con molta
diligenza.
In Venetia,Appresso Fabio,& Agostino Zoppini,
fratelli.MDLXXXII.

8°. 7p.l.,284 numb.l. 15cm.
Printers' mark on t.-p.
Wormed.

NT   0047750   MH CtY

PQ
4634
.T6
Z45
1585

Tasso, Bernardo, 1493-1569.
⸤Letters. 1585⸥
Lettere. Di nuouo ristampate, riuedute &
corrette. In Venetia, Appresso G. Cornetti,
1585.
284 p. 15 cm.

NT   0047751   DCU ICU ICN DFo WU MH

TASSO, Bernardo, 1493-1569.
Le lettere di M. Bernardo Tasso. Vtili
non solamente alle persone priuate, ma
anco à Secretarij de prencipi, per le
materie che vi si trattano, & per la maniera dello scriuere. Lequali per giudicio
de gli intendenti sono le più belle, &
correnti dell'altri. Di nuouo ristampate,
riuedute & corrette con molta diligenza.
Venetia, appresso Ioan. Griffio, 1591.
8 l., 284 numb.l. 15 cm.
Printer's device on t.p.; initials.

NT   0047752   MnU ICN NjP FU MH

Rare
Books
Dept.

Tasso, Bernardo, 1493-1569.
Le lettere di M. Bernardo Tasso ... Di nuouo ristampate,
riuedute & corrette con molta diligenza. Venetia, Appresso il
Griffio, 1597.
[7], 284 p. 15cm.

Several errors in paging.
Printer's device on t. p.

1. Italian letters.

NT   0047753   CU ICN OU

Tasso, Bernardo, 1493-1569.
Lettere inedite di Bernardo Tasso, precedute dalle notizie
intorno la vita del medesimo, per cura di G. Campori. Bologna, G. Romagnoli, 1869.
222 p. 19 cm. (Scelta di curiosità letterarie inedite o rare dal
secolo XIII al XVII. Dispensa 103)
"Edizione di soli 202 esemplari ordinatamente numerati. N. 72."

I. Campori, Giuseppe, marchese, 1821-1887, ed. (Series)
PQ4204.A3C6 vol. 103   A 53-4306

Cincinnati. Univ. Libr
for Library of Congress   ⸤1⸥†

NT   0047754   OCU PU CtY IU MdBP ICN MH DLC

T.ASSO, Bernardo, 1493-1569.
Lettere inedite di Bernardo e Torquato
Tasso, e Saggio di unabibliografia delle let-
tere a stampa di Bernardo Tasso. [Edited by
Giuseppe Ravelli]. Bergamo, tipo-litog.
frat. Bolis, 1895.

f°.pp.39+. Port.
"Bibliographia ," pp.25-39+
110 copies.
"Nel terzo centenario della morte di
Torquato Tasso".

NT   0047755   MH PU

PQ4634   TASSO,BERNARDO,1493-1569.
.T7A29   ...Lettere inedite di Bernardo Tasso. Verona[etc.]
Fratelli Drucker,1895.
[3]-36(i.e.37),[1]p. 20cm.
Page 37 wrongly numbered 36.
At head of title:Giuseppe Bianchini.
"Queste lettere...si conservano all' Archivio di
stato in Venezia in una busta-miscellanea di varietà,
che porta provvisoriamente il num.I."

NT   0047756   ICU MH

---

*IC5   Tasso, Bernardo, 1493-1569.
B4225   Libro primo de gli Amori di Bernardo Tasso.
530r   [Venice,1531]
60 numb.l. 21.5cm.
Colophon: In Vinegia per Giouan Antonio &
fratelli da Sabbio. MDXXXI.
Leaf 4 is blank except for the number.
Errata: l.60.
Bound with Pietro Bembo's Rime, [1530].

NT   0047757   MH ICN CtY NIC

Tasso, Bernardo, 1493-1569.
Hd28   Libro primo[-secondo] de gli Amori di
752   Bernardo Tasso. [Colophon: In Vinegia
Per Ioan. Ant. da Sabio,Dol XXXIIII[1534].
Del mese di Settembre]
127mmb.l.,+l. 14cm. [Bound with his
Libro terzo de gli Amori. Vinegia,1537]
Signatures: A-Q8+4(R4 blank)
"Libro secondo" begins on leaf 30 verso;
followed (with special t.-p., leaf [74])
by "Hinni et ode" (including "Egloghe"

and "Elegie").
Imperfect: leaf 1 (title-page?) wanting;
title, as above, taken from leaf 7.

NT   0047759   CtY

Case
Y   [TASSO, BERNARDO] 1493-1569.
712   [Libro primo[-terzo] de gli amori. Vinegia,
T 1546   1534-37]
2v.in 1. 15cm.

Colophon of first vol.: In Vinegia per Ioan.
Ant. da Sabio, del XXXIIII; colophon of "libro
terzo": In Vinegia per Barnardino Stagnino.
M.D.XXXVII.
"Favola di Leandro et d'Hero di Bernardo Tas-
so": l.lii-lxiiii of "libro terzo."
Imperfect   t.-p. wanting.

NT   0047760   ICN CtY

Rare Book   Tasso, Bernardo, 1493-1569.
Room   Libro terzo de gli Amori di Bernardo
Hd28   Tasso. [Colophon: In Vinegia Per Ber-
752   nardino Stagnino L'anno di nostra salute.
1537]
LXIIIImumb.l. 14cm.
Signatures: A-H8.

NT   0047761   CtY PU

Tasso, Bernardo, 1493-1569.
*IC5   Ode di messer Bernardo Tasso ...
T1852   In Vinegia Appresso Gabriel Giolito
560r   de'Ferrari.MDLX.
12°. 142p.,1l. 14cm. (In his Rime,[1560])
Probably also issued separately.
First word of title within cartouche at head;
printer's marks on t.-p. and recto of last
leaf.

NT   0047762   MH-H MWelC MiU IU PU NjP CtY

.Case
3A   TASSO, BERNARDO, 1493-1569.
2600   Prima[-secunda] parte delle lettere di M.
Bernardo Tasso alle qvali nvovamente si sono
aggiunti gli argomenti per ciascuna lettera:
di nuouo ristampata. Con la tavola nel fine.
In Vinegia, Appresso Gabriel Giolito de'
Ferrari, 1560-62 [v.1, 1562]
2v. 16cm.

Incomplete: Library has v.1 only.

NT   0047763   ICN ICU

Tasso,Bernardo, 1493-1569.
Hd28.748   Prima [-seconda] parte delle lettere di M.
Bernardo Tasso, alle qvali nvovamente si sono
aggiunti gli argomenti per ciascuna lettera: di
nuouo ristampata ...Vinegia,Appresso G.Giolito
de' Ferrari,1562-75.
2v. port. 16cm.
Title vignettes; printer's mark; initials.
Vol.2 has title: Delle lettere di M. Bernardo
Tasso nvovamente posto in lvce ... 1575.

NT   0047764   CtY

Rare Book   Tasso, Bernardo, 1493-1569.
Room   Ragionamento della poesia di M. Bernardo
Hd25   Tasso ... In Vinegia Appresso Gabriel Gio-
231   lito de' Ferrari,1562.
15numb.l.,1l. 19cm.
Signatures: A-D4.
Imperfect: t.-p. bled, with very slight
damage to device.

NT   0047765   CtY

Rare   Tasso, Bernardo, 1493-1569.
PQ   Rime di Bernardo Tasso. [Vinegia, per
4634   Ioan. Ant. da Sabio, 1534]
T6A7   127, [4] l. 15cm.
1534
Title supplied in manuscript.
Colophon (l. [4b]): In Vinegia per Ioan.
Ant. da Sabio del XXXIIII. del mese di Set-
tembre.
Contents.--Libro primo de gli amori.--
Libro secondo de gli amori.--Hinni et ode.

NT   0047766   NIC

Tasso, Bernardo, 1493-1569.
*IC5   Rime di messer Bernardo Tasso. Divise in
T1852   cinqve libri novamente stampate. Con la sua
560r   tauola per ordine di alfabeto ...
In Vinegia Appresso Gabriel Giolito
de'Ferrari.[1560]
12°. 5 pts.in 1v. 14cm.
Each part has separate signatures, separate
paging or foliation, & special t.-p.; pt.3
(Salmi) & pt.4 (Ode) both called for in Tavola
on verso of t.-p., probably also issued
separately.

First word of titles within cartouche at
head; printer's marks on t.-p.'s & at end of
each pt. (except 1st).
Contents: [pt.1] Rime [Tre libri de gli
amori].--[pt.2] Delle rime ... libro qvarto.--
[pt.3] Rime ... libro qvinto.--[pt.4] Salmi.--
[pt.5] Ode.
Other recorded copies have date in imprint;
in this copy date has apparently failed to
print.

NT   0047768   MH-H NjP MiU CtY DCU MdBP PU ICN IU CU

851.3   Tasso, Bernardo, 1493-1569.
T214r   Rime di M. Bernardo Tasso. Edizione
1749   la più copiosa finora uscita. Colla
vita nuovamente descritta dal Sig.
Abate Pierantonio Serassi. Bergamo,
Appresso P. Lancellotti, 1749.
2v. 15cm.

I. Serassi, Pietro Antonio, 1721-
1791, ed.

NT   0047769   IEN PPL PU CtY

PQ   Tasso,Bernardo,1493-1569.
4634   Salmi di messer Bernardo Tasso ... Vinegia,
.T6   Appresso G.Giolito de' Ferrari, 1560.
1560   24,37-48 numb.l. 13½ x 7 cm.
Title vignette (printer's device); in variant
form on verso of last leaf.
Nos.25-36 omitted in foliation.
With,as issued,his Rime. 1560.

NT   0047770   MiU PU CtY

Tasso, Bernardo, 1493-1569.

Petrarca, Francesco, 1304-1374.
Traduzioni dall'italiano di Barbarina lady Dacre.
[London, C. Whittingham, priv. print.] 1836.

SPECIAL COLLECTIONS
B851T1851
O3   Tasso, Bernardo, 1493-1569.
1555   I tre libri de gli Amori di M. Bernardo
Tasso. A i qvali nvovamente dal proprio autore s'è aggiunto il qvarto libro, per adie-
tro non piu stampato ... In Vinegia, Appresso
Gabriel Giolito de Ferrari et fratelli, 1555.
496, [6] p. 17cm.

Printers' devices on title page and on verso
of last leaf.

NT   0047772   NNC CU MH-H LNT DFo PU WU

SPECIAL COLLECTIONS
B851T1851
S62   Tasso, Bernardo, 1493-1569.
1559   Li tre libri delle Lettere di M. Bernardo
Tasso. Alli quali nuovamente s'è aggiunto
il quarto libro. Venetia, G. Giglio, 1559.
[15], 255, [7] p. 16cm.

Title-vignette.

NT   0047773   NNC PU

Case
3A   TASSO, BERNARDO, 1493-1569.
457   I tre libri delle lettere di M. Bernardo
Tasso. Alli quali nuovamente s'è aggiunto il
quarto libro. Vinegia, Appresso F.Lorenzini,
da Turino, 1561.
[8],255,[3]l. 16cm.
Printer's device on t.-p.
Numerous errors in foliation.

NT   0047774   ICN

Tasso, Bernardo, 1493-1569.
I tre libri delle lettere di M. Bernardo
Tasso. Alli quali nuovamente s'e aggiunto il
quarto libro. In Vinegia, Appresso Francesco
Lorenzini, da Turino, MDLXIII.
[8], 255, [3] l. 15cm.

Signatures: *8, A-Z8, AA-II8, KK2.
Many errors in foliation.
Manuscript notes.
Printer's device on t.-p.

NT   0047775   OO

Tasso, Bruno, tr.
   La letteratura americana

   see under

   Cahen, Jacques Fernand, 1908–

Tasso (Dominique) [1858–]. *Les scrofu-
lides chez les enfants du premier âge; notes cliniques. 50 pp. 1 l. 4°. Paris, 1895. No. 29.

NT   0047777   DNLM

---

*IC5   Tasso, Ercole, 16th cent.
T18523   Il confortatore di Hercole Tasso ...
595c   In Bergamo, Per Comin Ventura.CIOIOXCV.
    4°. 4p.ℓ.,166p. 18.5cm.
    First word of title within cartouche at
head; printer's mark on t.-p.
    Prefatory verse by G. B. Lícino.

NT   0047778   MH-H CtY MH ICN

PQ4634   Tasso, Ercole, 16th cent.
.T75   Dell'ammogliarsi; piacevole contesa frà i due
D35   moderni Tassi, Hercole, cioè, & Torqvato, gen-
1594   tilhuomini bergamaschi. Bergamo, C. Ventura,
Rare   1593.
Bk   ₊4₊, 55 l. 19 cm.
    Printer's device on t. p.; initiale.

    1. Marriage. I. Tasso, Torqvato, 1544-1595.
II. Title.

NT   0047779   ICU

Tasso, Ercole, 16th cent.
    Dell' ammogliarsi piacevole; contesa fra i
due moderni tassi, Hercoie, ...Bergamo,
C. Ventura, 1606.

    4 o   4 editione.

NT   0047780   MiU

Spec.   Tasso, Ercole, 16th century.
Arnold   Della realtà & perfettione delle
PN   Imprese di Hercole Tasso, con
6349   l'essamine di tutte le openioni infino
T 3   a qul scritte sopra tal' arte.
    All'illustrissimo Sig. Cardinale
Givstiniani.   Bergamo, Comino Ventura,
1612.
    [14] p. ℓ., 428, [4] p. 21 cm.
    Contemporary vellum.
    Illus. t.- p.; initials; head- and
tail-pieces.
    Praz 511.

    1. Emblems. I. Title

NT   0047781   MoSW MoSU OU NcU FU NcD DFo MH-H

Hd22   Tasso, Ercole, 16th cent.
684   Della realtà & perfettione delle imprese di
Hercole Tasso con l'essamine di tutte le opinioni
infino a qul scritte sopra tal' arte. 2.ed.
Bergamo,per C.Ventura,1614.
    13p.ℓ.,428,[4]p. 22cm.
    With printer's mark,having motto "Fortunae
bona," on title-page.
    "Lettera scritta al ... Cardinal Giustiniani":
[4]p. at end.

NT   0047782   CtY

Tasso, Ercole, *16th cent.*
    Dello ammogliarsi piacevole; contesa fra i due moderni
Tassi, Hercole, cioè, & Torqvato, gentilhuomini bergamaschi. Nouamente in più luoghi al confronto de' loro originali corretta ... Bergamo, C. Ventura, 1594.

    4 p. L, 64 (i. e. 60) numb. l. 20ᵐ.

    1. Marriage. I. Tasso, Torqvato, 1544-1595.

                           8-22022

    Library of Congress   HQ731.T22

NT   0047783   DLC MH-H

STC   Tasso, Ercole, 16th cent.
23690   Of mariage and wiuing. An excellent, pleasant,
and philosophicall controuersie, betweene the two
famous Tassi now liuing, the one Hercules the
philosopher, the other, Torquato the poet. Done
into English, by R. T. gentleman. London, Printed
by Thomas Creede, and are to be sold by Iohn
Smythicke, 1599.

    A-K⁴, L². (A1, probably blank, lacking.) 4to.
    Translated by Robert Tofte.
    'The declamation   against' is by Ercole Tasso;
the 'Defence', be-   ginning on sig. H1r., is by
Torquato Tasso.
    Harmsworth copy.

NT   0047784   DFo

FILM

    Tasso,Ercole,16th cent.
    Of mariage and vviuing. An excellent,pleasant,
and philosophicall controuersie,betweene the
two famous Tassi now liuing,the one Hercules
the philosopher,the other, Torquato the poet.
Done into English,by R.T..ofte?. ... London
Printed by Thomas Creede,and are to be sold by
Iohn Smythicke ... 1599.
    University microfilms no.15620 (case 60,carton 358)
    Short-title catalogue no.23690.

    1.Marriage. I.Tasso,Torquato,1544-1595. II.Tofte,
Robert,d.1620,tr.

NT   0047785   MiU CSmH MH WaPS

Case   TASSO, ERCOLE, 16th cent.
Y   Poesie del sig. Hercole Tasso...composte da
712   lui, in sua giouanile età, e già spartatamente
.T 16   stampate in Bologna, in Vinegia & in Bergamo.
Con brieui dichiarationi, annesse con gl'indici,
sopra le più di loro del sig. Christoforo Cor-
belli...   Bergamo,Per C.Ventura,1593.
    72(i.e.74)numb.leaves. illus.

    Error in foliation: leaf 74 incorrectly num-
bered 72.

NT   0047786   ICN CtY DFo NIC MH-H MiU

Tasso, Ercole, 16th cent.   Emb 16.1.
    Risposte di Hercole Tasso alle assertioni del M. R. P. Horatio
Montalto, overo Montaldo Giesuita, contra il trattato suo dell'
imprese, publicate sotto il nome di Cesare Cotta. Bergamo, per
C. Ventura, 1613.
    4°. pp. (6), 47 [51].
    With printer's mark on title-page.

    Montalto, Orazio

NT   0047787   MH-H INS DFo ICN

Tasso, Faustino, d. 1597.
    De sermoni in honore della Beata Vergine,
sopra l'evangelio Exurgens Maria abiit in montana.
E. sopra il Magnificat anima mea Dominum. Del...
Faustino Tasso...
In Venetia, presso Gio. Battista Somasco, 1589.
    2 v.   21.5 cm.

NT   0047788   NNUT

BV 4914   Tasso, Faustino,d.1597.
.T21   Della conversione del peccatore ...
(Rare)   libro primo [-terzo] Venetia, D. & G.B.
Guerra, fratelli, 1578.
    3 v. in1. illus. 20 cm.
    Titles within ornamental borders;
initials.

    1. Conversion. 2. Penance. I. Title.

NT   0047789   ICU MdSsW

Case   TASSO, FAUSTINO, d.1597.
D   Le historie de'successi de'nostri tempi_
17   Nelle quali si contengono tumulti, ribellioni,
864   seditioni_guerre de'popoli_& altre cose occorse
fra Catolici, & heretici, dal fine dell'anno
M D LXVI. fino al principio dell'anno M D LXXX_
Venetia, Presso D.& G.B.Guerra,fratelli,1583.
    ₊56₊,815,₊1₊p. 21cm.

    Printers' device on t.-p. and on verso of
last leaf; head and tail pieces, initials.

NT   0047790   ICN P ICU MdSsW

Hd22.685   Tasso, Faustino, d. 1597.
    Il primo [-secondo] libro delle rime toscane
del r. Faustino Tasso Vinitiano academico
detto Il Somerso. Raccolte da diversi lvoghi, &
date in luce da Girolamo Campeggio. Al
serenissimo Emanvel Filiberto dvca di Savoia ...
Tvrino,Francesco Dolce e co.,1573.
    2v. 19cm.
    Vol.2 has title: Il secondo libro delle rime
toscane del r. Favstino Tasso Vinitiano,
academico, detto Il Somerso. Rime spiritvali,
raccolte, e date in lvce per Girolamo Campeggio.
Al prencipe di   Piemonte ... Tvrino,
Francesco Dolce   e co.,1573.

NT   0047791   CtY ICN MH

Tasso, Francesco Maria, *conte*
       see
Tassi, Francesco Maria, *conte,* 1710–1782.

Tasso, Francois, 1911–
    ... Sur un cas demétastase de cancer du sein
à la choroide...   Paris, 1940.
    Thèse - Univ. de Paris.

NT   0047793   CtY

Tasso, Henri, 1882–

France. *Assemblée nationale, 1871–   Chambre des
députés. Commission de la marine marchande.*
    ... Rapport fait (au cours de la précédente législature)
au nom de la Commission de la marine marchande sur la
proposition de loi tendant à la création de zones franches
maritimes et fluviales, par m. Henri Tasso. Paris, Imprimerie
de la Chambre des députés, 1932.

Tasso (Joseph). *Propositions présentées et
soutenues dans l'Université impériale de Gênes.
2 l. fol. Gênes, De-Grossi, an 1807. [P., v.
2146.]

NT   0047795   DNLM

697.6   Tasso, Mario.
T18r   Riscaldamento a nafta; impianti e installazi-
one. ₊Milano₊ A. Vallardi ₊1954₊.
    118p. illus. 20cm. (Biblioteca di cultura
250)

    1. Heating. 2. Oil burners. 3. Petroleum
as fuel. I. Title.

NT   0047796   IU

[TASSO, Sefrino]
    Le calunnie smascherate dell' amo. Patuzzi
sedicente generale delle guardie civiche bo-
lognesi, sul sistema amministrativo di Roma.
n.p., 1832.

    24°.pp.48.

NT   0047797   MH

PQ4636 Tasso, Torquato, 1544-1595.
.A1
1922   Le opere ... Raccolte por Giuseppe Mauro ₍pseud.
₎ ... Venezia, C. Buonarrigo, 1722-42.
    12 v. front., illus.
    Vols.2-12, edited by A. F. Seghezzi, have title:
Delle opere di Torquato Tasso, con le controversie
sopra la Gerusalemme liberata, e con le annotazioni intere di vari autori, notabilmente in questa
impressione accresciute.
    Imprint varies: vols.2-12, Venezia, S. Monti e
N. N. Campagno.
    Engraved front., printors' dovices and initials

NT 0047798   ICU CtY RPB NbU CU-S PU NN MA MH NcD

Tasso, Torquato, 1544-1595.
    Opere di Torquato Tasso ... Firenze, Nella stamperia di
S. A. R. per li Tartini, e Franchi, 1724.
    6 v. port. 34ᶜᵐ.
    Engraved title vignettes; head and tail pieces; initials.
    Vol. 1 has added t.-p. (with vignette) : Opere di Torquato Tasso colle
controversie sopra la Gerusalemme liberata, divise in sei tomi.
    Edited by G. G. Bottari.
    "Vita di Torquato Tasso scritta da Gio : Batista Manso": v. 1, p. i-
cxij.
    "Varie edizioni della Gerusalemme liberata": v. 1, p. xxxix-xxxxiij.
    I. Bottari, Giovanni Gaetano, 1689-1775, ed. II. Manso, Giovanni
Battista, 1561-1645.

       29-9376

    Library of Congress   PQ4636.A1 1724

NT 0047799   DLC CtY PPAmP CU OrU PU MiU

Tasso, Torquato, 1544-1595.
    Opere. Milano, 1804-25.
    5 v. 8°. ₍Classici Italiani.₎
    ₍V. 1. 2, Gerusalemme liberata con annota-
zione. 3, Discorsi dell'arte poetica, e lettere. 4.
L'Aminta el poesie amorose.5. Prose scelte.₎

NT 0047800   CtY

851.46 Tasso, Torquato, 1544-1595.
T214OC
    Opere, colle controversie sulla Gerusa-
lemme, poste in migliore ordine, ricorretto
sull'edizione fiorentina, ed illustrate dal
professore Gio. Rosini. Pisa, N. Capurro,
1821-32.
    33 v. 22 cm.
    Each vol. has also special t. p.
    Contents.-1. Il Rinaldo.-v. 2. Aminta,
aggiuntovi Il rogo di Corinna.-v. 3-4. Rime.
t. 1-2. pt. 1.-   v. 5-6. Rime. t. 3-4.

    pt. 2.-v. 7-9. Dialoghi, con gli argomenti del
cavaliere A. Mortara.-v. 10. Prose varie.-v.
11-12. Discorsi.-v. 13-17. Lettere.-v. 18-23.
Controversie sulla Gerusalemme liberata.-v.
24-26. La Gerusalemme liberata.-v. 27. Il
mondo creato.-v. 28-29. La Gerusalemme conquistata.-v. 30. Postille alla Divina commedia

    di Dante Alighieri.-v. 31. Rimario della
Gerusalemme liberata.-v. 32. Rime inedite
o disperse.-v. 33. Saggio sugli amori e sulle
cause della sua prigionia.
    I. Rosini, Giovanni, 1776-1855, comp.

NT 0047803   NcD OrU NIC NcU CtY MH NN OCU ICN

Tasso, Torquato, 1544-1595.
    Opere di Torquato Tasso. ₍Milano, Società tip. de'
Classici italiani, 1823-25₎
    5 v. front. (port.) 22½ᶜᵐ
    Each volume has general half-title and special t.-p.
    Edited by G. Gherardini.
    Contents.—v. 1-2. La Gerusalemme liberata (incl. Fabroni's Elogio di
Tasso)—v. 3. Discorsi del poema eroico di Torquato Tasso e lettere poeti-
che dello stesso e d'altri particolarmente intorno alla Gerusalemme.—v. 4.
L'Aminta e rime scelte.—v. 5. Prose scelte.

    I. Gherardini, Giovanni, 1778-1861, ed. II. Fabroni, Angelo, 1732-1803.

       17-5378

    Library of Congress   PQ4636.A1 1823

NT 0047804   DLC CU NcD PU

PQ
4636   Tasso, Torquato, 1544-1595
+A1   Opere. ₍Napoli₎ Stabilimento del Gutten-
1840   berg, 1840.
    4 v. in 2. illus., ports., plates. 27
cm.

    Each volume has general half-title.
    Vol. 2 has special t.-p.

NT 0047805   WU PU

PQ
4636   Tasso, Torquato, 1544-1595.
.A1   Opere; a cura di Bruno Maier. Milano,
1963   Rizzoli ₍19
    v. port. 20cm. (I Classici Rizzoli)

    Bibliographical footnotes.
    Contents.-

    3. Gerusalemme liberata.

    I. Maier, Bruno.   ed. II. Series.

NT 0047806   OrU

PQ4636   Tasso, Torquato, 1544-1595.
A1   ... Opere. Bari, G. Laterza & figli,
1936   1930-36.
    4 v. 21 cm. (Scrittori d'Italia, 130,
148-149, 158

    Vol. 1-2, 4-5, edited by Luigi Bonfigli.
    Contents. - t. 1. Rinaldo. 1936. - t. 2.
Gerusalemme liberata. 1930. -

    t. 4-5. Gerusalemme conquistata. 1934. 2 v.

    I. Bonfigli,   Luigi, ed.

NT 0047807   OU CU

851
T18   Tasso, Torquato, 1544-1595.
A2   Opere. A cura di Bortolo Tommaso Sozzi.
    [Torino] Unione Tipografico-Editrice Tori-
nese [1955-
    v. illus. 25cm. (Classici italiani,
v.45)
    CONTENTS.--v.1. Gerusalemme liberata, e
passi scelti della Gerusalemme conquistata
e dei Discorsi.--v.2. Dal Rinaldo, dalle
Rime, Aminta, Il re Torrismondo, Rogo amoroso, dal Mondo creato.
    I. Sozzi, Bartolo Tommaso, 1909-   ed.

NT 0047808   TxU ICarbS MiU MH CU InU IEN ICU IaU

853T185 Tasso, Torquato, 1544-1595.
OpGr   Der adeliche hausvatter/ vor vielen jahren/ von
dem hochgelarten italiäner Torquato Tasso in welscher sprache beschrieben/ hernach auss derselben/
durch J. Baudoin in die französische übergesetzet/
₍unmehr aber verteütschet/in gewisse abtheilung
verfasset/ und mit nützlichen erläuterungen ver-
mehret und aufgezieret durch Johan Rist. Lüne-
burg/ Gedruckt vnd verlegt bey Johan vnd Heinrich
Sternen/ 1650.
    24 p.l., 235, ₍16₎p. front., plates. 13½cm.
    Title vignette.
    Imperfect: upper   part of p.7-8 torn away.

NT 0047809   IU CtY

FILM   Tasso, Torquato, 1544-1595.
4333
FT   Der adeliche Hausvatter/vor vielen jahren/von
Rcol   dem hochgelarten Italiäner Torquato Tasso in wel-
75   scher Sprache beschrieben/hernach auss derselben/
durch J. Baudoin in die Französische übergesetzet/
nunmehr aber verteütschet/in gewisse Abtheilungen
verfasset/...durch Johan Rist. Lüneburg, J. vnd
H. Stern, 1650.
    25p.ℓ.,235,₍16₎p. plates. 13cm.
    Added engrave t.-p.
    (German Baroque Literature, No.392, reel No. 75
Research Publications, Inc.)
    Microfilm.

NT 0047810   CU PSt

Tasso, Torquato, 1544-1595.
    The age of gold; a chorus translated out of Tasso's "L'Aminta"
by Clifford Bax. Derby, The Grasshopper press, 1944. 2 l.
21cm.

    One of 250 copies "printed for Kenneth Hopkins, The Grasshopper press...in
March 1944."

    464561B. I. Bax, Clifford, 1886-   , tr. II. Title.
N. Y. P. L.   January 12, 1949

NT 0047811   NN

Tasso, Torquato, 1544-1595
    Alcune illustri prose ed. by
Gamba. Bologna, Masi, 1830.

    88 p.

NT 0047812   PU MeB

M2   Tasso, Torquato. Alma cortes' e bella.
.T67
vol. 2   **Gabrieli, Giovanni,** 1557-1612.
    ₍Works, vocal. Selections₎

    ₍Composizioni₎
    (*In* Torchi, Luigi, ed. L'arte musicale in Italia. Milano ₍1897-
191-?₎ 32 cm. v. 2, p. 149-200₎

Tasso, Torquato, 1544-1595.
    Aminta, comedia pastorale del sig. Torquato Tasso; ₍a repro-
duction of ms. 795 (olim 1197), part 5, in the R. Biblioteca
Universitaria, Bologna, Italy₎
    2 p. l., facsim.: 47 negatives (each representing two confronting pages
of the original, except that the first represents the upper and lower cover
pages) mounted on 24 leaves. 28½ x 32ᶜᵐ. ₍The Modern language association of America. Collection of photographic facsimiles, no. 289. 1934₎
    Deposited in the Library of Congress by the M. L. A. Committee on
the reproduction of manuscripts and rare printed books.
    Collation of the original (a ms. on paper, dated at Ferrara, 28 Nov.
1577) based on the facsimile, which, however, omits fol. 116ᵛ-120ᵛ
(blank) : 51 follos (numbered 116-166 in a modern foliation) 15 x 11½ᵉⁿ.

    Signatures: A-M⁴ (M₍ᵢᵢ₎ recto is the last page of text). On fol. 166ᵛ
(*i. e.* M₍ᵢᵢ₎ verso) : "Registro. A ... M. Tutti sono fogli intieri." On fol.
166ᵛ, after the text, an ornament (an urn?) and the colophon: "In Ferrara, A'xxviij di di Novembre, ᴍᴅʟxxviɪ." Doubtless a ms. prepared
for printing, with the eight blank pages perhaps left for a preface.
    On the first prelim. leaf, half-title: Library of Congress. The Modern
language association of America. On the second prelim. leaf: a photostat
of the printed description of the ms. in Mazzatinti, Inventari dei manoscritti delle biblioteche d'Italia, xix (Firenze, 1912), p. 143; also a copy
of the description in A. Solerti, Teatro di Torquato Tasso (Bologna,
1895), p. xci-xcii, in whose ed. this ms. is designated as Ub.

    1. Manuscripts, Italian—Facsimiles. I. Bologna. Università. Biblio-
teca. Mss. (Ital. 795). II. Title.

    Library of Congress   Manuscript Div.

       Pho M 34-9

NT 0047815   DLC

---

854   **Tasso, Torquato,** 1544-1595.
T185ams   L'Aminta e il Torrismondo, precedono
    alcune pagine di C.L.Sismondi. Milano,
    Istituto editoriale italiano ₍n.d.₎
    214p. port. 19cm. (Classici italiani;
novissima biblioteca. Ser.2,v.47)

    I. Title. II. Title: Torrismondo.
III. Series.

NT 0047816   OrU PHC GU IaU RPB

PQ
4639   Tasso, Torquato, 1544-1595
.A2   L'aminta e L'amor fuggitivo; Il pastor fido
1812   del Batista Guarini. Edizione formata sopra
    i testi indicati nel seguente Avviso. Vene-
    zia, Vitarelli, 1812.
    455 p. ports. 13 cm.

    I. Guarini, Giovanni Battista, 1538-1612. / Il pastor
fido. II. Title. III. Title: L'amor fuggitivo.

NT 0047817   WU WaT OrU MH PU

PQ4639　Tasso, Torquato, 1544-1595.
A2　　　[Aminta. 1824]
1824　　　L'aminta e L'amor fuggitivo di Torquato Tasso; Il pastor fido del Cav. Batista Guarini. Ed. formata sopra i testi indicati nel seguente avviso. Firenze, presso Leonardo Ciardetti, 1824.
　　　　453 p.　2 ports.　23cm.

　　　　Modern red morocco.
　　　　On spine: Pastor fido.
　　　　Bookplate of S. Griswold Morley.

　　　　I. Tasso, 1544-1595. Amor fuggitivo. 1824.
　　　　II. Guarini, Giovanni Battista, 1538-1612. Il pastor fido. 1824.
　　　　III. Title. IV. Title: L'amor fuggitivo. V. Title: Il pastor fido.

NT　0047818　　CU-BANC FTaSU NIC TU MH MiU PU

Tasso, Torquato, 1544-1595.
　　　L'Aminta e l'Amor fuggitivo.　　Cremona, De Micheli, 1828.
　　　324 p.

NT　0047819　　PU

TASSO, Torquato, 1544-1595.
　　Aminta. Coll' aggiunta dell'amore fuggitivo
Nuova ed., corretta e migliorata. Firenze,
Tipog. A. Salani, 1890.

NT　0047820　　MH

Tasso, Torquato, 1544-1595.
　　　L'Aminta e le poesie amorose.　　Milano, Soc. tip. de'classici italiani, 1805.
　　　238 p.

NT　0047821　　PU

Tasso, Torquato, 1544-1595.
　　L'Aminta, e Rime scelte. Per cura di F.S. Orlandini. Firenze, G.Barbèra, 1862.

NT　0047822　　MH

853T195 Tasso, Torquato, 1544-1595.
Oa.Er　　　　　　　　　　Aminta Englisht. To this is
1528　　added Ariadne's complaint in imitation of Angvillara; written by the translator of Tasso's Aminta ... London, Printed by Avg: Mathewes for William Lee; and are to bee sold at the signe of the Turkes Head in Fleetstreet, 1628.
　　　[93]p.　18½cm.

　　　Signatures: A-M¹²(verso of M³ and last leaf blank)
　　　Illus. t.-p.

　　　Closely trimmed.
　　　Translated by Henry Reynolds. cf. Check list of the Huntington library; Dict. of nat. biog.

　　　I. Reynolds, Henry, fl.1630, tr. II. Reynolds, Henry, fl.1630. Ariadnes complaint.

NT　0047824　　IU CtY MH CSmH ICN DFo

FILM
Tasso,Torquato,1544-1595.
　　Aminta Englisht [by Henry Reynolds] To this is added Ariadne's complaint in imitation of Angvillara; written by the translater of Tasso's Aminta. London, Printed by A.Mathewes for W.Lee, 1628.
　　Short-title catalogue no.23696 (carton 941)
　　Microfilm.

　　I.Reynolds,Henry,fl.1630,tr. II.Reynolds, Henry,fl.1630. Ariadnes complaint. III.Title.

NT　0047825　　MiU

Tasso, Torquato, 1544-1595.
　　Aminta Englisht [translated] from the Italian [by] Henry Reynolds. London, 1628.
　　(In Three centuries of drama: English, 1512-1641)
　　Microprint.
　　Translation ascribed also to John Reynolds.

　　I. Reynolds, Henry, fl. 1628, tr. II. Reynolds, John, fl. 1628, tr. III. Title.

NT　0047826　　MoU

852　　Tasso, Torquato, 1544-1595.
T185aE　　Aminta, Englisht [by Henry Reynolds] To this is added Ariadne's complaint in imitation of Angvillara, written by the translater of Tasso's Aminta. London, Printed by Avg. Mathewes for William Lee, 1628.
　　1 v. (unpaged)

　　Xerox copy of the original.

NT　0047827　　WaU

Tasso, Torquato, 1544-1595.
　　Aminta de Torcvato Tasso. Traduzido de Italiano en Castellano, por don Iuan de Iauregui. A D. Fernando enriqvez de Ribera Duque de Alcala, &c. En Roma, Por Estevan Paulino, MDCVII.
　　Con licencia de los Superiores.
　　Tasa, Dedication, Sonnets, Approbation, List of characters, p. 87, 8°., morocco, gilt edges.

NT　0047828　　NNH PU

FILM　　Tasso, Torquato, 1544-1595.
x853T185 Aminta. Traduzido de italiano en castellano,
Oa.SPj　　por Iuan de Iauregui.　Roma, Por E. Paulino, 1607.
　　[16]s, 87p.

　　Microfilm copy.　New York, The Hispanic Society of America, 1971.　1 reel.　35mm.

　　I. Jáuregui y Aguilar, Juan de, 1583-1641, tr.

NT　0047829　　IU

Tasso, Torquato, 1544-1595.
　　Aminta, fábula pastoril; traducida por don Juan de Jáuregui. Madrid, Edición Estereotípica, 1804.
　　86 p.　17 cm.

　　I. Jáuregui y Aguilar, Juan de, 1583-1641, tr.　II. Title.
　　PQ4642.S22J3　1804　　　　　　52-46211

NT　0047830　　DLC MoU KU IU NjP IaU

Tasso, Torquato, 1544-1595.
　　Aminta, fabula pastoril de Torquato Taso, traducida por Don Juan de Jauregui. Madrid, Edicion estereotípica, 1804.
　　86p.
　　Microcard edition.

NT　0047831　　ICRL

PQ4642　Tasso, Torquato, 1544-1595.
S22J3　　Aminta, fabula pastoral de Torcuato Tasso;
1820　　traducida del Italiano por D.Juan de Jauregui. Barcelona, J.Busquets, 1820.
　　119p.　16cm.

　　I. Jáuregui y Aguilar, Juan de, 1583-1641, tr. II. Title.

NT　0047832　　IaU NNH

PQ4642 Tasso, Torquato, 1544-1595.
.S22J4　Aminta, fábula pastoril; traducida por D. Juan de Jáuregui. Madrid, E. Aguado, 1829.
　　78 p.　port.

　　I. Jáuregui y Aguilar, Juan de, 1583-1641, tr. II. Title.

NT　0047833　　ICU NNH PU

Tasso, Torquato, 1544-1595.
　　L'Aminta, favola boscareccia del signor Torquato Tasso; [a reproduction of ms. Barberinianus lat. 3910, in the Vatican library]
　　2 p. l., facsim.: 70 negatives (each, except the first, representing two confronting pages of the original) mounted on 35 leaves.　23 x 33cm.　[The Modern language association of America. Collection of photographic facsimiles, no. 291.　1934]
　　Deposited in the Library of Congress by the M. L. A. Committee on the reproduction of manuscripts and rare printed books.
　　Collation of the original (a 16th cent. ms. on paper) based on the facsimile: 69 folios (paged 1-74, 74bis-137; with a final page, blank

and unnumbered, not here reckoned in)　17 x 12½cm. From the library of the Barberini family, at Rome.
　　Msgr. Eugène Tisserant, of the Vatican library, finds the first 48 pages to be on paper bearing the watermark no. 652 of Briquet, from Salo, 1567, which would date this ms. among the earliest extant, soon after the composition of the poem (1573)
　　On the first prelim. leaf, half-title: Library of Congress. The Modern language association of America. On the second prelim. leaf: a copy of the printed description of the ms. in A. Solerti, Teatro di Torquato Tasso, Bologna, 1895, p. xcii.

　　1. Manuscripts, Italian—Facsimiles.　I. Vatican. Biblioteca vaticana. Mss. (Cod. Barb. lat. 3910)　II. Barberini family.　III. Title.

　　　　　　　　　　　　　　　　　　　　Pho M 35-36
　　Library of Congress　　　　　Manuscript Div.

NT　0047835　　DLC

Tasso, Torquato, 1544-1595.
　　Aminta, favola boschereccia del signor Torquato Tasso, corretta et accresciuta per Vittorio Baldini in Ferrara; [a reproduction of ms. Magliabechiano, VII, 333, in the Biblioteca nazionale centrale, Florence, Italy]
　　2 p. l., facsim.: 41 negatives (each, except the first and last, representing two confronting pages of the original) mounted on 21 leaves. 23 x 30½cm.　[The Modern language association of America. Collection of photographic facsimiles, no. 277.　1934]
　　Deposited in the Library of Congress by the M. L. A. Committee on the reproduction of manuscripts and rare printed books.

　　Collation of the original (a 16th cent. ms. on paper) based on the facsimile: 40 folios.　17 x 11cm. From the library of Antonio Magliabechi, 1633-1714. On fol. 1', the stamp of the Biblioteca nazionale, dated 182[4?]
　　The manuscript was doubtless the basis of the edition printed by V. Baldini, Ferrara, 1581, with which it agrees in text throughout.
　　On the first prelim. leaf, half-title: Library of Congress. The Modern language association of America. On the second prelim. leaf, a copy of the printed description of the manuscript in Mazzatinti, Inventari dei manoscritti delle biblioteche d'Italia, XIII (1905) p. 64, and also of the description in A. Solerti, Teatro di Torquato Tasso (Bologna, 1895) p. xciii.

　　1. Manuscripts, Italian—Facsimiles.　I. Baldini, Vittorio, 16th cent.　II. Florence. R. Biblioteca nazionale centrale. Mss. (Cod. Magl. VII, 333)　III. Title.

　　　　　　　　　　　　　　　　　　Pho M 34-5 Revised
　　Library of Congress　　　　　Manuscript Div.

NT　0047837　　DLC

*IC5　　Tasso, Torquato, 1544-1595.
T1853A　　Aminta, favola boscareccia di m. Torqvato
1580　　Tasso ...
　　　In Vinegia.M.D.LXXXI[i.e.1580].
　　　8°.　4p.l.,70p.　14.5cm.
　　　Printer's mark of Aldo Manuzio on t.-p.
　　　Dedication dated "Di Vinegia, a' xx. di dicembre, M.D.LXXX", signed, "Aldo Mannucci"; Tasso acknowledged receipt of a copy in a letter to Manuzio dated Dec. 3, 1580. (See Angelo Solerti, Bibliografia delle opere minori in versi di　　　　Torquato Tasso (1893) p.106).

NT　0047838　　MH-H

*IC5　　Tasso, Torquato, 1544-1595.
T1853A　　Aminta, favola boschereccia, del sig.
1581　　Torqvato Tasso. Corretta, & accresciuta.
　　　In Ferrara, Per Vittorio Baldini.1581.
　　　8°.　83,[1]p.　15.5cm.
　　　Printer's marks on t.-p. & p.[84].
　　　"Vittorio Baldini a'lettori" (p.[3-4]) dated: Della mia stamperia, il primo di febraro. 1581.

NT　0047839　　MH-H

*IC5
T1856
581a
  Tasso,Torquato,1544-1595.
    Aminta,favola boscareccia di m.Torqvato Tasso.
  Con privilegio.
    In Vinegia. [Presso Aldo Manuzio] M. D. LXXXI.
  4p.ℓ.,70p.   16cm.

    Publisher's device on t.-p.
    Dedication signed: Aldo Mannucci.

NT   0047840   PU MH CtY

853T185
Oa.m
1583
 Tasso, Torquato, 1544-1595.
    Aminta,favola boscareccia del s. Torqvato
 Tasso. Di nouo corretta, & di vaghe figure adornata ... In Vinetia, Presso Aldo, 1583.
  92p. illus. 12½cm.

    Signatures: A-D¹²(last two leaves blank)
    Device of printer on t.-p.
    Italic type; head and tail-pieces; initials.
    Dedicatory epistle signed: Aldo Mannucci.
    Originally printed as part of v.1 of the Aldine
  edition: Delle rime del signor T. Tasso.

NT   0047841   IU MH-H

PQ
4639
A2
1584
Cage
 Tasso, Torquato, 1544-1595.
    Aminta, fauola boscareccia...In Parigi, Appresso
 Abel l'Angelier¹ , 1584.
  46 [2] l. 12mo.

NT   0047842   DFo

853T185
Oa1589
 Tasso, Torquato, 1544-1595.
    Aminta, favola boscareccia del s. Torqvato Tas-
 so. Di nouo corretta, & di vaghe figure adornata
 ... In Vinetia., Presso Aldo, 1589.
  92p. illus. 13½cm.

    Signatures: A-D¹²(last 2 leaves blank)
    Device of printer on t.-p.
    Head and tail-pieces; initials.
    Italic type.
    Dedicatory epistle signed: Aldo Mannucci.
    First edition 1581.

    The woodcut illustrations are those of the 1583
  ed. of Tasso's works. cf. Renouard. Annale de
  l'imprimerie des Alde.

    I. Manuzio, Aldo, 1547-1597, ed. II. Title.

NT   0047844   IU MH-H

Rare Book
Room
Hd18
38
 Tasso, Torquato, 1544-1595.
    Aminta favola boschereccia del Sig.
 Torqvato Tasso. Di nouo corretta, & di
 bellissime ... figure adornata ... In
 Venetia,1590.Presso Aldo.
  4p.ℓ.,80p. illus,(incl.port.) 19cm.
  Signatures: *A-K*.
  Dedication signed: Nicolò Manassi.

NT   0047845   CtY

---

*IC5
T1856
581a
1599
 Tasso,Torquato,1544-1595.
    Aminta,favola boscareccia del signor Torqvato
 Tasso. Di nuouo corretta,& di bellissime¹,&
 vaghe figure adornata.
    In Ferrara, MDXCIX, Per Vittorio Baldini,
 stampator camerale. Con licenza de' superiori.
  82p.,1ℓ. illus. 13cm.

    Title vignette (portrait)
    Printer's device,p.[83]
    Illustration on p.32 signed: BF.

NT   0047846   PU ICU

IC5
1856
31a
503
 Tasso,Torquato,1544-1595.
    Aminta,favola boscareccia,del signor Torqvato
 Tasso. Di nvovo corretta,& di vaghe figure
 adornata.
    In Venetia, M D C III. Appresso Marc' Ant.
 Zaltieri,a San Giuliano,al segno del struzzo.
  72p. illus. 12cm.

    Publisher's device on t.-p.
    Title and imprint within woodcut border.

NT   0047847   PU

Q 4639
A2
1622
(Rare)
 Tasso, Torquato, 1544-1595.
    Aminta, favola boscareccia ... Di
 nouo corretta & di vaghe figure
 adornata ... Venetia, E. Deuch, 1622.
  88 p. illus. 13 cm.
    Title vignette (Tasso's port.)

NT   0047848   ICU

PQ4639
.A2
1650
 Tasso, Torquato, 1544-1595.
    L'Aminta, di Torquato Tasso, favola boscareccia. Tas-
 so's Aminta, a pastoral comedy, in Italian and English.
 2d ed. ... Oxford, Printed by L. Lichfield, for J. Fletcher,
 and sold by J. Nourse [1650?]
  [12], 135, [1] p. 16½ᵐᵐ.
  Italian and English on opposite pages.

NT   0047849   ICU CLU-C KU NNC

 Tasso, Torquato, 1544-1595.
    Aminta, favola boscareccia di Torqvato Tasso, con le annota-
 tioni d'Egidio Menagio. Parigi, A. Cvrbe, 1655.
  5 p. l., xviii, [4], 341 p., 13 l. 22ᵐᵐ.
  Engraved title vignette (printer's device)
  Engraved initials and head pieces.
  "Egidio Menagio [i. e. Gilles Ménage,] a' lettori": p. i-x.
  "Testimonii di diversi scrittori circa l'Aminta di Torqvato Tasso":
  p. xi-xviii.
  "Osservationi sopra l'Aminta": p. 91-334. "Aggivnta alle Osserva-
  tioni": p. [335]-341.
  "Amore fvggitivo" : p. 85-90.
  I. Ménage, Gilles, 1613-1692, ed. II. Title.   2-14053 Revised

Library of Congress   PQ4639.A2 1655

NT   0047850   DLC NNU NcU MH-H NcU PU InU

Rare
PQ
4639
A2
1656
 Tasso, Torquato, 1544-1595.
    Aminta, favola boscareccia.   Leida, Pre-
 so Giovanni Elsevier, 1656.
  [22], 84 p. 13cm.

    "Marque: le Solitaire."--A. C. J. Willems,
 Les Elseviers ... p. 197.

NT   0047851   NIC PU PPT MoSW PPFR

---

*IC5
T1853A
1656
 Tasso, Torquato, 1544-1595.
    Aminta, favola boscareccia del signor
 Torqvato Tasso. In questa vltima e
 correttissima impressione è stato aggiunto
 vn'elogio historico dell'autore.
    In Parigi,Appresso Clavdio Cramoisy,nella
 strada del Carmine,al Sacrificio di Abele.
 M.DC.LVI.
  4°. 4p.ℓ.,78p. 23cm.
    A reissue of the sheets of the 1654 Cramoisy
 edition with cancel t.-p.
    Publisher's de-   vice on t.-p.
    "Elogio   historico di Torqvato
 Tasso": recto of   2d prelim. leaf.

NT   0047852   MH-H PU

851.4
T214a
 Tasso, Torquato, 1544-1595.
    Aminta favola boschereccia del sig.
 Torquato Tasso. Di nuouo corretta, &
 accresciuta d'un breue Argomento. Dedicata
 all'illustriss. eccellentiss. Signore Don
 Givseppe de Medici, principe d'Ottaiano.
 [Printer's fleuron] In Nap. per nouello
 de Bonis Stamp. Arciuese, 1671. Con
 licenza de'Superiori. Ad instanza di
 Adriano Scultore.
  [12], 85 p. 12cm.

    Title within double line border.
    Added t.-p., engr.

NT   0047854   FU DFo MH-H

---

t PQ4639
A2
1678
 Tasso, Torquato, 1544-1595.
    [Aminta. 1678]
    Aminta, favola boscareccia. Amsterdam, Stamperia del s. D.
 Elsevier; Parigi, appresso Thomaso Jolly, 1678.
  85 p. 7 plates. 11cm.

    Calf; gilt spine.
    Imperfect copy: plate 2 wanting.
    Illustrated by Sébastien LeClerc.
    Cf. Brunet, v. 5, c. 672.

    I. LeClerc, Sébastien, 1637-1714, illus. II. Title. // t. Elsevier,
 Daniel, 1626-1680 (1678) t. Jolly, Thomaso (1678) c. 1678. Holland.
 c. 1678. France.

NT   0047855   CU-BANC PU

Tasso, Torquato, 1544-1595.
    L'Aminta di Torquato Tasso difeso, e illustrato da
Giusto Fontanini ... Roma, Stamperia del Zenobj, e del
Placho, 1700.
  xcv, 391, [33] p., 1 l. 16ᵐᵐ.
  Half-title: L'Aminta, fauola boscareccia di Torquato Tasso, con alcune
 varie lezioni cavate dal manoscritto originale.
  The text follows that of the Aldine ed. of the "Rime e prose del Sig. Torquato Tasso," Venezia, 1583, which Fontanini, p. 383, speaks of as the 1st
 ed. of the Aminta, though the latter had been printed at least three times
 before that, the editio princeps being the Aldine of 1581.
                                   2-14345

NT   0047856   DFo NcD CU PU CtY DLC

---

*IC5
T1856
581a
1705
 Tasso,Torquato,1544-1595.
    Aminta. Favola boscareccia di Torquato Tasso.
 In Venezia. M. DCCV. Appresso Gio:Gabriel
 Hertz.
  92p. illus. 10cm.

    Title vignette.
    Added t.-p.,engraved,with imprint: In Parigi,
 appresso Tomaso Iolly. 1700.
    Engraved illustrations signed Ant: Luciani.

NT   0047857   PU

Tasso, Torquato, 1544-1595.
    L'Aminta, favola boschereccia di Torquato Tasso; e l'Alceo,
favola pescatoria di Antonio Ongaro ... Tratte da' migliori
esemplari emendatissime. Padova, G. Comino, 1722.
  xxiv, 187, [1] p. 18½ᵐᵐ.
  Title vignette.
  Dedicatory letter signed by the editor, Gio: Antonio Volpi.
  "Edizioni dell' Aminta" : p. ix-xiv.   "Traduzioni dell' Aminta in diverse lingue" : p. xv-xvii.
  "L'Alceo" (p. [81]-187) with special t.-p., is from the Venetian edition
 of 1582.
  "Alcune notizie intorno alla persona di Antonio Ongaro, e alla sua
 favola pescatoria intitolata l'Alceo": p. 83-86. "Alcune edizioni dell'
 Alceo" : p. 87-89.
  I. Ongaro, Antonio, cn.   1569-1599. II. Volpi, Giovanni Anto-
 nio, 1686-1766, ed.   III. Title. IV. Title: L'Alceo.
                                  4—11869

Library of Congress   PQ4639.A2 1722

NT   0047858   DLC MH-H PU ICU PBL MiU

---

x853T185
Oa1726
 Tasso, Torquato, 1544-1595.
    L'Aminta, favola boscherecchia. Tasso's
 Aminta, a pastoral comedy, in Italian and English
 by P. B. Du-Bois.   Oxford, Printed by L.
 Lichfield, and sold by C. Combes, 1726.
  135p. 16cm.

    Italian and English on opposite pages.

    I. Du Bois, Peter B. II. Title.

NT   0047859   IU CSmH CtY

Tasso, Torquato, 1544-1595.
    Aminta, favola boscareccia del signor Tor-
quato Tasso, con alcune annotazioni, ed un
elogio historico dell' autore. Osford, Teatro
Sceldoniano, 1726.
  107 p.

NT   0047860   TxDaM-P CSmH

PQ4639
A2
1729
 Tasso, Torquato, 1544-1595.
    Aminta, favola boscareccia. Ed. nuova, riv.,
 e corr. per l'Abbate Antonini. In Parigi,
 Appresso Rollin, Cavalieri, Bordelet, 1729.
  vi,88 p. 21cm.

    I. Antonini, Annibale, 1702-1755, ed.
  II. Title.

NT   0047861   CU PU CaBVaU

PQ4639
.A2F7
 Tasso, Torquato, 1544-1595.
    L'Aminta. Difeso, e illustrato da Giusto
 Fontanini, con alcune osservazioni d'un acca-
 demico fiorentino [U. Benvoglienti, Venezia,
 S. Coleti [1730].
  2 pts. in 1 v. [391 p.]

    I. Fontanini, Giusto, Abp. of Anoyra,
 1666-1736. II. Title.

NT   0047862   ICU PU MH CU CtY

TASSO, Torquato, 1544-
Aminta; favola boschereccia. A correct
edition of the original Italian with a literal
English translation. By a gentleman. 2d ed.
Oxford, L.Lichfield, etc., 1731.

NT 0047863   MH

Tasso, Torquato, 1544-1595.
Aminta, favola boschereccia di Torquato Tasso, con le
annotazioni d'Egidio Menagio, accademico della Crusca.
In questa prima veneta edizione accresciuta & migliorata.
Venezia, G. B. Pasquali. 1736.
xlii p., 1 l., 387, [1] p. 19cm.
CONTENTS.—Dedicatoria.—Prefazione.—Testimonii di diversi scrittori.—
Edizioni dell'Aminta.—Traduzioni dell'Aminta.—Prefazione dell'editore.—
L'Aminta .... — Amore fuggitivo. — Varie lezioni .... —Osservazioni sopra
l'Aminta. —Tavola delle cose più notabili ....—Errori. Correzioni.
"Aminta ... con le annotazioni d'Egidio Menagio" [i. e. Gilles Ménage]
was first pub. at Paris, 1655, though the major portion of the book, the "Osservazioni sopra l'Aminta," appeared at Paris in 1655.
2-14346

NT 0047864   DLC MH PSt CU PHC PU

Tasso, Torquato, 1544-1595
L'Aminta, favola boschereccia di
Torquato Tasso; e l'Alceo, favola
pescatoria di Antonio Ongaro.....
Venezia, 1741

208 p.

NT 0047865   OU PPL

Tasso, Torquato, 1544-1595.
Hd18   Aminta, favola boschereccia, di Torquato Tasso.
44   In Parigi, Appresso Prault, 1745.
xix[i.e.xiv],103p. illus. 14½cm.
Dedicatory letter by l'abbate Antonini.
"Amore fuggitivo": p.[95]-103.

[Antonini, Annibale, 1702-1755, ed.

NT 0047866   CtY MdBJ MH NjP

Tasso, Torquato, 1544-1595.
L'Aminta, di Torquato Tasso, favola boschereccia. Tasso's Aminta, a pastoral comedy,
in Italian and English. Second edition ...
Oxford, Printed by L. Lichfield, for James
Fletcher; and sold by J. Nourse, London [ca.
1750?]
[12], 135, [1] p. 17cm.

Cf. Bibl. Nat. Cat. note for date from A.
Solerti, who attributes translation to P. B.
Du Bois; Brit. Mus. Cat. gives date as [1650?]

NT 0047867   NNC PPL MH-H OrU MWA

Tasso, Torquato, 1544-1595.
Hd18   Aminta; favola boschereccia di Torquato
45   Tasso. Glasgua, Della stampa di R.ed A.Foulis,
1753.
2p.l., [3]-74p. 16cm.
Illustrated by Sebastien Le Clerc.
"Amore fuggitivo": p.70-74.

I. Le Clerc, Sébastien, 1637-1714, illus.

NT 0047868   CtY CSt InU IEN MiDU ICN OrU OO PU

PQ4639 Tasso, Torquato, 1544-1595.
.A2C5   Aminta, favola boschereccia di Torqvato Tasso colla maniera d'imparar l'italiano. Dedicata ... da Nicolo Ciangulo
... Lipsia, Appresso G. S. Heinsio ed heredi, 1753.
[8], 94 p. 17¾cm.

NT 0047869   ICU

Tasso, Torquato, 1544-1595.
Aminta, favola boschereccia, di Torquato
Tasso. Parigi, Appresso Marcello Prault,
1758.
1 p.l., xlviii, 143 p. 14cm.

Illustrated t.-p.
Head pieces.

NT 0047870   NcD CaBVaU

Typ   Tasso, Torquato, 1544-1595.
725   L'Aminta, favola boschereccia di Torquato
62.822   Tasso. Aggiuntovi il poemetto Amore fuggitivo
(A)   In Venezia,MDCCLXII.Presso Antonio Zatta,
con licenza de'superiori.
12°. 1p.l., xvj,96p. front.,plates. 19.5cm.
Signatures: π², a⁸, A-D¹².
Title-page with vignette, frontispiece and
plates engraved by Ferdinando Fambrini after
Pietro Antonio Novelli.

Another copy. 17cm., in case 18.5cm.
This copy contains "Catalogo d'alcuni libri
usciti dalle stampe di Antonio Zatta ...
Venezia 1762": 6p. at end, signed E⁴ (E4
blank).
Limp yellow boards; in cloth case.

NT 0047872   MH-H ICU

Tasso, Torquato, 1544-1595.
*IC5   L'Aminta, favola boschereccia di Torquato
T1853A   Tasso, e L'Alceo, favola pescatoria di Antonio
1763   Ongaro ... Tratte da'migliori esemplari
emendatissime.
In Padova.CIƆIƆCCLXIII.Presso Gio: Antonio
Volpi. Cor licenza de'superiori.
8°. xxiv,187,[1]p. 19.5cm.
Colophon: [Volpi arms] In Padova.
CIƆIƆCCLXIII. addi 1. ottobre. Presso Gio:
Antonio Volpi.

Printer's mark on t.-p.
Edited by the printer's father, G. A. Volpi.
"Edizioni dell'Aminta": p.ix-xiv; "Traduzioni
dell'Aminta in diverse lingue": p.[xv]-xvii.
"L'Alceo ..." (p.[81]-187) has special t.-p.
"Alcune notizie intorno alla persona di
Antonio Ongaro e alla sua favola pescatoria
intitolata L'Alce": p.83-86; "Alcune edizioni
dell'Alceo": p.87-89.

NT 0047874   MH-H PU

853T185 Tasso, Torquato, 1544-1595.
Oa1765   Aminta, favola boschereccia con varie
lezioni tratte da un ms. originale
postumo dello stesso autore, conserva-
to dal ... Girolamo Baruffaldi, giusta
la testimonianza di monsignor Fontanini. Parma, per li fratelli Borsi,
1765.
80p.

NT 0047875   IU

Tasso, Torquato, 1544-1595.
L'Aminta, favola boschereccia di Torquato Tasso; aggiuntovi
il poemetto Amore fuggitivo. Venezia, Presso Antonio Zatta,
1769.   1 p.l., xxiv, 84 p.   illus., plates.   19cm. (12°.)

Morazzoni: Libro illustrato veneziano del settecento, 256.   See: Lanckorońska:
Venezianische Buchgraphik des XVIII. Jahrhunderts, no. 237.   See: Venice (City).
Mostra degli incisori veneti del settecento, 1941: Catalogo a cura di Rodolfo Pallu-
chini, no. 539.
Illustrations: 29 engravings (comprising frontispiece, illustrated t.p., 7 full-page
and 20 head- and tailpieces), by Ferdinando Fambrini after Pietro Antonio Novelli.
Engraved pictorial initials.

Includes "Edizioni dell'Aminta," p. x-xvi, and "Traduzioni dell'Aminta in diverse
lingue," p. xvii-xix.
With monogrammed wax seal on flyleaf.
Binding, 18th century Italian, of red leather, gilt.

1. Drama, Italian. 2. Engravings,   Italian. 3. Bindings, 18th cent.,
Italian. I. Novelli, Pietro Antonio,   1729-1804, illus. II. Fambrini,
Ferdinando, engr. III. Title.

NT 0047877   NN MH-H PU NjP

Tasso, Torquato, 1544-1595.
Aminta, favola boschereccia di Torquato Tasso. Ed. novissima, riveduta, e cor. Londra [Napoli?] 1774.
2 p. l., x, 104 p. front. (port.) 15cm.
"Amore fuggitivo": p. 98-104.

I. Title.
17-13124

Library of Congress   PQ4639.A2 1774

NT 0047878   DLC

Tasso, Torquato, 1544-1595.
L'Aminta; favola boschereccia,
e L'Alceo di Antonio Ongaro. Padova,
Comina, 1776.

140 p.

NT 0047879   PU NjP

Tasso, Torquato, 1544-1595.
Aminta; favola boschereccia di Torquato Tasso.   Londra:
G. T. Masi e Comp., 1780.   261 p.   plates.   16°.
Engraved t.-p.
In five acts.
"Canzoni amorose di Torquato Tasso," p. [107-]261.

1. Drama, Italian. 2. Title.
N. Y. P. L.   October 5, 1927

NT 0047880   NN NNC NBuG

Tasso, Torquato, 1544-1595.
*AC85   Aminta favola pastorale di Torquato Tasso.
H8395   Nella stamperia di Fr.Amb.Didot,Parigi,a spese
Zz781t   di Gio.Cl.Molini,librajo,rue du Jardinet.
M. DCC. LXXXI.
xvj,112p. 22.5cm.
Publisher's device on t.-p.
Printed on vellum.
"Prefazione di Egidio Menagio": p.[v]-xvj.
Imperfect: stained throughout; parts of the
title restored in ms.
Mildred   Howells's copy.

NT 0047881   MH

PQ4639 Tasso, Torquato, 1544-1595.
.A2   Aminta, favola pastorale. Parigi, F. A.
1781   Didot; G. C. Molini, Librajo, 1781.
Rare Bk   xvi, 349 p. 22 cm.

NT 0047882   ICU

Tasso, Torquato, 1544-1595.
*IC5   Aminta, favola pastorale di Torquato Tasso.
T1853A   Nuova edizione.
1781   Parigi,Presso G.C.Molini,librajo,rue du
Jardinet.M.DCC.LXXXI.
12°. 3p.l., [v]-xvj,127p. 15cm.
Another edition with the same
date has Didot & Molini imprint & xvj, 112p.
Added engr. t.-p. by Nicolas de Launay after
C. P. Marillier.
"Prefazione di Egidio Menagio": p.[v]-xvj.

"Amore fuggitivo": p.[117]-127.
Leaves containing p.77-78 and 99-100 are
cancels.

NT 0047884   MH-H

Tasso, Torquato, 1544-1595.
L'Aminta; favola boschereccia.
Nizza, Soc. tipografica, 1784.

100 p.

NT 0047885   PU

Tasso, Torquato, 1544–1595.
Aminta: favola pastorale di Torquato Tasso. Parigi: Cazin, 1786. xiv, 158 p. 24°.

Engraved t.-p. Added t.-p. has imprint: Orleans, C. A. I. Jacobs, 1785.
In five acts.
"Prefazione di Edigio Menagio."
"Amore fuggitivo," p. ₁81–₁86.
"Il congresso di citera, del conte Algarotti, accresciuto d'alcune Lettere e del Giudizio d'amore," p. ₁87–₁197 ₁really 147₁.

1. Drama, Italian. 2. Ménage, Gilles, 1613–1692. 3. Algarotti, Francesco, conte, 1712–1764. 4. Title.
N. Y. P. L. October 11, 1927

NT 0047886 NN CtY NjP TxU

Tasso, Torquato, 1544–1595.
Aminta, favola boschereccia di Torquato Tasso, ora per la prima volta alla sua vera lezione ridotta. Crisopoli ₁i. e. Parma₁ Impresso co' caratteri Bodoniani, 1789.

6, 142 p. 31ᶜᵐ.
Engraved title vignette (portrait of author) ; engraved head-piece.
Dedicatory letter in verse by Vincenzo Monti.
CONTENTS.—Prefazione dell' abate Pierantonio Serassi.—Aminta.—Intermedj rappresentati nel recitarsi l'Aminta.—Amore fuggitivo.

1. Tasso, Torquato—Portraits. I. Serassi, Pietro Antonio, 1721–1791, ed. II. Title. III. Title: Amore fuggitivo.
2–789

Library of Congress PQ4639.A2 1789

OrU InU ViU OClW OO MH
NT 0047887 DLC PSt FU OC NcD KyLoU OrU PU CtY ICU

Tasso, Torquato. 1544–1595.
Aminta, favola boschereccia di Torquato Tasso; ora alla sua vera lezione ridotta. Crisopoli ₁i.e. Parma₁ Impresso co' tipi Bodoniani, MDCCXCIII.
xxxv p., 1 l., ₁3₁–117 p. 45ᶜᵐ.
CONTENTS.—₁Lettera dedicatoria in versi₁.—Prefazione dell' abate Pier-Antonio Serassi.—Giambatista Bodoni à benevoli.—Aminta.—Intermedj ... rappresentati nel recitarsi L'Aminta.—Amore fuggitivo.
I. Serassi, Pietro Antonio, 1721–1791, ed. II. Title.

NT 0047888 ViU N MH MiU NcU OU

Tasso, Torquato, ₁1544–1595₁.
Aminta, favola boschereccia. Venezia, Stamp palese. 1735.

88 p.

NT 0047889 PU

Tasso, Torquato, 1544–1595.
Aminta, favola boschereccia di Torquato Tasso; ora alla sua vera lezione ridotta. Crisopoli ₁i. e. Parma₁ Impresso co' tipi Bodoniani, 1796.

xxxvii, 142 p. 24½ᶜᵐ.
Engr. title vignette (portrait of author)
CONTENTS.—₁Lettera dedicatoria in versi sciolti di Vincenzo Monti₁—Prefazione dell' abate Pierantonio Serassi.—Giambatista Bodoni à benevoli.—Aminta.—Intermedj ... rappresentati nel recitarsi L'Aminta.—Amore fuggitivo.
I. Serassi, Pietro Antonio, 1721–1791, ed. II. Monti, Vincenzo, 1754–1828. III. Title.
17–12347

Library of Congress PQ4639.A2 1796

NT 0047890 DLC MH CU PU NNC NcD CtY NN

Tasso, Torquato, 1544–1595.
Aminta, favola boschereccia di Torquato Tasso, ora alla sua vera lezione ridotta. Crisopoli ₁i. e. Parma₁ Impresso co' tipi Bodoniani, 1796.

xliv, 150 p. 17ᶜᵐ.
CONTENTS.—₁Lettera dedicatoria in versi sciolti di Vincenzo Monti₁—Prefazione dell' abate Pierantonio Serassi.—Giambatista Bodoni à benevoli.—Aminta.—Intermedj ... rappresentati nel recitarsi L'Aminta.—Amore fuggitivo.
I. Serassi, Pietro Antonio, 1721–1791, ed. II. Monti, Vincenzo, 1754–1828. III. Title.
17–12348

Library of Congress PQ4639.A2 1796 b

NT 0047891 DLC

Tasso, Torquato, 1544–1595.
L'Aminta favola boschereccia... aggiuntovo. Venezia, Zatto, 1799.

209 p.

NT 0047892 PU

Tasso, Torquato, 1544–1595.
Aminta; favola boschereccia di Torquato Tasso... Parigi: P. Didot e F. Didot, 1800. xvii, 99 p. 24°.

"Edizione stereotipa."
In five acts.
"Prefazione dell'abate Pierantonio Serassi."
"Amore fuggitivo," di Torquato Tasso, p. ₁97–₁99.

1. Drama, Italian. 2. Serassi, Pietro Antonio, 1721–1791. 3. Title.
N. Y. P. L. September 30, 1927

NT 0047893 NN MH CtY NjP ViLxW PPL PMA PU

PQ4639 Tasso, Torquato, 1544–1595.
.A285 Aminta, favola boschereccia di Torquato Tasso. Parigi, Appresso A.A.Renouard, IX–1800.
144 p. front. 15ᶜᵐ.
Title-vignette(port.)
"Prefazione dell' abate Pierantonio Serassi."
"Vita di Torquato Tasso":p.[5]–23.

NT 0047894 ICU PU OrP MH

Hd18 Tasso, Torquato, 1544–1595.
77 Aminta, favola con altre poesie di Torquato Tasso. Livorno,G.Gamba,1802.
xviii,218p.,1l. 17cm.
"Prefazione dell'abate Pierantonio Serassi": p.[111]–xviii.

I.Serassi, Pietro Antonio, 1721–1791, ed.

NT 0047895 CtY WaU PPA PU MH

Tasso, Torquato, 1544–1595.
Aminta, favola boschereccia di Torquato Tasso. Firenze, Presso Molini, Landi e comp., 1804.

2 p. l., iv, xv, 114 p., 1 l. 40½ x 26ᶜᵐ.
Dedicatory letter dated 1806.
Preface by Pierantonio Serassi.
Contains also "Intermedj dello stesso autore rappresentati nel recitarsi l'Aminta" and "Amore fuggitivo".

I. Title.
10–20210

Library of Congress PQ4639.A2 1804

NT 0047896 DLC ScU PU

*IC5 Tasso, Torquato, 1544–1595.
T1853A Aminta, favola boschereccia di Torquato
1811 Tasso.
Parigi,Appresso A.Nepveu.1811.
xvj,104p. 10 col.plates. 12.5cm.
Copy on pink paper; there were also copies on papers of other colors & on vellum, and the ordinary paper edition.
Printer's imprint on p.104: Stampato da Gillé.
Ten different colored engravings by Charles Johannot after A. J. Desenne, 5 on pink paper, & 5 on heavy paper.

"Prefazione dell'abate Pierantonio Serassi": p.[v]–xvj.
"Intermedi ...": p.[91]–96.
"Amore fuggitivo ...": p.[97]–104.

NT 0047898 MH-H PP

Tasso, Torquato, 1544–1595.
Aminta, favola boschereccia. Parigi, Presso Nepveu libraio, 1813.

xx, 115 p. illus. (part col.) 17 cm.
Pref. by Pierantonio Serassi.
Illustrations include 1 plate engr. after P. P. Prud'hon, 5 plates (each in both plain and colored impressions) and 5 colored vignettes engr. after A. J. Desenne.
"Intermedi de lo stesso autore rappresentati nel recitarsi l'Aminta": p. ₁101–106; "Amore fuggitivo": p. ₁107–115.

I. Prud'hon, Pierre Paul, 1758–1823, illus. II. Desenne, Alexandre Joseph, 1785–1827, illus. III. Title.

PQ4639.A2 1813 Rosenwald Coll. 75–206964

NT 0047899 DLC OO MH CtY

Tasso, Torquato, 1544–1595.
Aminta ... favola boschereccia. Firenze, Nicolo, 1819.

239 p.

NT 0047900 PU

Tasso, Torquato, 1544–1595.
Aminta di Torquato Tasso. Parigi, Lefevre, 1819.

123 p. front. 11 cm.

NT 0047901 NcD PU PSC MA

Tasso, Torquato. Aminta.

Jáuregui y Aguilar, Juan de, 1583–1641.
Rimas de don Juan de Jáuregui. Por d. Ramon Fernandez ₁pseud.₁ ... Madrid, Imprenta real, 1819.

TASSO, Torquato. 1544–1595.
L'Aminta; dramma pastorale [Pref. di V. Monti]. Firenze, G. Marini, 1820.

f°.

NT 0047903 MH

Tasso, Torquato, 1544–1595.
L'Aminta; favola boschereccia. Firenze, Lib. di Pallade, 1821.
97 p.

NT 0047904 PU

Tasso, Torquato, 1544–1595.
Aminta; favola boschereccia di Torquato Tasso. Milano, Dalla Soc. tipografica de' classici italiani, 1822. 127 p. 32°.

In five acts.
"Notizie intorno alla vita e agli scritti di Torquato Tasso," p. ₁3–₁12.
"Amore fuggitivo," p. ₁121–₁127.

Italian. 2. Title.
October 5, 1927

NT 0047905 NN AAP PU NjP

PQ4639 Tasso, Torquato, 1544–159 .
.A2 Aminta; favola boschere cia ... Padova, V. Crescini, 1822.
1822 xl, 134, ₁3₁ p. illus.
Manly Engraved portrait of Ta so on title-page; engrave tail-pieces.
"A' benevoli il tipograf o editore, Jacopo Crescini": p.v–xii.
"Prefazione di Giovanni Zuccala": p.xv–xl.
"La presenta edizione di soli 100 esemplari numerati in carta velina bi nca ... Esemplare no.24."
"Descrizione bil iografica e critica delle edizioni dell' Aminta₁: p.121–134.

NT 0047906 ICU MWiW-C

PQ
4639
A2
1824
Tasso, Torquato, 1544-1595.
Aminta, favola boschereccia di Torquato
Tasso. Firenze, Presso G. Molini All'insegna
di Dante, 1824.
viii, 487 p. plates. 15 cm.
Contents. Aminta. Le poesie scelte.- Dis-
cori dell' arte poetica.

I. Tasso, Torquato, 1544-1595. / Selected
works. 1824. II. Title.

NT 0047907   DCU MB MH MeB PU

TASSO, Torquato, 1544-1595.
Aminta favola boschereccia - L'Amor fuggitivo idillio - Carme del cav. Vincenzo Monti
steso a nome del tipografo Bodoni. Firenze,
1825.

24°.

NT 0047908   MH

Tasso, Torquato, 1544-1595.
Aminta; favola boscareccia di Torquato Tasso.   Firenze:
P. Borghi e comp., 1826.   101 p.   32°.

Title vignette.
In five acts.
"Amore fuggitivo," p. [95-]100.
Bound with: MAFFEI, F. S. Merope. Firenze, 1826.

1. Drama, Italian. 2. Title.
N. Y. P. L.   October 11, 1927

NT 0047909   NN PU MH

---

ar U
1180
Tasso, Torquato, 1544-1595.
Aminta; favola boschereccia; pubblicata
da A. Buttura. Parigi, Aimé-André, 1828.
121 p. 11cm.

I. Buttura, Antonio, 1771-1832, ed. II.
Title.

NT 0047910   NIC DLC

Tasso, Torquato. Aminta.
Buttura, Antonio, 1771-1832, ed.
I quattro poeti italiani, con una scelta di poesie italiane dal 1200 sino a' nostri tempi. Pub. secondo l'edizione del 1833 da A. Buttura. Parigi, Lefèvre [etc.] 1836.

PQ
4639
A2
1837
Tasso, Torquato, 1544-1595.
Aminta; favola boschereccia. 2. ed.
Milano, Società tipografica de' classici italiani, 1837.
213 p. 11 cm.

On spine: Tasso. Opere.

NT 0047912   CU-S

851.46
A5ge
Tasso, Torquato, 1544-1595.
L'Aminta.
(In Tasso, Torquato, 1544-1595. La
Gerusalemme liberata e l'Aminta. Paris,
Didot, 1854. 18 cm. p. [493-558.

NT 0047913   MoSU

Tasso, Torquato, 1544-1595
Aminta; favola boschereccia.
Torino, Guigoni, 1857.

93 p.

NT 0047914   PU

Y
7134
.14
Tasso, Torquato,   1544-1595.
L'Aminta, favola boschereccia di
Torquato Tasso.   (in [Camerini,
Eugenio] ed. I drammi de' boschi
e delle marine. 1874. p.[21]-82)

Half-title.
"Intermedi dello stesso autore
rappresentati nel recitarsi l'Aminta":
p.[75]-76.
"Amore fug   gitivo…": p.[77]-82.

NT 0047915   ICN

Tasso, Torquato. Aminta.
I drammi de' boschi e delle marine, ossiano L'Aminta di Torquato Tasso, Il pastor fido di Battista Guarini, La Filli di
Sciro di Guidubaldo Bonarelli, L'Alceo di Antonio Ongaro;
ora per la prima volta raccolti in un solo volume; aggiuntevi
le notizie degli autori. Milano, E. Sonzogno, 1878.

Tasso, Torquato, 1544-1595.
Aminta; favola boscareccia.
(in Tasso, Torquato. Il Rinaldo.
1884. p.263-352.)

NT 0047917   OU

TASSO, Torquato, 1544-1595.
Aminta; favola boscareccia, con gl'inter-
mezzi. Edita con prefazione e note da
Achille Mazzoleni. Bergamo, I. Carnazzi,
1895.

NT 0047918   MH

Tasso, Torquato, 1544-1595.
…Aminta; favola boscareccia. Firenze,
Quattrini [1914]
106 p. 18½ cm.

NT 0047919   NjP CtY

PQ4639
.A2P4
TASSO,TORQUATO,1544-1595.
…Aminta,dramma pastorale preceduto dalla dedica
di V.Monti;introduzione e commento di G.B.Pellizzaro.
2.ed.riv.e cor. Napoli[etc.]F.Perrella[1925?]
117,[1]p. 21cm. (Biblioteca classica italiana)
Bibliographical foot-notes.

NT 0047920   ICU CU

PQ4639
.A2
1926
Tasso, Torquato, 1544-1595.
Aminta, favola boscareccia; con introd.
e note di Angelo Solerti. Torino, G. B.
Paravia [1926]
xx, 138 p. port. 20cm. (Biblioteca di
classici italiani)

I. Solerti, Angelo, 1865-1907, ed. II. Title.

NT 0047921   ViU MiU ICU RPB MH CtY CU NNR

Tasso, Torquato, 1544-1595.
Aminta. Traduction française par Arthur de Rudder.
Domenico Belli, 1616: Orfeo dolente. Reconstitution et
harmonisation par A. Tirabassi. Bruxelles, Maison Del-
vigne, 1927.

79 p., 39 p. of music. facsims., plates. 34 cm.

On spine: J. Belli. Orfeo dolente.
"Il a été tiré de l'Aminta 250 exemplaires, dont 50 exemplaires de
grand luxe sur papier Van Gelder. Exemplaire n° 0041."
The music consists of the 5 intermedi, principally for 1-3 voices
and continuo or for chorus, which comprise D. Belli's Orfeo dolente,
previously published 1616 for performance between acts of Tasso's
pastoral drama, Aminta.

The words, in Italian, of the Orfeo dolente are in part constituted
from G. Chiabrera's dramatic poem, Il pianto d'Orfeo, scena 1.-3.

I. Rudder, Arthur de, tr. II. Belli, Domenico. Orfeo dolente. III.
Tirabassi, Antonio, 1882-   ed. IV. Chiabrera, Gabriello, 1552-
1638. v. Title. VI. Title: Orfeo dolente.

PQ4642.F22R8   76-200474

NT 0047923   DLC MH-Mu MiU

PQ4639
.A2L75
TASSO,TORQUATO,1544-1595.
… Aminta, favola boschereccia con prefazione di
Giuseppe Lipparini. Milano,C.Signorelli[1930]
97,[1]p. 15cm. (On cover:Biblioteca di lette-
ratura. No.27)

NT 0047924   ICU FTaSU

PQ4639
.A2M4
TASSO,TORQUATO,1544-1595.
…Aminta,con introduzione e commento di Giulio
Marzot. Milano,L.Trevisini,1930.
151 p. 20cm.

NT 0047925   ICU MH OU CtY

PQ4639
.A2A9
TASSO,TORQUATO,1544-1595.
… Aminta, introduzione e commento di Ettore
d'Avanzo. Napoli,A.Rondinella,1931.
157,[1]p. 20½cm. (On cover:Classici italiani)
Bibliographical foot-notes.

NT 0047926   ICU

Tasso, Torquato. L'Aminta.
Poliziano, Angelo, 1454-1494.
A translation of the Orpheus of Angelo Politian and the
Aminta of Torquato Tasso, with an introductory essay on the
pastoral by Louis E. Lord … London, Oxford university
press, H. Milford, 1931.

PQ4639
.A2F3
TASSO,TORQUATO,1544-1595.
… Aminta, con introduzione e commento di Luigi
Fassò… Firenze,G.C.Sansoni[1932]
xxiii,[1],111 p. 19½cm. (On cover:Biblioteca
scolastica di classici italiani…)
Contains bibliography.

NT 0047928   ICU DCU CtY MH OO CU IU

PQ4639
.A2T7
TASSO,TORQUATO,1544-1595.
…Aminta,note,bibliografia,introduzione su le fa-
vole delle selva e della riviera,a cura di Alessandro
Tortoreto. Milano,A.Vallardi[1932]
[3]-114,[1]p. plates. 19½cm.
"Postilla bibliografica":p.[19]-20.

1.Pastoral poetry,Italian. 2.Pastoral drama.

NT 0047929   ICU MiU NNF

Hd18
92
Tasso, Torquato, 1544-1595.
Aminta, con introduzione e commento di
Giuseppe Petronio. Napoli,F.Perella,1933.
xiv,106p. 21cm. (Semina Flammae. Biblioteca
classica italiana)

I. Petronio, Giuseppe   ed.
II. Title (1)

NT 0047930   CtY PPT

W.C.L.
851.46
T214AC
Tasso, Torquato, 1544-1595.
Aminta, con introd. e commento di Carmelo
Previtera. Milano, F. Villardi, 1936.
120 p. 20 cm. (Biblioteca dei classici
italiani annotati)

I. Previtera, Carmelo.

NT 0047931   NcD OrU

Tasso, Torquato, 1544-1595.
Aminta / di Torquato Tasso. Verona :
stampato per i Cento Amici del Libro,
1939.
127 p. ill.
"Favola boscareccia (1573)"
"Questa edizione ... composta a mano
con caratteri "Griffo" ... è stata
stampata in centoventi esemplari ... su
carta appositamente fabbricata nelle
cartiere a tino dai Fratelli Magnani de
Pescia. Le sette acqueforti sono di
Francesco Chiappelli ... "
"Questo esemplare è stampato per
Erardo Aeschlimann."
In slipcase.
I. Chiappelli, Francesco, ill.
II. Officina   Bodoni. III. Title

NT 0047932   TxDaM-P

PQ4639
A2
1943
Tasso, Torquato, 1544-1595.
Aminta / Tasso Torquato ; con
introduzione e commento di Luigi Fassò.
3. ed. Firinze : G. C. Sansoni, 1943.
xxiii, 111 p. ; 21 cm.

I. Fassò, Luigi. II. Title

NT 0047933   OU

PQ4639
.A2C8
Tasso, Torquato, 1544-1595.
Aminta. Introd. di Giuseppe Citanna. ₍Re-
visione di testo a cura di Carlo Cordie₎ Milano,
A. Martello ₍1944₎
126, ₍12₎ p. (I classici di filarete)
"Intermedi": p.₍127₎-₍135₎

1. Pastoral poetry, Italian. 2. Pastoral drama.

NT 0047934   ICU MiU

PQ4639
.A2T72
Tasso, Torquato, 1544-1595.
Aminta. Note, bibliografia, introd. su le
favole della selva e della riviera a cura di
A. Tortoreto. Milano, A. Vallardi ₍1946₎
114 p. plates.
"Postilla bibliografica": p.₍19₎-20.

1. Pastoral poetry, Italian. 2. Pastoral drama.

NT 0047935   ICU PLF InU MWelC

PQ4639
A2
1952
Tasso, Torquato, 1544-1595.
Aminta, favola boscareccia in cinque atti, un prologo e un
epilogo. Testo stabilito e commentato con introduzione da
Paul Renucci ₍e₎ Renzo Milani. Paris, Société d'édition Les
Belles Lettres, 1952.
xi,118 p. (Publications de la Faculté des lettres de
l'Université de Strasbourg. Textes d'étude, 13)

I. Renucci, Paul, ed.   II. Title.

CaBVaU
NT 0047936   CU CtY ICU OCU IU MiU NcD CSt ICarbS

Tasso, Torquato, 1544-1595.
... Aminta; favola boscareccia, con introduzione e commento di Bruno Maier. Milano,
Casa editrice L. Trevisini ₍1953?₎
186 p. 20cm. (On cover: Scrittori italiani con introduzione e commento)

NT 0047937   NcD

851.3
T21a
ed.3
Tasso, Torquato, 1544-1595.
Aminta. Introduzione e commento di Luigi
Fassò. ₍3. ed.₎   Firenze, Sansoni ₍1954₎
xxiii, 111 p. 21cm.
Bibliographical footnotes.

1. Fassò, Luigi, 1882-   ed. I. Title.

NT 0047938   CSt VtMiM

PQ4639
.A2
1955
Also in
General
Library
Tasso, Toquato, 1544-1595.
Aminta, favola boscareccia. [A cura di
Pia Piccoli Addoli. 1.ed. B.U.R. Milano]
Rizzoli [1955]
94 p. 16 cm. (Biblioteca universale Riz-
zoli, 926)

I.Piccoli Addoli, Pia, ed.   II.Title.

NT 0047939   MB MiU ICarbS NRU

Tasso, Torquato, 1544-1595.
... Aminta, a pastoral drama, edited with an essay on
renaissance pastoral drama and prose translation, by
Ernest Grillo, M. A. New York, E. P. Dutton & co.; Lon-
don, J. M. Dent & sons ltd., 1924.
vii, 200 p. 19ᶜᵐ.
Printed in Great Britain.
Lists of English, French and Spanish translations of Aminta, English
translations of Italian pastorals, and English pastoral plays: p. 193-198.
Bibliography: p. 199-200.

1. Pastoral drama.   I. Grillo, Ernesto, 1877-   ed. and tr. II. Title.
                                                    24-26920
Library of Congress   PQ4639.A2 1924

CU PU PPT NIC OOxM
NT 0047940   DLC CaBViP PSC OrP PRosC MiU MH OCU NN

Tasso, Torquato, 1544-1595
Aminta, a pastoral drama, edited with an essay on
renaissance pastoral drama and prose translation, by
Ernest Grillo. New York, Dutton, 1924

vii,200 p.
Microfilm, master preservation negative, of Harvard
College Library copy
I. Grillo, Ernesto, 1877-   ed.

NT 0047941   MH

Tasso,Torquato,1544-1595.
Aminta: the famous pastoral. Written in
Italian by Signor' ₍sic₎ Torquato Tasso. And
translated into English verse by John Dancer.
Together with divers ingenious poems. London,
Printed for J.Starkey,1660.
7 p.ℓ.,134 p. 17ᶜᵐ.
"Ex libris E.M.Cox."

I.Dancer,John,fl.1675, tr. II.Title.

NT 0047942   MiU NNC DFo NcD CSmH PU CtY

Tasso, Torquato, 1544-1595.
Aminta: the famous pastoral. London, J.
Starkey, 1660.
Microfilm copy from Mill.
Woodward & McMannaway No. 305.

NT 0047943   ViU

---

*IP7
P2427
v.24
(A)
[Tasso, Torquato, 1544-1595]
Aminta, Alceo [di Antonio Ongaro], Egle [di
G.B. Giraldi Cintio], favole teatrali del
secolo XVI.
Venezia,MDCCLXXXVI,Presso Antonio Zatta e
figli.Con licenza de' sup. e privilegio.
4p.ℓ.,304(i.e.318)p. 16cm. (Parnaso
italiano ovvero Raccolta de' poeti classici
italiani ... t.24)
Engraved t.-p.; title vignette.
Head pieces engraved by Dall'Acqua, with one

by Zuliani after Novelli.
Numbers 192-205 repeated in paging; p.191-192
(1st count) blank except for page number "191"
and signature "Alceo. Atto V."
Preface by Andrea Rubbi; editor of the
series.

*IP7
P2427
v.24
(B)
Another copy. 18cm.
In this copy, p.191-192 (1st count) not
present.

NT 0047945   MH ICN PU CtY

[TASSO, Torquato] 1544-
Aminta, Alceo, Egle. Favole. teatrali
del secolo xvi. [Edited by Andrea Rubbi]
Venezia, coi tipi di P. Bernardi, 1815.

24°. 332, [3].

Contents:-Tasso, Torquato, Aminta.-
Ongaro, Antonio. Alceo.- Giraldi Cintio,
Giovanni Battista Egle.

NT 0047946   MH

Tasso, Torquato, 1544-1595.
... Aminta. Madrigali e ballate. Introduzione e commento
di Tommaso Martella. ₍Roma₎ Editoriale romana ₍1944₎
213 p., 2 l. incl. front. (port.) 19ᶜᵐ. (Half-title: Collezione "Alfa," v)
On cover: Grandi scrittori d'ogni tempo.
At head of title: Tasso.
"Il testo seguito è quello delle edizioni critiche curate dal Solerti
('Aminta,' Torino, Paravia, 1901; 'Rima d'amore,' Bologna, Romagnoli-
Dall' Acqua, 1898)"—p. ₍16₎

I. Martella, Tommaso, ed. II. Title. III. Title: Madrigali e ballate.
                                                    45-16745
Library of Congress   PQ4639.A2 1944
                                                    852.4

NT 0047947   DLC NjP IU CtY

PT5659
.H92A66
1711
TASSO,TORQUATO,1544-1595.
Amintas;bosch-tonneel-spel van Torquato Tasso,uit
het Italiaansch vertaald. Amsterdam,By d'erfgenaamen
van J.Lescailje,1711.
₍16₎110,₍2₎p. 17cm.
Dedicatory letter signed:C.Hoofman.

NT 0047948   ICU

PT5737
.W45A72
1715
TASSO,TORQUATO,1544-1595.
Amintas. Herderspel,van Torquatus Tasso;met
eenige verklaaringen. Beneven eene verhandeling
van het herderdicht. Door Jan Baptista Welle-
kens. Amsterdam,J.Oosterwyk en H.van de Gaete,
1715.
[26],211 p. front. 20cm.
Title vignette.

1.Pastoral poetry.

NT 0047949   ICU

---

*NC7
B6446
B735t
Tasso, Torquato, 1544-1595.
Amintas. Herderspel. Uit het italiaensch van
T. Tasso.
Te Delf by Reinier Boitet.MDCCXXII.
71p. 17.5cm.
Title vignette, engr.
Translated by Cornelis Boon van Engelant.
No.5 in a volume lettered on spine: K. Boon
Tooneel poezy.

NT 0047950   MH

PR
3316
.A7
Z4
T2a
Tasso,Torquato,1544-1595.
Amintas,a dramatick pastoral written origi-
nally in Italian by Torquato Tasso. Tr.into
English verse,by Mr.William Ayre. [London,
1737]

6 p.ℓ.,3-96 p. front. 20cm.
Title vignette,engraved.
Imperfect: three preliminary leaves wanting.

I.Ayre,William, tr. II.Title.

     NcD NjP MdBP
NT   0047951   MiU CU IU ICU CSmH CtY MH-H ICN TxU PBL

Tasso, Torquato, 1544-1595.
Amintas.[translated] from the Italian [by]
William Ayre. n. p., 1737.
(In Three centuries of drama: English,
1701-1750)

Microprint.
Frontispiece, title page and prologue on
cd. 1, text on cd. 2.

I. Ayre, William, tr. II. Title.

NT   0047952   MoU

Tasso, Torquato, 1544-1595.
Amintas... Translated from Tasso by
William Ayre. Edinburgh, 1792.

v. 6

NT   0047953   PPL

Tasso, Torquato, 1544-1595.
Amintas. A pastoral, acted at the Theatre Royal.
Made English out of Italian from the Aminta of Tasso,
by Mr. Oldmixon ... London, Printed for Rich. Parker,
at the Unicorn, under the Piazza of the Royal Exchange
in Cornhil. 1698.

4 p. l., 56 p. 22cm.
[Longe, F. Collection of plays. v. 178, no. 5]
Fly-leaf contains a long manuscript note on Oldmixon.

I. Oldmixon, John, 1673-1742, tr. II. Title.

                                      26-2235

Library of Congress   PR1241.L6 vol. 178

     NjP ICN
NT   0047954   DLC DFo CSmH OU CtY TxU CaBVaU InU MiU

FILM
P-750
Tasso, Torquato, 1544-1595.
Amintas [tr. by John Oldmixon] [London]
R. Parker, 1698.

Microfilm copy
Woodward & McManaway No. 865.
Translation of: Aminta.

I. Oldmixon, John, 1673-1742, tr. II. Title.

NT   0047955   ViU

---

*IC5
T1853A
Eh591cb
Tasso, Torquato, 1544-1595.
Aminte, pastorale de Torqvato Tasso.
A Tovrs,Chez Iamet Mettayer,imprimeur
ordinaire du roy.D.M.XCIII[i.e.1593].

12°. 71 numb.ℓ. 13.5cm.
Prose translation of his Aminta by de la
Brosse.
With this is bound G. P. Guarini's Le berger
fidelle, 1609.
Bound in dark red morocco, gilt, with the
monogram "CM" within a border of s fermés.
Imperfect: wormed, slightly affecting
text.

NT   0047956   MH-H

Tasso, Torquato, 1544-1595.
L'Aminte dv Tasse. Tragi-comedie pastoralle, accommodée
au theatre françois, par le Sievr de Rayssigvier. Paris, Avgv-
stin Covrbé, M.DC.XXXII.

8 p. l., 148 (i. e. 150) p. 17½cm.
Signatures: A–B⁴, A–T⁴ (Q4, probably blank, wanting) [Q5] and [R1]
unpaged between p. [126] and 127. Title vignette: Device of Courbé.
"Avtres oevvres poetiqves dv Sievr de Rayssigvier. A Paris,
M.DC.XXXI.": 1 l., p. 127-148.

I. Rayssigvier, N. de, tr. II. Title.

                                   30-7371

Library of Congress   PQ4642.F22R3

NT   0047957   DLC OCU

---

x853T185
OaFd
Tasso, Torquato, 1544-1595.
L'Aminte dv Tasse. Pastorale. Fidellement
traduitte de l'italien en vers françois, &
enrichie de figures. Paris, P. Rocolet, 1632.
158p. fold.plates. 21cm.

Translated by Charles Vion, sieur de Dalibray.
Every leaf has been trimmed and mounted; the
corners of the last 5 leaves have been cut away,
with some loss of text.

Binder's title: Theatre de Dalibray.
Bound with Cremonini, C. La pompe fvnebre.
Paris, 1634, Dalibray, C. Vion sieur de. Le
Torrismon dv Tasse. Paris, 1636, and Bonarelli
della Rovere, P. Le Soliman. Paris, 1637.

NT   0047959   IU PU

CAGE
PG 1642
.F22 T6
1666
Tasso, Torquato, 1544-1595.
L'Aminte dv Tasse. Pastorale, traduite
de l'Italien en vers François. [Vignette]
A Paris, Chez Gabriel Qvinet, au Palais, à
l'entrée de la Gallerie des Prisonniers, à
l'Ange Gabriel. MDCLXVI.
[12], 185, [33 p. 6 plates. 15cm.
Engraved half title: L'Aminte dv Tasse,
pastorale, tradvite en vers libres.
Italian and French on opposite pages.
Translator's dedication "Av roy" signed
D. T. [i.e., l'ab bé de Torche] Cf. Brunet.

Plates signed L. Cossinus.
Duodecimo. ã⁶, A-G¹², H¹⁰.
Imperfect: stained.

I. Torche, Antoine de, abbé, 1631-1675,
tr. II. Cossin, Louis, 1627-1686(ca.) illus.
III. Title.

NT   0047961   MdBJ PBm

Tasso, Torquato, 1544-1595.
L'Aminte du Tasse. Pastorale, traduite de l'italien en vers
françois. Paris, Claude Barbin, M.DC.LXXVI.

6 p. l., 185, [2] p. 15½cm.
Title vignette: head and tail pieces.
Translator's epistle "au roy", signed: D. T. [i. e. l'abbé de Torche]
Italian and French.

I. Torche, Antoine de, abbé, 1631-1675, tr. II. Title.

                                   30-7372

Library of Congress   PQ4642.F22T6

NT   0047962   DLC PSt PU CU

Tasso, Torquato, 1544-1595.
L'Aminte du Tasse. Pastorale. Traduite de l'Italien en vers François.
Avec figures. Ital. et Fr. La Haye,
1679.

NT   0047963   PPL

Tasso, [Torquato] 1544-1595.
L'Aminte dv Tasse. Pastorale. Tr. de l'italien en vers
françois. Ed. nouv., rev. & enrichie des tailles douces.
Suivant la copie de Paris. La Haye, L. van Dyk, 1681.

5 p. L., 185, [2] p. plates. 16cm.
Added t.-p., engr.
Italian and French.
The translator's dedicatory letter "Au roy" is signed "D. T." i. e. l'abbé
de Torche.

I. Torche, —— de, abbé, tr.

                                     4-6792

NT   0047964   DLC ViU CLU DFo NjP PU

---

*IC5
T1853A
Eh785fb
Tasso, Torquato, 1544-1595.
L'Aminte du Tasse. Traduction nouvelle, par
m. Fournier de Tony.
A Londres[i.e.Paris?].M.DCC.LXXXIX.
12°. xxix,[31]-176p. 12.5cm.
False imprint.
Added engraved t.-p. with imprint: A Paris,
M.DCC.LXXXVI. Edition de Cazin, rue des
Maçons, n? 31.
"1789. Catalogue des petits formats qui
se trouvent à Paris, rue des Maçons, n°. 31":
p.165-176.

NT   0047965   MH-H

854
T185smF
Tasso, Torquato, 1544-1595.
Aminte, traduction du sieur de la Brosse,
avec une préf. par H. Reynald, compositions
de Victor Ranvier, gravées à l'eau-forte par
Champollion, dessins de H. Giacomelli.
Paris, Librairie des bibliophiles, 1882.
xcvi,115p. illus. 16cm. (Collection
Bijou)

NT   0047966   OrU MH

Tasso, Torquata, 1544-1595.
Gl' amori d'Armida, La fvga d'Erminia del
signor Torqvato Tasso. La cortesia di Leone
à Ruggiero, del sig. Lodovico Ariosto.
Ridotti in favola scenica da Giovanni
Villifranchi Volterrano. A' molti illvstri
signori il signor Marcello & il signor Ascanio
Agostini ... Venetia, Presso Gio. Battista
Ciotti, 1600.

NT   0047967   IEN

Hd18.43
Tasso, Torquato, 1544-1595.
The Amyntas of Tasso. Translated from the
original Italian by Percival Stockdale.
London,Printed for T Davies,1770. xviii,
[6],170pp. 20½cm.
Title-vignette.

I. Stockdale, Percival, 1736-1811, tr.

NT   0047968   CtY ICU TxU NcU RPB MH CtW CSmH CSdS

Tasso, Torquato, 1544-1595.
Amyntas [translated by] Percival Stockdale.
London, 1770.
(In Three centuries of drama: English,
1751-1800)

Microprint.

I. Stockdale, Percival, 1736-1811, tr. II.
Title.

NT   0047969   MoU

Tasso, Torquato.
Amyntas, a pastoral play from the Italian of
Torquato Tasso. Adapted from Leigh Hunt's translation ... 1902.
see under Bartholeyns, A O'D.

Tasso, Torquato, 1544–1595.
Amyntas, a sylvan fable by Torquato Tasso; now first rendered into English by Frederic Whitmore; drawings and cover by Wm. R. Whitmore. Springfield, Mass., The Ridgewood press, 1900.

1 p. l., iii, ₃₁, 72 p. front., plates. 12½ x 25ᶜᵐ.

I. Whitmore, Frederic, tr. II. Title.

1-29591 Revised

Library of Congress   PQ4642.E22W6 1900

NT   0047971   DLC

Tasso, Torquato, 1544–1595.
Amyntas, a tale of the woods; from the Italian of Torquato Tasso. By Leigh Hunt. London, T. and J. Allman, 1820.

3 p. l., ₇viii–xxxii, 146 p. front. (port.) 18ᶜᵐ.

"Imperfect; wanting the cuts, which should be at the beginning of each act."—Brit. mus. Catalogue.

I. Hunt, James Henry Leigh, 1784–1859, tr. II. Title.

17-7403

Library of Congress   PQ4642.E22H8 1820

WaU MiU NNC IU PBL OO NjP MB CSmH CU WU CSt TU MiEM
NT   0047972   DLC ScU InU MWiW-C NIC PBm MH MdBP NcD

B808
T18
no.20   Tasso, Torquato, 1544–1595.
Amyntas, schäferspiel von Torquato Tasso. Uebersetzt von H. L. von Danford. Zwickau, Im verlage der gebrüder Schumann, 1821.

xvi, 174, ₁1₁ p. front. 10ᶜᵐ. (Half-title: Taschenbibliothek der ausländischen klassiker, in neuen verdeutschungen. n⁰. 20)

I. Danford, H   L   von,   tr.

NT   0047973   NNC PU CU

---

*IC5
T1853A   [Tasso, Torquato, 1544–1595]
Eb638a   L'Amynte, pastorale, tradvction novvelle avec les figvres.
A Paris, Chez Tovssainct Qvinet, au Palais, sous la montée de la Cour des aydes. M. DC. XXXVIII. Avec privilege dv roy.
4°.   7p. l., 110p. 10 double plates. 23cm.
Reissued in 1659 with cancel t.-p.
Publisher's device (engr.) on t.-p.; plates engraved.
"Acheué d'imprimer pour la premiere fois le 28 may, 1638."
Translation   ascribed to R. Bonneau; also sometimes   ascribed to T. Quinet, the publisher.

NT   0047974   MH-H

---

*FO6
A100   [Tasso, Torquato, 1544–1595]
B650t3   L'Amynte pastorale tradvction novvelle.
A Paris, Chez Tovssainct Quinet, au Palais, sous la montée de la Cour des aydes. M. DC. XXXIX. Avec privilege dv roy.
3p. l., 110p. 22.5cm.
Publisher's device engraved on t.-p.
Errors in paging.
Probably printed from the same setting as the 1638 edition.
Imperfect? the 1638 ed. included 10 plates not present in this   copy.
No.8 in a vol-   ume labelled on spine:
Theatre françois.   Tom.3.

NT   0047975   MH

Case
Y
712   **TASSO, TORQUATO,** 1544–1595.
T 2345   Apologia del Sig. Torquato Tasso. In difesa della sua Gierusalemme liberata. Con alcune altre opere, parte in accusa, parte in difesa dell'Orlando furioso dell'Ariosto, della Gierusalemme istessa, e dell'Amadigi del Tasso padre. Ferrara, G. C. Cagnacini, et Fratelli, 1585.
2v. in l.   15cm.

Printer's device on t.-p.
Signatures: †⁸ († 8 blank), A-G⁸; A-O⁸, P².
Edited by G.B.   Licino.

Imperfect: sig. D 1 (first group) wanting.
Contents.--Dialogo del Sig. Camillo Pellegrino.--Chiose dell'Academia della Crusca di Fiorenza.--Apologia del Signor Torquato Tasso. --Lettere del medesimo, e d'altri in materia della Gierusalemme.--Lettera del medesimo, in lode dell'Ariosto.--Parere del Signor Francesco Patritio.--Difese del Furioso fatte dal Signor Horatio   Ariosto.

MH MnU NjP TxU CtY
NT   0047977   ICN InU MiU MWelC IEN PPL CSt PU NcD CU

PG 1656
.A 1
1585 R   Tasso, Torquato, 1544–1595.
Apologia del S. Torqvato Tasso. In difesa della sva Giervsalemme Liberata. Ferrara, Appresso Giulio Cesare Cagnacini & fratelli, 1585.
114 l.   15cm.

A detached copy of the 3d-7th parts of the collection edited by Giovanni Battista Licino, with the t.-p. of the 3d part, from which the collec-   tion takes its name. cf. Solerti, A.   Appendice alle opere

in prosa di Torquato Tasso. Firenze, 1892. p. 36-37.
Contents.- Apologia del S. Torqvato Tasso.- Lettere diverse scritte dal Sig. Torqvato Tasso. Et da altri in materia della Gierusalemme Liberata. Con vna del Tasso medesimo, in lode dell'Ariosto.- Parere del Signor Francesco Patrici, in difesa   dell'Ariosto.- Difese dell'Orlando   Fvrioso dell'Ariosto. Fatte dal Signor   Horatio Ariosto.

NT   0047979   MdBJ

PG 1656
.A 1
1585a R   Tasso, Torquato, 1544–1595.
Apologia del S. Torqvato Tasso. In difesa della sva Giervsalemme liberata. Con alcune altre opere, parte in accusa, parte in difesa dell' Orlando Furioso dell' Ariosto. Della Gierusalemme istessa, e dell' Amadigi del Tasso Padre ... Mantoua, Per Francesco Osana, 1585.
8 p.l., [122], 219 p.   13½cm.

Title vignette (printer's mark)
Consists of 7   (actually 6) parts, the third, from which   the collection takes its name, having   a special t.-p.

Edited by Giovanni Battista Licino.
Contents.- Chiose dell' Academia della Crusca di Fiorenza.- De gli accademici della Crvsca difesa dell' Orlando Furioso dell' Ariosto contra'l Dialogo dell' epica poesia di Camillo Pellegrino.- Apologia del S. Torquato Tasso. In difesa della sua Gierusalemme liberata.- Lettere diverse scritte   dal Signor Torquato Tasso. Et da   altri in materia della

Gierusalemme Liberata. Con una del Tasso medesimo in lode dell' Ariosto.- Parere del Signor Francesco Patrici, in difesa dell' Ariosto.- Difese dell' Orlando Fvrioso dell' Ariosto fatte dal S. Horatio Ariosto.
With this are bound [Salviati, Leonardo] Dell'Infarinato, academico della Crvsca ... Mantova, 1585; Tasso,   Torquato. Risposta ... alla lettera   di Bastian Rossi ...

Mantova, 1585; Lombardelli, Orazio. Discorso intorno a'contrasti, che si fanno sopra la Gierusalemme liberata del Signor Torquato Tasso ... Mantoua, 1586 and Tasso, Torquato. Parere ... sopra il Discorso del Signor Horatio Lombardello intorno a' contrasti, &c ... Mantoua, 1586.

NT   0047983   MdBJ

Case
Y
712   TASSO, TORQUATO, 1544–1595.
T 2346   Apologia del S. Torquato Tasso. In difesa della sua Gierusalemme liberata. Con alcune altre opere, parte in accusa, parte in difesa dell'Orlando furioso dell'Ariosto, della Gierusalemme istessa, e dell'Amadigi del Tasso padre. Mantoua, Per F. Osana, 1585.
₇138₁, 219p. 14cm.
The "Apologia" has special t.-p. Printer's device on title-pages; initials, head and tail-pieces.
Contents.--Dialogo del Sig. Camillo Pellegrino.--Chiose dell'Academia della Crusca di Fiorenza.--Apologia del Sig. Torquato Tasso.-- Lettere del medesimo,   e d'altri in materia della Gierusalemme.   --Lettera del medesimo in lode dell'Ariost   o.--Parere del S. Frances- co Patritio.--Difese   del Furioso fatte dal   S. Horatio Ariosto.

NT   0047984   ICN PPL CtY MH MdBJ PU

PQ4656 Tasso, Torquato, 1544–1595.
.A2A3   Apologia del S. Torq. Tasso, in difesa della sua Gieru-
1586   salemme liberata, a gli accademici della Crvsca. Con le accuse, & difese dell'Orlando furioso dell'Ariosto. Et alcvne lettere, pareri, & discorsi di diuersi auttori nel medesimo genere. Di nuouo cor., & ristampata. Aggiontovi la risposta dell'istesso Tasso, al discorso del Lombardelli ... Ferrara, G. Vasalini, 1586.

₁16₁, 227 (i. e. 327) p. 15ᶜᵐ.
Title vignette.
Errors in paging.

"Apologia" (p. ₁121₁–115, i. e. 215) has special t.-p., with vignette, and is preceded by "Difesa dell'Orlando fvrioso ... contra'l Dialogo ... di Cammillo Pellegrino. De gli accademici della Crvsca."
Edited by G. B. Licini.

1. Tasso-Ariosto controversy, 1584–1590. 2. Tasso, Torquato. Gerusalemme liberata. 3. Ariosto, Lodovico, 1474–1533. Orlando furioso. 4. Pellegrini, Camillo, fl. 1585. 5. Lombardelli, Gregorio, d. 1613.

MnU DFo InU CLU
NT   0047986   ICU DFo PV NPV PU MH MWelC NcD CU IU

Tasso, Torquato, 1544–1595.
Appendice alle opere in prosa di Torquato Tasso a cura di Angelo Solerti. Firenze, Successori Le Monnier, 1892.

456, ₃₁ p. 19¼ᶜᵐ.

"È questo volume una appendice divenuta ormai necessaria alla edizione delle opere in prosa del Tasso, procurata dal compianto Cesare Guasti ... Lettere (1853-55) ... Dialoghi (1858-59) ... Prose diverse (1875)"—Avvertimento.
Includes "Intrichi d'amore. Commedia."
Bibliography: p. ₁11₁-67.

I. Solerti, Angelo, 1865–1907, ed.

14-22193

Library of Congress   PQ4640.A1 1892

NT   0047987   DLC MiU NIC PBm CU NjP

Tasso, Torquato, 1544–1595.
Argante e Tancredi (studio sul Tasso) [With selections from Gerusalemme liberata and Gerusalemme conquistata] 1888
see under   Mocavini, Roberto.

Tasso, Torquato, 1544–1595.
Armida und Rinaldo... *Melodrama 1793.*
see under   [Babo, Joseph Marius,] 1756–1822.

---

tPQ4642 Tasso, Torquato, 1544–1595.
G2   Auserlesene Gedichte. Deutsch von Karl
1821   Förster. Zwickau, Gebrüder, Schumann, 1821.
2 v. in l.   11cm.

Contents.- 1. Büchen. Sonette.-
2. Büchen. Canzonen, Madrigale und Stanzen.

I. Förster, Karl August, 1784–1841, tr.

NT   0047990   CU PU NNC MiU

PQ4642 Tasso, Torquato, 1544–1595.
G23F6   Auserlesene lyrische Gedichte. Aus dem
1844   Italienischen übers. von Karl Förster. Mit einer Einleitung: "Ueber Torquato Tasso als lyrischen Dichter." 2. verm. und verb. Aufl. Leipzig, F.A. Brockhaus, 1844.
2 v. in l. ₇Ausgewählte Bibliothek der Classiker im Auslande. 31.-32.Bd.₁

I. Förster, Karl August, 1784–1841. tr.

NT   0047991   CU ICU

Tasso, Torquato, 1544-
Das befreite Jerusalem neu uebersetzt
Muenchen, Michaelis, 1827.

8v. in 4

NT 0048001   PU

Tasso, Torquato, 1544-1595.
Das befreite Jerusalem... aus dem italienischen
übersetzt von Karl Streckfuss. Ed. 4.   Leipzig,
Brockhaus, 1847.
2 v. in 1.

NT 0048002   PU

Tasso, Torquato, 1544-1595.
... Das befreite Jerusalem, uebers. von J. D. Gries, mit einer
einleitung von Siegfried Samosch. Berlin & Stuttgart, W.
Spemann [1883]
338 p. 18ᶜᵐ. (Collection Spemann. [Deutsche hand- und hausbiblio-
thek, 256.])
At head of title : Torquato Tassos werke, 1.

I. Gries, Johann Diederich, 1775-1842, tr.
17—12351

Library of Congress   PQ4642.G2G7   1883

NT 0048003   DLC PPT OC1

Tasso, Torquato, 1544-1595.
Das befreite Jerusalem. Grosses pantomim. Ballet
see under   Samengo, Paolo.

TASSO, Torquato.
Befreites Jerusalem. Übersetzt von J.D.
Gries. 4 theile (in 1 vol.) Jena, F.
Frommann, 1800-03.

sm.4°.

NT 0048005   MH

PQ4642 Tasso, Torquato, 1544-1595.
.G21G76   Torquato Tasso's Befreites Jerusalem, übers. von J. D.
Gries. 2. umgearb. aufl. ... Jena, F. Frommann, 1810.
2 v. 21ᶜᵐ.

NT 0048006   ICU MH

PQ
4642
G.
S83   Tasso, Torquato, 1544-1595.
1822   Torquato Tasso's befreites Jerusalem, über-
HRC   setzt von Karl Streckfuss ... Mit gegenüber
gedrucktem Original-Text.   Leipzig, Brockhaus, 1822.
2v. 21cm.

German and Italian on opposite pages.
Translation of La Gerusalemme liberata.

I. Streckfuss, Adolf Freidrich Karl, 1778-
1844, tr. II. Title: Befreites Jerusalem.

NT 0048007   TxU MH

Tasso, Torquato, 1544-
Befreites Jerusalem; übersetzt von
J. Gries. Neue bearb.   Stuttgart,
Macklot, 1822.

2 v. in 1

NT 0048008   PPLT CU RPB

Y   TASSO, TORQUATO, 1544-1595.
712   Torquato Tasso's Befreites Jerusalem, über-
.T 223   setzt von J.D.Gries. 4. rechtmässige auflage,
von neuem durchgesehen...   Jena,F.Frommann,1824.
2v. 21½cm.

NT 0048009   ICN PU OO MH IU

Tasso, Torquato, 1544-
Befreites Jerusalem. Übersetzt von Karl
Streckfuss. 2.verbesserte Aufl. Leipzig, F.A.
Brockhaus, 1835.

2 v. in 1.

NT 0048010   MH

PQ4642 Tasso, Torquato, 1544-1595.
.G21G8   Torquato Tasso's Befreites Jerusalem, übers. von J. D.
Gries. 5. rechtmässige aufl., von neuem durchgesehen ...
Jena, F. Frommann, 1837.
2 v. 17½ᶜᵐ.

NT 0048011   ICU KyLoU OC1 TxU

Tasso, Torquato, 1544-
Befreites Jerusalem uebersetzt von
Karl Streckfuss. Ed. 3.
(in Streckfuss, A.F.K. comp. & tr.
Meisterwerke italiaenischen dichtkunst.
(binder's title) 1839-40.)

NT 0048012   PU

TASSO, Torquato, 1544-
Befreites Jerusalem. Im versmaasse der
urschrift übersetzt   von F. M. Duttenhofer,
Stuttgart, Hoffmann, 1840.

Front.

NT 0048013   MH

TASSO, Torquato, 1544-
Befreites Jerusalem. Übersetzt   von J.D.
Greis. 6e aufl. 2 theile (in 1 vol.),
Leipzig, Weidmann, 1844.

24°.

NT 0048014   MH

Tasso, Torquato, 1544-1595.
Befreites Jerusalem. Übersetzt von J.D. Gries.
Leipzig, P.Reclam, jun. [185- ?]

451 p.

NT 0048015   MH PPG IU

Tasso, Torquato, 1544-1595.
Torquato Tasso's Befreites Jerusalem, übersetzt von J. D.
Gries. 8. aufl. ... Leipzig, Weidmann, 1851.
2 v. in 1. 15ᶜᵐ.

I. Gries, Johann Diederich, 1775-1842, tr.
32—8859

Library of Congress   PQ4642.G21G7   1851   851.46

NT 0048016   DLC

PQ4642   TASSO,TORQUATO,1544-1595.
.G21D8   Torquato Tasso's Befreites Jerusalem. Uebersetzt
von prof.dr.Duttenhof.r. Neue gänzlich umgearb.ausg.
... Berlin,A.Hofmann & comp.,1854.
2 v.in 1. 15½cm.

NT 0048017   ICU MH PU

Tasso, Torquato, 1544-
Befreites Jerusalem, im versmasze
der urschrift übersetzt von F.M.Dutten-
hofer.   Stut. Rieger, 1855.

560 p.

NT 0048018   PU PPG

Tasso, Torquato, 1544-1595.
Befreites Jerusalem neu und in reinen reimen
übersetzt von F. C. Jochem.   Giessen, Picker,
1862.
2 v. in 1.

NT 0048019   PU PHC

Tasso, Torquato, 1544-1595.
[Torquato Tasso's Befreites Jerusalem, über-
setzt von J.D.Gries. 12.aufl. ... Berlin,
Weidmann, 1865.

NT 0048020   MdBJ

Tasso, Torquato, 1544-1595.
Torquato Tasso's Befreites Jerusalem, übersetzt von J. D. Gries. 13.Aufl. ... Berlin,
Weidmann, 1873.
2v.in 1. 19cm.

Translation of Gerusalemme liberata.

NT 0048021   NBC OC1

Tasso, Torquato, 1544-1595.
Torquato Tasso's Befreites Jerusalem, übersetzt von J. D.
Gries...   Berlin: Weidmann, 1880.   2 v. in 1.   14. ed.
12°.

221995A. 1. No subject. 2. Gries,   Johann Diederich, 1775-1842, trans-
N. Y. P. L.   lator.   July 13, 1926

NT 0048022   NN

853T185 Tasso, Torquato, 1544-1595.
OgGgr   Torquato Tassos Befreites Jerusalem ... Uebersetzt von J. D. Gries. Mit einer biographischen
einleitung von Hermann Fleischer ... Stuttgart,
J. G. Cotta [etc., 1893]
2v. front.(port., v.1)   (On cover: Cotta'sche
bibliothek der weltlitteratur)

I. Gries, Johann Diederich, 1775-1842, tr. II.
Fleischer, Hermann.

NT 0048023   IU ODW ViLxW MH

Tasso, Torquato, 1544-1595.
Das befreyte Jerusalem, von Torquato Tasso ... Mit aller-
höchstem kaiserlichen und höchstem kuhrfürstlichpfälzischen
privilegium. Mannheim, Im verlage der herausgeber der ausländischen schönen geister, 1781.
4 v. in 2. front.(port.) 16ᵐ.
Engraved title vignettes.
Prose translation (facing text on opposite pages) by J. J. W. Heinse,
to whom was awarded the prize offered for the best translation by the
editor Anton, edler von Klein. cf. "Ein wort des herausgebers an das
publicum", signed "Professor Klein", v. 4, verso of p. 375.
"Leben des Torquato Tasso": v. 1, p. 1-48 (i. e. 84)
I. Heinse, Johann Jakob Wilhelm, 1749-1803, tr. II. Klein, Anton, edler
von, 1748-1810, ed. III. Title.

Library of Congress   PQ4638.C81   2—15828

NT 0048024   DLC CtY MH PU

Tasso, Torquato, 1544-1595.

Hd17
410
Das befreyte Jerusalem von Torq.Tasso ...
Zurich,Orell,Gessner,Füssli u.Comp.,1782.
2v. 17½cm.
"Leben des Torquato Tasso": [v.1]p.[vii]-lix.
Translated by W.Heinse.

NT 0048025 CtY

Tasso, Torquato, 1544-1595.

Zg18
M323
791t
Das befreyte Jerusalem. 1.Theil. Leipzig,
im Verlage der Dykschen Buchhandlung,1791.
2p.ℓ.,[3]-304p. front. 19cm.
Translated by J.K.F.Manso
No more published.

NT 0048026 CtY

Tasso, Torquato, 1544-1595.
Torquato Tasso's Befreytes Jerusalem ... übersetzt von
A. W. Hauswald ... Görlitz, C. G. Anton, 1802.
2 v. fronts. 21ᶜᵐ.

ɪ. Hauswald, August Wilhelm, 1749-1804, tr. ɪɪ. Title: **Befreytes
Jerusalem.**

34-34370

Library of Congress   PQ4642.G21H3   851.46

NT 0048027 DLC NcU OCU TNJ PPL ICU

TASSO, Torquato, 1544-
Befreytes Jerusalem. Teutsch durch A.L.
Follen. Neunter gesant als probe des
gansen. Frankfurt a. M., in auftrag bey
Eichenberg, [1817]
pp.(4).23.

NT 0048028 MH

TASSO, Torquato, 1544-1595.
Befriade Jerusalem; öfversättning
af A.F.Skjöldebrand. . 2bde in 1.
Stockholm, tryckt hos J. Hörberg, 1825.

NT 0048029 MH PU OC1W NN

Tasso, Torquato, 1544-1595.
Torquato Tasso's Befriade Jerusalem, öfversatt af Carl A.
Kullberg ... Stockholm, J. L. Brudin [1860]
2 v. in 1. 21½ᶜᵐ.

ɪ. Kullberg, Carl Anders, 1815-1897, tr.

34-37910

Library of Congress   PQ4643.S61K8   851.46

NT 0048030 DLC MH

Tasso, Torquato, 1544-1595.
Det befriede Jerusalem, paa dansk ved Christini
Daugard. Kjobenhavn, Schonberg, 1884.
391 p.

NT 0048031 PU

Tasso, Torquato. La bella pargoletta.

M2
.T67
vol. 1
Bell' Haver, Vincenzo, *ca.* 1530-*ca.* 1588.
Madrigale [ɪ-ɪɪɪ, di] Vincenzo Bell' Haver.
(*In* Torchi, Luigi, ed. L'arte musicale in Italia ... Milano [etc.,
1897-191-?] 21½ cm. v. 1, p. 390-422)

D851T18
O328
Tasso, Torquato, 1544-1595.
Bellezze della Gerusalemme liberata, con L'epilogo del poema e con note di Enrico Mestica. Per
le scuole secondarie di grado superiore. 6. ed.
Livorno, Giusti [1922]
4 p. l., 206, [2] p. 19ᶜᵐ. (Biblioteca di
classici italiani commentati per le scuole)

1. Mestica, Enrico, 1856-1936, ed.

NT 0048033 NNC

TASSO,Torquato,1544-1595.
Canzone inedita,foggiata sulla Cantica.
Genova,1823.
pp.8.

NT 0048034 MH

Case
4A
1501
TASSO, TORQUATO, 1544-1595.
Canzone nella coronatione del serenissimo
sig. Don Vincenzo Gonzaga. Dvca di Mantova
... Del Sig. Torqvato Tasso ... In Mantova, Appresso F. Osanna, 1587.
[4]ℓ. 21cm.
Title vignette (printer's device)
Imperfect: all leaves water-stained;
last leaf partly crumbled away, with loss of
text.

NT 0048035 ICN CtY

Tasso, Torquato, 1544-
Canzone nella oreatione del santis-
simo Papa Gregorio XIII. In Roma,
Fincenzo Accolti, 1591.
11 p.

NT 0048036 PU

TASSO, Torquato, 1544-
Canzone sagra. Ed. 3. napoletana.
Napoli, dalla Stamperia reale, 1823.
pp.(18).

NT 0048037 MH

Tasso, Torquato, 1544-1595.

PQ4637
A5
1895
Carmina latina Torquati Taxi; editio altera
cum prooemio et notis Antonii Martinii.
Romae, Ex officina typographica Forzani et s.,
1895.
58 p., 1 l. fold. facsim. 26 1|2 cm.
Bibliography: p. [29]-32.

I. Martini, Antonio ed.
II. Title.

NT 0048038 CSmH

Tasso, Torquato, 1544-1595.
Le cinquanta conclusioni amorose del Tasso ...
see under Neri, Ippolito, 1652-1709.

Tasso, Torquato, 1544-1595.
Cinquanta madrigali inediti del Signor Torquato Tasso
alla granduchessa Bianca Cappello nei Medici. Firenze,
Tip. di M. Ricci, 1871.
2 p. l., 60 p. 23ᶜᵐ.
Edited by Gargano Gargani.
"Edizione di ccɪ. esemplari non venali."
"Altri madrigali del Tasso alla Signora Bianca Cappello precedentemente
editi": p. [34]-43.
"Madrigali due del Tasso di argomento amoroso (inediti)": p. [45]-48.
Added entries: Gargani, Gargano, ed.

4-2190

NT 0048040 DLC PU

M1500
.M78M33
Case
Tasso, Torquato, 1544-1595.

Monteverdi, Claudio, 1567-1643.   FOR OTHER EDITIONS
[Madrigali guerrieri et amorosi.   SEE MAIN ENTRY
Combattimento di Tancredi e
Clorinda]
Combattimento di Tancredi e Clorinda. Parole del Signor
Torquato Tasso, a cura di G. Francesco Malipiero. New ed.
with English text by Peter Pears. London, J. & W. Chester
[1954]

Tasso, Torquato, 1544-1595.
Conjectures and researches concerning the love
madness and imprisonment of Torquato Tasso
see under Wilde, Richard Henry, 1789-1847.

TASSO, Torquato, 1544-
Costanza, [Rime]. Torquato, Bernardo
Tasso, e poetesse del secolo XVI. Venezia,
A.Zatta e figli,1787.
Vigns.
Half-title: Parnaso italiano,30.

NT 0048043 MH

PQ
4642
E21
D6
1761
Tasso, Torquato, 1544-1595
The delivery of Jerusalem; an heroick poem.
Translated by Philip Doyne. To which is
added the life of Tasso and an essay on the
Gerusalemme liberata. Dublin, G. and A.
Ewing, 1761.
2v. 23cm.
Translation of La Gerusalemme liberata.
I. Doyne, Philip, tr. II. Title

NT 0048044 WU

Tasso, Torquato, 1544-1595.
La delivrance de Hiervsalem mise en vers françois de l'italien
de Torquato Tasso par Iean Dv Vignav sʳ de Vvarmont Bour-
delois a monseignevr le prince de Conty. Auec priuilege du
roy. A Paris, Chez Nicolas Gilles rue Sᵗ Jacques aus trois
couronnes et au Pallais [1595]
3 p. l., 259 numb. l., [18] p. 13½ᶜᵐ.
Signatures: t.-p., Rˣ, A-Yᵛᴵᴵ Zⁱ.
Engraved t.-p. within architectural border with portrait of Tasso in
the upper part.
"Acheué d'imprimer le 9. Iuillet. 1595" (Privilege)
"Ex bibliotheca R. Toinet."
ɪ. Du Vignau, Jean, fl. 1595, tr. ɪɪ. Title.

33-787

Library of Congress   PQ4642.F21D8 1595   851.46

NT 0048045 DLC NIC ICU IU CtY MH

Tasso, Torquato, 1544-
Dell' arte poetica discorsi
tre... e lettere poetiche del medesimo.
Bologna, Marsigli, 1845.

288 p.   (Eletta di opere utili e
dilettevoli, ser. 1. v.6)

NT 0048046   PU

Tasso, Torquato, 1544-1595.
Della Gervsalemme conqvistata libri xxiv, novellamente
ristampati. Con gli argomenti a ciascvn libro del signor Gio.
Battista Massarengo, et la tauola de' principij di tutte le
stanze. Pavia, A. Viani, 1594.

308 p. 21 cm.

L. C. copy imperfect: part of prelim. leaves (?) and "Tauola" at
end, wanting.
Bound with the author's Il Goffredo. Venetia, 1582.

I. Title: Gerusalemme conquistata.

PQ4638.A82 1582   50-52740

NT 0048047   DLC NIC PU ICU

Bonaparte
Collection TASSO, TORQUATO, 1544-1595.
No.5426   Della tradottione della Giervsalemme libe-
rata del Tasso in lingva bolognese popolare di
Gio. Francesco Negri...   [Bologna,1628]
228p. 20cm.
Caption title.
Incomplete: ends with 34th stanza of the 13th
canto. No more published.
Manuscript note on flyleaf, at end: L'edizio-
ne restò imperfetta per proibizione del cardinale
Spada, allora legato di Bologna.
Original text   and translation in par-
allel columns.

NT 0048048   ICN

Tasso, Torquato, 1544-
Della virtù dei Romani. Orazione.
(In Albèri, Eugenio. Tesoro della prosa italiana. Pp. 537-562.
Firenze, 1841.)

E5517 — Rome. Manners.

NT 0048049   MB

Tasso, Torquato, 1544-1595.
Delle differenze poetiche; discorso del Signor
Torqvato Tasso per risposta al Sig. Horatio
Ariosto. In Verona, Appresso Hieronimo Dis-
cepolo, 1587.
PG 1656   7 l. 15cm. [With Lombardelli, Orazio.
.A2 L8 Discorso ... In Ferrara, 1586.]
1586 R
Title vignette (printer's mark)
Dedicatory epistle signed: Ciro Spontone.

NT 0048050   MdBJ

Tasso, Torquato, 1544-1595.
Delle Lettere Familiari Del Sig. Torqvato Tasso, Nuouamente
raccolte, e date in luce, Libro Primo[-Secondo]...   Bergamo,
Per Comino Ventura, e Compagni, 1588. 2 v. in 1. 25cm. (4°.)

Grässe, VI², 39.
Last leaf blank.
Edited by Giovanni Battista Licino.
With several ms. sonnets and notes about Tasso on prelim. l. 4°, last leaf and 2
flyleaves at end.
With ms. note indicating ownership by the heirs of Giulio Cesare Giovannini.

56R0307. I. Letters, Italian.   I. Licino, Giovanni Battista, ed.

NT 0048051   NN DFo CtY ICN NIC MnU MH PU MWelC

Tasso, Torquato, 1544-1595.
Delle opere di Torquato Tasso ... Venezia,
Steffano Monti

see his   Le opere ... Venezia, C. Buonarrigo, 1722-42.

PQ4201
C55   Tasso, Torquato, 1544-1595
v. 36-39   [Selected works]
Delle opere di Torquato Tasso. [Milano,
Società tipografica de' classici italiani,
1804-05]
4 v. port. 22 cm. [Classici italiani,
v. 36-39]

Half title.
Each vol. has also special t. p.
Contents. - v. 1-2. Gerusalemme, liberata.

- v. 3. Discorsi, e lettere. - v. 4.
L'Aminta e le poesie amorose.

ICN NN
NT 0048054   MeB MH WaSpG DCU MdBP CtY IaU CU CtW

Y
712   TASSO, TORQUATO, 1544-1595.
.T 168 Delle opere non piu' stampata del signor
Torquato Tasso, raccolte, e publicate da Marc'
Antonio Foppa, con gli agromenti del medesimo.
Roma, G. Dragondelli,1666.
3v. in 2. 23cm.

Contents.--v.1. Le prose.--v.2. Il giuditio
della sua Gerusalemme.--v.3. Poesie varie.

NT 0048055   ICN WU NcD NNC

Tasso, Torquato, 1544-1595.
Delle opere non piv' stampate del Signor Torqvato
Tasso raccolte, e publicate da Marc' Antonio Foppa, volume secondo. Che contiene il Giuditio della sua Gerusalemme ... Roma, G. Dragondelli, 1666.
6 p. l., 154, [8] p. 24ᶜᵐ.
Title vignette.
Title-page slightly mutilated owing to erasure of the words "volume
secondo." The missing words are supplied from the "Bibliografia delle
edizioni delle prose di T. Tasso" in Appendice alle opere in prosa di T.
Tasso a cura di A. Solerti, Firenze, 1892, p. 28.
Contemporary binding, limp vellum, gilt, Medici arms in center, front
and back.
1. Tasso, Torquato, 1544-1595. Gerusalemme liberata. I. Foppa, Marc'
Antonio, ed.

                                        4-5791 Revised
Library of Congress   PQ4656.A2T3

NT 0048056   DLC OO CU PU MB MH PPL

853T185 Tasso, Torquato, 1544-1595.
KM31   Delle rime del signor Torqvato Tasso parte prima[-seconda] Insieme con altri componimenti del
medesimo ...   In Vinegia, MDXXCCII [i.e.1582]
2 pt. in 1v. 13½cm.

Signatures: pt.1, ★¹², A-V¹²(V¹² and versos of
L¹² and N³ blank, P¹² wanting); pt.2, ✹¹², A-V¹²
(V¹² and versos of E⁸ and E¹² blank)
Device of printer, Aldus Manutius, on title-
pages; initials.
Dedicatory epistle signed: Aldo Mannucci.

Armorial book-plate of a royal knight of the
Garter, and, stamped on end paper, a crest with
the name J. M. Paine.

I. Manuzio, Aldo, 1547-1597, ed.

NT 0048058   IU MH PU IaU

TASSO, Torquato, 1544-1595.
Delle rime parte prima [-seconda]. Di novo
dal medesimo in questa nuova impressione
ordinate, corrette, accresciute & date in luce.
Con l'esposizione dello stesso autore. In
Brescia, appresso Pietro Maria Marchetti,1592-93.

2 pt. 15 cm.
Printer's mark on the title-page of each part.
Imperfect:-title-page of part 1 badly stained.

NT 0048059   MH DFo PU NIC NjP CtY ICU

850
T214   Tasso, Torquato, 1544-1595.
tR   DELLE RIME / Del Signor / TORQVATO /
1620 TASSO / ... / Con licentia & Priuilegio.
/ [Portrait vignette]   IN VENETIA, MDCXX
[i.e.1620] / Appresso Euangelista Deuchino. /
v.[n   15×7cm.

First published 1592-93.
CONTENTS:

—Parte Sesta.Morali.—Parte Settima.Lvgvbri.—-Parte
Ottaua.Sacres-Parte Roma.Varie.—

NT 0048060   CLSU NjP PU

Tasso, Torquato, 1544-1595.
Delle rime et prose del sig. Torquato Tasso ...
Di nuouo ristampate, con diligenza riuedute, e
corrette. Ferrara, G. Vasalini, 1583-1587.
6 v. in 5. 13cm.

Vols.3-6: Venetia.
Printer's device on title pages.
On 1ly-leaf of Vol.1, in pencil: "Printed while
Tasso was imprisoned at Ferrara. A reprint of the
Aldine edition with additions".

NT 0048061   NcU

Tasso, Torquato, 1544-1595.
Delle Rime, Et Prose Del S. Torqvato Tasso,
Di nuouo con diligenza riuedute, corrette, & di
vaghe Figure adornate, ... In Vinetia, Presso
Aldo MDXXCIII. [1583]
2 v. 12.8 cm. Red morocco, by Hardy-Mennil.
T.-ps. within woodcut border.
Each work has special t.-p. and pagination.
Printer's device on t.-ps.
From the Anderson galleries, Feb. 13-14, 1918,
no. 886.

NT 0048062   CSmH PU DFo

853T185 Tasso, Torquato, 1544-1595.
K1583   Delle rime, et prose del s. Torqvato Tasso, di
nuouo con diligenza riuedute, corrette, & di vaghe
figure adornate ... In Vinetia, Presso Aldo, 1583.
2v. illus. 13½cm.

Title-pages have ornamental borders with the Aldine anchor at base.
Head and tail-pieces; initials.
Dedicatory epistles at the beginning of the Rime
and the Aminta signed Aldo. Manucci; others by Lelio Gavardi.

—— Aggivnta alle Rime, et prose del sig. Torqvato Tasso ... In Vinetia, Presso Aldo, 1585.
12 p.l., 90p. port. 13½cm.

Dedicatory letter signed: Nicolò Manassi.
Bound at end of v.2.

I. Manuzio, Aldo, 1547-1597. II. Manassi, Nicolò, fl.1590. III. Gavardi, Lelio.

NT 0048064   IU OCl CLU TU

Tasso, Torquato, 1544-1595.
Delle rime et prose del Sig. Torquato
Tasso. Parte prima, di nuouo ristampate
con diligenza riuedure e corrette.
In Ferrara, Appresso Giulio Vasalini,
1585.
12 p.l., 144 [6] 90 [1] 95-120 [1] 7-
163 [14] 54 p., 14ᶜᵐ.

NT 0048065   NjPT CSt KMK PU MWelC

PQ
4636   Tasso, Torquato, 1544-1595.
A5   Delle rime, et prose...parte seconda, di nuouo
1585 ristampate...e corrette. In Ferrara, Appresso
Cage Simon Vasalini, 1585.

[24] 144, 263 [49] 84 [12] p. 12mo.

NT 0048066   DFo

Tasso, Torquato, 1544-1595.

Tasso, Ercole, *16th cent.*

Dello ammogliarsi piacevole; contesa fra i due moderni Tassi, Hercole, cioè, & Torqvato, gentilhuomini bergamaschi. Nouamente in più luoghi al confronto de' loro originali corretta ... Bergamo, C. Ventura, 1594.

Tasso, Torquato, 1544-1595.

Dello infarinato ...

see under   [Salviati, Leonardo] 1540-1589.

Film
3137
.31
.316

Tasso, Torquato, 1544-1595

Des berühmten italiänischen Poeten Torquati Tassi Amintas oder Waldgedichte. Aus dem Originale deutsch gegeben... von M. Michael Schneidern. Hamburgk, Bey Valentin Paulmann, 1642.

125 p.

Microfilm (negative) of the original in Thüringische Landesbibliothek, Weimar. 1 reel.

NT   0048069   NjP

Tasso, Torquato, 1544-1595.

Di Gervsalemme conqvistata del sig. Torqvato Tasso libri XXIIII ... Roma, G.Facciotti, 1593.

6 p.*l.*,290,[2] p.   22 x 17cm.
Title vignette (portrait of Tasso)
Dedication signed: Angelo Ingegneri.
Written to replace the Gerusalemme liberata, with which Tasso was dissatisfied.

I.Ingegneri,Angelo,1550-ca.1613.   II.Gerusalemme conquistata.

WU NIC
NT   0048070   MiU NcU PU MnU ICN MH ICU IU DFo CtY

PQ4640
.A4
1822

TASSO,TORQUATO,1544-1595.

Dialoghi di Torquato Tasso con gli argomenti del cavaliere Alessandro Mortara ... Pisa,N.Capurro, 1822-24.

3 v.in 2.   21cm.   [Opere...illustrate dal prof.Gio. Rosini. v.7-9]
Mutilated:added title-pages cut out.

NT   0048071   ICU PPT

851
T185
JM841d

Tasso, Torquato, 1544-1595.

Dialoghi di Torquato, con gli argomenti e cavaliere Alessandro Mortara. Pisa : Presso N. Capurro, 1822.

2 v. in 1 ; 22 cm. (His Opere..., v.7-8)

I. Mortara, Alessandro de, conte.

NT   0048072   VtU

PQ
4640
.A4
1824

Tasso, Torquato, 1544-1595

Dialoghi. Milano, Dalla Tipografia di Commercio, 1824-25.

3 v.

NT   0048073   INS PU

Tasso, Torquato, 1544-1595.

I dialoghi di Torquato Tasso, a cura di Cesare Guasti. ... Firenze, F. Le Monnier, 1858-59.

3 v.   19ᶜᵐ.

"Notizia bibliografica dei dialoghi compresi in questo volume" at beginning of each volume.

I. Guasti, Cesare, 1822-1889, ed.

NjP OCU MiU OO ICU MH NjP PBm
NT   0048074   MiU CU NIC IEN NcD NNC TU IaU CU-S ICU

Tasso, Torquato, 1544-1595

I dialoghi di Torquato Tasso a cura di Cesare Guasti ... Firenze, 1901.

3v.   18cm.

I. Guasti, Cesare, 1822-1889, ed.

NT   0048075   RPB NNC

Tasso, Torquato, 1544-1595.

Dialoghi, di Torquato Tasso, a cura di **Alessandro Tortoreto.** [Milano] Bompiani [1945]

256 p., 2 l.   18ᵐ.   (*Half-title:* Corona, collezione universale Bompiani, v. 60)
Bibliography included in introduction to each dialogue.

CONTENTS.—Il Tasso; ovvero, Dell' arte del dialogo.—Il padre di famiglia.—Il Gonzaga secondo; ovvero, Del giuoco.—La Cavalletta; ovvero, Della poesia toscana.—Il Minturno; ovvero, Della bellezza.

I. Tortoreto, Alessandro, ed.

                              46-20016

Library of Congress   PQ4640.A4 1945
                [2]   858.4

NT   0048076   DLC OrU NjP IU CtY OU MB

851.46
Od
1914

Tasso, Torquato, 1544-1595.

I dialoghi amorosi, con prefazione e bibliografia a cura di Nella Belletti. Lanciano, R. Carabba, 1914.

142p.   20cm.   (Scrittori nostri, 49)

I. Belletti,   Nella,   ed.

NT   0048077   KU CU NIC INS MdBJ ICU IU

Tasso, Torquato, 1544-1595.

Dialoghi et discorsi. Venetia, G. Vassalini, 1586.

[12], 201 p.   13cm.

With this is bound: Sannazaro, J. Rime. 1589.

NT   0048078   MnU

Tasso, Torquato, 1544-1595.

Dialoghi scelti di Torquato Tasso, con gli argomenti del cavaliere Alessandro Mortara.   Volume unico; edizione stereotipa. Milano: E. Sonzogno, 1878.   349 p.   18cm.

CONTENTS.—Prefazione, di F. Costèro.—Dell' arte del dialogo.—Il padre di famiglia.—Il Gonzaga.—Il Gonzaga secondo.—La Cavalletta.—Il Malpiglio.—Il Malpiglio secondo.—Il Minturno.—Il Costantino.—Il Cataneo.—Il Porzio.

586119A. 1. No subject. I. Mortara,   Alessandro. II. Costèro, Francesco.
N. Y. P. L.   October 21, 1933

NT   0048079   NN ICN IU

PQ
4640
A4
1930

Tasso, Torquato, 1544-1595

Dialoghi scelti, con saggio introduttivo di Gustavo Rodolfo Ceriello, Milano, C. Signorelli [1930]

130p.   16cm.   (Biblioteca di letteratura, n. 99-100)
Bibliographical footnotes.

I. Ceriello, Gustavo Rodolfo, ed.

NT   0048080   WU PPT CLSU

PQ
4640
A4
1894

Tasso, Torquato, 1544-1595

Dialogo dei casi d'amore. Roma, L. Roux, 1894.

247p.   20cm.

NT   0048081   WU NcU PU MH

Tasso, Torquato, 1544-

Dialogo dell' imprese. Napoli, nella stamparia dello Stigliola, ad instantia di P. Venturini, [1594].

4°.   pp. (4), 71.

With printer's mark, clasped hands with motto "Sine fraude, bona fide," on title-page.

Print. spec.

NT   0048082   MH PU

Tasso, Torquato, 1544-1595.

Dialogo dell'imprese del sig. Torqvato Tasso. All'illvstrissᵐᵒ e reverendissᵐᵒ signor cardinal San Giorgio. In Napoli, Nella stamparia dello Stigliola
Microfilm copy, made in 1962, of the original in Vatican. Biblioteca vaticana. Positive. Negative film in Vatican. Biblioteca vaticana.
Collation of the original, as determined

imprese.
from the film: 2 p. *l.*, 71 p.

1. Emblems. I. Title: Dialogo dell'Imprese. (Series: [Manuscripta, microfilms of rare and out-of-print books. List 38, no. 39])

NT   0048084   MoSU OU

Tasso, Torquato, 1544-1595.

Dialogo dell' imprese del sig. Torqvato Tasso ... Napoli, [1597?]

[With his Discorsi del poema heroico...Napoli, 1597?]

NT   0048085   MdBJ

Tasso, Torquato, 1544-1595.

Dialogo intorno alla Gerusalemme Liberata...

see under [Vagenti, Paolo]

Tasso, Torquato, 1544-1595.

Discorsi Del Signor Torqvato Tasso. Dell'Arte Poetica; Et In particolare del Poema Heroico. Et Insieme Il Primo Libro Delle Lettere scritte à diuersi suoi amici, lequali oltra la famigliarità, sono ripiene di molti concetti, & auertimenti poetici à dichiaratione d'alcuni luoghi della sua Gierusalemme liberata... Non Piv Stampati...   Venetia, Ad instanza di Giulio Vassalini Libraro à Ferrara, 1587.   4 p.l., 108 f.   20cm. (4°.)

Grässe, VI², 39.
Title vignette: printer's mark?
Dedication signed: Giouanni Battista Licinio.
With stamp: Bibl. Gvst. C. Galetti Flor., and bookplate of Baron Horace de Landau.

56R0091. 1. Poetry, Epic. 2. Letters,   Italian. I. Licino, Giovanni Battista, ed.

         CoU PU ICN MdBJ PBm MH NjP PU
NT   0048088   NN InU CLU NcD DeU WaU FU MnU ICU MoSW

Tasso, Torquato, 1544-1595.
... I discorsi dell'arte, poetica, Il padre di famiglia, e L'Aminta, annotati per cura di Angelo Solerti (con illustrazioni) Torino ₍etc.₎ Ditta G. B. Paravia e comp., 1901.

2 p. l., ₍3₎-305 p., 1 l. front. (port.) illus. (incl. facsim.) 19ᶜᵐ. (*On cover:* Biblioteca italiana ordinata per le scuole normali e secondarie (Collezione Paravia))

With facsimile of t.-p. of Aminta; favola boscareccia ... Vinegia, 1581. "Prologo per una rappresentazione di *I suppositi* di Ludovico Ariosto": p. ₍301₎-305.
1. Epic poetry. I. Solerti, Angelo, 1865-1907, ed. II. Title: Il padre di famiglia. III. Title: L'Aminta.

NT 0048089   MiU MH CU

Tasso, Torquato, 1544-1595.
Discorsi di Torquato Tasso ... Pisa, Presso N. Capurro, 1823.

2 v. 22ᶜᵐ.
On cover: Firenze, Libreria Dante.
The dedicatory letter to Giuseppe Antinori, dated "Pisa, 1 agosto, 1823," is signed "G. R." *i. e.* Giovanni Rosini.
CONTENTS.—v. 1. Considerazioni sopra tre canzoni di M. G. B. Pigna intitolate Le tre sorelle. Orazione fatta nell' aprirsi dell'Accademia Ferrarese. Lezione recitata nell'Accademia Ferrarese ₍sopra il sonetto Questa vita mortal ec. di monsignor Della Casa₎ Opposizioni d'incerto ad un sonetto di T. Tasso. Risposta all' opposizioni fatte ad un sonetto. Della fortuna, interpretazione d'un proprio sonetto al Sig. Ercole Cato. Orazione in lode della serenissima casa dei Medici. Orazione nella morte dell'illustrissimo cardinale

Luigi d'Este. Discorso sopra due quistioni amorose. Il segretario. Dell' ufficio del sinicsaleo. Del maritarsi. Dell' amor vicendevole fra il padre e il figliuolo. ₍Del giuramento falso₎ Della virtù eroica, e della carità. Della virtù femminile e donnesca. Della gelosia. Orazione in morte di Barbara d'Austria. Orazione nella morte del Santino. Discorso sopra varj accidenti della sua vita ₍scritto a Scipione Gonzaga₎ Risposta di Roma a Plutarco. Discorso intorno alla sedizione di Francia.—v. 2. Discorsi del poema eroico. Discorso dell' arte poetica in particolare sopra il poema eroico. Lettera di Marcantonio Foppa all' eminentiss. Sig. card. Sforza Pallavicino. Del giudizio sovra La Gierusalemme di T. Tasso. Estratti della Poetica del Castelvetro. Lettera politica, al Sig. Giulio Giordani.
2-18129

NT 0048091   DLC PU

Tasso, Torquato, 1544-1595.
Discorsi del poema heroico, del s. Torqvato Tasso ... Napoli, Stamparia dello Stigliola, ad instantia di P. Venturini ₍1594₎

3 p. l., 179, ₍1₎ p. 19½ᶜᵐ.
Title vignette.

1. Poetry—Early works to 1800.
4-5798 Revised
Library of Congress   PQ4640.D9 1594

ICU NcD
NT 0048092   DLC MWelC PU CtY WaU DFo IU MH FU NIC

Tasso, Torquato, 1544-1595.
Discorsi et annotationi sopra la Gierusalemme liberata ...
     see under   Guastavini, Giulio, 16th cent.

Tasso,. Torquato, 1544-1595.
Discorso Della Virtv Feminile, E Donnesca, Del Sig. Torqvato Tasso... Venetia, Appresso Bernardo Giunti, e fratelli, 1582. 8 f. 21cm. (4°.)

Grässe, VI², 39.

56R0208. 1. Woman, to 1750.

NT 0048094   NN

Tasso, Torquato, 1544-1595.
Discorso Della Virtv Heroica, Et Della Charità Del Sig. Torqvato Tasso. Al Serenis. Sig. Monsig. il Cardinale Cesareo. Venetia, Apresso Bernardo Giunti, e fratelli, 1582. 10 f. 21cm. (4°.)

Grässe, VI², 39.
Requests the dedicatee's assistance in ending the author's imprisonment.

56R0208. 1. Courage. 2. Charity.

NjP NcD OCl PU MH FU CSt IU MWelC
NT 0048095   NN FU NcU MiU NjP PU CtY DFo ICN MnU

Tasso, Torquato, ₍1544-₎
Discorso sopra varii accidenti della sua vita, scritto a Scipione Gonzaga.
(In Carrer, Luigi, compiler. Autori che ragionano di sè. Pp. 75-123. Venezia. 1840.)

NT 0048096   MB

Tasso, Torquato, ₍1544-₎
La disperatione di Guida.   45p.
Venetia, 1628.

NT 0048097   PU

Tasso, Torquato, 1544-1595. La Disperatione Di Givda, Poemetto Del Sig. Torqvato Tasso. All' Illustriss. Sig. D. Andrea Pacheco. ... In Cermona per Giacinto Belpieri. 1629...
8° pp (16) - 30
Bound with: Guasco's Ghismonda.

NT 0048098   MWelC

Tasso, Torquato, ₍1544-₎
La disperazione di guida...
New ed.   Parato Vestri, 1815.
34 p.

NT 0048099   PU

Tasso, Torquato, 1544-1595.
Dodici lettere e due sonetti di Torquato Tasso, ora per la prima volta pubblicati, con note di Antonio Enrico Mortara ... Casalmaggiore, Tipi dei fratelli Bizzarri, 1850.

32 p. 21ᶜᵐ.

1. Mortara, Antonio Enrico, ed.
4-8787

NT 0048100   DLC PU

Tasso, Torquato, ₍1544-₎
Dodici lettere.   Faenzu,
Marabini, 1868.
24 p.

NT 0048101   PU

Tasso, Torquato, 1544-1595.
Dodici madrigali di scuola ferrarese ...
     see under   Nielsen, Riccardo, 1908-

Tasso, Torquato, 1544-1595. Dolcemente dormiva la mia Clori

Pallavicino, Benedetto, d. 1616?
Due madrigali ₍di₎ Benedetto Pallavicino.
(In Torchi, Luigi, ed. L'arte musicale in Italia ... Milano ₍etc.₎ 1897-191-? ; 31½ᶜᵐ. v. 2, p. 307-322)

Tasso, Torquato, 1544-1595.
Du madrigali [di] Benedetto Pallavicino
     see under   Pallavicino, Benedetto, d. 1601.

TASSO, Torquato, ₍1544-₎
Due ottave inedite. Publicate da Giovanni Zannoni. Roma, Forzani e c., tipog. 1890.

pp.(8).
"Edizione di C.Esemplari."

NT 0048105   MH

Rare Book Collection
PQ4639
.M2
Tasso, Torquato, 1544-1595.
I dve primi giorni del mondo creato, poesia sacra, del S. Torqvato Tasso dedicati al ... Gregorio Barbarigo, con licentia di superiori et privilegio. In Venetia, Presso Gio. Battista Giotti, MDC.
4 p. l., 1-59 p. 19 1/2 cm.

Title vignette. Head and tail pieces.
First two cantos of Tasso's Creation of the world.

NT 0048106   NcU

PQ4639
.A2
15-
Mss room
TASSO,TORQUATO, 1544-1595.
Egloga del Tasso. [16th cent.]
3 l.,21 numb.l. 28cm.
Contemporary manuscript of Tasso's Aminta. Incomplete; ends with Act II,scene 3,verse 68. From the library of Francesco Novati.

1.Manuscripts,Italian.

NT 0048107   ICU

Tasso, Torquato, 1544-1595.

Pope, Alexander, 1688-1744.
Ироида I. Элоиза ко Абеларду. ₍Tasso, Torquato₎ Ироида II. Армида къ Ринольду. Изъ поэмы "Освобожденный Іерусалимъ." Санктпетербургъ, 17—₎

Tasso, Torquato, 1544-1595.

Chalmers, Alexander, 1759-1834, ed.
English translations, from ancient and modern poems, by various authors. London, J. Johnson ₍etc.₎ 1810.

850.8
Scr38
v.21-
22
Tasso, Torquato, ₍1544-₎
Epistolario. Con prefazione di Scipio Slataper. Lanciano, 1912.
2v. (Scrittori nostri, v.21-22)

NT 0048110   IU MWelC MiU MH TU

PQ4647
.A3
1932
TASSO,TORQUATO, 1544-1595
Epistolario; con prefazione di Scipio Slataper. Lanciano, Carabba ₍1932₎
2 v. in 1.

I. Slataper, Scipio, 1888-1915, ed.

NT 0048111   InU OU MH

Tasso, Torquato, 1544-1595.
... Epos italico; letture dalla Gerusalemme liberata e dall'Orlando furioso, scelte e commentate e ricongiunte col nesso dei poemi. Aggiuntivi i riepiloghi delle note di lingua, grammatica e stile ad uso delle scuole medie. Milano, C. Signorelli [1935]
263 p. 19 cm.
At head of title: Giuseppe Lipparini.
I. Ariosto, Lodovico, 1474-1533. Orlando furioso. II. Lipparini, Giuseppe, 1877- ed.

NT 0048112   CU

Tasso, Torquato, 1544-1595.
L'esprit, ou L'ambassadeur; Le secrétaire;
et Le père de famille. Traitez excellans de
Torquato Tasso, mis en nostre langue, par I.
Baudoin.   Paris, A. Courbé, 1632.
8 p.l., 701 p. port. 17ᵐ. (Morales de Torquato Tasso, v.2)

KB
1632

I. Baudoin, Jean, 1590?-1650, tr. II. Title:
L'esprit. III. Title: L'ambassadeur. IV. Title:
Le secrétaire. V.   Title: Le père de fa-
mille.

NT 0048113   CSt
_____

Tasso, Torquato, 1544-1595.
Esposizione della Gerusalemme liberata ... colla
scelta degli episodi
        see under   Ferrero, Costante, 1861-
_____

Tasso, Torquato, 1544-1595.

Perrodil, Victor de, tr.
Études épiques et dramatiques; ou, Nouvelle traduction en
vers des chants les plus célèbres des poèmes d'Homère, de
Virgile, du Camoens et du Tasse, avec le texte en regard et des
notes, par Victor de Perrodil ... Nouv. éd. Paris, L'éditeur,
1839.
_____

Tasso, Torquato, 1544-1595.
El Fernando; o, Sevilla restavrada; poema
heroico escrito con los versos de la Gervsalemme
liberata del insigne Torqvato Tasso
        see under   Roca, Juan Antonio Vera
Zúñiga y Figueroa, conde de la, 1588-1658.
_____

Tasso, Torquato, 1565-1635.
Festa secolare della nascita di Torquato Tasso
celebrata in Torino il giorno XI marzo MDCCCXLIV
        see under title
_____

Tasso, Torquato, 1544-1595.
  ₍Gerusalemme liberata. Selections. 1946₎
Les flèches d'Armide. Texte italien présen-
té et traduit par ₍Jacques₎ Audiberti. ₍Paris₎
Éditions du Seuil ₍1946₎
  152 p. 17 cm. (Collection poétique ₍bilin-
gue₎ Le don des langues)
  Italian and French on opposite pages.

PQ
4638
.Z5
1946

I. Audiberti, Jacques, 1899-   ed. and tr.
II. Title.

NT 0048118   DCU OrU NBuU DLC-P4 ScU
_____

Tasso, Torquato, 1544-1595.
  ₍Il₎ fiore della Gerusalemme liberata,
con note illustrarive e riassunti del Professore Ersilio Bicci, Firenze. 1892.
  207 p.

NT 0048119   OC1W
_____

Tasso, Torquato, 1544-1595.
  ...Florilegio della Gerusalemme liberata con
commento di Nicola Scarano. Lanciano, Giuseppe
Carabba, 1926.
  1 p.l., 188p., 1ℓ. 23cm. (On cover:Classici
italiani e stranieri)

I. Scarano, Nicola, ed. II. Title.

NT 0048120   NNF RPB
_____

Tasso, Torquato, 1544-1595.
  Florilegio della Gerusalemme liberata con
commento di Nicola Scarano.   Lanciano, G.
Carabba, [1934]
  188 p.   19 cm. (On cover: Classici italiani
e stranieri)

NT 0048121   PV
_____

TASSO, TORQUATO, 1544-1595.
  Il Forno, Overo Della Nobiltà Dialogo Di M. Torquato Tasso. Nuouamente posto in luce, & con diligenza
corretto.   Vicenza, Appresso Perin libraro, & Giorgio
Greco compagni, 1581.   4 p.l., 49 f., 1 l.   18cm.(4°.)

  Brunet, V, 674. BM (Italian), p. 660.
  Last leaf blank.
  Edited by Lodovico Botonio.
1. Nobility. I. Botonio, Lodo-   vico, ed.

NT 0048122   NN PU DFo OC1W MH CtY
_____

Tasso, Torquato, 1544
  Il Forno della nobilita.
Ferrara, Baldini, 1582.
  118 p.

NT 0048123   PU
_____

TASSO, Torquato, 1544-
  Il Forno, overo Della nobiltà; dialogo.
[Edited by Lelio Gavardo.] Vinetia, presso
Aldo, 1583.
  24°. pp.172, (19).

NT 0048124   MH
_____

Tasso, Torquato, 1544-1595.
  Il Forno, overo, della nobilita
dialogo Colophon. In Ferrara, nella stamp
eria di Giulio Cesare Cagnacini & fratelli M.DLXXXV.   Ferrara, Cagnacini,
1585.
  171 p.

NT 0048125   PU
_____

Tasso, Torquato₎ 1544-1595.
  Genesis; verses from a manuscript of William Blake.
₍Cummington, Mass.₎ Cummington Press, 1952₎
  xxviii p. 3 col. illus. 30 cm.
  "170 copies printed by Wightman Williams, who cut the wood-
blocks, & Harry Duncan, who set the type."
  "Translation, probably by Hayley, of the opening lines of Tasso's
Le sette giornate del mondo creato ... Blake was merely the
amanuensis."—G. E. Bentley. A Blake bibl. ₍1964₎ p. 48.
  Accompanied by folder containing signed proofs of the illustra-
tions.
  I. Blake, William, 1757-1827. II. Williams, Wightman, illus.
III. Title.
PQ4639.M2E5 Rosenwald Coll.   67-115708 rev

        MdBP TxU CU MiU NRU CoU
NT 0048126   DLC CLU-C KyU WaU MWelC MiDW PPULC ICN
_____

Bonaparte
Collection TASSO, TORQUATO, 1544-1595.
No.5858   La Gerosalem liberada del Tasso, portada in
          lengua rustega belunes da Barba Sep Coraulo, dit
          dal Piai, e spartida in tre libri. Libro prin-
          Belun, S. Tis, 1782.
            192p. 16cm.
          No more published?

NT 0048127   ICN PU
_____

Tasso, Torquato, 1544-1595.
  ... Gerusalemme conquistata, a cura di Luigi Bonfigli ...
Bari, G. Laterza & figli, 1934.
  2 v. 21ᶜᵐ. (Half-title: T. Tasso. Opere. IV-v)
  Scrittori d'Italia. ₍148-149₎
  "Ragguaglio della favola tra Gerusalemme conquistata e Gerusalemme liberata a cura di Angelo Solerti": v. 2, p. ₍385₎-407; "Ragguaglio
delle stanze tra la Gerusalemme conquistata e la Gerusalemme liberata":
v. 2, p. ₍409₎

  I. Bonfigli, Luigi, ed. II. Solerti, Angelo, 1865-1907. III. Title.

Minnesota. Univ. Libr.   A 34-2128
  for Library of Congress   PQ4638.Z9 1934
                                    ₍a40d1₎   851.46

        CtY OCU ViU DLC OU
NT 0048128   MnU GU PBm PU VtMiM MU TNJ NcU CSt OrU
_____

Bonaparte
Collection TASSO, TORQUATO, 1544-1595.
No.5475   Ra Gerusalemme deliverà dro signor Torquato
          Tasso, tradúta da diversi in lengua zeneize.
          Zena, Tarigo₍1755₎
            2v. 17cm.
          Text and translation on opposite pages.
          Translated by Stefano de Franchi, A. Conti,
          G. Gallin, P. Toso, G. Guidi, and G.A. Gastaldi.

NT 0048129   ICN MH
_____

Tasso, Torquato, 1544-1595.
  La Gerusalemme liberata.
  For a musical composition based on this work see Pallavicino,
Carlo, 1630-1688. La Gerusalemme liberata.
_____

Tasso, Torquato, 1544-1595.
  Gerusalemme liberata.
  For a musico-dramatic work based on this see Rossini, Gioacchino
Antonio, 1792-1868. Tancredi.
_____

Tasso, Torquato, 1544-1595.
  Gerusalemme liberata.
  For operas based on this work
      see
Campra, André, 1660-1744.
  Tancrède.
_____

Tasso, Torquato, 1544-1595.
  La Gerusalemme liberata, con un discorso di
Ugo Foscolo.   Istituto editoriale Italiano, n.d.
  illus.
  Translated under the title: Jerusalem deliverd.

NT 0048133   OrP
_____

Tasso, Torquato, 1544-1595.
  La Gerusalemme liberata. Ridotta
e commentata per l'uso scolastico da
Achille Pellizzari. 2. edizione.
Genova, F. Perrella
  316 p.

4PQ
It
508

NT 0048134   DLC-P4
_____

Tasso, Torquato, 1544-1595.
  La Gerusalemme liberata di Torquato Tasso.
Con brevi note storiche o letterario ad uso delle
scuole del Prof. A. Fassini ... Torino, Roma
[etc.] Ditta G.B. Paravia e comp. [n.d.]
  viii, 442 p. 19cm.

851.46
T214GD

NT 0048135   NcD

Rare
PQ
4638
A73

Tasso, Torquato, 1544-1595.
La Gervsalemme liberata ... Adornata con bellisime figure a ciascun canto.
In Venetia, Per Gio. Giacomo Herts, 1573.
244 p. illus., plates. 23cm.

NT   0048136   NIC

Tasso, Torquato, 1544-1595.
La Gervsalemme liberata di Torqvato Tasso, con le annotationi di Scipion Gentili, e di Givlio Guastauini, et li argomenti di Oratio Ariosti. Genova, Stampata per G. Pauoni, ad instanza di B. Castello, 1617.
8 p. l., 255, 71, ⟨1⟩, 36, ⟨4⟩ p. incl. 20 pl. 29ᶜᵐ.
Added ornamental t.-p., engr. (with portrait of the Duke of Savoy):
La Gervsalemme di Torqvato Tasso figvrata da Bernardo Castello a Carlo Emanvello dvca di Savoia.
Ornamental t.-p., engr., with portrait of author; head-pieces; initials.
Each "argomento" within ornamental border.
The text is continued on the rectos of 12 plates.
"Tvtte le stanze intere, che dall'avtore sono state rifivtate in qvesto libro": p. 245-255.
    i. Gentili, Scipione, 1563-   ii. Guastavini, Giulio, 16th cent.
    iii. Ariosto, Orazio, 1555-   1593.   iv. Castello, Bernardo, 1557-
    1629, illus.   v. Title.
    Library of Congress   PQ4638.B17   17-16500

    MWA
NT   0048137   DLC FU IaU CtY NIC PU NjP ViU CSmH MH

Typ
625
25.822

Tasso, Torquato, 1544-1595.
La Gervsalemme liberata, di Torqvato Tasso, con la vita di lui e con gli argomenti dell'opera del cav: Gvido Casoni ...
In Venetia dal Sarzina. Con licenza de superiori e priuilegio. 1625.
4°. 12p.ℓ.,255p.incl.illus.,plates. 25cm.
Dedication signed: Giacomo Scaglia.
Plates engraved by Francesco Valesio & others.

NT   0048138   MH PU NN ODW PPL PU

851.3
T21gb

Tasso, Torquato, 1544-1595.
La Gervsalemme liberata di Torqvato Tasso con la vita di lui, con gli argomenti á ciascun canto di Bartolomeo Barbato con le annotationi di Scipio Gentile, e di Giulio Guastavino, e con le notitie historiche di Lorenzo Pignoria.
In Padova, per Pietro Paolo Tozzi, 1628.
8 p.l., 408 p. illus., plates. 22½cm.
Initials, head and tail-pieces; t.-p. and all illustrative material engraved.
    I. Barbato, Bartolomeo, ed. II. Gentili, Scipione 1563-1616, ed. III Guastavini, Giulio, ed.
IV. Pignoria, Lorenzo, 1571-1631, ed. V. Title.

NT   0048139   CSt PU CtY MH IU

TASSO, Torquato, 1544-
La Gerusalemme liberata, con la vita di lui [by Guido Casoni]. Con gli argomenti a ciascun canto di Bartolomeo Barbato. Venetia, S. Curti, [1665]
4°. 20 plates.
With manuscript notes.

NT   0048140   MH PPL PU

Tasso, Torquato, 1544-1595.
La Gervsalemme liberata di Torqvato Tasso, adornata con bellissime figure a ciascun canto. Venetia, Si uende all' insegna della Sapienza, 1673.
4 p. l., 244 p. incl. 19 pl. 25ᶜᵐ.
Ornamental t.-p., engraved, with portrait of author; head-pieces; initials.
The text is continued on the rectos of 10 plates.
Dedication signed: Gio. Giacomo Herz.
    I. Title.
                         42-89409
    Library of Congress   PQ4638.B73

NT   0048141   DLC CtY NIC PU MH

Tasso, Torquato, 1544-1595.
La Gerusalemme liberata, del signor Torquato Tasso. Con l'allegoria universale dell'istesso. Et con gli argomenti del sig. Oratio Ariosti. Corretta, & adornata di bellissime figure in rame.
In Parigi 1698[i.e.1700]. Appresso Tomaso Jolly.
32°. 2v. in 1. illus.,plates,port. 10cm.
Another issue has imprint: In Venetia, M.DCCV. Appresso Gio: Gabriel Hertz; both issues have added engr. t.-p. in v.1 with imprint: In Parigi MDCC. Appresso   Tomaso Jolly.

"Vita di Torquato Tasso, scritta dal cavalier Guido Casoni": 15ℓ. at end of v.2; here misbound following p.16, v.1.

NT   0048143   MH PU

TASSO, Torquato, 1544-
La Gerusalemme liberata. Con l'allegoria universale dell'istesso, etc., Venetia, appresso G.G Hertz, 1705.
2 tom. 32°.
Vol. 1 has also an engraved titlepage, reading Parigi, 1700, appresso T. Jolly,

NT   0048144   MH

Tasso, Torquato, 1544-1595.
La Gerusalemme Liberata, colla vita estratta da Grasso. Neapolitan version only. Napoli, 1706.
12mo.

NT   0048145   NN MH

Tasso, Torquato, 1544-1595.
La Gerusalemme liberata di Torquato Tasso, con la vita del medesimo, allegoria del poema, argomenti incisi ne' rami del Tempesta, ed indice di tutti i nomi proprj, e materie principali contenute nell' opera; e con le annotazioni di Scipione Gentili, e di Giulio Guastavini... Urbino, G. Mainardi, Stampator camerale, 1735.
10 p. l., 316 p. incl. illus., plates. 1 pl. 25½ᵐ.
    i. Gentili, Scipione, 1563-1616.   2. Guastavini, Giulio, 16th cent.
                              4-24635

NT   0048146   DLC MH PU NN ICN

Tasso, Torquato, 1544-1595.
La Gerusalemme liberata ... trasportata in lingua calabrese in ottava rima in questa prima edizione da C. Cusentino ... Cosenza, 1737.
4 p. l., 345 p. 8°.
Italian and Calabrian in parallel columns.
                              It—107

NT   0048147   DLC NcU PU CU RPB

PQ4638
C40

Tasso, Torquato, 1544-1595.
Gerusalemme liberata. Osservazioni di Nicolo Clangulo. Lipsia, A spese del medesimo, 1740.
2 v. in 1.
    I. Clangulo, Nicolo,   ed. II. Title.

NT   0048148   CU PU

Tasso, Torquato, 1544-1595.
La Gerusalemme liberata, con le figure di Giambatista Piazzetta. Venezia, Stampata da G. Albrizzi, 1745.
253 l. illus., port. 45 cm.
    I. Piazzetta, Giovanni Battista, 1682 or 3-1754, illus.   II. Title.
    PQ4638.C45   Rosenwald Coll.   50-49561

NT   0048149   DLC IU NN PU NIC MH CtY NcU NBu MB ICN

Tasso, Torquato, 1544-
La Gerusalemme liberata. Vinezia, Remondini, 1756.
436 p.

NT   0048150   PU

Tasso, Torquato. La Gerusalemme liberata.
Portal, Abraham, fl. 1758-1796.
Olindo and Sophronia. A tragedy. The story taken from Tasso ... By Abraham Portal. The 2d ed. London, J. Graham [etc.] 1758.

PQ
4638
C64

Tasso, Torquato, 1544-1595.
La Gerusalemme liberata, colle osservazioni di N. Cianculo e di S. Gentili. Avignione, L. Chambeau, 1764.
2 v. 17cm.
Vol. 2 has imprint: Nîmes, M. Gaude.
    I. Cianculo, Niccolò, ed. II. Gentili, Scipione, 1563-   1616, ed.

NT   0048152   NIC

TASSO, Torquato, 1544-
La Gerusalemme liberata. 2 tom. Parigi, appresso M. Prault, 1768.
Front.

NT   0048153   MH

Tasso, Torquato, 1544-1595.
La Gerusalemme liberata. Parigi, A. Delalain, 1771.
2 v. illus., plates, ports. 24 cm.
Illustrative matter engr. after designs by Gravelot.
Bound by Derôme le jeune, with coat of arms on covers. Bookplate of Edward Taylor.
    I. Gravelot, Hubert François Bourguignon, known as, 1699-1773,
illus.   II. Title.
    PQ4638.C71   Rosenwald Coll.   20-5566*

NT   0048154   DLC CaBVaU CtY ViU MH PU PPRF

[TASSO, Torquato] 1544-1595.
La Gerusalemme liberata, travestita in lingua milanese [by Domenico Balestrieri]. Ital. and Milan. 1 vol. in 2 Milano, appresso G.B. Bianchi, 1773.
f°.

NT   0048155   MH

PQ4638   Tasso, Torquato, 1544-1595.
C72   La Gerusalemme liberata travestita in
lingua milanese <da Domenico Balestrieri.
Milano, Appresso G.B. Bianchi, 1772.
4 v.

     Original and Milanese on opposite pages.

     I. Balestrieri, Domenico, 1714-1780,
II. Title.

NT   0048156   CU PU IU

SPECIAL COLLECTIONS
B851T185
R
1776   Tasso, Torquato, 1544-1595.
     La Gerusalemme liberata di Torquato Tasso ...
Parigi, Appresso Delalain, 1776.
2 v. plate, port. 14cm.

     Engraved title-pages.
     Dedicatory letter by the editor, Giuseppe
Pezzana, lacking.

     I. Pezzana, Giuseppe, 1735-1802, ed.

NT   0048157   NNC NPV MdBJ DCU-H CtY

TASSO, Torquato, 1544-
     La Gerusalemme liberata. 2 tom. Londra,
presso G.T. Masi e com., 1778.

     The title-pages are engraved.

NT   0048158   MH NN NjP CU PU

---

tPQ4638   Tasso, Torquato, 1544-1595.
C79   La Gerusalemme liberata. Bassano, a spese Remondini di
Venezia, 1779.
     443 p. 14cm.

     I. Title. II. Remondini, Giuseppe (1779). III. 1779.
Italy.

NT   0048159   CU-BANC CU PU

Tasso, Torquato, 1544-1595.
     La Gerusalemme liberata di Torquato Tasso ...
In Mannhemio, [n.p.], 1782.
     2 v. in 1. front. 16cm.

NT   0048160   FU

PQ4638   Tasso, Torquato, 1544-1595.
1783   Gerusalemme liberata. Parisiis, Benedicti Morin, 1783.
     2v. 18cm.

     Binding: Blue calf with gilt tooled borders by R. P. Ginain.
     Bookplate: Caroli ac Mariae Lacaitae filiorumque. Selham,
Sussex.
     Provenance: Florence S. Walter.

     I. Title. II. Morin, Benedict (1783). III. 1783. France.

NT   0048161   CU-BANC MH PU RPB

Tasso, Torquato, 1544-1595.
     La Gerusalemme liberata di Torquato Tasso. Stampata d'ordine
di Monsieur.   Parigi, Presso Franc. Ambr. Didot, 1784[-88?]
2 v.   plates.   31cm. (4°.)

     This copy contains the illustrations only (41 full page engravings by Tilliard and
others after Charles Nicolas Cochin), without the text.
     Brunet, V, 667 and suppl. II, 730.   Cohen-DeRicci, col. 976-977.   Grésy, Hilaire.
Catalogue. Paris, 1869. no. 6.   Portalis: Dessinateurs, I, 125.   Portalis and
Béraldi, I, 543.
     Presumably issued in 4 parts.

     Accompanied by Cochin's 41 original drawings, 40 additional drawings which were
never engraved (on each of which a stanza of the text has been printed between the
vignette and the fleuron), and an original title-page drawing dated 1790 and lettered:
La Gerusalemme liberata... Raccolta di' disegni originali. All the drawings are
signed.
     With description of the drawings, in French, 13 l. of ms. (presumably in the hand
of Cochin) laid in.
     With letter dated 29 August 1785 laid in, in which Cochin's patron, later Louis
XVIII, accepts the proffered drawings ...

NT   0048163   NN MH PP CtY

Tasso, Torquato, 1544-1595.
     La Gerusalemme liberata, di Torquato Tasso; 2. ed.,
coi rami della edizione di Monsieur ... Parigi, Stamperia di F. A. Didot l'aîné [1785-86]
     2 v. front., plates. 31ᶜᵐ.
     Reprint of 1784 edition. *cf.* Quérard, La France littéraire.
     Plates by C. N. Cochin.

     I. Cochin, Charles Nicolas, 1715-1790, illus.   II. Title.

                                      20-11726
     Library of Congress   PQ4638.Z3P3

NT   0048164   DLC PSt MH NN PU MeB ICarbS

RARE BKS
PQ4638   Tasso, Torquato, 1544-1595.
.A11   The Gerusalemme liberata of Tasso:
with explanatory notes on the syntax in
obscure passages, and references to the
author's imitations of the ancient
classics. To which is prefixed; a
compendious analysis of Italian metre.
By Agostino Isola ... Cambridge,
Printed by F. Archdeacon, printer to
the University; and sold by the editor,
and F. & F. Merrill [etc.] 1786.
     2 v. 18 1/2 cm.

     I. Isola, Agostino, ed.   II. Title

NT   0048165   NRU OO

Tasso, Torquato, 1544-1595.
     La Gerusalemme liberata.   In Dresda: Appresso i fratelli
Walther, 1786.   xi, 568 p.   front.   16½cm.
     Title vignette: portrait of Tasso.

NT   0048166   NN MiU PU MH

Tasso, Torquato, 1544-1595.
     Gerusalemme liberata di Torquato Tasso ... Venezia,
A. Zatta e figli, 1787.
     2 v. 15½ᶜᵐ. (*Half-title:* Parnaso italiano; ovvero, Raccolta de' poeti clas-
sici italiani. t. XXVIII-XXIX)
     Title vignette (port.); head pieces.   4-5794

NT   0048167   DLC ICN PU

Tasso, Torquato, 1544-1595.
     La Gerusalemme liberata di Torquato Tasso... In Parigi:
Appresso Bossange, Masson e Besson, 1792.   2 v.   fronts.,
plates, ports.   4°.
     Engraved title-pages.

NT   0048168   NN NjP OKentU NIC

Tasso, Torquato, 1544-
     La Gerusalemme liberata.
Basilea, Tourneisen, 1793.

     2v.

NT   0048169   PU

Tasso, Torquato, 1544-1595.
     La Gerusalemme liberata di Torquato Tasso.   Parma, Nel
regal palazzo co' tipi Bodoniani, 1794.
     2 v. 32½ᶜᵐ.
     "Ediz di soli 130 esemplari." Based upon the collations of Pietro An-
tonio Serassi. *cf.* Pref.

     I. Serassi, Pietro Antonio.

     Library of Congress   PQ4638.C94   4-30423

NT   0048170   DLC NcD OC1 NN MdBJ MH

Tasso, Torquato, 1544-1595.
     La Gerusalemme liberata ...   Londra, Polidori
e Nardini, 1796.
     2 v.   15.5 cm.

NT   0048171   CtY PU

Tasso, Torquato, 1544-
     La Gerusalemme liberata, di
Torquato Tasso... In Avignone, Appresso la vedova Seguin, l'anno VI, 1798.

     4v. in 1

NT   0048172   PU

Tasso, Torquato, 1544-
     La Gerusalemme liberata.
Nizza, Reymann, 1799.

     2v. in 1

NT   0048173   PU

Tasso, Torquato, 1544-
     La Gerusalemme liberata.
Livorno, Gamba, 1802.

     2v.

NT   0048174   PU

Tasso, Torquato, 1544-1595.
     La Gerusalemme liberata, di Torquato Tasso.
Parigi, Crapart, Caille e Ravier, 1805.

     2 v.

NT   0048175   MH PU NN

Tasso, Torquato, 1544-1595.
     Gerusalemme liberata; con note. Ossia
spiegazione de' luoghi più oscuri, dilucidazioni
grammaticali ed imitazioni dai Classici antichi. Il
tutto riveduto da Romualdo Zotti, ad uso degli
studiosi della lingua italiana.   Londra, B. Dulau,
1806.
     2 v.   18 cm.

NT   0048176   PBm

Pq351   Tasso, Torquato, 1544-1594.
T214ge   La Gerusalemme liberata.   Parma,
nel Regal Palazzo, Co'Tipi Bodoniani,
1807.
     2v.

     No.1017 in Brooks.   Edizione
Bodoniane.

     I. Title.   II. Bodoni Press, Parma.
III. 1807. Bodoni Press, Parma.

NT   0048177   RP PU ICN MH DGU PU MWiW-C

Spec.   Tasso, Torquato, 1544-1595.
Coll.   La Gerusalemme liberata, di Torquato Tasso.
PQ   Nuova edizione, nella quale si è adoperato
4638.   il modo più semplice di notare le voci coll'
D9   accento di prosodia. Avignone, Fratelli
Seguin, 1809.

     2 v. in 1.   15 cm.
     Illustrated colored lining papers.
     "Vita del Tasso, estratta dagli elogj di
Lorenzo Crasso"; vol. 1, p. [v]-xi.
     I. Crasso, Lorenzo, 17th century.   II.
Title.   mf

NT   0048178   IEdS MH NjP PU

Tasso, Torquato, 1544-1595.
La Gerusalemme liberata del Signor Torquato Tasso,
con gli argomenti del Signor Gio: Vincenzo Imperiale...
Venezia, Dai torchj di G. Molinari, a spese di G. Martini,
1811.
2 v. in 1. front. 17ᶜᵐ.
"Vita dell Signor Torquato Tasso, estratta dagli elogi del Signor Lorenzo Crasso": vol. I, p. v-xii; "Allegoria del poema": vol. I, p. xiii-xxiv.

I. Imperiale, Giovanni Vincenzo, d. 1645.
4-5796

NT 0048179 DLC WaSpG MH MB PU MdBJ

PQ4638
.E12 Tasso, Torquato, 1544-1595.

La Gerusalemme liberata, di Torquato
Tasso... Firenze, Baudry [1812?]
2 v. 15cm.

"Genni biografici sopra Torquato
Tasso;" v.1,p.i-xvi.

NT 0048180 OCU

858
T214ge.z Tasso, Torquato, 1544-1595
1812 Gerusalemme liberata. Illustrata
di note o sia di spiegazioni utili, e
dilucidazioni grammaticali, da Romualdo Zotti... 2.ed... Londra,
Zotti, 1812.
2v. S.
Vol.1, Leigh Hunt's autographed presentation copy to Laura V. Kent.

NT 0048181 IaU

Tasso, Torquato, 1544-
La Gerusalemme liberata.
Pisa, Nistri, 1812.

2v. (Collezione di poeti classici
italiani. v.1)

NT 0048182 PU CU

TASSO, Torquato, 1544-
La Gerusalemme liberata. Firenze, 1813.

2 vol. 32°.
(Collezione dei quattro primi poeti
italiani, XII., XIII.)
"Vita di Torquato Tasso", by Lorenzo
Crasso, I. v-ix.

NT 0048183 MH

853T185 Tasso, Torquato, 1544-1595.
Og1816 La Gerusalemme liberata ... Nuova ed., nella
quale si è adoperato il modo più semplice di notare le voci coll'accento di prosodia. Avignone, F. Seguin, 1816.
4v. in 2.

NT 0048184 IU PPL NjP MH

Bonaparte
Collection TASSO, TORQUATO, 1544-1595.
No.13710 La Gerusalemme liberata, travestita in dia-
letto milanese da Domenico Balestrieri. Milano,
G.Pirotta,1816.
503p. 17cm.

NT 0048185 ICN

Tasso, Torquato, 1544-
Gerusalemme liberata, con note o sia
spiegazioni utili, e dilucidazioni grammaticali da Romualdo Zotti. 3 ed. Londra,
1817.

2v.

NT 0048186 PPL

Tasso, Torquato, 1544-1595.
La Gerusalemme liberata. Ora ridotta alla più esatta ed.
Prato, L.Vannini, 1817.

2 v. port., plates. 15 cm.

NT 0048187 MH PU

Tasso, Torquato, 1544-1595.
La Gerusalemme liberata, poema di Torquato Tasso.
Firenze: G. Molini e Cia., 1818. 2 v. in 1. front. (port.)
8°.
Edited by G. Molini.
"Vita di Torquato Tasso estratta dall'elogio del medesimo di Monsi-
gnore Angelo Fabron": v. 1, p. ix-xlvi.

———— ———— A second copy.

Bound in 2 v.
With book-plate of James Lenox.

1. Poetry (Italian). 2. Fabroni,   Angelo, 1732-1803. 3. Molini,
Giuseppe, 1772-1856, editor.   4. Title.
N.Y.P.L.   September 21, 1916.

NT 0048189 NN CtY MH NjP IU

854
T185g Tasso, Torquato, 1544-1595.
1818 La Gerusalemme liberata. Livorno, T.
Masi, 1818.

2v. illus.,port. 17cm.

NT 0048190 OrU

Tasso, Torquato, 1544-1595.
La Gerusalemme liberata. Firenze, dalla Stamperia di
Pallade, 1818.
2 v. port. 12 cm.
Includes index.

1. Godefroid de Bouillon, 1058?-1100—Poetry. 2. Crusades—First,
1096-1099—Poetry.   I. Title.
PQ4638.D18 Batchelder Coll.   76-526747

NT 0048191 DLC MH NN NjP CU PU

Tasso, Torquato, 1544-1595.
La Gerusalemme liberata, di Torquato Tasso. ... Ed.
stereotipa. Parigi, F. Didot, 1819.
2 v. in 1. 13½ᶜᵐ.
"Notizie storiche sopra Torquato Tasso tratte dalle Memorie storiche sopra
Tasso, premesse all'operetta: Veglie di Tasso, di G. Compagnoni": v. 1, p. vi-
xxiii.

1. Compagnoni, Giuseppe, 1754-1833. II. Title.

NT 0048192 MiU LU ViU PPL MWA IU MH

TASSO, Torquato, 1544-
La Gerusalemme liberata. Edizione formata
sopra quella di Bartoli del 1590. 2 tom.
Venezia, Molinari,1819.

24°. Port.
"Debole imitazione della edizione del
Vitarelli del 1811."- Ulisse Guidi's Annali,
p.61.

NT 0048193 MH ViU

Tasso, Torquato, 1544-
La Gerusalemme liberata...
con varianti e note del Colombo, del
Gherardini e del Cavedoni. Mantova,
Caranenti, 1820-28.

2v.

NT 0048194 PU OClW

+*Y TASSO, TORQUATO, 1544-1595.
712 La Gerusalemme liberata. Firenze,G.Ma-
.T 2082 renigh,1820.
2v. 46cm.

NT 0048195 ICN IU NN MH PP

858
T21g Tasso,Torquato,1544-1595.
Z88 Gerusalemme liberata di Torquato Tasso,con
1820 note o sia spiegazioni utili,e dilucidazioni
grammaticali,da Romualdo Zotti,ad uso degli
studiosi lingua italiana. 4.ed. ... Londra,
R.Zotti, 1820.

2 v. 16cm.

I.Zotti,Romualdo,d.1819,ed. II.Title.

NT 0048196 MiU

PQ4638 Tasso, Torquato, 1544-1595.
.D20 La Gerusalemme liberata. Milano,
P.A. Tosi, 1820.
2 v. front. 21 cm.

"Edizione formata sopra quella di
Mantova, Osanna, 1584."

NT 0048197 TU PU

Tasso, Torquato, 1544-1595.
La Gerusalemme liberata di Torquato Tasso, con annotazioni
... Padova, Tip. della Minerva, 1820.
2 v. front. (port.) 18ᶜᵐ.
"Elogio di Torquato Tasso": vol. I, p. [1]-lxv.
"Argomenti" of Orazio Ariosto.
"Indice delle voci della 'Gerusalemme liberata' citate nel Vocabolario
della Crusca": vol. II, p. [347]-357.

1. Ariosto, Orazio, 1555-1593.   II. Title.
4-5784

Library of Congress   PQ4638.D20

NT 0048198 DLC MH PU

Tasso, Torquato, 1544-1595.
La Gerusalemme liberata ... Firenze, Dal gabinetto
all' insegna di Pallade, 1821.
3 p. l., [iii]-vii, 182 p. front. (port.) 23ᶜᵐ. (In Parnaso classico italiano ... v. 4)
"Vita di Torquato Tasso estratta dagli elogj di Lorenzo Crasso":
p. [iii]-iv.
L'Aminta: p. [151]-182.

1. Crasso, Lorenzo, 17th cent.   II. Title.
1-19908

Library of Congress   PQ4201.P2

NT 0048199 DLC PU

Tasso, Torquato, 1544-1595.
La Gerusalemme liberata di Torquato Tasso ... Lon-
dra, Presso C. Corrall; a spese di G. Pickering, 1822.
2 v. front. (port.) 9 x 5½ᶜᵐ.
Paged continuously.
Vol. 1 has added t.-p., engr.

1. Title.
17-12350

Library of Congress   PQ4638.D22

NT 0048200 DLC PP PU CtY MB ICU MH InU NN

Tasso, Torquato, 1544–1595.
La Gerusalemme liberata di Torquato Tasso; publicata da A. Buttura ... Parigi, Presso Lefevre, 1822.
4 v. front. (port.) 10ᵐ. (*Half-title:* Biblioteca poetica italiana, t. XVI–XIX)
"Cenni su l'autore e sul poema": v. 1, p. [5]–8.

I. Buttura, Antonio, 1771–1832, ed.   II. Title.

2–14754 Revised

Library of Congress   PQ4638.D22 b

NT   0048201   DLC PU PPL MH

Tasso, Torquato, 1544–1595.
La Gerusalemme liberata di Torquato Tasso. Firenze, Presso L. Ciardetti, 1823.
2 v. 21½ᵐ.
"Vita di Torquato Tasso": vol. I, p. [vii]–xxv.

I. Title.

27–4472

Library of Congress   PQ4638.D23

NT   0048202   DLC NN WaSpG PP NIC OKentU

J54
t185g
1823

Tasso, Torquato, 1544–1595.
La Gerusalemme liberata, diligentemente riveduta sull'esemplare di Firenze del 1818. Napoli, Da'torchi di Raffaello di Napoli, 1823–
   v./ 16cm.

NT   0048203   OrU

Tasso, Torquato, 1544–1595.
La Gerusalemme, e l'Aminta di Torquato Tasso; con note di diversi per diligenza e studio di Antonio Buttura... Parigi: Lefevre, 1823. 2 v. front. (port.) 12°.
Notizie intorno a Torquato Tasso scritte dal cavaliere Girolamo Tiraboschi, p. ii–[xxx.

1. Poetry (Italian). 2. Drama (Italian). 3. Buttura, Antonio, 1771–1832, editor. 4. Tiraboschi, Girolamo, 1731–1794. 5. Title: La Gerusalemme liberata. 6. Title: Aminta.
N. Y. P. L.   April 10, 1922.

NT   0048204   NN MH NjP PHC

Tasso, Torquato, 1544–1595.
La Gerusalemme liberata, poema di Torquato Tasso, ridotta a miglior lezione; aggiuntovi il confronto delle varianti tratto dalle più celebri edizioni, con note critiche sopra le medesime ... Firenze, Presso G. Molini, all'insegna di Dante, 1824.
2 v. front. (port.) 23½ᵐ.
"Elogio di Torquato Tasso, scritto da Monsignor Fabroni": v. 1, p. [xvii]–lxxv.
"Michele Colombo ... fu il compilatore delle belle osservazioni poste al fine d'ogni volume."—Gamba, Serie dei testi di lingua, 4. ed., no. 951.
I. Fabroni, Angelo, 1732–1803. II. Colombo, Michele, 1747–1838. III. Title.

18–19336

Library of Congress   PQ4638.D24

NT   0048205   DLC CU PU NN MH

Tasso, Torquato, 1544–1595.
Gerusalemme liberata; poema di Torquato Tasso, secondo l'edizione di Mantova per Francesco Osanna, M.D.LXXXIIII. Firenze, Presso G. Molini, all'insegna di Dante, 1824.
3 p. l., [v]–vii, 548 p., 1 l. front. 15ᵐ.
Added t.-p., engr.
Title vignette (Printer's device?)
"Vita di Torquato Tasso": p. [1]–16.
"Argomenti" of Orazio Ariosto.

I. Ariosto, Orazio, 1555–1593. II. Title.

4–5790

Library of Congress   PQ4638.D24 c

NT   0048206   DLC MeB MiU

TASSO, Torquato, 1544–
La Gerusalemme liberata. Milano, G. Silvestri, 1824.

Portr.
(BIBLIOTECA scelta di opere italiane antiche e moderne, 142.)   Ital 7458.24.4
"Memorie storiche sopra Tasso scritte dal cav. Giuseppe Compagnoni", pp. ix–xxxii.

NT   0048207   MH PU OU IU

Tasso, Torquato, 1544–1595.
La Gerusalemme liberata del Sig. Torquato Tasso, confrontata, e corretta sul migliore originale. Prato, Stamp. Vestri, 1824.
2 v. in 1. 16½ᵐ.
"Vita del Signor Torquato Tasso, estratta dagli elogj del Sig. Lorenzo Crasso": p. 3–[8]
"Argomenti" of G. V. Imperiale.

I. Imperiale, Giovanni Vincenzo, d. 1645.

4–8785

NT   0048208   DLC PU

PQ4201
.C8
v.29–30
1827

Tasso, Torquato, 1544–1595.
... La Gerusalemme liberata ... Firenze, P. Borghi e comp., 1827.
2 v. 12ᶜᵐ. (*Added t.-p.:* Collezione portatile di classici italiani. Vols. XXIX–XXX)
Title vignettes.

NT   0048209   ViU

---

xPQ4638
.D27

Tasso, Torquato, 1544–1595.
La Gerusalemme liberata. Milano, Società Tipogr. de'Classici Italiani, 1827.
2v. 12cm. (Raccolta di poeti classici Italiani antichi e moderni, v.54–55)

NT   0048210   FMU

TASSO, Torquato, 1544–
La Gerusalemme liberata. [Edited by Angelo Sicca]. Padova, tipog. della Minerva, 1827.
(In PARNASO classico italiano. [4].)

NT   0048211   MH PU

Tasso, Torquato, 1544–1595.
La Gerusalemme liberata, di Torquato Tasso. Firenze, Presso Giuseppe Galletti, 1828.
2 v. front(port.) 22 cm.

NT   0048212   KAS PU

Tasso, Torquato, 1544–
La Gerusalemme liberata ... col riscontro della conquistata. [Riscontri e considerazioni di Luigi Carrer.] Padova. Alla Minerva. 1828. 3 v. in 2. 24°.
The title-page is missing from vol. I.

F2662 — T.r. — Carrer, Luigi, ed. 1801–1850.

NT   0048213   MB MH PP

Tasso, Torquato, 1544–
La Gerusalemme liberata. Torino, Pomba, 1828.
3v. in 1

NT   0048214   PU

Dante
PQ
4302
E29

Tasso, Torquato, 1544–1595.
La Gerusalemme liberata. Firenze, Passigli, Borghi e Compagni, 1830.
[708]–835 p. port. 23cm. (Biblioteca portatile del viaggiatore, v.1, p. [708]–835)
Added t. p., engraved.

NT   0048215   NIC

Tasso, Torquato, 1544–1595.
La Gerusalemme liberata. Tomo 1–2. Venezia, G. Antonelli, 1831.
2 v. in 1. port. 48°.

NT   0048216   NN

Dante
PQ
4302
E32

Tasso, Torquato, 1544–1595.
La Gerusalemme liberata. Firenze, Tipografia Borghi e Compagni, 1832.
[706]–833 p. port. 22cm. (Biblioteca portatile del viaggiatore, v.1, p. [706]–833)
Added t. p., engraved.
Reprint of the edition of 1830, with the same portrait.

NT   0048217   NIC

Dante
PQ
4302
E33

Tasso, Torquato, 1544–1595.
La Gerusalemme liberata. Firenze, Tipografia Borghi e Compagni, 1833.
[706]–833 p. port. 21cm. (Biblioteca portatile del viaggiatore, v.1, p. [706]–833)
Added t. p., engraved, has date 1832, of which this edition is a reissue.

NT   0048218   NIC PU

Tasso, Torquato, 1544–1595.
La Gerusalemme liberata di Torquato Tasso. Venezia, G. Antonelli, 1834.
2 p. l., [ix]–xxxii col., 1 l., [5]–326 col., 1 l. front. (port.) 24½ᵐ. (*In* Parnaso italiano, v. 1)

2–12006

NT   0048219   DLC PPLas PU

Tasso, Torquato, 1544–
La Gerusalemme liberata con argomenti. Firenze, Baudry, 1835.
2v. in 1

NT   0048220   PU

853T185
0g.z5

Tasso, Torquato, 1544–
Gerusalemme liberata con note da Romualdo Zotti, ad uso degli studiosi della lingua italiana. 5.ed., riv. e cor. Londra, 1835.
2v. in 1.

NT   0048221   IU MH PU

Tasso, Torquato, 1544–95.
La Gerusalemme liberata. Nuova ed., diligentemente corretta. Napoli, Presso S. Starita, 1835
2 v. in 1

NT   0048222   MH MiU

851 Tasso, Torquato, 1544-1595.
T185g   La Gerusalemme liberata. Brusselles, L.
      Hauncan; Londra, P. Rolandi, 1836.
1836   2 v. 16 cm.
      Vol. 2 wanting.
      Imperfect copy: without covers.

NT 0048223 MsSM PHC

TASSO, Torquato, 1544-1595.
      La Gerusalemme e l'Aminta. Con note di di-
      versi. Parigi, Baudry, 1836.

NT 0048224 MH

Tasso, Torquato. Gerusalemme liberata.
Buttura, Antonio, 1771-1832, ed.
      I quattro poeti italiani, con una scelta di poesie ita-
liane dal 1200 sino a' nostri tempi. Pub. secondo l'edizione del 1833 di A. Buttura. Parigi, Lefèvre [etc.] 1836.

Tasso, Torquato, 1544-1595.
      La Gerusalemme liberata, di Torquato Tasso... Édition
stereotype, d'après le procédé de Firmin Didot. Paris: Crochard
et Cie, 1838. 2 v. in 1. 24°.

1. Poetry (Italian). 2. Title.
N. Y. P. L.   December 10, 1917

NT 0048226 NN MH NjP

PQ4638 Tasso, Torquato, 1544-1595.
.D38   La Gerusalemme liberata di Torquato Tasso. Ed. critica,
      riveduta e cor. da Gio. Gaspare Orelli ... Zurigo, F. Schul-
      thess, 1838.
      viii, 615 p. 21¼[cm].

NT 0048227 ICU MH OCX

TASSO, Torquato, 1544-
      La Gerusalemme liberata. 2 tom. (In 1.)
      Firenze, presso G. Moro, 1839.

      32°. Portr. and plates.

NT 0048228 MH

Tasso, Torquato, 1544-95
      La Gerusalemme liberata. Con le annotazioni di
      G.Gherardini. Firenze, Passigli, 1840

      p. [1357] - 1552 plate
      Bound as issued with Ariosto, L.L'Orlando
      furioso. Firenze, 1840

NT 0048229 MH PU IU

Tasso, Torquato, 1544-1595
      La Gerusaleme liberata ...Publicata da A.
      Buttura... Parigi, Baudry, 1840.

      4 v.

NT 0048230 OO

Tasso, Torquato, 1544-1595.
      Gerusalemme liberata, di Torquato Tasso. Con
note da Romualdo Zotti ad uso degli studiosi della
lingua italiana. 6. ed. riv. e cor. ... Londra,
Dulau e cia. [etc.] 1842.
      2 v. 17 cm.

NT 0048231 CU

Tasso, Torquato, 1544-1595.
      La Gerusalemme liberata, e L'Aminta, di Torquato Tasso.
      Paris, Firmin Didot frères, 1843.
      2 p. l., viii, 558 p. 18¼[cm].
      "Vita di Torquato Tasso": p. [i]-viii.

      I. Title. II. Title: Aminta.
                                    17—12349
      Library of Congress   PQ4638.D43

NT 0048232 DLC ViU OrU TU MB MiU

PQ4638 Tasso, Torquato, 1544-1595.
D44   La Gerusalemme liberata; colla vita dell'au-
      tore e note storiche ad ogni canto per Giuseppe
      Bertinatti. Brusselle, Meline, Cans, 1844.
      xvi,592 p. illus.

      I. Bertinatti, Giuseppe, ed. II. Title.

NT 0048233 CU MH OO PPL PP DLC-P4 IaU ICN

PQ4638 Tasso,Torquato,1544-1595.
.D44a   La Gerusalemme liberata,di Torquato Tasso,pre-
      ceduta da un discorso critico letterario di Ugo
      Foscolo,e seguita da note storiche. Firenze,F.
      Le Monnier,1844.
      xxiii,480 p. 18cm.
      Italian translation by F.D.Guerrazzi of Fos-
colo's "Discorso",'estratto dal LXII[i.e.XLII]
della Quarterly Review;settembre[i.e.April]1819.'
      "Note storiche" by Pietro J.Fraticolli.

NT 0048234 ICU PU NcU

PQ4638 Tasso, Torquato, 1544-1595.
.D44   Gerusalemme liberata di Torquato Tasso. Con note sto-
      riche di G. Sacchi ... Milano, L. Sacchi, 1844, '42.
      2 v. in 1. front., illus (incl. ports.) map 27¼[cm]
      T.-p. illus.
      Head and tail pieces.

NT 0048235 ICU MH OU PU OrU CtU

PQ4638 Tasso, Torquato, 1544-1595.
1845   La Gerusalemme liberata, e L'Aminta, di Torquato
      Tasso. Paris, Firmin Didot frères, 1845.
      2 p. l., viii, 558 p. 18¼[cm].
      "Vita di Torquato Tasso": p. [i]-viii.

NT 0048236 ViU MB CtY FMU PPL PU MH NcU OOxM

TASSO, Torquato, 1544-
      La Gerusalemme liberata. Edizione quasi
      del tutto conforme alla milanese dell'anno
      1844. Padova, 1846.

      24°.

NT 0048237 MH

Tasso, Torquato, 1544-1595.
      La Gerusalemme liberata. Brusselles, L.
      Hauman [185-?]
      2 v. 17 cm.

NT 0048238 CtY

TASSO, Torquato, 1544-
      La Gerusalemme liberata. preceduta da
      un discorso di Ygo Foscolo, etc., 3a ed.
      Firenze, 1850.

      12 x 19.

NT 0048239 MH-AH

Tasso, Torquato, 1544-1595.
      La Gerusalemme liberata e L'Aminta. Paris,
      F. Didot frères, 1850.

NT 0048240 MH PPL

TASSO,Torquato,1544-1595.
      La Gerusalemme liberata. Prato,a spese di
D.Cassuto,1851.

      18 cm.

NT 0048241 MH

TASSO, Torquato, 1544-
      La Gerusalemme liberata.

      (In BUTTURA, Antonio, editor. I quattro
poeti italiani, 1852.)

NT 0048242 MH

Tasso, Torquato, 1544-1595.
      La Gerusalemme liberata, di Torquato Tasso: prece-
      duta da un discorso critico letterario di Ugo Foscolo, ed
      illustrata da note storiche. 4. ed. Firenze, F. Le Mon-
      nier, 1853.
      xx, 460 p. 18[cm].
      The "Discorso" translated from the Quarterly review, April 1819, no.
      XLII, by F. D. Guerrazzi.
      "Note storiche" by P. J. Fraticelli.

      I. Foscolo, Ugo [i. e. Niccolò Ugo, 1778-1827. II. Guerrazzi, Francesco
Domenico, 1804-1873, tr. III. Fraticelli, Pietro Jacopo, 1803-1866. IV. Title.
                                    2—14059
      Library of Congress   PQ4638.D53

      CtY FTaSU WU CU OU MB ViU OClW NjP NN OCU
NT 0048243 DLC OrU PU NIC OKentU NRU PSC PPL PV

TASSO, Torquato, 1544-1595.
      La Gerusalemme liberata; poema epico.
      Ed. ad uso dei giovani studenti. Genova,
      Stabilimento tipografico ligustico, 1853.

      24°.

NT 0048244 MH PU

851.46
A5ge   Tasso, Torquato, 1544-1595.
      La Gerusalemme liberata e l'Aminta ...
      Paris, Didot, 1854.
      viii, 558 p. 18 cm.
      Stamped on title-page, Ex Biblioteca
      Universitatis, Sti Ludovici.

NT 0048245 MoSU ViU MH MiD

PQ4638   TASSO,TORQUATO,1544-1595.
.D57   La Gerusalemme liberata,di Torquato Tasso. Torino,
        M.Guigoni,1857.
        [2],400 p. 16cm.

NT   0048246   ICU

Tasso, Torquato, 1544-1595.
        La Gerusalemme liberata e l'Aminta.   Paris,
    1858.
        12°.

NT   0048247   CtY

TASSO, Torquato, 1544-1595.
    La Gerusalemme liberata. Firenze, G.
Barbèra, 1862.

    nar.32°. pp.(2). 659. Port.

NT   0048248   MH OO

PQ4638 Tasso, Torquato, 1544-1595.
.Z4   La Gerusalemme liberata di Torquato Tasso, illustrata in
1865   ordine alla critica letteraria e storica ad uso della gioventu'
        studiosa da un Vercellese. Ed. 3. Torino, Per G. Marietti,
        1865.
        ccxv, 623, [1] p. 14½ᶜᵐ.
        With reproduction of the t.-p. of the ed. pub. Torino, 1855.

NT   0048249   ICU PU

PQ   Tasso, Torquato, 1544-1595.
4638   La Gerusalemme liberata e l'Aminta.
D67   Paris, Didot, 1867.
        viii, 658 p. 18cm.

        I. Aminta.

NT   0048250   NIC CU OC1W

PQ   Tasso, Torquato, 1544-1595.
4638   La Gerusalemme liberata; illustrata col
D68   presidio della filologia, della storia e del
        disegno. 4. ed., rifusa su più ampio con-
        cetto. Modena, Tip. editrice dell' Imm.
        Concezione, 1868.
        xvi, 752 p. map, plan. 19cm.

        Edited by Camillo Mela.

        I. Mela, Camillo, ed. II. Title.

NT   0048251   NIC OU PV

Tasso, Torquato, 1544-
            La Gerusalemme liberata,
    poema epico.   Torino, Marietti, 1868.

        623 p.

NT   0048252   PU

        Tasso, Torquato, 1544-1595
WA   La Gerusalemme liberata. Firenze, G.
14152   Barbèra, 1869.
        659 p. illus.

NT   0048253   CtY IU NNC MH

PQ4638 Tasso, Torquato, 1544-1595.
.D71   La Gerusalemme liberata di Torquato Tasso. Riveduta
    nel testo e corredata di note critiche ed illustrative per cura
    di G. A. Scartazzini. Leipzig, F. A. Brockhaus, 1871.
    xlvi, [1], 411, [1] p. 18½ᶜᵐ.   (*Half-title:* Biblioteca d'autori italiani. t. 12)

NT   0048254   ICU CtY PU

Tasso, Torquato.
        La Gerusalemme liberata. Volume unico.   Milano: M.
Guigoni, 1871. 404 p. 16°.

    On cover: Collegio italiano d'Alessandria d'Egitto. Premio.

1. Poetry (Italian). 2. Title.
N. Y. P. L.   June 3, 1914.

NT   0048255   NN

Tasso, Torquato, 1544-
    La Gerusalemme liberata, con note
raccolte e ordinate per cura di
Eugenio Damerini; edizione integra.
Milan, 1875.

NT   0048256   ODW

Tasso, Torquato, 1544-1595.
    ...La Gerusalemme liberata, cantos I, II. With introduction
and notes by H. B. Cotterill ... Oxford, Clarendon press, 1875.
    2 p. l., [vii]-xxii, [2], 95p. 17cm. (Clarendon press series)

    I. Cotterill, Henry Bernard, 1846- ed. II. Title.

    Printed by Wesleyan   University Library

NT   0048257   CtW PV NN PU ViU OU NjP MdBP MH

Tasso, Torquato, 1544-1595.
    La Gerusalemme liberata, e L'Aminta, di
Torquato Tasso.   Paris, Firmin Didot et cie.,
1876.
    2 p. l., viii, 558 p. 18.5 cm.
    "Vita di Torquato Tasso": p. [i]-viii.

NT   0048258   CU

853T185 Tasso, Torquato, 1544-
Og.c   La Gerusalemme liberata, con note rac-
        colte e ordinate per cura di Eugenio Ca-
        merini. Ed. integra.   Mil. 1879.
        400p.

NT   0048259   IU CtY

PQ4638 Tasso, Torquato, 1544-1595.
.D80   La Gerusalemme liberata di Torquato Tasso. Corredata
    di note filologiche e storiche e di varianti e riscontri colla
    conquistata per cura di Domenico Carbone . 5. ed. stereo-
    tipa. Firenze, G. Barbèra, 1880.
    xvi, 224 p. 20ᶜᵐ.
    "Vita di Torquato Tasso": p. [ix]-xvi.

NT   0048260   ICU

851.46 Tasso, Torquato, 1544-1595.
Og   La Gerusalemme liberata. Preceduta da un
        discorso critico letterario di Ugo Forcolo,
        ed. illustrata da note storiche. 4. ed.
        Firenze, Successori Le Monnier, 1881.
        460p. 19cm.

NT   0048261   KU

PQ4638 Tasso, Torquato, 1544-1595.
.Z4F2   La Gerusalemme liberata di Torquato Tasso, annotata ad
    uso delle scuole con prefazione di Guido Falorsi. Firenze,
    Successori Le Monnier, 1882.
    xlv, [iii]-xx, 222 p 17½ᶜᵐ.

NT   0048262   ICU PU

Tasso, Torquato, 1544-
    La Gerusalemme liberata di T. Tasso. Riveduta nel
testo e corredata di note critiche ed illustrative, e di
varianti e riscontri colla Conquistata per cura di G. A.
Scartazzini. 2. ed. intieramente rifatta. Leipzig, F. A.
Brockhaus, 1882.
    viii, 474 pp., 1 l. 12°. (Biblioteca d'autori italiani. t. 12)
                                                        1-29909—M 2

NT   0048263   DLC PU CtY NN MdBP MiU ViU OU

PQ 4638
D82   Tasso, Torquato, 1544-1595.
1882   La Gerusalemme liberata. Milano,
            Guigoni, 1882.
            400 p. 16 cm.

NT   0048264   CaBVaU

        Tasso, Torquato, 1544-1595.
851.46   La Gerusalemme liberata; con pref. di
T214   Guido Mazzoni. Firenze, G. C. Sansoni, 1883.
GEA   xxvi, 492 p. 11 cm.

NT   0048265   NcD MH CU

Tasso, Torquato, 1544-
    La Gerusalemme liberata. Con prefazione di Guido Falorsi.
= Firenze. Le Monnier. 1884. cxliv, 516 pp. 32°.

F3 — Falorsi, Guido, prefacer.

NT   0048266   MB

        Tasso, Torquato, 1544-1595.
        La Gerusalemme liberta. Firenze,
    Salani, 1884.

        611 p. 18½ cm.

NT   0048267   WaTU

Tasso, Torquato, 1544-1595.
    La Gerusalemme liberata, di Torquato Tasso, con note rac-
colte et ordinate per cura di Eugenio Camerini. Ed. integra.
Milano, E. Sonzogno, 1884.
    399, [1] p. 18¼ᶜᵐ.

    I. Camerini, Eugenio, 1811-1875, ed. II. Title.

                                                        33-39093
    Library of Congress   PQ4638.D84   , 851.46

NT   0048268   DLC FMU OC1W

Tasso, Torquato, 1544-
            La Gerusalemme liberata.
    Lipsia, Fleischer, 1886.

        256 p.   (Il parnasso italiano.)

NT   0048269   PU

PQ4638
1888   Tasso, Torquato, 1544-1595.

La Gerusalemme liberata; preceduta da
un discorso critico letterario di Ugo
Foscolo, ed illustrata da note storiche. 4.
ed. Firenze, Successori Le Monnier, 1888.
xx, 460 p.   18cm.
"Note storiche" by P. J. Fraticelli.

I. Foscolo, Ugo, 1778-1827. II. Fraticelli,
Pietro Jacopo, 1803-1866. III. Title.

NT 0048270   ViU MiU NNC CtY MH OClW NjP

---

fPQ4638   Tasso, Torquato, 1544-1595.
D88   La Gerusalemme liberata, con le figure di Giambatista
Piazzetta.   Venezia, Stampata da G. Albrizzi, 1745; Milano,
Fratelli Treves, 1888.
xxiii, 512 p. illus., port. 45cm.

I. Piazzetta, Giovanni Battista, 1682-or 3-1754, illus.
II. Title.

NT 0048271   CU PU

TASSO, Torquato, 1544-
La Gerusalemme liberata. Con note raccolte
e ordinate per cura di Eugenio Camerini.
Ed. integra. Milano, 1889.

NT 0048272   MH

PQ4638 Tasso, Torquato, 1544-1595.
.D90   La Gerusalemme liberata di Torquato Tasso, con commento del prof. Severino Ferrari. Firenze, G. C. Sansoni,
1890.
xiii, [1], 233, [2] p. 20cm. (On cover: Biblioteca scolastica [di classici italiani])

NT 0048273   ICU MH MiU PU

PQ4638 TASSO,TORQUATO,1544-1595.
.D91   La Gerusalemme liberata,di Torquato Tasso. Firenze,
Rare bk G.Barbèra,1891.
room   [1], 659 p. front.(port.) 10½cm.
Preface signed:C.Guasti.

NT 0048274   ICU PPFr PU

Tasso, Torquato, 1544-1595.
La Gerusalemme liberata di Torquato
Tasso; con prefazione e note di Domenico
Galeazzi, per uso della gioventù.
Napoli,A.Morano,1891.
11,732p. 11½cm.

I. Galeazzi, Domenico. II. Title.

NT 0048275   MWelC

Tasso, Torquato, 1544-
La Gerusalemme liberata; con raccolte e ord.nate per cura
di Eugenio Camerini.   Milano: Edoardo Sonzogno, 1892.
300 p.   12°.

NT 0048276   NN NIC CU OClW InStme

Tasso, Torquato, 1544-1595.
Gerusalemme liberata; poema eroico di Torquato Tasso. Ed.
critica sui manoscritti e le prime stampe a cura di Angelo
Solerti e cooperatori ... Firenze, G. Barbèra, 1895-96 [v. 1, '96]

3 v. front. (port.) 19ᵐᵐ.

CONTENTS.—v. 1. Discorso sul testo. Bibliografia. Cinque Canti, di
Camillo Camilli aggiunti al Goffredo. Rimario. Indice.—v. 2-3. I primi
tre canti della Gerusalemme secondo un primitivo abbozzo. Gerusalemme
liberta.

I. Solerti, Angelo, 1865-1907, ed. II. Camilli, Camillo. III. Title.

1—23910

Library of Congress   PQ4638.D96

NjP MeB MiU
NT 0048277   DLC CtY NcD OrU PU MdBP NN NIC TU OrPS

PQ4638 Tasso, Torquato, 1544-1595.
.D95a   La Gerusalemme liberata di Torquato Tasso. Riveduta
nel testo e commentata dal prof. Pio Spagnotti. Milano,
U. Hoepli, 1895.
xxxix, 486 p. 19ᵐᵐ.
"Opere consultate": p. [ix]
"Torquato Tasso. Cenni intorno a la vita e a le opere": p. [xi-xvi]

NT 0048278   ICU CtY MB MH DCU PU

Tasso, Torquato, 1544-1595.
La Gerusalemme liberata. Riv. nel testo e
commentata dal Prof. Pio Spagnotti. 2. ed.
riv. Milano, Hoepli, 1898.
xxxix, 486 p.

I. Spagnotti, Pio. II. Title.

NT 0048279   WaU PHC MA MH IU IaU NNC MiU

TASSO, Torquato, 1544-
La Gerusalemme liberata. Con note storiche,
critiche, e filologiche, raccolte dal dott.
G. B. Francesia. 22a ed. Torino, libr.
Salesiana, 1899.

NT 0048280   MH

PQ
4638   Tasso, Torquato, 1544-1595.
E01   La Gerusalemme liberata di Torquato
Tasso. Corredata di note filologiche
e storiche e di varianti e riscontri
colla Conquistata, per cura di Domenico
Carbone. 13.ed.stereotipa. Firenze,
G.Barbèra,1901.
xvi,224p. 20cm.

I.Carbone Domenico, 1880-   ed.
II.Title.

NT 0048281   CLSU

TASSO Torquato,1544-
La Gerusalemme liberata. Ridotta con
annotazioni di Riccardo Cornali. Milano.
Albrighi, Segati & co., 1901.

NT 0048282   MH

TASSO,TORQUATO, 1544-1595.
La Gerusalemme liberata, di Torquato Tasso,
con commento di Severino Ferrari. Nuova ed.
riveduta e corretta.   Firenze,G.C.Sansoni,
1903.
xii,[iii],233,[1]p. 20cm. [Biblioteca
scolastica di classici italiani]

NT 0048283   PU

850
T214   Tasso, Torquato, 1544-1595.
tG.1   Gerusalemme liberata, poema eroico.
Firenze, G.Barbèra, 1904.
498p. port. 7x5cm. (Edizione vademecum)

In case.

NT 0048284   CLSU MH PPC

Tasso, Torquato, 1544-
La Gerusalemme liberata. Con commento di S. Ferrari.
Firenze: G. C. Sansoni, 1905.   xii, 2 l., 233 p., 1 l.   rev. ed.
12°.

1. Poetry (Italian). 2. Ferrari,   Severino, editor. 3. Title.
N.Y. P. L.   June 23, 1914.

NT 0048285   NN NIC

Tasso, Torquato, 1544-1595.
La Gerusalemme liberata, di Torquato Tasso.
Corredata di note filologiche e storiche e di
varianti e riscontri colla Conquistata, per cura di Domenico Carbone. Volume unico. 14.ed.
stereotipa. Firenze, G. Barbèra, 1906.
224p. 20cm.

I. Carbone, Domenico, 1880-   ed. II.
Title.

NT 0048286   NcU MH

PQ 4638 TASSO,TORQUATO,1544-1595
.D06   La Gerusalemme liberata; edizione di
Giovanni Giorgio Keil. Tomo 1-2. Gotha,
Steudel e Keil, 1906.
2 v. (Biblioteca italiana, v.1-2)

1. Keil, Johann Georg,1781-1857,ed. II. Title.

NT 0048287   InU

Tasso, Torquato, 1544-1595
La Gerusalemme liberata. Con commento di Severino
Ferrari. Nuova ed.riv.e corr. Firenze, Sansoni, 1907
xii, 233 p.

NT 0048288   MH

Tasso, Torquato, 1544-
La Gerusalemme liberata; riveduta nel tresto e commentata
dal Prof. Pio Spagnotti.   Milano: Ulrico Hoepli, 1907.   xxxviii
(i), 486 p. 3. ed. 12°.

1. Spagnotti, Pio, editor. 2. Title.
N.Y. P. L.   November 20, 1911.

NT 0048289   NN NNC ICU WaS

Tasso, Torquato, 1544-1595.
La Gerusalemme liberata; con commento di
Severino Ferrari. New ed. rev. Firenze,
Sansoni, 1908.
233 p. D.

NT 0048290   NcU CU

PQ4638 TASSO,TORQUATO,1544-1595.
.E08   ...Gerusalemme liberata;poema eroico. Prefazione
di Guido Mazzoni,note di Arnaldo della Torre... Torino[etc.]G.B.Paravia & c.[1908]
ix,[1],416,[1]p. front.(port.) 20cm.

NT 0048291   ICU MH IaU NNC

Tasso, Torquato, 1544–
La Gerusalemme liberata, preceduta
da un discorso critico e letterario di
N.U. Foscolo ed illustra da note storiche
Ed. 4.   Florence, Le Monnier, 1910.

460 p.

NT 0048292   PU

Tasso, Torquato, 1544–
La Gerusalemme liberata di T. Tasso; con commento di S.
Ferrari.   Firenze: G. C. Sansoni, 1910.   xii p., 2 l., 233 p., 1 l.
new ed.   12°.   (Biblioteca scolastica di classici italiani.)

1. Poetry (Italian). 2. Ferrari,   Severino, editor. 3. Title.
N. Y. P. L.   June 20, 1911.

NT 0048293   NN

TASSO, Torquato, 1544–
La Gerusalemme liberata, illustrata da
Edoardo Matania con note di Eugenio Camerini
e prefazione di Carlo Romussi . Milano,
Sonzogno, [1911].

f°
"La crociata, 1095-1099",pp. 315-317.

NT 0048294   MH NN

Tasso, Torquato, 1544–1595.
La Gerusalemme liberata di Torquato Tasso;
riveduta nel testo e commentata da Pio Spagnotti.
4 ed., con proemio di Michele Scherillo.   Milano,
U. Hoepli, 1912.
x l., 488 p.   19 cm.

NT 0048295   MtU WaT CtY MH

Tasso, Torquato, 1544–1595.
Hd17   ... La Gerusalemme liberata, ampiamente
101m   tradotta in prosa, ad uso del popolo italiano
dal prof. Giuseppe Castelli. Milano,Societa'
editoriale milanese[1913]
958p. illus. 24½cm.

NT 0048296   CtY

Tasso, Torquato, 1544–1595.
La Gerusalemme liberata, di Torquato Tasso. Ad uso delle
scuole, con introduzione e commento di Michele Martina
Torino [etc.] Libreria editrice internazionale, 1913.   xcix, 658 p.
illus. (map.)   19cm.

With bookplate of John Finley.

68905B. 1. No subject. I. Martina,   Michele.
N. Y. P. L.   November 4, 1940

NT 0048297   NN CU

TASSO, Torquato. 1544–1595.
Gerusalemme liberata. Con introduzione
e note di Guido Falorsi. Firenze, successori Le
Monnier, [1915?]

pp. lxxxvii, (4). 641-. Port.
(SCRITTORI italiani per la scuola e per la
cultura).

NT 0048298   MH MA

Tasso, Torquato, 1544–1595.
La Gerusalemme liberata di Torquato
Tasso, con commento di Severino Ferrari;
nuova ed. riveduta e corretta (nuova tiratura).   Firenze,G.C.Sansoni,1916.
xii p.,2 l.,233p.,1 l. 20½cm.

I.Ferrari, Severino, 1856–1905, ed.
II.Title.

NT 0048299   MWelC

Tasso, Torquato, 1544–1595.

Pallavicino, Carlo, 1630–1688.
... La Gerusalemme liberata. Herausgegeben von Hermann
Abert. Leipzig, Breitkopf & Härtel, 1916.

Tasso, Torquato, 1544–1595.
La Gerusalemme liberata, con commento de
Serverino Ferrari. Nuova ed. curata e riveduta
da Pietro Papini; con le illustrazioni di Bernardo
Castello.   Firenze, Sansoni [1917]
268 p. illus.
I. Ferrari, Severino, 1856–1905, ed. II. Papini,
Pietro, ed.

NT 0048301   IU

PQ4638
E18   Tasso, Torquato, 1544–1595
Gerusalemme liberata. Con note di Pio
Spagnotti, e proemio di Michele Scherillo.
5. ed. Milano, U. Hoepli, 1918.
xxxviii, 488 p. 20 cm.

I. Spagnotti, Pio   ed. II.
Scherillo, Michele, 1860–1930.

NT 0048302   MeB IU MiD NjP

Tasso, Torquato, 1544–1595.
... Gerusalemme liberata; introduzione e note di Umberto Bucchioni ... Torino, Unione tipografico-editrice
torinese [1919]

2 v. plates, port. 18½ cm.   (Added t.-p.: Collezione di classici
italiani ... vol. LVII–LVIII)
Some of the plates are printed on both sides.

I. Bucchioni, Umberto, ed. II. Title.
PQ4201.C7 vol. 57–58   22—5032

NT 0048303   DLC CtY ICU PV

TASSO, Torquato, 1544–1595.
La Gerusalemme liberata, con note storiche,
critiche, e filologiche raccolte dal dotor
G.B. Francesia. 40° migliaio. Torino, etc.,
Soc. ed. internazionale, 1920.

NT 0048304   MH

---

854   Tasso, Torquato, 1544–1595.
T185gv
La Gerusalemme liberata e le opere
minori in prosa e in versi a cura di Guido
Vitaletti. Torino, P. Viano, 1920.
xxviii,332p. illus.,ports. 22cm.

Bibliography: p. [xxvii]–xxviii.

I. Vitaletti, Guido, ed.

NT 0048305   OrU OClW

Tasso, Torquato, 1544–1595
La Gerusalemme liberata...13.ed...
Firenze, Barbèra, 1921.

659 p.

NT 0048306   PP

Hum
PQ   Tasso, Torquato, 1544–1595.
4638   Gerusalemme liberata; con note di Pio
E23   Spagnotti e proemio de Michele Scherillo.
6. ed. Milano, U. Hoepli, 1923.
xxxviii,488p.

I. Scherillo, Michele, 1860–1930.
II. Spagnotti, Pio   III. Title.

NT 0048307   ODW PHC OrP OrCS

Tasso,Torquato,1544–1595.
La Gerusalemme liberata di Torquato Tasso,
corredata di note filologiche e storiche e di
variante e riscontri colla conquistata per cura
di Domenico Carbone. Ediz.illustrata con 16
composiz.artistiche (21.tiratura). Firenze, G.
Barbèra, 1924.

xvi,254 p.incl.plates. front.(port.) pl. 20½cm.
(On cover: Edizioni di classici italiani)

I.Carbonne,Domenico,1823–1883, ed. II.Title.

NT 0048308   MiU MH ICU NcD NIC CtY NNC LU OClW

851.4   Tasso, Torquato, 1544–1595.
T21g   La Gerusalemme liberata, dieci canti
1925   commentati da Francesco Biondolillo.
Messina, G. Principato [1925]
345p. 20cm.

I. Biondolillo, Francesco, ed.

NT 0048309   IEN MH

Tasso, Torquato, 1544–
...La Gerusalemme liberata...   Fir.,
Sansoni, 1926.

335 p.

NT 0048310   PBm

Tasso, Torquato, 1544–1595.
Gerusalemme liberata, con note di Pio Spagnetti
e proemio di Michele Scherillo. aesta edizione.
Milano, Ulrico Hoopli, 1926.
488 p.

NT 0048311   PPT

Tasso, Torquato, 1544–1595.
La Gerusalemme liberata di Torquato
Tasso, con commento di Severino Ferrari.
Nuova ed.curata e riveduta da Pietro
Papini. Con le illustrazioni di Bernardo Castello ... Firenze, G.C.San-
soni, 1927.

xii,268p. illus. 20cm.

NT 0048312   CLSU

PQ Tasso, Torquato, 1544-1595.
4638 La Gerusalemme liberata, con note raccolte e
D22 ordinate per cura di Eugenio Camerini. Edizione
1927 integra. Milano, Casa Editrice Sonzogno [1927]
HRC 399p. (Biblioteca classica economica no. 3)

NT 0048313 TxU

PQ4638 Tasso, Torquato, 1544-1595.
E28 Gerusalemme liberata. Introduzione e note di Umberto Bucchioni. Torino, Unione Tipografico-editrice torinese [1928-
29 (v.1, 1929)]
2 v. illus.,port. (Collezione di classici italiani, v.57-58)

Vol. 2 (cop.1) imperfect copy: added t. p. with series note
wanting.
Bibliography: v.1, p.xxxvi.

I. Bucchioni, Umberto, ed. II. Title.

NT 0048314 CU OCU ViU NBuU

D851T18
03343
Tasso, Torquato, 1544-1595.
... La Gerusalemme liberata, con note di Augusto Sainati. Canti scelti. Firenze, Vallecchi [1928]
x, 159 p., 1 l. 20cm. (Classici italiani
commentati)

I. Sainati, Augusto ed.
II. Classici italiani commentati.

NT 0048315 NNC MH IU

TASSO, Torquato, 1544-
La Gerusalemme liberata. Con le parafrasi
in prosa preposte a ciascuno dei canti, note
illustrative ed appendice dei nomi storici
di personaggi, fatti e cose più notevoli.
Milano, etc., A. Vallardi, 1928.

pp.705. Port. and plates.
At head of title: Florilegio dei classici
italiani.

NT 0048316 MH OCU

D851T18
0334
Tasso, Torquato, 1544-1595.
... La Gerusalemme liberata, con introduzione
e commento estetico, a cura di Siro Attilio Nulli,
Palermo, Sandron, 1928.
660 p., 1 l. 20cm. (Collezione "Sandron"
di classici italiani)

I. Nulli, Siro Attilio ed.

NT 0048317 NNC

Tasso, Torquato, 1544-
La Gerusalemme liberata. Firenze, Salani
c1929,
538 p.

NT 0048318 OClW

851.46 Tasso, Torquato, 1544-1595.
OG La Gerusalemme liberata, canti scelti,
1929 collegati e annotati ad uso delle Scuole
Medie Superiori da Piero Nardi. Milano, A. Mondadori, 1929.
546p. 21cm. (Edizioni Mondadori per
le Scuole Medie)

NT 0048319 KU NNC OU OCU

Tasso, Torquato, 1544-1595.
... Gerusalemme liberata, a cura di Luigi Bonfigli. Bari,
G. Laterza & figli, 1930.
2 p. l. 598 p. 1 l. 21cm. (Half-title: Scrittori d'Italia. [130] T.
Tasso. Opere. II)
"Appendice: Stanze rifiutate dall'autore": p. [493]-530.

I. Bonfigli, Luigi, ed. II. Title.

Title from Univ. of Minn. A 31-583
Library of Congress [PQ4638]

NT 0048320 MnU PBm NcU InU ViU MH OCU OU MiU

Hd17 Tasso, Torquato, 1544-1595
104 La Gerusalemme liberata, con introd. e
commento di Ettore Allodoli. Milano,F.Vallardi
1933.
2v. fronts(v.1,port.) 19cm. (Biblioteca
di classici italiani annotati)
Collezione Vallardi.

NT 0048321 CtY

Tasso, Torquato, 1544-1595
...La Gerusalemme liberata;......Torino
Societa editrice internazionale 1933.

689 p.

NT 0048322 OCU

Tasso, Torquato, 1544-1595.
La Gerusalemme liberata di Torquato Tasso, con
commento di Severino Ferrari. Nuova ed., curata
e riveduata di Pietro Papini. Con le illustrazioni di
Bernardo Castello... Firenze, G. C. Sansoni
[1935]
xii p., 2 l., 268 p., 1 l. illus. 21 cm.
(On cover: Biblioteca scolastica di classici italiani
gia diretta da Giosuè Carducci)

NT 0048323 CU

858
T21g Tasso, Torquato, 1544-1595.
L77 ... La Gerusalemme liberata, con introduzione
e note di Giuseppe Lipparini. Milano, C.
Signorelli [1936]
373 p.,1 l. 20cm.
"Per il testo,ho creduto opportuno di seguire ...
quello fissato da Luigi Bonfigli nella edizione later-
ziana degli 'Scrittori d'Italia'".--Avvertenza.

I.Lipparini,Giuseppe,1877- ed. II.Title.

NT 0048324 MiU OU NNF

Tasso, Torquato, 1544-1595.
Gerusalemme liberata, con introduzione e commento di Giovanni Ziccardi. Torino, G. B. Paravia
& C. [1936]
xxiv, 664 p. front. (port.) plates. 20 cm.

NT 0048325 OrU

PQ Tasso, Torquato, 1544-1595.
4638 La Gerusalemme liberata, con commento di Se-
.E37 verino Ferrari. Nuova edizione, curata e riv.
da Pietro Papini, con le illustrazioni di Bernardo Castello. Firenze, G. C. Sansoni [1937]
xii, 268 p. illus. 21 cm. (Biblioteca scolastica di classici italiani)

I. Ferrari, Severino, 1856-1905, ed. II.
Papini, Pietro, ed III. Title.

NT 0048326 DCU MiU

Hd17 Tasso, Torquato, 1544-1595.
108 Le Gerusalemme liberata di Torquato Tasso,
con introduzione, commenti e riassunti di
Emilio Zanette. 2ª ristampa. Torino[etc.]
Società editrice internazionale[1937]
lxviip.,2l.,596p.,1l. front.(port.) 20cm.

NT 0048327 CtY

Y TASSO, TORQUATO, 1544-1595.
712 ...La Gerusalemme liberata, con introduzione e
T 2085 commento di Silvio Adrasto Barbi. Nuova tiratura.
Firenze,Le Monnier,1938.
548p.

NT 0048328 ICN

Tasso, Torquato, 1544-1595
...La Gerusalemme liberata; introduzione,
note e commento di Massimo Sasso. Nuova
edizione riveduta e corretta. Milano, "La
Prora" 1938

693 p.

NT 0048329 CU

Hd17 Tasso, Torquato, 1544-1595
106 Gerusalemme liberata, con introd. e
commento di Giovanni Ziccardi. [2.ristampa]
Torino,G.B.Paravia[1938?]
xxii,664p. illus.,port. 19cm.

NT 0048330 CtY

PQ Tasso, Torquato, 1544-1595.
4638 La Gerusalemme liberata. Introd. e commenti
E39 di Onorato Castellino, tavole illustrative fuori
testo di Federico Zuccheri e Bernardo Castello.
2. ed. Torino, Libraria Italiana, 1939.
xxxv,523 p. illus. 21cm.

"Ad uso delle scuole medie."

I. Castellino, Onorato, ed. II. Title.

NT 0048331 NIC

PQ Tasso, Torquato, 1544-1595.
4638 La Gerusalemme liberata; scelta con introduzione,
Z5R2 commento e note di Gaetano Ragonese. Palermo,
G.B. Palumbo[194-?]
256 p. 20cm. (I Nostri classici...4)

I. Ragonese, Gaetano ed. II. Series

NT 0048332 CLSU

854 Tasso, Torquato, 1544-1595.
T185gfe La Gerusalemme liberata, con commento
di Severino Ferrari. Nuova ed., curata e
riv. da Pietro Papini, con illustrazioni
di Bernardo Castello. Firenze, Sansoni
[1940]
xii,268p. illus. 20cm.

I. Ferrari, Severino, 1856-1905.
II. Title.

NT 0048333 OrU

Tasso, Torquato, 1544-1595.
... La Gerusalemme liberata, e prose scelte; biografia, introduzione e commento di Claudio Varese. Stampe di Giam-
battista Piazzetta dalla edizione veneziana dell'Abrizzi, 1745 ...
[Firenze] Vallecchi [1940]

lvi, 386 p. plates. 19½ᵐ. (On cover: Biblioteca di classici italiani)
"Edizioni de 'La Gerusalemme' in vita del Tasso": p. [373] "Altre
opere": p. [375]-378.
"Bibliografia essenziale": p. lvi.

i. Varese, Claudio, ed. ii. Title.

Library of Congress   PQ4638.E40   44-48567
                          [2]   851.46

NT   0048334   DLC NNC OrU PPT MiD MB

Tasso, Torquato, 1544-1595.
La Gerusalemme liberata. Testo intero, con
pref. note e postille critche di Luigi Russo. 2. ed.
Messina, G. Principato [1943]
vii, 322 p.   20 cm.

NT   0048335   CtY

Tasso, Torquato, 1544-1595.
La Gerusalemme liberata, con discorsi intro-
duttivi del Foscolo e del Michelet, note a chia-
rimento e indice dei nomi e delle cose più notevoli, a cura di L.G. Tenconi. Milano, La Universale Barion [1943]

398 p.   20 cm.

I. Foscolo, Ugo, 1778-1827. II. Michelet,
Jules, 1798-1874. III. Title.

NT   0048336   CFS RPB MH

PQ   Tasso, Torquato, 1544-1595.
4638   La Gerusalemme liberata. Con introd. e
E43   commento di Piero Nardi. 10. ed.
          [Verona] A. Mondadori [1943]
          821 p.   20cm.

"Ad uso dell'ordine superiore."

I. Nardi, Piero, ed. II. Title.

NT   0048337   NIC

Tasso, Torquato, 1544-1595.
... La Gerusalemme liberata, con introduzione e note di Giuseppe Lipparini.
Milano, C. Signorelli [1944]
373, [1]p.   20cm.

NT   0048338   PSt

          Tasso, Torquato, 1544-1595.
851.3   La Gerusalemme liberata e Prose scelte. Bio-
T21gv   grafia, introduzione e commento di Claudio Va-
          rese. Stampe di Giambattista Piazzetta dalla
          ed. veneziana dell'Albrizzi - 1745.   [Firenze]
          Vallecchi [1945]
          lvi, 365p. illus. 19ᵐ.
          "Bibliografia essenziale": p. lvi.

I. Varese, Claudio,   ed.

NT   0048339   CSt

Tasso, Torquato, 1544-1595.
La Gerusalemme liberata [riassunti a cura di]
Nicola Feliciani. Bologna, L. Cappelli [1946]
67 p. (Enciclopedia scolastica, n. 174)
I. Feliciani, Nicola.

NT   0048340   ICU

---

854   Tasso, Torquato, 1544-1595.
T185gm   La Gerusalemme liberata, edizione integrale
           commentata da Attilio Momigliano.   Firenze,
           La Nuova Italia [1946]
           viii,326p.   21cm.   (Classici Italiani)

No.689.

I. Momigliano, Attilio, 1883- ed.
II. Title. III. Series.

NT   0048341   OrU NcD IaU

PQ 4638   Tasso, Torquato, 1544-1595.
E46   La Gerusalemme liberata / di Torquato
           Tasso ; con commento di Severino
           Ferrari. Nuova ed. / Curata e riveduta
           da Pietro Papini ; con illustrazioni di
           Bernardo Castello. Firenze : G. C.
           Sansoni, 1946.
           268 p. ; 21 cm.

NT   0048342   OU

851.3   Tasso, Torquato, 1544-1595.
T21gr   La Gerusalemme liberata per le scuole medie.
           Introduzione e commento di Riccardo Rugani.
           Firenze, Sansoni [1948]
           xxviii, 400 p.   20ᵐ.
           Bibliography: p. xxvii-xxviii.

I. Rugani, Riccardo,   ed. II.
Title: La Gerusa   lemme liberata.

NT   0048343   CSt TNJ CU

Tasso, Torquato, 1544-1595.
La Gerusalemme liberata; con introd. e com-
mento di Piero Nardi. [11. ed.   Verona]
Edizioni scolastiche Mondadori [1948]
823 p.   20 cm.
"Guida bibliografica": p. [815]-823.
I. Nardi, Piero, 1891-   ed.

NT   0048344   IU CtY

Tasso, Torquato, 1544-1595.
La Gerusalemme liberata. [Note a cura di
Lodovico Magugliani.]   Milano, Rizzoli [1950]
495 p.   16 cm.   (Biblioteca universale Rizzoli,
113-117)
I. Magugliani, Lodovico, ed.

NT   0048345   NB MB TU CU

PQ 4638   Tasso, Torquato, 1544-1595.
E52   La Gerusalemme liberata ; e la
           Gerusalemme conquistata / Torgato
           Tasso. Edizioni integrali a raffronto.
           Corrispondenza e varianti a cura di
           Francesco Flora e Ettore Mazzali.
           Milano : Edizioni Universitarie
           Malfasi, 1952.
           2 v. ; 25 cm.

I. Flora, Francesco, 1891-1962.
II. Mazzali, Ettore. III. Title.
IV. Title: La Gerusalemme conquistata.

NT   0048346   OU DLC-P4 RPB MH InU NNC IU

PQ 4638   TASSO, TORQUATO, 1544-1595
.23 F5   La Gerusalemme liberata; edizione scola-
           stica commentata da Attilio Momigliano.
           Firenze, "La Nuova Italia" [1954]
           8+326 p.   (Scrittori italiani)

1st ed. 1946; 5th reprint 1954.

I. Momigliano, Attilio, 1883-   II. Title.

NT   0048347   InU CaBVaU NjP

1851   Tasso, Torquato, 1544-
T185g2   La Gerusalemme liberata, con introduzione e
           note di Federico Ravello.   Turin, Società edi-
           trice internazionale, [1954].   illus.

NT   0048348   WaSp

Tasso, Torquato, 1544-1595.
Gerusalemme liberata
see also   [Corbould, Henry] 1787-1844.
Proof impressions of the engravings executed
for the Jerusalem delivered of Tasso.

Tasso, Torquato, 1544-1595.
La Gerusalemme liberata
see also   Pascale, Pietro.
La Gerusalemme liberata; tragi-commedia.

Bonaparte
Collection   TASSO, TORQUATO, 1544-1595.
No.5593   La Gierosalemme libberata de lo sio Torquato
           Tasso, votata a llengua napoletana, da Grabiele
v.13-14 Fasano.   Napoli, G.M.Porcelli, 1786.
           2v.in 1.   16½cm.   (Collezione di tutti i
           poemi in lingua napoletana.   t.13-14)

NT   0048351   ICN CtY MH CU DGU PU MdBP   OCl NN

Tasso, Torquato, 1544-
Gierusalemme liberata; poema heroico. Tratta dal vero origi-
nale, con aggiunta di quanto manca nell'altre edittioni [by Febo
Bonnà], & con l'allegoria dello stesso autore. Ferrara, [per V.
Baldini], 1581.
4°.   pp. (8), 208, (12).
With printer's mark at end.
With coat-of-arms of Alphonso II, duke of Ferrara, on title-page.

Print. spec.

          MoSW
NT   0048352   MH MnU PU NjP NcD NN DFo ICN OU MA MWiW-C

---

*IC5   Tasso, Torquato, 1544-1595.
T1853G   Giervsalemme liberata, poema heroico del s.
1582   Torquato Tasso ... Tratta dal vero originale,
           con aggiunta di quanto manca nell'altre
           edittioni, con l'allegoria dello stesso autore.
           Et con gli argomenti à ciascun canto del sig.
           Horatio Ariosti. Aggiuntoui l'annotationi
           d'incerto autore. Et alcune stanze in lode del
           poeta ...
           In Ferrara, Appresso Domenico Mammarelli, e
           Giulio Cesare Cagnacini, 1582.

           12°.   12p.l.,576,[12]p.   13cm.
           Edited by Febo Bonnà; includes the annotations
           of Bonaventura Angeli, somewhat abridged.
           Woodcut arms of the dedicatee, Alfonso II
           d'Este, duke of Ferrara, on t.-p.
           Imperfect: prelim. leaves 6-7 wanting; p.373-
           374 & 495-496 mutilated.

NT   0048354   MH ICU

Tasso, Torquato, 1544-1595.
La Giervsalemme liberata, con le figure di Bernardo
Castello e le annotationi di Scipio Gentili e di Giulio
Gvastavini. Genova [Appresso G. Bartoli] 1590.
11, 255, 71, 40 p.   illus.   27 cm.
The illustrations engraved by Agostino Carracci and Giacomo
Franco.

i. Gentili, Scipione, 1563-1616, ed. ii. Guastavini, Giulio, 16th
cent., ed. iii. Castello, Bernardo, 1557-1629, illus. iv. Carracci,
Agostino, 1557-1602, engr. v. Franco, Giacomo, d. 1620, engr. vi.
Title.

PQ4638.A90 1590 Rosenwald Coll.   65-59164

          MH   NNC CU CtY MB NN
NT   0048355   DLC OrU PU PPD CSmH CLU-C MWiW-C NBuG

Tasso, Torquato, 1544 –
La Gierusalemme. Con gli argomenti del Sig. Gio. Vincenzo Imperiale; figurata da Bernardo Castello. Genova, stampata per G. Pavoni, 1604.
nar. 24°. pp. (24), 572, (2). Engrs.
The title-page is engraved.

||Imperiale

NT 0048356   MH MoU DFo PU

---

*IC5
T1853G
1604aa
Tasso, Torquato, 1544-1595.
La Giervsalemme, del signor Torqvato Tasso, con gl'argomenti del sig. Gio. Vincenzo Imperiale, figurata da Bernardo Castello. Stampata in Genova per Gioseppe Pauoni.1615. Con licenza de superiori.
12°. 11p.ℓ.,572p.,1ℓ.incl.illus.,plates. pl. 14.5cm.
Colophon: [printer's mark] In Genova, appresso Giuseppe Pauoni. MDCIV ...

A reissue of the sheets of the 1604 blue-paper issue, with the first gathering reset.
Engraved t.-p.; title within architectural border.

NT 0048358   MH FTaSU

TASSO, Torquato, 1544 - 1595.
La Gierusalemme liberata. Traducida por Antonio Sarmiento de Mendoça. Madrid, D. Diaz de la Carrera, 1649.
                Ital 7477.4

NT 0048359   MH NNH

Cℓ
PQ4638
.B73
Tasso, Torquato, 1544-1595.
La Giervsalemme liberata; poema heroico. [Cinque canti di Camillo Camilli aggiunti al Goffredo del sig. Torquato Tasso. Con gli argomenti a ciascun canto del sig. Francesco Melchiori Opitergino] Roma, M. Hercole, 1673.
667 p. 13cm.

I. Camilli, Gamillo, fl. 1585. II. T.

NT 0048360   MiDW

Tasso, Torquato, 1544-1595.
La Gierusalemme liberata di Torquato Tasso; con le figure di Bernardo Castelli, e le annotazioni di Scipio Gentille e di Giulio Guastavini. Aggiuntovi la Vita dell' autore scritta da Gio. Battista Manso, marchese di Villa. E la tavola delle rime; con altre aggiunte, e correttioni.
In Londra, Appresso Giacob Tonson & Giovanni Watts, 1724.
2 v. 20 plates, port.

Based on the text of the Geneva edition of 1590.
Plates designed by Bernardo Castelli and re-engraved in England by Gerard van der Gucht.
Bookplate (1 in each vol.) engraved by Johann Friedrich and Johann David Schleuen, Berlin, for the German poet, Johann Wilhelm Ludwig Gleim.—cf. Leiningen-Westerburg, German book-plates, London, 1901, p. 276.

I. Castello, Bernardo, 1557-1629, illus. II. Van der Gucht, Gerard, 1696-1776, illus. III. Gentili, Scipione, 1563-1616. IV. Guastavini, Giulio. V. Manso, Giovanni Battista, 1561-1645. Vita di Torquato Tasso. Ref. from Gucht, Gerard van der.

NT 0048363   CaOTP DFo OCU PU MH

Z
232
.F767
1763
Tasso, Torquato, 1544-1595.
La Gierusalemme liberata di Torquato Tasso ... In Glasgua, Della stampa di Roberto ed Andrea Foulis; e si vendono appresso loro, e Giovanni Balfour in Edinburgo, 1763.
2 v. front.(port.) 20 pl. 15½ cm.
Vol.1 has illustrated and engraved half-title.
"Tutte le stanze intere, che dall' autore sono state rifiutate in questo libro": v.2, p.[339]-372.
I.Title: La Gierusalemme liberata.

NT 0048364   MiU NjP PU ICN

Tasso, Torquato, 1544 - 1595.
La Gierusalemme liberata; con le figure di Bernardo Castello... Genova, Bartoli, 1890.
255 p.

NT 0048365   PPD

Tasso, Torquato, 1544-1595.
Il "Gierusalemme" nella storia della poesia tassiana [a cura di] Antonio di Pietro. Milano, Vita e pensiero [1951]
160 p. 25 cm. (Pubblicazioni dell'Università cattolica del Sacro Cuore, nuova ser., v. 37)
Text of Il Gierusalemme with corresponding text from Gerusalemme liberata and Gerusalemme conquistata, with introduction and commentary.
Bibliographical footnotes.
1. Tasso, Torquato. Gerusalemme liberata. I. Pietro, Antonio di, ed. (Series: Milan. Università cattolica del Sacro Cuore. Pubblicazioni, nuova ser., v. 37)
AS222.M63 n. s., vol. 37   A 52-8474 rev

Harvard Univ. Library
for Library of Congress   [r55bⅡ]†

NT 0048366   MH ICU NN NcD NIC ViU MiU OrU DLC

Tasso, Torquato, 1544-1595.
Gioie di rime e prose del Sig. Torquato Tasso
    see his   Rime et prose ... 1587-90.

TASSO, Torquato, 1544-1595.
O Godfredo, ou Hierusalem libertada. Traduzido na lingua portugueza por Andre Rodriguez de Mattos. Lisboa, M. Deslandes, 1682.
sm.4°.pp.(32), 659. Plate.
Also with an engraved title-page.

NT 0048368   MH PU

Tasso, Torquato, 1544-1595.
O Godfredo; ou, Jerusalem libertada, poema heroico composto no idioma toscano por Torquato Tasso ... traduzido na lingua portugueza ... por André Rodrigues de Mattos ... Edição feita pela de 1689; e precedida agora d'uma noticia sobre a vida e escriptos de Torquato Tasso. Editor—Olympio Nicolau Ruy Fernandes. Coimbra, Imprensa da Universidade, 1859.
3 p. l., [5]-32, 496, 47, [1] p. 20½ᶜᵐ.
"Torquato Tasso, estudo historico por João Joaquim d'Almeida Braga": 47 p. at end.
L. C. copy imperfect: 47, [1] p. at end wanting.
I. Rodrigues de Mattos, Andre, 1638-1698, tr. II. Fernandes, Olympio Nicolau Ruy, 1820-1879, ed. III. Almeida Braga, João Joaquim de, 1838-1871. iv. Title. v. Title: Jerusalem libertada.
                                                 39-15917
Library of Congress   PQ4642.P21R6
                           [2]   851.46

NT 0048369   DLC CLU PV NN

Tasso, Torquato, 1544-1595.
Godfrey Of Bvlloigne, Or The Recoverie of Hiervsalem. An Heroicall poeme written in Italian by Seig. Torquato Tasso, and translated into English by R. C. Esquire: And now the first part containing fiue Cantos, Imprinted in both Languages. London: Imprinted by Iohn Windet for Christopher Hunt of Exceter, 1594. 2 p.l., 235 p. 19cm. (4°.)
STC 23697.
Preface "To the Reader" signed: C. H.
With autograph of Wh. Kennett.

I. No subject. I. Carew, Richard,   Card revised
N.Y.P.L.   1555-1620, tr.   August 27, 1943

NT 0048370   NN InU PU DFo MH ICN CtY MWiW-C CSmH NIC

FILM
S-8
reel
1190
Tasso, Torquato, 1544-1595.
Godfrey of Bvlloigne; or, The recouerie of Hiervsalem. An heroicall poeme written in Italian by seig. Torquato Tasso, and translated into English by R.C. ... And now the first part containing fiue cantos, imprinted in both languages. London, Imprinted by I.Windet for C.Hunt, 1594.
Short-title catalogue no.23697 (carton 1190)
Microfilm.
I.Carew, Richard, 1555-1620, tr. II.Title.

NT 0048371   MiU ViU NNC

Humanities
Library
Microfilm
AC
4
E5
Reel
no.
359
Tasso, Torquato, 1544-1595.
Godfrey of Bvlloigne, or The recouerie of Hiervsalem.
An heroicall poeme written in Italian by Seig. Torquato Tasso, and translated into English by R. C.[arew] ... And now the first part containing fiue cantos, imprinted in both languages. London Imprinted by Iohn Windet for Thomas Man ... [1594?]
Editor's note signed: C. H[unt?]
University microfilms no. 15623 (case 60, carton 359)
Short-title catalogue no. 23697a.
I. Carew, Richard, 1555-1620, tr.

NT 0048372   MiU WaPS

Tasso, Torquato, 1544 –
Godfrey of Bulloigne, or The recoverie of Jerusalem. Done into English heroicall verse by Edward Fairefax. London, imprinted by A. Hatfield for J. Jaggard and M. Lownes, 1600.
pp. (8), 392.
First issue of first edition in English. With manuscript copy of the later issue of the first stanza.
This book may be consulted in the room of the Widener Collection.

||Fairfax

          CtY PU-F PPL ICN NjP   PBL MB NIC ScU
NT 0048373   MH GEU MiDW IU PU CSmH CLU-C MWiW-C DFo

Humanities
Library
Microfilm
AC
4
E5
Reel
no.
333
WaPS
Tasso, Torquato, 1544-1595.
Godfrey of Bulloigne, or The recouerie of Ierusalem. Done into English heroicall verse, by Edward Fairefax ... Imprinted at London by Ar. Hatfield, for I. Iaggard and M. Lownes. 1600.
University microfilms no. 15624 (case 56, carton 333)
Short-title catalogue no. 23698.
I. Fairfax, Edward, d. 1635, tr.

NT 0048374   MiU WaPS

Humanities
Library
Microfilm
AC
4
E5
Reel
no.
359
Tasso, Torquato, 1544-1595.
Godfrey of Bulloigne, or The recouerie of Ierusalem. Done into English heroicall verse by Edward Fairefax ... Imprinted at London by Ar Hatfield, for I. Iaggard and M. Lownes. 1600.
University microfilms no. 15624A (case 60, carton 359)
Short-title catalogue no. 23698 (variant).
I. Fairfax, Edward, d. 1635, tr.

NT 0048375   MiU WaPS

Humanities
Library
Microfilm
AC
4
E5
Reel
no.
333
Tasso, Torquato, 1544-1595.
Godfrey of Bulloigne, or The recouerie of Ierusalem. Done into English heroicall verse, by Edward Fairefax ... Imprinted at London by Ar. Hatfield, for I. Iaggard and M. Lownes. 1600.
University microfilms no. 15624B (case 56, carton 333)
Short-title catalogue no. 23698 (variant).
I. Fairfax, Edward, d. 1635, tr.

NT 0048376   MiU WaPS

[Tasso, Torquato] 1544–1595.
Godfrey of Bovlogne: or, The recouerie of Iervsalem.
Done into English heroicall verse, by Edward Fairefax,
gent., and now the second time imprinted ... together with
the life of the said Godfrey. London, Printed by I. Bill,
1624.

12 p. l., 392 p. 27½ᶜᵐ.
Engr. t.-p.
1st ed., 1600.

I. Fairfax, Edward, d. 1635, tr. II. Title.

15–1151

Library of Congress   PQ4642.E21F3 1624

NT CU
0048377   DLC MB NcU DFo IU FU PU MH NcD CtY PBL

FILM

Tasso, Torquato, 1544–1595.
Godfrey of Bovlogne: or The recouerie of
Iervsalem. Done into English heroicall verse,
by Edward Fairefax. And now the second time
imprinted ... together with the life of the
said Godfrey. London, Printed by I.Bill, 1624.
Short-title catalogue no.23699 (carton 1036)
Microfilm
I.Fairfax,Edward,d.1635.tr. II.Title.

NT 0048378   MiU

Tasso, Torquato, 1544–1595.
Godfrey of Bulloigne: or, The recovery of Jerusalem
Done into English heroical verse, by Edward **Fairfax**
gent., together with the life of the said Godfrey ... London, Printed by J. M. for R. Chiswell [etc.] 1687.

16 p. l., 655 p. 19½ᶜᵐ.

I. Fairfax, Edward, d. 1635, tr. II. Title.

17–7412

Library of Congress   PQ4642.E21F3 1687

NT   NPV WU OrU CtY MH NIC NNC OU NN
0048379   DLC TU NcU MnU CSt IU CU-BANC CLU-C NRU

Tasso, Torquato, 1544–1595.
Godrey of Boulogne; or, The recovery of
Jerusalem. Done into English heroical verse, by
Edward Fairfax.   London, 1725.

NT 0048380   PPL

---

*
PQ4642
.E21F3   Tasso, Torquato, 1544–1595.
1726
Godfrey of Bulloigne: or the recovery of
Jerusalem. Done into English heroical verse,
by Edward Fairfax. Together with the life
of the said Godfrey. Licensed to be reprinted. Ro. L'Estrange. Dublin: Printed
by and for A. Rhames, 1726.
xxvi, 659 p. 21cm.

I. Fairfax, Edward, d. 1635, tr. II. L'Estrange,
Sir Roger, 1616–1704, ed. III. Title.

NT 0048381   ViU CSt WU NPV NNC KMK

TASSO, Torquato, 1544–1595.
Godfrey of Bulloign, or The **Gierusalemme
liberata**, abridge and altered. London, J.
Dodsley, 1774.

NT 0048382   MH CtY KyLx

Tasso, Torquato, 1544–1595.
Godfrey of Bulloigne, or Jerusalem delivered, by Tor-
quato Tasso.   Tr. by Edward Fairfax, gent. ... London,
Printed by Bensley and son, for R. Triphook [etc.] 1817.

2 v. front. (port.) 17½ᶜᵐ.
Head and tail pieces.
"The editor's preface," signed: S. W. Singer.
With reproduction of original t.-p.: Godfrey of Bulloigne or The re-
coverie of Jerusalem. Done into English heroicall verse, by Edward
Fairfax, gent. London, 1600.
"Fairfax's Fourth eclogue": vol. I, p. xxv–xxxii.
"Carew's translation, book the fourth": vol. I, p. xxxiiii–lvii.
I. Fairfax, Edward, d. 1635, tr. II. Singer, Samuel Weller, 1783–1858,
ed. III. Carew, Richard, 1555–1620, tr. IV. Title.

17–7411

Library of Congress   PQ4642.E21F3 1817

NT OO
0048383   DLC CtY OrU OrCS NN MdBP LNT WU MH ICU

Tasso, Torquato, 1544–1595.
Godfrey of Bulloigne; or, The recovery of Jerusalem:
done into English heroical verse, from the Italian of
Tasso, by Edward Fairfax.   5th ed., reprinted from the
original folio of 1600.   To which are prefixed, a glossary, and the lives of Tasso and Fairfax, by the editor ...
Windsor, Printed by and for Knight and son; and pub.
by R. S. Kirby, London, 1817.

2 v. in 1. 19ᶜᵐ.

I. Fairfax, Edward, d. 1635, tr. II. Knight, Charles, 1791–1873, ed.
III. Title.

17–7414

Library of Congress   PQ4642.E21F3 1817 b

NT 0048384   DLC

Tasso, Torquato, 1544–1595.
Godfrey of Bulloigne; or, The recovery of Jerusalem: done
into English heroical verse, from the Italian of Tasso, by Edward Fairfax.   The 7th ed., reprinted from the original folio
of 1600.   To which are prefixed, a glossary, and the lives of
Tasso and Fairfax.   By the editor ...   London, C. Knight
& co., 1844.

2 v. front., illus. 15ᶜᵐ. [Knight's weekly volume, x, xiv]
Edited by C. Knight.

I. Fairfax, Edward, d. 1635, tr. II. Knight, Charles, 1791–1873, ed.
III. Title.

17—7407

Library of Congress   PQ4642.E21F3 1844

NT OU OO
0048385   DLC OrP NcD IU MeB OCX CtY PU NjP NN

Tasso, Torquato, 1544–1595.
Godfrey of Bulloigne; or, The recovery of Jerusalem: done
into English heroical verse, from the Italian of Tasso, by Edward Fairfax.   1st American from the 7th London ed., reprinted from the original folio of 1600.   To which are prefixed,
an introductory essay, by Leigh Hunt, and the lives of Tasso
and Fairfax, by Charles Knight ...   New-York, Wiley & Putnam, 1845–46.
2 v. in 1. 18½ᶜᵐ. (Half-title: Wiley and Putnam's foreign library)
Vol. 2 has half-title: Wiley & Putnam's library of choice reading.
I. Fairfax, Edward, d. 1635, tr. II. Hunt, Leigh, 1784–1859.
III. Knight, Charles, 1791–1873, ed. IV. Title.

33—35852

Library of Congress   PQ4642.E21F3 1845

[40c1]

851.46

NT MiU CU NBuG
0048386   DLC N ViU NN MH PU ICU NN MiU OC1JC OCX

Tasso, Torquato, 1544–1595.
Godfrey of Bulloigne; or, The recovery of Jerusalem: done into English heroical verse, from the
Italian of Tasso, by Edward Fairfax. 1st American
from the 7th London ed., reprinted from the original folio of 1600.   To which are prefixed, an
introductory essay, by Leigh Hunt, and the lives
of Tasso and Fairfax, by Charles Knight. New ed.,
complete in one volume.   New York, G. P. Putnam,
1848.
2 v. in 1. 19.5 cm. (On cover: Putnam's
choice library)

On spine: Fairfax's Tasso.
Caption and running title: The recovery of
Jerusalem.
Error in paging: p. 96, v. 2, numbered 6.

I. Fairfax, Edward, d. 1635, tr. II. Hunt,
Leigh, 1784–1859. III. Knight, Charles, 1791–
1873, ed. IV. Title. V. Title: The recovery
of Jerusalem.

NT 0048388   Vi NWM MeB PPL

Tasso, Torquato, 1544–1595.
Godfrey of Bulloigne; or, The recovery of Jerusalem; done into English heroical verse from the
Italian of Tasso, by Edward Fairfax. 1st American
from the 7th London ed., reprinted from the original
folio of 1600. To which are prefixed an introductory
essay by Leigh Hunt, and the lives of Tasso and
Fairfax by Charles Knight. New ed.   New York,
Putnam, 1849.

2 v. in 1.   20 cm.

I. Fairfax, Edward, d. 1635. II. Knight,
Charles, 1791–1873. III. Hunt, Leigh, 1784–1859.
IV. Title. V. Title: The recovery of Jerusalem.

NT 0048390   NIC PP NcA-S MH OC1

Hd17
367
Tasso, Torquato, 1544–1595.
Godfrey of Bulloigne; or, The recovery of
Jerusalem: done into English heroical verse,
from the Italian of Tasso, by Edward Fairfax.
1st American from the 7th London ed., reprinted
from the original folio of 1600. To which are
prefixed, an introductory essay, by Leigh Hunt,
and the lives of Tasso and Fairfax, by Charles
Knight. New ed., complete in one volume.   New
York, George P. Putnam, 1851.
lxvi, 201, 244p. 19½cm.
In two parts,   paged separately.

NT 0048391   CtY OC1W OO NjP MH PU

Tasso, Torquato, 1544–1595
Godfrey of Bulloigne; or, The recovery of Jerusalem: done into English heroical verse, from the Italian of Tasso, by
Edward Fairfax. The 7th ed. reprinted from
the original folio of 1600. To which are
prefixed a glossary, and the lives of
Tasso and Fairfax. By the editor.   London, G. Cox, 1853.

2v. in 1. 15cm.
Vol.2.: London, C. Knight, 1844.

NT 0048392   PV NcD MH

PQ
4642
.E21   [Tasso, Torquato] 1544–1595.
F3
1855
Godfrey of Bulloigne; or, The recovery of
Jesusalem, done into English heroical verse
from the Italian of Tasso, by Edward Fairfax.
First American from the seventh London edition
... to which are prefixed, An introductory
essay, by Leigh Hunt, and The lives of Tasso
and Fairfax, by Charles Knight.   New ed.
Philadelphia, C.G. Henderson, 1855.
lv. (various pagings) 20cm.

I. Fairfax, Edward, d. 1635, tr. II. Hunt,
Leigh, 1784–1859. III. Knight, Charles, 1791–
1873.

NT 0048393   OrU NjP MH NNC

Tasso, Torquato, 1544–1595.
Godfrey of Bolloigne; or, Jerusalem delivered, by Torquato
Tasso.   Translated by Edward Fairfax.   Edited by Robert Aris
Willmott ... illustrated by Corbould.   London: G. Routledge
and Co., 1858.   xlviii, 445 p.   front., plates.   16°.

485686A. 1. No subject. I. Fairfax,
II. Willmott, Robert Eldridge Aris,
Edward Henry, illustrator. IV. Title.
N. Y. P. L.

Edward, d. 1635, translator.
1809–1863, editor. III. Corbould,
V. Title: Jerusalem delivered.
January 19, 1931

NT 0048394   NN CaBVaU MH

PQ
4642
.E21F3
1687

Tasso, Torquato, 1544-1595.
    Godfrey of Bulloigne : or, The
recovery of Jerusalem. Done into
English heroical verse, by Edward
Fairfax, gent., together with the life
of the said Godfrey ... London,
Printed by J. M. for R. Chiswell
[etc.] 1687.
    16 p. l., 655 p. 20 cm.

    I. Fairfax, Edward, d. 1635, tr.
II. Title

NT 0048395   TU ViU MWA NcD

Tasso, Torquato, 1544-1595.
    Tasso's 'Godfrey of Bvlloigne'. (Five cantos.) Translated
by Richard Carew, esq. (1594.) Ed., with introduction and
notes and illustrations, by the Rev. Alexander B. Grosart ...
[Blackburn, Eng.] Printed for the subscribers [by C. E. Simms,
Manchester] 1881.
    xiv, 133 p. 22½ᶜᵐ. [Grosart, A. B. Occasional issues of unique or
very rare books ... no. 36]
    "Limited to sixty-two copies—fifty ... [to subscribers; and twelve
editor's copies. This is no. 27. Proof-sheets and waste pages have been
des'royed."
    With reproduction of original t.-p.: Godfrey Of Bvlloigne. or The
Recouerie of Hiervsalem. An Heroicall poeme written in Italian by
Seig. Torquato Tasso, and translated into English by R. C. Esquire:
And now the first part containing fiue Cantos, Imprinted in both lan-
guages. London, Imprinted by Iohn Windet for Christopher Hunt of
Exeter, 1594.
    Pages 129–133 (Notes) were issued in 1883 with no. 38 of the series
("Fly-leaves, or Additional notes and illustrations" ...)
    Omits the Italian of the original edition, 1594.

    I. Carew, Richard, 1555-1620, tr. II. Grosart, Alexander Balloch,
1827-1899, ed. II. Title: Godfrey of Bvlloigne.

                                                        28-7664
    Library of Congress   PR1121.G7 no.36

          MiU MdBP ViU
NT 0048397   DLC NcU NIC OrU IU MH NjP CU PU-F OCU

Tasso, Torquato, 1544-1595.
    Godfrey of Bulloigne, or The recovery of
Jerusalem, done into English heroical verse,
from the Italian of Tasso, by Edward Fairfax.
1st American from the 7th London ed., reprinted
from the original folio of 1600. To which are
prefixed, an introductory essay, by Leigh Hunt,
and the lives of Tasso and Fairfax, by Charles
Knight. New York, Wiley & Putnam, 1946.

NT 0048398   MH

Tasso, Torquato, 1544-1595.
    El Godofredo; ó, La Jerusalen restaurada; poema
épico del Sr. Torquato Taso. Tr. del italiano á verso
castellano por D. Melchor de Sas ... Barcelona, Impr.
de T. Gorchs, 1817.
    2 v. 16½ᶜᵐ.
    "Vida del Sr. Torquato Taso": vol. I, p. [iii]-xix; "Discurso preliminar":
vol. I, p. [xxi]-xlvii.

    I. Sas, Melchor de, tr.
                                                    4-8786

NT 0048399   DLC MH PU

Tasso, Torquato, 1544-1595.
    Il Goffredo; overo, Giervsalemme liberata, poema he-
roico del Signor Torquato Tasso. Con l'allegoria dell'istesso; et con gli argomenti del Signor Horatio Ariosti.
Aggiuntiui di nuouo I cinque canti di Camillo Camilli.
Bassano, G. A. Remondini [n. d.]
    1 p. l., 5-672 p. 11 x 6½ᶜᵐ.
    "Vita del Signor Torquato Tasso, estratta dagli Elogij del Signor Lo-
renzo Crasso": p. 5-11.
    "I cinqve canti di Camillo Camilli" (with special t.-p.): p. [531]-672.
    I. Ariosto, Orazio, 1555-1593. II. Camilli, Camillo, fl. 1585. III. Crasso,
Lorenzo, 17th cent. IV. Title.

                                                    17-13143
    Library of Congress   PQ4638.Z3B2

NT 0048400   DLC

*IC5
T1853G
1580

Tasso, Torquato, 1544-1595.
    Il Goffredo, di m. Torqvato Tasso. Nvovamente
dato in lvce ...
    In Vinegia. Appresso Domenico Caualcalupo.
A instantia di Marc'Antonio Malaspina. MDLXXX.
    4°. 2p.l.,61 numb.l.,[2]p. 23cm.
    First edition.
    First word of title within cartouche;
printer's mark on t.-p.
    Also published with title: Gierusalemme
liberata.

NT 0048401   MH

Tasso, Torquato, 1544-1595.
    [Il Goffredo. Novamente corretto e ristampato. Con gli
argomenti & allegorie a ciascun canto, d'incerto auttore. Aggiuntovi molte stanze, etc. Venetia, G. Perchacino, 1582]
    [10], 118 l. 21 cm.
    L. C. copy imperfect: leaves [1] (t. p.) and 115-118 wanting; title
supplied from Brit. Mus. Cat.
    Edited by C. Malespini.
    Bound with the author's Della Gervsalemme conquistata libri xxiv.
Pavia, 1594.

    I. Malespini, Celio, b. 1531, ed. II. Title.

    PQ4638.A82 1582   50-52741

NT 0048402   DLC OC1 MWe1C CtY ICU IU MH DFo PU NN

*IC5
T1853G
1583

Tasso, Torquato, 1544-1595.
    Il Goffredo del s. Torqvato Tasso, novamente
corretto, et ristampato. Con gli argomenti, &
allegorie à ciascun canto d'incerto auttore.
Aggiontoui molte stanze leuate, con le varie
lettioni ... Con l'aggiunta de'cinque canti
del sig. Camillo Camilli ...
    In Venetia, presso Francesco de'Franceschi
senese 1583.
    4°. 13p.l.,2-118 numb.l.,[18]p.; 4p.l.,29
numb.l. 21.5cm.

    Edited by Celio Malespini.
    Printer's mark on t.-p.
    "I cinqve canti di Camillo Camilli ..." (4p.l.,
29 numb.l.) has separate signatures & paging
& special t.-p.
    In this copy, 20 engraved plates have been
inserted; these plates, which were used as
illustrations in the text in the 1590 ed., were
also issued separately in that year without
text.

NT 0048404   MH PU CtY

Tasso, Torquato, 1544-1595.
    Il Goffredo; overo Gierusalemme liberata,
poema heroico ... Tratto dal vero originale,
con aggiunta di quanto mancava nell'altre
edittioni, etc. Vinegia, A. Salicato, 1584.
    576 p. 14 cm.

    Title page missing; title from Brit. Mus.
With this is bound Camilli, Camillo. Cinqve
canti. Vinegia, 1584.

    I. Title.   II. Title: Gerusalemme liberata.

NT 0048405   CU-S NNC IU MH DFo PU

*IC5
T1853G
1585

Tasso, Torquato, 1544-1595.
    Il Goffredo, overo Gervsalemme liberata,
poema heroico del s. Torqvato Tasso. Nel quale
sono state aggiunte molte stanze leuate, con
le varie lettioni; & postiui gli argomenti, &
allegorie a ciascun canto d'incerto auttore.
Con l'aggiunta de cinque canti del s. Camillo
Camilli, & i loro argomenti, del s. Francesco
Melchiori ... Di nuouo con somma diligenza
corretto, & ristampato ...
    In Vinegia, Presse Altobello Salicato. 1585.
Alla libraria   della Fortezza.

    4°. 11p.l.,2-127 numb.l.; 32 numb.l. 21cm.
    Edited by Celio Malespini; includes [prelim.
leaves 3ᵛ-4ᵛ] "Discorso del s. Filippo
Pigafeta, mandato al signor Celio Malespina in
materia de i due titoli di questo poema."
    Printer's mark on t.-p.
    "Cinqve canti di Camillo Camilli ..." has
separate signatures & paging and special t.-p.

Continued in next column

Continued from preceding column

    In this copy, 20 engraved plates have been
inserted; these plates, which were used as
illustrations in the text in the 1590 ed., were
also issued separately in that year without
text.
    Imperfect: engr. headpiece from t.-p. of the
1590 ed., including port. of Tasso, mounted on
t.-p., obscuring printer's mark.

NT 0048408   MH PU NNH NNC

Tasso, Torquato, 1544-
    Il Goffredo, overo Gierusalemme liberata; poema heroico. Con
aggiunta di quanto mancava nell'altre edittioni, et con gli argomenti del Signor Horatio Ariosti. Aggiuntovi l'annotationi d'incerto auttore, et anco i Cinque canti del Signor Camillo Camilli.
Vinegia, presso A. Salicato, 1588.
    nar. 16°. pp. (24), 576, (22), 143.
    With printer's mark on title-pages.
    "Cinque canti di Camillo Camilli," pp. 143, has individual title-page.

Print. spec.

NT 0048409   MH GEU CtY PU

Tasso, Torquato, 1544-
    Il Goffredo, overo Gierusalemme liberata; poema heroico. Con
l'allegoria universale dell' istesso, et con gli argomenti à ciascun
canto del Signor Horatio Ariosti. Aggiuntovi l'annotationi d'incerto auttore, et le figure à ciascun canto, et alcune stanze in lode
del poeta. Venetia, presso G. B. Ciotti, 1599.
    nar. 24°. pp. (24), 576, (22). Wdcts.
    Printer's mark, with motto "Micat aurea Phæbo," on title-page.

Print. spec.

NT 0048410   MH CU NIC PU

Tasso, Torquato, 1544-1595.
    Il Goffredo, ò vero Giervsalemme liberata,
del sig. Torqvato Tasso.
    In Roma [app]resso Gio:Angelo Ruffinelli
l'[anno 16]01.
    12°. 24p.l.,502p.,1l. 11.5cm.
    Colophon: [printer's mark] In Roma, per Luigi
Zannetti. L'anno del giub M.DC. Con licenza
de'svperiori. Ad istanza di Gio: Angelo
Ruffinelli.
    Engraved t.-p.; title within ornamental border
surmounted by a   port. of Tasso & including

    [16]01.

    the arms of the dedicatee, Cardinal Alessandro
d'Este.
    Imperfect: t.-p. wormed, affecting imprint.

NT 0048412   MH PHC

PQ4638 Tasso, Torquato, 1544-1595
.B08   Goffredo, overo Gierusalemme liberata, poema
        heroico del Sig. Torqvato Tasso. Con l'Allegoria
        vniuersale dell' istesso. Et con gli Argomenti del
        Sig. Horatio Ariosti. Di nuouo ricorretto, & di
        figure ornato. Venetia, [B.?] Deuchino e G.B.
        Pulciano, 1608?
            [40], 503p. port. 14cm.
            Date of 1608 on t.p. changed in ms. to 1688.
            Allegoria del poema: p.[3-18]
            Tavola di tvtti i nomi proprii: p.[19-40]
            I. Ariosto, Oraz   io, 1555-1593. II. Title.
        III. Title: Giervsa   lemme liberata. IV. Au/
        t for III.

NT 0048413   PSt

Tasso, Torquato, 1544–1595.

Il Goffredo, overo Giervsalemme liberata, poema heroico del Sig. Torquato Tasso. Con l'allegoria uniuersale dell'istesso. Et con gli Argomenti del Sig. Horatio Ariosto, & di bellisime figure adornato. In Venetia, P Bernardo Giunti, & Gio. Battista Ciotti, 1609.
16 p.l., 502 p., wdcts.   10 x 6ᶜᵐ.
Title within woodcut border; margins cropped.

I. Ariosto, Orazio, 1555–1593. II. Title. III.
Title: Giervsalemme liberata.

NT   0048414   ViU PU

Tasso, Torquato, 1544-1595.

Goffredo, overo Giervsalemme liberata, poema heroico del Sig. Torqvato Tasso. Nel quale sono state aggiunte molte stanze leuate, con le varie lettioni, & postiui gli argomenti, & allegorie a ciascun canto d'incerto auttore. Con l'aggiunta de' cinque canti del Signor Camillo Camilli & i loro argomenti del Signor Francesco Melchiori opitergino. Di nuouo aggiontoui le figure in rame, & con somma diligenza corretto, & ristampato. Con vna copiosissima tauola de' nomi proprij, & materie principali ... Venetia, G. Vincenti, 1611.

8 p. L., 117 numb. l., 63 p. illus. 21 x 16ᶜᵐ.
Engr. t.-p.
Paging irregular: no. 73 and 74 repeated; 77 and 78 omitted; 81, 87, 89, 90, 95, 96, 114 numbered respectively 89, 95, 97, 98, 103, 104, 89.
The "argomenti" of the Gerusalemme are by Orazio Ariosto. They are printed at the top of the page, above the vignettes of G. Grispoldi, both being surrounded by ornate borders.
Discorso del S. Filippo Pigafeta, mandato al Signor Celio Malespina in materia de due titoli di questo poema, p. [iii-iv] Allegoria del poema, p. [v-viii] Tavola di tvtti i nomi proprij, p. [ix-xiv] Oda del Sig. Guido Casoni in morte del Sig. Torqvato Tasso, p. [xv]
2-14755

NT   0048416   DLC MH PU

Tasso, Torquato, 1544-1595.

[Il Goffredo; overo, Giervsalemme liberata, poema heroico del sig. Torquato Tasso. Con l' allegoria uniuersale dell' istesso; e[t] con l' agguinta de' cinque canti del sig. Camillo Camilli E i loro argomenti de sig. Francesco Melchiori opitergino] [in Venetia, 1613]
3-334, [1] L. illus. 11 x 6ᶜᵐ.
Title-page and first pages lacking; also various pages throughout book. Title-page and missing pages printed in ink and bound in.
"I cinque canti de Camillo Camilli" (with special t.-p.) :   L.262-334.

NT   0048417   PMA MH

851.4
T214g
1616

Tasso, Torquato, 1544-1595.

Il Goffredo, overo Giervsalemme liberata, poema heroico del sig. Torqvato Tasso, con l'Allegoria vniuersale dell' istesso. Et con gli Argomenti à ciascun Canto, del Signor Horatio Ariosti. Aggiunteui l'annotationi à ciascun Canto d'incerto autore. Et alcune stanze in lode del poeta. Aggiunti i cinque canti di Camillo Camilli. Et aggiuntaui la prefatione di Filippo Paruta, Nobile Venetiano. Con licenza de'

Superiori. [Ornament] In Venetia, MDCXVI. Appresio Pietro Milocho.
[54], 576, 144 p., 1 *l*. 13cm.

Title within single line border.
Second vol. has special t.p.
Initials. Catchwords.
First endpaper inscribed: J. Toby given to him as a token   of friendship by Rosalia Velasco.

I. Ariosti, Orazio - 1555-1593. II. Camilli, Camillo. III. Paruta, Filippo, 1550?-1629. IV. Title.

NT   0048420   FU CU-BANC MH NN PPL PU ICU WU

---

tPQ4638   Tasso, Torquato, 1544-1595.
1620   [La Gerusalemme liberata. 1620]
Il Goffredo, overo Gierusalemme liberata, poeme heroico del Signor Torquato Tasso. Con l'Allegoria universale del stesso. Et con gli Ar gomenti del Signor Oratio Ariosti. Venetia, appresso Nicolò Misserini, 1620.
2v. in l. 10cm.

v. 2 has special t.-p.: I cinque canti di Camillo Camilli. Aggiunti al Goffredo ... Venetia, N. Misserini, 1620.
Cf. Guidi p. 21.

I. Title. II. Ariosto, Orazio, 1555-1593. III. Camilli, Camillo. fl. 1585 I cinque canti. 1620. IV. Misserini, Nicolò (1620) V. 1620. Italy.

NT   0048421   CU-BANC NjP PU IWW

---

*IC5
T1853G
1632

Tasso, Torquato, 1544-1595.

Il Goffredo, overo Giervsalemme liberata, del sig. Torqvato Tasso. Con gli argomenti, e con l'allegoria ...
In Roma, Appresso Guglielmo Facciotti. 1632. Ad instanza di Pompilio Totti. Con licenza de'superiori.
24⁰. 2p.*l*., 3-540p. incl. illus., plates. 9.5cm.
Added engr. t.-p.: La Gervsalemme liberata, di Torqvato Tasso. In Roma appresso Pompilio Totti. 1632.
Imperfect: p.133-134 torn, removing some text.

NT   0048422   MH IU

TASSO, Torquato, 1544-
Il Goffredo, overo Gierusalemme liberata, con gli argomenti del sig. Horatio Ariosti, Aggiuntovi i Cinque canti del sig. Camillo Camilli. Roma, F. Cavalli, 1639.

24⁰.
The work by Camilli is wanting.

NT   0048423   MH

TASSO, TORQUATO, 1544-1595
Il Goffredo; overo, la Gervsalemme con- qvistata del sig. Torqvato Tasso. In questa vltima impressione megliorata. All' illvstre signor Lodovico Caballino dedicata ... Venetia, Per li Turrini, 1642.
4 p.*l*., 304 p. 4to

Bound in vellum.

NT   0048424   InU-Li PU MH

Tasso, Torquato, 1544-
Il Goffredo overo Gierusalemme liberata. [Added] Cinque canti di Camillo Camilli. Venetia, 1643
496, 154p. 12⁰

NT   0048425   MWA NjR

TASSO, TORQUATO, 1544-1595.
Il Goffredo overo La Gierusalemme liberata di Tor- qvato Tasso. Parigi, Nella Stamperia reale, 1644.
6 p.l., 502 p., 1 l.   41cm. (f⁰.)

Brunet, V, 666.   Bergamo: Raccolta tassiana, 215.
Illustrations: engraved pictorial t. p. by G. Rousselet after J. Stella. Engraved head- and tailpieces which include a repeated group of 5

armorial devices (papal, royal, Mazarin, etc.) and pictorial and ornamen- tal initials. Large coat of arms with interlaced SF at foot on last leaf. The same arms occur in one of the headpieces.
In ms. on t. p.: Présenté à Sa Majesté la reine de Suede par...cardinal Mazarini premier ministre du roy tres chrestien le 2 janvier 1647.
With leather label of C. A. and V. Baldwin.
The Ottoboni--W. K. Bixby--W. C. Van Antwerp copy.
Binding, 17th century French, probably by the royal binder, of tan

Continued in next column

Continued from preceding column

morocco, gilt, with supra-libros of Christina, queen of Sweden, to whom the copy was presented. --cf. Lindberg, S. G. Queen Christina bindings, p. 199, 209-211. (In: Platen, M. v. Queen Christina of Sweden; docu- ments and studies. [Stockholm, 1966] p. 199-225. illus.)

1. Engravings, French, 17th cent. 2. Bindings, 17th cent., French. I. Stella, Jacques, illus. II. Rousselet, Gilles, d. 1686, engr. III. Tasso, Torquato, 1544-1595. La Gieru-   salemme liberata.

NT   0048428   NN PPL MH

Tasso, Torquato, 1544-1595.

Il Goffredo; overo, Gierusalemme liberata, poema heroico del Signor Torqvato Tasso. Con l'allegoria uni- versale del istesso: et con gli argomenti del Signor Hora- tio Ariosto. Aggiuntovi i cinque canti del Camillo Ca- milli. [Amsterdam, Per gli Combi et La Noy] 1652.
436, 239, 186 p. 11 x 6ᶜᵐ.
Added t.-p., engr.
Customarily listed with productions of L. Elsevier's press, but probably printed by Severyn Mathys, of Leyden. cf. Willems, no. 1673; Berghman, no. 956.

1. Ariosto, Orazio, 1555-1593. II. Camilli, Camillo, fl. 1585. III. Title.
22-13110

Library of Congress   PQ4638.B52

NT   0048429   DLC MH OC1W

PQ
4638
B57
Cage

Tasso, Torquato, 1544-1595.
Il Goffredo ouero Gierusalemme liberata...
In Roma, Per Filippo de' Rossi, 1657.
[16] 521 [3] p. 12mo. illus.

NT   0048430   DFo CSmH MH

TASSO, Torquato, 1544-1595.
Il Goffredo, overo Gierusalemme liberata; poema heroico. Con gli argomenti del Sig. Oratio Ariosti. Aggiontovi i Cinque canti del Camillo Camilli. Venetia, appresso B. Bruni, 1668.

nar.32⁰. pp.(24). 710 .
Half title is engraved.

NT   0048431   MH

PQ4638   Tasso, Torquato, 1544-1595.
1670   [La Gerusalemme liberata. 1670]
Il Goffredo ... Travestito alla rusticana Bergamasca da Carlo Assonica. Venetia, appresso, Nicolò Pezzana, 1670.
[8], 400p. 28cm.

Original text and Bergamese dialect version in parallel columns.
Cf. Guidi p. 14.

I. Assonica, Carlo, tr. II. Pezzana, Nicolò (1670) III. 1670, Italy. IV. Title

NT   0048432   CU-BANC MH PU CU ICU

Bonaparte
Collection   Tasso, Torquato,   1544-1595.
No. 5304
Il Goffredo del Signor Torqvato Tasso, trauestito alla rustica berga- masca da Carlo Assonica. 2.impres- sione... Venetia, 1674.   Q.

Parallel columns of Italian and Bergamasco.

NT   0048433   ICN

X36Y Tasso, Torquato, 1544-1595.
.T18 Il Goffredo, overo Giervsalemme liberata, poema
1676 heroico. Tratto dal vero originale, con aggiunta
di quanto mancaua nell'altre editioni, con
l'allegoria dell' istesso auttore; et con gli
argomenti à ciascun canto del sig. Horatio Ariosti;
et i Cinque canti del sig. Camillo Camilli; con i
loro argomenti, del sig. Francesco Melchiori opitergino. Venetia, Appresso li Prodotti, 1676.
12, 490, 141 p. 14cm.
"Cinqve canti di Camillo Camilli" has special
t.-p. and separate paging.

NT 0048434 WU

tPQ4638 Tasso, Torquato, 1544-1595.
1678 [La Gerusalemme liberata. 1678]
Il Goffredo, overo Gierusalemme liberata ... con gli
Argomenti del Sig. Horatio Ariosti, & di bellissime figure
adornato. Amsterdam, Stamperia del S. D. Elsevier. Parigi,
appresso Thomaso Jolly, 1678.
2v. in 1. front., plates, port. 11cm.
Illustrated by Sébastien Leclerc.
Cf. Guidi, Annali delle edizione ... della Gerusalemme
liberata, p. 30-31; Brunet, v.5 c. 666.
Armorial bookplate of Hardress Robert Saunderson.

NT 0048435 CU-BANC MdBJ PU MWelC

Tasso, Torquato, 1544-1595.
El Goffredo del Tasso canta' alla barcariola, dal dottor
Tomaso Mondini, e dedica' al lustrissimo, e celentissimo sior
Francesco Dvodo. Venetia, Per Il Lovisa, 1693.
345 p. illus., plates. 24 cm.
Original text and dialect version in parallel columns.

I. Mondini, Tomaso, tr. II. Title.

PQ4638.B93 58-53117

NT 0048436 DLC CU-BANC

Bonaparte
Collection TASSO, TORQUATO, 1544-1595.
No.5848 El goffredo del Tasso cantà alla barcariola
dal dottor Tomaso Mondini. Venezia,D.Lovisa,
1704.
345p. 23cm.
Added t.-p., engraved.
Italian text and Venetian translation in
parallel columns.

NT 0048437 ICN PU

t PQ4638 Tasso, Torquato, 1544-1595.
1714 [La Gerusalemme liberata. 1714]
Il Goffredo; poema heroico del Torquato Tasso, con gli
Argomenti del Gio: Vincenzo Imperiale. In questa nova
impressione corretto, e di belle figure ornato con la vita
dell'auttore. appresso Gio: Battista Zuccato, 1714.
550 p. plates. 14 cm.
Added t.p., engraved with port.
I. Imperiale, Giovanni Vincenzo, 1571-1648. / t. Zuccato,
Giovanni Battista (1714) c. 1714. Italy.

NT 0048438 CU-BANC PU

PQ4638 Tasso, Torquato, 1544-1595.
.C19 Il Goffredo; ovvero, La Gerusalemme liberata,
rincontrato co' migliori testi: con gli argomenti
di Orazio Ariosti. Aggiuntovi un ristretto della
sua vita, e nel fine varie varie lezioni tratte da' più
esemplari, e gli argomenti di Gio: Vincenzo Imperiale. Napoli, Stamperia di F. Mosca, 1719.
636 p. port.
I. Ariosto, Orazio, 1555-1593, ed. II. Imperiale, Gian Vincenzo, 17th cent. III. Title.

NT 0048439 ICU

R.B.R. Tasso, Torquato, 1544-1595.
Il Goffredo; poema eroico del signor Torquato Tasso, con
gli argomenti del signor Gio. Vicenzo Imperiale. Padova,
Stamperia del seminario, appresso G. Manfrè, 1728.
23, [1], 550 p. incl. front., plates. 14 x 8cm.
"Vita del signor Torquato Tasso estratta dagli Elogj del sig. Lorenzo
Crasso": p. [5-9]
"Allegoria del poema": p. 10-23.
"Tutte le stanze intere, che dall'autore sono state rifiutate in questo
libro": p. 524-550.
I. Imperiale, Giovanni Vincenzo, 1571?-1645? II. Crasso, Lorenzo, 17th
cent. III. Title.
Library of Congress PQ4638.C63 2-14757

NT 0048440 DLC MH ViU CU PU ICU NcD

4PQ Tasso, Torquato, 1544-1595.
It. El Goffredo del Tasso, canta'alla
3034 barcariola dal dottor Tomaso Mondini.
Venezia, T. Bettinelli, 1746-
Pt. 1
Italian and Venetian dialect;
added t.p. in Italian.

NT 0048441 DLC-P4

PQ 4638 Tasso, Torquato, 1544-1595.
C63 Il Goffredo, poema eroico. Con gli
1754 argomenti del Gio. Vicenzo Imperiale.
In Padova, Nella stamperia del Seminario,
Appresso Gio. Manfrè, 1754.
550 p. illus.
"Vita del Signor Torquato Tasso, es-
tratta dagli elogi del Sig. Lorenzo
Crasso."
I. Imperiale, Giovanni Vincenzo, 1571?-
1645? II. Crasso, Lorenzo,
17th cent. III. Title.

NT 0048442 CaBVaU

TASSO, Torquato, 1544-
Il Goffredo, poema eroico. Con gli argomenti
di Orazio Ariosti, in quaesta nuova impressione corretto, e di belle figure ornato,
con la vita dell'autore, e con l'aggiunta
de' Cinque canti di Camillo Camilli. Lucca,
G.Marescandoli,1758.
nar.24°. pp.663. Wdcts.
"Cinque canti di Camillo Camilli aggiunti
al Goffredo", pp.525-663.

NT 0048443 MH

SPECIAL COLLECTIONS
B851T185 Tasso, Torquato, 1544-1595.
R Il Goffredo, ovvero Gerusalemme liberata di
1760 Torquato Tasso. Nuova edizione arricchita di
figure in rame, e d' annotazioni colla vita
dell' autore ... In Venezia, Presso Antonio
Groppo, 1760-61.
2 v. illus., plates, port. 30cm.
Edited by Scipione Gentili and Giulio Guastavini.
Plates and illus. engraved by Jacopo Leo-
nardis after designs by Bernardo Castelli and
Pietro Antonio No- velli.

NT 0048444 NNC NN MH CtY ICN PU PHC CU MoU

Tasso, Torquato, 1544-1595.
Il Goffredo; poema eroico del signor Torquato Tasso, con
gli argomenti del signor Gio. Vicenzo Imperiale. Padova,
Stamperia del seminario, appresso G. Manfrè, 1763.
23, [1], 550 p. incl. front., plates. 14 x 7cm.
"Vita del signor Torquato Tasso estratta dagli Elogj del sig. Lorenzo
Crasso": p. [5-9].
"Allegoria del poema": p. 10-23.
"Tutte le stanze intere, che dall' autore sono state rifiutate in questo
libro": p. 524-550.
I. Imperiale, Giovanni Vicenzo, d. 1645. II. Crasso, Lorenzo, 17th cent.
III. Title.
Library of Congress PQ4638.C63 2-14757

NT 0048445 DLC CU OU

Tasso, Torquato, 1544-1595
Il Goffredo, poema eroico del Signor
Torquato Tasso con gle argomenti del Signor
Gio: Vicenzo Imperiale. Parma. 1765.
548 p.

NT 0048446 OU

Hdl7 Il Goffredo; poema eroico del Signor
23p Torquato Tasso con gli argomenti del Signor
Gio: Vincenzo Imperiale. Napoli,1766.
xxiii,520p. front.,plates. 14½cm.
Added engraved t.-p.: La Gervsalemme liberata
del Sig. Torquato Tasso.
Vita del Signor Torquato Tasso estratra
dagli elogj del Sig. Lorenzo Crasso":
p.[iii-vii]

NT 0048447 CtY

tPQ4638 Tasso, Torquato, 1544-1595.
C77 Il Goffredo; poema eroico. Con gli argomenti [di] Gio:
Vincenzio Imperiale. Padova, Stamperia del Seminario,
appresso G. Manfrè, 1777.
23, 550 p. illus. 13cm.
I. Imperiale, Giovanni Vincenzo, 1571?-1645. II. Title.

NT 0048448 CU PU MH

Bonaparte
Collection Tasso, Torquato, 1544-1595.
No5305 Il Goffredo; poema eroico...con il
travestimento alla rustica bergamasca
del dottor Carlo Assonica alla moderna
ortografia ridotto... Bergamo,1778.
2v.nar.D.
Italian and Bergamasco on opposite
pages.

NT 0048449 ICN MH

Tasso, Torquato, 1544-
Il Goffredo; poemo eroico, con
gli argomenti del... G.V. Imperiale.
Venezia, Astolfi, 1782.
521 p.

NT 0048450 PU

Tasso, Torquato, 1544-1595.
Il Goffredo; peoma eroico del signor Torquato
Tasso con gli argomenti del signor Torquato
Tasso in questa nuova impressione corretto, e di belle figure ornato,
con la vita dell'autore e con l'aggiunta de'cinque canti
di Camillo Camilli. Lucca, D. Marescandoli,
1785.
23, [1], 663 p. incl. plates. 14.5 x 7.5 cm.
"Vita del signor Torquato Tasso estratta dagli
Elogj del sig. Lorenzo Crasso": p. 5-9.

NT 0048451 NcD

Tasso, Torquato, 1544-1595.
Hdl7 Il Goffredo; ovvero, La Gerusalemme liberata,
30 poema eroico .. Con gli argomenti a ciascun
canto d'incerto autore ... Venezia,A spese
della società,1790.
2v. 18cm.
Both vols. have also added t.-p.: El
Goffredo del Tasso, canta' alla barcariola del
dottor Tomaso Mondini.
The original and the Venetian texts on
opposite pages.
"Vita del Signor Torquato Tasso, estratta
dagli Eloji del Sig.Lorenzo Crasso": v.1,
p.5-8.

NT 0048453 CtY MH ICN

TASSO, Torquato, 1544-1595.
Il Goffredo; poema eroico con gli argomenti di
Orazio Ariosti in questa nuova impressione,
corretto, e di belle figure ornato, con la vita
dell'autore e con l'aggiunta de' cinque canti
di Camillo Camilli. Lucca, D.Marescandoli,1795.

14 x 7 cm. pp.663. Wdcts.
Half-title: La Gerusalemme liberata.

NT 0048454   MH MA PU

Y
712
.T 2079

TASSO, TORQUATO, 1544-1595.
Il Goffredo; poema eroico...con gli argomenti
del signor Gio: Vincenzo Imperiale. Edizione
arriechita di un rame ad ogni canto. Venezia,
A.Astolfi,1797.
xxiv,523p. illus. 16cm.

"Vita del signor Torquato Tasso, estratta
dagli Elogi del signor Lorenzo Crasso": p.v-x.

NT 0048455   ICN

Tasso, Torquato, 1544-
Il Goffredo, poema eroico con gli
argomenti del signor Gio. Vincenzo
Imperiale. Venezia, 1800.

521 p.

NT 0048456   PHC

PQ4638
D28

Tasso. Torquato, 1544-1595.
Il Goffredo, poema eroico; con gli argomenti di Orazio Ariosti in questa nuova
impressione corretto e di belle figure
ornato, con la vita dell'autore e con
l'aggiunta de'Cinque canti di Camillo
Camilli. Roma, Presso P. Aurelj, 1828.
2 v. in 1. illus.

NT 0048457   CU

Tasso, Torquato, 1544-1595.
El Goffredo del Tasso, canta a la barcariola
del dottor Tomaso Mondini co i argomenti a
ogni canto d'un incerto autor. Venezia, 1840.
666, ʃ20ʃ p. front. (port.) 25ᶜᵐ.

Colophon: Venezia, Tipografia all'Ancora,
1842.

NT 0048458   NNC NN MH ICN

Tasso, Torquato, 1544-
Goffred, abo Ieruzalem wyzwolona. Przekł. Piotra
Kochanowskiego. Wyd. Lucyan Rydel. Kraków, Wydawn.
Akad. Umiejętności, 1901-1903
2v. facsim. (Biblioteka pisarzów polskich [Ser.A],
41, 46)
Photoreproduction
Film Mas 738
Microfilm, negative, of copy in the British
Museum

NT 0048459   MH

Tasso, Torquato, 1544-1595.
Goffred; abo, Ieruzalem wyzwolona. Przekładania Piotra
Kochanowskiego. Wydał Lucyan Rydel. Kraków, Nakł.
Akademii Umiejętności, 1902-03.
2 v. 21 cm. (Biblioteka pisarzów polskich, nr. 41,46)
Wydawnictwa Akademii Umiejętności w Krakowie.
"Słowniczek. Ułożył Jan Czubek": t. 2, p. ʃ337ʃ-366.
ɪ. Kochanowski, Piotr, 1566-1620, tr. ɪɪ. Title. (Series)
AC60.B47 no. 41, 46   4-17466 rev

NT 0048460   DLC ICU CoU NNC

Tasso, Torquato, 1544-
Gofred; albo, Jerusalem wyzwolona;
poemat bohaterski przekład Piotra Kochanowskiego. Sanok, Pollake, 1856.

492 p.

NT 0048461   PU

PG7005
B5
ser. 2
no. 4

Tasso, Torquato, 1544-1595.
Gofred; abo Jeruzalem wyzwolona. Przekładania Piotra
Kochanowskiego; na podstawie pierwodruku wydał, wstępem i
objaśnieniami zaopatrzył Roman Pollak. Wyd. 3., całkowite.
Wrocław, Wydawn. Zakładu Narodowego im. Ossolińskich [1951]
li, 697 p. facsim. (Biblioteka narodowa. Seria 2, nr. 4)

ɪ. Kochanowski, Piotr, 1566-1620, tr. ɪɪ. Title.

NT 0048462   CU MiD MiU CtY

858.4
T214g

Tasso, Torquato, 1544-1595.
Il Gonzaga Secondo, overo del Givoco,
dialogo del Signor Torqvato Tasso. [Orna-
ment] In Venetia, Bernardo Giunti, e
fratelli, 1582.
20 numb. l. 21cm.

Initials. Catchwords.
Text stained.
Rebound.
Listed in Brit. mus. gen. cat. v. 235,
col. 77 in this single edition.

NT 0048463   FU NN MiU MnU ICU NcD NcU CSt

ʃTasso, Torquatoʃ 1544-1595.
Gottfried von Bulljon, oder Das erlösete Jerusalem.
Erst von dem hochberühmbten poeten Torquato Tasso in
welscher sprache beschrieben: vnd nun in deutsche heroische poesie gesetzweise / als vormahls nie mehr gesehen /vberbracht. Getruckt zu Franckfurt am Mayn / In
verlegung Daniels vnd Davids Aubrj vnd Clemens
Schleichen. Anno M.DC.XXVI.
30 p., 1 l., 259 numb. l., 1 l. illus. 23ᶜᵐ.
Engraved t-p.

Added t-p.: Glücklicher heerzug in das Heylig Landt / oder Das er-
löste Jerusalem ...
"O du / der du diss werck durch Gottes hülff geendt .... Du bist zu ross
vnd fuss ein Werdter rittersmann."—Salutatory, leaf 259, signed: C K.

ɪ. Werder, Dietrich von dem, 1584-1657, tr. ɪɪ. Title. ɪɪɪ. Title: Das
erlösete Jerusalem. ɪᴠ. Title: Glücklicher heerzug in das Heylig Landt.

Library of Congress   PQ4642.G21W4 1626   25-19710

NT 0048465   DLC CU WaU CtY PU ICU

FILM
4333
PT
Reel
42

Tasso Torquato, 1544-1595.
Gottfried von Bulljon; oder, Das erlösete Jeru-
salem. Erst von dem Hochberührmbten Poeten Torquato
Tasso in welscher Sprache beschrieben; vnd nun in
deutsche heroische Poesie gesetzweise, als vormals
nie mehr gesehen, vberbracht. Getruckt zu Franck-
furt am Mayn, In Verlegung Daniels vnd Davids
Aubrj vnd Clemens Sonleichen, 1626.
30p., 1l., 259 numb.l., 1l. illus.   23cm.
Title within engraved illustrated border.
Added t-p.: Glücklicher Heerzug in das Heylige
Landt, oder, Das erlösete Jerusalem.
Translated by Dietrich von dem Werder.
(No.179, German Baroque Literature, Microfilm,
reel No. 42, ʻReebaɕoh, Publications, Inc.)

NT 0048466   CU PSt

Tasso, Torquato, 1544-1595.
Gottfried. Oder Erlösetes Jerusalem. Deutsch. Verbessert.
Zum zweyten Mahl gedruckt. Frankfurt am Mayn, Gedruckt
bey Caspar Röteln, Jn Verlegung Johann Pressen, 1651. 10 p.l.,
520 p. illus., ports. 24cm.(4°.)
See: Neufforge: Versuch einer deutschen Bibliothek, p. 169. Guidi: Gerusalemme
liberata, p. 132.
Translated by Diederich von dem Werder.—cf. dedication.
Illustrations: 25 engravings, comprising illustrated t. p. border, one portrait, and 23
full-page (one signed) by Matthaeus Merian; one portrait of Ferdinand III, the dedicatee, engraved by Sebastian Furck. These illustrations probably appeared first in the
1626 edition of this work.

Continued in next column

Continued from preceding column

With bookplate: Nordkirchen.
Binding, contemporary German, of vellum, gilt, with the Hesse supra-libros; with
ties.

1. Engravings, German. 2. Bind-   ings, 17th cent., German. I. Werder, Diederich von dem, 1584-1657, tr.   II. Merian, Matthaeus, 1593-1650,
illus. III. Furck, Sebastian, 1600?-   1665, engr. IV. Title.

NT 0048468   NN CtY PU InU IEN OU TNJ

[Tasso, Torquato] 1544-1595.
Gottfried; oder Erlösetes Jerusalem. Deutsch.
Verbessert. Zum zweyten Mahl gedruckt. Franck-
furt am Mayn, Gedruckt bey Caspar Röteln, in
Verlegung Johann Pressen, 1651.
1 reel   35 mm.
Translated by Dietrich von dem Werder.
In verse.
(German Baroque Literature, reel 43, No. 180)
Translation of La Gersalemme liberata.

Research Publications, New Haven, Conn., 1970.
Microfilm (positive)
Collation of the original: 10 p. l., 520 p.
I. Title. II. Title: Erlösetes Jerusalem.
III. Werder, Dietrich von dem, 1584-1657.

NT 0048470   PSt CU

Tasso, Torquato, 1544-1595.
Hierosolyma vindicata, sev heroicvm poema Torqvati
Tassi epico carmine donatum ab Adm. R. D. Hieronymo
de Placentinis Foroliviensi; cum indice locupletissimo
nominum, & præcipuarum rerum, quæ in opere continentur. Forolivii, typis Iosephi Syluæ, 1673.
12 p. l., 336 p. 15½ᵐᵐ.

ɪ. Hieronymus de Placentinis, tr.   4-20128

NT 0048471   DLC PU

TASSO, Torquato, 1544-1595.
La Hierusalem. Renduë françois par Blaise
de Vigenère . Paris, impr. d'A. du Brueil,
1610.

pp.(20). 658, (12). Vign. of Tasse.

NT 0048472   MH PU

Tasso, Torquato, 1544-1595.
La Hiervsalem delivrée. Poëme heroïqve de
Torqvato Tasso. Tradvit en vers françois. Par m.
Le Clerc. A Paris, Chez Clavde Barbin,
MDCLXVII.
7 p. l., 235 p. front., 5 pl. 29.5 cm.
Signatures: a⁴, e³, A-Z⁴, Aa-Ff⁴, Gg².
Illustrated by François Chauveau (frontispiece
signed) cf. Le Blanc, Manuel and Bryan, i, p. 286.
Contains only chants I-V.
Italian text on margins.

The "Privilege" is granted to Denys Thierry and
Claude Barbin.

NT 0048474   NcD

Tasso, Torquato, 1544-1595.
La Hiervsalem delivrée. Poëme heroïqve de Torqvato
Tasso. Tradvit en vers françois. Par m. Le Clerc. A Paris,
Chez Clavde Barbin, M.DC.LXVII.
7 p. l., 235 p. front., 5 pl. 29½ᶜᵐ.
After "Avertissement", 1 leaf (p. 131-132) signed Qᵢᵢ inserted. Dif-
fers noticeably from corresponding pages of text in book (Rᵢᵢ)
Illustrated by François Chauveau (frontispiece signed) cf. Le Blanc,
Manuel and Bryan, ɪ, p. 286.
Contains only chants ɪ-ᴠ.
Italian text on margins.
The "Privilege" is granted to Denys Thierry and Claude Barbin.
"Ex bibliotheca R. Tolnet."
ɪ. Le Clerc, Michel, 1622-1691, tr. ɪɪ. Chauveau, François, 1613-1676,
illus. ɪɪɪ. Title.
30-33525

Library of Congress   PQ4642.F21L45

NT 0048475   DLC MH

Tasso, Torquato, 1544–1595.
La Hierusalem deliurée dv Tasse ... A Paris chez Denis Thierry rue S¹. Iacques. Auec priuilege du roy 1671.
2 v. 20 pl. 12½ᶜᵐ.
Engraved t.-p. with vignette (device of D. Thierry)
Vol. 2 has half-title only : Godefroy ou La Jerusalem delivrée. Poëme heroïque, en vers françois ...
The privilege is granted to Monsieur Sablon.
The first edition, 1656, containing only 5 cantos, appeared under title: Le Godefroy, ou Hierusalem delivrée.
Anonymous book-plate, with the letter R in the center and motto: Bona fide sine fravde.
"Ex bibliotheca R. Tolnet."
I. Sablon, Vincent, 1619–1693, tr.

                                              31–12271
Library of Congress   PQ4642.F21S3
──── Copy 2. 11½ᶜᵐ   Imperfect: v. 1 wanting.   851.46

NT   0048476   DLC

─────────────────────────────

Tasso, Torquato, 1544–1595.
Broughton, John Cam Hobhouse, *1st baron*, 1786–1869.
Historical illustrations of the fourth canto of Childe Harold : containing dissertations on the ruins of Rome; and an essay on Italian literature. By John Hobhouse ... London, J. Murray, 1818.

─────────────────────────────

FILM
Tasso, Torquato, 1544–1595.
The housholders philosophie. VVherein is perfectly and profitably described the true oeconomia and forme of housekeeping ... First written in Italian by ... Torquato Tasso, and now translated by T.K. [yd. Whereunto is anexed a dairie booke for all good huswiues. At London Printed by J.C. [harlwood] for Thomas Hacket ... M.D.LXXXVIII.
"A dairie booke" has special t.-p. with imprint: At London Printed for Thomas Hacket ... 1588.
University microfilms no.15626 (case 56, carton 333)
Short-title catalogue no.23705.
1. Conduct of   life. 2. Dairying. I. Kyd,
Thomas, 1558–1594,   tr. II. Title.   Trans-
lation of Il padre   di famiglia.

NT   0048478   MiU WaPS CSmH

─────────────────────────────

RARE
BOOKS
DEPT.   Tasso, Torquato, 1544–1595.
Iervsalem libertada, poema heroyco. Traduzido al sentido de lengua toscana en castellana por Iuan Sedeño ... Madrid, P. Madrigal, 1587.
8 p. ℓ., 341 numb. ℓ., [34] p. 16cm.

Title vignette (coat of arms)

I. Sedeño, Juan, 16th cent., tr.

NT   0048479   CU InU MH NNH PU

─────────────────────────────

Tasso, Torquato, 1544–1595, supposed author.
La impenitenza di Giuda
see under Liliani, Giulio.

─────────────────────────────

TASSO, Torquato, 1544–
Intrichi d'amore; comedia. Venetia, presso G.B. Giotti, 1605.
nar. 24°. A–L in 6's. ff. 132.
Title-page is engraved.
Haym and Allacci attribute the above work to Tasso; Graesse believes the attribution to be incorrect.

NT   0048481   MH

─────────────────────────────

Tasso, Torquato, 1544–1595.
Intrichi d'amore, comedia del Sign. Torquato Tasso. Rappresentata in Caprarola, all' ill.ᵐᵒ et rever.ᵐᵒ Sig. card. Farnese ... Venetia, G. B. Ciotti, 1613.
274 p. 14ᶜᵐ.
Title vignette (device of Ciotti).
Dedication signed: Scipione Perini, 9. di nouemb. 1603.
Solerti (Vita di Torquato Tasso, v. 1, p. 474) after considering the disputed authorship of this drama, concludes that in plot and structure it was the work of Tasso, but that, having been left unfinished by him, it was completed and possibly remodeled by the Accademici di Caprarola.
First published Viterbo, 1604.
I. Perini, Scipione, ed. II. Title.

                                              17–13120
Library of Congress   PQ4639.I 2 1613

NT   0048482   DLC

─────────────────────────────

PQ4437
.T3
1831   Tasso Torquato. Intrichi d'amore.

Tasso, Torquato, 1544–1595.
Postille di Torquato Tasso alla Divina commedia di Dante Alighieri. Pisa, N. Capurro, 1831.

─────────────────────────────

354
T185i   Tasso, Torquato, 1544–1595.
Intrighi d'amore; commedia in cinque atti con uno studio introduttivo Il nuovo volto del Tasso e commento di Francesco Pedrina. Milano, Trevisini [1954?]
286p. 23cm.

            I. Pedrina, Francesco,   ed.
II. Title.   III. Title: Il nuovo volto
del Tasso.

NT   0048484   OrU

─────────────────────────────

Case
Y
712   TASSO, TORQUATO, 1544–1595.
.T 2173   Tasso's Jerusalem, an epic poem. Translated from the Italian, by Henry Brooke esq... London, Printed by J.Hughs for R.Dodsley, 1738.
3v. in 1.

Bookplate of T.R.Jenkinson.

NT   0048485   ICN InU TxU MH CtY

─────────────────────────────

PQ4642
E21W6   Tasso, Torquato, 1544–1595.
The Jerusalem delivered of Torquato Tasso. Translated into English Spenserian verse, with life of the author, by J.H. Wiffen. New York, Crowell [n.d.]
493p. front. 19cm.

            I. Wiffen, Jeremiah Holmes, 1792–1836, tr.
II. Title.

NT   0048486   IaU NcU ViW OrCS WaWW NcRS

─────────────────────────────

Tasso, Torquato, 1544–1595.
Tasso's Jerusalem delivered: or, Godfrey of Bulloign. An heroic poem. Done into English, in the reign of Queen Elizabeth, by Edward Fairfax, gent. The 4th ed., with a glossary, and index. London, Printed by J.Purser for J.Clark [etc.] 1749.
12p. ℓ., 500, [25]p. 22cm.
Dedication signed: John Bill.

         NcD PPL NjP ICN MoU IU OrU NmU WaSpG
NT   0048487   CtY PU DFo NIC CLU-C NcU TxU ViU CLU

─────────────────────────────

Tasso, Torquato, 1544–1595.
Jerusalem delivered; an heroick poem: translated from the Italian of Torquato Tasso, by John Hoole ... London, Printed for the author, 1763.
2v. 22cm.

Title vignettes; tail-pieces.
Translation of La Gerusalemme liberata.
The dedication to the queen was written by Samuel Johnson.
"The life of Tasso": v.1, p. xvii–xlviii.

         ViU IU PPL CaBVaU
NT   0048488   MoU RPB OC1W CtY WaU TxU MH ICN KU NcU

─────────────────────────────

Rare Book
Collection
PQ4642   Tasso, Torquato, 1544–1595.
.E21   Jerusalem delivered; an heroic poem: trans-
H7   lated from the Italian of Torquato Tasso,
1764   by John Hoole. The second edition. London, Printed for R. and J. Dodsley, MDCCLXIV.
2 v. 17 cm.

Illustrated title-pages.

I. Hoole, John, 1727–1803, tr. II. Title.

NT   0048489   NcU PPL PU OU MH

─────────────────────────────

854
T185gE2   Tasso, Torquato, 1544–1595.
            Jerusalem delivered; an heroic poem
WaSpG   translated from the Italian by John Hoole.
3d ed. London, Printed for T. Davies and J. Dodsley, 1767.
2v. 18cm.

I. Hoole, John, 1727–1803, tr. II. Title.

NT   0048490   OrU TxU CtY MiEM WaSpG

─────────────────────────────

Am
H765
763td   Tasso, Torquato, 1544–1595.
Jerusalem delivered; an heroic poem: translated from the Italian of Torquato Tasso, by John Hoole ... The fourth edition. London: Printed for J.Dodsley, in Pall-Mall; and T.Davies, in Russel-Street, Covent-Garden. 1772. 2v. 17cm.
Engr. title vignettes.
Autograph of Richard Heber.

NT   0048491   TxU NN

─────────────────────────────

Tasso, Torquato, 1544–
Jerusalem delivered, an heroic poem. Translated from the Italian of Torquato Tasso, by John Hoole. Dublin, 1778.

NT   0048492   PPL

─────────────────────────────

Am
H765j
1783   Tasso, Torquato, 1544–1595.
Stark   Jerusalem delivered; an heroic poem: translated
Lib'y   from the Italian of Torquato Tasso, by John Hoole. In two volumes. The 5th ed., with notes. London, Printed for J. Dodsley, 1783.
2v. plates. 22cm.
Errors in paging: v.1, 302 and 303 numbered 202 and 203; v.2, p.81 wants no.
TxU copy has plates bound as fronts.
Vol. 2 has autograph of Sarah Wetenhill.

NT   0048493   TxU MH ICN KyU NIC IaU

─────────────────────────────

PQ4642
.E21H7
1787   Tasso, Torquato, 1544–1595.
Jerusalem delivered; an heroic poem. Translated from the Italian of Torquato Tasso, by John Hoole. 6th ed., with notes. London, Printed for J. Dodsley, 1787.
2 v. illus. 22 cm.
"The life of Tasso": v. 1, p. [xix]–xlvii.

I. Hoole, John, 1727–1803, tr. II. Title.

NT   0048494   MB PMA MH

─────────────────────────────

Tasso, Torquato, 1544–1595.
Jerusalem delivered; an heroic poem: translated from the Italian of Torquato Tasso, by John Hoole... London: J. Dodsley, 1792. 2 v. fronts. 7. ed. 8°.

With bookplate of James Alexander Frampton.

I. No subject. 2. Hoole, John,   1727–1803, translator.
N. Y. P. L.   March 24, 1921.

NT   0048495   NN TxU MdBJ PPL CLSU CaBViPA

PQ4642
.E21H7
1797   Tasso, Torquato, 1544–1595.

    Jerusalem delivered: an heroic poem.
Tr. from the Italian by John Hoole. With
four elegant engravings. London: Printed
for J. Johnson ₍etc.₎ 1797.
    2 v. front. 22cm.

    I. Hoole, John, 1727–1803, tr.   II. Title.

NT   0048496   ViU MB PU MoSU CU DeU NIC CtY NjP MiU MH

Tasso, Torquato, 1544–1595.
    Jerusalem delivered; an heroic poem. Tr. from the
Italian of Torquato Tasso, by John Hoole ... 8th ed.,
with notes. London, Printed by T. Bensley, for J. Johnson ₍etc.₎ 1802.
    2 v. fronts. (v. 1, port.) plates. 21ᶜᵐ.
    "The life of Tasso": v. 1, p. ₍xix₎–xlvii.

    I. Hoole, John, 1727–1803, tr.   II. Title.
                                17–7405

Library of Congress   PQ4642.E21H7 1802

NT   0048497   DLC MH ICN

Tasso, Torquato, 1544–1595.
    Jerusalem delivered; an heroic poem. Tr. from the
Italian of Torquato Tasso, by John Hoole ... 8th ed.
with notes. London, Printed by T. Bensley, for J. Johnson ₍etc.₎ 1803.
    2 v. fronts. (v. 1: port.) 13 pl. 28ᶜᵐ.

    I. Hoole, John, 1727–1803, tr.   II. Title.

Library of Congress   ₍31c1₎
                     PQ4642.E21H7 1803   4–19850

    ViU NcU CSmH NN MB
NT   0048498   DLC OGK OrCS OrPR PV CtY PU TxU MeB

Tasso, Torquato, 1544–1595.
    Jerusalem delivered: an heroic poem. Tr. from the
Italian of Torquato Tasso, by John Hoole.
    (*In* Chalmers, Alexander, ed. The works of the English poets ... Lon-
don, 1810. 24ᶜᵐ. v. 21, p. ₍385₎–516)

    I. Hoole, John, 1727–1803, tr.
                             12–3673

Library of Congress   PR1173.C5 vol. 21

NT   0048499   DLC NN MdBP

Tasso, Torquato, 1544–1595.
    Jerusalem delivered: an heroic poem. Tr. from the
Italian of Torquato Tasso, by John Hoole ... 1st American, from the 8th London ed. With notes. Newbury-
port ₍Mass.₎ Pub. and sold by Edward Little & co.; Exeter ₍N. H.₎ Printed by C. Norris and co. and E. C. Beals,
1810.
    2 v. front. (port.) plates. 22ᶜᵐ.
    "Life of Tasso": v. 1, p. ₍xix₎–xlvii.

    I. Hoole, John, 1727–1803. II. Title.
                             17–7408

Library of Congress   PQ4642.E21H7 1810

    NcD PU PP PV KyLx OGK NcU MH NN CU MWA ViU MB
NT   0048500   DLC PPL NCshB NjP N PPT CSt NBu InU MWH

Tasso, Torquato, 1544–1595.
    Jerusalem delivered; an heroic poem. Translated from the
Italian of Torquato Tasso, by John Hoole. The tenth edition,
with notes. London: Printed for Johnson and co. ₍etc.₎ 1811.
xxxii, 505 p. front. (port.), plates. 25½cm.

150703B. 1. No subject. I. Hoole,   John, 1727–1803, tr. II. Title.
N. Y. P. L.   December 16, 1941

    NcD CaOTP WaS
NT   0048501   NN MdBP MB MH ViU OCl OrPS TxU CSt NcU

Tasso, Torquato, 1544–1595.
    Tasso's Jerusalem delivered, an heroic poem. With
notes and occasional illustrations. Tr. by the Reverend
J. H. Hunt ... London, Printed for J. Mawman, by
T. Miller, 1818.
    2 v. 22ᶜᵐ.
    "Sketch of the life of Tasso": v. 1, p. ₍xiii₎–xxi.

    I. Hunt, John Higgs, 1780–1859, tr.   II. Title.
                             17–7406

Library of Congress   PQ4642.E21H8 1818

NT   0048502   DLC CtY InU TxU OKentU CU MH NBuG PV NjR

TASSO, TORQUATO, 1544–1595.
    Jerusalem delivered; an heroic poem, translated from
Torquato Tasso, by John Hoole... London: Suttaby, Evance
& Fox, 1819. 443 p. front. 15x8cm.

    Engraved t.–p., title vignette.

595854A. 1. No subject. I. Hoole, John, 1727–1803, translator.
II. Title.

NT   0048503   NN CtY NcD MH

Tasso, Torquato, 1544–1595.
    Tasso's Jerusalem delivered, an heroic poem. With
notes ... Tr. by the Rev. J. H. Hunt ...
    (*In* The works of the British poets ... Philadelphia, 1819–23. 15ᶜᵐ.
v. 48–49. fronts.)

    I. Hunt, John Higgs, 1780–1859, tr.
                             11–31338 Revised

Library of Congress   PR1173.B64

NT   0048504   DLC ViU PV DGU

PQ4642
.F21
W5
1821   Tasso, Torquato, 1544–1595.
    Jerusalem delivered. Book of the fourth.
From the Italian of Tasso, being the speci-
men of an intended new translation in English
Spenserian verse. With a prefatory disserta-
tion on existing translations, by J. H.
Wiffen. London, Warren, 1821.
    120p.

    ₍I.₎ Wiffen, Jeremiah Holmes, 1792–1836, tr.
    II.₎ Title.

NT   0048505   NcU InU MiD CtY FMU

Tasso, Torquato, 1544–1595.

    Jerusalem delivered, an heroic poem,
with notes and occasional illus.; tr. by
J. H. Hunt. Philadelphia, S. F. Bradford,
1822.
    2 v. fronts. 15cm. (Works of the British
Poets: Translations, v. 9–10)
    Tr. of: La Gerusalemme liberata.

    I. Hunt, John Higgs, 1780–1859, tr. II. Title.
    III. Ser.

NT   0048506   ViU KyLx PV PPL PU

Tasso, Torquato, 1544–1595.
    Jerusalem delivered; an epic poem, in twenty cantos;
tr. into English Spenserian verse from the Italian of
Tasso: together with a life of the author, interspersed
with translations of his verses to the Princess Leonora
of Este; and a list of English crusaders. By J. H. Wiffen ... London, Hurst, Robinson and co.; ₍etc., etc.₎
1824–25.
    2 v. front. (port.) facsim. 24½ᶜᵐ.
    Head and tail pieces.
    "This edition in royal octavo consists of 250 copies."
    I. Wiffen, Jeremiah Holmes, 1792–1836, tr. II. Title.
                             17–7416

Library of Congress   PQ4642.E21W6 1824

NT   0048507   DLC TxU PV InU CSmH

Tasso, Torquato, 1544–1595.
    Jerusalem delivered. Part of 7th canto in which the incidents of
pastoral life are described.
    (In Capuzzi, E., translator. A literal prose translation of five
select pieces from the works of Tasso ... Vol. 1, pp. 215–228.
Leghorn. 1826.)
    English and Italian on opposite pages.

Ls877 — T.r. made.

NT   0048508   MB

---

*Y
712
.T 2182   TASSO, TORQUATO, 1544–1595.
    Jerusalem delivered; translated into English
Spenserian verse from the Italian with a life of
the author, by J.H.Wiffen. 2d edition. London,J.Murray,1826.
    3v. 22cm.

NT   0048509   ICN CLSU CSmH

PQ
4642
E21
W6
1830   Tasso, Torquato, 1544–1595
    The Jerusalem delivered, of Torquato Tasso.
Tr. into English Spenserian verse with a life
of the author. By J. H. Wiffen. 3rd. ed.
London, Longman, etc., 1830.
    2 v.

    Wiffen, Jeremiah Holmes, 1792–1836, tr.
    The Jerusalem delivered, of Torquato Tasso

NT   0048510   KMK OrU ICN PSC NN PU

Tasso, Torquato, 1544–1595.
    The Jerusalem delivered of Torquato Tasso, tr. by
J. R. Broadhead ... London, R. H. Evans, 1837.
    2 v. 19¼ᶜᵐ.

    I. Broadhead, J. R., tr.   II. Title.
                             17–7413

Library of Congress   PQ4642.E21B7

NT   0048511   DLC PV MB CU

Tasso, Torquato, 1544–
    The Jerusalem delivered. Translated into English Spenserian
verse, with a life of the author: by J. H. Wiffen. First American
from the last English edition... New York: D. Appleton & Co.,
1846. 624 p., 5 pl., 1 port. 16°.

I. Poetry (Italian). 2 Wiffen, Jere-   miah Holme, translator.
N. Y. P. L.   April 12, 1911.

NT   0048512   NN MB ICN PPL NNUT ViU OClW NjP

PQ
4642
E21
W6
1850
HRC   **Tasso, Torquato, 1544–1595.**
    The Jerusalem delivered of Torquato
Tasso. Translated into English
Spenserian verse, with a life of the
author: by J.H. Wiffen. 2d American
from the last English ed. Illustrated
with six fine steel engravings. New
York, Appleton, 1850.
    624p. illus. 18cm.
    Inscribed: Wilmot Johnson, Dec.
25th, 1851.

    I. Wiffen, Jeremiah Holmes, 1792–
1836, tr. II. TITLE. AF Johnson,
Wilmot. CO+ CRS

NT   0048513   TxU

PQ4642
.E21W6
1850   Tasso, Torquato, 1544–1595.
    The Jerusalem delivered of Torquato Tasso. Tr. into Eng-
lish Spenserian verse, with a life of the author: by J. H.
Wiffen. 3d American from the last English ed. Illustrated
with six ... steel engravings. New-York, D. Appleton & company, Phila., G. S. Appleton, 1850.
    624 p. front. 5 pl. 17 ᶜᵐ.
    Published also under title: Godfrey of Bulloigne

NT   0048514   ViU MH

Tasso, Torquato, 1544–1595.
The Jerusalem delivered of Torquato Tasso. Tr. into English Spenserian verse, with a life of the author: by J. H. Wiffen. 3d American from the last English ed. Illustrated with six ... steel engravings. New-York, D. Appleton & co.; Philadelphia, G. S. Appleton, 1851.
624 p. front, 5 pl. 17½ᶜᵐ.

NT 0048515   ViU MB NjP

PQ
4642
.E21
W65
1852
Tasso, Torquato, 1544–1595.
Jerusalem delivered. Tr. by J. H. Wiffen. 3rd American from the last English ed. New York, D. Appleton, 1852.
624 p. facsim. 17 cm.

I. Wiffen, J   H   , tr. II. Title.

NT 0048516   DCU

Tasso, Torquato, 1544–1595.
The Jerusalem delivered, of Torquato Tasso, tr. by Alex. Cuningham Robertson ... With an appendix ... Edinburgh and London, W. Blackwood and sons, 1853.
2 p. l., [viii–xii p, 1 l., 527 p. 18½ᶜᵐ.

I. Robertson, Alexander Cuningham, 1816–1884, tr. II. Title.

17–9058

Library of Congress   PQ4642.E21R6   1853

NT 0048517   DLC CtY PU

851
T21gxW
1853
Tasso, Torquato, 1544–1595.
The Jerusalem delivered of Torquato Tasso. Tr. into English Spenserian verse, with A life of the author, by J.H. Wiffen. 3d. American from the last English ed. Illus. with six fine steel engravings. New York, D. Appleton & co., 1853.
624p. illus. 17cm.

Translation of: Gerusalemme liberata.

I. Wiffen, Jeremiah Holmes, 1792–1836, tr. II. Title.

NT 0048518   NcU MoSU

PQ
4642
.E21
W6
1854
Tasso, Torquato, 1544–1595.
The Jerusalem delivered, of Torquato Tasso. Tr. into English Spenserian verse with a life of the author. By J. H. Wiffen. 5th ed. London, Henry G. Bohn, 1854.
500 p. illus., plates. 18 cm.

I. Wiffen, Jeremiah Holmes, 1792–1836, tr. II. Title.

NT 0048519   MoSU NNC LU IU MH NjP

Tasso, Torquato, 1544–1595.
The Jerusalem delivered of Torquato Tasso. Translated into English Spenserian verse, with a life of the author: by J. H. Wiffen. Third American from the last English edition... New York: D. Appleton & Co., 1856.   624 p. front. (port.), plates. 16°.

282008A. 1. No subject. 2. Wiffen,   Jeremiah Holmes, 1792–1836, translator.
N. Y. P. L.   April 11, 1927

NT 0048520   NN OCX ViU MH T KyTrA

TASSO, Torquato, 1544–
Jerusalem delivered. Translated into English Spensarian verse, with a life of the author, by J.H.Wiffen. 5th ed., London, H.G.Bohn, 1857.
lxiv, 500 p. front. (port.) illus., pl., facsim.
Portrs., plates, and otherillustr.
(Bohn's illustrated library)

NT 0048521   MH MiD MdBP PP PPL

Tasso, Torquato, 1544–1595.
The Jerusalem delivered of Torquato Tasso. Tr. into English Spenserian verse, with a life of the author: by J. H. Wiffen. 3d American from the last English ed. Illustrated with six ... steel engravings. New-York, D. Appleton & company, 1858.
624 p. front., 5 pl. 17½ᶜᵐ.

I. Wiffen, Jeremiah Holmes, 1792–1836, tr. II. Title.
7–42583

Library of Congress   PQ4642.E21W6   1858
[40p1]   851.46

NT 0048522   DLC WaWW Or OC1MN NcD OC1JC MnU

PQ
4642
.E21
W60
1859
Tasso, Torquato, 1544–1595.
The Jerusalem delivered of Torquato Tasso / Trans. into English Spenserian verse, with a life of the author by J. H. Wiffen. 3d American from the last English edition. New York : D. Appleton, 1859.
624 p. : plates. ; 18cm.
Translation of Gerusalemme liberata.

NT 0048523   GU

851.4
T214gEw
Tasso, Torquato, 1544–1595
The Jerusalem delivered of Torquato Tasso. Tr. into English Spenserian verse, with a life of the author: by J. H. Wiffen. New York, Hurst & Co., [1860?].
493p. front., 5pl. 17.5cm

I. Wiffen, Jeremiah Holmes, 1792–1836, tr. II. Title.

NT 0048524   ICarbS MiU Or ViU

PQ
4642
E21
W6
1863
Tasso, Torquato, 1544–1595.
The Jerusalem delivered of Torquato Tasso. Trans. into English Spenserian verse, with a life of the author by J. H. Wiffen. 3d American from the last English edition. New York, D. Appleton, 1863.
624 p. plates. 18 cm.
Translation of Gerusalemme liberata.

I. Wiffen, Jeremiah Holmes, 1792–1836, tr. II. Title

NT 0048525   NBuC OCU OWorP

PQ4642
.E21W6
1864
Tasso, Torquato, 1544–1595.
The Jerusalem delivered, of Torquato Tasso. Tr. into English Spenserian verse with a life of the author. By J. H. Wiffen. New ed. With twenty-four engravings on wood by Thurston, and eight engravings on steel. London, Bell & Daldy, 1864.
2 p. l., lxiv (i. e. lxviii), 500 p. front. (port.) illus., plates. 19cm.
(On cover: Bohn's illustrated library)
Published also under title: Godfrey of Bulloigne.

NT 0048526   ViU NBuG

TASSO, TORQUATO, 1544–1595
The Jerusalem delivered of Torquato Tasso; translated into English verse by John Kingston James ... London, Longman, Green, Longman, Roberts, & Green, 1865.
2 v.   12mo
Bound by Riviere in full red morocco, with gilt design of bees; gilt edges.

I. James, Sir John Kingston, bart., 1815–1893, tr.

NT 0048527   InU-Li CtY PU ViU

oPQ
4642
.E21
W6
1866
TASSO, TORQUATO, 1544–1595.
[La Gerusalemme liberata. English 1866] The Jerusalem delivered of Torquato Tasso / Torquato Tasso ; tr. into English Spenserian verse, with a life of the author: by J.H. Wiffen. — 3rd American from the last English ed. — New York : D. Appleton, 1866.
624 p. : port. ; 18cm.
On t.p.: Illustrated with six fine steel engravings.

NT 0048528   ICN IaU I NN NjNbS

PQ4642
E21W6
1868
Tasso, Torquato, 1544–1595
[Gerusalemme liberata. English]
The Jerusalem delivered. Translated into English Spenserian verse, with a life of the author, by J. H. Wiffen. 3d American from the last English ed. New York, D. Appleton, 1868.
624 p. 6 plates. 18 cm.

I. Wiffin, Jeremiah Holmes, 1792–1836, tr.

NT 0048529   MeB OC1 ViU PPL

TASSO, Torquato, 1544–1595.
The Jerusalem delivered. Translated into English Spenserian verse, with a life of the author, by J.H.Wiffin [Wiffen]. 3d American from the last English ed. New York, D. Appleton & Company, 1869.
17 cm. pp.624.

NT 0048530   MH

Tasso, Torquato, 1544–1595.
The Jerusalem delivered, of Torquato Tasso. Tr. into English Spenserian verse with a life of the author. By J. H. Wiffen. 3rd American ed. from the last English ed. New York, D. Appleton, 1870.
624 p. front. (port.) illus., plates. 18 cm.

I. Wiffen, Jeremiah Holmes, 1792–1836, tr. II. Title.

NT 0048531   IEdS NIC

Tasso, Torquato, 1544–1595.
The Jerusalem delivered, of Torquato Tasso. Tr. into English Spenserian verse with a life of the author. By J. H. Wiffen. New ed. With twenty-four engravings on wood by Thurston, and eight engravings on steel. London, Bell & Daldy, 1872.
2 p. l., lxiv (i. e. lxviii), 500 p. front. (port.) illus., plates. 18ᶜᵐ.

I. Wiffen, Jeremiah Holmes, 1792–1836, tr. II. Title.   17–21272

Library of Congress   PQ4642.E21W6 1872

NT 0048532   DLC IdU PPMoI

Tasso, Torquato, 1544-1595
     The Jerusalem delivered. 3d American from
the last English ed. New York, D. Appleton and
company, 1872.
     624 p.

NT   0048533   OU

Tasso, Torquato, 1544-1595.
     The Jerusalem delivered of Torquato Tasso, tr. in the
metre of the original, by the Rev. Charles Lesingham
Smith ... 2d ed., priv. print. London, R. Barrett & sons,
printers, 1874.
     xii, 401 p. 19ᶜᵐ.

     I. Smith, Charles Lesingham, 1806-1878, tr.   II. Title.

     Library of Congress   PQ4642.E21S5   15-17089

NT   0048534   DLC

Tasso, Torquato, 1544-1595.
     The Jerusalem delivered of Torquato Tasso, translated in
the metre of the original, by the Rev. Charles Lesingham
Smith ... London, S. Harris & co., 1876.
     2 p. l., 496 p. 15ᶜᵐ.
     Errata slip inserted.

     I. Smith, Charles Lesingham, 1806-1878, tr.   II. Title.

                                                        29-29813
     Library of Congress   PQ4642.E21S5 1876

NT   0048535   DLC MiU OCl MiU OrPR PPT

Tasso, Torquato, 1544-
     The Jerusalem delivered of Torquato
Tasso. Translated...with a life. By J.
H. Wiffen. New ed. illustrated.   L.,
1878.

     (Bohn's illustrated library)

NT   0048536   PPL

Tasso, Torquato, 1544-1595.
     The Jerusalem delivered of Torquate Tasso.
Tr. into English Spenserian verse, with a
life of the author; by J.H. Wiffen. 3d
American from the last English ed. New York,
D. Appleton & company, 1880.
     624 p.

NT   0048537   OFH

Tasso, Torquato, 1544-1595
     The Jerusalem delivered, of Torquato Tasso.
Tr. into English Spenserian verse with a life
of the author. By J.H. Wiffen. New ed. With
twenty-four engravings on wood by Thurston, and
eight engravings on steel. London, Bell and
sons, 1881.
     500 p.

NT   0048538   OCU

PQ   Tasso, Torquato, 1544-1595.
4642   Jerusalem delivered. Translated into
E21   English Spenserian verse, by J.H. Wiffen.
W6   New York, American Book Exchange, 1881.
1881   493p. 18cm.

     I. Wiffen, Jeremiah Holmes, 1792-1836.
II. Title.

     MH PHC NN NjP KAS
NT   0048539   CCSC OClW WaTU OrSaW ODW OCX OCl OClND

Tasso, Torquato, 1544-1595.
     Jerusalem delivered, by Torquato Tasso, translated into
English Spenserian verse, by J. H. Wiffen.   New York: S. W.
Green's Son, 1882.   493 p.   12°.

10139A. 1. No subject. 2. Wiffen,   Jeremiah Holmes, 1792-1836, trans-
N. Y. P. L.   lator.   June 27, 1921.

NT   0048540   NN MoU IU WaSpG

Tasso, Torquato, 1544-
     The Jerusalem delivered of Torquato Tasso.
Translated... with a life of the author by J. H.
Wiffen.   new ed.   Lond. Bell. 1883.
     500p. front. illus. (Bohn's Illus. lib.)

NT   0048541   PPMoI

SPEC COLL
PQ
4642   Tasso, Torquato, 1544-1595.
E21   The Jerusalem delivered. Trans. into
J3   English verse by Sir John Kingston James, Bart.
         London, Kegan, Paul, Trench, 1884.
             2v. 21cm.

             Translation of his Gerusalemme liberata.
             Engraved title pages.
             Butler Library copy in white leather.

             I. James, Sir John Kingston, bart, 1815-1893
         tr. II. Title. III. Ti: Gerusalemme liberata.

NT   0048542   NBuC ICN MH MdBP

Tasso, Torquato, 1544-1595
     The Jerusalem delivered of Torquato Tasso.
Tr. into English Spenserian verse, with a
life of the author; by J.H. Wiffen. 3d
American from the last English ed. Illus-
trated with six ... steel engravings. New
York, D. Appleton & company, 1884.

NT   0048543   OO

Tasso, Torquato, 1544-1595
     The Jerusalem delivered of Torquato Tasso.
Tr. into English Spenserian verse, with a life
of the author; by J.H. Wiffen. 3d American
from the last English ed. Illustrated with
six ... steel engravings. N.Y., Appleton,
1886.
     624 p. front., 5 pl.

NT   0048544   OClW

Tasso, Torquato, 1544-
     Jerusalem delivered; tr. into
Eng. Spenserian verse; with a life of...
Tasso, by J.H.Wiffen. New ed.   Lon-
don, Bell, 1887.

     500 p.

NT   0048545   PPD NN

Tasso, Torquato, 1544-1595.
     Jerusalem delivered; a poem by Torquato Tasso; tr. by Ed-
ward Fairfax, ed. by Henry Morley ... London, New York
[etc.] G. Routledge and sons, limited, 1890.
     2 p. l., [9]-446 p. 20ᶜᵐ.
     Includes reprint of an early t.-p.: Godfrey of Bulloigne; or, The re-
coverie of Ierusalem ... London, 1600.
     "Introduction: Torquato Tasso, Edward Fairfax": p. [9]-26.

     I. Fairfax, Edward, d. 1635, tr.   II. Morley, Henry, 1822-1894, ed.
III. Title.

                                                        4-14034
     Library of Congress   PQ4642.E21F3 1890
                                  [a391]   -851.46

     DGU WaE WaWW CaBVaU
     ODW MiU OU ODW ViU OrCS NcD RPB WaSp IU NBuU MB KU
NT   0048546   DLC TU NN OOxM CU CtY NcU PHC PU PPL PPF

PQ4642   Tasso, Torquato, 1544-1595.
.E21W6   The Jerusalem delivered of Torquato
1893   Tasso. Translated into English Spenserian
         verse, with a life of the author, by J.H.
         Wiffen. New ed. London, New York, G. Bell,
         1893.
             xiv, 500 p. illus., port. 19 cm.

             I. Wiffen, Jeremiah Holmes, 1792-1836, tr.
         II. Title.

NT   0048547   MB KEmT MtU CtY PP PU IaU

PQ   Tasso, Torquato, 1544-1595.
4642   The Jerusalem delivered of Torquato
.E21   Tasso. Trans. into English
W6   Spenserian verse, with a life of the
1898   author by J. H. Wiffen. 3d American
         from the last English edition. New
         York, D. Appleton, 1898.
             624 p. plates. 18 cm.
             Translation of Gerusalemme liberata.

             I. Wiffen, Jeremiah Holmes, 1792-
         1836, tr. II. Title

NT   0048548   MoWgW Wa

Tasso, Torquato, 1544-1595.
     The Jerusalem delivered of Torquato Tasso.
Translated into English Spenserian verse,
with a life of the author, by J.H. Wiffen.
London, O. Bell and sons, 1900.
     500 p.

NT   0048549   OO

PQ4642   Tasso, Torquato, 1544-1595.
.E21   Jerusalem delivered; trans. by Edward
F3   Fairfax; ed. by Henry Morley. Rev. ed.
1901   New York, Collier [c1901]
             446 p. 21cm. (World's greatest litera-
         ture)

NT   0048550   OrCS

Tasso, Torquato, 1544-1595.
     Jerusalem delivered, by Torquato Tasso; tr. by Edward
Fairfax, ed. by Henry Morley ... Rev. ed. New York, The
Colonial press [1901]
     2 p. l., ii-xxii p., 2 l., 446 p. front. (port.) 2 pl., 2 col. facsim. 24ᶜᵐ.
     (Added t.-p.: The World's great classics)
     Each plate preceded by leaf with descriptive letterpress.
     "Introduction" (life of Tasso) : p. iii-xiii; "Edward Fairfax": p. xv-
xix.

     I. Fairfax, Edward, d. 1635, tr.   II. Morley, Henry, 1822-1894, ed.
III. Title.

                                                        1-15171
     Library of Congress   PQ4642.E21F3 1901
     ———— Copy 2.   PN6013.W8 vol. 35

     OClND CU PP TNJ NIC MtBC CaBVaU IdPI
     MsU WaTU NcD OrP IdB WaT OrU NNU-W OCl OCl OClW OO
NT   0048551   DLC PSt UU PU-F NN AAP ScU KMK OClMN NcRS

Tasso, Torquato, 1544-1595.
     Jerusalem delivered (Gerusalemme liberata) by Torquato
Tasso; translated by Edward Fairfax. Éd. de luxe; [New
York] The National alumni [c1907]
     3 p. l., v-xii, 323 p. col. front., 3 pl. 23ᶜᵐ. (Added t.-p.: The litera-
ture of Italy, 1265-1907. Ed. by Rossiter Johnson and Dora Knowlton
Ranous)

     I. Fairfax, Edward, d. 1635, tr.

                                                        7-19474

     NN OKentU OClMN OClJC CoU
NT   0048552   DLC OrPR IdU NmU CU NBuC PP OCU ODW MB

PQ
4642
E21W6
1908

Tasso, Torquato, 1544–1595.
    The Jerusalem delivered of Torquato Tasso.
Tr. into English Spenserian verse, with a
life of the author: by J.H. Wiffen. London,
G. Bell,1908.
    500p. illus. 19cm.

NT   0048553   MU OrPR MH OOxM OCU

TASSO, Torquato, 1544–
    The Jerusalem Delivered. Translated
into English Spenserian Verse with a
Life of the Author by J. H. Wiffen.
London, G. Bell, 1913. 44, 500p pls.
18.5cm.
    1.Title. 2.Poetry-English.
3.Wiffen.

NT   0048554   NNJ CtY MB

Tasso, Torquato, 1544–1595.
    Jerusalem delivered; tr. into English Spenserian
verse from the Italian ... with a life of the author,
by J.H. Wiffen. 2. ed.   Lonson, J. Murray,
1926.
    3 v.   front. (port.) illus.   22 cm.

NT   0048555   NcU

PQ4642
.F21L4

Tasso, Torquato, 1544-1595.
    Jérusalem délivrée; poëme heroïque du Tasse.
Amsterdam, La Compagnie, 1764.
    2v.(405p.)18cm.

NT   0048556   NBC

Tasso, Torquato, 1544–95.
Jerusalem delivrée; poëme héroïque. Amsterdam,
1767
    405 p.

NT   0048557   MH

Tasso, Torquato, 1544–1595.
    Jérusalem délivrée, poëme du Tasse. Nouvelle traduction.
Paris, Musier fils, 1774.
    2 v. fronts. (ports.) plates. 22ᵐ.
    Title vignette, head and tail pieces, engr.
    Prose translation, by C. F. Lebrun.

    I. Lebrun, Charles François, duc de Plaisance, 1739–1824, tr.   II. Gravelot, Hubert François Bourguignon, known as, 1699–1773, illus.
                  18—16967

    Library of Congress   PQ4642.F21L4   1774

NT   0048558   DLC PU NNC PSt CtY

Tasso, Torquato. 1544–1595.
Jérusalem délivrée. Poëme du Tasse. Nouvelle traduction.
À Londres. M.DCC.LXXX. 2 v. Plates. Vignette. 24°.

NT   0048559   MB

[Tasso, Torquato] 1544–1595.
    La Jérusalem délivrée, en vers françois. Par
L.P.M.F. Baour-Lormian ...   Paris, P. Didot
L'aîne, 1796.
    2 v. in 1   plates   30.8cm.

NT   0048560   CSmH MH NNC

Tasso, Torquato, 1544–1595.
    Jérusalem délivrée, poème du Tasse. Nouv.
traduction ...   Paris, Société littéraire, an VII
[1799]
    2 v. in 1.   14 cm.
    Prose translation, by C. F. Lebrun (?)

NT   0048561   CU

[Tasso, Torquato,] 1544–1595.
    Jérusalem délivrée. Poëme, traduit de l'italien. Nouvelle
édition revue et corrigée; enrichie de la vie du Tasse: ornée de son
portrait et de vingt belles gravures.   Paris: Bossange, Masson et
Besson, 1803.   2 v.   front. (port.), pl.   12°.

    Translated by C. F. Le Brun.
    Preliminary matter of v. 1 contains: Preface...1774. Notice sur la vie et le
caractère du Tasse, par M. Suard. Appendice. Jugement sur l'Arioste et le Tasse,
traduit d'une lettre de Pietro Metastasio...
    Bound in stained calf, gilt tooled and with gilt edges.

1. Poetry (Italian). 2. Le Brun,   Charles François, duc de Plaisance,
1739–1824, translator. 3. Suard, Jean   Baptiste Antoine, 1734–1817. 4. Ariosto, Lodovico, 1474–1533. 5. Metas-   tasio, Pietro Antonio Domenico
Buonaventura, 1698–1782.
N. Y. P. L.   September 3, 1915.

NT   0048562   NN PU NcD MH

PQ4642
F21S8
1808

Tasso, Torquato, 1544–1595.
    Jérusalem délivrée; poème. Traduit de
l'italien. Enrichie de la vie du Tasse [par
M. Suard] Nouvelle éd., rev. et corr.
Paris, Bossange, 1808.
    2 v. 17cm.
    Translation of Gerusalemme liberata.

NT   0048563   CSt IU

Tasso, Torquato, 1544–1595.
    Jérusalem délivrée; poëme traduit de l'italien,
nouv.éd., rev. et cor., enrichie de la vie du Tasse.
Paris, Bossange et Masson, 1810.

    2 v.

NT   0048564   MH PPCCH PPL PU

851.3
T21gFL
f

[Tasso, Torquato,] 1544–1595.
    Jérusalem délivrée; poëme traduit de l'italien.
Nouv. ed., précédée de la vie du Tasse.   Paris,
Imprimerie de Bossange et Masson, 1811.
    2 p.l.,xlix,[1] p.,1 l.,176 p.   engr. front.,
engr.plates.   44ᶜᵐ.
    Prose translation by Lebrun first published
1774.
    "Notice sur la vie et le caractère du Tasse
[par Suard]" p.iii-xi.   "Appendice [bibliographique]" p.[xlii]–xlvi.   "Jugement sur l'Arioste et
le Tasse, traduit d'   une lettre de Pietro
Metastasio, à Don   Domenico Diodati":p.[xlviii]–
l.
    Plates by C.N.Cochin.

NT   0048565   CSt

[Tasso, Torquato,] 1544–1595.
    Jérusalem délivrée, poëme tr. de l'italien; nouv. éd.,
rev. et cor., enrichie de la vie du Tasse ...   Paris, Bossange et Masson, 1814.
    2 v. fronts. (v. 1, port.) plates. 21ᶜᵐ.
    Prose translation by Lebrun, first published 1774.
    "Notice sur la vie et le caractère du Tasse [par Suard]": v. 1, p. [iii]–lxxiij. "Appendice [bibliographique]": p. [lxxiv]–lxxxiij. "Jugement sur l'Arioste et le Tasse, traduit d'une lettre de Pietro Metastasio, à Don Domenico Diodati": p. [lxxxiv]–xc.
    I. Lebrun, Charles François, 1739–1824, tr.   II. Suard, Jean Baptiste
Antoine, 1734–1817. III. Lebarbier, Jean Jacques François, 1738–1826, illus.
IV. Title.
                  18–16960

    Library of Congress   PQ4642.F21L4   1814

NT   0048566   DLC NcD KU PBL

[TASSO, Torquato] 1544–
    Jérusalem delivreé ; poëme traduit de
l'italien [by C.F. Le Brun]. Nouvelle ed.
revue et corrigée , enrichie de la vie de
Tass. [By M. Suard]. Paris, Bossange et
Masson,1818.

    2 vol. Plates.

NT   0048567   MH PU

Tasso, Torquato, 1544–1595.
    La Jérusalem délivrée. En vers français, par P. L. M.
Baour-Lormian ...   Paris, Delaunay, 1819.
    3 v. fronts. (v. 1 : port.) pl.   21ᶜᵐ.
    "Notice sur la vie et les ouvrages de Torquato Tasso," signed J. A.
Buchon: v. 1, p. [i]–clxxxviii.

    I. Baour-Lormian, Pierre Marie François Louis, 1770–1854, tr.
    II. Buchon, Jean Alexandre, 1791–1846. III. Title.
                  2–14055 Revised

    Library of Congress   PQ4642.F21B3

NT   0048568   DLC TxU PPL PU

851.46
T21gF
B2

[Tasso, Torquato] 1544–1595.
    La Jérusalem délivrée, tr. en vers français
par Pl. M. Baour-Lormian ... 2. éd ... Paris,
A. Tardieu, 1821.
    2v. fronts. plates. 23cm.

    I. Baour-Lormian, Pierre Marie François
Louis, 1770–1854, tr. II. Title.

NT   0048569   TNJ

[Tasso, Torquato] 1544–1595.
    La Jérusalem délivrée, tr. en vers français par Pl. M.
Baour-Lormian ...   3. éd. ...   Paris, A. Tardieu, 1822.
    3 v. fronts. (v. 1, port.) plates. 15½ᶜᵐ.
    Engr. title-pages, with vignettes.

    I. Baour-Lormian, Pierre Marie François Louis, 1770–1854, tr.   II. Title.
                  17–9062

    Library of Congress   PQ4642.F21B3   1822

NT   0048570   DLC

Tasso, Torquato, 1544–1595.
    La Jérusalem délivrée, poëme tr. de l'italien par Lebrun ...   Londres, Dulau et co., 1824.
    2 v. 18ᶜᵐ.
    Text and translation on opposite pages.
    "Epitome della vita di Torquato Tasso, scritta da Stefano Egidio Petronj": v. 1, p. [vi]–xx.

    I. Lebrun, Charles François, 1739–1824, tr.   II. Petronj, Stefano Egidio,
1770–1837. III. Title.
                  17–7410

    Library of Congress   PQ4642.F21L4

NT   0048571   DLC CtY PHi LU

Tasso, Torquato, 1544–1595.
    Jérusalem délivrée, traduction nouvelle par C. J.
Panckoucke ... 2. éd. ... Paris, C. L. F. Panckoucke,
1824.
    4 v. 12 x 7½ᶜᵐ.
    Half-title: Œuvres du Tasse.
    Text and translation on opposite pages.
    "Fait partie d'une collection intitulée : Traduction de chefs-d'œuvre des
classiques. Le libraire éditeur a fait disparaître des titres de cette réimpression le nom du collaborateur de Panckoucke (Framery) dans cette traduction."—Quérard, La France littéraire, v. 9, p. 351.
    "Notice sur la vie et le caractère du Tasse" [par Suard]: v. 1, p. [viii]–lxxii.
    I. Panckoucke, Charles Joseph, 1736–1798, tr.   II. Panckoucke, Charles
Louis Fleury, 1780–1844, ed. III. Framery, Nicolas Étienne, 1745–1810,
joint tr. IV. Suard, Jean   Baptiste Antoine, 1734–1817. v. Title.
                  17–7415

    Library of Congress   PQ4642.F21P3

NT   0048572   DLC

Tasso, Torquato, 1544-1595
Jérusalem délivrée, Paris, Le Normant, 1832.
4 v.

NT 0048573   OU

854
T185gF3   Tasso, Torquato, 1544-1595.
Jérusalem délivrée; poème traduit de
l'italien. Nouv. éd., rev., cor., et enrichie
d'une notice sur la vie et les ouvrages du
Tasse; ornée de jolies vignettes gravées en
taille-douce sur acier, d'après les dessins de
m.C. Rogier. Paris, Camuzeaux, 1835.
xx,462p. illus.,port. 21cm.

NT 0048574   OrU

854
T185gFle   Tasso, Torquato, 1544-1595.
Jérusalem delivrée, poème traduit de
l'italien par le Prince Lebrun, avec une
notice sur le Tasse traduite de l'italien de
Davide Bertolotti, par M. Laass d'Aguen.
Paris, Chez Corbet Aîné, 1836.
xii,369p. illus. 19cm.

NT 0048575   OrU

PQ4642
F21L4
1836   Tasso, Torquato, 1544-1595.
Jérusalem délivrée, poème du Tasse traduit en françois par le
prince Le Brun. Paris, Lefèvre, 1836.
lii, 475 p. port.

I. Lebrun, Charles François, 1739-1824, tr. II. Title.

NT 0048576   CU CtY MH MeB PPiU

[Tasso, Torquato] 1544-1595.
La Jérusalem délivrée, traduction nouvelle et en prose,
par M. V. Philipon de la Madelaine, augm. d'une description de Jérusalem, par M. de Lamartine … Ed. illustrée
par MM. Baron et C. Nanteuil. Paris, J. Mallet et cⁱᵉ,
1841.
4 p. l., xx, 525 p., 1 l. front. (port.) illus, 20 pl. 25ᶜᵐ.
Title vignette.

I. Philipon de la Madelaine, V., tr. II. Lamartine, Alphonse Marie Louis
de, 1790-1869. III. Title.
17-7409

Library of Congress   PQ4642.F21P5

NT 0048577   DLC CtY GU TNJ LU NN PU CU

Tasso, Torquato, 1544-1595.
Jérusalem délivrée … Traduit en français par le prince Le Brun.
Illustré de … Célestin Nanteuil. Édition épurée.
= Paris, Lehuby. 1848. lx, 406 pp. Illus. Plates. [Bibliothèque
littéraire de la jeunesse.]

M3089 — S.r. — Le Brun, Charles François, Duc de Plaisance, 1739-1824. —
Nanteuil, Celestin, illus.

NT 0048578   MB PP

Tasso, Torquato, 1544-1595.
La Jérusalem délivrée. Traduit en français par
le prince Le Brun. Nouv. éd., précédée d'une
notice sur la vie et les ouvrages du Tasse, par
Suard. Paris, Didier, 1852.
lvi, 392 p. plates, port. 18 cm.
I. Lebrun, Charles François, duc de Plaisance,
1739-1824, tr. II. Suard, Jean Baptiste Antoine,
1734-1817.

NT 0048579   OCU

---

ar Y
107   Tasso, Torquato, 1544-1594.
La Jérusalem délivrée, traduite de
l'italien par le prince Lebrun. La vie du
Tasse, par A.d'Albanes. Ed. illustrée par
Baron, Celestin Nanteuil, etc. Paris,
Marescq, 1856.
72 p. illus. 30cm.

Cover title.
No. 2 in volume lettered: Romans du
jour illustres.

NT 0048580   NIC

Tasso, Torquato, 1544-
Jérusalem délivrée, traduction
française par le prince Lebrun, précédée
d'une notice sur la vie et le caractere
du Tasse par Suard. Par. Didot, 1864.

369 p.

NT 0048581   PU MBrZ

Tasso, Torquato, 1544-1595.
La Jerusalem délivrée, traduction nouvelle et
en prose par m. V. Philipon de la Madelaine,
précédée d'une introduction par m. Jules Janin,
Illustrations de mm. Baron et C. Nanteuil. Paris,
Morizot, 1864.
361 p. front. (port.) illus., plates. 25 cm.

NT 0048582   PV MH

PQ4642 Tasso, Torquato, 1544-1595.
.F21L4   … La Jérusalem délivrée, traduction du prince Lebrun.
Paris, Librairie de la Bibliothèque nationale, 1877.
2 v. in 1. 13½ᶜᵐ. (Bibliothèque nationale. Collection des meilleurs auteurs
anciens et modernes)
At head of title: Le Tasse.

NT 0048583   ICU MH

Tasso, Torquato, 1544-1595.
… La Jérusalem délivrée; vingt-quatre planches hors
texte en couleurs de O.-D.-V. Guillonnet. Paris, H. Laurens [1921]
xii, 52 p. xxiv col. pl. 27½ᶜᵐ. (Les grandes œuvres; pages célèbres
illustrées)
At head of title: Le Tasse.
Selections from La Gerusalemme liberata, translated into French by
Teodor de Wyzewa; introduction by Henri Focillon.

I. Wyzewa, Teodor de, 1862-1917, ed. and tr. II. Focillon, Henri,
1881-   III. Guillonnet, O. D. V., illus. IV. Title.
22-6339
Library of Congress   PQ4642.F21W8

NT 0048584   DLC

854
T185gFî   Tasso, Torquato, 1544-1595.
Le Jérusalem délivrée. Traduction française.
Notices et notes par P. Ladouê. Paris, A.
Hatier [1949]
95p. 18cm. (Les classiques pour tous)

I. Ladouê, Pierre, 1881-   ed. II. Series

NT 0048585   OrU

Tasso, Torquato, 1544-
[Baour-Lormian, Pierre Marie François Louis] 1770-1854.
Jérusalem délivrée, opéra en cinq actes, représenté pour la
première fois, sur le théâtre de l'Académie impériale de musique, le 8 septembre 1812 … Paris, Roullet, 1812.

853T185 Tasso, Torquato, 1544-1595.
Og.Lp   … Jerusalem liberata, in sermonem
latinum translata, atque epico carmine
modulata a … D. Mario Parente …
v.1.   Neapoli, 1824.
v.1, 1 por.

NT 0048587   IU

TASSO, Torquato, 1544-1595.
La Jerusalem libertada. Trasladada al
castellano de la traduccion francesa hecha
en prosa en 1774, corregida despues por
Antonio Izquierdo de Wasteren. 2 tom.
Madrid, impr. D.T. Jordan,1832.

Port., and plates.

NT 0048588   MH

TASSO, Torquato, 1544-
La Jerusalem libertada. Puesta en verso
castellano por el teniente general de la
Pezuela. Madrid. Aguado, impreso, 1855.

f°. 20 plates.
The title-page is engraved.
2 tom.

NT 0048589   MH CU

Tasso, Torquato, 1544-1595.
A Jerusalem libertada, de Torquato Tasso, vertida em oitava-
rima portugueza por José Ramos Coelho. Lisboa, Typographia universal, 1864.
5 p. l., 597 p., 1 l. 23ᶜᵐ.

I. Ramos Coelho, José, 1832-1914, tr. II. Title.
34-28719
Library of Congress   PQ4642.P21R3   851.46

NT 0048590   DLC MB OrU

Tasso, Torquato, 1544-1595.
La Jerusalem libertada trad. do original italiano
em verso endecasyllabo, estancia por estancia por
estancia por J. F. Pereira … Lisboa, Typ.
commercial 1877.
496 p.

NT 0048591   PU

Tasso, Torquato, 1544-
(La) Jerusalem libertada.   Barcelona, 1884.

555 p.

NT 0048592   PSC

853T185 Tasso, Torcuato, 1544-1595.
OgSPg   La Jerusalem libertada. Traducción en verso
castellano por Francisco Gomez del Palacio.
México, Ofic. Tip. de la Secretaría de Fomento,
1886.
575p. 23cm.
Imperfect copy: p.571-572 wanting.
Translation of Gerusalemme liberata.

I. Gómez del Palacio, Francisco, tr.
II. Title.

NT 0048593   IU TxHU

851   Tasso, Torcuato, 1544-1595.
T215g3   La Jerusalem libertada. Traducción en
E   verso castellano por Francisco Gómez del
Palacio precedida de un estudio biográfico
y crítico de Tasso y su poema por Emilia
Pardo Bazán. Madrid, Librería de la Viuda
de Haernado y Ca., 1893.
2 v.   (Biblioteca clásica, t. 168)

Translation of Gerusalemme liberata.

NT 0048594 PrU

Tasso, Torquato, 1544-
Jerusalem libertada; poema de T. Tasso, vertido estancia por
estancia do original italiano. ¡By J. Ramos-Coelho.¿ Terceira
edição revista e melhorada. (In: J. Ramos-Coelho, Obras
poeticas. Lisboa, 1910 . 8°. p. 443-766.)

1. Poetry (Italian). 2. Ramos-   Coelho, José. 3. Title.
N. Y. P. L.   May 27, 1913.

NT 0048595 NN MB

PQ   Tasso, Torquato, 1544-1595.
4642   La Jerusalen libertada, poema heroico;
.S22   escrito en italiano. Trad. en octavas
S4   castellanas por Juan Sedeño. Barcelona,
Impr. Gorchs, 1829.
2 v. in 1.   16 cm.

I. Sedeño, Juan, 16 th cent. tr.

NT 0048596 WU

851.46   Tasso, Torquato, 1544-1595.
OgNs   Jerusalen libertada, poema en 20
1841   cantos. Traducido por D. T. Caamaño
y D. A. Ribot. Valencia, Imprenta de
Cabrerizo, 1841.
2v. illus. 21cm.

NT 0048597 KU

TASSO, Torquato, 1544-
La Jerusalén libertada. Puesta en verso
castellano por Juan de la Pezuela, conde
de Cheste. Barcelona, tipolitografia
de L. Tasso, [1855].

2 tom. in 1.

NT 0048598 MH

PQ4642 Tasso, Torquato, 1544-1595
.S21   La Jerusalén libertada, de Torcuato Tasso;
P49   puesta en verso castellano por el Juan de la
Pezuela. Barcelona, Imp. de L. Tasso,
1915?-
v. 18cm.

Translation of the Italian Gerusalemme
liberata.

I. Pezuela, Juan de la   II. Title.

NT 0048599 PSt

PQ 4642 Tasso, Torquato, 1544-1595.
S21 R8   Jerusalén libertada ¿por¿ Tasso. Ed. ilustrada
1932   ejecutades en 1745 por Juan Bautista Piazzetta.
¿Trad. de J. Rubio. 1. ed.¿ Barcelona, Ediciones Populares Iberia ¿1932¿
142 p. illus. 27 cm. (Las Grandes obras
maestras de la literatura universal)

I. Piazzetta, Giovanni Battista, 1682 or 3-
1754, ed. II. Title.

NT 0048600 OU

Tasso, Torquato, 1544-1595.
Judas desesperado: breve poema, de Torqvato
Tasso, traducido de toscano al castellano por Don
Juan Antonio de Vera y Figueroa, Conde de la Roca.
Segunda Impression. Con Licencia, En Madrid,
Año de 1730.
A costa de D. Pedro Joseph Alonso y Padilla,
Librero de Camara de su Magestad: Se hallará en su
Imprenta, y Librería, Calle de Santo Thomas, junto
al Contraste.
List of translator's works, License, Errata,
Tasa, Dedication, p 54, Printer's notes, 8°.,
vellum.

NT 0048601 NNH

Tasso, Torquato, 1544-1595.
The lamentations of Amyntas ...
see under [Watson, Thomas] 1557-1592?

[Watson, Thomas] 1557?-1592?
The Lamentations of Amintas for the death of
Phillis. Paraphrasticallie translated out of Latine
into English Hexameters, by Abraham Fraunce.
Newly Corrected. London, Printed by Robert
Robinson, for Thomas Newman and Thomas Gubbin.
... 1589.
sm. 4 to.
Bound (4) with: Fenton, Sir Geoffrey. Monophylo..
1572.

NT 0048603 CSmH

[Tasso, Torquato] 1544-1595.
Lamynte pastoralle, tradvction novvelle.
A Paris, Chez Tovssainct Qvinet, 1639.
PH 3735   7 p.l., 110 p.   23½cm. [With [Chapoton,
.C78 D4   de] La descente d'Orphee avx enfers.
1640 C   Paris, 1640]
Title vignette, engr.
Many errors in paging.
Imperfect: t.-p. mutilated, most leaves
stained.
Translated by Toussaint Quinet.

NT 0048604 MdBJ

Tasso, Torquato, 1544-1595.
Hd16.20   Later work of Torquato Tasso rendered into
English verse; also a short essay: Affinities
Tassian and Miltonic; by Henry Cloriston.
[London]Postal literary alliance,1907.
47p. front.(port.) 20½cm. ([Postal literary
alliance] Poems in prose and verse. Series A,
no.1)

NT 0048605 CtY NIC

PQ4640   Tasso, Torquato. Lettere.
.S4
1588   Tasso, Torquato, 1544-1595.
Rare Bk   Il secretario, et il primo volvme, delle Lettere familiari,
Coll   ¿el sig. Torquato Tasso. Nouamente ristampate. Venetia,
G. Vincenzi, 1588-90.

---

x B   Tasso, Torquato, 1544-1595.
T214tl ℓe Lettere del signor Torqvato Tasso non piv'
stampate ... In Bologna, Presso Bartolomeo
Cochi, 1616.
8 p.l., 480p. 21cm.

Device of printer on t.-p.; head and tail-
pieces; initials.
Italic type.
Dedication signed: Giulio Segni.

I. Segni, Giulio, fl.1584-1616.

NT 0048607 IU PU PP MdBP NjP MH ICU CSt

Tasso, Torquato, 1544-1595.
Lettere di Torquato Tasso a Luca Scalabrino, ora per
la prima volta pub. da Bartolommeo Gamba. Venezia,
Tip. di Alvisopoli, 1833.
62 p., 1 l. 20½ᵐ.
Half-title: In occasione delle nozze favstissime della nobil donzella
Bernardina Nievo di Vicenza col chiarissimo vomo dottore Carlo Mal-
mvsi di Modena.
"Alcune altre ¿lettere¿ che si leggono nel ms. della Marciana": p. 62.

1. Nozze, Per. Nievo-Malmusi.   ɪ. Gamba, Bartolommeo, 1776-
1841, ed.
    17-7402
Library of Congress   PQ4647.A5S4 1833

NT 0048608 DLC PU

Tasso, Torquato, 1544-1595.
Le lettere di Torquato Tasso, disposte per ordine di tempo ed
illustrate da Cesare Guasti ... Firenze, F. Le Monnier, 1852-
55.
5 v. front. (port.) 18ᵐ.
"Notizie bibliografiche intorno all' edizioni delle Lettere": v. 1, p. ¿xxi¿-
xxxiv.
"Notizie storiche e bibliografiche intorno alle lettere" at end of each
volume.

ɪ. Guasti, Césare, 1822-1889, ed.

    It-44 Revised
Library of Congress   PQ4647.A3 1852

    IaU NjP MH TxU
NT 0048609 DLC OrU PPL PU CU OCU MiU NcD CU-S MdBP

PQ   Tasso, Torquato, 1544-1595.
4647   Lettere; disposte per ordine di tempo
A3   ed illustrate da C. Guasti. Firenze, F.
1853   Le Monnier, 1853-55.
5 v. in 2. 18cm.

I. Guasti, Césare, 1822-1889, ed.

NT 0048610 NIC

Tasso, Torquato, 1544-1595.
Le lettere di Torquato Tasso; disposte per ordine di
tempo ed illustrate da Cesare Guasti. 1. ed. napolitana
diligentemente cor. ... Napoli, G. Rondinella, 1857.
5 v. front (port.) 19½ᵐ.
"Notizie bibliografiche intorno all' edizioni delle lettere di Torquato
Tasso": v. 1, p. ¿xxiii¿-xxxvi.
"Notizie storiche e bibliografiche intorno alle lettere": at end of each
volume.

ɪ. Guasti, Césare, 1822-1889, ed.

    18-310
Library of Congress   PQ4647.A3 1857

NT 0048611 DLC

TASSO, Torquato, 1544-
Lettere; scelte e commentate dal prof.
Achille Mazzoleni. Con prefazione, bibliografia, ed indice delle materie. Bergamo,
tip. corti e Ronzoni, 1895.

Port.

NT 0048612 MH RP PU

Tasso, Torquato. Lettere.

Solerti, Angelo, 1865-1907.
Vita di Torquato Tasso ... Torino, Roma, E. Loescher,
1895.

Tasso, Torquato, 1544-1595.
... Lettere autobiografiche, a cura di Alessandro
Tortoreto. Milano, C. Signorelli [1929]
104 p. 15 cm. (On cover: Biblioteca di
letteratura)
"Nota bibliografica": p. [13]

NT 0048614 CU

Tasso, Torquato, 1544-1595.
... Lettere autobiografiche.
Milano, Signorelli [1934]
104p. 16cm. (On cover: Biblioteca di letteratur [81-82])

NT 0048615   PPT

Tasso, Torquato, 1544-
Lettere di grave argomento ed
altre prose... scelta per cura di G.
Ignazio Montanari.   Parma, Fiaccadori,
1847.
2v.

NT 0048616   PU

---

*PQ4647
.A3   Tasso, Torquato, 1544-1595.
1822   Lettere ed altre prose, raccolte da
Pietro Mazzucchelli. Milano, G. Pogli-
ani, 1822.
vii, 247 p. port. vignette. 28cm.
Printed on gray paper.
Bibliographical footnotes.

I. Mazzucchelli, Pietro, ed., 1762-
1829.

NT 0048617   MB MH

Tasso, Torquato, 1544-1595.
Lettere familiare. vol.1,2. Venetia, 1607.
8°

NT 0048618   MeB

TASSO, Torquato, 1544-
Lettere familiari, non più stampate.
Con un dialogo dell'imprese, del quale
in esse lettere si fa mention; [Edited by
Antonio Costantini]. Praga, T.Leopoldi, 1617.

4°.

NT 0048619   MH

Tasso, Torquato, 1544-1595.
Lettere familiari di Torquato Tasso; con annotazioni
istoriche e critiche di Cristiano Giuseppe Jagemann ...
Lipsia, A. Schumann, 1803.
xvi, 295, [1] p. 22cm.
"Tavola cronologica delle principali vicende della vita di Torquato
Tasso": p. ix-xiv.
"Aggiunta di rime, relative alle lettere familiari": p. 267-295.

I. Jagemann, Christian Joseph, 1735-1804, ed.
17-7401

Library of Congress   PQ4647.A4 1803

NT 0048620   DLC

PQ4647   TASSO,TORQUATO,1544-1595.
.A4   Lettere inedite di Torquato Tasso, poste insieme
1827   dall'abate Pier' Antonio Serassi. Pisa,N.Capurro,
1827.
[2] ,vii,274,[1]p. fold.facsim. 21½cm. [Opere
...illustrate dal prof.Gio.Rosini. v.17]

NT 0048621   ICU PU

Tasso, Torquato, 1544-1595.
Wiffen, Jeremiah Holmes, 1792-1836.
Life of Torquato Tasso. By J. H. Wiffen, with an appendix
on the "Jerusalem delivered", by m. Simonde de Sismondi.
New York, Delisser & Procter, 1859.

Tasso, Torquato, 1544-1595.
A literal prose translation of five select pieces
from the works of Tasso
see under   Capuzzi, E., tr.

Tasso, Torquatto, 1544-1595.
Manoscritti, cimeli e ricordi di Torquato...
see under   Biagi, Guido, 1855-1925.

Tasso, Torquato, 1544-1595.
Manoscritti inediti di Torquato Tasso, ed altri
pregevoli documenti per servire alla biografia
del medesimo, posseduti ed illustrati dal Conte
Mariano Alberti, e pubblicati con incisioni e
fac-simili per cura di Romualdo Gentilucci e c.
Lucca, Giusti, 1837.
70p. illus.

NT 0048625   ICRL PPL PU

PQ4640   Tasso, Torquato, 1544-1595.
.M3   Il Manso, o vero Dell'amicitia, dialogo ...
1596   Napoli, G. I. Carlino & A. Pace, 1596.
Rare   [8], 35, [1] p. 21cm.
Bk   Printer's device on t. p. and at end; date
at end: 1595.

NT 0048626   ICU

TASSO, Torquato, 1544-
Il Manso, overo Dell'amicitia dialogo.
Ferrara, appresso V. Baldini,1602.

pp.(8). 86. Vign. of Tasso.

NT 0048627   MH

Tasso, Torquato, 1544-1595.
Guizot, François Pierre Guillaume, 1787-1874.
Méditations et études morales; conseils d'un père sur l'éducation, suivis de Idées de Rabelais, de Montaigne et du Tasse en
fait d'éducation, par Guizot ... Paris, Didier et c[ie], 1883.

Tasso, Torquato, 1544-1595.
Il messaggiero, dialogo del Signor Torqvato Tasso ...
Venetia, B. Giunti, e fratelli, 1582.
2 p. l., 36 numb. l. 20cm.
Title vignette.
2-14004

ICU
NT 0048629   DLC NcD CSt NN IaU NjP CtY PU ICN MWelC

Tasso, Torquato, 1544-1595.
... Minturno; oder, Von der schönheit. Berlin, A. Juncker
[1923]
3 p. l., 9-63, [1] p., 2 l. 33cm.
"Einleitung und Übersetzung von Karl Paul Hasse."
"Dieses werk wurde im herbst 1923 in einer einmaligen auflage von
200 numerierten exemplaren herausgegeben ... Nummer 161."
Half-title: Dialog.

1. Esthetics.   I. Hasse, Karl Paul, tr.   II. Title.
34-20454

Library of Congress   PQ4640.M8G4   [701]   851.46

NT 0048630   DLC

Tasso, Torquato, 1544-1595.
[Glassford, James] d. 1845.
Miscellanea. [By] J. G. [Edinburgh, Priv. print. by
Walker and Greig] 1818.

Tasso, Torquato, 1544-1595.
Il mondo creato. Pisa, Niccolò Capurro, 1823.
296 p. 22 cm.

NT 0048632   CaBVaU CU

TASSO, Torquato, 1544-
Il mondo creato. Firenze. 1825-26.
2 vol. 24°.

NT 0048633   MH PU

PQ4639
.M2   Tasso, Torquato, 1544-1595.
Il mondo creato. Ed. critica con introd. e note di Giorgio
Petrocchi. Firenze, F. Le Monnier, 1951.
L, 338 p. diagrs. 25 cm.

I. Petrocchi, Giorgio, 1921-   ed.
A 52-6733
Brown Univ. Library   PQ4639.M2 1951
for Library of Congress   [3]

OU OCU IaU   MB CU-S TxU NNCU-G OrU NNU ViU MiU
NT 0048634   RPB IU NcD MH NNC CSt WaU ICU CU IEN

---

*IC5   Tasso, Torquato, 1544-1595.
T1853   Il Montoliveto del signor Torqvato Tasso
605ma   nuovamente posto in luce.
Con licenza de'superiori.M.DC.V.In Ferrara,
Per Vittorio Baldini,stampatore camerale.
4°. [32]p. 20.5cm.,in case 22cm.
Signatures: A⁴ (±A1),B-D⁴.
This issue is without the dialogue, "Il
miracoloso principio de la congregatione di S.
Maria di Montoliveto" by Michelangelo
Bonaverti; cancel t.-p. with ornamental border

has group of type ornaments below title in
place of dialogue statement; verso of t.-p. is
blank.
"Nel venerdi santo": p.[29-31].
"Sonetto fatto nel monistero di Montoliveto
maggiore": p.[32].
Left unfinished at the author's death.

NT 0048636   MH-H

Tasso, Torquato, 1544-1595.
Nächtliche Klagen der Liebe
see [Compagnoni, Giuseppe] 1754-1833.
Torquato Tasso's Naechtliche klagen der liebe.

Tasso, Torquato, 1544-1595, supposed author.
Noches de Torcuato Taso
see under   Compagnoni, Giuseppe, 1754-
1833.

TASSO, Torquato, 1544–
  Nuovo discorso nel quale si hà notitia di
molti accidenti della sua vita, e d'altri
curiosi particolari. Publicato hora dal
sig. Martino Sandelli. Padova, appresso G.B.
Martino, 1629.

  4°.pp.(96).

NT 0048639   MH

Spec. Coll.

1643 Tasso, Torquato, 1544–1595.
.T214   Nvovo discorso del Signor Torqvato **Tasso**
scritto gia dal medesimo all' illustrissimo
Signor Scipione Gonzaga... Publicato dal Sig.
D. Martino Sandelli Padouano...
  In Este, per il Cruiellari, Stamp. della
Mag. Communità 1643. Con lic. de' Sup.
  ₍86₎ p.   19 cm.

  Signatures: (–)², A–K⁴, L².

NT 0048640   DGU

Tasso, Torquato, 1544–1595.

Ramos Coelho, José, 1832–
  Obras poeticas de Ramos-Coelho ... contendo: as poesias originaes publicadas e ineditas; as versões de muitas
d'ellas pelos Snrs. Thomaz Cannizzaro, Prospero Pera-
gallo ... e Henrique Faure; as versões de varias poesias
de Ovidio, Horacio, Lamartine, Victor Hugo, Millevoye,
André Chénier, Lamartine, Byron, Torquato Tasso,
Dante, Miguel Angelo, Strozzi, Manzoni, Rubió y Ors, e
Sarran d'Alard, e a traducção do poema Jerusalem
libertada de Torquato Tasso. Lisboa, Typ. Castro
irmão, 1910.

Ms. ₍Tasso, Torquato₎ 1544–1595
T21o   Ode to the golden age ₍tr.₎ by
  Leigh Hunt. First published in The
Leigh Indicator March 15, 1820, and later
Hunt incorporated in Amyntas, published in
Coll. the same year.
  ₍3₎. ℓ.
  Typed t.-p.
  Ms. in Hunt's autograph. Each leaf inlaid.
Bound. A copy of The Indicator, no.XXIII,
March 15, 1820, containing printed copy of the
poem, is mounted at back.

NT 0048642   IaU

Tasso, Torquato, 1544–1595.
  Olinde et Sophronie, tiré du Tasse, traduction
du commencement du second chant de la Jérusalem
deliveree. (In Rousseau, J.J. Oeuvres complettes.
1793. v. 15.)

NT 0048643   RPB

Tasso, Torquato, 1544–1595.
  Olindo & Sophronia; Tancred & Clorinda, Rinaldo
& Armida, tr. into English prose.
  (In Hunt, Leigh. Works. 1859. v. 1)

NT 0048644   PU

Tasso, Torquato, 1544–1595.

Casa, Giovanni della, abp., 1503–1556.
  Opere di Monsig. Giovanni della Casa, con una copiosa
giunta di scritture non più stampate ... Firenze, Appresso G. Manni, per il Carlieri, 1707.

Tasso, Torquato. 1544–1595.
  Opere minori in versi e in prosa di Torquato
Tasso, scelte e commentate da Rosolino Guastalla.
Livorno, 1915.

NT 0048646   MdBJ OClW

Tasso, Torquato, 1544–1595.
  ₍Original document, supposedly in the handwriting and with the signature of Torquate Tasso,
dated July 14th, 1582₎
  1 l. 27ᶜᵐ. in 34½ᶜᵐ.

  Portrait of Tasso, typewritten transcription and
English translation of the document also in the
volume. Also letter on stationery of the British
museum attesting the authenticity of the document.
The document certifies the receipt of certain
money by Tasso.

NT 0048647   NNC

Tasso, Torquato, 1544–1595.

Lathom, Francis, 1777–1832.
  Orlando and Seraphina; or, The funeral pile. An heroic
drama, in three acts. By Francis Lathom. As performed at
the Theatre-Royal, Norwich. London, Printed for the author,
and sold by Longman and Rees ₍1800?₎

WID-LC
PQ   Tasso, Torquato, 1544–1595.
4644   Torquata Tassa Osvobozený Jerusalem / formou
.B23 originálu přel. Jaroslav Vrchlický ; ₍úvod, dosl
F74x Jaroslav Vrchlický₎. -- V Praze : Nákl. Aloisa
  R. Lauermana, 1887.
  726, xvi p. ; 19 cm.
  Errata slip inserted.
  Includes bibliographical references.

  I. Frída, Emil Bohuslav, 1853–1912, tr.

NT 0048649   MH

PQ   Tasso, Torquato, 1544–1595.
4644   Osvobozený Jerusalem. Nové laciné vyd.
B2F91 Formou originalu přeložil Jaroslav Vrchlický.
1890 [Poznámky sest. Fr. Pover] V Praze, Storch,
  1890.
  726 p.

  Translator's autograph presentation copy
to Xavier da Cunha.

  I. Frida, Emil Bohuslav, 1853–1912. II.
Title.

NT 0048650   CLU

Tasso, Torquato, 1544–1595.
  Освобожденный Ιерусалимъ. Перевелъ съ итальян-
скаго подлинника А. Ш. Санктпетербургъ, Тип. Н. Греча,
1818–19.
  2 v. in 1. 27 cm.

  I. Shishkov, Aleksandr Semenovich, 1754–1841, tr. II. Title.
  Title transliterated: Osvobozhdennyi Ierusalim.

PQ4644.R2S4   52–48825

NT 0048651   DLC

Case
Y   TASSO, TORQUATO, 1544–1595.
712   Il padre di famiglia; dialogo...nel quale breue-
.T 237 mente trattando la vera economia, s'insegna, non
  meno con facilità, che dottamente, il gouerno non
  pur della casa, tanto di città, quanto di contado;
  ma ancora il vero modo di accrescere, & conseruar
  le ricchezze. Con la tauola delle cose notabili.
  Vinetia, Presso Aldo, 1583.
  84, ₍12₎p. 13½ cm.
  Printer's device on t.-p.
  Dedication signed: Lelio Gauardo.
  Listed in Re— nouard as no.3 in pt.2
of "Delle rime del signor T.Tasso". Probably
extracted from that work.

NT 0048652   ICN PU

TASSO, Torquato, 1544–1595.
  Le palais d'Armide (Il palazzo di Armida)
Traduction en vers français du seizieme
chant de la Jérusalem delivrée, par
Leopold Pelzer. Liège, impr. H.Vaillant-
Carmanne, 1883.

  pp.36.

NT 0048653   MH

      Tasso, Torquato, 1544–1595.
      Parere del Signor Torqvato Tasso. Sopra
    il Discorso del Signor Horatio Lombardello
    intorno a'contrasti, &c. ... Mantoua, Per
    Francesco Osanna, 1586.
PG 1656   33 p. 13½ cm. [With Tasso, Torquato.
.A 1 Apologia ... In difesa della sva Giervsalemme
1585a R liberata. Mantoua, 1585]

      Title vignette (printer's mark)

NT 0048654   MdBJ

Tasso, Torquato, 1544–1595.
  ... Il Pensiero Filosofico
    see under   Bianchini, Giuseppe, 1871–1903.

Tasso, Torquato, 1544–1595.
  Per terzo centennale della morte di Torquato
Tasso
    see under title

FILM
FP   Tasso, Torquato, 1544–1595.
1085   Plvtonis concilium. Ex initio qvarti libri
  Solymeidos. Londini, Apud I.Wolfium, 1584.
  Latin version, by Scipione Gentili, from the
fourth book of Gerusalemme liberata.
  Short-title catalogue no.23702 (carton 1085)
  Microfilm.

    I. Gentili, Scipione, 1563–1616, tr. II. Title.

NT 0048657   MiU NNC

Tasso, Torquato, 1544–1595.
  Poemi minori di Torquato Tasso. Ed. critica a cura di
Angelo Solerti, con studi di G. Mazzoni e C. Cipolla ...
Bologna, Ditta N. Zanichelli, 1891.
  2 v. 20ᶜᵐ. (*On cover:* ... Opere minori in versi ... Ed. critica a cura
di Angelo Solerti. ₍vol. I–III₎)
  At head of cover-title: Biblioteca di scrittori italiana. ₍xv₎

  I. Solerti, Angelo, 1865–1907, ed. II. Mazzoni, Guido, 1859– III. Cipolla, Carlo, conte, 1854–

                               14–21713

  Library of Congress   PQ4636.A9 1891

MdBP
NT 0048658   DLC MH NIC PU CU MiU OClW OCU NjP NcD

Tasso, Torquato, 1544–1595.
  ... Poesie, a cura di Francesco Flora. Con 10 illustrazioni.
Milano-Roma, Rizzoli & c. ₍1934₎
  997 p., 1 l., ₍3₎ p. incl. front. (port.) facsims. 19½ᶜᵐ. (*Half-title:* I
classici Rizzoli, diretti da Ugo Ojetti)

  I. Flora, Francesco, 1891– ed.

                               A C 35–1965

  Title from Illinois Univ.   Printed by L. C.

NT 0048659   IU CtY OU OC1JC CU FU

Tasso, Torquato, 1544–1595.
   Poesie; a cura di Francesco Flora. Milano, R. Ricciardi [1952]
   xlvi, 1027 p. 23 cm. (La Letteratura italiana; storia e testi, v. 21)
   Bibliography: p. [xlv]–xlvi.

   I. Flora, Francesco, 1891–   ed.   (Series)

   PQ4637.A1 1952   851.46   53–32535

MoSU
   PBm NN DCU CSt C WaU ICU MdU CaQMM FTaSU NBuU NSyU
   MtU OrU CaBVaU OrU MoU CU IU NNC MB MoSU CtY TU TxU
NT   0048660   DLC ViU FMU LU OU NcD RPB NIC MH WaSpG

PQ
4201
I4   **Tasso, Torquato,** 1544–1595.
v.21   Poesie; a cura di Francesco Flora. Milano, R. Ricciardi [1954]
   xlvi, 1027 p. 23 cm. (La Letteratura italiana; storia e testi, v. 21)
   Bibliography: p. [xlv]–xlvi.

NT   0048661   NBuC

PQ4636
A1
1955a   Tasso, Torquato, 1544–1595
   Poesie e prose, a cura di Siro Attilio Nulli. Milano, U. Hoepli [1955]
   lx, 658 p.

   "Nota biobibliografica": p.[lix]–lx.

   Contents. – Gerusalemme liberata. – Aminta. – Liriche varie. – Il padre di famiglia. – Lettere varie.

   I. Nulli, Siro Attilio, ed.

NT   0048662   CU OU CtY MH MB NB

Tasso, Torquato.

Gosse, Henry, *fl.* 1800–1820.
   Poetical translations. By Henry Gosse ... London, Printed by A. J. Valpy, 1822.

PQ4437
.T2
1829   TASSO,TORQUATO,1544–1595.
   Postille di Torquato Tasso sopra i primi XXIV canti della Divina commedia di Dante Alighieri ora per la prima volta date alle stampe con alcune annotazioni a maggiore intelligenza delle medesime. Bologna,R.Masi 1829.
   ix,[1],26,[1]p. 22cm.
   Dedication signed: Gaetano Majocchi.

   1.Dante Alighieri. Divina commedia. Inferno.

NT   0048664   ICU MH NIC PU

Tasso, Torquato, 1544–1595.
   Postille di Torquato Tasso alla Divina commedia di Dante Alighieri. Pisa, N. Capurro, 1831.
   v p., 1 l., 361, [3] p. 22cm. [Opere, v. 30]
   Edited by Luigi Maria Rizzi.
   "Intrighi d'amore; commedia": p. [203]–361.

   1. Dante Alighieri. Divina commedia. 2. Dante—Commentaries. I. Tasso Torquato, Intrichi d'amore. II. Rizzi, Luigi Maria, 1785–1857, ed.
        4–30450

   Library of Congress   PQ4437.T3 1831

NT   0048665   DLC RPB CU PU NjP NIC

Tasso, Torquato, 1544–1595.
   ... Postille alla Divina commedia; edite sull' autografo della R. Biblioteca Angelica da Enrico Celani, con prefazione di Tommaso Casini. Città di Castello, S. Lapi, 1895.
   97 p., 1 l. 19cm. (*Added t.-p.:* Collezione di opuscoli danteschi inediti o rari, diretta da G. L. Passerini. vol. XX)
   Autograph marginalia, covering Inf. I–XXIV, from Tasso's long lost copy of the 1536 Giolito ed. of the Commedia, recently rediscovered by Casini in the Biblioteca Angelica, Rome.

   In the Effemeridi letterarie di Roma, 1823, tomo XIII, p. 121–128, Filippo de Romanis printed inaccurate transcriptions of these notes, based on ms. copies in the Chigi and Barberini collections. In 1829 they were printed at Bologna, "per nozze Rusconi-Davia," edited by Gaetano Majocchi from the Chigi ms. They were also incorporated (with another series of notes) in "La divina commedia, postillata da T. Tasso," 3 v., Pisa, 1830, and in v. 30 of Tasso's "Opere," Pisa, 1831.
   "L'edizione giolitina della Divina commedia postillata da Torquato Tasso" (p. [7]–22) by T. Casini, reprinted from Giornale dantesco, 1895, anno III, p. 3–9.
   "Note all' edizione di Gaetano Maiocchi": p. [83]–97.   3–31399

NT   0048667   DLC MiU CU CLU NIC

Tasso, Torquato, 1544–
   Postille alla Divina commedia, edite sull' autografo della R. biblioteca angelica da Errico Celani, con prefazione di Tommaso Casini.   Città di Castello Lapi, 1896.

   95 p.   (Collezione di opuscoli danteschi inediti o rari. 1893–'98. v.20)

NT   0048668   PU

Tasso, Torquato, 1544–1595, defendant.
   Processo fatto in Bologna l'anno 1564 a Torquato Tasso
   see under   Gualandi, Michel Angelo, 1793–1865.

Tasso, Torquato, 1544–1595.
   Prof på öfversättningar från T. Tasso, som, méd philosophiska facultetens tillstånd, och under inseende af C. A. Hagberg ...komma att för philosophiska gradens erhållande offentligen försvaras af F. W. Sjöbohm [and others]...d. 18. Juni 1844. Lund: Berling, 1844.   6 parts.   12°.
   [Part] 1, by F. W. Sjöbohm; [part] 2, by G. E. Warholm; [part] 3, by F. T. Carlson; [part] 4, by J. Andersson; [part] 5, by M. W. Pihl; [part] 6, by S. K. Peterson.
   Dissertations, Lund.
   Italian and Swedish. Paging continuous. Separate title-page to each part.
   In: NNK p. v. 14, no. 5.

   1 Poetry (Italian). 2. Hagberg, Wilhelm. 4. Warholm, Gustaf Eddor. 6. Andersson, Johan. 7. Pihl, Salomon Knut. N.Y.P.L.   Carl August. 3. Sjöbohm, Folke vin. 5. Carlson, Fredrik Theo-Mårten Wilhelm. 8. Peterson,   August 22, 1913.

NT   0048670   NN

PQ4640
.A1
1612   Tasso, Torquoto, 1544–1595.
   Le prose del Signor Torqvoto Tasso, diuise in cinque parti. Nuouamente poste in luce separate dalle Rime, al reuerendiss. P.D. Angelo Grillo Abbate, e prefid. Generale. Con licenza de superiori et privilego. Venetia, Appresso Evangelista Deuchino, 1612.
   461 p. 15 cm.

   Title within decorative border.
   With this is bound his Il padre di famiglia...   Venetia, 1612.

NT   0048671   TU MH PU NcGU

Tasso, Torquato, 1544–1595.
   ... Prose, a cura di Francesco Flora. Con 6 illustrazioni. Milano–Roma, Rizzoli & c. [1935]
   1016 p. incl. front. plates, ports., facsims. 19½cm. (*Half-title:* I classici Rizzoli, diretti da Ugo Ojetti)

   I. Flora, Francesco, 1891–   ed.
                   A C 36–2427
   Title from Illinois Univ.   Printed by L. C.

NT   0048672   IU CU OU

PQ4640
.A1G8   **Tasso, Torquato,** 1544–1595.
   Le prose diverse di Torquato Tasso, nuovamente raccolte ed emendate da Cesare Guasti ... Firenze, Successori Le Monnier, 1875.
   2 v. 18mm.

00
NT   0048673   ICU NIC NNC MeB CU IaU PBm NjP MH NRU

Tasso, Torquato, 1544–1595.
   Prose filosofiche di Torquato Tasso ... Firenze, Per A. Parenti, 1847.
   2 v. 19mm. (*Half-title:* Antologia di insigni scrittori italiani)
   "Intorno a Torquato Tasso, frammenti di un discorso di Paolo Emiliani-Giudici": v. 1, p. [vii]–xxxvi.   3–22700

NT   0048674   DLC PU MB

852
8   Tasso, Torquato, 1544–1595.
   Prose scelte di Torquato Tasso. Milano, Dalla società tipografica de' classici italiani, 1825.
   574 p.   22 1/2 cm.   (Opere, v. 5)

NT   0048675   ViLxW

Tasso, Torquato, 1544–1595.
   Prose varie de Torquato Tasso.   Pisa, Capurro, 1824.
   254 p.   21.5 cm.

NT   0048676   PPT

PQ
4638
.Z5
F5   Tasso,Torquato,1544–1595.
   Qvatre chants de la Hiervsalem de Torqvato Tasso. Par Pierre de-Brach,sieur de La Motte Montussan ... Paris, A.L'Angelier, 1596.
   5 p.l.,96 numb.l.   16½cm.
   Title vignette.
   Imperfect? Portrait lacking? "In effigiem P.Drachi", stanza by Scévole de Sainte Marthe: 2d prelim.leaf. Manuscript note on fly-leaf: Edition originale ... manque le portrait."
   "Les chants sont ptépcsterez [;] en leur ordre,mais ... entiers en ce qu'ils traitent & l'vn ne depend de l'autre."--Av lecteur.

   CONTENTS.--Chant XVI.--Chant IIII.--Chant XII (Italian and French on opposite pages)--Chant II.
   Binding signed: Hardy.

   I.Brach,Pierre de,sieur de La Motte-Montussan,b. 1549,tr.

NT   0048678   MiU PU CSt

Tasso, Torquato, 1544–
   Raccolta di sentenze, massime concetti sublimi.

   (in Bizzarri, Anacleto, & Bocci, Ippolito, comp. Raccolta di sentenze... dei quattra classici italiani. 1873)

NT   0048679   PU

853T185
K1789   Tasso, Torquato, 1544–1595.
   Raccolta di varie poesie di Torquato Tasso ricavate da'suoi manoscritti inediti. [Roma] Si vendono da M. Nicoli, 1789.
   cc p. 17cm.

   Bibliographical note concerning this edition, in ms. on fly-leaf, signed: Giulio Bernardino Tomitano.

NT   0048680   IU PU

Tasso, Torquato, 1544–1595.
Il re Torrismondo, tragedia del Sig. Torqvato Tasso. Al sereniss.ᵐᵒ Sig.ᴿᵉ Don Vicenzo Gonzaga, dvca di Mantova, & di Monferrato, &c. In Vinegia, Per Girolamo Polo, 1587.
63 numb. l. 15¼ᶜᵐ.
Signatures: A–H⁸ (₁H₈₎ blank)
Title vignette (device of G. Polo? with motto: Vis vincitur arte); italic type: initials.
Dedicatory letter to Don Vicenzo Gonzaga dated: Di Bergamo il 1. di Settembre. M.D.LXXXVII.
Seventh in the order of the twelve editions of the same year, described by Angelo Solerti, in Teatro di Torquato Tasso, 1895, p. cxxix (the first being that of Bergamo, Comino Ventura, with dedication dated Sept. 1)
cf. also Solerti's Vita di   Torquato Tasso, 1895, v. 1, p. 555–556.
   I. Title.   II. Title: Torrismondo.
                              25–17230
   Library of Congress   PQ4639.T2   1578 g

     DFo MH-H ICN PU
NT   0048681   DLC IU ICU NIC FU MWiW-C MWelC CtY MH

1607
851
T214r   **Tasso, Torquato,** 1544–1595.
A923   Il Re Torrismondo, tragedia. Del S. Torquato Tasso. In Perugia, Nella Stampa Augusta, 1607.
117p.

     Signatures: A–E¹².
     Engraved vignette on title-page.
     Bound in vellum.
     First published Bergamo, 1587.

     I. Title.   II. Title: Torrismondo.   Date cd.

NT   0048682   FTaSU

TASSO, Torquato, 1544 –
Il re Torrismondo; tragedia.   Di nuovo revista & ricoretta.   Perugia, stampa Augusta, 1608.

NT   0048683   MH

Tasso, Torquato, 1544–1595.
Il re Torrismondo; tragedia del sig. Torqvato Tasso. Di nuouo in questa nostra vltima impressione con somma diligenza ricorretta. In Venetia, Appresso Gio: Antonio, & Gio: Maria Misserini fratelli, MDCXXXVII.
116 p.   17¼ x 9¼ᶜᵐ.
In verse.

     I. Title.   II. Title: Torrismondo.

                            31–16479
   Library of Congress   PQ4639.T2 1637   852.49

NT   0048684   DLC WU CU MH

Tasso, Torquato, 1544–1595.
Il re Torrismondo. Tragedia [in five acts and in verse.]
   (In: Teatro italiano. Verona, 1723. 16.°
Tomo 2. p. 9–144.)

NT   0048685   NN MB

Tasso, Torquato, 1544–1595.
Il re Torrismondo; tragedia.   (In Collezione de'classici italiani. 1802–14. v. 246, p. 5–137)

NT   0048686   CU

Tasso, Torquato, 1544 –
Il Re Torrismondo; tragedia. [In five acts and in verse]
(Teatro italiano antico. Milano, 1809. 12°. v. 7, p. 3–137.)

   I. Drama (Italian). 2. Title.
N. Y. P. L.   February 21, 1912.

NT   0048687   NN MB

PQ4639
T2   Tasso, Torquato, 1544–1595.
1821   Il re Torrismondo; tragedia.   Pisa, N. Capurro, 1821.
     159 p.

     I. Title.   II. Title: Torrismondo.

NT   0048688   CU

Tasso, Torquato, 1544–1595.
Il re Torrismondo; tragedia di Torquato Tasso. Milano, Casa editrico Sonzogno [1884]
   96 p.   18 cm.   (Biblioteca universale)

NT   0048689   CU

PQ
4639   Tasso, Torquato, 1544–1595.
.T6   [Il re Torrismondo. 1921]
1921   Torrismondo; tragedia.   Milano, Sonzogno [1921]
     96 p.   18 cm.   (Biblioteca universale, n. 102)

NT   0048690   DCU

Tasso, Torquato, 1544–95.
   Le renaud amoureux, imité de l'italien. Paris, Passot, 1724.
   513 p.   front.
   A French prose version of his Il rinaldo

NT   0048691   MH

Tasso, Torquato, 1544 –
   Rime, parte prima. Insieme con altri componimenti del medesimo. Vinegia, [Aldus, the younger], 1581.
     Printer's mark on title-page.
     Contents: — Rime, 1ª parte, pp. (8), 160. — Aminta, pp. (8), 74. — Conclusioni amorose, pp. (4), 9. — Il Romeo, pp. (3), 22. — Lettera nella quale paragona l'Italia alla Francia, pp. (2), 27. — All' eccellentiss. signor duca di Urbino. (3), 4. — Dialogo dell' amor, pp. (2), 17. — Tavola, pp. (21). All are signatured continuously.

NT   0048692   MH

Lilly
PQ 4637   TASSO, TORQUATO, 1544–1595
.A1   Rime ... di nvovo datte in lvce ...
1593   [Brescia] Appresso Pietro Maria Marchetti, 1593.
     7 p.l., 341, [1] p., [3] l., 194, [6] p. 8vo(15.2 cm.)

     Adams, H.M., Cambridge, T258; cf. T254.
     From Queen Elizabeth's library; with the rose and crown in gilt on both covers.
     Bound in vellum.

NT   0048693   InU

---

x853T185   Tasso, Torquato, 1544–1595.
K1608   Rime, diuise in sei parti.   Venetia, G. B. Pulciani, 1608.
     2v. in 1.   13cm.

     Title within architectural border; title vignette, v.2.
     Comtemporary vellum binding.

NT   0048694   IU WU

Y
712   TASSO, TORQUATO, 1544–1595.
.T 239   Rime del signor Torquato Tasso, diuise in sei parti.   Milano, Per G.B. Bidelli, 1619.
     2v. in 1.   13cm.

NT   0048695   ICN PU

Tasso, Torquato, 1544–1595.
   Rime del Signor Torquato Tasso. Divise in amorose, boscherezze, maritime, imenei, heroiche, morali, lugubri, sacre, e varie. Con gli argomenti ad ogni compositione. Fatica del Sig. Carlo Fiamma. Aggiuntoui la vita, & sentenze dell'autore scritta dall'illustriss. Sig. Gio. Battista Manso. ... Venetia, Appresso E. Deuchino, 1621.
   9 pt. in 1 v.   port.   13½ᶜᵐ.
     Each part separately paged; each, except the first and the eighth, has

     special t.-p. with vignette (port.): Delle rime del Signor Torquato Tasso parte 2 [–9] ... Venetia, Appresso E. Deuchino, 1620.
     Without the "vita, & sentenze dell'autore scritta dall'illustriss. Sig. Gio. Battista Manso" mentioned on t.-p.

     I. Fiamma, Carlo, fl. 1621, ed.

NT   0048697   MiU IU PU OrU PU CtY

Tasso, Torquato, 1544–1595.
   Rime di Torquato Tasso, di nuovo corrette ed illustrate ... Pisa, Presso N. Capurro, 1821–31.
   5 v.   port.   22ᶜᵐ.   (Added t.-p.: Opere ... III–VI, XXXII)
     Edited by G. Rosini.
     Vol. 5 has title: Rime inedite o disperse ...
     "Elogio di Torquato Tasso," by A. Fabroni: v. 5, p. 1–74.
     "Orazione in lode di Torquato Tasso, fatta nell'Accademia degli Alterati in Firenze da Lorenzo Giacomini Tebalducci Malespini": v. 5, p. [75]–115.

     I. Rosini, Giovanni, 1776–1855, ed.   II. Giacomini Tebalducci Malespini, Lorenzo, d. 1599.   III. Fabroni, Angelo, 1732–1803.

                         18–3616
   Library of Congress   PQ4637.A1   1821

NT   0048698   DLC CU OrU

853T185   Tasso, Torquato, 1544–1595.
KB63   Rime di Torquato Tasso con emendazioni di mano dello stesso autore la più parte inedite.   Milano, dalla Tipografia e libreria Pirotta, 1856.
     39, clxxxix p.   facsim.

     "Edizione di 100 esemplari."
     Published by Leopoldo Boldi.
     Text of 1582 and text with emendations in italics on opposite pages.

NT   0048699   IU

Tasso, Torquato, 1544–1595.
   Le rime di Torquato Tasso. Ed. critica su i manoscritti e le antiche stampe a cura di Angelo Solerti ...
   Bologna, Romagnoli-dall' Acqua, 1898–
   v.   23ᶜᵐ.   (Half-title: Collezione di opere inedite o rare ... IV.
77–

     I. Tasso, Torquato, 1544–1595—Bibl.

                         15–24346
   Library of Congress   PQ4204.A3C5

NT   0048700   DLC CtY MiU NcD OU OCU OCl MB

853T185   Tasso, Torquato, 1544–1595.
K1949   Rime.   Roma, Edizioni numerate per sé e per pochi di Colombo, 1949.
     v.   22cm.

     500 copies printed. Vol.1 and 3: "esemplare n.9"; v.2: "esemplare no.6."

NT   0048701   IU OrU

Tasso, Torquato, 1544-1595.
... Rime amorose (con prefazione)
Milano,Sonzogno[1909]
103p. 17cm. (Biblioteca universale,
n.389)
"Le 'Rime amorose'", signed C.E.A: p.
[3]-6.

NT 0048702   CtY

Tasso, Torquato, 1544-1595.
Rime divise in amorose, boscherezze, maritime
imenei ... 1620-21
see his Rime ... 1621.

Brancacci
Library
1975
380

Tasso, Torquato, 1544-1595.
Rime, et prose del S. Torqvato Tasso.
Parte prima. Di nouo reuiste, et corrette,
con aggiunta di quanto manca nell'altre
editioni. In Ferrara, Ad instanza di Giulio
Vassallini, 1583.
12 p.ɫ., 335, 118, [1] p. 13 cm.
Colophon: In Ferrara, appresso Vittorio
Baldini. 1582.
Signatures: +12A-O12A-g12
Imperfect: slightly damp-stained.

1. Ralegh, W.- Autograph. 2. Berard, L.-
Autograph. 3. Bruce, Charles, Earl of Elgin,
1682-1747 - Bookplate, 1712.

NT 0048705   CtY MWelC

Case
Y
712
.T 1683

TASSO, TORQUATO, 1544-1595.
Rime et prosa. Accresciute, & corrette..in
questa nova impressione.   Ferrara,G.Vasalini,
1587-90.
v.in   14cm.

The t.-p. of pt.5 reads: Gioie di rime et
prose. Quinta, e sesta parte. Some portions
have special title-pages. Pt.1-3 bear the imprint of Ferrara; 4-6: that of Venetia.
Title vignette (coat-of-arms); head and tail-
pieces; initials.

NT 0048706   ICN NjPT IU PU

Tasso, Torquato, 1544-1595.

[Caldani, Floriano] 1772-1836, ed.
Rime inedite di Torquato Tasso, Girolamo Verità, Vincenzo
Querini, Francesco M. Molza, Pompeo Figari. Padova, Tip.
della Minerva, 1819.

Tasso, Torquato, 1544-
Rime inedite o disperse.
Pisa, Capurro, 1831.
176 p.

NT 0048708   PU

Tasso, Torquato, 1544-1595.
Rime inedite, raccolte e pubblicate da Marco Vattasso.
Roma, Tip. poliglotta vaticana, 1915-
v. facsims. 25 cm. (Studi e testi, 28

I. Vattasso, Marco, 1869-1925, ed.   (Series: Vatican. Biblioteca
vaticana. Studi e testi, 28

PQ4637.A45 1915   52-1528

MoSU MH IU
CU-S WaU NcD OU CtY-D CSt MCW PBm OrU TNJ CtY ODaU
NT 0048709   DLC CU OCU TxU OCl ICU IMunS PU NN RPB

Tasso, Torquato, 1544-
Rime nove; con altre compositioni del medesimo ultimamente
poste in luce. Ferrara, ad instantia di G. Vasalini, 1589.
nar. 24°. pp. 72.
With coat-of-arms of Alphonso II, duke of Ferrara, on title-page.

Print. spec.

NT 0048710   MH CtY PU

Tasso, Torquato, 1544-1595.
Rime scelte e Aminta di Torquato Tasso, col discorso
sulle differenze poetiche e col carme del cav. Vincenzo
Monti ... Milano, G. Silvestri, 1824.
4 p. l., xii, 298 p., 1 l., 75, [1] p. 17cm. (Biblioteca scelta di opere italiane antiche e moderne. v. 146)
The "Rime scelte" and "Aminta" have each special t.-p. and separate
paging.
2-14066

NT 0048711   DLC PU

Tasso, Torquato, 1544-1595.
Rime scelte di Torquato Tasso. Milano, Dalla Società tipogr. de'classici italiani, 1827.
213, [1] p. 11½cm. (Added t.-p.: Raccolta di poeti classici italiani antichi e moderni. v. LVI)

NT 0048712   MiU NN FMU

Tasso, Torquato, 1544-1595.
Le rime scelte di Torquato Tasso.   Milano: N. Bettoni,
1828. 2 p.l., (1)8-232 p.   24°.

1. Poetry (Italian).
N.Y.P.L   October 19, 1915.

NT 0048713   NN

WA
26368

Tasso, Torquato, 1544-1595.
Rime scelte: Aminta, Intermedii, Amor
fuggitivo, Rime amorose, Sonetti, Canzoni.
Roma, Tip. Eredi Botta, 1871.
243 p.

NT 0048714   CtY

854
T185r2

Tasso, Torquato, 1544-1595.
Rime, scelte e annotate, a cura di A.C.
Volpe. Firenze, "La Voce" [1924]
48p. 21cm.

I. Volpe, Angelo Camillo, ed.

NT 0048715   OrU

Tasso, Torquato, 1544-1595.
Rime spiritvali del Signor Torqvato Tasso,
nuouamente raccolte, e date in luce. Bergamo,
Comin Ventura, 1597.
7 p. l., 40 numb. l. 19 cm.

NT 0048716   CtY DFo

Tasso, Torquato, 1544-1595.
Rinaldo.

For a musical composition based on this work see Sacchini, Antonio
Maria Gasparo, 1730-1786. Armida.

---

xPQ4639
R2

Tasso, Torquato, 1544-1595.
Il Rinaldo di Torquato Tasso.   Venetia,
Appresso Francesco Senese, 1562.
66ɫ. 21cm.

First edition.

NT 0048718   IaU MH MH-H

Tasso, Torquato, 1544-
Il Rinaldo.   Vinegia, Senese,
1570.
100 p.

NT 0048719   PU

Tasso, Torquato, 1544-1595.
Il Rinaldo del S.Torquato Tasso.Di nuouo
riueduto,& con diligenza corretto:aggiuntoui le
figure,argomenti, & allegorie à ciascun canto.Con
due tavole... [Vinetia,Aldo,1583]
276, [35]p.illus.14cm.

NT 0048720   PBm PU

TASSO, Torquato, 1544-
Il Rinaldo. Di nuovo riveduto & corretto;
aggiuntovi gli argomenti & le allegorie à
ciascun canto. Milano, 1618.
sm.12°.

NT 0048721   MH

Hd18
200

Tasso, Torquato, 1544-1595.
Il Rinaldo del Sig. Torqvato Tasso. Di nvovo
rivedvto, & con diligenza corretto ... In
Venetia, 1621.Appresso Euangelista Deuchino.
261,[3]p. 14cm.
Signatures: A-L12.

NT 0048722   CtY

Tasso, Torquato, 1544-1595.
Il Rinaldo, del Sig. Torqvato Tasso. Di nvovo
rivedvto, & con diligenza corretto; aggiuntoui gli
argomentĭ, & le allegorie à ciascun canto. Con la
tavola delle cose piu notabili. In Venetia, Appresso
G. A. & G. M. Misserini fratelli, 1637.
261, [3] p. 14 cm.

NT 0048723   CU PU

Tasso, Torquato, 1544-1595.
Il Rinaldo; poema di Torquato Tasso. Pisa, N.
Capurro, 1821.
viii, 269 p., 1 l. front. (port.) 21 cm.
Edited by Giovanni Rosini.

NT 0048724   CU

Tasso, Torquato, 1544-1595.
Rinaldo, a poem, in XII. books: tr. from the Italian of
Torquato Tasso. By John Hoole ... London, J. Dods-
ley, 1792.
xix, 326, [14] p. 2 port. (incl. front.) 22cm.
The heads of Tasso and Hoole mentioned by Lowndes (Bibliog. manual.
New ed., v. 5, p. 2576) are wanting in this copy.

I. Hoole, John, 1727-1803, tr. II. Title.
17-9059

Library of Congress   PQ4642.E27H7 1792

OCU PP PPL MiEM NjP
NT 0048725   DLC NcU TxU OU KMK InU ViU CtY NPV OCl

PQ4639
.R2
    Tasso, Torquato, 1544-1595.
    Il Rinaldo di Torquato Tasso. Alla sua vera lezione ridotto da Leonardo Nardini. Londra, Presso Lorenzo dà Ponte 1801.
    ix, 249 p. 16¼cm. bds.

    I. Nardini, Leonardo,   ed.   II. Title: Rinaldo.

NT   0048726   NjR NcU

Tasso, Torquato, 1544-
    Il Rinaldo.   Venezia, Antonel. li, 1840.

    178 p.

NT   0048727   PU NN

Tasso, Torquato, 1544-1595.
    ... Rinaldo; a cura di Luigi Bonfigli. Bari, G. Laterza & figli, 1936.
    3 p. l., [3]-370 p., 1 l. 21 cm. (*Half-title:* Opere. I)
    Scrittori d'Italia. 158.
    "Appendice: Il Gierusalemme. I canti IV, IX e XII della Gerusalemme liberata": p. [255]-355.
    Bibliography included in "Nota" (p. [357]-370)

    I. Bonfigli, Luigi, d. 1931, ed.   II. Title.   III. Title: Il Gierusalemme. IV. Title: Gerusalemme liberata.

    PQ4639.R2 1936   A 37-445 rev
    Minnesota. Univ. Libr.
    for Library of Congress   [r51e²]†

NT   0048728   MnU CSt DLC OCU ViU OrU PU PBm

Tasso, Torquato, 1544-1595.
    Dennis, John, 1657-1734.
    Rinaldo and Armida: a tragedy: as it is acted at the theatre in Little-Lincoln's-Inn-Fields. Written by Mr. Dennis ... London, Printed for Jacob Tonson at Graye's-Inn-Gate in Graye's-Inn-Lane. MCDXCIX [!] [1699]

Tasso, Torquato, 1544-1595.
    Il Rinaldo e l'Aminta. Per cura di Guido Mazzoni. Firenze, G.C. Sansoni, 1884.
    2 p. l., xvi, 364 p. 10.5 cm. (On cover: Piccola biblioteca italiana)

NT   0048730   OrU PU IU CU MH OClW

PQ
4656
.A2T3
    Tasso, Torquato, 1544-1595.
    Risposta del S. Torqvato Tasso alla lettera di Bastian Rossi...in difesa del svo Dialogo del piacere honesto, et detta lettera. Et vn discorso del medesimo Tasso sopra il parere critto dal Sig. Franc. Patricio in d'fesa di Lodouico Ariosto. Ferrara, Nella stamperia di V. Baldini ad instanza di G. Vassalini, 1585.
    117, [2] p.

    #Tasso-Ariosto controversy, 1584-1590.
    #Patrizi, Francesco, 1529-1597.
    #Pellegrino, Camillo, fl. 1585.
    Rossi, Bastiano de', fl. 1585-1605.
    Lettera di Bastiano de' Rossi, cognominato lo Inferigno.
    Risposta del S. Torqvato Tasso alla lettera di   Bastian Rossi.

    PU NcD MH
NT   0048732   MoU MWelC RPB MdBJ NN NcD FU CSt MoU

Tasso, Torquato, 1544-1595.
    Risposta Del S. Torq. Tasso, Al Discorso Del Sig. Oratio Lombardelli Intorni à i contrasti, che si fanno sopra la Gierusalemme liberata. Ferrara, Ad instäza di G. Vasalini, 1586.   31 p. 15cm. (8°.)
    Grässe, VI⁴, 39.   BM (Italian), p. 661.

    1. Lombardelli, Orazio, 1542?- che si fanno sopra la Gierusalemme 1595. Gerusalemme liberata.
    1608. Discorso intorno ai contrasti liberata. 2. Tasso, Torquato, 1544-

NT   0048733   NN MnU MdBJ DFo NcU MH PU InU IU

Tasso, Torquato, 1544-
    Il rogo di Corinna et La Fenice...   Venetia, Deuch, 1621.

    35 p.

NT   0048734   PU

Tasso, Torquato, 1544-
    Il rogo di Corinna poemetto pastorale... restituito alla sua vera lezione sopra un testo inedito del seco lo XVI... dal G de Poveda.   Firenze, Ciardetti, 1824.

    64 p.

NT   0048735   PU

PQ
4637
.A2
1929
    Tasso, Torquato, 1544-1595.
    Scelta dalle rime e dai poemi minori; introduzione e commento a cura di Gino Francesco Gobbi.   Milano, C. Signorelli [1929]
    123 p.   (Scrittori italiani e stranieri, 21)
    Bibl. footnotes.

    I. Gobbi, Gino Francesco   ed. II. Title. Series.

NT   0048736   NBuU MH CtY

Tasso, Torquato, 1544-1595.
    [Scelta delle Rime di Torquato Tasso. Parte Prima e seconda All'Illustriss. ed Eccellentiss. Madama la Sig. D. Lucrezia d'Este Duchessa d'Urbino. In Ferrara per Vittorio Baldini.]
    4°(6) pp. - 96. II Part Separate Pagination.

NT   0048737   MWelC

X36Y
.T18
S
    Tasso, Torquato, 1544-1595.
    Scelte poesie italiano di Torquato Tasso, Vincenzio da Filicaia, Alessandro Manzoni e Camillo Piciarelli.   Napoli, R. Marotta e Vanspandoch, 1831.
    2 p.l.,[7]-180 p.   14cm. (Cover-title: Scelta enciclopedica di opere italiane e tradotte in pretto Toscano in prosa ed in verso...)

    I. Filicaia, Vincenzio da, 1642-1707. II.Manzoni, Alessandro, 1785-1873. II.Piciarelli, Camillo. IV.Title.

NT   0048738   WU

Tasso, Torquato, 1544-
    ...Scelte rime lirich.   Milano, Bettoni, 1828.

    160 p.

NT   0048739   PU

Tasso, Torquato, 1544-1595.
    Scene und arie... aus... Das befreite Jerusalem
    see under   Eberwein, Traugott Maximilian, 1775-1831.

Tasso, Torquato, 1544-
    Scielta delle rime del Sig. Torquato Tasso. Ferrara, per V. Baldini, 1582.
    2 pt.   4°.
    With printer's mark at end.
    With coat-of-arms of Alphonso II, duke of Ferrara, on title-page.

    Print. spec.

NT   0048741   MH NcGU CtY PU CSt

PQ
4637
A1
1582
Cage
    Tasso, Torquato, 1544-1595.
    Scielta delle rime...Prima, e seconda parte... In Ferrara, Appresso Domenico Mammarelli, e Giulio Cesare Cagnacini compagni, 1582. Colophon:...Nella stamperia delli heredi di Francesco di Rossi.

    [16] 93 [1] p. 8vo.

NT   0048742   DFo PU

---

*IC5
T1853
B590s
    Tasso, Torquato, 1544-1595.
    Il secondo volvme delle Lettere familiari del sig. Torqvato Tasso. Nuouamente ristampate, & corrette.
    In Venetia,Appresso Giacomo Vincenti.M.D.XC. 8°.   4p.l.,174(i.e.176)p. 15cm.
    Also issued with imprint date 1589.
    Printer's mark on t.-p.
    Numbers 95-96 repeated in paging.
    Bound with his Il secretario, et il primo volvme delle Lettere familiari, 1588.

NT   0048743   MH

Tasso, Torquato, 1544-1595.
    Il Secretario Del S. Torqvato Tasso. Diusio in duoi Trattati All'Illustriss. & Eccellentiss. Sig. Don Cesare D'Este ... In Ferrara. Appresso Giulio Cesare Cagnacini, & Fratelli. M.D.LXXXVII. 8° pp (6) - 39. Colophon;

NT   0048744   MWelC

Tasso, Torquato, 1544-1595.
    Il secretario, et il primo volvme, delle Lettere familiari, del sig. Torqvato Tasso. Nouamente ristampate. Venetia, G. Vincenzi, 1588-90.
    2 v. 15 cm.
    Vol. 2 has title: Il secondo volvme delle Lettere familiari ... Nuouamente ristampate, & corrette.

    I. Tasso, Torquato. Lettere. II. Title.

    PQ4640.S4 1588   4-5789

NT   0048745   DLC CtY ICN PU DFo

TASSO,TORQUATO,1544-1595
    Il secretario, et il primo e-secondo volvme delle Lettere familiari. Novamente ristampate ... Venetia, P. Vgolino, 1601
    2 v. in 1.

    Bound in full vellum.

NT   0048746   InU-Li

PQ 4636 A5 1605 Cage Tasso, Torquato, 1544-1595.
Il secretario, et il primo (-secondo) volume delle lettere familiari...Di nuouo ristampate, & ricorrette. In Venetia, Appresso Lucio Spineda, 1605.
Colophon to v.1.

2 v. in 1. 8vo.

NT 0048747   DFo

PQ4640 .S4 1607 Tasso, Torquato, 1544-1595.
Il secretario, et il primo (-secondo) volume delle Lettere familiari. Di nuouo ristampate & con somma diligenza ricorrette. Venetia, Heredi di D. Farri, 1607.
2 v. in 1.
Title vignette; initials; printer's device at end of v.1.

I. Tasso, Torquato, 1544-1595. Lettere familiari. II. Title.

NT 0048748   ICU MH

Tasso, Torquato, 1544-1595.
Sei lettere, e tre sonetti di Torquato Tasso, tratti dagli autografi
see under   Gambara, Veronica, 1485-

Tasso, Torquato, 1544-1595.
Le sette giornate del mondo creato del S. Torqvato Tasso. All'illustrissimo signore il S. Gio. Battista Vittorio nepote di N.S.   Viterbo, appresso G. Discepolo, 1607.
322 p.   15 cm.
Dedicatory letter signed: Angelo Ingegneri.

NT 0048750   IEN CtY MWelC MH

Tasso, Torquato, 1544-1595.
Le sette giornate del mondo creato, del sig. Torqvato Tasso. All'illustrissimo signore il s. Gio. Battista Vittorio, nepote di N. S. ... Venetia, B. Giunti, G. B. Ciotti, & compagni, 1608.
307, (1) p. illus. 13½ᵐ.
Title vignette.
Dedicatory letter signed: Angelo Ingegneri.

I. Ingegneri, Angelo, 1500-ca. 1613, ed.
4—5788
Library of Congress   PQ4639.M2 1608

NT 0048751   DLC NcD FU PU MH NcU ICU

Tasso, Torquato. 1544-1595.
Le sette giornate del mondo creato. Di nouo in questa nostra vltima impressione con somma diligenza ricorretta.
= In Venetia, M DC XXXVII. Appresso Gio: Antonio, & Gio: Maria Misserini fratelli. 310 p⟩. Vignette. 12½ cm., in 12s.

K523 — T.r. — Bible. O.T. Genesis. Crit.

NT 0048752   MH PU MH

Tasso, Torquato, 1544-
Le sette giornate del mondo creato... alle qualli si aggiungono gli argomenti per ciascun canto ed. un copioso indice...   Parma, Borsi, 1765.

285 p.

NT 0048753   PU

PQ 4639 .M2 1780 Tasso, Torquato, 1544-1595
Le sette giornate del mondo creato.
Londra, G. T. Masi, 1780.
330 p.

Illustrated t. p.

I. Title.   II. Title: Il mondo creato.

NT 0048754   INS NcU KU PU NN MH

PG3361 .S45 1818 Tasso, Torquato.

Shishkov, Aleksandr Semenovich, 1754-1841.
Собраніе сочиненій и переводовъ. Санктпетербургъ, Въ Тип. Имп. Россійской академіи, 1818-34.

PQ4204 .A3C6 vol. 205 Tasso, Torquato, 1544-1595.

Trissino, Giovanni Giorgio, 1478-1550.
La Sofonisba di Giangiorgio Trissino con note di Torq.ᵒ Tasso, edite a cura di Franco Paglierani. Bologna, G. Romagnoli, 1884.

Y 712 .O 57 TASSO, TORQUATO, 1544-1595.
La Sofronia del sig. Torquato Tasso. Ridotta in favola scenica. Da Giovanni Villifranchi. Venetia Appresso G.B.Ciotti,1603.
35p. 14cm. (with Ongaro, Antonio. Rime. 1602)

Title vignette.

NT 0048757   ICN

TASSO, Torquato, 1544-1595.
Sofronia e Olindo, episodio della Gerusalemme liberata. Tradotto in dialetto lodigiano dal poeta Francesco de Lemene. Prima pubblicazione per cura di Cesare Vignati. Milano, tipi di C.Wilmant, 1852.

f°.pp.(35).

NT 0048758   MH

Humanities Library Microfilm AC 4 E5 Reel no. 359 Tasso, Torquato, 1544-1595.
Torqvati Tass Solymeidos, liber primvs latinis nvmeris expressvs a Scipio Gentili. Londini excudebat Iohannes VVolfius. 1584.
Translation of first book of Gerusalemme liberata.
University microfilms no. 15625 (case 60, carton 359)
Short-title catalogue no. 23700.

I. Gentili,   Scipione, 1563-1616, tr.

NT 0048759   MiU WaPS

STC 23701 Tasso, Torquato, 1544-1595.
Scipii Gentilis Solymeidos libri duo priores ... Italicis expressi. Londini, Apud Iohannem Wolfium, 1584.

*⁴, B-H⁴ (*2 and *3 signed *1 and *2 respectively; H4 blank). 4to.

NT 0048760   DFo

TASSO, Torquato, 1544-1595.
Soneto italiano, enderegado como encomio ao nosso Luiz de Camões. Com as versões em portuguez [by Jose Ramos Coelho], Frances [By Duperron de Castera, and by Millie], e inglez [By Mickle, and by Fanshaw], antecedidas d'um preambulo do professor Pereira Caldas. Braga, Imprensa commercial, 1883.
pp.24.
"66 exemplares. No.   11".
Printed on yellow   paper.

NT 0048761   MH

Tasso, Torquato, 1544-
Sonnets.
(In Lafond and Lafond, translators. Dante, Pétrarque, Michel-Ange. Tasse. Pp. 427-473. London. 1848.)

NT 0048762   MB

Tasso, Torquato, 1544-1595.
... Sonette an Lucrezia Bendidio, aus dem italienischen von Paul graf Thun-Hohenstein. München, K. Alber, 1942.
56 p. 20½ x 11½ᵐ.
"Zweite auflage. Drittes bis neuntes tausend."
Italian and German on opposite pages.

I. Thun-Hohenstein, Paul, graf, 1884-   tr.
PQ4637.A21 1942   A F 47-4910
Yale univ. Library
for Library of Congress   (2)†

NT 0048763   CtY MH DLC IU NjP

Tasso, Torquato, 1544-1595.
Sonette an Lucrezia Bendidio. Aus dem Italienischen von Paul Graf Thun-Hohenstein. München, K.Alber, 1944.
56 p. 21 cm.
"3.Aufl."

NT 0048764   MH

Tasso, Torquato, 1544-1595.
Sonetti. (Firenze, 1933)
xv p. 29 cm.

PQ4637.A2 1933   58-53118

NT 0048765   DLC CtY

TASSO, Torquato, 1544-
Sonetti inediti. Con le varie lezioni di altre sue rime già pubblicate. [Edited by Celestino Cavedoni. Modena, 1832.]

pp.(26).
Extracted from Continuazione delle Memorie di religione, di morale, etc., 1832, i. 293-318.

NT 0048766   MH

Tasso, Torquato,   1897.
Sonetto beginning Io non contesi,...

NT 0048767   NIC

Tasso, Torquato. 1544-1595.
Sopra le verdi chiome
see under Falcone, Achille, d. 1600.

[Tasso, Torquato], 1544-
Stanze della Gerusalemme liberata; scelte
annotate e collegate dal racconto dell'intero
poema ad uso delle scuole da Severino Ferrari
e Alfredo Straccali. Bologna, N. Zanichelli,
1886.

NT 0048769 MA

PQ
4638
.Z5
F4
Tasso, Torquato, 1544-1595.
Stanze della Gerusalemme liberata.
Scelte ed annotate e collegate dal racconto
dell' intero poema ad uso delle scuole da
Severino Ferrari e Alfredo Straccali. Bologna,
Nicola Zanichelli [1917]
432p.

I. Ferrari, Severino, ed. II. Title:
Gerusalemme li-   berata.

NT 0048770 OC1JC

D851T18
O336
Tasso, Torquato, 1544-1595.
... Stanze della Gerusalemme liberata, scelte
ed annotate e collegate dal racconto dell'intero
poema ad uso delle scuole da Severino Ferrari e
Alfredo Straccali. Bologna, Zanichelli [1929]
2 p. l. [3]-432 p., 2 l. 19cm.

1. Ferrari, Severino, 1856-1905. ed.
II. Straccali, Alfredo. 1854-   ed.

NT 0048771 NNC

[TASSO, Torquato] 1544-
Stanze scelte de la Gerusalemme liberata,
annotate e collegate, con il racconto de l'ini-
tiere poema, da G. Mazzatinti e G.Padovan,
Torino, etc., E.Loescher, 1885.
iv, 242 p. 21cm.

(Classici italiani annotati per uso
delle scuole.)

NT 0048772 MH CaBVaU CtY MiU

Tasso, Torquato, 1544-1595.
FOR OTHER EDITIONS
SEE MAIN ENTRY
Hunt, Leigh, 1784-1859.
Stories from the Italian poets: with lives of the writers.
By Leigh Hunt ... London. Chapman and Hall. 1846.

Tasso, Torquato, 1544-1595.
Tales from Tasso, and other poems and translations,
by G. Grinnell-Milne ... London, D. Nutt, 1909.
vii, 315 p. plates. 22½cm.
"Errata" slip inserted before p. vii.
Contains the original text of the selections translated (Italian and
English on opposite pages)
CONTENTS.—Tales from Tasso's "Jerusalem delivered": Introduction.
Torquato Tasso. About the epic. The story and the episodes. Life of
Tancred. Life of Godfrey. Notes.—Ginevra, a tale of Florence [poem
by G. Grinnell-Milne]—Sonnets and madrigals of Michael Angelo.—
Francesca di Rimini from Dante's Inferno.
I. Buonarroti, Michel Angelo. Rime. II. Dante Alighieri. Div. com.
Inferno. Canto v. III. Milne, G. Grinnell-, ed. and tr. IV. Title.
18-22861
Library of Congress   PQ4642.E21M5

NT 0048774 DLC OCU OC1 OO PPL MB NN CtY

[Tasso, Torquato.] 1544-1595.
Tancreds envig med Clorinda. Fragment ur Gerusalemme
liberata (12 sången 48-71 st.). Fri öfversättning som...under
inseende af C. W. Böttiger...för philosophiska graden utgifven
och författad af A. Falk...offentligen försvaras...d. 11 Junii
1845. Upsala: Wahlström & Låstbom, 1845. 16 p. 8°.
Dissertation, Upsala.
In: NNK p. v. 15, no. 11.

1. Poetry (Italian). 2. Böttiger, Karl   Wilhelm. 3. Falk, Axel. 4. Title.
N. Y. P. L.   September 27, 1913.

NT 0048775 NN

Tasso, Torquato, 1544-1595.
Le Tasse
see under Mellier, Emile.

TASSO, [Torquato] 1544-
Il Tasso minore; Aminta, Liriche, il dialogo
"De la Bellezza", Lezioni e discorsi, Lettere
Con introduzione e Illustrazioni storico es-
tetiche di Fortunato Rizzi. Catania, C.
Galatola, 1929.

NT 0048777 MH

SPECIAL COLLECTIONS
B851T185
R
1689
Tasso, Torquato, 1544-1595.
[Gerusalemme liberata]
Lo Tasso napoletano; zoe La Gierosalemme
libberata de lo sio Torquato Tasso votata a
llengua nosta da Grabiele Fasano ... Napole,
Iacovo Raillardo, 1689.
[18], 410, [1] p. plates. 35 cm.

Italian text and translation in Neapolitan
dialect in parallel columns.
Title vignette (armorial device)

NT 0048778 NNC ICN DCU-H PU PPL DGU NN CtY NIC MH

Tasso, Torquato, 1544-1595.
Tasso's Enchanted Ground. The Story of the
'Jerusalem delivered.' London, Hatchards, 1877.
viii, 288 p.

NT 0048779 MB

Tasso, Torquato, 1544-1595.
Tasso's Jerusalem delivered; or Godfrey of
Bulloign
see his Jerusalem delivered.

Tasso, Torquato, 1544-1595, supposed author.
Tasso's Nächte
see under Compagnoni, Giuseppe, 1754-
1833.

Tasso, Torquato, 1544-1595.
Teatro di Torquato Tasso. Ed. critica a cura di Angelo
Solerti, con due saggi di Giosue Carducci. Bologna, Ditta N. Zanichelli, 1895.
3 p. l., [iii]-clv, [1], 531, [2] p. 20cm. (On cover: ... Opere minori in
versi ... Ed. critica a cura di Angelo Solerti. vol. III)
At head of cover-title: Biblioteca di scrittori italiani. (XVII)

1. Solerti, Angelo, 1865-1907, ed. II. Carducci, Giosuè, 1836-1907.
14-21712
Library of Congress   PQ4636.A7 1895

CU
NT 0048782 DLC NIC MeB MdBP OC1W OCU NcD NjP MiU

Tasso, Torquato, 1544-1595.
Teatro italiano, o sia Scelta di tragedie per uso della scena
... Premessa un' istoria del teatro, e difesa di esso. Verona,
J. Vallarsi, 1723-25.

PQ
4213
A5
T3
1591
Cage
[Tasso, Torquato] 1544-1595, ed.
Tempio fabricato da diuersi... ingegni, in lode
dell'... Flauia Peretta Orsina... Dedicatole da
Vranio Felice [pseud.]... In Roma, Appresso Gio-
uanni Martinelli.
Colophon:... 1591.

[6], 250 [i.e. 350] [10] p. [A]^4, A^4, B-Z^8.
([A]2 lacking or cancelled) 4to.

NT 0048784 DFo

Tasso, Torquato, 1544-1595.
Terzo centenario dalla morte di Torquato Tasso,
25 aprile, 1895
see under Circolo Romano Di San Sebastiano.

Ak
B610
718t
TASSO, TORQUATO, 1544-1595.
The third book of Tasso's Jerusalem. Written
originally in Italian. Attempted in English.
By Mr. Bond ...
London: Printed and sold by W.Lewis in Russel-
street, Covent-Garden, H.Clements, at the Half-
Moon in St.Paul's-Church-yard, and T.Warner, at
the Black-Boy in Pater-noster-row.1718. xii,
59p. 20cm.
Fairfax's stanzaic translation and Bond's
translation in heroic couplets on parallel
pages.

NT 0048786 TxU CtY MH

Tasso, Torquato, 1544-1595.
Hd16
67
Torquato Tasso. A brief biographical sketch,
and choice selections from his works ... New
York, Chicago, J.B.Alden[1891]
cover-title, 8p. 18½cm. (Elzevir library,
v.X,no.517)
The selections are translated by Wiffen and
R.H.Wilde.

NT 0048787 CtY

854
T185F
Tasso, Torquato, 1544-1595.
Torquato Tasso. Introd., traduction et
notes, par Gustave Charlier. Paris, La
Renaissance du livre [1928]
175p. port. 17cm. (Les cent chefs-
d'oeuvre étrangers)

Bibliography: p.34-37.

I. Charlier, Gustave, 1885-   ed.
and tr. II. Series.

NT 0048788 OrU

Tasso, Torquato, 1544-1595.
... Torquato Tasso (1544-1595) Torino, Milano [ecc.] G. B.
Paravia & c. [1937]
135 p. 19½cm. (Scrittori italiani con notizie storiche e analisi este-
tiche)
At head of title: ... Giovanni Ziccardi.
Paraphrases, selections, biography and criticism of Tasso and his
poetry.
"Nota bibliografica": p. [131]-133.

I. Ziccardi, Giovanni, 1881-   ed.
A C 39-1636
Pennsylvania. Univ. Libr.
for Library of Congress   [2]

NT 0048789 PU

TASSO, Torquato, 1544-
　　Torquato Tasso e la casa di Savoia nel terzo centenario dalla morte del poeta, Roma.
25 aprile, 1895; [Lettere, sonetto, ed estratti, pubblicati da P.D.Pasolini e Angelo
Solerti. Roma, Forzani e C., tipog., 1895.

　　f°. pp.xii, 4 facsimile plates.
　　"150 esemplari".

NT　0048790　　MH

Tasso, Torquato, 1544-1595.
　　Le Torrismos du Tasse
　　　　see under　Dalibray, Charles Vion, sieur de,
ca. 1600- ca. 1655.

Tasso, Torquato, 1544-1595.
　　Torrismondo
　　　　see his　Il re Torrismondo.

Tasso, Torquato, 1544-95.
　　Traduction libre de l'Aminte par M. le compte de
Choiseul-Meuse. Londres, Desenne, 1784
　　118 p.

NT　0048793　　MH

TASSO, Torquato, 1544-
　　Translations from the Jerusalem delivered;
with various original poems,&c., by the author,
[of the translation]. London, [Printed by
C. Roworth], 1813.

　　With manuscript notes, evidently corrections.

NT　0048794　　MH PU

Tasso, Torquato, 1544-1595.
　　Trattato della dignità ed altri inediti scritti di Torqvato
Tasso; premessa vna Notizia intorno ai codici manoscritti di
cose italiane, conservati nelle biblioteche del mezzodì della
Francia, ed vn cenno svlle antichità di qvella regione, del cava-
liere Costanzo Gazzera. Torino, Stamperia reale, 1838.
　　3 p. l., 3), 202 p., 1 l. fold. facsim. 21½ x 13¾ᶜᵐ.
　　Book-plate of Mr. Anatole de Montaiglon.
　　CONTENTS.—Notizia.—Scritti inediti del Tasso: Preambolo. Trattato
della dignità. Lettera prima ad N. N. Favola della Gerusalemme.
Lettera seconda ad N. N. Dubbi e riposte. Dubbi sulle parole. Varie
lezioni del Mondo creato. Stanze del Monte Oliveto.
　　1. Manuscripts. France. 2. Manuscripts, Italian.　　I. Gazzera,
Costanzo, 1779-1859, ed.
　　　　　　　　　　　　　　　　　　　　　　　　2-14061 Revised
　　Library of Congress　　　　PQ4640.D4　1838

NT　0048795　　DLC CtY MiU WU

Tasso, Torquato, 1544-1595.
　　Tre madrigali di Torquato Tasso, op. 13
　　　　see under　Lewkovitch, Bernhard, 1927-

PQ　　Tasso, Torquato, 1544-1595.
4643　　Vapautettu Jerusalem. Suomentanut Elina
F5V11　Vaara. Porvoo, Söderström, 1954.
　　554 p. illus.

　　Kuvittanut Charles Nocolas Cochin (1784)
　　Translation of La Gerusalemme liberata.

　　I. Vaara, Elina.　II. Cochin, Charles
Nicolas, 1715-1790. III. Title.

NT　0048797　　CLU

Tasso, Torquato, 1544-1595, supposed author.
　　Veglie
　　　　see under　　[Compagnoni, Giuseppe] 1754-
1833.

Tasso, Torquato, 1544-1595, supposed author.
　　Les veillées du Tasse
　　　　see under　　[Compagnoni, Giuseppe] 1754-
1833.

Tasso, Torquato, 1544-1595.
　　Ventiquattro sonetti / di Torquato Tasso. — [Vienna] :
A l'insegna del Santuccio, 1939.
　　34, [1] p. ; 22 cm.
　　"Cesare Olschki selected the sonnets."—Amateur book collector.
v. 6, 1955-56, no. 5, p. 5.
　　"A trial printing, V. H. [i. e. Victor Hammer]"—Pencilled note
on p. [35]

　　PQ4637.A2　1939　　　　　　　　　75-571636

NT　0048800　　DLC OCU InU MWelC NIC LU ICN NN

Tasso, Torquato, 1544-1595.
　　Het verloste Jeruzalem ... vertaald door J.
Dullaart. Rotterdam, Naeranus, 1658.
　　778 p.

NT　0048801　　PU

Tasso, Torquato, 1544-1595.
　　Vers inédits de Tasse tirés d'un nouvel auto-
graphe. Paris [A. Lanier et ses fils] 1889.
　　21 p.　19 cm.
　　"Tiré a 99 exemplaires numérotés a la presse.
36."

NT　0048802　　NcD MH

851.46
T185v　　**Tasso, Torquato, 1544-1595.**
　　　**Versi inediti. Parma, Co'tipi Bodoniani,
1812.**
　　viii,19 p. 23cm.

　　Pref. by Bartolommeo Borghesi.

　　I. Borghesi, Bartolomeo, Conte, 1781-
1860.

NT　0048803　　MiDW MH PU MiU

Tasso, Torquato, 1544-
　　**Versi tratti dagli autografi di
Torquato Tasso ed. by Mario Valdrighi.
Modena, Vincenzi, 1827.**

　　23 p.

NT　0048804　　PU

853T185
OgYs　　Tasso, Torquato, 1544-1595.
　　Versiones castellanas de la Jerusalem libertada
de Torcuato Tasso; estudio bibliográfico leido en
el Liceo hidalgo, por el socio de número Francisco
Sosa.　México, Oficina tipografica de la Secre-
taria de fomento, 1885.
　　58p.

　　1. Tasso, Torquato. Gerusalemme liberata.

NT　0048805　　IU MH

PQ　　Tasso, Torquato, 1544-1595.
4642　　Versuch einer poetischen Uebersetzung des
G21　Tassoischen Heldengedichts genannt: Gott-
K65　fried, oder das Befreyte Jerusalem, ausge-
1744　arbeitet von Johann Friedrich Koppen ...
HRC　Leipzig, B.C. Breitkopf, 1744.
　　[30],600p.　front.　20cm.

　　I. Koppen, Johann Friedrich, tr.
II. Title. III. Title: Gottfried. IV. Title:
Befreyte Jerusalem.

NT　0048806　　TxU CtY CaBVaU InU WU CSt OU TU CU PU

Tasso, Torquato, 1544-1595, supposed author.
　　Vigilias...
　　　　see under　　[Compagnoni, Giuseppe] 1754-
1833.

Tasso Fragoso, Augusto
　　　see
　　Fragoso, Augusto Tasso, 1867-1945.

PQ　　Tasso Serra, Torcuato
6637　　Esclofollas.　Barcelona, Tipolitografía de
.A77　L. Tasso Serra, 1893.
E8　　159 p.　18 cm.

　　Alternate pages blank.

NT　0048809　　WU

TASSO　　SERRA, Torcuato,
Polsina.　Barcelona, I. Lopez, etc., [1893]

NT　0048810　　MH

Tasso Serra, Torcuato.
　　Vislumbres por Torcuato Tasso Serra.
Barcelona, Antonio Lopez, editor rambla del
centro, 20 Alvaro Verdaguer rambla del centro, 5
y principales librerias.　Madrid, Fernando Fe
Carrera de San Jerónimo.　A. López Robert,
impresor, 1897.

NT　0048811　　NNH

Il Tasso a Castelvetro e la sala dell'antico
palazzo
　　　see under　　[Masinelli, Antonio]

PQ　　Il Tasso. A dialogue. The speakers, John Milton,
4646　Torquato Tasso. In which, new light is thrown on
T2　their poetical and moral characters...London, R.
Cage　Baldwin, 1762.
　　[4] 19 [1] p.　[A]², B-C⁴, D². 8vo.

NT　0048813　　DFo CtY IU MH

Il Tasso, il Manzoni e i romantici
　　　see under　　[Bosco, Umberto] 1900-

Il Tasso piangente
    see under   [Boccia, Severino] d. 1697.

Tasso por memor de los intereses qve podram lleriar las deputaciones... [Mexico, 1584]
    Bd. in vol.: Spaniards in South America

NT 0048816   RPJCB

Tasso y ordenanzas para el reyno de Chile ... Lima, 1620

NT 0048817   RPJCB

Tassolambros, L
   see
   Tasolampros, L

Tassolo, Domenico.
  I Trionfi Feste, Et Livree Fatte Dalli Signori Conservatori, & Popolo Romano, & da tutte le arti di Roma, nella felicissima, & honorata entrata dell'Illustrissimo Signor Marcantonio Colonna. Venetia, 1571.   4 l.   21cm. (4°.)

    Signed: Domenico Tassolo, & Baldassare Mariotti.

                                   Proudfit Collection
1. Colonna, Marco Antonio, 1535-   1584. 2. Lepanto, Battle of, 1571.
I. Mariotto, Baldassare, joint author.   II. Title.

NT 0048819   NN

[TASSOLO, Domenico]
  La felicissima et honorata entrata in Roma del illustrissimo signor Marcantonio Colonna con li trionfi. Viterbo, [1571].

    4°. pp.(8).
    The work is signed "Domenico Tassolo & Baldassarre Mariotti".
    With unidentified printer's mark on title-page.   Ott 315.12

NT 0048820   MH

GT   [Tassone, Ercole Estense]
4252   L'isola beata. Torneo fatto nella citta di
F4   Ferrara per la venuta del ... principe Carlo
T3   arciduca d'Austria, a XXV di maggio M.D.LXIX.
1569   [n.p., 1569?]
Cage

    43 [1] l. A-L⁴. 4to.

NT 0048821   DFo

Tassoni, Alessandro
  I dimenticati.   Roma, E. Perino, 1886.
    (1) 62, p.
    At head of title: Biblioteca patriottica [6]
    Back cover lists the author of this work as Tommassoni.
    Short biographical sketches of ten men of the risorgimento period.

NT 0048822   MH

Tassoni, Alessandro, 1565-1635.
  ... Opere.   [Bari, G. Laterza & figli, 1930-
    2 v.   21 cm.   (Scrittori d'Italia. 129)
    Half-title; each volume has special t.-p.

NT 0048823   DLC

851.5   Tassoni, Alessandro, 1565-1635.
T21   Opere. A cura di Luigi Fasso.   Milano-
    Roma, Rizzoli [1942]
    1153p. port. facsims. 19cm. (Classici Rizzoli)

    I. Fasso, Luigi, ed.

NT 0048824   IEN NNC ICU CU

Tassoni, Alessandro, 1565-1635, supposed author.
    Annotazioni sopra il Vocabolario degli Accademici della Crusca...
        see under Ottonelli, Giulio, 1550-1620.

Cl   Tassoni, Alessandro, 1565-1635.
PQ4478   Avvertimenti di Crescenzio Pepe da svsa al
.A2T3   Sig. Giosefo de gli Aromatari, intorno alle
    Risposte date da lui alle Considerazioni del
    Sig. Alessandro Tassoni sopra le rime del
    Petrarca. Modona, G. Cassiani, 1611.
    223 p. 16cm.

    1. Aromatari, Giuseppe degli, 1586-1660. Risposte de Gioseffe de gli Aromatari alle Considerazioni del Sig. Alessandro Tassoni sopra le rime del Petrarca. 2. Petrarca, Francisco, 1304-1374. I.T.

NT 0048826   MiDW IU ICN NIC NcU

    Tassoni, Alessandro, 1565-1635.
*IC6   Considerazioni sopra le rime del Petrarca
T1857   d'Alessandro Tassoni col confronto de'luoghi
609c   de'poeti antichi di varie lingue. Aggiuntaui nel
    fine vna scelta dell'annotazioni del Muzio
    ristrette, e parte esaminate.
    In Modona.M.DC.IX.Appresso Giulian Cassiani.
    Con licenza de'superiori.
    8°. 8p.l.,576(i.e.574)p.,1l. 17cm.
    Printer's mark (engr.) on t.-p.
    Numbers 481-482 omitted in paging.

              NSchU
NT 0048827   MH WU OU CU PU DLC-P4 MnU NIC CSt ICN

DG975 Tassoni, Alessandro, 1565-1635.
f.M6M8   Cronache modenesi di Alessandro Tassoni, di
v.15   Giovanni da Bazzano e di Bonifazio Morano, secondo
    l'esatta lezione dei codici e con le varianti del
    Muratori, ora per la prima volta nella loro integrità pub., a cura di L. Vischi, T. Sandonnini,
    O. Raselli. Modena, Società tipografica, 1838.
    xxxi, 376 p. 33cm. (Monumenti di storia patria delle provincie modenesi; serie delle cronache, t.15)

NT 0048828   ICU

Cl   Tassoni, Alessandro, 1565-1635.
PQ4663   De' pensieri diversi di Alessandro Tassoni,
.A16   libri dieci; corretti, ampliati, e arricchiti in
    questa vltima impressione per tutto dall'autore
    di nuoue curiosità; ne' quali per via di quisiti
    con nuoui fondamenti, e ragioni si trattano le
    piu curiose materie naturali, morali, ciuili,
    poetiche, istoriche, e d'altre facoltà, che
    soglion venire in discorso fra caualieri, e
    professori di lettere. Con due copiosissime
    tauole: vna de' libri, quisiti, e capitoli;
    e l'altra delle cose più notabili, e memorabili.

Continued in next column

Continued from preceding column

Venetia, Per il Barezzi, all'insegna dell'abbondanza, 1646.
    [xiv],445,[70] p. 23cm.

    Bibliography of Tassoni's works: p.[iii-v]

NT 0048830   MiDW NIC OrU CU InU MH NcU ICN

Tassoni, Alessandro, 1565-1635.
  De'pensieri diversi di Alessandro Tassoni libri dieci. Correti, ampliati, e arrichiti per tutto dall'autore di nuoue curiosita: ne'quali per via di quisiti con nuoui fondamenti, e ragioni si trattano le più curiose materie naturali, morali, ciuili, poetiche, istoriche, e d'altre facoltà, che soglion venire in discorso fra caualieri, e professori di lettere. ... Venetia, Appresso C. Conzatti, 1665.
    5 p. l., 422, [8] p. 21½ᶜᵐ.
    Title vignette.
    "Ex nova Leonis Allatii Apium vrbanarum recensione" (Bibliography of Tassoni): 4th-5th prelim. l.

NT 0048831   MiU MtU OU ICU CLSU NN MH

PQ4663 Tassoni, Alessandro, 1565-1635.
.A16   De' pensieri diversi. Correti, ampliati,
    earrichiti per tutto dall'autore di nuoue
    curiosita... Consacrati all'illustriss &
    eccellentiss. Antonio Barbarigo, dell'
    illustriss & eccellentiss. Gio: Francesco.
    Venetia, Carlo Conzatti, 1665.
    422 p.
    "Tavola de' quisiti." p.[423]
    Xerox-copy, by SUNY at Buffalo, 1966.

NT 0048832   NBuU

Tassoni, Alessandro, 1565-1635.
  De' pensieri diversi di Alessandro Tassoni, libri dieci. Corretti, ampliati, e arricchiti in questa vltima impressione per tutto dall'auttore di nuoue curiosita ne' quali per via di quesiti con nuoui fondamenti, e ragioni si trattano le più curiose materie naturali, morali...e d'altre facolta... In Venetia, Per D.Miloco, 1676.
    4 l.,361,[5] p. 22 ᶜᵐ.

NT 0048833   NjP PHC TU NNC

Tassoni, Alessandro, 1565-1635.
*IC6   Dieci libri di pensieri diversi
T1857   d'Alessandro Tassoni, ne'quali per via di quisiti
608pd   con nuoui fondamenti, e ragioni si trattano le
    più curiose materie naturali, morali, ciuili,
    poetiche, istoriche, e d'altre facoltà, che
    soglian venire in discorso fra caualieri, e
    professori di lettere. Aggiuntoui nuouamente
    il decimo libro del paragone de gl'ingegni
    antichi, e moderni, e la confutazione del moto
    della terra, con altri varj quisiti. E corretti,

    e ampliati, e arricchiti in questa terza
    impressione per tutto dall'autore di nuoue
    curiosità ...
    In Carpi,Appresso Girolamo Vaschieri.1620.
    Con licenza de'superiori.
    4°. 48p.l.,584p. 21cm.
    Woodcut arms of the dedicatee, Paolo Coccapani, on t.-p.
    An expanded version of his Parte de qvisiti;
    also pub-   lished under title
    Varietà di   pensieri.

NT 0048835   MH ICN CtY

Tassoni, Alessandro, 1565-1635.
*IC6   Dieci libri di pensieri diversi d'Alessandro
T1857   Tassoni, ne'quali per via di quisiti con nuoui
608pe   fondamenti, e ragioni si trattano le più
    curiose materie naturali, morali, ciuili,
    poetiche, istoriche, e d'altre facoltà, che
    soglian venire in discorso fra caualieri, e
    professori di lettere. Aggiuntoui nuouamente il
    decimo libro del paragone de gl'ingegni antichi,
    e moderni con altri varij quisiti. Corretti,
    ampliati, e arricchiti in questa quarta
    impressione per tutto dall'autore di nuoue
    curiosità ...

Continued in next column

Continued from preceding column

In Venetia,MDCXXVII.Appresso Marc'Antonio
Brogiollo. Con licenza de'superiori, &
priuilegio.
     4°. 48p.ℓ.,679(i.e.683),[1]p. 22cm.
     Engraved arms of the dedicatee, G. B. Gambara,
on t.-p.
     Numbers 389-392 repeated in paging.

*IC6
T1857
608pe
     An expanded version of his Parte de qvisiti;
also published under title Varietà di pensieri.
Manuscript notes & autograph of Convers
Francis on front flyleaves.

NT 0048838   MH ICN PU OU NNC PPL DFo

Tassoni, Alessandro, 1565-1635.
     Dieci libri di pensieri diversi d'Alessandro
Tassoni... Milano, Per G.B. Bid. [i. e. G. B.
Bidelli] 1628.
     60 p.l., 630 p. 18 cm.
     1st ed., 1613, has title; Varietà di pensieri.
     Title vignette.

NT 0048839   CU PP NcU

Tassoni, Alessandro, 1565-1635.
*IC6
T1857
608pg
     Dieci libri di pensieri diversi di Alessandro
Tassoni ne'quali per via di quisiti con nuoui
fondamenti, e ragioni si trattano le più
curiose materie naturali, morali, ciuili,
poetiche, istoriche, e d'altre facolta, che
sogliam venire in discorso fra caualieri, e
professori di lettere. Corretti, ampliati, e
arricchiti in questa ottaua impressione per
tutto dall'autore di nuoue curiosità ...
     In Venezia,MDCXXXVI.Appresso Marc'Antonio
Brogiolo. Con licenza de'superiori, &
priuilegio.

     4°. 52p.ℓ.,551(i.e.547)p. 21.5cm.
     Printer's mark on t.-p.
     Numbers 401-404 omitted in paging.
     An expanded version of his Parte de qvisiti;
also published under title Varietà di pensieri.
         YA 3340

NT 0048841   MH NcD WU NNC MWelC DNLM DLC

Tassoni, Alessandro, 1565-1635.
857.51
T215D
     Difesa di Alessandro Macedone, divisa in
tre dialoghi con appendice di altri scritti
tassoniani, a cura di Giorgio Rossi. Livorno,
R. Giusti, 1904.
     2 v. in 1. 19 cm. (Raccolta di rarità
storiche e letterarie, v. 8-9)

     "400 esemplari."
     1. Alexander the Great, 353-323 B. C. I.
Rossi, Giorgio, 1873- ed. II. Title.

NT 0048842   NcD NIC MH ICU MiU RPB ICN CtY CU

[TASSONI,Alessandro,1565-1635.
     Due lettere inedite]. Per le nozze dell'
amica Baronessina Emmy Levi,con l'onorevole
Louis Louis-Dreyfus. [Milano,U.Allegretti,
1906.]

     pp.13+.
     "100 esemplari."
     Edited by Fiorella Gelli.

NT 0048843   MH

[TASSONI,Alessandro,1565-1635.]
     Filippica 1[-2. Modena?,1615?]

     20 cm. pp.(14).
     Imperfect: Lacks frontispiece.

NT 0048844   MH DLC MnU

Tassoni, Alessandro, 1565-1635. Filippiche
        contro gli Spagnuoli.
[Cambiagi, Francesco] *comp.*
     Ricordi di famiglia. Per le nozze di Eugenio Miche-
lozzi con la marchesa Eleonora Tassoni. Firenze, Stamperia granducale, 1854.

F
355
.863
     TASSONI, ALESSANDRO, 1565-1635.
     Le filippiche contro gli Spagnuoli. Precedute
da un Discorso di G. Canestrini sulla Politica
Piemontese nel sec. XVII e seguite dalla risposta
del Tassoni al Soccino in difesa del Duca di Savoia
e dal Manifesto dell'autore intorno alle sue relazioni coi Principi di Savoia. Firenze,A.Volpato
[1855]
     xi,199p. 16cm.

     "Al lettore" signed: Silvio Giannini.
     Against Philip   III, King of Spain, and
the Spanish rule in   Italy.--cf. Brit. Mus.
Catalogue.

NT 0048846   ICN CSt IaU MiDW OU NjP CU

Tassoni, Alessandro
     Le filippiche contra gli Spagnuoli; dicorso
di G. Canestrini sulla politica piemontese...
Firenze, Monnier, 1895.
     199 p.

NT 0048847   OCl

Tassoni, Alessandro, 1565-1635.
Hd32
752
     Le filippiche di Alessandro Tassoni nel III
centenario dalla morte del poeta riprodotte
per la prima volta in facsimile, con introduzione narrativa di Fausto Bianchi. Modena,
Dante Cavallotti,1935.
     2p.ℓ.,[3]-81p.,facsim:[16]p. front.,illus.
20cm.

     1. Piedmont - Hist. 2. Savoy, House of. I.
Bianchi,Fausto

NT 0048848   CtY IU CU CLU

PQ
4663
.F4
     Tassoni, Alessandro, 1565-1635.
     Le filippiche, con introd. a cura di
Augusto de Marco; con aggiunte le altre
dell'Anonimo sincrono. Milano, Signorelli
[1928]
     91 p.
     Bibl. footnotes.

     1. Phillip II, King of Spain 1527-1598.
I. Marco, Augusto di, ed. II. Title.

NT 0048849   NBuU IU

Tassoni, Alessandro, 1565-1635.
     Der geraubte Eimer: ein heroisch-komisches
Gedicht. Aus den Italienischen mit Anmerkungen
von Friedrich Schmit. Hamburg, Bey C. E.
Bohn, 1781.
     546 p. 16 cm.
     Translation of Secchia rapita.
     I. Schmit, Friedrich, 1744-1822, ed. and tr.

NT 0048850   NjP InU

PQ
4716
M87
A44
     Tassoni, Alessandro, 1565-1635
     Der geraubte Eimer. Aus dem Italienischen
übers. von P. L. Kritz. Leipzig, F. A.
Brockhaus, 1842.
     250p. illus. 17cm.
     Translation of La secchia rapita.
     Bound with Meli, Giovanni. Lieder. Leip-
zig, 1856.

     I. Kritz, Paul Ludolph, 1788-1869, tr.
II. Title

NT 0048851   WU

PQ4663
.S43K8
     TASSONI,ALESSANDRO,1565-1635.
     Der geraubte eimer,von Alessandro Tassoni. Aus dem
italienischen übersetzt von P.L.Kritz. Mit einer die
in dem gedichte vorkommenden geographischen oertlich-
keiten darstellenden karte. Leipzig, F.A.Brockhaus,
1842.
     xi,250 p. fold.map. 19cm. (On cover:Bibliothek
italienischer classiker. 25.bd.)

NT 0048852   ICU

Tassoni, Alessandro, 1565-1635.
     Le lettere di Alessandro Tassoni, tratte da autografi e da
copie e pubblicate per la prima volta nella loro interezza da
Giorgio Rossi. Bologna, Romagnoli dall' Acqua, 1901-10.
     2 v. 23ᶜᵐ. (*Half-title:* Collezione di opere inedite o rare dei primi tre
secoli della lingua. [84, 100])

     I. Rossi, Giorgio, 1873- ed.   A 41-2873
Northwestern univ. Libr.
for Library of Congress   [PQ4204.A3C5 vol. 84, 100]
       [2]   (850.82)

MH ICU
NT 0048853   IEN OCU MB CU ICN NcD MdBP MH MiU CSmH

Tassoni, Alessandro, 1565-1635
     Manifesto di Alessandro Tassoni intorno le
relazioni passate tra esso e i principi di Savoia.

     (In Archivio storico italiano. Firenze, 1849.
22 1/2 cm. Appendice, t. 7, p. [447]-495)

DG401
.A7

NT 0048854   DLC

TASSONI,Alessandro,1565-1635.
     La mastèla rubà ed Sandrein Tassón,tradotta
in bulgnèis. Bologna,G.Cenerelli,1902.

     At head of title: Raffaele Bonzi.

NT 0048855   MH

Tassoni, Alessandro, 1565-1635.
     Miscellanea Tassoniana
       see under Casini, Tommaso, 1565-1635.

Tassoni, Alessandro, 1565-1635.
     Opere minori. A cura di Giovanni
Nascimbeni e Giorgio Rossi, xilografie di
Benito Boccolari. [Modena,G. Ferraguti,
1926]
     3v. in 1. illus. 20cm. (Classici del
ridere)

NT 0048857   MtU OrU

851.5
T21o
     Tassoni, Alessandro, 1565-1635.
     Opere minori, a cura di Giovanni Nascimbeni
e Giorgio Rossi; xilografie di Benito Boccolari.
Roma, Formiggini [1926]
     3v. in 1. illus. 21cm. (Classici del
ridere, 62-64)

     I. Nascimbeni, Giovanni, ed. II. Rossi,
Giorgio, 1873l   jt. ed.

DLC-P4 PP CtY
NT 0048858   IEN ICU MH WU TU NN MiU OrU NcD PBm

DG
441
.T3
    Tassoni, Alessandro, 1565-1635.
    Paragone degl'ingegni antichi e moderni.
Venezia, Tip. di Alvisopoli, 1827.
    247 p.   17cm.

1. Italy - Civilization I. Title

NT   0048859   WU TU

DG442
T3
    Tassoni, Alessandro, 1565-1635.
    Paragone degli ingegni antichi e moderni (libro x, ed altro,
dei pensieri diversi) di A. Tassoni; a cura e con introduzione
di M. Recchi ... Lanciano, R. Carabba ɩpref. 1915ɩ
    2 v. 19½ᶜᵐ. (*On cover:* Cvltvra dell'anima. n. 56-57)

NT   0048860   CU MH

F
3589
.863
    TASSONI, ALESSANDRO, 1565-1635.
    Paragone degli ingegni antichi e moderni
(libro X, ed altro, dei Pensieri diversi)
a cura e con introduzione di M. Recci.
Lanciano, R. Carabba, 1918-19.
    2v.inl. 20cm.   (Cvltvra dell'anima, n.
56-57)

NT   0048861   ICN NRU IU

    Tassoni, Alessandro, 1565-1635.
    Paragone degli ingegni antichi e moderni (libro x, ed altro,
dei Pensieri diversi) di A. Tassoni; a cura e con introduzione
di M. Recchi ... Lanciano, R. Carabba ɩ1934ɩ
    2 v. 19½ᶜᵐ. (*On cover:* Cvltvra dell'anima. n. 56-57)

1. Italy—Civilization.   I. Recchi, Mario, ed. II. Title.
                         A C 35-2591

Title from Wellesley   College. Printed by L. C.

NT   0048862   MWelC CaBVaU AzU OCU CSmH

---

*IO6
T1857
608p
    Tassoni, Alessandro, 1565-1635.
    Parte de qvisiti del s. Alessandro Tassoni ...
Dati in lvce da Givlian Cassiani ...
    In Modona,Per Givlian Cassiani.1608. Con
licenza de'superiori.
    8°. 8p.ℓ.,144p. 14.5cm.
    Printer's mark (?) on t.-p.
    Also published with title: Varietà di pensieri;
a much expanded version later published with
title: Dieci libri di pensieri diversi.

NT   0048863   MH ICN DFo

    Tassoni, Alessandro, 1565-1635.
    La Pate enlevade, poïeme coumique
      see under title

    Tassoni, Aleskandro, 1565-1635.
    Per dare un saggio del satirico ingegno del
Tassoni... [n.d.]

NT   0048865   NIC

PQ4201
.P65
r.6
    TASSONI,ALESSANDRO,1565-1635.
    Le più belle pagine di Alessandro Tassoni,scelte da
Adolfo Albertazzi. ɩMilano,Fratelli Treves,1922.
    ɩ6ɩ,viii,300 p.incl.front.(mounted port.) 16½cm.
    (Half-title: Le più belle pagine degli scrittori ita-
liani,scelte da scrittori viventi... ɩ6ɩ)
    Bibliography:p.ɩ279ɩ-280.

NT   0048866   ICU OCl MH IU MB CaBVaU CtY CU PPT PP

    Tassoni, Alessandro, 1565-1635.
    Le postille del Tassoni, inserte a propii luoghi,
sono state trascritte dalla copia lattano in Roma
dal Dr. Domenico Vandelli sull' originale
posseduto dal marchese Alessandro Copponi.
    (In Dante Alighieri. La divina commedia 1515)

NT   0048867   PU

TASSONI,Alessandro, 1565-1635.
    Postille scelte alla Divina commedia di
Dante Alighieri. Reggio,1826.

    pp.44+.   12°
    The notes are of the briefest,and are taken
from the margins of a copy of the Aldine edition of Divina commedia.

NT   0048868   MH NIC PU

    Tassoni, Alessandro, 1565-1635.
    Postille scelte alla Divina commedia di Dante
Alighieri.   Reggio, 1836.
    44 p.   12°.
    In: Romeo, S., Prolegomeni alla Divina
commedia... 1898.

NT   0048869   RPB

    Tassoni, Alessandro, 1565-1635.
    ... Prose politiche e morali, a cura di Giorgio Rossi. Bari,
G. Laterza & figli, 1930.
    3 p. l., ɩ3ɩ-461 p. 21ᶜᵐ.   (*Half-title:* A. Tassoni. Opere. II)
    Scrittori d'Italia, 129.
    CONTENTS.—I. Il primo dialogo della difesa di Alessandro Mace-
done.—II. Dai pensieri diversi.—III. Opuscoli politici.—Appendice.—Nota.

    I. Rossi, Giorgio, 1873-   ed.   A 31-582 Revised

Minnesota. Univ. Libr.
for Library of Congress   PQ4663.A16 1930
                         ɩr43f2ɩ†

    OCU OU GU NN MH ViU DLC CaBVaU
NT   0048870   MnU CU NcU CaOTP ViMiM PBm MU NBuU MiU

TASSONI,Alessandro, 1565-1635.
    Ragionamento inedito tra Furio Carandino e
Gaspare Prato intorno ad alcune cose notate
nel xii.dell'Inferno ɩvv.109-111ɩ Published by
Carolina Cutting nei Guitera,with a prefatory
note by Oreste Raggi.] Modena,[1867].

    pp.46.
    "Nozze Carandini - Bastogi."

NT   0048871   MH PU NIC RPB

Bd.w.
PR
3658
P3
P3
1714
Cage
    Tassoni, Alessandro, 1565-1635.
    The rape of the bucket. An heroi-comical poem.
The first of the kind. Made English from the
original Italian ... by Mr. Ozell. 2d. ed.
London: Printed for E. Curll, 1715.
    70 ɩ2ɩ p. A-D⁸, E⁴. (A2, title-page, is a
cancel.) 8vo.
    "Books printed for E. Sanger", sig. E4v.
    John Hales Calcraft copy.

NT   0048872   DFo NjR OrU NN TxU IU CtY

    Tassoni, Alessandro, 1565-1635.
    The rape of the bucket. An heroi-comical
poem. The first of the kind. Made English
from the original Italian of Tassoni by Mr.
ɩJohnɩ Ozell. The second edition. London:
Printed for E. Curll ... 1715.
    70,ɩ1ɩ,54 p.incl.front. 20ᵐ.
    Translation of the first two cantos, with a
part of the third, of the author's La secchia
rapita.
    Signatures: A-   D⁸, E⁴ (A₁ frontis-

Continued in next column

Continued from preceding column

piece; E₄, verso, advertisements); A-C8, D3.
    "La secchia rapita ... con le dichiarazioni
del Sig. Gasparo Salviani ɩpseud. for Tas-
soniɩ. ɩn.p.ɩ 1710", containing the original
Italian of the first two cantos, has special
title-page and separate signaturing and paging.
Bound in half brown cloth.

NT   0048874   CLU-C ICN

    Tassoni, Alessandro, 1565-1635.
    Rime; raccolte su i codici e le stampe da Tommaso Casini.
Bologna, G. Romagnoli, 1880.
    79 p. 20 cm. (Scelta di curiosità letterarie inedite o rare dal
secolo XIII al XVII. Dispensa 174)
    "Edizione di soli 202 esemplari ordinatamente numerati. N.° 137."

    I. Casini, Tommaso, 1859-1917, ed.   (Series)
    PQ4204.A3C6   vol. 174   A 53-4656

Cincinnati. Univ. Libr.
for Library of Congress   ɩ¾ɩ†

NT   0048875   OCU MdBP CtY OrU PBm MdBP MH ICN DLC

    Tassoni, Alessandro, 1565-1635.
    Le rime di Francesco Petrarca... "aggrungono
le considerazioni rivedute eampliate d'Alessandro
Tasoni. Modena, 1711
      see under   Petrarca, Francesco, 1304-1374.

Y
712
T 302
    Tassoni, Alessandro,   1565-1635.
    Le seau enlevé, poeme heroï-satiro-
comique, nouvellement tr. de l'italien
du Tassoni…   Par.1758-59ɩv.1,1759ɩ
3v.nar.T.

    Italian and French on opposite pages
    Translated into French by De Cá-
dors.-cf.Quérard.

NT   0048877   ICN

    Tassoni, Alessandro
    Le seau enlevé. Paris, 1871.
    2 v. in 1 24°

NT   0048878   NN

PQ4663 **Tassoni, Alessandro, 1565-1635.**
.S42B8   ... Le seau enlevé, poëme héroï-comique en douze chants,
    tr. de l'italien par Miltiade de Bresse ... Paris, Librairie
    de la Bibliothèque nationale, 1875.
    2 v. in 1. 13½ᶜᵐ. (Bibliothèque nationale. Collection des meilleurs auteurs
anciens et modernes)
    At head of title: Tassoni.

NT   0048879   ICU NBuG

    Tassoni, Alesandro, 1565-1635.
    La secchia; contiene sonnetti burleschi inediti
del Tassoni e molte invenzioni piacevoli...
Modena, 1908
      see under title

---

*IO6
T1857S
1622a
    [Tassoni, Alessandro, 1565-1635]
    La secchia, poema eroicomico d'Androvinci
Melisone [pseud.]. Con gli argomenti del can.
Alber. Baris. Aggiuntoui in vltimo il primo
canto de l'Oceano del medesimo autore.
    In Pariggi.Presso Tvssan dv Bray,à la strada
di S.Giacomo all'insegna delle Spiche mature.
M.DC.XXII. Con priuilegio del rè.
    12°. 6p.ℓ.,166 numb.ℓ.,[1]p. 14.5cm.
    First edition.
    In this issue, the dedication occupies prelim.

Continued in next column

Continued from preceding column

leaves 2-3 & the preface prelim. leaves 4-6;
another issue has 10 prelim. leaves, with the
preface on prelim. leaves 2-4 & a longer
dedicatory epistle on prelim. leaves 5-10.
 There are two settings of prelim. leaf 5ʳ in
this issue; in this setting, the author's real
name is given in ℓ.15, and the last line ends
"pensieri di-"; in the other setting, the
author's real name is not given and the last

line ends "riuscivano que-"
 Edited by P. L. Barocci, with notes by
Albertino Barisoni.
 With this is bound G. B. Marino's
Epithalami, 1616.

NT 0048883   MH MB OU NN

Tassoni, Alessandro, 1565-1635.
    La secchia rapita, poema eroicomico, e'l
primo canto dell'Oceano del Tassone.
[Roma,1624]Ristampati con licenza de'superiori,
e con priuilegio.
    12°. 15p.ℓ.,166 numb.ℓ.,1ℓ. 14.5cm.
    Added engr. t.-p. by Claude Mellan has false
imprint: In Ronciglione [i.e. Rome]. Ad
istanza di Gio. Batista Brogiotti [!]. L'anno
M.D.CXXIV.
    Dedication to Antonio Barberini (prelim.

*IC6
T1857S
1624

leaves 3-12) signed "Gio. Battista Brugiotti",
the printer, probably by Tassoni.
    Preface "A chi legge" (prelim. leaves 13-15)
signed Il Bisquadro accademico Vmorista di Roma
[pseud.].
    "Primo canto dell'Oceano": leaf 150ᵛ-166ᵛ.
    Errata: recto of unnumbered leaf at end.
    Prelim. leaf 14 is a cancel.

NT 0048885   MH-H NNC MH ICN ViU

Tassoni, Alesandro, 1565-1635.
    La secchia rapita, poema eroicomico, e'l canto
dell'Oceano, del Tassone. Con licenza de'
superiori, e priuilegio. [Printer's device]
In Venetia, presso Giacomo Sarzina, MDCXXV.
    [xxii] 333 p. 13 cm.
    Initials. Catchwords.
    Bound in limp vellum.
    Listed in Brit. Mus. in variant edition.

NT 0048886   FU

Tassoni, Alessandro, 1565-1635.
    La secchia rapita, poema eroicomico, del sig.
Alessandro Tassoni, con le dichiarazioni del
sig. Gasparo Saluiani [pseud.], e'l primo canto
dell'Oceano nell'vltimo corretti con gli
originali ...
    In Venetia M.DC.XXX.Presso Giacomo Scaglia.
    12°. 7p.ℓ.,384(i.e.388)p.,1ℓ. 13cm.
    Title vignette (printer's mark?).
    "Pavlino Castelucchio [pseud. of the author]
ai lettori": prelim. leaves 6ᵛ-7ᵛ.

*IC6
T1857S
1630

    The "Dichiarazioni del sig. Gasparo Saluaini
[pseud. of the author]" follow each canto.
    Errata: recto of leaf at end.
    Numbers 285-288 repeated in paging.
    Imperfect: p.11-14 wanting.

NT 0048888   MH-H MH ICN

R.B.R. Tassoni, Alessandro, 1565-1635.
    La secchia rapita; poema eroicomico con
le dichiarazioni del Sig. Gasparo Saluiani
[pseud.] e'l primo canto dell'Oceano nell'vltimo corretti con gli originali. In Venetia,
1642.
    384 p. 13 cm.

NT 0048889   NcD MH

854T18 Tassoni, Alessandro.
Os1651   La secchia rapita; poema eroicomico.
    Con le dichiarazioni del Signor Gasparo
    Saluiani [pseud.], e'l primo canto dell'
    Oceano nell'vltimo, corretti con gli
    originali ...   Bologna, 1651.
    319p. front.

    Gasparo Saluiani, pseud. of the author.

NT 0048890   IU

TASSONI,Alessandro,1565-1635.
    La secchia rapita;poema eroicomico. Con le
dichiarazioni del signor Gasparo Salviani,e 'l
primo canto dell'Oceano nell'ultimo,corretti
con gli originali. In Bologna,1651,appresso
Carlo Zenero.
    14 x 7 cm.
    Imperfect:-bottom of title-page bearing im-
print cut off,hence the possibility that this
volume is the Bologna reprint of 1673;the imprint is supplied from a copy of the 1651
edition. Two leaves   of the first signature are wanting.

NT 0048891   MH NjP

Tassoni, Alessandro, 1565-1635.
    La secchia rapita; poema eroicomico.
con le dichiarationi del sig.Gasparo Salviani [pseud.] el primo canto dell'oceano
nell'vltimo corretti con gli originali.
In Bologna, Per G.Longhi [1670]
    311 p. 16 ᶜᵐ.

    Edited by P.Castelucchio.

    I.Castelucchio,Paulino, ed.

NT 0048892   NjP

Tassoni, Alessandro, 1565-1635.
    La secchia rapita poema eroicomico del signor Alessandro Tas-
soni, con le dichiarationi del sig. Gasparo Salviani [pseud.], e'l
primo canto dell'Oceano nell'vltimo corretti con gli originali.
In Bologna: Per G. Longhi, 1673.   300 p.   15½cm. (12°.)

    See: Sabin 94402.   See: Brunet, V, 675.
    Signature L (p. 241-264) wrongly folded.
    Gasparo Salviani is a pseud. of the author.
    The argument at the beginnig of each canto is by Albertino Barisoni. — cf. foreword
by the editor, Paulino Castelvecchio.

    "Primo¡secondo¡ canto dell'Oceano del medesimo avtore. Con la copia d'vna lettera
scritta ad vn'amico sopra la materia del Mondo Nuovo," p. 276-300.

    1. Poetry, Italian. 2. America—   Discovery—Poetry. 3. Columbus,
Christopher—Poetry. I. Barisoni,   Albertino, bp., 1587-1667. II. Castel-
vecchio, Paulino, ed. III. Title.   IV. Title: Oceano.   *Revised*
N. Y. P. L.   December 10, 1936

NT 0048894   NN

Bd.w. Tassoni, Alessandro, 1565-1635.
PR   La secchia rapita, poema eroicomico ... Con le
3658   dichiarazioni del ... Gasparo Salviani [pseud.]
P3   [n.p.] 1710.
P3
1714   54 [2] p. A-C⁸, D⁴. 8vo.
Cage   John Hales Calcraft copy.

NT 0048895   DFo

---

851   Tassoni, Alessandro.
T185sEo La secchia rapita, poema eroicomico
    con le dichiarazioni del Sig. Gasparo
    Salviani. Lond. 1720.
    54p.

    Bound with the English translation
    by John Ozell entitled The rape of the
    bucket.

NT 0048896   IU

3A
2025   TASSONI, ALESSANDRO, 1565-1635.
    La secchia rápita, poema eroicomico, del
Signor Alessandro Tassoni. Aggiuntovi la
vita del medemo, con le dichiarazioni del Sig.
Gasparo Salviani [pseud.], e'l primo canto
dell'Oceano nell'ultimo corretti con gli
originali.   In Venezia, Per D. Lovisa,
1726.
    [4]ℓ.,276(i.e.280)p. 14cm.

    Numbers 236-239 repeated in paging.

NT 0048897   ICN

Y
712   TASSONI, ALESSANDRO, 1565-1635.
.T2994   La secchia rapita. Poema eroicomico del sig.
    Gasparo Salviani [pseud.] accresciute, ed ammen-
    date dal sig. abate Marchioni... Osford,Teatro
    sceldoniano,1737.
    2v.in 1. 23cm.

    Paged continuously.
    Edited by Giovanni Fabro.

NT 0048898   ICN NIC NjP CtY

Tassoni, Alessandro, 1565-1635.
    La secchia rapita. Poema eroicomico, di Alessandro
Tassoni, colle dichiarazioni di Gaspare Salviani [pseud.]
... e le annotazioni del dottor Pellegrino Rossi ... Venezia, G. Bettinelli, 1739.

    6 p. l., xlviii, 450, [2] p. front., port. 17¼ᶜᵐ.

    Gaspare Salviani, pseud. of the author.
    "Vita di Alessandro Tassoni scritta dal Sig. proposto Lodovico Antonio
Muratori": p. i-xlviii.
    "L'Oceano": p. 401-430.

    I. Rossi, Pellegrino, d. 1776. II. Muratori, Lodovico Antonio, 1672-1750.
III. Title.
                                                        17-10156

    Library of Congress   PQ4663.S4 1739

NT 0048899   DLC

Tassoni, Alessandro, 1565-1635.
    La secchia rapita, poema eroicomico di Alessandro
Tassoni ... colle dichiarazioni di Gaspare Salviani [pseud.]
... s'aggiungono la prefazione, e le annotazioni di Giannandrea Barotti ... le varie lezioni de'testi a penna, e
di molte edizioni; e la vita del poeta, composta da Lodovico Antonio Muratori ... Modena, B. Soliani, Stamp.
ducale, 1744.

    lx, 92, 489 p., 1 l. front., illus., plates (part fold.) port., fold. maps, fold.
facsim., fold. geneal. tab. 26ᶜᵐ.
    Engr. title vignette; initials.
    Gaspare Salviani, pseud. of the author.
    "Catalogo delle edizioni della Secchia": p. liv-lx.
    "Primo¡secondo¡ canto dell' Oceano": p. 425-448.
    I. Barotti, Giovanni   Andrea, 1701-1772. II. Muratori,
Lodovico Antonio, 1672-   1750. III. Title.
                                                        17-10157

    Library of Congress   PQ4663.S4 1744

NT 0048900   DLC PU PPD FU CtY MH

PQ4663 Tassoni, Alessandro, 1565-1635.
.S4   Le secchia rapita, poema eroicomico ...
1744   colle dichiarazione di Gaspare Salviani [pseud.]
Rare Bk ... s'aggiungono la prefazione, e le annotazioni
    di Giannandrea Barotti ... le varie lezioni
    de'testi a penna, e di molte edizioni e la vita
    del poeta composta d'a Lodovico Antonio Muratori
    ... 2. ed. Modena, B. Bartolommeo, 1744.
    [4], 508 p. illus., facsim., geneal. table.
    22 cm.
    I. Barotti, Giovanni Andrea, 1701-1772. II.
    Muratori, Lodovico   Antonio, 1672-1750.

NT 0048901   ICU CU CU-BANC

PQ4663 Tassoni, Alessandro, 1565-1635.
.S4   La secchia rapita; poema eroicomico. Colle
1744   dichiarazioni di Gaspare Salviani. S'aggiun-
    gono la prefazione, e le annotazioni di
    Giannandrea Barotti. Le varie lezioni de'
    testi a penna, e di molte edizioni; e la
    vita del poeta composta dâ Lodovico Antonio
    Muratori. 2. ed. Modena, B. Soliani,
    1744.
    129 p. front.
    Xerox-copy, by SUNY at Buffalo, 1966.

NT 0048902   NBuU

Typ
725
47.822

Tassoni, Alessandro, 1565-1635.
La secchia rapita, poema eroicomico di
Alessandro Tassoni, colle dichiarazioni di
Gaspare Salviani [pseud.] ... e le annotazioni
del dottor Pellegrino Rossi ... rivedute, e
ampliate.
Venezia,MDCCXLVII.Presso Giuseppe Bettinelli.
Con licenza de'superiori,e privilegio.
8°. 8p.ℓ.,1vℓ,495p. front.,12 plates,port.
18.5cm.
Gaspare Salviani: pseud. of the author.

"Vita di Alessandro Tassoni" by L. A.
Muratori: p.i-1vℓ.
Tassoni's "L'oceano": p.433-462.
Plates engraved by Giuseppe Filosi after
Giustino Menescardi & Giorgio Gradizzi.
Another copy. 18cm.
Imperfect: portrait wanting.

NT 0048904   MH CU NcD MsSM

Rare
PQ
4663
S4
1763

Tassoni, Alessandro, 1565-1635.
La secchia rapita, poema eroicomico, colle
dichiarazioni di Gaspare Salviani ... et le
annotazioni del Dottor Pellegrino Rossi ...
rivedute, e ampliate. Venezia, Presso Giuseppe Bettinelli, 1763.
xxxviij, 488 p. 18cm.

"Vita di Alessandro Tassoni, scritta dal
Sig. proposto Lodovico Antonio Muratori": p.
x-xxxviij.
"L'Oceano": p. 433-462.

Gaspare Salviani, pseud. of the author.

I. Rossi, Pellegrino, d. 1776. II. Muratori, Lodovico Antonio, 1672-1750. III.
Title. IV. Title: L'oceano.

NT 0048906   NIC CtY

PQ4663
S4
1766

Tassoni, Alessandro, 1565-1635.

La secchia rapita; poema eroicomico di
Alessandro Tassoni. Parigi, Appresso Lorenzo Prault e Pietro Durand, 1766.
227 p. illus., plates.

NT 0048907   HU

Tassoni, Alessandro, 1565-1635.
Le secchia rapita, poema eroicomico di Alessandro Tassoni...
Parigi, Appresso Lorenzo Prault e Pietro Durand [da' torchj di
Prault] 1766. 2 v.   illus., plates, port. 24cm. (8°.)

Cohen-de Ricci, col. 980-981.   Rothschild: Catalogue, I, 1037.
Includes A. Muratori's "Vita di Alessandro Tassoni," P. Perrault's "Riflessioni"
and the author's "Dichiarazioni."
Dedicatory leaf signed: G. Conti.
Illustrations: 41 copper engravings by J. Le Roy and others after H. F. B. Gravelot,

C. P. Marillier and others, comprising 2 title-pages, dedication, 15 full-page engravings,
13 headpieces (incl. small port. of the author) and 10 tailpieces.
Binding, 18th century French, of mottled calf.

1. Engravings, French. I. Grave-   lot, Hubert François Bourguignon,
1699-1773, illus. II. Le Roy,   Jacques, b. 1739, engr. III. Marillier, Clément Pierre, 1740-1808, illus. IV. Marillier, Clément Pierre, 1740-ca.1790.
V. Title.   IV. Conti, Giusto, ca. 1720-ca.1790.

NT 0048909   NN ICN MH MiU PU PP

Rare
PQ
4663
S4
1768

Tassoni, Alessandro, 1565-1635.
La secchia rapita, arricchita di annotazioni. Parigi, Appresso Marcello Prault,
1768.
xx, 386, [1] p. port. 15cm.

Engraved t.p. and port. mounted.
"Compendio della vita di Alessandro Tassoni": p. [1]-xiv.
"A chi legge, prefazione dell'autore, sotto il nome Accademico di Bisquadro": p. [xv]-
xx.

Continued in next column

Continued from preceding column

"Prefazione di Alessandro Tassoni, alle
dichiarazioni da lui fatte alla Secchia,
sotto il finto nome di Gaspare Salviani": p.
[301]-303.
"Dichiarazioni": p. [304]-386.
With autograph: G. Waring, Shirehampton,
Dec. 2, 1868.

NT 0048911   NIC NN MH

Tassoni, Alessandro, Conte, 1565-1635
—— Secchia rapita, poema eroicomico con alcune scelte annotazioni, e varie lezione. Venezia, 1772. 12°.   2305

NT 0048912   MdBP

Tassoni, Alessandro, 1565-1635.
La secchia rapita di Alessandro Tassoni.   Londra, 1779.
4 p.l., (i)viii-xxiii, 330 p., 1 l.   front. (port.)   12°.

Engraved t-p. with ornamental border.
In verse.
"Compendio della vita di Alessandro Tassoni," p. [vii-]xviii.
"Dell' Oceano canto primo [-secondo]. Del medesimo autore," p. [305-]330.

1. Poetry, Italian. I. Title.
N. Y. P. L.   November 18, 1931

NT 0048913   NN

Tassoni, Alessandro, 1565-1635.
La secchia rapita, poema eroicomico, di Alessandro Tassoni.
In Orleans: Nella Stamperia di C. A. I. Jacob, 1786.   3 p.l.,
260 p., 1 l.   18°.

Added engraved t.-p. with imprint: A Paris: Édition de Cazin, 1786.
Ornamental tail-pieces.
"Canto primo [-secondo] dell' Oceano, del medesimo autore," p. [233-]260.

1. Poetry, Italian. I. Title.
N. Y. P. L.   November 18, 1931

NT 0048914   NN OCU NcU CtY NjP

PQ
4663
S4
1788

Tassoni, Alessandro, 1565-1635.
La secchia rapita : poema eroicomico / di
Alessandro Tassoni ; con alcune scelte annotazioni e varie lezioni. -- Orléans : L. P.
Couret de Villeneuve, 1788.
vℓ, 293 p. ; 21 cm. -- (Bibliothèque des
meilleurs poètes italiens ; 28.vol.)

CONTENTS: La secchia rapita.--L'Oceano.

NT 0048915   CLSU

*IP7
P2427
v.34

Tassoni, Alessandro, 1565-1635.
Secchia rapita di Alessandro Tassoni.
Venezia,MDCCLXXXVIII,Presso Antonio Zatta e
figli.Con licenza de superiori e privilegio.

4p.ℓ.,304p. 18cm. (Parnaso italiano ovvero
Raccolta de' poeti classici italiani ..., t.34)
Engraved t.-p., with medaillon port. of
Tassoni.
Head pieces engraved by Daniotto.
Preface by Andrea Rubbi, editor of the
series.

NT 0048916   MH CtY IU ICN

Tassoni, Alessandro, 1565-1635.
La secchia rapita. Di Alessandro Tassoni.
Venezia, A. Zatta, 1797.
240 p. 18 cm.

NT 0048917   CU MdBP

Y
7109
.82
v.163

TASSONI, ALESSANDRO, 1565-1635.
La secchia rapita; poema eroicomico di
Alessandro Tassoni, con la vita e con le note
compilate da Robustiano Gironi.   Milano,
Società tipografica de'classici italiani,
1806.
xxxiv,333p.   [Classici italiani, v.163]

Bookplate of the Marquis of Stafford.
"Canto primo-secondo dell'Oceano di Alessandro
Tassoni": p.307-333.

ICU MdBP MeB
NT 0048918   ICN CU CtY PU NIC RPB WaSpG CtW NN MH

+
PQ4663
.S38

Tassoni, Alessandro, 1565-1635.
La secchia rapita di Alessandro Tassoni.
Pisa, Dalla tipografia della Società
letteraria, 1811.
3p.l.,vi,303p. 37cm.
Title vignette (port. of author)

NT 0048919   NNU-W MH

Tassoni, Alessandro, 1565-1635.
La secchia rapita, poema eroicomico di
Alessandro Tassoni, con clune scelte annotazioni.
Nuova Edizione, nella quale si è adoperato il modo
più semplice di notare le voci coll' accento di
prosodia. Avignone, 1813.
2 v. in 1.

NT 0048920   PPDrop PPL MH

Y
712
.T 3

TASSONI, ALESSANDRO, 1565-1635.
La secchia rapita; poema eroicomico di
Alessandro Tassoni. Edizione formata sopra
quella di Soliani del 1744.   Venezia,Vita-
relli,1813.
389p.

Bookplate of Edmund Venables.
"Prefazione di Giannandrea Barotti, distesa
per l'edizione di Modena del 1744": p.xv-lxxix.

NT 0048921   ICN MdBP ICU

Tassoni, Alessandro, 1565-1635.
La secchia rapita.   Pisa, 1814.
374 p. front. (por.) 14 cm.

NT 0048922   CU

TASSONI,Alessandro,1565-1635.
La secchia rapita; poema eroicomico.
Firenze,P.Caselli,1823.

32°. Port.

NT 0048923   MH NN

PQ 4663
.S4
1826

TASSONI,ALESSANDRO,1565-1635
La secchia rapita. Milano, Società
Tipografica de' Classici Italiani, 1826.
xx+335 p. port. (Added t.-p.: Raccolta di poeti classici italiani antichi e
moderni, v. 41)

Notizie intorno alla vita di A. Tassoni
di Girolamo Tiraboschi: p.[vii]-xx.

I. Tiraboschi,Girolamo,1731-1794. II. Title.

NT 0048924   InU PU FMU

Tassoni, Alessandro, 1565-1635.
La secchia rapita. Lipsia, Fleisher,
1826-33.

60 p.   (Il parnasso italiano, v.2)

NT 0048925   PU

Tassoni, Alessandro.
La secchia rapita: poema. Mil., Silvestri,
1828.

NT 0048926   MA

TASSONI, Alessandro.
La secchia rapita; poema eroicomico e il
primo canto dell'oceano.   Torino, 1830.

32°.

NT 0048927   MH

Tassoni, Alessandro, 1565-1635.
La secchia rapita, di Alessandro Tassoni, arricchita di
incisioni in rame. Volume unico. Firenze, Presso spirito
Batelli, 1840.

376 p.   plates, port., fold. geneal. tab.   25½ᶜᵐ.

CONTENTS.—Vita di Alessandro Tassoni, compilata da Robustiano Gironi.—
La secchia rapita.—Dell'oceano.—Poesie e prose.

I. Gironi, Robustiano, 1769-1838.   II. Title.

NT 0048928   MiU MH

Tassoni, Alessandro, 1565-1635.
La secchia rapita. Tomo 1-2.   Venezia,
G. Antonelli, 1850.
2 v. in 1.   48°.

NT 0048929   NN

858
T212s   Tassoni, Alessandro, 1565-1635.
1858   La secchia rapita e L'oceano di Alessandro
Tassoni, con note. Firenze, Barbèra, Bianchi e
comp., 1858.
xlii, 477 p., 1 ℓ.   front. (port.)   11 cm.

NT 0048930   MiU

Tassoni, Alessandro, 1565-1635.
La secchia rapita e altre poesie di Alessandro Tassoni.
2. ed. Firenze, G. Barbèra, 1861.

liii, 453 p., 1 l. front. (port.) 11 x 7ᶜᵐ. ¡Collezione diamante¡

CONTENTS.—A. Tassoni da G. Carducci.—Quattro prefazioni alla Secchia
rapita fatte da Alessandro Tassoni sotto diversi nomi.—La secchia rapita.—
Canto primo dell' Oceano.—Sonetti.—Note.

I. Carducci, Giosuè, 1836-1907.   II. Title.

Library of Congress   PQ4663.S4   1861   1-24386

NT 0048931   DLC MdBP PHC NjP

Tassoni, Alessandro, 1565-1635.
857.51   La secchia rapita e altre poesie di Alessandro Tassoni.
T215S   2. ed. Firenze, G. Barbèra, 1861.

L. 485 p.   front. (port.)   11 x 7ᶜᵐ.

CONTENTS.—A. Tassoni da G. Carducci.—Quattro prefazioni alla Secchia
rapita fatte da Alessandro Tassoni sotto diversi nomi.—La secchia rapita.—
Canto primo dell' Oceano.—Sonetti.—Note.

NT 0048932   NcD PHC

854T18 Tassoni, Alessandro.
Os.1878 La secchia rapita e altre poesie, con
note. ¿Pref. da Francesco Costèro.
Mil. 1878.
335p.

La secchia rapita.— Dell' oceano.—
Sonetti.

NT 0048933   IU

Tassoni, Alessandro, 1565-1635.
La secchia rapita, L'oceano e Le rime;
aggiuntevi Le prose politiche, a cura di Tommaso
Casini. Firenze, G.C. Sansoni, 1887.
xlvi, 447 p.   11 cm.   (Piccola biblioteca
italiana)
"Dichiarazioni di Gaspare Salviani [pseud.]
alla Secchia rapita"; p. 403-444.
I. Casini, Tommaso, ed. II. Title. III. Title;
L' oceano. IV. Title: Le rime. V. Title: Le
prose politiche.

NT 0048934   NcD CU ICU OClW

Tassoni, Alessandro, 1565-1635
La secchia rapita; poema eroicomico, ¿di
Alessandro Tassoni, castigato ad uso della
costumata gioventu per cura di I. Gobio
G. B. Barnabita. 3. ed. Torino, Tipografia
e libreria salesiana, 1883.
233, ¿1¿ p. (On cover; Biblioteca della
gioventu italiana. Pubblicazione mensuale
...)

NT 0048935   OU

Tassoni, Alessandro, 1565-1635.
La secchia rapita di Alessandro Tassoni, con prefazione
di G. Stiavelli, e con note. Roma, E. Perino, 1890.

239, (1) p. 18ᶜᵐ. (On cover: Biblioteca classica per il popolo. vol. no. 17)

NT 0048936   MiU

PQ4663
.S4   Tassoni, Alessandro, 1565-1635.
La secchia rapita e altre poesie di
Alessandro Tassoni con note. Volume
unico. Milano, Sonzogno ¿19-?¿
335p. 18cm.
Contents.—La secchia rapita.— Dell'o-
ceano.— Sonetti.

I. Title. II. Title: Dell'oceano.

NT 0048937   NNU-W

PQ4663 TASSONI, ALESSANDRO, 1565-1635.
.S4   La secchia rapita e altre poesie di Alessandro Tas-
1902   soni, con note... Milano, Società editrice Sonzogno¡1902¡
335 p. 18½cm. (On cover: Biblioteca classica economica. n.30)
"Prefazione" signed: Francesco Costèro.

NT 0048938   ICU

857.5
T21s   Tassoni, Alessandro, 1565-1635.
1910   La secchia rapita, e altre poesie. Milano,
Sonzogno [1910]
335p. 18cm. (Biblioteca classica economica,
30)

NT 0048939   IEN NN

Tassoni, Alessandro, 1565-1635.
La secchia rapita, di Alessandro Tassoni, col commento
di Pietro Papini. Ed. per le scuole. Firenze, G. C. Sansoni, 1912.

vii, 219 p., 2 l. 20½ᶜᵐ. (On cover: Biblioteca scolastica di classici italiani, già diretta da Giosue Carducci)

"Questa edizione, ridotta per la scuola, è derivata dalla edizione integra, che
nello stesso tempo si pubblica."—Avvertenza.
"Le opere consultate, che più frequentemente si citano nel commento": p.
¡iii¡-iv.

I. Papini, Pietro, ed.   II. Title.

NT 0048940   MiU OrU MH

.S4
1914   Tassoni, Alessandro, 1565-1635.
La secchia rapita. Secondo l'edizione
veneta del 1630, integrata coi manoscritti e
le stampe anteriori. A cura di Giovanni
Nascimbeni. Lanciano, R. Carabba, 1914.
197 p. 20cm. (Scrittori nostri, 39)

"Dichiarazioni di Gaspare Salviani ¿pseud¿
alla Secchia rapita." p.¿175¿-197.

I. Nascimbeni, Giovanni, ed. II. Title.

NT 0048941   OCU ICU IU NN

Tassoni, Alessandro, 1565-1635.
... La secchia rapita con una prefazione di
Giosue Carducci. Milano, Istituto editoriale
italiano [1916]
xxiii [1] 275 [1] p., 2 l.   port.   19 cm.
(Half-title; Classici italiani novissima biblioteca,
diretta da Ferdinando Martini. Serie IV, volume
XCV)
At head of title: Tassoni.
Illustrated lining papers.
I. Carducci, Giosuè, 1836-1907.

NT 0048942   CSmH TU RPB IU

Tassoni, Alessandro, 1565-1635.
... La secchia rapita, a cura di Giorgio Rossi. Con 114
disegni di A. Majani (Nasica). Roma, A. F. Formiggini ¿1918¿

2 p. l., ¡vii¡-xiv p., 2 l., 3-315 p., 2 l. incl. front., illus. 20½ᶜᵐ. (Classici del ridere)

Title within ornamental border, with vignette.
Reproduces the text of the edition of Venezia, 1630.

I. Rossi, Giorgio, 1873- ed. II. Title.

NT 0048943   MiU CU MH ODW PBm CLSU

TASSONI, Alessandro, 1565-1635.
La secchia rapita. A cura di G. Rossi con
114 disegni di A. Majani, (Nasica) [pseud.]
2a ed. Roma, F. Formiggini, [1924].

At head of title: Classici del ridere.

NT 0048944   MH OU PP

Tassoni, Alessandro, 1565-1635.
... La secchia rapita. Introduzione e note di Francesco
Luigi Mannucci. Con due tavole. Torino, Unione tipo-
grafico-editrice torinese ¿1928¿

xlvi p., 1 l., 350 p., 1 l. II pl. (incl. port.) 18ᶜᵐ. (Added t.-p.: Collezione di classici italiani ... 2. ser., diretta da Gustavo Balsamo-
Crivelli. vol. LVIII)

"Nota ¡bibliografica¡ alla presente edizione": p. ¡xxxiii¡-xxxvii.

I. Mannucci, Francesco Luigi, ed.   II. Title.

Library of Congress   PQ4201.C7   2. ser., vol. 58   38-9406
¡3¡   (850.82) 857.51

NT 0048945   DLC CU CtY MH IU ICU

Tassoni, Alessandro, 1565–1635.
... La secchia rapita, L'oceano e Le rime; a cura di Giorgio
Rossi. Bari, G. Laterza & figli, 1930.

3 p. l., ₍3₎–382 p. 21 cm. (*Half-title:* Opere. I)

Scrittori d'Italia. 125.
"Dichiarazioni di Gaspare Salviani ₍pseud.₎ alla Secchia rapita":
p. ₍233₎–258.
Bibliography included in "Nota" (p. ₍349₎–357)

I. Rossi, Giorgio, 1873–   ed. II. Title. III. Title: L'oceano.

PQ4663.A17 1930   A 31–578 rev

Minnesota. Univ. Libr.
for Library of Congress   ₍r51e₂₎

CtY OrU CaBVaU DLC
NT 0048946   MnU PBm CaQMM NcU OClJC MiU OCU OU ViU

Hd32
776
Tassoni, Alessandro, 1565–1635.
... La secchia rapita, secondo l'edizione
veneta del 1630, integrata coi manoscritti e
le stampe anteriori a cura di Giovanni
Nascimbeni. Lanciano, R. Carabba[1935]
197p., 1 l. 19cm. (Scrittori nostri)

NT 0048947   CtY

851
T185la
TASSONI, ALESSANDRO, 1565–1635.
... La secchia, nella redazione del codice
Sassi, pubblicata nel terzo centenario della
morte del poeta. Prefazione e introduzione di
Giulio Bertoni, testo curato da Cesare Angeli
(VII fac-simili) Modena, Dante Cavallotti,
1935.
2p. l., vii–xlvp., 1 l., 409p., 1 l. illus. (incl.
facsim.) 20½cm.

I. Angeli, Cesare   ed. II. Title.

NT 0048948   TxU IU ICN CU CtY

---

*PQ
4663
S4
1935
Tassoni, Alessandro, 1565–1635.
La secchia di Alessandro Tassoni, nella redazione più antica secondo la lezione del
codice Sassi. Pubblicata nel terzo centenario della morte del poeta. Pref. e introd.
di Giulio Bertoni, e pref. di Renato Simoni
ai cinquantadue disegni eroicomici di Alberto Martini; testo curato da Cesare Angeli.
Modena, D. Cavallotti, 1935.
2 ix, 438 p. illus., facsims.

I. Angeli, Cesare.

NT 0048949   CLU

851.59
T18al
Tassoni, Alessandro, 1565–1635.
... La secchia rapita. A cura di G.
Rossi con 114 disegni di A. Majani
(Nasica) Terza edizione.   Milano,
Bietti ₍1939₎
xivp., 1 l., 311p., 2 l. incl. col. front.,
illus. 21cm. (Classici del ridere
₍33₎)

Title-page illustrated.

NT 0048950   KU PRosC OrU OU

PQ
4663
S4
1945
Tassoni, Alessandro, 1565–1635.
La secchia rapita; a cura di Francesco
Luigi Mannucci.   Torino, Unione Tipografico,
1945.
xlviii, 420 p. 18cm. (Collezione di
classici italiani, 60.)

I. Mannucci, Francesco Luigi, 1880–   ed.

NT 0048951   CLU

PQ4663
.S4
1950
Tassoni, Alessandro, 1565–1635.
La secchia rapita. (A cura di Dino Proven-
zal. 1. ed. Milano₎ Rizzoli ₍1950₎
296 p. 16 cm. (Biblioteca universale
Rizzoli, 161–163)
On cover: 3. ed.

I. Provenzal, Dino, 1877–   editor.
II. Title.

NT 0048952   MB IEdS NBuU OrPS

854T18
KZ6
Tassoni, Alessandro, 1565–1635.
La secchia rapita. Rime e prose scelte.
A cura di Giovanni Ziccardi. ₍Torino₎
Unione tip.–editrice torinese ₍1952₎
579p. ports., facsims. 24cm. (Classici
italiani, v.53)

Classici UTET.
"Nota bibliografica": p.29–32.

I. Ziccardi, Giovanni, 1881–   ed.
II. Title. (Series)

NT 0048953   IU OU InU ICN CU MnU MtU

Tassoni, Alessandro, 1565–1635.   Ital 7986.26*
La secchia rapita: The trophy bucket; a mock-heroic poem, done
into English rhime by Mr. Ozell. To which is annex'd a correct
copy of Tassoni's original, together with Salviani's notes from the
Venetian edition. Pt. I. London, printed by J. D. for Egbert
Sanger, 1710.
pp. 70, (2), 54. Engraved front.
"La secchia rapita; poema eroicomico," pp. 54, has individual title-page.

||Au:° trophy|Au°: La   secchia rapita; poema|Ozell

NT 0048954   MH MnU ICN NcD

Tassoni, Alessandro, 1565–1635.
La secchia rapita; or, The rape of the bucket: an heroi-
comical poem, in twelve cantos. Tr. from the Italian of
Alessandro Tassoni. With notes. By James Atkinson
... London, J. M. Richardson, 1825.
2 v. in 1. front. 19½ᶜᵐ.

I. Atkinson, James, 1780–1852, tr. II. Title. III. Title: The rape of the
bucket.
17–10159

Library of Congress   PQ4663.Z32

NT 0048955   DLC CtY NIC OCU

Tassoni, Alessandro, 1565–1635.
La secchia rapita; or, The rape of the bucket: an
heroicomical poem, in twelve cantos. Tr. from the
Italian of Alessandro Tassoni. With notes. By
James Atkinson... London, J. M. Richardson,
1825–27.
2 v. front. 19.5 cm.

NT 0048956   NcU PBm

Tassoni, Alessandro
La secchia rapita; or, The rape of the
bucket; an heroi-comical poem, in twelve
cantos; tr. from the Italian of Alessandro
Tassoni; with notes by James Atkinson, esq.
London, 1827.
2 v.

NT 0048957   ODW NjP PSC

Tassoni, Alessandro, 1565–1635.
La secchia rapita. Le seau enlevé. Poeme heroicomique du
Tassoni. Nouvellement traduit d'italien en françois ... A
Paris, Chez Guillaume de Luyne, et Jean Baptiste Coignard.
M.DC.LXXVIII.
2 v. front. 15½ᵐ.
The privilege is granted to Sieur P**.
Translated by Pierre Perrault who in the preface renews the attack on
the ancient writers in answer to Racine's and Boileau's defense.
Italian text and French prose translation on opposite pages.
Anonymous armorial book-plate.
"Ex bibliotheca R. Toinet."
1. Literature, Comparative—Classical and modern. 2. Literature, Com-
parative—Modern and classical.   I. Perrault, Pierre, 1611–(ca.) 1680,
tr. II. Title: Le seau   enlevé.
32–10146

Library of Congress   PQ4663.S4 1678   857.51

NT 0048958   DLC NjP NcD

TASSONI, Alessandro.
La seccia rubâ. [Translated into Bolognese
by F.M.Longhi.]

(COLLEZIONE di componimenti scelti in
idioma bolognese,[1827,etc.],III.57–206.)

NT 0048959   MH

---

*IC6
T1857
613t
[Tassoni, Alessandro, 1565–1635]
La tenda rossa, risposta di Girolamo
Nomisenti [pseud.]. A i dialoghi di Falcidio
Melampodio [pseud.]...
In Francfort[i.e.Modena].MDCXIII.
8°. 2p. l.,269,[2]p. 16cm.
False imprint.
A 1702 counterfeit has collation: 2p. l.,270p.
A response to G. degli Aromatari's Dialoghi.
With this are bound Plato, Il Liside, 1548, &
Tacitus, De moribus & populis Germaniae, 1519.

NT 0048960   MH NIC DFo CU

---

*IC6
T1857S
Eiz767b
[Tassoni, Alessandro, 1565–1635]
Al'trionf di mudnis pr'una segia tolta ai
bulgnis, poema ridicol traspurtà in lingua
bulgneisa da un'accademich dal tridell.
In Modna,Per j'ered d'Bertelmî Sulian,
stampadur ducal,Con licenzia di superiur.1767.
4°. 5p. l.,iii–ccxli,[2]p.incl.illus.,plates.
24cm.
Translation of his La secchia rapita.
Dedication signed "G.B."; the translation has
been ascribed to G. M. Buini, to Giuseppe
Boriani & to G. G. Bolletti.
Printer's   mark on t.-p.

NT 0048961   MH CU ICN PU

Y
712
.T3024
TASSONI, ALESSANDRO, 1565–1635.
Varietà di pensieri divisa in IX parti,
nelle quali per via di quisiti con nuoui fondamenti, e ragioni si trattano le più curiose
materie naturali, morali, ciuili, poetiche,
istoriche, e d'altre facolta, che foglian venire in discorso fra caualieri, e professori
di lettere.   Modona,Appresso gli eredi di
G.M.Verdi,1612.
₍102₎,592p. 21cm.

NT 0048962   ICN

PQ
4663
V3
1613
Cage
Tassoni, Alessandro, 1565–1635.
Varietà di pensieri ... diuisa in IX parti,
nelle quali per via di quisiti con nuoui
fondamenti, e ragioni si trattano le più
curiose materie naturali, morali, ciuili,
poetiche, istoriche, e d'altre facoltà, che
soglian venire in discorso fra caualieri, e
professori di lettere. In Modona, Appresso gli
eredi di Gio. Maria Verdi, 1613.
₍64₎ 396 ₍4₎ p. a–d⁸, A–3D⁴. 4to.
Francesco Carcano   copy.

NT 0048963   DFo NIC NNC

Tassoni^{NIC} Alessandro, 18th century.
Un Zoccolante mandd ad Alessandro Tassoni,...

NT 0048964   NIC

Tassoni, Bernardo.
    Rime...   **376p.**   **Bergamo, 1749.**

NT 0048965   PU

Tassoni, Ernesto.
    Contro la gloria: dramma in tre atti.
Catanzaro, G. Mauro (tip. Bruzia) 1931.

NT 0048966   NN

Tassoni, Giovanni.
    Proverbi e indovinelli; folklore mantovano. Firenze, L. S. Olschki, 1955.
    xiv, 256 p.   22 cm.   (Biblioteca di "Lares," v. 2)

    1. Proverbs, Italian.   2. Italian language—Dialects—Mantua.
I. Title.
    PN6475.M3T3   57–25188

  NIC MH MB ICU IU IaU
NT 0048967   DLC NN GU NBuU NBuC OC1 MiU ICN InU CU

WZ   TASSONI, Giulio, d. ca. 1615
240   ... Microcosmographia, seu parvi mundi brevis descriptio juxta
T215m   tres scientias philosophiam, medicinam, & sacram theologiam ...
1588   Bononiae, Apud Jo. Rossium, 1588.
      51, [4] p.   22 cm.

NT 0048968   DNLM

Tassoni, Giuseppina Allegri
    see
    Allegri Tassoni, Giuseppina.

LD3907   Tassoni, Joseph Paul, 1923–
.G7   Studies on the nitrogen and phosphorus
1953   content of insect protein.
.T3   45p.
       Thesis (Ph.D.) - N.Y.U., Graduate
       School, 1953.
       Bibliography: p.[41]-45.

NT 0048970   NNU-W

D274   Tassoni Estense, Alessandro, marchese di
E8T18   Castolvecchio, 1909–
      Eugenio de Saboya. Tr. y prólogo de Isabel
de Ambía. Madrid, Espasa-Calpe, 1943.
      196 p.   illus., ports.   22cm.

      1. Eugène, prince of Savoie-Carignan, 1663–
1736.   2. Europe - Hist. - 1648-1715.   I.
Ambía, Isabel de,   tr.

NT 0048971   CLSU ICU

Tassoni Estense, Alessandro, *marchese di Castelvecchio,*
1909–
     ... Eugenio di Savoia. Con 20 tavole. [Milano] A. Garzanti [1939]
     4 p. l., [3]-224 p., 2 l.   plates, ports., facsims.   20^{cm}.   [Piccola collana storica]

     1. Eugène, prince of Savole-Carignan, 1663–1736.   2. Europe—Hist.—
1648–1715.
                                 44–23431
     Library of Congress   D274.E8T3
                       [2]   923.5436

NT 0048972   DLC MWelC CU

Tassoni Estense, Alessandro, *marchese di Castelvecchio,*
1909–
     Uomini di un tramonto. [1. ed. Milano] Garzanti [1947]
     216 p.   ports.   20 cm.

     CONTENTS.—Maurizio di Sassonia.—Struensee.—La grande avventura del finanziere Law.—La tragica vita del barone Trenck.—Armfelt.—Giovanni Axel di Fersen.—Rivarol.—I cavalieri della regina.—Il galo principe di Ligne.

     1. Biography.   I. Title.
     CT167.T3   A 48–4774*
     Harvard Univ.   Library
     for Library of Congress   [1]†

NT 0048973   MH IEN NN DLC

Tassony, Ernő
     Aki a párját keresi; regény a Salmeci
Diákéletből... Selmecbánya, Joerges Á.
Özv. és fia kiadása. 1912.
     352 p.

NT 0048974   OC1

Law   Tassonyi, Ernő, joint ed.

     Hungary. *Laws, statutes, etc.*
     Magyar bányajog; a bányaszatra vonatkozó törvények, rendeletek, döntvények és elvi jelentőségű határozatok teljes gyüjteménye. Hivatalos adatok alpján összeállították és kiadják: Alliquander Ödön, d^r Bán Imre [és] Tassonyi Ernő. Budapest, Athenaeum irodalmi és nyomdai r.-t., 1931.

Tassopoulos (Anastase) [1894–]. *La mort subite chez l'enfant et ses rapports avec hypertrophie du thymus. 52 pp. 8°. Paris, 1926.
No. 525.

NT 0048976   DNLM CtY

Tasso's La fenice
     see under   [Cook, Albert Stanburrough]
1853–1927.

---

ar W   Tassot, Fabien.
54141   Le rachat du canal du midi; étude historique de la propriété de l'oeuvre de
no.3   Riquet. Toulouse, A. Nauze, 1912.
      215 p.   24cm.

      Thèse—Toulouse.

NT 0048978   NIC CtY ICRL

Tassovatz, Borivoie.
     Les formes pleuro-pulmonaires de la lymphogranulomatose malingne.
     Inaug. diss. Strassbourg, 1928.
     Bibl.

NT 0048979   ICRL CtY

Tassovatz, Sinicha, 1899–
     Contribution a l'étude de la glande thécale chez la femme.
     Thèse, 1927 Strasbourg.
     Bibl.

NT 0048980   DLC CtY ICRL

Tassulo, Carlo Antonio Pilati di
     see   Pilati, Carlo Antonio, 1733–1802.

Tassus, E., ed.

     Héronval, *France.*
     Cartulaire de Héronval, pub. par le Comité archéologique de Noyon. Noyon, D. Andrieux, impr., 1883.

944.08   Tassy,   abbé.
T2155m   Ménilmontant sous la Commune :
       épisodes / recueillis par M. l'abbé
IN: Tassy. Paris : F. Wattelier, [1872]
spec   34 p. ; 14 cm.
       Magis catalog 38, item 1153
       Cover title.

      1. Paris--History--Commune, 1871.   2.
Paris. Ménilmontant.   I. TITLE.

NT 0048982   IEN

Tassy, Edme, 1876–
     L'activité psychique; les réactions centrales dans les phénomènes cérébraux, par Edme Tassy. Paris, F. Alcan, 1925.
     2 p. l., [vii]-xvi, 126 p., 1 l. 19^{cm}.   (On cover: Bibliothèque de philosophie contemporaine)

     1. Psychology, Physiological.   I. Title.

     Library of Congress   BF182.T3   26–16750

NT 0048983   DLC MB NIC

Tassy, Edme, 1876–
     L'activité psychique; les réactions centrales dans les phénomènes cérébraux, par Edme Tassy. Nouv. éd. Paris, F. Alcan, 1931.
     2 p. l., [vii]-xvi, 126 p., 1 l.   18½^{cm}.   (On cover: Bibliothèque de philosophie contemporaine)

     1. Psychology, Physiological.   I. Title.

                                 38–23700
     Library of Congress   BF192.T3 1931

NT 0048984   DLC

Tassy, Edme, and P. Léris.
     ...La cohésion des forces intellectuelles.   Paris: Gauthier-Villars & Cie, 1922.   77 p.   12°.
     Reprinted in part from Mercure de France, Jan. 15, 1922.
     Bibliographical footnotes.

     1. Societies (Learned), France.   2. Léris, Pierre, jt. au.
     N. Y. P. L.   September 11, 1922

NT 0048985   NN

Tassy, Edme.

... La philosophie constructive ; l'orientation de la pensée moderne.—Le passage du positivisme au constructivisme.—Les méthodes constructives et l'avenir des sciences.—La constructivité mentale & sociale et l'avenir de l'intelligence.—L'esprit constructif et le pouvoir de cérébration consciente. Paris, E. Chiron (1921)

321 p., 1 l. 19ᶜᵐ. (Bibliothèque de philosophie moderne)

1. Philosophy, Modern.

Library of Congress　　　　B2430.T33P4　　　　23–622

NT　0048986　DLC

Tassy, Edme, 1876–　　*comp.*

... Les ressources du travail intellectuel en France, par Edme Tassy et Pierre Léris. Avec une préface de m. le général Sebert ... Paris, Gauthier-Villars et cⁱᵉ, 1921.

xxi, 711, (1) p. 22½ᵐ.

At head of title: ... Publié sous le patronage du Bureau bibliographique de Paris et de l'Union française.

CONTENTS.—Renseignements généraux. — Sociétés savantes. — Associations professionnelles. — Encouragements et aides financiers. — Créations diverses pour le perfectionnement des études et pour l'expansion intellectuelle.—Services et établissements scientifiques spéciaux.—Périodiques spéciaux.—Bibliothèques et dépôts d'archives.—Bibliothèques circulantes, d'échange, de prêt.—Indications bibliographiques.

———— Supplément (1921–1923) ouvrage honoré d'une souscription du Ministère de l'instruction publique. Publié sous le patronage du Bureau bibliographique de Paris et de l'Union française. Paris, Gauthier-Villars et cⁱᵉ (1924)

2 p. l., (iii)–viii p., 1 l., 100 p. 22½ᵐ.

1. France—Learned institutions and societies. 2. Association and associations—France. I. Léris, Pierre, joint comp. II. Bureau bibliographique de France. III. Union française, Paris.

22–10063

Library of Congress　　　　AS155.T3 Suppl.

NT　0048988　MiU OC1 DBS OU　DLC CaBVaU MH NN ICJ PSC CtY NcU NjP

Tassy, Edme, & Léris, Pierre
Les ressources du travail intellectuel en France...organes d'information et de documentation...societes savantes; cours, laboratoires...collections d'etudes; bibliotheques et archives...indications bibliographiques. Par., Gauthier-Villars, 1921.

100 p.

NT　0048989　PU

Tassy, Edme, 1876–　　153.1 R100
Le travail d'idéation. Hypothèses sur les réactions centrales dans les phénomènes mentaux, par Edme Tassy. Paris, F. Alcan, 1911.

(4), 316 p. 23½ᵉᵐ. (*On cover:* Bibliothèque de philosophie contemporaine.)

NT　0048990　ICJ ICRL

Tassy, Georges Mannevy-
see Mannevy-Tassy, Georges.

Tassy, Henri-Félix de, Bp. of Châlon-sur-Saône, d. 1711.
Explication des épitres et évangiles de tous les dimanches de l'année et de tous les mistères de Nôtre Seigneur et de la tres-sainte Vierge ...
see under title

Tassy, Henri Félix de, bp. of Châlon-sur-Saône.
Instructions pour les nouveaux catholiques. Où tous les points principaux de la religion sont familierement expliquez par l'écriture, les conciles & les pères, par Monseigneur l'Evêque & Comte de Châlon sur Saône. Paris, Chez Antoine Dezallier ... 1586. [i.e. 1626]

13 , 487 p. 17cm.

1. Catholic church. Catechisms and creeds.

NT　0048993　NcD NcU

Tassy (Jean-François-Félix). *Propositions médico-chirurgicales 20 pp. 4°. Paris, 1855, No. 239, v. 289.

NT　0048994　DNLM PPC

Tassy (Jean-Joseph-Victor). *Propositions et observations de médecine et de chirurgie. 20 pp. 4°. Paris, 1831, No. 257, v. 245.

NT　0048995　DNLM PPC

Tassy, Joseph Héliodore Sagesse Vertu Garcin de

see

Garcin de Tassy, Joseph Héliodore Sagesse Vertu, 1794–1878.

Tassy, Laugier de
see Laugier de Tassy, fl. 1720.

Tassy, Louis, 1816–
Aliénation des forets de l'état, encore un mot pusiqu' on y revient. A messieurs les députés. Paris, 1866.
16 p. 8°.
Signed: Aloys Wisst [pseud.]

NT　0048998　MH–A

Tassy, Louis, 1816–
L'aménagement des forets, par L. Tassy; troisième édition, revue et augmentée. Paris, Octave Doin, 1887.
1 v, 591 p. tables, 23 cm.
1. Forest management.

NT　0048999　NcD MH–A MiU CU

1816–
Tassy, Louis, A l'état des forêts en France, travaux à faire et mesures à prendre pour le rétablir dans les conditions normales. Paris, 1887. 8°.
"Ce travail est extrait de la 3ᵉ édition de l'Aménagement des forêts."

NT　0049000　MH–A

Tassy, Louis, b. 1816.
Etudes sur l'aménagement des forets, par L. Tassy... Paris, , 1858.
3 p. l., xi, 375 p. 22 cm.

NT　0049001　NcD CtY MH–A

Tassy, Louis, b. 1816.
Études sur l'aménagement des forêts, par L. Tassy ... 2. éd., rev. et augm. Paris, J. Rothschild, 1872.

3 p. l., xxxiv, 498 p. 22ᵐ.

1. Forests and forestry.

12–29208

Library of Congress　　　　SD431.T2

NT　0049002　DLC NcD CtY MH–A GU NNBG

TASSY, LOUIS, b.1816.
Lorentz et Parade, par L. Tassy. Paris: Bureau de la Revue des eaux et forets, 1866. 159 p. pl., ports. 22½cm.

587118A. 1. Lorentz, Bernard, 1775–1865. 2. Parade, Adolphe Louis François, 1802–1865. 3. Forestry—France.

NT　0049003　NN CtY MH

Tassy, Louis, 1816–
M. Parade, sa vie et ses œuvres. Paris. 1865. 8°.
pp. 58. Port.

NT　0049004　MH–A

Tassy, Louis, 1816–
Note sur le défrichement des bois. Paris. 1854.
8°. pp. 74.

NT　0049005　MH–A

Tassy, Louis, b. 1816.
Réorganisation du service forestier. Lettres, 1–4. Paris, 1879–80.
4 v. 22 cm.
France. Administration des eaux et forets.

NT　0049006　CtY–FS MH–A

Tassy, Louis, b. 1816.
Réorganisation du service forestier par M. de Mahy & M. Meline. Paris, 1884.
55 p. 22 cm.
France. Administration des eaux et forets.

NT　0049007　CtY–FS MH–A

Tassy, Louis, 1816–
Réorganisation du service forestier; reforme de la du juin 1853 sur les pensions civiles, par Aloys Wisst [pseud.] Paris, 1875.
23 cm.

NT　0049008　CtY–FS MH–A

Tassy, Louis, 1816–
La restauration des montagnes; étude sur le projet de loi présenté au sénat. Paris. 1877. 8°.

NT　0049009　MH–A

Tassy, Louis, *b.* 1816.
Restauration et conservation des terrains en montagne, loi du 4 avril, 1882, par L. Tassy ... Paris, J. Rothschild, 1883.

2 p. l., 89 p. fold. map. 23ᶜᵐ.

"Loi relative à la restauration et à la conservation des terrains en montagne": p. ₍82₎–89.

1. Forests and forestry—France. 2. Reforestation. ɪ. France. Laws, statutes, etc., 1879–1887 (Grévy)

24–23699

Library of Congress   SD193.T3

NT 0049010   DLC

Tassy, Pál.
Az európai nemzetközi jog vezérfonala, jogtanulók, szigorlók részére és magánhasználatra források, valamint jeles franczia és német forrásművek nyomán. Kecskeméten, Scheiber J., 1887.

208 p. 23 cm.

1. International law. ɪ. Title.

JX3695.H9T3   60–56248 ‡

NT 0049011   DLC

Tassy, Raphaël Jacques Justin, 1889–
... Hygiène d'un bataillon de chasseurs en campagne ... Bordeaux, Y. Cadoret, 1916.

52 p. 25½ᶜᵐ.

Thèse n° 24—Univ. de Bordeaux, fac. de méd. et pharm., année 1915–16.

1. Military hygiene. 2. European war, 1914–   —Medical and sanitary affairs.

S G 18–97

Library, U. S. Surgeon-   General's Office

NT 0049012   DNLM CtY

Tast, Albert.
... Untersuchungen über kreso-sapoformal auf seine brauchbarkeit als desinfiziens, desodorans, antiparasitikum und wundheilmittel ... Hannover, Buchdr. F. Culemann, 1910.

28 p. 22ᶜᵐ.

Inaug.-diss.—Bern.

1. Creso-sapoformal.

Agr 12–219

Library, U. S. Dept. of   Agriculture 396T18

NT 0049013   DNAL DNLM

Tast, E
Ce que l'on vous cache; documents troublants. [Paris, Technique du livre 1954]

64 p.

NT 0049014   MH

A tast [!] of the saints submission, loyalty and moderation; before and since the restoration of King Charles II. Giving an account of their fréquent conspiracies, insurrections and rebellions, &c. Also an instance of St. Baxter's moderation and piety... London, Printed for, and sold by the booksellers of London and Westminister, 1705.
20 p.   21 cm.
1. Dissenters - England. I. Title; A taste of the saints submissions.

NT 0049015   MB

Tastaldi, Henrique.
... Sobre a determinação microfotométrica da sulfocianemia medicamentosa e da adsorção do sulfocianato na desproteinização tricloracética ... São Paulo ₍Tip. Rossolillo₎ 1941.

84 p. incl. tables, diagrs. 23ᶜᵐ.

"Tese apresentada à Faculdade de farmácia e odontologia da Universidade de S. Paulo, para concorrer à cátedra de química biológica." Errata slip inserted.
"Bibliografia": p. ₍81₎–84.

1. Thiocyanates. 2. Chemistry, Medical and pharmaceutical. 3. Microphotometer.

45–41501

Library of Congress   RS431.T47T3

NT 0049016   DLC

TASTAMANTITORKAMIK agdlagsimassut ilait okalugtuarissat, ajokersûtinik ilasimassut. 1871.
180pp. 18.2cm. Dialect of Greenland)

NT 0049017   ICN

Tastavy, André
La Forme Hépato-Renale de la Maladie de Carré. Toulouse, 1948
Thèse - Toulouse

NT 0049018   CtY-M

Taste, Mr., pseud.
Mr. Taste's tour...
see under [Pope, Alexander] 1688–1744.

Tasté, Jacques, tr.

Citrine, *Sir* Walter McLennan, 1887–
... A la recherche de la vérité en Russie (I search for truth in Russia) traduit de l'anglais par Jacques Tasté. Avec 14 reproductions photographiques et une carte itinéraire. Paris, Berger-Levrault. 1937

Taste (Léon) [1872–   ]. * De l'inversion utérine; indications et traitement. 100 pp. 8°. *Lyon.* 1897, No. 68.

NT 0049021   DNLM

Taste, Lodoïs la
see
Lataste, Louis Lodoïs, *b.* 1842.

Taste, Louis Bernard de La
see
La Taste, Louis Bernard de, *bp.*, 1692–1754.

Tᴀsᴛᴇ (Timothy), *pseud.* The Freaks of Columbia; or, The Removal the Seat of Government: a Farce, accompanied by an interlude, called "The Metamorphosis;" to which is added, The New Prospect Before Us. Written by Timothy Taste, Author of that well-known novel, entitled, "The Pepper Box;" and also, the moral tale of "The Worn-out Pantaloons," which actually became threadbare, from too many editions having been published, without one having been read, by a single sans-culotte, and yet all of them were printed in France. ... *Washington City: Printed for the Benefit of the Author.* 1808. 12mo, pp. 70, errata (1).
B., BA., C. 94403

Purports to be written by a Portuguese visitor to the United States.

NT 0049024   RPB ICN MB PU MBAt DLC

Taste, Timothy, pseud.
Freaks of Columbia; Metamorphosis; and, The new prospect before us. Washington, 1808.
(In Three centuries of drama: American)

Microprint.

I. Title. II. Title: Metamorphosis. III. Title: The new prospect before us.

NT 0049025   MoU

Taste
see under   Foote, Samuel, 1720–1777.

*EC7
A100
746t
Taste. A satire. In an epistle to a friend ... London: [1746?]
f°. 10p. 25.5cm.
Political satire in verse; Walpole, Pulteney, & Chesterfield are cited.
Not to be confused with "Taste; an epistle to a young critic" by John Armstrong.
Imperfect: too closely trimmed throughout; imprint date based on reference to Chesterfield's resignation as Lord-lieutenant of Ireland.

NT 0049027   MH

Taste; an essay, by J.S., D.S.P. 2d ed.
see under   [Swift, Jonathan] 1667–1745, attributed author.

Dublin, 1739

Taste, an essay. London, 1732
see under   [Rollin, Charles] 1661–1741.
₍supplement₎

*fEC7
A100
732t3
Taste and beauty. An epistle to the Right Honourable the Earl of Chesterfield.
London: Printed for J.Roberts at the Oxford-Arms in Warwick-lane.1732. <Price six-pence.>
f°. 12p. 34.5cm.
In verse.

NT 0049030   MH CtY GASU IU MdBJ NNC OCU

MICPT
822.08
Taste and feeling. 1790. (Larpent collection. Ms. #877) New York, 1954.
(In Three centuries of drama: English, Larpent collection)

Microprint.

I. Larpent collection. Ms. #877.

NT 0049031   MoU

Taste and odor control in water purification
see under   West Virginia Pulp and Paper Company. Industrial Chemical Sales Division.

D628.16
T18
Taste and odor control journal ...
v. 1-
Sept. 1934-
New York, N. Y., 1934-
v.   illus., ports., diagrs.   23ᵐ.
(v. 1, no. 4: 30½ᶜᵐ) monthly.

Sept. 1934-Sept. 1938 have title: Taste and odor control.
Published by Industrial chemical sales division, West Virginia pulp and paper company.

Jan. 1942 supplement is "Index for the first seven volumes" (4 p.)
The March, May, July, Sept. and Nov. 1942 numbers comprise a Bibliography on articles pertaining to taste and odor control in water purification, published from 1912 up to the end of 1941.
Library has another copy of the bibliography issued in one cover, with title: Bibliography, 1912-1941. Taste and odor control in water purification. (32,   8, 8 p.)

NT 0049034   NNC IU ICJ NIC NN OrCS NNCC

TASTE life's glad moments. To which are added, Begone dull care. Lovely Nan. The woodman. Cuckoo. Edinburgh, Printed for the booksellers in town and country, 1823.   8 p. 17cm.

Weiss: Chapbooks, 724.
In verse.

NT 0049035   NN

---

*Defoe
30
.712
.A107A
A taste of philosophical fanaticism; in some speculations upon the four first chapters of Mr. Green's Principles of natural philosophy. By a gentleman of the University of Gratz [pseud.] ... London, Printed for J. Morphew, 1712.
71 p. 19cm.

NT 0049036   MB

A taste of the saints submission
see A tast [!] of the saints submission.

The taste of the town: or, A guide to all publick diversions
see under   [Ralph, James] d. 1762.

Tastes,   Marcel de
see   Marcel de Tastes,   , 1851-

Tastes, Maurice de.
Avis donnés aux agriculteurs en prévision de temps. Tours. 1877.
12 p. 8.

NT 0049040   DAS

Tastes, Maurice de.
Etude sur les courants aériens. Limoges, n. d.
12 p.   8°.

NT 0049041   DAS

Tastet, Émile.
... Rapport de M. Émile Tastet sur l'introduction en France des vers à soie sauvages de la Chine.   Paris, Impr. S. Raçon et cⁱᵉ, 1854.
30 p. 23ᶜᵐ.
"Extrait du Bulletin de la Société zoologique d'acclimatation. n° 3.— mai 1854."

1. Silk-worm, Chinese.   Agr 4-3618

Library, U. S. Dept. of   Agriculture 425T18.

NT 0049042   DNAL

Tastet, Étienne.
Capbreton : ses origines, son fleuve, son histoire, ses curiosités, ses richesses, le climat, la population, son avenir. Bayonne, Impr. Le Courrier, 1955.
54 p. illus. 21 cm.

1. Capbreton, France—Hist.

DC801.C215T3   57-26325 ‡

NT 0049043   DLC NN

[Tastet, Etienne]
L'église de Capbreton (Landes) notice historique et descriptive. [Capbreton (Landes) Imprimerie Spéciale des Editions Chabas, 1951]
20 p.
Paper-cover: Histoire de l'Église de Capbreton.

NT 0049044   MH MH-FA

Tastet, Jean.
Réponse à Eluard [poem] Paris, l'auteur, 1946.

NT 0049045   MH

Tastet, Tyrtée.
Histoire des quarante fauteils de l'Académie française depuis la fondation jusqu'à nos jours. 1635-1844...   Paris, Au Comptoir des imprimeurs unis, 1844-55.
4 v.   23 cm
Vol. 3-4 cover period 1635-1855.
1. Académie française, Paris.

NT 0049046   CtY NSchU

DC
36
T3
Tastet, Tyrtée
Histoire des quarante fauteuils de l'Académie française; depuis la fondation jusqu'a nos jours, 1635-1844 [i. e. 1855] Paris, Comptoir des imprimeurs-unis, 1844-66.
4 v. 22cm.

1. France – Biog.   I. Academie française, Paris II. Title

NT 0049047   WU

AS
162
.P281
T22
Tastet, Tyrtée.
Histoire des quarante fauteuils de l'Académie française depuis la fondation jusqu'à nos jours, 1635-1855. Par M. Tyrtée Tastet ... Paris, Lacroix-Comon, 1855.
4 v. 21ᶜᵐ.

NT 0049048   MiU CU NN ICU InU

Tastet, Tyrtée.
Le toréador, drame en cinq actes ... [Paris, Imp.J.-R.Mevrel, 1838]
46 p. 22ᶜᵐ.
Caption title.
No.7 in volume lettered Drames et mélodrames [v.51]

NT 0049049   MiU

Tastet, Victor Auguste Pierre, 1900-
... Du volvulus de la vésicule biliaire... Bordeaux, 1926.
Thèse - Univ. de Bordeaux.
Bibliographie: p. [57]-59.

NT 0049050   CtY

Tastevin, A
Guide complet du voyageur à Moscou
see under   Tastevin, Félix, 1858-1911.

Tastevin, A
Guide du voyageur à Moscou, par A. et F. Tastevin. 2. éd. revue et corrigée. Moscou, Impr. Th. I. Hagen, 1897.
194, 29, xiii p. illus., 2 fold. maps. 16 cm.
1. Moscow - Descr. - Guide - Books.
I. Tastevin, F

NT 0049052   NIC ICN MH

DK
26
T3
MAIN
Tastevin, A
Guide du voyageur en Russie. Moscou, Th. Hagen [1891?-
v. illus. 16cm.

CONTENTS.--v.1
--v.2 Moscu. [1891]

1. Russia - Descr. & trav. - Guide-books.
2. Moscow - Descr. - Guide-books. I. Title.

NT 0049053   TxU

DK549
T37
[Tastevin, A   ]
Guide du voyageur en Russie: St.-Pétersbourg et Moscou. [Moscou, T. Hagen, 1891]
1 v. (various pagings) illus., fold. maps.

1. Leningrad - Descr. - Guide-books. 2. Moscow (City) - Descr. - Guide-books. I. Title.

NT 0049054   CU NcU

PL 5373
T36
Tastevin, Constant F.
Africanité du Malgache. (Préfixes, radicaux, suffixes) [n. p., 195?]
1 v. (various pagings) 27 cm.
Cover title.
Extracts from L'Ethnographie, no. 45, années 1947-1950.

1. Malagasy language.

NT 0049055   OU NN

TASTEVIN, Constant F
D'où viennent les Noirs malgaches?; ou, L'émigration des Noirs, d'Afrique à Madagascar, avant l'arrivée des Hovas. (IN: L'Ethnographie. Paris. 29cm. Nouv. Sér., no. 39 (1941) p.[19]-32)

1. Malagasy language.   2. Ethnology--Madagascar.

NT 0049056   NN

Tastevin, Constant F
Grammática da lingua tupy. ¡1921?¡
p.¡535¡-763. O.

Manuscript note on title-page: Publicado en los Anales del Museo de São Paulo "Vocabulario tupy-portugues": p.¡599 y 686.
"Nomes de plantas e animaes em lingua tupy": p.¡687¡-763.

NT 0049057 NcU

498
T186g Tastevin, Constant F
Grammatica da lingua tupy. [São Paulo, Officinas do "Diario Official," 1923]
152 p. 23 cm.

Separata do Tomo XIII da Revista do Museu Paulista.

1. Tupi language--Grammar. 2. Tupi language--Dictionaries--Portuguese. I. Title.

NT 0049058 MoSU

Tastevin, Constant F
La langue tapïhïya dite tupï ou néēngatu (belle langue) grammaire, dictionnaire et textes... Vienne, A. Hölder, 1910.
4 p.l., 307 p. 23.5 cm. (Kaiserliche Akademie der Wissenschaften. Schriften der Sprachenkommission. Bd. 2)

NT 0049059 CtY

Tastevin, Constant F
Les langues des Purús...
see under Rivet, Paul, 1876-1958.

Tastevin, Constant.
... The middle Amazon: its people and geography, eleven articles, by Constant Tastevin. Translated by the Strategic index of the Americas. ¡Washington, 1943¡
ii, 166 (i. e. 160) p. 32ᶜᵐ.
Caption title.
At head of title: Coordinator of inter-American affairs. Office for emergency management. Washington, D. C., Research division ...
Reproduced from type-written copy.
Bibliography: p. ¡163¡-166.

1. Amazon valley — Descr. & trav. 2. Indians of South America — Amazon valley. 3. Rivers—Brazil. I. Strategic index of the Americas. II. U. S. Office of inter-American affairs. Research division. III. Title.

Library of Congress F2546.T2 46-25837
¡1¡ 918.1

NT 0049061 DLC PP PU TxU

Tastevin, Constant F
Petite clef des langues africaines, essai de manuel de linguistique africaine, suivant une méthode analytique intégrale. Vanves, Imp. franciscaine missionnaire ¡1946¡
196 p. 21 cm.

1. African languages—Grammar. I. Title.

PL8005.T3 51-35176 ‡

NT 0049062 DLC PU CU MH TxU IU OU MiU NBuU

Tastevin, Constant F
Les tribus indiennes des bassins du Puri
see under Rivet, Paul, 1876-1958.

Tastevin, Constantino
see Tastevin, Constant F

Tastevin, Félix, 1858-1911
Guide complet du voyageur à Moscou, par F.et A. Tastevin. Moscou, Gautier, 1881.

186, xiii p., illus.

NT 0049065 MH-FA

DK 43
.T215 TASTEVIN, FELIX, 1858-1911
Histoire de la colonie française de Moscou depuis les origines jusqu'à 1812. Moscou, Librairie F. Tastevin, 1908.
191 p.

1. French in Russia.

NT 0049066 InU CtY

Tastevin, F¡élix¡, 1858-1911. Slav 3197.1.6
Histoire de la colonie française de Moscou depuis les origines jusqu'à 1812. Moscou, Librairie F. Tastevin, etc. etc., 1909.
pp. (6), 191.

French–Russia|Moscow–Descr.

NT 0049067 MH

Tastevin (Joseph) [1874-   ]. *L'asthénomanie post-épileptique. 58 pp. 8°. *Paris, J. Rousset, 1911.*

NT 0049068 DNLM

Tastevin, Maria.
Les héroïnes de Corneille, par Maria Tastevin ... Paris, E. Champion, 1924.
vii, 250 p., 1 l. 20ᶜᵐ.
"Bibliographie": p. 245–250.

1. Corneille, Pierre, 1606-1684. I. Title.

Library of Congress PQ1782.T3 26-4391

NT 0049069 DLC CU LU TU NIC FTaSU ViU NBuC NBuU OU
CtY NcD CU-I CLSU MiU OCU WaSp CaBVaU OrPR

Tastevin, Paul.
Dictionnaire des termes économiques et financiers allemands et français ... par Paul Tastevin ... Paris, Éditions Le Pont ¡pref. 1942-
v. 18ᶜᵐ.
Vols. 1-   have added t.-p.: Finanz- und wirtschaftstechnisches handwörterbuch in deutscher und französischer sprache.
CONTENTS.—I. ptie. Allemand-français.

1. Commerce — Dictionaries—German. 2. Commerce—Dictionaries—French. 3. German language — Dictionaries — French. 4. French language—Dictionaries—German. I. Title.

HF1002.T3 A F 47-5007
Yale univ. Library
for Library of Congress ¡2¡†

NT 0049070 CtY ICRL DLC

Tastevin, Confrérie des chevaliers du
see Confrérie des chevaliers du tastevin.

Tastevin frères, tr.
BD431
.T6 Tolstoĭ, Lev Nikolaevich, graf, 1828-1910.
... De la vie; seule traduction rev. et cor. par l'auteur. Paris, C. Marpon & E. Flammarion ¡1889¡

Tastmona, Thothnu, pseud.
see
Platt, Paul T 1897-

Tastu, Abdon Lennen, 1754-1808.
Rapport fait par Tastu au nom d'une commission spéciale chargée d'examiner un message du Directoire exécutif
see under France. Corps législatif, 1795-1814. Conseil des Cinq-Cents.

Tastu, Abdon Lennen, 1754-1808.
Rapport fait par Tastu (des Pyrénées-Orientales) au nom d'une commission spéciale, sur une demande du tribunal civil du département de l'Aude
see under France. Corps législatif, 1795-1814. Conseil des cinq-cents.

Tastu, Amable (Voïart), 1798-1885, comp.
Album poétique des jeunes personnes; ou, Choix de poésies. Extrait des meilleurs auteurs par Mme Amable Tastu. Nouvelle édition. Paris: Didier et cie, 1869. iv, 460 p. front., ports. 18cm.

171491B. 1. Poetry, French—Collections.
N.Y.P.L. July 31, 1942

NT 0049076 NN

841.08
T186a Tastu, Amable (Voïart) 1798?-1885, comp.
D56 Album poétique des jeunes personnes; ou,
1876 Choix de poésies extrait des meilleurs auteurs. Nouv. éd. Paris, Didier, 1876.
460 p. front., ports. 18cm.

1. French poetry (Collections) I. Title.

NT 0049077 AU

Tastu, Mme. Amable Voïart.
1798-1885.
Chevalerie française. [Paris], 1821. 16°.

NT 0049078 MdBP

Tastu, Amable (Voïart) 1798?-1885.
Chroniques de France, par Mme. Amable Tastu.
2d éd. Paris, Didier, 1820.

NT 0049079 PPL

Tastu, Mme. Amable (Voïart) 1798?-1885.
Chroniques de France. Par Madame Amable Tastu.
3. éd. Paris, Didier, 1839.
2 p. l., 313 p., 1 l. front. 13ᶜᵐ. (Half-title: Œuvres poétiques. III)

I. Title.
¡Full name: Sabine Casimire Amable (Voïart) Tastu¡
13-2657 Revised
Library of Congress PQ2449.T7 1839 vol. 3

NT 0049080 DLC

Tastu, Mme Amable (Voïart) 1798?-1885.
Cours d'histoire de France. Lectures tirées des chroniques et des mémoires avec un précis de l'histoire de France ... par mme. Amable Tastu ... Paris, Lavigne, 1837
v. 22 cm.
1. France - Hist.

NT 0049081 CU

Tastu, Amable
Education maternelle, simples lecons d'une mère a ses enfants. Paris, Didier, 1843.
xii, 54 p. illus. 27 cm.

NT 0049082 PPStCh MWA

Tastu, Mme. Amable (Voïart) 1798?-1865.
Education maternelle. Simples leçons d'une mère a ses enfants ... 3. éd. rev. et corr. Paris, 1848.
26.5 cm.

NT 0049083 CtY

Tastu, Mme. Sabine Casimire Amable (Volart) 1798-1885.
Education maternelle, simples lecons d'une mère a ses enfants. Ed. 4. Paris, Didier, 1852.
488 p.

NT 0049084 PU

LC 37 .T3 1861
Tastu, Amable (Voïart) 1798?-1885.
Éducation maternelle; simples leçons d'une mère à ses enfants, par Mme. Amable Tastu. 6. éd., rev. et corr. Paris, Didier, 1861.
xv, 493p. illus. (part col.) color chart, maps (part col.) music. 26cm.
"Utile aux mères qui ont le désir de diriger elles-mêmes la première de leurs enfants..."
CONTENTS.--1. ptie. Le livre de lecture.--2. ptie. Le livre d'écriture.--3. ptie. Le livre de mémoire.--4. ptie. Le livre d'arithmétique.--5. ptie. Le livre de grammaire.--6. ptie. Le livre d'orthographe.--7. ptie. Le livre de géographie.--8. ptie. Le livre d'histoire sainte.--9. ptie. Le livre de récréations.
1. Domestic education. 2. Education of children. 3. Primers, French. I. Title.

NT 0049086 NSbSU

4LB 853
Tastu, Amable (Voïart) 1798?-1885.
Éducation maternelle; simples leçons d'une mère à ses enfants. 7. éd., rev. et corr. Paris, Didier, 1869.
485 p.

NT 0049087 DLC-P4

Tastu, Mme. Amable (Voïart) 1798?-1885.
Education morale populaire, imitée de l'italien de César Cantù, par Madame Amable Tastu. Ce volume comprend: L'honnête homme, lectures pour la jeunesse. Le portefeuille d'Ambroise, lectures pour tous les âges. Paris: Didier, 1842. xi, 252, vii, 192 p. illus. 18cm. (Bibliothèque d'élite pour la jeunesse.)
256069B. 1. Christian life. 2. Conduct of life. I. Tastu, Amable (Volart), 1798-1885, tr. II. Title: L'honnête homme. III. Title: Le portefeuille d'Ambroise. N.Y.P.L. February 18, 1944

NT 0049088 NN OO CtY

TASTU, Amable.
Éloge de Mme de Sévigné.
(Sévigné. Lettres choisies. Pp. iii-lviii. Paris, 1841.)

NT 0049089 MB

Tastu, Mme. Amable (Voïart) 1798-1885, comp.
Livre de jeunesse et de beauté. Morceaux en prose et en vers recueillis par Madame Amable Tastu. Paris, L. Janet [1834]
4 p. l., 259 p. plates. 14cm.
Added t.-p., engr., with vignette.
1. Children's literature, French. 2. Gift-books (Annuals, etc.) 3. French literature--19th cent. I. Title.
(Full name: Sabine Casimire Amable (Voïart) Tastu)
20-11054
Library of Congress PZ22.T3

NT 0049090 DLC CtY PU

Tastu, Amable i.) e. Sabine Casimire Amable (Voïart) 1798-1885, joint comp.
Dufrénoy, Adélaïde Gillette (Billet) 1765-1825, comp.
Le livre des femmes, choix de morceaux extraits des meilleurs écrivains français, sur le caractère, les moeurs et l'esprit des femmes, par Mmes Dufrénoy et Amable Tastu. Ouvrage enrichi de plusieurs fragmens inédits ou peu connus orné de 4 portraits lithographiés par MM. Colin et Boulanger ... Paris, Persan [etc.] 1823.

Tastu, Madame de Genlis. Amable Voïart. 2648.38
(In Genlis. Mademoiselle de Clermont. Pp. i-xii. Paris, 1844.)
F4990 — Genlis, Stéphanie Félicité Ducrest de St. Aubin, Comtesse de.

NT 0049092 MB

DC 611 N848 T22
Tastu, Mme. Amable (Voïart) 1798?-1885.
La Normandie historique, pittoresque et monumentale; ou, Souvenirs d'un voyage sur les bords de la Seine [par Amable Tastu]. Illustrée de 50 dessins par mm. Godefroy, Rossigneux et Lemercier, gravés par Brugnot. Paris, P.-C. Lehuby, 1847.
2 p. l., 375, [1] p. front., illus., plates port. 22 cm.
Head and tail pieces.
1. Normandy-Descr. & travel. I. Lemercier, C., illus. II. Rossigneux, Charles, illus. III. Godefroy, F., illus. IV. Title.

NT 0049093 MiU

Tastu, Mme. Amable (Voïart) 1798?-1885.
Oeuvres de madame Amable Tastu. Bruxelles, E. Laurent, 1835.
2 p. l., 449 p., 3 l., [7]-212 p. 11½cm.
CONTENTS.--Chroniques de France.--Poésies.--Peau-d'âne. Mythe.--[Poésies]
(Full name: Sabine Casimire Amable (Voïart) Tastu)
34-22618
Library of Congress PQ2449.T7 1835 840.81

NT 0049094 DLC NNUT

Tastu, Amable (Voïart) 1798?-1885.
[Oeuvres poétiques] Paris, Didier, 1838.
3 v. fronts. 13cm.
Each vol. has special t.-p.
Vol. 1, 6. éd.; v. 2, 3. éd.; v. 3, 2. éd.
Contents.--I. Poésies.--II. Poésies nouvelles.--III. Chroniques de France.

NT 0049095 NNC

Tastu, Amable (Voïart) 1798?-1885
Les oiseaux du sacre. [P,] 1825
10 p.

NT 0049096 MH

Tastu, Amable Voïart. **G.3910.19
Poésies.
[Paris. Dupont & cie. 1826.] (3), 344 pp. Vignettes. Decorated borders. 25 cm., in 4s.

NT 0049097 MB MH IU

* 841 T186P
Tastu, Mme. Amable (Voïart) 1798?-1885
Poésies. [Paris] I. Tastu, imprimeur, 1826.
vii, 344p. illus. 24½ cm.
"Edition original" pencilled on flyleaf.

NT 0049098 KyU

Tastu, Mme. Amable (Voïart) 1798?-1885.
Poésies. Par Madame Amable Tastu. 2. éd. [Paris, I. Tastu, 1827]
347 p. front. (Half-title: OEuvres poétiques. 1)
[Full name: Sabine Casimire Amable (Voïart) Tastu]

NT 0049099 NcD

Tastu, Amable (Voïart), 1798-1885.
...Poésies, par Madame Amable Tastu. 3e édition. Paris, J. Tastu, imprimeur, 1827. 5 p.l., (1)8-344 p. mounted front., illus. 22cm.
See: Vicaire: Manuel de l'amateur de livres du XIXe siècle, VII, 760.
At head of title: Éditeurs: Ambroise Dupont et cie, libraires ...
Illustrations: engraved frontispiece by A. Fauchery after A. Devéria (on China paper, mounted) and numerous small wood engravings, probably after Devéria.
Binding, by Messier, of red leather, gilt and blind tooled, in the Romantique style.
1. Engravings, French. 2. Wood engravings, French. 3. Bindings, 19th cent., French--Messier. I. Fauchery, Auguste, 1798-1843, illus. II. Devéria, Achille, 1800-1857, illus.

NT 0049100 NN CtY

TASTU, Mme. Amable.
Poésies. 4e éd. [Paris, 1827].
Engr. front.

NT 0049101 MH

PQ2449 .T7 A17 1830
Tastu, Amable (Voïart) 1798?-1885.
Poésies. Par Madame Amable Tastu. 4. éd. [Paris?, A. Dupont?, 1830?]
347p. 17cm.
P.S.U. copy imperfect: t.p. lacking; added t.p., engraved.

NT 0049102 PSt

Tastu, Mme. Amable (Voïart) 1798?-1885.
Poésies, par Madame Amable Tastu. 5. éd. [Paris] A.J. Dénain, 1833.
5 p.l., 347 p. front. 15cm.
"Shakspeare": p.[293]-326.

NT 0049103 MiU

Tastu, Amable.
Poésies.
Paris, 1839.
3v.

NT 0049104   DCU-IA

Tastu, *Mme.* Amable (Voïart) 1798?-1885.
Poésies. Par Madame Amable Tastu. 7. éd. Paris,
Didier, 1839.
2 p. l., 315 p. front. 13ᶜᵐ. (Half-title: Œuvres poétiques. I)

I. Title.
ₜFull name: Sabine Casimire Amable (Voïart) Tastuₗ
13-2655 Revised
Library of Congress   PQ2449.T7 1839 vol. 1

NT 0049105   DLC

Tastu, *Mme.* Amable (Voïart) 1798-1885.
Poésies complètes ... de Mᵐᵉ Amable Tastu. Nouvelle
éd. Paris, Didier et cⁱᵉ, 1858.
2 p. l., 552 p. front., plates. 18ᶜᵐ.

NT 0049106   MiU CtY

4PQ   Tastu,   . Amable (Voïart) 1798?
Fr.   -1885.
2360   Poésies nouvelles. Paris,
Denain et Delamare, 1835.
378 p.

NT 0049107   DLC-P4 MH

Tastu, *Mme.* Amable (Voïart) 1798?-1885.
Poésies nouvelles. Par Madame Amable Tastu. 4. éd.
Paris, Didier, 1839.
2 p. l., 316 p. front. 13ᶜᵐ. (Half-title: Œuvres poétiques. II)

I. Title.
ₜFull name: Sabine Casimire Amable (Voïart) Tastuₗ
13-2656 Revised
Library of Congress   PQ2449.T7 1839 vol. 2

NT 0049108   DLC

PN35   Tastu, Mme. Amable (Voïart) 1798?-1885.
.M4   Porcia ... [Paris, Krabbe, 1851?]
no. 17   [9] -12 p. 22 cm.
Caption title.
From "Les femmes de Shakespeare."
No. 17 of volume of pamphlets lettered
"Mélanges littéraires."

NT 0049109   DLC

PQ   Tastu, Amable (Voïart), 1798?-1885.
2449   Prose. Bruxelles, Meline, Cans, 1837.
.T7P7   2v. 16cm.
1837   Contents:--t.1.Fabien le rêveur. Rouget--de
--L'Isle. Le souhait. Susanne Centlivre. La
protégée. La belle cauchoise. La bonne idée de
Norah Clary. La guirlande, conte du village.--
t.2. Esther à Saint-Cyr. Trop tard. Und journée
de dupe. Le bracelet maure. Deux visites à la
Malmaison. Les expériences.
Collection of pieces which appeared originall
in various literary journals. Cf.Quérard. La
France litté-   raire.

I.Title: Fabien le rêveur. II.Title:
Esther à Saint-Cyr.

NT 0049111   LLafS

Tastu, Mme. Amable (Voïart) 1798?-1885.
Les récits du maître d'école, lectures pour l'enfance, suivis
de M. Bonhomme; ou, L'adolescent conduit à la vertu, au savoir et
à l'industrie, lectures pour l'adolescence. Ouvrages imités de
l'italien de César Cantu, par Madame Amable Tastu. Paris:
Didier, 1844.   viii, 192, viii, 296 p.   front., plates.   18½cm.
(Bibliothèque d'ouvrages d'élite pour la jeunesse.)

Line engravings by Mme. Thorel after Louis Lasalle.

646715A. 1. Juvenile literature.   French. I. Tastu, Amable
(Voïart), 1798-1885, translator.   II. Lasalle, Louis, illustrator.
III. Title.   IV. Title: M. Bonhomme.
N. Y. P. L.   August 28, 1933

NT 0049112   NN CU MH

Tastu, *Mme.* Amable (Voïart) 1798?-1885.
Les récits du maître d'école. Lectures pour l'enfance et
pour l'adolescence imitées de César Cantu, par Mᵐᵉ Amable
Tastu. Nouv. éd. Paris, Didier et cⁱᵉ, 1880.
2 p. l., 328 p. 18ᶜᵐ.
Title vignette.

I. Cantù, Cesare, 1805-1895. II. Title.
ₜFull name: Sabine Casimire Amable (Voïart) Tastuₗ
27-11979
Library of Congress   PZ23.T3R4 1880

NT 0049113   DLC

---

*FC8   Tastu, Amable (Voïart) 1798?-1885, ed.
T1866   Soirées littéraires de Paris. Recueil publié
832s   par madame Amable Tastu.
Paris, Janet, éditeur-libraire, rue Saint-
Jacques, nᵒ 59. [18³²?]
4p.l.,300p. plates. 16.5cm.,in case 18cm.
This issue is in 12°; there were also a few
copies imposed in 8° with the plates on chine.
Announced in the Bibliographie de la France,
Dec. 15, 1832.
Plates engraved by Charles Rolls, J. T.

Willmore & others after G. S. Newton, Thomas
Uwins, Ary Scheffer & others.
Includes pieces by George Sand, Sainte-Beuve,
Jules Janin, Charles Nodier, Marceline
Desbordes-Valmore, etc.
Original rose and gilt boards; in rose and
gilt board slip-case, in cloth case.
Pages 293-296 misbound in order 295-296,293-
294.

NT 0049115   MH-H ICU

Rkl   Tastu, *Mme.* Amable (Voïart) 1798?-1885.
13   Tableau de la littérature allemande depuis
l'établissement du christianisme jusqu'à nos
jours ... Nouvelle édition. Tours, Aᵈ Mame et
cⁱᵉ, 1858.
3p.l.,380p. front.(port.) 22cm. (Bibliothèque de la jeunesse chrétienne)
Added engraved t.-p.

1. German literature - Hist. & crit.

NT 0049116   CtY MB MdBP

Tastu, *Mme.* Amable (Voïart) 1798?-1885.
Tableau de la littérature italienne depuis l'établissement du christianisme jusqu'à nos jours. Par Mᵐᵉ.
Amable Tastu. Tours, A. Mame et cⁱᵉ, 1843.
392 p. front. (port.) 22ᶜᵐ. (Half-title: Bibliothèque de la jeunesse
chrétienne)

1. Italian literature--Hist. & crit. 2. Italian literature (Selections: Extracts, etc.)
ₜFull name: Sabine Casimire Amable (Voïart) Tastuₗ
15-6991 Revised
Library of Congress   PQ4044.T3

NT 0049117   DLC NcD

Tastu, Mme. Amable (Voïart) 1798?-1885.
Trop tard. Conte d'aujourd'hui. Par Madame Ama-
ble Tastu.
(In Heures du soir. Paris, 1833. 22ᶜᵐ. t. 2, p. [1]-139)

I. Title.
ₜFull name: Mme. Sabine Casimire Amable (Voïart) Tastuₗ
CA 13-1817 Unrev'd
Library of Congress   PQ1107.H4 vol.2

NT 0049118   DLC

Tastu, *Mme Amable (Voïart)* 1798?-1885.
Le voyage autour du monde. ₜWith translations by D. Mar-
telli, L. Craigie, and L. Müller. Paris:ₗ F. Locquin, 1836. 249-
275 p. 4°. (Veillées de famille. livr. 6.)
French, Italian, English and German, in parallel columns.
In: †NKD p. v. 6, no. 11.

1. Fiction (French). 2. Martelli, D.,   translator. 3. Craigie, L., translator.
4. Müller, Lida, translator. 5. Title.
N. Y. P. L.   April 24, 1913.

NT 0049119   NN

Tastu, *Mme.* Amable (Voïart) 1798?-1885.
Voyage en France, par Mᵐᵉ Amable Tastu. Tours, A.
Mame et cⁱᵉ, 1846.
3 p. l., 620 p. illus., plates, fold. map. 25ᶜᵐ.
Added t-p., illus. in colors.

1. France—Descr. & trav.
ₜFull name: Sabine Casimire Amable (Voïart) Tastuₗ
3-31165 Revised
Library of Congress   DC27.T21

NT 0049120   DLC NN IEN CaBVaU

Tastu, *Mme.* Amable (Voïart) 1798?-1885.
Voyage en France, par Mᵐᵉ Amable Tastu. Tours, A.
Mame; New York, R. Lockwood, 1846.
3 p. l., 620 p. illus., plates, fold. map. 25ᶜᵐ.
Added t.-p., illus. in colors.

NT 0049121   MeB

TASTU, Mme. Amable (Voïart), 1798?-1885.
Voyage en France. Tours, Aᵈ Mame et Cⁱᵉ,
1852.

24 cm. Plates, map and other illustr.
The plates are drawn and engraved by the
brothers Rouargue; most of the illustrations
are by K.Girardet engraved by Badoureau.

NT 0049122   MH

Tastu,   Amable Voïart.   *4661.38
Voyage en France. Nouvelle édition augmentée.
— Tours. Mame & cⁱᵉ. 1862. (2), 563 pp. Illus. Plates. Map. 8°.

G2173 — France. Geog.

NT 0049123   MB

Tastu, *Mme.* Amable (Voïart) 1798?-1885.
Voyage en France, par Mme. Amable
Tastu. Nouvelle edition, revue et
augmentée. Tours, A, Mame et fils, 1879.
399 p. illus., plates. fold. map.
30cm.

NT 0049124   PBL

Tastu, Amable (Voïart) 1798?-1885
Voyage en France. Nouvelle éd. Tours, A.
Mame et fils, 1885.
400p. illus.,map.

NT 0049125   OC1

Tastu, Sabine Casimire Amable (Voïart).
See
Tastu, Amable (Voïart), 1798-1885.

TX717
.O 85   Tasty dishes, Author of.
Rare bk.
coll.   Our girls' cookery, by the author of "Tasty dishes."
London, J. Clarke [1899]

**Tasty dishes made from tested rec-
ipes...eightieth thousand.   L., 1889.**

NT 0049128   PPL

Tasty dishes, made from tested receipes;
showing what we can have for breakfast,
dinner, tea and supper ... Lond., Clarke,
1894.
160 p.

NT 0049129   OC1

Tasty dishes made from tested recipes; showing what
we can have for breakfast, dinner, tea and supper. New
York, R. F. Fenno & company, 1902.
1 p. l., 6, 9-181 p. 18ᶜᵐ.   2-24745

NT 0049130   DLC ICJ MB

Tasty tropical treats; a cookbook specially prepared for
people who live in the tropics. Corrected. Manila, Philippine Pub. House [1952, *1951]
160 p. illus. 20 cm.

1. Cookery, Tropical.

TX725.T3 1952   55-40325 ‡

NT 0049131   DLC

W   **Tasville T   , Jorge**
4   El albucid y su aplicación en los
C53   procesos inflamatorios agudos de la
1942   cavidad oral. Santiago, Dirección
       General de Prisiones, 1942.
       74 p. illus.

       Tesis - Univ. de Chile.

NT 0049132   DNLM

Tasvir. Günlük siyasi gazete. sayi: 1-
30 Mart, 1945-
Istanbul[Ebüzziya Matbaasi]
illus. 58cm. daily.
Supersedes: Tasviri Efkâr. Müstakil yevmî
gazete.
Editor: 1945-   Z.T.Ebüzziya.

NT 0049133   CtY

Tasviri Efkâr. Müstakil yevmî gazete.

Istanbul[Ebüzziya Matbaasi]
illus. 58cm. daily.

Ceased publication with no. 5888, Sept.30,1944.
Superseded by Tasvir.

Editor: Z.T.Ebüzziya.

NT 0049134   CtY MH

[Taswell,   ]
The Deviliad
see under title

Taswell, Edward, 1696?-1720.
*EC7   Miscellanea sacra, consisting of three divine
T1873   poems; viz. The song of Deborah and Barak. The
718m   lamentation of David over Saul and Jonathan,
        The prayer of Solomon at the dedication of the
        Temple. With a proposal for publishing a large
        collection of the said poems, never before
        printed, in two volumes octavo. By Mr. E.
        Taswell ...
        London:Printed for the author,and sold by J.
        Morphew,near Stationers-hall.1718. <Given gratis
        to the sub-   scribers.>
          8°. 4p.l.,   31p. 19cm.
          Each poem   has divisional t.-p.

NT 0049136   MH CtY ICN

Taswell, Guilelmus
see Taswell, William, 1652-1731.

Taswell, Henry, tr.
Taswell, William, 1652-1731.
Autobiography and anecdotes by William Taswell, D. D.,
sometime rector of Newington, Surrey, rector of Bermondsey,
and previously student of Christ church, Oxford, A. D. 1651-
1682. Edited by George Percy Elliott ... [London] Printed
for the Camden society, 1852.

Taswell, James, fl.1648.
*EC65   Ten necessary quaeries touching the per-
T1873   sonall treatie very usefull and necessary to
648t   be considered. Also a right description of a
        Cavalier: with some drops to quench the fiery
        bull of Colchester. By James Tasvvell, a true
        lover of King, Parliament, truth and peace.
        London,Printed by R.I.for A.H.1648.
        15p. 18cm.
        Pages 3, 6, 7 misnumbered 1, 4, 5.
        Directed against Charles I and the royalists.

NT 0049139   MH

Taswell, Stephen Taylor Taylor-
see Taylor-Taswell, Stephen Taylor.

Taswell, William, 1652-1731.
**Antichrist reveal'd among the sect of
Quakers. In answer to a book entitled,
The rector corrected ... London:Printed
for Richard Sare,1723.
2p.l.,72p. 19cm.**

NT 0049141   PSC-Hi

Taswell, William, 1652-1731.
The artifices and impostures of false-
teachers. Discover'd in a visitation sermon,
preach'd at Croydon in Surrey, May the 8th,
1712. By William Taswell ... London, Printed
for Henry Clements, 1712.
31 p. 21cm.

Volume of pamphlets.

NT 0049142   NNC

Taswell, William, 1652-1731.
Autobiography and anecdotes by William Taswell, D. D.,
sometime rector of Newington, Surrey, rector of Bermondsey,
and previously student of Christ church, Oxford, A. D. 1651-
1682. Edited by George Percy Elliott ... [London] Printed
for the Camden society, 1852.
40 p. 22½ cm. [The Camden miscellany, v. 2, no. 6]
Forms part of the society's Publication no. LV.
"This autobiography was originally written in Latin, but has been
preserved only in the present translation, which was made by the author's
grandson, the Rev. Henry Taswell, vicar of Marden, in Herefordshire."—
Introd.
1. Taswell family. 2. London—Fire, 1666. I. Taswell, Henry, tr.
II. Elliott, George Percy, ed.   A C 36—657

Columbia univ. Libraries
for Library of Congress   [DA20.C17 vol. 55]

        VtU DLC MnU MB MH NN PU PPT
NT 0049143   NNC WaSpG MdBP OrPR OrU TxFTC CU PSt UU

x283   Taswell, William, 1652-1721.
T187c   The Church of England not superstitious.
         Shewing what religions may justly be charged
         with superstition. London, Printed for H.
         Clements, 1714.
         47p. 17cm.

NT 0049144   IU

Spec.
Q   Taswell, William, 1652-1731. ed.
157   Physica Aristotelica modernae accomodatio in
T37   usum juventutis academicae. Authore Gulielmo
1718   Taswell, S. T. P.   Londini:Impensis Gul.& Joh.
        Innys ad insignia principis in Coemeterio D.
        Pauli,1718.
        156p.

        1. Physics. I. Aristoteles.

NT 0049145   DeU

Augustan
BX 7734 TASWELL,WILLIAM, 1652-1731.
.T2   The popish priest unmasked. Or, The Quaker's
         plea for non-payment of tithes answer'd. By
         William Taswell ... London, Printed for R.
         Sare,1722.
         2 p.l., 51 p.

         1. Bugg,Francis,1640-1724?

NT 0049146   InU PHC

         [Taswell, William] 1652-1731.
Mhc8   A vindication of the orthodox clergy, in
1720   answer to two scurrilous libels, pretending
T18   to be vindications of the Lord archbishop of
         Canterbury ... London,J.Bowyer,1720.
         46p. 20½cm.

NT 0049147   CtY DNC

Taswell, William, 1709?-1775.
The propriety and usefulness of sacred musick. A sermon preach'd in the Cathedral-church of Gloucester, at the
anniversary meeting of the three choirs of Gloucester,
Worcester, and Hereford, September 8, 1742. And published at their joint request, (for the use of their charity)
by William Taswell ... Gloucester, C. Hitch; [etc., etc.,
1742]
31 p. 18ᶜᵐ.

1. Music in churches.
                        20-14641

Library of Congress   ML3001.T15

NT 0049148   DLC

Taswell-Langmead, Thomas Pitt, 1840–1882.
Wilshere, Alured Nathaniel Myddelton. FOR OTHER EDITIONS SEE MAIN ENTRY
An analysis of Taswell-Langmead's English constitutional history, by A. M. Wilshere ... 5th ed. London, Sweet & Maxwell, limited, 1929.

NT 0049150   CaBVaU

Taswell-Langmead, Thomas Pitt, 1840–1882.
English constitutional history from the Teutonic conquest to the present time. [1st ed.]–
London, Stevens & Haynes [etc., 18–]–
v.
1. Gt. Brit. - Constitutional history.

NT 0049150   CaBVaU

JN118
.T18
1875

Taswell-Langmead, Thomas Pitt, 1840–1882.
English constitutional history. A text-book, for students and others. By Thomas P. Taswell-Langmead ... London, Stevens & Haynes, 1875.
xx, 736 p. 22 1/2cm.

1. Gt. Brit.—Constitutional history.

NT 0049151   MB PU MdBP CtY MH PU-L

Taswell-Langmead, Thomas Pitt, 1840–1882.
English constitutional history from the Teutonic conquest to the present time. By Thomas Pitt Taswell-Langmead ... 2d ed. Rev. throughout, with additions. London, Stevens & Haynes, 1880.
xxiv, 803 p. 22½cm.

1. Gt. Brit.—Constitutional history.

10–5436 Revised

Library of Congress   JN118.T18 1880

NT 0049152   DLC CtY MiU MB MH NN NjP OC1

Taswell-Langmead, Thomas Pitt, 1840–1882.
English constitutional history from the Teutonic conquest to the present time. By Thomas Pitt Taswell-Langmead ... 2d ed., rev. throughout, with additions. London, Stevens and Haynes; Boston, Houghton, Mifflin & co., 1881.
xxiv, 803 p. 21½cm.

1. Gt. Brit.—Constitutional history.

17–8678

Library of Congress   JN118.T18 1881

NT 0049153   DLC NcD PHC NjR MH OU

JN
118
.T18
1881a

Taswell-Langmead, Thomas Pitt, 1840–1882.
English constitutional history from the Teutonic conquest to the present time. By Thomas Pitt Taswell-Langmead. 4th ed., rev. throughout, with notes and appendices. London, Stevens & Haynes; Boston, Houghton, Mifflin & co., 1881.
xli, 883 p. 22 cm.

1. Great Britain—Constitutional history. I. Title

NT 0049154   OKentU

Taswell-Langmead, Thomas Pitt, 1840–1882.
English constitutional history from the Teutonic conquest to the present time.
3d ed., rev. throughout, with notes and appendices, by C. H. E. Carmichael. London, Stevens & Haynes; Boston, Houghton, Mifflin, 1886.
xxxiii, 826 p. 22cm.
Bibliography: p. [xxix]–xxxiii.
1. Gt. Brit.—Constitutional history. I. Carmichael, Charles Henry Edward, 1842–1895, ed. II. Title.

OKentU WaWW
NT 0049155   ViU PU OC1W CtY OO MH NN NcD-L OCU OU

Taswell-Langmead, Thomas Pitt 1840–1882.
English constitutional history from the Teutonic conquest to the present time... 2d ed. London, 1887.

NT 0049156   PPL

Taswell-Langmead, Thomas Pitt, 1840–1882.
English constitutional history from the Teutonic conquest to the present time. By Thomas Pitt Taswell-Langmead ... 4th ed. Rev. throughout, with notes and appendices by C. H. E. Carmichael ... London, Stevens & Haynes, 1890.
xli, 883 p. 22cm.
"List of authors and editions cited by the editor": p. [xxxiii]–xli.

1. Gt. Brit.—Constitutional history. I. Carmichael, Charles Henry Edward, 1842–1895, ed. II. Title.

10–5437

Library of Congress   JN118.T18 1890

MB ICJ ODW OCU
NT 0049157   DLC PPT PHC PPD PU OrSaW CaBVaU PPB CtY

JN
118
T18
1890a
HRC

Taswell-Langmead, Thomas Pitt, 1840–1882.
English constitutional history from the Teutonic conquest to the present time. By Thomas Pitt Taswell-Langmead ... 4th ed. Rev. throughout, with notes and appendices by C. H. E. Carmichael ... London, Stevens & Haynes; Boston, Houghton, Mifflin, 1890.
xli, 883 p. 22cm.
"List of authors and editions cited by the editor": p. [xxxiii]–xli.

NT 0049158   TxU

Taswell-Langmead, Thomas Pitt, 1840–1882.
English constitutional history from the Teutonic conquest to the present time, by Thomas Pitt Taswell-Langmead ... 5th ed., rev. throughout, with notes. By Philip A. Ashworth ... London, Stevens & Haynes, 1896.
xxvi, 669 p. 19½cm.

I. Ashworth, Philip Arthur, 1853– ed.
Library of Congress   5–11636
———— Copy 2.   JN118.T8 1896

NT 0049159   DLC CtY MiU OO MiU-L KMK MH

Taswell-Langmead, Thomas Pitt, 1840–1882.
English constitutional history from the Teutonic conquest to the present time, by Thomas Pitt Taswell-Langmead ... 6th ed., rev. throughout, with notes. By Philip A. Ashworth ... London, Stevens & Haynes, 1905.
xxiv, 639 p. 22 cm.

1. Gt. Brit.—Constitutional history. I. Ashworth, Philip Arthur, 1853–1921, ed.
N118.T18 1905   8—12155

[5711]

MiU-L OEac OCX ICJ NNCU-G
NT 0049160   DLC OrP WaT KMK RPB PPB PU-L PWcS MB

Taswell-Langmead, Thomas Pitt, 1840–1882.
English constitutional history from the Teutonic conquest to the present time, by Thomas Pitt Taswell-Langmead ... 6th ed., rev. throughout, with notes. By Philip A. Ashworth ... London, Stevens, Houghton, Mifflin and co. 1905.
xxiv, 639 p.

NT 0049161   OU

Taswell-Langmead, Thomas Pitt.   342.42-L
English constitutional history from the Teutonic conquest to the present time; revised throughout, with notes, by Philip A. Ashworth. London: Stevens and Haynes, 1911.   651 p. 7. ed.   8°.

1. Great Britain.—Constitutional law   and history.
N. Y. P. L.   October 24, 1916.

NT 0049162   NN OrSaW OCU OOxM OC1W NjP MiU-C MH-L

Taswell-Langmead, Thomas Pitt
English constitutional history from the Teutonic conquest ot the present time... 7th ed. rev. throughout, with notes, by Philip A. Ashworth. London, Stevens and Haynes, Boston, Houghton, Mifflin & co., 1911.
651 p.

NT 0049163   PBa OU

Taswell-Langmead, Thomas Pitt, 1840–1882.
English constitutional history from the Teutonic conquest to the present time, by Thomas Pitt Taswell-Langmead... 8th ed., by Coleman Phillipson... Boston, Houghton Mifflin Company, 1919.
xxiv, 830 p. 22 cm.

NT 0049164   PU MtU IU ViU OCX PPT PPDrop

Taswell-Langmead, Thomas Pitt, 1840–1882.
English constitutional history from the Teutonic conquest to the present time, by Thomas Pitt Taswell-Langmead ... 8th ed., by Coleman Phillipson ... London, Sweet & Maxwell, limited, 1919.
xxiv, 830 p. 22cm.

1. Gt. Brit.—Constitutional history. I. Phillipson, Coleman, 1878– ed.

Library of Congress   JN118.T18 1919   20–7504

OCU
NT 0049165   DLC WaS WaU-L NjP CSt-Law MiU-L ViU-L

Taswell-Langmead, Thomas Pitt, 1840–1882.
English constitutional history from the Teutonic conquest to the present time, by Thomas Pitt Taswell-Langmead ... 9th ed. By A. L. Poole ... London, Sweet & Maxwell, limited, 1929.
xxvi, 784 p. 22cm.
"List of some of the more important books cited in the foot-notes": p. xxiii–xxvi.

1. Gt. Brit.—Constitutional history. I. Poole, Austin Lane, 1889–

Library of Congress   JN118.T18 1929   30—4538

O OC1W OC1JC OO MiU OCU ViU IdU-SB WaU-L WaSpG
NT 0049166   DLC NN IU NjN MH-L PPLas CtY PV PU NcD

9289
22

Taswell-Langmead, Thomas Pitt, 1840–1882.
English constitutional history from the Teutonic conquest to the present time / by Thomas Pitt Taswell-Langmead. 10th ed.; rev. and enl. / by Theodore F.T. Plucknett. Boston : Houghton Mifflin, 1946.
xxviii, 833 p. ; 22 cm.
Includes bibliographical references and index.

1. Great Britian—Constitutional history. I. Plucknett, Theodore Frank Thomas, 1897– II. Title

NT 0049167   MiDW MiU ViU OkU MtU Mi CoU NcD

Taswell-Langmead, Thomas Pitt, 1840–1882.
English constitutional history, from the Teutonic conquest to the present time. 10th ed. rev. and enl. by Theodore F. T. Plucknett. London, Sweet & Maxwell, 1946.
xxviii, 833 p. 22ᶜᵐ.
"First edition 1875."
Bibliographical footnotes.

1. Gt. Brit.—Constitutional history.   I. Plucknett, Theodore Frank Thomas, 1897–   ed.

JN118.T18 1946   342.4209   47–24880*

       CaBVa PPT CtY ICU NBuU-L NNUN
NT   0049168   DLC WaU-L OrPS CaBVaU OrCS OrPR OrU-L

Taswell-Langmead, Thomas Pitt, 1840–1882.
English constitutional history, from the Teutonic conquest to the present time. 10th ed. rev. and enl. by Theodore F. T. Plucknett. Boston, Houghton Mifflin Co. ₁1947₎
xxviii, 833 p. 22 cm.
Bibliographical footnotes.

1. Gt. Brit.—Constitutional history.   I. Plucknett, Theodore Frank Thomas, 1897–   ed.

[JN118T   ]   342.4209   A 48—6414*
Iowa. State Univ of   Science and Technology.   Library
for Library of Congress   ₁a61g1₎

NT   0049169   IaAS WaWW WaS PU TxU

Taswell-Langmead, Thomas Pitt, 1840–1882, ed.
The Law magazine and review
see under title

Taswell-Langmead, Thomas Pitt, 1840–1882.
Parish registers: a plea for their preservation. By T. P. Taswell-Langmead ... London, S. Palmer, 1872.
30 p. 20ᶜᵐ.

1. Registers of births, etc.—England.

                     5–41706 Revised

Library of Congress   CD1068.A2T3

NT   0049171   DLC MB

Taswell-Langmead, Thomas Pitt, 1840–1882.
The parochial registers preservation bill, 1882. The preservation of parish registers ... By T. P. Taswell-Langmead ... With preface, by William Copeland Borlase ... London, Printed by Pewtress & co., 1882.
27 p. 20ᶜᵐ. ₁*With his* Parish registers: a plea for their preservation. London, 1872₎
Reprinted from the "Law magazine and review" for May, 1878.
"Parochial registers preservation bill, 1882. (Prepared and brought in by Mr. Borlase, Mr. Bryce, Mr. Cochran-Patrick, and Mr. Mellor" : p. ₁24–27. "₁Langmead₎ drafted Mr. W. C. Borlase's abortive parish registers bill of 1882."—Dict. nat. biog.
1. Registers of births, etc.—England.   I. Borlase, William Copeland, 1848–

                     5–41707 Revised

Library of Congress   CD1068.A2T3

NT   0049172   DLC

       Taswell-Langmead, Thomas Pitt, 1840–1882.
Lmd92   The reign of Richard the Second. The Stanhope
St2   prize essay for 1866 ... Oxford[etc.]
1866   Rivingtons, 1866.
       51p. 20½cm. (Stanhope historical essay, 1866)

       1.Gt.Brit. – Hist. – 1377-1400 (Richard II) I.Ser.

NT   0049173   CtY

4PL   **Taszáry, Tamás.**
Hung. 3   Mezõgazdasági öregségi biztositás. Budapest, Madách-Myomda, 1939.
       160 p.

NT   0049174   DLC-P4

Taszkent
see **Tashkend.**

Taszycki, Mikolaj, fl. 1532.
Poland. *Laws, statutes, etc.*
Correctura statutorum et consuetudinum regni Poloniae anno ᴍᴅxxxɪɪ decreto publico per Nicolaum Taszycki, Bernardum Macieiowski, Georgium Myszkowski, Benedictum Izdbieński, Albertum Policki et Nicolaum Koczanowski confecta et Conventioni generali regni anno ᴍᴅxxxɪᴠ proposita. Ex rarissima editione authentica opera Michaelis Bobrzyński nunc iterum edita. Cracoviae, sumptibus Academiae litterarum, typis V. Kornecki, ᴍᴅᴄᴄᴄʟxxɪᴠ.

NT   0049177   DLC-P4   CSt WU PU MiU ICU MiDW NIC CU MH NNC InU

PG6707   **Taszycki, Witold,** 1898–
T38   Dawność tzw. ₁i.e. tak zwanego₎ mazurzenia w języku polskim. Warszawa, Nakł. Tow. Naukowego Warszawskiego, 1948.
       33 p. 25cm.
       At head of title: Towarzystwo Naukowe Warszawskie. Wydział I: Językoznawstwa i historii literatury.
       Added t.p.: L'ancienneté du "Masourisme" en Polonais.
       1.Polish language – Dialects. I.Title. II.Title: Mazurzenie.

       DLC-P4
NT   0049177   CSt WU PU MiU ICU MiDW NIC CU MH NNC InU

T A S Z Y C K I , W I T O L D , 1898-
Dawność tzw. mazurzenia w języku polskim. Warszawa. Nakł. Tow. naukowego warszawskiego, 1948.   33 p. 24cm.

Film reproduction. Negative.
At head of title: Towarzystwo naukowe warszawskie. Wydział I: językoznawstwa i historii literatury.

"Rzecz przedstawiona... dnia 24 maja 1948 r."
Added t.p. in French.
Bibliographical footnotes.

1. Polish language--Hist.   I. Towarzystwo naukowe warszawskie. Wydział I: językoznawstwa.   historji i sztuki.

NT   0049179   NN

Taszychi, Witold, ₁1898–₎ ed.
Dzieła wszystkie
see under
Rej, Mikołaj, z Naglowic, 1505-1569.

491.857   **Taszycki, Witold,** ₁1898–₎
T187g   Gwary ludu polskiego. Lwów, Nakł. Państwowego Wydawn. Książek Szkolnych, 1934.
       35 p. maps. 18cm. (Bibljoteka szkoły powszechnej)

       1.Polish language – Dialects. I.T.

NT   0049181   MiDW MH

PG6311   **Taszycki, Witold,** 1898–
T37   Imiesłowy czynne, teraźniejszy i przeszły I. w języku polskim. W Krakowie, Nakł. Polskiej Akademji Umiejętności, 1924.
       74 p. 26cm. (Polska Akademja Umiejętności. Wydział Filologiczny. Rozprawy, t. 61, nr. 5)

       Bibliographical footnotes.

       1. Polish language – Participle. (Series: Polska Akademia Umiejętności, Kraków. Wydział Filologiczny.   Rozprawy, t. 61, nr. 5)

NT   0049182   CoU InU WU NIC CSt

Taszycki, Witold, 1898–
Jan Łoś w czterdziestolecie pracy naukowej. Kraków, Nakł. Koła Polonistów U. U. J.; skł. gł. w księg. Gebethnera i Wolffa, 1926.
35 p. illus. 25 cm.

1. Łoś, Jan, 1860–1928.

PG6064.L63T3   59–50407 ‡

NT   0049183   DLC

Taszycki, Witold.
Język polski na Śląsku w wiekach średnich. Kraków, Polska Akademja Umiejętności, 1930.
17 p. maps. 24 cm.
"Osobne odbicie z 'Historji Śląska,' wydawnictwa Polskiej Akad. Um."
Bibliographical footnotes.

1. Polish language—Dialects—Silesia.   I. Title.

PG6780.Z9T3   53–47002

NT   0049184   DLC

Taszycki, Witold.
Najdawniejsze polskie imiona osobowe. W Krakowie, Nakładem Polskiej Akademji Umiejętności, 1925.
124 p. 26 cm. (Polska Akademja Umiejętności. Wydział Filologiczny. Rozprawy, t. 57, nr. 3)
Includes bibliographical references.

1. Names, Personal—Polish. 2. Polish language—Etymology—Names.   I. Title.   II. Series.

AS142.K86   t. 57, nr. 3   74–231546
[PG6576]

NT   0049185   DLC ICN WU PCamA

PG   **Taszycki, Witold,** ed.
6027   Najdawniejsze zabytki języka polskiego, opracował Witold Taszycki. Kraków, Krakowska
T36   Spółka Wydawnicza [1927]
       xlii, 150 p. (Biblioteka Narodowa. Seria 1, no.104)

       Includes bibliographies.

       1. Polish language - Old Polish. I. Title.

NT   0049186   WaU IU CoU NN MH

Taszycki, Witold, ed.
Najdawniejsze zabytki języka polskiego. Wyd. 2, przejrz. Wrocław, Wydawn. Zakładu Narodowego im. Ossolińskich ₁1950₎
210 p. 18 cm. (Biblioteka narodowa. Seria 1., nr. 104)

1. Polish literature—Old Polish.   I. Title.

PG6701.T3 1950   58–21026–

NT   0049187   DLC ICU InU MH

PG
6701
T19
1951

Taszycki, Witold, ed.
Najdawniejsze zabytki języka polskiego.
Wyd. 3.   Wrocław, Wydawn. Zakładu Naro-
dowego im. Ossolińskich ₍1951?₎
210 p.   18cm.   (Biblioteka narodowa.
Seria 1., nr. 104)

1. Polish literature--Old Polish.   I.
Title.

CLSU MiU IaU
NT   0049188   NIC PU WU KU NNC MiD NN UU ViU MnU OU

491.8509
T187nm

Taszycki, Witold, 1898–
Nasza mowa ojczysta. Lwów, Nakł.
Państwowego Wydawn. Książek Szkolnych, 1933.
34 p. facsims. 18cm. (Bibljoteka szkoły
powszechnej)

1. Polish language - Hist.   I. T.

NT   0049189   MiDW

1899

Taszycki, Witold, ed.
Obrońcy języka polskiego, wiek xv–xviii. ₍Wyd. 1.₎
Wrocław, Zakład im. Ossolińskich; wydawn. Polskiej Akademii Nauk ₍1953₎
393 p. 18 cm. (Biblioteka narodowa. Seria 1, nr. 146)

1. Polish language.   I. Title.

PG6071.T3   56–19890 ‡

NNC OU NcD NBuU CaBVaU
NT   0049190   DLC KU CSt ICU MH CtY InU PU MiU NN CU

Taszycki, Witold.
Patronimiczne nazwy miejscowe na Mazowszu. Kraków,
Nakł. Polskiej Akademii Umiejętności, 1951.
105 p. fold. map. 26 cm. (Polska Akademia Umiejętności. Prace
onomastyczne, nr. 3)

Bibliography: p. ₍88₎–89.

1. Polish language—Etymology—Names. 2. Names, Geographical—Masovia.   I. Title.   (Series: Polska Akademia Umiejętności, Kraków. Prace onomastyczne, nr. 3)

PG6576.T3   59–41878

₍2₎

NT   0049191   DLC MiDW NN CtY ICU PSt CSt CoU OU MH PU

Taszycki, Witold.
Die polnische Sprache in Schlesien im Mittelalter. Język
polski na Śląsku w wiekach średnich. Vertrauliche Uebersetzung der Publikationsstelle des Preuss. Geheimen Staatsarchivs in Berlin-Dahlem, ausgeführt von Bertold Spuler
im Auftrage der Historischen Kommission für Schlesien.
₍Berlin? 1935?₎
14 l. 30 cm. (₍Publikationsstelle Berlin-Dahlem. Polnische Reihe.
Bücher und grössere Aufsätze; 30)
In German.
Reprinted from "Historja Śląska (Geschichte Schlesiens) Heraus-
gegeben von der Krakauer Akademie" v. 1, p. 72–88.
1. Polish language—Dialects—Silesia.   I. Title.   (Series:
Germany. Publika-   tionsstelle Berlin-Dahlem. Polnische
Reihe. Bücher und   grössere Aufsätze, 30)
PG6780.Z9T315   56–51955

NT   0049192   DLC

Taszycki, Witold.
Polskie nazwy osobowe. Kraków, Gebethner i Wolff,
1924.
32 p. 18 cm. (Bibljoteczka Towarzystwa Miłośników Języka
Polskiego, nr. 5)

1. Polish language—Etymology—Names.   I. Title.

PG6576.T33   59–58150

NT   0049193   DLC WU MiU NN

Taszycki, Witold.
Die schlesischen Ortsnamen. Śląskie nazwy miejscowe.
Vertrauliche Uebersetzung der Publikationsstelle des Preuss.
Geheimen Staatsarchivs in Berlin-Dahlem, ausgeführt von
Fritz Goehrke. ₍Berlin, 1936?₎
23 l. map. 30 cm. (₍Publikationsstelle Berlin-Dahlem. Polnische
Reihe. Bücher und grössere Aufsätze, 27)
In German.
"Aus dem Vortragszyklus: 'Das polnische Schlesien' herausgegeben
vom Schlesischen Institut Kattowitz 1935."
"Anmerkungen" (bibliographical) : leaves 20–23.
1. Polish language—Etymology—Names. 2. Names, Geographical—
Silesia.   I. Title.   (Series: Germany. Publikationsstelle Berlin-
Dahlem. Polnische Reihe. Bücher und grössere Aufsätze, 27)

PG6576.T35   60–59541

NT   0049194   DLC

PG7158
S42T3

Stack

Taszycki, Witold, 1898–
Sienkiewicz w piśmiennictwie Łużyckiem.
Kraków, Gebethner i Wolff, 1931.
30 p. 22⅝.
"Uzupełniona odbitka z 'Ruchu słowiańskiego'
R.III.Nr.8–9."

1.Sienkiewicz, Henryk, 1846-1916.   I.Title.

NT   0049195   CSt

DD
491
.S43
T3

Taszycki, Witold
Śląskie nazwy miejscowe. Katowice, Wydawn.
Instytutu Śląskiego; skł. gł.: Kasa im. Mianowskiego, 1935.
35 p. 24 cm. (Polski Śląsk, cykl odczytów wygłoszonych w Katowicach w sezonie
1934/5)

Includes bibliography.

1. Names, Geographical - Silesia.
I. Title.

NT   0049196   WU ICU NN

Taszycki, Witold, 1898–
Słowiańskie nazwy miejscowe; ustalenie podziału. Kraków, Nakł. Polskiej Akademii Umiejętności; skł. gł. w
księg. Gebethnera i Wolffa, 1946.
64 p. 25 cm. (Polska Akademia Umiejętności. Prace Komisji
Językowej, nr. 29)

1. Slavic languages—Etymology—Names. 2. Names, Geographical—Slavic.   I. Title.   (Series: Polska Akademia Umiejętności,
Krakow. Komisja Językowa. Prace, nr. 29)

PG303.T3   59–42178

NT   0049197   DLC InU ICU MnU NNC CU NcU IU OU CSt

PG6146
.J6
1951

Taszycki, Witold, joint author.
₍1898₎
Jodłowski, Stanisław.
Słownik ortograficzny i prawidła pisowni polskiej,
według uchwał Komitetu Ortograficznego Polskiej Akademii Umiejętności z r. 1936. Wyd. 2. Wrocław, Wydawn.
Zakładu Narod. im Ossolińskich, 1951.

Taszycki, Witold, editor.
...Wybór tekstów staropolskich XVI – XVIII wieku.
Lwów: K. S. Jakubowski, 1928.   viii, 264 p.   8°.   (Lwow-
ska bibljoteka slawistyczna. Tom 7.)

516837A. 1. Polish literature—   Collections. I. Ser.
N. Y. P. L.   April 24, 1931

NT   0049199   NN CU NNC

Taszycki, Witold, ed.
Wybór tekstów staropolskich xvi–xviii wieku. ₍Wyd. 2.₎
Warszawa, Państwowe Wydawn. Naukowe, 1955.
xi p., facsim. (264 p.), ₍265₎–276 p. 25 cm.
"Przedruk fotooffsetowy z wydania 1928 r." : p. 1–264.
Bibliographical references included in "Przedmowa do wydania
drugiego" (p. ₍ix₎–xi)

1. Polish literature (Selections: Extracts, etc.)   I. Title.

PG7134.T3 1955   56–34965

MiU ICU OU MiDW MH NN
NT   0049200   DLC NIC MU CU NcD KU CtY TxU NNC CSt MnU

Taszycki, Witold, 1898–
...Z dawnych podziałów dialektycznych języka polskiego.
Część   We Lwowie: Nakładem Towarzystwa
naukowego, 1934–   v. maps. 25cm. (Towarzystwo
naukowe we Lwowie. Wydział I: filologiczny. Archiwum.
Tom 6

"Wykaz źródeł,"   część 2, p. 92.
CONTENTS.—
Część 2. Przejście ja ⁻ⁱ je.

1. Polish language—Dialects.
N. Y. P. L.   June 30, 1936

NT   0049201   NN

Taszycki, Witold, 1898 –
Z dawnych podziałów dialektycznych języka polskiego.
We Lwowie, Nakł. Tow. Naukowego, 1934.
92, 98 p. maps. 26 cm. (Archiwum Towarzystwa Naukowego we
Lwowie. Dział I, t. 6, zesz. 1–2)
Part 2 has also special t. p.
Includes bibliographies.

1. Polish language—Dialects.   (Series: Towarzystwo Naukowe
we Lwowie. Wydział I. Filologiczny. Archiwum, t. 6, zesz. 1–2)

P19.T65 t. 6, zesz. 1–2   59–59860

NT   0049202   DLC MH IU

PG6145
.J6
1948

Taszycki, Witvold, joint author.
₍1898₎
Jodłowski, St   FOR OTHER EDITIONS
                                   SEE MAIN ENTRY
Zasady pisowni polskiej interpunkcji ze słownikiem orto-
graficznym, według uchwał Komitetu Ortograficznego Polskiej Akademii Umiejętności z 21 kwietnia 1936 r. Wyd. 7.
Wrocław, Wydawn. Zakładu Narodowego im. Ossolińskich,
1948.

W 1
AN2318
sayı 37
1953

TAT, A   Lûtfû
Deri hastalıkları. Ankara ₍Yeni
Matbaa, 1953₎
.. xvi, 423 p. illus. (Ankara
Üniversitesi Tip Fakültesi yayınlarından,
no. 37)
.. 1. Skin - Diseases   Series: Ankara.
Üniversite. Tip Fakültesi. Yayınlar,
sayı 37

NT   0049204   DNLM

Tat, Ayda.
The emancipation of women in the Republic of Turkey.
Cairo, 1950.
51 l. 34 cm.

Typewritten.
Thesis (M. A.)—American University at Cairo.
Bibliography : leaves 41–43.

1. Women in Turkey.   I. Title.

HQ1777.T3   50–57114

NT   0049205   DLC

PZ
3
T3
Do
HRC
GRA

Tat, Robert Desmond
The doughman; a novel. [1st ed.] Sydney, Endeavour Press, 1933.
228p. 22cm.

NT   0049206   TxU

Tat-Sat, Om
see   Om Tat-Sat, pseud. ?

720.5 Tat.
TAT
⌐Cape Town⌐
no. illus. 25cm.

"The magazine of the School of Architecture
of the University of Cape Town and the official
organ of the Cape Architects Association."

NT 0049208   IU

Die Tat.
Jahrg. 1–

Leipzig: Verlag Die Tat, G.m.b.H. ⌐etc.⌐, 1909–   8°.
v.   illus.

Editors: April, 1909 –   Ernst Horneffer;   March,
1913, Ernst Horneffer and Karl Hoffmann; April, 1913 –   Eugen
Diederichs.
Subtitle varies

1. Periodicals, Germany.
N. Y. P. L.   August 30, 1924

NT 0049209   NN DLC-P4 NcD PBm

Die Tat. Apr. 1950-Mar. 1956, May-June 1960,
Sept. 1960-Jan. 1961. Zurich, 1950-1961.
50v. daily.

NT 0049210   ICRL

Die Tat; deutsche Monatschrift. Jahrg.   –30;
–März 1939.
Jena, E. Diederichs.
v. plates. 24 cm.

Subtitle varies: Monatschrift zur Gestaltung
neuer Wirklichkeit.
Editors: Eugen Diederichs.–   –Mar. 1939, Giselher Wirsing, E. W. Eschmann.
Superseded by Das xx Jahrhundert.

I. Diederichs, Eugen, 1867–1930, ed. II. Wirsing, Giselher, 1906–
ed.
AP30.T36   053   48–39240*

NT 0049211   DLC DAU InU NNC TxU

Die Tat; deutsche monatschrift.
Beiheft.
⌐Nr.⌐ 1
Jena: E. Diederichs, 1919
v. maps.

Contents:
⌐Nr.⌐ 1. Neue Wege zum Aufbau Deutschlands. 1919.

1. Periodicals—Germany.
N. Y. P. L.   September 19, 1927

NT 0049212   NN IEN NNU-W NRU NjP

Tat-Buecher für Feldpost
Heft 1–
Jena: E. Diederichs, 1914–
v.

"Die Feldpostbuecherei trat waehrend des ersten Kriegshalbjahrs an die Stelle
der Kulturzeitschrift des Verlages: Die Tat, die aber vom Maerz an wieder
erscheint." cf. Heft 10, back cover.

Contents: Heft 1. ⌐Buchwald, R.⌐ Der heilige Krieg. 1914.
Heft 2. ⌐Buchwald, R.⌐ Deutsches Volkstum. 1914.
Heft 3. ⌐Michel, E.⌐ Deutscher Glaube. 1914.
Heft 4. ⌐Buchwald, R.⌐ Der Kampf. 1915.
Heft 5. ⌐Höfer, C.⌐ Die Heimat; neue Kriegsgedichte. 1915.
Heft 6. ⌐Höfer, C.⌐ Sieg oder Tod; neue Kriegsgedichte. 1915.
Heft 7. ⌐Neckel, G.⌐ Germanisches Heldentum. 1915.

Heft 9. Treitschke, H. von. Deutsche Politik. 1915.
Heft 10. ⌐Crusius, O.⌐ Mannhaftigkeit und Bürgersinn. 1915.

NT 0049214   NN DLC

Tat-flugschriften... ⌐–
Jena, 1914–

DLGO
.T3

NT 0049215   DLC NcD NN

Tat im bild; zwei jahre NSG-Kraft durch freude
see under   [Kiehl, Walter]

W 1   The TAT newsletter. / v. ⌐1⌐-5; Sept. 1946-
T109   spring 1952. Topeka, Kan.
5 v.
Merged into the Journal of projective
techniques with v. 3, Aug. 1949, but also
continued to appear separately as a
reprint of a section of the Journal through
v. 5, spring 1952.
"Book reviews" section is sometimes
issued separately.

NT 0049217   DNLM LU

TAT Schriften.
Jena: E. Diederichs Verlag[, cop. 1931
v.

NT 0049218   NN

Tat Seng Company, *Shanghai*
see Shanghai Tat Seng Company.

Tat shag pin; or, Midwifery made easy. Translated from the Chinese by J.G. Kerr. Transcribed by R.P. Harris.   Philadelphia, 1881.
111 p.

NT 0049220   PPC

551.21 ⌐Tata, Domenico⌐ 1723–
T18d   Descrizione del grande incendio del Vesuvio
successo nel giorno otto del mese di agosto del
corrente anno 1779.   Napoli, V. Mazzola-Vocola,
1779.
38p.

Dedication by Domenico Tata.
Bibliographical foot-notes.

1. Vesuvius, Eruption of, 1779. I. Title.

NT 0049221   IU

DG975   TATA, DOMENICO, b.1723.
.V95T22   Lettera sul Monte Volture a sua eccellenza il sig-
nor d.Guglielmo Hamilton ... dell' abate Domenico
Tata. Napoli,Nella stamperia Simoniana,1778.
235,⌐4⌐p. illus.,V pl. 20cm.
Title vignette.
"Dell' etimologia del Monte Volture. Lettera al
... Domenico Tata di Ciro Saverio Minervino" with
special t.-p.(p.⌐63⌐-235)
1.Vulture,Monte,Italy.

NT 0049222   ICU OkU

Tata, Domenico, 1723–
Memoria dell'Abate domenico Tata sulle acque
di Modena.

NT 0049223   PPAN

Tata, Domenico, 1723–
Memoria sulla pioggia di pietra avvenuta nella
campagna Sanese ...   Napoli, 1794.
74 p.   8 °.

NT 0049224   CtY

HC435   Tata, Jehangir R. D., 1904–   joint author.
.T5
Thakurdas, *Sir* Purshotamdas, 1879–
... A brief memorandum outlining a plan of economic devel-
opment for India by Sir Purshotamdas Thakurdas, J. R. D.
Tata, G. D. Birla ⌐and others⌐ ... Harmondsworth, Middlesex,
Eng., New York, Penguin books ⌐1944⌐

HC435   Tata, Jehangir R. D., 1904–   joint author.
.T52
1945   Thakurdas, *Sir* Purshotamdas, 1879–
... Memorandum outlining a plan of economic development
for India, parts one and two, by Sir Purshotamdas Thakurdas,
J. R. D. Tata, G. D. Birla ⌐and others⌐ ... Harmondsworth,
Middlesex, Eng., New York, Penguin books ⌐1945⌐

Tata, Jehangir R. D., 1904–   joint author.
HC435
.T52   Thakurdas, *Sir* Purshotamdas, 1879–
1944   A plan of economic development for India, by Sir Purshotamdas Thakurdas, J. R. D. Tata, G. D. Birla ⌐and others⌐ ...
⌐Bombay, Printed by S. Ramu, at The Commercial printing
press, 1944–45⌐

Tata, Juan Carlos de.
... El sistema dentario como auxiliar en el esclarecimiento
de un hecho e identificación de cadáver; tesis de doctorado del
dr. Juan Carlos de Tata. ⌐Buenos Aires⌐ 1938.
38, ⌐2⌐ p. incl. illus., tables. 26⌐ᵐ⌐.
At head of title: Universidad nacional de Buenos Aires. Facultad de
ciencias médicas. Escuela de odontología.

1. Identification. 2. Dental jurisprudence.
43–22424
Library of Congress   RA1055.T3
⌐2⌐   340.6

NT 0049228   DLC

Tata, Lady Mehrbai Dorab, 1879–1931.
Lady Tata ...
see under   Natarajan, Kamakshi, 1868–

Tata Air Lines.
Monthly bulletin. Mar. 31, 1941–
Bombay.
v. in   illus. 34 cm.

TL720.9.T3A2   387.7065   52–15507

NT 0049230   DLC

Tata-Bhisotype Syndicate.
Bhisotype; the method and economy of the new single type caster and composer. London ₍1908?₎
cover-title, 27 p. illus. 18cm.

Imprint on label pasted on cover.

1. Type-setting machines. I. Title.

NT 0049231   NNC

Tata Chemicals Limited.
Report.
₍Bombay₎
v. 28 cm. annual.

HD9657.I 44T33   55–40164 ‡

NT 0049232   DLC

Tata Engineering and Locomotive Company, ltd.
see
Tata Locomotive and Engineering Company, ltd.

Tata Graduate School of Social Work, *Bombay*
see
Tata Institute of Social Sciences, *Bombay.*

Tata Hydro-electric Power Supply Company, ltd.
Report.
₍Bombay₎
v. diagrs. 28 cm. annual.
Report year ends June 30.

HD9685.I 44T323   51–23803 ‡

NT 0049235   DLC

Tata Industries Limited.
Sixty years; the story of Tatas ...
see under   Menen, Aubrey, 1912–

Tata Industries Limited. *Dept. of Economics and Statistics.*
Statistical outline of India.
Bombay.
v. 16 cm.

1. India—Econ. condit.—1945–   I. Title.

HC431.T33   55–25623 ‡

    TxU NSyU MoU
NT 0049237   DLC NIC IdPI DS MiU NjP MCM WaWW DNAL

Tata Industries Limited. *Dept. of Industrial Health.*
Report.
₍Bombay₎
v. 28 cm. annual.

1. Industrial hygiene—India.

HD7481.T3A35   54–40118 ‡

NT 0049238   DLC NN

510.6
T18L
Tata Institute of Fundamental Research, Bombay.
Lectures on mathematics and physics. Mathematics. no.1–   1953–   Bombay, 1953–
v. diagrs. 29 cm.

Some are reprints.

1. Mathematics—Collected works.   I. Title.

NT 0049239   LU KU NN

Tata Institute of Fundamental Research, *Bombay.*
Report.
₍Bombay₎
v. 19 cm. annual.

Q73.T334   51–35900

NT 0049240   DLC

Tata Institute of Fundamental Research, Bombay.
Report of an international conference on elementary particles
see under   International Conference on Elementary Particles, Bombay, 1950.

Tata Institute of Social Sciences, *Bombay*
Current trends in social work

see under

Current trends in social work.

Tata Institute of Social Sciences, *Bombay.*
Director's report.
Bombay.
v. 19–25 cm. annual.
Title varies: Report.

I. Title.

H67.B435A38   54–40187

NT 0049243   DLC

Tata Institute of Social Sciences, Bombay. Students' Union.
Students and social work, for students by students. Bombay, Bureau of Research and Publications, Tata Institute of Social Sciences ₍1948₎
x, 66 p. 22 cm.
Bibliography: p. 65–66.

1. Students—India. 2. Social workers—India. 3. Social service. 4. Community development—India.   I. Title.

HV393.T3   61–28439

NT 0049244   DLC

Business
HD
8690
.J5
T18
Tata Iron and Steel Company, ltd.
Answers to the questionnaire of the Labour Enquiry Committee, Bihar. Bombay ₍Commercial Printing Press₎ 1938.
x, 245 p. tables.

"Answers ... in regard to the Jamshedpur Works."

NT 0049245   NNC WaU

Tata Iron and Steel Company, ltd.
Answers to the questionnaire of the Labour Enquiry Committee, Bihar, for collieries and Noamundi ore mine. Bombay, 1938.
149 p. 25 cm.

1. Coal-miners—Bihar, India (State)   I. Bihar, India (Province) Labour Enquiry Committee.   II. Title.

HD8039.M62 I 43   S A 68–6690

NT 0049246   DLC NNC

Tata Iron and Steel Company, ltd.
An economic guide to India. ₍Calcutta, 1947₎
6 col. maps. 35 cm.
Cover title.
A reprint of the maps originally appearing in the company's 1947 calendar.

1. India—Economic conditions—Maps.   I. Title.

G2281.G1T3 1947   912′.1′33095405   72–185753
                                   MARC

NT 0049247   DLC

NA9252
.J3K6
folio
    Tata iron and steel company, limited.

Koenigsberger, Otto H
Jamshedpur development plan, by Otto Koenigsberger; prepared for the Tata iron & steel company limited. With a foreword by J. R. D. Tata. ₍Bombay, Printed by S. Ramu at the Commercial printing press, 1945?₎

4HD
1558
Tata Iron and Steel Company, ltd.
Oral evidence given by the representatives of the Tata Iron and Steel Company, limited, before the Tariff Board at Jamshedpur...August, 1923. Calcutta, Superintendent Govt. Print., India, 1923.
105 p.

NT 0049249   DLC-P4

TF258
.W7
    Tata Iron and Steel Company, ltd.

Wraight, Ernest Alfred, 1879–1946.
Production and inspection of rails at the works of Messrs. the Tata Iron and Steel Company, ltd., Jamshedpur, by E. A. Wraight. Calcutta, Central Publication Branch, Govt. of India, 1928.

Tata Iron and Steel Company, ltd.
Reference book. Calcutta, Pub. for the Tata Iron & Steel Co. by the Press Syndicate, 1941.
v–xxxviii, 355 p. illus. 21 cm.

1. Steel.

TN730.T3   669.1   48–36102*

NT 0049251   DLC

Tata Iron and Steel Company, ltd.
Report.
₍Bombay₎
v. diagrs. 28 cm. annual.
Report year ends Mar. 31.

HD9526.I 64T33   51–23788 ‡

NT 0049252   DLC NN NSyU

Business
HN
690
.J5
T18

Tata Iron and Steel Company, ltd.
Report on the conditions affecting the labourers of the Jamshedpur works of the Tata Iron & Steel Co., Ltd. Jamshedpur, 1937.
217 p. charts, tables.

1. Tata Iron and Steel Company, ltd.
2. Jamshedpur – Social conditions.

NT 0049253   NNC

Tata iron and steel company, limited.
... Representation submitted to the Tariff board by the Tata iron and steel company, limited, regarding the steel industry in India. Jamshedpur, July 1923. Calcutta, Superintendent government printing, India, 1923.
cover-title, [84] p. incl. tables (part fold.) 24½ᶜᵐ.
At head of title: Tariff board.
Various pagings.

1. Steel industry and trade—India.   ɪ. India. Tariff board.
ɪɪ. Title.

                         31–17846
Library of Congress   HF2651.I 771T3

NT 0049254   DLC

Tata Iron and Steel Company, ltd.
TS300
.T57   **Tisco** review.
[Calcutta]

Tata Iron and Steel Company, limited.
TISCO; technical journal of the Tata iron and steel company
    see under title

Tata Locomotive and Engineering Company, ltd.
Report.
[Bombay]
v. illus. 28 cm. annual.

Report year ends Mar. 31.
HD9712.I 44T33   57–24346 ‡

NT 0049257   DLC

Tata Mills, ltd.
Report.
[Bombay?]
v. 28 cm. annual.

HD9886.I 44T33   56–30680 ‡

NT 0049258   DLC

Tata Oil Mills Company, ltd.
Report.
[Bombay]
v. illus. 28 cm. annual.

Report year ends Mar. 31.
HD9490.I 44T33   57–24349 ‡

NT 0049259   DLC

Tata Power Company, ltd.
Report.
[Bombay]
v. diagrs. 28 cm.
Report year ends June 30.

HD9685.I 44T343   51–23804 ‡

NT 0049260   DLC DS

Tata quarterly; a review of economic & financial conditions in India. Jan. 1946–
[Bombay, Published by Y. S. Pandit for Tata Sons]
v. in   diagrs. 25 cm.

1. India—Econ. condit.—Period.   ɪ. Tata Sons, ltd.

HC431.T35   330.954   50–19730

     CaBVaU NN DAU MiU DS OrU
NT 0049261   DLC CU-SB TxDaM IU GU MB NNUN ICRL DNAL

Tata sons limited.
Tata enterprises.   [Bombay? 195–]
24 p.   21cm.
Cover-title.

NT 0049262   NN

HC431
.T35   Tata Sons, ltd.
Tata quarterly; a review of economic & financial conditions in India. Jan. 1946–
[Bombay, Published by Y. S. Pandit for Tata Sons]

Tata sons, limited.
Tata studies in current affairs

         see

Tata studies in current affairs.

Tata studies in current affairs.   Tata Sons ltd.,
1–   1944–

NT 0049265   DLC

Tata Subbaraya Sastri
   see Subbaraya Sastri, Tata, *mahamahopadhyaya.*

Tata Subrahmanya Sastri
   see Subbaraya Sastri, Tata, *mahamahopadhyaya.*

Tatachar, D. Ramaswamy
   see Ramaswamy Tatachar Iyengar,
Dindigal, 1899–

PK3521
.I 8E57   Tatacharya, Desika Tirumalai, 1892–   tr.
Venkaṭanātha, 1268–1369.
ईशावास्योपनिषद्भाष्यम्. श्रीमन्निगमान्तमहादेशिकानुगृहीतम्.
Isavasyopanishad-bhashya. Critically edited with introd., translation and notes by K. C. Varadachari and D. T. Tatacharya. Tirupati, India, Sri Venkatesvara Oriental Institute [cover 1942]

NT 0049270   DLC-P4 MH

4PK
Ind.   Tatacharya, Desika Tirumalai, 1892–
132   Rupakaparisuddhi; a study in the figures Rupaka and Upama. Tirupati, Tirumalai-Tirupati Devasthanams Press, 1946.
      59 p.
(Sri Venkatesvara Oriental Institute studies, no. 2)

NT 0049270   DLC-P4 MH

Tatacharya, Desika Tirumalai, 1892–
(Viśiṣṭādvaitakośaḥ)
विशिष्टाद्वैतकोशः. सम्पादकः देशिकतातार्यकुमारः तिरुमलै तातार्यैः. [With a foreword by K. C. Varadachari. Trivellore, श्रीमद्-अहोबिलमठस्थाने द्विदशवारिखपट्टे मूर्धाभिषिक्तानां श्रीवण् शठकोप श्री श्री-रङ्गशठकोप यतीन्द्रमहादेशिकानां दिव्याज्ञानुगृहाभ्यां प्रकाशितः, 1951.
iii, xxiv, 374, 2 p. ports. 29 cm.
Added t. p. in English.
In Sanskrit; foreword in English.

1. Visiṣṭādvaita. 2. Vedanta.   I. Title.

B132.A35T38   74–218707

NT 0049271   DLC

GN
63   TATAFIORE, Enrico
T216c   La costituzione morfologica normale del
1935   neonato e del lattante italiano. Napoli, Morano, 1935.
     xi, 163 p. illus.
     1. Anthropometry - Italy 2. Body constitution

NT 0049272   DNLM

WJ
840   TATAFIORE, Enrico
T216c   Criptorchismo e pseudocriptorchismo;
1947   importanza, diffusione, rapporti con l'ernia inguinale, profilassi, trattamento medico [di] E. Tatafiore [e] A. Cappelli. Napoli, Pironti, 1947.
     58 p.   WJ840 T216c
     1. Testis - Abnormalities & deformities I. Cappelli, Attilio

NT 0049273   DNLM

Tatafiore, Enrico.
Elementi di auxologia. Pref. del prof. S. de Stefano. Napoli, Edizioni scientifiche italiane, 1954.
182 p. illus., tables. 24 cm. (Collana di studi pediatrici)
Bibliographical footnotes.

1. Children—Growth.

                         A 54–5989
Temple Univ. Library   RJ131.T38
for Library of Congress   [1]

NT 0049274   PPT

W1
CO168F   **Tatafiore, Enrico.**
n.2   Elementi auxologia. Napoli, Edizioni scientifiche
1954   italiane, 1954.
     204 p. illus. (Collana di studi pediatrici, n. 2)

1. Growth I. Title II. Series

NT 0049275   DNLM

DS851
.A2T37
Orien
Japan

Tatai, Shirōji, 1884–

日本神代文化研究總論　卽思善導根本策　田
多井四郎治著　東京　昭和12 ₍1937₎

3, 2, 6, 10, 150 p. illus., map. 23 cm.

Cover title.

1. Japan—Hist.—To 645. I. Title. *Nihon jindai bunka kenkyū sōron.*
Title romanized: Nihon jindai bunka kenkyū sōron.

J 60–3165

Hoover Institution
for Library of Congress

NT 0049276   CSt-H DLC

Tatakai no wa.

斗いの環　小說集　新日本文學會・勞農救援會
靜岡支部共編 ₍東京₎ 新日本文學會 1950₎

234 p. 19 cm.

CONTENTS: 序文　中野重治著—翼なき小鳥　中本たか子著—愛鷹
は少しもかくれて　間宮茂輔著—怒るハルプ　松田解子著—分水嶺　堀田昇
一著.

1. Short stories, Japanese—Japan—Shizuoka (Prefecture) 2. Labor
and laboring classes—Stories. I. Shin Nihon Bungaku Kai. II.
Rōnō Kyūenkai. Shizuoka Shibu.

PL770.T37   72–805404

NT 0049277   DLC

(Tatakau Doku-So)

鬪ふ独ソ　時局情報編輯部編 ₍東京₎ 東京日日新
聞社 ₍昭和16 i. e. 1941₎

162 p. illus. 18 cm.

1. World War, 1939–1945—Diplomatic history. 2. World War,
1939–1945—Russia. 3. World War, 1939–1945—Germany. I. Tōkyō
Nichinichi Shimbun Sha. Jikyoku Jōhō Henshūbu.

D748.T37   77–798084

NT 0049278   DLC

W 4
A86
1954

TATAKĒ, Hērō I

Περὶ τῶν κλωστηριδίαν τῆς ἀεριο-
γόνου γαγγραίνης: καὶ δι-
πλοῦματικοῦ. Ἀθῆναι, 1954.

64 p.
Title transliterated: Peri tōn
klōstēridiōn tēs aeriogonou gangrainēs.
Diatribē epi didaktoria - Athens.
1. Clostridium

NT 0049279   DNLM

Tatakēs, Basileios Nikolaou
    see
    Tatakēs, Vasileios, 1896–

Tatakēs, V. N.

Γράμματα Μικρασιατων προς τον Θεοφιλο
Καῖρη. (IN: Mikrasiatika chronika.
Athēnai. tomos 6(1955)p. ₍101₎–136. port.)

Title transliterated: Grammata Mik-
rasiatōn pros ton Theophilo Kaīrē.
Includes letters from Ath. Kyzikēnos.

1. Kaīrēs, Theophilos. I. Kyzikēnos, Ath.

NT 0049282   NN

Tatakēs, Vasileios, 1896–
   ... Panétius de Rhodes, le fondateur du moyen stoicisme;
sa vie et son œuvre, par Basile N. Tatakis. Paris, J. Vrin,
1931.

2 p. l., II, 234 p. 23 cm. (Bibliothèque d'histoire de la philosophie)

"Bibliographie": p. ₍227₎–228.

1. Panaetius. I. Title.

B595.Z7T3   188.4   A C 33–2442
Princeton Univ. Libr.   rev 2
for Library of Congress   ₍73₍2₎₎†

NBuU ScU MoU CSt GEU TNJ NcD
NT 0049283   NjP DLC CU IU MH CaBVaU NNC OCU DDO PBm

B161
B9B7

Tatakēs, Vasileios, 1896–
   ... La philosophie byzantine, par Basile
Tatakis. Paris, Presses universitaires de
France, 1949.

vii,₍i₎, 323,₍l₎ p. (Histoire de la philosophie. Fascicule supplémentaire No. II)

"Bibliographie générale": p. ₍315₎.
Bibliographical footnotes.

1.Philosophy-Hist. 2.Byzantine philosophy.
I.Title. II.Series. III.Bréhier, Émile, ed.

NT 0049284   MBtS ICN MH IU OCl TxU MeB MnCS

889
B292
ser.1
v.8

Tatakēs, Vasileios, 1896–
Σκόθρος, Μηνιάτης, Βούλγαρις, Θεοτόκης. Ἐπιμελεία Βασιλείου Τατάκη. Ἀθῆναι, Ἀετός ₍1953₎

356p. 25cm. (Βασικὴ βιβλιοθήκη, 8)

Biographical sketches of the individual writers,
with bibliography, preceding the selections
from their works (speeches, sermons, treatises,
etc.)
Bibliographical footnotes.
Title transliterated: Skouphos, Mēniatēs
Boulgaris. Theotokēs.

NT 0049285   IU IEN NN MB

Tatakēs, Vasileios, 1896–
Θέματα Χριστιανικῆς καὶ Βυζαντινῆς φιλοσοφίας ₍ὑπὸ₎ B. N.
Τατάκη. Ἀθῆναι, Ἐκ τοῦ τυπογραφείου τῆς Ἀποστολικῆς Δια-
κονίας τῆς Ἐκκλησίας τῆς Ἑλλάδος, 1952.

206 p. 24 cm. (Βιβλιοθήκη Ἀποστολικῆς Διακονίας, 37)

1. Christianity—Philosophy. 2. Philosophy—History—Byzantine
Empire. I. Title. II. Series: Bibliothēkē Apostolikēs Diakonias,
37)
Title transliterated: Themata Christianikēs
kai Byzantinēs philosophias.

BR100.T27   74–223648

NT 0049286   DLC NBuU NNC MH

Tatakis, Basile Nicolas
   see
   Tatakēs, Vasileios, 1896–

Tatamiya, Eitarō, 1909–

鳩山ブームの舞台裏—政治記者の手記—田々宮
英太郎著　東京　実業之世界社　昭和30 ₍1955₎

222 p. illus. 19 cm.

1. Japan — Pol. & govt. — 1945— 2. Hatoyama, Ichirō, 1883–
1959. I. Title.
Title romanized: Hatoyama būmu no butaiura.

DS889.T287   J 61–146 ‡

NT 0049288   DLC

Tatanan njerat basa Djawi
   see under   Indonesia. Tjabang Bagian
Bahasa.

Tatang Sastrawiria
   see
   Sastrawiria, Tatang.

Tatang Sontani, Utuy
   see
   Sontani, Utuy Tatang, 1920–

QD501
T3

Tatanskii, S V
Catalysts from obtaining synthetic fuels from
coal, by S. V. Tatanskii, K. K. Papok and E. G.
Semenido. ₍n.p., n.d.₎

7 l. (p. 113–119) 20 cm.
Photocopy (positive)
Translation from Neftianoe khoziaistvo,
24(2), 52–55, 1946.
RT–2646.

1.Catalysis.   2. Synthetic liquid
fuels.

NT 0049292   DI

Tatar, Peter.
    Tamas bátya
      see under   Stowe, Harriet Elizabeth
(Beecher)

Tatar A. S. S. R. Constitution.

Конституция (основной закон) РСФСР ₍с изменениями и
дополнениями, принятыми на 1. и 2. сессиях Верховного
Совета РСФСР 3. созыва₎ Конституции (основные законы, автономных советских социалистических респуб-
лик, входящих в состав РСФСР. Москва, Гос. изд-во
юрид. лит-ры. 1952.

Tatar A. S. S. R. *Gosudarstvennyĭ arkhiv*
   see
   Tatar A. S. S. R. *TSentral'nyĭ gosudarstvennyĭ arkhiv.*

Tatar A. S. S. R. Laws, statutes, etc.
    Chto skazal desi͡atyĭ Vsetatarskiĭ s ezd
Sovetov o kul'ture i prosveschenii
     see under   Tatar A. S. S. R. TSentral'nyĭ
Ispolnitel'nyĭ Komitet.

Tatar A. S. S. R. *Laws, statutes, etc. (Indexes)*
Алфавитно-предметный указатель декретов и распоря-
жений. 1920–
Казань, Изд. ЦИК и СНК ₍etc.₎

v. in.   27 cm.

1. Law—Tatar Republic—Indexes.
*Title transliterated: Alfavitno-predmetnyĭ
ukazatel' dekretov i raspori͡azhenii.*

60–58124

NT 0049297   DLC

Tatar A. S. S. R. *Narodnyĭ komissariat finansov.*
Гербовый сбор в нотариальных органах при соверше-
нии нотариальных действий. I. Засвидетельствование.
II. Надписи о протесте. III. Надписи исполнительные.
IV. Документы, выдаваемые. V. Документы, подаваемые.
VI. Удостоверение сделок. Под ред. Н. В. Кибардина.
Казань, Официальное издание НКФ ТАССР, 1929.

11 p. 17 cm.

1. Notaries—Tatar republic—Fees. I. Kibardin, N. V., ed.
II. Title. *Title transliterated: Gerbovyĭ sbor.*

47–44669

NT 0049298   DLC

Tatar ASSR. Narodnyĭ komissariat po
prosveshcheniĭu.
Kazanskiĭ muzeĭnyĭ vestnik
see under title

Tatar A. S. S. R. *Narodnyĭ komissariat po prosveshcheniĭu.*
Сборник материалов к докладам на весенних методических конференциях в ТССР. Казань, 1928.
113 p. illus. 22 cm.
At head of title: Академический центр Народного комиссариата по просвещению ТССР.
Includes bibliographies.

1. Education—Tatar Republic. I. Title.
Title transliterated: Sbornik materialov k dokladam.
LA853.T34A5 1928   53–48326

NT   0049300   DLC

Tatar A. S. S. R. *Narodnyĭ komissariat truda.*
Краткие итоги работы между VII и VIII съездами профсоюзов Т. С. С. Р. (1926–1929 годы) Казань, 1929.
48 p. 23 cm.

1. Labor and laboring classes—Tatar Republic.
Title transliterated: Kratkie itogi raboty.
HD8529.T3A53   53–49013

NT   0049301   DLC

Tatar A. S. S. R. *Narodnyĭ komissariat truda i sotsial'nogo obespechenīĭa.*
Материалы к докладу народного комиссара труда и СО ТССР тов. Измайлова по работе Наркомата на VII-м С'езде профсоюзов, за время с 1 июля 1926 г. по 1 июля 1927 г. Казань, 1927.
42 p. 22 cm.

1. Labor and laboring classes—Tatar Republic. I. Izmaĭlov,
——. II. Title.
Title transliterated: Materialy k dokladu narodnogo komissara truda ... Izmaĭlova.
HD8529.T3A54   55–51152

NT   0049302   DLC

Tatar A. S. S. R. *Narodnyĭ komissariat zdravookhranenīĭa.*
Иженский минеральный источник. Казань, Ижминвод, 1930.
56 p. (p. 53–56 advertisement) illus. 22 cm.
Bibliography: p. [51]–52.

1. Mineral waters—Tatar Republic. I. Title.
Title transliterated: Izhevskiĭ mineral'nyĭ istochnik.
RA878.T3A5 1930   53–48465

NT   0049303   DLC

Tatar A. S. S. R. *Narodnyĭ komissariat zemledelīĭa.*
Основы перспективного плана по восстановлению и реорганизации сельского хозяйства Татреспублики на ближайшее пятилетие, 1926–1931 г.г. (в сокращенном популярном изложении) Казань, 1927.
x, 50 p. 23 cm.

1. Tatar Republic—Economic policy. I. Title.
Title transliterated: Osnovy perspektivnogo plana po vosstanovleniĭa ... sel'skogo khozĭaĭstva.
HC337.T3A52   53–47064

NT   0049304   DLC

Tatar A. S. S. R. *Narodnyĭ komissariat zemledelīĭa.*
Пути переустройства сельского хозяйства Татарской Республики; сборник материалов руководящего характера для повседневной работы в области сельского хозяйства. Казань, 1928.
88 p. 23 cm.

1. Agricultural laws and legislation—Tatar Republic. I. Title.
Title transliterated: Puti pereustroĭstva sel'skogo khozĭaĭstva Tatarskoĭ Respubliki.
52–58288

NT   0049305   DLC

Tatar A. S. S. R. *Narodnyĭ komissariat zemledelīĭa. Upravlenie zemleustroĭstva i melioratsii*
see **Tatar A. S. S. R.** *Upravlenie zemleustroĭstva i melioratsii.*

Tatar A. S. S. R. *Respublikanskaĭa detskaĭa ėkskursionno-turistskaĭa stantsīĭa.*
Маршрутный путеводитель по экскурсионным объектам Татарии. [Ответственный редактор М. Н. Елизарова] Казань, 1939.
96 p. illus. 15 cm.

1. Tatar Republic—Descr. & trav.—Guide-books. I. Elizarova,
M. N., ed. II. Title.
Title transliterated: Marshrutnyĭ putevoditel' po ėkskursionnym ob"ektam Tatarii.
DK511.T17A5 1939   61–22076 ‡

NT   0049307   DLC

Tatar A. S. S. R. *Statisticheskoe upravlenie. Otdel tekushcheĭ sel'sko-khozĭaĭstvennoĭ statistiki.*
Числовое выражение видов на урожай. Казань, 1-я Гос. тип., 1920.
40 p. 26 cm.
At head of title: Татарская Социалистическая Советская Республика. Статистическое управление. Отдел текущей сельскохозяйственной статистики.

1. Field crops—Russia—Statistics. 2. Crop yields. I. Title.
Title romanized: Chislovoe vyrazhenie vidov na urozhaĭ.
SB187.R8T37   75–581653

NT   0049308   DLC

Tatar A. S. S. R. *S"ezd Sovetov.*
Стенографический отчет.
Казань.
v. 26 cm.

1. Tatar Republic—Pol. & govt.
Title transliterated: Stenograficheskiĭ otchet.
JS7.R9T33   52–41909

NT   0049309   DLC

LC156
.R9T3
Tatar A. S. S. R. *S"ezd Sovetov. 10th, 1934.*
Что сказал x Всетатарский с'езд Советов о культуре и просвещении. Казань, Таттосиздат, Учпедсектор, 1935.

Tatar A. S. S. R. *S"ezd sovetov. 10th, 1934.*
Вопросы местной промышленности на x С'езде советов Татарской АССР. Казань, Таттосиздат, 1935.
40 p. 18 cm.

1. Tatar Republic—Indus.
Title transliterated: Voprosy mestnoĭ promyshlennosti.
HC337.T3T34   50–42340

NT   0049311   DLC

Russia (*1923–   U. S. S. R.*) *Laws, statutes, etc.*
Директивы по рационализации производства и хозрасчету; сборник официальных материалов. Казань, 1931.

52–58288

Tatar A. S. S. R. *Sovet Narodnykh Komissarov.*
Доклад председателя Совета народных комиссаров ТССР К. Г. Мухтарова на торжественном заседании Казанского горсовета ЦИК, СНК, ОК РКП(б) Совета профессиональных союзов и представителей Красной Армии в день трехлетней годовщины Автономной Татарской Социалистической Советской Республики 25 июня 1923 года. Казань, 1923.
47 p. 22 cm.

1. Tatar Republic—Pol. & govt. I. Mukhtarov, K. G.
Title transliterated: Doklad predsedatelĭa.
DK511.T17A5 1923   55–49772 ‡

NT   0049313   DLC

J7
.R7T3
Tatar A. S. S. R. *Sovet Narodnykh Komissarov.*

Tatar A. S. S. R. *TSentral'nyĭ Ispolnitel'nyĭ Komitet.*
Отчет ЦИК и СНК.

Tatar A. S. S. R. *Statisticheskoe upravlenie.*
Статистический справочник по промышленности Т. С. С. Р. Казань, 1924.
172 p. 16 cm. (*Its* Серия популярных справочников, вып. 2)
Russian and Tatar.
Added t. p., pref., and contents in Tatar.

1. Tatar Republic—Indus.—Stat. (Series: Tatar A. S. S. R. Statisticheskoe upravlenie. Seriĭa populĭarnykh spravochnikov, vyp. 2) *Title transliterated:* Statisticheskiĭ spravochnik.
HC337.T3A5 1924   50–50877

NT   0049315   DLC

Tatar A. S. S. R. *Statisticheskoe upravlenie. Otdel tekushcheĭ sel'sko-khozĭaĭstvennoĭ statistiki.*
Числовое выражение видов на урожай. Казань, 1-я Гос. тип., 1920.
40 p. 26 cm.
At head of title: Татарская Социалистическая Советская Республика. Статистическое управление. Отдел текущей сельскохозяйственной статистики.

1. Field crops—Russia—Statistics. 2. Crop yields. I. Title.
Title romanized: Chislovoe vyrazhenie vidov na urozhaĭ.
SB187.R8T37   75–581653

NT   0049316   DLC

D550
.T8
Tatar A. S. S. R. *TSentral'nyĭ gosudarstvennyĭ arkhiv.*
Царская армия в период Мировой войны и Февральской революции (материалы к изучению истории империалистической и гражданской войны). Вступ. статья М. Вольфович. Составители: А. Максимов, Е. Медведев и Ш. Юсупов. Под ред. А. Максимова. Казань, Татиздат, 1932.

Tatar A. S. S. R. *TSentral'nyĭ Ispolnitel'nyĭ Komitet.*
Что сказал x Всетатарский с'езд Советов о культуре и просвещении. Казань, Таттосиздат, Учпедсектор, 1935.
59 p. illus. 23 cm.
Includes legislation.

1. Education—Tatar Republic. 2. Illiteracy—Tatar Republic. I.
Tatar A. S. S. R. S"ezd Sovetov. 10th, 1934. II. Tatar A. S. S. R.
Laws, statutes, etc. III. Title
Title transliterated: Chto skazal desĭatyĭ Vsetatarskiĭ s"ezd Sovetov o kul'ture i prosveshchenii.
LC156.R9T3   54–50389

NT   0049318   DLC

Tatar A. S. S. R. *TSentral'nyĭ Ispolnitel'nyĭ Komitet.*
Отчет ЦИК и СНК.

Казань.
v. 26 cm.
Russian and Tatar.

1. Tatar Republic—Pol. & govt.   I. Tatar A. S. S. R. Sovet
Narodnykh Komissarov.   *Title transliterated:* Otchet TSIK i SNK.

J7.R7T3   52–58863

NT   0049319   DLC

Tatar A. S. S. R. *TSentral'nyĭ Ispolnitel'nyĭ Komitet.*
Сборник руководящих материалов к перевыборам Советов в ТССР в 1929 г. Казань, Изд. Орготдела ЦИК ТССР, 1928.

vi, 58 p. 23 cm.
Bibliography: p. 58.

1. Election law—Tatar Republic.   I. Title.
Title transliterated: Sbornik rukovodi͡ashchikh materialov k perevyboram Sovetov v TSSR.

52–54104

NT   0049320   DLC

Tatar republic *(A. S. S. R.) Upravlenie narodno-khozi͡aĭstvennogo ucheta.*
... Социалистическое строительство Татарской АСС республики за 15 лет. Экономико-статистический сборник, посвященный пятнадцатилетию АТССР. Казань, 1935.

199 p. diagrs. 17½ᵐ.
At head of title: ... Управление народно-хозяйственного учета Татарской АСС республики.
Errata slip mounted on p. 187.

1. Tatar republic—Stat.   I. Title.
Title transliterated: Sot͡sialisticheskoe stroitel'stvo Tatarskoĭ ASS.

Library of Congress   HA1448.T3A5   1935
                                                           44–33530
                                                               ₂₎

NT   0049321   DLC

HC337
.T3T35

Tatar A. S. S. R. Upravlenie narodno-khozi͡aĭst-
vennogo ucheta.
Татарская АССР; экономический справочник. 1932–
Казань, Татиздат.

Tatar A. S. S. R. *Upravlenie zemleustroĭstva i melioratsii.*
Правила по технической части производства землестроительных работ в Татреспублике; дополнение Инструкции по производству землеустроительных работ на основе Земельного кодекса Р. С. Ф. С. Р. 1928 г. ч. 3. Геодезическая техника при землеустройстве. (См. Справочник землеустроителя, ч. 2, Москва, 1928 г.) Казань, 1929.
16 p. 23 cm.
———— Приложения. Составил инженер Барчан. Казань, 1929.
24 p. tables. 22 cm.

1. Earthwork.   TA715.T312 Suppl.
Title transliter-   I. Barchan.   II. Title.
ated: Pravila po tekhnicheskoĭ chasti proiz-
TA715.T3   vodstva zemleustroitel'nykh rabot.
                                                           54–50689

NT   0049323   DLC

Tatar A. S. S. R. *Upravlenie zemleustroĭstva, melioratsii i gosudarstvennykh zemel'nykh imushchestv*
see **Tatar A. S. S. R.** *Upravlenie zemleustroĭstva i melioratsii.*

Tatar A. S. S. R. *Verkhovnyĭ Sovet.*
Заседания; стенографический отчет.
₍Казань₎
v. 23 cm.

Title transliterated: Zasedanii͡a; stenograficheskiĭ otchet.

JS6070.T3A3   57–19668

NT   0049325   DLC

AP50
.A9

Tatar-Bashkirskiĭ natsional'nyĭ komitet, Munich.
Azat vatan. № 1–16; март 1952–авг. 1953. München.

Tatar republic (A. S. S. R.)
see   Tatar A. S. S. R.

Tatar yili
see
Rocznik tatarski.

Tatara-Hoszowska, Władysława
see
Hoszowska, Władysława.

PL6515
A1T3
no. 76
x

Te tatara raa no te mau numera i roto i te ravea e papu ai te manao i te numera. / [Tahiti. Printed at the London Missionary Society's Press, 1852]
24 p. (incl. cover) 18cm.   [Tahitian imprints, no. 76]

Caption title.
Running title: Tatara raa no te peau toru.
O'Reilly, Bibliographie de Tahiti et de la Polynésie française, no. 5940.
Provenance: Alphonse Pinart; Thomas W. Streeter.

1. Arithmetic – 1846–1880.   2. Linguistics – Tahitian – Texts.
I. London Missionary Society.   (Series)

NT   0049330   CU–BANC

TATARANO, C. A.
Les nouvelles tendances économiques de la Roumanie d'après la littérature économique et les discussions parlementaires. Thèse. Paris, Jouve et cie, 1922.

"Bibliography", pp. [141]–142.

NT   0049331   MH CtY

W 6
P3

TĂTĂRANU, I
Odihna și tratamentul in stațiunile de pe litoral. ₍Bucureşti₎ Centrul de Educație Sanitară, 1955.
71 p. illus.
1. Health resorts – Rumania

NT   0049332   DNLM

Tatarasco, Gh.
see
Tatarescu, George, 1886–

Tatarchenko, Aleksandr Evgen'evich.
Вертолет. Москва, Воен. изд-во, 1955.
148 p. illus. 21 cm.

Negative film in the Library of Congress.
——— Microfilm copy (positive)
Made   –by the Library of Congress.
1. Helicopters.   I. Title.   *Title transliterated:* Vertolet.

TL716.T26   56–35184

NT   0049334   DLC

UG635
.F8L35

Tatarchenko, Evgeniĭ Ivanovich, tr.

Lapchinskiĭ, Aleksandr Nikolaevich, 1882–   ed.
... Воздушный флот; история, тактика, техника. Перевод с французского В. В., С. А. Меженинова, Е. И. Татарченко и С. Г. Хорькова; под редакцией и с предисловием А. Лапчинского. Москва, Издание журнала "Вестник воздушного флота", 1924.

Tatarchenko, Evgeniĭ Ivanovich.
... Воздушный флот Америки (Северо-Американских соединенных штатов). 2. значительно дополненное изд. ... Москва ₍Военный вестник₎ 1924.

137, ₍2₎ p. illus. 19¼ᵐ. (Библиотека Общества друзей воздушного флота)

At head of title: Евгений Татарченко ...
On cover: Общество друзей воздушного флота.
Bibliography: p. 8.

1. Aeronautics – U. S.   I. Obshchestvo druzeĭ vozdushnogo flota,
Moscow.   II. Title.
                                                           40–19049
Library of Congress   TL521.T3 1924

NT   0049336   DLC

Tatartscheff, Assène
see **Tatarchev, Assen.**

Tatarchev, Asen.
Mémoire sur la situation de la minorité bulgare en Yougoslavie. Exposé de quelques faits qui illustrent la politique de contrainte morale et physique appliquée par le gouvernement yougoslave à la population bulgare de Macédoine. ₍Par, Dr. Assène Tatartcheff. ₍Genève, 1933₎
1 p.l., 3, 18 ₍i.e., 21₎ numb. l. 34 cm.

NT   0049338   NNC

₍Tatarchev, Asen₎
₍A petition to the League of nations by Asen Tatarchev, in the name of the Bulgarian minority, protesting their treatment by Yugoslavia₎ / ₍Genève, 1933₎ 1 v.   33cm.

₍Text in French.
₍Includes his Mémoire sur la situation de la minorité bulgare en Yougoslavie.

1. Bulgars in Yugoslavia.   I. League of nations.
N. Y. P. L.   December 1, 1947

NT   0049339   NN

Tatarchev, Viktor.
... Опит върху политическите престъпления (юридико-социологичен етюд) ... София, Кооперативна печатница "Типограф", 1929.

262, ₍2₎ p. 23ᵐ.
"Библиография": p. ₍263₎

1. Political crimes and offenses.   I. Title.

                                                           37–21705

NT   0049340   DLC

Tatarchukov, A   N
(Birzhi truda)
Биржи труда / А. Н. Татарчуков. — Петроград : Жизнь и знание, 1916.

64 p. ; 19 cm. – (Дешевая библиотека ; кн. 93)
"Литература о биржах труда": p. 61–62.

1. Labor supply.   I. Title.

HD5861.T37   75–578829

NT   0049341   DLC

Tatarchukov, A   N
Центрально-Черноземная область в хозяйственном отношении. Воронеж, 1925.
45 p. illus. 22 cm.
At head of title: Областная плановая комиссия Ц. Ч. О.

1. TSentral'no-Chernozemnaiâ oblast'—Econ. condit.
Title transliterated: TSentral'no-Chernozemnaiâ oblast'.
HC337.T75T3 1925   54–49144 ‡

NT 0049342   DLC

Tatarchukov, A   N
Центрально-Черноземная область (экономический очерк) 2. доп. и совершенно перер. изд. Воронеж, 1928.
107 p. fold. col. maps, diagrs. 26 cm.
At head of title: Воронежский губисполком и Воронежское бюро Госплана Р. С. Ф. С. Р.

1. TSentral'no-Chernozemnaiâ oblast'—Econ. condit.
Title transliterated: TSentral'no-Chernozemnaiâ oblast'.
HC337.T75T3 1928   52–57076

NT 0049343   DLC

Tatarchukov, A   N
Центрально-Черноземная область (экономический очерк) 3. доп. и перер. изд. Воронеж, Коммуна, 1929.
98 p. maps (part fold. col.) 27 cm.
At head of title: Центрально-Черноземная областная плановая комиссия.

1. TSentral'no-Chernozemnaiâ oblast'—Econ. condit.
Title transliterated: TSentral'no-Chernozemnaiâ oblast'.
HC337.T75T3 1929   52–57071

NT 0049344   DLC

Tatarczuk, Vincent Anthony, 1925–
Infamy of law; a historical synopsis and a commentary.
Washington, Catholic University of America Press, 1954.
xii, 119 p. 23 cm. (Catholic University of America. Canon law studies, no. 357)
Thesis—Catholic University of America.
Vita.
Bibliography: p. 110–114.

1. Infamy (Canon law) 2. Infamy (Roman law)   i. Title. (Series)
    A 54–4838
Catholic Univ.
for Library of Congress
   America. Library ₃₎

NT 0049345   DCU OrStbM GU-L NN OU NcD DLC

Tatarė, A   *kunigas.*   **891.92 T18**
Pamoksėai izzminties ir teisybes, iszguldinėti gałwocziu wisu amžiu, del lietuvos waikelu. Antras izzdawimas. New York, Spausdinta kasztu J. Papłaucko, 1887.
vii, 121 p. 16ᵐᵒ.
"Prakalba" signed: Kun. Tatarė.

NT 0049346   ICJ

Tatarė, A
Hvc46   Pamokslai gražių žmonių Kun. A. Totoriaus.
U2   Shenandoh, Pa., V.J. Staparo spaustuvėje,
1   1900.
T188   95p.

"Atspauda iš 'Dirvos'".

NT 0049347   CtY OC1

Tatarė, A
Hvc46   Pamokslai izzminties ir teisybes, iszguldi-
U2   nėti galvoczių visu amžiu del Lietuvos vaikeliu.
1   3. laida. Chicago, Spaustuwėje "Lietuvos",
T187   1899.
        ix,182p.

NT 0049348   CtY OC1

Tataresco, Georges
   see
Tatarescu, George, 1886–

Tatarescu, George, 1886–
... Bessarabie et Moscou; discours prononcé ₍!₎ à la Chambre des députés de Bucarest le 9 décembre 1925.
Bucarest, Cvltvra naţională, 1926.
47 p. incl. illus. (ports., map, facsims.) tables. 23 cm.
At head of title: Georges Tataresco, sous-secrétaire d'état au Ministère de l'intérieur.

1. Bolshevism—Bessarabia. 2. Bessarabia—Pol. & govt.   i. Title.
DK511.B4T3   947.7   36—4753

NT 0049350   DLC GU CtY MH CU MChB MB NIC TxU ViU

TATARESCO, GEORGES, 1886–
Discursuri-program, expozeuri, cuvântări.
₍Bucureşti? Partidul naţional-liberal, 1946?₎ 112 p.
21cm.

Film reproduction. Negative.

1 Rumania—Politics, 1944-1946. 2. Partidul naţional-liberal.

NT 0049351   NN

Rum
949.8
T216e   **Tatarescu, Georges, 1886–**
Evacuarea Basarabiei si a Buccvinei de Nord.
Craiova, Rumania, Editura Scrisul Romanesc
S. A., ₍1940₎.
26p.   24cm.

NT 0049352   OKentU

Tataresco, Georges, 1886–
Quatre années de gouvernement, 1933–1937; exposé fait devant le Comité central du Parti national-libéral le 1 novembre 1937.
Bucarest, 1937.   59 p.   port.   17cm.

1. Rumania—Politics, 1933–1937.

NT 0049353   NN

JN9638   **Tatarescu, Georges, 1886–**
.T2   ... Le régime électoral et parlementaire en Roumanie ...
Paris, M. Giard & E. Brière, 1912.
191, ₍1₎ p. 25ᶜᵐ.
Thèse—Univ. de Paris.

1. Rumania—Pol. & govt. 2. Rumania—Constitutional history.

NT 0049354   ICU MH

Tatarescu, Gh.
   see **Tatarescu, Georges, 1886–**

4DD   **Tatarescu, Ştefan**
4174   Procesul iudaismului in faţa
conştiinţei naţionale, contribuţiuni la lichidarea visului israelit de hegemonie mondiala. Bucureşti, Tip. Dimitrie Cantemir, 1934.
64 p.

NT 0049356   DLC-P4

Tataretus, Petrus
   see Tartaretus, Petrus, 15th cent.

Tatarin-Tarnheyden, Edgar, 1882–
Die berufsstände, ihre stellung im staatsrecht und die deutsche wirtschaftsverfassung, von dr. Edgar Tatarin-Tarnheyden ... Berlin, C. Heymann, 1922.
xix, ₍1₎, 260 p. 24ᶜᵐ.
"Literaturauswahl" at beginning of most of the chapters.

1. Professions. 2. Germany—Occupations. 3. Trade and professional associations—Germany.   i. Title.
    26–6510
Library of Congress   HD3616.G4T3

NT 0049358   DLC CtY CU

TATARIN-TARNHEYDEN, EDGAR, 1882–
Berufsverbaende und Wirtschaftsdemokratie; ein Kommentar zu Artikel 165 der Reichsverfassung, von Dr. Edgar Tatarin-Tarnheyden... Berlin: R. Hobbing, 1930. 118 p. 8°.

Bibliographical footnotes.

588735A. 1. Constitutions—Germany, 1919—Commentaries.
2. Employee representation   —Germany.

NT 0049359   NN

Tatarin-Tarnheyden, Edgar, 1882–
Die betriebsvereinbarung im verhaeltnis zum einzelsarbeitvertrag und zum tarifvertrag.
(Auszug) Rostock, 1924.
Inaug.-diss. - Rostock.

NT 0049360   ICRL

JC 264   **Tatarin-Tarnheyden, Edgar, 1882–**
T37   Der Einfluss des Judentums in Staatsrecht und Staatslehre / von E. Tatarin-Tarnheyden. Berlin : Deutscher Rechts-Verlag, ₍1938?₎
35 p. ; 25 cm. (Das Judentum in der Rechtswissenschaft ; 5.)

1. State, The. 2. Lawyers, Jewish.
3. Jews in Germany—History I. Title
II. Series

NT 0049361   OU CU NN NNC CSt CSt-H

Tatarin-Tarnheyden, Edgar, 1882–
Die enteignung des deutschen doms zu Riga im lichte des modernen staats-, verwaltungs- und völkerrechts, unter berücksichtigung der kirchenrechtlichen grundlagen, von dr. Edgar Tatarin-Tarnheyden ... Breslau, J. U. Kern, 1932.
2 p. l., 69, ₍1₎ p. 24½ᶜᵐ. (On cover: Zeitschrift für völkerrecht ... Ergänzungsheft zu band xvi)

1. Riga. St. Marien (Cathedral) 2. Ecclesiastical law—Latvia.
i. Title.
    37–13087
Library of Congress   JX5.Z6 bd. 16
         (341.05) 274.74

NT 0049362   DLC CtY NNC CU-L WU

Tatarin-Tarnheyden, Edgar, 1882–   ed.
Festgabe für Rudolf Stammler zum 70. geburtstage am 19. februar 1926. Hrsg. von Edgar Tatarin-Tarnheyden ...
Berlin und Leipzig, W. de Gruyter & co., 1926.

Tatarin-Tarnheyden, Edgar, 1882-
Rechtsgutachten zur Frage der Monopolstellung der drei herrschenden Gewerk-
schaftsrichtungen im allgemeinen und ins-
besondere zu der Festlegung dieser Monopolstellung im Reichsknappschaftsgesetz,
in der Verordnung über den Vorläufigen
Reichswirtschaftsrat und in den Gesetz-
entwürfen über den endgültigen Reichswirk-
schaftsrat, erstattet von: Dr. E. Tatarin-
Tarnheyden ... Berlin, Deutschland-Verlag
[1929]

40 p. incl. chart. 23cm.

Advertising matter: p. 35-40.
"Gliederung des R. v. A.": diagram on
p. [3] of cover.
"... Betrifft: Beseitigung der verfas-
sungswidrigen Monopolstellung der Gewerkschaften": [3] p. (21 x 33cm. fold. to 16
x 21cm.) laid in.

NT 0049365   MH-L

Tatarin-Tarnheyden, Edgar, 1882–
... Die rechtsstellung des amtshauptmanns in Mecklenburg-
Schwerin, in verwaltungs- und staatspolitischer beleuchtung;
zugleich ein beitrag zum problem einer reichsverwaltungsre-
form, von dr. Edgar Tatarin-Tarnheyden ... Rostock, C. Hinstorff, 1931.

62 p. 22½ᶜᵐ. (Rostocker abhandlungen ... hft. 12)

1. Administrative law — Mecklenburg-Schwerin. 2. Mecklenburg-
Schwerin—Constitutional law. 3. Mecklenburg-Schwerin—Pol. & govt.
4. Mecklenburg-Schwerin—Officials and employees. I. Title.

35-9640

Library of Congress   JN4370.T3

[3]   354.4307

NT 0049366   DLC

Tatarin-Tarnheyden, Edgar, 1882-
Staat und recht in ihrem begrifflichen
verhältnis; eine studie über die konsequenzen
der Stammlerschen rechtslehre, von professor
dr. Edgar Tatarin-Tarnheyden ... Berlin und
Leipzig, Walter de Gruyter & Co., 1926.
1 p.l., 72 p. diagrs. 24cm.

"Sonderausgabe aus Festgabe für Rudolf
Stammler zum 70. Geburtstage."
Paged also: [477]-548.

NT 0049367   NcD DLC-P4 MH-L

TATARIN-TARNHEYDEN, E[dgar].
Die staatsrechtliche entwicklung des räte-
gedankens in der russischen und deutschen
revolution;marburger antrittsvorlesung,gehal-
ten am 4.märz 1922. München,[1925].

NT 0049368   MH-L

TATARIN-TARNHEYDEN, E[dgar]1882-
Völkerrecht und organische staatsauffassung.
Berlin, 1936.
8°   29 p.
"Erstmalig erschienen in: Rudolf Stammler
Festschrift zu seinem 80. geburtstag am 19.
februar 1936, herausgegeben im auftrag der In-
ternationalen vereinigung für rechts- und
sozialphilosophie, von C. A. EMGE."

NT 0049369   MH-L NcD

Tatarin-Tarnheyden, Edgar, 1882-
Werdendes staatsrecht; gedanken zu einem organischen und
deutschen verfassungsneubau, von dr. Edgar Tatarin-Tarnheyden ... Berlin, C. Heymann, 1934.
viii, 183 p. 22½ᶜᵐ.

1. Germany—Constitutional law. 2. Germany—Pol. & govt.—1933-
I. Title.

35-14916

Library of Congress   JN3954.T3

[2]   342.4303

NT 0049370   DLC CU MH

Tatarinoff, Adèle
see
Tatarinoff-Eggenschwiler, Adele.

Tatarinoff, Eugen, 1868-
Die beteiligung Solothurns am Schwabenkriege bis zur
schlacht bei Dornach 22 juli 1499. Nebst 172 urkund-
lichen belegen und 24 lithographischen beilagen. Festschrift verfasst im auftrage der hohen regierung des
kantons Solothurn zur iv. säkularfeier der schlacht bei
Dornach von Eugen Tatarinoff. Solothurn, A. Lüthy,
1899.
ix, [3], 171 p. xxiv pl. (incl. col. front., map, facsim.) 27ᶜᵐ.
Half-title: Die schlacht bei Dornach.
"Bemerkungen zur darstellung der schlacht bei Dornach": p. 197-202.
1. Dornach, Battle of, 1499. 2. Swabian war, 1496-1499.
4-5428

Library of Congress   DQ617.5.F23

NT 0049372   DLC

Tatarinoff, Eugen, 1868-
Die Briefe Glareans an Johannes Aal aus den
Jahren 1538-1550... Solothurn, Zepfel'sche
Buchdruckerei, 1895.
59 p. front. (facsim.) facsims. 23 cm.
(Mitteilungen des Solothurnischen Historischen
Vereins)

NT 0049373   ICN

Tatarinoff, Eugen, 1868—
Die entwicklung der probstei Interlaken...
Inaug. diss. Zurich,1892.

NT 0049374   ICRL

Tatarinoff, Eugen, 1868—
Festschrift Eugen Tatarinoff.   1938
see under title

DQ610
.5T3   Tatarinoff, Eugen, 1868—
Die Kultur der Völkerwanderungszeit
im Kanton Solothurn.   Solothurn, A.
Lüthy, 1934.
152p. illus.,fold.map. 23cm.
Bibliographical footnotes.

1.Solothurn, Switzerland (Canton) -
Antiquities. I.Title.

NT 0049376   NNU

Tatarinoff, Mario.
Das nachbarliche Baurecht des Kantons Solothurn.
Zürich, 1947.
151 p. 23 cm.
Inaug.-Diss.—Bern.
Bibliography: p. 5-6.

1. Adjoining landowners—Solothurn (Canton)   I. Title.

56-56164

NT 0049377   DLC

Tatarinoff, Paul
Ueber methylguanidine verschiedenen Ursprungs. München,
M.Rieger, 1879.

30 p. diagrs.

NT 0049378   MH-C

Tatarinoff-Eggenschwiler, Adele
Albert Nyfeler; dem Gebirgsmaler in Lötschental zum
siebzigsten Geburtstag am 26.Sept.1953. [Solothurn,
Selbstverlag der Verfasser, 1953]

31 p. illus. (part.col.) port.

NT 0049379   MH

Tatarinoff-Eggenschwiler, Adele.
Der Berghof Mieschegg auf der zweiten Jurakette. [Solo-
thurn, Buch- und Kunstdruckerei Union, 1947 or 8]
108 p. illus., map. 21 cm.
"Quellenangabe": p. 102-103.

1. Mieschegg, Switzerland.   I. Title.

DQ851.M64T3   51-34098

NT 0049380   DLC

Tatarinoff-Eggenschwiler, Adele.
Die Familie Wisswald von Solothurn. Solothurn, Buch-
und Kunstdr. Union, 1939.
52, [3] p. illus., fold. geneal. table, ports. 23 cm.
Bibliography: p. [55]

1. Wisswald family.   I. Title.

CS999.W58 1939   72-241278

NT 0049381   DLC MH

DQ609
.8
.S35   Tatarinoff-Eggenschwiler, Adele.
Schnyder, Willy, 1921-
Der Schützenmatthof. Nach Material und Vorarbeiten
von Willy Schnyder, bearb. und dargestellt von Adele Tatarinoff-Eggenschwiler. [Solothurn, 1953]

Tatarinoff-Eggenschwiler, Adele.
Der Weissenstein bei Solothurn; Beiträge zur Natur und
Geschichte unseres Juraberges. Solothurn, Buchdruckerei
Union, 1952.
143 p. illus., fold. col. map. 21 cm.
"Zum grössten Teil erschienen in den 'Sankt-Ursen-Glocken,'
Beilage zum 'Solothurner Anzeiger.'"

1. Weissenstein, Switzerland.   I. Title.

DQ841.W4T3   914.94   53-30594

NT 0049383   DLC MdBJ NN

TATARINOV, Aleksandr
Catalogus medicamentorum sinensium. St. Petersburg, 1856.

NT 0049384   MiU

Tatarinov, Aleksandr.
Catalogus medicamentorum Sinensium quæ Pedini
comparanda et determinanda. Ectropole; 1886.
1 v.   65 p.

NT 0049385   MiU

Tatarinov, Aleksandr Alekseevich, d. 1886.
(Semimi͡esi͡achnyĭ pli͡en v Bukhari͡i)
Семимѣсячный плѣнъ въ Бухарѣ / А. Татаринова. —
Санктпетербургъ : Изд. М. О. Вольфа, 1867.
iii, 136 p., ₁₁ leaf of plates : fold. map ; 23 cm.

1. Bukhara—Description and travel. 2. Tatarinov, Aleksandr
Alekseevich, d. 1886. I. Title.

DK873.T35   76-500684

NT   0049386   DLC   *

Tatarinov, Fedor Stepanovich.

... "Вѣстникъ воздухоплаванія" ("Библіотека воздухоплаванія") ₁Научно-популярный иллюстрированный жур-
налъ₁ Дек. 1909-

С.-Петербургъ, 1909-

Tatarinov, M. P.

Akademii͡a nauk SSSR.
Александр Семенович Ильичев, 1898–1952. Составил
М. П. Татаринов. ₁Глав. редактор А. Н. Несмеянов₁ Мо-
сква, 1953.

TN140
.I4A6

Tatarinov, M. P.

Akademii͡a nauk SSSR.
Александр Семенович Ильичев, 1898–1952. Составил
М. П. Татаринов. ₁Глав. редактор А. Н. Несмеянов₁ Мо-
сква, 1953.

Tatarinov, M   P

Горная механика; рудничные вентиляторные и водоот-
ливные установки. 2. изд., испр. и доп. Москва, Углетехиздат, 1948.
254 p. diagrs. 26 cm.

1. Mine ventilation. 2. Mine pumps.   I. Title.
Title transliterated: Gornai͡a mekhanika.

TN301.T3 1948   54-26665

NT   0049390   DLC

Tatarinov, M   P

Русские ученые—создатели шахтных насосов и венти-
ляторов. Москва, Углетехиздат, 1951.
198 p. illus., ports., facsims. 20 cm.

1. Mine pumps.   2. Mine ventilation.   3. Scientists–Russia
I. Title.
Title transliterated: Russkie uchenye -
sozdateli shakhtnykh nasosov.

TN325.T3   54-22793

NT   0049391   DLC

Tatarinov, Pavel Mikhaĭlovich.
Асбест. П. М. Татаринов и Е. И. Дворщан. Asbestos.
Ленинград, Глав. ред. геолого-разведочной и геодезиче-
ской лит-ры, 1935.
31, ₁1₁ p. diagrs., map, tables. 23 cm. (Минерально-сырьевая
база СССР, вып. 38)
Errata slip inserted.
Bibliography: p. 31-₁32₁

1. Asbestos.   I. Dvorshchan, Evgeniĭ Il'ich, joint author.   II. Title.
(Series: Mineral'no-syr'evai͡a baza SSSR, vyp. 38)
Title transliterated: Asbest.

TN85.M43 vol. 38   53-48860

NT   0049392   DLC

Tatarinov, Pavel Mikhaĭlovich, ed.
... Индерские бораты; сборник статей под редакцией
П. М. Татаринова ... Ленинград, Москва, ГОНТИ НКТП
СССР, Главная радакция горно-топливной и геолого-разве-
дочной литературы, 1938.
241, ₁1₁ p. illus., plates, maps (part fold.) tables, diagrs., profiles
(part fold.) 25¼ᵉᵐ.
At head of title: ГГУ НКТП СССР. Центральный научно-исследо-
вательский геолого-разведочный институт (ЦНИГРИ).
Errata slip mounted on t.-p.
"Литература" at end of some articles.
1. Geology— Kazakh S.S.R.   2. Mineralogy— Kazakh S.S.R.   3.
Borates.   I. Leningrad. T͡Sentral'nyĭ nauchno-issledovatel'skiĭ geologo-
razvedochnyĭ institut.   II. Title.
Title transliterated: Inderskie boraty.
44-13813

Library of Congress   QE315.T23

NT   0049393   DLC

Tatarinov, Pavel Mikhaĭlovich.
Магнезит. П. М. Татаринов и Е. И. Дворщан. Magne-
site. Ленинград, Глав. ред. геолого-разведочной и геоде-
зической лит-ры, 1935.
21, ₁3₁ p. diagr., tables. 23 cm. (Минерально-сырьевая база
СССР, вып. 11)
Errata slip inserted.
Bibliography: p. 21-₁22₁

1. Magnesite.   I. Dvorshchan, Evgeniĭ Il'ich, joint author.
II. Title.   (Series: Mineral'no-syr'evai͡a baza SSSR, vyp. 11)
Title transliterated: Magnezit.

TN85.M43 vol. 11   53-48072

NT   0049394   DLC

Tatarinov, Pavel Mikhaĭlovich, ed.
... Слюды СССР; сборник статей по минералогии, кри-
сталлографии, геологии и экономике слюд и обзор месторождений мусковита в СССР, под редакцией П. М. Татаринова ... Ленинград, Москва, ОНТИ-НКТП-СССР, Главная редакция геолого-разведочной и геодезической литературы, 1937.
540, ₁1₁ p., 1 l. illus., plates, maps, profiles, diagrs. 26ᵉᵐ.
At head of title: НКТП-СССР. Главное геологическое управление.
Центральный научно-исследовательский геолого-разведочный институт (ЦНИГРИ)

Part of the illustrative material is folded.
Errata slip mounted on leaf at end.
The article by A. K. Boldyrev on mica has a summary in English.
"Литература" at end of some articles.

1. Mica.   2. Mines and mineral resources—Russia.   I.
Leningrad. T͡Sentral'nyĭ nauchno-issledovatel'skiĭ geologo-razvedochnyĭ
institut.   II. Title.
Title transliterated: Sli͡udy SSSR.
44-34487

Library of Congress   TN933.T3

NT   0049396   DLC

Tatarinov, Pavel Mikhaĭlovich.
Тальк и тальковый камень. Talc and soapstone. П. М.
Татаринов и Е. И. Дворщан. Ленинград, Глав. ред.
геолого-разведочной и геодезической лит-ры, 1935.
18, ₁2₁ p. 23 cm. (Минерально-сырьевая база СССР, вып. 19)
Errata slip inserted.
Bibliography: p. ₁19₁

1. Talc.   2. Soapstone.   I. Dvorshchan, E.   (Series: Mineral'no-syr'evai͡a baza SSSR, vyp. 19)
Title transliterated: Tal'k i tal'kovyĭ kamen'.

TN948.T2T3   51-47260

NT   0049397   DLC

Tatarinov, Pavel Mikhaĭlovich.
Условия образования месторождений рудных и неруд-
ных полезных ископаемых. Москва, Гос. научно-техн.
изд-во лит-ры по геологии и охране недр, 1955.
279 p. illus. 23 cm.
Bibliography: p. 277-₁278₁
——— Microfilm copy (negative)
Made in 1955 by the Library of Congress.
Call No. ———————————→ Microfilm Slavic 543 T
1. Ores.   2. Geology.   I. Title.
Title transliterated: Uslovii͡a obrazovanii͡a mesto-
rozhdeniĭ rudnykh i poleznykh iskopaemykh.

TN265.T3   56-39746

Library of Congress

NT   0049398   DLC

Film
1091
no. 4

TATARINOV, Pavel Pavlovich
Ueber die Bedeutung des Glutins als
Nahrungsstoff. Zürich, Zürcher &
Furrer, 1879.
14 p.
Film copy.
Translation of *Materialy dli͡a
raz"i͡asnenii͡a znachenii͡a gli͡utiny, kak
pishchevago veshchestva.*

NT   0049399   DNLM

Film
1091
no. 3

TATARINOV, Pavel Pavlovich
Ueber Methylguanidine verschiedenen
Ursprungs. München, Rieger, 1879.
30 p. illus.
Film copy.

NT   0049400   DNLM

PN4788
.K6

Tatarinov, V. T., ed.

Kommunisticheskai͡a partii͡a Sovetskogo Soi͡uza. *Vysshai͡a
partiĭnai͡a shkola. Kafedra zhurnalistiki.*
Газетные жанры; учебное пособие по журналистике.
₁Составлено по лекциям, прочитанным в ВПШ при ЦК
КПСС₁ Под ред. К. А. Ковалевского и В. Т. Татаринова.
Москва, 1955.

Tatarinov, Vasiliĭ Georgievich.
Учебник анатомии и физиологии человека. Рекомендо-
ван для школ мед. сестер. Москва, Медгиз, 1954.
361 p. illus. 23 cm.

1. Anatomy, Human.   2. Physiology.   I. Title.
Title transliterated: Uchebnik ana-
tomii i fiziologii cheloveka.

RT69.T35   55-44469 ‡

NT   0049402   DLC

Tatarinov, Vladimir Fokich.
Уравнительный сбор с торговых и промышленных предприятий; краткое руководство для плательщиков, состав-
лено ... В. Татариновым. Москва, Издательство Мосфинотдела, 1926.
1 p. l., 19, ₁1₁ p. 17ᵉᵐ.

1. Taxation—Russia—Law.   2. Industrial laws and legislation—Russia.   I. Title.

Library of Congress   HJ3536.1926.T3
40-15054

NT   0049403   DLC

Tatarinov, Vladimir Fokich, *comp.*
Уравнительный сбор с торговых и промышленных предприятий. Содержание: i. Основные практические сведения
по уравнительному сбору. ii. Табель %% облож. уравсбо-
ром. iii. Пояснение к табели. Составили: Татаринов,
В. Ф., Трофимов, А. П., Николаев, Б. К. Москва, Издательство Мосфинотдела, 1928.
49 p. 17¼ᵉᵐ.

1. Taxation—Russia—Law.   I. Trofimov, Aleksandr Petrovich, joint
comp.   II. Nikolaev, Boris Konstantinovich, joint comp.   III. Title.

Library of Congress   HJ3536.1928.T3   41-42474

NT   0049404   DLC

PQ2254
.R6R8
1937

Tatarinova, I. S., ed.

France, Anatole, 1844–1924.
Восстание ангелов. Пер. с французского Н. Рыковой и
З. Шпитальниковой, под ред. И. С. Татариновой. Мо-
сква, Academia, ₁etc.₁ 1937.

Tatarische Lieder
see under Paasonen, Heikki, 1865-1919.

Tatariahvili, Akaki.
Die industrievereinigungen in der U.d.SSR.
... von Akaki Tatarischwili ... Göttingen,
Göttinger handelsdruckerei, 1932.
iv,116 p. 20½ᶜᵐ.
Inaug.-diss.—Göttingen.
"Literaturverzeichnis": p.₍115₎-116.

1.Russia—Econ.policy. I.Title.

NT 0049407 MiU ICRL NNC CtY CSt-H

Tatarka, Dominik, 1913-
Družné letá. ₍Vyd. 1. Bratislava₎ Slovenský spisovateľ,
1954.
200 p. illus. 21 cm. (Pôvodná próza, zv. 63)

ɪ. Title.

PG5438.T34D7   62-28654 ‡

NT 0049408 DLC CU

PG 5438 Tatarka, Dominik, 1913-
.T2P2   Farská republika. [Vyd. 1. V
1948   Turčianskom sv. Martine] Matica
slovenská [1948]
250 p. (Knižnica slovenských
pohl'adov, sv. 138)

NT 0049409 ICU OC1 NSyU DLC-P4

TATARKA, DOMINIK.
Farská republika. [2. wyd. Turčiansky Sv. Martin]
Matica slovenská [1948] 250 p. 22cm. (Slovenské
pohľady. Knižnica Slovenských pohľadov. sv. 138)

ɪ. Fiction, Slovak. I. Series. II. Title.

NT 0049410 NN

Tatarka, Dominik
Farská republika. [Ze slovenského převedla Kamila
Jíroudková. Praha] Československý spisovatel, 1949
310 p.

NT 0049411 MH DLC-P4

Tatarka, Dominik.
Farská republika. ₍Vyd. 2.₎ Martin, Matica slovenská,
1951.
260 p. 22 cm. (Knižnica Slovenských pohľadov, sd. 138)

ɪ. Title.

PG5438.T34F3 1951   54-25489

NT 0049412 DLC IU CLU

PG5438 Tatarka, Dominik.
T34F3   Farská republika. ₍vyd.3.₎ vo vyd-ve Slovenský
1955   spisovateľ prepracované 1. Bratislava, Slovenský
spisovateľ, 1955.
321 p. illus. (Pôvodná próza, zv.76)

NT 0049413 CU

891.87 Tatarka, Dominik, 1913-
T18   Panna Zázračnica. ₍Turčiansky Sv. Martin₎
Op1944 Matica slovenská ₍1944₎
118p. 20cm.

NT 0049414 IU ICU MH NSyU

Tatarka, Dominik.
Prvý druhý úder. Bratislava, Pravda, 1950.
323 p.
Slovak.

NT 0049415 OC1

PG5438 TATARKA,DOMINIK
.T2P9   Prvý a druhý úder. ₍2. oprav. vyd.₎
Bratislava, Slovenský spisovateľ, 1951.
310 p.

The first and second blow ₍novel₎

NT 0049416 InU

Tatarka, Dominik.
Prvý a druhý úder. ₍Vyd. 3. Bratislava₎ Slovenský
spisovateľ, 1954.
234 p. 20 cm. (Pôvodná próza, zv. 49)

ɪ. Title.

PG5438.T34P7 1954   61-39783 ‡

NT 0049417 DLC ICU

PG5438 Tatarka, Dominik, 1913-
.T2R2   Radostník. ₍Vyd. 1. Bratislava₎ Slovenský
1954   spisovateľ, 1954.
227 p. (Edícia Pôvodná próza, zv.56)

NT 0049418 ICU

Tatarka, Dominik, 1913-
V úzkosti hľadania; novely. ₍V Turčianskom sv. Mar-
tine₎ Matica slovenská, 1942.
150 p. 20 cm. (Knižnica Slovenských pohľadov, sv. 84)

ɪ. Title.

PG5438.T34V2   63-42185 ‡

NT 0049419 DLC MiU CU CtY IU NN

PG 5438 Tatarka, Dominik, 1913-
.T2V2   V úzkosti hľadania; novely. [Vyd.
1948   2., dop.] Turčiansky Sv. Martin
[Matica slovenská, 1948]
194 p. (Knižnica slovenských
pohl'adov, sv. 84)

NT 0049420 ICU NSyU NjP

ND   Tatarkiewicz, Władysław, 1886-
699   Aleksander Orłowski. Warszawa, Nakł.
.O74 Gegethnera i Wolffa [1926]
T33   23p. 32 plates. 19cm. (Monografje
artystyczne, t.7)
Cover title: Al. Orłowski.
Bibliographical footnotes.

1. Orłovskiĭ, Aleksandr Osipovich,
1777-1832. I. Title

NT 0049421 DGW MH

Tatarkiewicz, Władysław: Die Disposition der Aristotelischen
Prinzipien. Marburg 1910: (Hof-Buchdr., Weimar). IV,
102 S. 8° ¶(Ersch. auch als: Philos. Arbeiten. Bd 4, H. 2.)
Marburg, Phil. Diss. v. 16. März 1910, Ref. Cohen, Natorp
[Geb. 3. April 86 Warschau; Wohnort: Marburg; Staatsangeh.: Rußland;
Vorbildung: 5. Gymn. Warschau Reife O. 03; Studium: Warschau 3, Zürich 1,
Berlin 3, Marburg 6 S.; Rig. 18. Dez. 09.]   [U 10. 3396

NT 0049422 ICRL MH PU

Tatarkiewicz, Władysław, 1886-
Die disposition der aristotelischen prinzipien, von Wla-
dyslaw Tatarkiewicz ... Giessen, A. Töpelmann, 1910.
iv, 102 p. 22ᶜᵐ. (On verso of t.-p.: Philosophische arbeiten, hrsg. von
Hermann Cohen und Paul Natorp, iv. bd., 2. hft.)
Issued also as author's inaugural dissertation, Marburg, 1910.

1. Aristoteles.
                                            A 20-732
Title from Univ. of Chicago   B485.T28 Printed by L. C.

NT 0049423 ICU CaBVaU InU NN NjP ScU PU

Tatarkiewicz, Władysław, 1886-
Dominik Merlini. ₍Wyd. 1. Warszawa₎ Budownictwo i
Architektura, 1955.
193 p. (chiefly illus.) 25 cm. (Mistrzowie architektury polskiej)
At head of title: Instytut Urbanistyki i Architektury.
Bibliography: p. 32-₍33₎

1. Merlini, Dominik, 1730-1797.

NA1199.M4T3   59-32897

NT 0049424 DLC ICA NSyU MB InU CtY CU

Pol.Rm. Tatarkiewicz, Władysław, 1886-
NA   Dominik Merlini. [Warszawa] Budownictwo i
1199   Architektura, 1955.
.M4T3   258 p. (chiefly illus.) 25 cm.
(Mistrzowie architektury polskiej)
At head of title: Instytut Urbanistyki i
Architektury.
Bibliography: p. 32-[33]

1. Marlini, Dominik, 1730-1797. Series.

NT 0049425 NBuU OU MH NN

Tatarkiewicz, Władysław, 1886-
... Dwa klasycyzmy, wileński i warszawski; rzecz czytana 12
czerwca 1920 na posiedzeniu Tow. Przyjaciół Nauk w Wilnie.
Warszawa: E. Wende i S-ka, 1921. 32 p. mounted illus. 8°.
(Towarzystwo Straży Kresowej, Warsaw. Biblioteka Wydziału
Zabytków. Tom 1.)

1. Architecture, Poland: Vilna.   2. Architecture, Poland: Warsaw.
3. Series.
N. Y. P. L.   September 9, 1922.

NT 0049426 NN

Tatarkiewicz, Władysław, 1886-
Ethical bases of reparations. Warsaw,
1945. 23 p. 21cm. (Poland.
Ministerstwo kultury i sztuki. Biuro
rewindykacji i odszkodowań. Publications.
no. 3)
1. World war, 1939-1945—Atrocities—
Poland. I. Series.

NT 0049427 NN

Tatarkiewicz, Władysław, 1886-
Historja filozofji. Lwów, Wydawn.
B99   Zakładu Narodowego im. Ossolińskich, 1931.
F62T32 2 v. ports. 26cm.
Includes bibliographies.
Contents.-t.1.Filozofja starożytna i śred-
niowieczna.-t.2.Filozofja nowożytna.

1.Philosophy - Hist. 2.Philosophers.
I.Title.

NT 0049428 CSt MH

Tatarkiewicz, Władysław, 1886–
... Historja filozofji ... Wyd. 2. Lwów, Wydaw. Zakładu
narodowego imienia Ossolińskich, 1933.
2 v. ports. 25½ᵐ.
Includes bibliographies.
Contents.—I. Filozofja starożytna i średniowieczna.—II. Filozofja
nowożytna.

1. Philosophy—Hist. 2. Philosophers.   I. Lemberg. Zakład naro-
dowy imienia Ossolińskich.
42–9815
Library of Congress   B99.P62T3

NT   0049429   DLC CoU

Tatarkiewicz, Władysław, 1886–
Historia filozofii. Wyd. 3. przejrz. i uzup. ₍W Krakowie₎
Czytelnik, 1946–
v. ports. 25 cm.
Includes bibliographies.
Contents.—t. 1. Filozofia starożytna i średniowieczna.

1. Philosophy—Hist. 2. Philosophers.   I. Title.
B99.P62T32   55–20512

NT   0049430   DLC MiU InU CtY MH NN

B99
P62T3   Tatarkiewicz, Władysław, 1886–
1948   Historia filozofii. Wyd.4. przejrzane i
uzupełnione. ₍Warszawa₎ Spółdzielnia wydawn.
"Czytelnik", 1947– ₍v.1, 1948₎
v. ports.
Includes bibliographies.
Contents.– t.1. Filozofia starożytna i
średniowieczna.– t.2. Filozofia nowożytna
do roku 1830. Wyd.3.

NT   0049431   CU

Tatarkiewicz, Władysław.
Historia filozofii. Wyd. 4., przejrzane i
uzupełnione.   [Warszawa] "Czytelnik" [c1948]
1949.
2 v.
Contents: v.1. Filozofia starożytna i średniowieczna. v.2. Filozofja nowożytna do roku 1830.

NT   0049432   MiD

Tatarkiewicz, Władysław, 1886–
Michał Płoński. Warszawa, Nakł. Gebethnera i Wolffa
[1926]
19 p. 32 plates. (Monografje artystyczne, 10)

1. Płoński, Michał, 1778–1812.

NT   0049433   MH

ВЛ405   Tatarkiewicz, Władysław, 1886–
P6T38   O bezwzględności dobra. Warszawa, Gebethner i Wolff, 1919.
172 p.

1. Good and evil.   I. Title.

NT   0049434   CU

TATARKIEWICZ, WŁADYSŁAW, 1886–
O szczęściu.   Kraków, Wiedza, zawód, kultura,
1947. 507 p. 22cm.
Includes bibliography.

1. Happiness.   i. Sub·· for main entry without date

NT   0049435   NN KU

Tatarkiewicz, Władysław, 1886–
O szczęściu / Władysław Tatarkiewicz. -- Wyd.2. --
Kraków : Wiedza, Zawód, Kultura, 1949.
483 p. ; 22 cm.
Includes bibliographical references and index.

NT   0049436   MH MiD CU

Tatarkiewicz, WŁadysŁaw, 1886–
Outline of the history of philosophy in Poland to World War
II / WŁadysŁaw Tatarkiewicz ; translated from the Polish by
Christopher Kasparek. — San Francisco : Polish Arts and Cul-
ture Foundation, ₍1947₎
57 p. ; 22 cm.
Cover title.
Translatio of Zarys dziejów filozofii w Polsce.

1. Philosophy, Polish—History.   I. Title.
B4689.T3713   199'.438   75–312969
MARC

NT   0049437   DLC

Tatarkiewicz, Władysław, 1886–
Pięć studjów o Łazienkach Stanisława Augusta, napisał Władysław Tatarkiewicz...   Lwów ₍etc.₎ Książnica-Atlas, 1925.
169 p. illus., plans. 24cm. (Nauka i sztuka. t. 15.)
Bibliography included.

474444B.   I. Warsaw. Lazienki   krolewskie.   I. Ser.
N. Y. P. L.   June 8, 1949

NT   0049438   NN MH NNC

Tatarkiewicz, Władysław, 1886–
Rządy artystyczne Stanisława Augusta. Warszawa,
Skł.w Księg.Gebethnera i Wolffa, 1919
107 p. illus. (Wydawnictwa Towarzystwa Naukowego
Warszawskiego. Wydział II)
Includes text of Stanisław August's letters in
French

NT   0049439   MH NN

BH208   Tatarkiewicz, Władysław, 1886–
P6   Skupienie i marzenie; studia z zakresu este-
T37   tyki. Kraków, Wydawn. M. Kot, 1951.
(LC)   140 p. 21 cm. (Literatura, sztuka, kryty-
ka. Biblioteka naukowa, nr. 12)
Bibliographical references included in "Przy-
pisy" (p. 137-140)

1. Aesthetics - Addresses, essays, lectures.
2. Aesthetics, Polish - Addresses, essays, lectures. I. Title (1)

NT   0049440   CtY DLC-P4 MH MiD CU NIC NBuU

Tatarkiewicz, Władyslaw, 1886–
Ueber die natürliche Weltansicht. (In: Philosophische Abhandlungen, Hermann Cohen zum 70sten Geburtstag (4. Juli
1912) dargebracht. Berlin, 1912. 8°. p. 24-43.)

1. Cosmology.
N. Y. P. L.   October 8, 1912.

NT   0049441   NN

Tatarkiewicz, Władysław, 1886 –
...Z dziejów filozofji na wszechnicy warszawskiej.
(Pierwszy wykład na Uniwersytecie warszawskim
18 listopada 1915 roku)   Warszawa, 1916.
15 p.   25 cm.
Reprint from Przeglad filozoficzny, 1915.

NT   0049442   CtY

Tatarkiewicz, Władysław, 1886–
Zarys dziejów filozofii w Polsce. Kraków, Nakł. Polskiej
Akademii Umiejętności ; skł. gł. w księgarniach Gebethnera i
Wolffa, 1948.
36 p. 25 cm. (Polska Akademia Umiejętności. Historia nauki
polskiej w monografiach, 32)
Summary in French.

1. Philosophy, Polish.   I. Title.   (Series: Polska Akademia
Umiejętności, Kraków. Historia nauki polskiej w monografiach, 32)
AS142.K825   vol. 32   52–38135

NT   0049443   DLC CSt ViU OU MiU NN NNC

Tatarkiewiczowa, Teresa.

Conrad, Joseph, 1857–1924.
... Wśród prądów ... przełożyła Teresa Tatarkiewiczowa.
Warszawa, Dom książki polskiej, spółka akcyjna, 1928.

Tataroff, Dmitry.
Die Dorpater wasserbacterien...   Dorpat,
C. Mattiesen, 1891.
77 [1] p.   24 cm.   [Dorpat. Universitet.
Dissertationen.   v. 22, no. 4]
Inaug.-diss. - Dorpat.

NT   0049445   CU DNLM

HIST SCI
QL   Tataroff, Dmitry.
878   Zur vergleichenden Anatomie des Musculus
T21   Cremaster externus...   Strassburg, J. H.
Ed. Heitz (Heitz & Mündel) 1888.
68 p.   23cm.
Diss.--Strasbourg.

1. Generative organs, Male.

NT   0049446   NIC MBCo

DB
929   A tatárok betörése Magyarországra és pápai
.T38   szövetségeseik. / ₍Az előadást kidolgozta
az HDP Központi Előadói Irodájának törté-
nelmi munkaközössége. Vezetb Andics Erzsébet, előadó Lederer Emma. Budapest, Szikra,
1952.
39 p. 20 cm. (A Magyar Dolgozók Pártja
Központi Előadói Irodájának előadásai)

NT   0049447   NNC

Tatarov, Boris.
Заразни болести по новороденните и млади домашни
животни. София, Земснаб, 1949.
132 p.   21 cm.
At head of title: Борис Татаров, Иван Ченчев.

1. Communicable   diseases in animals.   i. Chenchev,
Ivan, joint author.   *Title transliterated: Zarazni bolesti.*
SF781.T3   51–21087

NT   0049448   DLC

Tatarov, G. D., tr.

Rynin, Nikolaĭ Alekseevich, 1877–   ed.
Безмоторный полет. Переводъ с нѣмецкаго. С приложением статей—В. Дудакова: "Авиэтты" и К. Виганда: "К
расчету планера". Под редакцией проф. Н. Рынина. Москва, НКПС—"Транспечать" ₍1923₎

JN6598
S6K58

Tatarov, Isaak L'vovich, 1901–

Kommunisticheskaiā partiiā Sovetskogo Soiūza.
История Р. К. П. (б) в документах. Составили Ш. М. Левин и И. Л. Татаров. Предисл. В. И. Невского. Ленинград, Гос. изд-во, 1926–

Tatarov, Isaak L'vovich, 1901–
… Классовая борьба вокруг законов о труде и образовании рабочей молодежи во второй половине XIX века. Москва-Ленинград, Молодая гвардия ₍1928₎
384, ₍3₎ p. 20ᵐ.
At head of title: Истмол ЦК ВЛКСМ. И. Татаров.

1. Labor laws and legislation—Russia. 2. Children—Employment—Russia. 3. Educational laws and legislation—Russia. I. Vsesoiūznyĭ leninskiĭ kommunisticheskiĭ soiūz molodezhi. II. Title.

37–36694

NT   0049451   DLC

Tatarova, A
Филипп Стрелец. ₍Москва, "Молодая гвардия," 1944.
53, ₍3₎ p. 17 cm. (*On cover:* Герои отечественной войны)

1. Streleḟ, Filipp. 2. Guerrillas.
         Title transliterated: Filipp Streleḟ.

D811.T35   49–33809

NT   0049452   DLC

Tatarova, A
Гениальный русский механик. Москва, Трудрезервиздат, 1952.
73 p. 20 cm. (Русские изобретатели)
At head of title: А. Татарова, С. Зимин.

1. Kulibin, Ivan Petrovich, 1735–1818. I. Zimin, S., joint author. II. Title.   *Title transliterated:* Genial'nyĭ russkiĭ mekhanik.

TJ140.K8T3   56–34111

NT   0049453   DLC

Pam.   Tatarova, A
Coll.
18225   Was die kollektivbäuerin Awdotja Pasuchina erzählt, niedergeschrieben von A. Tatarowa. Moskau, Verlagsgenossenschaft ausländischer arbeiter in der UdSSR, 1932.
75 p. front., illus. 17 cm.

1. Agriculture, Cooperative. Russia. Fiction.

NT   0049454   NcD

HIST SCI
QD
3
C51
v.2
no 16

Tatarowicz, Zdzisław von.
Ueber einige Chlorbromsubstitutionsproducte der Methanreihe. Tübingen, H. Laupp, 1879.
18 p. 21cm.

Diss.--Technische Hochschule, Karlsruhe.
No. 16 in a vol. lettered: Chemistry pamphlets. 2.
1. Bromo-derivatives (Organic chemistry)
2. Chlorine organic compounds. 3. Methane.

NT   0049455   NIC DLC ICRL

Татарская АССР; экономический справочник. 1932–
Казань, Татиздат.
v. il.   26 cm.
Issued by Upravlenie narodno-khoziāĭstvennogo ucheta ATSSR.

1. Tatar Republic—Econ. condit. I. Tatar A. S. S. R. Upravlenie narodno-khoziāĭstvennogo ucheta.
      Title transliterated: Tatarskaiā ASSR.

HC337.T3T35   50–42341

NT   0049456   DLC

Tatarskaiā avtonomnaiā sovetskaiā sofsialisticheskaiā respublika
     see
Tatar A. S. S. R.

Tatarskaiā lesnaiā opytnaiā stanfsiiā, *Kazan*
     see
Kazan, Russia (City)   Tatarskaiā lesnaiā opytnaiā stanfsiiā.

Tatarskaia literatura v perevodakh na russkiĭ iāzyk
M, Gos.izd-vo

1 (1923) - Validov, Dzhamaliutdin
         Ocherki istorii obrazovannosti i literatury [volzhskikh] Tatar, do revoliutsii 1917 g.

NT   0049459   MH DLC

Tatarski, W   B
     see
Tatarskiĭ, Vitaliĭ Borisovich.

(Tatarskie rasskazy)
Татарские рассказы. Москва, Советский писатель, 1951.
445 p. 21 cm.

1. Short stories, Tatar—Translations into Russian. 2. Short stories, Russian—Translations from Tatar. I. Amir, Mirsāĭ, 1907–

PL65.T36T3   1951   52–31202

NT   0049461   DLC

549.1
T216a

Tatarskiĭ, Vitaliĭ Borisovich.
Methods for the determination of rock-forming carbonate minerals. Translated by Associated Technical Services. East Orange, N.J., 1954.
39 ℓ. diagrs., table. 28½.　(₍Associated Technical Services₎ Translation: RJ-198)
Translation of Vsesoiūznyĭ neftiānoi nauchno-issledovatel'skiĭ geologo-razvedochnyĭ institut, Trudy, n.s., no. 53, 1952.
Bibliography: leaves 38–39.

1. Mineralogy,   Determinative.
2. Carbonates.

NT   0049462   CSt

Tatarskiĭ, Vitaliĭ Borisovich.
Metody oznaczania skałotwórczych minerałów węglanowych. ₍Tłum. Helena Bogdanowicz. Wyd. 1.₎ Warszawa, Wydawn. Geologiczne, 1955.
52 p. illus. 21 cm. (Biblioteka zawodowa geologa. Metody pracy, 12)
Includes bibliography.

1. Carbonates.   I. Title.

QE389.61.T286   62–42123 ‡

NT   0049463   DLC

Tatarskiĭ, Vitaliĭ Borisovich.
Микроскопическое определение карбонатов групп кальцита и арагонита. Ленинград, Гос. научно-техн. изд-во нефтяной и горно топливной лит-ры, Ленинградское отделение, 1955.
61, ₍3₎ p. illus. 22 cm.
Errata slip inserted.
Bibliography: p. 60–₍62₎

1. Carbonates. 2. Microscope and microscopy. I. Title.
       Title transliterated: Mikroskopicheskoe opredelenie karbonatov grupp kal'fsita.

QE389.61.T3   55–40815

NT   0049464   DLC

Tatarskiĭ institut marksizma-leninizma, *Kazan*
    see Kazan, Russia (City)   Tatarskiĭ nauchno-issledovatel'skiĭ institut marksizma-leninizma.

Tatarskiĭ nauchno-issledovatel'skiĭ institut iāzyka, literatury i istorii

     The Tatarskiĭ nauchno-issledovatel'skiĭ institut iāzyka, literatury i istorii was founded in 1939. In 1945 it was placed under the Kazanskiĭ filial of the Akademiiā nauk SSSR and renamed Institut iāzyka, literatury i istorii. In 1963, when the filial was abolished, the name was changed to Kazanskiĭ institut iāzyka, literatury i istorii and the institute was placed directly under the academy. In 1967 the name was changed again to Institut iāzyka, literatury i istorii. In 1973 Kazanskiĭ filial was reinstated and the institute was placed again under the filial.
     Works by this body are found under the following headings according to the name used at the time of publication:

     Tatarskiĭ nauchno-issledovatel'skiĭ institut iazyka, literatury i istorii.
     Akademiiā nauk SSSR. Kazanskiĭ filial. Institut iāzyka, literatury i istorii.

Tatarskiĭ sovet narodnogo khoziāĭstva
     see
Tatar A. S. S. R.   Sovet narodnogo khoziāĭstva.

Tatarsky (Abraham) [1880–]. *Experimentelle Untersuchungen über die Wirkung der Röntgenstrahlen auf tierisches Blut ₍Breslau.₎ 39 pp. 8°. Leipzig, J. A. Barth 1907.

NT   0049469   DNLM ICRL

Tatarsky (Esther). *Œsophagogastrostomie transdiaphragmatique. 74 pp. 8°. Paris, A. Michalon, 1904.

NT   0049470   DNLM

"Tatarstan," Lesnaiā opytnaiā stanfsiiā, *Lopatino*
    see
Kazan, Russia (City)   Tatarskaiā lesnaiā opytnaiā stanfsiiā.

Tatartscheff
    see also   Tatarchev.

Tatartscheff (Bojirad [Sterjo] A.) *Die Uro-
  genitalstörungen bei Tabes dorsalis. 32 p[
8°. *Berlin, G. Schade.* [1892].

NT 0049473   DNLM MH

Tatartscheff (Christo N.) [1867–]. *Be-
  schäftigungsneurose. 42 pp., 1 l. 8°. *Berlin,
G. Schade.* [1892].

NT 0049474   DNLM

BT   Tatarynovic, Pietro
2409   S. Cirillo Vesc. di Turov e la sua
.C9   dottrina spirituale. Roma, 1950.
T4   94, [2] p. 22cm.
      Excerpt from dissertation—Pontificium
Institutum Orientalium Studiorum.

    1. Cyril, Saint, Bp. of Turov, d. 1182.
2. Asceticism.

NT 0049475   DCU

Tatay, Emilio Ruiz.
    See
Ruiz Tatay, Emilio.

PH   Tatay, István
3136   Költészeti és szónoklati remekek, magyar
.T38   prosodiával, metrikával, s a költői és szó-
1857   noki beszédnemek és fajok rövid elméleti
    felvilágositásával eme' nemek és fajok sze-
rint osztályozva. Olcsó kiadás. Pesten,
Kilián Gy., 1857.
    579 p. 22 cm.

NT 0049477   NNC

Tatay, José María.
    La mano de Dios; ó, Roman el enmascarado. Drama en tres
actos y en verso original de Don José María Tatay. Habana,
1902. 114 p. 12°.

1. Drama (Cuban). 2. Title.
N. Y. P. L.   August 10. 1923.

NT 0049478   NN MH

Tatay, Luis Donderis
    see
Donderis Tatay, Luis.

Tatay, Ramón.
    La caza en Guinea. Madrid, Espasa-Calpe, 1955.
    278 p. illus., fold. col. map. 23 cm.

    1. Hunting—Guinea, Spanish. I. Title.

SK255.G8T3   56–43320 ‡

NT 0049480   DLC CtY NNC MoU IEN

Tatay, Sándor
    Jelek a porban, elbeszélések. [Budapest,
Magyar élet kiadás, [1929]
    179 [1] p.

    Contents: Kék hang.- Jelek a porban.
Hungarian.

NT 0049481   OC1

4PH   Tatay, Sándor
Hung   A Simeon-Ház; regény. [Budapest,
613   Szépirodalmi Könyvkiadó, 1955.
     441 p.

NT 0049482   DLC-P4

W   Tatcheff, Boris, 1904-
4   Abcès chroniques primitifs des os.
N17 Nancy, André, 1933.
1932/33 73 p. (Nancy. Université. Faculté
    de médecine. Thèse. 1932/33. no. 183)

    Bibliography: p. [71]-73.

NT 0049483   DNLM CtY

Tatchell, Frank.
    The happy traveller; a book for poor men, by Frank
Tatchell ... London, Methuen & co., ltd. [1923]
    xii, 271, [1] p. 19¼[cm].
    CONTENTS.—The art of travelling.—The Mediterranean countries.—The
Far East.—Islands.

    1. Travel.   I. Title.

Library of Congress   G153.T3   23—12182

NT 0049484   DLC WaT OC1 OU CU-S

Tatchell, Frank.
    The happy traveller; a book for poor men, by Frank Tat-
chell ... New York, H. Holt and company, 1924.
    xii, 271, [1] p. 19[cm].
    "Printed in Great Britain."
    CONTENTS. — The art of travelling. — The Mediterranean countries.—
The Far East.—Islands.

    1. Travel.   I. Title.

Library of Congress   G153.T3 1924   42–30702

NT 0049485   DLC PU NN

TATCHELL, Frank.
    The happy traveller; a book for poor men.
[5th ed.] London, Methuen & Co., ltd., [1927].

NT 0049486   MH-AH WaS

Tatchell, Frank.
    Walks and rides round Midhurst ...
[N.p.]Privately printed,1923.
    S.

NT 0049487   CaBViP

Tatchell, Frank.
    Walks and rides round Midhurst ...
Privately printed, 1930.
    65p.

NT 0049488   ICRL

TA425   Tatchell, Sydney Joseph, 1877–
.G7
1946   **Gt. Brit.** *Ministry of Public Building and Works. Standards Committee.*
    Further uses of standards in building; second progress
report. London, H. M. Stationery Off., 1946.

TH425   Tatchell, Sydney Joseph, 1877–
.G7
1944   **Gt. Brit.** *Ministry of public building and works. Standards
committee.*
    ... The use of standards in building. First progress report
of the Standards committee. London, Published for the
Ministry of works by H. M. Stationery office, 1944.

Tatchell, William Arthur.
    Booth of Hankow; a crowded hour of glorious life by W. Ar-
thur Tatchell ... London: C. H. Kelly [1915]. 125(1) p., front.
(port.), 3 pl. 12°.

1. Booth, Robert T., 1873–1912.   2. Missions (Medical), China.
3. China.—History, 1900–12. 4.   Title.
N. Y. P. L.   September 24. 1915.

NT 0049491   NN CtY OO

Tatchell, William Arthur.   209.51 R400
    Healing and saving, the life-story of Philip Rees, medical mis-
sionary in China. By W. Arthur Tatchell, ... With seven
illustrations. London, C. H. Kelly, [1914].
    154 p. front. (port.), plates. 19¼[cm].

NT 0049492   ICJ NIC OC1 DNLM PPC

Tatchell, William Arthur.   209.51 Q900
    Medical missions in China in connexion with the Wesleyan Metho-
dist Church, by Rev. W. Arthur Tatchell, ... With an appreciation by the Hon. E. H. Fraser, ... With forty-six illustrations. London, R. Culley, [pref. 1909].
    351, [1] p. incl. plates, ports. 19[cm].

NT 0049493   ICJ OU NIC CtY MSaE

Tate, Mr., poet laureat
    see   Tate, Nahum, 1652–1715.

Tate, Professor
    see   Tate, Ralph, 1840–1901.

Tate, Alberta Hinds, joint author.

PS3515
.I7424H6
    Hinds, Gladys.
      Howdy, soldier! (Letters from the gal back home) written
and illustrated by Gladys Hinds and Alberta Hinds Tate. New
York, M. S. Mill co., inc. [1944]

Tate, Alexander Norman, 1837–1892.
    Du pétrole & de ses dérivés: histoire, origine,
composition, propriétés, emplois & valeur
commerciale du pétrole ... Paris, Author, pref.
1863.
    140 p.

NT 0049497   PPF

TP691
T2   **Tate, Alexander Norman,** 1837-1892.
        The examination of petroleum and other mineral
        oils, according to the Petroleum act, 1868.
        London, H. Greenwood, 1869.
        12 l.   illus.   21 cm.
        Photocopy (positive)

        1. Petroleum – Testing.   I. Title.

NT   0049498   DI

TN870
.H617   **Tate, Alexander Norman,** 1837-1892.
        Hirzel, Heinrich, 1828-1908.
        (Gornoe maslo i ego produkty)
        Горное масло и его продукты. Г. Гирцеля. Состав-
        ленное по A. Norman Tate "The petroleum and its prod-
        ucts." Переводъ съ нѣмецкаго. С.-Петербургъ, Тип.
        А. С. Голицына, 1865.

TN870
.T38   **Tate, Alexander Norman,** 1837-1892.
        Petroleum and its products: an account of
        the history, origin, composition, properties,
        uses, and commercial value, &c., of petrole-
        um, the methods employed in refining it, and
        the properties, uses, &c., of its products.
        London, J.W. Davies, 1863.
        116 p.   18 cm.

        1. Petroleum.

NT   0049500   T MH-BA DI CU PPF PU

Spec.
TP
680   Tate, Alexander Norman, 1837-1892.
.T37   Petroleum and its products : an
        account of the history, origin,
        composition, properties, uses, and
        commercial value, &c., of petroleum,
        the methods employed in refining it,
        and the properties, uses, &c., of its
        products / by A. Norman Tate ... London
        : J. W. Davies ; Liverpool : H.
        Greenwood, 1863.
        [2], ii, iv, 116, iv p. : ill. ; 18
        cm.
        Paper label on cover.

        1. Petroleum. 2. Petroleum products.
        I. Title

NT   0049501   DeU CtY DSI

        Tate, Alexander Norman, 1837-1892, ed.

        Research: a monthly illustrated journal of science. Ed. by
        A. Norman Tate ... v. 1-2; July 1888-June 1890. London,
        E. W. Allen; [etc., etc., 1888-90]

        Tate, Alexander Norman, 1837-1892.
        Das steinöl und seine producte
              see under   Hirzel, Heinrich, 1828-1908.

342.7294
D367Ya
MICROFILM   **Tate, Alexandre.**
        Les ressources et les nécessités
        financières d'Haïti. [Port-au-Prince,
        Bouchereau, 1862]
        32 p.   27cm.

        Microfilm (negative) Gainesville, Uni-
        versity of Florida Library, 1964.
        On reel with Armand, Joseph. Encore
        l'article 7! Port-au-Prince, 1874.

        1. Finance – Haiti.   I. Title.

NT   0049504   FU

        Tate, Alfred, joint author.

S623
.W23   **Walker, Ernest De Witt,** 1887-
        Conserving our soil resources: an outline for teachers in the
        elementary schools. Prepared in the College of agriculture,
        University of Illinois, by E. D. Walker ... W. F. Purnell ...
        Alfred Tate ... and H. R. Beeson ... Issued by Vernon L.
        Nickell, superintendent of public instruction. [Springfield]
        1944.

        Tate, Alfred O   1863-1945.
        Edison's open door; the life story of Thomas A. Edison, a
        great individualist, by Alfred O. Tate, his private secretary.
        New York, E. P. Dutton & co., inc., 1938.
        320 p. front. (port.) illus. (facsim.) 22½ cm.
        "First edition."

        1. Edison, Thomas Alva, 1847-1931.   I. Title.
                                                           38—18208
        Library of Congress   TK140.E3T3
                                     [a50t1]   [925.3] 926

        WaTU CaBViP WaSpG NN NcC MoU PPPrHi
        OU TxU CoU OKentU CU IdB GAT WaE OrU CaBVaU OrPS PU
NT   0049506   DLC Wa OrP WaS PPD PPF PPFr OC1 OC1h OO

        Tate, Mrs. Allen
              see   Gordon, Caroline, 1895-

Spec.
PS 3539 Tate, Allen, 1899-
A 74   Allen Tate. New Haven [ca. 1954]
A 17   14 p. 25 cm. (Yale series of recorded
1954   poets)
        Text of poems "to accompany album YP300."

NT   0049508   MoSW

        Tate, Allen, 1899-   joint ed.

        Johnson, A   Theodore, 1890-   ed.
        America through the essay, an anthology for English courses,
        edited by A. Theodore Johnson ... and Allen Tate ... New
        York, Oxford university press, 1938.

        Tate, Allen, 1899-   ed.
        American harvest; twenty years of creative writing in the
        United States, edited by Allen Tate and John Peale Bishop.
        New York, L. B. Fischer [1942]
        544 p. 23½ᵐ.

        1. American literature—20th cent.   I. Bishop, John Peale, 1892-
        joint ed.   II. Title.
                                              [Full name: Orley Allen Tate]
                                                           42—23613
        Library of Congress   PS536.T3
                                     [25]   813.50822

        MiHM OrP WaS OrSaW OrU Wa CaBVaU OrCS WaE MH
        FTaSU O ODW OLak OO OC1W OC1C OC1 OCU OOxM NmLcU Or
NT   0049510   DLC MsU PSC PV PSt PBm WU TxU MoSW NcD

        Tate, Allen, 1899-   ed.
        American harvest; twenty years of creative writing in the
        United States, edited by Allen Tate and John Peale Bishop.
        Garden City, N. Y., Garden City publishing co., inc. [1943]
        544 p. 22 cm.

        1. American literature—20th cent.   I. Bishop, John Peale, 1892-
        1944, joint ed.   II. Title.
                                              Full name: Orley Allen Tate.
        PS536.T3 1943   813.5082   45—2164

        OC1ND OU KEmT GU FU WaSpG
NT   0049511   DLC OrStbM WaBeW MU TU AAP NmLcU MiU MH

        Tate, Allen, 1899-
        Les ancêtres (The fathers) tr. de l'américain par Marie
        Canavaggia. Roman. [Paris] Gallimard [1948]
        282 p. 21 cm.

        I. Title.
                                              Full name: Orley Allen Tate.

        PS3539.A74F33   813.5   49-17915*‡

NT   0049512   DLC ViU

Spec.
PS 3539 Tate, Allen, 1899-
A 74   Les ancêtres (The fathers) tr. de l'améri-
F 313   cain par Marie Canavaggia. Roman. [Paris]
1948   Gallimard [1948]
            282 p. 21 cm. (Du monde entier, LXX)
            Paper wrappers.
            210 copies printed.
            Translation of The fathers.
            First edition of this translation.

NT   0049513   MoSW

PS525
.S7B5   Tate, Allen, 1899-   joint ed.

        Bishop, John Peale, 1892-1944, ed.
        Antología de escritores contemporáneos de los Estados Uni-
        dos; prosa y verso compilados por John Peale Bishop y Allen
        Tate. Versión de la prosa a cargo de Ricardo A. Latcham;
        versión de la poesía a cargo de varios traductores ... Santiago,
        Chile, Nascimento, 1944.

PS3503
.I79A17 Tate, Allen, 1899-   ed.
1948   **Bishop, John Peale,** 1892-1944.
        The collected poems of John Peale Bishop, ed. with a
        pref. and a personal memoir by Allen Tate. New York,
        C. Scribner's Sons, 1948.

SPECIAL COLLECTIONS
B612C849
DT   **Tate, Allen,** 1899-
        Comment: Hart Crane and the American mind.
        [1932]
        [7] p. 21cm.

        From Poetry; a magazine of verse. July
        1932, Vol. XI, No. IV, p. 210-216.

        1. Crane, Hart, 1899?-1932.

NT   0049516   NNC

Spec.
PS 3539 Tate, Allen, 1899-
A 74   Dostoevsky's hovering fly. [n.p.] Re-
D 6   printed from the summer number of The Sewanee
1943a   review, 1943.
            19 p. 24 cm.
            Paper wrappers; stapled.
            Later reprinted as The hovering fly.
            This reprint not listed in M. Fallwell,
        Allen Tate: a bibl., 1969.
            Bears the author's signed autograph pre-
        sentation inscription to Sidney Kramer [2]

NT   0049517   MoSW

        Tate, Allen, 1899-
        The fathers, by Allen Tate. New York, G. P. Putnam's
        sons, 1938.
        6 p. l., 3-306 p. 21ᵐᵐ.

        I. Title.
                                              [Full name: Orley Allen Tate]
                                                           38-27756
        Library of Congress   PZ3.T183Fat

        IdB OrCS OrU Or ICarbS InU MoSW
        KyBgW OEac OCU OLak TxU ViU NN MiU CaBVaU OrP IdU
NT   0049518   DLC TNJ WU OU DCU NcD PSC PPT PP PU OO

AC-L
T187fa
1938

Tate, Allen, 1899–
    The fathers, by Allen Tate. New York, G. P. Putnam's
sons, 1938.
    6 p. l., 3–306 p. 20½cm.

    Proof copy.

    I. Title.   X [Full name: Orley Allen Tate]

NT 0049519   TxU

Spec.
PS 3539
A 74
F 3
1939

Tate, Allen, 1899–
    The fathers. London, Eyre & Spottiswoode,
1939 [c1938]
    6 p. l., 3–306 p. 21 cm.
    Yellow-gold cloth; purple lettering on
spine; purple designs on front cover and spine.
    First English edition. –M. Fallwell, Allen
Tate: a bibl., 1969, p. 12.

NT 0049520   MoSW NjP

Tate, Allen, 1899–
    The forlorn demon; didactic and critical essays. Chicago,
Regnery, 1953.
    vii, 180 p. 22 cm.

    1. Literature–Addresses, essays, lectures.   I. Title.

    PN37.T28   804   53–5778

OrPR OrU WaSpG MnU MoSW
    PRosC OO GU MoU TxU TNJ NRU WU CU MB CaBVaU OrP OrCS
    OC1W MB TU NN OU ODW OCU AAP Or NcRS OOxM MiU PPD
NT 0049521   DLC WaSp MtU WaT IdPI KEmT NSyU PSt NcD

Tate, Allen, 1899–
    Fragment of a meditation, MCMXXVIII, by Allen Tate...
[Cummington, Mass., The Cummington press] Christmas 1947.
4 l. 23cm.

    In original gray covers with red label on front cover; sewn with red thread.

    * KPC
    ——— Second copy.
    In original tan covers with title lettered by hand; unsewn.

NT 0049522   NN MH MoSW NIC ICN IEdS TxU CU NNC

Rare
PS
261
T21

Tate, Allen, 1899–
    The Fugitive, 1922–1925: a personal
recollection twenty years after.
    (In The Princeton University library
chronicle. Princeton. 24cm. v. 3 (1942)
p. 75–[84])

    1. The Fugitive. 2. The Fugitives. 3.
American literature––Southern States––Hist.
& crit.

NT 0049523   NIC

PS3545
.I 5958
G6
Rare bk.
Coll.

Tate, Allen, 1899–

Wills, Ridley.
    The golden mean, and other poems by Ridley Wills and
Allen Tate. [n. p., c1923]

PZ1
.G653
Ho

Tate, Allen, 1899–   joint ed.

Gordon, Caroline, 1895–   *ed.*
    The house of fiction; an anthology of the short story, with
commentary, by Caroline Gordon and Allen Tate. New
York, Scribner, 1950.

Tate, Allen, 1899–
    The hovering fly, and other essays. [Cummington, Mass.]
Cummington Press, 1949.
    102 p. illus. 25 cm.
    Illustrated by Wightman Williams.
    "Two hundred and forty-five numbered copies; the first twelve,
each with an original drawing and the woodcuts hand-colored, and
the next ninety-three are on Van Gelder paper and signed at the
colophon by the author and the illustrator." No. 11.
    CONTENTS.—The hovering fly.—The new provincialism.—Techni-
ques of fiction.—A reading of Keats.—Stephen Spender's Poems.—An
exegesis on Dr. Swift.—Longinus.—A suppressed preface.
    1. Literature—Addresses, essays, lectures.   I. Williams, Wight-
man, illus.   II. Title.
    PN37.T3   Rosenwald Coll.   804   49–10947 rev*

                    MB NjP NcU MH–Lm TU
NT 0049526   DLC IaU CoU LU KyU MoSW ViU OU PPL PU

Ex
3952
.88
.349

Tate, Allen, 1899–
    The immortal woman. [Camden, N.J., 1933]
    [592]–609 p. 23 cm.

    Forms part of Hound & Horn, VI, no.4, Jul.–
Sept. 1933.

NT 0049527   NjP

Tate, Allen, 1899–   joint author.

Cairns, Huntington, 1904–
    Invitation to learning [by] Huntington Cairns, Allen Tate
[and] Mark Van Doren. New York, Random house [c1941]

Aq
E846
T931t
Rare
Books
Col

Tate, Allen, 1899–
    Irony and humility. [Concord, N.H.,
c1931]
    p.290–297. 22½cm.

    Review of T.S. Eliot's Ash Wednesday.
    In a whole no. of Hound & Horn, v.4, no.2.

    1. Eliot, Thomas Stearns, 1888–   Ash
Wednesday.

NT 0049529   TxU

Tate, Allen, 1899–
    Jefferson Davis: his rise and fall, a biographical narra-
tive, by Allen Tate ... New York, Minton, Balch & company, 1929.
    6 p. l., 3–311 p. front., ports. 21 cm.
    Maps on lining-papers.
    "Bibliographical note": p. 303–306.

    1. Davis, Jefferson, 1808–1889.
                            [Full name: Orley Allen Tate]
    Library of Congress   E467.1.D26T21
                                        29—20277

Or OrCS WaWW OrPS
WaTU OrP WaS WaT IdU WaSp OrPR OrSaW OrU CaBVaU IdPI
OC1W–H MiU OKentU NWM InU NcRS OOxM OC1 NBuHi TNJ WU
TxU KyBgW CLU KyU Ky–LE MeB PWcS PPA PHC WaU KyLxT
NT 0049530   DLC NcD DAL MB NN NcC ViU PU OU FU MsU TU

E
467.1
D26
T21
1929a

Tate, Allen, 1899–
    Jefferson Davis: his rise and fall, a biographical narra-
tive, by Allen Tate ... New York, Minton, Balch & company, 1929.
    6 p. l., 3–311 p. front., ports. 21 cm.

    "Bibliographical note": p. 303–306.
    Photocopy (positive) Washington, Library of
Congress. Photoduplication Service. n.d.
    Printed on double leaves.
    1. Davis, Jefferson, 1808–1889.

NT 0049532   NBuC

Spec.
PS 3539
A 74
J 4
1929b

Tate, Allen, 1899–
    Jefferson Davis: his rise and fall; a
biographical narrative. New York, Minton,
Balch, 1929.
    311 p. front., ports. 21 cm.
    Light blue cloth; black lettering and
illus. on spine; dust jacket.
    "Second printing, October, 1929."
    "Bibliographical note": p. 303–306.

    1. Davis, Jefferson, 1808–1889.

NT 0049533   MoSW T

AC-L
T187je
1932

Tate, Allen, 1899–
    Jefferson Davis: his rise and fall, a biographical narrative.
by Allen Tate ... New York, Minton, Balch & company
[1932, c1928] 6 p. l., 3–311 p. front., ports. 21cm. [Minton, Balch
American biographies]
    "Bibliographical note": p. 303–306.
    At foot of dust jacket spine: New popular
edition.

NT 0049534   TxU

Tate, Allen, 1899–   *ed.*
    The language of poetry, by Philip Wheelwright [and
others] ... Edited by Allen Tate. Princeton, Princeton university press; London, H. Milford, Oxford university press
[c1942]
    2 p. l., vii–viii p., 2 l., 3–125 p. diagr. 21 cm. [The Mesures series
in literary criticism]
    "Essays ... read ... at Princeton university in the spring of 1941
under the auspices of the Creative arts program."—Pref.
    CONTENTS.—Poetry, myth, and reality, by Philip Wheelwright.—
The language of paradox, by Cleanth Brooks.—The interactions of
words, by I. A. Richards.—The noble rider and the sound of words, by
Wallace Stevens.

    1. Poetry—Addresses, essays, lectures.   I. Wheelwright, Philip
Ellis, 1901–   II. Brooks, Cleanth, 1906–   III. Richards, Ivor
Armstrong, 1893–   IV. Stevens, Wallace, 1879–   V. Title.
                            Full name: Orley Allen Tate.
    PN1055.T35   808.1   42—14242

WaS OrCS WaWW OrU WaT IdU
OU OOxM NIC MoSU NcD KEmT FTaSU CoU MU NmLcU OrP Or
NT 0049536   DLC PHC TxU PU PBm PSC OC1 OC1C ODW OO

Tate, Allen, 1899–
    The man of letters in the modern world;
selected essays, 1928–1955. Cleveland, World
Publishing Co. [1955]
    352p. 18cm. (Meridian books, M13)

    1. Literature - Addresses, essays, lectures.
I. Title.

NT 0049537   NcU

Tate, Allen, 1899–
    The man of letters in the modern world; selected essays,
1928–1955. New York, Meridian Books, 1955 [c1953]
    352 p. 18 cm. (Meridian books, M13)

    1. Literature—Addresses, essays, lectures.   I. Title.
                            Full name: Orley Allen Tate.
    PN37.T32   804   55–9698 ‡

NNR OrP FMU AAP WU NSyU CaBVaU Wa OC1W
MtBC NcD ViU MiU NIC AU KyU MH CLSU KyU–F WaU NRU
PPT OO TxU TU OC1 NN MsSM OrLgE IdPI OrCS OrStbM
NT 0049538   DLC WaSpG ICarbS OOxM KyTrA IU CU PP PV

Tate, Allen, 1899–
    The Mediterranean and other poems...
[n.p.] Privately printed, 1936.
    58 p.,1 l. 28½ cm.

    In portfolio.
    No.9 of an edition of 12 copies
printed on Italian handmade paper, with
author's autograph.
    First edition, first issue.

NT 0049539   NjP

Tate, Allen, 1899–
The Mediterranean and other poems, by Allen Tate. New York, The Alcestis press, 1936.
5 p. l., 15–56, ₍1₎ p. 24ᶜᵐ.
"This first edition ... limited to 165 numbered copies, signed by the author and printed on Strathmore permanent all rag paper ... This is copy number 38."
Errata slip inserted.

I. Title.
₍Full name: Orley Allen Tate₎
A 39–768
Brown univ. Library
for Library of Congress ₍2₎

ScU ICU NjP MoSW DeU NSyU
NT 0049540   RPB ViU TNJ InU MnU NcU NIC OU FU IaU NN

Tate, Allen, 1899–
Mr. Pope and other poems, by Allen Tate ... New York, Minton, Balch & company, 1928.
viii, 52 p. 19¼ cm.

I. Title.
₍Full name: Orley Allen Tate₎
28—20433
Library of Congress   PS3539.A74M5 1928

OCU ViU MoSW NjP OkU OOxM NIC FU MH-H ICarbS
NT 0049541   DLC OO WU OU PU MH TNJ TxU CaBVaU OC1

Ex 3952 .88 .367 1943₎
Tate, Allen, 1899–
New poems. ₍Gambier, Ohio, Kenyon college, 1943₎
184–188 p. 23 cm.

Contents: - Jubilo. - More sonnets at Christmas.
Forms part of the Kenyon review, V, no.2, Spring 1943.

NT 0049542   NjP

Tate, Allen, 1899–
Ode to the Confederate dead, being the revised and final version of a poem previously published on several occasions; to which are added Message from abroad and The cross. By Allen Tate. New York, Pub. for the author by Minton, Balch & company, 1930.
₍20₎ p. 19 x 15ᶜᵐ.
Cover-title: Three poems.
"Private edition of 125 copies of which 25 are numbered and signed by the author."
I. Title. II. Title: Message from abroad. III. Title: The cross.
44–26423
Library of Congress   PS3539.A74O3
₍2₎   811.5

NT 0049543   DLC MoSW NIC TNJ ViU NjP

Tate, Allen, 1899–
Ode to the Confederate dead; choral setting by Elizabeth Holmes
see under   Holmes, Elizabeth.

1901 T21672o 1952 Harris Collection
Tate, Allen, 1899–
Ode to the Confederate dead, with a French translation by Jacques and Raissa Maritain, and a note on the French version, by Jackson Mathews.
Reprinted, with corrections, from The Sewanee Review, summer, 1952, vol. 60, no. 3.
24 cm. 11 p.

I. Maritain, Jacques, 1882–   tr.
II. Maritain, Raïs   tr. III. Mathews, Jackson.

NT 0049545   RPB MoSW NNC WU NjP

Tate, Allen, 1899–
On the limits of poetry, selected essays: 1928–1948. New York, Swallow Press, 1948.
xviii, 379 p. 22 cm.
Selected from the author's previously published works: The hovering fly, Reactionary essays on poetry and ideas, and Reason in madness.

1. Poetry. I. Title.
PN1031.T3   808.1   48—8822*

WaT OrU OrP WaS WaSpG WaWW
MiU ICU OO GU CaBVa CaBVaU IdPI MH OU MtU Or OrCS
MoSW MoWgW PPLas MiU PPT NcRS InU MoU OC1W IEN MB
NT 0049546   DLC PPD PSC ViU PBm NjP TxU OrPR CoU TNJ

Tate, Allen, 1899–
Poems: 1928–1931, by Allen Tate ... New York, London, C. Scribner's sons, 1932.
x, 52 p. 19¼ᶜᵐ.

I. Title.
₍Full name: Orley Allen Tate₎
32–8185
Library of Congress   PS3539.A74P6 1932
———— Copy 2.
Copyright A 50280   ₍2₎   811.5

GU AAP ViU ICarbS OrP OrPR OrU MWiW-C CoU ViU
NT 0049547   DLC TxU MoSW NN MH OC1 NcD PSC FU WU TNJ

AC-L T187B4 1947a
Tate, Allen, 1899–
Poems, 1920–1945; a selection by Allen Tate. London, Eyre & Spottiswoode, 1947.
x, 114p. 22½cm.
"Somewhat more than half of the present collection appeared in Selected poems in New York in 1937."

IU MH CU WU InU MdBP MoSW
NT 0049548   TxU OCU RPB NcU ICU CaBVaU NjR MnU TNJ

Tate, Allen, 1899–
Poems, 1922–1947. New York, C. Scribner's Sons, 1948.
xiv, 206 p. 21 cm.
Most of these poems appeared in the author's Selected poems, 1937, or The winter sea, 1944.

PS3539.A74P58   811.5   48—5674*

OrCS WaSp
IdU OrP OrPR MoSW MH MtU WaS ICN InU NjP Or WaT ICU
TNJ NmLcU PBm ViU MB PPCCH TxU PHC MiU OC1W NIC PU
NT 0049549   DLC AU CoU PSt TU PBm PLF ICarbS AAP ODaU

PS3509 .L43Z876 1929
Tate, Allen, 1899–
Poetry in the laboratory.
(In The New republic. New York. 30cm. Vol. 61, no. 785, pt. 2. (Dec. 18, 1929) p. 111–113)
"Practical criticism, by I. A. Richards. New York: Harcourt, Brace and Company."
T. S. Eliot mentioned on p. 112.

1. Eliot, Thomas Stearns, 1888–   2. Richards, Ivor Armstrong, 1893–   Practical criticism. I. Title.

NT 0049550   ViU

PS3509 .L43Z8762 1926
Tate, Allen, 1899–
A poetry of ideas.
(In The new republic. New York. 30cm. Vol. 47, no. 604 (June 30, 1926) p. 172–173)
"Poems: 1909–1925, by T. S. Eliot. London: Faber and Gwyer."

1. Eliot, Thomas Stearns, 1888–
Poems: 1909–1925. I. Title.

NT 0049551   ViU

Tate, Allen, 1899–   *ed.*
Princeton verse between two wars, an anthology, edited, with a preface, by Allen Tate. Princeton, N. J., Princeton university press, 1942.
3 p. l., ix–xx, 112 p. 23½ᵐ.

1. College verse—Princeton. 2. American poetry—20th cent. I. Title.
₍Full name: Orley Allen Tate₎
42–13062
Library of Congress   PN6110.C7T25
₍4₎   811.50822

ScU MoSW
NT 0049552   DLC Or TNJ ICU GU FU PU PBm NjP OO CoU

Z881 .U5Q3
Tate, Allen, 1899–   ed.
U. S. *Library of Congress.*
... Quarterly journal of current acquisitions ... July/Sept. 1943–
₍Washington, 1943–

Tate, Allen, 1899–
Reactionary essays on poetry and ideas, by Allen Tate ... New York, C. Scribner's sons; London, C. Scribner's sons, ldt., 1936.
xii p., 2 l., 3–240 p. 21 cm.

1. Poetry—Addresses, essays, lectures. 2. American literature—Hist. & crit. 3. Poets, American. I. Title.
PN511.T3   811.09   36—9280

NN WaWW OrU WaSpG MtU WU MoSW
KEmT OrP OrCS IdU MB NjP ICarbS WaT CaBVaU WaE CoU
PPLas NcRS OCU ODW OOxM OC1 MiU ScU GU ViU OKentU
NT 0049554   DLC PSC OU PU TxU PPT OO PV KMK PRosC NcD

PN 511 .T3
Tate, Allen, 1899–
Reactionary essays on poetry and ideas. New York, Scribner, 1936.
240 p.
Xerox reprint, Ann Arbor, Mich., 1967.

1. Poetry - Addresses, essays, lectures. 2. American literature - Hist. & crit. 3. Poets, American. I. Title.

NT 0049555   NBuU

Tate, Allen, 1899–
Reason in madness; critical essays by Allen Tate. New York, G. P. Putnam's sons ₍ᶜ1941₎
xiii, 230 p. 22ᶜᵐ.
Contents.—The present function of criticism.—Literature as knowledge.—Tension in poetry.—Understanding modern poetry.—Miss Emily and the bibliographer.—Hardy's philosophic metaphors.—Narcissus as Narcissus.—Procrustes and the poets.—Nine poets: 1937.—The function of the critical quarterly.—Liberalism and tradition.—What is a traditional society?

1. Literature—Hist. & crit. 2. Criticism. I. Title.
₍Full name: Orley Allen Tate₎
41–6601
Library of Congress   PN511.T33
₍10₎   804

NcD NjP OOxM ODW OU OC1 OC1W ViU OrCS OrPR Or OrU
NT 0049556   DLC FMU MB KMK CoU TxU PSC PBm PV PPFr

PN 511 T33 1941a
Tate, Allen, 1899–
Reason in madness; critical essays by Allen Tate. New York, G. P. Putnam's sons ₍ᶜ1941₎ ₍Ann Arbor, Mich., 1967₎
xiii, 230 p. 22 cm.
Contents.—The present function of criticism. — Literature as knowledge. — Tension in poetry. — Understanding modern poetry.—Miss Emily and the bibliographer. — Hardy's philosophic metaphors.—Narcissus as Narcissus.—Procrustes and the poets.—Nine poets: 1937.—The function of the critical quarterly.—Liberalism and tradition.—What is a traditional society?
Photocopy (positive) made by University Microfilms.
Printed on double leaves.
PN511.T33 1941a   804

NT 0049557   NBuC

Tate, Allen, 1899–

Z1231
.P7U5

U. S. *Library of Congress.*
... Recent American poetry and poetic criticism, a selected list of references. Compiled by Allen Tate, chair of poetry. Washington, 1943.

Tate, Allen, 1899–
Selected poems, by Allen Tate ... New York, C. Scribner's sons; London, C. Scribner's sons, ltd., 1937.

xiv p., 1 l., 112 p. 21ᶜᵐ.

ₗFull name: Orley Allen Tateₗ

		37–22933
Library of Congress	PS3539.A74S4 1937	
——— Copy 2.		
Copyright A 109749	₍₃₎	811.5

CoU GU IEN
OC1 OCU PV ViU WaS MB OrU CU-BANC MoSW NjP ViU MsU
NT 0049559 DLC OrPR OrP NBuU PP PU NcD NcRS ODW OU

Tate, Allen, 1899–

Z1231
.P7U55

U. S. *Library of Congress. General reference and bibliography division.*
... Sixty American poets, 1896–1944, selected, with preface and critical notes, by Allen Tate, the chair of poetry. A preliminary check list by Frances Cheney. Washington, 1945.

20th

Tate, Allen, 1899–
Sonnets at Christmas / Allen Tate ; [line drawings by Ralph Pendleton] Cummington, Mass. : Cummington Press, 1941.
4 leaves, sewn at center; unpaged : ill. ; 18.7 cm.
Title from labels on cover.
"Reprinted ... from Allen Tate's Selected poems."
"... 100 numbered copies on Worthy Sterling Laid paper and 50 lettered copies on Worthy Hand & Arrow ... This copy is number [in ink] 87."
Bound in blue wrappers printed in gold on front cover. Gold paper labels printed in b   lack on front cover.
I. Cumming   ton Press.

NT 0049561 ICarbS MH NIC NN NjP

Tate, Allen, 1899– ed.
A southern vanguard. New York, Prentice-Hall ₍1947₎

x, 331 p. 22 cm.

"Stories, poems, and critical essays offered for the John Peale Bishop memorial literary prize contest conducted between April 1 and September 15, 1945, by the Sewanee review and Prentice-Hall, inc."

1. American literature—Southern States. I. Title.

Full name: Orley Allen Tate.

| PS551.T37 | 810.82 | 47–5284* |

OrPR WaE OrP WaS PP WaTU CaBVaU IdU WaSpG MtU OrCS
NjP ViU TxU ICU NcGU TNJ NcD PPLas PSt PBm WU OrU Or
NT 0049562 DLC MiU FU CoU NIC MU PPT NSyU MoWgW OU

Spec.
PS 3539   **Tate, Allen,** 1899– ed.
A 74   A southern vanguard. The John Peale Bishop
S 65   memorial volume. New York, Prentice-Hall ₍1947₎
1947   x, 331 p. 22 cm.
Brown cloth; green lettering and design on front cover; lettering on spine is green printed on brown and brown printed on green; dust jacket.
First edition. –M. Fallwell, Allen Tate: a bibl., 1969, p. 18.
1. American literature – Southern States.
I. Bishop, John Peale, 1892–1944. I. Title.

NT 0049563 MoSW InU

Tate, Allen, 1899–
Stonewall Jackson, the good soldier; a narrative by Allen Tate ... New York, Minton, Balch & company, 1928.

viii p., 2 l., 3–322 p. front., illus. (maps) plates, ports. 21 cm.

Bibliography: p. 321–322.

1. Jackson, Thomas Jonathan, 1824–1863.

E467.1.J15T23   28—12052

OrSaW Or InU MoSW
NN TU CaBVaU OrP IdU CoU MB O WaS OrU OrAshS NmU WU
OCU OC1W OLak OOxM ViU NcD NcRS PPA PSC PPD DAL NWM
NT 0049564 DLC FU TNJ NNC LU KyLx MsSM OKentU PPL TU

AC-L
T187sto **Tate, Allen,** 1899–
1928b   Stonewall Jackson, the good soldier; a narrative by Allen Tate ... New York, Minton, Balch & company, 1928.
viii p., 2 l., 3–322 p. front., illus. (maps) plates, ports. 21ᶜᵐ.
Bibliography: p. 321–322.
"Second printing, April 1928."

NT 0049565 TxU

Lilly
PS 3539
.A74 S88   TATE, ALLEN, 1899–
1930   Stonewall Jackson, the good soldier. A narrative by Allen Tate ... London ₍etc.₎ Cassell & Company ₍1930₎
viii p. ₍2 l.₎, 3–322 p. front. (port.), map, plates. 20.4 cm.

Fallwell, p. 3.
In navy boards.

NT 0049566 InU FMU NcU

AC-L
T187sto **Tate, Allen,** 1899–
1932   Stonewall Jackson, the good soldier; a narrative by Allen Tate ... New York, Minton, Balch & company [1932, c1928]
viii p., 2 l., 3–322 p. front., illus. (maps) plates, ports. 21ᶜᵐ.
[Minton, Balch American biographies]
Bibliography: p. 321–322.
At foot of spine of dust jacket: New popular edition.

NT 0049567 TxU

Tate, Allen, 1899–
PR6019
0829   Three commentaries: Poe, James, and Joyce.
T21   (In The Sewanee review. Sewanee, Tenn., 1950. 24ᶜᵐ. Vol.58, no.1, Winter 1950. p. ₍1₎–15)
Detached copy.

1. Joyce, James, 1882–1941. 2. Fiction - Technique. I. Title.

NT 0049568 CSt

Tate, Allen, 1899–
Three poems. New York, Minton, Balch & Co., 1930.

NT 0049569 ViU

Tate, Allen, 1899–
Two conceits for the eye to sing, if possible. ₍Cummington, Mass.₎ Cummington Press, 1950 ₍i. e. 1949₎

₍8₎ p. 19 cm.

300 copies printed.
Poems.

I. Title.

Full name: Orley Allen Tate.

| PS3539.A74T9 | 811.5 | A 51–4858 rev |

Wisconsin. Univ. Libr.
for Library of Congress

MoSW
NT 0049570   NcGU IaU TNJ TxU MiEM CtY DLC CtU CLU-C DeU KyU WU
WU MA CU GU TU MH NN NIC NNC NNU NjP InU

Tate, Allen, 1899–
818.5
T216T   Two conceits for the eye to sing, if possible. ₍Cummington, Mass.₎ Cummington Press ₍1950₎

₍8₎ p. 26 cm.

Poems.

NT 0049571 NcD ViU ScU

Tate, Allen, 1899–   tr.
PA6557
.P3
1943   Pervigilium Veneris.
The vigil of Venus. Pervigilium Veneris. The Latin text with an introduction and English translation by Allen Tate. ₍Cummington, Mass.₎ The Cummington press ₍1943₎

Tate, Allen, 1899–
Whitman in America. Chicago, Poetry, 1937.
p. 350–353. 21 cm.
In a whole issue of Poetry, v. 50, no. 6, Sept., 1937.
Review of Whitman, by E. L. Masters.
1. Masters, Edgar Lee, 1869–1950. Whitman.
2. Whitman, Walt, 1891–1892. I. Poetry, v. 50, no. 6.

NT 0049573 TxU

◆**Tate, Allen,** 1899–   joint ed.

Agar, Herbert, 1897–   ed.
Who owns America? A new declaration of independence, edited by Herbert Agar & Allen Tate. Boston, New York, Houghton Mifflin company, 1936.

Tate, Allen, 1899–
... The winter sea, a book of poems. ₍Cummington, Mass.₎ The Cummington press, 1944.

₍51₎ p. 20½ᶜᵐ.

"Three hundred thirty copies ... Number 165."

I. Title.

Full name: Orley Allen Tate.

		45–5558
Library of Congress °	PS3539.A74W5	
	₍5₎	811.5

ViU MoSW OrPR WaS
NIC WU TxU NN ViU MWelC NjP MnU MeB CaBVaU InU WaU
NT 0049575   DLC PU OCU OO OU OC1 PHC OOxM TNJ NcGU

20th

Tate, Allen, 1899–
The winter sea : a book of poems / Allen Tate. [Cummington, Mass.] : Cummington Press, printers & publishers, 1944.
[1–7]⁴ ; unpaged [i.e., 56 p.] ; 20 cm.
"Printed ... in an edition of three-hundred-thirty copies, those numbered 1 to 300 on Sterling Laid paper, and the others, i to xxx, signed by the author and bound with an original painting by Wightman Williams ... This copy is number [in ink] 276."
From the collection of Joseph D. Hirschberg.
Bound in b   lack boards stamped in white on spi   ne. Brown label printed in w   hite pasted on front

I. Cummington Press.

NT 0049577 ICarbS PSC

Tate, Arthur F.

Somewhere a voice is calling. Words by Eileen Newton. Music by Arthur F. Tate. ₍n. p.₎ J. H. Larway, c1911.

First line: Dusk and the shadows falling.

I. Newton, Eileen. II. Song   index (2).
N. Y. P. L.   February 23, 1951

NT 0049578 NN OrU OrP

qM784.3   Tate, Arthur F
T187s2
    Somewhere a voice is calling, song. Words by
Eileen Newton. In D.   New York, T. B. Harms
& Francis, Day & Hunter ₍c1911₎
    4p.   35cm.

    Cover title.
    For voice and piano.

NT   0049579   IU

V
6
R441t18
1845
v

Tate, Benjamin.
    The American form book: containing legally
approved precedents for agreements, arbitrations, assignments, bonds, bills of exchange,
promissionary notes, conveyancing, letters of
attorney, partnerships, receipts, releases,
transfers, wills, deeds in trust, and other
matters of importance. With a complete
index to the whole. By Benjamin Tate ...
Richmond, Va.: Drinker & Morris, 1845.
    261, ₍1₎, vi, ix p.   20½cm.
    1. Forms (Law)   - U. S.   I. Title.

NT   0049580   ViW NcD-L NcU-L ViN

Tate, Benjamin.
    The American form book: containing legally approved
precedents for agreements, arbitrations, assignments, bonds,
bills of exchange, promissory notes, conveyancing, letters of
attorney, partnerships, receipts, releases, transfers, wills,
deeds in trust, and other matters of importance. With a
complete index to the whole. By Benjamin Tate ..
    Richmond, Va., Drinker & Morris₍ Philadelphia₎
Thomas, Cowperthwait & co., 1845.
    261, ₍1₎, vi, ix p.   20cm.

NT   0049581   ViU

Tate, Benjamin.
    The American form book: containing legally approved
precedents for agreements, arbitrations, assignments, bonds,
bills of exchange, promissory notes, conveyancing, letters of
attorney, receipts, partnerships, releases, transfers, wills,
deeds in trust, and other matters of importance. With a
complete index to the whole. By Benjamin Tate ... A new
and rev. ed.   Richmond, Va., Drinker & Morris, 1847.
    261, ₍1₎, xvii p.   21½ᶜᵐ.

    1. Forms (Law)—U. S.   I. Title.

                   32–21989

NT   0049582   DLC ICRL NSbSU

300
Am3
440-1

Tate, Benjamin.
    The American form book, containing legally
approved precedents for agreements, arbitrations, assignments, bonds, bills of exchange,
promissory notes, conveyancing, letters of
attorney, receipts, partnerships, releases,
transfers, wills, deeds in trust, and other
matters of importance. With a complete index
to the whole. A new and rev. ed.   Richmond,
Drinker & Morris, 1847. ·
    261, xvii p.

    Microfilm (positive) Ann Arbor, Mich.,
University Microfilms, 1970. 1st title of 10.
35 mm. (American culture series, reel 440.1)

    1. Forms (Law) - U. S.   I. Title.

NT   0049584   KEmT PSt

Tate, Benjamin.
    The American form book: containing legally
approved precedents for agreements, arbitrations,
assignments, bonds, bills of exchange, promissory
notes, conveyancing, letters of attorney, receipts,
partnerships, releases, transfers, wills, deeds
in trust, and other matters of importance. With a
complete index to the whole. By Benjamin Tate...
A new and rev. ed.   Richmond, Morris & brothers
1850.
    261, [1] xvii p.   21 cm.

NT   0049585   ViU-L KyU

Tate, Benjamin.
    The American form book: containing legally approved
precedents, for agreements, arbitrations, assignments, bonds,
deeds, wills, &c. with an index. By Benjamin Tate ... To
which is added a Supplement, containing forms of deeds of
bargain and sale, lease, trust and release, under Code of Virginia; also, forms of attachments under same; mode of holding to bail under acts of 1851 and 1852; and other forms
valuable to clerks, attorneys, notaries, sheriffs, and coroners.
With an index.   By Alexander H. Sands ...   Richmond, Va.,
A. Morris, ~~1888~~.   1851.
    4 p. l., ₍5₎ 261, ₍1₎, xvii. 110 p.   21ᶜᵐ.

    Added t.-p.: The American form book: containing legally approved
precedents ... A new and rev. ed.   Richmond, Va., Morris & brother,
1850.
    The Supplement has special t.-p. and separate paging (110 p.)

    Title-page wanting.

NT   0049587   NcD

Tate, Benjamin.
    The American form book: containing legally approved
precedents, for agreements, arbitrations, assignments, bonds,
deeds, wills, &c. with an index. By Benjamin Tate ... To
which is added a Supplement, containing forms of deeds of
bargain and sale, lease, trust and release, under Code of Virginia; also, forms of attachments under same; mode of holding to bail under acts of 1851 and 1852; and other forms
valuable to clerks, attorneys, notaries, sheriffs, and coroners.
With an index.   By Alexander H. Sands ...   Richmond, Va.,
A. Morris, 1853.
    4 p. l., ₍5₎–261, ₍1₎, xvii, 110 p.   21ᶜᵐ.

    Added t.-p.: The American form book: containing legally approved
precedents ... A new and rev. ed.   Richmond, Va., Morris & brother,
1850.
    The Supplement has special t.-p. and separate paging (110 p.)

    1. Forms (Law)—U. S.   2. Forms (Law)—Virginia.   I. Sands,
Alexander Hamilton, 1828–1887.   II. Title.

                  32–21938

NT   0049589   DLC CSmH ViU ViU-L

Tate, Benjamin.
    The American form book, containing
legally approved precedents for agreements, arbitrations, assignments, bonds,
wills, deeds, etc.; a new ed., edited by
Alexander H. Sands...
Richmond, Va. Morris, 1854.
    3, ₍43₎-338 p. D.

NT   0049590   PP

V
6
R441t18
1857
v

Tate, Benjamin.
    The American form book ... containing
legally approved precedents for agreements,
arbitrations, assignments, bonds, deeds,
wills, etc. By Benjamin Tate ... also forms
of deeds of bargain and sale, lease, trust
and release, under the Code of Virginia; forms
of attachments under same, mode of holding to
bail under acts of 1851 and 1852; and other
forms, for the use of clerks, attorneys, notaries, justices, and sheriffs. By Alexander

H. Sands ...   Richmond, A. Morris, 1857.
    2 v. 22cm.

    1. Forms (Law) - U. S.   2. Forms (Law) -
Va. I. Sands, Alexander Hamilton, 1828–1887.
II. Title.

NT   0049592   ViW ViU ViU-L

Tate, Benjamin.
    An analytical digested index of the reported cases of the
Court of appeals and General court of Virginia; from Washington to second Grattan inclusive ₍1790–1846₎   With a repertorium of the cases doubly and systematically arranged.   By
Benjamin Tate ...   Richmond, Va., Drinker & Morris; Philadelphia, T. & J. W. Johnson ₍etc.₎ 1847.
    2 v. 24ᶜᵐ.

    1. Law reports, digests, etc.—Virginia.   I. Virginia.   Supreme
court of appeals.   II. Virginia.   General court.

                  32–22867

NT   0049593   DLC PPB ViU NcD

Tate, C   H   joint author.
    Floods of April 1955 in southwestern Alabama

    see under

    U.S.   Geological Survey.

Tate, C   M
    The songs I love ... ed and pub. by C. M. Tate.
Thornfield, Mo. c1910.
    unp.   20 cm.

NT   0049595   RPB

Tate, C   M.
    Tate's theory of music for singing schools and elemen-
tary normals, by C. M. Tate.   Mansfield, Mo., C. M. Tate,
ᶜ1914.
    44 p.   19½ᶜᵐ. $0.15
    On cover: Shaped notes only.
    Includes hymns with music.

    1. Music—Manuals, text-books, etc.   15–14100

    Library of Congress   MT7.T29

NT   0049596   DLC

Tate, Carolyn (Gordon)
    see   Gordon, Caroline, 1895–

Tate, Charles M
    The capabilities of the harbor of
Quebec.   Q₍ue₎ 1863.

NT   0049598   PPL

₍Tate, Charles M   ₎
    Report. To the chairman of the Road committee ₍upon a
plan of sewerage for Montreal₎   ₍Montreal, 1854₎
    16 p. 21ᶜᵐ.

    ₍Technological pamphlets. 23ᶜᵐ. v. 12, no. 8₎
    Caption title.
    Signed: Charles M. Tate, c. e.

    1. Montreal—Sewerage.

    Library of Congress   T7.T25   CA 5—843 Unrev'd

NT   0049599   DLC PPAN

[Tate, Mrs. Charles Montgomery]
    Early days at Coqualeetza.   [Toronto, The
Woman's Missionary Society] n.d.
    cover-title, 7 [1] p.   illus.   T.

NT   0049600   CaBViPA

Tate, Charles Montgomery, 1852–1933.
    Chinook as spoken by the Indians of Washington territory,
British Columbia and Alaska   For the use of traders, tourists
and others who have business intercourse with the Indians.
Chinook-English.   English-Chinook.   By Rev. C. M. Tate.
Victoria, B. C., M. W. Waitt & co. ₍1889₎
    47 p.   16¼ᵐ.

    I. Title.   6—17513

    Library of Congress   PM848.T3

    InU CaBVaU CtY WaU CU-BANC
NT   0049601   DLC WaS CaBViPA OrP WaSp MH ICN WaWW NN

PM
848
T21c
1914
Tate, Charles Montgomery
Chinook jargon as spoken by the Indians of the Pacific coast. For the use of missionaries, traders. tourists and others who have business intercourse with the Indians. Chinook-English, English-Chinook. By C.M.Tate. ₍Rev.ed.₎, Victoria, B.C., Printed by T.R.Cusack, 1914 ₍c1889₎ 48p. 17cm.

1. Chinook jargon - Dict. - English. 2. English language - Dict. - Chinook jargon. 3. Hymns, Chinook. I. Title.

NT 0049602   NRU NN CtY CLSU CaBVaU

Tate, Charles Montgomery.
Chinook jargon as spoken by the Indians of the Pacific coast. For the use of missionaries, traders, tourists and others who have business. Chinook-English. English-Chinook. By C. M. Tate. Victoria, B. C., Thos. R. Cusack, 1914. 48 l. 17 cm.

Alternate pages blank.
Photocopy (positive)
22 hymns in Chinook.

1. Chinook jarg   on - Glossaries, vocabularies, etc.   I. Title.

NT 0049603   Wa CaBViPA CaBVaU OrCS Or

PM848
T5
1931
₍Tate, Charles Montgomery₎
Chinook jargon as spoken by the Indians of the Pacific Coast for the use of missionaries, traders, tourists and others who have business intercourse with the Indians. Chinook-English. English-Chinook. ₍Victoria, B. C., Printed by Diggon's limited, 1931₎ 50 p. 23cm.

Cover-title: Dictionary of the Chinook jargon.
Caption title: Revised dictionary of the Chinook jargon.
Includes hymns and the Lord's prayer in Chinook.

NT 0049604   CU-BANC CaBViPA WaU CaBViP CaBVaU

TATE, CHARLES MONTGOMERY, tr.
I'm going home to die no more.
1p. 20.8cm.

NT 0049605   ICN

Tate, Charles Montgomery, *tr.*
Indian Methodist hymn-book; staylim-paypa ta Methodist-ts' hayilth. Hymns used on the Fraser river Indian mission, of the Methodist church, B. C. conference. To which are appended hymns in Chinook, and the Lord's prayer and Ten commandments. Translated by Rev's. Thos. Crosby, Chas. M. Tate, and Wm. H. Barraclough ... Compiled and printed by Rev. W. H. Barraclough. Chilliwack, B. C., 1898.
1 p. l., 48, ₍2₎ p. 13 x 10ᶜᵐ.

Caption title: Ts'hayilth staylim.
Translated mainly by C. M. Tate.
"The following hymns are in the Chill-way-uk dialect of the language of the Alkomaylum nation of Indians, who live along the Fraser river, from Yale to the coast, and on Vancouver island, at Cowichan and Nanaimo."—Verso of t.-p.

1. Chilliwack dialect—Texts. 2. Hymns, Chilliwack.   i. Crosby, Thomas, 1840-1914, joint tr. ii. Barraclough, William H., comp. iii. Title.
6-17205 Revised 2
Library of Congress   PM803.Z71 1898
₍r43c2₎   245.97

NT 0049607   DLC CaBViPA CaNSWA

Tate, Charles Montgomery.

Nothing but the blood of Jesus.
1p. 20.8cm. Ms.

NT 0049608   ICN

Tate, Charles Montgomery, 1852-1933.
Our Indian missions in British Columbia. [Toronto, Methodist young people's forward movement for missions] n. d.
16 p.   port. map, nar. O.

NT 0049609   CaBViPA CtY

Tate, Charles Montgomery, 1852-1933, tr.
St. Mark's Kloosh yiem kopa nesika Saviour Jesus Christ. London, 1912
see under Bible. N. T. Mark. Chinook. 1912. Tate.

TATE, CHARLES MONTGOMERY, tr.
Sweet by and by.
1p. 20.8cm. Ms.

NT 0049611   ICN

Tate, Charles Spencer, 1865–
Pickway; a true narrative. By Charles Spencer Tate. Chicago, The Golden rule press, 1905.
3 p. l., 9–159 p. front., illus., ports. 19½ᶜᵐ.

I. Title.
5–13948
Library of Congress   BV3785.T27A3
₍a41b1₎   922

NT 0049612   DLC CaBViPA NN

Tate, Colin C, Rev.
Correspondence touching the action of the American Church Union in the case of the Rev. C. C. Tate, of Ohio.   N. Y., 1869.

NT 0049613   PPL

Tate, D   N
My experience in seeking eternal life ... By Rev. D. N. Tate, Richmond County, Va. Ed. 6. Philadelphia, Ullrich printing house, 1894.
44 p.   16.5 cm.

NT 0049614   PHi

LD3907
.E3
1952
.T4
also
Film
T334
Tate, Donald Joseph, 1913–
An outline of topics for a secretarial syllabus developed from job analyses.
viii,285p. tables,forms.
Final document (Ed.D.) - N.Y.U., School of Education, 1952.
Bibliography: p.282-285.

NT 0049615   NNU-W

Tate, Dorothy Dean.
The story of Yuku, by Dorothy Dean Tate. Toronto, W. Briggs, 1910.
240 p. 18½ᶜᵐ.

10-11470
Library of Congress   PZ3.T185S

NT 0049616   DLC CaBVaU CaOTU IaU TxU

QC100
.U555
no. 446
Tate, Douglas Roy, 1912–   joint author.
Wilson, Bruce Lee, 1908–
... Dead-weight machines of 111,000- and 10,100-pound capacities, by Bruce L. Wilson, Douglas R. Tate ₍and₎ George Borkowski. ⟨Issued June 1943⟩ Washington, U. S. Govt. print. off., 1943.

QC100
.U555
no. 454
Tate, Douglas Roy, 1912–   joint author.
Wilson, Bruce Lee, 1908–
... Proving rings for calibrating testing machines, by Bruce L. Wilson, Douglas R. Tate, and George Borkowski. ⟨Issued August 14, 1946⟩ Washington, U. S. Govt. print. off., 1946.

QC1
.U52
vol. 37,
no. 1
Tate, Douglas Roy, 1912–   joint author.
Wilson, Bruce Lee, 1908–
... Temperature coefficients for proving rings, by Bruce L. Wilson, Douglas R. Tate, and George Borkowski ...
(R P 1726, *in* U. S. National bureau of standards. Journal of research of the National bureau of standards. Washington, U. S. Govt. print. off., 1946. 26ᶜᵐ. July, 1946, v. 37, no. 1, p. 35–41. 2 pl. on 1 l., diagrs.)

Tate, E. Ridsdale, illus.
Shaw, Patrick John.
An old York church: All Hallows in North street. Its mediaeval stained glass and architecture. Depicted by Mabel Leaf & E. Ridsdale Tate. Ed. by the Rev. P. J. Shaw, rector. York, Church shop, 1908.

Tate, E. Risdale.
Quaint & historic York
see under Benson, George, architect.

Tate, E. Ridsdale, illus.
Cooper, Thomas Parsons, 1863–
With Dickens in Yorkshire, by T. P. Cooper ... With an introduction by B. W. Matz ... Numerous illustrations by E. Ridsdale Tate. London, B. Johnson & co., ltd. ₍1923₎

15
Tate, Edgar & Co.
Hand book. [New York, 1894]
1 p.l., 31 p. incl. 5 pl. obl. 18 °.

NT 0049623   DLC

T215
.T21
Tate, Edgar, & co., *comp.*
Manual of foreign patents. Compiled by Edgar Tate & co. ... ₍New York₎ ᶜ1898.
cover-title, 16 p. 13½ᶜᵐ.

1. Patents.
CA 5-1541 Unrev'd

NT 0049624   DLC

TX820
.L5

Tate, Edith (Belcher) 1919–   joint author.

Lifquist, Rosalind Caribelle, 1903–
Planning food for institutions, by Rosalind C. Lifquist and Edith B. Tate. Washington, U. S. Govt. Print. Off., 1951

Tate, Edward Mowbray, 1902–
Church school curricula and education for Protestant church unity; an analysis of religious education materials used by six denominations in training children for church membership, in the light of denominational pronouncements favoring the movement for church unity, by Edward Mowbray Tate ... New York city, 1932.
95 p. 23ᶜᵐ.
Thesis (PH. D.)—Columbia university, 1932.
Vita.
Published also without thesis note.
"List of textbooks": p. 11–14; Bibliography: p. 92–94.
1. Religious education.   2. Christian union.   I. Title.   II. Title: Education for Protestant   church unity.

33–302

Library of Congress   BV1558.T3 1932
Columbia Univ. Libr.   ₍2₎   268.6

NT 0049626   NNC DLC DHEW NIC NcU

Tate, Edward Mowbray, 1902–
Church school curricula and education for Protestant church unity; an analysis of religious education materials used by six denominations in training children for church membership, in the light of denominational pronouncements favoring the movement for church unity, by Edward Mowbray Tate ... New York city, 1932.
94 p. 221ᶜᵐ.
Issued also as thesis (PH. D.) Columbia university.
"List of textbooks": p. 11–14; Bibliography: p. 92–94.
1. Religious education.   2. Christian union.   I. Title.   II. Title: Education for Protestant church unity.

33–301

Library of Congress   BV1558.T3 1932 a
—— —— Copy 2.
Copyright A 55869   ₍3₎   268.6

NT 0049627   DLC OrP WaWW

Tate, Elizabeth.
Little Teddy and the big sea. Pictures by Kurt Werth. New York, Lothrop, Lee & Shepard, ᶜ1954.
unpaged. illus. 28 cm.

I. Title.

PZ10.3.T1396Li   53–6733 ‡

NT 0049628   DLC Or WaSp OCl

Tate, Ellalice, pseud.
see
Hibbert, Eleanor, 1906–

Tate, Ethel T.
Roster and ancestral roll, Maine Daughters of the American Revolution
see under   Daughters of the American Revolution. Maine.

TATE, Faithful.
See TEATE, Faithful, 1621–

Tate, Farish Carter, 1856–
Appropriations ... Speech of Hon. F. C. Tate ...in the House of representatives, Thursday, March 24, 1898. Washington ₍Gov't print. off.₎ 1898.
8 p. 24 cm.

1. Finance, Public—U. S.—1875–1900—Speeches in Congress.

HJ2373.T22   1–4869

NT 0049632   DLC

Tate, Farish Carter, 1856–
The tariff ... Speech of Hon. F. C. Tate, of Georgia, in the House of representatives, Wednesday, March 24, 1897. Washington ₍Govt. print. off.₎ 1897.
14 p. 23ᵐ.

1. Tariff—U. S.—Speeches in Congress.

1–3852

Library of Congress   HF1755.T19

NT 0049633   DLC

Tate, Florence (Lee)
Echoes ₍by₎ Florence Lee Tate. ₍Chilhowie, Va., 1940₎
63 p. 20¼ᵐ.
Poems.

I. Title.
42–82417
Library of Congress   PS3539.A742E3
₍2₎   811.5

NT 0049634   DLC

Tate, Florence (Lee)
Random reveries; true incidents and echoes. Copyrighted ... by Florence Lee Tate. ₍Chilhowie, Va.₎ ᶜ1943.
204 p. 1 col. illus., mounted col. port. 20¼ᵐ.
Verse.

I. Title.
43–13610
Library of Congress   PS3539.A742R3
₍2₎   811.5

NT 0049635   DLC ViU

Tate, Francis, 1560–1616.
The opinions of several learned antiquaries, viz. Dodridge, Agar, Tate, Camden, Holland, Cotton, Selden, touching the antiquity, power, order, state, persons, manner, and proceedings of the high court of Parliament in England. London, Printed by F. L. for M. Gilliflower, 1685.

TATE, FRANCIS G   H
... Alcoholometry; an account of the British method of alcoholic strength determination. With an historical introduction written by the author in collaboration with George H. Gabb ...
London:Published by His Majesty's stationery office.1930.
xviii,92,[1]p. front.(port.),plates(incl.facsims.) 24½cm.
Royal arms on t.-p.
Orig. green cloth.
Inscribed: To Dʳ A. S.   W. Rosenbach, with
kind regards from George   H. Gabb. May 1930.

NT 0049637   PPRF DLC MiD WU MnU NN

TP609
.L62

Tate, Francis G. H., comp.

London. Laboratory of the Government Chemist.
Tables showing the relation between the specific gravity of spirits at 60°/60° Fahrenheit, the corresponding percentage of proof spirit, and the percentage of alcohol by weight. London, H. M. Stationery Off., 1933.

Tate, Frank, 1863–1939

Victoria, Australia. Education dept.
... Preliminary report of the director of education upon observations made during an official visit to Europe and America; with recommendations referring to state education in Victoria. Melbourne, J. Kemp, government printer ₍1908₎

Tate, Frank, 1863–1939.
...Some lessons from rural Denmark, by Frank Tate... Being results of observations made during an official visit to Europe in 1923. Melbourne, H. J. Green, 1924. iv, 83 p. illus. 26cm.

At head of title: Education department, Victoria.

275448B. 1. People's high schools   —Denmark. I. Victoria, Australia.
Education department.
N. Y. P. L.   June 12, 1944

NT 0049640   NN

Tate, Frank C., jt. author.
Tate's atlas of Des Moines
see under   Tate, John C

Tate, Frank J.
Red wilderness, by Frank J. Tate. London, New York ₍etc.₎ Oxford university press, 1938.
3 p. l., 461 p. 21¼ᵐ.
"Printed in Canada."

I. Title.
39–17807
Library of Congress   PZ3.T187Re

NT 0049642   DLC

070.46
T216t
MICROFILM

Tate, Frank Joseph.
Television as the new news' medium. [Columbus] Ohio State University, 1950.

Microfilm copy (negative) of typescript, made by Ohio State University Library in 1961.
Collation of the original, as determined from the film: 72 *l*.
Thesis (M.A.) - Ohio State University.
Bibliography: *l*. 71-72
1. Television broadcasting of news   I. Title

NT 0049643   FU

BF1999
(Rd)

Tate, Frank William, 1916–
A rank pattern analysis of verbal behavior occurring in client–centered psychotherapy. 1953.
129 l.

Thesis--Univ. of Chicago.

1. Psychotherapy. I. Title.

NT 0049644   ICU

Western
Americana
Broadsides
Zc52
857ta

Tate, Fred.
The public debt.To the voters of Fayette, Austin and Colorado counties. [Brenham, Tex.? 1857]
broadside. 49 x 20 cm.

Signed and dated: Fred Tate. LaGrange, July, 1857. Brenham enquirer copy.

NT 0049645   CtY

Tate, Fred Alonzo
The chain terminating step in the free radical polymerzation of allyl acetate

Thesis - Harvard, 1951

NT 0049646   MH-C

Tate (G.). Report on vaccination in the northwest frontier province for tho year 1919-20.
4 pp., 10 l. roy. 8°. Peshawar, 1920.

NT 0049647   DNLM

QD305 Tate, George.
.A2T21   Ueber die unsymmetrische dimethylbernsteinsaure
und die propyl- und isopropylmalonsaure.
Wuersburg, 1880.
26p.
Inaug. diss. Wuersburg.

NT 0049648   DLC PPAN

Tate, George, M.R.C.S.
A treatise on hysteria.   London,
Highley, 1830.

134 p.

NT 0049649   PU DNLM PPPH

Tate, George, M. R. C. S.
A treatise on hysteria. By George Tate ... Philadelphia, E. L. Carey and A. Hart, 1831.
134 p. 24½ᶜᵐ.

1. Hysteria.

Library of Congress   RC403.T2   7-19081†

NT 0049650   DLC CU PP PPHa PPJ Nh MiU DNLM ViU WU-M

Tate, George, M.R.C.S.   616.852 L800
A treatise on hysterical affections. By George Tate, ... Third
edition, revised. London, J. Churchill, 1858.
x, 110 p. 16½ᶜᵐ.

NT 0049651   ICJ OCIW-H

Tate, George, 1805-1871.
The ancient British sculptured rocks of Northumberland
and the eastern borders, with notices of the remains associated
with these sculptures. By George Tate ... Alnwick, Printed
by H. H. Blair, 1865.
2 p. l., ₃-46 p. illus., xii pl. (incl. front.) 28 x 21½ᶜᵐ.
Reprinted from the Proceedings of the Berwickshire Naturalists'
club, for 1864.—Pref.

1. Northumberland—Antiq. 2. Petroglyphs.   2-21076

Library of Congress   GN806.N8T2

NT 0049652   DLC CtY

Tate, George, 1805-1871.
The antiquities of Yevering Bell and Three Stone Burn,
among the Cheviots, in Northumberland, with an account
of excavations made into Celtic forts, hut dwellings, bar-
rows, and stone circle. By George Tate ... Reprinted
from the Berwickshire naturalists' transactions, 1862.
Alnwick, Printed by H. H. Blair, 1862.
25 p. incl. plan. 1 pl., fold. map. 21½ᶜᵐ.

Subject entries: 1. Yevering Bell. 2. Three Stone Burn.   2-20897

Library of Congress, no.   DA140.T219.

NT 0049653   DLC

Tate, George 1805-1871.
The Cheviots; the geographical range, physical
features, mineral characters, relation to Stratifield
rocks, origin, age, botanical peculiarities, read at
the meeting at Dunsdale, July, 1867. np [1867?]
12 p.
Caption title
Reprinted from the Berwickshire Naturalists' Club
Proceedings, 1867

NT 0049654   MH

Tate, George, The fossil flora of the mountain limestone
formation of the eastern borders, in connection with the
natural history of coal. (In JOHNSTON, George. The botany
of the eastern borders, 1853, pp. 289-317.)

NT 0049655   MH-A DLC MH

Tate, George, 1805-1871.
The geology and archæology of Beadnell, Northumber-
land, with descriptions of fossil annelids, by George Tate
... The land and freshwater Mollusca of Alnwick, by
Geo. Ralph Tate ... Alnwick, Printed by W. Davison,
1858.
25 p. front. 21½ᶜᵐ.
"From the Transactions of the Berwickshire naturalists' club for 1858."

1. Paleontology—England—Northumberland. 2. Mollusks—England—
Northumberland. 3. Annelida, Fossil. I. Tate, George Ralph.

CA 17-1110 Unrev'd

Library of Congress   QE754.T21

NT 0049656   DLC

QE783 Tate, George, 1805-1871.
.S8T2   Geology & archæology of the borders.
Description of a sea star, cribellites carbonarius,
from the mountain limestone of Northumberland.
Alnwick, 1863.
21 p.
"Reprinted from the Bewickshire Naturalists'
Transactions, 1863.

NT 0049657   DLC

Tate, George, 1805-1871
Harbottle Castle, read at Alwinton, June 25, 1868.
np [18-?]

11 p.

NT 0049658   MH

Tate, George, 1805-1871.
The history of the borough, castle, and barony of Alnwick, by George Tate ... Alnwick, H. H. Blair, 1866-69.
2 v. illus., 21 pl. (partly col.) incl. plans. 22ᶜᵐ. (v. 2: 27ᶜᵐ.)
Originally issued in 14 parts.

Subject entries: 1. Alnwick, Eng. 2. Natural history—England—Alnwick. 3. Alnwick castle.   3-16660

Library of Congress, no.   DA690.A4T2.

NT 0049659   DLC CtY NN MB MdBP MiU FU PPFr

Tate, George, 1805-1871.
The life of the Rev. Gilbert Rule, M. D.
Alnwick [dated, 1860]
10 p. 8°. [In v. 626, College Pamphlets]

NT 0049660   CtY

Tate, George, 1805-1871.

Baker, John Gilbert, 1834-
A new flora of Northumberland and Durham, with
sketches of its climate and physical geography, with a
map, by J. G. Baker ... and G. R. Tate ... with a sketch
of the geology of the two counties and a map, by G. Tate
... [London, Williams & Norgate; etc., etc., 1868]

*6559.1.
Tate, George, 1805-1871, and William Hylton Dyer Longstaffe.
The pedigrees and early heraldry of the Lords of Alnwick. A chap-
ter from the history of the Borough Castle, and Barony of Aln-
wick, by George Tate. The Vescy heraldry and pedigrees of
Tyson, Vescy, Aton, and Bek, by W. H. D. Longstaffe.
Alnwick. Blair. 1866. 36 pp. Illus. 4°.
The genealogy of the family of Percy is also given.

E768r — Longstaffe, William Hylt Dyer, jt. auth. — Alnwick, England.
Biog. and genealogy. — Genealogy. Alnwick.

NT 0049662   MB

Tate, George, 1805-1871.
The polished and scratched rocks in the
neighbourhood of Alnwick, viewed in connection
with the boulder formation in Northumberland.
Alnwick, Mercury office [1860]
8 p. 8°.

NT 0049663   DLC

QD697 Tate, George, 1805-1871.
.T21   Records of glaciated rocks in the eastern
borders. [Alnwick? 186-]
5 p.

NT 0049664   DLC

Tate, George, 1805-1871.
The vill, manor, and church of Longhoughton, North-
umberland. By George Tate ... Reprinted from the
"Alnwick Mercury" Dec. 1, 1864. Alnwick, Printed by
H. H. Blair [1864?]
11 p. 21½ᶜᵐ.

Subject entries: Longhoughton, Eng.   3-15688

Library of Congress, no.   DA690.L83T2.

NT 0049665   DLC

Tate, George, 1914-   ed.
London's struggle for socialism, 1848-1948, edited by
George Armstrong [pseud.] With a foreword by John
Mahon. London, Thames Publications, 1948.
viii, 56 p. 22 cm.

1. Socialism in London. 2. Labor and laboring classes—London.
I. Title.

HX250.L6T3   335   50-22549 rev

NT 0049666   DLC MH OkU

QL345 Tate, George Henry Hamilton, 1894-   joint
.A1C3   author.

Carter, Thomas Donald, 1893-
Animals of the Pacific world, including whales, seals and
dugongs of neighboring waters, by T. Donald Carter, John Eric
Hill and G. H. H. Tate ... Washington, The Infantry journal
[1944]

S9.206 Tate, George Henry Hamilton, 1894–
718   ... An apparently new fruit bat of the
Pteropus hypomelanus group from Gower island,
Solomon islands ... [New York, 1934]
2p. 24cm. (American museum novitates,
no.718)
Caption title.

1. Pteropus goweri. x.ser.

NT 0049668   CtY

QH1 Tate, George Henry Hamilton, 1894–
A14   The banded anteater, Myrmecobius
no.1521 Waterhouse (Marsupialia). New York, 1951.
8 p. tables. 24 cm. (American Museum
of Natural History, New York. American
Museum novitiates no. 1521)
Bibliography: p. 7–8.

1. Marsupialia. I. Title. (Series)

NT 0049669   DI

S9.206 Tate, George Henry Hamilton, 1894–
713   ... Bats from the Pacific islands, including
a new fruit bat from Guam ... [New York,1934]
3p. 24cm. (American museum novitates,
no.713)
Caption title.

1. Chiroptera - Islands of the Pacific.
x.ser.^

NT 0049670   CtY

Tate, Geo. Henry Hamilton, 1894 –
Botanical results of the Tyler-Duida
expedition
see under Gleason, Henry Allan,
1882–

Tate, George Henry Hamilton, 1894–
... Brief diagnoses of twenty-six apparently
new forms of Marmosa (Marsupialia) from South
America ... [New York, 1931]
14 p. 24 cm. (American museum novitates,
no. 493)
Caption title.
1. Marmosa.

NT 0049672   CtY

QL Tate, George Henry Hamilton, 1894–
3   [Collected reprints, 1938–1952]
W94T21+ 1 v. illus. 28cm.

1. Rodentia. 2. Marsupialia.

NT 0049673   NIC

S9 Tate, George Henry Hamilton, 1894–
206   ... Further notes on the Rhinolophus
1219   philippinensis group (Chiroptera) ... [New
York,1943]
7p.incl.table. 23½cm. (American museum
novitates, no.1219)
Caption title.
Results of the Archbold expeditions, no.49.
"References": p.5.

NT 0049674   CtY

Tate, George Henry Hamilton, 1894–
A list of the mammals of the Japanese war area ... by G. H.
H. Tate ... New York, The American museum of natural
history, 1944.
4 v. illus. (maps) 19ᵐ.
Cover-title.
"It is recommended that these pamphlets be used in conjunction with
... 'Mammals of the Pacific world' by T. D. Carter, J. E. Hill, and G. H. H.
Tate."—Foreword.
CONTENTS.—pt. 1. New Guinea and eastward. — pt. 2. The Greater
Sunda area (islands of the northeast margin of the Indian ocean: Anda-
mans, Nicobars, Sumatra, Java, Bali)—pt. 3. Lesser Sunda islands, Mo-
luccas, Celebes.—pt. 4. Borneo and the islands of the China sea.
1. Mammals—Oceanica. I. American museum of natural history,
New York.

Library of Congress   JL735.A1T3   46–1890

[2]   599

MnU OClW
NT 0049675   DLC CaBViP OrP WaS CU DI PPAN TxU CtY

QH1 Tate, George Henry Hamilton, 1894–
A12   Mammals of Cape York Peninsula, with notes on the
v.98   occurrence of rain forest in Queensland.
no.7   New York, 1952.
[2], 567–616 p. 27 cm. (American Museum
of Natural History, New York. Bulletin, v. 98,
art. 7)
"Literature cited": p. 614–616.

1. Mammals – Cape York Peninsula. 2. Forests &
forestry – Queensland. I. Title: The Archbold Expeditions, Results of. No. 66. (Series)

NT 0049676   DI

Tate, George Henry Hamilton, 1894–
Mammals of eastern Asia, by G. H. H. Tate ... New York,
The Macmillan company, 1947.
xiv p., 1 l., 366 p. illus. (incl. maps) 21ᶜᵐ. [The Pacific world
series, under the auspices of the American committee for international
wild life protection]
"First printing."

1. Mammals—East (Far East)
QL729.A1T3   599   47–1666

Wa WaT WaS WaTU OrStbM
OClMN ScU VtU ICU TxU PPAN PU–BZ GU CaBViP OrP OrU
NT 0049677   DLC CaBVaU OrLgE IdB MtBC OrCS OU CU PP

S9 Tate, George Henry Hamilton, 1894–
206   ... Molossid bats of the Archbold collections
1142   ... [New York,1941]
4p. 24½cm. (American museum novitates,
no.1142)
Caption title.
"Results of the Archbold expeditions, no.38."

NT 0049678   CtY

S9 Tate, George Henry Hamilton, 1894–
206   ... A new Galidia (Viverridae) from
1112   Madagascar by G. H. Tate and A. L.
Rand [New York,1941]
1l. 24½cm. (American museum novitates,
no.1112)
Caption title.

NT 0049679   CtY

S9 Tate, George Henry Hamilton, 1894–
206   ... A new genus and species of fruit bats,
1204   allied to Nyctimene ... [New York,1942]
2p. 23½cm. (American museum novitates,
no.1204)
Caption title.
Results of the Archbold expeditions, no.46.

NT 0049680   CtY

QH1 Tate, George Henry Hamilton, 1894–
A14   A new Rhinolophus from Queensland (Mammalia,
no.1578 Chiroptera). New York, 1952.
3 p. table. 24 cm. (American Museum of
Natural History, New York. American Museum
novitates no. 1578)
"References": p. 3.

1. Bats. I. Title: The Archbold expeditions,
Results of. No. 67 (Series)

NT 0049681   DI

S9 Tate, George Henry Hamilton, 1894–
206   ... New rodents and marsupials from New
1101   Guinea, by G.H.H.Tate and Richard Archbold.
[New York,1941]
9p. 24½cm. (American museum novitates,
no.1101)
Caption title.
"Results of the Archbold expeditions, no.31."

NT 0049682   CtY

QH1 Tate, George Henry Hamilton, 1894–
A14   A new squirrel from Burma. New York, 1954.
no.1676 2 p. 24 cm. (American Museum of Natural
History, New York. American Museum novitates
no. 1676)

1. Squirrels. (Series)

NT 0049683   DI

S9 Tate, George Henry Hamilton, 1894–
206   ... Notes on oriental Taphozous and allies
1141   ... [New York,1941]
5p. 24½cm. (American museum novitates,
no.1141)
Caption title.
"Results of the Archbold expeditions, no.37."

NT 0049684   CtY

S9 Tate, George Henry Hamilton, 1894–
206   ... Notes on the types of certain early
1061   described species of monotremes, marsupials,
Muridae and bats from the Indo-Australian
region ... [New York,1940]
10p. 24cm. (American museum novitates, no.
1061)
Caption title.

NT 0049685   CtY

Tate, George Henry Hamilton, 1894–
The rodents of Australia and New Guinea. New York,
1951.
187–430 p. maps, tables. 27 cm. (Bulletin of the American Museum of Natural History, v. 97, article 4)
"Results of the Archbold expeditions, no. 65."
Bibliography: p. 414–417.

1. Rodentia. 2. Zoology—Australia. 3. Zoology—New Guinea.
I. Title.   (Series: American Museum of Natural History, New
York. Bulletin, v. 97, article 4)
QH1.A4 vol. 97, art. 4   599.32   53–2467

NT 0049686   DLC DI OrPS

QH 1 TATE, GEORGE HENRY HAMILTON, 1894–
.A445   Rodents of the genera Rattus and Mus from
v.68   the Pacific Islands. Collected by the
art.3   Whitney South Sea Expedition, with a discussion
of the origin and races of the Pacific Island
rat. New York, 1935.
145–178 p. illus. (American Museum of
Natural History. Bulletin, v.68, art.3)

1. Rodentia. Biol. cds.

NT 0049687   InU CtY

QH 1 TATE, GEORGE HENRY HAMILTON, 1894–
.A445   Some Muridae of the Indo-Australian region.
v.72   (Results of the Archbold Expeditions, no.13)
art.6   New York, 1936.
501–728 p. illus., maps. (American Museum
of Natural History. Bulletin, v.72, art.6)

1. Muridea. Biol. cds.

NT 0049688   InU

S9.206 / 557
Tate, George Henry Hamilton, 1894-
... The South American Cricetidae described by Felix Azara ... [New York,1932]
5p. 24cm. (American museum novitates, no.557)
. Caption title.

1. Cricetidae - South America. 2. Azara, Félix de, 1746-1821. x.ser.^

NT 0049689 CtY

Tate, George Henry Hamilton, 1894-
Studies in the Peramelidae (Marsupialia) New York, 1948.
317-346 p. illus. 27 cm. (Bulletin of the American Museum of Natural History, v. 92, article 6)
At head of title: Results of the Archbold Expeditions, no. 60.
Includes bibliography.

1. Peramelidae.
QH1.A4 vol. 92, art. 6   599.2   53-34587 ‡

NT 0049690 DLC PPAN NBuU

S9 / 201 / 66
Tate, George Henry Hamilton, 1894-
A systematic revision of the marsupial genus Marmosa ... New York,1933.
cover-title,250,2,p. illus.(incl.maps), XXVIpl.,9 fold.tables(in pocket at end) 24½cm (Bulletin of the American museum of natural history, vol.LXVI,1933, art.I)
Descriptive letterpress on versos facing the plates.
"Bibliography": p.237-246.

NT 0049691 CtY

S9.206 / 583
Tate, George Henry Hamilton, 1894-
... The taxonomic history of certain South and Central American cricetid Rodentia: Neotomys, with remarks upon its relationships; the cotton rats (Sigmodon and Sigmomys); and the "fish-eating" rats (Ichthyomys, Anotomys, Rheomys, Neusticomys, and Daptomys) ... [New York,1932]
10p. 24cm. (American museum novitates, no.583)
Caption title.
"List of references": p.9-10.

NT 0049692 CtY

S9.206 / 529
Tate, George Henry Hamilton, 1894-
... The taxonomic history of the genus Reithrodon Waterhouse (Cricetidae) ... [New York,1932]
4p. 24cm. (American museum novitates, no.529)
Caption title.

1. Cricetidae. 2. Reithrodon. 3. Mammals - Classification. x.ser.^

NT 0049693 CtY

S9.206 / 562
Tate, George Henry Hamilton, 1894-
... The taxonomic history of the neotropical cricetid genera Holochilus, Nectomys, Scapteromys, Megalomys, Tylomys and Ototylomys ... [New York,1932]
19p. 24cm. (American museum novitates, no.562)
Caption title.
Bibliography: p.16-19.

NT 0049694 CtY

S9.206 / 661
Tate, George Henry Hamilton, 1894-
... Taxonomic history of the neotropical hares of the genus Sylvilagus, subgenus Tapeti ... [New York,1933]
10p. 24cm. (American museum novitates, no.661)
Caption title.
"List of references": p.8-10.

NT 0049695 CtY

S9.206 / 541
Tate, George Henry Hamilton, 1894-
... The taxonomic history of the South American cricetid genera Euneomys (subgenera Euneomys and Galenomys), Auliscomys, Chelemyscus, Chinchillula, Phyllotis, Paralomys, Graomys, Eligmodontia and Hesperomys ... [New York,1932]
21p. 24cm. (American museum novitates, no.541)
"List of references": p.18-21.

NT 0049696 CtY

S9.206 / 582
Tate, George Henry Hamilton, 1894-
... The taxonomic history of the South and Central American akodont rodent genera: Thalpomys, Deltamys, Thaptomys, Hypsimys, Bolomys, Chroeomys, Abrothrix, Scotinomys, Akodon (Chalcomys and Akodon), Microxus, Podoxymys, Lenoxus, Oxymycterus, Notiomys, and Blarinomys ... [New York,1932]
32p. 24cm. (American museum novitates, no.582)
Caption title.
"List of references": p.30-32.

NT 0049697 CtY

S9 / 206 / 579-580
Tate, George Henry Hamilton, 1894-
... The taxonomic history of the South and Central American cricetid rodents of the genus Oryzomys ... [New York,1932]
2 nos. illus.(maps) 24cm. (American museum novitates, no.579-580)
Caption title.
"List of references": pt.2, p.12-17.

NT 0049698 CtY

S9.206 / 581
Tate, George Henry Hamilton, 1894-
... The taxonomic history of the South and Central American Oryzomine genera of rodents (excluding Oryzomys): Nesoryzomys, Zygodontomys, Chilomys, Delomys, Phaenomys, Rhagomys, Rhipidomys, Nyctomys, Oecomys, Thomasomys, Inomys, Aepeomys, Neacomys and Scolomys ... [New York,1932]
28p. illus.(map) 24cm. (American museum novitates, no.581)
Caption title.
"List of references": p.24-28.

NT 0049699 CtY

S9 / 201 / 68
Tate, George Henry Hamilton, 1894-
The taxonomy of the genera of neotropical hystricoid rodents ... New York,1935.
cover-title,p.295-447. 24½cm (Bulletin of the American museum of natural history, vol.LXVIII,1935, art.V)
"List of references": p.436-447.

NT 0049700 CtY InU

Tate, George Passman, 1856-
The frontiers of Baluchistan; travels on the borders of Persia and Afghanistan, by G. P. Tate ... With an introduction by Col. Sir A. Henry McMahon ... With a coloured frontispiece, thirty-six plates and two maps. London, Witherby & co., 1909.
xv, [1], 261 p. 37 pl. (incl. col. front., ports.) 2 fold. maps. 23 cm.

1. Baluchistan—Descr. & trav. 2. Sistan arbitration mission, 1903-1905. I. Title.

DS485.B17T3   9—22569

NcD CtY CU MiU
NT 0049701 DLC PP CaBVaU WU KyLoU NcU MB NN ICJ OC1

4DS / Ind. / 467
Tate, George Passman, 1856-
Kalat; a memoir on the country and family of the Ahmadzai Khans of Kalat. From a ms. account by the Akhund Muhammad Sidik, with notes and appendices from other manuscripts, as well as from printed books. Calcutta, Office of the Superintendent of Govt. Print., 1896.
55 p.

NT 0049702 DLC-P4

Tate, George Passman, 1856-
The kingdom of Afghanistan: a historical sketch, by G. P. Tate ... With an introductory note by the Right Hon'ble Sir Henry Mortimer Durand ... Bombay & Calcutta, "Times of India" offices, 1911.
3 p. l., [iii]-ix, 224 p. maps (part fold.) 24cm.

1. Afghanistan—Hist. I. Title.
A 12-1594
Title from Enoch Pratt   Free Libr. Printed by L. C.

NT 0049703 MdBE GU CU OC1 IU LU MiU

Tate, George Passman, 1856-
Seistan; a memoir on the history, topography, ruins and people of the country, in four parts, by G. P. Tate. Calcutta, Superintendent government printing, 1910-12.
2 v. plates, maps, plans. 31cm.
In four parts, paged continuously, v. [1] covering pt. I-III.

1. Seistan, Persia.
A 15-1347
Title from Columbia Univ. Printed by L. C.

NT 0049704 NNC CtY CU OC1 ICJ NN

Tate, George Ralph.

Tate, George, 1805-1871.
The geology and archæology of Beadnell, Northumberland, with descriptions of fossil annelids, by George Tate ... The land and freshwater Mollusca of Alnwick, by Geo. Ralph Tate ... Alnwick, Printed by W. Davison, 1858.

Tate, George Ralph, 1835-1874, joint author.

Baker, John Gilbert, 1834-
A new flora of Northumberland and Durham, with sketches of its climate and physical geography, with a map, by J. G. Baker ... and G. R. Tate ... with a sketch of the geology of the two counties, and a map, by G. Tate ... [London, Williams & Norgate; etc., etc.. 1868]

Tate, Gerald Ainslie
Elizabeth Wydeville, a play in one act, by Gerald A. Tate. Oxford. Printed at the Shakespeare head press and sold by B. Blackwell, 1933.
24 p.   19½ᶜᵐ.

1. Elizabeth, queen consort of Edward IV, king of England, 1437?–1492—Drama.   I. Title.

Library of Congress   PR6039.A75E5 1933   34–12571
⸂2⸃   822.91

NT   0049707   DLC CtY NN

Tate, Gerald Ainslie
The captivity and trial of Marie Antoinette, by Gerald Tate. With two illustrations. London, Methuen & co., ltd. ⸂1923⸃
2 p. l., 59, ⸂1⸃ p. front., port. 17¾ᶜᵐ.

1. Marie Antoinette, queen consort of Louis XVI, king of France, 1755–1793.

Library of Congress   DC137.17.T3   24–763
⸂2⸃

NT   0049708   DLC NN

Tate, Gerald Ainslie
Louis XVI; the last phase, by Gerald A. Tate...   London: Methuen & Co., Ltd. ⸂, 1929.⸃   vi, 57 p.   front., port.   16°.

417547A. 1. Louis XVI, king of   France, 1754–1793.
N. Y. P. L.   June 28, 1929

NT   0049709   NN MA KU OC1

DC146
R7T3   **Tate, Gerald** Ainslie
Madame Roland, a biographical study. New York, Fifth Avenue Pub. Co. ⸂1917⸃
106 p. 19cm.

1. Roland de la Platière, Marie Jeanne (Phlipon) 1754–1793.

NT   0049710   GU NN

QA43
.K5
1946   **Tate, Gladys,** joint author.   FOR OTHER EDITIONS SEE MAIN ENTRY
Knight, Frederic Butterfield, 1891–1947
Mathematics and life, by F. B. Knight, J. W. Studebaker and Gladys Tate. ⸂New ed.⸃ Chicago, Scott, Foresman ⸂1946–

QA39
.H365   **Tate, Gladys,** joint author.
Hawkins, George Edmon, 1901–
Your mathematics, by George E. Hawkins ⸂and⸃ Gladys Tate; illus. by Raymond E. Craig, Julia Kolb and Gladys Rabung. Chicago, Scott, Foresman ⸂1948⸃

Tate, Harold Simmons.
Analysis and evaluation of the job of the state supervisor of trade and industrial education. Ann Arbor, University Microfilms, 1951.
⸂University Microfilms, Ann Arbor, Mich.⸃ Publication no. 3286)
Microfilm copy of typescript. Positive.
Collation of the original, as determined from the film: xiii, 308 l. maps.
Thesis—Pennsylvania State College.
Bibliography: leaves 300–306.
1. Business education—Michigan. 2. Technical education—Michigan.
Microfilm AC-1 no. 3286   Mic 53–136

NT   0049713   DLC MiU

Tate, Harry, and W. Pink.
Motoring; a farce written by Harry Tate and Wal Pink...
London: Reynolds & Co.⸂, 1925?⸃   15 p.   12°.   (French's acting edition, no. 1846.)

1. Drama, English. 2. Pink, Wal,   jt. au. 3. Title.
N. V. P. I.   July 14, 1926

NT   0049714   NN OC1

Tate, Helen Meyers.
Remembered voice ⸂by⸃ Helen Meyers Tate. Philadelphia ⸂Camden, N. J., The Haddon craftsmen, inc.⸃ 1942.
2 p. l., 28 p. 21ᶜᵐ.
Poems.

I. Title.

Library of Congress   PS3539.A743R4   42–16449
⸂2⸃   811.5

NT   0049715   DLC

Tate, Henry.
Aaron Crane.   New York, The Abbey Press. [cop. 1901]
v, 7–248 p.   3 pl.   8°.

NT   0049716   NN

PS
2978
.T37B5x   **Tate, Henry.**
Bicycle yarns. New York [etc.] F. Tennyson Neely [1899]
154 p. illus. 20 cm.

NT   0049717   OKentU

FILM
4274   **Tate, Henry**
PR   Bicycle yarns, by Ex-Judge Henry Tate.   New
v.3   York, F. Tennyson Neely [c1899]
reel   154 p. front. (Wright American Fiction,
T3   v.III, 1876–1900, no. 5372, Research Publications, Inc. Microfilm, Reel T-3)

NT   0049718   CU NNC

Tate, Sir Henry, 1819–1899.
The Tate collection
see under title

DRAMATIC LIBRARY
D780.994
T18   **Tate, Henry,** 1873–1926.
Australian musical possibilities. With an introduction by Bernard O'Dowd. Melbourne, E. A. Vidler ⸂1924⸃
72 p. 22 cm.

"Compositions by Henry Tate": p. 65–72.

NT   0049720   NNC CaBVaU TxU PSt

W921.99
T216p   Tate, Henry, 1873–1926.
The poems of Henry Tate. With introduction by Elsie Cole.   Melbourne, Edward A. Vidler ⸂1928⸃
182p. front.(port.) 20cm.

NT   0049721   NcU NN CtY TxU

821
T187r   **Tate, Henry,** 1873–1926.
The rune of the Bunyip (four grotesques) and other verse. Melbourne, G. Robertson [1910]
35p. 19cm.

NT   0049722   TxU CLU

Tate, Henry Clay, 1902–
Building a better home town; a program of community self-analysis and self-help. ⸂1st ed.⸃ New York, Harper ⸂1954⸃
236 p. 22 cm.
Includes bibliography.

1. Suburbs. 2. Bloomington, Ill.—Suburbs. 3. Cities and towns—U. S. I. Title.
HT351.T35   *301.36 323.353   54—6451 ‡

WaS WaT OrLgE OrU OrCS IdPI
PP PSC TxU OU PSt KEmT PU–FA MH–PA Wa CaBVaU MtU Or
NT   0049723   DLC OKentU OrU PPD NcRS ViU MB NN OOxM

SPECIAL COLLECTIONS
X898C442
T18   **Tate, Henry W**
Tate manuscripts ⸂American Indian tales, written down by Henry W. Tate, a Tsimshian Indian, and assembled by Franz Boas. / 190-?–1910?⸃
213–349, 365–2017 l. in 2 manuscript boxes.
Tales numbered: 5–10, 12–44. Text in the Tsimshian language, with English translation.
Included also are 7 folders (variously paged) of supplementary material, 5 with text in English, 2 with text (typescript) in Indian without translation.

NT   0049724   NNC

Tate, Henry W.
Boas, Franz, 1858–
Tsimshian mythology, by Franz Boas; based on texts recorded by Henry W. Tate.
(In U. S. Bureau of American ethnology. Thirty-first annual report, 1909–1910. Washington, 1916. 24½ᶜᵐ. p. 29–1037. illus., plates)

Tate, Herbert 1894–
Elementary mathematical analysis. Toronto, Pitman, 1946.
299 p.   24 cm.

1. Mathematics. I. Title.

NT   0049726   CaBVaU

332.8
T216e   Tate, Herbert, 1894–
1937   Elements of the mathematical theory of interest. 2d ed. Toronto, I. Pitman, 1937.
viii, 130 p.   tables.

1. Interest and usury. I. Title.

NT   0049727   CaQML

Tate, Herbert 1894–
Interest annuities and bonds.   Toronto, Sir Isaac Pitman & sons, ltd. [c1929]
viii, 103p.   22cm.

NT   0049728   NBuG

Tate, Herbert, 1894–
Intermediate algebra. 2d ed. Toronto, Pitman, 1944. 218p. tables.

NT 0049729   CaBVa

Tate, Herbert, 1894–
Mathematical theory of interest. Rev. ed. Toronto, I. Pitman, 1947.
112 p. 24 cm.

1. Interest and usury.   i. Title.

HF5695.T35 1947   332.82   48–21102*

NT 0049730   DLC

Tate, Herman Douglas, 1905–   and
Klostermeyer, E.C.
Cockroach control...
Lincoln, ¡1943¿
8 p. illus.
(Nebraska. Agricultural experiment station ¡Lincoln¿ Circular 72)

Cover-title.

NT 0049731   PP

Tate, Herman Douglas, 1905–
... Insects as vectors of yellow dwarf, a virus disease of onions ... by H. D. Tate ... ¡Ames, Ia., 1940¿
cover-title, 287–294 p. 25½ᵐ.
Thesis (PH. D)—Iowa state college of agriculture and mechanic arts, 1936. Doctoral thesis no. 403.
"Condensed from a thesis."
"Journal paper no. J–718 of the Iowa Agricultural experiment station, Ames, Iowa. Project no. 135."
"Reprinted from Iowa state college journal of science, vol. xiv, no. 3, April, 1940."
"Literature cited": p. 293–294.
1. Onions—Diseases and pests. 2. Yellow dwarf disease. 3. Insects as carriers of plant diseases.   i. Title.

41–21599 Revised

Library of Congress   SB608.O5T3
                                         ¡r43c2¿   632.3

NT 0049732   DLC PPT

Tate, Herman Douglas, 1905–
Transmission of sugarcane mosaic by aphids. By H. D. Tate ... S. R. Vandenberg ...
(*In* U. S. Dept. of agriculture. Journal of agricultural research. v. 59, no. 1, July 1, 1939, p. 73–79. 23ᶜᵐ. Washington, 1939)
Contribution from Bureau of entomology and plant quarantine (K–802)
In cooperation with the Puerto Rico Experiment station, U. S. Dept. of agriculture, Mayaguez, P. R.
Published July 19, 1939.
"Literature cited": p. 78–79.
1. Plant-lice. ¡1. Aphdidae¿ 2. Insects, Injurious and beneficial. ¡2. Insects and plant diseases¿ 3. Mosaic disease. 4. Sugar-cane—Diseases and pests. ¡3, 4. Mosaic disease of sugar-cane¿   i. Vandenberg, Sidney Rendall, 1894–   joint author.

Agr 39–637

U. S. Dept. of agr.   Librar,   1Ag84J   vol. 59, no. 1
for Library of Congress   [S21.A75   vol. 59, no. 1]
                                         ¡6*¿   (630.72)

NT 0049733   DNAL DLC

Tate, Homer R
The name and family of Tate, compiled by Homer R. Tate. Effingham, Ill., 1945.
22 l. incl. coat of arms.   29 x 23ᵐ.

1. Tate family (Henry Tate, d. 1793)

CS71.T196 1945   43–21982

NT 0049734   DLC

Tate, Humphrey D   , jt. author.
Formation and regulation of corporations in Pennsylvania
see under   Meredith, M   M

Tate, I   N.
... Modern trends in lumber selling, by I. N. Tate ... An address delivered at Yale university, November 16, 1925, under the auspices of the School of forestry on the 20th Engineers' memorial foundation ... New Haven, Yale university, School of forestry, 1925.
29 p. 21ᵐ.   (Yale university. School of forestry ... Lumber industry series. no. 6)

1. Lumber trade—U. S.

Library of Congress   HF6201.L7T3   31–2847
                                         ¡2¿   658.974

NT 0049736   DLC OrU WaS ViU NN MH–BA

Tate, J.
Medulla grammatices: or The reasons of grammar. / Being a new method to render ingenious persons ... considerable proficients in a very short time. There is also prefix'd a brief synopsis of ... rules ... By J. Tate. Licensed, June the 4th. 1687. London, Printed by J. Leake, for Edward Poole ... 1687.
¡6¿,55,¡1¿ p. illus. 19½ᶜᵐ.
An introduction to latin grammar.
Signatures: A⁴,   B–D⁸, E⁴.
Title within   double line border.
Unbound, in mar-   bled cloth folding case.

NT 0049737   CLU–C

Tate, J. The names of families, children's names, and time of births, in the town of Somersworth, March ye 26, 1767.¡
Note. Copied by John R. Ham.   ★

NT 0049738   NhDo

Tate, J   M   jr.
The decline and dissolution of the Harmony Society. ¡n.p.,¿ 1931.
¡4¿p. 18cm.

1. Harmonists.   I. Title.

NT 0049739   NcU

Tate, J   M   jr.
Some notes, pictures and documents relating to the Harmony Society and its homes at Harmony, Pennsylvania, New Harmony, Indiana, and Economy, Pennsylvania.   Sewickley, Pa., 1925.
14p. 26cm.
Inserted: Old Economy letters, by J.M.Tate, jr.; The decline and dissolution of the Harmony Society, by J.M.Tate, jr.
Pictures and documents referred to in the Foreword wanting.

J
28
.864

NT 0049740   ICN

Tate, James.
Works by this author printed in America before 1801 are available in this library in the Readex Microprint edition of Early American Imprints published by the American Antiquarian Society.
This collection is arranged according to the numbers in Charles Evans' American Bibliography.

NT 0049741   DLC

Tate, James.
Major est Veritas, & praevalebit. A modern vindication of infant baptism, extracted from Sacred Scripture...Savannah, James & Nicholas Johnston, M,DCC,XC (1790)
16 p. 18 cm.
Cover title on p. [1]

NT 0049742   MBAt

Tate, James, 1771–1883, ed.

Dalzel, Andrew, 1742–1806.
'Ανάλεκτα ἑλληνικὰ μείζονα, sive Collectanea graeca majora: ad usum academicae juventutis accommodata. Cum notis philologicis, quas partim collegit, partim scripsit Andreas Dalzel ... Londini, T. Cadell; ¡etc., etc.¡ 1825–27.

Tate, James, 1771–1843.

Disney, John, 1746–1816.
A catalogue of some marbles, bronzes, pictures, and gems, at the Hyde, near Ingatestone, Essex. The greater part successively the property of Thomas Hollis ... and Thomas Brand-Hollis ... and now of John Disney ... With an appendix. ¡2d ed.¿ ¡London, T. Gillet, printer¿ 1809.

Tate, James, 1771–1843.
The Christian rule of equity enforced and applied A sermon preached ... March 20, 1825... York, J. Wilson & sons, 1825.
16 p. nar. 8°.
In * C. p. v. 1263.

NT 0049745   NN MB

G
1033
T21+
Tate, James, 1771–1843
First classical maps, with chronological tables of Grecian and Roman history. London, George Bell, 1845.
11,¡13¿ p. maps. 27cm.

1. Geography, Ancient—Maps. 2. Classical geography—   Maps. I. Title.

NT 0049746   NIC NN

TATE, James, 1771–1843.
First classical maps, with chronological tables of Grecian and Roman history; by James Tate. London, G.Bell, etc., etc., 1845.
4°.
Atlas with 5 maps.
Autograph of C.L.Dodgson.

NT 0049747   MH NN

Tate, James, 1771–1843.
The Horæ Paulinæ of William Paley, D. D., carried out and illustrated in a continuous history of the apostolic labours and writings of St. Paul, on the basis of the Acts, with intercalary matter of sacred narrative supplied from the Epistles, and elucidated in occasional dissertations. By James Tate ... London, Printed for Longman, Orme, Brown, Green, & Longmans, 1840.
xix, 202 p., 3 l., 219, ¡1¿ p. fold. map. 22½ᵐ.
Half-title: The continuous history of St. Paul: with the Horæ Paulinæ subjoined.

The "Horæ Paulinæ" (3 l., 219, ¡1¿ p. at end) has special t.-p.: Horæ Paulinæ: or, The truth of the Scripture history of St. Paul, evinced by a comparison of the epistles which bear his name, with the Acts of the apostles, and with one another. By William Paley ... First printed in 1790, now carefully reprinted, with occasional notes, which are marked in brackets. ¡London, Printed by A. Spottiswoode¿ 1840.

1. Paul, Saint, apostle. 2. Bible. N. T. Epistles of Paul—Evidences, authority, etc. 3. Bible. N. T. Acts—Evidences, authority, etc. 4. Bible—Evidences, authority, etc.—N. T. Epistles of Paul. 5. Bible—Evidences, authority, etc.—N. T. Acts.   i. Paley, William, 1743–1805. Horæ Paulinæ. ii. Title. iii. Title: The continuous history of St. Paul.

34–19084

Library of Congress   BS2505.T3   [922.1]   225.92

NT 0049749   DLC MH

Gb3
4
3

Tate, James, 1771-1843.
An introduction to the principal Greek tragic and comic metres in scansion, structure, and ictus. 2d ed. With an Appendix on syllabic quantity in Homer and Aristophanes ... London, Printed for Baldwin and Cradock; and sold by J.Parker,Oxford;[etc.,etc.]1829.
xp.,1l.,46p. 21½cm. [Binder's title: Greek language,3]

NT 0049750   CtY MiU NIC NjP MH

486.5
T216I

Tate, James, 1771-1845.
An introduction to the principal Greek tragic and comic metres, with an appendix on syllabic quantity in Homer and Aristophanes. To which are now added treatises on the Sapphic stanza and the elegiac distich. 4th ed. London, Baldwin and Cradock, 1834.
x, 67 p. 23 cm.

1. Greek language. Metrics and rhythmics.
I. Title.

NT 0049751   NcD MH MdBP InU

Tate, James, 1771-1843.
Gb31.32 ... Letters on the Analogia linguae graecae, &c. which first appeared in the Gentleman's magazine for 1832. By James Tate ... Now reprinted, with a preface. London,W.Pickering and G.Bell,1843.
viii,44p. 21½cm.
At head of title: Greek etymology.
Addressed to Mr. Urban.

1.Greek language - Etymology. 2.Urban, Sylvanus,   pseud.

NT 0049752   CtY

Tate, James, 1771-1843.
[Preliminary] dissertation on the chronology of the works, and on the localities and life and character of Horace. London, 1837.
[In Horatius Flaccus, Quintus. Horatius restitutus, p. 1-202]

NT 0049753   DLC

Tate, James, 1771-1843, ed.
Richmond rules to form the Ovidian distich; with some hints on the transition to the Virgilian hexameter... London, Baldwin, 1835.
30 p.

NT 0049754   PU

Tate, James, 1771-1843.

Moor, James, 1712-1779.
Tracts on the cases, prepositions and syntax of the Greek language. By James Moor ... and by James Tate ... Richmond [Yorkshire] 1830.

Tate, James, M. E., *1894-*
Building a model of the Flying Cloud.   4097.05-132
— Mineola. Mineola Ship Supply Co. 1929. x, 51 pp. Illus. Diagrams. 23½ cm.

N8157 — Models. Ship. — Flying Cloud, clipper ship.

NT 0049756   MB

Tate, James, 1894—   ed.

Delta manufacturing company, *Milwaukee.*
Getting the most out of your drill press. (5th ed.) A Delta-craft publication. Edited by James Tate. A complete manual covering all phases of drill press operation in the home workshop, with over two hundred photographic illustrations and line drawings. Milwaukee, Wis., The Delta manufacturing co., °1937.

TK6550
.H2

Tate, James, 1894—   joint author.

Haan, Enno R   1899-
Radio practice; a practical presentation of radio set building, including simple and clear instructions on trouble shooting and maintenance, prepared by Enno R. Haan ... James Tate ... and Charles B. Hayward ... Chicago, American technical society [°1927]

Tate, James Murray, 1852-
Foundry practice; a treatise on molding and casting in their various details, by James M. Tate and Melvin O. Stone, M. E. Prepared for the use of students in the College of engineering, University of Minnesota. Minneapolis, The H. W. Wilson company, 1904.
iv, 236 p. illus., diagrs. 20cm.

1. Founding.   I. Stone, Melvin Oscar, 1877—   joint author.

Library of Congress   TS230.T2   4—23733

NT 0049759   DLC MtBC Or PU-Sc MB ICJ PPF

ar V
19905

Tate, James Murray, 1852-
Foundry practice; a treatise on moulding and casting in their various details. [2d ed.] Prepared for the use of students in the College of Engineering, University of Minnesota. Minneapolis, H. W. Wilson, 1906.
iv, 236 p. illus. 20cm.

I. Stone, Melvin Oscar, 1877-   joint author.

NT 0049760   NIC IdU MH NN OCl OOxM PP

Tate, James Murray, 1852-
Foundry practice; a treatise on molding and casting in their various details, by James M. Tate and Melvin O. Stone, M. E. Prepared for the use of students in the College of engineering, University of Minnesota. 3d ed., rev. New York, J. Wiley & sons; [etc., etc.,] 1909.
vi, 234 p. illus., diagrs. 19cm. $2.00

1. Founding.   I. Stone, Melvin Oscar, 1877—   joint author.

Library of Congress   TS230.T23   9—1599

NT 0049761   DLC WaS OrP NcD OCl OU NN

Tate, James Murray, 1852-
Training in wood-work, designed for use in manual training and technical school; consisting of three parts: carpentry, wood-turning and pattern work, by James M. Tate ... 1st ed. Minneapolis, Minn., School education company [1902]
2 p. l., [7]-120 p. illus., diagr. 20cm.

1. Woodwork (Manual training)

Library of Congress   TT185.T2   2—23331

NT 0049762   DLC NcRS DHEW ICJ

Tate, James Murray, 1852-
Training in wood-work, designed for use in manual training and technical school; consisting of three parts: carpentry, wood-turning and pattern work, by James M. Tate... 2d ed. Minneapolis, Minn., Northwestern school supply co. [1902]
2 p. l. [7]-22 p. illus., diagr. 20 cm.

NT 0049763   MtBC OCl

Tate, J[ames] Roddam.
Madeira; or, The spirit of Anti-Christ in 1846, as exhibited in a series of outrages perpetrated in August last, on British subjects and Portuguese Protestant Christians.   London: J. Nisbet and Co., 1847.   4 p.l., (i)iv-viii p., 1 l., 126 p.   8°.

1. Madeira.—History, 1846. 2. Per-   secutions (against Protestants),
Madeira, 1846.
N. Y. P. L.   June 30, 1913.

NT 0049764   NN

Tate, James Roddam.
A practical treatise on naval book-keeping in all its branches, comprising the duties of a captain's clerk, an admiral's secretary, an officiating judge advocate, and an officer in charge of accounts connected with treasure received on freight, with marginal references, notes, and copious appendices, illustrative of the subjects. By James Roddam Tate ... Portsmouth, Printed for the author, sold by W. Woodward, Portsea [etc.] 1840.
xvi, 220 p., 1 l., 14 p. incl. tables (4 fold.) 24½cm.

1. Naval art and science—Accounting.
                                                          13-20675

Library of Congress   VC505.G7T2

NT 0049765   DLC

Tate, James S.
Surcharged and different forms of retaining walls. By James S. Tate, c. e. New York, D. Van Nostrand, 1873.
59 p. incl. tables, diagrs. 15cm. (On cover: Van Nostrand's science series, no. 7)

1. Retaining walls.
                                                          A 11-2351

Title from U. S. Engineer   School. Printed by L. C.

        NN ICJ OCl
NT 0049766   ViFbE MiHM CU PSt PU NIC MiU OU DI-GS

Tate, James William, 1875–1922.
[The beauty spot. With piano]
...The beauty spot. A musical play in three acts. Adapted from the French of P. L. Flers by Arthur Anderson. Lyrics by Clifford Harris and Valentine. (Additional lyrics by Arthur Anderson.) Music by Jas. W. Tate... London: Francis, Day & Hunter [etc., etc.] cop. 1918.   Publ. pl. no. F. & D. 14700. 141 p. 27½cm.
Vocal score. English words.

757312A. 1. Operas, Comic—Vocal   score. I. Anderson, Arthur. The
beauty spot. III. Harris, Clifford.   beauty spot. IV. Valentine. The
beauty spot. IV. Flers, Pierre Louis   Puyol, called, 1867—   The
N. Y. P. L.   July 19, 1935.

NT 0049767   NN

Tate, James William, 1875–1922.

I've told his Missus all about him. By John P. Harrington and James W. Tate.   New York, Francis, Day and Hunter [c1907]

First line: You've heard me tell the story.
Chorus: I'm the girl he left in the lurch!
Portrait of Vesta Victoria on t-p.

1. Victoria, Vesta—Port. I. Har-   rington, John P. II. Song index (3).
N. Y. P. L.   May 31, 1949.

NT 0049768   NN

Tate, Jane Beverlin, 1922–
Equinox, a collection of poems. New York, William-Frederick Press, 1952.
46 p. 22 cm. (The William-Frederick poets, 94)

I. Title.

PS3539.A746E6   811.5   52–13406 ‡

NT   0049769   DLC NN NcD PU OCl OOxM ViU

Tate, Jane Beverlin, 1922–
These are for you. Portland, Me., Falmouth Pub. House ₁1949₎
62 p. 21 cm.
Poems.

I. Title.

PS3539.A746T5   811.5   50–5934

NT   0049770   DLC

Tate, John
At home among the atoms. Portadown, Publ. for the Author at the Portadown and Lurgan News Offices, 1885
60 p.

NT   0049771   MH NjP

4QB
200   **Tate, John**
The sun: its constitution; how the sun fire is sustained. Portadown, Printed by S. Farrell, 1881.
33 p.

NT   0049772   DLC-P4 MH

Tate, John, 1887–
Die experimentelle Bestimmung der Verdampfungswärme einiger Metalle. Berlin, Ebering, 1914.
49 p. 23.5 cm.
Berlin, Phil. Diss. v. 5. Aug. 1914, Ref. Wehnelt, Planck.

NT   0049773   CtY MH

Tate, J₍ohn₎ C   *and* **Tate, F₍rank₎ C.**
Tate's atlas of Des Moines and plat directory to additions, subdivisions, and official plats in Des Moines, Iowa/ ... Completed to January 1, 1899. Des Moines, Ia., J. C. & F. C. Tate ₁1898₎
₁13₎ p. map. 35 plans. fol.

Jan. 5, 99–106

NT   0049774   DLC

Tate, J₍ohn₎ C. & F. C.
Tate's atlas of Des Moines and plat directory to additions, subdivisions and official plats in Des Moines, Iowa. Giving a complete ward map of the city and the plats as shown in the county records, compiling all of the plat records in one, showing their relative position one to another, including plat index giving the correct name and date of filing of plats, giving book and page now in use in the recorder's office in Polke county, Iowa. Completed to jan., 1899. 9 p. l., 35 maps. fol. Des Moines, J. C. & F. C. Tate, 1899.
————— 1709

NT   0049775   DLC

Tate, John Orley Allen.

See

Tate, Allen, 1899–

Tate, John Torrence, 1889–   joint author.

Hustrulid, Andrew, 1905–
The development of a high intensity, high resolving power mass spectrograph and a study with it of the dissociation products of the benzene molecule under electron impact ... by Andrew Hustrulid ... ₁New York, 1938₎

Tate, John Torrence, 1889–

National research council. *Committee on electrodynamics of moving media.*
... Electrodynamics of moving media. Report of the National research council Committee on electrodynamics of moving media, by W. F. G. Swann, John T. Tate, H. Bateman, E. H. Kennard. Washington, D. C., Published by the National research council of the National academy of sciences, 1922.

Tate, John Torrence, 1889–   ed.

Journal of applied physics. v. 1–
July 1931–
₁Lancaster, Pa. and New York, etc., 1931–

Tate, John Torrence, 1889–

Vaughan, Alfred Leland, 1906–
Mass spectrograph analyses, and critical potentials for the production of ions by electron impact, in nitrogen and carbon monoxide ... by Alfred Leland Vaughan ... ₁New York, 1935₎

Tate, John Torrence, 1889–
... Resonance and ionization potentials for electrons in cadmium vapor, by John T. Tate, assistant physicist, and Paul D. Foote, associate physicist ... ₁Washington, Govt. print. off., 1918₎
479–486 p. incl. illus., diagrs. 27½ cm. (₁U. S.₎ Bureau of standards. Scientific papers, no. 317)
At head of title: Department of commerce. Bureau of standards. S. W. Stratton, director.
₍Issued February 9, 1918₎
1. Electric discharges through gases. 2. Cadmium. I. Foote, Paul Darwin, 1888– Joint author. II. Title.

QC711.T3   18–26342 rev

NT   0049781   DLC OrMonO WaWW OrU CaBVaU

Tate, John Torrence, 1925–
Class field theory. [195?]
see under Artin, Emil, 1898–

Film
6172   **Tate, John Torrence,** 1925–
Fourier analysis in number fields and Hecke's zeta-functions. ₍n.p., 1950₎
₍55₎ *l.*
Thesis (Ph.D.) – Princeton University.
Includes bibliography.
Microfilm copy of typescript. Ann Arbor, University Microfilms, 1950? 1 reel. 35 mm.

NT   0049783   MiEM

QA247
-T37   **Tate, John** Torrence, 1925–
Fourier analysis in number fields and Hecke's zeta-functions. [Princeton, N.J., 1950]
1 v. (various pagings) 28 cm.

Caption title.
Xerox copy of typewritten dissertation, Princeton University.
Includes bibliography.

NT   0049784   RPB

PA3062
T3   **Tate, Jonathan,** 1899–1958
Grammarian's progress. Inaugural lecture delivered 23rd January, 1946. / ₁Sheffield, Eng., Univ. of Sheffield, 1947?₎
cover-title, 17p. 22 cm.

NT   0049785   RPB

Tate, Jonathan, 1899–1958, *tr.*

Persius Flaccus, Aulus.
The Satires of A. Persius Flaccus, rendered into English verse with an introduction and notes by Jonathan Tate ... Oxford, B. Blackwell, 1930.

Tate, Joseph.
A digest of the laws of Virginia, which are of a permanent character and general operation; illustrated by judicial decisions: to which is added, an index of the names of the cases in the Virginia reporters. By Joseph Tate ... Richmond, Shepherd and Pollard, printers, 1823.
viii, 562 p. 23ᵐ.

1. Law—Virginia—Digests. I. Virginia. Laws, statutes, etc.

35–31323

NT   0049787   DLC NcD CSmH IU ViU OCX ViU-L

Tate, Joseph.
Digest of the laws of Virginia, which are of a permanent character and general operation; illustrated by judicial decisions: to which is added, an index of the names of the cases in the Virginia reporters. By Joseph Tate ... 2d ed. Richmond, Smith and Palmer, 1841.
viii, 959 p. 24ᵐ.
"The present edition includes most of the decisions contained in the ninth volume of Leigh's Reports, and the acts of assembly of 1839–40, and a part of the acts of 1840–41."—Pref. to the 2d ed.
This edition attributed, in ms. note on t.-p., to George Wythe Munford.
1. Law—Virginia—Digests. I. Munford, George Wythe, 1803–1882. II. Virginia. Laws, statutes, etc.

35–24007

Library of Congress

NT   0049788   DLC NcD ViU-L

345.12   **Tate, Joseph**
V81s   Digest of the laws of Virginia, which
1841   are of a permanent character and general operation; illustrated by judicial decisions: to which is added, an index of the names of the cases in the Virginia reporters. By Joseph Tate. 2d ed. Richmond, 1841.
933p.

NT   0049789   IU PU-L

Tate, Joseph, ed.

U. S. *Circuit court (4th circuit)*
The opinion of Chief Justice Marshall, in the case of Garnett, ex'r of Brooke v. Macon et al. Published by Joseph Tate ... Richmond, Printed by Shepherd & Pollard, 1825.

Law

Tate, Joseph, ed.

Virginia. *Supreme court of appeals.*
Reports of cases argued and adjudged in the Court of appeals
of Virginia. ₁June term–Nov. term, 1790; Apr. term, 1797–
May term, 1803₎ By Daniel Call ... 2d ed. To which are
added, notes referring to subsequent adjudications of the same
court, and other authorities, and a complete table of cases cited.
By Joseph Tate ... Richmond, P. Cottom, 1824.

JK32
O1

Tate, Joseph *of Plainfield, N.J.*
Fine American paintings, including examples
by George H. Durrie, Ralph Blakelock, Thomas
Moran, George Inness and many other noted XIX
century artists. The collection of the late
Joseph Tate, Esq., of Plainfield N.J. With
additions ... To be sold at public auction
Thursday evening, November 2nd, 1933 ...
C.H. Seavey, auctioneer. [New York, 1933?]
pamphlet
At head of cover-title: The New England
galleries ... New York city.

NT   0049792   CtY

Tate, Joseph A
Essay on dysentery.   1816.

Ms.

NT   0049793   PU

Tate, Leland Burdine, 1905–   ed.

Conner, Maynard Calvin.
... An economic and social survey of Patrick county, by
Maynard Calvin Conner and William K. Bing; a laboratory
research study in the School of rural social economics of the
University of Virginia. ₁Charlottesville₎ University of Vir-
ginia, 1937.

Tate, Leland Burdine, 1905–
... An economic and social survey of Russell county, by
Leland-Burdine Tate; a laboratory study in the School of rural
social economics of the University of Virginia. ₁Charlottes-
ville₎ University of Virginia, 1931.
126 p. front. (map) plates. 23ᶜᵐ. (University of Virginia record.
Extension series. vol. XVI, no. 1)
"Sixteenth in the series of Virginia county surveys."
"History of Russell county, by Daniel Trigg": p. ₁9₎–28.

1. Russell co., Va.—Econ. condit. 2. Social surveys.   I. Trigg,
Daniel, 1877–   31—27895
Library of Congress   HC107.V82R86
——— Copy 2.   HC107.V8V8   no. 16
                         ₁aCaH₎   [309.1755755] 330.9755755

NT   0049795   DLC PU OCU OC1 ViU NN DHEW

Tate, Leland Burdine, 1905–
... The health and medical-care situation in rural Virginia,
by Leland B. Tate. Blacksburg, Va., 1944.
51 p. incl. illus., maps, tables. 23ᶜᵐ. (Virginia. Agricultural experiment station, Blacksburg. Bulletin 363)
"Some medical needs in Virginia, as seen by Dr. Louis Reed": p. 47–49.
"Recommendations of the Virginia sponsoring committee for research
on rural health and medical care": p. 49–51.
Bibliographical foot-notes.

1. Hygiene, Rural. 2. Medical economics.   I. Reed, Louis Schultz,
1902–   II. Virginia rural health and medical care committee. III.
Title.
                                                A 45–107
Va. poly. inst. Library
for Library of Congress   [S123.E2   no. 363]
                                              (630.72)

NT   0049796   ViBlbV ViU

Tate, Leland Burdine, 1905–
... Lebanon: a Virginia community, by Leland B. Tate.
Blacksburg, Va., 1943.
55 p. incl. illus., maps, tables. 23ᶜᵐ. (Virginia. Agricultural experi-
ment station, Blacksburg. Bulletin 352)
Bibliographical foot-notes.

1. Lebanon, Va.—Soc. condit.   A 43–2254
Va. poly. inst. Library
for Library of Congress   [S123.E2   no. 352]
                                    ₃₎   (630.72)

NT   0049797   ViBlbV

Tate, Leland Burdine, 1905–   comp.
Rural fiction and biography; a descriptive list
of ninety books.   University of Virginia, 1937.
7 l.
Mimeographed.

NT   0049798   ViU

Tate, Leland Burdine, 1905–
The rural homes of city workers and the urban-rural migra-
tion ... by Leland B. Tate. ₁Ithaca, N. Y.₎ 1934.
cover-title, 53 p. illus. (incl. maps) diagrs. 22ᶜᵐ.
Thesis (PH. D.)—Cornell university, 1934.
Cornell university, Agricultural experiment station, Bulletin 595, with
cover having thesis note.
A survey of Monroe county, New York.
Bibliography: p. 49–50.

1. Monroe co., N. Y. 2. Sociology, Rural. 3. Social surveys. 4. Cost
and standard of living—Monroe co., N. Y.   I. Title.

                                                35–16564
Library of Congress   HT153.T3   1934
                            ₃₎   309.174788

NT   0049799   DLC NIC PU PPD NcD OU ViU

Tate, Leland Burdine, 1905–   , ed.
The South's health: a picture with promise...
see under   U.S. Congress. House.
Committee on Agriculture.

---

*
HB935
.V8T3
1930

Tate, Leland Burdine, 1905–
A summary of regional population trends
in Virginia since 1870. ₁n. p., 193–?₎
3, ₁2₎ l.   28cm.
Mimeographed copy.
Caption title.

1. Virginia—Statistics, Vital. 2. Population—Va.
I. Title: Regional population trends in Virginia
since 1870.

NT   0049801   ViU

Tate, Leland Burdine, 1905–
The Virginia guide; a manual of information about Virginia
... compiled, published and copyrighted ... by Leland B. Tate.
Lebanon, Va., 1929.
189 p. front., illus. (maps) plates. 23½ᶜᵐ.
Contains advertising matter.

1. Virginia—Descr. & trav.—Guide-books.   I. Title.

                                                29–10235
Library of Congress   F231.T22

NT   0049802   DLC ViU

Tate, Lou.
Cape Breton coverlet patterns, Florence Mackley
collection. ₁Louisville, Ky., Little Loomhouse,
1952₎
₁38₎ p.

NT   0049803   Wa

Tate, Lou.
Exhibition catalog: Contemporary American
handwoven textiles
see   Contemporary American handwoven
textiles exhibition.

₁Tate, Lou, dir.₎
Little loomhouse country fair. Contemporary
American handwoven textiles 7th season, 1945–
1946. ₁1946₎
80 p. illus. diagrs. 28cm.

NT   0049805   OOxM

Tate, Lou.
Kentucky coverlets, by Lou Tate. ₁Louisville, Commercial
litho co., *1938₎
33, ₁2₎ p. illus. (incl. facsims.)   27½ᶜᵐ.

1. Coverlets.   I. Title.
                                                39–4007 Revised
Library of Congress   TT835.T3
                            ₁r41d2₎   746

OCU TU PPPTe
NT   0049806   DLC WaT WaE Or WaS InU NcRS OC1 OC1MA

Tate, Lou.
The little loomhouse.   [Louisville, Ky., 1949]
v. p.   illus., ports., plans.
cover-title.

NT   0049807   OC1 WaS

TT 848
.T216

TATE, LOU
Some historic Kentucky coverlets. ₁Louisville, Ky., 19— ₎
₁33₎ p. (chiefly illus.)

1. Hand weaving. 2. Coverlets.   I. Title.

NT   0049808   InU

[Tate, Lou]
Some historic Kentucky coverlets.   Louisville
14, Little loomhouse [1954?]
unpaged, illus.

NT   0049809   Or

Tate, Lou.
Weaving at the little loomhouse, by Lou Tate. ₁Louisville,
Ky., *1940₎
35 p. illus. 27½ᶜᵐ.

1. Weaving.   S 41–60
Smithsonian inst. Library
for Library of Congress   ₃₎

OEac NN OC1h TU WaT
NT   0049810   DSI WaS Or WaE Wa InU PPD PSt NcRS OC1

Tate, Lou.
Weaving is fun ₁by₎ Lou Tate. ₁Louisville, Ky.₎ 1946.
cover-title, 64 (i. e. 66) p. illus., diagrs. 28 x 21½ᶜᵐ.
Index on p. ₁3₎ of cover.
Instruction manual for the Little loomhouse group's program "Weav-
ing is fun." cf. p. ₁2₎ of cover.

1. Weaving.   I. Little loomhouse group.   II. Title.

TT848.T3   745.52   47–30002

NcGU NcRS OrP WaS WaT Wa
NT   0049811   DLC CaBViP CaBVa PP PPD PSt OC1 TxU Or

Tate, Louisa S.
 The child's cookery book.   London : Alexander Moring Ltd.
₁190–?₁   141 p.   12°.

1. Cooking. 2. Title.
N. Y. P. L.   March 18, 1912.

NT   0049812   NN OC1

Tate, Louisa S.   **Z.5of 11.1**
 The child's cookery book.
— London. Alexander Moring, Ltd. [1913.] 141 pp. 17 cm., in 8s.

K2725 — T.r. — Cookery. Children's cookery books.

NT   0049813   MB

Tate, Lucius Eugene, 1879–
 History of Pickens county, by Luke E. Tate. Atlanta, Ga.,
Press of W. W. Brown publishing company ₁°1935₁
 1 p. l., 5–322 p. illus. 24ᶜᵐ.
 "Family accounts": p. 291–308.
 "Errata" slip mounted on lining-paper.

1. Pickens co., Ga.—Hist. 2. Pickens co., Ga.—Geneal.

Library of Congress   F292.P57T3   36–4808
— — — Copy 2.
Copyright A 90332   ₁3₁   975.8

NT   0049814   DLC PHi NcD ViU ICN

Tate, Luke E.

see

Tate, Lucius Eugene, 1879–

Tate (Magnus A.) [1868–   ]. Rupture of the
uterus. 9 pp. 8°. *Cincinnati*, 1894.
 Repr. from: Cincin. Lancet-Clinic, 1894, xxxii.

NT   0049816   DNLM

TG350
.M66   Tate, Manford Ben, joint author.

Moorman, Robert Burrus Buckner, 1904–
 Influence lines for horizontally curved fixed-end beams of
circular-arc plan, by Robert B. B. Moorman and Manford
B. Tate. Columbia, 1947.

Tate, Manford Ben.
 Shear lag in tension panels and box beams. ₁Ames₁ Iowa
State College, 1949 ₁i. e. 1950₁
 v, 189 p. illus. 23 cm. (Iowa Engineering Experiment Station,
Iowa State College. Engineering report no. 3)
 The Iowa State College bulletin, v. 49, no. 7.
 Thesis—Iowa State College of Agriculture and Mechanic Arts.
 Bibliography: p. 82–85.

1. Monocoque construction. 2. Shear (Mechanics)   I. Title.
(Series: Iowa. State College of Agriculture and Mechanic Arts,
Ames. Engineering Experiment Station. Engineering report no. 3)

TA7.I 83   no. 3   624.171   A 51–9108
Iowa. State Coll. Libr.
for Library of Congress   ₁2₁†

NT   0049818   IaAS ViU DI MsU NBPol PP PU-Sc UU DLC

Tate, Marguerite (Gaylord) 1898–
 Twelve walked away. ₁1st ed.₁ New York, Harcourt,
Brace ₁1948₁
 150 p. map. 21 cm.

1. Aeronautics—Accidents.   I. Title.

TL553.5.T3   629.13255   48–6110*

    DSI CU Or OrCS OrP WaS WaSp WaT WaE
NT   0049819   DLC CaBVa CaBViP NN MiU PU-PSW PPAN PSt

Tate, Mavis Constance (Hogg)
 … Equal work deserves equal pay! By Mavis Tate, M. P.,
on behalf of the Equal pay campaign committee. ₁London,
The Equal pay campaign committee, 1945₁
 11, ₁1₁ p. illus. 21½ᶜᵐ.

1. Wages. 2. Woman—Employment.   I. Equal pay campaign committee. II. Title.

Library of Congress   HD6061.T3   45–18929
                  ₁3₁   331.42

NT   0049820   DLC

Tate, Merle Wesley.
 Statistics in education. New York, Macmillan ₁1955₁
 597 p. illus. 22 cm.

1. Education—Stat.

LB2846.T3   371.2   55–2723 ‡

    MtU OrCS OrLgE OrMonO OrPS WaS IdPI IdU
    ViU OOxM PU PP PWcS TU TxU NcRS OCU NcD MB FTaSU
NT   0049821   DLC OrU NNCU-G KU OC1W CaBVaU KEmT WaU

Tate, Merle Wesley.
 Individual differences in speed of response in
mental test materials of varying degrees of
difficulty.

 Thesis - Harvard, 1947.

NT   0049822   MH

Tate, Merze, 1905–
 The disarmament illusion; the movement for a limitation
of armaments to 1907, by Merze Tate … New York, The
Macmillan company, 1942.
 xiv, 398 p. 21 cm.
 Half-title: Bureau of international research, Harvard university
and Radcliffe college.
 "First printing."
 Bibliography: p. ₁363₁–378.

1. Disarmament.   I. Bureau of international research of Harvard
university and Radcliffe college.

JX1974.T3   341.6   42—17792

    MH-PA NNUN OO OCU OC1 OC1W ViU PSt PHC PPT PU
NT   0049823   DLC WaS OrP OrU Or WaSpG OrCS MtU AAP O

Tate, Merze
 The movement for a limitation of armaments to
1907
 Thesis - Radcliffe, 1941

NT   0049824   MH

Tate, Merze, ed.
 Trust and non-self-governing territories;
Papers and proceedings of the tenth annual con-
ference …
    see under Howard University, Washington,
D. C. Graduate School. Division of the
Social Sciences.

Tate, Merze.
 The United States and armaments. Cambridge, Harvard
Univ. Press, 1948.
 xii, 312 p. 24 cm.
 "Much of the material of Part I … is in ₁the author's₁ The disarma-
ment illusion."
 "Short titles used in footnotes": p. ₁275₁–27₈. "Selective bibliogra-
phy": p. 278–286.

1. Disarmament. 2. U. S.—Defenses.   I. Title.

JX1974.T32   341.6   48–5607*

             ₁3₁

    TxU PPT PSC PHC PBL PPD NcGU NWM MH-PA DSI MsU WaT
NT   0049826   DLC MH MtU OrP Or MB OrU WaS ICU ViU MiU

TX167
.H28   Tate, Mildred Bertha (Thurow) 1905–   joint
1946   author.   FOR OTHER EDITIONS
                              SEE MAIN ENTRY
Harris, Jessie Wootten, 1888–
 Everyday living ₁by₁ Jessie W. Harris … Mildred T. Tate …
₁and₁ Ida A. Anders … edited by Alice F. Blood … Boston,
New York ₁etc.₁ Houghton Mifflin company ₁1946₁

412.7   Tate, Murphy O.
T18   Deer farming. 1st ed., 1934... Chicago,
    Ill., Moose lake fur and animal farm, 1934.
    16 p. illus. 23cm.

NT   0049828   DNAL

Tr.R.   Tate, Nahum, 1652–1715.

     The ingratitude of a common-wealth; or,
    The fall of Caius Martius Coriolanus, as it
    is acted at the Theatre-Royal … London,
    Printed by T. M. for Joseph Hindmarsh, 1682.
    64 p. 21cm.

NT   0049829   NcD

FILM   Tate, Nahum, 1652–1715.
800   The ingratitude of a common-wealth; or,
no.49   the fall of Caius Martius Coriolanus, as
    it was acted at the Theatre-Royal. London,
    J. Hindmarsh, 1682.
    1r.

    Microfilm copy of original in the Library
    of the University of California at Los
    Angeles. Positive.

NT   0049830   CLSU ViU

Tate, Nahum, 1652–1715.
    The ingratitude of a common-wealth; of, The
    fall of Caius Martius Coriolanus. As it is acted
    at the theatre-royal. London, Printed by L.M.
    for Joseph Hindmarsh, 1682.
    55p. facsim. 25cm.

    Reprint ₁1929?₁
    "This edition is limited to twenty-five copies,
    numbered and signed, of which this is no.6
    ₁Signed₁ Horace Howard Furness Jr."
    Letter to S.A. Tannenbaum, signed H.H. Furness
    tipped inside back cover.
    I. Title.

NT   0049831   NcU NjP

Microfilm   Tate, A
1630   The ingratitude of a common-wealth or, The
    fall of Caius Martius Coriolanus as it is
    acted at the Theatre-Royal. London, Joseph
    Hindmarsh, 1683.
    64 p.
    A play.
    Microfilm. N.p., University of California,
    n.d. 1 reel. 35mm.

NT   0049832   CoU

Rare
PR
3729
T19
058+
1685

Tate, Nahum, 1652-1715.
On the sacred memory of our late sovereign: with a congratulation to His present Majesty. 2d ed. London, Printed by J. Playford for H. Playford, 1685.
6 p. 29cm.

NT 0049833 NIC

Tate, Nahum, 1652-1715.
Church of England. Book of common prayer.
Abridgement of the Book of common prayer, and administration of the sacraments, and other rites and ceremonies of the church, according to the use of the Church of England: together with the Psalter, or Psalms of David, pointed as they are to be sung or said in churches. London: Printed in the year MDCCLXXIII.

DA452
.W72
Rare Bk
Coll

Tate, Nahum, 1652-1715, tr.
Wright, John Michael, 1625?-1700.
An account of His Excellence Roger, earl of Castlemaine's embassy, from His Sacred Majesty James the IId., king of England, Scotland, France, and Ireland. &c., to His Holiness Innocent XI. Published formerly in the Italian tongue, by Mr. Michael Wright ... And now made English, with several amendments, and additions ... London, Printed by T. Snowden for the author, 1688.

Tate, Nahum, 1652-1715, tr.

FOR OTHER EDITIONS
SEE MAIN ENTRY

Heliodorus, *of Emesa.*
Aethiopian adventures: or, The history of Theagenes and Chariclea. Written originally in Greek, by Heliodorus. In ten books. The first five tr. by a person of quality, the last five by N. Tate. To which are prefixed, the testimonies of writers, both ancient and modern, concerning this work. ¡London? Reprinted. 1753.

Tate, Nahum, 1652-1715, tr.

Heliodorus, *of Emesa.*
The Æthiopian history of Heliodorus. In ten books. The first five tr. by a person of quality, the last five by N. Tate. To which are prefixed, the testimonies of writers, both ancient and modern, concerning this work ... London, Printed by J. L. for E. Poole, 1686.

Tate, Nahum, 1652-1715.

Angling: a poem ... 2d ed. London, H. Slater ¡etc.¡ 1741.

Tate, Nahum, 1652-1715.
The anniversary ode for the fourth of December, 1697. His Majesty's birth-day. Another for new-year's-day, 1697-8. Both set to Musick, and perform'd at Kensington. First edition. London, for Richard Baldwin, 1698.
2 p.l., 7 p. small quarto. Bound in 3/4 black calf.

NT 0049839 CSmH

FILM
821
T18a

Tate, Nahum, 1652-1715.
The anniversary ode for the fourth of December 1697. His Majesty's birth-day. Another for New Year's-Day, 1698. Both set to musick, and perform'd at Kensington. London, Printed for R. Baldwin, 1698.
Microfilm copy (negative) made in 1962 of the original in the Huntington Library.
Collation of the original, as determined from

Continued in next column

Continued from preceding column

the film: ¡3¡ 7p.
The two poems have caption titles: The ode upon His Majesty's birth-day. Set to musick by Dr. Staggins and The ode for New Year's day, 1696. Set to musick by Dr. Blow, respectively. Without the music.

NT 0049841 IU

Tate, Nahum, 1652-1715.
An arrangement of the most suitable verses for singing, selected from each of the one hundred and fifty Psalms of the present authorized version of Tate and Brady ... Dublin, 1814
see under Bible. O.T. Psalms. English. Paraphrases. 1814. Tate and Brady.

Tate, Nahum, 1652-1715.
Church of England. Book of common prayer.
The Book of common prayer, and administration of the sacraments, and other rites and ceremonies of the Church, according to the use of the Church of England: together with the Psalter or Psalms of David, pointed as they are to be sung or said in churches. London, Printed by M. Ritchie, for J. Good and E. Harding, 1794.

---

*pEB65
T1878
706b

Tate, Nahum, 1652-1715.
Britannia's prayer for the Queen. By Mr. Tate, poet laureat to Her Majesty.
London:Printed for John Chantry,at the sign of Lincolns-Inn-square at Lincolns-Inn back-gate,1706. Price two pence.
2p. 35x20.5cm.
Caption title; imprint on p.2.
Narcissus Luttrell's copy, priced & dated in his autograph: 2d [&] 23. May. 1706.

NT 0049844 MH

FILM
x821
T18b

Tate, Nahum, 1652-1715.
Britannia's prayer for the Queen. ¡London, Printed for J. Chantry, 1706¡
Microfilm copy (negative) made in 1964 of the original in the British Museum Library.
Collation of the original, as determined from the film: ¡2¡p.
Caption title.

NT 0049845 IU

Tate, Nahum, 1652-1715.
Brutus of Alba: or, The enchanted lovers. A tragedy. Acted at the Duke's theatre. Written by N. Tate ... Licensed July 15. 1678. Roger L'Estrange. London, Printed by E. F. for Jacob Tonson, at the sign of the Judge's head ¡in Chancery-lane, near Fleet-street. 1678¡
4 p. L, 56, ¡1¡ p. 22cm.
¡Longe, F. Collection of plays. v. 113, no. 7¡
Imperfect: part of imprint trimmed away; imprint taken from Hoe's Catalogue of Early English books; Catalogue of library of J. H. Wrenn. v. 5, p. 2.
¡ Title 26—2237
Library of Congress PR1241.L6 vol. 113

NT 0049846 DLC MH MiU PU CtY CSmH OU NjP ICN TxU

FILM
P-666

Tate, Nahum, 1652-1715.
Brutus of Alba; or, The enchanted lovers. ¡London¡ E. F. for J. Tonson, 1678.
Microfilm copy from TxU.
Woodward & McManaway No. 1194.

I. Title. II. Title:The enchanted lovers.

NT 0049847 ViU

Tate, Nahum, 1652-1715.
Characters of vertue and vice
see under Hall, Joseph, bp. of Norwich, 1574-1656.

Tate, Nahum, 1652-1715.
Comitia lyrica: sive Carmen panegyricum
see under [Maidwell, Lewis] 1649 or 50-1716.

---

*fEC65
T1878
714c

Tate, Nahum, 1652-1715.
A congratulatory poem, on Her Majesties happy recovery, and return to meet her Parliament. By Mr. Tate, poet-laureat to Her Majesty.
London:Printed for James Holland,at the Bible and Ball in St Paul's church-yard;and sold by John Morphew,near Stationers-hall 1714.
1p.ℓ.,10p. 31.5cm.
Title vignette.

NT 0049850 MH CtY TxU

Wj
T188
+701c

TATE, NAHUM, 1652-1715.
A congratulatory poem on the new parliament assembled on this great conjuncture of affairs. By N. Tate ...
London:Printed for W.Rogers,at the Sun against St.Dunstan's Church in Fleetstreet, 1701. 12p. 32cm.

NT 0049851 TxU CLU-C CSmH CtY MB MH NcU

FILM
821
T18con

Tate, Nahum, 1652-1715.
A congratulatory poem on the new Parliament assembled on this great conjuncture of affairs. London, Printed for W. Rogers, 1701.
Microfilm copy (negative) made in 1963 of the original in the University of Texas Library.
Collation of original, as determined from the film: 12p.

NT 0049852 IU

R.B.R.
no.2

Tate, Nahum, 1652-1715.
A Congratulatory poem to his Royal Highness Prince George of Denmark, Lord High Admiral of Great Britain, upon the glorious successes at sea. To which is added a happy memorable song, on the fight near Audenarde, between the Duke of Marlborough and Vendome, etc. London, Printed by H. Hills, 1708.
16 p. 18 cm.
No. [2] in a collection of pamphlets.
1. George, Prince of Denmark, 1653-1708, 2. Marlborough, John Churchill, 1st duke of, 1650-1722. I. Title.

NT 0049853 TxHU ViU DFo CLU-C CtY NjR PU NcD IU ICN MH NIC ViW WU NjP PU CU IEN

PR
3729
.T115
C7

Tate,Nahum,1652-1715.
A congratulary poem to His Royal Highness Prince George of Denmark,Lord High Admiral of Great Britain. Upon the glorious successes at sea. By N.Tate ... London, Printed by H.Meere, for J.B.and sold by R.Burrough and J.Baker, 1708. 18 (i.e.20) p. 23 cm.
Numbers 17-18 repeated in pagination.
1.George,Prince of Denmark,Consort of Queen Anne,1653-1708-- Poetry. I.Title.

NT 0049854 MiU InU

Aj
T183
706c

Tate, Nahum, 1652–1715.
    A congratulatory poem, to the Right Honourable
Richard earl Rivers, upon his lordship's expedi-
tion. Written by Mr.Tate poet-laureat to Her
Majesty.
    London,Printed and Sold by B.Bragge,at the
Raven in Pater-Noster-Row.1706. 8p. 24cm.

NT 0049855   TxU

Tate, Nahum, 1652–1715.
    A consolatory poem to the Right Honourable
John Lord Cutts, upon the death of his most
accomplish'd lady. By N. Tate, servant to
His Majesty ... London: Printed by R. R.
for Henry Playford ... 1698.
    1 p.l.,9 p. 31½cm. [Miscellaneous poems
and tracts. London, 1681-1704. v.2, no.44]

    First edition.
    Signatures: A-C².

NT 0049856   CLU-C CSmH CtY MH NjP TxU

---

*fEC65
T1878
698cb

Tate, Nahum, 1652–1715.
    A consolatory poem to the Right Honourable
John lord Cutts, upon the death of his most
accomplish'd lady. By N. Tate, servant to His
Majesty ... The second edition.
    London:Printed by R.R.for Henry Playford in
the Temple-Change.MDCXCVIII.

    1p.l.,9p. 32cm.

NT 0049857   MH

FILM
821
T18co
1698a

Tate, Nahum, 1652–1715.
    A consolatory poem to the Right Honourable
John Lord Cutts, upon the death of his most
accomplish'd lady. 2d ed.   London, Printed
by R. R. for H. Playford, 1698.

    Microfilm copy (negative) made in 1962 of the
original in Harvard University Library.

    1. Cutts, Elizabeth (Pickering) baroness,
d.1697—Poetry.

NT 0049858   IU

Tate, Nahum, 1652–1715.
    Cuckolds-Haven: or, An alderman no conjurer. A
farce. Acted at the Queen's theatre in Dorset Garden.
By N. Tate. London, Printed for J. H. and are to be
sold by Edward Poole, next door to the Fleece Tavern
in Cornhill. 1685.
    5 p. l., 45, ₍2₎ p. 21½ᵐᵐ.
    Adapted from Chapman's, Marston's, and Jonson's "Eastward hoe" and
Jonson's "The devil is an ass".
    I. Chapman, George, 1559?–1634. II. Jonson, Ben, 1573?–1637. III. Title.
                                                          26–2238
    Library of Congress   PR3729.T115C8   1685
    ———— Copy 2.   22ᵐᵐ.   ₍Longe, F. Collection of plays.
    v.113, no.3₎   PR1241.L6 vol.113

    MiU
NT 0049859   DLC PU MWiW-C CtY PBL NjP MH CSmH TxU

FILM
P-667

Tate, Nahum, 1652–1715.

    Cuckolds-haven; or, An alderman no conjurer.
₍London₎ J. H., sold by E. Poole, 1685.

    Microfilm copy from TxU.
    Woodward & McManaway No. 1195.

    I. Title. II. Title:An alderman no conjurer.

NT 0049860   ViU

M1503
.P994D555
1925

Tate, Nahum, 1652–1715. Dido and Aeneas.

Purcell, Henry, 1658 or 9–1695.
    ₍Dido and Aeneas. Piano-vocal score. English & German₎

    Dido and Aeneas; an opera. Newly edited by Edward
J. Dent. ₍Vocal score₎ London, Oxford University Press
₍¹1925₎

M1500
.P98D5
1942
Case

Tate, Nahum, 1652–1715. Dido and Aeneas.

Purcell, Henry, 1658 or 9–1695.
    ₍Dido and Aeneas. English₎

    ... Dido and Aeneas, an opera. Score. New York, Broude
bros. ₍1942?₎

Tate, Nahum, 1652–1715.   FOR OTHER EDITIONS
                                SEE MAIN ENTRY

₍Cokayne, Sir Aston, bart.₎ 1608–1684.
    A duke and no duke. A farce. As it is acted by Their
Majesties servants. Written by N. Tate. With several
songs set to music, with thorow basses for the theorbo, or
basse viol. London, H. Bonwicke, 1685.

Tate, Nahum, 1652–1715.
    Duke and no duke
Cokayne, Sir Aston, bart., 1608–1684.
    The devil of a duke: or, Trapolin's vagaries. A (far-
cical ballad) opera, as it is acted at the Theatre-Royal
in Drury-Lane. To which is prefix'd the musick to each
song ... 2d ed. London, C. Corbett ₍etc.₎ 1732.

Tate, Nahum, 1652–1715.
    Elegies on I. Her Late Majesty of blessed memory.
II. Late Arch-Bishop of Canterbury. III. Illustrious Duke of Ormond and Earl of Ossory. IV.
Countess of Dorset. V. Consolatory poem, &c. Together with A poem on the promotion of several
eminent persons, &c. By N. Tate ... London:
Printed for J. Wild ... 1699.
    4 p.l.,125 p. 18ᵐ.

    First edition.
    Signatures: A⁴,   B-I⁸, (B₂, E₅ incorrectl₎

signed A₂, E₅, respectively; I₈, advertisements)
    Page 32 incorrectly numbered 23.
    Title within double line border.
    Each poem, except the first, has special t.-p.
    Armorial book-plate of Robert, lord viscount
Tamworth; armorial book-plate, unidentified.
    Bound in old paneled calf.
    Cf. A catalogue of the library of ... John Henry
Wrenn. Austin, Tex. 1920. v.5, p.5-6.
                                        CtU-C

NT 0049866   CLU-C MB CtY CSmH ICN TxU MH NjP

FILM
821
T18e2h

Tate, Nahum, 1652–1715.
    Elegies on I. Her late Majesty of blessed
memory. II. Late Arch-bishop of Canterbury.
III. Illustrious Duke of Ormond and Earl of
Ossory. IV. Countess of Dorset. V. Consolatory poem, &c. Together with a poem, on
the promotion of several eminent person, &c.
London, Printed for J. Wild, 1699.

    Microfilm copy (negative) made in 1962 of the

original in Harvard University Library.
    Collation of the original, as determined from
the film: ₍7₎, 125p.
    Each work, except the first has special t.p.,
with no imprint.
    Published in 1700 with title: Funeral poems.

NT 0049868   IU

Tate, Nahum, 1652–1715.
    An elegy in memory of the much esteemed and
truly worthy Ralph Marshall, esq; one of His
Majesty's Justices of peace, &c. By N. Tate,
servant to His Majesty ... London: Printed
by R. Roberts for the author. 1700.
    2 p.l.,8 p. 31½ᵐ. [Miscellaneous poems
and tracts. London, 1681-1704. v.2, no.49]

    First edition.
    Signatures: ₍A₎-C².
    Cf. A catalogue   of the library of ...
John Henry Wrenn.   Austin, Tex., 1920.
v.5, p.6.

NT 0049869   CLU-C CSmH TxU

FILM
821
T18eℓ

Tate, Nahum, 1652–1715.
    An elegy in memory of the much esteemed and
truly worthy Ralph Marshall, Esq; one of His
Majesty's justices of peace, &c.   London:
Printed by R. Roberts for the author, 1700.

    Microfilm copy (negative) made in 1962 of the
original in the Huntington Library.
    Collation of the original, as determined from
the film: ₍3₎, 8p.

    1. Marshall, Ralph, d.1700?

NT 0049870   IU

Rare Book
Room
Ij
T186
+695E

[Tate, Nahum] 1652–1715.
    An elegy on His Grace John Lord Arch-
bishop of Canterbury. A pindaric. London
Printed.And are to be sold by John Whitlock near Stationers-Hall,1695.Price 3 d.
    8p. 33cm.
    Signatures: A-B².

NT 0049871   CtY InU MiU

FILM
821
T18e

₍Tate, Nahum₎ 1652–1715.
    An elegy on His Grace John Lord Archbishop of
Canterbury. A Pindaric.   London, Printed, and
are to be sold by J. Whitlock, 1695.

    Microfilm copy (negative) made in 1962 of the
original in the University of Michigan Library.
    Collation of the original as determined from
the film: 8p.

    1. Tillotson, John, Abp. of Canterbury, 1630–
1694—Poetry. I. Title.

NT 0049872   IU

Tate, N₍ahum₎, 1652-1715.   15485.34.8.5*
    An elegy on John, late lord archbishop of Canterbury. London,
printed for B. Aylmer and W. Rogers, 1695.
    f°. pp. (4), 11.

NT 0049873   MH CtY CSmH TxU

[Tate, Nahum] 1652–1715, supposed author.
    An epistle to Charles, earl of Dorset and
Middlesex
        see under   Halifax, Charles Montagu,
Earl of, 1661–1715.

Tate, Nahum, 1652–1715.
    An elegy on the Most Reverend Father in God,
His Grace, John, late lord archbishop of Canter-
bury. By N. Tate ... London: Printed for B.
Aylmor ... and W. Rogers ... 1695.
    2 p.l.,11 p. 28½ᵐ.

    First edition.
    Signatures: ₍A₎-D².
    Title within heavy line border.
    Unbound, in cloth case; a few upper margins

closely trimmed.
    Cf. Grolier club, New York. Catalogue of
original and early editions of some ... English
writers from Wither to Prior. New York, 1905.
v.3, p.113-114.

NT 0049876   CLU-C TxDaM-P ICN InU TxU OU NjP MH

FILM 821 T18e2e
Tate, Nahum, 1652-1715.
An elegy on the Most Reverend Father in God, His Grace, John, late Lord Archbishop of Canterbury. London, Printed for B. Aylmer, 1695.

Microfilm copy (negative) made in 1962 of the original in Harvard University Library.
Collation of original, as determined from the film: ₄₄₎, 11p.

NT 0049877   IU

Tate, Nahum, 1652-1715.
An epistolary poem to N. Tate
    see under   Pittis, William, 1674-1724.

₍Tate, Nahum₎ 1652-1715.
An essay for promoting of psalmody. London. Printed for J. Holland, 1710.
5 p. l., 38 p. 16½ᵐ.
Dedication signed: N. Tate.

1. Music in churches. 2. Bible. O. T. Psalms—Paraphrases. 3. Bible—Paraphrases—O. T. Psalms. 4. Psalmody. ɪ. Title.

8—33176

Library of Congress   ML3001.T16

NT 0049879   DLC CtHT MB CtY-Mus

FILM x264.2 T187e
₍Tate, Nahum₎ 1652-1715.
An essay for promoting of psalmody. London, Printed for J. Holland, 1710.
Microfilm copy (negative) made in 1964 of the original in the Library of Congress.
Collation of the original as determined from the film: ₄10₎, 38p.
Dedication signed: N. Tate.
Original closely trimmed with loss of part of imprint.

NT 0049880   IU

Tate, Nahum, 1652-1715.
An essay of a character of the Right Honourable Sir George Treby kt., lord chief justice of His Majesty's court of Common-pleas. Address'd to the learned Dr. Fowke: By N. Tate ... [London, R. Roberts, 1699]
4 p. 28 cm.
Caption title.

NT 0049881   CtY MH

FILM 821 T18es
Tate, Nahum, 1652-1715.
An essay of a character of the Right Honourable Sir George Treby kt lord chief justice of His Majesty's Court of Common-Pleas. Address'd to the learned Dr. Fowke. ₍London, Printed for R. Roberts, 1699₎
Microfilm copy (negative) made in 1962 of the original in Harvard University Library.
Collation of the original, as determined from the film: 4p.

Caption title.
Verse.

1. Treby, Sir George, 1644?-1700--Poetry.

NT 0049883   IU

T187.2
Tate, Nahum, 1652-1715.
An essay of a character of the late right honourable Sir George Treby Kt. lord chief justice of his majesty's Court of common-pleas ...
Colophon: London, Printed by R. Roberts, and sold by A. Baldwin, 1700.

Single folio leaf.

NT 0049884   DFo CLU-C

Tate, Nahum, 1652-1715.
An essay of a new version of the Psalms of David... London, 1695
    see under   Bible. O. T. Psalms. English. Paraphrases. 1695. Tate and Brady.

Tate, Nahum, 1652-1715.
An essay upon poetry ...
    see under   Buckingham, John Sheffield, 1st duke of, 1648-1721.

Tate, Nahum, 1652-1715, ed.
The four epistles of A.G. Busbequius, concerning his embassy into Turkey
    see under   Busbecq, Ogier Ghislain de, 1522-1592.

Tate, Nahum, 1652-1715.
Funeral poems on I. Her late Majesty of blessed memory. II. Late Arch-bishop of Canterbury. III. Illustrious Duke of Ormond and Earl of Ossory. IV. Countess of Dorset. V. Consolatory poem, &c. Together with a poem on the promotion of several eminent persons, &c. By N. Tate ... London: Printed by J. Gardyner, and sold by J. Nutt ... 1700.
4 p.l.,125 p. 18½ᶜᵐ.

A reissue, with cancel title-page, of the first edition, published (1699) under title: Elegies ...
Signatures: A⁴, B-I⁸ (A₁, title-page, cancel; B₂, E₃ incorrectly signed A₂, E₅, respectively; I₈, advertisements)
Page 32 incorrectly numbered 23.
Title within double line border.
Each poem, except the first, has special title-page.
Bound in old ₌calf.

NT 0049889   CLU-C MH

FILM 821 T18e2h 1700
Tate, Nahum, 1652-1715.
Funeral poems on I. Her late Majesty of blessed memory. II. Late Arch-bishop of Canterbury. III. Illustrious Duke of Ormond and Earl of Ossory. IV. Countess of Dorset. V. Consolatory poem, &c. Together with a poem on the promotion of several eminent persons, &c. London, Printed by J. Gardyner, and sold by J. Nutt, 1700.
Microfilm copy (negative) made in 1962 of the original in Harvard University Library.
Collation of the original, as determined from the film: ₄7₎, 125p.
Each work except the first has special t.p. with no imprint.
Published in 1699 with title: Elegies.

NT 0049891   IU

Tate, Nahum, 1652-1715.   FOR OTHER EDITIONS SEE MAIN ENTRY
₍Shakespeare, William₎ 1564-1616.
The history of King Lear, a tragedy. As it is now acted at the Theatres Royal in Drury-Lane and Covent-Garden. Revived, with alterations, by N. Tate, esq London, F. and J. Noble ₍etc.₎ 1771.

Tate, Nahum, 1652-1715
The history of King Lear
Shakespeare, William, 1564-1616.
Shakespeare adaptations: The tempest, The mock tempest, and King Lear. With an introduction and notes by Montague Summers. London, J. Cape. 1922

₍Shakespeare, William₎ 1564-1616.
The history of King Richard the Second, acted at the Theatre royal, under the name of the Sicilian usurper. With a prefatory epistle in vindication of the author. Occasion'd by the prohibition of this play on the state. By N. Tate ... London. Printed for R. Tonson and J. Tonson, 1681.

Tate, Nahum, 1652-1715.   charity-
An hymn to be sung by the children of the ^ parish St. Bride's ...
    see under title

Tate, Nahum, 1652-1715.
In memory of Joseph Washington, esq; late of the Middle Temple, an elegy. Written by N. Tate ... [London: Printed for Richard Baldwin ... 1694]
4 p. 29½ᵐ.
First edition.
Signature: A².
Caption title.
Unbound, in cloth case.

Cf. Grolier club, New York. Catalogue of original and early editions of some ... English writers from Wither to Prior. New York, 1905. v.3, p.113.

NT 0049897   CLU-C CSmH MH DFo CtY

FILM 821 T18i
Tate, Nahum, 1652-1715.
In memory of Joseph Washington, Esq; late of the Middle Temple, an elegy. ₍London, Printed for R. Baldwin, 1694₎
Microfilm copy (negative) made in 1962 of the original in Harvard University Library.
Collation of the original, as determined from the film: 4p.
Caption title.

NT 0049898   IU

Tate, Nahum, 1652-1715.
₍Shakespeare, William₎ 1564-1616.
The ingratitude of a common-wealth: or, The fall of Caius Martius Coriolanus. As it is acted at the Theatre-Royal. By N. Tate. ₍Three lines from Horace₎ London, Printed by T. M. for Joseph Hindmarsh, at the Black-Bull in Cornhill. 1682.

Tate, Nahum, 1652-1715.
₍Webster, John₎ 1580?-1625?
Injur'd love: or, The cruel husband. A tragedy. Design'd to be acted at the Theatre Royal. Written by Mr. N. Tate ... ₍London, R. Wellington, 1707₎

Tate, Nahum, 1652-1715, ed.
The innocent epicure: or, The art of angling. A poem ...
    see under title

Tate, Nahum, 1652-1715.
    The island-princess
        see under   Fletcher, John, 1579-1625.

Tate, Nahum, 1652-1715.
    Majestas imperij Britannici
        see under   Maidwell, Lewis, 1649 or 50-
1716.

Tate, Nahum, 1652-1715.
    A monumental poem in memory of the Right
Honourable Sir George Treby k^t. late lord chief
justice of His Majesty's Court of common-pleas:
consisting of his character and elegy. By N.
Tate ...   London, Printed for Jacob Tonson ...
1702.
    2 p.l.,12 p. 30½^cm.

    First edition.
    Signatures: 2 leaves unsigned, A-C^2.

    Pages 6-7 incorrectly numbered 2-3.
    Title within double line border.
    Folded portrait of Sir George Treby, engraved
by R. White, at front.
    Unbound, in cloth case.

NT 0049919   CLU-C CSmH MH

---

*fEC65   Tate, Nahum, 1652-1715.
T1878   The Kentish worthies. A poem, by Mr. Tate.
701k   Poet--laureat to His Majesty.
    London,Printed for A.Baldwin in Warwick-lane,
1701.
    4p. 31cm.
    Caption title; imprint on p.4.
    Narcissus Luttrell's copy, priced & dated in
his autograph: 1^d [&] l. Aug. 1701.

NT 0049903   MH TxU CLU-C

FILM   Tate, Nahum, 1652-1715.
821   The Kentish worthies. A poem. ₍London,
T18k   Printed for A. Baldwin, 1701₎

    Microfilm copy (negative) made in 1963 of
the original in the University of Texas Library.
    Caption title.
    Collation of original, as determined from the
film: 4p.

NT 0049904   IU

FILM   Tate, Nahum, 1652-1715.
x821   A monumental poem in memory of the Right
T18mo Honourable Sir George Treby k^t. late lord
    chief justice of His Majesty's Court of Com-
mon-Pleas; consisting of his character and
elegy.   London, Printed for J. Tonson, 1702.

    Microfilm copy (negative) made in 1964 of the
original in Harvard University Library.
    Collation of the original, as determined from
the film: 12p.

    The "Character" and the "Elegy" have caption
titles: An essay of a character of the Right
Honourable Sir George Treby k^t. and A panegyrical
elegy, pursuant to the fore-written Character.
In a dialogue between the poet and his muse,
respectively.

NT 0049921   IU

    Tate, Nahum, 1652-1715.   FOR OTHER EDITIONS SEE MAIN ENTRY
Shakespeare, William, 1564-1616.
    ... King Lear, a tragedy; altered from Shakspeare, by
Nahum Tate. With prefatory remarks ... Faithfully
marked with the stage business, and stage directions, as
it is performed at the Theatres Royal. By W. Oxberry,
comedian. London, Pub. for the Proprietors, by W.
Simpkin, and R. Marshall ₍etc.₎ 1820.

DC130   Tate, Nahum, 1652-1715, tr.
.C7C3
Rare Bk ₍Coste, Pierre₎ 1668-1747.
Coll   The life of Lewis of Bourbon, late prince of Conde. Di-
gested into annals. With many curious remarks on the trans-
actions of Europe for these last sixty years. Done out of
French. London, T. Goodwin, 1693.

Tate, Nahum, 1692-1715.
    The loves of Dido and Aeneas, an
opera ...
        see under   Purcell, Henry, 1658 or 9-
1695.

    Tate, Nahum, 1652-1715.
    The loyal general, a tragedy. Acted at the Duke's
theatre, written by N. Tate. London, Printed for Henry
Bonwicke, at the Red Lion in St. Paul's Church-yard.
1680.
    6 p. l., 59, ₍1₎ p. 22½^cm.
    ₍Longe, F. Collection of plays. v. 134, no. 1₎
    Prologue by Dryden.
    Pages 57-59 torn.

    I. Title.
                              26-2236

Library of Congress   PR1241.L6   vol. 134

NT 0049908   DLC OU TxU CtY MiU ICN CSmH MH NjP InU

FILM
P-666   Tate, Nahum, 1652-1715.

    The loyal general. ₍London₎ H. Bonwicke,
1680.

    Microfilm copy from TxU.
    Woodward & McManaway No. 1205.

NT 0049909   ViU PU

Tate, Nahum, 1652-1715.

    Mausolaeum: a funeral poem on our late
gracious sovereign Queen Mary of blessed
memory. By N. Tate, servant to His Majesty.
WILLIAM   London: Printed for B. Aylmer ... And W.
ANDREWS Rogers ... And R. Baldwin ... 1695.
CLARK   1 p.l.,19 p. front. 31½^cm.   [Miscellaneous
MEMORIAL poems and tracts. London, 1681-1704. v.2,
LIBRARY no.4]

    First edition.

    Signatures: ₍A₎-F^2 (₍A1₎ frontispiece; F2,
verso, advertisement)
    Title within heavy line border.
    Cf. A catalogue of the library of ... John
Henry Wrenn. Austin, Tex., 1920. v.5, p.5.

MWiW-C CSmH ViW MH
NT 0049912   CLU-C TxU FU NRU ICN OU InU NjP CtY DFo

FILM   Tate, Nahum, 1652-1715.
821   Mausolaeum: a funeral poem on our late
T18ma   gracious sovereign Queen Mary, of blessed
memory.   London, Printed for B. Aylmer,
1695.
    Microfilm copy (negative) made in 1962 of
the original in Harvard University Library.
    Collation of the original, as determined
from the film: ₍1₎, 19p. front.

NT 0049913   IU

AG104   Tate, Nahum, 1652-1715, ed.
.M4
Rare Bk.
Coll.   A memorial for the learned: or, Miscellany of choice
    collections from most eminent authors. In history, philos-
    ophy, physick, and heraldry. By J. D., Gent. London, G.
    Powell, 1686.

Tate, Nahum, 1652-1715,   comp.

    Miscellanea sacra: or, Poems on divine &
moral subjects. vol.I. Collected by N. Tate
...   London: Printed for Hen. Playford ...
MCIXCVI[i.e.1696]
    8 p.l.,140,₍4₎ p.,1 l.,12 p. front. 16½^cm.

    First edition.
    Signatures: A-L^8(L^8 wanting)
    Imperfect copy: half-title and 12 p. at end
(sig.L^8) wanting.

    Title within double line border.
    No more published.
    Bound in old black morocco, gold tooled,
gilt edges.
    Cf. Case, A.E. A bibliography of English
poetical miscellanies, 1521-1750. Oxford,
1935, p.145-146, no.207.

NT 0049916   CLU-C MH TxU NNUT ICN CSmH

Ex   Tate, Nahum, 1652-1715
3952   Miscellanea sacra; or, Poems on divine &
.89   moral subjects. 2d ed., with additions of
.364   several poems and meditations in prose.
    London, Printed for H. Playford, 1698
    12 p.l.,140,₍6₎,12 p. front. 17 cm

NT 0049917   NjP CtY CtY-D OU NNC MH ICN

IJ   Tate, Nahum, 1652-1715.
T186   The muse's bower, an epithalamium on the
713   auspicious nuptials of the Right Honourable
    the the [sic] Marquis of Caermarthen, with
the Lady Elizabeth Harley, daughter of the
Right Honourable Earl of Oxford and Mortimer,
lord high treasurer of Great Britain ...
London:Printed for the author,and sold by
J.Morphew,1713.
    15p. 21½cm.

NT 0049922   CtY ICN MH

FILM   Tate, Nahum, 1652-1715.
821   The muse's bower, an epithalamium on the aus-
T18mu picious nuptials of the Right Honourable the
    Marquis of Caermarthen, with the Lady Elizabeth
Harley, daughter of the Right Honourable Earl
of Oxford and Mortimer lord high treasurer of
Great Britain.   London, Printed for the author, and sold by J. Morphew, 1713.

    Microfilm copy (negative) made in 1963 of the

    original in the Newberry Library.
    Collation of the original, as determined from
the film: 15p.
    Original closely trimmed with loss of part
of title.

NT 0049924   IU

Tate, Nahum, 1652-1715.
    The muse's memorial of His Royal Highness, Prince George
of Denmark. Written by Mr. Tate ... London, 1708.
    2 p. l., ₍3₎-18 (i. e. 20) p. 23^cm.

    Signatures: 2 leaves unsigned; A-E^2.
    Error in paging; nos. 17-18 repeated.

    1. George, prince of Denmark, 1653-1708.   I. Title.
                              27-863

Library of Congress   PR3729.T115M8 1708

NT 0049925   DLC

Tate, Nahum, 1652-1715.
The muse's memorial of the happy recovery of
the Right Honourable Richard Earl of Burlington,
from a dangerous sickness, in the year 1706, a
congratulary poem. With an account of the present state of poetry. By N. Tate ... First edition.
London, for Tho. Osborne, and sold by B. Bragge,
1707.
24 p. ([A]-F in 2's) 4to. Brown paper
covers.

NT 0049926   CSmH

Tate, Nahum, 1652-1715.
The muse's memorial, of the Right Honourable
Earl of Oxford, lord high treasurer of Great
Britain. Written by Mr. Tate ... London:
Printed by E. Berington, and sold by J. Baker
... and B. Berington ... 1712.
16 p. 35ᵐ.

First edition.
Signatures: [A]-D².
Title within double line border.

Unbound, uncut, in blue cloth case.
Cf. A catalogue of the library of ... John
Henry Wrenn. Austin, Tex., 1920. v.5, p.9.

NT 0049928   CLU-C MH TxU

FILM   Tate, Nahum, 1652-1715.
821   The muse's memorial, of the Right Honourable
T18mum   Earl of Oxford, lord high treasurer of Great
         Britain.   London, Printed by E. Berington,
         and sold by J. Baker, 1712.

         Microfilm copy (negative) made in 1963 of
         the original in the University of Texas Library.
         Collation of the original, as determined from
         the film: 16p.

NT 0049929   IU

Tate, Nahum, 1652-1715.
A new version of the Psalms of David...
[London, 1695?]
           see under Bible. O. T. Psalms.
English. Paraphrases. 1695? Tate and Brady.

and   later editions identified by the names
of Tate and Brady after the date in the heading.

Tate, Nahum, 1652-1715.
Nova grammatices experimenta
           see under [Maidwell, Lewis] 1649 or 50-
1716.

Tate, Nahum, 1652-1715, supposed author.
Ode for the Thanksgiving Day
   see under title

Tate, Nahum, 1652-1715.
An ode upon Her Majesty's birth-day, April
the thirtieth. Set to musick by Mr. Henry
Purcell, and perform'd before Her Majesty at
Whitehall, Monday May the 1st. 1693.   Written
by N. Tate, servant to Their Majesties.
[London: Printed for Richard Baldwin ... 1693]
[2] p. 31½ᵐ. [Miscellaneous poems and
tracts. London, 1681-1704. v.1, no.26]

Caption title.
Signature: 1 leaf   unsigned.
Without the mu   sic.

NT 0049933   CLU-C

Tate, Nahum, 1652-1715
An ode upon Her Majesty's birth-day, April the
thirtieth. Set to musick by Henry Purcell, and
perform'd before Her Majesty at Whitehall, Monday,
May the 1st, 1693. Written by N. Tate. [London,
Printed for R. Baldwin, 1693]
[2] p.
Microfilm copy (negative) made in 1962 by
Clark Library, University of California, L. A.
Without the music.

NT 0049934   IU

TATE, N[ahum], 1652-1715.
An ode upon His Majesty's birth-day, set to
musick by Dr. Staggins; performed at Whitehall,
November, 1694. [London, printed for R. Baldwin,
1694].

f°. pp.(2).
Caption-title.

NT 0049935   MH

Ex
3952   Tate, Nahum, 1652-1715.
.89   An ode upon the assembling of the new
.366   parliament, to be sung before His Majesty
       on New-Years-Day, 1702. [n.p.] 1702.
           4 p. 21 cm.

NT 0049936   NjP CLU-C TxU MH

Tate, Nahum, 1652-1715.
An ode upon the New Year, performed before
their Majesties ...
   see under Blow, John, d. 1708.

FILM   Tate, Nahum, 1652-1715.
821   An ode upon the ninth of January 169¾ the
T18o   first secular day since the University of
       Dublin's foundation by Queen Elizabeth.
       Dublin, Printed by J. Ray, 1694.

       Microfilm copy (negative) made in 1962 of
       the original in the Bodleian Library.
       Collation of original, as determined from
       the film: broadside.
       In double columns.

NT 0049938   IU

Tate, Nahum, 1652-1715.

On the sacred memory of our late sovereign:
with a congratulation to His present Majesty
... Written by N. Tate.   London, Printed
by J. Playford, for Henry Playford ... 1685.
1 p.l., 6 p. 31ᵐ. [Poetry longwaies.
London, 1683-85. no.132]

First edition.
Signatures: A-B².
Title within heavy line border.

Narcissus Luttrell's copy, dated 17. feb.
169½.

_____ Another copy. [Miscellaneous poems
and tracts. London, 1681-1703. v.1, no.8]

___ ___ Microfilm copy (negative)

NT 0049940   CLU-C PU OU MH CtY NjP ICN TxU CSmH DFo

*fEC65   Tate, Nahum, 1652-1715.
T1878   On the sacred memory of our late sovereign:
685ob with a congratulation to His present Majesty...
       Written by N. Tate. The second edition.
       London, Printed by J.Playford, for Henry Play-
       ford, near the Temple-church: 1685.

       1 p.l., 6p. 30.5cm.
       In verse.

NT 0049941   MH TxU CU DLC

TATE, Nahum, 1652-1715.
The oration and poem spoken at the entertainment of divine musick. Perform'd at Stationers-hall on the 6th of Jan. 1702. 1702.

The ode and poem composed by Nahum Tate.

NT 0049942   MH

Tate, Nahum, 1652-1715.

Weedon, Cavendish, fl. 1700, ed.
The oration, anthems and poems, spoken and sung at the
Performance of divine musick. For the entertainment of the
Lords spiritual & temporal, and the honourable House of commons. At Stationers-Hall, January the 31st 1701. Undertaken by Cavendish Weedon, esq; London, Printed for H.
Playford, and are to be sold by J. Nutt, MDCII [!] [i. e. 1702]

Tate, Nahum, 1652-1715, ed.

Davies, Sir John, 1569-1626.
The original, nature, and immortality of the soul. A
poem. With an introduction concerning human knowledge. Written by Sir John Davies ... With a prefatory
account concerning the author and poem. The 3d ed.
London, Printed for W. Mears and J. Browne, 1715.

Tate, Nahum, 1652-1715, tr.

Ovidius Naso, Publius.
Ovid's Art of love; Remedy of love; and Art of beauty. To
which is added Chaucer's Court of love. Also several miscellaneous pieces by various authors, in imitation of Ovid.
London. Published for the booksellers [1884?]

Tate, Nahum, 1652-1715.
Oxford. A poem...
   see under Tickell, Thomas, 1868-1740.

Tate, Nahum, 1652-1715.
Panacea: a poem upon tea: in two canto's. By N. Tate ...
London, Printed by and for J. Roberts, 1700.

8 p. l., 34, [5] p. 18½ᶜᵐ.

Later edition issued with title: A poem upon tea.
"The tea-table": p. [35-36].
Have also another copy with which are bound: Gay, J. Wine, a poem. London,
1708. and Philips, J. Cyder. A poem. London, 1709.

CLU-C
NT 0049947   ICJ TxU ICN CSmH DNLM CtY TxU NjP MH

[Tate, Nahum.] 1652-1715.   15481.36.4F
A pastoral dialogue; a poem. London, printed for R. Baldwin,
1690.
f°. pp. (16), 27.
The later edition is entitled: "A poem occasioned by the late discontents & disturbances in the state."

NT 0049948   MH

FILM   [Tate, Nahum] 1652-1715.
821   A pastoral dialogue. A poem.   London,
T18pa Printed for R. Baldwin, 1690.

       Microfilm copy (negative) made in 1962 of the
       original in Harvard University Library.
       Collation of the original, as determined from
       the film: [6], 27p.
       Published also with title: A poem occasioned
       by the late discontents & disturbances in the
       State.

NT 0049949   IU

[Tate, Nahum.] *1652-1715*   15481.36.5F
A pastoral dialogue; a poem. London, printed for R. Baldwin, 1691.
f°. pp. (6), 27.
Another edition is entitled. "A poem occasioned by the late discontents & disturbances in the state."

NT 0049950   MH CtY ICN NNC NjP DFo CSmH

[Tate, Nahum] 1652-1715.
A pastoral dialogue. A poem. Liberius si Dixero quid, si forte Jocosius, Hoc mihi juris Cum Venia dabis. Hor. Vincit Amor Patriae. Virg. [Ornament of thistle and crown] London, Printed for Richard Baldwin, near the Oxford-Arms in Warwick-Lane, 1691
[iv] 27 p.   31 cm.
Bound in gray boards.
Wing T202b.

NT 0049951   FU

Tate, Nahum, 1652-1715.
A pastoral elegy on the death of Mr. John Playford ...
see under Purcell, Henry, 1658 or 9-1695.

Tate, Nahum, 1652-1715.
A pastoral in memory of His Grace the illustrious Duke of Ormond; deceased July the 21st, 1688 ... Written by N. Tate. London, Printed, and to be sold by Randal Taylor, near Stationers-Hall, 1688.
2 p. l., 15 p.   30 cm.
Signatures: [A]-E2.

NT 0049953   CtY MnU MH

FILM
821
T18p
Tate, Nahum, 1652-1715.
A pastoral in memory of His Grace the illustrious Duke of Ormond; deceased July the 21st. 1688. London, Printed, and to be sold by R. Taylor, 1688.
Microfilm copy (negative) made in 1962 of the original in Harvard University Library.
Collation of the original, as determined from the film: ₄₄₃, 15p.

NT 0049954   IU

Tate, Nahum, 1652-1715.
The pocket psalmist.... Dublin, 1834
see under Bible. O.T. Psalms.
English. Paraphrases. 1834. Tate and Brady.

Tate, Nahum, 1652-1715.
A poem, occasioned by His Majesty's voyage to Holland, the congress at the Hague, and present siege of Mons ... Written by N. Tate. London: Printed for Richard Baldwin ... 1691.
15 p.   31½ᶜᵐ. [Miscellaneous poems and tracts. London, 1681-1704. v.1, no.24]
First edition.
Signatures: ₄A₃-D².

NT 0049956   CLU-C IU NjP

FILM
321
T18po
Tate, Nahum, 1652-1715.
A poem, occasioned by His Majesty's voyage to Holland, the congress at The Hague, and present siege of Mons. London, Printed for R. Baldwin, 1691.
Microfilm copy (negative) made in 1962 of the original in Harvard University Library.
Collation of the original, as determined from the film: 15p.

NT 0049957   IU

Tate, Nahum, 1652-1715.   15481.34.8F
A poem occasioned by the late discontents & disturbances in the state; with reflections upon the rise and progress of priest-craft. London, printed for R. Baldwin, 1691.
f°. pp. (6), 27.
An earlier edition is entitled. "A pastoral dialogue."

NT 0049958   MH CtY NjP CSmH DFo InU OU PU

FILM
821
T18poe
Tate, Nahum, 1652-1715.
A poem, occasioned by the late discontents & disturbances in the State. With reflections upon the rise and progress of priest-craft. London, Printed for R. Baldwin, 1691.
Microfilm copy (negative made in 1962 of the original in Harvard University Library.
Collation of the original, as determined from the film: ₄6₃, 27p.
Published in 1691 also with title: A pastoral dialogue.

NT 0049959   IU

Tate, Nahum, 1652-1715.
A poem on the late promotion of several eminent persons in church and state. By N.Tate, servant to Their Majesties ... London; Printed for Richard Baldwin, near the Oxford-Arms in Warwick-lane.1694.
2p.ℓ.,12p. 29cm.
Signatures: A-D².

NT 0049960   CtY ICN CSmH MH InU NjP OU DFo CLU-C

[Tate, Nahum] 1652-1715, ascribed author.
A poem on the present assembling of the Parliament. March the 6th. 1678 [1679]
[London, 1679]
4 p.   28 cm., in case 33 cm.
Caption title.
Author's(?) autograph at end: N. Tate.

NT 0049961   TxU CtY

FILM
x821
T18poe
1716
Tate, Nahum, 1652-1715.
A poem sacred to the glorious memory of Her late Majesty Queen Anne. ₄London₃ 1716.
Microfilm copy (negative) made in 1964 of the original in the British Museum Library.
Collation of the original, as determined from the film: 20p.
Original closely trimmed with some loss of text.

NT 0049962   IU

Tate, Nahum, 1652-1715.
A poem upon tea: with a discourse on its sov'rain virtues; and directions in the use of it for health. Collected from treatises of eminent physicians upon that subject. Also a preface concerning beau-criticism. By Mr. Tate ... London, J. Nutt, 1702.
8 p. l., 47 p. front. 20½ᶜᵐ.
Signatures: A-D⁶.
Published in 1700 under title: Panacea: a poem upon tea.
Book-plate: Lieutenant General William Thornton, M. P.

1. Tea.   I. Title.   II. Title: Panacea.

27–859

Library of Congress   PR3729.T115P6 1702

NT 0049963   DLC InU NN PPC MH

820
T217
tP
1677
Tate, Nahum, 1652-1715.
Poems. By N.Tate. London, Printed by T.M. for Benj.Tooke at the Signe of the Ship in St.Pauls, Church-yard, M DC LXX VII.[i.e.1677]
t.-p.,[12],133p. 18cm.

NT   OU CLU-C
0049964   CLSU MB CtY MH CSmH DFo NNU NcU MWiW-C

FILM
821
T18
1677
Tate, Nahum, 1652-1715.
Poems. London, Printed by T. M. for B. Tooke, 1677.
Microfilm copy (negative) made in 1962 of the original in Harvard University Library.
Collation of the original, as determined from the film: ₄14₃, 133p.

NT 0049965   IU

Ex
3598
.895
.2
Tate, Nahum, 1652-1715.
Poems written on several occasions. 2d ed., enl. London, Printed for B. Tooke, 1684.
223(i.e.225) p.   19 ᶜᵐ.

NT   MH OU WU FU NPV
0049966   NjP MiU ICN TxU DFo CSmH CLU-C IEN CtY

Tate, Nahum, 1652-1715.
Poems by several hands, and on several occasions. Collected by N. Tate. London, J. Hindmarsh, 1685.
8 p. l., 445 p. 19ᶜᵐ.
Poems by Cowley, Rochester, Sir Francis Fane, P. Ayres, J. Evelyn, Waller, Tate and others.
Signatures: A-Z, Aa-Ee⁸, Ff² (last verso blank)

1. English p etr.—Early modern (to 1700)

17–28255

Library of Congress   PR1213.T3

NT   MH NNUT MnU OU IEN CtY
0049967   DLC NcU OrU IaU NjN PU ICN ViU NjP CSmH

Tate, Nahum, 1652-1715, tr.
Cowley, Abraham, 1618-1667.
The poetical works of Abraham Cowley ... From the text of Dr. Sprat, &c. with the life of the author ... Bell's 2d ed. Edinburg, At the Apollo press, by the Martins, 1784.

Tate, Nahum, 1652-1715.
Portions of Psalms, selected from the version of Brady and Tate, and adapted to fifty-tunes ... Bristol, [1798?]
see under Bible. O.T. Psalms. English. Paraphrases. 1798? Tate and Brady.

TATE, Nahum, *1652-1715.*
Portrait-royal, a poem upon Her Majesty's (Queen Anne's) picture set up in Guild-hall, by order of the Lord Mayor and court of aldermen of London; drawn by Mr.Closterman. [With notes.] London, printed by J.Rawlins for J. Nutt, 1703.
4°. pp.(8),24.

NT 0049970   MH CSmH CtY

FILM
x821
T18por
Tate, Nahum, 1652-1715.
Portrait-royal. A poem upon Her Majesty's picture set up in Guild-Hall; by order of the Lord Mayor and Court of Aldermen of the city of London. Drawn by Mr. Closterman. London, Printed by J. Rawlins for J. Nutt, 1703.
Microfilm copy (negative) made in 1964 of the original in the British Museum Library.
Collation of the original, as determined from

the film: 24p.
"Notes alphabetically referr'd to in the poem" p.21-24.

NT 0049972   IU

Tate, Nahum, 1652-1715.
A present for the ladies: being an historical vindication of the female sex. To which is added, The character of an accomplish'd virgin, wife, and widow, in verse. London, Printed for Francis Saunders, at the Blue Anchor in the New Exchange in the Strand, 1692.

NT 0049973   MdBG MH PPL CtY DFo TxU

FILM
396
T187p
[Tate, Nahum] 1652-1715.
A present for the ladies: being an historical vindication of the female sex. To which is added, The character of an accomplish'd virgin, wife, and widow, in verse. London, Printed for F. Saunders, 1692.
Microfilm copy (negative) made in 1962 of the original in Harvard University Library.
Collation of the original, as determined from the film: [16], 101, [1], 22p.

NT 0049974   IU

PR3729
.T11P9
1693
TATE, NAHUM, 1652-1715.
A present for the ladies: being an historical account of several illustrious persons of the female sex. To which is added, The character of an accomplish'd virgin, wife, and widow, in verse. Written by N.Tate... 2d ed. cor., with additions. London, Printed for F.Saunders, 1693.
[22], 101, [1], 22 p. 17½cm.

NT 0049975   ICU CLU-C MH ICN CtY

Tate, Nahum, 1652-1715.
The prologue to the last new play; A duke and no duke
see under [Duffet, Thomas] fl. 1678.

TATE, Nahum, 1652-1715.
The prologue [!] to King William & Queen Mary at a play acted before Their Majesties at Whitehall, on the 15th of Nov.1689. [London, printed for F. Saunders, and published by R. Baldwin, 1689.]
f°. pp.2.
Without title-page. Caption title.

NT 0049977   MH

FILM
821
T18pr
Tate, Nahum, 1652-1715.
The prologue [sic] to King William & Queen Mary. At a play acted before Their Majesties at Whitehall, on Friday the 15th of November 1689. [London, Printed for F. Saunders, 1690?]
Microfilm copy (negative) made in 1962 of the original in Harvard University Library.
Collation of the original, as determined from the film: 1p.

NT 0049978   IU

Tate, Nahum, 1652-1715.
The Psalms of David in metre ...
see under Bible. O. T. Psalms. English. Paraphrases. 1780. Tate and Brady.
Also with date : 1791

Tate, Nahum, 1652-1715.

Reformed church in America.

The Psalms of David, with the Ten commandments, Creed, Lord's prayer, &c. in metre. Also, the Catechism, Confession of faith, liturgy, &c. Translated from the Dutch. For the use of the Reformed Protestant Dutch church of the city of New-York. New-York: Printed by James Parker, at the new printing-office in Beaver-street. MDCCLXVII.

Tate, Nahum, 1652-1715.
Psalms, to be sung in churches and chapels; selected chiefly from the new version ...
see under Bible. O. T. Psalms. English. Paraphrases. 1799. Tate and Brady.
Also with date: 1844

Tate, Nahum, 1659?-1726.
The Psalter, or Psalms of David in metre ...
see under Bible. O. T. Psalms. English. Paraphrases. 1843. Tate and Brady.
Also with date: 1654

Tate, Nahum, 1652-1715, tr.

FOR OTHER EDITIONS SEE MAIN ENTRY

Juvenalis, Decimus Junius.
The satyrs of Decimus Junius Juvenalis: and of Aulus Persius Flaccus. Translated into English verse by Mr. Dryden, and several other eminent hands. To which is prefix'd a discourse concerning the original and progress of satyr ... The 5th ed., adorn'd with sculptures. London, Printed for J. Tonson, 1726. **OTHER EDITIONS UNDER AUTHOR**

PR3370
.A1
1689
Rare bk.
Coll.
Tate, Nahum, 1652-1715, tr.

Cowley, Abraham, 1618-1667.
The second and third parts of the works of Mr Abraham Cowley, the second containing what was written and published by himself in his younger years: now reprinted together. The 6th ed. The third containing his six books Of plants, never before published in English ... Now made English by several hands. With necessary tables to both parts, and divers poems in praise of the author ... London, Printed for Charles Harper, at the Flower-deluce over against S. Dunstan's church in Fleet-street, 1689.

[Tate, Nahum] 1652-1715.
- The second part of Absalom and Achitophel. A poem ... Dublin, Printed for Robert Thornton ... 1682.
[32] p. 21cm.
This work was supervised by John Dryden, who contributed 200 lines.
Signatures- [A]-D⁴.
Upper margins closely trimmed; some page numbers wanting.
Unbound, in cloth case.
Cf. Macdonald, Hugh. John Dryden; a bibliography. Oxford 1939. p.32-33, no.15c.

NT 0049985   CLU-C DFo PU

[Tate, Nahum] 1652-1715.
The second part of Absalom and Achitophel. A poem ... London: Printed for Jacob Tonson, at the Judges Head in Chancery-Lane, near Fleet-Street. 1682.
1 p.l., 34 p. 32½cm. [With Dryden, John. Absalom and Achitophel ... London, 1681]
First issue, first issue, with 10 lines on p.34.
Signatures: 1 leaf unsigned, B-I², K¹.
This work was supervised by John Dryden who contributed 200 lines.
Cf. Macdonald, Hugh. John Dryden; a bibliography. Oxford, 1939, p.32.

NT 0049986   CLU-C DLC TxU NjP ICN MWiW-C CtY

Disbd
Part II
1682
RARE BOOK
COLLECTION
Tate, Nahum, 1652-1715.
The second part of Absalom and Achitophel. A poem. - Si quis tamen Haec quoque, si quis captus amore leget - London, Printed for Jacob Tonson, at the Judges Head in Chancery-Lane, near Fleet-Street, 1682.
34 p. 32cm.
Head piece. Catchwords. Title stained.
Disbound.
Wing, D2350.

I. Title: Absalom and Achitophel, second part. II. Title.

MiU IEN MWiW-C PU DFo
NT 0049988   FU NIC CSmH TxU DLC MShM MB InU MH CSt

AJ
D848
+681a2b
[TATE, NAHUM] 1652-1715.
The second part of Absalom and Achitophel. A poem ... The second edition.
London: Printed for Jacob Tonson, at the Judge's Head in Chancery-Lane, near Fleet-Street. 1682. 1p.l., 34p. 30½cm., in case 35cm.
Dryden wrote two hundred lines, added "some touches in other places," and in general supervised the composition of this poem.
Marginal ms. annotations.

NT 0049989   TxU DFo MH PBL NcD

FILM
x821
T18se
1682a
[Tate, Nahum] 1652-1715.
The second part of Absolom and Achitophel. A poem. 2d ed. London, Printed for J. Tonson, 1682.
Microfilm copy (negative) made in 1963 of the original in the Newberry Library.
Collation of the original, as determined from the film: 34p.
By Nahum Tate, assisted by John Dryden. Cf. Dict. nat. biog.

NT 0049990   IU

Tate, Nahum, 1652-1715.
The second part of Absalom and Achitophel. London, J. Read, 1709.

NT 0049991   DFo

Tate, Nahum, 1652-1715.
A selection from Tate and Brady's version of the Psalms ... for the use of the church in Brattle Square ...
see under Boston. Brattle Square Church.

Tate, Nahum, 1652-1715.
A selection of Psalms and hymns from the new version of the Church of England, and others ... London, 1813
see under Bible. O. T. Psalms. English. Paraphrases. 1813. Tate and Brady.

Tate, Nahum, 1652–1715.

₍Shakespeare, William₎ 1564–1616.
 The Sicilian usurper : a tragedy, as it was acted at the Theatre-Royal. With a prefatory epistle in vindication of the author, occasioned by the prohibition of this play on the stage. Written by N. Tate ... London: Printed for James Knapton, at the Crown in St. Paul's Church-yard. 1691.

Tate, Nahum, 1652–1715.
 Some of the Psalms of David in metre...
Cambridge [Eng.], 1699
  see under Bible. O.T. Psalms.
English. Paraphrases. 1699.

TATE, ₍Nahum₎, 1652–1715.
 The song for Her Majesty's birthday, February the 6th, 1710/11. Set by Mr. Eccles, master of musick to Her Majesty, the words by Mr. Tate, poet-laureat. [London, 1711.]

 4°. pp. 4.
 The music is wanting.

NT 0049996 MH

TATE, N₍ahum₎, 1652–1715.
 A song for St. Caecilia's day, 1685. Written by Mr. N. Tate, and set by Mr. William Turner. [London?, 1685].

 f°. pp. (2). Broadside.
 Words only. Printed on one side of the leaf.

NT 0049997 MH

FILM Tate, Nahum, 1652–1715.
821 A song for St. Cecelia's day 1685. Written
T18s by Mr. N. Tate, and set by Mr. William Turner.
  ₍London? 1685?₎

 Microfilm copy (negative) made in 1962 of the original in Harvard University Library.
 Collation of the original, as determined from the film: ₍1₎p.
 In manuscript following title: 23. Nov. 1685.

 "In 1685 he ₍Turner₎ was selected to compose the ode, which that year was written by Nahum Tate. The result was probably unsatisfactory; the music was not printed — and is now lost." Dict. nat. biog.

 I. Turner, William, 1651–1740.

NT 0049999 IU

Ohio State

Tate, Nahum, 1652–1715.
 The song for New-Years-Day, 1705. Perform'd before Her Majesty. Set by Mr. Eccles, master of Her Majesty's musick. The words by Mr. Tate, poet-laureat to Her Majesty. ₍London, Printed for J. Nutt, 1705₎
 ₍5₎ p. 21 cm.

NT 0050001 OU

FILM Tate, Nahum, 1652–1715.
x821 The song for New-Years-day, 1705. Perform'd
T18so before Her Majesty. Set by Mr. Eccles, master
  of Her Majesty's musick. The words by Mr. Tate.
  ₍London, Printed for J. Nutt, 1705₎

 Microfilm copy (negative) made in 1964 of the original in the British Museum Library.
 Collation of the original, as determined from the film: 3p.
 Caption title.
 In manuscript on p. 1: 2 Januar. 170$\frac{2}{3}$.

NT 0050002 IU

---

*EB65 Tate, Nahum, 1652–1715.
T1878 The song for the New-year 1708. Set by Mr.
708s Eccles master of Her Majesty's musick. The
 words by Mr. Tate poet-laureat to Her Majesty.
 [London, 1708]

 broadside. 32x19.5cm.
 Without the music.

NT 0050003 MH

Tate, Nahum, 1652–1715.
 A supplement to the New version of Psalms by... Tate and... Brady... London, 1700
  see under Bible. O.T. Psalms. English. Paraphrases. 1700. Tate and Brady.

and later editions identified by the names of Tate and Brady after the date in the heading.

---

*fE065 Tate, Nahum, 1652–1715.
T1878 The triumph of peace. A poem, on the magnifi-
713t cent publick entry of His Excellency the illustrious Duke of Shrewsbury, ambassador extraordinary from Her Majesty of Great Britain, to the Most Christian King. And the magnificent publick entry of His Excellency the illustrious Duke D'Aumont, ambassador extraordinary from His Most Christian Majesty, to the Queen of Great Britain. With the prospect of the glorious procession for a general thanksgiving at St. Paul's. By Mr. Tate, poet- laureat to her Majesty.

 London: Printed for James Holland, in St. Paul's church-yard; and are sold by J. Morphew, near Stationers-hall. 1713.

 12p. 30.5cm.
 Page 10 misnumbered 01.

NT 0050006 MH CLU-C TxU

FILM Tate, Nahum, 1652–1715.
x821 The triumph of peace. A poem, on the mag-
T18tr nificent publick entry of His Excellency the illustrious Duke of Shrewsbury, ambassador extraordinary from Her Majesty of Great Britain, to the most Christian king. And the magnificent publick entry of His Excellency the illustrious Duke D'Aumont, ambassador extra-ordinary, from His Most Christian Majesty, to

 the Queen of Great Britain. With the prospect of the glorious procession for a general thanksgiving at St. Paul's. London, Printed for J. Holland, and sold by J. Morphew, 1713.

 Microfilm copy (negative) made in 1964 of the original in Harvard University Library.
 Collation of the original, as determined from the film: 12p.

NT 0050008 IU

FILM Tate, Nahum, 1652–1715.
x821 The triumph of union: with the muse's address
T18tri for the consummation of it in the Parliament of Great Britain. London, 1707.

 Microfilm copy (negative) made in 1964 of the original in the British Museum Library.
 Collation of the original, as determined from the film: 16p.

NT 0050009 IU

Tate, Nahum, 1652–1715.
 The triumph, or, Warriours welcome: a poem on the glorious successes of the last year. With The ode for New-year's day. 1705. By Mr. Tate, poet-laureat to Her Majesty ... London, Printed by J. Rawlins for J. Holland ₍etc.₎ 1705.

 2 p. l., 30 (i. e. 32) p. 21½ᵐ.

1. Blenheim, Battle of, 1704—Poetry. I. Title.

             45–34636

NT 0050010 DLC CtY InU

FILM Tate, Nahum, 1652–1715.
821 The triumph, or, Warriours welcome: a poem on the glorious
T18t successes of the last year. With The ode for New-year's day.
 1705. By Mr. Tate, poet-laureat to Her Majesty ... London,
 Printed by J. Rawlins for J. Holland ₍etc.₎ 1705.

 Microfilm copy (negative) made in 1963 of the original in the Library of Congress.
 Collation of the original, as determined from the film: ₍4₎, 30(i.e. 32)p.
 Errors in paging: 30–32 numbered: 22, 30, 30.

NT 0050011 IU

Tate, Nahum, 1652–1715.
 The triumph, or Warriours welcome: a poem on the glorious successes of the last year. With The ode for New-Year's day, 1705. By Mr. Tate ... The second edition ... London: Printed by J. Rawlins for J. Holland ... Sold by J. Nutt ... 1705.
 2 p.l., 28 p. 21½cm.
 Signatures: A–D⁴.
 Book stamps of Harvard college library on t.-p.
 Bound in half light green cloth; a few lower margins closely   trimmed.

NT 0050012 CLU-C TxU NN MH

Z43 Tate, Nahum, 1652–1715.
.S395 Upon this performance of penmanship, a poem
Rare bk. Seddon, John, 1644–1700.
coll. The penman's magazine: or, A new copy-book, of the Eng-
Folio lish, French and Italian hands, after the best mode; adorn'd with about an hundred new and open figures and fancies, never before publish'd: after the originals of the late incomparable Mr. John Seddon. Perform'd by George Shelley ... ₍London₎ T. Read ₍etc.₎ 1705.

Tate, Nahum, 1652–1715.
 While shepherds watched their flocks by night, by Nahum Tate, with twelve ideal hymns and poems... Boston: D. Lothrop and co. ₍c1886₎ 14 l. front., illus., plates. 23½cm.

 Without music.

NT 0050014 NN MH

PR3729 Tate, Nahum, 1652–1715.
.T115W5 While shepherds watched their flocks by
1886 night. With twelve ideal hymns and poems.
 Boston, D. Lothrop ₍1886₎
 ₍47₎ p. illus. 24cm.

 1. Christmas—Poetry. I. Title.

NT 0050015 ViU

PN6110.C5 Tate, Nahum, 1652–1715.
T2 While shepherds watched, by Tate & Brady.
 Buffalo, N. Y., Berger publishing company ₍c1908₎

 ₍16₎p. incl. front. illus. 17½cm.

 Text within colored borders.

 I. Brady, Nicholas, 1659–1726, jt. auth. II. Title

NT 0050016 NBuG

Tate, Nahum, 1652–1715.
 The whole book of Psalms, in metre; with hymns, suited to the feasts and fasts of the church ...
  for editions of this work (titles may vary slightly) see under: Bible. ₍O. T. Psalms. English. Paraphrases. [year of publication] Protestant Episcopal Church.

Tate, Newman.
    The builder's materials. London, Chapman and Hall, 1947.
    viii, 168 p. illus. 25 cm.

    1. Building materials.

    TA403.T3   691   49–14087*

NT   0050018   DLC CaBVa MH

Tate, Newman.
    Practical building mechanics, by Newman Tate ... London, Chapman & Hall ltd., 1945.
    viii, 227 p. illus., diagrs. (1 fold.) 22ᶜᵐ.
    "First published 1945."

    1. Building. 2. Strains and stresses.   I. Title: Building mechanics.
                              45–8301
    Library of Congress   TH845.T34
                      ₅₎   624.1

NT   0050019   DLC PSt Or OCl NcC

Tate, Newman.
    Reinforced concrete. London, G. Allen & Unwin ₍1948₎
    85 p. illus. 19 cm. (The World builders' handbook no. 5)

    1. Concrete construction. 2. Concrete, Reinforced.   (Series)

    TA683.T28   693.5   49–27839*

NT   0050020   DLC CaBVa

Tate, Orley Allen
    see
    Tate, Allen, 1899–

Tate, Paul
    Letter to Lord Melville enclosing a letter to William Astell of the East India company, on the cotton trade and the methods of cleaning India cotton. 1816.
    [16]p.

    Manuscript.

NT   0050022   OCl

Tate, Phyllis, 1911–
    ₍Concerto, saxophone & string orchestra ; arr.₎

    Concerto for alto saxophone and strings. Reduction for saxophone and piano ₍by Peter Wishart₎ London, Oxford University Press ₍1949₎
    score (41 p.) and part. 32 cm.
    Reproduced from ms.
    Duration : about 21 minutes.

    1. Concertos (Saxophone with string orchestra)—Solo with piano.

    M1106.T3C6   49–52059*

NT   0050023   DLC FTaSU CU–SB IU IEN OCU

Tate, Phyllis, *1911–*
    I sing of a maiden. Words anon., 15th century, set to music by Phyllis Tate. ₍London₎ Oxford univ. press ₍c1932₎   4 p. 31cm.

    For 1 voice with piano accompaniment.
    Cover-title.

    1. Songs, English.
    N.Y.P.L.   June 20, 1944

NT   0050024   NN

M1621
.T38L3
1949
    Tate, Phyllis, 1911–   arr.
    The lark in the clear air; an Irish air for voice and piano. Medium key. [London] Oxford University Press ₍c1949₎
    3 p. 28 cm.
    Cover title.
    Words by Sir Samuel Ferguson.

    1. Songs (Medium voice) with piano.
    I. Title.

NT   0050025   MB DCU KU

    Tate, Phyllis, 1911–   joint composer.

M1393
.M8M6
    Murray, Eleanor.

    More tunes for my violin, by Eleanor Murray and Phyllis Tate. London, New York, Hawkes; sole selling agents, Boosey & Hawkes ₍1950₎

    Tate, Phyllis, 1911–
    ₍Nocturne for four voices. English₎

    Nocturne for four voices, a chamber cantata for soprano, tenor, baritone and bass soli, string quartet, double bass, bass clarinet and celesta. The poem by Sidney Keyes. Full score. London, Oxford University Press ₍1949₎
    41 p. 26 cm.
    Duration : about 25 minutes.
    1. Cantatas, Secular—Scores.   I. Keyes, Sidney Arthur Kilworth, 1922–1943. Nocturne for four voices.

    M1531.T3N5   49–51363*

NT   0050027   DLC CLU LU NN

    Tate, Phyllis, 1911–
    ₍Sonata, clarinet & violoncello₎

    Sonata for clarinet and cello. London, Oxford University Press ₍1949₎
    score (29 p.) 25 cm.
    Duration : 19 minutes, 30 seconds.

    1. Sonatas (Clarinet and violoncello)

    M291.T   50–28444

NT   0050028   DLC OrU NN IU IEN INS

KEPT IN
BROWN MUSIC
COLLECTION
*M452
.T365S8
    Tate, Phyllis, 1911–
    [Quartet, strings, F major]
    String quartet in F. London, New York, Oxford University Press [c1955]
    miniature score (43 p.) 20cm.

    1. String quartets—Scores.

NT   0050029   MB IU MH

    Tate, Phyllis, 1911–   arr.
    Suite from Handel's 'Water Music'
        see under   Händel, Georg Friedrich, 1685–1759.

    Tate, Ralph, 1840–1901.
    ... The anniversary address of the president, Professor Ralph Tate ... ₍Adelaide? 1879?₎
    cover-title, 36 p. 21ᶜᵐ.
    At head of title: The Adelaide philosophical society.
    "From the Transactions of the Philosophical society of Adelaide, 1879."
    Subject of address : Leading physical features of South Australia.

    1. Geology—South Australia.   I. Geology, Adelaide.
                              12–31582
    Library of Congress   QE345.T3

NT   0050031   DLC PPAN

    Tate, Ralph, 1840–1901.
    Appendix to the Manual of mollusca of S. P. Woodward, containing such recent and fossil shells as are not mentioned in the second edition of that work. London, Straham & co., 1869.
    86 p. illus. nar. D.

NT   0050032   CaBViP

    1840–1901.
    Tate, Ralph, ₍Botany ₍of central Australia₎. With an appendix, ₍" Notes on some vegetable exudations "₎, by J. H. Maiden. (*In* Horn, W. A. Report on the work of the Horn scientific expedition to central Australia, 1896, iii, 117–197.)

NT   0050033   MH–A MH MB

    Tate, Ralph, 1840–1901.
    Brief diagnosis of mollusca from central Australia; notes on the organic remains of the osseous clays at Lake Callabonna.
    (Trans. Royal Soc. South Australia. 1894)
    Conch. T. v. 2a.

NT   0050034   PPAN

    Tate, Ralph, 1840–1901.
    The Cambrian fossils of South Australia.
    (Trans. Roy. Soc. South Australia. 1892)
    Geol. T. v.

NT   0050035   PPAN

    Tate, Ralph, 1840–1901.
    Census of the mollusca of Australia. 1888.
    (Trans. Roy. Soc. South Australia)
    Conch. T. v. 11ᵃ

NT   0050036   PPAN

    Tate, Ralph, 1840–1901.
    Check list of fresh water shells of Australia by Ralph Tate & John Brazier. 1881.
    Conch. T. v. 12.

NT   0050037   PPAN

    Tate, Ralph, 1840–1901.
    Correlation of the marine tertiaries of Australia by Ralph Tate & J. Dennant.
    (Trans. Roy. Soc. South Australia. 1893)
    Geol. T. v. 4b.

NT   0050038   PPAN

    Tate, Ralph, 1840–1901.
    Critical remarks on the A. Bittner's "Echiniden des Tertiars von Australia".
    (Trans. Roy. Soc. South Australia. 1892)
    Geol. T. v.

NT   0050039   PPAN

    Tate, Ralph, 1840–1901.
    Description of some new species of South Australian marine and fresh water mollusca. Oct. 5, 1886.
    Conch. T. v. 1a.

NT   0050040   PPAN

Tate, Ralph, 1840–1901.
   Descriptions of new species of Australian
mollusca, recent and fossil.
   (Trans. Roy. Soc. South Australia. 1891)
   Conch. T. v. 11ᵃ.

NT 0050041   PPAN

Tate, Ralph, 1840–1901.
   Descriptions of some new species of marine
mollusca from Australia.
   (Trans. Roy. Soc. South Australia, 1892)
   Conch. T. v. 11a

NT 0050042   PPAN

Tate, Ralph, 1840–1901.
   Descriptions of some new species of marine
mollusca from South Australia and Victoria.
   (Trans. Roy. Soc. South Australia.)
   Conch. T. v. 11a

NT 0050043   PPAN

1840-1901.
Tate, Ralph, ⸌ Flora belfastiensis. The plants around Bel-
fast with their geographical and geological distribution.
Belfast. 1863. 24°. pp. xx. 92.

NT 0050044   MH-A MH-G

Tate, Ralph, 1840–1901.
   General geology. By Ralph Tate and
J. Alexander Watt.
   Pls.   (In Horn scientific expedition to
Central Australia. Report. Part 6 , p. 26–75.
London, 1896)

NT 0050045   MB

TATE, Ralph, 1840-1901.
   Geology and botany of the Horn Scientific
Expedition to Central Australia. London, 1896.

   4°. pp. 204.
   By Ralph Tate and J. A. Watt.

NT 0050046   MH PPAN

Tate, Ralph, 1840–1901.
   A handbook of the flora of extratropical South Australia,
containing the flowering plants and ferns. By Ralph Tate …
Adelaide, Education department, 1890.
   vi p., 1 l., 303 p. double map. 19ᶜᵐ.

   1. Botany—South Australia. ₍1. South Australia—Botany₎   I. Title.
                                      Agr 22-127 Revised
   Library, U. S. Dept. of   Agriculture 460.35T18

NT 0050047   DNAL NNBG OCl MH-A

Tate, Ralph, 1840–1901.
   A handbook of the flora of extratropical South Australia, containing the flowering plants and ferns. By
Ralph Tate … Adelaide, Education department, 1920.
   vi p., 1 l., 303 p. double map. 19ᶜᵐ.

   1. Botany—South Australia. ₍1. South Australia—Botany₎   I. Title.
                                      Agr 22-127
   Library, U. S. Dept. of   Agriculture 460.35T18

NT 0050048   DNAL

Tate, Ralph, 1840–1901.
Tietkens, William Henry.
   Journal of the Central Australian exploring expedition, 1889, under command of W. H. Tietkens. De-
spatched by the Central Australian exploring and pros-
pecting association, limited, under the auspices of the
Royal geographical society of Australasia, South Australian branch. Together with map; list of botanical
specimens, described by Baron Sir Ferd. von Mueller …
and Professor R. Tate … also catalogue of geological
specimens, described by H. Y. L. Brown … with geo-

logical sketch of the country passed over. Adelaide,
C. E. Bristow, government printer, 1891.
   1 p. l., 84 p. fold. map, fold. col. profile. 21ᶜᵐ.

   1. Australia—Disc. & explor. 2. Scientific expeditions. I. Central Australian exploring expedition, 1889. II. Royal geographical society of Australasia. South Australian branch, Adelaide. III. Müller, Ferdinand, freiherr von, 1825–1896. IV. Tate, Ralph, 1840–1901. v. Brown, Harry York
Lyell.

   Library of Congress   DU390.T52   6-19822

NT 0050050   DLC

Tate, Ralph, 1840-1901.
Winnecke, Charles.
   Journal of the Horn scientific exploring expedition,
1894, by C. Winnecke, F. R. G. S., together with maps and
plans; and report of the physical geography of central
Australia, by Professor R. Tate and J. A. Watt, B. SC.
Adelaide, C. E. Bristow, gov't printer, 1897.

Tate, Ralph, 1840-1901.
   List of plants collected during Mr. Tietkens'
expedition into central Australia
      see under   Mueller, Ferdinand, freiherr von,
1825-1896.

Tate, Ralph, 1804–1901.
   A list of the Lammellibranch and Pallibranch
mollusca of South Australia. Supplement.
   (Trans. Roy. Soc. South Australia)
   Conch. T. v. 11a.

NT 0050053   PPAN

Tate, Ralph, 1840–1901.
Woodward, Samuel Peckworth, 1821–1865.
   A manual of the *Mollusca;* being a treatise on recent and
fossil shells, by S. P. Woodward … 3d ed., with an appendix
of recent and fossil conchological discoveries, by Ralph Tate
… Illustrated by A. N. Waterhouse and Joseph Wilson
Lowry. London, Lockwood & co., 1875.

Tate, Ralph, 1840–1901.
   Manuel de conchyliologie, ou Histoire
naturelle des mollusques vivants et fossiles
      see under   Woodward, Samuel Peckworth,
1821-1865.

TATE, Ralph, 1840-1901.   *5820a.15.
   Mollusca. With an appendix on anatomical characters by C. Hedley
   Illus. Pls.
      (In Horn scientific expedition to Central Australia. Report. Par
2, pp. 182–226. London, 1896.)

NT 0050056   MB PPAN

Tate, Ralph, 1840–1901.
   The natural history of the country around the
head of the Great Australian Bight.   1879.
   G. N. H. T. v. 2ᵃ.

NT 0050057   PPAN

DU395
.S63
Tate, Ralph, 1840–1901.
Sowden, *Sir* William John, 1858–1943.
   The Northern territory as it is. A narrative of the South
Australian parliamentary party's trip, and full descriptions
of the Northern territory; its settlements and industries. By
William J. Sowden. With an appendix, containing reports
on the general resources of the territory by Professor Tate,
F. G. S. Adelaide, W. K. Thomas & co., 1882.

Tate, Ralph, 1840–1901.
   Notes on the correlation of the coral bearing
strata of South Australia.   1878.
   Geol. T. v. 20ᵃ.

NT 0050059   PPAN

Tate, Ralph, 1840–1901.
   On some new species of Australian marine
Gasteropoda.
   (Trans. Roy. Soc. South Australia. 1893)
   Conch. T. v. 11ᵃ .

NT 0050060   PPAN

Tate, Ralph, 1840–1901.
   On the classificatory position and synonyms of
Eatoniella Rufilabris.
   Conch. T. v. 11ᵃ.

NT 0050061   PPAN

Tate, Ralph, 1840-1901.
—— On the geographic relations of the floras of Norfolk
and Lord Howe islands. [Sydney. 1893.] 4°. pp. [17].
From "Macleay memorial volume."

NT 0050062   MH-A PU PPAN

Tate, Ralph, 1840–1901.
   On the occurrence of the Fissurellid Genus
Zidora in Australian waters.
   (Trans. Roy. Soc. South Australia, 1894)
   Conch. T. v. 2ᵃ.

NT 0050063   PPAN

Tate, Ralph, 1840–1901.
   On the oldest British Belemnite.   1869.
   Geol. T. v. 38.

NT 0050064   PPAN

Tate, Ralph, 1840–1901.
   On two new cretaceous bivalves. On some
Australian species of Eulimidae and Pyramidellidae,
On some recent and fossil Australian species of
Philobryae.
   (Trans. Roy. Soc. South Australia. 1898)
   Geol. T. v. 21ᵇ.

NT 0050065   PPAN

Tate, Ralph, 1840–1901.
   Palaeontology.
   (Horn Expedition to Central Australia
Pt. III. 1896)
   Geol. T. v. 52ᵇ.

NT 0050066   PPAN

Tate, Ralph, 1840–1901.
Physical geography.
(In Horn scientific expedition to Central
Australia. Report Part 3, p.1-25. London, 1896
I. J. Alexander Watt.

NT 0050067   MB PPAN

Tate, Ralph, 1840–1901.
A plain and easy account of the land and
fresh-water mollusks of Great Britain; containing descriptions, figures, and a familiar account of the habits of each species. By Ralph
Tate ... London, R. Hardwicke, 1866.
viii, 244 p. illus., XI col. pl. (incl. front.) 17ᶜᵐ.

1. Mollusks--Gt. Brit.

NT 0050068   MiU LU NcU PPAN DSI CLSU CaBVaU CU

Tate, Ralph, 1840–1901.

South Australia. *Geological dept.*
... Professor Tate's report on Northern Territory ...
₍Adelaide, 1882₎

Tate, Ralph, 1840–1901.
Report on the physical geography of Central
Australia, by Ralph Tate and J. A. Watt. 1897.
Text & maps.

NT 0050070   PPAN

Tate, Ralph, 1840–1901.
A revision of the recent Lamellibranch and
Pallibranch mollusca of South Australia.
Oct. 5, 1886.
Conch. T. v. 1ᵃ.

NT 0050071   PPAN

Tate, Ralph, 1840–1901.
Rudimentary treatise on geology ⟨partly based on
Major-Gen. Portlock's Rudiments of geology⟩ By Ralph
Tate ... London, Lockwood & co., 1871.
2 v. fronts., illus., diagrs. 17½ᶜᵐ. (On cover: Weale's rudimentary
series. 173-174)
CONTENTS.—pt. I. Physical geology.—pt. II. Historical geology.

1. Geology.   I. Portlock, Joseph Ellison, 1794–1864.

Library of Congress   QE28.T21   6-41553

NT 0050072   DLC PPFr MiHM MB

Tate, Ralph, 1840–1901.
Rudimentary treatise on geology. ⟨Partly based on
Major-Gen. Portlock's Rudiments of geology⟩ ... By
Ralph Tate ... 2d ed. ... London, Lockwood & co., 1874–
v.   front., illus. 17½ᶜᵐ. (On cover: Weale's rudimentary series.
173-)
CONTENTS.—pt. I. Physical geology.

1. Geology.   I. Portlock, Joseph Ellison, 1794–1864.

Library of Congress   QE28.T22   4-25267†* Cancel

NT 0050073   DLC DNLM

Tate, Ralph, 1840–1901.
Rudimentary treatise on geology. 3d ed.
1887.

NT 0050074   DI-GS

---

arV
20597

Tate, Ralph, 1840–1901.
Rudimentary treatise on geology (partly
based on Major-Gen. Portlock's Rudiments
of geology) 4th ed. London, C. Lockwood, 1890-95.
2 v. in 1. illus. 18cm. (Weale's
scientific and technical series)

I. Portlock, Joseph Ellison, 1784-1864.

NT 0050075   NIC CaBVaU DNLM

Tate, Ralph, 1840–1901.
Some additions to the list of the marine
Gasteropoda of South Australia.
(Trans. Roy. Soc. South Australia. 1893)
Conch. T. v. 11a.

NT 0050076   PPAN

Tate, Ralph, 1840–1901.
The Yorkshire Lias. By Ralph Tate ... and J. F.
Blake ... London, J. Van Voorst, 1876.
viii p., 2 l., 475, xii p. illus., plates, fold. map, fold. col. profiles, diagrs.
(part fold., part col.) 23ᶜᵐ.
"Literature of the Yorkshire Lias": p. 5–11.

1. Geology, Stratigraphic—Jurassic.   2. Geology—England—Yorkshire.
3. Paleontology — England — Yorkshire.   4. Paleontology — Jurassic.
I. Blake, John Frederick, 1839–1906, joint author.   II. Title.

          G S 14–228

Library, U. S. Geol.   survey   342(520) T19

NT 0050077   DI-GS PPAN GU CU OO ICJ

Tate, Ralph, 1840–1901.
Zoologica et Palæontologica Miscellanea,
chiefly relating to South Australia. 1879.
G. N. H. T. v. 2ᵃ.

NT 0050078   PPAN

Tate ₍Ricardus₎. *De tetano. 1 p. l., 19 pp.
8°. *Edinburgi, J. Pillans et filius,* 1822. ₍F., v.
1072.₎

NT 0050079   DNLM

4053   **Tate, Robert.**
A practical treatise upon several different and useful
subjects. To which are added, the opinions of some
learned men concerning the Church of England, and
Archbishop Tillotson's Discourse against transubstan-
tiation. London, 1732. 4°.
Includes relief of clergymen's widows and of South
sea sufferers.

NT 0050080   MH RPJCB CSmH

Tate, Robert, 1774–1867.
... Rev. Robert Tate's history of Black river chapel (a short
and imperfect sketch of the rise and progress of the Black
river church, commonly known by the name of the Black river
chapel) ... Copyright ... ₍by₎ Elizabeth Janet Black ... Wilmington, N. C., The National press, inc., 1925.
cover-title, ₍7₎ p. 28ᶜᵐ. (Publications of the Scottish institute of
America. Bulletin no. 1)

1. Ivanhoe, N. C.   Black river church.   2. Presbyterians in North
Carolina.   3. Scotch in North Carolina.   I. Black, Elizabeth Janet.

          35–8810
Library of Congress   BX9211.I 88B6
———— Copy 2.
Copyright A 880587   ₍3₎   285.1756

NT 0050081   DLC NcU

Tate, Robert Brian.
Italian humanism and Spanish historiography of the fif-
teenth century; a study of the Paralipomenon Hispaniae of
Joan Margarit, Cardinal Bishop of Gerona.
(In John Rylands Library, Manchester. Bulletin. Manchester.
27 cm. v. 34 (1951) p. 137–165)
Bibliographical footnotes.

1. Margarit y Pau, Juan de, Cardinal, 1421–1484. Paralipome non
Hispaniae libri decem.   2. Humanism.   3. Spain—Historiography.
I. Title.

Z921.M18B   vol. 34   A 52–3715
New York Univ.   Libraries
for Library of Congress   rev   ₍r71c2₎†

NT 0050082   NNU DLC

Tate, Robert Brian.
Joan Margarit i Pau, Cardinal-Bishop of Gerona; a bio-
graphical study. ₍Manchester, Eng.₎ Manchester University
Press ₍1955₎
xi, 155 p. map, geneal. tables. 22 cm. (Publications of the
Faculty of Arts of the University of Manchester, no. 6)
Bibliography: p. 149–151.

1. Margarit y Pau, Juan de, Cardinal, 1421–1484.   (Series: Victoria University of Manchester.   Faculty of Arts.   Publications, no. 6)

BX4705.M32513T3   922.246   56–58517

        AU ViU MU WaU TNJ NBuU CU ICN OU LU InU NN NcD
NT 0050083   DLC NNC MH IdU ICU MiU CtY-D NIC CtY PU

PZ
3
.T187
Do

Tate, Robert Desmond
The doughman; a novel. ₍1st ed.₎ Sydney,
Endeavour Press, 1933.
228 p. 22cm.

NT 0050084   WU CaBVaU

QA276
T3

Tate, Robert Flemming, 1921–
Contributions to the theory of random
numbers of random variables. ₍Berkeley,
1952₎
v, 76 l.
Thesis (Ph.D. in Statistics) - Univ. of
California, June 1952.
Bibliography: p. 74-76.

NT 0050085   CU

Tate, Robert S.
The grass roots of Kenton county, Kentucky. ₍A paper read...
December 8th, 1953, before the Christopher Gist historical society
at the Covington women's club house, Covington, Kentucky.
Covington, Ky., 1953₎   13 l.   28cm.
Cover title.

1. Kenton county, Ky.

NT 0050086   NN WHi N ICN

Tate, *Sir* Robert William, 1872–   *tr.*
Carmina dublinensia, by Sir Robert William Tate ... Dublin, Hodges, Figgis & co.; ₍etc., etc.₎ 1943.
xix, 117 p. 21½ᶜᵐ. (On cover: Dublin university press series)
Translations into Latin or Greek of passages from English literature.

1. English literature—Translations into Latin.   2. English literature—
Translations into Greek.   3. Latin literature—Translations from English.
4. Greek literature—Translations from English.   I. Title.

         A 43–3070
Harvard univ.   Library
for Library of Congress   ₍2₎

NT 0050087   MH CtY

Tate, *Sir* Robert William, 1872–   tr.
Carmina dublinensia. Dublin, Hodges, Figgis
& co., etc., etc., 1946.
xxi, 150 p. 22 cm.

NT 0050088   MH OCU FU

Tate, *Sir* Robert William, 1872–
Orationes et epistolae dublinensis (1914–40), by Sir Robert
William Tate ... Dublin, Hodges, Figgis & co.; ₍etc., etc.₎ 1941.
xix, 203 p., 1 l. 22½ᶜᵐ.
Latin speeches and letters, written by the author as public orator in
the University of Dublin.

I. Dublin.   University.   II. Title.

         A 42–8825
Yale univ.   Library
for Library of Congress   ₍2₎

NT 0050089   CtY

Tate, Sally.
Fluffy, the pink bunny; story and pictures by Sally Tate. New York, Cupples and Leon company [1943]
[20] p. col. illus. 23 x 18ᶜᵐ.

I. Title.
43–8951

Library of Congress PZ7.T2113Fl

NT 0050090 DLC PBa OOxM

PZ10
.3
.H71
Ft
Hoke, Helen, 1903–
The furry bear. Story by Helen Hoke; pictures by Sally Tate. New York, J. Messner, inc., ᶜ1943.

Tate, Sally, illus.

PZ8
.G397
Gi
3

Tate, Sally, illus.

FOR OTHER EDITIONS
SEE MAIN ENTRY

Gingerbread boy.
The gingerbread man. Illus. by Sally Tate. Racine, Wis., Whitman Pub. Co., ᶜ1947.

PZ8
.3
.R47
Jo

Tate, Sally, illus.

Riley, James Whitcomb, 1849–1916.
Joyful poems for children [by] James Whitcomb Riley, illustrated by Sally Tate. Indianapolis, New York, The Bobbs-Merrill company [1946]

PZ8
.3
.M85
1947

Tate, Sally, illus.

Mother Goose.
Mother Goose; illus. by Sally Tate. Racine, Wis., Whitman Pub. Co., ᶜ1947.

PZ10
.3
.H71
Wo

Tate, Sally, illus.

Hoke, Helen, 1903–
The woolly lamb, by Helen Hoke & Natalie Fox, pictures by Sally Tate. New York, J. Messner, inc., ᶜ1942.

Tate, Samuel.
The dedication of Mount Oglethorpe; an everlasting monument to the founder of Georgia
see under title

Tate, Sylvia, 1919–
Never by chance. [1st ed.] New York, Harper [1947]
282 p. 22 cm.

I. Title.
PZ3.T1874Ne
47–5150*

NT 0050097 DLC PP TxU ViU CaBVa OrP WaE

914.165
T187t

Tate, T M
Tales and legends of Lecale, County Down. Foreword by C.K. Pooler. Downpatrick, Printed at Down Recorder Office [193–?]
63p. 19cm.

1. Lecale, Northern Ireland. I. Title.

NT 0050098 TxU

Tate [Thomas]). Experimental chemistry for the use of beginners. (Gleig's school series.) 102 pp. 18°. *London, Longman [and others],* 1850.

NT 0050099 DNLM

Tate, Thomas.
Notes on a voyage to the Arctic seas in 1863. By Thomas Tate ... Alnwick [Eng.] Printed by H. H. Blair, 1864.
50 p. 18 x 10½ᶜᵐ.
"Reprinted from the 'Alnwick Mercury.'"

1. Arctic regions.

Library of Congress G545.T21
5–22643†

NT 0050100 DLC

Tate, Thomas Rouse, 1888–
U. S. *Federal power commission.*
... National power survey. Interim report ... 1935. Washington, U. S. Govt. print. off., 1935.

Tate, Thomas S
Surcharged & different forms of retaining walls. New York, Van Nostrand, 1873.
59 p.

NT 0050102 PPF

Tate, Thomas Turner, 1807–1888.
Algebra made easy. Chiefly intended for the use of schools. By T. Tate ... New ed. London, Longmans, Brown, Green, and Longmans, 1848.
vi, 114 p. 17ᶜᵐ.

1. Algebra.
3–1082†

Library of Congress QA152.T21

NT 0050103 DLC CtY

Tate, Thomas Turner, 1807–1888.
An elementary course of natural and experimental philosophy, for the use of beginners... By T. Tate... v. London: Longman, Brown, Green, and Longmans, 1855. v. diagrs., illus. 16°.

1. Physics.—Elementary and popular works, 1855.
N. Y. P L. December 6, 1921.

NT 0050104 NN MH

Tate, Thomas Turner, 1807–1888.
An elementary course of natural and experimental philosophy ... By T. Tate ... American ed., rev. and improved by C. S. Cartée ... Boston, Hickling, Swan and Brown, 1856.
528 p. illus., diagr. 19ᶜᵐ.

1. Physics.
3–25680

Library of Congress QC23.T23

NT 0050105 DLC MH NN PPeSchw CU NjR MB OO PV

Tate, Thomas Turner, 1807–1888.
The elements of mechanism: containing a familiar explanation of the construction of various kinds of machinery, &c. For the use of schoolmasters and private students. By Thomas Tate ... London, Longman, Brown, Green, and Longmans, 1851.
viii, 176 p. illus. 17ᶜᵐ.

1. Machinery, Kinematics of.
6–27861

Library of Congress TJ175.T21

NT 0050106 DLC TxU

Tate, Thomas [Turner] 1807–1888. 531.8 L100
The elements of mechanism: containing a familiar explanation of the construction of various kinds of machinery, &c. For the use of schoolmasters and private students. By Thomas Tate ... London, Longman, Brown, Green, and Longmans, · 1857.
viii, 176 p. illus. 17ᶜᵐ.
4ᵗʰ ed.

NT 0050107 ICJ

Tate, Thomas Turner, 1807–1888.
The elements of mechanism; containing a familiar explanation of the construction of various kinds of machinery, &c... 5th ed. London, Longman, Green, Longman, and Roberts, 1859.
viii, 176 p. incl. illus., diagrs. 17.5 cm.
1. Machinery, Kinematics of.

NT 0050108 CtY

[Tate, Thomas Turner] 1807–1888.
Exercises in arithmetic for elementary schools. After the method of Pestalozzi. Under the sanction of the Committee of council on education. London, J. W. Parker, 1844.
iv [5]–172 p. diagrs. 19 cm.
1. Arithmetic – Study and teaching. 2. Pestalozzi, Johann Heinrich, 1746–1827. I. Title.

NT 0050109 CU

Tate, Thomas [Turner] 1807–1888.
Exercises on mechanics and natural philosophy; or, An easy introduction to engineering, for the use of schools and private students: containing various applications of the principle of work; the theory of the steam engine, with simple machines; theorems and problems on accumulated work; the equilibrium of structure, with the theory of the arch; the pressure and efflux of fluids; calculations on railway cuttings; &c. &c. By Thomas Tate ... 2d ed., with additions and improvements. London, Longman, Brown, Green, and Longmans, 1847.
1 p. l., [vi]–viii, 163, [1] p. tables, diagrs. 18ᶜᵐ.
1. Mechanical engineering.
6–28097†

Library of Congress TJ146.T21

NT 0050110 DLC

Tate, Thomas Turner, 1807–1888.
Exercises on mechanics and natural philosophy; or, An easy introduction to engineering, for the use of schools and private students: containing various applications of the principle of work; the theory of the steam engine, with simple machines; theorems and problems on accumulated work; the equilibrium of structure, with the theory of the arch; the pressure and efflux of fluids; calculations on railway cuttings; &c., &c. By Thomas Tate ... New ed. London, Longman, Brown, Green, and Longmans, 1849.
viii, 163, [1] p. diagrs. 18ᶜᵐ.
1. Mechanical engineering.
15–1170

Library of Congress TJ146.T21 1849

NT 0050111 DLC PV MB MH CtY PPF

Tate, Thomas Turner, 1807–1888.
First lessons in philosophy; or, The science of familiar things ... By Thomas Tate ... American ed., rev. and improved by C. S. Cartée ... Boston, Hickling, Swan and Brown, 1856.
252 p. illus., diagr. 19½ᶜᵐ.
CONTENTS.—pt. 1. The chemistry of familiar things.—pt. 2. Mechanics of familiar things.—pt. 3. Physics of familiar things.

1. Physics. I. Cartée, Cornelius Soule, ed.
3—25681

Library of Congress QC23.T21

NT 0050112 DLC MH CtY OO ICJ

QC 145
T38
1851
Tate, Thomas Turner, 1807-1888.
    Hydrostatics, hydraulics, and pneumatics.
New ed. London, Longmans, Green [1851]
    96 p. illus.
At head of title: Gleig's school series.
    1. Hydrostatics. 2. Hydraulics. 3.
Pneumatics. I. Title.

NT 0050113   CaBVaU

TATE, Thomas, 1807-1888.
    Key to Tate's Exercises on Mechanics and
Natural Philosophy. New ed. London, Longman,
Brown, Green, and Longmans, 1853.

NT 0050114   MH PPF

Ujb23
847ta
Tate, Thomas Turner, 1807-1888.
    Key to Tate's Exercises on mechanics and
natural philosophy ... New ed. London,
Longmans, Green, and co., 1879.
    iv, 167p. illus.(diagrs.) 18cm.

NT 0050115   CtY

TATE, Thomas *Turner, 1807-1888.*
    The little philosopher, or The science of
familiar things. Forming a series of instructive reading books for young people. New ed.
Vol. I. London, Longman, Green, Longman, Roberts,
& Green, 1863.

    24°. Illustr.

NT 0050116   MH IU

Tate, Thomas Turner, 1807-1888.
    ...On light and heat; for the use of beginners, in which the
principles of the sciences are familiarly explained and illustrated
by numerous experiments and diagrams, by Thomas Tate...
New ed. London, Longmans, Green, and co. [n. d.] iv, 102 p.
illus. 14cm. (Gleig's school series.)

1. Light. 2. Heat.
N. Y. P. L.   September 24, 1947

NT 0050117   NN

Tate, Thomas Turner, 1807-1888.
    ... On magnetism ... London, 1854.

NT 0050118   PPL

Tate, Thomas Turner, 1807-1888.
    ... On magnetism, voltaic electricity, and
electro-dynamics for the use of beginners, in
which the principles of the sciences are familiarly
explained and illustrated by numerous experiments
and diagrams. New ed. Longmans [1862 ?]
    106 p. illus. diagrs. (Gleig's series)

NT 0050119   MiD

Tate, Thomas Turner, 1807-1888.
    On the strength of materials; containing various origi-
nal and useful formulæ, specially applied to tubular
bridges, wrought iron and cast iron beams, etc. By
Thomas Tate ... London, Printed for Longman, Brown,
Green, and Longmans, 1850.

1 p. l., [v]-x p., 1 l., 96 p. diagrs. 22½ᶜᵐ.

1. Strength of materials.

Library of Congress   TA405.T2
                                               4—1467

NT 0050120   DLC CtY PPF CU OrP NjP NWM

Tate, T[homas Turner] 1807-1888.
    The philosophy of education; or, The principles and
practice of teaching. In five parts. Part I. On method
as applied to education. Part II. The intellectual and
moral faculties considered in relation to teaching. Part
III. On systems and methods of instruction. Part IV. On
systems and methods as applied to the various branches
of elementary education. Part V. On school organization
and discipline. By T. Tate ... London, Longman,
Brown, Green, and Longmans, 1854.

iv p., 1 l., 162 p. incl. illus., forms. 22ᶜᵐ.

1. Teaching.

Library of Congress   LB1025.T19   6-29208†

NT 0050121   DLC KEmT

Tate, Thomas Turner, 1807-1888.
    The philosophy of education; or, The principles
and practice of teaching. In five parts. Part I.
On method as applied to education. Part II. On
the cultivation of the intellectual and moral
faculties. Part III. On the comparative advantages
of different methods and systems of instruction.
Part IV. On the application of differenet systems
and methods to the various branches of elementary
education. Part V. On school organisation and
discipline. By T. Tate ... 2d ed rev. and
considerably enl. London, Longman, Brown,

Green, Longmans & Roberts, 1857.
    xii, 388 p. incl. illus., forms. 18 cm.

NT 0050123   CtY

Tate, Thomas Turner, 1807-1888.
    Philosophy of education, or The principles &
practice of teaching. In five parts. Ed. 3, rev.
and enl. London, Longman, 1860.
    p. 12-338. D.

NT 0050124   OO

Tate, Thomas Turner, 1807-1888.
    The philosophy of education; or, The principles and
practice of teaching. In five parts. Part I. On method as
applied to education. Part II. On the cultivation of the
intellectual and moral faculties. Part III. On the comparative advantages of different methods and systems of instruction. Part IV. On the application of different systems and methods to the various branches of elementary
education. Part V. On school organization and discipline.
By T. Tate, F. R. A. S. With an introduction by Col. Francis W. Parker. 1st American, from 3d London ed. Syracuse, N. Y., C. W. Bardeen, 1884.
    xvi, 330 p. 17½ᶜᵐ.
1. Teaching.   [31d1]
Library of Congress   LB1025.T2   6-30089†

NT 0050125   DLC WaSp MtBC KMK DHEW OC1

Tate, Thomas Turner, 1807-1888.
    The philosophy of education; or, The principles and prac-
tice of teaching, by T. Tate ... Edited by Edward E. Sheib ...
New York and Chicago, E. L. Kellogg & co. [*1885]
    xii, [13]-331 p. diagrs. 19ᶜᵐ. (Kellogg's teachers' library. vol. x)
    Educational foundations ... December, 1900. vol. XII, no. 4.

    1. Teaching.   I. Sheib, Edward E., ed.   II. Title.
                                               E 9—1640
U. S. Off. of educ. Library   LB1025.T22
for Library of Congress   LB1025.T2 1885
————— Copy 2.   L11.E3 vol. 12, no. 4

                      ICJ MiU DLC
NT 0050126   DHEW PWcS PSC PPT PU MH-Ed NNC NcU OCU

Tate, Thomas Turner, 1807-1888.
    The philosophy of education; or, The principles and prac-
tice of teaching. In five parts... By T. Tate... With an introduction by Col. Francis W. Parker. Syracuse: C. W. Bardeen,
1885. xv, 400 p. 2. Amer. ed. 12°. (Standard teachers'
library.)

    Imprint of J. R. Holcomb & Co., Cleveland, Ohio, pasted over original imprint.
    On method as applied to education. On the cultivation of the intellectual and
moral faculties. On the comparative advantages of different methods and systems
of instruction. On the application of different systems and methods to the various
branches of elementary education. On school organization and discipline.

1. Teaching.—Principles, etc.   2. Parker, Francis Wayland, 1837-
1902. 3. Title.
N. Y. P. L.   June 14, 1915.

NT 0050127   NN NcD NIC MiU OU CtY NcC PU LU PPFr

Tate, Thomas Turner, 1807-1888.
    Principles of geometry, mensuration, trigonometry,
land-surveying, and levelling: containing ... demonstrations and illustrations of the most important propositions
in Euclid's elements; proofs of all the useful rules and
formulae in mensuration and trigonometry, with their application to the solution of practical problems in estima-
tion, surveying, and railway engineering. By Thomas
Tate ... 3d ed. London, Longman, Brown, Green, and
Longmans, 1848.
    viii, 2 l., 261, [1] p. diagr. 18ᶜᵐ.
    1. Geometry. 2. Mensuration. 3. Trigonometry. 4. Surveying.
                                               3—20981
Library of Congress   QA529.T21

NT 0050128   DLC

TATE, Thomas, 1807-1888.
    Principles of geometry, mensuration, trigono-
metry, land-surveying, and levelling. 7th ed.
London, 1855.

    Wdcts. and diagrs.

NT 0050129   MH OO

Tate, Thomas Turner, 1807-1888.
    The principles of mechanical philosophy applied to in-
dustrial mechanics: forming a sequel to the author's
"Exercises on mechanics and natural philosophy." By
Thomas Tate ... London, Longman, Brown, Green, and
Longmans, 1853.
    xv, 342 p. tables, diagrs. 22ᶜᵐ.

    1. Mechanical engineering.
                                               6—28096
Library of Congress   TJ146.T22

NT 0050130   DLC CtY NjR PPF PU MiU NjP ICJ NN

Tate, Thomas Turner, 1807-1888.
    The principles of the differential and integral calculus,
simplified, and applied to the solution of various useful
problems in practical mathematics and mechanics. By
Thomas Tate ... London, Printed for Longman, Brown,
Green, and Longmans, 1849.
    viii, 245, [1] p. diagrs. 16½ᶜᵐ.

    1. Calculus.
                                               3-20299 Revised
Library of Congress   QA303.T19

NT 0050131   DLC CtY MH OO CU

Tate, Thomas Turner, 1807-1888.
    Principles of the differential and integral
calculus simplified ... 5. ed. London, 1863.

NT 0050132   NjP

Tate, Thomas Turner, 1807-1888.
    The principles of the differential and integral
calculus simplified and applied to the solution of
various useful problems in practical mathematics
and mechanics ... New ed. London, Longmans,
Green, and co., 1873.
    viii, 245 [1] p. diagrs. 18 cm.
    1. Calculus.

NT 0050133   CtY CoU

Tate, Thomas Turner, 1807-1888.   512.4 K400
    A treatise on factorial analysis, with the summation of series;
containing various new developments of functions, &c. By Thomas Tate, ... London, G. Bell, 1845.
    [2], x, 51, [1] p. 22½ᶜᵐ.

NT 0050134   ICJ CtY DAU

Tate, Thomas Turner, 1807–1888.
    A treatise on the first principles of arithmetic, after the method of Pestalozzi ... By Thomas Tate ... 7th ed. London, Longman, Brown, Green, and Longmans, 1849.
    2 p. l., ₁ix₎– xii, 108 p. 18ᶜᵐ.

    1. Arithmetic—1846–1880.

    Library of Congress   QA101.T2   3—28092

NT   0050135   DLC

Z1007
.A477

Tate, Vernon Dale, 1909–   ed.

    American documentation; a quarterly review of ideas, techniques, problems and achievements in documentation.   v. 1–

    Jan. 1950–
    ₁Washington, American Documentation Institute₎

Tate, Vernon Dale, 1909–
    Books in libraries, architect vs. librarian; two rounds to a decision. ₁Papers read at the Club of Odd Volumes, March 21, 1951, by Vernon D. Tate and Ralph Walker. Boston? 1951₎
    38 p. 18 cm.

    1. Library architecture.   ɪ. Walker, Ralph, 1889–   ɪɪ. Title.

    Z679.T3   022   56–32514 ‡

NT   0050137   DLC CU NIC IU MoU

₁**Tate, Vernon Dale**₎ 1909–
    Books in libraries. Architect vs. librarian; two rounds to a decision. ₁Portland, Me., Printed for the Friends of the Massachusetts institute of technology library by the Anthoensen press, 1951₎   38 p., 1 l.   18cm.

    Cover-title.
    Comprises "The librarian and the building of a library, by Vernon D. Tate" and "The architect and the university library, by Ralph Walker," two papers read at the Club of odd volumes, March 21, 1951.

    52R0253. 1. Libraries—Architecture.   I. Tate, Vernon Dale, 1909–
    The librarian and the building of a   library. II. Walker, Ralph T
    The architect and the university li-   brary. III. Friends of the library
    of the Massachusetts institute of   technology. IV. Title.
    NN

NT   0050138   NN NNC TxU ViU MeB MiU MB

Tate, Vernon Dale, 1909–
    The founding of the port of San Blas, by Vernon Dale Tate ... [Berkeley, Calif., 1934]
    4 p. l., ii, 287 numb. l. plates (mounted photos) 29 cm.
    Thesis (Ph. D.) - University of California, May, 1934.
    Bibliography: p. 266–287.
    1. San Blas, Mexico—History.

NT   0050139   CU

Z265
.J86

Tate, Vernon Dale, 1909–   ed.

    The **Journal** of documentary reproduction; a quarterly review of the application of photography and allied techniques to library, museum and archival service. v. 1–5; winter 1938– Dec. 1942. ₁Chicago, American Library Association₎

Tate, Vernon Dale, 1909–
    The Librarian and the building of a library
        see his   Books in libraries.

Tate, Vernon Dale, 1909–
    Memorandum on the American Documentation Institute
        see under   American Documentation Institute.

₁**Tate, Vernon Dale**₎ 1909–
    Micro-copying as an aid to research. ₁n. p., 1935₎   10 f. 26½cm.

    Caption-title.
    Reproduced from typewritten copy.
    Signed: Vernon D. Tate.
    "Paper read at the fiftieth annual meeting of the American Historical Association, Chattanooga, Tennessee, December 27, 1935."

    869920A. 1. Microphotography.   2. Photography—Reproduction of books.
    N. Y. P. L.   February 25, 1937

NT   0050143   NN

Tate, Vernon Dale, 1909–
    ... Microfotografía, traducción, prólogo y notas de Carlos Víctor Penna ... Buenos Aires, 1944.
    ₁27₎ p. illus. 22½ᶜᵐ. (On cover: Contribuciones al conocimiento de la bibliotecología, 1)
    At head of title: Comité argentino de bibliotecarios de instituciones científicas y técnicas. Vernon D. Tate.
    Reproduced from type-written copy.

    1. Microphotography.   ɪ. Penna, Carlos Víctor, ed. and tr. ɪɪ. Comité argentino de bibliotecarios de instituciones científicas y técnicas, Buenos Aires. ɪɪɪ. Title.

    Library of. Congress   TR835.T278   45–17292
                            ₁3₎   778.315

NT   0050144   DLC

778
T18m

Tate, Vernon Dale, 1909–
    Microphotography for the special library ... ₁Washington? D.C., 1937₎
    18 numb. l.

    Caption title.
    Multigraphed.
    "Address delivered before the New York chapter of the Special libraries association, New York city, January 27, 1937."– leaf 18.

    1. Microphotography.

NT   0050145   IU PPAmP

Tate, Vernon Dale, 1909–
    Microphotography in archives, by Vernon D. Tate. [Washington, D. C.] 1940.
    10 numb. l. 27 cm. (National archives. Office of the executive officer. Staff information circulars, no. 8, April 1940)
    Reproduced from typewritten material.
    "This paper is a revision ... of ... ₁the₎ article bearing the same title in American library.

NT   0050146   PU PPPCPh

Tate, Vernon Dale, 1909–
    ... The present status of equipment and supplies for microphotography, a report prepared for the Committee on scientific aids to learning, by Vernon D. Tate ... ₁Chicago, American library association, 1938₎
    cover-title, 62 p. plates, tables (1 fold.) 21½ᶜᵐ.
    Issued as v. 1, no. 3, part 2 of the Journal of documentary reproduction, summer 1938.
    "Abridged directory of sources of further information": p. 57–62.

    1. Microphotography. 2. Photography — Apparatus and supplies. ɪ. National research council. Committee on scientific aids to learning.
                                        46–40134
    Library of Congress   Z265.J86   vol. 1, no. 3, pt. 2

NT   0050147   DLC PHi PPT PPAmP CaBViP CSmH

    The year's progress in microphotography... [Washington, D.C., 1937]   38 p.   23cm.

    Signed: Vernon D. Tate.
    Reproduced from typewritten copy.

    1. Photography—Reproduction of books.

NT   0050148   NN DLC

Tate, W. G.　　　　　　　　　**527 Q002**
    The theory and practice of navigation and nautical astronomy. [6],118 p. il. 1 table. O. North Shields: W. J. Potts, 1900.

NT   0050149   ICJ

Tate, William, ed.
    Documents and memoirs, genealogical tables, the Tates of Pickens county.   Marietta, Ga., Continental book co., 1953.   94 l.   28cm.

    1 Tate family. I. Tate, William.

NT   0050150   NN

Tate, William, chemist
    ... On the connection between the critical temperatures of gases and vapours and their absorption coefficients and the viscosity of the solvent medium, by W:m Tate. Uppsala & Stockholm, Almqvist & Wiksells boktryckeri-a.-b.; ₁etc., etc.₎ 1906.
    cover-title, 9 p. 22½ᶜᵐ. (Meddelanden från K. Vetenskapsakademiens Nobelinstitut. bd. 1, n: o 4)

    1. Solubility. 2. Gases.

    Library of Congress   Q64.S92   8-22769
    ———— Copy 2.   Library of Congress   QD543.T3

NT   0050151   DLC NN

Tate, William, chemist.
Thorpe, *Sir* **Thomas Edward,** 1845–1925.
    A series of chemical problems with key for use in colleges and schools ₁by₎ Sir Edward Thorpe ... rev. and enl. by W. Tate ... With a preface by Sir H. E. Roscoe ... London, Macmillan and co., limited, 1911.

Tate, William, chemist.
Lundén, Harald L   R.
    ... Über einen einfachen toluolregulator und eine einfache schüttelvorrichtung für thermostaten, von Harald Lundén und W. Tate. Uppsala & Stockholm, Almqvist & Wiksells boktryckeri-a.-b.; ₁etc., etc.₎ 1906.

Tate, William, Engineer of Scranton
    Questions and answers for American mine examinations, by Wm. Tate ...   Scranton, Pa., The Colliery engineer co., 1897.
    v. illus. 19ᶜᵐ.
    CONTENTS.— pt. I. Mine ventilation, theoretical and practical. — pt. II. Economic coal mining.

    1. Coal mines and mining. 2. Mining engineering.

    Library of Congress   TN151.T21   6-19491†

NT   0050154   DLC CaBVaU NNC ICJ

Tate, William, *the younger*
　　A complete system of commercial arithmetic,
its application to the principal branches
of commerce according to the existing practices
of trade, & numerous rules for facilitating &
performing mental calculations; with an app....
By W.Tate... 3d ed. London, E. Wilson ,etc.,
etc., 1837.
　　122 p.

NT　0050155　　MiU

Tate, William, *1781?-1848.*
　　The elements of commercial arithmetic. New edition, with additional questions.
London. Wilson. 1857. vi, (2), 218 pp. Sm. 8°.

3936.22

H3881 — Commercial arithmetic.

NT　0050156　　MB

Kress
Room
Tate, William, 1781?-1848.
　　The elements of commercial calculations,
and an introduction to the more important
branches of the commerce & finances of this
country. By W.Tate ... London, Printed
by Richards and co., 1819.
　　2 v. forms, tables. 22.5 cm.

　　Vol.2 has imprint: London, Sold by Sherwood, Neely and Jones, 1819.

NT　0050157　　MH-BA CtY MB MH PU

SPECIAL COLLECTIONS
MONTGOMERY

Tate, William, 1781?-1848.
　　An introduction to merchants' accounts, or,
Commercial book-keeping, by double entry; with
an examination of the principles of single
entry. For the use of schools and counting
houses. London, Printed for C. Law ,etc.,
1810.
　　xxii, ,2, 192 p. 18cm.

　　1. Bookkeeping.

NT　0050158　　NNC

Tate, William, *1781?-1848.*
　　A manual of foreign exchanges, in the direct, indirect, and
cross operations of bills of exchange and bullion; including an
extensive investigation of the arbitrations of exchange, according to the practice of the first British and foreign houses, with
numerous formulæ and tables of the weights and measures of
other countries, compared with the imperial standards. By
William Tate. London, E. Wilson; ,etc., etc.,) 1831.
　　xiv, 224 p. 23cm.
Later editions pub. under title: The modern cambist.

　　1. Foreign exchange. 2. Weights and measures. I. Title.
　　　　　　　　　　　　　　　　　　　　　　10—34789
Library of Congress　　　　HG3863.T2 1831

NT　0050159　　DLC NjP MiU

HG3856
.T25
Tate,William,1781⸗1848.
　　The modern cambist;forming a manual of foreign
exchanges,in the direct,indirect,and cross operations of bills of exchange and bullion;including
an extensive investigation of the arbitrations
of exchange,according to the practice of the first
British and foreign houses. With numerous formulae
and tables of the weights and measures of other
countries,compared with the imperial standards.
By William Tate. 2d ed. London,E.Wilson;,etc.,
etc.,,1834.
　　xiv,224 p. 23cm.

NT　0050160　　ICU PU-L

C.4260 Tate, William, 1781?-1848.
　　The modern cambist, forming a manual of foreign exchanges . . . 3d. ed. with extensive alterations and additions [1] ... London, E.Wilson, 1836.
　　2 p l., [iii]-xiv (i.e.xvi), 224 p. 22 cm.

NT　0050161　　MH-BA ViU CtY

Tate, William, *1781?-1848.*
　　The modern cambist, forming a manual of foreign
exchanges ... By William Tate. 4th ed. with extensive
alterations and additions ... London, E. Wilson, 1842.
　　2 p. l., iiii-xviii, 212 p. 22½ᶜᵐ.

　　1. Foreign exchange. 2. Money—Tables, etc.
　　　　　　　　　　　　　　　　　　6-35927†
Library of Congress　　　　HG3856.T22

NT　0050162　　DLC NN

Tate, William, 1781?-1848.
　　Modern cambist. London, 1849

NT　0050163　　NjP

Tate, William, 1781?-1848.
　　The modern, cambist, forming a manual of
foreign exchanges ... By William Tate. 7th ed.
with extensive alterations and additions ...
London, E. Wilson, 1852.
　　22.5 cm.
　　Edited by his son William Tate.

　　1st ed. pub. 1829 under title : A manual of
foreign exchanges.
　　1. Foreign exchange. 2. Money. Tables, etc.
I. Tate, William, ed. 3. Weights and measures.

NT　0050164　　CtY

Tate, William, *1781?-1848.*　　　332.45 M100
⁸⁷⁰⁴⁶ The modern cambist: forming a manual of foreign exchanges, in
the different operations of bills of exchange and bullion, according
to the practice of all trading nations; with tables of foreign weights
and measures, and their equivalents in English and French. By
William Tate, ... Eleventh edition. With extensive alterations
and additions, brought down to the present time. London, E.
Wilson, 1862.
　　x, 262 p. 23ᶜᵐ.

NT　0050165　　ICJ

HG3856
.T255
Tate William,1781⸗1848.
　　The modern cambist:forming a manual of foreign
exchanges,in the different operations of bills
of exchange and bullion,according to the practice
of all trading nations;with tables of foreign
weights and measures,and their equivalents in
English and French. By William Tate... 12th ed.,
with extensive alterations and additions,brought
down to the present time,and tables of the new
French tariff rates of gold and silver. London,
E.Wilson,1863.
　　x,262 p. 22½cm.

NT　0050166　　ICU CtY

Tate, William, 1781?-1848.
　　The modern cambist: Forming a manual of
foreign exchanges ... with tables of foreign
weights and measures ... London, E. Wilson,
1868.
　　iii-x, 262 p. 8°.
　　14. ed.

NT　0050167　　NN

Tate, William, *1781?-1848.*
　　Tate's modern cambist ... forming a manual of foreign
exchanges ... 16th ed., re-written and enlarged; with a
copious index. By G. L. M. Strauss. London, E. Wilson,
1874.
　　xii, 311 p. 22½ᶜᵐ.

　　1. Foreign exchange. 2. Weights and measures. 3. Money—Tables, etc.
I. Strauss, Gustave Louis Maurice, 1807?-1887, ed.
　　　　　　　　　　　　　　　　　　6—35928
Library of Congress　　　　HG3856.T25

NT　0050168　　DLC DAU NN

TATE,William, *1781?-1848.*
　　'Tate's modern cambist;' a manual of foreign
exchanges and bullion,etc., 17th ed. by Hermann Schmidt. London,E.Wilson,1880.

　　pp.xi,245+.

NT　0050169　　MH

Tate, William, 1781?-1848.
　　Tate's modern cambist; a manual of foreign
exchanges and bullion, with the moneys and other
mediums of exchange of all trading nations; also
tables of foreign weights and measures, with
their equivalents in English and French. 19th ed.,
by Hermann Schmidt. London, E. Wilson, 1884.
　　245 p. tables.

NT　0050170　　MH-BA

TATE,William, *1781?-1848.*
　　Tate's *Modern cambist*: a manual of foreign
exchanges and bullion,with the moneys and
other mediums of exchange of all trading
nations;also tables of foreign weights and
measures,with their equivalents in English and
French. 20th ed.,by Hermann Schmidt. London,
1887.

NT　0050171　　MH INS DN

Tate, William, 1781?-1848.
　　Tate's modern cambist; a manual of foreign exchanges and
bullion, with the moneys and other mediums of exchange of all
trading nations; also, tables of foreign weights and measures,
with their equivalents in English and French. 23d ed. By
Hermann Schmidt. London, E. Wilson & co., 1893.
　　xi, 249 p. 22ᶜᵐ.

　　1. Foreign exchange. 2. Weights and measures. 3. Money—Tables,
etc. I. Schmidt, Hermann, economist.
　　　　　　　　　　　　　　　　　　38-25380
Library of Congress　　　　HG3863.T2 1893

NT　0050172　　DLC CoU CtY ICJ OU CU

Tate, William, *1781?-1848.*
　　Tate's Modern cambist: a manual of foreign exchanges
and bullion, with the monetary systems of the world and
foreign weights and measures. 24th ed. By H. T. Easton ... London, E. Wilson, 1908.
　　xv, 345 p. 22ᶜᵐ.

　　1. Foreign exchange. 2. Weights and measures. 3. Money—Tables, etc.
I. Easton, Harry Tucker, ed.
　　　　　　　　　　　　　　　　　　9—22045
Library of Congress　　　　HG3856.T26

NT　0050173　　DLC MiU ViU ICJ

Tate, William, *1781?-1848.*
　　Tate's Modern cambist: a manual of foreign exchanges
and bullion, wih the monetary systems of the world
and foreign weights and measures, with chapters on exchange and bullion operations. 25th ed. By H. T. Easton ... London, E. Wilson, 1912.
　　xvii, 375 p. 21½ᶜᵐ.

　　1. Foreign exchange. 2. Weights and measures. 3. Money—Tables,
etc. I. Easton, Harry Tucker, ed.
　　　　　　　　　　　　　　　　　　13-579
Library of Congress　　　　HG3856.T26 1912

NT　0050174　　DLC CtY PU-W NN

Tate, William, 1781?-1848.
　　Tate's Modern cambist; a manual of foreign
exchanges and bullion, with the monetary systems
of the world and foreign weights and measures.
25th ed. by H. T. Easton ... New York,
Colonial Pub. Co., 1919.
　　345 p.

NT　0050175　　PPFRB

HG 3863
T3
1921
Tate, William, 1781?-1848.
Tate's modern cambist: a manual of foreign exchanges and bullion, with the monetary systems of the world and foreign weights and measures. With chapters on exchange and bullion operations. 26th ed., by H. T. Easton. London, E. Wilson, 1921.
xviii, 438 p. 22 cm.

NT 0050176 OU DBS MB

Tate, William, 1781?-1848.
Tate's modern cambist: a manual of the world's monetary systems, the foreign exchanges, the stamp duties on bills of exchange in foreign countries, the principal rules governing bills of exchange and promissory notes, foreign weights and measures and bullion and exchange operations. 27th ed. By William F. Spalding ... London, E. Wilson; New York, Bankers publishing co., 1926.
xxxi, 477 p. 22cm.
"Re-written by William F. Spalding."
1. Foreign exchange. 2. Weights and measures. 3. Money—Tables, etc. I. Spalding, William Frederick, 1879- ed.

Library of Congress   HG3856.T26 1926
                                                    26- 5400

NT 0050177 DLC NcD MU CaBVaU WaU CU NN MiU

Tate, William, 1781?-1848.
Tate's Modern cambist: centenary edition; a manual of the world's monetary systems, the foreign exchanges, the stamp duties on bills of exchange in foreign countries, the principal rules governing bills of exchange and promissory notes, foreign weights and measures, bullion and exchange operations. 28th ed. By William F. Spalding ... London, Sir I. Pitman & sons, ltd., 1929.
xiv, 734 p, 1 l. 22cm.
Rewritten by William F. Spalding.
Contains advertising matter.
"Appendix: Biographical account of the activities of William Tate—Editions of Tate's 'Cambist'—Editors of Tate's 'Cambist' ": p. 687-696.

——— Tate's money manual, being the first— annual edition of additions, alterations, and amendments to the centenary edition of Tate's Modern cambist, by William F. Spalding ... London, Sir I. Pitman & sons, ltd. [1931]—
v. fold. tab. 22cm.
Includes list of books on banking and allied subjects.
1. Foreign exchange. 2. Weights and measures. 3. Money—Tables, etc. I. Spalding, William Frederick, 1879- ed.
                                                    36-14093
Library of Congress   HG3863.T2 1929 a Suppl.
                                [2]   332.45

NT 0050179 DLC CoU MB

Tate, William, 1781?-1848.
Tate's Modern cambist: centenary edition; a manual of the world's monetary systems, the foreign exchanges, the stamp duties on bills of exchange in foreign countries, the principal rules governing bills of exchange and promissory notes, foreign weights and measures, bullion and exchange operations. 28th ed. By William F. Spalding ... London, E. Wilson; New York, Bankers publishing co., 1929.
xiv, 734 p, 1 l. 21½cm.
Rewritten by William F. Spalding.
Contains advertising matter.
"Appendix: Biographical account of the activities of William Tate—Editions of Tate's 'Cambist'—Editors of Tate's 'Cambist' ": p. 687-696.

——— Tate's money manual, being the first— annual edition of additions, alterations and amendments to the centenary edition of Tate's Modern cambist, by William F. Spalding ... London, E. Wilson; New York, Bankers publishing co. [1931]—
v. 22cm.
Includes list of books on banking and allied subjects.
1. Foreign exchange. 2. Weights and measures. 3. Money—Tables, etc. I. Spalding, William Frederick, 1879- ed.
                                                    30-16793 Revised
Library of Congress   HG3863.T2 1929 Suppl.
                                [2]   332.45

PPT MB NN ICJ OC1 OC1C
NT 0050181 DLC CaBVaU WaS WaSp MtU NcC PP PPFRB CU

Tate, William, 1781?-1848.
Tate's Money manual
see his Tate's Modern cambist: centenary edition ... 1929.

368.2
T188p
Tate, William.
The practice of marine insurances; containing a summary of the most important legal decisions, the regulations of the policy office, of Lloyd's, and of the assurance companies ... and the principles of making up statements of general and particular averages, and salvage losses. London, 1819.
80p.

NT 0050183 IU

Tate, William, 1781?-1848.
Steel, David.
Steel's shipmaster's assistant; for the use of merchants, owners, and masters of vessels, officers of customs, and other persons connected with the ownership, charge, and management of ships and their cargoes: containing the acts of Parliament relating to such subjects; treaties of navigation and commerce; shipping rates and rates of pilotage in the ports and harbours of the United Kingdom; regulations and duties in the East India and China trade, and the British colonies; with treatises on the duties of owners and masters; of agents; on the carriage of goods; stoppage in transitu; marine insurance and averages; bottomry and respondentia; bills of exchange, foreign moneys, weights, measures, and exchanges; and naval book-keeping. New ed., re-written throughout, dedicated (by permission) to the General shipowners' society. Ed. by Graham Willmore ... The customs and shipping department by George Clements ... The commercial department and naval book-keeping by William Tate ... London, Longman, Brown, Green, and Longmans, 1846.

Tate, William, 1781?-1848.
A system of commercial arithmetic, upon a new and improved plan. By W. Tate ... London, Printed by W. Flint, for S. Tipper, 1809.
xii, 228, [11] p. 18cm.
——— A key to the new System of commercial calculations ... London, J. Asperne, C. Law [etc.] 1811.
1 p. l., x, 195, [x] p. 18cm.
Appendix: ix p.
1. Arithmetic, Commercial.

Library of Congress   QA101.T21
                                                    3-28093-4

NT 0050186 DLC MH

QA101
.T2
Tate, William, 1781?-1848.
A system of commercial arithmetic; containing a new and improved arrangement of the theory of the science, with an extensive application of its principles to various calculations... by W. Tate...
London, Printed for C. Law, 1810.
1 p. l., xii, 228, [32] p. 18cm.
With answers.
1. Arithmetic, Commercial.

NT 0050187 NNU-W

Kress
Room
Tate, William, 1781?-1848.
The system of the London bankers' clearances, and their effect upon the currency. Explained and exemplified by formulae of the clearing-house accounts ... London, E. Wilson, 1841.
2 p. l., ii, [3]-32 p. 21.5 cm.
1. Banks and banking - London. I. Title.

NT 0050188 MH-BA PU CtY ICJ

Tate, William Edward.
A hand-list of Buckinghamshire enclosure acts and awards, by W. E. Tate ... Aylesbury, Clerk of the Bucks county council, 1946.
vi, 46 p, 1 l. plan, facsim. 21½ cm.
Bibliographical foot-notes.
1. Inclosures. 2. Real property—Buckinghamshire, Eng.

HD594.6.T3   333.31   47-25297

NT 0050189 DLC NN LU AU CU ICU MB MnU ViU NcD

Tate, William Edward.
A handlist of Sussex inclosure acts and awards. Chichester, Clerk of the West Sussex County Council, 1950.
iv, 47 p. maps. 22 cm. (Sussex Archaeological Society. Record publication no. 1)
"Reprinted from Sussex Archaeological Society's collections, vol. 88."
Bibliographical footnotes.
1. Inclosures. I. Title: Sussex inclosure acts. (Series)
DA670.S97S917 no. 1   58-43767

NT 0050190 DLC TxU LU NcU NN ViU MH CSt

Tate, William Edward.
Inns and inn signs in and near Burslem, in Stoke on Trent. By W. E. Tate ... Burslem, W. Savage, 1944.
46 p. incl. col. front. (coat-of-arms) illus. 22cm.
1. Signs and sign-boards. 2. Burslem, Eng.—Hotels, taverns, etc. I. Title.
Library of Congress   GT3910.T3   45-2863
                                [4]   647.94

NT 0050191 DLC

Tate, William Edward.
The parish chest, a study of the records of parochial administration in England, by W. E. Tate ... Cambridge [Eng.] The University press, 1946.
x, 346 p. front., plates, maps, facsims. 22cm.
Bibliography: p. 326-332.
1. Archives—Gt. Brit. 2. Gt. Brit.—History, Local—Sources. 3. Gt. Brit.—Church history—Sources. I. Title.
CD1068.A2T43   942   47-401

NcD CtY NBuU
NT 0050192 DLC PU MCE PBL PPWe CaBViP MB ICN ICU CU

Tate, William Edward.
The parish chest; a study of the records of parochial administration in England. 2d ed., rev. and enl. Cambridge [Eng.] University Press, 1951
xi, 346 p. illus. maps. 23 cm.
Bibliography: p. 326-332.
1. Gt. Brit.—History, Local—Sources. 2. Gt. Brit.—Church history—Sources. I. Title.
CD1068.A2T43 1951   942   51—13231

NT 0050193 DLC MB Vi CtY NIC NcD ViU PPCCH LU

Tate, William Edward, ed.
Parliamentary land enclosures in the county of Nottingham during the 18th and 19th centuries (1743-1868) by William Edward Tate ... with a foreword by T. M. Blagg ... Nottingham, Printed for the Thoroton society by Cooke & Vowles, ltd., 1935.
xxvii, 215 p. v pl. (incl. front., maps, diagr.) on 3 l. 22½cm. (Half-title: Thoroton society. Record series, vol. v)
1. Inclosures. 2. Agriculture—England—Nottinghamshire. I. Gt. Brit. Parliament. II. Title.
                                                    38-14647
Library of Congress   DA670.N89T6 vol. 5
                                [5]   (942.52) 333.3094252

NT 0050194 DLC WU ICN NN CtY CSmH

Tate, William Edward
333.094238
T217s
Somerset enclosure acts and awards, by W. E. Tate. Also a detailed list of the enclosure award maps prepared at the Somerset County Record Office. Frome [Eng.] Printed for the Society by Butler & Tanner, 1948.
107 p. 23 cm.
At head of title: Somerset Archaeological and Natural History Society.
1. Inclosures. 2. Somerset. Hist. I. Somersetshire Archaeological and Natural History Society. II. Title.

NT 0050195 NcD

Tate, William H.

Gt. Brit. *Ministry of health. Advisory committee on the welfare of the blind.*
... Report of the sub-committee on home teaching ... London, H. M. Stationery off., 1937.

Tate, William Harold.
... Growth and food habit studies of smallmouth black bass in some Iowa streams.
[n. p. , n. pub.] 1949.
p. 343–354. O.

NT 0050197   CaBViP

Tate, William J[ames]
East coast scenery; rambles through towns and villages; nutting, blackberrying and mushrooming; sea fishing, wild-fowl shooting, etc. By William J. Tate. London, Jarrold & sons, 1899.
261, [1] p. incl. front., illus., plates. 21½ᶜᵐ. (*On cover:* Jarrold's holiday series)

Title in red and black. Title vignette.
"The majority of these sketches were contributed to ... the Civil service guardian, in 1890–91, and the Bristol times and mirror, in 1897–98."

1. England—Descr. & trav.

Library of Congress   DA670 E14T2   5–38341

NT 0050198   DLC

Tate, William James.   354-42 P800
A new and complete practical guide to H. M. civil service. Containing qualifications of candidates, limits as to age, subjects to be examined in, official regulations, specimens of examination papers, etc., etc. Sixth thousand. iv,328 p. D. London: J. Blackwood & Co., [1898].

NT 0050199   ICJ

Tate, William James.
Somerset in bygone days, by William J. Tate. London, Simpkin, Marshall, Hamilton, Kent and co., ltd., 1912.
4 p. l., 128 p. 19½ᶜᵐ.
CONTENTS. — The father of English botany, Dr. W. Turner, dean of Wells.—The Blakes, Alleines and Normans.—Arthur's Point, near Wells.—How the cavaliers were driven out of Wells.—The condition of the Wells, West of England, and South Wales clothiers and woolcombers in the early part of the XVII century. From state papers.—Arrests and examinations for sedition in Somersetshire. From state papers.—A few hours in the law courts 600 years ago. From the Year books of Edward I.—The Norman conquest, and what followed it in the West of England. From the "Saxon chronicle."—Miscellaneous entries from the Stuart state papers.—Some state papers of Henry VIII's reign relating to Wells and neighbourhood.—The Somersetshire visitation of A. D. 1623, etc.—The Somersetshire visitations of A. D. 1573, 1591 and 1623.—Names of the electors who voted at the Wells parliamentary election, 1765.—Saxon spells and charms and remedies.
1. Somerset, Eng.

Library of Congress   DA670.S5T3   13–358

NT 0050200   DLC IU NjP

[Tate, William James] writer on Wright brothers flight
Brochure of the 25th. anniversary celebration of the first successful airplane flight, 1903–1928. Kitty Hawk, N. C., Dec. 17, 1928.
12 p. illus.
No imprint.
Contains also: Program of unveiling ceremonies Wright Brothers Memorial Marker, May 2d, 1928, Kitty Hawk, N. C.

NT 0050201   NcD NcU

Tate, William James, writer on Wright brothers Flight
Wings over Kill Devil
see under Albertson, Catherine Seyton, 1868–

Tate, William Knox, 1870–1917.

Withers, Sarah.
The child's world readers manual, by Sarah Withers ... Hetty S. Browne ... and W. K. Tate ... Atlanta, Richmond [etc.] B. F. Johnson publishing company [°1917]

Tate, William Knox, 1870–1917.
Country school movements and ideals in South Carolina, by W. K. Tate ... Columbia, S. C., The State company, printers, 1914.
31 p. 23ᶜᵐ. (*Added t.-p.:* Bulletin of the University of South Carolina ... no. 36, pt. II)
Reprinted from the forty-fifth Annual report of the state superintendent of education, 1913 (p. 41–61)

1. Rural schools—South Carolina.   I. Title.

         17–11081

Library of Congress   LA361.T3

NT 0050204   DLC DL MH ScU

Tate, William Knox, 1870–1917.
Enrichment of rural life in South Carolina. (University of South Carolina Bulletin, No. 26, pt. 1, Founders' day, 1911. p. 17–23. 12°.)

NT 0050205   ScU

Tate, William Knox, 1870–1917.
Farm supplement to Milne's Progressive arithmetic. Second book. South Carolina edition. New York, American Book Company, [°1912]
p. 305–323
1. Arithmetic – Study and teaching. I. Milne, William James, 1843–1914. Progressive arithmetic. Book 2.

NT 0050206   ScU

Tate, William Knox, 1870–1917.

Withers, Sarah.
Manual to accompany the Child's world readers, by Withers, Browne, and Tate. Enl. ed. with a chapter on the use of tests in teaching reading, by William A. McCall ... Richmond, Va., Johnson publishing company [°1921]

Tate, William Knox, 1870–1917.
The new country school; a survey of development, by W. K. Tate ... The Youth's companion and school improvement; an address delivered by Warren Dunham Foster before a meeting of the Inter-state league for the betterment of public schools, held under the auspices of the Summer school of the South, at the University of Tennessee. Boston, Mass., The Youth's companion [1914]
cover-title, 16 p. illus. 23ᶜᵐ.
1. Rural schools. 2. Youth's companion.   I. Foster, Warren Dunham.

         E 14–820

Library, U. S. Bur. of   Education LB1567.T2

   MB NN
NT 0050208   DLC ICJ Or PWcS PU ICU DHEW DL MiU OO

Tate, William Knox, 1870–1917.
... Some suggestive features of the Swiss school system, by William Knox Tate ... Washington, Govt. print. off., 1914.
119 p. 26 pl. (incl. front., plans) 23ᶜᵐ. (U. S. Bureau of education. Bulletin, 1913, no. 56. Whole no. 567)

1. Education—Switzerland.   I. Title.   II. Title: Swiss school system. Some suggestive features of ...

U. S. Off. of educ. Library   L111.A6   E 14–297
———— Copy 2.   LA932.T2
for Library of Congress   [a43b1]

   CaBVaU
NT 0050209   DHEW PPPL PPAN PBm PU PP DL ICJ NN MB OCl

Tate, William Knox, 1870–1917.
South Carolina. *Dept. of education.*
Special instructions for the organization of rural graded schools, prepared for the State dept. of education by W. K. Tate, state supervisor of elementary rural schools. Issued by J. E. Swearingen, state supt. education. [Columbia, S. C., The State co., printers] 1913.

Tate, William Knox, 1870–1917.
... Special supervision of country schools in South Carolina, by W. K. Tate ... Columbia, S. C., The University, 1913.
44 p. 23½ᶜᵐ. (Bulletin of the University of South Carolina. no. 32, pt. IV, January, 1913)
Reprinted from the Forty-fourth annual report of the state superintendent of education, 1912 (p. 101–144)

1. School supervision—Rural schools. 2. Rural schools—South Carolina.

         E 13–1629

Library, U. S. Bur. of   Education

NT 0050211   DHEW DL ScU ViU

Tate, William Knox, 1870–1917.
... A statement of the rural school problem in South Carolina [by] W. K. Tate ... Columbia, S. C., The University, 1911.
19 p. 23ᶜᵐ. (Bulletin of the University of South Carolina. no. 24, pt. II, January, 1911)
Reprinted from the Forty-second annual report of the state superintendent of education, 1910.

1. Rural schools—South Carolina.

         E 11–812

Library, U. S. Bur. of   Education LB1567.S5T2

NT 0050212   DHEW ScU

Tate, William Knox, 1870–1917.
... Suggested solutions for some rural school problems in South Carolina, by W. K. Tate ... Columbia, S. C., The University, 1912.
43 p. 23ᶜᵐ. (Bulletin of the University of South Carolina. no. 28, pt. VI, January, 1912)
Reprinted from the Forty-third annual report of the state superintendent of education.

1. Rural schools—South Carolina.

         E 12–830

Library, U. S. Bur. of   Education LB1567.S5T22

NT 0050213   DHEW PP ScU NN

Tate, William Knox, 1870–1917.
South Carolina. *Dept. of education.*
Suggestions for county fairs and field days, prepared for the State dept. of education by W. K. Tate, state supervisor of elementary rural schools. Issued by J. E. Swearingen, state supt. of education. [Columbia, S. C., The State co., printers] 1913.

Tate, William Knox.
South Carolina. *Dept. of education.*
Suggestions for county teachers' associations, prepared for the State dept. of education by W. K. Tate, state supervisor of elementary rural schools ... Issued by J. E. Swearingen, state superintendent of education. Columbia [The State co., printers] 1913.

Tate, William Knox, 1870–1917.
Teachers' manual for the elementary schools of South Carolina...
see under South Carolina. Dept. of Education.

Tate, William Ramage, 1873–
Criminal commercialism; the true story of the systematic frauds of a big corporation of interest to all and especially the clothing trade, by William R. Tate ... New York, Nicoletti bros. press [°1909]
61 p. incl. port. 19ᶜᵐ. $0.50

1. Clothing trade—U. S. 2. Business ethics. 3. American woolen company.

Library of Congress   HD9899.A5T3   10–12441

NT 0050217   DLC

Tate, Willis McDonald, 1911-
Portrait of a University. Program of inauguration
see under Dallas. Southern Methodist
University.

Tate, Zetta C
Susan and Little Black Boy. Illus. by Stanley E. Long.
Mountain View, Calif., Pacific Press Pub. Association [1952]
unpaged. illus. 24 cm.

1. Title.

PZ10.3.T14Su 52-14714 ‡

NT 0050219 DLC

N 1080 The TATE collection. London, Photographed
T38 by J. Thomson [1898]
1898 1 v. of illus. 24 x 31 cm.
Cover title.
Inscribed to the architect of the Tate
Gallery, Mr. Sidney R. James Smith, by Mrs.
Henry Tate.
1. Paintings, British. I. Smith, Sidney
R James. II. Tate, Sir Henry, 1819-
1899.

NT 0050220 CaBVaU

Tate County Baptist Association
see
Baptists. Mississippi. Tate County Association.
Baptists. Tennessee. Tate County Association.

MIC Tate County Democrat.
1891-
Senatobia, Miss.
v. illus. weekly.
Title varies: 1891-Jan. 2?, 1897, North
Mississippi Democrat; Jan. 8, 1897-Jan. 22?,
1925, Senatobia Democrat.
Microfilm. Wooster, Ohio, Bell & Howell, Micro
Photo Division. reels.

1. Newspapers – Mississippi. I. Title: North
Mississippi Democrat. II. Title: Senatobia
Democrat.

NT 0050222 MsSM

Pam Tate Epsom Spring, Tate Spring, Tenn.
76- Annual pamphlet of Tate Epsom Spring
1139 containing information relative to location,
analysis of water, means of access, accomo-
dations, diseases for which the water is
highly recommended ... -- Knoxville, Tenn. :
S.B. Newman, 1901?
40 p. : ill.

1.Tate Epsom Spring, Tate Spring, Tenn.
2.Mineral waters--Tate Spring, Tenn.

NT 0050223 WHi

The Tate family of Fayette county, Indiana ...
see under [Rynearson, Ruby (Tate)] 1903-

ND Tate Gallery, London.
212 American painting from the eighteenth
.T1 century to the present day. London,
The Tate Gallery, 1946.

19 [1] p., 8 plates on 4 l. 23 cm.
"An exhibition assembled by the National
Gallery of Art, Washington, D. C."

1. Painting, American. I. U. S. National
Gallery of Art. II. Title.

NT 0050225 DNGA CtY NBC

N5055 Tate Gallery, London.
.A7
Arts Council of Great Britain.
Art treasures from Vienna; an exhibition held at the Tate
Gallery, London. [London] 1949.

Tate Gallery, London.
Ben Nicholson; a retrospective exhibition, June-July
1955. [L] 1955

[8] p. 12 plates (part col.)

NT 0050227 MH-FA IaU OC1MA

R708.2 TATE gallery, London.
T187B British school; a concise catalogue by
Mary Chamot.
Lond. 1953. 306p. illus.

Earlier ed. has title: Catalogue, British
school. 25th ed.

NT 0050228 WaS WaT FTaSU CaBVa

Tate Gallery, London.
Catalogue, book illustration of the sixties,
January 18 to December 31, 1923. [London, 1923]

44 p. 22 cm.
At head of title: National Gallery, Millbank
"Under revision"

NT 0050229 MH-FA

Tate Gallery, London.
Catalogue, British school.

London, Printed by order of the Trustees by Harrison [etc.]
v. 19-23 cm.
Title varies: 18 -1907, Descriptive and historical catalogue of the
pictures and sculpture.—1908-14, Catalogue, with descriptions, histori-
cal notes.
Other slight variations in title.
Vols. for 18 - 1914 issued by the gallery when under the adminis-
tration of the National Gallery.
Each issue includes biographical notices of deceased artists.
Vol. 25, 1936/37, includes suppl. 1937/46.
1. Art—London—Catalogs. 2. Art—Gt. Brit. 3. Artists, British.
British.

N1080.A6 -708.2 1-13283 rev*

WaSpG GU ICJ MtU NNU KU MdBWA
MiD ViU ICU MiU OC1MA NN MiDA NcD CtY DSI MH OrU
NT 0050230 DLC OC1 NNC WaS NjP OU CU NIC PSt MH-FA

Tate Gallery, London.
Catalogue, British school
see also its Complete catalogue of the
British school.

Tate Gallery, London.
Catalogue; loan exhibition of paintings and draw-
ings of the 1860 period, Apr.27 to July 29, 1923.
[L, 1923]

56 p.
At head of title: National Gallery, Millbank

NT 0050232 MH-FA

Tate Gallery, London.
Catalogue, loan exhibition of works by Charles
Conder (1868-1909) Open July 1-September 25,
1927. [London, 1927]

19 p. 22 cm.
At head of title: National Gallery, Millbank

NT 0050233 MH-FA

ND497 Tate Gallery, London
W6L7 ... Catalogue: loan exhibition of works by
Richard Wilson, June 26 to September 30, 1925.
[London, 1925]

23 p. 22 cm.
At head of title: Under revision.
"Bibliography": p. [3] of cover.
Collins Baker fund, with stamp of Collins Bake
on title.
Ms. notations in margins.
1. Wilson, Richard, 1714-1782.

NT 0050234 CSmH

Tate Gallery, London
J437 Catalogue, modern foreign school. 1st ed.
T18H [London, Waterlow] 1926.
1926 71 p. illus. 22 cm.
At head of title: National Gallery, Millbank.

1. Paintings - London - Catalogs.

NT 0050235 CtY NNU

W.C.L. Tate Gallery, London.
759.0838 Catalogue, modern foreign school. 2d ed.
T216C [London] 1928.
83 p. plan, plates. 21 cm.
At head of title: National Gallery,
Millbank.

1. Paintings, French. Catalogs. 2.
Paintings. London. Catalogs.

NT 0050236 MWelC

708.2 Tate Gallery, London.
T18c Catalogue; modern foreign school. 3d ed.
1934 [London] 1934.
69p. 1 col.illus., plan. 22cm.

1. Paintings—London—Catalogs.

NT 0050237 IU KyU WaS

Tate Gallery, London.
Catalogue of an exhibition of pictures by
Richard Wilson and his circle
see under Birmingham, Eng. Museum and
Art Gallery.

Tate Gallery, London.
Catalogue of cartoons, paintings and drawings by Alfred
Stevens for the decoration of the dining room at Dorchester
house, lent by Sir George Holford and Alfred Drury. [Lon-
don] 1915.

27 p. plan. 20 cm.

1. Stevens, Alfred, 1817-1875. 2. Art, British—Exhibitions.

N6797.S7T3 15-21288 rev*

NT 0050239 DLC MH

Tate Gallery, London
Catalogue of loan collection of works by
Alfred Stevens [Exhibition] November 15, 1911
to January 15, 1912, The National Gallery,
British Art. [London, 1911]

18 p. 19 cm.
Cover title

NT 0050240 MH-FA

Tate Gallery, *London.*
  Catalogue of loan collection of works by Alphonse Legros.
June to Sept. 1912. [London, 1912]
    24 p. 20 cm.

    1. Legros, Alphonse, 1837-1911. 2. Paintings, French—Exhibitions.

    ND553.L65T3   13-20001 rev*

NT   0050241   DLC NN

Tate Gallery, *London.*
  Catalogue of loan collection of works by James McNeill Whistler. July to Oct., 1912. [London, H. M. Stationery Off., 1912]
    7 p. 19 cm.

    1. Whistler, James Abbott McNeill, 1834-1903. 2. Paintings, American—Exhibitions.

    ND237.W6T3   48-40261*

NT   0050242   DLC CtY

Tate Gallery, *London.*
  Catalogue of loan exhibition of works by pre-Raphaelite painters, from collections in Lancashire. July to Sept., 1913. [London, 1913]
    16 p. 19 cm.

    1. Paintings, British—Exhibitions. 2. Preraphaelitism.

    ND467.T25   14-11842 rev*

NT   0050243   DLC MH

Tate Gallery, *London.*
  Catalogue of loan exhibition of works by William Blake. [Prepared by Archibald G. B. Russell] Oct. to Dec., 1913. [2d ed.] London, Printed under the authority of H. M. Stationery Off. by Darling, 1913.
    75 p. 21 cm.
    Bibliography: p. [7]

    1. Blake, William, 1757-1827. 2. Art, British—Exhibitions. I. Russell, Archibald George Blomefield, 1879-
    ND497.B6T27 1913   14-9638 rev*

NT   0050244   DLC

Tate Gallery, London.
  Catalogue of the drawings and sketches by J.M.W. Turner, R.A.
    see under   Ruskin, John, 1819-1900.

Tate Gallery, London.
  ... A catalogue of the National gallery of British art at South Kensington with a supplement containing works by modern foreign artists and old masters. New ed.
London, Printed by G. E. Eyre and W. Spottiswoode, 1878.
    vi, 203, 1 p. 22 cm.
    At head of title: Science and art department of the Committee of Council on education, South Kensington museum.

    1. Paintings - London - Catalogs.

NT   0050246   DSI

Tate Gallery, London.
  ... A catalogue of the National gallery of British art at South Kensington with a supplement containing works by modern foreign artists... New ed.
London, Printed by Eyre and Spottiswoode for H. M. Stationery off., 1884.
    v. 2   21½ cm.
    At head of title: Science and art department of the Committee of Council on education, South Kensington museum.

    Contents. -
    Part II. Water colour paintings. 1884.

NT   0050247   DSI

Tate Gallery, London.
  ... A catalogue of the National gallery of British art at South Kensington with a supplement containing works by modern foreign artists and old masters. New ed. Pt. I-II.
London, 1893.
    2 v. in 1.   21½ cm.
    At head of title: Department of science and art of the Committee of Council on education, South Kensington museum.
    Contents.—Pt.1. Oil paintings.—Pt. 2. Water-colour paintings, etc.

NT   0050248   DSI

Tate Gallery, *London.*
  Catalogue of the National Gallery of British Art (Tate Gallery) ed. with an introd. by Lionel Cust, assisted by Edward H. Fitchew. London, Eyre & Spottiswoode, Her Majesty's Printers [1899]
    48 p. illus., plan. 25 cm.
    Cover title: Gems from the galleries.

    1. Art—London—Catalogs. 2. Art, British. I. Cust, Sir Lionel Henry, 1859-1929, ed.
    N1080.A615   45-27365 rev 2*

NT   0050249   DLC NN

Tate Gallery, London.
  ... A catalogue of the Prescott-Hewett gift of water-colour paintings forming part of the National gallery of British art at South Kensington.
London, Printed for H. M. Stationery office by Eyre and Spottiswoode, 1891.
    8 p.   25 cm.
    At head of title: Department of science and art of the Committee of Council on education.

    1. Water-color painting.
    I. Title: Prescott-Hewett gift of water-colour paintings...

NT   0050250   DSI

Tate Gallery, London.
ND497   ... Catalogue, Turner collection ... London,
T8L6   Printed by H. M. Stationery off., 1920.
    xii, 158 p. 24 1/2 cm.

    At head of title: National gallery, Millbank.

    1. Turner, Joseph Mallord William, 1775-1851.— Bibl.

NT   0050251   CSmH CaBVaU CaBViP MiDA OClMA NBuG

Tate Gallery, London.
  Catalogue, with descriptions, historical notes and lives of deceased artists
    see its   Catalogue, British School.

Tate Gallery, London.
  ... Centenary exhibition of paintings and drawings by Sir Edward Burne-Jones ... June 17th to August 31st, 1933.   [London, 1933]
    1. Burne-Jones, Sir Edward Coley, 1833-1896.

NT   0050253   CtY MH-FA

ND497   TATE GALLERY, London.
.C75T22   Centenary exhibition of paintings and water-colours by John Constable, 1776-1837, May 4th to August 31st, 1937. Illustrated catalogue.
London, 1937.
    47 p. illus.

    1. Constable, John, 1776-1837. I. Title.

NT   0050254   ICU CtY CSmH OClMA

Tate Gallery, London.
  Centenary exhibition of paintings and water-colours by William McTaggart, R.S.A. (1835-1910) May 1st to July 31st, 1935 [London, 1935]
    19 p. illus. 24 cm.

NT   0050255   MH-FA

709.71   Tate Gallery, London.
T187c   A century of Canadian art; catalogue [of exhibition]   London, 1938.
    36 p. plates. 22 cm.

    "Organised by the National Gallery of Canada."

    1. Art, Canadian - Exhibitions. I. Ottawa. National Gallery of Canada. II. Title.

NT   0050256   TxU DSI NcD CaOTU FMU KU WaU WU CtY WU

Tate Gallery, London.
N5055   [A collection of exhibition catalogues of the
T3   Tate gallery.   London, 1911-1936]
    23 v.   18-23 1/2 cm.   In green buckram case.
    26 1/2 cm.

    1. Art—Exhibitions. 2. Art—London.

NT   0050257   CSmH

Jd18   *Tate Gallery, London*
506.   ... Complete catalogue of the British school (exclusive of the Turner collection), with brief descriptions and lives of deceased artists ... 22d ed. London, H.M. Stationery off., 1920.
    viii, 331 p. incl. plan. 24 cm.
    At head of title: Under revision. National gallery, Millbank.
    Includes also works at Trafalgar Square and on loan to other galleries or institutions - cf. p. vii.

NT   0050258   CtY

Tate Gallery.
  ... Cotman exhibition, April 7 to July 9, 1922 [London, 1922]
    see its   Exhibition of works by John Sell Cotman.

Tate Gallery, London.
  Degas; an exhibition sponsored by ...
    see under   Edinburgh. Royal Scottish Academy of Painting, Sculpture and Architecture.

Tate Gallery, *London.* Descriptive and historical **catalogue** of the pictures and sculptures
see its   Catalogue, British school.

Tate Gallery, *London.*
  Drawings and paintings by Alexander Cozens, arr. by Paul Oppé. London, 1946.
    55 p. plates. 25 cm.
    Cover title: Illustrated catalogue: drawings and paintings by Alexander Cozens.

    1. Cozens, Alexander, 1717 (ca.)-1786. 2. Paintings, English—Exhibitions. 3. Drawings, English—Exhibitions. I. Oppé, Adolf Paul, 1878-
    ND497.C85T3   759.2   48-11508*

NT   0050262   DLC CtY

Tate Gallery, London.
Epstein; an exhibition held at the Tate gallery,
September 25 to November 9, 1952. [2. ed.]
[London, 1952]
36 p.   18 cm.
At head of title: The Arts council of Great
Britain.
Bibliography, p. 20.
1. Epstein, Jacob, 1880–

NT 0050263   NN MH InU TxU

NB497   Tate Gallery, London.
E6A72   Epstein; an exhibition held at the Tate Gallery, September
25 to November 9, 1952.   [3d ed.   London, 1952]
36 p.

1. Epstein, Sir Jacob, 1880–1959.

NT 0050264   CU

NB497   Tate Gallery, London.
E6A7   Epstein, book of illustrations, including a number of works not
exhibited.   An exhibition held at the Tate Gallery, 25th September - 9th November.   [London] Arts Council of Great Britain.
1952.
[2] p., 29 plates, ports.

1. Epstein, Sir Jacob, 1880–1959.   I. Tate Gallery, London.

NT 0050265   CU MH FMU

Tate Gallery, London.

Ethel Walker, Frances Hodgkins, Gwen John; a
memorial exhibition, 7 May to 15 June 1952.
London, 1952

32 p.   plates

NT 0050266   MH-FA

Tate Gallery, London.
An exhibition of a selection from the acquisitions
of the Contemporary Art Society
see under   Contemporary Art Society.

Tate Gallery, London.
An exhibition of cricket pictures from the
collection of Sir Jeremiah Colman
see under   Colman, Sir Jeremiah, bart.,
1859–1942.

Tate Gallery, London.
Exhibition of Jugoslav sculpture and painting,
April 10th–May 31st, 1930, under the auspices of
the Jugoslav Society of Great Britain and the
Friends of Great Britain in Jugoslavia. [London]
The Jugoslav Society of Great Britain [1930]

40 p.   map 22 cm.

NT 0050269   MH-FA

N6550   Tate Gallery, London.
.E95
**Exhibition of Mexican art from pre-Columbian times to
the present day,** organized under the auspices of the
Mexican Government.   Tate Gallery, 4 March to 26 April.
London, Arts Council, 1953.

Tate Gallery, London.
An exhibition of paintings by Cézanne...
see under   Arts Council of Great Britain.

Tate Gallery, London.
An exhibition of paintings by Jack B. Yeats
see under   Arts Council of Great Britain.

Tate Gallery, London.
An exhibition of paintings by Joanna Mary
Boyce (Mrs. H.T. Wells) 1831–1861, June 14th
to July 27th, 1935. [London, 1935]

15 p.   illus.   24 cm.

NT 0050273   MH-FA

Tate Gallery, London.
Exhibition of paintings of scenes of Gaucho
life in the province of Entre Rios, by C. Bernaldo
de Quirós, January 1931. [London, 1931?]

10 p.   illus.   23 cm.
Cover title
At head of title: National Gallery, Millbank

NT 0050274   MH-FA

Tate Gallery, London.
Exhibition of the Eton leaving portraits
see under   Eton college.

Tate Gallery, London.
An exhibition of the sculpture of Matisse

see under

Arts Council of Great Britain.

ND497   Tate Gallery, London.
T8T3   Exhibition of Turner's early oil- paintings (1796–1815)
July to September, 1931.   Illustrated catalogue.   [London, 1931]
16 p.   illus.

Cover title.
At head of title: National Gallery, Millbank.

1. Turner, Joseph Mallord William, 1775–1851.

NT 0050277   CU CSmH

Tate Gallery, London.
Exhibition of works by John Sell Cotman, and
some related painters of the Norwich School,
Miles Edmund Cotman, John Joseph Cotman, John
Thirtle. [April 7 to July 9, 1922. London, 1922]

47 p.   21 cm.
Added t.p.: Cotman exhibition
At head of title: National Gallery, Millbank
Includes bibliography

NT 0050278   MH-FA CSmH

Tate Gallery, London.
Gauguin, an exhibition of paintings

see under

Arts Council of Great Britain.

Tate Gallery, London.
George Frederic Watts, 1817–1904

see under

Arts Council of Great Britain.

Tate Gallery, *London.*
Illustrated catalogue. Pub. by authority of the Trustees.
London, New York, Cassell, 1903.
128 p.   illus.   17 cm.

1. Art—London—Catalogs. 2. Art, British.

N1080.A618   49–30721*

NT 0050281   DLC NN NNC ICU OO MB MH

708.2   Tate Gallery, London.
T187n   The National Gallery of British art
(the Tate Gallery).   Illustrated catalogue.   London, Published by authority
of the Trustees, Cassell, 1905.
128p.   illus.

NT 0050282   MiDA

(SA)
NA1030 Tate Gallery, London.
.T18A33   The National Gallery of British Art (The Tate
1906   Gallery): illustrated catalogue with Turner
supplement; published by authority of the
trustees. London, Cassel, 1906.
[8], 128 p.: ill.; 18 cm.

1. Art - London - Catalogs. 2. Art, British.

NT 0050283   NjP

N   Tate Gallery, London.
1080   Illustrated catalogue. Pub. by authority
.A618   of the Trustees.   London, New York. Cassell,
1907.
128p.   illus.   17cm.

1. Art.   London.   Catalogs.   2. Art,
British.

NT 0050284   OrU IU

Tate Gallery, *London.*
The Tate Gallery illustrated catalogue. [With Turner
supplement] Pub. by authority of the Trustees. London,
New York, Cassell, 1909.
128 p. illus. 17 cm.

1. Paintings, British—London—Catalogs.

N1080.A62 1909   43–32979 rev*

NT 0050285   DLC MH NNC

N   Tate Gallery, London.
1080   Illustrated catalogue, published by
A6   authority of the trustees.   London, Cassell,
1910   1910.
138 p. illus. 17cm.

"Turner supplement:" p. [129]–138.

1. Paintings—London—Catalogs.

NT 0050286   NIC TU

708.2 Tate Gallery, London.
T18t The Tate Gallery illustrated catalogue.
1911 ⟨With Turner supplement⟩ Published by
authority of the trustees. London, New
York, Cassell, 1911.
138p. illus. 17cm.

At head of title: The National Gallery,
British Art.

1. Paintings—London—Catalogs. 2. Paintings, British.

NT 0050287   IU NcD

Tate Gallery, London.
The Tate Gallery; illustrated catalogue ⟨with
Turner suppl.⟩ London, Pub. by authority of the
trustees, Cassell, 1913.
128-⟨16⟩ p. illus.

NT 0050288   MiD

Tate Gallery, *London.*
Illustrated catalogue, British school. 1st ed. London,
Printed by H. M. Stationery Off., 1921.
v, 101 p. illus. 21 cm.

1. Art—London—Catalogs. 2. Art, British.

N1080.A65 1921   22–16646 rev*

NT 0050289   DLC OClMA

Tate Gallery, *London.*
Illustrated catalogue, loan collection of works by English
pre-Raphaelite painters lent by the Art Gallery Committee
of the Birmingham Corporation. Open Dec. 1911 to Mar.
1912. London, H. M. Stationery Off., 1911.
v, 21 p. 13 plates. 21 cm.
At head of title: Under revision.

1. Preraphaelitism. 2. Paintings, British—Exhibitions. i. Birmingham, Eng. Museum and Art Gallery.

N1080.A7   12–26188 rev*

NT 0050290   DLC

Tate Gallery, London.
ND467 ... Illustrated catalogue of works by English
L8 pre-Raphaelite painters, lent by the Art gallery
1912 committee of the Birmingham corporation, Decem-
ber, 1911 to March, 1912. London, Printed for
His Majesty's Stationery office, 1912.

v, [1], 22 p. plates. 21cm.
Ms. underscorings and notes in text.

1. Paintings, British—Exhibitions. 2. Painters, British.   3. Preraphaelitism. (T.
Birmingham, Eng.   Museum and art gallery.

NT 0050291   CSmH NjP

Tate Gallery, London.
Illustrated catalogue
see also its   The national Gallery of
British Art (The Tate Gallery) Illustrated
catalogue ...

708.2 Tate Gallery, London.
T187b Illustrated guide, British school.
1925 Glasgow, R. Maclehose, 1925.
ix, 165p. illus. 25 cm.

At head of title: National Gallery,
Millbank.

1. Art, British.

NT 0050293   MiDA NRU NjR NNC MH OClMA GU MdBWA MiU

Tate Gallery, London.
...Illustrated guide, British school. Glasgow,
R. Maclehose, 1927.
165 p. illus.

At head of title: National gallery, Millbank.

NT 0050294   MiD DSI NN

Tate Gallery, *London.*
Illustrated guide, British school. Glasgow, Printed by R.
Maclehose and sold at the gallery, 1928.
ix, 165 p. illus. 24 cm.

1. Art—London—Catalogs. 2. Art—Gt. Brit.

N1080.A72   49–30723*

    ViU
NT 0050295   DLC OrU KyLoU MiU FMU DSI NN CaBVaU IU

N1080 Tate Gallery, London.
.A72 Illustrated guide, British school. Glasgow,
1931 Printed by R. Maclehose and sold at the gallery,
1931.
ix, 165p. illus. 24cm.

1. Art - London - Catalogs. 2. Art - Gt.
Brit.

NT 0050296   FMU MWiCA GEU

N
1080 Tate Gallery, London.
.A72 Illustrated guide, British school.
1931 Glasgow, The University Press, c1931.
ix, 165 p. illus. 24 cm.
At head of title: National Gallery,
Millbank.

1. Art—London—Catalogs. 2. Art—
Great Britain.

NT 0050297   OKentU NcD

M.A.G.
N1080 Tate Gallery, London.
.A1i Illustrated guide, British school /
1936 Tate Gallery, Millbank. Glasgow :
Printed by R. Maclehose at the
University Press and sold at the
Gallery, 1936.
ix, 165 p., [1] leaf of plates :
ill. ; 24 cm.
Includes index.

1. Art—London—Catalogs. 2. Art—
Great Britain. I. Title

NT 0050298   NRU LU

708.2 Tate Gallery, London.
T18i Illustrations, National Gallery Millbank.
1923 London, Published by the Trustees, 1923.
v, 101p.(chiefly illus.) 21cm.

"A companion to the Official catalogue."

1. Art—London—Catalogs. 2. Art, British.

NT 0050299   IU MiD NN PPPM MsU

N1080
A8 *Tate Gallery, London.*
Illustrations; paintings & drawings,
National gallery, Millbank. Glasgow,
Printed by Robert Maclehose & co., ltd.
at the University press, 1926.
1p.ℓ.⟨3⟩p. plates. 23½cm.

1. Paintings.–London.–Catalogs.
x. London.–National gallery, Millbank.

NT 0050300   NBuG GU MdBWA MH

N Tate Gallery, London.
1080 Illustrations; paintings & drawings, National Gallery, Millbank.
A5 Glasgow, printed by R. Maclehose at the University Press and sold at
1928 the Gallery, 1928.
199 illus.

"A companion to the official catalog ... contain[ing] illustrations
of 199 paintings, drawings and sculpture in the National Collection."
Spine: ... Tate Gallery.

1. Paintings, British - London - Catalogs. 2. Drawings, British -
London - Catalogs. 3. Sculpture, British - London - Catalogs.

NT 0050301   CLU CSt IU CaBVaU TxLT IaU CtY MiDA NNU

Tate Gallery, London.
Loan collection of paintings, drawings and
engravings by contemporary British artists
recently exhibited in New Zealand and Australia
under the auspices of the Empire Art Loan Collections Society, October 17th to October 31st,
1935. [London, 1935]
15 p. 22 cm.

NT 0050302   MH-FA

Tate Gallery, London.
... Loan exhibition of the Burrell collection,
1924. [London, 1924]
15 p. 22 cm.
At head of title: National gallery, Millbank.

NT 0050303   CtY-A

Tate Gallery, London.
Manet and his circle; paintings from the Louvre..
see under   Arts Council of Great Britain.

ND699 Tate Gallery, London.
.C5A7
Arts Council of Great Britain.
Marc Chagall; an exhibition of paintings, prints, book
illustrations and theatre designs, 1908–1947, at the Tate
Gallery, 4th–29th February, 1948. [London, 1948]

Tate Gallery, London.
Masterpieces from the São Paulo Museum

see under

Arts Council of Great Britain.

Tate Gallery, London.
Matthew Smith; paintings from 1909 to 1952. [London]
1953.
23 p. illus. (part col.) 19 x 25 cm.

1. Smith, Matthew, 1879–1959. I. Smith, Matthew, 1879–1959.

ND497.S57T38 1953   759.2   74–185915
                                                    MARC

NT 0050307   DLC MiU WaS MH MdBWA KyU NN

Tate Gallery, London.
Matthew Smith, paintings from 1909 to 1952.
[2d ed.] London, Tate Gallery, 1953.
23 p. 16 plates (part col.) 18 x 25 cm.
Catalogue of exhibition at the Tate Gallery,
1953, with an introduction by Sir John
Rothenstein.
1. Smith, Matthew, 1879–1959. I. Tate
Gallery, London. II. Title.

NT 0050308   CoU

Tate Gallery, London.
　　Mexican arts from 1500 B.C. to the present day
　　　see under　Arts Council of Great Britain.

N
6512
.T1
　　Tate Gallery, London.
　　　... Modern art in the United States. A selection from the collections of the Museum of Modern Art, New York. The Tate Gallery 5 January to 12 February 1956. [London, Arts Council of Great Britain, 1955 ?]
　　51 p. 　xliv plates. 　26 cm.
　　At head of title: An exhibition organized by the Tate Gallery and the Arts Council.
　　1. Art, American. I. Arts Council of Great Britain. II. New York. Museum of Modern Art. III. Title: Modern Art in the United States.

NT　0050310　　DNGA

Tate Gallery, *London.*
　　Modern British pictures from the Tate Gallery, exhibited under the auspices of the British Council ... [Continental exhibition] 1946–47. London [1947]
　　24 p. 24 plates. 24 cm.

　　1. Paintings, English—Exhibitions. 　ɪ. Title.
　　　　　　　　　　　　　　　　　　　A 49–3825*
Harvard Univ. Library
for Library of Congress　　　[1]

NT　0050311　　MH NN

Tate Gallery, *London.*
　　Modern foreign pictures in the Tate Gallery, with an introd. by John Rothenstein. London, Pub. by order of the Trustees, 1947 [i. e. 1949]
　　13 p. 100 plates. 34 cm.
　　Errata slip inserted.

　　1. Paintings—London. 　ɪ. Rothenstein, John Knewstub Maurice, 1901– 　ɪɪ. Title.
　　N1080.A73　　　　759.084　　　49–53982*

NT　0050312　　DLC CLSU CtY ICU OrU LU MB CaBViP WaS

Tate Gallery, London.
　　Modern Italian art
　　　see under　Amici di Brera, Milan.

Tate Gallery, London.
　　Mural painting in Great Britain, 1919–1939; an exhibition of photographs; illustrated catalogue. Collected and arr. at the Tate Gallery. [London, 1939]
　　20 p. plates. 22 cm.

　　1. Mural painting and decoration. 2. Decoration and ornament—Gt. Brit.
　　ND2728.T3　　　751.73　　　44–15518 rev*

NT　0050314　　DLC NN CtY OC1MA

[Tate Gallery, London]
　　[\ National Gallery, Millbank. A record of ten years, 1917–1927. [Glasgow, Printed by Robert Maclehose & Co. Ltd. at the University Press, 1927.
　　112 p. incl. plates, 26 cm.

NT　0050315　　DNGA OC1MA NN

Tate Gallery, London.
　　(The National gallery of British art (The Tate Gallery)) Illustrated catalogue. Pub. by authority of the Trustees. 　London, N. Y. [etc.] Cassell & co., 1908.
　　128 p.

NT　0050316　　MiU OC1 OO OC1MA OrP

Tate Gallery, London.
　　The national Gallery of British Art (The Tate Gallery) illustrated catalogue
　　　see also its　Illustrated catalogue.

Tate Gallery, *London.*
　　The National Gallery of British Art (the Tate **Gallery**) with an introd. by Sir Charles Holroyd. With 24 Rembrandt photogravure plates and numerous other illus. London, New York, Cassell, 1905.
　　100 p. illus. 38 cm.

　　1. Art—London—Catalogs. 2. Art, British. 　ɪ. Holroyd, Sir Charles, 1861–1917.
　　　　　　　　　　　　　　　A 15–1642 rev*
Forbes Library
for Library of Congress　　　[r48b1]

NT　0050318　　MNF DSI IU

Tate Gallery, *London.*
　　Paul Nash, 1889–1946. Memorial exhibition: paintings, watercolours, and drawings. At the Tate Gallery, Mar. 17th–May 2nd, 1948. Arr. by the Tate Gallery and the Arts Council of Great Britain. [London] 1948.
　　16 p. 16 plates, port. 25 cm.

　　1. Nash, Paul, 1889–1946. 2. Paintings, English—Exhibitions. 3. Drawings, English—Exhibitions. 　ɪ. Arts Council of Great Britain.
　　ND497.N3T3　　　759.2　　　48–11507*

NT　0050319　　DLC CaBVa MiDA CLU GU InU

Tate Gallery, London.
　　Pictures in the Tate Gallery. London ... 1905
　　　see under　Hartley, Catherine Gasquoine, 1867–1928.

Tate Gallery, London.
　　The Pleydell-Bouverie collection of impressionist and other paintings, lent by the Hon. Mrs. A.E. Pleydell-Bouverie. London, The Tate gallery, 1954.
　　12 p. 4 pl. 21 cm.
　　Exhibition held at the Tate gallery from January 26th to April 25th, 1954.
　　I. Pleydell-Bouverie, Mrs. A.E.

NT　0050321　　OC1MA NN

750.74　Tate Gallery, London.
T18p　　Pre-Raphaelite brotherhood, 1848–1948. Catalogue of a centenary exhibition. [London, 1948]
　　[83]p. 29cm.

　　Cover title.
　　"This edition — is limited to one hundred and seventy-five copies."

NT　0050322　　IU

Tate Gallery, *London.*
　　Report by the trustees. London, H. M. Stationery Off.
　　v. illus. 25 cm. annual.
　　Report year ends Mar. 31.
　　Report covering 1953/54 includes a brief summary covering 1938/53 during which time annual reports were not issued.

　　N1080.A3　　　　　　　　55–40266 ‡

NT　0050323　　DLC WaS MiU OC1MA

Tate Gallery, London.
　　... Review of the acquisitions... 　Glasgow, R. Maclehose & co.
　　v.

NT　0050324　　OC1MA

N
1080
.A8
　　Tate Gallery, London.
　　　...Review of the acquisitions during the years July, 1927 – December, 1929... London Printed...at the Univ.Press, Glasgow and sold at the gallery, 1930.
　　58[2]p. incl. pl. 26 cm.

NT　0050325　　PPPM CtY

Tate Gallery, London.
　　Samuel Courtauld, memorial exhibition, the Tate Gallery, 1948. [London, 1948]
　　24 p. col. plates, port. 15 x 22 cm.

NT　0050326　　MH-FA KyU

Tate Gallery, London.
　　Sculpture and drawings. Catalogue of an exhibition arranged by the Arts Council of Great Britain and held on the occasion of the Festival of Britain 1951, May 2–July 29 at the Tate Gallery, London
　　　see under　Moore, Henry Spencer, 1898–

Tate Gallery, *London.*
　　A selection from the Tate Gallery's wartime acquisitions. [London] C. E. M. A., 1942.
　　7 p. 23 cm.
　　Cover title.

　　1. Art—Exhibitions.
　　N1080.A752　　　708.2　　　43–6406 rev*

NT　0050328　　DLC

Tate Gallery, *London.*
　　Sir William Rothenstein, 1872–1945; a memorial exhibition: paintings, drawings, etchings and lithographs. An appreciation by Augustus John. Biographical and critical notes by John Piper. May 5th–June 4th, 1950. London [1950]
　　32 p. 13 illus. 25 cm.
　　Bibliography: p. 12.

　　1. Rothenstein, Sir William, 1872–1945. 2. Art, English—Exhibitions.
　　N6797.R6T3　　　708.2　　　50–33477

NT　0050329　　DLC CLU NN NBC KU NNU DSI

Tate Gallery, London.
　　Sir William Rothenstein, 1872–1945. A selection from the memorial exhibition ...
　　　see under　Arts Council of Great Britain.

Tate Gallery, London.
　　Stanley Spencer; a retrospective exhibition Nov. – Dec.1955. [L] 1955
　　31 p. 8 plates

NT　0050331　　MH-FA WaS OC1MA

Tate Gallery, London.
Tableaux britanniques modernes appartenant à la Tate Gallery. Exposés sous les auspices du British Council. 1946. Berne, Switzerland, 1946.
24 p. [15] illus. 24.5 cm.
Exposition: 3-25 Aout 1946, Kunst-museum, Bern.

NT 0050332   PPPM PPULC

Tate Gallery, London.
Tableaux britanniques modernes appartenant a la Tate Gallery, exposés sous les auspices du British council. Paris, Musee de jeu de paume, 1948.

23 p. plates.

NT 0050333   MH-FA

Tate Gallery, London.
... The Tate gallery (the National gallery of British art) London, Paris, New York, Toronto and Melbourne, Cassell & company, 1907.
63 [1] p. incl. front., illus. 14 cm. (At head of title: The great galleries of Europe)
1. London. National gallery, British art.
2. Painting. Great Britain.

NT 0050334   NBuG DAU NN ODW

Tate Gallery, London.
...The Tate Gallery ⟨The National Gallery of British Art⟩. London: Cassell & Co., Ltd., 1908. front., plates. 24°. (The great galleries of Europe.)
Reproductions of 60 masterpieces, without text.
At head of title: Great art galleries

1. Paintings.—Collections, Gt. Br.:
2. Series.
N. Y. P. L.   England: London: Tate gallery.
    October 7, 1921.

NT 0050335   NN CU

N
1080   Tate Gallery, London.
T384   The Tate Gallery; (the National Gallery,
HRC   British art) London, New York,
NON-CIRC   Cassel, 1909.
MOR   63p.(chiefly illus.) 14cm. (Great
    art galleries)
    Inscribed: C.D.M. [Christopher
    Darlington Morley] March, 1911.

1. Tate Gallery, London—Catalogs.

NT 0050336   TxU

Tate Gallery, London.
The Tate Gallery, the National Gallery, British Art. [Reproductions of sixty masterpieces] London, New York Cassell, 1912.
63 p. illus. 14 cm. (Great art galleries)

1. Paintings, British—London—Catalogs. (Series)

N1080.A63   759.2   37–15672 rev*

NT 0050337   DLC

Tate Gallery, London.
The Tate gallery; the national collection of British painting and of modern foreign art. By John Rothenstein; ed. and designed by Jill Simon. London, The Trustees, 1947. 14 p. illus. 15cm.

I. Rothenstein, John Knewstub   Maurice, 1901- . II. Simon,
Jill, ed.
N. Y. P. L.   January 3, 1950

NT 0050338   NN

N25   Tate Gallery, London.
A73   La Tate Gallery. Introd. par R. A. Butler. Préf. de Sir John
v. 27   Rothenstein. [Traduit par M. A. Bera. Paris, 1953]
    1 v. (unpaged) plates(part mounted col.) ports. (Art et style, 27)

    Text also in English.

1. London, Eng. (City) Tate Gallery. I. Rothenstein, Sir John Knewstub Maurice, 1901-

NT 0050339   CU PSC PPT

Tate Gallery, *London.*
The Tate Gallery, a brief history and guide, by John Rothenstein and Mary Chamot. London, 1951.
20 p. 15 cm.

1. Rothenstein, John Knewstub Maurice, 1901-

N1080.A74   708.2   53–38007 ‡

NT 0050340   DLC CtY

Tate Gallery, *London.*
Tate Gallery, 1897–1947; pictures from the Tate Gallery foundation gift, and exhibition of subsequent British painting. London [1947]
xi, 24 p. 25 plates. 25 cm.

1. Paintings, British—Exhibitions.

ND467.T26   759.2   48–12184 rev*

NT 0050341   DLC CtY

Tate Gallery, *London.*
The Tate Gallery's wartime acquisitions. [London] National Gallery, 1942.
13 p. plates. 23 cm.
Cover title.

1. Art—Exhibitions.

N1080.A75   708.2   43–6405 rev*

NT 0050342   DLC CLSU CtY OC1MA

Tate Gallery, *London.*
The Tate Gallery's wartime acquisitions. Second exhibition, June–July 1945. [London, 1945]
8 p. 8 plates. 23 cm.
Cover title.

1. Paintings, British—Exhibitions.

N1080.A77 1945   708.2   A 48–498 rev*
Harvard Univ. Library
for Library of Congress   [a48b1]†

NT 0050343   MH CtY DLC

ND497   Tate Gallery, London.
.T8G7   Gt. Brit. *British Council.*
    Turner, 1775–1851, esposizione di quadri organizzata dalla Tate Gallery per il British Council. Padiglione britannico, Esposizione d'arte internazionale della xxiv biennale. Venezia, 1948.

ND497
.T8G72   Tate Gallery, London.

Gt. Brit. *British Council.*
Turner, 1775–1851, exposition de peintures organisée par la Tate Gallery pour le British Council. Paris, 1948.

Tate Gallery, London.
XXth century masterpieces

see under

Arts Council of Great Britain.

Tate Gallery, *London.*
Two centuries of British drawings from the Tate Gallery. [London] C. E. M. A., 1944.
10 p. 19 cm.
Robin Ironside selected the drawings and prepared this catalogue for a C. E. M. A. exhibition.

1. Drawings, British—Exhibitions. I. Arts Council of Great Britain. II. Ironside, Robin. III. Title.

NC27.T3   741.942   45–1904 rev*

NT 0050347   DLC CtY ICU

Tate Gallery, London.
The unknown political prisoner. International sculpture competition, Tate gallery 14 March to 30 April
see under London. Institute of Contemporary Arts.

ND497   Tate Gallery, London.
.B6G7
1947   Gt. Brit. *British Council.*
    William Blake (1757–1827) [London] Tate Gallery, 1947.

N6797   Tate Gallery, *London.*
.S7T6   Towndrow, Kenneth Romney.
    The works of Alfred Stevens, sculptor, painter, designer, in the Tate Gallery. With an introd. and descriptive catalogue of classified works, by Kenneth Romney Towndrow and a foreword by John Rothenstein. London, Published by order of the Trustees [distributed by Longmans, Green] 1950.

Tate Gallery, London.
The works of James Ensor
see under Arts Council of Great Britain.

Tate Gallery, London.
Yugoslav medieval frescoes

see under

Arts Council of Great Britain.

Tate-Jones & Company, Inc., *Pittsburgh.*
Fuel oil and its use ...　　Pittsburgh: Tate-Jones & Co., Inc.,
cop. 1918.　31 p.　illus.　8°.

1. Petroleum as fuel.
N. Y. P. L.　　　　　　　　　　　　　　　　June 28, 1921.

NT　0050353　　NN PPF

BV
4005
.T3　　　Tate lectures.
　　　　　Oxford, Eng., Manchester College, 194 –

　　　1. Pastoral theology-Collections.

NT　0050354　　DAU OO

Tate manuscripts [American Indian tales, written
down by Henry W. Tate, a Tsimshian Indian,
and assembled by Franz Boas
see under　Tate, Henry W

Ga
F292
P5T2　　Tate Mountain Estates, Inc., Jasper, Ga.
　　　　　Play above the clouds. [Atlanta, Townley,
　　　　Webb & Martin, 193-]
　　　　　1 v. (unpaged)　illus., map.　25cm.

　　　　1. Tate Mountain Estates, Inc., Jasper, Ga.
　　　2. Pickens County, Ga. - Descr. & trav.　I.
　　Title.

NT　0050356　　GU

Tate, Müller & co., *Baltimore.*
... The Baltimore export cable code for use between Tate,
Müller & co., and their correspondents ... [Baltimore, Gug-
genheimer, Weil & co., ᶜ1890]
viii, 128 p.　17ᵐᵐ.

1. Cipher and telegraph codes—Grain trade.
　　　　　　　　　　　　　　　　CA 7—4214 Unrev'd
Library of Congress　　HE7677.G7T2

NT　0050357　　DLC

Tate Public Library, *Streatham, Eng.*
　Report.
　London, J. Hitchcock.
　　v.　21 cm.　annual.
　Report year ends Mar. 25.

Z792.S884　　　　　　　　　　　56–48855 ‡

NT　0050358　　DLC

Tatebayashi, Masaki, 1909–
　(Autaruki no kenkyū)
　アウタルキイの研究 / 建林正喜著．— 東京：
　冨山房，昭和18 [1943]
　9, 4, 342 p. ; 22 cm.
　Includes bibliographical references.

　　　1. Autarchy.　I. Title.
　　　HD85.J3T43　　　　　　　74-819594

NT　0050359　　DLC

Tateish, Sajiro, 1869–
　Japans internationale handelsbeziehungen, mit beson-
derer berücksichtigung der gegenwart ...　Halle a. S.,
Hofbuchdruckerei von C. A. Kaemmerer & co., 1902.
　2 p. l., 98 p., 1 l.　22ᶜᵐ.
　Inaug.-diss.—Halle.
　"Litteratur": p. [97]–98.
　Vita.

　1. Japan—Comm.

Library of Congress　　HF3826.T25　　　3—13275

NT　0050360　　DLC CtY PU CU

Tatekawa, Danjūrō
　see
　Utei, Emba, 1743-1822.

Tatekawa, Emba
　see
　Utei, Emba, 1743-1822.

Tatekawa, Harushige, 1897–
　(Kabuki)
　歌舞伎　立川春重著　[東京　元々社　昭和30
　i.e. 1955]
　2, 2, 217 p.　3 col. plates.　18 cm.　(民族教養新書　25)

　　1. Kabuki.
　　PN2924.5.K3T37　　　　　　73-815924

NT　0050363　　DLC

Tatekawa, Harushige, 1897–
　(Sempaku no riron to jissai)
　船舶の理論と實際　立川春重著　[東京]　有象
　堂出版部　[昭和17 i.e. 1942]
　6, 8, 491 p.　illus.　22 cm.
　Includes bibliographical references.

　　1. Ships.　2. Naval architecture.　I. Title.
　　VM145.T37　　　　　　　73-816227

NT　0050364　　DLC

Tatelis, Gabriel, 1899–
　Ueber behandlung der malaria.
　Inaug. diss. Bonn, n.d.
　Bibl.

NT　0050365　　ICRL CtY

HS397
.T3
1832a　　Tatem, Henry.
　　　　　... Rev. H. Tatem's reply to the summons of
　　　　the R. I. Royal arch chapter. [Providence?
　　　　1832]
　　　　　8 p.　23 1/2ᶜᵐ.
　　　　　Caption title.
　　　　　At head of title: Second edition.

　　　　1. Freemasons.

NT　0050366　　MB MWA PHi MHi CtY M

Tatem, Henry.
　... Rev. H. Tatem's reply to the summons of the R. I.
Royal arch chapter. [3d ed.] [Providence? 1832]
　8 p.　22ᶜᵐ.
　[Freemasonry pamphlets, v. 3, no. 10]
　Caption title.

　1. Freemasons.
　　　　　　　　　　　　　　　　9–34093†
Library of Congress　　HS371.F85　vol. 3

NT　0050367　　DLC PHi MnU

Tatem, Henry.
　A compendious grammar of the Egyptian
language, as contained in the Coptic and Sapidic
dialects, etc. By the Rev. H. Tatem, with an
appendix of a dictionary of the rudiments of the
ancient Egyptian language in the Enchorial
character. By Thomas Young.　London, 1830.

NT　0050368　　PPL PPWa

Tatem, Henry.　... Reply to the summons of the
Rhode Island Royal Arch chapter.
A collection of letters on freemasonry.　In chronological
order. Boston, Press of T. R. Marvin, 1849.

Tatem, John H.
　The monitor of the eastern star; ...
　　see under　Order of the Eastern Star.

Tatem, M. H., *pseud.*
　The heights of Eidelberg.　1871
　　see
Hazlett, Helen.

P95
.779
(Ex)　　Tatem, William, complainant.
　　　　　The evidence in a cause depending in
　　　　the Court of chancery of the state of
　　　　New-Jersey, between William Tatem,
　　　　esquire, and others, complainants, and
　　　　Jeffery Chew, and others, defendants...
　　　　Trenton, Printed by G.Craft, 1799.
　　　　　136 p.　25½ᶜᵐ.
　　　　　Richard Stockton, Princeton, class of
　　　　1779, was attorney for the defendants.-
　　　　p.4.　I.Chew,Jef-　　fery defendant. II.
　　　Stockton,Richard,　1764-1828.

NT　0050372　　NjP

Tatem, William Richardson

Turks and Caicos Islands. *Hurricane relief administration
office.*
　... Report on the hurricanes of 1926 and 1928 by William
Richardson Tatem, J. P., hurricane relief officer. London,
Printed by Waterlow & sons limited, 1929.

Icono-　　Tatem Label Co., *Salem, Ohio.*
graphic　　Labels. -- Salem, Ohio, 189-?
sect.　　[86] p. : ill.
Lot
3590
985
　　　　　1.Labels--Catalogs. I.Title.

NT　0050374　　WHi

Tatemi-Storma, Giuseppe, *pseud.*
Elegia macaronica de famosa storia sfogliatel-
lae impepatissime Pii IX. [Napoli, 1848]
Broadside. f°.
In: BWL p.v. 1, no. 152.

Real name: Giuseppe Mastromattei de Giorgio

NT 0050375   NN

Tatemoto, Masahiro.
A stabilization model for the postwar Japanese
economy, 1953-62, by Masahiro Tatemoto [and
others. Osaka, 1954.
v. (Institute of Social and Economic
Research, Osaka University. Discussion paper,
37)
1. Japan - Econ. policy.

NT 0050376   MH

Tatén, *Doctor, pseud.*
see
Trongé, Faustino Juan Nereo, 1870–

Die Taten Bogda Gesser Chan's
see under   Gesar (Romances, etc.)

Die TATEN der "Emden" und anderer kreuzer.
Nach berichten des kapitänleutnants von Mücke
und anderer. Mit einer einführung von Hermann
Kirchhoff. Leipzig, Hesse & Becker, [19-.]
pp.79.
Cover: Hesses volksbücherei, 1031.

NT 0050379   MH CtY

Tatène, veue Tchanchet; journal satirique
illustré. 1e-4e (no. 4) année; 18 25 fév.
1911-7 14 mars 1914. Liège.
4 v. in 1. illus. 55 cm. weekly.

NT 0050380   OU

Wason
Film   Tatengkeng, J   E   , 1907–
N1533   Rindoe-dendam. Solo, Drukkerij Djawi,
1934.
37 p. 20cm.

Microfilm (negative) Netherlands, 1967.
1 reel. 35mm.

NT 0050381   NIC

Wason
PL5089   Tatengkeng, J   E   , 1907–
T21R5+   Rindoe-dendam. Solo, Drukkerij Djawi,
1967   1934.
37 p. 20cm.

Photocopy. [Syracuse? N.Y., 1967]
37 p. (on double leaves) 28cm.

NT 0050382   NIC

Tatenhill, *Eng.* (Parish)
... Tatenhill parish register [1563-1812] ... [n. p.] Priv.
print. for the Staffordshire parish register society, 1905.
v, 228 p. 23ᶜᵐ. (Staffordshire parish registers society. [Publications])
Deanery of Tutbury.
Title from cover.

1. Registers of births, etc.—Tatenhill, Eng.

Library of Congress   CS435.S5   23-16876

NT 0050383   DLC PHi NN IdRR

Tateno, Kakuji, 1904–
(Hanzai sōsa zensho hōkihen)
犯罪捜査全書・法規篇 / 舘野覚治著. ― 東京 :
警察新報社, 昭和24 [1949]
267 p. ; 18 cm.

1. Criminal investigation—Japan. 2. Criminal procedure—Japan.
I. Title.
77-802563

NT 0050384   DLC

Tateno, Kakuji, 1904–
問題少年―犯罪と補導―舘野覚治著 東京 警
察新報社 昭和29 [1954]
386 (i. e. 286) p. tables. 19 cm.

1. Juvenile delinquency—Japan. 2. Children—Law—Japan. I.
Title.   *Title romanized:* Mondai shōnen.
J 60-2515
Hoover Institution
for Library of Congress   [3]

NT 0050385   CSt-H

Tateno, Nobumi, 1914–
日本の恐怖 立野信実著 徳富蘇峰序文 東京
政経指針社 昭和29 [1954]
4, 7, 258 p. 19 cm.

1. Japan—Pol. & govt.—1945– 2. Japan—Soc. condit.
I. Title.   *Title romanized:* Nihon no kyōfu.

DS889.T29   J 64-668

NT 0050386   DLC

Tateno, Nobumi, 1914–
葦のずいから―政治と行政の矛盾―立野信実著
東京 大系社 昭和28 [1953]
268 p. 18 cm.

1. Japan—Pol. & govt.—1945–   I. Title.
Title romanized: Yoshi no zui kara.
J 60-2397
Hoover Institution
for Library of Congress   [3]

NT 0050387   CSt-H

Tateno, Nobuyuki, 1903–
(Guntaibyō)
軍隊病―兵士と農民に關する短篇集―立野信之
著 日本プロレタリア作家同盟編輯 [東京] 戦
旗社 [昭和5 i. e. 1930]
246 p. 19 cm. (日本プロレタリア作家叢書 第5篇)
CONTENTS: 標的になつた後―赤い空―軍隊病―闘警をあげる―溝
堀―豪雨―若者―少年隊
1. Soldiers—Japan—Fiction. 2. Farmers—Japan—Fiction. I.
Title. II. Series: Nihon puroretaria sakka sōsho, dai 5-hen.
PL839.A75G8   74-819385

NT 0050388   DLC

Tateno, Nobuyuki, 1903–
叛亂 立野信之著 東京 六興出版社 昭和
28 [1953]
377 p. illus. 18 cm.

1. Japan—Hist.—February 26 Incident, 1936—Fiction.   I. Title.
Title romanized: Hanran.

PL839.A75H3   J 62-181 ‡

NT 0050389   DLC CSt-H

Tateno, Nobuyuki, 1903–
菊薫る 立野信之著 東京 青磁社 昭和17
[1942]
280 p. 19 cm.
Fiction.

I. Title.   *Title romanized:* Kiku kaoru.

PL839.A75K5   J 62-183 ‡

NT 0050390   DLC

Tateno, Nobuyuki, 1903–
(Kōshaku Konoe Fumimaro)
公爵近衛文麿 / 立野信之. ― 東京 : 講談社,
昭和25 [1950]
6, 368 p. ; 19 cm.
Editions for 1951 and 1964 published under title: Taiyō wa mata
noboru.

1. Konoye, Fumimaro, 1891-1945—Fiction.   I. Title.
PL839.A75T3 1950   77-803228

NT 0050391   DLC

Tateno, Nobuyuki, 1903–
肉親の倫理 立野信之著 東京 昭森社 昭和
17 [1942]
334 p. 19 cm.
Fiction.

I. Title.   *Title romanized:* Nikushin no rinri.

PL839.A75N5   J 62-182 ‡

NT 0050392   DLC

Tateno, Nobuyuki, 1903–
(Ōdo chitai)
黄土地帯 立野信之著 [東京] 高山書院
[昭和16 i. e. 1941]
4, 4, 380 p. illus. 19 cm.

1. China—Description and travel—1901-1948.   I. Title.
DS710.T34   73-818232

NT 0050393   DLC

Tateno, Nobuyuki, 1903–
(Ryojun)
旅順 百五十五日間の死闘と一兵卒の生涯 小
説 立野信之著 [東京] 金星堂 [昭和19 i. e.
1944]
142 p. 19 cm.

1. Port Arthur—Siege, 1904-1905—Fiction.   I. Title.

PL839.A75R9   78-788713

NT 0050394   DLC

Tateno, Nobuyuki, 1903–
    (Taiyō wa mata noboru)
太陽はまた昇る：公爵近衛文麿 / 立野信之
著. — 東京：六興出版社. 昭和26-27 ₍1951-
1952₎
    3 v. : ports. : 19 cm.
    Edition for 1950 published under title: Kōshaku Konoe Fumimarō.

    1. Konoye, Fumimarō, 1891–1945—Fiction.   I. Title.
    PL839.A75T3 1951   77–803244

NT 0050395   DLC

Tateno, Norimitsu
    see
    Tateno, Tonan, 1889–

Tateno, Tanemasa.
治罪法註解 立野胤政 編輯 ₍改正増補₎ 東京
₍山中市兵衛 明治14 i. e. 1881₎
    7, 521, 73 p. : 19 cm.

    1. Criminal procedure—Japan. 2. Criminal courts—Japan.
    ɪ. Japan. Laws, statutes, etc. Chizaihō. 1881. ɪɪ. Title.
                    Title romanized: Chizaihō chūkai.

                                                77–818443

NT 0050397   DLC

Tateno, Tonan, 1889–
    (Nampō keirin)
南方經綸 立野斗南著 ₍東京   野田經濟研究
所 秋豊園出版部發賣 昭和11 i. e. 1936₎
    6, 8, 275 p. : 19 cm.

    1. Japan — Foreign economic relations — Asia, Southeastern. 2.
    Asia, Southeastern—Foreign economic relations—Japan. I. Title.
    HF1602.15.A75T38   73–819654

NT 0050398   DLC

Tateno, Japan (Ibarski Prefecture: Tsukuba-gun)
    Aerological Observatory
    see Kōso Kishodai.

Tateno, Japan (Ibarski prefecture: Tsukuba-gun)
    Kōso kishodai
    see Kōso Kishodai.

Tateo, Giuseppe.
    Amor per gelosia: un monologo e cinque scene...
    Pallanza, E. Vercellini, 1889.
    32 p.   16°.   (Collezione delle opere dram-
    matiche di G. Tateo, v. 1)

NT 0050401   NN

Tater, Miroslav.
    Dobrodruh: ₍básně. Žatec, M. Nodl, 1934₎
    42 p. : 21 cm.   (Edice Průsvit)
    Cover title.

    I. Title.
    PG5038.T32D6   72–217134

NT 0050402   DLC

Tater, Miroslav.
    Úzkost schýlení. Žatec, 1936.
    17 p. 17 cm.

    I. Title.

    PG5039.3.A8U9   72–216808

NT 0050403   DLC

Tater Tooter
    see Pacific semaphore.

Taterka, Hans, Volontärarzt: Untersuchungen am Nervus
    opticus mit Leducschem Strome. Aus d. neurol. Abt. d.
    Allerheil.-Hosp. zu Breslau. [In Maschinenschrift.] 23 S.
    4°(2°). — Auszug: Breslau 1921: Breslauer Genossensch.-
    Buchdr. 2 Bl. 8°
    Breslau, Med. Diss. v. 2. Mai 1921, Ref. Foerster
    [Geb. 3. März 95 Breslau; Wohnort: Breslau; Staatsangeh.: Preußen; Vor-
    bildung: Friedrich-Wilhelms-G. Posen Reife 13; Studium: Freiburg 1, Berlin 6,
    Breslau 9 S.; Coll. 2. Nov. 20; Approb. 27. Sept. 20.]   [U 21. 3119

NT 0050405   ICRL

Taterka, Heinz. Chinin in der Geburtshilfe. [Maschinenschrift.] 65 S.
    4°. — Auszug: Breslau 1923: Bresl. Genoss.-Buchdr. 2 Bl. 8°
    Breslau, Med. Diss. v. 1. Aug. 1923   [U 23. 1408

NT 0050406   ICRL

TATERSAL, Robert.
    The bricklayer's miscellany, or Poems on
    several subjects. 2d ed. London, printed for
    the author, and sold by J. Wilford, 1734.

    pp.vi,(2),32.

NT 0050407   MH

TATERSAL, Robert.
    The bricklayer's miscellany. Pt.II.
    London, 1735.

    II.Poems on several subjects, 1735.

NT 0050408   MH

75.8
T18   The Taterstater.
          Presque Isle, Me., Aroostook potato growers,

NT 0050409   DNAL

Tate's atlas of Des Moines and plat directory to
    additions, subdivisions, and official plats in
    Des Moines, Iowa
    see under Tate, John C

Tate's Creek Baptist Association
    see Baptists. Kentucky. Tate's Creek
    Association.

Tateum, William A
    ... James D. Turnbull, relator, vs. J.
    Wight Giddings et al, respondents; Thomas E.
    Barkworth, relator, vs. William A. Tateum...
        see under Cooley, Thomas McIntyre, 1824–
    1898.

Tateum, William Aldrich
    "Before the blazing back-log." Little tales
    of woods, fields, waters. Grand Rapids, Mich.,
    1907.
    99 p.

NT 0050413   OCU

LJw5   Tateum, William Aldrich,   comp.
+1   ₍Popular songs at Wesleyan university, as
        sung by students and Glee club ... Middle-
        town, Conn., Pelton & King, 1882.
        20p. 17cm.
        Additional song, 1 leaf inserted at end.
        Without music.

NT 0050414   CtY

Tatevosov, Konstantin Georgievich.
    Производственные мощности цехов. ₍Ленинград₎ Ле-
    нинградское газетно-журнальное и книжное изд-во, 1948.
    197 p. illus. 22 cm.
    At head of title: К. Г. Татевосов.

    1. Factory management.   *Title romanized:* Proizvodstven-
                                  nye moshchnosti ĭsekhov.
    TS155.T22   49–53746

NT 0050415   DLC

Tatevin, C
    La langue tapĭhīya dite tupĭ ou ñeẽngatu (belle langue)
    Grammaire, dictionnaire et textes. Vienne, En commission
    chez A. Hölder, 1910.
    307 p. 24 cm. (Kaiserliche Akademie der Wissenschaften.
    Schriften der Sprachenkommission, Bd. 2)

    1. Tupi language.   (Series: Akademie der Wissenschaften,
    Vienna. Kommission zur Erforschung von Illiteraten Sprachen Aus-
    sereuropäischer Völker. Schriften, Bd. 2)
    PM7171.T3   56–51945

NT 0050416   DLC ICU NN TxU

Tatevskiĭ, Vladimir Mikhaĭlovich.
    (Khimicheskoe stroenie uglevodorodov)
    Химическое строение углеводородов и закономер-
    ности в их физико-химических свойствах. ₍Москва₎
    Изд-во Московского университета, 1953.
    319 p. diagrs., tables. 27 cm.
    Errata slip inserted.
    Includes bibliographies.

    1. Hydrocarbons.   I. Title.
    QD305.H5T3   54–22482

NT 0050417   DLC GAT

Tatevskiĭ, Vladimir Mikhaĭlovich.
    (Spektroskopiía)
    Спектроскопия. Под ред. А. В. Фроста. ₍Москва₎
    1951.
    189 p. illus. 20 cm. (Практические работы по физической хи-
    мии)
    At head of title: Московский государственный университет.
    Errata slip inserted.
    Bibliography: p. ₍188₎

    1. Spectrum analysis. I. Title. II. Series: Moscow. Universi-
    tet. Prakticheskie raboty po fizicheskoĭ khimii.
    QD95.T3   52–21664

NT 0050418   DLC

895.652
T187
   Tatewaki, Kanaya
     Tatewaki's short cut to Japanese conversation,
for beginners; practical and grammatical.
₍Tokyo₎ K. Tatewaki ₍1938₎
     2 p.l., 3, ₍1₎, 126 p., 1 l. 22ᶜᵐ.

     1. Japanese language - Conversation and phrase
books. 2. Japanese language - Grammar.

NT   0050419   NNC OC1

   Tatewake, Misao, 1889-
     A contribution to the flora of the Aleutian
Islands. By Misao Tatewaki and Yoshio
Kobayashi. 1934.
     (In Hokkaido university. Faculty of agri-
culture. Journal. v. 36, p. 1-119. illus.,
VIII pls., fold. map)

NT   0050420   PPAN

   Tatewaki, Misao, 1899-
     (Kita Karafuto no shokubutsu)
     北樺太の植物 ₍舘脇操著 東京₎ 東亞研究所
昭和18₍1943₎
     68 p. col. map. 26 cm. (東ソ自然調査資料 第6輯) ₍東亞研究所
資料 丁第30號C₎
     Cover title.
     Bibliography: p. 13-14.

     1. Botany—Sakhalin.   I. Title.   II. Series: Tōso shizen chōsa
shiryō, dai 6-shū.   III. Series: Tōa Kenkyūjo. Tokyo. Shiryō. Tei dai
30-gō C.
QK375.T38   72-802404

NT   0050421   DLC

1889-

Tatewaki, Misao, *Notes on plants of the western Aleutian
Islands collected in 1929. i, ii. (In Transactions of the
Sapporo natural history society, 1930-31, xi, 152-156, 200-
209.)*

NT   0050422   MH-A

460.15
T18
   Tatewaki, Misao, *1889-*
     Vascular plants of the northern Kuriles,
by Misao Tatewaki. ₍n.p.,1934₎
     p. ₍257₎-334. illus. 22½cm.

     Reprinted from the Bulletin of the Bio-
geographical society of Japan, vol.4,no.4,
pp.257-334, February, 1934.
     Bibliography: p.333-334.

NT   0050423   DNAL

   Tatewaki, Sadayo, 1904-
     現代女性十二講 帯刀貞代櫛田フキ監修 東京
ナウカ社 1950.
     339 p. tables. 19 cm.
     Includes bibliographies.

     1. Women in Japan.   I. Kushida, Fuki, 1899–   II. Title.
                       Title romanized: Gendai josei jūnikō.
HQ1762.T35   J 61-4217
Hoover Institution
for Library of Congress   ₍1₎†

NT   0050424   CSt-H DLC

   Tatewaki, Sadayo, 1904-
     (Hataraku josei no tame ni)
     働く女性のために ₍帯刀貞代著 東京 雄文
社 昭和24 i.e. 1949₎
     220 p. 19 cm.
     Title on cover: 働く婦人のために
     Colophon inserted.
     CONTENTS: 働く女性のために—新しいモラルについて—生活の合
理化について
     1. Woman—Employment—Japan. 2. Woman—Social and moral ques-
tions. 3. Home.   I. Title.
HD6197.T35   74-817860

NT   0050425   DLC

Tat⁽ewats⁽i, Movses
   see
   Movsēs III Tat⁽ewats⁽i, Catholicos of
   Armenia, 1577?-1633.

   Tatewossianz, Artem, 1879-
     Ueber die Identitaet oder Nichtidentitaet der
Bacillen menschlicher und Rindertuberkulose.
Tuebingen, 1906.
     Inaug. - diss. - Tuebingen.
     Bibl.

NT   0050427   ICRL

   Tateyama, Toshitada.
     (Dai Tōa Kyōeiken no bōeki to tsūka)
     大東亞共榮圈の貿易と通貨 竪山利忠著 ₍大
阪₎ 日本出版社 ₍昭和18 i.e. 1943₎
     6, 2, 243 p. 21 cm.

     1. Asia—Commerce.   2. Currency question—Asia.   3. Greater
East Asia co-prosperity sphere.   I. Title.
HF3766.T36   77-799101

NT   0050428   DLC CSt-H

   Tateyama, Zennoshin, 1856-1915.
     (Heike ongaku shi)
     平家音樂史 / 舘山漸之進著. — 東京：木村安
重, 明治43 ₍1910₎
     1203, ₍162₎ p., ₍72₎ plates (6 fold.) ; ill. ; 23 cm.
   ——— ₍附錄₎：經世小策. — 東京：木村安重, 明
治43 ₍1910₎
     315, 51, ₍30₎ p. ; ill. ; 23 cm.
     CONTENTS: 自鳴花筵機史—武道金湯史

                      ML3750.T35 1910 suppl.

     1. Heike monogatari.   2. Music—Performance.   I. Title.   II.
Title: Keisei shōsaku.
ML3750.T35 1910   75-792108

NT   0050430   DLC

   Tatford, Barrington.
     The story of British railways, by Barrington Tatford ...
London, S. Low, Marston & co., ltd. ₍1946₎
     xvi, 343 p. incl. front., illus. col. plates. 21½ x 17½ᵐ.

     1. Railroads—Gt. Brit.—Hist.
                             46-20846
Library of Congress   HE3018.T27
                   ₍3₎   385

NT   0050431   DLC TxU CoU ICU WaS NcU CtY

   Tatford, Frederick. A.   *1901 —*
     The climax of the ages; studies in the prophecy
of Daniel. With an appendix by F. F. Bruce ...
London, Marshall Morgan & Scott, [1953]
     270 p.

NT   0050432   PPWe

Scm
241
T18e
   Tatford, Frederick A.   1901-
     Early steps in the Christian life. Fort
Dodge, Iowa, Walterick Pub. Co., n.d.

     55 p.

     1. Christian life. I. Title. II. Cd., Sem.

NT   0050433   CLamB

   Tatford, Frederick A   1901-   *ed.*
     The faith, a symposium. London, Pickering & Inglis,
1952.
     350 p. 22 cm.
     On spine : A symposium of Bible doctrine.
     Bibliography : p. 332-340.

     1. Theology, Doctrinal.   I. Title.

BT75.T28   230   54-29665

NT   0050434   DLC PU NjPT

   Tatford, Frederick A   1901-
     The Master; reflections on the glories of Christ. ₍1st ed.₎
New York, Loizeaux Bros. ₍1950₎
     124 p. 20 cm.

     1. Jesus Christ—Person and offices.   I. Title.

BT201.T2   232   50-58043

NT   0050435   DLC MH-AH

BS
2825
.T21
n.c.
   Tatford, Frederick A   1901-
     Prophecy's last word; an exposition of the
Revelation. With a foreword by W.E. Vine.
London, Pickering & Inglis, 1947.
     270 p. illus. (part col.) map. 22cm.
     "List of authors quoted": p.258.

     1. Bible. N.T. Apocalypse - Criticism, inter-
pretation, etc. I. Title.

NT   0050436   DCU CLamB

Z5524
.C3T38
1954
   Tatge, Eleanor,   comp.
     Bibliography on the less ordered forms of
carbon, February 1954, by Eleanor Tatge ₍and₎
H. F. McMurdie. Washington, U. S. Dept. of
Commerce, National Bureau of Standards ₍1954?₎
     22 l. 28cm. (NBS report 3141)
     "NBS project 0907-10-4430."
     Contract no. Na-Onr-123-52.
     Xerox copy.
     1. Carbon—Bibl. I. McMurdie, Howard F
1905-   joint comp.

NT   0050437   ViU

QC100
.U555
no. 539
   Tatge, Eleanor, joint author.

   Swanson, Howard Eugene, 1915-
     Standard X-ray diffraction powder patterns ₍by₎ Howard
E. Swanson and Eleanor Tatge. Washington, U. S. Dept.
of Commerce, National Bureau of Standards, 1953-

PC2121
.S4
1933
   Tatge, Oscar.

   Schmitz, Bernhard, 1819-1881.
     Deutsch-französische phraseologie in systematischer ord-
nung, von prof. dr. Bernhard Schmitz; unter mitwirkung von
A. Gornay neubearbeitet von prof. dr. Karl Schmidt. 27. aufl.,
durchgesehen und ergänzt von prof. Oscar Tatge. Berlin-
Schöneberg, Langenscheidt ₍°1933₎

PC2121
.C8
1934
   Tatge, Oscar, ed.   FOR OTHER EDITION
                                    SEE MAIN ENTRY

   Coursier, Édouard.
     Handbuch der französischen und deutschen umgangs-
sprache, von Eduard Coursier; neubearbeitet von prof. Oscar Tatge. 1. aufl. Berlin-Schöneberg, Langenscheidt,
1934.

788
T18p Tatgenhorst, Ted C
Precision marching with the band, by
Ted C. Tatgenhorst and Donald L. Wolf.
The answer to your problem of creating
shows for the half time. New York,
Bourne [*1954]
48 p. illus. 27 cm.

Cover title.

1. Drill and minor tactics. 2. Bands
(Music). I. Wolf, Donald L
jt. author. II. Title.

NT 0050441 LU InU TxU ICarbS MtBC TxFTC OB1C

Tath, Prêa Krou Sangvichêa H
Quelques monuments d'Angkor; guide rédigé
sous les auspices de la Bibliothèque royale du
Cambodge. Phnom-Penh, Impr. du gouvernement, 1928.
95 p. plates, fold. plans. 25 cm.
Title and text in Khmer; added t. p. in French.
1. Angkor, Cambodia.

NT 0050442 NIC

Wason
PL4328.9 Tath, Prêas Visuddhivongs H
T21 Sattaparitta-dvādasaparitta; suivis de
quelques sûtras et de diverses stances,
tirés de Bhānavāra Pāli. Phnom-Penh, Edition
de la Bibliothèque royale, 1935.
199 p. 24cm.

Title and text in Khmer; added t. p. in
French.

1. Buddha and Buddhism. I. Title.

NT 0050443 NIC

Tathāgata
see
Gautama Buddha.

Tathagata, A.
...Septinveidīgā pasaule un psīchiskā enerġija; zinātniski-
ezoterisks apcerējums... Ventspili: K. Gūtmaņa apgādībā,
1935. 15 p. 24cm.

1. Occult sciences.
N. Y. P. L. September 25, 1940

NT 0050445 NN

Tathāgataguhyaka
see
Tantras. *Guhyasamājatantra.*

Tathāgataguṇajñāna
see
Tantras. Guhyasamāja tantra.

Tathagatha-oudana. FOR OTHER EDITIONS
SEE MAIN ENTRY
Bigandet, Paul Ambrose, *bp., d.* 1894.
The life, or legend, of Gaudama, the Buddha of the Bur-
mese. With annotations. The ways to neibban, and Notice on
the phongyies, or Burmese monks. By the Right Reverend
P. Bigandet ... 3d ed. London, Trübner & co., 1880.

Tathai, Saint. Legend.
Vita Sancti Tathei and Buched Seint y Katrin
see under title

Tatham, Benjamin.
Indians, soldiers and civilization ...
see under title

Tatham, C Ernest.
Beginning over again, and other talks; a few practical messages
for Christian young people, by C. Ernest Tatham. New York,
Loizeaux Bros. [195-?]
78 p. 19 cm. (Treasury of truth, no. 173)

1. Sermons, American. I. Title. II. Series.
BV4253.T37 252'.55 75-304236
MARC

NT 0050451 DLC CLamB

Tatham, C Ernest.
Elijah; the prophet of faith and fire, by C. Ernest Tatham.
New York, Loizeaux Bros. [19—?]
47 p. 19 cm.

1. Elijah, the prophet.
BS580.E4T26 222'.5'0924 75-303645
[B] MARC

NT 0050452 DLC

Tatham, C Ernest.
Forever secure, now and hereafter [An invita-
tion home – plus the fare !] Chicago, Moody press
[n. d.]
63 p.
1. Assurance (Theology) 2. Perseverance of the
saints.

NT 0050453 CM1G

Tatham, C Ernest.
He lives ! Seven studies of the resurrection
appearances of the Lord Jesus Christ, with foreword by H. G. Lockett. London, Pickering &
Inglis [pref. 1938]
80 p. 19 cm.

Messages given in the summer of 1938 to students of Guelph Bible School, Guelph, Canada.

1. Jesus Christ—Resurrection. I. Title.

NT 0050454 KKcB CLamB

Tatham, C M.
The airman, by C. M. Tatham. 2d impression. London,
New York [etc.] H. Milford, Oxford university press, 1917.
15, [1] p. 20cm.
In verse.

1. Aeronautics—Poetry. 2. European war, 1914-1918—Poetry.
I. Title. 18—20660
Library of Congress PR6039.A8A4 1917

NT 0050455 DLC

XN5
T218 [Tatham, C M]
"I believe in the Holy Ghost." A book of
daily devotion ... London[etc.]Society for
promoting Christian knowledge;New York,
E.& J.B.Young & co.[1891]
126,[2]p. 18cm.
Preface signed: C.M.T.

NT 0050456 NNUT

Tatham, Campbell, *pseud.*
see Elting, Mary, 1909–

Tatham, Carl von
see Tatham, Charles Heathcote, 1771–1842.

Tatham, Charles Heathcote, 1771–1842.
Auserlesene Muster antiker Bau-Ornamenten
gezeichnet nach den besten Originalen in Rom und
andern Theilen von Italien in den Jahren 1794,
1795, 1796. Von Carl Heathcote Tatham.
Weimar, im Verlage des Landes-Industrie-
Comptoirs, 1805.
8 p. 78 plates. 45 cm.
A translation of Tatham's Etchings, representing the best examples of ancient ornamental
architecture.
1. Architecture – Details. 2. Decoration and
ornament – Italy. 3. Architecture – Italy.

NT 0050459 TxU

Tatham, Charles Heathcote, 1771–1842.
Designs for ornamental plate, many of which have been
executed in silver, from original drawings. By Charles Heathcote Tatham ... London, Printed for T. Gardiner, by J. Barfield, 1806.
2 p. l. 3 p. 41 pl. 46cm. [With his Etchings, representing the best
examples of ancient ornamental architecture ... London, 1803]

1. Plate. 2. Design, Decorative. I. Title.
11—34695
Library of Congress NA3341.T3

NT 0050460 DLC NN NNC

f
NA
3341 Tatham, Charles Heathcote, 1771–1842.
TJ75 [Drawings, mainly of fragments of
HRC Grecian and Roman architectural
NonCirc ornament. England, 18—]
14 ink and pencil drawings. 57 x
39cm.

1. Decoration and ornament,
Architectural. 2. Decoration and
ornament, Ancient. CO- WEI

NT 0050461 TxU

Tatham, Charles Heathcote, 1771–1842.
Etchings, representing the best examples of
originals in Rome, and other parts of Italy, during
the years 1794, 1795, and 1796. By Charles
Heathcote Tatham ... facsimile reproduction by
photo-lithography. New York, Wm. Helburn
[n. d.]
[52] plates. 42.5 cm.

NT 0050462 WA

f729
T187e Tatham, Charles Heathcote, 1771–1842.
Arch Etchings, representing the best examples of an-
Lib'y cient ornamental architecture; drawn from the
originals in Rome, and other parts of Italy, during
the years 1794, 1795, and 1796. London, Printed
for the author, and sold by T. Gardiner, 1799.
12p. 98,[3] plates. 47cm.

1. Architecture – Details. 2. Decoration and
ornament – Italy. 3. Architecture – Italy. I.
Title: Ancient ornamental architecture.

NT 0050463 TxU DeU NcD OCl CaBVaU

Tatham, Charles Heathcote, 1771–1842.
Etchings, representing the best examples of ancient ornamental architecture; drawn from the originals in Rome, and
other parts of Italy, during the years 1794, 1795, and 1796.
2d ed. By Charles Heathcote Tatham ... London, Printed
for T. Gardiner, by J. Barfield, 1803.
12 p. 102 pl. 40ᶜᵐ.
With this is bound the author's "Etchings, representing fragments of
antique Grecian and Roman architectural ornament ... 1806".
1. Architecture—Details. 2. Decoration and ornament—Italy. 3. Architecture—Italy. I. Title.

Library of Congress   NA3341.T3   11–34697

NT 0050464   DLC

Tatham, Charles Heathcote, 1771–1842.
Etchings, representing fragments of antique Grecian and
Roman architectural ornament; chiefly collected in Italy, before the late revolutions in that country, and drawn from the
originals. By Charles Heathcote Tatham ... London, Printed
for T. Gardiner, by J. Barfield, 1806.
2 p. l., 3 p., 24 pl. 46ᶜᵐ. ₍With his Etchings, representing the best examples of ancient ornamental architecture ... London, 1803₎
1. Decoration and ornament, Architectural. 2. Decoration and ornament, Ancient. 3. Architecture—Details. I. Title: Architectural ornament.

Library of Congress   NA3341.T3   11–34696

NT 0050465   DLC NBB

NA2341
.T3   Tatham, Charles Heathcote, 1771–1842.
1810   Etchings, representing the best examples of
          ancient ornamental architecture; drawn from the
          originals in Rome, and other parts of Italy,
          during the years 1794, 1795, and 1796. 3d ed.
          London, Printed for T. Gardiner, by J. Barfield,
          1810.
             8 p. 102 plates. 46cm.
             1. Architecture—Details. 2. Decoration and
          ornament—Italy. 3. Architecture—Italy. I.
          Title.

NT 0050466   ViU TxU

Tatham, Charles Heathcote, 1771-1842.   *Cab.80.114.5
Etchings representing the best examples of Grecian and Roman
architectural ornament drawn from the originals and chiefly collected in Italy, before the late revolutions in that country.
London. Priestley & Weale. 1826. 8 pp. Plates. 48½ cm., in
2s.

K3651 — Architectural ornament. — Italy. Fine arts. Arch. — Rome. Fine arts.
Arch.

NT 0050467   MB TxU OClW OCU OOxM NWM

Tatham, Charles Heathcote, 1771–1842.
Etchings, representing the best examples of Grecian
and Roman architectural ornament; drawn from the
originals, and chiefly collected in Italy, before the late
revolutions in that country. By Charles Heathcote Tatham, architect ... London, J. B. Nichols and son, 1843.
10 p. 126 pl. 50ᶜᵐ.
1. Decoration and ornament, Architectural. 2. Decoration and ornament, Ancient. 3. Architecture—Details. I. Title: Architectural ornament.

                                               15–11125
Library of Congress   NA3341.T4

NT 0050468   DLC MWiW CtY PBL

Tatham, Charles Heathcote, 1771–1842.
Etchings, representing the best examples of ancient ornamental architecture; drawn from the originals in Rome, and other
parts of Italy, during the years 1794, 1795, and 1796. By
Charles Heathcote Tatham, architect; facsimile reproduction
by photo-lithography. New York, W. Helburn ₍189–₎
1 p. l., 102 pl. 43ᶜᵐ.
1. Architecture—Details. 2. Decoration and ornament—Italy. 3. Architecture—Italy.

Library of Congress   NA3341.T28   44–14696

NT 0050469   DLC CU PP MiD AAP CtY NcRS ICU NN

W
245   TATHAM, CHARLES HEATHCOTE, 1771–1842.
75   The gallery at Castle Howard, in Yorkshire…
          London, T. Gardiner, 1811.
             3 leaves. 6 pl. 49cm.   (with Robinson,
          Peter Frederick. Vitruvius britannica… 1833)

NT 0050470   ICN TxU NNC

BV4813   Tatham, Christopher
T3   Power from on high; a study in meditation
          and action.   London, Hodder & Stoughton
          ₍1947₎
             160 p.

             1. Meditation.   I. Title.

NT 0050471   CU

[Tatham, Edward] 1749–1834.
An address to the members of Convocation at
large, on the proposed new statute respecting
public examination, in the University of Oxford.
By the Rector of Lincoln college. 3d ed.   Oxford,
R. Bliss [etc., etc.] 1807.
   1 p. l., 18 p.   26.5 cm.   (In his Oxonia
purgata ... Oxford, 1811)
   Signed: Edward Tatham.

NT 0050472   CtY

LF
507   Tatham, Edward, 1749–1834.
.T22   ₍Addresses. Oxford, N.Bliss for R.Bliss
          etc., 1807-11₎
             6 pamphlets in 1 v. 28½ᶜᵐ.
          All but two of the pamphlets have special title-
          pages.
             CONTENTS.—A fourth address to the members of con-
          vocation respecting the new statute upon public ex-
          amination. 2d ed.1807.—A fifth address to free and
          independent members of convocation on the new statute
          respecting public examination; and the new alterations.
          2d ed.1808.—A new address to the free and independent
          members of convocation. 1810.—An address to the mem-

          bers of the Hebdomadal meeting ₍1810₎—A particular
          address to the members of convocation ₍1810₎—An ad-
          dress to the Right Honourable Lord Grenville ...
          upon great and fundamental abuses in ... ₍Oxford₎
          university. 1811.

             1.Oxford. University—Examinations. I.Grenville,
          William Wyndham Grenville,baron,1759–1834.

NT 0050474   MiU CU ICU CtY

Tatham, Edward, 1749–1834.
The chart and scale of truth, by which to find the cause of
error. Lectures read before the University of Oxford, at the
lecture founded by the Rev. John Bampton, M. A. By Edward
Tatham ... Oxford, Sold by J. Fletcher; ₍etc., etc.₎ M DCC XC–
₍M DCC XCII₎
   2 v. 22ᶜᵐ.
   Binder's title: Bampton lectures. 1789.
1. Truth. 2. Logic—Addresses, essays, lectures. 3. Theology—Addresses, essays, lectures. I. Title.
                                               38–16035
Library of Congress   BR45.B3 1789
                          ₍2₎   (230.082) 230

NT 0050475   DLC NN RPB ODW CtY MeB MH PL

Tatham, Edward, 1749–1834.
The chart and scale of truth, by which to find the cause of
error; lectures read before the University of Oxford at the
lecture founded by the Rev. John Bampton, M.A. By Edward
Tatham ... A new ed., rev., cor. and enl. from the author's
manuscripts, with a memoir, preface and notes by E. W. Grinfield ... London, W. Pickering. 1840.
   2 v. 22½ᶜᵐ.
   Half-title: Dr. Tatham's Bampton lectures. MDCCLXXXIX.
1. Truth. 2. Logic—Addresses, essays, lectures. 3. Theology—Addresses, essays, lectures. I. Grinfield, Edward William, 1785–1864, ed.
II. Title.
                                               37–23390
Library of Congress   BC171.T3 1840
                          ₍2₎   (230.082) 230

     MH CtY NN MCE
NT 0050476   DLC OKentU PP PBm NcD NjNbS DL PPRETS

[Tatham, Edward] 1749–1834.
A fourth address to the members of Convocation
respecting the new statute upon public examination.
By the Rector of Lincoln college.   Oxford,
R. Bliss, 1807.
   8 p.   27 cm.
   Signed: Edward Tatham.
   1. Oxford. University - Examinations.

NT 0050477   CtY

[Tatham, Edward] 1749–1834.
A fifth address to free and independent members
of Convocation, on the new statute respecting
public examination; and the alterations to be
proposed in Convocation. By the Rector of
Lincoln college.   Oxford, M. Bliss, 1808.
   11 p.   28 cm.
   Signed: Edward Tatham.
   1. Oxford. University - Examinations.

NT 0050478   CtY

[Tatham, Edward] 1749–1834.
A letter to the Reverend the Dean of Christ-
Church respecting the new statute upon public
examination. To which is added a third address
to the members of Convocation on the same
subject. By the Rector of Lincoln college.
Oxford, R. Bliss, 1807.
   34 p.   26.5 cm.   (In his Oxonia purgata ...
Oxford, 1811)
   Signed: Edward Tatham.
   1. Oxford. University - Examinations.

NT 0050479   CtY

₍Tatham, Edward₎ 1749–1834.
.md26   A letter to the Reverend the Dean of Christ-
807tc   Church respecting the new statute upon public
          examination. To which is added a third address
          to the members of Convocation on the same sub-
          ject. By the Rector of Lincoln college. 3d ed.
          Oxford,R.Bliss,1807.
             1p.ℓ.,34p. 28cm.
             Signed: Edward Tatham.

             1.Oxford. University - Examinations. (stamp)

NT 0050480   CtY

Tatham, Edward, 1749–1834.
Letter to the Right honorable Lord Grenville...on
the metallic standard ...   Ox., Munday, 1820.
   29 p.   (In Political economy pamphlets. v.d.
v. 147)

NT 0050481   PU CtY

Ngc95   Tatham, Edward, 1749–1834.
G5   A letter to the Right Honourable Lord
820tb   Grenville ... on the metallic standard ...
          2d ed. Oxford,Munday and Slatter,1820.
             1p.ℓ.,35p. 21cm.

             1.Currency question —Gt.Brit. 2.Paper
          money - Gt.Brit. 3.Grenville, William Wyndham
          Grenville, baron, 1759–1834.

NT 0050482   CtY

By62   Tatham, Edward, 1749–1834.
1   A letter to the Right Honourable Viscount
1820t   Sidmouth ... on the difficulty of the times ...
          Oxford,Printed and sold by Munday and Slatter
          ₍etc.,etc.₎ 1820.
             15p. 23ᶜᵐ.

             1.Sidmouth, Henry Addington, 1st viscount,
          1757–1844.

NT 0050483   CtY

Tatham, Edward, 1749, 1834, attributed author.
A letter to the Right Honourable William Pitt...
see under Bexley, Nicholas, vansittart,
baron, 1766-1851.

DA   Tatham, Edward, 1749-1834.
507   Letters to the Right Honourable Edmund Burke
1791   on politics. By Edward Tatham... Oxford, J.
T18 1   Fletcher, D. Prince, and J. Cooke [etc.; etc.]
     1791.
     1 p.l., 111 p.   20½ cm.

     1. Liberty. 2. Political science. 3. Great
Britain - Pol. & govt. I. Burke, Edmund, 1729?-
1797.

NT   0050485   CLU MH ICU ICN

[Tatham, Edward] 1749-1834.
A new address to the free and independent
members of Convocation. By the Rector of
Lincoln college. Oxford, N. Bliss, 1810.
     1 p.l., 26 p.   26.5 cm.   (In his Oxonia purga-
ta... Oxford, 1811)
     Signed: Edward Tatham.
     Concerns the illegality of the passing of the
new examination statute.
— --- Oxford, N. Bliss, 1810.
     1 p.l., 26 p.   28 cm.
     There is an additional line in the imprint of
this issue.

NT   0050486   CtY

B.6821 **Tatham, Edward,** 1749-1834.
Observations on the scarcity of money; and its effects
upon the public...Oxford, N. Bliss, 1816.
2 p.l., 47 p.   21 cm.

NT   0050487   MH-BA PU CtY MdBP

Tatham, Edward, 1749-1834.
Observations on the scarcity of money; and its effects
upon the public. By Edward Tatham ... 3d ed. Oxford, N. Bliss, 1816.
26 p.   20½ᶜᵐ.

1. Currency question—Gt. Brit.

Library of Congress   HG938.T2   7-6510†

NT   0050488   DLC KMK ICN

Tatham, Edward, 1749-1834.
On the scarcity of money; and its effects upon the public,
with the expedients by which alone they can be remedied, and
the nation saved from ruin. By Edward Tatham ... 5th ed.,
adapted to the present time. Oxford, Printed by Munday and
Slatter, 1819.
66 p.   21ᶜᵐ.

1. Currency question—Gt. Brit.

                     CA 6—485

Library of Congress   HG938.T22

NT   0050489   DLC CtY

[Tatham, Edward, 1749-1834]
Lmd65   Oxonia explicata & ornata. Proposals for
773T   disengaging and beautifying the University and
     city of Oxford. London, Sold by J.Wilkie,1773.
     25p. 20cm.

NT   0050490   CtY

[Tatham, Edward] 1749-1834.
Oxonia explicata & ornata. Proposals for dis-
engaging and beautifying the university and city of
Oxford. 2d ed. improved and enlarged...
London, 1777.
     viii, 43 p.   front.   cm.
     1. Oxford. University.-Buildings. 2. Oxford,
Eng. Descr. 1820. I. Title. Madan card.

NT   0050491   CtY

Tatham, Edward, 1749-1834.
Oxonia explicata et ornata ... A new edition.
Oxford, Printed & sold by Munday and Slatter,
1820.
     1 p.l., 24 p.   28 cm.

NT   0050492   CtY

Tatham, Edward, 1749-1834.
Oxonia purgata. An attempt to correct the errors and abuses
of the University of Oxford, in a series of addresses; first to the
members of convocation, and afterwards to the chancellor, relating to the new discipline of that university. By the Rector of
Lincoln college... Oxford, N. Bliss [etc., etc.] 1811.   1 v.
27cm.

Most of the addresses have special t-p., dated: 1807-11.
With armorial bookplate of F. Hayward Joyce.

321785B. 1. Oxford university—   Examinations. I. Title.
N.Y.P.L.   July 3, 1946

NT   0050493   NN CtY

[Tatham, Edward] 1749-1834.
A particular address to the members of
Convocation. [Oxford, 1810]
     2 p.   26.5 cm.   (In his Oxonia purgata ...
Oxford, 1811)
     Caption title.
     Signed: Edward Tatham.
     Supplementary to his An address to the members
of the Hebdomadal meeting.

NT   0050494   CtY

[Tatham, Edward] 1749-1834.
A second address to the members of
Convocation at large, on the proposed new statute
respecting public examination, in the University of
Oxford. By the Rector of Lincoln college. 3d ed.
Oxford, N. Pliss, 1811.
     8 p.   26.5 cm.   (In his Oxonia purgata ...
Oxford, 1811)
     Signed: Edward Tatham.

NT   0050495   CtY

Tatham, Edward, 1749-1834.
Second letter to the Right honourable
William Pitt ... on a national bank.   London,
n.p., 1797.
     31 p.   (In Political economy pamphlets. v.d.
v. 70)

NT   0050496   PU

Tatham, Edward, 1749-1834.
A sermon preached before the University of
Oxford, on the 5th of November 1791 ... London,
1791   Sold by W.Richardson,J.F.and C.Rivington,and
T18   T.Cadell;[etc.,etc.]1791.
     39p. 23cm.

NT   0050497   CtY

Tatham, Edward, 1749-1834.
A sermon preached before the University of
Oxford, on the 5th of November 1791 ... 2d ed.
1792   London,Sold by W.Richardson;J.F.and C.
T18   Rivington,and T.Cadell;[etc.;etc.]1792.
     40p. 22½cm.

NT   0050498   CtY

Mwv27   Tatham, Edward, 1749-1834.
T181   A sermon, preached before the University of
     Oxford, on Sunday morning, April 20, 1817 ...
     Oxford,Printed and published by N.Bliss,1817.
     25p. 22cm.
     "Second edition" on cover.

NT   0050499   CtY

Mwv27   Tatham, Edward, 1749-1834.
T182   A sermon, preached before the University of
     Oxford, on Sunday morning, April 20, 1817 ...
     3d ed. Oxford,Printed and published by N.
     Bliss,1817.
     25p. 23cm.

NT   0050500   CtY

RARE   Tatham, Edward, 1749-1834.
BOOKS   A sermon suitable to the times, preached at St. Mary's, Oxford,
DEPT.   on Sunday the 18th of November, at St. Martin's on Sunday the
     25th, and at St. Peter's in the East on Sunday the 2d of December.
     2d ed.   London, J. F. and C. Rivington, 1792.
     19 p.

NT   0050501   CU OCU

         Tatham, Edward, 1749-1834.
*EC8   A sermon suitable to the times, preached at
T1875   St. Mary's, Oxford, on Sunday the 18th of
792sc   November; at St. Martin's, on Sunday the 25th;
     at St. Peter's in the East, on Sunday the
     2d; and at All Saints, on Sunday the 9th of
     December. By Edward Tatham ... The third edi-
     tion.
     London:Sold by J.F.and C.Rivington,St.Paul's
     church-yard;W.Richardson,in the Strand:by J.
     Fletcher,J.Cooke,and R.Bliss,Oxford;and by the
     booksellers in   every principal town in
     England.   MDCCXCII. Price 3d.
     or 2s. 6d.   per dozen.
     8°. 19p. 20.5cm.

NT   0050502   MH

         Tatham, Edward, 1749-1834.
*EC8   A sermon suitable to the times, preached at
T1875   St. Mary's, Oxford, on Sunday the 18th of
792sd   November; at St. Martin's, on Sunday the 25th;
     at St. Peter's in the East, on Sunday the 2d;
     and at All Saints, on Sunday the 9th of December.
     By Edward Tatham ... The fourth edition.
     London:Sold by J.F.and C.Rivington,St.Paul's
     church-yard;W.Richardson,in the Strand:by J.
     Fletcher,J.Cooke,and R.Bliss,Oxford;and by the
     booksellers in every principal town in England.
     MDCCXCII. Price   3d. or 2s. 6d. per
     dozen.
     8°. 19p.   21.5cm.

NT   0050503   MH CtY

B.3517 **Tatham, Edward,** 1749-1834.
A third letter to the Right Honourable William Pitt, chancellor of the Exchequer, on the state of the nation, and the
prosecution of the war...London, Rivington [etc.] 1797.
2 p.l., 31 p. 23 cm.

NT   0050504   MH-BA

Tatham, Edward, 1749-1834.
Twelve discourses introductory to the study of
divinity, in which the principles of the Christian
religion are attempted to be laid down with
plainness and precision. London, Sold by
Richardson and Urquhart, 1780.
     xiv, vii, 314 p.   22 cm.

NT   0050505   OU CtY

Tatham,   Edward Henry Ralph, 1858-1938.
Erasmus in Italy. 21 pp. (*Eng. Hist. Rev.* v. 10, 1895.
p. 642.)

NT   0050506   MdBP

Tatham, Edward Henry Ralph, 1857–1938.
　Francesco Petrarca, the first modern man of letters, his life and correspondence; a study of the early fourteenth century (1304–1347) ... by Edward H. R. Tatham ... London, The Sheldon press; New York and Toronto, The Macmillan co., 1925–

　　　v. fronts. (v. 1: port.) 25½cm.

　　CONTENTS.—I. Early years and lyric poems.—II. Secluded study and public fame.

　　1. Petrarca, Francesco, 1304–1374.
　　　　　　　　　　　　　　　　　26–6217 Revised
Library of Congress　　　　　　　PQ4505.T3

OrPR IdU OrU
MiU OU ViU NN NjP MB OCU CU OrP MeB GU NIC CaBVaU
NT　0050507　　DLC MiU LU PP PU PBm PPT WaTU DGU ODW OO

E　　TATHAM, EDWARD HENRY RALPH, 1857–1938.
5　　　John Sobieski…　Oxford,A.T.Shrimpton &
.S 6773 son,1881.
　　　72p. 22cm.　(Lothian prize essay for 1881)

　　Bibliographical foot-notes.

NT　0050508　　ICN NjP CtY INS

Tatham, Edward H[enry] R[alph], 1857– 1938
　Lincolnshire in Roman times.　A paper read before the Louth antiquarian and naturalists' society, by Edward H. R. Tatham ...　Printed by request.　Louth, J. W. Goulding and son, 1902.

　　52 p. front. (fold. map) 21½cm.

　　Subject entries: 1. Lincolnshire, Eng.—Antiq.　2. Gt. Brit.—Antiquities, Roman.
　　　　　　　　　　　　　　　　　3–7827
Library of Congress, no.　　　　DA145.T21.

NT　0050509　　DLC

Tatham, Emma.
　The dream of Pythagoras and other poems.　By Emma Tatham.　Second edition, revised and enlarged.　London, Longman and co. [etc.]　Edinburgh, Oliver and Boyd [etc., etc., 1854]
　　3 p. l. [v]–vi, 216 p.　17.5 cm.

NT　0050510　　NNUT

Tatham, Emma
　The dream of Pythagoras and other poems.
3d ed. London, Hamilton, 1858.
　248 p.

NT　0050511　　OCl

Tatham, Emma, 1830–1855.
　The dream of Pythagoras, and other poems.　By Emma Tatham.　4th ed., with several additional pieces, complete in one volume.　With memoir by Rev. B. Gregory. (Abridged)　London, Hamilton & co., 1864.
　　viii, 344 p.　front. (port.)　18 cm.

NT　0050512　　CtY

PR 5548　　Tatham, Emma.
T18　　　The dream of Pythagoras, and other
D74　　poems.　5th ed., with several additional
1872　　pieces, and memoir by B. Gregory.　London,Wesleyan Conference Office, 1872.
　　iv, 327 p.　port.　18 cm.

NT　0050513　　CaBVaU PU

Tatham, F. S. Future of South Africa. 1. Voice
from Natal. 9 pp. (*Nineteenth Cent.* v. 47, 1900. p. 881.)

NT　0050514　　MdBP

Tatham, Frederick, 1805–1878.

Blake, William, 1757–1827.
　The letters of William Blake, together with a life by Frederick Tatham; ed. from the original manuscripts with an introduction and notes by Archibald G. B. Russell. With 12 illustrations. New York, C. Scribner's sons, 1906.

Tatham, Geoffrey Bulmer.
　Dr. John Walker and the Sufferings of the clergy, by G. B. Tatham ...　Cambridge [Eng.] University press, 1911.
　　vii, [1], 429 p. 19cm.　(Half-title: Cambridge historical essays.　No. xx)
　The Prince Consort prize, 1910.
　　CONTENTS.—The genesis of the work.—Contemporary criticism.—Walker as an historian.—Appendix: I. Calendar of the Walker collection of mss. in the Bodleian library.　II. Two letters from John Walker.　III. A list of the principal printed authorities cited by Walker in part I of the Sufferings of the clergy.
　　1. Walker, John, 1674?–1747.　An attempt towards recovering an account of the numbers and sufferings of the clergy.　2. Church of England—Hist.　I. Oxford.　University.　Bodleian library.　Mss. (Walker collection)
　　　　　　　　　　　　　　　　11–23796 Revised
Library of Congress　　　　　　BX5075.W23T3

NN
NT　0050516　　DLC CtY–D MiU CSt MSohG OO OU CU MB MnU

Tatham, Geoffrey Bulmer.
　The Puritans in power; a study in the history of the English church from 1640 to 1660, by G. B. Tatham ...　Cambridge [Eng.] The University press, 1913.
　　vi, [2], 282 p.　23cm.

　　1. Puritans.　2. Gt. Brit.—Church history—17th cent.　I. Title.
　　　　　　　　　　　　　　　　14—1740
Library of Congress　　　　　　ZX9334.T3

Vi MBrZ
NN MiU–C NjP CU MnU MB OC1 OU OOxM OO IdU CaBVaU PU
NT　0050517　　DLC MiU NIC ScU NcD PHC KEmT PU ViU WaU

TATHAM, GEOFFREY BULMER.　The sale of episcopal lands during the Civil wars and the Commonwealth.
Eng. hist. rev. 23:91-108.

NT　0050518　　MnU

Tatham, George N.
　An exposition of the character and management of the New Jersey joint monopolies, the Camden and Amboy railroad and transportation company: the Delaware and Raritan canal company, and their appendages.　By George N. Tatham.　Philadelphia, King & Baird, printers, 1852.
　　32 p. 23½cm.
　　[Technological pamphlets, v. 28, no. 11]
　　1. Camden and Amboy railroad and transportation company.　2. Delaware and Raritan canal company.
　　　　　　　　　　　　　　　CA 5—2440 Unrev'd
Library of Congress　　T7.T25
———— Copy 2.　22½cm.　[Miscellaneous pamphlets, v. 459, no. 10]

NT　0050519　　DLC PHi PPF PPL IU

Tatham, George N
　Memorial relative to the New Jersey consolidated monopolies, the Philadelphia & Trenton railroad company, the Camden & Philadelphia S. B. ferry co. and other associated companies, presented April 18, 1852.　Harrisburg, 1852.
　　11 p.

NT　0050520　　PPAmP PPL PHi

Tatham, George N
　... The railroad and canal monopolies of N. Jersey ...　Philadelphia, 1852.

NT　0050521　　PPL

F
149　　Tatham, George N
.5　　　Statement on behalf of the owners of
P41　　Windmill Island, by George N. Tatham,
v.1　　January 1, 1855.　Philadelphia, Printed
no.5　　by King and Baird, 1855.
　　　12 p.　23cm.

　　Cover title.

　　1. Windmill　　Island, Pa.

NT　0050522　　NIC PPAmP

Tatham, Herbert Francis William, d. 1909.
　The footprints in the snow, and other tales, by H. F. W. Tatham ...　With a memoir by A. C. Benson ...　London, Macmillan and co., limited, 1910.
　　xxix, 187 p. front. (port.) 21cm.
　　Preface signed M. T. T.
　　CONTENTS.—Preface.—Memoir.—The footprints in the snow.—The ordeal.—The dice.—The priest's curse.—Brother Ambrose.—The shepherd.—An eye for an eye.—Manfred's three wishes.—The house in the wood.—The Countess Kathleen.—The fourth wise man.—The travelling-companion.—The Lady Alicia.—King Richard's story.—The debt.—The true king.—The phonograph bewitched.
　　1. Tatham, Herbert Francis William, d. 1909.　I. Benson, Arthur Christopher, 1862–　II. Title.
　　　　　　　　　　　　　　　　A 12–694
Title from Enoch Pratt　　　　Free Libr.　Printed by L. C.

NT　0050523　　MdBE GU NBuU CaBVaU MB

Tatham, Herbert Francis William, d. 1909, joint comp.

Benson, Arthur Christopher, 1862–1925, comp.
　Men of might; studies of great characters, by A. C. Benson, M. A., and H. F. W. Tatham, M. A.　London, E. Arnold, 1892.

Tatham, James.
　A grammar, in which the orthography, etymology, syntax and prosody of the Latin language are minutely detailed, and rendered easy to the juvenile capacity.　By James Tatham ...　Philadelphia, Kimber & Sharpless, 1822.
　　2 p. l., 140, [2] p.　18½cm.

　　1. Latin language—Grammar—1800–1870.
　　　　　　　　　　　　　　　　11–9588
Library of Congress　　　　　　PA2087.T218

NT　0050525　　DLC PU NjP

xq828　　Tatham, John, fl.1632–1664.
T18a　　Acqua triumphalis; being a true relation of the honourable the city of Londons entertaining their sacred majesties upon the river of Thames, and well coming them from Hampton-Court to White-Hall.　Expressed, and set forth in severall shews and pageants the 23. day of August 1662.　London, Printed for the author by T. Childe and L. Parry, 1662.
　　[8], 12p.　31cm.

NT　0050526　　IU DFo CSmH TxU CtY

FILM
P-197　Tatham, John, fl. 1632–1664.

　　　Aqua triumphalis.　London, T. Childe and L. Parry, 1662.
　　Microfilm copy from TxU.
　　Woodward & McManaway No. 1206.

NT　0050527　　ViU MoU

Tatham, John, fl. 1632–1664.
　The character of the Rump
　　see under title

[Tatham, John] *fl.* 1632–1664.
The distracted state, a tragedy. Written in the yeer, 1641. By J. T. Gent... London, Printed by W. H. for Iohn Tey, and are to be sold at his shop at the Sign of the White Lion in the Strand, neer the New Exchange, 1651.

4 p. l., 30 p. 18¼ᶜᵐ.
[Longe, F. Collection of plays. v. 81, no. 3]
Dedication signed: J. Tatham.

1. Title.   26–2239

Library of Congress   PR1241.L6   vol. 81

NT   0050529   DLC NjP CtY PU MiU OU CSmH TxU

Tatham, John, *fl.* 1632–1664.
The dramatic works of John Tatham. With introductions and notes. Edinburgh. W. Paterson; [etc., etc.] 1879.

xii, 304 p. 20ᶜᵐ. (*Half-title:* Dramatists of the restoration)
Edited by James Maidment and W. H. Logan.
CONTENTS.— Introductory notice.—Love crownes the end.—The distracted state.—The Scotch figgaries.—The Rump.—The character of the Rump.—London's glory.
I. Maidment, James, 1795?–1879, ed.   II. Logan, William Hugh, d. 1883, joint ed.   III. Title: Love crownes the end.   IV. Title: The distracted state.   V. Title: The Scotch figgaries.   VI. Title: The Rump. VII. Title: The character of the Rump.   VIII. Title: London's glory.

1—10983

Library of Congress   PR3729.T12 1879

OrPS NSyU KEmT ScU WaSp MtU WaS
CtY MiU OO OCU OClW OCl ViU TxU TU NN NjP I ICN MH
NT   0050530   DLC NcD CaBVaU NIC PPT PSC PBm PP TxDaM

Rare Book Room
Ij
T187
640F

Tatham, John, fl. 1632–1664.
The fancies theater. By Iohn Tatham gent. ... London. Printed by Iohn Norton, for Richard Best, and are to be sold at his shop neere Grayes-Inne-gate in Holborne. 1640.
[162]p. 13ᶜᵐ.
Signatures: (∗)⁸((∗))₁, blank, wanting)
A⁴B–E⁸F⁴G–K⁸L².
"Love crownes the end. A pastoral" has special t.-p. (leaf I₄)
Reissued in 1657 with new title: The mirrour of   fancies.

NT   0050531   CtY DFo MH CSmH

Tatham, John, fl. 1632–1664.
The fancies theater. London, Printed by I. Norton, for R. Best, 1640.
"Love crownes the end. A pastorall ..." has special t.p.
Short-title catalogue no.23704 (carton 977)

I. Title.   II. Title: Love crownes the end.

NT   0050532   MiU

Tatham, John, fl.1632–1664.   FOR OTHER EDITIONS
                                   SEE MAIN ENTRY

Grim the collier of Croydon.
Grim the collier of Croydon.
(*In* Dodsley, Robert, ed.   A select collection of old English plays. 4th ed. by W. C. Hazlitt. London, 1874–76. 21½ᶜᵐ. v. 8, p. [385–470])

Tatham, John, fl. 1632–1664.

Knavery in all trades: or, The coffee-house. A comedy. As it was acted in the Christmas holidays by several apprentices with great applause. With license. London, Printed by J. B. for W. Gilbertson, and H. Marsh; and are to be sold at the Royal Exchange, Fleet-Street, and Westminster-Hall. 1664.

[Tatham, John] *fl.* 1632–1664.
[London]s Glory Represented by Time, Trvth and Fame: At The Magnificent Triumphs and Entertainment of His most Sacred Majesty Charls the II. The Dukes of York and Glocester, The two Houses of Parliament, Privy Councill, Judges, &c. At Guildhall on Thursday, being the 5ᵗʰ day of July 1660. and in the 12ᵗʰ Year of His Majestie most happy Reign. Together With the Order and Management of the whole Days Business. Published according to Order. London, Printed by William Godbid in Little Brittain. 1660.
2 p. l., 10 p. 19 x 15ᶜᵐ.
Signatures: A², B².
Title within ornament-   al border.
1. Gt. Brit.—Hist.—   Restoration, 1660–1688.   1. Title.
                                                        15–12522
Library of Congress   DA432.1660.T3

NT   0050535   DLC NjP ViU

Tatham, John, fl. 1632–1664.
Londinum triumphans. Londons triumphs celebrated in honour of the truely deserving Sir Anthony Bateman. Lord Maior of the Honourable city of London.   London, Printed by W. G. for Henry Brome, 1663.
Small 4 to.   Red morocco extra, gilt edges. First Edition.

NT   0050536   CSmH TxU

Rare Book Room
Ij
T187
664

Tatham, John, *fl.* 1632–1664.
Londons triumphs celebrated the 29ᵗʰ of October, 1664. In honour to ... Sir Iohn Lawrence knight, lord maior of ... London: and performed at the costs ... of the Worshipful company of haberdashers ... Written by John Tatham gent. Lond. Printed by W.G. for H. Brome at the Gun in Ivylane. 1664.
2 p. l., 18p. 17½ᶜᵐ.
Signatures: 2l. unsigned, B–C⁴D²(D₂ blank)
Imperfect: p.17–18 bled at top, with damage to page-numbers.

NT   0050537   CtY GU CSmH

Tatham, John, *fl.* 1632–1664.
London's triumph.   1662.

NT   0050538   CSmH

[Tatham, John] fl. 1632–1664.
London's tryumph, celebrated the nine and twentieth day of October in the year 1659. In honour of the much honoured Thomas Allen, Lord Mayor of said city. Presented and personated by an Europian, an Egyptian and a Persian. London, Printed by Thomas Mabb, 1659.
Small 4 to   Orange morocco, gilt edges.
First Edition. The authors name appears at the end of each of the two dedications.

NT   0050539   CSmH

Tatham, John, fl. 1632–1664.
Londons tryumph, presented by industry and honour: with other delightfull scaenes, appertaining to them: celebrated in Honour of the right Honourable Sr. John Ireton, Knight, Lord Mayor of the said city, on the 29th. day of October, 1658 ... London, by Thomas Mabb, 1658.
14 p.   Sm 4 to.   Unbound.   Formerly in Dev. vol. 57(6)

NT   0050540   CSmH

Tatham, John, fl. 1632–1664.
Londons tryumphs presented in several delightfull scoenes, both on water and land and celebrated in honour to the deservedly honored Sir John Frederick, Lord Mayor of the city of London. By John Tatham.   London, Printed by Thomas Mabb, 1661.
Small 4to.   Orange morocco, gilt edges. First Edition.

NT   0050541   CSmH CtY

Case
Y
135
.T 1756

TATHAM, JOHN, fl.1632–1664.
Love crownes the end. A pastorall presented by the schollees of Bingham in the county of Notingham, in the yeare 1632... London, Printed by I.N. for R.Best, 1640.
[30]p.

Signatures: J 4–8, K 8, L 2.
Signatures continuous with his "The fancies theater" (STC 23704)

NT   0050542   ICN

MiCPT
822.08

Tatham, John, fl. 1632–1664.
Love crowns the end. London, 1640.
44 p.
(In Three centuries of drama: English, 1512–1641)

Microprint.

NT   0050543   MoU

Tatham, John,   fl. 1632–1664.   **G.4076.25
The mirror of fancies. [Verse.] With a tragicomedy. Intitled, Love crowns the end. Acted by the Schollars of Bingham in the county of Nottingham.
London, Printed for W. Burden ... 1657. (162) pp. 13½ cm., in 8s.
Contains an allusion to Shakespeare on page (12).
The play has a separate title-page.

L9635 — Shakespeare, William. Allu...ns to, in literature. — T.r. — Love crowns the end. Play.

NT   0050544   MB CtY DFo CSmH

[Tatham, John] *fl.*1632–1664.

Neptunes address to His Most Sacred Majesty Charls the Second: king of England, Scotland, France and Ireland, &c. congratulating his happy coronation celebrated the 22th. day of April, 1661. In several designements and shews upon the water, before White-hall, at His Majesties return from the land-triumphs. London, Printed by William Godbid for Edward Powel. 1661.
8 p. 28ᶜᵐ.

Signatures: 4 leaves unsigned.
Title within double line border. Initial.
In verse.
Signed: John Tatham.
Unbound, in cloth case.
Cf. A catalogue of the library of ... John Henry Wrenn. Austin, Tex., 1920. v.5, p.10.

NT   0050546   CLU-C MH TxU CtY

Case
Y
185
.T 183

[TATHAM, JOHN] fl.1632–1664.
Ostella: or The faction of love and beauty reconcil'd. By I.T. Gent.   London, J. Tey, 1650.
[8], 115p. 16cm.
Dedication signed: John Tatham.
In verse.
Imperfect: t.–p. mutilated: closely trimmed.
Errors in paging.
STC II T 231.
Bound by Williams, Cheltenham.
Bookplate of William Holgate.

NT   0050547   ICN CtY CSmH MH NcU DFo

Tatham, John,   Fl. 1632–1664.   **2537.12
The royal oake, with other various and delightfull scenes ... celebrated in honour of ... Sir Richard Brown, Lord Mayor of the City of London, the 29th day of October ... 1660, and performed at the costs and charges of the Right Worshipfull Company of Merchant Taylors ... London. Printed by S. G. for R. B. 1660.
(In Lord Mayors' pageants. Pp. 87–106. London, 1843.)

E5491 — T.r.

NT   0050548   MB CtY MdBP CSmH

Tatham, John, fl. 1632–1664.
Royal oake [celebrated in honour of ... Sir Richard Brown] London, 1660.
(In Three centuries of drama: English, 1642–1700)

Microprint.

1. Brown, Sir Richard, bart., fl. 1660.
I. Title.

NT   0050549   MoU

Tatham, John, *fl.* 1632–1664.
The Rump: or, The mirror of the late times. A new comedy, written by J. Tatham, gent. Acted many times with great applause, at the private house in Dorset-Court. London, Printed by W. Godbid for R. Bloome. 1660.

2 p. l., 68 p. 19ᶜᵐ.

₍Longe, F. Collection of plays. v. 117, no. 5₎
Dramatis personæ are actual Roundheads with the names transposed.

1. Gt. Brit.—Hist.—Commonwealth and protectorate, 1649–1660—Drama.
I. Title.
26–2240
Library of Congress　　　　PR1241.L6 vol. 117

NT 0050550　　TxU NjP
　　　　DLC MH DFo NPV NIC CtY CSmH　　MiU OU I

FILM
P–544 **Tatham, John,** *fl.* 1632–1664.

The rump; or, The mirrour of the late times. London, W. Godbid for R. Bloome, 1661.

Microfilm copy from TxU.

Woodward & McManaway No. 1219.

I. Title. II. Title: The mirrour of the late times.

NT 0050551　　ViU

Tatham, John, *fl.* 1632–1664.
The rump
Behn, *Mrs.* **Aphra (Amis)** 1640–1689.
The Roundheads, or, The good old cause, a comedy. As it is acted at His Royal Highness the Dukes theatre. By Mrs. A. Behn. London, Printed for D. Brown ... and Benskin ... and H. Rhodes, 1682.

₍**Tatham, John,**₎ *fl.* 1632–1664.
The Scots figgaries: or, A knot of knaves. A comedy. London, Printed by W. H. for Iohn Tey, at the White-Lion in the Strand, near the New Exchange, 1652.

2 p. l., 52 p. 18ᶜᵐ.

Dedication signed: Jo. Tatham.
Signatures: 2 leaves unsigned (t.-p.; dedication), B–G⁴, H².

I. Title.
28–5743
Library of Congress　　　　PR3729.T12S4

NT 0050553　　DLC MH CtY MWiW-C NjP TxU MB

₍**Tatham, John**₎ *fl.* 1632–1664.
The Scotch figgaries: or, A knot of knaves. A comedy. London, Printed 1652; Reprinted, W. Mears ₍etc.₎ 1735.

59 p. incl. front. 16½ᶜᵐ.

₍Longe, F. Collection of plays. v. 73, no. 6₎

I. Title.
26–2241
Library of Congress　　　　PR1241.L6 vol. 73

NT 0050554　　DLC InU CSmH CtY

Tatham, John, *fl.* 1687–1699.
The case put and decided by George Fox, George Whitehead ...
　　see under　Leeds, Daniel, 1652–1720, ed.

Tatham, John, *Francis Walkingame.*
Annual report on the health of Salford by the medical officer of health
　　see　Salford₍Eng.₎(Lancashire) Medical Officer of Health.
　　　Annual report.

Tatham, John *Francis Walkingame*
Health bulletins
　　see under　Salford, Eng. (Lancashire)
Medical Officer of Health.

Tatham, John Francis Walkingame

——. Letter to the registrar-general, on the mortality of males engaged in certain occupations in its three years 1890–92; and on an English healthy district life table for the ten years 1881–90. cxriv, 166 pp. 8°. *London,* 1897.
Forms pt. 2 of: Suppl. 55, Ann. Rep. Registrar-Genl. ... in England.

NT 0050558　　DNLM

Tatham, John Francis Walkingame

——. Manchester life tables (new edition, 1893), comprising separate tables for I. The city of Manchester. II. The Manchester township. III. Manchester outlying townships. vi, 57 pp. roy. 8°. *Manchester, H. Blacklock & Co.,* 1893.

NT 0050559　　DNLM MB

Tatham, John Francis Walingame.
Quarterly health returns
　　see under　Manchester, Eng. Public Health Office. ₍Supplement₎

Tatham, John *Francis Walkingame.*
Remarks of the medical officer of health on existing hospital provision for infectious diseases
　　see under　Salford. Eng. (Lancashire) Medical Officer of Health.

Tatham, John Francis Walkingame.
Report on the health of Greater Manchester, 1891–3
　　see under　Manchester, Eng. Public Health Office.　[Supplement]

Tatham, John *Francis Walkingame.*
——. Smallpox, vaccination and re-vaccination. A lecture. 8 pp. 8°. *Manchester & London, J. Heywood ₍and others₎,* 1888.

NT 0050563　　DNLM

Tatham, John Francis Walkingame.
Weekly health returns of the city of Manchester
　　see under　Manchester, Eng. Public Health Office.

Tatham, Joseph
Considerations on the existence, operation and fruits of the Holy Spirit. York, W. Alexander & Son, 1830.
77p.

NT 0050565　　ICRL PPL PSC-Hi

Tatham, Joseph, d. 1843
The ground of Christian discipline... By Joseph Tatham... York: W. Alexander ₍etc., etc.₎ 1824.　x, 12–57 p.　18cm.

1. Friends, Society of—Govt.　　　　and discipline.
N. Y. P. L.　　　　　　　　　　　　　December 7, 1943

NT 0050566　　NN ICN NjPT MH PSC-Hi PHC

Tatham, Joseph, d. 1843.
The ground of Christian discipline briefly explained; and the necessity of the influence of heavenly widsom for its proper support, enforced; by Joseph Tatham ...　Dublin, Printed by Thomas I. White, MDCCCXXXIV [1834]
vi [7]–45 p.　16.5 cm.
"Appendix: containing selections from the writings of Friends ..." p. [31]–45.

NT 0050567　　PSC-Hi OC1WHi PHC

Tatham, Joseph.
The ground of Christian discipline briefly explained; and the necessity of the influence of heavenly wisdom for its proper support enforced... Sherwoods, N. Y., D. Heston, 1852.
24 p.　(In Pamphlets connected with the Gurney controversy. No. 32)

NT 0050568　　PHC

Tatham, Joseph, d. 1843
The ground of Christian discipline... Sherwoods, N. Y., 1862.

NT 0050569　　PHC

Tatham, Joseph, d. 1843
Rules and instruction of the Seminary at Leeds. Leeds, 1806.

NT 0050570　　PSC-Hi

Tatham, Julie (Campbell)
Behind the white veil. New York, Grosset & Dunlap ₍1951₎
vii, 214 p.　illus.　20 cm.　(The Vicki Barr flight stewardess series)

I. Title.
PZ7.T2114Be
51–1373 rev

NT 0050571　　DLC

Tatham, Julie (Campbell)
Cherry Ames at Spencer. New York, Grosset & Dunlap ₍1949₎
vii, 213 p.　front.　20 cm.

I. Title.
PZ7.T2114Ch
49–3929 rev*

NT 0050572　　DLC NN

Tatham, Julie (Campbell)
Cherry Ames, clinic nurse. New York, Grosset & Dunlap ₁1952₎
208 p. illus. 20 cm. (The Cherry Ames stories)

ɪ. Title.

PZ7.T2114Chf   52–10255 rev ‡

NT 0050573   DLC

Tatham, Julie (Campbell)
Cherry Ames, country doctor's nurse. New York, Grosset & Dunlap (ᶜ1955₎
214 p. illus. 20 cm. (The Cherry Ames stories ₁16₎)

ɪ. Title.

PZ7.T2114Chfl   55–1360 ‡

NT 0050574   DLC

Tatham, Julie (Campbell)
Cherry Ames, dude ranch nurse. New York, Grosset & Dunlap ₁1953₎
210 p. 20 cm. (The Cherry Ames stories)

ɪ. Title.

PZ7.T2114Chg   53–2323 ‡

NT 0050575   DLC InU

Tatham, Julie (Campbell)
Cherry Ames, mountaineer nurse. New York, Grosset & Dunlap ₁1951₎
212 p. front. 20 cm. (Her The Cherry Ames stories ₁12₎)

ɪ. Title.

PZ7.T2114Cj   51–4230 rev

NT 0050576   DLC NN

Tatham, Julie (Campbell)
Cherry Ames, night supervisor. New York, Grosset & Dunlap ₁1950₎
vii, 209 p. illus. 20 cm. (The Cherry Ames stories)

ɪ. Title.

PZ7.T2114Ci   50–4001 rev

NT 0050577   DLC

Tatham, Julie (Campbell)
Cherry Ames, rest home nurse. New York, Grosset & Dunlap ₁1954₎
214 p. illus. 20 cm. (Her The Cherry Ames stories ₁15₎)

ɪ. Title.

PZ7.T2114Cjd   54–8564 ‡

NT 0050578   DLC

Tatham, Julie (Campbell)
The clue of the broken blossom. New York, Grosset & Dunlap ₁1950₎
211 p. front. 20 cm. (The Vicki Barr flight stewardess series)

ɪ. Title.

PZ7.T2114Cl   50–5645 rev

NT 0050579   DLC

Tatham, Julie (Campbell)
Ginny Gordon and the lending library; illustrated by Margaret Wesley. Racine, Wis., Whitman Pub. Co. ₁1954₎
282 p. illus. 20 cm.

ɪ. Title.

PZ7.T2114Gf   54–4377 ‡

NT 0050580   DLC

Tatham, Julie (Campbell)
Ginny Gordon and the missing heirloom. Illustrated by Margaret Jervis. Racine, Wis., Whitman ₁1950₎
249 p. illus. 21 cm.

ɪ. Title.

PZ7.T2114Gh   50–8331 rev

NT 0050581   DLC

Tatham, Julie (Campbell)
Ginny Gordon and the mystery at the old barn. Illustrated by Margaret Jervis. Racine, Wis., Whitman Pub. Co. ₁1951₎
250 p. illus. 21 cm.

ɪ. Title.

PZ7.T2114Ghc   51–6063 rev ‡

NT 0050582   DLC

Tatham, Julie (Campbell)
Ginny Gordon and the mystery of the disappearing candlesticks. Illus. by Margaret Jervis. ₁Authorized ed.₎ Racine, Wis., Whitman Pub. Co. ₁1948₎
248 p. illus. 21 cm.

ɪ. Title.

PZ7.T2114Gi   49–3810 rev*

NT 0050583   DLC

Tatham, Julie (Campbell)
The mongrel of Merryway Farm; illustrated by Edwin Megargee. ₁1st ed.₎ Cleveland, World Pub. Co. ₁1952₎
232 p. illus. 21 cm.

ɪ. Title.

PZ10.3.T142Mo   52–8422 ‡

NT 0050584   DLC Or WaS

Tatham, Julie (Campbell)
The mystery at Hartwood House. New York, Grosset & Dunlap ₁1952₎
210 p. illus. 20 cm. (The Vicki Barr flight stewardess series ₁7₎)

ɪ. Title.

PZ7.T2114My   52–7176 rev ‡

NT 0050585   DLC

Tatham, Julie (Campbell)
Rin Tin Tin's Rinty; an original story featuring Rinty, son of the famous movie dog, Rin Tin Tin. Illustrated by Rene Martin. Authorized ed. Racine, Wis., Whitman Pub. Co. ₁1954₎
282 p. illus. 20 cm.

ɪ. Title.

PZ10.3.T142Ri   54–33177 ‡

NT 0050586   DLC

Tatham, Julie (Campbell)
Trixie Belden and the gatehouse mystery. Illustrated by Mary Stevens. Racine, Wis., Whitman Pub. Co. ₁1951₎
250 p. illus. 21 cm.

ɪ. Title.

PZ7.T2114Tp   51–6062 rev ‡

NT 0050587   DLC ICarbS

Tatham, Julie (Campbell)
Trixie Belden and the mysterious visitor; illustrated by Mary Stevens. Racine, Wis., Whitman Pub. Co. ₁1954₎
282 p. illus. 21 cm.

ɪ. Title.

PZ7.T2114Tq   54–3747 ‡

NT 0050588   DLC

Tatham, Julie (Campbell)
Trixie Belden and the red trailer mystery. Illustrated by Mary Stevens. Racine, Wis.. Whitman ₁1950₎
248 p. illus. 21 cm.

ɪ. Title.

PZ7.T2114Ts   50–8332 rev

NT 0050589   DLC ICarbS

Tatham, Julie (Campbell)
Trixie Belden and the secret of the mansion. Illus. by Mary Stevens. ₁Authorized ed.₎ Racine, Wis., Whitman Pub. Co. ₁1948₎
248 p. illus. 21 cm.

ɪ. Title.

PZ7.T2114Tr   49–3808 rev*

NT 0050590   DLC ViBlbV

Tatham, Julie (Campbell)
World book of dogs; illustrated by Edwin Megargee. [1st ed.] Cleveland, World Pub. Co. [1953]
126 p. illus. 29 cm.

1. Dogs. I. Title.

SF423.T22   636.7   53–6641 ‡

WaS OrP DNAL
NT 0050591   DLC ViU OOxM OC1 PP MB WaT IdB Or WaE

Tatham, Meaburn, *ed.*
The Friends' ambulance unit, 1914–1919, a record, ed. by Meaburn Tatham and James E. Miles. London, The Swarthmore press ltd. [1919]
xxiv, 263, [1] p. col. front., plates (part col.) ports., 3 fold. maps, 2 fold. diagr. 24½ᶜᵐ.

1. Friends' ambulance unit, 1914–1919. I. Miles, James Edward, joint ed. II. Title.

Library of Congress   D629.G7T3   20–6971

NT 0050592   DLC PPFr ICRL IU PHC DNLM ICJ

TATHAM, RICHARD.
Science, politics and the masses. Is mass enlightenment a political fallacy? [London] Social science association [1944] 15 p. 18cm.
(Social science series. no. 1)

Published also with title: Understanding the mass mind.

1. Political science, 1918– . I. Tatham, Richard. Understanding the mass mind.

NT 0050593   NN

[Tatham, Richard]
... Understanding the mass mind ... [London] The Social science association [1944?]
cover-title, 15, [1] p. 18ᶜᵐ. (Social science series, no. 1)
"First published under the title of 'Science, politics and the masses'."

1. Social psychology. I. Title.

                     45–6425
Library of Congress   HM251.T33 1944
       [3]   301.15

NT 0050594   DLC

Tatham, Richard Ecroyd, 1839–1861.
The Sabbath school teacher; a memoir
    see under   Ford, John, 1801–1875.

Tatham, Ronald.
Aeronautical engineering for national certificate. London, English Universities Press [1949–52]
2 v. illus. 23 cm. (The Technical college series)

1. Aeronautics. 2. Aeroplanes—Design and construction. I. Title. II. (Series)

TL546.T3   629.13   50–761 rev

NT 0050596   DLC PSt DSI CaBVaU MB

Tatham, S
Observations on the Glasgow, Paisley, and Ardrossan canal, and the harbour at Ardrossan. Glasgow, 1807.
8°

NT 0050597   MBAt

Tatham, Sandford, *plaintiff.*
A verbatim report of the cause Doe dem. Tatham v. Wright, tried at the Lancaster Lammas assizes, 1834, before Mr. Baron Gurney and a special jury. By Alexander Fraser ... Lancaster, W. Barwick [etc.] 1834.
2 v. 22½ᶜᵐ.
Will cause in ejectment.

I. Wright, George, defendant. II. Fraser, Alexander, reporter.

                             14–5715

NT 0050598   DLC OU MH

[Tatham, *Mrs.* Sarah Theresa (Roe)] 1872–
Airman [by] Sands-Roux [pseud.] New York, The Poets press [ᶜ1937]
61, [1] p. 23½ᶜᵐ.
Poems.
"First edition."

I. Title.

                             39–18598
Library of Congress   PS3539.A75A7 1937
————— Copy 2.
Copyright A 128790   [2]   811.5

NT 0050599   DLC

Tatham, W. P.
A contribution to meteorology. Mr. Espy; Dr. Hare; tornadoes; hailstorms. By W. P. Tatham... Philadelphia: Franklin Institute, 1889. 9 p. 8°.

Cover-title.
Repr.: Jour. of the Franklin Institute, June, 1889.
Bibliographical foot-notes.

1. Meteorology.—Essays and   misc.
N. Y. P. L.   January 13, 1916.

NT 0050600   NN DAS

Tatham, William, 1752–1819.
Works by this author printed in America before 1801 are available in this library in the Readex Microprint edition of Early American Imprints published by the American Antiquarian Society. This collection is arranged according to the numbers in Charles Evans' American Bibliography.

NT 0050601   DLC

VCC636
T21   Tatham, William, 1752–1819.
Auxiliary remarks on an essay on "Comparative advantages of oxen for tillage in comparison with horses." In a letter to Sir John Talb. Dillon, Knt. &c. &c., to which is added sundry communications on this interesting subject. London, Printed by and for R. B. Scott, 1801.
53 p. 21cm.

1. Domestic animals 2. N.C.—Live stock I. Auxiliary remarks II. Comparative advantages of oxen for   tillage.

NT 0050602   NcU

Tatham, William, 1752–1819.
Circular architecture, being a new method of building ... London, Lawrence, 1803.
24 p.

NT 0050603   PPAmP

Tatham, William, 1752–1819, *ed.*
Communications concerning the agriculture and commerce of America: containing observations on the commerce of Spain with her American colonies in time of war. Written by a Spanish gentleman in Philadelphia, this present year, 1800. With sundry other papers concerning the Spanish interests. Ed. in London, by William Tatham. London, Printed for J. Ridgway, 1800.
viii, 120 p. 21ᶜᵐ.

1. Spain—Colonies—America. 2. U. S.—Comm. 3. Spain—Commercial policy.

Library of Congress   HF3025.T22   6–17321†

NT 0050604   DLC ViW NN ViU MH NIC NjP RPJCB

---

*
TC625
.D673   Tatham, William, 1752–1819.
1808
A comparative view of the four projected coastwise canals, which are supposed by some to be in competition for the trade between Norfolk and North-Carolina. Norfolk, Printed by J. O'Connor, 1808.
27 p. 21cm.

1. Dismal Swamp Canal. 2. Suffolk Canal. 3. Great Bridge Canal. 4. Kempsville Canal.

NT 0050605   ViU PPAmP

Tatham, William, 1752–1819.
Copy of manuscript report by William Tatham on survey of the coast of North Carolina from Cape Hatteras to Cape Fear, 1806. Washington, 1807.
56 p. Q.
Photographic reproduction from the original typed manuscript which was evidently made from another manuscript.

NT 0050606   NcU

1752–1819.
Tatham, William, A few hints and remarks for the use of the officers, physicians and students of His M: C: Majesty's botanic garden at Madrid, intended to introduce a botanical correspondence with the principal botanists of the United States of N. America, thereby exchanging good offices for the benefit of mankind in the science of botany in general; and to add to the very extensive and laudable collection of His M. C. Majesty in particular the numerous productions of the several American states which appear to have been hitherto omitted. Humbly submitted to their reflection by William Tatham, a traveller from the said United States now sojourning in Madrid 10th June, 1796. Illustr.
A typewritten copy of the original manuscript, made in North Billerica, Mass., [1921?] 27 sheets in 1. 8° cover.

NT 0050607   MH-A

Tatham, William, 1752–1819.
An historical and practical essay on the culture and commerce of tobacco. By William Tatham. London, Printed for Vernor & Hood, 1800.
xv. 330 p. 4 pl. (2 col.) 21½ᶜᵐ.

1. Tobacco.

Library of Congress   SB273.T21   12—11608

NcD MWiW-C MHi
MsU NN OC ViU ViW RPJCB NNC KyU CU MH-BA MH CaBVaU
NT 0050608   DLC OC1 ICRL PP ViW MU PPL ScU NHi MBAt

Tatham, William, 1752–1819.
An historical and practical essay on the culture and commerce of tobacco. London, Printed for Vernor & Hood, 1800.
Microcard edition (4 cards) (Travels in the Old South II, 170) microprinted by the Lost Cause Press, Louisville, 1959.

1. Tobacco. I. Ser.

NT 0050609   ViU FMU TxU ICRL PSt FU

Tatham, William.
Letter to John Vaughan. In relation to a paper on longevity written by him. 1808.
Ms. communications to the A. P. S., Vol. on Medicine, Anatomy and Physiology.

NT 0050610   PPAmP

Tatham, William, 1752–1819.
National irrigation, or the various methods of watering meadows; affording means to increase the population, wealth, and revenue of the kingdom, by an agricultural, commercial and general economy in the use of water. By William Tatham ... London, Printed for J. and T. Carpenter, 1801.
1 p. l., [v]–xix, 427, [1] p. illus., plates, plans. 21½ᶜᵐ.

1. Irrigation—Gt. Brit. I. Title.

                             Agr 29—457
U. S. Dept. of agr. Library   55T18
for Library of Congress   [a40b1]

MBH PPUSDA
NT 0050611   DNAL MH-BA FMU CtY PPL DI-GS ICJ MiU

B.4739 **Tatham, William,** 1752-1819.
Navigation and conservancy of the river Thames.
Report on a view and examination of certain impediments and obstructions in the navigation of the river Thames, made pursuant to a resolution of the worshipful the navigation committee, dated the 7th December, 1802: and also pursuant to farther indulgences, communicated by their clerk on the 12th day of the same month...from a survey of the premises, made in co-operation with Samuel Miller. London, C. Whittingham [etc.] 1803.
2 p.l., 126 p. 22·5 cm.

NT 0050612   MH-BA

Tatham, William, 1752-1819.
Plan for improving the city of London by means of navigable canals & commercial basons. n.p., 1799.
163 p.

NT 0050613   PU

Tatham, William, 1752-1819.
The political economy of inland navigation, irrigation, and drainage; with thoughts on the multiplication of commercial resources; and on means of bettering the condition of mankind, by the construction of canals, by the improvement of their various capacities for commerce, transfer, agriculture, household supplies, and mechanical power; and by the unlimited extension thereof into the remotest interior of Great Britain and of foreign parts. London, Faulder, 1799.
xvi, 500, [7] p. illus., maps (1 col.) 27 cm.

Appendix and "A filtering machine": p. [501]-[507]
Bibliographical footnotes.

1. Inland water transportation—Gt. Brit. 2. London—Canals. 3. Inland water transportation—U. S. 4 Canals.

HE663.T36   68-126433 rev

    DeU MH-BA PU
NT 0050615   DLC PPAmP ScU MiU NN MnU CtY NWM NjP

Microfm
WB
22
Tatham, William, 1752-1819.
The political economy of inland navigation, irrigation, and drainage; with thoughts on the multiplication of commercial resources; and on means of bettering the condition of mankind, by the construction of canals, by the improvement of their various capacities for commerce, transfer, agriculture household supplies, and mechanical power; and by the unlimited extension thereof into the remotest interior of Great Britain and of foreign parts. London, Faulder, 1799.
Negative.
Appendix and "A filtering machine": p. [501]-[507]
Bibliographical footnotes.

1. Inland water transportation—Gt. Brit. 2. London—Canals. 3. Inland water transportation—U.S. 4. Canals.

NT 0050617   ICU

Tatham, William, 1752-1819.
Proposals, for publishing a large and comprehensive map of the southern division of the United States of America. (By subscription only.)
[Richmond, 1790]
Broadside. 52.5 x 42.5 cm.
With printed power of attorney to collect subscriptions attached: Dear sir, The magnitude of the undertaking ... 1 l.
Evans 22924; Sabin 94410.

NT 0050618   RPJCB

X22
A
90
Tatham, William, 1752-1819.
Remarks on inland canals, the small system of interior navigation, various uses of the inclined plane, &c. &c. In a letter from William Tatham, to a proprietor in the Colebrook-Dale and Stratford canals. London, Printed for J. Taylor, 1798.
20 p.

NT 0050619   MiU

Tatham, William, 1752-1819.
U. S. *Congress. House. Committee on letter of William Tatham.*
Report from the Committee appointed on the tenth of February last, on the letter of William Tatham to the speaker ... City of Washington, A. & G. Way, printers, 1806.

[Tatham, William] 1752-1819, comp.
Report of a case decided ... the 16th of Nov. 1793
     see under   Kamper, Peter, plaintiff.

Cm912
1807t
Tatham, William, 1752-1819.
Rough hydrographick map of the N: Carolina junction canals, being an inland coastwise navigation, designed for improving the commerce & defence of the United States. [n.p.] October 31, 1807.
50 x 85 cm. on 2 sheets 46 x 57 cm.
Scale about 7.5 nautical miles to the inch.
Negative photocopy of manuscript map in the Library of Congress.
1. N.C.—Maps 2. N.C.—Waterways

NT 0050622   NcU

RARE BOOK
DEPT.
*XG
.324
.13
no.18
Tatham, William, 1752-1819.
Schedule of vouchers tending to prove that William Tatham has served the U. States near forty years, zealously ... that he has been thereby ruined ... and that he ought to be equitably and honorably remunerated, for a life-time employed so advantageously to the community, and affording to the government an unparalleled mass of information & economical resources.
[Washington, D.C.?] December, 1815.

12p. 20.5cm.

NT 0050623   MB DLC

551.36
T187
Tatham, William, 1752-1819.
The separate report of William Tatham, one of the commissioners appointed to survey the coast of North Carolina from Cape Hatteras to Cape Fear inclusive, under the Act of Congress of the 10th of April last. [Addressed] to the Hon. Albert Gallatin, Secretary of the Treasury, &c. &c. [Washington, D.C., 1807]
52 l. 27 cm.

Caption title.
Manuscript corrections in text.

Photocopy (positive) "From the original manuscript in the Library of the U.S. Coast and Geodetic Survey."

NT 0050625   KyU

Rare Book
Room
c23
88
[Tatham, William] 1752-1819.
To His Excellency Henry Lee, Governor, and the respective gentlemen of the Council ... to the share-holders and others interested in the canals of Virginia; to the commercial interest and property-holders thereof ... [Richmond, 1794]
16p. 23cm.
Signature: A⁸.
Caption title.
Signed: William Tatham. Richmond, Virginia, May 1794.

NT 0050626   CtY

---

*pAB7
T1877
791tb
Tatham, William, 1752-1819.
A topographical analysis of the commonwealth of Virginia: compiled for the years 1790-1. Shewing the extent, and relative situation of the several counties, their distance from the seat of government; population; force; county lieutenants; representatives, &c. Also the district and county courts; the civil list of the commonwealth, &c. carefully collected from public records, and other authorities. To be continued annually ...
<Philadelphia,   printed by Charles Cist.> [1791]

Continued in next column

Continued from preceding column

broadside. 60x46.5cm.
Evans 23821.
Copyright by William Tatham.

NT 0050628   MH NN ViU PHi RPJCB

Tatham, William, 1752-1819.
A topographical analysis of the Commonwealth of Virginia [a table] compiled for the years 1790-1. Shewing the extent and relative situation of the several counties; their distance from the seat of government; population, force, county lieutenants, representatives, &c. also the district, and county courts, the civil list of the Commonwealth, &c. carefully collected from public records and other authorities. To be continued annually. Richmond: Printed by Thomas Nicolson exclusive printer for the author at that place [1791].
Microcard edition.
Copy owned by Thomas Jefferson.
Evans 23820. Sabin   94413. Sowerby 3159.
1. Virginia—Officials   and employees. I. Title.

NT 0050629   ViU PSt

B.4988 **Tatham, William,** 1752-1819.
Traité général de l'irrigation, contenant diverses méthodes d'arroser les prés et les jardins, la manière de conduire les prairies, pour les récoltes du foin; avec les moyens d'augmenter ses revenus...avec huit planches représentant diverses machines pour élever et conduire l'eau...tr. de l'anglais. Paris, Galland, an XIV, 1805.
xii, [2], 309, [3] p. diagrs. 21 cm.

NT 0050630   MH-BA

Tatham, William P.
On the restoration of the standard of value, and the proper limit to the use of bank credit as money. By W. P. Tatham ... Philadelphia, Printed by Sherman & co., 1869.
cover-title, 19 p. 23ᶜᵐ.

1. Currency question—U. S.

     CA 7-5140 Unrev'd
Library of Congress   HG525.T2

NT 0050631   DLC NN PPL PHi OClWHi PPB

Tatham, *Eng. (Parish)*
The registers of Tatham. 1558-1812. Indexed by Henry Brierley ... Preston, Printed for the Lancashire parish register society, by R. Seed & sons, 1922.
4 p. l., 240 p. 22½ᶜᵐ. (Half-title: Lancashire parish register society. [Publications] 59)

1. Registers of births, etc.—Tatham, Eng. 2. Tatham, Eng.—Geneal. I. Brierley, Henry, 1847-   ed.

Library of Congress   CS435.L3 vol. 59   24-8532

NT 0050632   DLC

Tatham, *Eng. (Parish)*
... The register of Tatham Fells church (Church of the Good Shepherd) The register of Tatham church (S. James the Less) Preston, Printed for the Lancashire parish register society by R. Seed & sons, 1940.
vii, [1], 84, ili, [1], 33 p. 22½ᶜᵐ. (Lancashire parish register society. [Publications] 78)
Each register has also special t.-p. and separate paging.
"In 1939 the parishes of Tatham and Tatham Fells, still remaining separate parishes, became by order in council a united benefice, of which the rector of Tatham is the incumbent."—p. v.
"Transcribed by Dr. E. Bosdin Leech."
1. Leech, Ernest Bosdin, 1875-
       41-13061
Library of Congress   CS435.L3 vol. 78
     [3]   (929.094272) 929.3004272

NT 0050633   DLC InU

Tatham Sales Co.
Frame specifications. Detroit, Mich. [The Author] c1939.
unp. illus.
Cover title: Blue prints of automobile frames (1935-1939)

NT 0050634   MiD

Tathan, Saint, 5th cent.
Vita Sancti Tathei
see under title

NT   0050636   DNLM

Tatheus, Saint
see   Tathan, Saint, 5th cent.

Tathéwatsi, Gr.
see   Dathewatsi, Krikor, 1340–1410.

Tathum, George, 1907–
The Cumberland Valley of Pennsylvania, a study in regional geography. [Worcester, Mass., 1934]
ix, 277 l.   fold. maps, photos, tables (part fold.)   28 cm.
Thesis – Clark University.
Vita.
Bibliography: leaves 276–277.

NT   0050639   IEN

Tathwell, S L   1864–
The old settlers' history of Bates county, Missouri. From its first settlement to the first day of January, 1900. Amsterdam, Mo., Tathwell & Maxey [1900]
212 (i. e. 284) p. incl. illus., ports., fold. map. front. 23ᵐ.
Compiled by S. L. Tathwell and H. O. Maxey. *cf.* Publishers' announcement.

1. Bates co., Mo.—Hist.   I. Maxey, H. O., joint author.   II. Title.
            45–48353
Library of Congress   F472.B3T3

NT   0050640   DLC NcD NNC ICN CtY ICU

4PZ   Tati, Jacques, 1908–
Fr-   Jour de fête; imagé par E. Lamotte. [Paris]
5072   Hachette [1950]
     47 p.

NT   0050641   DLC-P4

Tati Remita, pseud.

See

[Merati, Giovanni Battista]

Tatia, Nathmal.
Nayas, ways of approach & observation. Bangalore City, Jain Mission Society [195–?]
11 p.   22 cm.

1. Jaina logic.   I. Title.
B132.J3T3   S A 63–1098 ‡

NT   0050643   DLC CtY NN

4B   Tatia, Nathmal
1062   Studies in Jaina philosophy. With a foreword by Mahāmahopādhyāya Gopinath Kaviraj. Banaras, Jain Cultural Research Society [1951]
     327 p.

(Sanmati publication, no. 6)

MH ICU
MiU PPT NBuU CU CaBVa CaBVaU FU NNC NcD IaU OU MiEM
NT   0050644   DLC-P4 NN CtY INS CtY-D ICarbS DHU NIC

Tatia, Rughunathji Nichhabhai.
The Hindu theology, by Rao Bahadur Rughunathji Nichhabhai Tatia...   Vadifalia[, India]: R. N. Tatia [1917].   iv p., 1 l., 360 p.   1. ed.   8°.

1. Hinduism.
N. Y. P. L.   February 21, 1920.

NT   0050645   NN

Tatiana (Motion picture script)
"Tatiana" a drama for the screen
see under   Sheldon, Harry Sophus, d. 1940.

Tat'ianin, A   **R**
Производство витамина D. Москва, Пищепромиздат, 1943.
62 p. illus. 21 cm.
Bibliography : p. [60]

D.
1. Vitamin A   I. Title.
           Title transliterated: Proizvodstvo vitamina D.
TP374.V5T3   56–53540

NT   0050647   DLC

Tat'ianin, D
(Sergeĭ Mironovich Kirov Kazanda)
Сергей Миронович Киров Казанда / Д. Татьянин. — Казан : Таттосиздат, 1944.
30 p. ; 13 cm.

1. Kirov, Sergeĭ Mironovich, 1886–1934.
DK268.K5T37   75–549300

NT   0050648   DLC

Tatianus, 2d cent.   *B.110.2.2, Part 2
[Opera.]
(*In* Maxima Bibliotheca vetervm patrvm. Vol. 2, part 2, pp. 194–212. Lvgdvni. 1677.)
Contents.—Oratio ad Græcos. — SS. euangeliorum diatessaron, id est, vnum ex quatuor.

[013] — Bible. N.T. Gospels. Harmonies. Latin.

NT   0050649   MB CtY

Tatianus, 2d cent.
Address to the Greeks tr. by J.E. Ryland.
(In Roberts, Alexander & Donaldson, James, ed.   Ante-Nicene fathers. 1885–87.   v. 2)

NT   0050650   PU CU

CF43.7   Tatianus, 2d cent.
1841   Ammonii Alexandrini quae et Tatiani dicitur Harmonia evangeliorum in linguam latinam et inde ante annos mille in francicam translata; indicem tam antiquaē quam hodiernaē dividendi singula evangelia methodo accommodatum, addidit J.A. Schmeller. Viennaē, Fr. Beck universitatis bibliopolam, 1841.
     xiv, 212 p.   27 cm.

Latin text (translated from the Greek by Victor, bp. of   Capua) and Old High German, in   parallel columns.

NT   0050651   CtY-D CU

Tatianus, 2d cent.
Die Beiruter Diatessaron-Fragmente, herausgegeben und übersetzt von Georg Graf.
(In Euringer, Sebastian. Die Überlieferung der arabischen Übersetzung des Diatessarons. p. 61–71. Freiburg im Breisgau. 1912)
[The Arabic harmony is, presumably, based on the (Greek? Syriac?) one compiled by Tatianus]
I. Graf, Georg, 1875–   ed. and tr.   II. Bible. N.T. Gospels. German. Harmonies. 1912. Graf. III. Bible. N.T. Gospels. Arabic. Harmonies. 1912.

NT   0050652   MB NN

Tatianus, 2d cent.
... Tatian's Diatessaron. Erlangen, 1881
see under [Zahn, Theodor von] 1838–1933.

BS   Tatianus, 2d cent.
2550   Tatians Diatessaron, aus dem Arabischen übersetzt von Erwin Preuschen. Mit einer einleitenden abhandlung und textkritischen anmerkungen. Hrsg. von August Pott. Heidelberg, Carl Winters Universitätsbuchhandlung, 1926.
     ix, 241 p.
T2A45
1926

1. Jesus Christ – Biography – Sources, Biblical.   I. Preuschen, Erwin, 1867–1920, tr. II. Pott, August, 1870–   ed. III. Title.

NT   0050654   PPT CPFT TxDaM CU CtY-D OCH TNJ-R

Tatianus, 2d cent.
... Diatessaron de Tatien; texte arabe etabli, traduit en français, collationné avec les anciennes versions syriaques, suivi d'un évangéliaire diatessarique syriaque et accompagné de quatre planches hors texte. Beyrouth, Imprimerie catholique, 1935.
5 p. l., cxl, 586, 84* p.   iv facsim.   25ᵐ.
Name of editor and translator, A.-S. Marmardji, at head of title.
Added t.-p. in Arabic. Arabic and French on opposite pages.
"Traduction arabe faite ... sur un manuscrit syriaque, et attribuée à Abul-Faraj 'Abdallah ibn at-Tayyib."—Avant-propos, p. i.
"Bibliographie": p. iv–v.
1. Jesus Christ—Biog.—Sources, Biblical.   I. Abū al-Faraj 'Abd Allāh ibn al-Tayyib, 11th cent.   II. Marmardji, A. Sebastianus, 1887– ed. and tr.   III. Title.
Library of Congress   BS2550.T2A43   39–25830
               [2]   226

MiU NjP ICU UU
NT   0050655   DLC InStme NcD DDO CtY-D OCH CtY CSt

[Tatianus] 2d cent.
... Il Diatessaron in volgare italiano; testi inediti dei secoli XIII–XIV, pubblicati a cura di prof. Venanzio Todesco, p. Alberto Vaccari s. i. [e]† mons. Marco Vattasso. Città del Vaticano, Biblioteca apostolica vaticana, 1938.
xii, 382 p., 1 l.   25ᵐ.   ([Vatican. Biblioteca vaticana] Studi e testi, 81)
"Elenco delle opere più frequentemente citate": p. [xi]–xii.
CONTENTS.—Il Diatessaron veneto a cura del prof. Venanzio Todesco.—Diatessaron toscano, per mons. Marco Vattasso e p. Alberto Vaccari.
I. Todesco, Venanzio, ed.   II. Vaccari, Alberto, 1875–   ed. III. Vattasso, Marco, 1869–1925, ed.   IV. Title.
Library of Congress   BS2550.T2A46   45–29016
               [2]   226

WaU TNJ PPT CU-S CSt ViU MCW LU
NT   0050656   DLC OrU CtY-D WU OU NcD PU MoSU TxU CtY

Tatianus, 2d cent.
The Diatessaron of Tatian, by Rev. Hope W. Hogg... (In: Ante-Nicene Fathers. Buffalo, 1886–96. 4°. v. 9, p. 33–138.)

In English.

    I. Hogg, Hope W., 1863––1912, tr. II. Bible. N.T. Gospels. English. Harmonies. 1886–96. Hogg.

NT 0050657   NN

BS3560   Tatianus, 2d cent.
.A3T2H5   The Diatessaron of Tatian; a harmony of the four Gos-
1888   pels compiled in the third quarter of the second century; now first ed. in an English form with introduction and appendices. By the Rev. Samuel Hemphill ... London, Hodder & Stoughton; [etc., etc.] 1888.

[2], xxxi, 78 p. 22ᶜᵐ.

    I. Hemphill, Samuel, 1859-1927, ed. [and tr. ?] II. Bible. N.T. Gospels. English. Harmonies. 1888. Hemphill

NT 0050658   ICU MH NN ODW PHC

Tatianus, 2d cent.
The Diatessaron of Tatian, by Hope W. Hogg.
(In Menzies, Allan, ed. Early Christian works. Edinburgh, 1897.)

In English.

    L Hogg, Hope W., 1863––1912, tr. II. Bible. N.T. Gospels. English. Harmonies. 1897. Hogg.

NT 0050659   MB OU

Tatianus, 2d cent.
Diatessaron persiano. [A cura di] Giuseppe Messina. Roma, Pontificio Istituto biblico, 1951.

cxiv, 387 p. facsims. 25 cm. (Biblica et orientalia; Sacra Scriptura antiquitatibus orientalibus illustrata, 14)

Includes bibliographical references.
CONTENTS: Introduzione.—Testo e traduzione.

1. Jesus Christ—Biography—Sources, Biblical. 2. Florence. Biblioteca Medicea-Laurenziana. Mss. (Persian XVII (81)) I. Messina, Giuseppe, 1893-   ed. II. Title. III. Series.

BS2550.T2A47 1951   75–858848

    NhD UU NjP NNC NN
    ICU PPiPT CBGTU CtY-D GEU-T MH-AH MnCS MoU NIC NcD
NT 0050660   DLC KyLxCB NjP CLU MnU TNJ-R NjPT IU MH

Tatianus.
... Il discorso ai Greci. Versione italiana di Paolo Ubaldi. Torino, Società editrice internazionale [etc., etc.] 1921.

1 p. l., lxiv, 1 l., 89 p. 20 cm. (Studi superiori. n. 7)

NT 0050661   CU

BR63   TATIANUS, 2d cent.
.S43   Discorso ai Greci; a cura di Maria Ferni.
no.8   Roma, Libreria di Cultura, 1924.
116 p. (Scrittori cristiani antichi, n.8)
Italian translation only.
"Appendice bibliografica": p.114.

1. Apologetics—Early church.

    Translation of Oratio ad Graecos.

NT 0050662   ICU MH MiU PU

CF43.7   Tatianus, 2d cent.
H553   The earliest life of Christ ever compiled from the four Gospels, being the Diatessaron of Tatian (circ. A.D. 160) Literally translated from the Arabic version and containing the four Gospels woven into one story, with an historical and critical introd., notes, and appendix by J. Hamlyn Hill. Edinburgh, T. & T. Clark, 1894.
viii, 379 p. 23 cm.

Continued in next column

Continued from preceding column

Bibliography: p. 378–379.

    I. Hill, James Hamlyn   ed.
    II. Title.

    MCE
    MH-AH NN CtY ICN MB NNC NRCR NcD NjNbS OO PBm PV
NT 0050664   CtY-D NIC WaU MoSU-D CLSU TxFTC OKentU

Tatianus, 2d cent.
The earliest life of Christ ever compiled from the four Gospels, being the Diatessaron of Tatian (circ. A. D. 160) Literally translated from the Arabic version and containing the four Gospels woven into one story, with an introduction and notes by the Rev. J. Hamlyn Hill ... 2d ed., abridged. Edinburgh, T. & T. Clark, 1910.

xv, 224 p. 22½ cm.
On cover: Popular edition.

I. Hill, James Hamlyn. II. Title.

Crozer Theol. Sem. Libr.   A 16—46
for Library of Congress   BS2550.T2A3 1910

    OCl ODW PSC PU PLF MiU CU
NT 0050665   NRCR DLC NjNbS NN CSt CU WaWW NIC MBU-T

BS3560   Tatianus, 2d cent.
.A4A6T3   ... Tatiani Evangeliorum harmonie arabice. Nunc
1888   primum ex duplici codice edidit et translatione latina donavit p. Augustinus Ciasca ... Romae, ex Typographia polyglotta S. C. de propaganda fide, 1888.
xv, 108, [211] p. plates. 29ᶜᵐ.
Arabic title precedes Latin title.

I. Ciasca, Agostino, cardinal, 1834-1902. II. Bible. N.T. Gospels. Arabic. Harmonies. 1888. III. Bible. N.T. Gospels. Latin. Harmonies. 1888.

    PPL NjP WaU CtY-D
NT 0050666   ICU GEU-T MB MH ICN DCU-H PPDrop OU CoU

Tatianus, 2d cent.
A Greek fragment of Tatian's Diatessaron, from Dura, edited with facsimile, transcription and introduction by Carl H. Kraeling, PH. D. London [etc.] Christophers [°1935]
4 p. l., [3]-37 p. fold. pl. 25ᶜᵐ. (Half-title: Studies and documents, edited by Kirsopp Lake ... and Silva Lake ... III)

"Printed in the U.S.A."
The folded plate contains (a) Facsimile of Dura parchment 24, (b) Transcription, (c) Composition and apparatus criticus.
"The fragment with which the following pages deal is now preserved in the parchment and papyrus collection of Yale university ... where it is listed as Dura parchment 24 (D Pg. 24)."—p. [3]

I. Kraeling, Carl Hermann, 1897-   ed. II. Yale university. III. Title.

Library of Congress   BS2550.T2K7   35–11046
—— Copy 2.
Copyright A 83193   [5]   226

    DDO OCU MiU TNJ-R CU CLSU PBm PPLT MCE
NT 0050667   DLC IEG IEN OrSaW PPAmP PU KyLxCB NcD OO

Rare   Tatianus, 2d cent.
BS
2549
A4   Tatiani Alexandrini Harmoniae evangelicae
1706   antiquissima versio Theotisca ut & Isidori Hispalensis ad Florentinam sororem De nativitate Domini, passione, resurrectione, &c. libri eadem lingua conversi fragmentum Jo. Philippus Palthenius e mss. codd. edidit & animadversionibus necessariis illustravit. Accessit Fragmentum veteris linguae Theotiscae à Lambecio ... Gryphiswaldiae, J. W. Fickweilerum,   1706.
420 p. 21cm.

Latin and Old High German in parallel columns.
Ex libris Frid. Zarncke.

I. Isidorus, Saint, bp. of Seville, d. 636. II. Palthenius, Johann Philipp. III. Title.

NT 0050669   NIC

[Tatianus] 2d cent.
The Liège Diatessaron, ed. with a textual apparatus by D. Plooij, with the assistance of C. A. Phillips. English translation of the Dutch text by A. J. Barnouw. Amsterdam, 1929–

v. 25 cm. (Verhandelingen der Koninklijke Akademie van Wetenschappen te Amsterdam. Afdeeling Letterkunde. Nieuwe reeks, deel 31)

Pts. 1-2 incorrectly numbered deel 29, no. 1, 6.
Pts. 5–   edited with a textual apparatus by D. Plooij, C. A. Phillips and A. H. A. Bakker.

Based on the Diatessaron of Tatianus.
Text in Dutch and English.

1. Jesus Christ—Biog.—Sources, Biblical. I. Plooij, Daniël, 1877-1935, ed. II. Phillips, Charles Augustine, joint ed. III. Barnouw, Adriaan Jacob, 1877-   tr. IV. Series: Akademie van Wetenschappen, Amsterdam. Afdeeling voor de Taal-, Letter-, Geschiedkundige en Wijsgeerige Wetenschappen. Verhandelingen, nieuwe reeks, deel 31.

AS244.A52   n. r., deel 31   A 48–1563*

Cleveland. Public Libr.
for Library of Congress   [3]†

    WU OCH MiU NjPT NcU OCU CBGTU NbU
NT 0050671   OCl WaSpG DLC PU CtY-D NN TNJ-R TU TxU

Tatianus, 2d century.
Het Luiksche diatessaron in het Nieuw-Nederlandsch vertaald met een inleiding over de herkomst van den Middelnederlandschen tekst... door Geertruida Catharina van Kersbergen. [Rijswijk, Drukkerij Nieuwvoorde, 1936]
160 p. maps. 26ᶜᵐ.

Editor's Proefschrift - Katholieke Universiteit te Nijmegen.

I Kersbergen,   Geertruida Catharina van

NT 0050672   NjPT MH

Tatianus, 2d cent.
Notizia su un diatessaron persiano, tradotto dal siriaco. [A cura di] Giuseppe Messina. Roma, Pontificio Istituto biblico, 1943.

127 p. facsims. 23 cm. (Biblica et orientalia; Sacra Scriptura antiquitatibus orientalibus illustrata, 10)

1. Jesus Christ—Biog.—Sources, Biblical. 2. Florence. Biblioteca Mediceo-Laurenziana. Mss. (Persian XVII (81)) I. Messina, Giuseppe, 1893-   ed. II. Title. (Series)

BS2550.T2A47   51–52181

    CLU IU NhD GU
NT 0050673   DLC TNJ-R NcD PPiPT CtY-D NN CU NNC NIC

Tatianus, 2nd century.
Tatianou pros 'Ellenae, oti Ouden ton Epithdeumaton, ois 'Ellenes kallopizontai, Ellenikon, alla ek Barbaron ten eureso exekos. Tatiani Assyrii Oratio ad Graecos, quod nihil eorum, quibus Graeci gloriantur, studiorum apud ipsos natum, sed omnia a Barbaris inventa sint.
(In, Sancti Patris Nostri Justini, Philosophi et Martyris, Opera. Coloniae, Apud Jeremiam Schrey, & Heinricum Joh. Meyerum, 1686. pp. [141]-17[4])

1. Apologetics—Early church.

NT 0050674   PLatS

BR65   Tatianus, 2d cent.
.T206   Tatiani Oratio ad Graecos. Hermiae Irrisio gentium philo-
1700   sophorum. Ex vetustis exemplaribus recensuit, adnotationibusque integris Conradi Gesneri, Frontonis Ducaei, Christiani Kortholti, Thomae Galei, selectisque Henrici Stephani, Meursii, Bocharti, Cotelerii, utriusque Vossii, aliorum, suas quaescunque adjecit Wilhelmus Worth, A. M. Oxoniae, e Theatro Sheldoniano, 1700.
[1], xvii, [14], 252 p. 20ᶜᵐ.
Title-page and "Monitum ad lectorem" bound after p. 212.
Added t.-p. in Greek with title vignette.
Greek text with Latin translation in parallel columns.
"Nicolai le Nourry Dissertatio in Tatiani Assyrii Opera": p. 159-209.
1. Apologetics   2. Philosophers, Greek.

    IU MH ViU NNUT NNC
NT 0050675   ICU CtY-D IEN ViLxW MH CLU-C PPL NN PBa

Tatianus, *2d cent.*
Tatiani Oratio ad Graecos. Ad optimos libros mss. partim denuo collatos recensuit, scholiis parisinis nunc primum integris ornavit, prolegomenis adnotatione versione instruxit, indices adiecit Ioann. Carol. Theod. Otto ... Cum speciminibus duorum codicum parisinorum. Ienae, prostat apud F. Mauke, 1851.

xl, 202 p., 1 l. 2 facsim. 22½ᶜᵐ. (*Added t.-p.:* Corpus apologetarum christianorum saeculi secundi. Edidit Ioann. Carol. Theod. Otto. vol. vi)

Greek and Latin on opposite pages.

1. Apologetics—Early church.   i. Otto, Johann Karl Theodor von, 1816–1897, ed.
38–33829

Library of Congress   BT1116.T1 1851
[2]   239.3

PPDrop OO OCU NNUT
NT   0050676   DLC WaSpG MH–AH PU PBm MH NcD MSohG NjP

Tatianus, *2d cent.*
Tatiani Oratio ad Graecos, recensvit Edvardus Schwartz. Leipzig, J. C. Hinrichs, 1888.

x, 105, [1] p. 22½ᶜᵐ. (Texte und untersuchungen zur geschichte der altchristlichen literatur, hrsg. von Oscar von Gebhardt und Adolf Harnack. iv. bd., hft. 1)

Contents.—Praefatio.—[Textus graecus]—Arethae scholia ex Codice parisino 174 (P) exscripta.—Fragmenta.—Testimonia.

1. Apologetics—Early church.   i. Arethas, abp. of Caesarea (Cappadocia) ca. 860–ca. 940.   ii. Schwartz, Eduard, 1858–   ed.   iii. Paris. Bibliothèque nationale. Mss. (Grecs 174)
37–11512

Library of Congress   BR45.T4 bd. 4, hft. 1
[2]   (281.1082) 239.3

MB ICU MH–BA OC1W OO ICMcC CtY–D
NT   0050677   DLC NcD PU PPLT PPiPT CBGTU OCU CtY MH

Tatianus, 2d cent.
Oratio adversus Graecos Gr. & Lat.
In Maran's ed. of Justin Martyr Venet., 1747.
fol.

NT   0050678   CtY

Tatianus, 2d cent.
Oratio adversus Graecos
In Caillau, Armand Benjamin.
Patres apostolici. Paris, 1842, vol. 1.

Tatianus, 2d cent.   *5461.4
Τατιάνου Πρὸς Ἕλληνας. Tatiani Oratio adversus Græcos. — Græce et Latine.
(In Patrologiæ cursus completus. Series Græca. Vol. 6, col. 803–888. Lutetiæ Parisiorum. 1857.)
Preceded by Analysis orationis Tatiani adversus Græcos, col. 801. 802.

K116 — Apologists.

NT   0050680   MB

Tatianus, 2d cent.
Oratio cõtra Graecos. [In Grk.] Tiguri, 1546.
fol.   (Ed. C. Gesner. With Sententiae Antonii & Maximi, &c.)

NT   0050681   CtY

---

n.d.

Tatianus, 2d cent.
Oration against the Greeks. (*In* Giles, J. A. tr. Writings of the early Christians)

NT   0050682   MBrZ

Tatianus, *2d cent.*
Tatian : Perfection according to the Saviour. Edited by Rendel Harris ...
(*In* John Rylands library, Manchester. Bulletin. Manchester. 1924. 25¼ᶜᵐ. v. 8, p. 15–51)
Running title: Perfection according to the Saviour.

1. Christian literature, Early.   i. Harris, James Rendel, 1852–   ii. Title: Perfection according to the Saviour.
A 38–462

Princeton univ. Library
for Library of Congress   [Z921.M18B   vol. 8]
[2]   (027.44272)

NT   0050683   NjP NcD DLC

Tatianus, 2d cent.
A primitive text of the Diatessaron; the Liège manuscript of a mediaeval Dutch translation. A preliminary study ... Leyden, 1923
see under Plooij, Daniël, 1877–1935.

Tatianus, 2d cent.
Pros Hellēnas [Greek]
see his   Oratio ad Graecos.

Tatianus, *2d cent.*
Puech, Aimé, 1860–
... Recherches sur le Discours aux Grecs de Tatien, suivies d'une traduction française du Discours avec notes; par Aimé Puech ... Paris, F. Alcan, 1903.

Tatian, *2d century.*
Tatians] Rede an die Bekenner des Griechentums, eingeleitet und übersetzt von Dr. R. C. Kukula. [Kempten: J. Kösel, 1913.] 83 p.   12°.   (In: Bibliothek der Kirchenväter. Bd. 12.)
Frühchristliche Apologeten und Märtyrerakten. Bd. 1.

1. No subject. 2. Kukula, Richard Cornelius, 1862–   , translator.
N.Y.P.L.   October 29, 1924

NT   0050687   NN DLC

Tatianus, 2d Cent.
Rede an die Griechen.
(In Saemmtliche Werke der Kirchen-Väter. Vol. 2, pp. 139–192. Kempten. 1830.)

L 5829

NT   0050688   MB

YLR   **Tatianus,** 2d cent.
36   Tatian's, des kirchenschriftstellers, rede an die griechen, übersetzt...von dr. Valentin Cröne. Kempten, 1872.
84 p.

(Bibliothek der kirchenväter)
With Severus, S. Ausgewählte schriften des Sulpicius Severus... Kempten, 1872.

NT   0050689   DLC NcD DCU MH PPeSchw PLatS

BT   Tatianus, 2d cent.
1116 Tatian's Rede an die Griechen.
T2H3 Übersetzt und eingeleitet von Adolf Harnack. Giessen, Wenzel'sche Universitäts-Buch- und Stein-Druckerei, 1884.
54 p.   23 cm.
At head of title: Festschrift Sr. Königl. Hoheit dem Grossherzoge von Hessen und bei Rhein Ludewig IV ... gewidmet...

1. Apologetics—Early Church, ca. 30–600. I. Harnack, Adolf von, 1851–1930, ed. II. Title

NT   0050690   OCH PHC NjP OCU NNUT MH

Tatianus, *2d cent.*
Tatian. Lateinisch und altdeutsch, mit ausführlichem glossar, herausgegeben von Eduard Sievers. Paderborn, F. Schöningh, 1872.

2 p. l., [vli]–x, 493, [1] p.   21½ᶜᵐ.

Cover-title.
Latin and Old High German in parallel columns.

i. *Sievers, Eduard, 1850–   ed.
30–3130

Library of Congress   PF3991.T2 1872

OC1W OCU NIC PHC PU
NT   0050691   DLC CtY InU CLSU IU CU NN MdBJ MB MiU

Tatianus, *2d cent.*
Tatian. Lateinisch und altdeutsch mit ausführlichem glossar, hrsg. von Eduard Sievers. 2. neubearb. ausg. Paderborn [etc.] F. Schöningh, 1892.

lxxv, 518 p.   21ᶜᵐ. (*Added t.-p.:* Bibliothek der ältesten deutschen litteraturdenkmäler. v. bd.)

Latin and German in parallel columns.

i. *Sievers, Eduard, 1850–1932, ed.
G–316

Library of Congress   PT1371.B5 5. bd.

NT   0050692   DLC NIC ICarbS MsSM IU LU

Tatianus, 2d cent.
Die Überlieferung der arabischen Übersetzung des Diatessarons ... Freiburg im breisgau, 1912
see under Euringer, Sebastian, 1865–

C   TATIANUS, 2d cent.
5   The writings of Tatian and Theophilus; and
04   the Clementine Recognitions. Edinburgh, T. & T.
Clark, 1867.
485p.   22½cm.   (Ante-Nicene Christian library. v.3)
The translation of Tatian is by J.E.Ryland.— cf. note, v.20, pt.2, p.4.
Contents.—Tatian: Address to the Greeks. Fragments of lost works.—Theophilus, translated by Rev. Marcus Dods: The three books of Theophilus of Antioch to Autol-   ycus.—Clement, translated by Rev. Thomas   Smith: The Recognitions
8531 of Clement.

IU NN MB MH
NT   0050694   ICN PPLT MBrZ KyTrA CLamB MH–AH NIC DCU

Tatianus, 2d cent.
The writings of Tatian and Theophilus, and the Clementine Recognitions, tr. by B. P. Pratten, Marcus Dods, and Thomas Smith.   Edinburgh, T. & T. Clark, 1868.
485 p.   23 cm.   (Ante-Nicene Christian library, v. 3)
I. Theophilus, Saint, Bp. of Antioch, 2d cent. II. Clemens Romanus.

NT   0050695   MdBP PPL

BR   Tatianus, 2d century.
63   The writings of Tatian and Theophilus, and
T188w the Clementine Recognitions; translated by
1883 B. P. Pratten, Marcus Dods and Thomas Smith. Edinburgh, Clark, 1883.
485 p.   (Ante-Nicene Christian library, v. 3)

1. Christian literature, Early. I. Theophilus, Saint, Bp. of Antioch, 2d cent. II. Clemens Romanus. Recognitiones. III. Title. IV. Series.

NT   0050696   CLU

Tatić, Žarko M.
Трагом велике прошлости; светогорска писма и монографске студије старе српске архитектуре. Са предговором од Радослава М. Грујића. Београд, 1929.
265 p. illus. 24 cm.

1. Architecture—Serbia—Hist.   I. Title.
Title transliterated: Tragom velike prošlosti.

NA1441.T38   54–46133 ‡

NT 0050697   DLC CSt DDO

Law

Tatics, Péter

Lányi, Márton, 1882–
... Igazságügyi iratmintatár. 3. kiad. Szerkesztették: dr. Lányi Márton, dr. Sándor Aladár ₁és₁ dr. Tatics Péter ... Budapest, Grill K., 1932.

Law

Tatics, Péter, ed.

Hungary. *Laws, statutes, etc.*
A telekkönyvi jog kézikönyve; a telekkönyvi anyagi és alaki jog ismertetése és magyarázata; a telekkönyvre vonatkozó rendeletek és törvények, valamint a birói joggyakorlat kapcsán, írta Tatics Péter dr. Budapest, Grill K., 1910–₁13₁

Law

Tatics, Péter, comp.

Hungary. *Courts.*
Uj döntvénytár; a magy. kir. Curia, kir. itélőtáblák, nemkülönben más legfelsőbb foku itélőhatóságok, elvi jelentőségü határozatai. Szerkeszti: Grecsák Károly ... Budapest, Grill Károly könyvkiadó vállalata, 1911–12.

Tatien
see
Tatianus, 2d cent.

Tatiev, Dmitrii Platonovich.
Акклиматизация офсетной бумаги. Москва, Изд-во геодезической и картографической лит-ры, 1951.
128 p. illus. 23 cm.
Bibliography: p. 125–127.

——— Microfilm.
Made by the Library of Congress.
Negative film in the Library of Congress.
Call No. ———————→   Microfilm Slavic 791 AC

1. Paper.   I. Title.
Title romanized: Akklimatizatsiia ofsetnoĭ bumagi.

TS1109.T28   58–17317

NT 0050702   DLC

Tatiev, Dmitrii Platonovich.
Картографическая бумага и работа с ней. Москва, Изд-во геодезической и картографической лит-ры, 1941.
99, ₁1₁ p. illus., diagrs. 23 cm.
"Использованная литература": p. ₁100₁

1. Paper making and trade. 2. Paper—Testing.   I. Title.
Title transliterated: Kartograficheskaia bumaga i rabota s neĭ.

TS1109.T3   49–33910

NT 0050703   DLC

Law

Tatiev, K   I
Судебная медицина; учебник для юридических школ. Москва, Юрид. изд-во, 1947.
126 p. illus. 20 cm.

1. Medical jurisprudence—Russia.   I. Title.
Title transliterated: Sudebnaia meditsina.

48–24599*

NT 0050704   DLC

---

*G.401
.86   Tatikian, B.
[Turkish, Greek and Armenian costume plates]
[Smyrna, ca. 1850]
26 col. plates. 34 cm.

1. Costume—Turkey. 2. Costume—Greece. 3. Costume—Armenia.

NT 0050705   MB

... Tatian's Diatessaron.   Erlangen, 1881
see under ₁Zahn, Theodor von₁ 1838–1933.

Tatin, A. Principes raisonnés et pratiques de la culture des
arbres fruitiers, l'alignement et forestiers, arbrisseaux et arbustes d'agrément, des graines, racines, plantes potagères et légumineuses, des prairies naturelles et artificielles. 2 pt. (in 1 vol.). 4° éd. Paris. [1811.] 8°.
1. pp. viii, 273.— ii. pp. [4], 270 +.
"Errata," at end.
The first three editions have the title: "Catalogue raisonné."

NT 0050707   MH–A

Tatin, Émile.
Lendemains de guerre: des Flandres à la Meuse; douze dessins rehaussés. Commentaire de René Gobillot. Paris, D.-A. Longuet, 1920.
7 p., 12 col. plates (in portfolio) 43 cm.
300 copies printed. "Exemplaire no 145."

1. European War, 1914–1918—Pictorial works.   I. Gobillot, René. II. Title.

NC1135.T3   59–59015

NT 0050708   DLC NjP

W 4   TATIN, Jean, 1923–
L99   Contribution à l'étude de la fonction
1950/51   sexuelle dans les aménorrhées.
no. 166   Lyon, 1951.
           58 p. (Lyons. ₁Université₁
           Faculté de médecine et de pharmacie.
           Thèse, 1950/51, no. 166)
           1. Amenorrhea

NT 0050709   DNLM

Tatin, René, 1905–
... Essai médico-psychologique sur Lamartine ... Lyon, 1929.
Thèse – Univ. de Lyon.
"Bibliographie": p. [87]–95.
1. Lamartine, Alphonse Marie Louis de, 1790–1869.

NT 0050710   CtY

Tatin, Victor, 1843–1913.

Gaston, Raymond de.
... Les aéroplanes de 1910–   ; étude technique avec plans cotés pour la plupart des principaux aéroplanes ... Paris, Librairie aéronautique ₁1913–

Tatin, Victor, 1843–1913.
Éléments d'aviation, par Victor Tatin ... Paris, H. Dunod & E. Pinat, 1908.
2 p. l., vi, 65 p., 1 l. illus. (incl. port.) diagrs. 27 cm.
"Publication de l' 'Aérophile': revue technique de la locomotion aérienne."

1. Aeroplanes.   I. Aérophile; revue technique de la locomotion aérienne.

32–25962

Library of Congress   TL670.T3 1908   629.13

NT 0050712   DLC NN CSt

Tatin, Victor, 1843–1913.
Éléments d'aviation, par Victor Tatin. Les expériences d'aviation de Wilbur et d'Orville Wright; description de l'aéroplane Wright ... Paris, H. Dunod & E. Pinat, 1909.
2 p. l., vi, 71 p., 1 l. illus. (incl. port.) diagrs. 27 cm.
"Publication de l' 'Aérophile': revue technique de la locomotion aérienne."
First edition, 1908.

1. Aeroplanes.   I. Aérophile; revue technique de la locomotion aérienne.

32–25961

Library of Congress   TL670.T3 1909   629.13

NT 0050713   DLC ICJ MB MiU CSmH

Tatin, Victor, 1843–1913.   5964.172
Les hélices aériennes.
(In Gaston, R. de. Les aéroplanes de 1910: ... Pp. (77–86.) Paris. [1910.])

H7333 — Screw-propellers.

NT 0050714   MB

Tatin, Victor, 1843–1913.
Théorie et pratique de l'aviation, par V. Tatin ... Ouvrage publié sous les auspices de l'Aérophile ... Paris, H. Dunod & E. Pinat, 1910.
vii, 318 p., 1 l. illus., diagrs. 18½ cm.

1. Aeronautics.

31–14681

Library of Congress   TL545.T35

NT 0050715   DLC MiU DAL ICJ MB NjP NN DSI

W 6   TATINGHOFF, Michaël Frederik, d. 1673, respondent
P3   ... Disputatio medica inauguralis, de pleuritide &
v.2561   peripneumonia ... Lugduni Batavorum, Ex officina Severini
no. 9   Matthaei, 1659.
          [8] p. 19 cm.
          Diss. – Leyden.

W 6   ----- Copy 2 [v.2561, no. 24]
P3

NT 0050716   DNLM

TATIO, GIOVANNI.
Oog30   La imagine del rettore della bene ordinata
T188   citta..ove si discorrono i modi, che dalla fan-
573   ciullezza per fino alla eta uirile si debbono
       tenere da quello, che deue esser eletto al
       gouerno d'alcuna citta. Alla qvale segve l'In-
       stitvtione del cancelliero che deue seruire al
       detto Rettore ... Vinetia, Appresso G. Giolito
       di Ferrarii, 1573.
       2 v. in 1. 20½ cm.

NT 0050717   ICN NcD IU CtY

Tatio, Giovanni.
L'ottimo reggimento del magistrato pretorio, di Giovanni Tatio Iustinopolitano ... Venetia, Appresso F. de' Franceschi, 1564.

8 p. l., 292, ⟨7⟩ p. 15ᶜᵐ.

Printer's mark on t.-p.; head-pieces and initials.

1. Political science.

10-10653

Library of Congress   JC143.T2

NT 0050718   DLC CtY

Tatiščev, Vasilij Nikitič
see
Tatishchev, Vasiliĭ Nikitich, 1686–1750.

Tatischeff, J de
see Tatischev, Ivan Ivanovich, 1743–1802.

Tatischeff, Jacques
See
Tati, Jacques, 1908–

Tatischeff, Michael
see
Tatishchev, Mikhail.

Tatischeff, Serge
see Tatischev, Sergeĭ Spiridonovich, 1846–1906.

DK127
.5
.T3D55

Tatishchev, Evgraf Vasil'evich, 1717–1781.

Dmitriev, Aleksandr Alekseevich, 1854–1902.
⟨Predsmertnoe uvĭeshchanīe V. N. Tatishcheva synu⟩
Предсмертное увѣщаніе В. Н. Татищева сыну. Ал. Дмитріева. С.-Петербургъ, Тип. В. С. Балашева, 1886.

Tatishchev, I͡U V
⟨Dĭei͡ateli Smutnago vremeni⟩
Дѣятели Смутнаго времени. Москва, Историко-родословное об-во, 1905.

46 p. 27 cm.

"Извлечено изъ 1-го выпуска Лѣтописи."
Includes bibliographical references.

1. Tatishchev, Mikhail Ignat'evich, d. 1609. 2. Russia—History—Epoch of confusion, 1605–1613. I. Title.

DK111.T37   73-207232

NT 0050725   DLC

Bonaparte
Collection Tatishchev, Ivan Ivanovich, *1743–1802.*
No. 12,791

Dictionnaire complet françois et russe. Composé sur la nouvelle édition de celui de l'Academie française et augmenté de mots nouvellement créés et de termes techniques… Moscou,1816. 2v. sq.Q.

Bookplate of William Plincke.
Each volume has added t.-p. in Russian charac- ter.

NT 0050726   ICN

Bonaparte
Collection Tatischev, Ivan Ivanovich, 1743–1802.
No. 12,676

Dictionnaire complet français-russe. Composé sur la cinquième édition de celui de l'Académie française. 3.éd. Saint-Pétersbourg,1824. 4v.in 2.

Added title-pages in Russian.
First edition edited by "une société de gens de lettres"; 2.ed., by Ivan Ivanovich Tatishchev.

NT 0050727   ICN

Tatishchev, Ivan Ivanovich, 1743–1802.
Полной французской и россійской лексиконъ, съ послѣдняго изданія лексикона Французской академіи на россійской языкъ переведенный. 2. изд., рачительнѣйше сличенное съ французскимъ оригиналомъ, испр. и доп. Въ Санктпетербургѣ, Тип. И. Вейтбрехта, 1798.

2 v. 23 cm.
Added t.-p. in French.

1. French language—Dictionaries—Russian.
Title transliterated: Polnoĭ frant͡suzskoĭ i rossīĭskoĭ leksikon.

PG2645.F5T35 1798   49-33879

NT 0050728   DLC CtY

PR3316
.A4E817
Rare Bk.
Coll.

Tatishchev, Luka, tr.

Arblay, Frances (Burney) d', 1752–1840.
Евелина; или Вступленіе въ свѣтъ молодой дѣвицы. Переводъ съ французскаго, сличенной съ англинскимъ оригиналомъ. Москва, Въ Унив. тип., у Ридигера и Клаудія, 1798.

Tatishchev, Mikhail, tr.
A description of the manner in which the commission, for establishing a new code of laws, was opened at Moscow
see under title

Law   Tatishchev, Mikhail, tr.

Russia. *Sovereigns, etc., 1762–1796 (Catharine II)*
The grand instructions to the commissioners appointed to frame a new code of laws for the Russian empire: composed by Her Imperial Majesty Catherine II., empress of all the Russias. To which is prefixed, a description of the manner of opening the commission, with the order and rules for electing the commissioners. Translated from the original, in the Russian language, by Michael Tatischeff ... and published by permission. London, Printed for T. Jefferys, 1768.

Tatishchev, Sergeĭ Spiridonovich, 1846–1906.
Alexandre Iᵉʳ et Napoléon d'après leur correspondance inédite 1801–1812 par Serge Tatistcheff. Paris, Perrin et cⁱᵉ, 1891.

xiii, 640p. 22½cm.

1. Alexander I, emperor of Russia, 1777–1825. 2. Napoléon I, emperor of the French, 1769–1821. 3. France. History. Consulate and empire to 1815. 4. Russia. History. 19th century. I. Alexander I, emperor of Russia, 1777–1825. II. Napoléon I, emperor of the French, 1769–1821.

    DNW OCl OCU MH
NT 0050732   CtW DLC-P4 NNF NjP MB MiU CtY NN PPL PU

Tatishchev, Sergeĭ Spiridonovich, 1846–1906.
Diplomacya rosyjska w kwestyi polskiej (1853–1863) przez S. Tatiszczewa. Warszawa, Nakład K. Treptego, 1901.

176 p. 19ᶜᵐ.

A translation of a series of articles published in the Russkij Wiestnik.
cf. Pref.

1. Russia—Pol. & govt.—1855–1881. 2. Russia—For. rel. 3. Poland—Pol. & govt. 4. Polish question.

22-25841

Library of Congress   DK437.Y3

NT 0050733   DLC CSt-H IU

Tatishchev, Sergeĭ Spiridonovich, 1846–1906.
Дипломатическія бесѣды о внѣшней политикѣ Россіи. С. С. Татищева. Г. 1–⟨II⟩ 1889–⟨1890⟩ С.-Петербургъ, Тип. И. Н. Скороходова, 1890–98.

2 v. in 1. 25ᶜᵐ.

Originally published in "Русскій вѣстникъ." 1889–90, as reviews of contemporary political events.

1. Russia—For. rel.—1881–1894. 2. Europe—Politics—1871–

CA 15-1169 Unrev'd

Library of Congress   DK241.T

NT 0050734   DLC

Tatishchev, Sergeĭ Spiridonovich, 1846–1906.
Императоръ Александръ II, его жизнь и царствованіе. С. С. Татищева ... С.-Петербургъ, А. С. Суворинъ, 1903.

2 v. 2 port. 28ᶜᵐ.

Title transliterated: Imperator Aleksandr II.

1. Alexander II, emperor of Russia, 1818–1881. 2. Russia—Hist.—Alexander II, 1855–1881.

12-344

Library of Congress   DK220.T

NT 0050735   DLC OrU TU TNJ

DK211
.T3

Tatishchev, Sergeĭ Spiridonovich, 1846–1906.
Императоръ Николай и иностранные дворы. Историческіе очерки С. С. Татищева ... С.-Петербургъ, Тип. И. Н. Скороходова, 1889.

xxv, 459 p. 25½ᵐ.

Contents.—Предисловіе.— Поѣздка императора Николая въ Англію.—Императоръ Николай и австрійскій дворъ.—Императоръ Николай и польская монархія во Франціи.—Императоръ Николай и прусскій дворъ.—Императоръ Николай и прусская армія.—Приложеніе: Императоръ Вильгельмъ I о Россіи.

1. Russia—For. rel.—1825–1855. 2. Europe—Politics—1815–1848. 3. Europe—Politics—1848–1871.
Title transliterated: Imperator Nikolaĭ
Library of Congress   12-9741

NT 0050736   DLC

Tatishchev, Sergeĭ Spiridonovich, 1846–1906.
Изъ прошлаго русской дипломатіи. Историческія изслѣдованія и полемическія статьи С. С. Татищева. С.-Петербургъ, А. С. Суворинъ, 1890.

xv, 567 p. 26 cm.

1. Russia—For. rel.—Bulgaria. 2. Bulgaria—For. rel.—Russia. 3. Eastern question (Balkan) I. Title.
Title transliterated: Iz proshlago russkoĭ diplomatīi.

DK67.5.B8T3   12-9758 rev

NT 0050737   DLC

Tatishchev, Sergeĭ Spiridonovich, 1846–1906.
⟨Padenie Tsar'grada⟩
Паденіе Царьграда; драматическая хроника въ пяти дѣйствіяхъ, въ стихахъ. Санктпетербургъ, Тип. Имп. Академіи наукъ, 1884.

xxi, 203 p. 23 cm.

1. Istanbul—Siege, 1453—Drama. I. Title.

PG3470.T36P3   76-527534

NT 0050738   DLC

Tatishchev, Sergeĭ Spiridonovich, 1846–1906.
⟨Rod Tatishchevykh⟩
Родъ Татищевыхъ, 1400–1900; историко-генеалогическое изслѣдованіе. С.-Петербургъ, Тип. С. Суворина, 1900.

xxvi, ii, 399 p. fold. geneal. table. 26 cm.

1. Tatishchev family. I. Title.

CS859.T38 1900   72-223304

NT 0050739   DLC

Tatishchev, Sergeĭ Spiridonovich, 1846–1906.
Внѣшняя политика Императора Николая Перваго; введеніе въ исторію внѣшнихъ сношеній Россіи въ эпоху Севастопольской войны. С.-Петербургъ, Тип. И. Н. Скороходова, 1887.
xviii, 639 p. 25 cm.
Includes bibliographical references.

1. Russia—Foreign relations—1825–1855. 2. Nicholas I, Emperor of Russia, 1796–1855. I. Title.
Title romanized: Vnīeshnīaīa politika Imperatora Nikolaīa Pervago.

DK215.T38 1887   70–261279

NT 0050740   DLC CSt

Tatishchev, Sergeĭ Vasil'evich.
Котлоагрегаты легких транспортных паросиловых установок. Москва, Гос. научно-техн. изд-во машиностроит. лит-ры, 1946.
217 p. illus. 20 cm.
At head of title: С. В. Татищев, Ю. А. Шебалин.

1. Steam-boilers. I. Shebalin, IU. A., joint author. II. Title.
Title transliterated: Kotloagregaty legkikh transportnykh parosilovykh ustanovok.

TJ285.T3   59–47710

NT 0050741   DLC

TP320
.K66
Tatishchev, Sergeĭ Vasil'evich.
Kornitskiĭ, S [A
Методика нормирования расхода топлива для отопления котлов малой и средней производительности, оборудованных слоевыми топками. Москва, Госпланиздат, 1948.

Tatishchev, Sergeĭ Vasil'evich.
Рациональные методы сжигания торфа в котельных установках. Москва, Гос. энерг. изд-во, 1946.
66 p. diagrs. 20 cm.

1. Peat. 2. Furnaces.
Title transliterated: Raṭsional'nye metody szhiganiīa torfa.

TP340.T3   50–29854

NT 0050743   DLC

TN880
.D9
Tatishchev, Sergeĭ Vasil'evich, joint author.
Dvoretskiĭ, Afanasiĭ Ivanovich.
Саратовский природный газ и рациональные методы сжигания газа в топках котлов. Москва, Гос. науч.-техн. изд-во нефтяной и горно-топливной лит-ры, 1947.

Bonaparte
Collection
No. 12,792
Tatishchev, Sergiĭ.
Nouveau dictionnaire français et russe, conforme à l'état actuel des sciences; rédigé d'après les meilleurs lexicographes, et contenant toutes les expressions propres à la langue française, avec le latin et la prononciation figurée des mots, lorsqu'elle s'écarte des règles générales… Moscou, 1832.
2v.

Each vol.   has added t.-p. in Russian.

NT 0050745   ICN

Tatishchev, Vasiliĭ Nikitich, 1686–1750.
Духовная … сочиненная въ 1733 году сыну … Евграфу Васильевичу. Печатана въ Санктпетербургѣ, 1773.
57 p. 20 cm.
Bound with Loccenius, Joannes. Общество пчел. Въ Санктпетербургѣ, 1772; and Нравоучительный разговоръ. [Москва] 1773.

I. Title.   *Title transliterated:* Dukhovnaīa.

DK127.5.T3A58   55–54392

NT 0050746   DLC

Tatishchev, Vasiliĭ Nikitich, 1686–1750.
Духовная моему сыну; тексты духовной и увѣщанія, содержаніе Разговора о пользѣ наукъ и др. сочиненія, объяснительные статьи. С.-Петербургъ, Изд. И. Глазунова, 1896.
II, 83 p. 20 cm. (Русская классная библіотека. Пособіе при изученіи русской литературы, вып. 22)

I. Title.   *Title transliterated:* Dukhovnaīa moemu synu.

DK127.5.T3A57   53–50327

NT 0050747   DLC CaBVaU CSt

Tatishchev, Vasiliĭ Nikitich, 1686–1750.
Исторія россійская съ самыхъ древнѣйшихъ временъ неусыпными трудами черезъ тритцать лѣтъ собранная и описанная. [Москва] Напечатана при Имп. Московскомъ университетѣ, 1768–1848.
5 v. in 6. 24 cm.
Vol. 1 in 2 pts.; pt. 2 has special t. p.
Vol. 4 has imprint: Санктпетербургъ, Тип. Вейтбрехта; v. 5: Москва, Изд. Имп. Об-ва исторіи и древностей россійскихъ при Имп. Московскомъ университетѣ.
Vols. 1–3 edited by G. F. Müller.
1. Russia—Hist.—To 1533. 2. Russia—Hist.—1533–1613.
Title transliterated: Istoriīa rossīĭskaīa s samykh drevnīeĭshikh vremen.

DK70.T3   57–34962 rev

NT 0050748   DLC

Tatishchev, Vasiliĭ Nikitich, 1686–1750.
Избранные труды по географіи Россіи. [Под ред., со вступ. статьей и комментаріями А. И. Андреева] Москва, Гос. изд-во геогр. лит-ры, 1950.
247 p. port. 23 cm.

1. Russia—Descr. & trav. I. Andreev, Aleksandr Ignat'evich, 1887– ed.
Title transliterated: Izbrannye trudy po geografii Rossii.

DK23.T3   51–16580

Library of Congress

NT 0050749   DLC AkU CaBVaU CaBViPA

DK127
.5
.T3D55
Tatishchev, Vasiliĭ Nikitich, 1686–1750. Predsmertnoe uvīeshchanie V. N. Tatishcheva synu.
Dmitriev, Aleksandr Alekseevich, 1854–1902.
(Predsmertnoe uvīeshchanie V. N. Tatishcheva synu)
Предсмертное увѣщаніе В. Н. Татищева сыну. Ал. Дмитріева. С.-Петербургъ, Тип. В. С. Балашева, 1886.

Tatishchev, Vasiliĭ Nikitich, 1686–1750.
(Razgovor o pol'zīe nauk i uchilishch)
Разговоръ о пользѣ наукъ и училищъ / В. Н. Татищева ; съ предисл. и указателями Нила Попова. — Москва : Въ Унив. тип., 1887.
xxvi, 171 p. ; 28 cm.
Includes indexes.

1. Education—Aims and objectives. 2. Education—Russia—History. I. Title.

LB41.T333 1887   76–517271

NT 0050751   DLC

Tatishchev, Vasiliĭ Nikitich, 1686–1750, ed.
Russia. *Laws, statutes, etc.*
Судебникъ Государя Царя и Великаго Князя Іоанна Васильевича, и нѣкоторые сего Государя и ближнихъ его преемниковъ указы, собранные и примѣчаніями изъясненные … Васильемъ Никитичемъ Татищевымъ. Изд. 2. Москва, Въ Унив. тип., у Н. Новикова, 1786.

Tatishchev, Vasiliĭ Nikitich, 1686–1750.
Testament de Basile Tatistchef; tr. du russe d'après le manuscrit déposé à la Bibliothèque impériale de Paris, par le R. P. J. Martynof, de la Compagnie de Jésus. Paris, B. Duprat, 1860.
xxii, 47 p. 20cm.

I. Martinov, Jean, 1821–1894, tr. II. Title.
20–15106

Library of Congress   DK127.5.T3A6

NT 0050753   DLC MB NN

Tatishchev, Vasiliĭ Nikitich, 1686–1750.
The testament of Basil Tatistchef; tr. from the Russian manuscript preserved in the Imperial library of Paris, by John Martinof. Paris, B. Duprat, 1860.
xv, 46 p. 19cm.
[Miscellaneous pamphlets, v. 1155, no. 1]

I. Martinov, Jean, 1821–1894, tr. II. Title.
20–15107

Library of Congress   AC901.M5 vol. 1155

NT 0050754   DLC

TATISHI, TEODORO, 1913–   defendant.
[Trial for war crimes committed in the Philippines: transcript of evidence, documents and exhibits. Manila, 1946]
1v.(various pagings) facsims. 33cm.
Mimeographed; typewritten title-page.
Presented to the Law Library by Lieut. E.W. Thode, assistant defense counsel.
Tatishi, a Japanese-Filipino mestizo, naturalized in 1941 as a Philippine citizen under the name of Teodoro Cantos or Cantus, was tried in May 1946 before a military commission convened in Manila by the commanding general, United States Army   Forces, Western Pacific.

He was charged with acting in concert with Japanese occupation forces in murdering Filipino civilians and looting private property in violation of the laws of war. Verdict: death by hanging.
Petition for writ of habeas corpus, on plea that defendant was a citizen of the Philippines not subject to the jurisdiction of an American military court, was dismissed by the Supreme Court of the Philippines, June 28, 1946.
Before a hear-   ing could be held before the U.S. Supreme   Court, the Philippines

became an independent nation (July 4, 1946) and the U.S. no longer had jurisdiction there; case dismissed as moot question (329 U.S. 686)

1. War crimes - Trials - Manila, 1946. 2. Military courts - Philippine Islands. I. U.S. Army. Forces in the Western Pacific. II. Philippines (Commonwealth) Supreme Court. III. Thode, Everett Wayne.

NT 0050757   TxU

Tatishvili, Vl
Грузины в Москве; исторический очерк, 1653–1722. Тбилиси, Заря Востока, 1950.
141 p. illus. 20 cm.
Includes bibliography.

1. Georgia (Transcaucasia)—Relations (general) with Russia. 2. Russia—Relations (general) with Georgia (Transcaucasia) 3. Georgians in Moscow. I. Title.
Title transliterated: Gruziny v Moskve.

DK511.G44T3   52–32171

NT 0050758   DLC

Tatistchef, Basil
   see Tatishchev, Vasiliĭ Nikitich, 1686–1750.

Tatitlek, Native Village of
   see Native Village of Tatitlek.

Tatius, Achilles
   see Achilles Tatius.

Tatius, Marcus, Alpinus
   see Alpinus, Marcus Tatius, ca.1500–1567.

Tatius, Theodorus Renaldus
   Dissertatio de sacerdote Castrensi Hebraeorum. In Ugolino Thes. Vol. 12.

NT 0050763   NN

Tatius, Theodorus Renaldus.
   Fundamentum theologiae theticae biblicum; sive, Girbertus ebraeo-graecus contractus... ac facilitatus atque... auctus. Lipsiae: I.C.Hendel,1752.
   [6],72 p.   16 cm.

NT 0050764   OCH

S 664.1 T187f
   Tatjer y Riqué, Juan
   Fabricación de azúcar de caña, tal como se practica con los aparatos mas modernos en la isla de Cuba ... obra ilustrada con seis laminas y veinte figuras en el texto. Habana, Impr. del "Avisador comercial", 1887.
   vi, [7]–218 p., 2 *l.* diagrs. (part fold.)

   1. Sugar – Manufacture and refining – Cuba. I. For. auth. cd.

NT 0050765   WaPS PPF

Tatjewski, Wadim.
   Planowanie w transporcie samochodowym ZSRR. [Wyd. 1] Warszawa, Wydawn. Komunikacyjne, 1952.
   182, [8] p. diagrs. 21 cm.
   Bibliography: p. [183]

   1. Transportation, Automotive—Russia. I. Title.

HE5675.A6T3   54-30964

NT 0050766   DLC

The Tatler, pseud.
   See
   Mitchell, Harley Bradford, 1855–1924.

Tatler, Tom.
   The Pope's bull, against the Romish priests and people that took the oaths: in a letter to Isaack Bickerstaffe
   see under title

Tatler. v. 1–   1889? –
   Athens, Ga.

NT 0050769   GU

The Tatler.
   Liberty, Mo.
   v. illus., ports. 28 cm. annual.
   Issued by the student body, William Jewell College. Issue for 1949 is centennial ed.

   I. William Jewell College, Liberty, Mo.

LD6051.W85   378.778   51-18219

NT 0050770   DLC DHEW RPB

Mfm.   **Tatler.** (London, 1709-1711)
   no.1-271; April 12, 1709-Jan.2, 1710. London, Jones and Company.
   v. illus. 23cm.
   Microfilm from the original sheets in the Rare Book Room, U.N.C. Library, Chapel Hill. Negative.

NT 0050771   NcRS

The Tatler (London, 1709-1711)
   The Tatler. By Isaac Bickerstaff esq; [pseud.]... no. 1-271 (Apr. 12, 1709 - Jan. 2, 1710 [i. e. 1711]). [London: Sold by J. Morphew, 1709-1711.] 33½cm. (f°.)

   Three times a week.
   Chiefly by Steele and Addison.
   No. has imprint: London: Printed for the author, 1709.
   Ceased publication with no. 271 (Jan. 2, 1711).
   Three spurious Tatlers were published later, one "sold by John Baker" (no. 272-273 only), one (q. v.) "sold by John Morphew," and one (q. v.) conducted by William Harrison and "sold by A. Baldwin."—cf. Crane, R. S., and F. B. Kaye. A census of British newspapers and periodicals, 1620-1800. Chapel Hill, N. C., 1927. no. 850.

   1. Periodicals—Gt. Br. I. Addison, Joseph, 1672-1719. II. Steele, Sir Richard, 1672-1729.
   N.Y.P.L.   Revised June 27, 1934

NT 0050772   NcU MH CU-Riv OU MB ICN RPB PU MiU ICU NN MWiW-C KyLx PPL NRU TxU OrU NNC KU IU

PR1361 **The Tatler.** By Isaac Bickerstaff, esq. [pseud.] no. 1-142; f.T172   Feb. 13, 1710-Jan. 9, 1711. [Edinburgh, Printed by J. Rare bk   Watson, 1710-11]
room   142 nos. in 1 v. 30½™.
   Caption title.
   A reprint of nos. 130-271 of the London Tatler with Edinburgh advertisements.

   1. English essays.

NT 0050773   ICU TxU

The Tatler (London, 1709-1711)
   The lucubrations of Isaac Bickerstaff esq; [pseud.] ... London, Printed: and to be deliver'd to subscribers, by Charles Lillie ... and and John Morphew ... 1710-11.
   4 v. 23™.
   First collected edition.
   Signatures: v.1. A⁷, B-Z⁸, Aa-Dd⁸, Eel (I₃ incorrectly signed I₅); v.2 A-Z⁸, Aa-Ff⁸ Gg⁴; v.3. A⁴, B-Z⁸, Aa-Hh⁸; v.4. A⁶, B-Z⁸, Aa-Gg⁸, Hh², I₁₃.

   Errors in paging: v.1, p.*57-*64 inserted following p.64, no.72-79 omitted in the paging, p.368 incorrectly numbered 863; v.2, p.377 incorrectly numbered 177; v.4, p.361 incorrectly numbered 261.
   Title within double line border.
   Running-title: The Tatler.
   Originally published in 271 tri-weekly numbers, Apr. 12, 1709-Jan. 2. 1711.

Continued in next column

Continued from preceding column

   Dedications, v.3-4, and last number signed: Richard Steele.
   Edited by Richard Steele who wrote 188 of the 271 issues himself. Joseph Addison contributed some essays.
   Armorial book-plate of Robert Bristow.
   Bound in old paneled calf.

   FU KU CoU InU LU CSt NIC
NT 0050776   CLU-C LNT MU CtY TxU ICN NRU ViU NNC MH

The Tatler (London, 1709-1711)
   The lucubrations of Isaac Bickerstaff, esq; revised and corrected by the author ... London, Printed by J. N. and sold by E. Nutt [etc.] 1710?-12.
   4 v. 14™.
   Caption and running title: The Tatler ...
   Imprint varies: v. 2. Printed by John Nutt, and sold by John Morphew, 1712.—v. 3-4, Printed: And sold by Charles Lillie ... and John Morphew, 1711. The date of v. 1 has been tampered with.
   271 numbers, originally issued in folio, three times a week, April 12, 1709, to January 2, 1710 [i. e. 1711]. About 188 numbers were by Steele, who was also the projector; 42 by Addison and 36 by them jointly.
   I. Steele, Sir Richard, 1672-1729. II. Addison, Joseph, 1672-1719.

   19-19001

Library of Congress   PR1365.T2 1710

   ICU TxDaM-P PHi
NT 0050777   DLC DFo IU PPL PPDrop PHC IU KU NjP WU

PR 1365 .T2 1711
   The Tatler. (London, 1709-1711)
   The lucubrations of Isaac Bickerstaff, esq; London, Printed by Charles Lillie and John Morphew, 1711-1713 [v. 1 and 2, 1713]
   4 v. 22 cm.
   Caption and running-title: The Tatler.
   271 numbers originally issued in folio, three times a week, April 12, 1709 to January 2, 1710 [i.e. 1711]. About 188 numbers were by Steele, who was also the projector; 42 by Addison and 36 by them jointly.
   I. Steele, Richard, Sir, 1672-1729. II. Addison, Joseph, 1672-1719. III. Title

NT 0050778   NSbSU CaBVaU IU PU PSt

[The Tatler] (London, 1709-1711)

   The lucubrations of Isaac Bickerstaff, Esq. Rev. and corr. by the author ... [Two lines of quotation in Greek: Homer] London, Printed by J. N. and sold by E. Nutt, 1716.
   4 v. 14½™.
   Caption and running-title: The Tatler.
   Title within double-line border.
   271 numbers, originally issued in folio, three times a week, April 12, 1709, to January 2, 1710 [i.e. 1711]. About 188 numbers were by Steele, who was also the projector; 42 by Addison and 36 by them jointly.
   Armorial bookplates of Edwᵈ. Pauncefort, Esq. I. Steele, Sir Richard, 1672-1729. II. Addison, Joseph, 1672-1719. III. Title.

NT 0050779   ViU ICU WyU

---

x824 St32 1.720
   The Tatler (1709-1711)
   The lucubrations of Isaac Bickerstaff Esq.; revised and corrected by the author. London, Printed by E. N. and sold by R. Gosling, 1720.
   4v. 17cm.
   Caption and running title: The Tatler.
   Chiefly by Steele and Addison.
   Originally published in 271 numbers, April 12, 1709 to January 2, 17111

NT 0050780   IU PU

The Tatler (London, 1709-1711)
   The lucubrations of Isaac Bickerstaff, esq. ... London, Printed for E. Nutt, A. Boll, J. Darby, A. Bettesworth, J. Pemberton, J. Hooke, C. Rivington, R. Cruttenden, T. Cox, J. Battley, F. Clay, and E. Symon, 1720-1723.
   5v. front.(port.v.1) 17cm.
   Caption and running-title: The Tatler.
   Vols. 2,3,4 have "Rev. and corrected by the author" on the t.p.; v.5 has "2d.ed." on t.p.
   V.2,3,4 are printed for E. and R. Nutt, J.

   Knapton, J. and B. Sprint, D. Midwinter, B. and S. Tooke, R. Gosling, W. Taylor, W. and J. Innys, J. Osborn, and R. Robinson. Vol. 5 is printed for the same as the imprint for v.1.
   271 numbers, originally issued in folio, three times a week, April 12, 1709, to January 2, 1710 [i.e.1711.] About 188 numbers were by Steele, who was also the projector; 42 by Addison and 36 by them jointly.

Continued in next column

Continued from preceding column

Bound in full calf leather with ornamental gilt borders; red leather labels with title on spine of books; sprinkled edges.

I. Steele, Sir Richard, 1672-1729. II. Addison, Joseph, 1672-1719. III. Title.

NT 0050783   ScU

PR
1365
T2
1723

The Tatler (London, 1709-1711)
The lucubrations of Isaac Bickerstaff.
Rev. and corr. London, Printed for E. and R. Nutt [and others] 1723.
4v. 17cm.
Originally published in 271 numbers, April 12, 1709 to January 2, 1711.

I. Steele, Sir Richard, 1672-1729
II. Addison, Joseph, 1672-1719

NT 0050784   WU IU CaBVaU NcD

PR1365
T2
1727
Rare
Book

The Tatler (London, 1709-1711)
The lucubrations of Isaac Bickerstaff, esq.; in five volumes ... London, Printed for E. and R. Nutt [and others] 1727-1733.
5 v. port. 17cm.
Imprint varies: v. 1, 1728; v. 2-4, 1733; v. 5, 1727.
V. 2-4 "Revised and corrected by the author"; v. 5 is 3d. ed.
Includes portrait of Isaac Bickerstaff, esq. Caption and running title: The Tatler

... v. 1-4 contain numbers 1-149 (April 12, 1709-March 23, 1709); numbers 150--270 (March 25, 1710 - December 30, 1710) and number 271 (January 2, 1710).
v. 5 contains numbers 1-30 (January 13, 1710 - March 29, 1710); numbers 31-52 (March 29, 1711 - May 19, 1711). Predictions for the year, 1708. The accomplishment of the first of Mr. Bickerstaff's precidtions:

being an account of the death of Mr. Partridge, the Almanack-maker ... written in the year, 1708. A vindication of Isaac Bickerstaff, esq. against what is objected to him by Mr. Partridge, ... 1709.; A Grub-street elegy on the supposed death of Partridge ... 1708.
v. 4 is imperfect copy. The dedication and preface are bound intermittenly with the index.

NT 0050787   GU PHi OCU DFo

The Tatler (London, 1709-1711)
The lucubrations of Isaac Bickerstaff, esq; [pseud] revised and corrected by the author ... Dublin: Printed by S. Powell, for George Risk ... George Ewing ... and William Smith ... 1728.
4 v. 16½cm.
Dedications of v.3-4 and the last number signed: Richard Steele.
Edited by Sir Richard Steele, who wrote 188 of the 221 issues himself. Joseph Addison contributed some es-   says.

Prize copy awarded to Thomas Parnell by Trinity College, Dublin; arms of Trinity College stamped in gold on covers.
Bound in old red morocco, gild tooled, gilt edges.

1. English essays - Collections. I. Steele, Sir Richard, 1672-1729. II. Addison, Joseph, 1672-1719. II. Title.

NT 0050789   CLU-C MB

824.53
Ot
T188l
1733

[The Tatler] (London, 1709-1711)
The lucubrations of Isaac Bickerstaff, esq; revised and corrected by the author. London, Printed for E. Nutt [etc.] 1733.
4v. 17cm.

Caption and running title: The Tatler...
Chiefly by Steele and Addison.
Originally published in 271 numbers, Apr. 12, 1709, to Jan. 2, 1711.

I. Steele,   Sir Richard, 1672-1729. II.   Addison, Joseph, 1672-1719.   O cd

NT 0050790   KU PU PPiPT IEN

---

x824
St32
1737

The Tatler (London, 1709-1711)
The lucubrations of Isaac Bickerstaff, esq. London, Printed for H. Lintot, 1737.
v. 18cm.

Caption and running title: The Tatler.
271 numbers, originally issued in folio, three times a week, April 12, 1709, to January 2, 1710 [i.e. 1711 n.s.] About 188 numbers were by Steele, who was also the projector; 42 by Addison and 36 by the two jointly.

NT 0050791   IU NcU IEN

The Tatler (London, 1709-1711)
The lucubrations of Isaac Bickerstaff, esq; [pseud.] ... London: Printed for H. Lintot [etc.] 1743.
4 v. 17½cm.
Dedications of v.3-4 and the last number signed: Richard Steele.
Edited by Sir Richard Steele, who wrote 188 of the 221 issues himself. Joseph Addison contributed some essays.
Bound in old   sprinkled calf.

NT 0050792   CLU-C MB IU NjPT

824.05
T219
1747-49

[The Tatler] (London, 1709-1711)
The lucubrations of Isaac Bickerstaff, esq. Glasgow, Foulis, 1747-1749.
4v. 17cm.

Caption and running-title: The Tatler.
Holdings: v.1-4.
I. Steele, Sir Richard, 1672-1729. II. Addison, Joseph, 1672-1719. III. Title.

NT 0050793   NcU

824
T219
1749

[The Tatler] (London, 1709-1711)
The lucubrations of Isaac Bickerstaff, esq. [pseud.] London, Printed for H. Lintot [and others] 1749.
4v. 16cm.

Caption title: The Tatler. by Isaac Bickerstaff, esq.
Chiefly by Steele and Addison.
Originally published in 271 numbers, April 12, 1709 to January 2, 1711.
I. Steele, Sir   Richard, 1672-1729. II. Addison, Joseph,   1672-1719. I. Title.

NT 0050794   DSI ICarbS PPL NPV IU MoU

Rare Book
Collection
PR1365
.T2
1751

[The Tatler] (London, 1709-1711)
The lucubrations of Isaac Bickerstaff, esq; vol. I. [quot.] Dublin, Printed for G. Risk, G. and A. Ewing, and W. Smith, 1751.
4 v. 17 1/2 cm.

Front and back covers stamped in gold with crest of Trinity college, Dublin.
Each volume has prize label of Trinity college, dated 1753.

NT 0050795   NcU PSC-Hi FU

PR1365
.T2
1752

[The Tatler] (London, 1709-1711)
The lucubrations of Isaac Bickerstaff, esq. ... London, Printed for H. Lintot, J. and P. Knapton [etc., etc.], 1752.
4 v. 13cm.
Caption and running title: The Tatler ...
271 numbers, originally issued in folio, three times a week, April 12, 1709, to January 2, 1710 [i.e. 1711. About 188 numbers were by Steele, who was also the projector; 42 by Addison and 36 by them jointly.
I. Steele, Sir Richard, 1672-1729. II. Addison, Joseph, 1672-1719. III. Title.

NT 0050796   ViU PU MB

Z17
224bb

The Tatler (London, 1709-1711)
The lucubrations of Isaac Bickerstaff, esq. ... London:Printed for H.Lintot[etc.]1754.
4v. 17½cm.

Caption and running title: The Tatler.
A reprint of 271 numbers, originally issued in folio, three times a week, April 12, 1709-Jan.2, 1710[i.e. 1711].
By Addison, Steele and others.
Front fly-leaves inscribed: John Haskins. 1759

NT 0050797   CtY KyU IU MH ICN

Tatler, London, 1709-176

*PR1365
.T2
1759

The Tatler; or, Lucubrations of Isaac Bickerstaff ... London, Printed for J. and R. Tonson, 1759.
4 v. fronts. 20 1/2cm.
Chiefly by Addison and Steele.
Originally published in 271 numbers, April 12, 1709 to January 2, 1711.

I. Steele, Sir Richard, 1672-1729. II. Addison, Joseph, 1672-1719. III. Title: Lucubrations of Isaac Bickerstaff.

NT 0050799   MB WaSpG WaU KU-S DFo PRosC ICU

Rare
PR
1365
T2
1760

The Tatler, by the Rt. Hon. Joseph Addison, esq. Glasgow, Printed for R. Urie, 1760.
258, [2] p. 17cm.

Publisher's catalogue: p. [259]-[260]
Chiefly by Addison & Steele.
Originally published in 271 numbers, April 12, 1709 to Jan. 2, 1711.

NT 0050800   NIC GS

Tatler (London, 1709-1711)

*A085
M4977
Zz764t

The Tatler; or, Lucubrations of Isaac Bickerstaff, esq;[pseud.] ...
London:Printed for J.and R.Tonson,J.Buckland, H.Woodfall,J.Rivington,J.Hinton,R.Baldwin,W. Johnston,T.Caslon,S.Crowder,T.Longman,B.Law, C.Rivington,R.Withy,E.Dilly,J.Wilkie,R.Ware, G.Kearsly,G.Keith,J.Coote,G.Burnet,H.Payne, W.Nicoll,A.Shuckburgh,M.Richardson,and J.Hinxman.1764.

4v. fronts. 17cm.
Title vignettes.

In v.3-4, the name "J. Fuller, jun." is included in imprint.
Chiefly by Steele and Addison.
Originally published in 271 numbers, Apr. 12, 1709 to Jan. 2, 1711.
Imperfect: v.4 wanting. (Houghton copy)
From the library of Herman Melville.

NT 0050802   MH MoU ViW NjP CU-I

824.08
T219
1772

The Tatler; or, Lucubrations of Isaac Bickerstaff, esq; in five volumes.
London, Printed for R.Crowder, C.Ware, and T.Payne, 1772.
5v. fronts. 16cm.

I.Steele, Sir Richard, 1672-1729. II. Addison, Joseph, 1672-1719. III.Title: Lucubrations of   Isaac Bickerstaff, esq.

NT 0050803   CLSU NjP

PR1365
.T2
1774

The Tatler; or, Lucubrations of Isaac
Bickerstaff, esq. London, C. Bathurst,
1774.
4 v. plates. 18cm.
Chiefly by Addison and Steele. Originally
published in 271 numbers, April 12, 1709 to January
2, 1711.

I. Steele, Sir Richard, 1672-1729. II. Addison,
Joseph, 1672-1719.

NT 0050804   ViU MH NjP PSC NNC WaSp

Tatler (London, 1709-1711)

x824
St32
1776

The Tatler: or, Lucubrations of Isaac
Bickerstaff, Esq. London, Printed for C.
Bathurst, 1776.
4v. plates. 18cm.

Chiefly by Steele and Addison.
Originally published in 271 numbers, April
12, 1709 to January 2, 1711.

I. Addison, Joseph, 1672-1719. II. Title.

NT 0050805   IU PPT

Tatler (London, 1709-1711)

x824
St32
1777

The Tatler: or, Lucubrations of Isaac Bickerstaff, Esq. Dublin, Printed for W. Whitestone, 1777.
4v. 18cm.

Chiefly by Steele and Addison.
Originally published in 271 numbers, April
12, 1709 to January 2, 1711.

I. Addison, Joseph, 1672-1719. II. Title.

NT 0050806   IU

Ib84
t785
v.3

... The Tatler; or, Lucubrations of Isaac Bickerstaff, esq. In four volumes. ... London:
Printed for Harrison and co.,1785.
641p. plates. 22cm. (Harrison's British
classicks. v.3)

At head of title: Harrison's edition.
A reprint; originally published in 271 numbers,
three times a week, April 12, 1709-Jan.2, 1711.
By Addison, Steele and others.

NT 0050807   CtY ICN PP MH IU PHC ViU

052
T188
1786
Rare
Books
Col

The Tatler. (London, 1709-1711)
The lucubrations of Isaac Bickerstaff,
esq. A new edition, with notes, in six
volumes ... London, Printed for C. Bathurst [etc.] 1786.
6v. fronts.(ports.) plates. 19cm.
Each vol. has added t.p.: The Tatler, with
illustrations and notes, historical, biographical and critical.
271 numbers, originally issued in folio,
three times a week, April 12, 1709, to January 2, 1710 [i.e. 1711] About 188 numbers
were by Steele, who was also the projector; 42 by   Addison and 36 by

them jointly.
"Additional Tatlers": v.6, p.457-475.
"Account of the Courten family": v.6,
p.488-502.
Edited by John Nichols.

1. Courten family. I. Steele, Sir Richard,
1672-1729. II. Addison, Joseph, 1672-1719.
III. Nichols, John, 1745-1826, ed. IV. Title.

NT 0050809   TxU PPL KU ICU CSmH IU MiDW MH InU

---

*
PR1365
.T2
1787

The Tatler: or, Lucubrations of Isaac
Bickerstaff, [pseud.] Dublin: Printed
for W. Whitestone, W. Watson [etc.], 1787.
v. 17cm.
Bookplate of Samuel M'Craw, Richmond.

I. Steele, Sir Richard, 1672-1729. II. Addison,
Joseph, 1672-1719.

NT 0050810   ViU

824
S814
T

The Tatler. London: Printed by Rivington,
Marshall, and Bye; For Messrs. Rivington, Davis,
Buckland, Longman, Dodsley, White, C. Riving-
ton, Law, H. Baldwin, Johnson, Nichols, Dilly,
Robinson, Cadell, Sewell, Flexney, Richardson,
H. Baldwin, Otridge, Hayes, Piguinet, Bent,
Newberry, and Wilkie. 1789.
4v. 22cm.
Imprint varies: v. 2-3 Printed by H. Goldney.
Title vignettes.
This ed. contains Steele's preface to the
original quarto ed   of 1710.

NT 0050811   TxFTC OClW
NCaS IaU OU MH CFS ICU   CU KU NjP IEN

RARE
828
T219Xp

The Tatler (London, 1709-1711)
The Tatler. By Isaac Bickerstaff, esq.
London, Printed for J. Parsons, 1794.
4 v. port., plates. 15 cm. (Parson's
select British Classics, v. 31-34)

271 numbers, originally issued in folio,
three times a week, April 12, 1709, to January 2, 1710 [i.e. 1711] About 188 numbers
were by Steele, who was also the projector;
42 by Addison and 36 by them jointly.
I. Steele, Sir Richard, 1672-1729. II.
Addison, Joseph,   1672-1719. III. Title.

NT 0050812   LNT IU ViU

The Tatler... London, Printed by Bye and Law for
Messrs. Longman, Dodsley, Law, [etc.] 1797.
4v. 4 illus. 26cm.

The title-pages carry the engraved illustration
for each volume.
Originally published in 271 numbers, issued
three times a week, Apr.12,1709, to Jan.2,1711.
By Sir Richard Steele, writing under the
pseudonym "Isaac Bickerstaff". Some forty or
more papers were contributed by Addison.

I. Steele, Sir Richard, 1672-1729. II. Addison,
Joseph, 1672-1719.

NT 0050813   MWelC TU IU CoU NPV MH CtY ICN ICU

The Tatler. By Isaac Bickerstaff, esquire; [pseud.] ... New-
buryport, Published by Angier March. 1803.
4 v. fronts. (port., v. 1) plates. 18cm. (Half-title: Select British clas-
sics, v. 23-26)
Imprint varies: v. 2, Newbury-Port: Published by Angier March.
T. L. Plowman, printer. 1803: v. 3, Newbury-Port: Published by Angier
March. Robert Carr, printer. 1803.
Chiefly by Steele and Addison.
Originally published in 271 numbers, April 12, 1709 to January 2,
1711.

I. Steele, Sir Richard, 1672-1729. II. Addison, Joseph, 1672-1719.

Library of Congress   PR1365.S4   vol. 23-26   34-17542
   [2]   (824.5082) 824.5

NT 0050814   DLC PPT MB MH NIC ScU OrU InU

The Tatler. v. 1-4. London: J. Sharpe, 1804. 4 v. illus.
17cm.

Plates bound out of order.
271 numbers originally issued from April 12, 1709 to Jan. 2, 1710 [i.e. 1711];
chiefly by Steele and Addison.

I. Essays, English. I. Addison,   Joseph, 1672-1719. II. Steele,
Sir Richard, 1672-1729.   March 2, 1943
N. Y. P. L.

NT 0050815   NN NNC MH PU NjP PPA NmLcU OrU IaU

The Tatler, a corrected edition; with prefaces
historical and biographical, by Alexander
Chalmers. London, Printed by Nichols and son,
1806.
4 v.
Title vignettes.
Chiefly by Steele and Addison.
Originally published in 271 numbers, April 12,
1709 to January 2, 1711.

I. Steele, Sir Richard, 1672-1729. II.Addison,
Joseph, 1672-1719.   III. Chalmers, Alexander,
1759-1834.

NT 0050816   TxDaM-P OrU

---

x824
St32
1809

The Tatler. By Isaac Bickerstaffe [pseud.]
With a preface, historical and biographical, by
Alex. Chalmers   New-York: Printed by D.& G.
Bruce. Published by E. Sargeant, and M. & W.
Ward; and Munroe, Francis & Parker, and Edward
Cotton, Boston, 1809.
5v. 16½cm.
Chiefly by Steele and Addison.
Originally published in 271 numbers, April 12,
1709 to January 2,1711.
I. Addison, Joseph, 1672-1719, joint author.
II. Chalmers, Alex-   ander, 1759-1834. III.
Title.

NT 0050817   IU NBu KyU MB CtY MH ViU PPLT WaS

P R
1365
.T19
1820

The Tatler; with notes and a general index... Royal octavo ed. designed to accompany the popular
work entitled Elegant extracts. London, C. Taylor, etc., 1820.
xii, 482 p. 24½cm. (Bound with: The Guardian
... Lond., C. Taylor,etc.,1820. viii, 264 p.)

NT 0050818   DNC

The Tatler; a new ed., carefully revised, in four volumes; with
prefaces, historical and biographical, by Alexander Chalmers ... London, F. C. and J. Rivington [etc.] 1822.
4 v. 22cm.
Title vignettes.
Chiefly by Steele and Addison.
Originally published in 271 numbers, April 12, 1709 to January 2, 1711.

I. Steele, Sir Richard, 1672-1729. II. Addison, Joseph, 1672-1719.
III. Chalmers, Alexander, 1759-1834, ed.

                     31-16207
Library of Congress   PR1365.T2   1822

NT 0050819   DLC ViU MdBP

PR1365
.T2
1822

The TATLER, with notes and illustrations ... London stereotype edition. London, I. Walker and
co., W. Baynes and son [etc., etc.] 1822.
3 v. illus. 16½cm.
Illus. missing.
Printed by A. Hancock.
271 numbers, originally issued in folio, three
times a week, April 12, 1709, to January 2, 1710
[i.e. 1711] About 188 numbers were by Steele, who
was also the projector; 42 by Addison and 36 by
them jointly.
I. Steele, Sir Richard, 1672-1729. II. Addison,
Joseph, 1672-1719.

NT 0050820   ViU MiU

Tatler. London, 1709-1711

Tatler ...
(In Chalmers, Alexander, ed. The British essayists ... London,
1823. 16cm. v. 1-2: ports.))
Chiefly by Steele and Addison.
Originally published in 271 numbers, April 12, 1709-January 2, 1711.
"Historical and biographical preface": v. 1, p. [xvii]-lxxxv.

I. Steele, Sir Richard, 1672-1729. II. Addison, Joseph, 1672-1719.

                     28-23155
Library of Congress   PR1365.C5   vol. 1-4

NT 0050821   DLC PPT PU CtY

PR
1365
L8
1-3

Tatler. no. 1-271. [April 12, 1709-Jan. 2,
1711. London. 1827]
3v. 16cm. (British essayists, v. 1-3)

Half title.
Chiefly by Steele and Addison.

NT 0050822   WU PV

The **Tatler**, complete in one volume. With notes, and a
general index ... no. 1-271: Apr. 12, 1709-Jan. 2, 1710.
London, Jones and co., 1829.

1 p. l., ₍ᵥ₎-xii, 482 p. front. (port.) 23ᶜᵐ.

By Addison, Steele, and others.

    i. Addison, Joseph, 1672-1719. ii. Steele, Sir Richard, 1672-1729.

                        5-16680

Library of Congress   PR1365.T2 1829

NT 0050823   DLC ODW NcD

824
St32   The Tatler, with notes, and a general index
1831   Philadelphia, J. J. Woodward, 1831.
     444p. front. 23½cm.

     Chiefly by Steele and Addison.
     Originally published in 271 numbers, April 12,
1709 to January 2, 1711.
     With this is bound: The Guardian. Philadelphia,
1831.

     I. Addison, Joseph 1672-1719. II. Title.

PG1B
NT 0050824   IU PHi MnU CU-I CSmH MdBJ MH NN ViU Vi

The **Tatler**, with notes and a general index... Complete in one
volume. Philadelphia: M. W. Woodward & Co., 1835.   vi,
7-444 p. 2 pl. 8°.

     Originally published in 271 numbers, April 12, 1709 to Jan. 2, 1710. About 188
numbers were by Steele, who was also the projector; 42 by Addison and 36 by them
jointly.
     With this is bound: The Guardian. Philadelphia, 1835. 8°.

6543A.   I. Essays, English.   *Revised*
N. Y. P. L.   *July 13, 1931*

NT 0050825   NN PP PPL DGU NjP ViU

The **Tatler**: or The lucubrations of Isaac
Bickerstaff, by Sir Richard Steele, assisted by
Addison, Swift, Hughes, Harrison, Fuller,
Asplin, Congreve, Twisden, Anthony, Henley,
Greenwood, Harrison, Dartiquenave. Stereotype
ed. London, Printed by W. Lewis, for Isaac,
Tuckey, and Co., 1836.
     xiv, 366 p. 24 cm.
     At head of title: British essayists.'
     271 numbers, originally issued in folio,
three times a week, April 12, 1709 to January 2,
1710 [i.e. 1711]
     Bound with The Spectator. London, 1836.

NT 0050826   T NN

The **Tatler**, with notes and a general index ... **Complete**
in one volume. Philadelphia, M'Carty and Davis,
1844.

     vi, 7-444 p. front., plates. 24ᶜᵐ.
     With this is bound the Guardian.
     By Addison, Steele, and others.

     i. Addison, Joseph, 1672-1719. ii. Steele, Sir Richard, 1672-1729.

NT 0050827   MiU IaB

PR 1365
T2   The TATLER, with notes and illustrations, in three
1845   volumes. 1845.

NT 0050828   CaBVaU

Tatler (London, 1709-1711)

The **Tatler** with notes & a general index.
London, Bohn, 1852.
     264 p.

NT 0050829   PU

Tatler (London, 1709-1711)

PR
1365   Tatler.
T2
1856   (In The British essayists: with prefaces,
     historical and biographical, by A. Chalmers.
     Boston, 1855-57 ₍v. 1, 1856₎ 18cm. v. 1-4
     (1856)

     Chiefly by Steele and Addison.
     Originally published in 271 numbers, April
12, 1709-January 2, 1711.
     "Historical   and biographical pref-
ace": v. 1,   p. 1-75.

NT 0050830   NIC NcU MH

The **Tatler**; with introduction and notes by George
A. Aitken; with twenty-four photogravures from
rare engravings. London, Boston, J. B. Millet
₍1898₎
     4 v. ports. 21cm.

     Chiefly by Steele and Addison.
     "Library edition. Limited to one hundred
numbered and registered copies, printed from type,
and type distributed. This copy is No. 15."
     Originally published in 271 numbers, April 12,
1709-January 2, 1711.

NT 0050831   IdPI CaBVaU WaU OrPR

PR1365   The **Tatler**; edited by George A. Aitken, in four
.T2   volumes. ₍London & Edinburgh, Printed by
1898   Ballantyne, Hanson, 1898.₎
     4v. 21cm.

     Chief by Steele and Addison.
     Originally published in 271 numbers, April 12,
1709 to January 2, 1711.

     i. Steele, Sir Richard, 1672-1729. ii.
Addison, Joseph, 1672-1719.

NT 0050832   FMU TxU MH NcRS KMK CSt NcU NcD PSC

PR1365   The **Tatler**. Edited with introduction & notes
T2   by George A. Aitken ... London, Duckworth
1898   & co., 1898-99.

     4 v. fronts. (ports.) 22 cm. Brown cloth.
Uncut.

     I. Steele, Sir Richard, 1672-1729. II. Addi-
son, Joseph, 1672-1719. III. Aitken, George
Atherton, 1860-1917, ed.

     IaU PBL DLC PSt PHC NcGU PU PPT MiU OU OCU
NT 0050833   CSmH PV KU-S GU MH TxU NIC ICN NcD NjP

Rare
PR
1365   The **Tatler** ₍London, 1709-1711₎
T2   Le babillard, ou Le nouvelliste philo-
1725   sophe. Traduit de l'Anglois par A.D.L.C.
     ₍i.e. Armand Boisbeleau de La Chapelle₎
     Amsterdam, F. Changuion, 1725.
     404 p. 17cm.

     Translations of issues from 12 April
1709 to 2 January 1711. Cf. p. 9.

     I. Title.   II. Title: Le nouvelliste
philosophe.

NT 0050834   NIC

Rare Book Room
PR
1365   The Tatler ₍London, 1709-1711₎
.T24   Le Babillard, ou, Le nouvelliste philosophe.
1737   Traduit de l'anglois, par A.D.L.C. ... Sui-
     vant l'edition d'Amsterdam. Basle, Chez J.
     Brandmuller & fils, 1737.
     2 v. 17 cm.
     Translated by Armand Boisbeleau de la
Chapelle.
     Selections from no. 1-76 of The Tatler,
which are chiefly by Steele, with a few contributions by Addison.
     Stamped on back of binding: M.D.
     I. Chapelle, Armand Boisbeleau de la, 1676-
1746. II. Steele, Sir Richard, 1672-1729.
III. Addison, Joseph, 1672-1719. IV. Title.

NT 0050835   MiU

PR3703   The **Tatler** ₍London, 1709-1711₎
.I 88   **Steele**, *Sir* Richard, 1672-1729.
     Il chiacchierone; a cura di Aldo Valori. ₍Roma₎ Colombo
₍1945₎

The **Tatler** ₍London, 1709-1711₎

Addison, Joseph, 1672-1719.
     ... An essay by Joseph Addison. The trial of the wine-brew-
ers, with an introduction and an inquiry into Mr. Addison's
drinking, by Edward F. O'Day ... San Francisco, Printed
by J. H. Nash, 1930.

The **Tatler** ₍London, 1709-1711₎

Sander, Carl, 1878-
     Die Franzosen und ihre literatur im urteil der moralischen
zeitschriften Steeles und Addisons ... von Carl Sander ...
Strassburg i. E., Druck von M. Du Mont-Schauberg, 1903.

The **Tatler** ₍London, 1709-1711₎

PR1365   **A General** index to the Spectators, Tatlers and Guardians ...
.A1G4   London, W. Owen, 1757.
Rare Bk.
Coll.

The **Tatler** ₍London, 1709-1711₎
     History, opinions, and lucubrations, of Isaac Bickerstaff, esq.
₍pseud.₎ From the "Tatler," by Steele and Addison. With introduction, notes, and illustrations by H. R. Montgomery ... London: Longman, Green, Longman and Roberts, 1861.   viii, xv,
304 p. illus. 18cm.

201060B.   1. No subject.   I. Steele,   Sir Richard, 1672-1729.   II. Addison, Joseph, 1672-1719.   III. Mont-   gomery, Henry Riddell, 1818-1904, ed.
N. Y. P. L.   *May 13, 1943*

NT 0050840   NN CaBVaU NSbSU TxU

PR
1365   The **Tatler**, ₍London, 1709-1711₎
T2   The motto's of the five volumes of Tatlers, and
M6   the two volumes of the Spectator, translated into
Cage   **English.** To which is added, A complete index to
     the two volumes of the Spectator. London: Printed
for John Morphew, 1712.

     ₍1₎ 34 ₍i.e. 68₎ ₍3₎ p. A-F in alternate 8's
and 4's. (F4 and all after lacking.) 12mo.
     Lacks the index to the 2 volumes of the Spec-
tator; perhaps never published at all.
     Latin and English on opposite pages.

NT 0050841   DFo NcD

     The Tatler ₍London, 1709-1711₎
     Motto's of the five volumes of Tatlers,
1971   and of the seven volumes of Spectators.
.488   With tables. In three parts. London: Prin-
     ted for Bernard Lintott at the Cross-keys
     between the Two Temple-Gates in Fleet-street
     [1713]
     3 pts. in 1 v. 16 cm.
     Signatures: [*]¹A-F⁸·⁴(F₄ wanting)A⁸B₄C⁶
A⁶C₄D²E².

     Imperfect? Index to The Spectator, called for
on t.-p. of parts I and II, not present.
     Part I-II dated 1712, pt.III 1713; pt.I has
imprint: London: Printed for John Morphew near
Stationers-Hall, 1712.
     1. Maxims. 2. Grosvenor, Sir Robert, 6th bart.
1695-1755 - Autograph and bookplate. I. The
Spectator. II. Title.

NT 0050843   CtY IaU

The Tatler (London, 1709-1711)
   Original and genuine letters sent to the Tatler
and Spectator ...
     see under   Lillie, Charles, ed.

The Tatler (London, 1709-1711)

   The Pantheon: a vision ... London, Printed for R.
Dodsley and sold by M. Cooper, 1747.

PR
1365
.T2
1888
   The Tatler (London, 1709-1711)
   Selected essays, with an introd. and
notes by Alex. Charles Ewald. London,
New York, F. Warne, 1888.
   478 p. (The Chandos classics)

   Steele, Sir Richard, 1672-1729.
   Addison, Joseph, 1672-1719.

MH MB WaTU WaSpG ViLxW
NT 0050846   MoU NcRS IdPI NNC PV OKentU KU PHC CU

The Tatler. (London, 1709-1711)
   Selections from the Tatler, the Spectator and their successors, edited, with an introduction, by Walter Graham ... New
York, T. Nelson & sons, 1928.
   4 p. l. 5-422 p. 16°. (*Half-title:* Nelson's English series; general
editor, E. Bernbaum.)
   "A reading list": p. 31-32.

   I. The Spectator. II. Graham, Walter James, 1885-   ed.

   Library of Congress   PR1365.G7
                             28—24633

  NRU OC1
NT 0050847   DLC NcU OrP OrSaW OrU MiU CoU WaU TU ViU

   The Tatler (London, 1709-1711)
     The Tatler [Addison's contributions only]
       see under Addison, Joseph, 1672-1719.

AC1
.E8
no.993
   The Tatler (London, 1709-1711)

   Steele, *Sir* Richard, 1672-1729.
   The Tatler. Edited by Lewis Gibbs [pseud.] London,
Dent; New York, Dutton [1953]

   The Tatler (London, 1709-1711)

   [Murphy, Arthur] 1727-1805.
   The upholsterer, or What news? a farce, in two acts.
As it is performed at the Theatre royal, in Drury lane ...
By the author of the Apprentice. London, Printed for
P. Vaillant, 1758.

---

q052
T188b
Rare
Books
Col
   The Tatler. [John Baker] no.272-273;
Jan. 4-6, 1711. London, Sold by John
Baker at the Black Boy in Pater-Noster
Row, 1711.
   2 no. 35cm. in envelope in folder 40cm.

   One of three spurious Tatlers published
after the last number of Steele's Tatler.

NT 0050851   TxU

The Tatler. v. 1-   July 3, 1901-
  London [1901-
     v.   illus. (part col. incl. ports.) 32½-35^{cm}. weekly.
  Title varies: July 3, 1901-   The Tatler; an illustrated
     journal of society and the stage.
               The Tatler.
  In L. C. set only v. 1-   have title-pages (with title: The Tatler;
an illustrated journal of society, the drama, and sport (varies slightly))
  Vols. 21-   include separately paged current supplement: Sporting
and country house supplement.

                                    39—13909

  Library of Congress   AP4.T3
               [2]   052

NT 0050852   DLC OAkU MeP TxU NN CaBVaU

   The Tatler, London, 1901-
     see also   The Tatler and bystander.

   The Tatler (London, 1901-)
   Coronation number (King George VI) [London]
1937.
   p. 295-366. illus.
   v. 144, no. 1873, May 19, 1937.
   In portfolio with the coronation numbers of The
Bystander and The Sketch.

NT 0050854   CaBVaU

   "The Tatler" (London, 1901)
   The first book of Eve
     see under   [Fish, Anne Harriet]

   The Tatler (London, 1901-)

   Fish, A   **H.**
   The third Eve book; drawings by Fish, written and designed by Fowl [pseud.] reproduced from & with the kind
permission of "The Tatler." London, John Lane; New
York, John Lane company, 1919.

   The Tatler.

   Tulane university of Louisiana. Spectators.
   The spectator, an anthology, 1933-1934. New Orleans, The
Spectators, 1935.

AP4
.T28
See
Periodi-
cal file
for hold-
ings
   The Tatler; a daily journal of literature
and the stage. v. 1-4 (no.1-493); Sept.
4, 1830-Mar. 31, 1832. New ser. [v.1]
(no. 1-59); Apr. 2-Oct. 6, 1832. London.
   5 v. in
   Frequency varies.
   Subtitle varies.

   1. English periodicals.

NT 0050858   NBuU CSmH IaU PU NN MiU NNC MB

S-65
no.120E
   Tatler; a daily journal of literature and the
stage. v. 1-4 (no. 1-493); Sept. 4, 1830-
Mar. 31, 1832; new ser., v. 1 (no. 1-59),
Apr. 2/4-Oct. 6, 1832. London.
   5 v. on 1 reel. (English literary
periodicals, 120E)

   Microfilm. Ann Arbor, Mich., University
Microfilms.

NT 0050859   ViU CLSU PSt NB

   The Tatler. A daily paper of literature, fine arts,
   music and the stage
     see   The Tatler; a daily journal of
   literature and the stage.

   The Tatler, a miscellany of literature, fine arts,
   music, and theatricals
     see   The Tatler; a daily journal of
   literature and the stage.

   Tatler: a record of books, fine arts, music,
   theatricals, and improvements
     see   The Tatler; a daily journal of
   literature and the stage.

   The Tatler; an illustrated journal of society and
   the stage
     see   The Tatler. London [1901-

   The Tatler; an illustrated journal of society, the
   drama, and sport
     see   The Tatler. London [1901-

   The Tatler ... being the annual publication of the senior
   class of the York high school.
   York, Pa. [19
     v. illus. (incl. ports.) plates. 27½^{cm}.

   I. York, Pa. High school.
                             CA 26-638 Unrev'd
   Library of Congress   LD7501.Y6755

NT 0050865   DLC

---

q052
T1885
Rare
Books
Col
   The Tatler. By Donald MacStaff [pseud.] of
the north. no.1-30; Jan. 10-Apr. 25,
1711. Edinburgh, Printed by James Wat-
son, 1711.
   v. 34cm. semiweekly.
   By Robert Hepburn.
   Included with this: The humble address of
Donald M'Staff of the north, in name of the
M'Staff's there, to Isaac Bickerstaff, cen-
sor of Great Britain. London printed, and
Edinburgh reprinted, 1710.
   I. Hepburn, Robert, 1690?-1712.

NT 0050866   TxU

   The Tatler ... published by the annual staff of the Technical
   high school ...
   Harrisburg, Pa. [19
     v. front., illus. (incl. ports.) plates. 27½^{cm}.

   I. Harrisburg, Pa. Technical high school.
                          CA 27-10 Unrev'd
   Library of Congress   LD7501.H28T55

NT 0050867   DLC

The **Tatler**; news and gossip about books.
v. 1[-4]   (Feb., 1926 – Spring, 1930)

New York, 1926–30.   4°.   illus. (incl. ports.)   8°.

Irregular.
Numbering continuous; v. 4 lacks v. numbering.
v. 1, no. 4 called The Christmas tatler.
Published by the Putnam Bookstore, New York.
Ceased publication with v. 4, no. 12 (Spring, 1930).

1. Bibliography—Per. and soc. publ   I. Putnam's, G. P., Sons.
N. Y. P. L.   December 7, 1931

NT 0050868   NN

... The **Tatler**; year book of Winthrop college, the South
Carolina college for women.   Rock Hill,
S. C.

    v. illus. (part col.) ports. 27ᶜᵐ.

    1. Winthrop normal and industrial college, Rock Hill, S. C.

    Library of Congress   LD7251.R465   23-8727

NT 0050869   DLC DHEW

Tatler and American sketch
    see   New York tatler; social digest.

---

052   The **Tatler & Bystander.**
T219   1–
         July 3, 1901–
         London.
            v. illus. 33–35cm. weekly.

         Title varies: v.1–158 (no.1–2053),
         1901–Oct.30 1940, The Tatler (with or
         without subtitle)

NT 0050871   CLSU NN N NBuG

The **Tatler & Bystander**
    see also The Tatler. London [1901–

... The **Tatler**, and the Guardian; complete in one volume.
London, Jones & co. [182–?]

    1 p. l., [vi]–viii p., 1 l., [ix]–xii, 482 p., 2 l., [vii]–viii, 264 p.   front. (port.)
    plates. 21½ᶜᵐ. (Jones's university ed. of British classics)
    Engr. t.-p.
    (Pt. 2) has separate t.-p.: The Guardian; complete in one volume. With
    notes, and a general index. London, Printed for J. Jones and co.
    A reprint of the Tatler, published 1709–11, and the Guardian, published
    1713, by Steele, Addison and others.

    I. Steele, Sir Richard, 1672–1729. II. Addison, Joseph, 1672–1719.
    III. Title: The Guardian.

    Library of Congress   PR1365.T2 1820   7-32911

NT 0050873   DLC CLU OU MB FTaSU NNC OClCC NNC

                                                    2552.22
The **Tatler and Guardian.** Chiefly by Sir Richard Steele and Jo-
seph Addison. And an account of the authors by Thomas Babington
Macaulay. With notes and general indexes.
    New York. Bangs & Co. 1852. 2 parts in 1 v. Plates. 8°.

*D6205 – Steele, Richard. – Addison, Joseph. – Macaulay, Thomas Babington.

NT 0050874   MB TxU

The **Tatler** and Guardian, chiefly by Sir Richard Steele,
and Joseph Addison. And an account of the authors,
by Thomas Babington [!] Macaulay, complete in one
volume. With notes and general indexes. New York,
Bangs, brother, & co., 1855.

    xii, 444, 244 p. front., plates. 23½ᶜᵐ.
    Imperfect: p. 21–36 and 85–100 in the Tatler, wanting; p. 437–444 du-
plicated.

    I. Steele, Sir Richard, 1672–1729. II. Addison, Joseph, 1672–1719. III.
Macaulay, Thomas Babington Macaulay, 1st baron, 1800–1859. IV. The
Guardian

                                                    25-24848
    Library of Congress   PR1365.T2 1855

NT 0050875   DLC CLSU OCX CaBViP WaWW OCl NN MB

The **Tatler and Guardian**, chiefly by Sir
Richard Steele, and Joseph Addison; and an
account of the authors, by Thomas Babbelington
Macaulay ... with notes and general indexes.
Derby & Jackson, 1858.
    2 v. in 1.

NT 0050876   Or

The **Tatler and Guardian**, chiefly by Richard
Steele and Joseph Addison, and an account of
the authors, by Thomas Babbington [!] Macaulay.
Cincinnati, Applegate & co., 1860.

NT 0050877   MH

The **Tatler and The Guardian** ... With notes and
a general index.   London and Edinburgh,
W. P. Nimmo, 1876.
    xii, 482 [4] [vii]–viii p., 1 l., 264 p.
    front. (port.) 24 cm.

NT 0050878   CU

The **Tatler and the Guardian**, Philadelphia, 1876
(Collection of articles ascribed to Addison)
    see under Addison, Joseph, 1672–1719.

PR1365   The **TATLER**, and the Guardian ... With notes, and
.T2   a general index. London and Edinburgh, W. P.
1877   Nimmo, 1877.
             1 p.l., [v]–xii p., 1 l., 482, vi p., 1 l.,
             264 p. front. (port.) 23½ᶜᵐ.
             The Guardian ... has special t.-p., and is
             paged separately.
             A reprint of the Tatler, published 1709–11, and
             the Guardian, published 1713, by Steele, Addison
             and others.

             I. Steele, Sir Richard, 1672–1729. II. Addison.
             Joseph, 1672–1719. III. Title: The Guardian.

NT 0050880   ViU OCl

824.508   The **Tatler and the Guardian.** Complete in
T219   in one volume. With notes, and a general
             index.   Edinburgh, W. P. Nimmo, 1880.
             xii, 482, vi, 264 p. port. 24ᶜᵐ.
             By Addison, Steele, and others.

             I. Addison, Joseph, 1672–1719. II. Steele,
             Sir Richard, 1672   –1729. III. The
             Guardian.

NT 0050881   CSt NNC

Tatler Club, Niagara Falls, N.Y.
             The Tatler Club, Niagara Falls, New
             York. [Niagara Falls? 1930]
             31p. 17cm.
             Includes constitution, by-laws, and
             membership list.

             1. Tatler Club, Niagara Falls, N.Y.

NT 0050882   NRU

The **Tatler, Guardian and Freeholder**
    see under   Addison, Joseph, 1672–1719.

PN4725   The **Tatler in Cambridge.**   Cambridge, E.
.T38   Johnson, 1871–2.
             2v.

             1. Periodicals – Gt. Brit. 2. Periodicals –
             Cambridge, Eng.

NT 0050884   NcU

The **Tatler** of society in Florida ... v. 1–
Jan. 9, 1892–
St. Augustine, Fla., 1892–
    v. illus., plates (partly col.) ports. 30½–32½ cm.
    Weekly during the winter season.
    Editor: Jan. 1892–   Anna M. Marcotte.

    I. Marcotte, Anna M., ed.

    F319.S2T2   8—12441

NT 0050885   DLC FU

The **tatler**; or, The history of Patty Steele
    see under   [Guernsey, Lucy Ellen] 1826–
1899.

The **Tatler Play Bill** for the Theatres of the
Metropolis ... June 4th to 16th, 1832 ...
[London, 1832]

NT 0050887   PU NN

The **Tatler revived**; by Isaac Bickerstaff, esq.
Num. 1–29. Oct. 16, 1727–Jan. 22, 1727/8.
s.-w. London, 1727–28.
    f°.
    One of the spurious continuations of
Steele's Tatler.

NT 0050888   MH

Ak   The **Tatler's character** (July 21.) of
St32   Æsculapius guessing diseases, without the
S723s   knowledge of drugs; apply'd to the British
             physicians and surgeons: or, The difficult
             diseases of the royal family, nobility and
             gentry will never be understood and recover'd,
             when the populace are oppress'd and destroy'd
             by the practising-apothecaries and empiricks,
             confess'd by the College and Mr. Bernard the
             surgeon. By a consultation of gentlemen of
             quality.

             London: Printed for M.Wotton, at the Three
             Daggers in Fleetstreet, 1709. 16p. 19cm.
             Lettered on cover: Swift, Steele, etc.

NT 0050890   TxU

Tatlock, Gulielmus
   see   Tatlock, William, S.J.

320.3
T21 Tatlock, Henry, *1848-1942.*
     An address on the regulation of the
   liquor business. Delivered in St. Andrew's
   church, Ann Arbor, 19 January, 1908, by the
   Rev. Henry Tatlock... [Ann Arbor, 1908]
     7 p.   23 cm.
     Caption title.
     Reprinted from the Ann Arbor daily
   times, January 22, 1908.

NT 0050892   MiU

Tatlock, Henry, 1848-1942.
    The Sunday question. A paper read at Church
  Congress held at Minneapolis, October 11, 1899.
  [New York, T. Whittaker, 1899?]
    6 p.   8°.

NT 0050893   NN

BT
89   Tatlock, Henry, 1848-1942.
.T22   Changes needed in some of the church's con-
   ceptions, by Rev. Henry Tatlock ... Ann Arbor,
   Mich., G. Wahr [c1927]
     47 p.   18½ cm.

   1. Theology, Doctrinal. I. Title.

NT 0050894   MiU

Tatlock, Jessie M.
   Merchants and merchant colonies in Sicily from
the twelfth through the fourteenth century.
   Thesis - Radcliffe, 1933.

NT 0050895   MH

Tatlock, Jessie May, 1878-
   Greek and Roman mythology, by Jessie M. Tatlock ...
New York, The Century co., 1917.
   xxviii, 372 p. incl. illus., plates. 21 cm.
   "A brief list of poems and dramas based on the myths": p. 356-361.

   1. Mythology, Classical.

   BL721.T3   292   17-3155

WaS OrStbM OLak
DGU NBuU PHC OC1W NcC PU NIC FMU WaSp CaBVaU OrPS
NN MB MH OC1 OC1h OC1W OEac OOxM TxU NNC NcD Wa WaE
NT 0050896   DLC PPPM NBuC OrP KEmT Or PCW PBm PPLas

Tatlock, John, 1860-
   [Mortality records of cities in the United
States collected by John Tatlock, 1887-1890]
   29½ cm.

   Manuscript sheets.

NT 0050897   NNC

Tatlock, John, *1860-*
   On the principal coefficients in the barometric formula of Laplace, as applied to the White
Mountain region. Boston. 1884.
   11p. 8°.

NT 0050898   DAS

Tatlock, John, 1860-

Willey, Nathan.
   ... Principles and practice of life insurance. Originally
prepared by Nathan Willey, actuary. Also new and extended tables based on the combined and American experience mortality tables, computed at 4½, 4, 3½ and 3 per
cent interest. New explanatory text and additions by
Henry Worthington Smith ... All tables carefully revised with the co-operation of John Tatlock, jr. ... New
York and Chicago, The Spectator company, 1892.

Tatlock, John, 1860-
   Variation of barometric measurements of altitude with the
season. By John Tatlock, jr. Read June 14, 1882. [Boston,
1882.]   147-155 p.   8°.

   Caption-title.
   Repr.: Appalachian Mountain Club. Appalachia. v. 3.

1. Altitude.—Measurement.
N. Y. P. L.   January 6, 1916.

NT 0050900   NN DAS

Tatlock, John Strong Perry, 1876- *1948.*
   Astrology and magic in Chaucer's "Franklin's
tale" [by] John Strong Perry Tatlock ... Boston, Ginn & co., 1913.
   cover-title, [339]-350 p. 26 cm.
   "Reprinted from Anniversary papers by colleagues and
pupils of George Lyman Kittredge."

   1. Chaucer, Geoffrey. Canterbury tales. Franklin's tale.

NT 0050901   MiU N NIC NN

Tatlock, John Strong Perry, 1876-1948.
   Boccaccio & the plan of Chaucer's Canterbury
tales.   [No imprint]
   [69]-117 p.   22.5 cm.
   Caption title.
   Extracted from Anglia, v. 37, 1913.

NT 0050902   MiU

828
C5k0 Tatlock, John Strong Perry, 1876-
T2   Chaucer. [No imprint]
     Various paging   28 cm.
     Caption title.
     Consists of contributions made by Prof.
   Tatlock to Modern language notes, v. 21 &
   22, 1906 & 1907, mainly on Chaucer.

NT 0050903   MiU

               1876-
12482.1 Tatlock, John Strong Perry, ∆ Chaucer and Dante.
   [Chicago. 1906.] l. 8°. pp. 6.
    " Reprinted from *Modern philology*, vol. iii. no. 3, Jan. 1906."

NT 0050904   MH NjP MiU

Tatlock, John Strong Perry, 1876-

Chaucer, Geoffrey, *d.* 1400.
   Chaucer's Canterbury tales; selections from The modern
reader's Chaucer, by John S. P. Tatlock ... and Percy Mac-
Kaye ... Chosen and edited by Carl W. Ziegler ... New York,
The Macmillan company, 1923.

B28
C50 Tatlock, John Strong Perry, 1876-
T22c   Chaucer's Retractions, by John S.P. Tat-
   lock...The Modern language association of
   America, 1913.
     cover-title, p. 521-529 23 cm.
     "Reprinted from the Publications of the
   Modern language association of America,
   xxiii, 4."

NT 0050906   MiU NcD

PR
2836 Tatlock, John Strong Perry, 1876-
.T22   The chief problem in Shakespeare, by John
   S.P. Tatlock ... [n.p., 1916?]
     cover-title, 19 p. 23 cm.
     "Reprinted from The Sewanee review for April, 1916."
   A study of Troilus and Cressida.
   Author's inscribed presentation copy.

   1. Shakespeare, William. Troilus and Cressida.

NT 0050907   MiU MeB

Tatlock, John Strong Perry, 1876-
             FOR OTHER EDITIONS
              SEE MAIN ENTRY
Chaucer, Geoffrey, *d.* 1400.
   ... The complete poetical works of Geoffrey Chaucer, now
first put into modern English, by John S. P. Tatlock ... and
Percy MacKaye ... Illustrations by Warwick Goble. New
York, The Macmillan company, 1938.

Tatlock, John Strong Perry, 1876-
   A concordance to the complete works of Geoffrey Chaucer
and to the Romaunt of the Rose, by John S. P. Tatlock ...
and Arthur G. Kennedy ... Washington, Carnegie institution
of Washington, 1927.
   xiii, 1110 p. 1 l. 29 cm. (*On verso of t.-p.:* Carnegie institution of
Washington. Publication no. 353)
   "Based on the 'Globe' edition of Chaucer's works."—Introd.

   1. Chaucer, Geoffrey—Concordances. 2. Roman de la Rose—Concordances.   I. Kennedy, Arthur Garfield, 1880-   joint author.

   Library of Congress   27-6088

WaSpG
MtBC WaSp OrPR WaWW WaS OrCS OrU IdPI OrSaW CaBVaU
   OC1W OU OCU OO OOxM ViU TU WaU MCW IdU OrP DAU
NT 0050909   DLC MeB MB PPT PBm PSC PP NcD MiU OC1W

TATLOCK, John Strong Perry, 1876-
   The dates of Chaucer's Troilus & Criseyde
   & Legend of good women. Chicago, [1903].

NT 0050910   MH OC1

Tatlock, John Strong Perry, 1876-1948.
   The development and chronology of Chaucer's works. By
John S. P. Tatlock ... [London] Pub. for the Chaucer so-
ciety, by K. Paul, Trench, Trübner & co., limited, 1907.
   xiii, 233, [1] p. 23 cm. (*On cover:* Chaucer society. [Publications.
Second series, 37])

   1. Chaucer, Geoffrey—Chronology of works.
                          7-29022
   Library of Congress   PR1901.A3 2d ser., no. 37

NIC CoU
OC1W OOxM OCU MiU ViU OrU CaBVaU MB WaSpG WaWW NNC
NT 0050911   DLC MH NjP NN PHC PSC PBm PU OC1 OO OU

Tatlock, John Strong Perry, 1876-1948.
   The development and chronology of
   Chaucer's works. By John S. P. Tatlock ...
   [London] Pub. for the Chaucer Society, by K.
   Paul, Trench, Trübner & co., limited, 1907.
   xiii, 233 [1] p. 23 cm. (Chaucer Society,
   London. Publications. [Microcard ed.] Ser.
   2, no. 37)

   Micro-opaque.

   1. Chaucer, Geoffrey, d. 1400 - Chronology
of works.

NT 0050912   NN

Tatlock, John Strong Perry, 1876-1948.
   The duration of Chaucer's visits to Italy.
   [No imprint]
     4 p.   22.5 cm.
     Caption title.
     Reprinted from the Journal of English & German
philology, v. 12, 1913.

NT 0050913   MiU NcD

Tatlock, John Strong Perry, 1876-1948.   ***2950.56.21**
The duration of the Canterbury pilgrimage.
(In Modern Language Association of America. Publications.
Vol. 21, pp. 478-485. Baltimore. 1906.)

G5706 — Chaucer, Geoffrey. — T.r.

NT   0050914   MB

TATLOCK, John Strong Perry, 1876-1948.
Essays at the chronology of Chaucer's poems.
Portions, revised and expanded, pub.as "The
development and chronology of Chaucer's works"
[London], Kegan Paul, 1907, pp.xiii, 233 (Chaucer
Soc.Publ., ser.2, 37). Smaller parts, revised and
expanded, pub.as "The dates of Chaucer's Troil-
us and Criseyde and Legend of Good Women,"in
Mod.Philol., 1903-04, 1:317-329;"Chaucer and
Dante," ibid., 1905-06, 3:367-372;"The
duration of the Canterbury pilgrimage,"in
Publ.Mod.Lang.Assoc.Amer., 1906, 21:478-485;

and "The Harleian manuscript 7334, and revision
of the Canterbury tales," [London], Kegan Paul,
etc., 1909, pp.viii, 33 (Chaucer Soc.Publ., ser.2,
41.)

Official copy of the thesis presented for a
doctor's degree at Harvard University.

NT   0050916   MH

Tatlock, John Strong Perry, 1876-1948.
The Harleian manuscript 7334 and revision of the Canterbury tales, by John S. P. Tatlock ... London, Pub. for the
Chaucer society by K. Paul, Trench, Trübner & co., ltd. ...
and by H. Frowde, Oxford university press, and in New
York, 1909, for the issue of 1904.
5 p. l., 33 p. 22½ cm. (*On cover:* Chaucer society ₁Publications.
2d series, 41₁)

1. Chaucer, Geoffrey. Canterbury tales. Harleian ms.

PR1901.A3 no. 41   10—2841

OU ViU PHC PBm PSC NIC OrU PP PU
NT   0050917   DLC CaBVaU WaSpG MB MiU NN OC1 OCU OC1W

Tatlock, John Strong Perry, 1876-1948.
The Harleian manuscript 7334 and revision
of the Canterbury tales, by John S. P.
Tatlock ... London, Pub. for the Chaucer
society by K. Paul, Trench, Trübner & co.,
ltd. ... and by H. Frowde, Oxford
university press, and in New York, 1909, for
the issue of 1904. 5 p. l., 33 p. 23 cm.
(Chaucer Society, London. Publications.
[Microcard ed.] Ser. 2, no. 41)

Micro-opaque.

1. Chaucer, Geoffrey, d. 1400. Canterbury
tales. Harleian ms. (TITLE)

NT   0050919   NN

Tatlock, John Strong Perry, 1876-
Idz   Has Chaucer's Wretched engendering been
+y2   found? J.S.P.Tatlock. Did Chaucer write An
holy medytacion? Germaine Dempster. An
affirmative reply. Carleton Brown. [New York?
1936]

Cover-title.
"Reprinted from Modern language notes, LI,
5, May, 1936."

NT   0050920   CtY

Tatlock, John Strong Perry, 1876-1948.
The intellectual interests of undergraduates.
Berkeley, 1921.
(Calif. University. Berkeley. Chronicle,
v. 23, no. 4. p. 364-391)

NT   0050921   PP

Tatlock, John Strong Perry, 1876-1948.
The legendary history of Britain: Geoffrey of Monmouth's
Historia Regum Britanniae and its early vernacular versions.
Berkeley, University of California Press, 1950.
xi, 545 p. 25 cm.
Bibliographical footnotes.

1. Geoffrey of Monmouth, Bp. of St. Asaph, 1100?-1154. Historia
Britonum.   I. Title.

DA140.G3T3 1950   942.01   50—7428

Wa MtU WaWW ViU PPT OU
MiU NcU TxU TU CaBVa IdU OrU WaS OrPR CaBVaU OrPS
NT   0050922   DLC NcGU OC1 OC1JC OCU OOxM MeB CU PSt

Tatlock, John Strong Perry, 1876-1948.
The mind and art of Chaucer. ₁Syracuse. N. Y., Syracuse
University Press ₁1950₁
ix, 114 p. 23 cm.
Bibliography: p. 108-114.

1. Chaucer, Geoffrey, d. 1400.   I. Title.

PR1905.T3   821.17   50—8074

CaBVa WaS WaWW
MtBC MtU OrCS OrMonO OrPR OrU WaSpG WaTU Or OrStbM
PBL PPD NcD MB MiU CaBVaU IdPI IdU OC1ND CoU CLSU
NT   0050923   DLC NcGU KEmT ICU MB NcU TxU TU OC1W OCU

TATLOCK, John S[trong] P[erry], 1876-
The modern reader's King Horn. n.p., [1928]
1.8°. pp.45.
"Reprint from the Univ.of California
Chronicle, Jan., 1928."

NT   0050924   MH

Tatlock, John Strong Perry, 1876-   ⁻²950.56.48
Muriel: the earliest English poetess.
(*In* Modern Language Association of America. Publications.
Vol. 48, pp. 317-321. Menasha, Wis. 1933.)

D8034 — Muriel, poetess.

NT   0050925   MB

Tatlock, John Strong, Perry, 1876-
Notes on Chaucer: The Canterbury tales.
₁The Plimpton fragment of the Canterbury
tales₁ By John S. P. Tatlock ... Baltimore,
The Johns Hopkins press ₁1914₁
cover-title, ₁4₁ p. 27ᶜᵐ.

Reprinted from Modern language notes, May,
1914.

1. Chaucer, Geoffrey, d. 1400. The Canterbury
tales. I. Plimpton library.

NT   0050926   NNC

Tatlock, John Strong Perry, 1876-   ed.
Representative English plays, from the middle ages to the
end of the nineteenth century, ed. with introduction and notes
by John S. P. Tatlock ... and Robert G. Martin ... New
York, The Century co., 1916.
6 p. l., 3–838 p. 23ᶜᵐ.
CONTENTS.—The middle ages: 1. The miracle play: Noah's flood.
Abraham and Isaac. The second shepherds' play. 2. The morality:
Everyman.—The Elizabethan period: Mother Bombie, by Lyly. The
troublesome reign and lamentable death of Edward the Second, by C.
Marlowe. The shoemakers' holiday; or, The gentle craft, by T. Dekker.
A woman killed with kindness, by T. Heywood. Philaster; or, Love lies
a-bleeding, by F. Beaumont and J. Fletcher. The alchemist, by B. Jon-
son. The Duchess of Malfi, by J. Webster. The wild-goose chase, by

Continued in next column

Continued from preceding column

J. Fletcher. The changeling, by T. Middleton and W. Rowley.—The
restoration: Almanzor and Almahide; or, The conquest of Granada, by
J. Dryden. Venice preserved; or, A plot discovered, by T. Otway. The
way of the world, by W. Congreve.—The eighteenth century: Cato, by
J. Addison. The conscious lovers, by Sir R. Steele. The tragedy of
tragedies; or, The life and death of Tom Thumb the Great, by H. Fielding. She stoops to conquer; or, The mistakes of a night, by O. Goldsmith. The school for scandal, by R. B. Sheridan.—The nineteenth
century: The Cenci, by P. B. Shelley. The lady of Lyons; or, Love and
pride, by E. Bulwer-Lytton. A blot in the 'scutcheon, by R. Browning.
Lady Windermere's fan, by O. Wilde.—Bibliography (p. 835-838.)

1. English drama (Collections)   I. Martin, Robert Grant, 1882-1931,
joint ed.   II. Title.

Library of Congress   PR1245.T3   16—15902

OrStbM PSC
Nc WaTU MtU MB OrP WaWW OrU WaT OrCS OrPS PPAmP IdU
MH MiU OCX OEac OOxM OC1W ViU OC1 PU NjP MtBC PP NN
NT   0050927   DLC OLak OrPR OrSaW CoU PRosC PPD PV NcD

Tatlock, John S[trong] P[erry], 1876-1948.   822-T
Representative English plays from the middle ages to the end
of the nineteenth century; edited with introductions and notes by
John S. P. Tatlock and Robert G. Martin. New York: The
Century Co., 1924.   838 p.   8°.

The middle ages: The miracle play, Noah's flood; Abraham and Isaac; The second shepherds' play. The morality, Everyman. The Elizabethan period: Mother

Bombie, John Lyly; The troublesome reign and lamentable death of Edward the Second,
Christopher Marlowe; The shoemakers' holiday, Thomas Dekker; A woman killed
with kindness, Thomas Heywood; Philaster, Francis Beaumont and John Fletcher;
The alchemist, Ben Jonson; The duchess of Malfi, John Webster; The wildgoose chase,
John Fletcher; The changeling, Thomas Middleton and William Rowley. The restora-
tion: Almanzor and Almahide, John Dryden; Venice preserved, Thomas Otway; The

of Malfi, John Webster; The wild-goose chase, John Fletcher; The changeling,
Thomas Middleton and William Rowley.
The restoration: Almanzor and Almahide, John Dryden; Venice preserved,
Thomas Otway; The way of the world, William Congreve.
The eighteenth century: Cato, Joseph Addison; The conscious lovers, Sir
Richard Steele; The tragedy of tragedies, Henry Fielding; She stoops to conquer,
Oliver Goldsmith; The school for scandal, Richard Brinsley Sheridan.
The nineteenth century: The Cenci, Percy Bysshe Shelley; The lady of Lyons,
Edward Bulwer-Lytton; A blot in the 'scutcheon, Robert Browning; Lady Winder-
mere's fan, Oscar Wilde.

1. Twenty-three au. anal.   2. Twenty-   five title anal.   3. Martin, Robert
Grant, jt. au.   September 20, 1916.
N. Y. P. L.

NT   0050931   NN

Tatlock, John Strong Perry, 1876-1948, *ed.*
Representative English plays, from the miracle plays to
Pinero; edited with introductions and notes by J. S. P. Tatlock and the late R. G. Martin. 2d ed., rev. and enl. New
York, London, D. Appleton-Century company, incorporated
₁ᶜ1938₁
x, 914 p.   24½ cm.

CONTENTS.—The middle ages: Miracle plays: Noah's flood. Abraham and Isaac. The second shepherd's play. The morality: Everyman.—The Elizabethan period: Mother Bombie, by J. Lyly. The
troublesome reign and lamentable death of Edward the Second, by

C. Marlowe. The shoemaker's holiday; or, The gentle craft, by T.
Dekker. A woman killed with kindness, by T. Heywood. Philaster;
or, Love lies a-bleeding, by F. Beaumont and J. Fletcher. The
alchemist, by B. Jonson. The Duchess of Malfi, by J. Webster. The
wild-goose chase, by J. Fletcher. The changeling, by T. Middleton
and W. Rowley.—The restoration: Almanzor and Almahide; or, The
conquest of Granada, by J. Dryden. Venice preserved; or, A plot
discovered, by T. Atway. The way of the world, by W. Congreve.—
The eighteenth century: Cato, by J. Addison. The conscious lovers,
by Sir R. Steele. The tragedy of tragedies; or, The life and death of

Tom Thumb the Great, by S. Fielding. The London merchant; or,
the history of George Barnwell by G. Lillo. She stoops to conquer;
or, The mistakes of a night, by O. Goldsmith. The school for scandal,
by R. B. Sheridan.—The nineteenth century: The Cenci, by P. B.
Shelley. The lady of Lyons; or, Love and pride, by E. Bulwer-Lytton.
Caste, by T. W. Robertson. Lady Windermere's fan, by O. Wilde.
The second Mrs. Tanqueray, by A. W. Pinero.—Bibliography (p.
911-914)

1. English drama (Collections)   I. Martin, Robert Grant, 1882-
1931, joint ed.   II. Title.

PR1245.T3 1938   822.0822   38—3805

MtBuM IdB IdPI IdU OrPR WaE WaPS WaSp WaSpG WaT
OCX OOxM OU KEmT PPLas MB PSC UU Or OrStbM OrU-M Wa
NT   0050934   DLC WaTU WaWW PP TU MiU CoU NN OC1 OCU

Tatlock, John Strong Perry, 1876-   ***4551.134.4**
St. Amphibalus.
(*In* University of California. Publications. English. Vol. 4. Essays in criticism. Ser. 2, pp. 247-257, 268-270. Berkeley, Cal.
1934.)

D6516 — Amphibalus, Saint.

NT   0050935   MB

Tatlock, John Strong Perry, 1876–
The scene of the Franklin's tale visited, by John S. P. Tatlock ... London, Pub. for the Chaucer society by K. Paul, Trench, Trübner & co. ltd., and H. Milford, Oxford university press ₁London₁ and New York, 1914, for the issue of 1911.

4 p. l., 77, ₁1₁ p. 23ᶜᵐ. (*On cover:* Chaucer society. ₁Publications₁ Second series, 51)

1. Chaucer, Geoffrey. Canterbury tales. Franklin's tale. ɪ. Title.
15—20625

Library of Congress   PR1901.A3 2d ser. no.51

    NjP ViU OrU CaBVaU WaSpG ICN MB
NT   0050936   DLC PHC PBm PP NIC PU OCl OU OClW MiU

Tatlock, John Strong Perry, 1876–1948.
The Siege of Troy in Elizabethan literature, especially in Shakespeare and Heywood. By John S. P. Tatlock. n.p., Modern Language Assoc. of America, 1915.
c. p.   O.   (In, Collected monographs. V. 297)

NT   0050937   NcD

1876-1948.
Tatlock, John Strong Perry,₁₁ ed.

₁Shakespeare, William₁ 1564–1616.
... Troilus and Cressida, ed. by John S. P. Tatlock ... New York, The Macmillan company, 1912.

Tatlock, John Strong Perry, 1876– *1948.*
... Why America fights Germany (Cantonment ed.) By John S. P. Tatlock, professor at Stanford university. Issued by the Committee on public information, Washington, D. C. ₁Washington, 1918₁

16 p. 22ᶜᵐ. (U. S. Committee on public information. War information series, no. 15. March, 1918)
List of publications of the Committee on public information: p. 14–16.

1. European war, 1914–1918—U. S. ɪ. Title.
18—26382

Library of Congress   D570.A2A35 no. 15
—— —— Copy 2.   D619.T4

    OClWHi OClW OCU
NT   0050939   DLC NRCR PPDrop PU PPFr Or MiU MB DAL OO

Tatlock, Orrett, 1884–   joint author.

Irwin, Frederick Charles, 1870–
Beginning chemistry and its uses ₁by₁ Frederick C. Irwin ... Byron J. Rivett ... Orrett Tatlock ... drawings by Dorothy Handsaker. Evanston, Ill., New York city ₁etc.₁ Row, Peterson and company ₁°1927₁

Tatlock, Orrett, 1884–   joint author.

Irwin, Frederick Charles, 1870–
Elementary and applied chemistry, with a laboratory manual, by Frederick C. Irwin ... Byron J. Rivett ... and Orrett Tatlock ... Chicago, New York, Row, Peterson and company ₁1915₁

Tatlock, Richard.
A Bible word-book; a dictionary, with examples of obsolete, unusual and ambiguous words commonly used in the authorized version. With a foreword by the Bishop of Croydon. London, Mowbray ₁1955₁

183 p. 13 cm.

1. Bible. English—Versions—Authorized. 2. Bible. English—Glossaries, vocabularies, etc. 3. English language—Words—Hist. ɪ. Title.
BS186.T3   56–26192 ‡

NT   0050942   DLC MiU CU

Tatlock, Richard, ed.
Pilgrim's progress at "Five to ten"; adapted for the daily broadcasts
   see   Bunyan, John, 1628–1688.
   Pilgrim's progress. Selections, abridgments ₁etc.₁ 1954.

Tatlock, Robert Rattray, 1889–   ed.
Chinese art ... London, B. T. Batsford Ltd., 1925.
62 p.

NT   0050944   PPPM–I

Tatlock, Robert Rattray, *1889-1954*
... In the heart of Russia, by Robert R. Tatlock ... London, Friends' war victims relief fund ₁1918₁

8 p. 24½ᶜᵐ.
At head of title: War victims' relief fund of the Society of Friends. "Reprinted from the Contemporary review, March, 1918."

1. European war, 1914– ——Russia. ɪ. Friends, Society of. War victims' relief committee. ɪɪ. Title.
18–17543

Library of Congress   D514.T3

NT   0050945   DLC

Tatlock, Robert Rattray, 1889–
English painting of the XVIIIth-XXth centuries, with some examples of the Spanish, French & Dutch schools, and of original drawings, together with a collection of historic & modern sculpture ... by R.R. Tatlock ... With an introduction by Roger Fry ... London, B.T. Batsford ₁1928₁

4 p. l., v-xiv, 187, ₁1₁ p. front. (port.) 113 plates. 33 1/2cm. (Port Sunlight, Eng. Lady Lever art gallery. A record of the collections ... v.1)

NT   0050946   OO

Tatlock, Robert Rattray, 1889–

Port Sunlight, Eng. Lady Lever art gallery.
A record of the collections in the Lady Lever art gallery, Port Sunlight, Cheshire, formed by the first Viscount Leverhulme, with introductory essays and descriptive text, by R. R. Tatlock, Roger Fry, R. L. Hobson and Percy Macquoid, and a foreword by C. Reginald Grundy ... London, B. T. Batsford, ltd., 1928

Tatlock, Robert Rattray, *1889-1954*
Russia and Russia's need. An account of what the Friends' war victims' relief fund has done to relieve distress in Russia, since July, 1916. Speeches by Prof. Gilbert Murray, Dr. J. Tylor Fox and Robert R. Tatlock. Delivered at the Central hall, Westminster, on March 6th, 1918. London, War victims' relief fund of the Society of Friends ₁1918₁

Tatlock, Robert Rattray, 1889–   ed.

Blum, André, 1881–
A short history of art from prehistoric times to the present day for the use of students and general readers, translated from the French of André S. Blum ... edited and enlarged by R. R. Tatlock ... London. R. T. Batsford, ltd ,1926₁

Tatlock, Robert Rattray, 1889–   *ed.*
... Spanish art, an introductory review of architecture, painting, sculpture, textiles, ceramics, woodwork, metalwork, by R. R. Tatlock, Royall Tyler ₁and others₁ ₁London, B. T. Batsford, ltd., 1927.

3 p. l., 121, ₁5₁ p. col. front., illus. (incl. map) plates (part col.) 31 x 24ᶜᵐ. (Burlington magazine monograph. ɪɪ)
CONTENTS.—Introduction. By R. R. Tatlock.—Architecture. By R. Tyler.—Painting: Spanish painting and the Spanish temper. By Sir C. Holmes. A chronology of Spanish painting. By H. I. Kay.—Sculpture. By G. Webb.—Textiles. By A. F. Kendrick.—Ceramics and glass: Hispano-Moresque pottery. By A. Van de Put. Renaissance and modern pottery. By B. Rackham. Glass. By B. Rackham.—Woodwork. By B. Bevan.—Metalwork. By P. M. de Artiñano.—Bibliography (p. 115–121)
1. Art. Spanish.   ɪ. Tyler, Royall, 1884–   27–23974

Library of Congress   N7101.T3
             ₁3₁

    NCorniC
    FU DDO CLU KEmT Or OrMonO CU-S CaBVaU NIC NcU CLSU
    NN MH ODW MdBWA OCl OU OO OClMA OClC OCU NBB ViU MB
NT   0050950   DLC PHC MtU WaS PPD OrPR PP OrU WaTU NjP

Tatlock, Rev. William, D.D.
Address. Delivered in St. John's Episcopal Church, Stamford, Conn., Monday, Sept. 26th, 1881. ₁Stamford, Conn. ? 1881₁
3 p.   8°.
In: AN Garfield p. v. 15. no. 12.

NT   0050952   NN

Tatlock, William, D.D.
Address, in memory of the Rev. Ebenezer Dibblee, D. D., May 29, 1881. Stamford, 1881
14p. 8°

NT   0050953   MWA PHi

Tatlock, William, D.D.
In memoriam. The Reverend William Tatlock
   see under title

₁**Tatlock, William, D.D.**₁
Our parish buildings. Address, delivered in St. John's Church, Stamford, on Sunday, March 21st, 1869, by the rector, together with the statement of the building committee, and other documents... Stamford: W. W. Gillespie & Co., 1869. 28 p. 8°.

Photograph of church inserted.

1. Stamford, Conn.—Churches.
N. Y. P. L.   April 10, 1912.

NT   0050955   NN

Tatlock, William, D.D.
The revelation of God in Christ, and other sermons, preached at St. John's Church, Stamford, Connecticut, by the late Reverend W. Tatlock. New York: J. Pott & Co., 1897. 3 p.l., 3-310 p. 12°.

1. Sermons (American).
N. Y. P. L.   July 14, 1911.

NT   0050956   NN MCE NNUT CtW

Tatlock, William, D.D.
Some reminiscences of W. T. Wilson. New York, T. Whittaker, ₁189- ?₁
15 p.   8°.
n. t.-p.
Title from cover.

NT   0050957   NN MWA

Tatlock, Rev. William S. J.
Manuale stenographiae Latinae; secundum systema Pitman, ad usum eorum praesertim qui studiis dant operam auctore Gulielmo Tatlock, S. I. Romae: prostat venale in Universitate Gregoriana ₁190–?₁. 54 p., 1 l. 16°.

1. Shorthand.—Systems (Latin), 190–. 2. Pitman, Sir Isaac.
N. Y. P. L. June 3, 1914.

NT 0050958 NN NNC ICN

Tatlock, William Stacy
An investigation of organosilanolates.

Thesis - Harvard, 1951.

NT 0050959 MH-C

Tatlock memorial lecture.
₁no.₁ 2

London, 1938 21½cm.
no. port.

Delivered at the Institute of chemistry of Great Britain and Ireland.

1. No subject. I. Institute of chemistry of Great Britain and
Ireland.
N. Y. P. L. September 27, 1938

NT 0050960 NN

Tatlow, A H ed.
Natal province. Descriptive guide and official handbook edited by A. H. Tatlow, manager—Publicity dept., South African railways. Published by authority. Durban, Natal, South African railways printing works, 1911.
xii. 574 p. incl. front., illus., plates, tables, diagrs. maps (part fold., 1 in pocket) plans (part fold.) 27ᶜᵐ.

1. Natal—Descr. & trav.—Guide-books. 2. Railroads—Natal. I. South
African railways. Publicity dept.
Library of Congress DT868.T3 23—5718

CaOTP KyLoU CU NcD ICJ NN WaT WaSp
NT 0050961 DLC PU-Mu OrU PP OrP WaS WU OCl CtY DNAL

TATLOW, A. H.
Trout fishing in Natal. Compiled under the authority of the acting general manager of railways by A.H. Tatlow. Publicity section general manager's dept. [n.p.],1909.

28 p.,illus.,map.fold.28 cm.

NT 0050962 MH

Tatlow, F. M., ed.
The St. Louis miller.

St. Louis, Midland publishing co.. 18

Tatlow, F. M., ed.
The Southwestern miller.

St. Louis, Midland publishing co. ₁etc.₁ 18

Tatlow, Herbert Johnson, 1862–
Institute of railway accounting; text-book of inter-line freight accounts, by Herbert J. Tatlow ... Chicago, Ill., ʿ1913.
86 p. 20ᶜᵐ.

1. Railroads — Accounts, bookkeeping, etc. 2. Railroads — Freight.
I. Title.
Library of Congress HE2241.T3. 15–14704

NT 0050965 DLC ICJ

Tatlow, Joseph, 1851–
Fifty years of railway life in England, Scotland and Ireland, by Joseph Tatlow ... London, The Railway gazette, 1920.
vi p., 1 l., 223, ₁1₁ p. front., plates, ports. 21½ x 16½ᶜᵐ.

1. Railroads—Gt. Brit.—Hist. I. Title.
Library of Congress HE3018.T3. 21–4160

NT 0050966 DLC PPiU NBC NcD WaU ICJ NN

313.5 Tatlow, Richard H
T2190 Orpah. A religious and historical novel with the principal scenes in Missouri, immediately preceeding, during and following the great Civil War, by Richard H. Tatlow and John D. Crisp. Chicago, Scroll publishing company [1902]
573 p. 21cm.

NT 0050967 NcD CoU IEdS ViU

NA9050 Tatlow, Richard Henry, 1906—
.T37
1952 Parkington: shopping center design.
₁n. p.₁ ʿ1952.
440–456 p. plans. 26cm.

"Reprinted ... from the October 1952 issue of Traffic quarterly."

1. Shopping centers. 2. Arlington, Va.
Parkington Shopping Center. I. Title.

NT 0050968 ViU OOxM

Tatlow, Tissington, 1876-1957.
Martyn Trafford. A sketch of his life and his work for the Student Christian Movement. By Tissington Tatlow. London: Student Christian Movement, 1910. 109 p. front. (port.), plates. 8°.

1. Trafford, Martyn, 1883–1910. 2. Student Christian movement of
Great Britain and Ireland. Theologi- cal College department.
N. Y. P. L. August 29, 1922.

NT 0050969 NN CtY-D

Tatlow, Tissington, 1876-1957.
Outline studies on India for use in missionary bands... 2. ed. London, Student volunteer missionary union, 1901
35 p., 19ᶜᵐ.

"References" at end of each section.

NT 0050970 NjPT CtY

MT70 Tatlow, Tissington, 1876-1957.
T1880 Outline studies on India, for use in missionary bands. 3d and rev. ed. London, Student Volunteer Missionary Union ₁1905₁
35, ₁1₁ p. 19 cm.

"An attempt to meet the need of college missionary bands."
Includes bibliographical references.

1. India - Missions. 2. Missions - Study and teaching. I. Title.

NT 0050971 CtY-D CtY

Tatlow, Tissington, 1876– 1957.
The story of the Student Christian movement of Great Britain and Ireland, by Tissington Tatlow ... London, Student Christian movement press ₁1933₁
xv, 944 p. front., plates, ports. 22½ᵐᵐ.
"First published October 1933."
Appendices: Men and women who have served as secretaries. Universities and colleges in which the S. C. M. has been organised: p. ₁889₁–919.
"These appendices are, in the main, the work of Miss Violet Latford, to whom I am also indebted for the index and much help in the preparation of the whole volume.—T. T."—p. 891.
1. Student Christian movement of Great Britain and Ireland.
I. Latford, Violet. II. Title.
Library of Congress BV970.86T7 34—7777
₁3₁ 267.1

NT 0050972 DLC NcD CtY OkEG CBPac CSt IEG

Tatlow, William Frederick Tissington.
A synopsis of neurology, by W. F. Tissington Tatlow, J. Amor Ardis, and J. A. R. Bickford. Baltimore, Williams and Wilkins, 1952.
513 p. illus. 19 cm.

1. Nervous system—Diseases. I. Title.
RC356.T3 616.8 52–1937 ‡

CtY CtY-D
NT 0050973 DLC ICJ CaBVaU DGW DNLM PU-Med-TS TxU OU

Tatman, Bernal L.
Jerusalem and the Jews, by Bernal L. Tatman; with an introduction by Rev. J. E. Godbey... St. Louis, Mo.: The National Masonic Research Soc., cop. 1926. 91 p. plan. 12°.

375781A. 1. Jerusalem—Hist.
N. Y. P. L. October 11, 1928

NT 0050974 NN IEdS NcD

Tatman, Beulah Bernice.
Auditorium values in character building ₁by₁ Beulah B. Tatman.
(*In* National education association of the United States. **Addresses and proceedings, 1932.** p. 325–327)

1. Moral education. ₁1. Character—Teaching₁ 2. ₁Auditoriums₁
I. Title. E 33–859
Library, U. S. Office of Education L13.N212 1932
Library of Congress L13.N4 1932

NT 0050975 DHEW

TATMAN, Charles Taylor, 1871–
The beginning of United States coinage.
Worcester. [1895.] 16 pp. [Amer. numismatic ser. 3.]

NT 0050976 MB

Tatman, Charles Taylor, 1871 –
Coin-collecting; an introduction to the study of numismatics. Worcester, Mass., ʻ1893.
10 p. illus. 18 cm. (American numismatic series, no. 1)
Cover title.

1. Numismatics—Collectors and collecting.   ɪ. Title.   (Series)

CJ85.T3   52–52584

NT 0050977   DLC MB

Tatman, Charles Taylor, 1871–
The Virginia coinage: proof that it was by legislative and royal authority. By Charles T. Tatman ... Worcester, Mass, c1894.
12 p. 1 illus. 19 cm. (On cover: American numismatic series, no. 2)

Title vignette.
"The substance of this paper is as published two years ago in the monthly magazine Plain talk, of New York city." p. ₍3₎
Bibliographical   foot-notes.
1. Numismatics   Virginia.   I. Title.
CJ1841.T2   12–41

NT 0050978   Vi MB MH

Tatnall, Edward, d. 1898.
Catalogue of the phænogamous and filicoid plants of Newcastle county, Delaware. Arranged according to the natural system, as recently revised by Prof. A. Gray and others. With the synonyms of modern authors. By Edward Tatnall. Published by the Wilmington institute. Wilmington, Del., sold by J. T. Heald. ₍Philadelphia, Collins, printer₎ 1860.
112 p. incl. tab. 23½ cm.
1. Botany — Delaware — Newcastle co.   ɪ. Wilmington institute, Wilmington, Del.

Library of Congress   QK152.T2   3–2905
——— Copy 2.
——— Copy 3. ₍Mis-   cellaneous pamphlets, v. 317, no. 7₎
                           AC901.M5 vol. 317
— Copy 4. ₍Bo-   tanical pamphlets, v. 14, no. 6₎
                           QK3.B77 vol. 14
                           ₍a33b1₎

       DeU MB NjP NcU MH–A TxU NNBG NN
NT 0050979   DLC PPWa PU PHi PHC PU ICJ CLSU MiU OU

E173
Am33
Reel
474

Tatnall, Edward, d. 1898.
Catalogue of the phænogamous and filicoid plants of Newcastle county, Delaware. Arranged according to the natural system, as recently revised by Prof. A. Gray and others. With the synonyms of modern authors. By Edward Tatnall. Published by the Wilmington institute. Wilmington, Del., sold by J. T. Heald. ₍Philadelphia, Collins, printer₎ 1860.
(American culture series, 474:6)
Microfilm copy made by University Microfilms, Ann Arbor, Mich.
Collation of original: 112 p.
1. Botany–Delaware–Newcastle co. I. Wilmington institute, Wilmington, Del.

NT 0050980   IaAS

Egleston
D669.11
Un291
no.4   **Tatnall,** Francis Gibbons.
Testing pressure vessels. New York, 1950.
p. 1-5. 29cm. (in Welding research council bulletin series, no. 4)

1. Pressure vessels.
   (Series)

NT 0050981   NNC

Tatnall, Robert
An Antidote Against the Sinfull Palpitation of the Heart, Or Fear of Death ...sadly occasioned by That Dreadfull Plague ... Made Up of That Singular and Soveraign Scripture, Hebrews 2. 15 ... London,Printed by J.Hayes, and are to be sold by S.Gellibrand ... and S.Thomson ... 1665.
3p. .,86p. 18½cm.

1.Christianity. 2. Faith.

NT 0050982   CtY-M MnU

Tatnall, Robert Richardson, 1870–
The arc-spectra of the elements; boron, beryllium, germanium, platinum, osmium, rhodium, ruthenium and palladium ... ₍Chicago, 1896₎
cover-title, 13, 286–291 p. tables. 24½ᶜᵐ.

Thesis (ᴘʜ. ᴅ.)—Johns Hopkins university.
Caption title: The arc-spectra of the elements ... By Henry A. Rowland and Robert R. Tatnall.
Published in Astrophysical journal, v. ɪ–ɪɪɪ, 1895–96.

1. Spectrum analysis.   ɪ. Rowland, Henry Augustus, 1848–1901.

Library of Congress   QC454.T22   5–31294†

NT 0050983   DLC NIC MdBP NjP MB

Tatnall, Robert Richardson, 1870–
Flora of Delaware and the Eastern Shore; an annotated list of the ferns and flowering plants of the peninsula of Delaware, Maryland and Virginia. ₍Wilmington₎ Society of Natural History of Delaware, 1946.
xxvi, 313 p. plates, map. 24 cm.
"Bibliography of botany of the peninsula": p. 289–290.

1. Botany—Delaware. 2. Botany—Maryland. 3. Botany—Virginia. ɪ. Title.

QK152.T23   581.9751   47–5894*

        DNAL
NT 0050984   DLC NcD PWcS PPAN PPFr PU–BZ TU NcU KEmT

Tatnall, Robert Richardson, 1870–

Rhoads, Joseph Edgar.
... How a leather belt transmits power, by Mr. J. Edgar Rhoads ... and Dr. R. R. Tatnall. A paper read at the educational session of the Leather belting exchange, November 16th and 17th, 1922. Philadelphia, Leather belting exchange ₍1923?₎

Tatnall, Robert Richardson, 1870–   joint author.
Crew, Henry, 1859–
A laboratory manual of physics for use in high schools, by Henry Crew ... and Robert R. Tatnall ... New York, The Macmillan co.; London, Macmillan & co., ltd., 1902.

Tatnall, Robert Richardson, 1870–   joint author.
Jones, Franklin Turner.
Laboratory problems in physics, to accompany Crew and Jones's "Elements of physics," by Franklin T. Jones ... and Robert R. Tatnall ... New York, The Macmillan company, 1912.

Tatnarkomtruda
see **Tatar A. S. S. R.** *Narodnyi komissariat truda.*

ND195
.M67

Tato, 1896–
Mostra d'arte internazionale la pittura in piccolo formato: catalogo. Ottobre 1953. ₍Roma, Pinci, 1953₎

Tato, 1896–
Tato raccontato da Tato (20 anni di futurismo) Con scritti poetici di: F. T. Marinetti ₍et al.₎ Milano, O. Zucchi ₍1941₎
240 p., ₍104₎ p. of illus. 24 cm.

1. Futurism (Art)—Italy. 2. Painters, Italian—Correspondence, reminiscences, etc. ɪ. Title. ɪɪ. Title: Venti anni di futurismo.

ND623.T32A56   72–227361

NT 0050990   DLC NN CU MH

HD8480
.M36

Tatò, Antonio, joint ed.

Mastrangeli, Augusto, ed.
Giuseppe di Vittorio per l'unità dei lavoratori e la rinascita dell'Italia. ₍A cura di Augusto Mastrangeli e di Antonio Tatò₎ Roma, Editrice Lavoro, 1952.

Tato, José.
El esfuerzo británico, por José Tato ...   Alicante: Imprenta Diario ₍1917?₎. 48 p. 8°.

1. European war, 1914– , Gt. Br.   2. Title.
N. Y. P. L.   January 24, 1919.

NT 0050992   NN

Tato, José F
... Temas (poesía) Avellaneda ₍Repúb. argent.₎ Editorial "Nueva vida," 1942.
63, ₍1₎ p. 18ᶜᵐ.

ɪ. Title.
                                              43–19283
Library of Congress   PQ7797.T33T4
                              ₍2₎   861.6

NT 0050993   DLC

Tato, Juan Bautista. Carta de agregación á la Congregacion del sagrado corazon ₍de Jesus, erigida apostólicamente desde el año de 1819 en la iglesia de S. Pedro y S. Pablo de México, é incorporada con las innumerables que hay establecidas y agregadas á la general de Roma, conocida con el nombre de La pia union. ₍n.p.,n.d.₎ 8p. 16mo. (Papeles varios. 137;7½)

NT 0050994   CU–BANC

Tato, Juan Manuel.
Antecedentes, títulos y trabajos, concurso para proveer la Cátedra de Oto-rino-laringología de la Facultad de Ciencias Médicas. Buenos Aires, Impr. A. Frascoli ₍1946?₎
78 p. 24 cm.

R483.T35A45   49–21385*

NT 0050995   DLC

WV
240
T219c
1944

TATO, Juan Manuel
La cirugía funcional conservadora de la petritis; técnica para el abordaje de los focos ánteroinferiores y del ápex. Buenos Aires, 1944.
56 p. illus.
1. Ear - Surgery 2. Temporal bone - Diseases

NT 0050996   DNLM

W 4
B92
no. 4665

TATO, Juan Manuel
La exploración radiográfica del hueso temporal. Buenos Aires, 1933.
187 p. illus. (Buenos Aires.
Universidad Nacional. Facultad de Ciencias Médicas. Tesis de doctorado, no. 4665)
1. Temporal bone - Radiography

NT 0050997   DNLM

Tato, Julio Fernando Guillén y
    see   Guillén y Tato, Julio Fernando, 1897–

Tato, Mario.
Tabla de cálculos de beneficios y descuentos por lectura directa, sin operaciones. 1. ed. Buenos Aires, Editorial Librería La Nena [1952]
18, [78] p. 16 x 23 cm.

1. Prices—Tables, etc. I. Title.

HF5702.T3   55–18937 ‡

NT 0050999   DLC

Tato, Santiago Gomez
see
Gomez Tato, Santiago

Tato Amat, Emigdio
Más que el oro, apunte de comedía en un acto, en prosa, original. Premio en el concurso del Ateneo Juvenil. Madrid, Establecimiento Tipográfico, 1909.
30 p.

In: Teatro español, v.24, no.16.
Teatro Lara, 18 de marzo, 1909.
List of author's works follows text.
Inscribed by the author.

NT 0051001   NcD MH NN

TATO AMAT, EMIGDIO.
Más que el oro; apunte de comedia en un acto, en prosa, original. Madrid, Establecimiento Tipográfico, 1909. 30 p. 20cm.

Film reproduction. Negative.

1. Drama, Spanish. I. Title.

NT 0051002   NN

DP   Tato   Amat, Miguel
236   Sol y Ortega y la política contemporánea.
S6   Apuntes biográficos, su actuación en la
T3   política y en el foro, discursos, anécdotas.
          Prólogo de Rafael Ginard de la Rosa, epílogo
          de Roberto Castrovido. Un artículo de
          Félix Azzati. Madrid, Impr. Artística
          Española, 1914.
          631p. illus. 19cm.
          Bibliographical footnotes.
          1. Sol y Ortega, Juan, 1849-1911 2. Spain -
          Hist. - 1868-1931 I. Title

NT 0051003   WU

Tato Amat, Miguel.
Los sueños del kaiser; fantasías del momento, por Miguel y Emigdio Tato Amat. Madrid: Tip. La Itálica, 1915.   222 p. 12°.

1. European war, 1914- . 2. Wil-   liam II., German emperor, 1859-
3. Tato Amat, Emigdio, jt. au.   4. Title.
N. Y. P. L.   April 19, 1916.

NT 0051004   NN MH

Tato Cumming, Gaspar.
DS710   China, Japón y el conflicto chino-japonés.
T219   1. ed. San Sebastián, Editorial Española
          [1939]
          160 p. plates. 25cm.

1. China - Descr. 2. Japan - Descr. 3.
Chinese-Japanese War, 1937-1945. I. Title.

NT 0051005   CSt-H

HV7961   **Tato Cumming, Gaspar.**
T219   El mundo del espionaje.   Barcelona,
          Tartessos [194-?]
          204 p. 20cm.

1. Secret service. I. Title.

NT 0051006   CSt-H

Tato Cumming, Gaspar.
El mundo del espionaje.   Barcelona, Tartessos, 1943.

204 p. 20 cm.

NT 0051007   MH

Tato Cumming, Gaspar.
...Nueva York. Un español entre rascacielos. Prólogo de Federico García Sanchiz... 2. ed.   [Madrid] Editorial Febo [1945] 370 p. illus. 20cm.   (Grandes reportajes)

331077B. 1. New York (City)—   Descr., 1900-
N. Y. P. L.   October 28, 1949

NT 0051008   NN IU

910.4   **Tato Cumming, Gaspar.**
T18p   ... Panorama mundial; prólogo de Francisco de
          Cossio.   Madrid, Editorial Tesoro, 1945.
          318p.

1. Voyages around the world. I. Title.

NT 0051009   IU

915.2   **Tato Cumming, Gaspar.**
T18t   Tokio. Un español entre geishas.   [Madrid]
          Editorial Febo [1945]
          250p. plates. 20cm.

1. Tokyo--Descr.

NT 0051010   IU

Tato Jaya, Yato Dharma
see
Jaya, Yato Dharma Tato.

HX312   **Tato Lorenzo, José.**
T219   ... Maximalismo y anarquismo, por José Tato
          Lorenzo. México, D.F., Imp. mundial, 1923.
          27 p. 19cm. (Biblioteca mundial [3])

1. Socialism in Russia. 2. Anarchism.
I. Title.

NT 0051012   CSt-H

Tato y Amat, Miguel
see Tato Amat, Miguel.

PN56   **Tato, raccontato, datato (20 anni di futurismo)**
F8T3   Con scritti poetici di F.T.Marinetti [et.
          al.   Milano, Casa editrice Oberdan Zuc-
          chi [1941]
          240p. 66 plates. 24cm.

1. Futurism. I. Marinetti, Filippo
Tommaso, .1876-1944. II. Title.

NT 0051014   IaU IEN DLC-P4

Z244   **Tatochenko, K. I.,** joint author.
.6
.R9A58   **Antonov-Rogachev, V   K**
          (Rukovodstvo po uchetu i otchetnosti poligraficheskikh predpriia-
          tii)
          Руководство по учету и отчетности полиграфических
          предприятий / В. К. Антонов-Рогачев, В. Д. Пашков,
          К. И. Таточенко. — [Смоленск : Смоленская гос. тип.
          им. Смирнова, 1929.

Tatochenko, Lev Kirillovich.
Промышленная гамма-дефектоскопия. Москва, Гос. научно-техн. изд-во лит-ры по черной и цветной метал-лургии, 1955.
151 p. illus., plates. 23 cm.
At head of title: Л. К. Таточенко, С. В. Медведев.
Errata slip inserted.
Bibliography: p. [128]

1. Metals—Testing. 2. Gamma rays. I. Medvedev, Sergei Vale-rianovich, joint author. II. Title.
Title transliterated: Promyshlen-naia gamma-defektoskopiia.

TA460.T33   56–19470

NT 0051016   DLC

636.32   **Tatocico, V**
T18r   La race de moutons Karakul-Boukhara
          à l'Ecole inférieure d'agriculture de
          Cocorozeni (District Orhei)   Bucarest,
          1925.
          18p. illus., table.

NT 0051017   IU

Tatoes, P., *pseud.*
Zc10   Mr. Simeon Slimpkins' trip through the
870ta   Far West. By P. Tatoes. Price 10 cents...
          Jamaica Plain,Mass.,Mackintosh,Hagar & Co.,
          1870.
          14 l. of illus. 11 x 8cm.
          Original wrappers.

NT 0051018   CtY

M82.1/798.1   **Tatom, John.**
T219we   Weather notes for pilots. Summer fogs and
          winter winds of the Aleutian islands and how to
          fly despite them. [n.p.] [n.d.]
          17p. illus. 19cm.

NT 0051019   DAS

BF   **Tatom, Mary Helen,** 1911-
698   A factorial isolation of psychiatric out-
.T21a   patient personality patterns. Washington, CUA,
          1952.
          v, 140 l. illus. 28cm.
          Thesis - CUA.
          Issued also on microcards.
          Bibliography: l. 136-140.
          1. Personality, Disorders of. 2. Personality
          tests. I. Title: Psychiatric out-patient
          personality patterns.

NT 0051020   DCU MiU

Tatom, Mary Helen, 1911–
A factorial isolation of psychiatric out-patient personality patterns. Washington, Catholic University of America Press, 1952.

4 cards. 7¼ x 12½ cm.

Microprint copy of typescript.
Collation of the original: v, 140 l. diagrs., tables. 28 cm.
Thesis—Catholic University of America.
Bibliography: leaves 136–140.

1. Personality, Disorders of.   I. Title.   II. Title: Psychiatric out-patient personality patterns.

Microcard BF6   Micp A 53–62

Catholic Univ. of   America. Library
for Library of Congress   ₍2₎†

NT   0051021   DCU DLC

Law   **Tatomir, Adam,** ed.

Poland. *Laws, statutes, etc.*
Odbudowa Państwa Polskiego w latach 1944–1946; najważniejsze dokumenty i informacje. Zestawili Wł. Kurkiewicz, W. Olszewski, A. Tatomir. Warszawa, Państwowe Zakłady Wydawn. Szkolnych, 1947–

Tatomir, Adam.
Pisarze Polski Ludowej; wybór sylwetek poetów i prozaików
see under title

Tatomir, Konstantin Ivanovich.
Вскрытие и разработка каменноугольных месторождений с расположением главных выработок в устойчивых породах. Киев, Изд-во Академии наук Укр. ССР, 1950.

134, ₍5₎ p. diagrs. 26 cm.

At head of title: Академия наук Украинской ССР. Институт горной механики.
Bibliography: p. ₍136₎

1. Coal mines and mining. 2. Mining engineering.   I. Title.
Title transliterated: Vskrytie i razrabotka kamennougol'nykh mestorozhdenii.

TN802.T3   52–16741

NT   0051024   DLC

TATOMIR, Lucjan, 1836–1901.
Geografia ogólna i statystyka ziem dawnej Polski. W Krakowie, w drukarni "Czasu" W. Kirchmayera, 1868.

22 cm.

NT   0051025   MH

PG7157   **Tatomir, Lucjan,** 1836–1901.
.K5728   Jan Kochanowski; opowiadanie z XVI. wieku.
T3   We Lwowie, Nakł. Seyfartha i Czajkowskiego, 1884.
163 p. port.

1. Kochanowski, Jan, 1530–1584.

NT   0051026   ICU

DK418.5   Tatomir, Lucjan, 1836–1901.
L5   Unia Litwy z Polska; wspomnienie historyczne
T37   na pamiatke 300-letniej rocznicy Unii Lubelskiej. Napisał L. Tatomir. We Lwowie, Nakł. Karola Wilda, 1869.
46 p. 19 cm.

1. Poland - For. rel. - Lithuania. 2. Lithuania - For. rel. - Poland. I. Title (1)

NT   0051027   XrT DLC-P4 NcD

Tatomir, Lucjan, 1836–1901.
... Wspomnienie o Janie III. Sobieskim. Napisał Lucyan Tatomir. Lwów, Nakł. Komitetu Wydawnictwa dziełek ludowych, 1909.

77 p. illus. (port.) 18ᵐ.   (Wydawnictwo ludowe)

1. Jan III Sobieski, king of Poland, 1629–1696.

Library of Congress   DK431.T36   43–38650

NT   0051028   DLC

QA75   **Taton, René.**
.T22   Le calcul mécanique. ₍1. éd.₎ Paris, Presses universitaires de France, 1949.

126, ₍2₎ p. illus. 18 cm. (Que sais-je? Le point des connaissances actuelles, 367)

"Bibliographie": p. ₍127₎

1. Calculating-machines.

QA75.T3 1949   50–55129

NT   0051029   DLC ICU OU MH NN

Taton, René.
Le calcul mental [1.éd.]   Paris, Presses universitaires de France, 1953.
134,[2] p.   18cm.   ("Que sais-je?; le point des connaissances actuelles. 605)

Bibliography, p.[135]

1. Arithmetic, Mental. t.1953.

NT   0051030   NN

Taton, René.
Causalités et accidents de la découverte scientifique; illustration de quelques étapes caractéristiques de l'évolution des sciences. Paris, Masson, 1955.

171 p. illus. 23 cm. (Collection Évolution des sciences, 6)

1. Research. 2. Science—Hist.   I. Title.

Q180.A1T3   55–40751 ‡

NT   0051031   DLC NN ICJ IU

Taton, René.
Gaspard Monge. Basel, Birkhäuser, 1950.

24 p. facsim., port. 25 cm. (Kurze Mathematiker-Biographien)
Beihefte zur Zeitschrift Elemente der Mathematik, Nr. 9.
Cover title.
Bibliography: p. 24.

1. Monge, Gaspard, comte de Péluse, 1746–1818. (Series: Elemente der Mathematik. Beihefte, Nr. 9)
A 65–61

Illinois. Univ. Library
for Library of Congress

TxFTC NjP MoU NcRS WU NjP PPT OrPR
NT   0051032   IU MU KMK WaU CU MH NIC NcD RPB CtY NjP

Taton, René.
La géométrie projective en France de Desargues à Poncelet; conférence faite au Palais de la découverte le 17 février 1951. ₍Paris, 1951₎

21 p. 18 cm. (Les Conférences du Palais de la découverte. Histoire des sciences)
At head of title: Université de Paris.

1. Geometry, Projective.

QA471.T3   A 53–147

Princeton Univ. Libr.
for Library of Congress

NT   0051033   NjP AzU NIC CaQMU NN CU DLC

Taton, René.
L'histoire de la géométrie descriptive; conférence faite au Palais de la découverte le 12 juin 1954. ₍Paris, Université, 1954₎

25 p. illus. 18 cm. (Les Conférences du Palais de la découverte, sér. D: Histoire des sciences, no 32)

1. Geometry, Descriptive—Hist.

QA501.T35   56–22607 ‡

NT   0051034   DLC OrCS NN CU AzU MH RPB IU OCU NcD

Taton, René.
... Histoire du calcul, par René Taton ... Paris, Presses universitaires de France, 1946.

123 p., 2 l. illus., diagrs. 17½ᵐ. ("Que sais-je?" Le point des connaissances actuelles. ₍198₎)
"1ᵉ édition."
"Bibliographie sommaire": 1st leaf at end.

1. Mathematics—Hist.

Library of Congress   QA21.T3   46–21684

                    510.9

NT   0051035   DLC TxU NN CU WaWW

Taton, René.
Histoire du calcul. ₍2. éd.₎ Paris, Presses universitaires de France, 1948.

126 p. illus. 18 cm. ("Que sais-je?" Le point des connaissances actuelles ₍198₎)
"Bibliographie": p. ₍124₎–126.

1. Mathematics—Hist.   (Series)

[QA21.T   ]   A 48–8561*

Princeton Univ. Libr.
for Library of Congress

NT   0051036   NjP OrStbM

QA559   **Taton, René,** ed.
.D38
1951   **Desargues, Gérard,** 1593–1662?
L'œuvre mathématique de G. Desargues. Textes publiés et commentés avec une introd. biographique et historique, par René Taton. ₍1. éd.₎ Paris, Presses universitaires de France, 1951.

Q5   Taton, René.
M74   L'oeuvre scientifique de Gaspard Monge.
951t   Paris, Presses universitaires de France, 1951.
441p. 22cm.
Thèse - Paris.
Bibliography: p.[395]–425.

NT   0051038   CtY MH

Taton, René.
L'œuvre scientifique de Monge. ₍1. éd.₎ Paris, Presses universitaires de France, 1951.

441 p. 23 cm. (Bibliothèque de philosophie contemporaine. Logique et philosophie des sciences)
Bibliography: p. ₍395₎–425.

1. Monge, Gaspard, comte de Péluse, 1746–1818.   I. Title.

QA29.M53T38   925.1   53–21708

IU NN ICU NcD NcU OU OO TU OrCS CaBVaU CSt
NT   0051039   DLC VtU FU InU MH NBC WU NNC NjP ICJ

Taton, René.
Pour continuer le calcul intégral, par René Taton ... avec une préface de l'abbé Th. Moreux ... Avec 53 figures dans le texte. Paris, G. Doin & cⁱᵉ, 1943.

2 p. l., ₍7₎–208 p. illus., diagrs. 17½ᵐ. (Half-title: Bibliothèque d'éducation scientifique. ₍Collection des "Pour comprendre"₎ Pub. sous la direction de l'abbé Moreux)

1. Calculus, Integral.

QA308.T3   517.3   A F 47–317
© 30Dec43; 1c 8May46; Gaston Doin et cⁱᵉ; AF1433.

Brown univ. Library
for Library of Congress   ₍4₎†

NT   0051040   RPB ICN NNC NcD NN DLC

Taton-Vassal,
   Rapport fait au nom de la Commission de la législation civile et criminelle chargée d'examiner le projet de loi ayant pour objet de substituer l'insertion au "Journal officiel" à l'insertion au "Bulletin des lois"
   see under   France. Assemblée nationale, 1871-1942. Chambre des députés. Commission de la législation civile et criminelle.

Wason
BS558
W76T21
  Tatopansi na Surat Refo na kahio Windĕsi. ₁Bijbelsche geschiedenissen in de Windessiche taal.₎ Amsterdam, Nederlandsch Bijbelgenootschap₁ 1911.
  105 p. illus. 20 cm.

     1. Bible stories, Windesian. 2. Windesian language--Texts.

NT   0051042   NIC

378.76
L930d
1948
  Tator, Benjamin Almon, 1914-
   Piedmont interstream surfaces of the Colorado Springs region... n.p., 1948.
   xi, 99p. maps (part fold.) diagrs. 28cm.

   Thesis (Ph.D.)- Louisiana state university. Baton Rouge, La. 1948.
   Biography.
   "References cited": p.95-99.
   Abstract.

   1. Geology--   Colorado. I. Title.

NT   0051043   LU

  Tator, Henry H
   Brother Jonathan's cottage... New York, 1854

NT   0051044   PU

Tator, Henry H.
  Brother Jonathan's cottage; or, A friend to the fallen. By Henry H. Tator ... New-York, F. Hart, 1854.
  3 p. l., 235 p. 20ᶜᵐ.

                  8-25558†

Library of Congress   PZ3.T188B

NT   0051045   DLC MnU

FILM
4274
PR
v.2
reel
T2
  Tator, Henry H
   Brother Jonathan's cottage; or, A friend to the fallen ... New York, F. Hart, 1854.
  235 p. (Wright American fiction, v.II, 1851-1875, no. 2429, Research Publications Microfilm, Reel T-2)

   1. Temperance - Fiction. I. Title.

NT   0051046   CU KEmT MiU

  Tator, Henry H
   Eulogy commemorative of the character of Henry Clay. Albany, 1852.
   2 p.   8°.   [In vol. of clay Memorials]
  -- ---- v. 73, Library of Americana.

NT   0051047   CtY

Tator, Henry H.
  An eulogy commemorative of the character of Hon. Henry Clay, by Henry H. Tator ... Albany, J. Munsell, 1852.
  22 p.   25½ᶜᵐ.

   1. Clay, Henry, 1777-1852.

                  14-19559

Library of Congress   E340.C6T2

NT   0051048   DLC

  Tator, Henry H
   Eureka; a Poem. Albany, 1856.
   15 p.   8°.   [In v. 112, Library of Americana - Pamphlets]

NT   0051049   CtY

  Tator, Henry H
   Hercules; a Poem. Albany, 1856.
   55 p.   8°.   [In v. 19 - Library of Americana - Pamphlets]

NT   0051050   CtY

---

*AC85
T1885
956h
  Tator, Henry H
   Hercules; a poem. In four books. By Henry H. Tator ...
   Albany:Joel Munsell,78 State street.1856.
   54,[1]p. 24cm.
   Original printed gray-green front wrapper preserved; bound in cloth.

NT   0051051   MH CSmH RPB

PS
2978
T22ℓ
  Tator, Henry H
   Leander; a poem. Springfield,Ill., B. A.Richards & co., 1859.
   48p. 17cm.
   Contents. - Leander. - Sonnets.

   1. Shelley in fiction, drama, poetry, etc. I. Title.

NT   0051052   NRU

  Tator, Henry H
   An oration commemorative of the birthday of Washington, delivered in the Methodist Episcopal church at Francisville, Schoharie co., N.Y., on the twenty-second of February, 1851... Albany, Joel Mansell, 1851.
   22 p.   22 cm.

NT   0051053   NcD CtY

  Tator, Henry H
   Oration, commemorative of the character of Alexander Hamilton, before the N.Y. Society of the Cincinnati, 1854.
  NY., 1854.

NT   0051054   MWA

  Tator, Henry H
   An oration commemorative of the character of Mrs. Mary Washington. Albany, 1851.
   20 p.   8°.

NT   0051055   CtY

  Tator, Henry H.
   An oration commemorative of the character of Mrs. Mary Washington. Albany, J. Munsell, 1851.
   20 pp.   8°.

             1-24365--M 1

NT   0051056   DLC CSmH

Tator, Henry H.
  An oration commemorative of the character of Patrick Henry. By Henry H. Tator ... Albany, J. Munsell, 1852.
  24 p.   25ᶜᵐ.
  "Dedicatory epistle," by Chas. Whitney.

   1. Henry, Patrick, 1736-1799.   I. Whitney, Charles.

                 11-22419

Library of Congress   E302.6.H5T2

NT   0051057   DLC

Tator, Henry H.
  An oration commemorative of the character of Thomas Jefferson, by Henry H. Tator ... Albany, J. Munsell, 1852.
  22 p.   25ᶜᵐ.

   1. Jefferson, Thomas, pres. U. S., 1743-1826.

                 11-22424

Library of Congress   E332.T22

NT   0051058   DLC PPAmP CtY OClWHi

Tatos, Ioan I
  Industria morăritului în România ₁de₎ I. I. Tatos și I. Ivănescu. București, Tip. "Lupta" N. Stroilă, 1941.
  145, ₁4₎, xv p. illus., fold. maps. 24 cm. (Biblioteca economică, 28)
  Bibliography: p. ₁147₎-₁149₎

   1. Flour and feed trade—Rumania.   I. Ivănescu, I., joint author. II. Title.

  HD9056.R8T3   50-46683

NT   0051059   DLC

HD9045
.R8M55
  Tatos, Ioan I., joint author.

  Mladenatz, Gromoslav, 1891-
   Tehnica valorificării cerealelor în campania anului 1940-1941 ₁de₎ Gr. Mladenatz și I. I. Tatos. ₁București₎ Independența Economică, 1940.

  Tatosov, A   K
  Опыт постройки наплавных железнодорожных мостов. Москва, Гос. трансп. жел-дор. изд-во, 1945.
  60 p. illus. 22 cm.
  At head of title: А. К. Татосов, Н. И. Петров.

   1. Railroad bridges. 2. Pontoon-bridges.   I. Petrov, N. I., joint author. II. Title.   *Title transliterated:* Opyt postroĭki naplavnykh zheleznodorozhnykh mostov.

  TF280.T3   57-45999

NT   0051061   DLC

DK879
.B58
T2
  Tatoušek, František, 1853-1927.
  Břevnovské obrázky; z pamĕti starého Břevnova. V Praze, A Neubert, 1920.
  175 p.

   1. Břevnov, Czechoslovak Republic--Hist. I. Title.

NT   0051062   ICU

Tatout, Christiane, Jeanne, 1911-
... De la gangrène cutanée progressive post-
opératoire (deux observations nouvelles)...
Paris, 1939.
Thèse – Univ. de Paris.

NT 0051063   CtY

Tatovici, Constantin T
... Les emprunts de l'état Roumain. ... Par
Constantin T. Tatovici. ... Paris, Imprimarie
Bonvalot-Jouve, 1906.
129 p. tables. 24.5 cm.
Thesis (Ph.D.) – University of Paris, 1906.
Bibliography; p. [125]-126.

NT 0051064   NcD CtY

T'at'owl, M
(Anowrjk' i Siõn)
Աևուրքք ի Սիոն / զրեսզ Մ. Թաթուլ. — Ճերուսաղէմ :
ի Տպարանի Առաքելական Աթոռոյ Ս. Յակոբեանց, 1869.
10, 44 p., [1] leaf of plates : ill. ; 15 cm.
A poem.

I. Title.

PK8548.T347A8   77-970596

NT 0051065   DLC

Tatra, Julius Keil-
see Keil-Tatra, Julius.

Tatra (*Automobile factory*)
Od kočáru k automobilu; 50 let automobilky Tatra v
Kopřivnici. [Autoři: Adolf Tůma et al. V Praze, 1947]
[94] p. illus. 25 cm.
Summaries in English, Russian, French, and German.

1. Automobiles, Czech. 2. Motor vehicles, Czech.   I. Tůma, Adolf.
II. Title.
TL215.T3A5   56-29872

NT 0051067   DLC

Tátra-almanach. 1938-   Bratislava,
Tátra-Kiadás, 1938-
v. 18 cm. annual.
Subtitle: Szlovenszkói városképek.
On added t. p.: Tátra-könyvek; szlovenszkói
írók munkái. I. sorozat, 3. köt.

NT 0051068   NNC

059.94511
TA   **Tátra**; a magyar élet és irodalom szlovenszkói
es ruszinszkói szemléje. 1.-2. évf.;
1937-38. Bratislava, Tátra-Kiadás.
2v. 24cm. monthly (except during summer)

NT 0051069   IU

Tatra banka
see also
Státní banka československá.

Film   TÁTRA-VIDÉK.
S186   1.-   szám; 1884-
Uj-Tátrafüred.
v. illus.
Film copy.
Editor: 1884-   Szontagh Miklós.
1. Balneology - Period. 2. Health
resorts - Hungary I. Szontagh, Miklós,
ed.

NT 0051071   DNLM

Tátrafüred vay Ó-Tátrafüred klimatikus gyógyhely ésvizgyógyintézet. (Curbad Schmecks
oder Alt-Schmecks), klimatischer Curort und
Wasserheilanstalt. 24 pp. 12°. Löcse, J. T.
Könyvnyomdája, 1893.
Hungarian and German text.

NT 0051072   DNLM

TATRAN; poucno-zábavný-obrázkový casopis.
Zodpovedný redaktor M.Bulgarsky. Rocník I, c.
1-6. 1.mája-15 julia 1878. Pestbudín, 1878.

4°.

NT 0051073   MH

Tatran, Slovenský akademický spolok vo Viedni
see
Slovenský akademický spolok "Tatran" vo Viedni.

AP 58   **Tatranka.** djl 1-3. W Presspurku, 1834-47.
S53   20 cm.
T37
(LC)   Vol. 2 has subtitle: Spis pokračugjcý zwlassté
Incomplete   pro Slowáky, Čechy a Morawany.

NT 0051075   CtY

Tatranka Slowáky, Čechy a Morawany. Díl. III.
Jiři Palkowic.

Pressporek, 1844.

NT 0051076   OClBHS

Tatranská Lomnica, Czechoslovakia. Ecole d'été
tchecoslovaque pour l'étude des problèmes de
l'Europe centrale
see Ecole d'été tchécoslovaque pour l'étude
des problèmes de l'Europe centrale, Tatranská
Lomnica.

057.87   **Tatranský orol.** roč.1-13; 1920-32.
TAT   Trnava [etc.]
13v. illus. 30cm. monthly.

NT 0051078   IU NN

PK8548   Tatrian, Vahram, 1900-1948.   Ariwnot mat-
.T37C5   nahetk'erě. 1952.
1952   Tatrian, Vahram, 1900-1948.
Orien   Զատրատած Համանուաագ, Աքիւնոտ մատնահետքերը, եւ
Armen   Հրապուիքի վրայ. զաղափ ոստկանենական պատումածքեէ :
Գաոսթ, Դիմել, Hairenik Press, 1952 :

Tatrian, Vahram, 1900-1948.
Զատրատած Համանուաագ, Աքիւնոտ մատնահետքերը, եւ
Հրապուիքի վրայ. զաղափ ոստկանենական պատումածքեէ :
Գաոսթ, Դիմել Hairenik Press, 1952.
III, 623 p. ports. 23 cm. (His Մատենաշար, թիւ 7)
Added t. p.: The unfinished symphony, The bloodstained finger-
prints, and On top of a volcano; three detective stories in Armenian,
by Vahram Dadrian.
I. Tatrian, Vahram, 1900-1948. Ariwnot matnahetk'erě. 1952.
II. Tatrian, Vahram, 1900-1948. Hrabowkhi vray. 1952. III. Title.
IV. Title: Ariwnot matnahetk'erě. V. Title: Hrabowkhi vray.
Title romanized: Ch'awartats hamanowagě.

PK8548.T37C5 1952   70-279255

NT 0051080   DLC MB

Tatrian, Vahram, 1900-1948.
Դէպի անապատ. թրգուած էքիք օրագրքս: Նիւ Եորք,
1945 :
563 p. ports. 22 cm. (His Մատենաշար, թիւ 1)

1. Armenian massacres, 1915-1923—Personal narratives.
I. Title.
Title romanized: Děpi anapat.
DS195.5.T38   70-279220

NT 0051081   DLC

Tatrian, Vahram, 1900-1948.
Գաբիկի արկածները. Հաբիբ եւ մէկ դրուագներ Գալւս
տական կեանքէ : Ֆրէզնο, 1947:
663 p. 22 cm. (His Մատենաշար, թիւ 4)

I. Title.
Title romanized: Gabiki arkatsnerě.
PK8548.T37G3   72-279253

NT 0051082   DLC MB

PK8548
.T37G4   Tatrian, Vahram, 1900-1948.
     Դերերմանեերի մէջեն. թրգուած էքիք օրագրքս: Նիւ
Also in   Եորք, Նոյեմ Տպարան, 1945: (His Մատենաշար, թիւ 2)
General   476 p. 22 cm.
Library   A novel.
     Bound with its sequel: Մս. Հաբիբ, Նիւ Եորք, 1945, by the same
     author.
     I. Title.
                    Title romanized: Gerermannerow mějěn.
PK8548.T37G4   70-279223

NT 0051083   MB DLC

Tatrian, Vahram, 1900-1948.
Գորդեան Հանգոյց. զագանիֆ ոստկանական երեք պատ
մուածքներ: Բ. Նուէրկկանիֆ խատաթաբումով: Գաոստ,
Տպագրութիւն Հայ Ճ. Ընկերման, 1949:
614 p. port. 22 cm. (His Մատենաշար, թիւ 5)
Added t. p.: The Gordian knot; three detective stories in Ar-
menian, by Vahram Dadrian.
CONTENTS.— Գորդեան Հանգոյց.—Չնքանուեր զել.—Թագակեoptique:
I. Title.
                    Title romanized: Gordean hangoyts'.
PK6561.T285G6 1949   75-279227

NT 0051084   DLC

Tatrian, Vahram, 1900-1948.
Հետապրքըրական նօթեր: [Detroit, Դիմել A. Dadrian]
1954.
637 p. ports. 23 cm. (His Մատենաշար, թիւ 9)
Added t. p.: An author's peregrinations, by Vahram Dadrian.
CONTENTS.—Հետապրքըական նօթեր.—Դրգամեներ ճեներու հետpih:

I. Title.
                    Title romanized: Hetak'rk'rakan nõt'er.
PK8548.T37H4 1954   76-279238

NT 0051085   DLC

Tatrian, Vahram, 1900–1948.
Հինգ Թատերախաղեր, եւ ծրուած էջեր : Detroit, Դ/միշ
A. Dadrian, 1950.
350 p. port. 22 cm. (His Մատեանը, ԺԲ 6)
Added t. p.: Five plays, and Scattered pages; in Armenian, by
Vahram Dadrian.
CONTENTS.— Հինգ Թատերախաղեր. Գատուեր դաղ. Զատագ
օրերին. Դատգուեիբ շաղապըԺեղ. Ներ/եբ ոերպ/սապաեդ. ԴրԺ/դ/ըՀ
Դարպիեբ—Թմնաե էջեր. ԴաետաադարԺ/շ ձս սգրԺեբ. Ոբ ոսաԺ/
ԺրպԺ/եբ. Ոեբ ոքբագ/ապամաիեԺ/ոը. Դատ/եը եԿ մգ. Դասաագա/ԺՀ
ծերու. ժԺ/. Ոգագ/ճ աՀԺ/եԺ/ը. Ծ/մդապալ/աoadd. Թոիգոբ Հ/ամ/ebe
ծԺ/եդ/ ժ/ճեԺ/ը. Դո/գԿ/եբ Ժ/ճ/տ/ե ոբ Ժ :
I. Title.
           Title romanized : Hing t'aterakhagher.
PK8548.T37H5 1950   76–279254

NT 0051086   DLC MB

PK8548
.T37C5
1952
Orien
Armen

Tatrian, Vahram, 1900–1948. Hrabowkhi vray.
1952.
Tatrian, Vahram, 1900–1948.
Ձատրատծ Համանեդաեր, Ոլրեծոա մամաեՆ/ոոեԺ/եբ, եւ
հքասԺ/եբ ժ/դաg. գագԺ/եԻ ոսրԺԺ/ռ/աԺան պատաՈ/oeԺ/քԺ/ե :
ԳատթԺ/Ե, Դ/տ/ձ/ Hairenik Press, 1952 :

Tatrian, Vahram, 1900–1948.
Ռ/ աեgdeo/դ. ՛ ԴորաԺ/Ք/դ գԻ/ատ/Հ/ե/ ԿԺ/աեԺ/ք : Ն/ք/ Ռ/տr/,
Գո/շ/աԿ Տ/աrpaե , 1946 :
82 p. 22 cm. (His Ս/ատԺ/ա/Ե/ոbr, ԹԺ/ 3)
Bound with his Ր/այբ Ոբե/— Ն/ք/ Ռ/տr/, 1946; and his Ն/ե/Ժ/ Ղ/ա/—
Ն/ք/ Ռ/տr/, 1946 :

I. Title.
           Title romanized : Ir ants'ealě.
PK6561.T285 I ''   77–279230

NT 0051088   DLC

Tatrian, Vahram, 1900–1948.
Ր/ոյբ Ոբե/— Դ/ոբaՆ/ք/դ գԻ/ատ/Հ/ե/ ԿԺ/աեԺ/ք : Ն/ք/ Ռ/տr/,
Գո/շ/աԿ Տ/աrpaե , 1946 :
128 p. 22 cm. (His Ս/ատԺ/ա/Ե/ոbr, ԹԺ/ 3–Բ)
Bound with his Ր/ աեgdeo/դ : Ն/ք/ Ռ/տr/, 1946 :

I. Title.
           Title romanized : K'oyr Anna.
PK6561.T285 I 7   79–279252

NT 0051089   DLC MB

Tatrian, Vahram, 1900–1948.
Ն/ե/Ժ/ Ղ/ա/— Դ/ոբaՆ/ք/դ գԻ/ատ/Հ/ե/ ԿԺ/աեԺ/ք : Ն/ք/ Ռ/տr/,
Գո/շ/աԿ Տ/աrpaե , 1946 :
374 p. 22 cm. (His Ս/ատԺ/ա/Ե/ոbr, ԹԺ/ 3–Բ)
Bound with his Ր/ աեgdeo/դ : Ն/ք/ Ռ/տr/, 1946 :

I. Title.
           Title romanized : Nelli Pella.
PK6561.T285 I 7   75–279251

NT 0051090   DLC MB

Tatrian, Vahram, 1900–1948.
Ո/ե/ Հ/ոg/Ե/. Ե/դpaՆ/aĿ/ոդ: Ն/ք/ Ռ/աrգ, Գո/շ/աԿ Տ/աrpaե,
1945 :
241 p. 22 cm. (His Ս/ատԺ/ա/Ե/ոbr, ԹԺ/ 2–Ձ)
Bound with the author's Ղ/ե/Ḳ/դՆ/ա/ե/բԽ/ոո/ Ժ/Ֆ/ե (Ն/ք/ Ռ/աrգ, 1945)
to which it is a sequel.
A novel.

I. Title.
           Title romanized : Sew hogin.
PK8548.T37G4   74–279224

NT 0051091   DLC

PG5235
.S8

Tatrín.
Štúr, Ľudovít, 1815–1856.
Nauka reči slovenskej. Vistavená od Ludevíta Štúra …
V Prešporku, Nákl. Tatrína, 1846.

Tatrishvili, N   F
Магматическая деятельность в Грузии в допалеозое и
палеозое. Тбилиси, Техника да шрома, 1948.
286 p. illus. 24 cm.
Bibliography : p. 274–[283]

1. Rocks, Igneous. 2. Petrology—Georgia (Transcaucasia) 3. Geology—Georgia (Transcaucasia) 1. Title.
          Title transliterated: Magmaticheskaiă
                 deiătel'nost' v Gruzii.
QE461.T27   52–20464

NT 0051093   DLC

QE461
.Z27

Tatrishvili, N. F., joint author.
Zaridze, Georgiĭ Mikhaĭlovich.
(Vvedenie v magmaticheskuiŭ geologiiŭ Gruzii)
Введение в магматическую геологию Грузии. Тби-
лиси, Техника да шрома, 1947.

Tatro, Earl E.
Safety for you! Written by Earl E. Tatro;
illustrations by Vincent Valentine; prepared under
supervision of Emil J. Novak, director of training,
Fairchild aviation corporation. Chicago, Deep
River, Conn. [etc.] National foremen's institute
[c1943]
34 p. illus.

Inserted in envelope in back of Faist, K.L.,
Job safety training manual, 1945.

NT 0051095   MH-BA NN

TATRO, EARL E
Safety for you! Illus. by Vincent Valentine
… Nat. foremen c1951.
34 p. illus.

NT 0051096   Or

Tatrosi, John.
… The Hungarians of Moldavia, by John Tatrosi. London,
Low, W. Dawson & sons; New-York, Steiger & comp.; [etc., etc.]
1920.
cover-title, 16 p. illus. (map) 19ᶜᵐ. (East-European problems, no. 8)

1. Hungarians in Moldavia. 2. Minorities.
                        43–43785
Library of Congress   DR281.M6T3

NT 0051097   DLC CSt-H

TATRY, P.
Loi du 21 janvier 1918 sur les marchés à
livrer et autres contrats commerciaux conclus
avant la guerre. Paris, 1920.

(4)+61+(2) p.
Thèse - Univ. de Paris.

NT 0051098   MH-L CtY-L

Tatry. Zdjęcia: K. Cełba i B. Straka. Przedm.: F. Kroutil;
teksty do zdjęć: J. Šimko. Praga, Artia, 1954.
unpaged (chiefly illus.) 30 cm.

1. Tatra Mountains—Descr. & trav.—Views. i. Cełba, K.

DK511.T3T25   56–34341 ‡

NT 0051099   DLC IU OClW

Tatrzański orzeł. The Tatra eagle.
[Passaic, N. J., Polish Tatra Mountaineers Alliance]
v. illus. 28 cm. quarterly.
Began with Sept. 1947 issue. Cf. Union list of serials.

I. Polish Tatra Mountaineers Alliance. II. Title: The Tatra eagle.

AP54.T35   72–622788

NT 0051100   DLC NN

DK511
T3Z5

Tatrzańskie towarzystwo narciarzy, Kraków.
[Zieliński, Adam K   ] ed.
Tatry—les Tâtra—the Tatra—die Tatra. Pologne—Poland—Polen … [Kraków, Tatrzańskie towarzystwo narciarzy,
1938]

Tatsachen! Etwas zum Nachdenken für den deutschen Arbeiter.
[Berlin, 1918?]   15 p.   8°.
Caption-title.

635264A. 1. Labor—Germany,   1918.
N. Y. P. L.   May 13, 1933

NT 0051102   NN

TATSACHEN! Wahrheiten! Zusammengestellt
vom Amt für Beamte beim Gau Kurmark.
Berlin, 1933. 47p 21cm

1. Antisemitism—Germany—Nazism.

NT 0051103   NNJ

Tatsachen des wirtschaftlichen und sozialen Lebens…
Heft 1–

Bonn: K. Schroeder, 1930
nos.

Published under the auspices of the Wirtschaftshistorischer Verein zu Koeln, e. V.
Editor : 1930, B. Kuske.

Contents:
Heft 1. Kuske, B. Entstehung und Gestaltung des Wirtschaftsraumes. 1930.
Heft 2. Klersch, ' Spargedanke und Sparkassen. 1930.

NT 0051105   NN

Tatsachen sprechen fuer den Sieg
see under   Speer, Albert, 1905–

Tatsachen sprechen … Für soziale Sicherheit in
ganz Berlin
see under   Freier Deutscher Gewerkschafts-
bund.

Tatsachen über den polnischen aufstand in
Oberschlesien, mai–juni, 1921. (n.p., 1921?)
56p. incl. plates, facsims. 33 x 21 cm.

Caption title.
Half-title: Der dritte aufstand in Oberschlesien.

NT 0051108   DNW

DB215.5 '. Tatsachen über die freiheit im "tschechischen
G3T219   paradiese" ... ₍n.p.₎ 1920.
              8 p.   24ᶜᵐ.
              At head of title: Nr. III.
              Contents.- Tschechische schulpolitik. Tsche-
            chische gewalttaten gegenüber einer deutschböh-
            mischen schule. Aussichten über den schutz der
            Deutschen in der Tschechoslovakei.

              1.Germans in Czechoslovak republic.
              2.Minorities.

NT 0051109   CSt-H

Tatsachen und Dokumente zum Streit um die
    Wünschelrute ...
        see under   Institut für Wünschelruten-
    und Pendelforschung, e.V., Munich.

Tatsachen und Lügen um Hitler
    see under   Nationalsozialistische deutsche
    Arbeiter-Partei. Reichspropagandaleitung.

Tatsachen und reime...   Berkeley, Cal., n.d.
    15 [1] p.   22 cm.
    Cover title.
    German text.

NT 0051112   RPB

V 1; Tatsachen und Stimmen. Materialsammlung
1. [Berlin? 1944?]

NT 0051113   MH

...Tatsachen und Zahlen aus der Kraftfahrzeug-Industrie.
19
Berlin₍, 19
    v.   illus.
    1928-   at head of title: Veröffentlichungen des Reichsverbandes der Auto-
mobilindustrie, e.V.

1. Automobiles—Trade and Stat.—
N.Y.P.L.   Germany.
                                          September 12, 1930

NT 0051114   NN

Tatsachen und Zahlen aus der Kraftverkehrswirtschaft.
Berlin, Union Deutsche Verlagsgesellschaft ₍etc.₎
    v. illus. 25 cm. annual. (Veröffentlichungen des Reichsver-
bandes de Automobilindustrie)
    Publication suspended 1939-47. Cf. Deutsches Bücherverzeichnis,
1941-50.
    Issued 19   by Reichsverband der Automobilindustrie.

1. Automobile industry and trade — Germany — Yearbooks.
I. Reichsverband der Automobilindustrie.

HD9710.G4R43   55-47003 rev ‡

NT 0051115   DLC MiD WU CaNSHD

Tatsachen zum Problem der deutschen Vertrie-
    benen und Flüchtlinge
        see under   Germany (Federal Republic,
    1949-   ) Bundesministerium für Vertriebene,
    Flüchtlinge und Kriegsgeschädigte.

Tatsachen zur geschichte der Komintern
    see under   Communist international.

Die tatsächliche Gestaltung des Verfassungs- und
Verwaltungsrechts...
    see under   Assmann, Hans.

G989   TATSCH, ALBERTO
T188v   ... A verdade sobre as apolices paraguayas
        emmittidas em virtude do Tratado de paz firmado
        a 9 de janeiro de 1873 [i.e. 1872]   Montevideo,
        1908.
          58p.   17½cm.
          "1873" on t.-p. corrected to "1872."
          A discussion of Brazilian claims as a result
        of the Treaty with Paraguay, 1872, closing the
        Paraguayan war.
          1. Brazil - Claims vs. Paraguay. 2. Paraguay
        - Claims vs. Brazil. 3. Paraguayan war, 1865-
        1870. I. Title.

NT 0051119   TxU

Tatsch, Jacob Hugo, 1888-1939.
    The facts about George Washington as a freemason, by
Major J. Hugo Tatsch ... with a foreword by Admiral
E. Coontz ...   New York, N. Y., Macoy publishing and ma-
sonic supply company, 1931.
    xvi p., 1 l., 94 p. front. (port.) illus., plates. 23ᶜᵐ.
    "First edition, September 1, 1931, 2000 copies."

    1. Washington, George, pres. U. S., 1732-1799. 2. Freemasons.
U. S.—Hist. 3. Freemasons. Alexandria, Va. Alexandria-Washington
lodge, no. 22.   I. Title.
    Library of Congress   E312.17.T29   31-31895
    ———— Copy 2.
    Copyright A 42515   923.173

NT 0051120   DLC WaS Wasp FTaSU ViU NjP

Tatsch, Jacob Hugo, 1888-
    The facts about George Washington as a freemason, by
Major J. Hugo Tatsch ... with a foreword by Admiral Robert
E. Coontz ...   New York, N. Y., Macoy publishing and ma-
sonic supply company, 1931.
    xvi p., 1 l., 96 p. front. (port.) illus., plates. 23½ᶜᵐ.
    "Laid paper edition limited to fifty-two copies." 52.
    "A list of ... books about George Washington": p. 89-92.

    1. Washington, George, pres. U. S., 1732-1799. 2. Freemasons. U. S.—
Hist. 3. Freemasons. Alexandria, Va. Alexandria-Washington lodge
no. 22.   I. Title.
    Library of Congress   E312.17.T292   32-4288
                                                       923.173

NT 0051121   DLC MB OKentU

Tatsch, Jacob Hugo, 1888-1939.
    The facts about George Washington as a freemason, by
Major J. Hugo Tatsch ... with a foreword by Admiral
Robert E. Coontz ...   3d ed. New York, N. Y., Macoy publishing and masonic supply company, 1932.
    xvi p., 1 l., 100 p. front., illus., pl., port. 22 cm.
    "Third edition, February 15, 1932, 2000 copies."
    "A list of masonic books about George Washington": p. 89; "Other
books on Washington": p. 90-91.

    1. Washington, George, pres. U. S.—Freemasonry. 2. Freemasons.
U. S.—Hist. 3. Freemasons. Alexandria, Va. Alexandria-Washington lodge, no. 22.   I. Title.
    E312.17.T294   923.173   32—5358

NT 0051122   DLC

Tatsch, Jacob Hugo, 1888-
    Freemasonry in the thirteen colonies, by J. Hugo Tatsch ...
Second issue. New York, Macoy publishing and masonic supply company, 1933.
    viii, ₍viiia₎-viiih, ix-xx, 245 p. illus. (facsim.) 2 port. (incl. front.)
21½ᶜᵐ.
    Bibliography at end of each chapter.

    1. Freemasons. U. S.—Hist.   I. Title.
    Library of Congress   HS521.T3 1933   33-7241
    ———— Copy 2.
    Copyright A 61012   ₍2₎   366.1

NT 0051123   DLC OWorP

Tatsch, Jacob Hugo, 1888-
    Freemasonry in the thirteen colonies, by J. Hugo Tatsch ...
New York, Macoy publishing and masonic supply company,
1929.
    xx, 245 p. 2 port. (incl. front.) 21½ᶜᵐ.
    Bibliography at end of each chapter.

    ¹ Freemasons—U. S.—Hist.   I. Title.
    Library of Congress   HS521.T3   30-578

NT 0051124   DLC NRCR PU ICU OCl OOxM MWA CaQML

Tatsch, Jacob   Hugo, 1888-
    High lights of Crescent history, by J. Hugo Tatsch ... a
series of sketches chiefly drawn from the old records of Crescent lodge no. 25, A. F. & A. M., Cedar Rapids, Ia., 1851-
1926. Cedar Rapids, Ia., Priv. print., Crescent lodge no. 25,
A. F. & A. M. ₍°1926₎
    63, ₍1₎ p. 2 port. (incl. front.) facsims. 24½ᶜᵐ.
    "Edition limited to 1,500 copies."

    1. Freemasons. Cedar Rapids, Ia. Crescent lodge no. 25.   I. Title.
    Library of Congress   HS539.C2S6C8   27-688

NT 0051125   DLC

Tatsch, Jacob Hugo, 1888-
    Isaiah Thomas, printer, patriot, free-
mason.
    74-80p. 8°

    (From Grand Lodge Bulletin, Iowa, Mar. 1929
vol. 30, no. 3)

NT 0051126   MWA

Tatsch, Jacob Hugo, 1888-
    John James Joseph Gourgas, 1777-1865, conservator of Scot-
tish rite freemasonry, by Ill∴ J. Hugo Tatsch ... with an introduction by Ill∴ Melvin Maynard Johnson ... Boston, Mass.,
Priv. print., Supreme council 33°, A. A. S. R., N. M. J., 1938.
    xii, 68 p. incl. front. (port.) pl., 8 port. on 2 pl., coat of arms. 23ᶜᵐ.
    "Edition limited to seven hundred and fifty copies."
    "A tentative genealogy of the Gourgas family": p. 59-63.
    "Footnotes and bibliography": p. 54-58.

    1. Gourgas, John James Joseph, 1777-1865. 2. Gourgas family.
I. Title.
    Library of Congress   HS511.G73T3   38-10343
    ———— Copy 2.
    Copyright A 116445   ₍3₎   923.673

NT 0051127   DLC MtHi WaS OClWHi ViU RPJCB

Tatsch, Jacob Hugo, 1888-
    Freemasons. *Massachusetts. Grand lodge. Library.*
    List of masonic subject headings for use in dictionary cata-
log, compiled for the library of the Grand lodge A. F. & A. M.
of Massachusetts by J. Hugo Tatsch and Muriel A. Davis ...
Boston, Mass., 1937.

Tatsch, Jacob   Hugo, 1888-
    The literature of freemasonry. Seattle,
Research Lodge no. 281, F. & A. M., 1939.
    ₍62-73₎ p. (Masonic papers, v. 1, no. 5)

NT 0051129   Wa

Tatsch, Jacob Hugo, 1888-
    Masonic bookplates, supplemented by a descriptive check
list of 586 ex libris of masonic interest, by J. Hugo Tatsch
and Winward Prescott. Cedar Rapids, Ia., The Masonic bibliophiles, 1928.
    101 p., 103-115 numb. l., ₍117₎-153 p. incl. xxxii pl. front. 28½ᶜᵐ.
    "Subscribers' edition limited to 102 copies. No. 101."
    "A selected bibliography of bookplate literature": p. 91-101.

    1. Book-plates. 2. Freemasons—Symbolism. I. Prescott, Winward,
1886-   , joint author. II. Title.
    Library of Congress   Z993.T21   28-16053

NT 0051130   DLC WaS WaSp OCl OU PP MiD OKentU MWA

Tatsch, Jacob Hugo, 1888–   joint author.

Smith, Harry.
Moses Michael Hays, merchant—citizen—freemason, 1739–1805; written in collaboration by Harry Smith ... and J. Hugo Tatsch ... Boston, Mass., Priv. print., Moses Michael Hays lodge, A. F. & A. M., 1937.

Tatsch, Jacob Hugo, 1888–

401
1

Notes on rare masonic books: the Franklin Constitutions of 1734 ...
(*In* The American collector. New York, 1927. v.5, p.103–106 incl.port.)

NT 0051132   CtY

Tatsch, Jacob Hugo, 1888–
A reader's guide to masonic literature, prepared for the use of freemasons and masonic lodges as an aid in the selection of available books, by J. Hugo Tatsch, P. M. New York, The Masonic bibliophiles, 1929.

32 p. 20ᶜᵐ.

"Copy number 1474 of a special edition printed on laid paper and limited to two thousand copies."
"The Masonic bibliophiles": p. 32.

1. Freemasons—Bibl.   I. Masonic bibliophiles, New York.   II. Title.

Library of Congress   Z5993.T22   30–22837
                        ₍2₎   016.3661

NT 0051133   DLC MiU PU MWA

Tatsch, Jacob Hugo, 1888–
A reader's guide to masonic literature, prepared for the use of freemasons and masonic lodges as an aid in the selection of available books, by J. Hugo Tatsch ... 4th ed., rev. New York, Macoy publishing and masonic supply company, 1930.

32 p. 17¼ᶜᵐ.

"5000 copies."
Advertising matter: p. 32.

1. Freemasons—Bibl.   I. Title.

Library of Congress   Z5993.T22 1930   30–32290
Copyright A 31168   ₍3₎   016.3661

NT 0051134   DLC

Tatsch, Jacob Hugo, 1888–
A reader's guide to masonic literature, prepared for the use of freemasons and masonic lodges as an aid in the selection of available books, by J. Hugo Tatsch ... 5th ed., rev. New York, Macoy publishing and masonic supply company, 1931.

40 p. 17¼ᶜᵐ.

"5000 copies."
"The Masonic bibliophiles": p. 40.
Advertising matter: p. 36–39.
"Fifth edition, revised. A price list of masonic books": 6 p. on fold. sheet laid in.

1. Freemasons—Bibl.   I. Masonic bibliophiles, New York.   II. Title.

Library of Congress   Z5993.T22 1931   32–9087
                                       016.3661

NT 0051135   DLC

Tatsch, Jacob Hugo, 1888–1939.
Short readings in masonic history; first series, a concise account of the rise and development of ancient craft masonry, prepared from authentic sources for the use of masonic study groups and individual brethren, by J. Hugo Tatsch ... Cedar Rapids, Ia., The Torch press ₍1926₎.

4 p. l., ₍7₎–59 p. 18ᶜᵐ.

1. Freemasons.   I. Title.

Library of Congress   HS405.T3   26–11920

NT 0051136   DLC OrStbM MiU NN

942.21 F13

Tatsfield, Eng.
The parish registers of Tatsfield, co. Surrey. Transcribed and edited by W. Bruce Bannerman. London, 1906.
48 p. (The publications of the Surrey parish register society ₍v.6, pt.2₎)

Bound with Farley, Eng. (Parish) The registers of Farleigh. London, 1906.

NT 0051137   CaOTP

Tatsfield, *Eng.*
The parish registers of Tatsfield, co. Surrey. Transcribed and ed. by W. Bruce Bannerman ... London ₍Mitchell, Hughes and Clarke, printers₎ 1906.

iv, 48 p. 2 pl. 23ᶜᵐ. ₍With Farley, Eng. (Surrey) The registers of Farleigh ... Ed. by R. Garraway Rice. London, 1906₎

1. Registers of births, etc.—Tatsfield, Eng.   I. Bannerman, William Bruce, ed.

                                        8–5187

NT 0051138   DLC MdBP NN MB

Tatsikovski, V
see
Tacikowski, Władysław.

Tatsinanana.
Tananarive.
v. illus. 27 cm. quarterly.
"Revue politique, économique, touristique, sociale."
French and Malagasy.

1. Madagascar—Periodicals.
DT469.M21T37   916.91   74–645363
                                     MARC-S

NT 0051140   DLC

Tatsios, Theodore G
The U. S. S. R. and revolution abroad: the question of their relationship as treated in three soviet politgramoti (1924, 1933, and 1937) ₍New York₎ 1949.
Microfilm copy of typewritten ms. Made by the Library of Congress. Negative.
Collation of the original, as determined from the film: 80 l.
Thesis (M. A.)—Columbia University.
Concerning Kovalenko's Knizhka politicheskoĭ gramoty, B. Volin's Politgramoty, and Politgramoty, by B. Volin and S. Inguliov.
Bibliography: leaf 80.
1. Russia—For. rel.—1917–1945. 2. Revolutions.   I. Title.

Microfilm 1540 reel 1 DK   Mic 51–133

NT 0051141   DLC

Tatsiyah.
The miracle play of Hasan and Husain
   see under   Hasan and Husain (Persian miracle play)

Tatsui, Matsunosuke, 1884–

Shiga, Naoya, 1883–   *ed.*
Gardens of Japan; a pictorial record of the famous palaces, gardens and tea-gardens, 150 plates. With explanations by Matsunosuke Tatsui ... Edited by Naoya Shiga and Motoi Hashimoto. Tokyo, The Zauho press, 1935.

SB
466
J3
T28

Tatsui, Matsunosuke, 1884–
Japanese gardens.   Tokyo, Japan Travel Bureau [etc.] 19
v. illus. 20 cm. irregular.
Vols. for 19   issued as Tourist library, 4; 19   as Tourist library [New ser.] 5
Began publication in 1934.
1. Gardens – Japan.   I. Nihon Kotsu Kosha.

NT 0051144   DLC MH AU NSyU

SB
466
J3
T28

Tatsui, Matsunosuke, 1884–
Japanese gardens, by Prof. Matsunosuke Tatsui. Tokyo, Maruzen Company, Ltd., 1934.
111 p. illus., plates, col. front. 20 cm. (Tourist library, 4)
"Editorial note" signed: Board of tourist industry, Japanese government railways.
Includes bibliography.

1. Gardens—Japan.   I. Japan. Board of Tourist Industry.   II. Title.

NT 0051145   MU WaS WaE KU OSW MdBP NN OCIMA MShM

SB466
.J3T28
1934

Tatsui, Matsunosuke, 1884–
Japanese gardens, by Prof. Matsunosuke Tatsui. (2d ed.) Tokyo, Maruzen company, ltd., 1934.
111 p. incl. illus., plates. col. front., plates. 19½ᶜᵐ. (Half-title: Tourist library. 4)
"Editorial note" signed: Board of tourist industry, Japanese government railways.
Bibliography: p. 111.

NT 0051146   TU

Tatsui, Matsunosuke, 1884–
Japanese gardens. 2d ed. [n. p.] Board of Tourist Industry, Japanese Government Railways [1936]
111 p. col. front., illus., plates. 20 cm. (Tourist library: 4)
Bibliography: p. 111.
Copy 1: From the library of Clarence Lewis.
1. Gardening – Japan.   2. Gardens – Japan.   I. Title.

NT 0051147   NNBG

Tatsui, Matsunosuke, 1884–
Japanese gardens, by Prof. Matsunosuke Tatsui. (2d ed.) Tokyo, Maruzen company, ltd., 1936.
111 p. incl. illus., plates. col. front., plates. 19½ᶜᵐ. (Half-title: Tourist library. 4)
"Editorial note" signed: Board of tourist industry, Japanese government railways.
Bibliography: p. 111.

1. Gardens—Japan.   I. Japan. Board of tourist industry.   II. Title.
                                 36–29881 Revised

Library of Congress   SB466.J3T28 1936
——— Copy 2.   ₍r39f2₎   712

NT 0051148   ODW ViU MB IdB KyU Wa WaT CaBVaU
                 DLC PHC PPAmP PBm CU PSt WaU MH OO OOxM

SB466
.J3T28
1936

Tatsui, Matsunosuke, 1884–
Japanese gardens. (3d ed.) ₍Tokyo₎ Board of Tourist Industry, Japanese Government Railways ₍1938₎
111 p. incl. illus., plates. col. front., plates. 20 cm. (Half-title: Tourist library. 4)
"Editorial note" signed: Board of tourist industry, Japanese government railways.
Bibliography: p. 111.

NT 0051149   TU OrP WaTU OCU MBSi ICN

Agriculture
SB
466
J3
T21

Tatsui, Matsunosuke.
Japanese gardens. ₍4th ed. Tokyo₎ Japan Travel Bureau ₍1947₎
70 p. illus. (part col.) 18 cm. (Tourist library, v. 5)

1. Gardens – Japan.   I. Japan Travel Bureau.   II. Title.

NT 0051150   NIC IU NNC DNAL

Tatsui, Matsunosuke, 1884–
Japanese gardens. ₍Tokyo₎ Japan Travel Bureau ₍ᶜ1949₎
70 p. illus. (part col.) 19 cm. (Tourist library. ₍New series₎ 5)
Bibliography: p. 70.

1. Gardens—Japan. ɪ. Title. (Series)

SB466.J3T28 1949   712.6   50–12558

NT 0051151   DLC OrP Wa OC1 CU MShM

SB466
.J3
T3
1949
Tatsui, Matsunosuke, 1884– ₍5th ed. Tokyo₎ Japan
Japanese gardens. Travel Bureau ₍1949₎
70 p. col. front., illus., plates. 19 cm.
(Tourist library: 5)

Bibliography: p.70.

1. Gardening – Japan. 2. Gardens – Japan.
i. t. ii. s.

NT 0051152   NNBG

SB
466
J3T28x
1952
Tatsui, Matsunosuke, 1884–
Japanese gardens / by Matsunosuke
Tatsui. Tokyo ; Japan Travel Bureau,
1952.
70 p., [19] leaves of plates : ill,
19 cm. (Tourist library. [New series]
5)
Bibliography: p. 70.
Includes index.

1. Gardens—Japan. I. Title
II. Series

NT 0051153   NmU TxFTC OrP

712
T188j
1952
Arch
Lib'y
Tatsui, Matsunosuke, 1884–
Japanese gardens. [6th rev. ed.] Tokyo,
Japan Travel Bureau [1952]
70p. illus.(part col) 19cm. (Tourist
library. [New series] 5)

Bibliography: p.70.

1. Gardens – Japan. I. Title. II. Series.

NT 0051154   TxU IU PBm PPMoI NcRS IEN CU–S PU

DS
821
.T6
v.5
Tatsui, Matsunosuke, 1884–
Japanese gardens. Tokyo, Japan Travel
Bureau ₍1953, c1952₎
70 p. (Tourist library series, v.5)

1. Gardens–Japan. I. Title. II. Series.

NT 0051155   DAU

Tatsui, Matsunosuke, 1884–
(Josei Nihon shi)
女性日本史 / 龍居松之助著. — 東京：章華社，
昭和8 ₍1933₎, 昭和10 ₍1935₎ printing.
308 p., ₍5₎ leaves of plates : ill. ; 23 cm.

1. Women—Japan—Social conditions. 2. Women—Japan—Biography.
I. Title.
HQ1762.T37 1935   77–813139

NT 0051156   DLC

Tatsui, Matsunosuke, 1884–
日本名園記 龍居松之助著 東京 嵩山房 大
正 13 ₍1924₎
10, 5, 195 p. illus. 28 cm.

1. Gardens—Japan. ɪ. Title. *Title romanised: Nihon meien ki.*
J 59–2593

Hoover Institution
for Library of Congress

NT 0051157   CSt–H

Tatsui, Matsunosuke, 1884–
₍Teien to fūzoku₎
庭園と風俗 龍居松之助著 ₍東京₎ 雄山閣
₍1929?₎
2, 120 p. illus. (part col.) 23 cm. (₍日本風俗史講座 第15号₎)

1. Gardens—Japan—History. ɪ. Title. II. Series: Nihon fū-
zoku shi kōza, dai 15–gō.
SB466.J3T29   72–804032

NT 0051158   DLC

Tatsujirō Honda
    see   Honda, Tatsujirō, 1868–

Tatsujirō Kumagai
   see
Kumagai, Tatsujirō.

Tatsuki, Yasuo.
General trend of Japanese opinion following the end of
war, based especially on public opinion surveys. Tokyo,
Nihon Taiheiyo Mondai Chosakai (Japan Institute of
Pacific Studies); distributed by International Pub. Co.,
1948.
54 p. 21 cm. (Pacific studies series)

1. Public opinion—Japan. ɪ. Title. (Series: Japan Institute
of Pacific Studies. Pacific studies series)
DS889.T3   301.154   48–27211*

WAS CaBVaU
NT 0051161   DLC PPD OU ScU ViU CSt–H CtY TxU CU OrU

HG5780
.M3M55
Orien
Japan
Tatsuki, Yasuo.
Minami Manshū Tetsudō Kabushiki Kaisha. Sōsai-
shitsu. Kōhōka.
(Nihon no taiman tōshi)
日本ノ對滿投資 ₍大連 南滿洲鐵道株式會社₎
總裁室弘報課 昭和13₍1938₎

Tatsukichi, Minobe
   see
Minobe, Tatsukichi, 1873–1948.

TATSUMI, HENRY SABURO.
Idiomatic Japanese; forms of greeting, useful phrases
pronunciation. Seattle, Far Eastern press, 1950.
6 p. 22cm. (Far Eastern language series. no. A–2)

1. Japanese language—Conversation and phrase books, English. I. Far
Eastern language series.

NT 0051164   NN WaS MB

495.25
T188t
TATSUMI, Henry Saburo
Simplified grammar table of the spoken
Japanese; a complete grammar condensed on
one chart. Seattle, Washington, The au-
thor, 1936.
4 p. fold. table in pocket at back.
Cover title.
Photostat of the original in the Univer-
sity of Washington archives.
Copy 1, negative.

NT 0051165   WaU CU–EAST WaS WaT

495.28
T188s
Tatsumi, Henry Saburo
Standard Japanese readers study aid.
Book 1–5. Boulder, Col., U. S. Navy
Language School, University of Colorado,
1946.
5 v. in 6

Reproduced from typewritten copy.

1. Japanese language – Text-books for
foreigners – English. I. Title.

NT 0051166   WaU

495.2
T18s
TATSUMI, Henry Saburo
Standard spoken Japanese; synoptical syn-
tactic charts for students and translators.
Seattle, Far Eastern press, 1949.
10 p. (Far Eastern language series, no. A–
1)

1. Japanese language – Grammar. I. Title.
II. Series.

NT 0051167   WaU

HB221
.H63
Orien
Japan
Tatsumi, Hirokazu, 1913–   joint author.
Hisatake, Masao, 1903–
(Kakaku riron) 価格理論 久武雅夫・巽博一著
₍東京₎ 春秋社 ₍1955₎

Tatsumi, Hirokazu, 1913–
ケインズ雇傭理論の分析－貨幣經濟の限界－巽
博一著 東京 日本評論社 昭和23 ₍1948₎
184 p. illus. 19 cm.

1. Keynes, John Maynard, 1883–1946. The general theory of em-
ployment, interest and money. ɪ. Title.
Title romanised: Keinzu koyō riron no bunseki.
HB171.K46T3   J 61–1728 ‡

NT 0051169   DLC

Tatsumi, Ineo, *pseud.*
   see
Takagi, Sōkichi, 1893–

Tatsumi, Keisei.
(Shihonron tokuhon)
資本論讀本 辰巳經世著 ₍東京₎ 清和書店
₍昭和10 i.e. 1935₎
198 p. 22 cm.

1. Marx, Karl, 1818–1883. Das Kapital. I. Title.
HB501.T3725   74–818890

NT 0051171   DLC

Tatsumi, Seika, 1905–
　〔Manshū no tsubame〕
　滿洲の燕　巽聖歌著　〔東京　中央公論社　昭
和18 i.e. 1943〕
　171 p.　illus.　18 cm.
　Poems.

　1. Manchuria—Description and travel—Poetry. 2. Poetry of places—Manchuria. I. Title.
　PL839.A77M3   72–805332

NT　0051172　DLC

TN145
.C45
Orien
Japan
    Tatsumi, Tatsuo, 1916–   ed.
　(Chika shigen)
　地下資源　災害と自然の改造　立見辰雄責任監修
羽賀貞四郎〔等〕執筆　〔東京　福村書店　1955〕

Tatsumi, Toshifumi, joint author.
Uemura, Rokurō, 1894–
　(Man'yō senshoku kō)
　萬葉染色考　上村六郎・辰巳利文著　東京　古
今書院　〔1930〕

Tatsumi, Toshifumi, comp.
　(Man'yōshū ron kō)
　萬葉集論考　辰巳利文編　山田考雄〔等〕著　佐
々木信綱序　東京　素人社書屋　昭和7 i.e.
1932〕
　6, 334 p.　23 cm.
　本書に收められた論文はすべて雑誌「奈良文化」誌上に掲載されたものに...筆を加へたものである
　1. Man'yōshū—Addresses, essays, lectures. I. Yamada, Yoshio, 1873–1958. II. Nara bunka. III. Title.
　PL728.173.T37   75–790695

NT　0051175　DLC

BF708
.J3T295
Orien
Japan
    Tatsuno, Chitoshi, 1920–   joint author.
Takemasa, Tarō, 1887–
　発達心理学概説　武政太郎・辰野千寿共著　〔東
京〕金子書房　〔1955〕

Tatsuno, Kyūshi, 1892–1962.
　(Aisei tsūshin)
　愛婿通信：ユーモア小説 / 辰野九紫著. — 東
京：南方書院，昭和16 〔1941〕
　314 p.；19 cm.
　Short stories.
　CONTENTS: 愛婿通信—表養—泥棒に告ぐ—駄猫太平記—お嬢ちゃん・坊ちゃん—御活風—軍國カメラ風脈—ぜんそく三銃士

　I. Title.
　PL839.A778A7   77–801785

NT　0051177　DLC

Tatsuno, Kyūshi, 1892–1962.
　(Meibutsu dōchū sugoroku)
　名物道中双六 / 辰野九紫著. — 東京：紫文閣，
昭和17 〔1942〕
　339 p.；19 cm.
　Short stories.
　CONTENTS: 名物道中双六—十六夜清心—四谷怪談—御守殿お熊—われらの虎徹—塚原卜傳—待たる、春—お伽快談・桃太郎—蛇だ・流だ・石炭だ！—これでも重役？—一貫衣裳は語る—舞疊の延長—スポーツ漫談

　I. Title.
　PL839.A778M44   77–803432

NT　0051178　DLC

Tatsuno, Kyūshi, 1892–1962.
　(Migawari shachō)
　身代り社長 / 辰野九紫著. — 東京：東成社，
昭和16 〔1941〕
　296 p.：19 cm. — 〔ユーモア文庫〕
　Fiction.
　Series romanized: Yūmoa bunko.

　I. Title.
　PL839.A778M5   77–803490

NT　0051179　DLC

Tatsuno, Nobuyuki
　　see
Tateno, Nobuyuki, 1903–

Tatsuno, Takashi
　　see
Tatsuno, Yutaka, 1888–1964.

PL758
.R4
Orien
Japan
    Tatsuno, Teiichi, 1889–
　(Rekidai kōgō miuta tokuhon)
　歴代皇后御歌讀本 / 小西重直序文，皆川治廣序文；
龍野定一謹編. — 東京：愛之事業社，昭和15
〔1940〕

Tatsuno, Teiichi, 1889–   comp.
　(Shindō jissen kyōten rekidai gyosei to goseitoku)
　臣道實踐教典歴代御製と御聖德　〔龍野定一輯
東京　日本文化研究會　昭和18 i.e. 1943〕
　〔46〕, 910, 〔109〕p.　26 cm.
　Bibliography: p. 〔11〕–〔14〕 (3d group)

　1. Japanese poetry. 2. Kings and rulers as poets. 3. Japan—Emperors—Biography. I. Japan. Sovereigns, etc. II. Title: Rekidai gyosei to goseitoku.
　PL757.T38   73–819256

NT　0051183　DLC

LB3605
.D24
Orien
Japan
    Tatsuno, Yutaka, 1888–1964, ed.
　(Daigaku seikatsu daini)
　大學生活第二　〔神西清等著〕　辰野隆編　〔東京〕
光文社　〔昭和25 i.e. 1950〕

Tatsuno, Yutaka, 1888–1964.
　(Furansu bungaku)
　佛蘭西文學　辰野隆著　〔東京〕　白水社
〔1954–
　v.　port.　21 cm.

　1. French literature—History and criticism. I. Title.
　PQ139.T319   72–802399

NT　0051185　DLC

Tatsuno, Yutaka, 1888–1964.
　フランス文學入門　辰野隆〔著　東京〕要書房
〔1951〕
　148 p.　19 cm.　〔要選書 18〕
　Colophon inserted.

　1. French literature—History and criticism. I. Title.
　　　　　Title romanized: Furansu bungaku nyūmon.
　PQ139.T32   70–821201

NT　0051186　DLC

Tatsuno, Yutaka, 1888–
　人生遍路　辰野隆著　東京　青林書院　昭和
28 〔1953〕
　278 p.　illus.　19 cm.
　Reminiscences.

　I. Title.
　　　　　Title romanized: Jinsei henro.
　PL713.T3A3   J 61–1601 ‡

NT　0051187　DLC

Tatsuno, Yutaka, 1888–   *ed.*
　近代日本の教養人　日夏耿之介博士華甲記念
文集　辰野隆編　東京　實業之日本社　昭和25
〔1950〕
　329 p.　ports.　19 cm.
　日夏耿之介博士著作年表: p. 316–327.
　　　　　For locations see Union Catalogs
　　　　　in Orientalia Division
　1. Authors, Japanese—Addresses, essays, lectures. 2. Hinatsu, Kōnosuke, pseud. I. Title.
　　　　　Title romanized: Kindai Nihon no kyōyōjin.
　PL723.T36   J 65–583

NT　0051188　DLC CSt-H

Tatsuno, Yutaka, 1886–1964.
　(Minami no kaze)
　南の風　佛蘭西飜案戯曲集　辰野隆〔著　再版
東京〕　白水社　〔1952〕
　249 p.　illus.　19 cm.
　CONTENTS: 南の風—父と子—一客一偶友

　I. Title.
　PL839.A79M5   72–804567

NT　0051189　DLC

Tatsuno, Yutaka, 1888–1964.
　(Nigorizake)
　濁り酒　辰野隆著　〔東京〕　創元社　〔1949〕
　306 p.　port.　19 cm.　(創元選書 177)
　Essays.
　List of the author's works: p. 299–306.

　I. Title.
　PL839.A79N5   74–818563

NT　0051190　DLC

Tatsuno, Yutaka, 1888–1964.
　老若問答　辰野隆〔著　東京〕　要書房　〔1950〕
　4, 230 p.　19 cm.
　Colophon inserted.

　I. Title.
　　　　　Title romanized: Rōnyaku mondō.
　AC146.T36   73–820185

NT　0051191　DLC

TP579
.S32
Orien
Japan
    Tatsuno, Yutaka, 1888–1964, ed.
　(Sakedangi)
　酒談義　辰野隆〔等編　東京　日本交通公社出版部
1949–50〕

Tatsuno, Yutaka, 1888–1964.
　(Tanizaki Jun'ichirō)
　谷崎潤一郎　辰野隆〔著　東京　イヴニング・ス
ター社　昭和22 i.e. 1947〕
　120 p.　19 cm.

　1. Tanizaki, Jun'ichirō, 1888–1964.
　PL839.A7Z845   72–804271

NT　0051193　DLC

Tatsuno, Yutaka, 1888–1964.
辰野隆選集 ｛東京｝ 改造社 ｛1948–50; v. 1,
1949｝
5 v. 19 cm.
Chiefly essays.
Bibliography: v. 3, p. 209–212.
CONTENTS.—1–2. 佛蘭西文學考—3. ボオドレエルとルナ
アル—4. 忘れ得ぬ人々と谷崎潤一郎—5. 信天翁の眼玉
1. French literature — Addresses, essays, lectures. 2. Authors,
Japanese—Correspondence, reminiscences, etc.
Title romanized: Tatsuno Yutaka senshū.

PQ139.T33   J 68–2102

NT   0051194   DLC

Tatsuno, Yutaka, 1888–1964.
(Zuihitsu senshū)
随筆選集 / 辰野隆. — 東京：要書房, 昭和21
｛1946｝, 昭和26 ｛1951｝ printing.
4, 344 p. ; 19 cm.
Essays.
Colophon inserted.

PL839.A79A16   1951   76–807639

NT   0051195   DLC

PS221
.T33
1941
Orien
Japan
Tatsunokuchi, Naotarō, 1903–   joint author.
Takagaki, Matsuo, 1890–1940.
｛Gendai no Amerika bungaku｝
現代のアメリカ文學 高垣松雄・龍口直太郎・杉
木喬共編 ｛東京｝ 三省堂 ｛昭和16 i. e. 1941｝

Tatsuo Honda
    see Honda, Tatsuo, 1904–

PL767
.N54
dai 8
Orien
Japan
Tatsuoka, Mansaku, 1742–1809. Aneimoto Date no ōkido.
1931.
(Kansei-ki Keihan adauchi kyōgen shū)
寛政期京坂仇討狂言集 / ｛編纂者 渥美清太
郎｝. — 東京：春陽堂, 昭和6 ｛1931｝

PL767
.N54
dai 8
Orien
Japan
Tatsuoka, Mansaku, 1742–1809. Katakiuchi An'ei roku.
1931.
(Kansei-ki Keihan adauchi kyōgen shū)
寛政期京坂仇討狂言集 / ｛編纂者 渥美清太
郎｝. — 東京：春陽堂, 昭和6 ｛1931｝

PL767
.N54
dai 7
Orien
Japan
Tatsuoka, Mansaku, 1742–1809. Keisei haru no tori. 1930.
(Kansei-ki Keihan jidai kyōgen shū)
寛政期京坂時代狂言集 / ｛編纂者 渥美清太
郎｝. — 東京：春陽堂, 昭和5 ｛1930｝

Tatsuta, Eizan, 1893–
(Seibutsu kagaku gairon)
生物科學概論 立田鐡二｛英山｝著 東京 前野
書店 ｛昭和6 i. e. 1931｝
2, 6, 247, 33 p. illus. 23 cm.
本書は高等學校文科に學ぶ諸君の爲に編輯したもの

1. Biology.   I. Title.
QH308.T32   73–818985

NT   0051201   DLC

Tatsuta, Eizan, 1893–
(Shimpen Hekiganshū kōwa)
新編碧巖集講話 / 立田英山著. — 市川：人間
禪教團；東京：発売所 オクムラ書店, 昭和28
｛1953｝
2, 2, 7, 619 p. ; 22 cm.
Colophon inserted.
「本書…は昭和｛二｝一年末から…二十六年い…たるまで人間禪教用信心
會において行われた…碧巖集提唱を…筆記したものを底本としそれに若干
の訂正を加え…たもの」

1. Hsüeh-tou, 980–1052. Pi yen lu.   I. Yüan-wu, 1063–1135.   II.
Hsüeh-tou, 980–1052. Pi yen lu. Japanese. Selections. 1953.   III. Title.
BQ9289.H783T37   75–793966

NT   0051203   DLC

Tatsuta, Shinobu.
｛Nihon sangyō kumiai ron｝
日本產業組合論 立田信夫著 東京 巖文閣
｛昭和15 i. e. 1940｝
5, 6, 352 p. 23 cm.
Includes bibliographical references.

1. Cooperation—Japan.   I. Title.
HD3547.A4T36   72–805918

NT   0051204   DLC

Tatsutaro Hida
    see Hida, Tatsutaro.

Tatsuwaka Shibuya
    see Shibuya, Tatsuwaka.

Tatsuyama, Chikayasu.
(Hama no isago)
濱のいさこ ｛龍山親祇著 横濱 昭和5 i. e.
1930｝
248 p. illus. 23 cm.

1. Kōtai Jingū. Yokohama.   2. Yokohama—History.   I. Title.
BL2225.Y6K67   73–817241

NT   0051207   DLC

Case
F
39
.326
1585ta
TATT, CHARLES.
    Brief discours de la magnifique reception
faicte par la Maiesté du roy Henry troisiesme…
aux ambassadeurs des puissans & libres potentats,
Suisses, Grisons, & leurs coalliez…   Paris, Chez
I. Mettayer, 1585.
    38, ｛1｝ p.   illus., fold. plate, port.   21 cm.

    Bibl. nat. Cat. de l'histoire de France,
v. 1, p. 304, no. 206.

NT   0051208   ICN

Tatta, Ken'ichi, 1891–1942.
(Chūtō muki kagaku)
中等無機化學 / 立田謙一著. — 東京：理化學
出版社：發賣所 工業圖書, 昭和16 ｛1941｝
8, 188 p. : ill. ; 22 cm.
Includes index.

1. Chemistry, Inorganic.   I. Title.
QD151.T29   75–794062

NT   0051209   DLC

QD453
.I 47
Orien
Japan
Tatta, Ken'ichi, 1891–1942, joint author.
Ikenoya, Kinjirō, 1900–
(Shokyū butsuri kagaku)
初級物理化學 池谷金次郎・立田謙一共著 増
補9版 ｛東京：産業圖書 ｛昭和25 i. e. 1950｝

PQ4843
A776
F2
Tatta, Vito
    Le facce della vita.   Milano, Gastaldi
｛1952｝
    186 p.   19 cm.   (Narratori d'oggi)

NT   0051211   RPB

Tattabhusan, Hemchandra Goswami
    see
    Goswami, Hemchandra, 1872–1928.

Tattam, Charles Maurice.
    … The metamorphic rocks of north-east Victoria, by C. M.
Tattam …   Melbourne, Australia, H. J. Green, government
printer, 1929.
    52 p. incl. illus., tables, diagrs.   x pl., fold. col. map.   24½ᵐ.   (Vic-
toria ｛Australia｝ Geological survey. Bulletin no. 52)
    At head of title: Victoria. Department of mines.

    1. Rocks, Crystalline and metamorphic.   I. Title.
                                    [QE347.A2 no. 52]   G S 30–72
    Library, U. S. Geological   Survey   (830) E no. 52

NT   0051213   DI-GS MtBuM OC1

Tattam, Charles Maurice.
Swinton, William Elgin, 1900–
    … On fossil *Reptilia* from Sokoto province, with 15 plates
and a map. By William Elgin Swinton … With a Preliminary note on the sedimentary rocks of Sokoto province, by
Dr. C. Raeburn and Dr. C. M. Tattam … ｛London｝ Published
by the Nigerian government, 1930.

Tattam, George J.   No. 10 in **M.190.8**
    A plain Te Deum. With solos for S. and T.
New York. Ditson & Co. 1876. (1), 2 pp. F°.

    F1193 — Te Deum. — Church music. Anthems, &c.

NT   0051215   MB

Tattam, Henry, 1789–1868, *ed. and tr.*
    The ancient Coptic version of the
Book of Job, the Just…   London,
1846   ｛Coptic and English｝
    see under Bible. O. T. Job.
Coptic (Bohaïric). 1846.

PJ408
.O6
vol. 63
Tattam, Henry, 1789–1868, ed. and tr.
Egyptian Heptateuch.
    The apostolical constitutions, or canons of the apostles in
Coptic. With an English translation by Henry Tattam …
London, Printed for the Oriental translation fund of Great
Britain and Ireland, 1848.

Tattam, Henry, 1789–1868.
A compendious grammar of the Egyptian language ... with an appx. consisting of the ancient Egyptian language... by Thomas Young.   London, 1830.
152 p.

NT 0051218   PPWe

Tattam, Henry, 1789–1868.
A compendious grammar of the Egyptian language as contained in the Coptic and Sahidic dialects; with observations on the Bashmuric: together with alphabets and numerals in the hieroglyphic and enchorial characters ... by the Rev. Henry Tattam ... With an appendix, consisting of the rudiments of a dictionary of the ancient Egyptian language in the enchorial character: by Thomas Young ...   London, J. and A. Arch, 1830.
xiv, 152 p., 2 l., ₍iii₎–x, 24 p., 1 l., 110, xv p.   4 pl. (1 fold.)   22ᶜᵐ.
The appendix has special t.-p. and separate paging.
1. Coptic language—Grammar.   2. Egyptian language—Writing.
I. Young, Thomas, 1773–1829.

Library of Congress   PJ2033.T3   11–⁵5458

NT 0051219   DLC CtY NBB MH CU MiU NN NjP DCU-H

Tattam, Henry, 1789–1868.
A compendious grammar of the Egyptian language as contained in the Coptic, Sahidic, and Bashmuric dialects; together with alphabets and numerals in the hieroglyphic and enchorial characters.   By the Rev. Henry Tattam ... 2d ed., rev. and improved. London and Edinburgh, Williams & Norgate, 1863.
xxiv, ₍4₎, 127 p.   24ᶜᵐ.

1. Coptic language—Grammar.   2. Egyptian language—Writing.

Library of Congress   PJ2033.T3 1863   13–21423

NT 0051220   DLC CtY NjNbS OCl PU MiD NjP MB IU NjP

Tattam, Henry, 1789–1868.
Compendious grammar of the Egyptian language ... app. ... by T. Young.   London, 1880.

Tattam, Henry, 1789–1868.
Compendious grammar of the Egyptian language ... app. ... by T. Young.   London, 1880.

NT 0051221   NjP

Tattam, Henry, 1789–1868, ed.
... Duodecim prophetarum minorum libros in lingua AEgyptiaca, vulgo Coptica seu Memphitica, ex manuscripto Parisiensi descriptos et cum manuscripto Johannis Lee collatos, Latine edidit H. Tattam.
Oxonii, 1836.
        see under   Bible. O.T. Minor prophets. Coptic (Bohairic) 1836.

1789-1868.
Tattam, Henry. A grammar of the Egyptian language as contained in the Coptic and Sahidic dialects; with observations on the Bashmuric: together with alphabets and numerals in the hieroglyphic and enchorial characters. London. 1830. 8°.   2265.11

NT 0051223   MH

Tattam, Henry, 1789–1868.
Lexicon ægyptiaco-latinum, ex veteribus linguæ ægyptiacæ monumentis, et ex operibus La Crozii, Woidii, et aliorum, summo studio congestum. Cum indice vocum latinarum. Ab Henrico Tattam ... Oxonii, e Typographeo academico, 1835.
vii, 958 p.   22ᶜᵐ.

1. Coptic language—Dictionaries—Latin.   2. Latin language—Dictionaries—Coptic.

                                11–13642
Library of Congress   PJ2181.T3

DCU-H MH
NT 0051224   DLC CCSC PPAmP PU ICU NjNbS NNUT NN

Tattam, Henry, 1789–1868.
Lexicon Aeguptiaes Latinum.   Oxford, 1885.

NT 0051225   NRCR

276.57 Tattam, Henry, 1789–1868.
T 221   Macarius the Great;–Homilies translated into Arabic for the use of the Coptic Church.   1846.
352 p.   23 cm.

NT 0051226   DCU-H

Tattam, Henry, 1789–1868, ed.
Prophetae majores in dialecto linguae Aegypticae Memphitica seu Coptica. Edidit cum versione Latina Henricus Tattam...
Oxonii, 1852
            see under   Bible. O.T. Major prophets. Coptic (Bohairic) 1852.

PJ2181 **Tattam, Henry,** 1789–1868.
.P3
        Parthey, Gustav Friedrich Constantin, 1798–1872.
Vocabularium Coptico-Latinum et Latino-Copticum e Peyroni et Tattami lexicis concinnavit G. Parthey. Berolini, F. Nicolai, 1844.

LD3907 Tattan, James Vincent, 1926–
.G7   Effects of electroshock convulsions
1954   on learning in rats as a function of
.T2   age.
        104p.   tables, diagrs.
        Thesis (Ph.D.) – N.Y.U., Graduate
        School, 1954.
        Bibliography: p.90–104.

NT 0051229   NNU-W

KE   Tattarano, Constantin N
1145   De la nature du mariage et des nullités qui
T38   le vicient à Rome, en France et en Roumanie /
        par Constantin N. Tattarano. -- Paris : A.
        Cotillon, 1880.

        1. Marriage law – France.   2. Marriage –
Annulment – France.   3. Marriage (Roman law).
4. Marriage – Annulment – Romania.   I. Title.

NT 0051230   CLU

Tattarinoff, Adrianus, b.1731, respondent.
Dissertatio medica inauguralis De pleuritide vera singulari casu illustrata
        see under   Richter, Georg Gottlob, 1694–1773, praeses.

Tattavī, Mīr ‘Alī Shīr Qāni‘
    see
‘Alī Shīr Qāni‘ Tattavī, Mīr, 1727 or 8–1788 or 9.

Tattay (Josephus). *De gurgulionis prolapsu.
34 pp., 1 l. 12°. *Buda, typ. C. Landerer vidua,*
₍1783₎.

NT 0051233   DNLM

Tattegrain, André.
... La fleur, médiatrice entre la pierre et l'homme ... Paris, Revue de la presse ₍*1938₎
4 p. l., ₍1₎–146 p., 2 l. 19¼ᶜᵐ.
"Édition originale."

1. Plants.   2. Flowers.   I. Title.
                                        40–23263
Library of Congress   QK46.T37 1938
Copyright A—Foreign   43006
                             ₍2₎   580

NT 0051234   DLC

Tattegrain, Henry.
... Le décor du livre, par Henry Tattegrain ... Causerie faite en l'Hôtel du Cercle de la librairie ... le 15 décembre 1923. ₍Foix, Imprimerie Gadrat aîné, 1923₎
19 p. 25ᶜᵐ.
At head of title: Conférences de la Société des aquafortistes français.
"Ouvrages à consulter": p. 19.

1. Book ornamentation.   2. Illustration of books.   I. Title.
                                        28–21625
Library of Congress   Z276.T22

NT 0051235   DLC OCU ICRL

BV   **Tattegrain, Robert**
192   Du temporel des bénéfices ecclésiastiques sous
.W2   l'ancien régime. Paris, Larose & Forcel, 1909.
T22   199 p. 25cm.
        "Bibliographie": p. ₍5₎–8.

        1. Benefices (Canon law)   2. Benefices,
Ecclesiastical - France.

NT 0051236   DCU

BQV192 Tattegrain, Robert
.W2   Du temporel des bénéfices ecclésiastiques sous
T221   l'ancien régime. Paris, Libraire de la Société
1909   du Recueil J.B. Sirey, 1909.
        199 p.

        Thèse. Paris. Faculté de Droit.
        Bibliography: p. ₍5₎–8.

        1.Benefices , Ecclesiastical (Canon law).
        I. Title.

NT 0051237   CU-L

Tattelbaum, Harvey Morton
Messianism in Jewish history; an interpretive
study in collective behavior, by Harvey M. Tattelbaum

Honors thesis - Harvard, 1955

NT 0051238   MH

Tattenbach, Eberhard Graf von, a. Landshut: Die Zuhälterei. Würzburg 1915: Memminger. 62 S. 8°
Würzburg, Rechts- u. staatswiss. Diss. v. 20. Mai 1915, Ref. Oetker
₍Geb. 6. Nov. 87 Frankfurt a. M.; Wohnort: Würzburg; Staatsangeh.: Bayern; Vorbildung: G. Büdingen Reife 06; Studium: München 1, Berlin 1, München 3, Würzburg 10 S.; Rig. 21. Juli 14.₎   ₍U 15.650

NT 0051239   ICRL PU MH-L

Tattenbach, Johann Erasmus, gróf, 1631–1671, defendant.
Aussführliche vnd warhaffte beschreibung wie es mit dem criminal-process vnd der darauff zu Grätz den 1. December 1671 erfolgten execution wider Johann Erasam von Tätenpach eigentlich hergangen. Wienn, Matthaeo Cosmerovio, 1672.
1 p.l., ₍24₎ p., 24 l. (part. fold.)
illus. 27½cm.

NT 0051240   MH-L

Tattenbach, Rázmán
   see   Tattenbach, Johann Erasmus, gráf, 1631-1671.

Tatter, Georgius Martinus, respondent.
   Disputationem anatomicam de sanguine peridromo
   See under   Major, Johann Daniel, 1634-1693, praeses.

Tatter, Henry.
   ... The preferential treatment of the actual settler in the primary disposition of the vacant lands in the United States; preemption: prelude to homesteadism ... by Henry Tatter. Evanston, Ill., 1932.
   2 p. l., ii-v, 517 (*i. e.* 516) xiv numb. l. 27½cm.
   Thesis (PH. D.)—Northwestern university.
   Type-written.
   Error in paging: no. 463 omitted.
   Bibliography: leaves i-xiv at end.
   1. Preemption law—U. S. 2. Squatter sovereignty. 3. Homestead law—U. S. I. Title.

   Library of Congress   HD197 1932a   34-7998
    (2)   336.130973

NT   0051243   DLC

HD197   Tatter, Henry.
1932   The preferential treatment of the actual settler in the primary disposition of the vacant lands in the United States to 1841, by Henry Tatter... (Evanston, Ill.) 1933.
   cover-title, p.89-95.   23cm.

   "Reprinted from Summaries of Ph.D. dissertations, volume 1, 1933."
   "The dissertation of which the preceding is an abstract was written under the guidance of   Professor I. J. Cox."

NT   0051244   MnHi

Tatter, Henry.
   State and federal land policy during the confederation period, by Henry Tatter... [Baltimore? Md., 1935]
   cover-title, p. 176-186.   26 cm.
   "Reprinted from Agricultural history, vol. 9, no. 4, October, 1935."
   1. U.S. Public lands. I. Title.

NT   0051245   IEN

SB357   **TATTER, W.**
.T22   Anleitung zur obsttreiberei, von W. Tatter... Stuttgart, E. Ulmer, 1879.
   (iii)-x, 336 p.   illus., diagrs.   21½cm.

   1. Fruit-culture.

NT   0051246   ICU

Tatter, W.
   Die praktische Obst-Treiberei sowohl in Treibhäusern, Treibkräften und Mistbeeten, wie auch in Talutmauern, bearbeitet für den praktischen Gärtner.   **3992.8**
   Hamburg. Kittler. 1861. vi, 228 pp. Illus. Plans. Tables. 21 cm., in 8s.

   M3806 — Fruit and fruit trees. — Forcing plants.

NT   0051247   MB

Tatter, W
   Das wichtigste aus der obsttreiberei. Unter zugrundlegung des vierten bandes der "Bibliothek für wissenschaft". Stuttgart, E. Ulmer, 1879.
   68 p.

NT   0051248   CU-A MB

Tattered battlements; a Malta diary, by a fighter pilot ... London, P. Davies (1943)
   2 p. l., 134 p. - plates, ports. 19cm.
   "First published June 1943. Second edition July 1943."

   1. World war, 1939- —Malta. 2. World war, 1939- —Personal narratives, English. I. A fighter pilot.

            A 44-148
   Harvard univ. Library
   for Library of Congress   (C)

NT   0051249   MH GU FTaSU

Tatters, *pseud.*
   The Diary of a Dog; three months in Kashmir... see under title

LB575   Tattersal, William.
.P7A2   Religious declension: a sermon preached before the dissenting ministers of Lancashire and Cheshire at their annual meeting at Bolton, June, 20, 1787. By William Tattersal. Warrington, Printed by W. Eyres, for J. Johnson, 1787.
   24 p.   21cm.   [With Priestley, Joseph. Miscellaneous observations relating to education... 1778]

   1. Religion-Addresses, essays, lectures.

NT   0051251   ICU

281.372   **Tattersall, Arthur.**
T18   Cotton. London [1950?]
   11 p.   (Purchasing Officers Association. Raw material survey series. no. 12)

   1. Cotton. Economic aspects. I. Purchasing Officers Association. Raw material survey series, no. 12)

NT   0051252   DNAL

TATTERSALL, Arthur C., compiler.
   The merry songsters' song book; favourite nursery rhymes. London, Weekes & Co., [18-?]
   4°.

NT   0051253   MH

Tattersall, Arthur Ewart.
   Modern developments in railway signalling. A treatise dealing with the theory and application of—(1) track-circuiting; (2) power signalling and (3) automatic train control. By A. E. Tattersall ... London, The "Railway engineer", 1921.
   4 p. l., 299 p. illus., diagrs. 22½cm.

   1. Railroads—Signaling. 2. Automatic train control.

            A 21-2045
   Title from bureau of   Railway Economics. Printed by L C

NT   0051254   DBRE ICJ NN

(Tattersall, Arthur Ewart) *ed.*
   Railway signalling and communications, installation and maintenance ... London, The St. Margaret's technical press limited (1940)
   xv, (1), 416 p. incl. illus., plates, diagrs. 2 pl. on 1 l. 22cm.
   On cover: 1st ed.
   Based on lectures, by A. E. Tattersall, E. G. Brentnall, J. H. Devine and others, given at training schools of the London and north eastern railway. A. E. Tattersall arranged the syllabus and edited the text, which has been prepared for publication by T. S. Lascelles. *cf.* Pref.
   1. Railroads—Signaling. 2. Railroads—Telegraph. 3. Railroads—Telephone. I. Lascelles, T. S. II. London and north eastern railway. III. Title.

   Library of Congress   TF615.T3   41-25583
    (4)   625.16

NT   0051255   DLC CaBVa

625.16   [TATTERSALL, ARTHUR EWART] ed.
T189r   Railway signalling and communications, 1946   installation and maintenance ... London, The
Engin   St. Margaret's technical press, ltd., 1946.
Lib'y   xv, (1), 416 p. incl. illus., plates, diagrs. 2 pl. on 1 l. 22cm.
   On cover: 2nd ed.
   Based on lectures, by A.E. Tattersall, E.G. Brentnall, J.H. Devine and others, given at training schools of the London and north eastern railway. A.E. Tattersall arranged the syllabus and edited the text, which has been prepared for publication by T.S. Lascelles.—cf. Pref.
   1. Railroads - Signaling. 2. Railroads - Telegraph. 3. Railroads - Telephone. I. Lascelles, T.S. II. London and north eastern railway. III. Title.

NT   0051257   TxU AzU

Mann
SF   Tattersall, C   H
472   A treatise on the dragoon pigeon, by
T22   C. H. Tattersall and S. F. Butterworth. Idle, Bradford (Eng.), "Pigeons", 1908.
   123 p. plates (part col.) plans. 22 cm.

   1. Pigeons. I. Butterworth, S
F   II. Title.

NT   0051258   NIC

Tattersall, Creassey Edward Cecil, 1877-
   The carpets of Persia; a book for those who use and admire them, by Creassey Tattersall ... London, Luzac & company, 1931.
   52 p. front., illus., xxxii pl., map. 19cm.
   "Published for the International exhibition of Persian art, Royal academy, 1931."

   1. Rugs, Persian. 2. Carpets. I. London. Royal academy of arts.

   Library of Congress   NK2809.P4T3   31-29179
    745

NT   0051259   DLC OCl OClMA OClW MiU NN MB PPPM MH-FA

Tattersall, Creassey Edward Cecil, 1877-
   Victoria and Albert museum, *South Kensington. Dept. of textiles.*
   Fine carpets in the Victoria & Albert museum; twenty examples, reproduced for the first time in colour, of old carpets from Persia, India, Caucasia, Armenia, Turkey, China, Spain and England, with an introduction and descriptive notes by A. F. Kendrick ... and C. E. C. Tattersall. London, E. Benn limited, 1924.

Tattersall, Creassey Edward Cecil, 1877-
   joint author.
   Kendrick, Albert Frank, 1872-
   Hand-woven carpets, Oriental and European, by A. F. Kendrick ... and C. E. C. Tattersall, with 205 plates, of which 19 are in colour. London, Benn brothers, limited, 1922.

Tattersall, Creassey Edward Cecil, 1877–
A history of British carpets, from the introduction of the craft until the present day, by C. E. C. Tattersall ... Benfleet, Essex, Eng., F. Lewis limited ₁1934₎

182 l. col. front., illus., cxvi pl. (part col.; incl. port., 2 facsim.) on 58 l. 32½ x 25 cm.
"First published 1934."
"List of British carpet manufacturers": p. 178–182.

1. Carpets. 2. Textile industry and fabrics—Gt. Brit. ɪ. Title.

TS1775.T3   [745] 677.640942   34—18006

PU–FA PP

NT   0051262   DLC OrP CaBVaU NN MB OO OC1 CtY NcGU

Tattersall, Creassey Edward Cecil, 1877–
FOR OTHER EDITIONS
SEE MAIN ENTRY
Victoria and Albert museum, *South Kensington. Dept. of textiles.*
... Notes on carpet-knotting and weaving, by C. E. C. Tattersall. London, Pub. under the authority of the Board of education, 1939.

TATTERSALL, CREASSEY EDWARD CECIL, 1877–
Notes on the end-game. Leeds, Whitehead and Miller, 1915. 1 v. illus. 22cm.

Part 1.
"Re-printed from The British chess magazine."
CONTENTS. --pt.1. King and pawn against king.

1. Chess--End-games.

NT   0051264   NN OC1

Tattersall, Creassey Edward Cecil, 1877–   ed.
... A thousand end-games ... a collection of chess positions that can be won or drawn by the best play. Edited and arranged by C. E. C. Tattersall. Leeds, "British chess magazine", 1910–11.

2 v. illus. 22ᶜᵐ.

1. Chess. ɪ. Title.
18–468 Revised

Library of Congress   GV1451.T3

NT   0051265   DLC CtY CaBVaU OC1 NN

Tattersall, E. W., illus.
DA684
.B87
Burnett, Richard George, 1898–
London lives on. Text by R. G. Burnett; photography by E. W. Tattersall. London, Phoenix House ₁1948₎

Tattersall, E. W., illus.
LF528
.B8
Burnett, Richard George, 1898–
Oxford and Cambridge in pictures. Text by R. G. Burnett. Photography by E. W. Tattersall. London, Phoenix House ₁1950₎

Tattersall, Edmund Harry, 1897–
Europe at play, by E. H. Tattersall. London ₁etc.₎ W. Heinemann ltd. ₁1938₎

xiv, 358 p. front., plates, ports. 22ᶜᵐ.
"First published 1938."

1. Europe—Soc. life & cust. 2. Europe—Descr. & trav.—1919–
3. Sports—Europe. ɪ. Title.

38–29219

Library of Congress   D921.T3 1938

Copyright A and int. 24223   ₁5₎   914

NT   0051268   DLC CaBVaU

Tattersall, Frederick W., ed.
... Tattersall's cotton trade circular.
Manchester ₁Eng.₎

42.9
T18   Tattersall, George, 1817–1849.
... Catalogue ... Newmarket ₁Eng.₎ December sales.
₁New Market?₎

1. Race horses. 2. Thoroughbred horse.
3. Auctions.

NT   0051270   DNAL

Tattersall, George, 1817–1849.
The cracks of the day. Edited by "Wildrake".
London, Ackermann, n. d.
1 v. Roy. 8°. brown (faded) cloth.
Illus. by fine steel engravings & cuts.

NT   0051271   CSmH

₁Tattersall, George₎ 1817–1849.
The cracks of the day. Ed. by Wildrake ₁pseud.₎
₁London₎ R. Ackermann ₁1840₎
1 p. l., iv, 271, ₁1₎ p. front., illus., plates. 25ᶜᵐ.

1. Horse-racing—Gt. Brit. ɪ. Title.

12–26807

Library of Congress   SF345.T3

NT   0051272   DLC CtY MiEM ScU

1817–1849.
Tattersall, George, ˄ Cracks of the day, edited by Wildrake [pseud.]. [London, 1841.] 8vo. Illus.   109567
Engraved title-page.
Through the racing season of 1840.

NT   0051273   CSmH

[Tattersall, George, 1817–49]
The cracks of the day, edited by Wildrake [pseud.] 2d ed., with additions, completing the work to Jan. 1843. London, Ackermann, 1843

286 p. illus.

NT   0051274   MH

Tattersall, George, 1817–1849
Cracks of the day...

——— ——— London, 1844. 8vo. Illus.   180060
Letterpress title-page reads: *The Pictorial Gallery of English Race Horses.*
This is No. 617 continued through the racing season of 1843.

NT   0051275   CSmH

Tattersall, George, 1817–1849, illus.
₁**Surtees, Robert Smith**₎ 1805–1864.
Hillingdon hall; or, The cockney squire, a tale of country life. By author of "Handley Cross," "Jorrocks's jaunts and jollities", etc. With twelve illustrations in colour by Wildrake-Heath-Jellicoe ₁pseud.₎ New York, William Farquhar Payson ₁1933?₎

₁**Tattersall, George**₎ 1817–1849.
☞ The lakes of England. ╱ London, Sherwood & co.; ₁etc., etc.₎ 1836₎
xii, 165, ₁1₎ p., 1 l. front., plates, fold. map. 19ᶜᵐ.

Engraved t.-p.
"Illustrations ... from original drawings by the author."—Pref.
Dedication signed: George Tattersall.

1. Lake district, Eng. ɪ. Title.
3–6114 Revised

Library of Congress   DA670.L1T2

NT   0051277   DLC NNUT InU MiU NBuG NIC

Tattersall, George, 1817–1849,   joint ed.
Chambers, Sir Thomas, 1814–1891, *ed.*
The laws relating to buildings, comprising the Metropolitan buildings act: fixtures; insurance against fire; actions on builders' bills; dilapidations; and a copious glossary of technical terms peculiar to building. Illustrated with numerous engravings. By Thomas Chambers ... and George Tattersall ... London, Lumley, 1845.

[Tattersall, George] 1817–1849.
The new sporting almanack, a manual of instruction and amusement. Edited by "Wildrake".
London, R. Ackermann, 1844.
82 p. front., illus., plates. 17 cm.
Added t.-p., engraved.

NT   0051279   PU PP

[Tattersall, George] 1817–1849.
Uzfe72   The pictorial gallery of English race horses;
G5   including portraits of all the winning horses
844   of the Derby, Oaks, and St. Leger stakes, during the last thirteen years; and a history of the principal operations of the turf ... by Wildrake Illustrated by seventy-five engravings ... after paintings by Cooper, Herring, Hancock, and others. London, H. G. Bohn, 1844.
2 p. ℓ., iv, 312 p. front., plates. 26½ cm.
Added t.-p.: The cracks of the day.

NT   0051280   CtY IU PP

Tattersall, George, 1817–1849.
The pictorial gallery of English race horses; containing portraits of all the winners of the Derby, Oaks, and St. Leger stakes, during the last twenty years; and a history of the principal operations of the turf. By George Tattersall. Illustrated by ninety engravings, chiefly on steel, after paintings by Cooper, Herring, Hancock, Alken, Hall, and others. London, H. G. Bohn, 1850.
viii, 386 p. front., illus., plates. 25½ cm.
Half-title: The royal gallery of English race horses.
1. Horse-racing—Gt. Brit., 2. Horse breeding—Gt. Brit. ₁2. Thoroughbred horse₎ ɪ. Title.

SF335.G7T3   Agr 17–297

U. S. Dept. of agr. Library   42T18
for Library of Congress   ₁a47b1₎†

NT   0051281   DNAL TxU NN NjR MB DLC PU–V CU

Tattersall, George, 1817–1849.
Sporting architecture. London, Bohn, n. d.
96 p.

NT   0051282   PU–V PPF

Tattersall, George, 1817–1849.
Sporting architecture. London, Bohn, 1840.
97 p.

NT   0051283   PU–V PU

Tattersall, George, 1817–1849.
Sporting architecture.
London. Bohn. [1841?] vi, 97 pp. Illus. Plates. Plans. 27 cm., in 4s.
Contents. — The stud farm. — The stall. — The kennel. — Race stands.

L547 — T.r. — Grandstands. — Stables. — Kennels. — Horse-breeding.

NT   0051284   MB

Tattersall, George, 1817-1849.
Sporting architecture. By George Tattersall ... London, R. Ackermann, 1841.
1 p. l., vi, 97, [1] p. front., illus., plates (incl. plans) 28½ᶜᵐ.
Engr. t.-p. with title vignette.
CONTENTS.—The stud farm.—The stall.—The kennel.—Race stands.

1. Architecture, Domestic. I. Title.

12-3169

Library of Congress   NA8202.T3

NT 0051285   DLC CtY PP DeU

Tattersall, George, 1817-1849.
Sporting architecture. By George Tattersall... London, H. G. Bohn [1850?]
1 p. l., vi, 97 [1] p. front., illus., plates (incl. plans) 28.5 cm.
Engraved t.-p., with title vignette.
Contents. - The stud farm. - The stall. - The kennel. - Race stands.

NT 0051286   CtY

Tattersall, Gulielmus
see Tattersall, William, fl. 1791.

Tattersall, Ivan, *pseud.*
see
Hodgkinson, Ivan Tattersall, 1891-

Humanities
Library
PR   Tattersall, J   F
5548   The baptism of the viking and other
T6   verses. London, Simpkin, Marshall, Hamilton,
B3   Kent [1890]
    viii, 150 p.

NT 0051289   CaBVaU WaPS

Tattersall, J   F
The baptism of the viking, and other verses.
London, Simpkin, Marshall, Hamilton, Kent & co.,
Limited; Burnley, Lupton Brothers [1890]
viii, 150, [1] p.

First edition.

NT 0051290   ScU CtY

Tattersall, John.
The lost Paradise, and other poems.
Edinburgh, G.A., Morton, 1904.
84 p. 16ᶜᵐ.

NT 0051291   NN

Tattersall, John Carlon, 1910-
Railway development and needs in China / John Carlon Tattersall. — [s.l. : s.n., pref. 1934]
152 leaves : map ; 26 cm.
Thesis—Georgetown University.
Bibliography: leaves 148-152.

1. Railroads—China—History. 2. Railroads—China. I. Title.

HE3288.T37   75-317807
    MARC

NT 0051292   DLC

Tattersall, John F., ed.

MacFarlane, Charles, 1799-1858.
Reminiscences of a literary life, by Charles MacFarlane, 1799-1858 ... with an introduction by John F. Tattersall. London. J. Murray, 1917.

Tattersall, M   A   S.
Jewish cookery book; comp. for use in the cookery centres under the School board of London. By Miss M. A. S. Tattersall ... London, Wertheimer, Lea & co., 1895.
128 p. 18½ᶜᵐ.

1. Cookery. I. Title.

Agr 6-1057

Library, U. S. Dept. of   Agriculture   389T18

NT 0051294   DNAL ICJ NN

Tattersall, Olive S., joint author.

QL444
.M8T18
Tattersall, Walter Medley, 1882-1943.
The British Mysidacea, by W. M. Tattersall, and Olive S. Tattersall. London, Ray Society; sold by Quaritch, 1951.

---

qQL
444
M8T22m
Invert.   **Tattersall, Olive S**
Zool.   Mysidacea. [Cambridge, Eng., University Press] 1955.
    190 p. illus. 31 cm. (Gt. Brit. Colonial Office. Discovery Committee. Discovery reports, v. 28)

1. Mysidacea. I. Title. II. Series.

    CSt AAP FTaSU CaBVaU
NT 0051296   DSI CU GU TxU NcU MiD NN NNC CU MB DI

Tattersall, Walter Medley, 1882-1943.
The British Mysidacea, by W. M. Tattersall, and Olive S. Tattersall. London, Ray Society; sold by Quaritch, 1951.
viii, 460 p. illus. 22 cm. (Ray Society, London. [Publications] no. 136)
Bibliography: p. 431-449.

1. Mysidacea. 2. Crustacea—Gt. Brit. I. Tattersall, Olive S., joint author. II. Title.   (Series)

QL444.M8T18   595.383   51-7998

NT 0051297   DLC ICJ OrCS CaBVaU

Tattersall, Walter Medley, 1882-1943.
Contributions to a knowledge of the *Mysidacea* of California ... I. On a collection of *Mysidae* from La Jolla, California ... by W. M. Tattersall ... Berkeley, Calif., University of California press, 1932.
cover-title, 1 p. l., [301]-314 p. illus. 28 cm. (University of California publications in zoology. v. 37, no. 13)
Issued in single cover with v. 37, no. 14 of the series.
"Literature cited": p. 314.

1. Mysidacea. I. Title.

[QL1.C15   vol. 37, no. 13]   A 32—1107

California. Univ. Libr.
for Library of Congress   [a35f1]

NT 0051298   CU CaBVaU OrU MU CoU ViU UU

Tattersall, Walter Medley, 1882-1943.
Contributions to a knowledge of the *Mysidacea* of California ... II. The *Mysidacea* collected during the survey of San Francisco bay by the U. S. S. "Albatross" in 1914, by W. M. Tattersall ... Berkeley, Calif., University of California press, 1932.
cover-title, 1 p. l., p. [315]-347 incl. illus., tables. 28 cm. (University of California publications in zoology. v. 37, no. 14)
Issued in single cover with v. 37, no. 13 of the series.
"Literature cited": p. 346-347.

1. Mysidacea. 2. Albatross (Steamer) I. Title.

A 32—1108

California. Univ. Libr.
for Library of Congress   [a65h1]

NT 0051299   CU CaBVaU OrU CoU MU ViU UU

S23   **Tattersall, Walter Medley,** 1882-
0817   Crustacea. Part VI. — Tanaidacea and Isopoda
3   ...
    (In British Antarctic ("Terra Nova") expedition, 1910-1913. Natural history reports. Zoology. London, 1915-23. 31½ᶜᵐ v.3, p.191-258. illus. XIpl.)
    Each plate accompanied by leaf with descriptive letterpress.
    "Issued 26th February, 1921", with cover-title, as vol.III, no.8 of the series.
    "List of papers referred to": p.252-254.

NT 0051300   CtY PPAN

S23   **Tattersall, Walter Medley,** 1882-
0817   Crustacea. Part VII. - Mysidacea ...
3   (In British Antarctic ("Terra Nova") expedition, 1910-1913. Natural history reports. Zoology. London, 1915-23. 31½ᶜᵐ v.3, p.273-304. IVpl.)
    Each plate accompanied by leaf with descriptive letterpress.
    "Issued 24th February, 1923", with cover-title, as vol.III, no.10 of the series.
    "List of papers referred to": p.301-302.

NT 0051301   CtY PPAN

Tattersall, Walter Medley, 1882-1943.
Crustacea. Tanaidacea and Isopoda. London, Brit. museum, 1921.
Pt. 6. (Brit. Antarctic ("Terra Nova") exped., 1910. Natural history rept. Zoology, v. 3, no. 8, p. 191-258)

NT 0051302   PPAmP

---

qQL
441.95
T22
Invert.   **Tattersall, Walter Medley,** 1882-1943.
Zool.   Crustacea. Parts 6-8. London, Printed by order of the Trustees of the British Museum, 1921-1924.
    3 v in 1. illus. 32 cm. (British Antarctic ("Terra Nova") Expedition, 1910-1913. Natural History report. Zoology. v. 3, no. 8, p. 191-258; v. 3, no. 10, p. 273-304; v. 8, no. 1, p. 1-36)
    Cover title.

NT 0051303   DSI

Tattersall, Walter Medley, 1882-1943.
Crustacea. Euphausiacea. London, British museum, 1924.
Pt. 8. (Brit. Antarctic ("Terra Nova") exped., 1910. Natural history rept., v. 8, no. 1. p. 1.-36)

NT 0051304   PPAmP

S23   **Tattersall, Walter Medley,** 1882-
0817   Crustacea. Part VIII. - Euphausiacea ...
8   (In British Antarctic ("Terra Nova") expedition, 1910-1913. Natural history reports. Zoology. London, 1924-30. 31½ᶜᵐ v.8, p. [1]-[36], IIpl.)
    Each plate accompanied by leaf with descriptive letterpress.
    "Issued 23rd February, 1924", with cover-title, as vol.VIII, no.1 of the series.
    "List of papers referred to": p.31-33.

NT 0051305   CtY

Tattersall, Walter Medley, 1882-
Crustaceans of the orders *Euphausiacea* and *Mysidacea* from the western Atlantic, by Walter M. Tattersall ...
(In U. S. National museum. Proceedings. Washington, 1927. 23½ᶜᵐ. v. 69, art. 8. 31 p. 2 pl. on 1 L)
Bibliography: p. 27-28.

1. Euphausiacea. 2. Mysidacea. 3. Crustacea—Atlantic Ocean.

Library of Congress   Q11.U55 vol. 69   28-7572

NT 0051306   DLC WaS

Tattersall, Walter Medley, 1882-1943.
Euphausiacea and Mysidacea.
(Austral. Antarctic Exped., 1911-14. Sci.
Reports. Ser. C. v. 5, pt. 4. 1918)

NT 0051307 PPAN

Tattersall, Walter Medley, 1882-1943.
Euphausiacea and mysidacea. Sydney, Government printer, 1918.
15 p. (Australasian antarctic expedition, 1911-1914... Scientific reports; series C. Zoology and botany, v. V, pt. 5)

NT 0051308 PPAmP

Tattersall, Walter Medley, 1882-
...Euphausiacea and mysidacea, by W. M. Tattersall...
Sydney: W. A. Gullick, 1918. 15 p. pl. f°. (Australasian Antarctic Expedition, 1911-1914. Scientific reports. Series C. v. 5, part 5.)
Bibliography, p. 13.

1. Euphausiacea. 2. Mysidacea. 3. Series.
N. Y. P. L. June 10, 1922.

NT 0051309 NN CtY

Tattersall, Walter Medley, 1882-1943.
The Euphausiacea and Mysidacea of the John Murray Expedition to the Indian Ocean. London, Printed by Order of the Trustees of the British Museum, 1939.
204-246 p. illus. 32 cm. (The John Murray Expedition, 1933-34. Scientific reports. v. 5, no. 8)
At head of title: British Museum (Natural History)
Cover title.
Bibliography: p. 245-246.
1. Euphausiacea — Indian Ocean. 2. Mysidacea — Indian Ocean.
I. British Museum (Natural History) II. Title. III. Series: John Murray Expedition, 1933-1934. Scientific reports, v. 5, no. 8.
Q115.J55   vol. 5, no. 8   508.3'165 s   74-153981
[QL444.E9]   [595'.384'09165]   MARC

NT 0051310 DLC CtY

Tattersall, Walter Medley, 1882-
... *Euphausiacea* and *Mysidacea* collected on the Presidential cruise of 1938, by W. M. Tattersall ... City of Washington, The Smithsonian institution, 1941.
1 p. l., 7 p. illus. 24½ᶜᵐ. (Smithsonian miscellaneous collections. v. 99, no. 13)
Publication 3508.
"References": p. 6-7.
1. Euphausiacea. 2. Mysidacea. 3. Presidential cruise to the Galapagos islands, 1938.
Library of Congress   Q11.S7   vol. 99, no. 13   41-50077
———— Copy 2.   Q115.P77T28
[12]   (506)   595.751

NBuU
NT 0051311   DLC PU-BZ OrSaW WaS OCU OO OU ViU FU

Tattersall, Walter Medley, 1882-
Glamorgan county history ... Cardiff, Printed and published for the Committee by W. Lewis (printers) limited, 1936-

Tattersall, Walter Medley, 1882-
S29.094   ... Mysidacea and Euphausiacea ... London,
5   Printed by order of the trustees of the British museum, 1936.
cover-title, p. [143]-176. illus. 31ᶜᵐ
(Great Barrier reef expedition, 1928-29.
Scientific reports, vol. V, no. 4)
"References": p.163; p.175-176.

1. Mysidacea - Great Barrier reef, Australia.
2. Euphausiacea - Great Barrier reef Australia.
I Ser.

NT 0051313 CtY

Tattersall, Walter Medley, 1882-
Uzi27   ... Mysidacea and Euphausiacea of Marine survey, South Africa ...
B5   (In South Africa. Fisheries and marine biological survey. Report no.4, June 1923-June 1925.
A2   Cape Town, 1925. 24½ᶜᵐ   12p.   IIpl.)
v.4   Caption title.
[Special reports, no.] V.
"List of references": p.11-12.

NT 0051314 CtY

Tattersall, Walter Medley, 1882-
... New species of mysidacid crustaceans, by **Walter M.**
Tattersall ... City of Washington, The Smithsonian institution, 1937.
1 p. l., 18 p. illus. 24½ cm. (Smithsonian miscellaneous collections. v. 91, no. 26)
Publication 3413.
Reports on the collections obtained by the first Johnson-Smithsonian deep-sea expedition to the Puerto Rican deep.
Johnson fund.
"References": p. 18.
1. Mysidacea. 2. Crustacea—Atlantic ocean.   I. Smithsonian institution. Johnson fund.
Q11.S7   vol. 91, no. 26   595.383   37—26479
———— Copy 2.   QL444.M8T3

NT 0051315   DLC WaSpG WaS MoU OCl OO OU ViU DNLM FU

Tattersall, Walter Medley, 1882-1943.   *3880a.79.6
Die nordischen Isopoden. Illus.
(In Nordisches Plankton. 6, pp. 181-313, (1). Kiel. 1911.)
Literatur-Verzeichnis, pp. 304-307.

H6000 — Isopoda.

NT 0051316   MB PPAN DSI

Tattersall, Walter Medley, 1882-
S29.094   ... The occurrence and seasonal distribution
2   of the Mysidacea and Euphausiacea ... London,
Printed by order of the trustees of the British museum, 1936.
cover-title, p. [277]-289 incl. tables, diagrs.
31cm. (Great Barrier reef expedition, 1928-29.
Scientific reports, vol.II, no.8. The zooplankton V)
"References": p.289.

NT 0051317 CtY

Tattersall, Walter Medley, 1882-1943.
On the Cephalochorda.
(Herdman, Pearl Oyster report, I. 1903)

NT 0051318 PPAN

Tattersall, Walter Medley, 1882-1943.
On the Leptostraca, Schizopoda and Stomatopoda.
(Herdman, Pearl Oyster report, V. 1906.

NT 0051319 PPAN

Tattersall, Walter Medley, 1882-1943.
A review of the Mysidacea of the United States National Museum. Washington, U. S. Govt. Print. Off., 1951.
x, 292 p. illus. 25 cm. (U. S. National Museum. Bulletin 201)
Bibliography: p. 263-283.

1. Mysidacea.   (Series)
Q11.U6   no. 201   595.383   51-61574
———— Copy 2.   QL444.M8T33

ViU NN TxU DI
NT 0051320   DLC WaS MoU MU MiAlbC OKentU FU MB MdBP

Tattersall, Walter Medley, 1882-1943.
Schizopoda, Stomatopoda and non arctic Isopoda of the Scottish National Antarctic Expedition.
(Rept. Scient. Res. Voy. "Scotia", 1902-1904.
v. 7. 1920)

NT 0051321 PPAN

Tattersall, Walter Medley, 1882-   *3360.1.49
The Schizopoda, Stomatopoda, and non-antarctic Isopoda of the Scottish Antarctic Expedition. Plate.
(In Royal Society of Edinburgh. Transactions. Vol. 49, pp. 865-894. Edinburgh. 1914.)
List of references, pp. 893, 894.

K5512 — Schizopoda.— Stomatopoda.— Isopoda.— Scottish National Antarctic Expedition.

NT 0051322 MB

Tattersall, Walter Medley, 1882-1943.
Schizopodous crustacea from the north-east Atlantic slope.
Second supplement. Dublin: Cahill & Co., 1911. 77 p., 8 pl. pap. 8°. (Ireland. Fisheries branch. Investigations. 1910. no. 2.)

1. Schizopoda, Atlantic ocean (North   east).
N. Y. P. L.   February 13, 1912.

NT 0051323 NN PU-BZ

Tattersall, William, joint author.

Naylor, Thomas Martin.
A first course in machine construction and drawing, by T. M. Naylor ... W. Tattersall ... London, H. F. & G. Witherby, 1923.

Tattersall, William, fl. 1791.
——. A brief view of the anatomical arguments for the doctrine of materialism; occasioned by Dr. Ferriar's argument against it. 30 pp. 8°.
London, J. Johnson, [1794].

NT 0051325 DNLM

W 4   TATTERSALL, William, fl. 1791.
E23   Disputatio medica de calculi et podagra nexu ... Edinburgi,
1791   Balfour et Smellie, 1791.
T.1   32 p. 20 cm.
Imperfect: preliminary pages (including title page) wanting.
Supplied in manuscript.
Diss. - Edinburgh.

NT 0051326 DNLM

Tattersall, William, 1847-1914.
Cotton trade circular
see   Tattersall's cotton trade circular.

1847-1914.
Tattersall, William, Lancashire and the cotton duties. 13 pp. (*Forts. Rev.* n. s. v. 59, 1896, p 291.)

NT 0051328 MdBP

Tattersall, William, 1847-1914, ed.
... Tattersall's cotton trade circular.
Manchester [Eng.]

Tattersall, William Dechair, 1752-1829.
Improved psalmody. Vol. 1. The Psalms of David, from a poetical version originally written by the late Reverend James Merrick ... Divided into stanzas for the purpose of public and private devotion, with new music collected from the most eminent composers, by the Reverend William Dechair Tattersall ... London, Rivingtons [etc.], 1794.
1 p. l., 44, 2, 329, 20 p. 21 x 26½ᶜᵐ.
Title-page and music engraved.
No more published.
1. Psalmody.   I. Merrick, James, 1720-1769. II. Bible. O. T.
Psalms. English. Paraphrases. 1794. III. Bible. English. Paraphrases. O. T. Psalms. 1794. IV. Title.
35-21833
Library of Congress   M2082.4.T3 I 5   783.9

NT 0051330   DLC CtY CtY-Mus

Tattersall, William Dechair, 1752-1829.
Improved psalmody, in three parts, printed separately for each voice: or, A poetical version of the psalms, originally written by...Rev. James Merrick...divided into stanzas, for parochial use, with new music, collected from the most eminent composers by the Rev. William Dechair Tattersall...   London: H. L. Galabin, 1795.   3 v.   8°.

With bookplates of Hugh Owen.
Words and music.

1. Bible.—Old Testament: Psalms   (Metrical). 1795. 2. Psalmody.
3. Merrick, James, 1720-69. 4. Tat-   tersall, William De Chair, 1752-
1829.   . July 11, 1919.

NT   0051331   NN PPL CtY MH-AH CtY-Mus CtHC

M
2082.4
T315
1795

Tattersall, William Dechair, 1752-1829.
Improved psalmody, in three parts, printed separately for each voice, or, a poetical version of the psalms, originally written by the late Rev. James Merrick ... Divided into stanzas, for parochial use, with new music, collected from the most eminent composers, by the Rev. William Dechair Tattersall ... London, Rivingtons [etc.] 1795.
270 p.   music.   23 cm.

Title-page and music engraved.

1. Psalmody. 2. Bi   ble. Old Testament Psalms—Paraphrases, English.   3. Bible—Music. I. Merrick,
James, 1720-1769.   II. Title.   dao

NT   0051332   IEdS NhD CtY-Mus

Rare
M
2082
.3
T221
134
1802

Tattersall, William Dechair, 1752-1829.
Improved psalmody; sanctioned by the King at Weymouth. The words selected from a poetical version of the Psalms originally written by ... James Merrick ... Divided into stanzas by ... William Dechair Tattersall ... The music adapted from the sacred compositions of Handel ... London, Broderip & Wilkinson, 1802.

score (58 p.)   19 x 26 cm.
For 3 mixed voices, unaccompanied.
Lowell Mason bookplate.

1. Choruses, Sacred (Mixed voices), Unaccompanied. 2. Psalms (Music) I. Merrick,
James, 1720-1769. II. Handel, Georg Friedrich, 1685-1759. Works, chorus. Selections;
arr. III. Titl

NT   0051334   CtY-Mus CtY

Tattersall, William Dechair, 1752-1829. ed.
A version [or paraphrase] of the Psalms, originally written by...James Merrick ...
see under   Bible. O. T. Psalms. Eng-
lish. Paraphrases. 1789, Merrick.   Also
with dates: 1790   1797   1801
1801?   1822

Tattersall, William Richard.
The dentist's handbook on law and ethics, with sections on forensic dentistry, income tax, and superannuation, by W. R. Tattersall and H. D. Barry. With a section on income tax by W. Donald, and a foreword by E. Wilfred Fish. London, Eyre & Spottiswoode, 1953.

328 p. illus. 23 cm.

1. Dental laws and legislation—Gt. Brit. 2. Dental jurisprudence—
Gt. Brit. 3. Medical ethics.   I. Barry, Hugh Desmond, joint author.
II. Title.

                    A 54-6746 ‡
New York. State Libr.
for Library of Congress

NT   0051336   N CaBVaU NNC DNLM PU-D NcU OU

... **Tattersall's cotton trade circular.**

Manchester [Eng.]
v.   31cm.

Printed monthly for private circulation.
Title varies: -Oct. 13, 1914, William Tattersall's cotton trade
        circular.
Nov. 11, 1914-   Frederick W. Tattersall's cotton trade circular.

1. Cotton trade—Period. 2. Cotton trade—Gt. Brit.   I. Tattersall,
William, 1847-1914, ed.   II. Tattersall, Frederick W., ed.

                   CA 15-1190 Unrev'd
Library of Congress   HD9070.1.T3

NT   0051337   DLC MH

SF299
T3

Tattersalls Incorporated, Lexington, Ky.
Fall sale trotting and saddle horses. 1,1940-
Lexington, Ky.
v. illus. 23cm. annual.

NT   0051338   IaAS

Tattersalls Limited, New York.
Catalogue of the ... annual sale of the Rancho del Paso trotting stock
see under   Rancho del Paso, Sacramento, Calif.

---

*
SF299
.T38
1893

Tattersalls Limited, New York.
Great sale of more extreme young speed than was ever offered at any one sale, in New York City February 23 and 24, 1893, commencing at 10 o'clock A. M. each day. New York, Thomas A. O'Keefe [1893]
[88] p.   22cm.
On cover: "Catalogue of highly-bred trotting stock ..."
1. Race horses—Catalogs.

NT   0051340   ViU

Tattersall's rules on betting, with notes and comments, with the rules of racing
see under   Stutfield, George Herbert, 1856-

RT
97
.T22

Tattershall, Louise M
Public health nursing in the United States, January 15,1931. Public health nursing in outlying possessions and territories of the United States, January 15,1931. Prepared for the National organization for public health nursing by Louise M. Tattershall ... Also Trained nurses in industry, U.S. Census of population 1930-Report on occupations. [New York, 1934]
2 p.l.,71 p.incl.illus.(maps) tables. 25cm.
1.Public health nursing—U.S. 2.Industrial nursing. 3.Nurses and nur-   sing—Stat. I.National
organization for   public health nursing.

NT   0051342   MiU

Tattershall, Thomas.
An account of Tobias Smith, a Gipsy : who was executed at Bedford, April 3d, 1792... By Thomas Tattershall.   [London?] 1792.   22 p.   16cm.

1. Smith, Tobias, 1773-1792.
N. Y. P. L.   September 7, 1945

NT   0051343   NN

248
S662Z
T
Theol.

Tattershall, Thomas
An account of Tobias Smith, a gipsy: who was executed at Bedford, April 3d, 1792. [Bedford?] Printed in the year 1796.
19p.   17cm.

1. Smith, Tobias, 1773-1792.

NT   0051344   TxDaM

Tattershall, Thomas, 1795-1846.
The integrity of the canon of Holy Scripture maintained against Unitarian objections: a lecture, delivered in Christ church, Hunter Street, Liverpool Feb. 13, 1839. Liverpool, Perris, 1839

p.61-104

NT   0051345   MH

Tattersall, Thomas, 1795-1846.
A sermon, preached at... Manchester, ... Sept. 28, 1823. ... Manchester, 1823.
24 p.   8°.   [In v. 777, College Pamphlets]

NT   0051346   CtY

Tattershall, Thomas, 1795-1846.
A sermon, preached at the Episcopal Jews' Chapel, ... May 2, 1839, before the London Society for promoting Christianity amongst the Jews.   [London]
33 p.   8°.   [In College Pamphlets, v. 1332]

NT   0051347   CtY

BV
2621
.L6

Tattershall, Thomas, 1795-1846.
A sermon preached at the Episcopal Jews' Chapel, Cambridge Heath, Bethnal Green, on Thursday evening, May 2, 1839, before the London Society for promoting Christianity amongst the Jews / by Thomas Tattershall. -- London : Printed by A. Macintosh; sold at the London Society's Office, 1839.
33 p. ; 21 cm.
No. 10 in a bound volume with binder's title: L. J. S. annual sermons 1809-1843.
1. Jews—Restoration. 2. Jews—Conversion to Christianity. I. London Society for Promoting Christianity Amongst the J   ews.

NT   0051348   MH-AH

BX5133
T3S4

Tattershall, Thomas, 1795-1846.
Sermons. With a memoir of the author by Thomas Byrth. London, Hatchard, 1848.
lxxxvi,429,2 p.   24cm.

1.Church of England - Sermons. 2.Sermons, English.

NT   0051349   CSt

Tatterson, Estelle M.
Three centuries of Biddeford. An historical sketch...   n. imp.
[31] p.

NT   0051350   MiD-B

Tatterson, Estelle M.
Three centuries of Biddeford; an historical sketch, by Estelle M. Tatterson. [Biddeford, Me.? 1916.] 16 l. 8°.

1. Biddeford, Me.—History.
N. Y. P. L.   June 9, 1923.

NT   0051351   NN ICN MWA

Tattet, Alfred.
La jeunesse dorée sous Louis-Philippe; Alfred de Musset, de Musard à la reine Pomaré, la Présidente. Documents inédits. Paris, Mercure de France, 1910.

367 p.   18 cm.   (Léon Séché. Études d'histoire romantique)

NT   0051352   MH

Tattet, Alfred.   4679a.157
Lettres.
(In Séché, Léon. La jeunesse dorée sous Louis-Philippe. Paris. 1910.)

H5594 — Letters. Colls.

NT 0051353   MB CU

Tattet, Eugène, 1869-1919.
...Journal d'un chirurgien de la grande armée (L.-V. Lagneau) 1803-1815. Avec une introduction de m. Frédéric Masson... Orné d'un portrait.
Paris, Émile-Paul frères, 1913.
2 p.l.,xiv,327p. front.(port.) 22.5cm.

1.Lagneau, Louis Vivant, 1781-1868.

NT 0051354   NNF

Tattet, Eugène, 1869-1919, ed.

Bugeaud de la Piconnerie, Thomas Robert, *duc d'Isly*, 1784-1849.
Lettres inédites du maréchal Bugeaud, duc d'Isly (1808-1849) colligées et annotées par M. le capitaine Tattet et publiées par Mademoiselle Féray-Bugeaud d'Isly ... Paris, Émile-Paul frères, 1922.

Tattet, Jean Louis Eugene

see

Tattet, Eugène, 1869-1919

W 4
S892
no. 693
1955   TATTEVIN, Louis
Influence de l'antibiothérapie sur les variations du taux de complément sérique chez les tuberculeux. Vannes, 1955.
78 p. illus. (Strasbourg. Université Faculté de pharmacie. Thèse, 1954/55, no. 693)
1. Antibiotics - Effects 2. Drugs - Antitubercular

NT 0051357   DNLM

Tattevin, Ludovic, 1892–
... Le sel et les microbes ... Vannes, Impr. A. Commelin, 1927.
100 p. illus. 24ᵐ.
Thèse—Univ. de Nancy.
"Bibliographie": p. ₁96₎-97.

1. Bacteriology. 2. Salt.

           Agr 28–67
Library, U. S. Dept. of   Agriculture   448.2T18

NT 0051358   DNAL CtY

Tatti, Francesco
   see   Sansovino, Francesco, 1521-1583.

Tatti, Giovanni, *pseud.*
Della agricoltvra ... 1560
see
Sansovino, Francesco, 1521-1586.

Tatti, Jacopo, 1486-1570.
Jacopo Tatti detto Il Sansovo
see under Sapori, Francesco, 1890-

---

q626.8
T18c   Tatti, Luigi.
Canali di irrigazione italiani, rete lombarda. Rapporto unito al progetto compilato d'incarico della Società concessionaria del canale Cavour, dagli ingegneri Tatti e Bossi, con due tavole dimostrative. Milano, G. Daelli & c., 1854.
70p. incl.tables. fold.map, fold.diagr.

"Estratto del Politecnico, vol.XXII."

1. Canals--Lombardy. I. Bossi, Giovanni Battista, joint author.

NT 0051362   IU

Tatti, Primo Luigi.
Degli Annali sacri della Citta di Como... Decade prima... C., 1663.
4ᵉ.

NT 0051363   CtY

TATTI, Primo Luigi.
Degli annali sacri della citta di Como raccolti e descritti Decade I,II. Como,etc., 1663-83.

NT 0051364   MH

Tatti, Primo Luigi.
De gli annali sacri della citta di Como. Raccolti e descritti dal P. D. Primo Lvigi Tatti. In Como, Per gli heredi di N. Caprani, 1663-1734.
3 v. 24 cm.
Title of vol, 3: Annali sacri della città di Como.
Imprint varies: v. 2, In Milano, G.B. Ferrario; v. 3. In Milano, C. G. Gallo.
Contents; [v. 1] Nella quale sono compresi i successi tanto ecclesiastici, quanto secolari della medesima città, dalla di lei fondatione sin all'anno ottocento ottantotto dell'incarnatiuono [sic] del

Figlio di Dio. - [v. 2] Dall'anno ottocento ottantotto sino al mille trecento di nostra salute. - [v. 3] Dall'anno 1300 sino all'anno di nostra salute 1582, con l'appendice del medesimo autore sino all'anno 1598. Riveduta, esaminata, corretta, e arricchita di varie osservazioni, e d'un indice copioso, dal P.A. Giuseppe Maria Stampa.

---- -------- Appendice alla terza deca degli annali di Como. In Milano, C.G. Gallo, 1735.
211, 67, 18 p. 24 cm.

NT 0051367   PU

---

q274.522
T189d   Tatti, Primo Luigi.
Degli annali sacri della città di Como raccolti, e descritti ... dalla di lei fondatione sino [all'anno di nostra salute 1582. Con l'appendice del medesimo autore fino all'anno 1598] Milano, 1663-1735.
3v. and app.

Vol. 1 pub. at Como.
Vol. 3 "riv., esaminata. cor.. e ar-

richita di varie osservazioni, e d'un indice copioso dal Giuseppe Maria Stampa".

NT 0051369   IU

922.2
T189s   Tatti, Primo Luigi.
Sanctvarivm, sev Martyrologivm sanctæ nouocomensis ecclesiæ; opvs ad augendam dei, & sanctorum ipsius gloriam fidelissime elaboratum tum ex m.s. codicibus, tum ex probatis auctoribus summa sedulitate Primi Aloysij de Tattis ... Novo comi, apud I. B. Arzonum, 1675.
263p.

Title vignette.

NT 0051370   IU

Bd.w.
DG
738.23
R5
1608a
Cage   Tatti, Prospero
... Ad feliciss. sereniss. Etruriae principum nuptias Hymenaeus... Florentiae, Apud Christophoru Marescotum, 1608.
₍A₎⁴. 4to.
Concerns the marriage of Cosimo II, de' Medici and Maria Maddalena of Austria.

NT 0051371   DFo

Gr6
220   Tatti, Prospero
In lode de serenissimi gran dvci di Toscana delle compositioni volgari e latine il terzo libro... Firenze,Appresso F.Tosi, 1587.
[19]p. 21cm.

NT 0051372   CtY

La tattica sindicalista in America [di] G. C.
New York, Libreria dei Lavoratori Industriali del Mondo [19--]
32 p. 17 cm.
1. Trade-Unions-U. S.

NT 0051373   NcD

Il tattilismo. Manifesto futurista letto al Théâtre de l'Oeuvre (Parigi) ...
see under [Marinetti, Filippo Tommaso] 1876-1944.

746.43
T189T   Tatting. Paris, Thiriez, n.d.
32p. illus.

NT 0051375   WaT

Tatting . 1939
see under Spool Cotton Company, New York.

Tatting book
see under Spool Cotton Co., New York.

... Tatting designs with instructions ...
see under Giessow, Paul Helmuth, 1876-

Tattje, Derk Hendrik Evert.
Stabilisatie en samenstelling van het glycosidenmengsel van folia digitalis. Groningen, 1952.
80 p. diagrs., tables. 24 cm.
Proefschrift—Groningen.
Summary in English.
"Stellingen": ₂₎ leaves inserted.
Bibliography: p. 76-80.

1. Digitalis. 2. Glycosides.

RS165.D5T3   56–41713

NT 0051379   DLC MiU NIC

Tattje, Pieter Hendrik Evert.
Beweeglijkheden van ionen in het AgJ sol. Utrecht,
1942.
87 p. illus. 25 cm.
Proefschrift—Utrecht.
Summary in English.
"Stellingen": [2] p. inserted.
Bibliographical footnotes.

1. Colloids.

QD549.T26   56–48884

Library of Congress

NT 0051380   DLC DNLM InU MH CtY InU

"Tattler" [pseud.]
National miniatures
see under [Leupp, Francis Ellington]
1849–1918.

Pam.
Coll.   Tattler, pseud.
Some objections to socialism considered
17293 and answered. By "Tattler" (of "Justice.")
... London, The Twentieth century press, 1907.
cover title, 22 p. 21 cm.

1. Devas, Charles Stanton. Plain words on
socialism. 2. Socialism

NT 0051382   NcD

Tattler, *pseud.*
Some objections to socialism considered and answered.
By "Tattler" (of "Justice"). London, The Twentieth
century press, limited [1910]
cover-title, 16 p. 22ᶜᵐ.

1. Socialism. 2. Devas, Charles Stanton. Plain words on socialism.
18–1811

Library of Congress   HX246.T3

NT 0051383   DLC

British
Tracts   **Tattler, Tom**
1718   An express from the stars, with a satchel-
T189   full of true news from the planets, for the
year 1719. Being a burlesque upon 'strologers,
conjurers ... By Tom.Tattler ... Dublin,
Printed by S.Powell [1718]
31, [1] p. 15 cm.
Signatures: [A]–D⁴.

NT 0051384   CtY

Tz
378.764
UQt   **Tattler.** v.1-
Photo-   spring term, 1924-
copy   Austin, Tex.
v. 28cm.

Photocopy (positive)
Published by students of the University of
Texas.

I. Texas. University.

NT 0051385   TxU

The **Tattler** ... an annual publication of the student body of
Blair high school.
Blair, Neb. [°19

v. illus. (incl. ports.) col. plates. 28ᶜᵐ.

1. Blair, Neb. High school.
CA 27–13 Unrev'd

Library of Congress   LD7501.B5765

NT 0051386   DLC

The tattler. (St Anthony)
see under   St. Anthony, Idaho.
High School.

The **TATTLER.**
Seattle. Young men's business club of
Seattle.

Weekly.
Mimeographed.

Library has:
v. ,no.1-v. ,no.   . ,19 -

NT 0051388   WaS

The tattler, [1863]
see under   Guernsey, Lucy Ellen,
1826–1899.

---

f F850   The Tattler, every Saturday, for the uplift of Santa Clara
T175   Valley. v.1 no.1-

Oct. 19, 1907-

San Jose, The Tattler Co.
v.   illus. 36cm.

1. Santa Clara Valley, Calif.

NT 0051390   CU-BANC

The **Tattling** tortilla; the "Mexican hayride" fortnightly newsette.
Issue 1–

[New York] 1944   29 – 35cm.

Biweekly (slightly irregular).
Issue 1–2 (March 15–24, 1944) called edition 1–2.
Issue 1–11 (March 15–June 1, 1944) lack subtitle.
Edited by Robert Lane of the Mexican hayride cast.

1. Fields, Herbert, 1897-   The Mexican hayride. I. Lane,
Robert, ed. II. Title: The "Mexican   hayride" fortnightly newsette.
N. Y. P. L.   April 12, 1948

NT 0051391   NN

Tattnal Baptist Association
see Baptists. Georgia. Tattnal
Baptist Association.

RARE BOOK
DEPT.   **Tattnall, Josiah.**
x XH   Proceedings of a naval general court martial,
.862   in the case of Captain Josiah Tattnall.
.T18P   Richmond: Macfarlane & Fergusson, 1862.

2 p.l.,90 p.,1 l. 23cm.
Crandall 878.
Pages 83–85 & 89 contain author's autograph
notations.
Inscribed: Wm. T. Thompson Esqr with Flag
Officer Tattnall's regards.
Ex libris   (signature): C.C. Coffin

NT 0051393   MB GEU MBAt

Tattnall-Evans Baptist Association
see Baptists. Georgia. Tattnall-Evans
Association.

Tattnall Square Presbyterian Church, Macon, Ga.
see Macon, Ga. Tattnall Square
Presbyterian Church.

945V425
T18   **Tatto, Giulio,** 1540–1620.
La cronaca varesina di Giulio Tatto (1540-
1620) ed i prezzi dei grani e del vino sul
mercato di Varese dal 1525 al 1620. [Varese,
Tip. Galli, 1954.
xli, 261 p. illus., fold. map, graphs,
tables. (Fonti storiche edite a cura della
Società storica varesina)

At head of title: Leopoldo Giampaolo.
"Supplemento della Rivista della Società
storica varesina."
"Notizie biogra-   fiche su Giulio Tatto":
p. viii–ix.

NT 0051396   NNC NN MH NIC

Tatton, Gabriel.
Maris Pacifici quod uulgo mar del zur...
nouissima descriptio, G. Tattonus auct.
1600. Benjamin Wright Anglus coelator.
21 x 28 in.
Full scale negative photostat from LC
Lowry No. 86.

NT 0051397   MiU-C

Tatton, Gabriel.
Maris Pacifici quod uulgo Mar del Zur, cum regionibus
circumiacentibus, insulisq, in eodem passi sparsis nouissima
descriptio. Beniamin Wright Anglus coelator. [n. p.] 1600.
map 40 x 52 cm.
Scale ca. 1 : 35,000,000.
Described in the Library of Congress Quarterly Journal of current
acquisitions, v. 6, no. 3, May 1949, p. 22.

1. Pacific Ocean—Charts, maps, etc. 2. Maps, Early.
G9230 1600.T3 Rosenwald Coll.   Map 49–968*

NT 0051398   DLC

Tatton, Gabriel.
Nova et rece tararum et regnorum Californiae,
novae Hispaniae Mexicanae et Peruviae.
London, 1616 [i. e. 1600]
Engraved by Benjamin Wright.

NT 0051399   RPJCB

Tatton, Gabriel.
Noua et rece terraum et regnorum Californiae,
...delineatio, d M. Tattonus celebrem Sydro-
geographo edita. Beniamin Wright Anglus
caelator. Ano. 1600.
16 1/4 x 21 1/4 in.
Photostat negative from LC. Full scale

NT 0051400   MiU-C

Tatton, Gabriel
Maris Pacifici quod Vulgo Mar del Zur
London, 1600   15.8 x 20.8 in.
Engraved by Benjamin Wright

NT 0051401   RPJCB

Tatton, Gabriel.   No. 4 in *Atlas.10.4.[15-?]
Nova Francia . . . [By Gabriel Tatton. Engraved by Benjamin
Wright. London, c. 1610.]
Map facsimile. (*In* British Museum, London. Department of
Maps and Plans. Six early printed maps . . . Size, 14¾ × 21⅛
inches. Scale, computed, approximately 200 miles to 1 inch. Lon-
don. 1928.)
"A rare map showing Canada, Labrador, Greenland, and the western coasts
of Europe."—*Page 3.*

D5092 — T.r. — Canada. Geog. Ma.   — Greenland. Geog. Maps. — Europe.
Geog. Maps. — Wright, Benjamin, of London, engraver.

NT 0051402   MB

Tatton, Jack Meredith, 1901–

... Mass in F, in honour of St. Catherine of Siena, for S. A.
T. B. or unison voices (by) J. Meredith Tatton ... (Boston,
McLaughlin & Reilly co.) °1944.

24 p. 27ᶜᵐ. (*On cover:* Liturgical masses by modern American composers. Ser. II)

Caption title.
Publisher's plate no.: M. & R. 1357.
With organ accompaniment.

1. Masses—Vocal scores with organ.

45–11414

Library of Congress   M2013.T27C3

NT 0051403   DLC

Tatton, Jack Meredith, 1901–
Quiet waters, poems. New York, Exposition Press (1951)

42 p. 23 cm.

I. Title.

PS3539.A76Q5   811.5   51–4353

NT 0051404   DLC MB TxU

PS566
.E9

Tatton, Jack Meredith, 1901–   joint ed.

Evans, Katharine, *ed.*
This friendly shore; poems from the Southwest Writers
Conference, edited by Katharine Evans and J. Meredith
Tatton. Foreword by Loring Williams. San Antonio,
Naylor Co. (1955)

---

fG160
H27
v.1
x

Tatton, John
An Account of a Voyage to the East-Indies, in the Pearl,
Commanded by Captain Samuel Castleton. Written by Mr. John
Tatton, Master of the same Ship.

(In Harris, John. Navigantium atque Itinerantium Bibliotheca
...London, 1705. 40cm. v.1, p. 114–115)

1. East Indies – Description and travel. 2. Castleton, Samuel.

NT 0051406   CU-BANC

---

fG159
P98
v.1
x

Tatton, John
A Iournall of a Voyage made by the Pearle to the East-
India, wherein went as Captaine Master Samvel Castelton of
London, and Captaine George Bathvrst as Lieutenant: written
by Iohn Tatton, Master.

(In Purchas, Samuel. Pilgrimes. Londn, 1625.
34cm. v.1, book 3, p. 328–332)

1. Castleton, Samuel 2. Bathurst, George

NT 0051407   CU-BANC

Tatton, John.
Reys na Gost-Indien van Samuel Costelton...
(In Davy, Johan: Negende reys na Gost-Indien
van de Englese Maatschappy)

NT 0051408   PU

Tatton, John. 17th cent.
Voyage of Capt. Samuel Castleton to Priaman in
1612.
6 p. (Green, J., Voyages, v. 1, p. 446:
Purchas, S., His pilgrimes, v. 1, p. 328)

NT 0051409   MdBP

Tatton, Reginald Arthur.

Gt. Brit. *Royal commission on sewage disposal.*
... Interim report of the commissioners appointed in 1898 to
inquire and report what methods of treating and disposing of
sewage (including any liquid from any factory or manufacturing process) may properly be adopted ... London, Printed
for H. M. Stationery off., by Wyman and sons, limited, 1901–
02.

Tatton (Reginald Arthur). The purification of
water after its use in manufactories, and experiments on the purification of waste water
from factories. By William Oliver Evelyn
Meade-King. 73 pp., 1 pl. 8°. *London,* 1900.
Repr. from: Proc. Inst. Civil Eng., Lond., 1899–1900, clx,
pt. 2.

NT 0051411   DNLM

Tatton, Robert Grey.

Rooper, Thomas Godolphin, 1847–1903.
Selected writings of Thomas Godolphin Rooper, M. A.
Balliol college, Oxford, late H. M. inspector of schools,
ed. with a memoir by R. G. Tatton ... London (etc.)
Blackie and son, limited, 1907.

Tatton, Lord Wilbraham Egerton

A description of Indian and oriental
armour... new ed. London, W.H. Allen & Co.,
Ltd., 1896.

168p. plates (part col.) 27.5cm.

NT 0051413   MdBWA

Tatton, Lord Wilbraham Egerton

An illustrated handbook of Indian arms;
being a classified and descriptive catalogue of
the arms exhibited at the India Museum...
London, W. H. Allen & Co., 1880.

162p. plates (part col.) 27cm.

NT 0051414   MdBWA

Tattoni, Antonio.
——. Antipirina e igiene nell' ileo-tifo. 17 pp.
8°. *Cagli, tipog. Balloni,* 1887.

NT 0051415   DNLM

Tattoni (Antonio). Il naftolo in alcune malattie cutanee. 13 pp. 8°. *Cagli, tipog. Balloni,*
1887.

NT 0051416   DNLM

Tattoni, Antonio.
——. Nota clinica su un caso di occlusione in-
testinale seguito da guarigione. 9 pp. 8°.
Cagli, tipog. Balloni, 1889.

NT 0051417   DNLM

Tattonus, G.
see **Tatton, Gabriel.**

The Tattoo, Aldershot, Eng.
Official programme...
19

Aldershot: Gale & Polden, ltd. (19   24½cm.
no.   illus.

"Produced by the officers of the Aldershot and Eastern commands."

1. Pageants—Gt. Br.—Eng.—   Aldershot.
N. Y. P. L.   October 10, 1939

NT 0051419   NN

The tattooed wrist; or, The deed of a night
see under Old Spicer, pseud.

Tattuva-kattalei
see under [Cesattiri Civanar] [Supple-
ment]

Tattva-bhūshaṇa, Hemachandra Gosvami
see
Goswami, Hemchandra, 1872–1928.

Micro-
film
AP95
9

Tattva bodhinī patrikā. v.1–
1842/43–
Calcutta.

In Bengali.
Positive; original in Bangiya Sahitya
Parishad, Calcutta.

1. Periodicals (Bengali)

NT 0051423   ICU

Tattva-darśana
see under Prasad, Jwala, 1890–

Tattvabhushan, Sitanath
see Sitanatha, Tattvabhushana.

Tattvabhushan, Sitanath Datta
see Sitanatha Datta, Tattvabhushana.

Tattvabodha
Tattwa bodha (Daseinserkenntnis) von San-
karacharya; aus dem sanskrit übers. von F.
Hartmann. vi,[2],55p. Leipzig, W. Friedrich [1894]

NT 0051427   OC1

(Tattvacintana)
तत्त्वचिन्तन.

जयपुर, दर्शन प्रतिष्ठान.
v. 24 cm. quarterly.
In Hindi.

1. Philosophy, Hindu—Periodicals.   I. Darśana Pratishthāna.
B131.T36   72–907580
                                        (MARC-S)

NT 0051428   DLC

তত্ত্বকৌমুদী.
(কলিকাতা, সাধারণ ব্রাহ্মসমাজ)
v. 25 cm. semimonthly.
In Bengali.

1. Brahmo-samaj.   I. Sadharan Brahmo Samaj.
                        Title romanized: Tattvakaumudī.

BL1263.T37   73–917851

NT 0051429   DLC

... Tattvamuktakalapa and Sarvarthasiddhi with
the Anadadayini and the Bhavaprakasa...
    see under [Vonkatanatha Vedantacharya]

BL1210 Tattvarāyasvāmi.
.V85   Sasivarna potham; or, The doctrine of Sasivarna. A Vedantic poem, translated from the Tamil
by the Rev. Thomas Foulkes. London, Williams and
Norgate, 1862.
  19 p. ₍With Vivēkachintāmani. A synopsis of
Hindu systems and sects. Madras, 1860₎

  1. Vedânta. I. Foulkes, Thomas. tr. II. Title.

NT 0051431   ICU CtY

Tattvarthadhigama sutra...
    see under Umasvati, ca. 135-ca. 219.

Tattwa bodha
    see Tattvabodha.

Tatu, Henri, 1902-
... L'analyse chimique dans l'industrie textile, par Henri
Tatu ... Paris, Les Éditions textile et technique ₍1938₎
  5 p. l., 9–439, ₍2₎ p., 2 l. incl. 1 illus., tables. 21½ᶜᵐ.
  At head of title: L'édition textile moderne.
  "Liste des ouvrages consultés": verso of t.-p.

  1. Textile chemistry.   I. Title. II. Title: L'édition textile moderne.
    ₍Full name: Henri Marie Louis Tatu₎
                     39–9800
  Library of Congress   QD139.T5T3
                    ₍2₎   677.02871

NT 0051434   DLC

Tatu, Henri, 1902-
... L'industrie moderne des parfums, par H. Tatu ... avec 26
figures intercalées dans le texte. Paris, J.-B. Baillière et fils,
1932.
  167, ₍1₎ p. incl. illus., tables, diagrs. 21ᶜᵐ. (Actualités scientifiques et
industrielles)

  1. Perfumery.
                         A C 33–87
  Title from N. Y. Pub.   Libr. Printed by L. C.

NT 0051435   NN NNC

Tatu (Jean) [1871-]. *L'otite moyenne
catarrhale avec épanchement. 74 pp., 1 l. 4°.
Lyon, 1895, No. 1188.

NT 0051436   DNLM

Tatuajurile in Romania
    see under   [Minovici]. Nicolae S.

TATUI BABA.

  See BABA, Tatui.

Tatui, Matunosuke
  see   Tatsui, Matsunosuhe, 1884-

Tatuini

  See

Tatwin, Abp. of Canterbury, d. 734.

    Tatulli, Leone
PQ4835   "I vecchi e i giovani" nella narrativa di
17   Luigi Pirandello. [Bari] Adriatica [1955]
Z984   149 p. 22 cm. [Biblioteca di studi let-
    terari, 1]

    Bibliographical footnotes.

NT 0051441   RPB

TATUM, ART.
  [WORKS. SELECTIONS]
  5 jazz piano solos. Transcribed and edited by
Frank Paparelli. New York, Leeds music corp.,
c1940.   24 p.   31cm.

  CONTENTS.--Carnegie hall bounce.--Gang o' nothin'.--Jumpin'
for sumpin'.--Live jive.--Night scene.--Pianotations.

  1. Piano (Jazz). I. Paparelli,   Frank, ed.

NT 0051442   NN

Tatum, Art.
  5 jazz piano solos; transcribed and edited by
Frank Paparelli. New York, Leeds musc corp.,
c1944.
  24 p.   F.

NT 0051443   PP

---

4   Tatum, Art
Music
2220   Improvisations; piano interpreta-
    tions of America's outstanding song
    hits; edited by Morris Feldman.
    New York, Robbins Music Corp. c1939.
    43 p.

NT 0051444   DLC-P4 MB

Tatum, Arthur Lawrie, 1884-
  Morphological studies in experimental Cretinism.
(From Journ. Exper. Med. XVII. 1913.)
A. & P. T. v. 71.

NT 0051445   PPAN

Tatum, Arthur Lawrie, 1884-
  ... Morphological studies in experimental cretinism ... by
Arthur Lawrie Tatum. Chicago, 1913.
  1 p. l., p. ₍1₎, 636–652. 24ᶜᵐ.
  Thesis (PH. D.)—University of Chicago, 1913.
  "Reprinted from the Journal of experimental medicine, vol. XVII,
no. 6, 1913."
  Bibliography: p. 651–652.

  1. Cretinism. 2. Thyroid gland.

                    13–33518 Revised
  Library of Congress   RC657.T3
  Univ. of Chicago Libr.   ₍r28c2₎

NT 0051446   ICU DLC NN IU NIC

Tatum, Arthur Lawrie, 1884-   joint author.

Pfeiffer, Carl Curt.
  A new experimental approach to the study of the rôle of
the reticulo-endothelial system in the cure of trypanosomiasis,
by Carl C. Pfeiffer and Arthur L. Tatum ... ₍Baltimore,
1935₎

Tatum, Arthur Lawrie, 1884-
  Prescription notes, by Arthur L. Tatum. Chicago, Ill.,
The University of Chicago press ₍1925₎
  vii, 22 p., 1 l. 16½ᶜᵐ.
  49 blank leaves at end for "Selected prescriptions".

  1. Prescription writing.   I. Title.

                             26–2138
  Library of Congress   RM139.T3

NT 0051448   DLC DNLM ICJ NBuU

Film
1307   Tatum, Beulah Benton.
    Teacher training in the South, 1875–1900; state
  training of white elementary teachers. Baltimore,
  1943.

    Microfilm copy (negative) of typescript.
  Thesis - Johns Hopkins University.

    1. Teachers, Training of - Southern States.

NT 0051449   TxU

R581.979 TATUM, Brooking.
T189F   Florachromes of the Pacific states.
    [Burlingame, Calif. n.d.] 20 col.pl.

    In portfolio.
  Botanical data in manuscript on versos.

NT 0051450   WaS

Tatum, David, 1823–1912.
  Important suggestions for the consideration of professors,
philanthropists, tax payers, and patriots. ₍Cleveland, n. d.₎
  ₍4₎ p. 28 cm.
  Caption title.

    1. Temperance—Addresses, essays, lectures.   I. Title.

  HV5089.T27   65–58656

NT 0051451   DLC

HV5105 Tatum, David, 1823–1912.
.T3   Important suggestions for the consideration of
  professors... [Cleveland, 187-

NT 0051452   DLC NN

Tatum, David, 1823–1912.
  Striking providences and touching incidents. Cleveland,
1884.
  92 p. diagr. 18 cm.
  Some chapter titles changed by mounted labels.

    1. Pastoral theology—Anecdotes, facetiae, satire, etc. 2. Friends,
Society of—Clergy—Correspondence, reminiscences, etc. I. Title.

  BV4014.T36   64–58436

NT 0051453   DLC OClWHi

Tatum, David, 1823-1912.
Striking providences and touching incidents.
Edition 7 rev. Cleveland, 1885. ₍c1884₎
92 p. D.

NT 0051454   OO OClWHi

Tatum, David, 1823-1912.
Striking providences. Chicago, Ill., 1887.

NT 0051455   PSC-Hi

Tatum, David, 1823-1912.
Striking providences and touching incidents;
the way of success, and shadow of life... Twelve
thousand issued. Rev. ed. Cleveland, O., 1888.
92 p., 1 l. diagr. 17.5 cm.

NT 0051456   PSC-Hi

Tatum, David, 1823-1912.
Striking providences and touching incidents;
the sunshine and shadow of life. Rev. ed.
Cleveland, 1890.
92p.

NT 0051457   ICRL

Tatum, David, 1823-1912.
Striking providences and touching incidents. The
sunshine and shadow of life, by David Tatum...
Denver, Colorado, 1893.
92 p. illus. (port.) 18 cm.
Includes poetry.

NT 0051458   RPB

Tatum, David, 1823-1912.
Striking providences and touching incidents...
Twentieth thousand... Denver, Colo. 1894.
92 p.

P 12,090

NT 0051459   OClWHi

Tatum, David, 1823-1912.
Striking providences and touching incidents:
the sunshine and shadow of life... Twenty-two
thousand issued. Denver, Col., 1896.
96 p. illus. (port.) 18.5 cm.
Diagram mounted on inside of back cover.

NT 0051460   PSC-Hi

Tatum, David, 1823-1912.
Striking providences and touching
incidents. The sunshine and shadow of
life. By David Tatum... Denver,
Colorado, 1897.
96 p. 1 illus. (port.) 19½cm.
"Twenty-four thousand issued."
"Copyright, 1884."

NT 0051461   NcD

Tatum, David, 1823-1912.
Striking providences and touching incidents. The sunshine and shadow of life.
Chicago, Ill., 1903 ₍1884₎
107 p. port. 18½ cm.
Twenty-nine thousand issued.
1. Temperance. 2. Smoking. I. Title.

NT 0051462   MoKU

Tatum, David, 1823-1912.
Striking providences and touching incidents:
the sunshine and shadow of life... Thirty-four
thousand issued. Chicago, Ill., 1907.
106 p. illus. (port.) 18.5 cm.
Diagram on inside of back cover.

NT 0051463   PSC-Hi

Tatum, E   C   comp.
Federal contractors guide. Copyright ... ₍by₎ E. C. Tatum.
Excelsior Springs, Mo., 1942.
₍171₎ p. 28ᶜᵐ.
Various pagings.
Reproduced from type-written copy.

1. Public contracts—U. S. 2. Sales—U. S. I. Title.

42-17738

NT 0051464   DLC

Tatum, Mrs. Edith, 1877–
The awakening of Iseult, by Edith Tatum. Oglethorpe Uni-
versity, Ga., Oglethorpe university press ₍c1933₎
6 p. l., 9–44 numb. l. 22½ᶜᵐ.
Printed on one side of leaf on opposite pages.
A narrative poem.

1. Tristan. I. Title.
₍Full name: Mrs. Edith Brittain (Crenshaw) Tatum₎
34-30071
Library of Congress   PS3539.A77A9 1933
———— Copy 2.
Copyright A 74868   811.5

NT 0051465   DLC

Tatum, Mrs. Edith, 1877–
Body servant ₍by₎ Edith Tatum. Emory University, Atlanta,
Banner press ₍c1940₎
32 p. 20½ᶜᵐ.

1. U. S.—Hist.—Civil war—Fiction. I. Title.
₍Full name: Mrs. Edith Brittain (Crenshaw) Tatum₎
40-12662
Library of Congress   PZ3.T189Bo

NT 0051466   DLC NcD IU TxU

Tatum, Edith, 1877–
Designs for living, by Edith Tatum. Dallas, Tex., The
Kaleidograph press ₍1947₎
x p., 1 l., 13–62 p. 19½ cm.
Poems.

I. Title.
PS3539.A77D4   811.5   47—20402

NT 0051467   DLC TxU

Tatum, Edith, 1877–
Hills of the spirit, by Edith Tatum. Dallas, Tex., The Kaleidograph press ₍1945₎
xi p., 1 l., 15–84 p. 19½ᶜᵐ.
Poems.

I. Title.
₍Full name: Edith Brittain (Crenshaw) Tatum₎
45-20064
Library of Congress   PS3539.A77H5
811.5

NT 0051468   DLC ViU

Tatum, Edith, 1877–
In a Chinese garden, and other poems, by Edith Tatum.
Dallas, Tex., The Kaleidograph press ₍c1937₎
xi p., 1 l., 15–80 p. 20½ cm.

I. Title.
PS3539.A77 I 6 1937   811.5   37—23669

NT 0051469   DLC NIC NNR ViU AU

Tatum, Edith, 1877–
Orchestra of wind and trees. ₍Poems₎ Emory University,
Ga., Banner Press ₍1954₎
91 p. 21 cm. (Verse craft series)

I. Title.
Full name: Edith Brittain (Crenshaw) Tatum.
PS3539.A77O7   811.5   54-43103 ‡

NT 0051470   DLC NN

Tatum, Mrs. Edith, 1877–
Pattern, by Edith Tatum ... Emory University, Ga., Banner press ₍c1931₎
72 p. 20½ᶜᵐ. ₍Verse craft series₎

I. Title.
₍Full name: Mrs. Edith Brittain (Crenshaw) Tatum₎
32–373
Library of Congress   PS3539.A77P3 1931
———— Copy 2.
Copyright A 46000   811.5

NT 0051471   DLC NcD IU

Tatum, Edith, 1877–
Through a window toward the south. ₍Poems₎ Dallas,
Kaleidograph Press ₍1950₎
72 p. 20 cm.

I. Title.
Full name: Edith Brittain (Crenshaw) Tatum.
PS3539.A77T5   811.5   51-2897

NT 0051472   DLC

Tatum, Edith, 1877–
When the bugle called, by Edith Tatum. New York and
Washington, The Neale publishing company, 1908.
132 p. 19ᵐᵐ.

8-11078
Library of Congress   PZ3.T189W
(Copyright 1908 A 201363)

NT 0051473   DLC NcD

Tatum, Edward Howland, 1908–   ed.

Serle, Ambrose, 1742–1812.
The American journal of Ambrose Serle, secretary to Lord
Howe, 1776–1778, edited with an introduction by Edward H.
Tatum, jr. San Marino, Calif., The Huntington library, 1940.

Tatum, Edward Holland, 1908–
Notes, and documents, letters of William
Henry Allen
see under
Allen, William Henry, 1784-1813.

Tatum, Edward Howland, 1908–
The United States and Europe, 1815–1823; a study in the background of the Monroe doctrine, by Edward Howland Tatum, jr. Berkeley, Calif., University of California press, 1936.

x, 315 p. 22½ᶜᵐ.
"Bibliographical essay: the historiography of the Monroe doctrine": p. 279–296.
Bibliography: p. 297–304.

1. U. S.—For. rel.—1809–1817. 2. U. S.—For. rel.—1817–1825. 3. Europe—Politics—1815–1848. 4. Public opinion—U. S. 5. Monroe doctrine. 6. Adams, John Quincy, pres. U. S., 1767–1848. I. Title.

Library of Congress   E183.7.T37   36–27754
———— Copy 2.
Copyright A 92091   ₍S₎   327.73

NcD PU PBm PSC OCU OU OC1 OC1W OO OC1U IU MB ViU
NT 0051476   DLC MtU OrSaW OrU MtBC WaT PPT OrP NcRS

Tatum, Edward Hubbert, 1878–
The story of Larchmont manor park, by Edward H. Tatum for Larchmont manor park society. ₍New York, Printed by F. Hubner & co., inc., 1946₎

48 p. incl. illus., mounted fold. maps. 23½ᶜᵐ.

1. Larchmont, N. Y.—Parks—Larchmont manor park.   I. Larchmont manor park society.

F129.L35T3   974.727   47–15630

NT 0051477   DLC

Tatum, Edward Lawrie, 1909–
Effect of associated growth on forms of lactic acid produced by certain bacteria, by Edward Lawrie Tatum, William Harold Peterson and Edwin Broun Fred. Cambridge ₍Eng.₎ The University press ₍1932₎
cover-title, [1], ₍846₎–852 p.
University of Wisconsin, 1934, Ph.D.
Thesis note stamped on cover.
"From the Biochemical journal, vol. XXVI, no. 3 ... 1932."

NT 0051478   DLC

QR82
.B23L44

Tatum, Edward Lawrie, 1909–
Lederberg, Joshua.
₍Genetic recombination in Escherichia coli. n. p., 1947₎

Tatum, Edward Lawrie, 1909–
Genetics of microorganisms by E. L. Tatum and David D. Perkins. 1950.
(In Annual review of microbiology, v. 4, p. 129–150)
Bibliography; p. 144–150.

NT 0051480   PPAN

Tatum, Edward Lawrie, 1909–
Über einen aktivator des stoffwechsels der propionsäurebakterien.
Berlin, J. Springer, 1933.
1 p. l., p. ₍360₎–375.
By Calude Fromageot and E. L. Tatum.
"Biochemische zeitschrift ... Sonderabdruck aus 267. band, 4.–6 heft."

NT 0051481   DLC

Tatum, Edward Lawrie, 1909–
An unknown factor stimulating the formation of butyl alcohol by certain butyric acid bacteria [by] E. L. Tatum, W. H. Peterson and E. B. Fred. [Baltimore, 1934]
p. 207–217.

"Reprinted from Journal of bacteriology, vol. XXVII, no. 2, February, 1934."

NT 0051482   DLC

Tatum, Elbert Lee.
The changed political thought of the Negro, 1915–1940; with a foreword by Lawrence A. Davis. New York, Exposition Press ₍1951₎
205 p. 23 cm.
Bibliography: p. 195–205.

1. Negroes—Politics and suffrage.   I. Title.

JK2275.N4T3   325.260973   51–11870

VIHaI
NT 0051483   DLC Or OrU DAU InU AAP ViU NN MH TxU MB

JK2275
.N4
T3
1973

Tatum, Elbert Lee.
The changed political thought of the Negro, 1915–1940. With a foreword by Lawrence A. Davis. New York, Exposition Press [1951]
205p.

Xerox copy by University Microfilms, 1973.

1. Negroes – Politics and suffrage.
I. Title.

NT 0051484   NcU ICIU

Tatum, Frances C   ed.
Old Westtown; a collection, edited by Frances C. Tatum. Philadelphia, Ferris brothers, 1888.

viii p., 2 l., 151 p. front., illus., plates. 22½ᶜᵐ.

1. Westtown school, Westtown, Pa.   I. Title.
                                                  24–4839
Library of Congress   LD7501.W4W527

NT 0051485   DLC PP PSC-Hi PPFr NBuG PHC OC1WHi NN

TATUM, GEORGE BISHOP.
Andrew Jackson Downing, Arbiter of American taste 1815–1852. N.J. Princeton University PhD, 1950.

NT 0051486   NjP

Tatum, George Bishop
Andrew Jackson Downing: arbiter of American taste, 1815–1852. ₍Ann Arbor, Mich., 1950₎
vii, 374 l. illus., ports., plans, table. ₍University Microfilms, Ann Arbor, Mich.₎ Publication no. 11,042₎

Microfilm of typewritten copy.
Thesis, Princeton.
Includes material on Downing's association with A. J. Davis.
Bibliography: l.   ₍322₎–337.

NT 0051487   NNC MoU

FINE ART
NA
737
D75
T22
1974

Tatum, George Bishop.
Andrew Jackson Downing; arbiter of American taste, 1815–1852. [Princeton, N. J., 1948]
vii, 374 l. illus., plans.
(Doctoral dissertation series. Publication no. 11,042)
Thesis—Princeton University.
Bibliography: p. 323–337.
Photocopy. Ann Arbor, Mich., Xerox University Microfilms, 1974. 21cm.

1: Downing, Andrew Jackson, 1815–1852.

NT 0051488   NIC

Tatum, George Bishop.
Directions for the use of altar societies...
see under   Vaughan, Herbert Alfred, cardinal, 1832–1903.

Tatum, George Bishop.
The Paliotto of Sant' Ambrogio at Milan. [New York, College art association of America, 1944]
[25]–47 p. illus. 31 cm.
Caption title.
Reprinted from The Art Bulletin, March, 1944. v. 26, no. 1.
Bibliographical footnotes.

NT 0051490   PU-FA

Diss.
378
N.U.
1954

Tatum, George Liston, 1919–
Communication in the sales training program of the International Business Machines Corporation.

Ph.D.

1. Communication in management. 2. International Business Machines Corporation.

NT 0051491   IEN

Tatum, George Liston, 1919–
Communication in the sales training program of the International Business Machines Corporation. Ann Arbor, University Microfilms ₍1954₎
(₍University Microfilms, Ann Arbor, Mich.₎ Publication no. 10,324)
Microfilm copy of typescript. Positive.
Collation of the original: 258 l. illus.
Thesis—Northwestern University.
Vita.
Bibliography: leaves 254–257.
1. Salesmen and salesmanship—Study and teaching. 2. International Business Machines Corporation.   I. Title.
Microfilm AC–1 no. 10,324   Mic 55–3904

NT 0051492   DLC MtU

HF5438
T32

Tatum, George Liston, 1919–
Communication in the sales training program of the International Business Machines Corporation. Evanston, Ill., 1954.
258 l. illus.

Thesis – Northwestern University.
Vita.
Photocopy of typescript. Ann Arbor, Mich., University Microfilms, 1969. 23cm. (Doctoral dissertation series)

NT 0051493   GU

Tatum, Georgia Lee.
Disloyalty in the confederacy, by Georgia Lee Tatum, PH. D. Chapel Hill, The University of North Carolina press, 1934.
xi, 176 p. 23½ cm.
"Prepared as a doctoral dissertation at Vanderbilt university ₍1933₎"—Pref.
"Selected bibliography": p. 167–170.

1. Confederate States of America—Hist. 2. Confederate States of America—Soc. condit. 3. Public opinion—Confederate States of America. 4. U. S.—Hist.—Civil war—Peace.   I. Title.

E487.T176   975   34–22569

FU
MB IU NcD NcRS ViU MiU TNJ AAP OKentU OC1 OU OCU OO
NT 0051494   DLC OrCS MtU OrU DNW PHC PU CLU NIC WHi

Tatum, Gordon Russell, 1904–

Harvard university. Cruft memorial laboratory.
History of the officers electronics training courses. Army electronics training center, Harvard division. Naval training school (pre-radar) Harvard university ... ₍Cambridge, Mass., Cruft laboratory, Graduate school of engineering, Harvard university ₍1945₎

PA6502
.F7

Tatum, Henry Francis, 1853–   joint tr.

Martialis, Marcus Valerius.
Martial's Epigrams, translations and imitations by A. L. Francis ... and H. F. Tatum ... Cambridge ₍Eng.₎ The University press, 1924.

Tatum, Howell, *fl.* 1775–1815.
... Major Howell Tatum's journal while acting topographical engineer (1814) to General Jackson, commanding the Seventh military district, ed. by John Spencer Bassett ... Northampton, Mass., Dept. of history of Smith college ₁1922₎

138 p. 23ᶜᵐ. (Smith college studies in history, vol. VII, nos. 1, 2 and 3)

1. U. S.—Hist.—War of 1812—Personal narratives. 2. New Orleans, Battle of, 1815. 3. Alabama River. I. Bassett, John Spencer, 1867– ed.

Library of Congress   E361.T2   22—16375

MiU OClW OCl OClWHi ViU MB NcU OO OU LN
NT   0051497   DLC WaTU OrU PHC PBm PU PPT PSt NIC CoU

Tatum, James Moore.
Coaching football and the split T formation, by James M. Tatum and Warren K. Giese. Dubuque, W. C. Brown Co. ₁1953₎

277 p. illus. 28 cm.

1. Football. I. Giese, Warren Kenneth, joint author. II. Title.

GV951.9.T3   796.33   54—3261 ‡

CaBVaU CaBVa OrLgE OrPS OrMonO OrCS Or
NT   0051498   DLC OClW OO PSt TU TxU PWcS NcU IU KEmT

Tatum, Jan Hendrik
... De adoptionibus ... submittit Janus Henricus Tatum ... Trajecti ad Rhenum, I. Broedelet, 1756.
2 p.l., 42, ₁8₎ p. 21cm.
Diss. - Utrecht.

NT   0051499   MH-L

Tatum, Joel Haywood, 1821–1886.
"Devitiæ veræ" and other poems. ₁By₎ Joel Haywood Tatum ... ₁n. p., 1895₎
76 p. 16¼ᶜᵐ.

I. Title.

Library of Congress   PS2978.T2D4   31—12885

NT   0051500   DLC

₁Tatum, Joseph W   ₎ 1875–   *comp.*
₁Information of great value to newly married people; a carefully compiled and edited collection of such knowledge as is most needed in the homes of the newly married, so indexed as to be readily found when needed. Philadelphia ed. ₁Philadelphia ?₎ The advertisers, ᶜ1909.

255 p. illus. 25ᶜᵐ.

Advertising matter interspersed.

1. Domestic economy. 2. Receipts. 3. Cookery, American. I. Title.

    10—2307

Library of Congress   TX153.T2

NT   0051501   DLC ICJ

Tatum, Joseph W   1875– comp.
Property-owner's hand-book; containing information and references of especial value to owners of property and names of reliable mechanics and supply houses, etc. Comp. ... by Joseph W. Tatum ... Philadelphia, Printed by the Boteler-Wick co., inc., ᶜ1904.

135 p. 15¼ᶜᵐ.

Advertising matter interspersed.
p. 40–129, street directory of Philadelphia.

1. Philadelphia—Streets.

    8—14853

Library of Congress   F158.5.T22
    (Copyright 1904 A 91324)

NT   0051502   DLC

Tatum, Joseph W   1875–
Resident Birds of Locust Grove Farms, Westville, N.J. Henry W. Leeds, of Chalfonte-Haddon Hall-Owner: A brief census made July 8, 1933. By Joseph W. Tatum, Haddonfield, N.J.
3 p.
Typewritten.

NT   0051503   PHi

Tatum, Josiah, ed.
The **Farmers'** cabinet and American herd-book, devoted to agriculture, horticulture, and rural and domestic affairs ... v. 1–12; July 1, 1836–July 15, 1848. Philadelphia Moore & Waterhouse; ₁etc., etc.₎ 1837–48.

378.76   Tatum, Julien Rundell, 1910-
L930d   The socio-economic correlatives of health: a
1948   study of factors affecting the health and the obtaining of health services of farm families in Columbia County, Arkansas, 1942. n.p., 1948.
[xvi], 220p. tables. 28cm.

Thesis (Ph.D.)- Louisiana state university. Baton Rouge, La. 1948.
Biography.
"Selected bibliography": p.204-210.
Abstract.

NT   0051505   LU

Tatum, L   A
Anti-religious invasion of higher education. ₁Belmont? 1932₎
₁8₎p. 23cm.

1. N.C. University--Liberalism

NT   0051506   NcU

F232   Tatum, L   B
J2T3   ... The James river tourist, a brief account of historical localities on James river, and sketches of Richmond, Norfolk, and Portsmouth. Published by L. B. Tatum ... Richmond, Dispatch steam presses, 1885 ₁ᶜ1878₎
4₁.₁₁9₎–64p. illus.,plates,map. 17½cm.

At top of page: Fourth edition. revised and enlarged.

NT   0051507   NBuG

₁Tatum, Laurence W
₁The Kalmia builder. ₁A reference book of great value, for lumber dealers, carpenters and contractors. 1st ed. ... ₁Cleveland, O., Brooks & co., printers, ᶜ1885₎
32, 48 p. incl. illus., plans, tables. 17¼ᵐ.

Table of contents on 3d page of cover.
Copyrighted by Laurence W. Tatum, also a notice "to the trade" signed by him, p. ₁4₎
"... Designs for model residences, cottages, barns, etc." (with special t.-p.) : 48 p.

1. Building—Estimates. 2. Lumber trade—Tables and ready-reckoners. 3. Architecture, Domestic.

    8-7284†

Library of Congress   TH435.T22
    (Copyright 1885: 886)

NT   0051508   DLC

Tatum, Lawrie.
Our red brothers and the peace policy of President Ulysses S. Grant, by Lawrie Tatum; with an introduction by Thomas C. Battey. Sixteen illustrations. Philadelphia, J. C. Winston & co., 1899.

xix, 21–366 p. front., plates, ports. 20ᵐ.

1. Indians of North America—Government relations. 2. Indians of North America—Missions. 3. Friends, Society of—Missions. I. Title

Library of Congress   E93.T22   31–591

NT   0051509   DLC WaSpG TxU PHC ICU ICN DAU CtY

PS593   Tatum, Lew.
.L9Te   ... Virginia songster... New York, c1883.

NT   0051510   DLC

UB342   Tatum, Lyle, ed.
.U5C4
1954   **Central Committee for Conscientious Objectors,** *Philadelphia.*
Handbook for conscientious objectors, edited by Lyle Tatum ₁executive secretary₎ 2d ed., rev. Philadelphia, 1954.

Tatum, Noreen (Dunn)
A round-the-world source book, especially prepared for use with missionary units found in closely graded junior courses, issued by Board of Christian education and Board of missions, Methodist Episcopal Church, South, Nashville, Tennessee, through the Joint Committee on co-operation and counsel. Nashville, Tennessee, Cokesbury press, ₁c1939₎
By Mary Noreen Dunn - CBI

NT   0051512   GEU

268.61   Tatum, Noreen(Dunn)
D922f   Friends at Bethlehem center, by Noreen Dunn; leaders' helps for World children's circles of the Woman's missionary society... Nashville, Dept. of education and promotion, Woman's section, Board of missions, Methodist Episcopal church, South ₁1933?₎
3p.l.,3–43p. 23cm.

1. Missions - Negroes. 2. Missions - Study and teaching. I. Title. II. Title: Bethlehem center.

NT   0051513   TxU

Tatum, Noreen (Dunn)
Let's see China; a world friendship unit for junior girls and boys. Nashville, Cokesbury Press ₁1937₎

78 p. illus. 23 cm.

"Issued by Board of Christian Education and Board of Missions, Methodist Episcopal Church, South, Nashville, Tennessee, through the Joint Committee on Co-operation and Counsel."
Bibliography: p. 76–78.

1. Missions—China. 2. Missions—Study and teaching (Elementary) 3. Religious education—Text-books for children. I. Title.

BV3415.T23   37–5074 rev 2*
    [915.1] 268.61

NT   0051514   DLC

Tatum, Noreen (Dunn)
Let's see Mexico; a world friendship unit for junior girls and boys. Nashville, Cokesbury Press ₁1936₎

80 p. music. 23 cm.

"Issued by Board of Christian Education and Board of Missions, Methodist Episcopal Church, South, Nashville, Tennessee, through the Joint Committee on Co-operation and Counsel."
Bibliography: p. 79–80.

1. Mexico—Soc. life & cust. 2. Missions—Mexico. 3. Missions—Study and teaching (Elementary) 4. Religious education—Text-books for children. I. Title.

BV2835.T3   [917.2] 268.61   38–7716 rev*

NT   0051515   DLC

E98   Tatum, Noreen (Dunn)
.M6G5
   Gladfelter, Katharine Eleanor.
Many moons ago and now, a world friendship unit for junior girls and boys, by Katharine E. Gladfelter, adapted by Noreen Dunn. ₁Nashville, ᶜ1938₎

Tatum, Noreen (Dunn)
Women and home missions. Nashville, Cokesbury Press ₁1936₎
80 p. 22 cm.

1. Methodist Episcopal church, South. Woman's missionary Council. 2. Women in church work. 3. Methodist Episcopal church, South--Missions. 4. Missions, Home. I. Title.

BV2766.M7T33   266.76   36--8088

NT   0051517   DLC ViU NcD

Tatum, Richard Parry, 1859-1925.
Tatum narrative, 1626-1925, by Richard P. Tatum. Philadelphia, Penna., 1925.
110 p. front., plates, ports., fold. geneal. tab. 24½ᶜᵐ.
The author died April 8, 1925, and his wife published the work in October, 1926.

1. Tatum family.   I. Tatum, Mrs. Sarah English (Green) ed. II. Title.
Library of Congress   CS71.T22 1926   26-21720

NN
NT   0051518   DLC PHC PHi PPL PP MiU-C OClWHi MB MWA

Tatum, Robert Lee.
Map of Bossier City, Louisiana, and environs. Mar. 15, 1948; revised Apr. 26, 1951. ₁Shreveport, La.₎ ᶜ1951.
map 33 x 56 cm.
Scale 1 : 12,000 or 1"=1,000'.
Blue line print.

1. Bossier City, La.--Maps.

G4014.B684 1951.T5   Map 51-1003

NT   0051519   DLC

Tatum, Samuel C., co.
Manual of machine bookkeeping... Cincinnati, The Author, C1902.
66 p. illus. forms.

NT   0051520   MiD

Tatum, Samuel C., Company.
...Tatum adjustable paper drills, punches and perforators... ₁Cincinnati, 1915.₎   48 p. illus. 8°.
Catalogue no. 32.

1. Punching machinery.--Catalogues.   2. Paper cutting machines.--Catalogues.
N. Y. P. L.   September 8, 1923.

NT   0051521   NN

Tatum, Mrs. Sarah English (Green) ed.
Tatum, Richard Parry, 1859-1925.
Tatum narrative, 1626-1925, by Richard P. Tatum. Philadelphia, Penna., 1925.

Mflm
279
Tatum, Scott L
Theology of John Bunyan. Austin, Tex., 1949.
xiii, 286 p. 28 cm.
Thesis (Th.D.)--Southwestern Baptist Theological Seminary.
Bibliography: p. 283-286.
Microfilm. Fort Worth, Tex., Southwestern Baptist Theological Seminary. Fleming Library, 1960. 1 reel. 35 mm.
1. Bunyan, John, 1628-1688. I. Title.

NT   0051523   MNtcA

N.J.-Y3
F119.5
.T38A3
Tatum, Sibyl.
Account of journey of Sibyl Tatum with her parents from N. Jersey to Ohio in 1830. ₁Woodbury, N.J., 1830₎
₁13₎1. 30 cm.

Typewritten copy
At end of last page:"About the Diary. Account was taken from a small fifteen page note book, 4x 6 inches. The notes are in longhand ... BibliOhioan, John Kolvoord, Independence, Ohio."

NT   0051524   NjR

F491
T3
Tatum, Sibyl
Account of journey of Sibyl Tatum with her parents from N. Jersey to Ohio in 1830. ₁Independence, Ohio, 1945?₎
1 v. (unpaged) 28cm.

Account taken from a small fifteen page notebook, 4 x 6 inches. The notes are in longhand.

1. Ohio - Descr & trav.   2. New York (State) - Descr. &   trav.

NT   0051525   GU

917.3
T189
Cov.
Coll.
Tatum, Sibyl.
Account of journey of Sibyl Tatum with her parents from N. Jersey to Ohio in 1830. [Independence, Ohio, BibliOhioan, J. Kolvoord, 1954]
₁13₎L. 30cm.

"Taken from a small fifteen page notebook, 4 x 6 inches...in longhand."
Mimeographed.

NT   0051526   OOxM

Tatum, Stewart L., comp.

Springfield, *O. Ordinances, etc.*
Codified ordinances of the city of Springfield, Ohio. Containing all the general ordinances of the city in force November 1, 1907, together with other municipal legislation of special interest and importance to the officers of the city and to the public. Revised, codified and compiled by Stewart L. Tatum, city solicitor. Published under the authority of the City council. Springfield, O., The Springfield publishing company, 1907.

Tatum, Stewart L.

Ohio. *Committee for an investigation of finances of municipalities.*
Report of the Committee for an investigation of finances of municipalities. Bulletin of the Ohio Legislative reference department. Columbus, February 3, 1915. Columbus, O., The F. J. Heer printing co., 1915.

PC4111
.A638
Tatum, Terrell Louise, 1902-

Arjona, Doris King.
Fronteras, a first₁-second₎ year course in Spanish. Chicago, Scott, Foresman, ᶜ1947-₁51₎

Tatum, Terrell Louise, 1902-
Pan American business Spanish, by Terrell Louise Tatum ... New York, London, D. Appleton-Century company incorporated ₁1945₎
xii, 255 p., 1 l. illus. (incl. maps) 22ᶜᵐ. (*Half-title:* The Century modern language series; Kenneth McKenzie, editor)
"Selected bibliography": p. 91-95.

1. Commercial correspondence, Spanish. 2. Spanish language--Business Spanish. 3. Spanish America. I. Title.
                           45-4391
Library of Congress °   HF3728.S7T3
          ₁7₎   651.75

KEmT MB
NT   0051530   DLC NcD NcC Or MtU WaSpG OCl OCU OO FMU

Tatum, Terrell Louise, 1902-
... Por onda corta; a radio journey to Latin America. Boston, New York ₁etc.₎ Published for Reynal & Hitchcock by Houghton Mifflin company ₁1942₎
xiii p., 1 l., 157, 49 p. plates. 19½ᶜᵐ.
Map on lining-papers.

1. Spanish language--Chrestomathies and readers. 2. Spanish America. I. Title. II. Title: A radio journey to Latin America.

Library of Congress   PC4127.G4T3   42-14352
         ₁4₎   468.6

NT   0051531   DLC OCl IU

Tatum, Terrell Louise, 1902-

Arjona, Doris King.
Spain and America ₁by₎ Doris K. Arjona, Rose L. Friedman ₁and₎ Esther P. Carvajal; a second year Spanish book in the Language, literature, and life program of Scott, Foresman and company. Chicago, Atlanta ₁etc.₎ 1940₎

Tatum, Terrell Louise, 1902-
Viñetas de la América Latina. New York, H. Holt ₁1947₎
vi, 168 p. illus., maps. 21 cm.

1. Spanish language--Chrestomathies and readers. 2. Spanish language--Composition and exercises. 3. Spanish America. I. Title.
PC4117.T38   468.6   47-12206*

NT   0051533   DLC IdPI FMU OCl FTaSU

PZ3
.E768
Wo
Tatum, Terrell Louise, 1902-   tr.

Espina, Concha, 1869-1955.
... The woman and the sea; authorized translation by Terrell Louise Tatum; introduction by Ernest Boyd. New York, R. D. Henkle ₁ᶜ1934₎

RD31
.H745
Tatum, Thomas.
Affections of the muscular system.
[In Holmes, T. System of Surgery. London, 1852. 22 cm. v. 3. p. 522-556]

NT   0051535   DLC

RD31
.H75
Tatum, Thomas.
Affections of the muscular system... By Thomas Tatum and J. Lockhart Clarke.
[In Holmes, T. ed. A system of surgery. 1st am. ed. 8°. Philadelphia, 1882. v. 3. p. 378-397]

NT   0051536   DLC

F869
S3P18
v. 18:6
x
Tatum and Bowen.
Catalogue of printing materials, printing presses, paper cutters, also, showing specimens of newspaper headings. San Francisco, 1889.
62 p. illus. 25cm. [Pamphlets on San Francisco. v. 18, no. 6]

1. Printing machinery and supplies - Catalogs. (Series)

NT   0051537   CU-BANC

B588.3
T 188
TATUNO, SEIZI.

Zytologische untersuchungen über die lebermoose von Japan, von Seizi Tatuno... ₁Hirosima, Japan, Hirosima university, 1941₎
115p. illus. (incl. maps) pl. 3-4, tables, diagrs. 26½cm. (On cover: Journal of science of the Hirosima university. Series B, div. 2 (Botany) vol. 4, no. 6)
Caption title.
"Literaturver zeichnis":p. 113-114.

NT   0051538   PU

S760
.R9U9

Tatur, Petr Kuz'mich

Uzbek S. S. R. *Upravlenie zemleustroĭstva.*
Справочник инженера-землеустроителя МТС. Под общей ред. М. П. Кунявского и П. К. Татур. Ташкент, Гос. изд-во Узбекской ССР, 1955.

HF3626
.B23

Tatur, Sergeĭ Koz'mich.

Bakanov, Mikhail Ivanovich.

Анализ хозяйственной деятельности торговых предприятий и организаций. Под ред. С. К. Татура. Допущено в качестве учебника для вузов. Москва, Госторгиздат, 1948.

Tatur, Sergeĭ Koz'mich.

Анализ хозяйственной деятельности предприятий. ₁Москва₎ Московский рабочий, 1949.

39 p. 20 cm. (В помощь слушателям вечерних партийных школ)

1. Finance.
Title transliterated: Analiz khozĭaĭstvennoĭ deĭatel'nosti predprĭatiĭ.

HF5550.T3   50–19808

NT 0051541   DLC

HG4186
.T3

Tatur, Sergeĭ Koz'mich.

Баланс как орудие управления предприятием; анализ финансового состояния промышленного предприятия. ₁Москва₎ Госполитиздат, 1941.

145 p. tables. 19 cm. (Библиотека по экономике промышленного предприятия)

1. Finance—Russia. 2. Financial statements. I. Title. (Series: Biblioteka po èkonomike promyshlennogo predprĭatĭa)
Title transliterated: Balans kak orudie upravlenĭa predprĭatiem.

NT 0051542   DLC

4-
HG-
276

Tatur, Sergeĭ Koz'mich.

Ewidencja środków trwałych przedsiębiorstwa przemysłowego. [Warszawa] Główny Instytut Pracy, 1950.

80 p.

NT 0051543   DLC-P4

HD57
.T38

Tatur, Sergeĭ Koz'mich.

Использование личных счетов экономии в борьбе за социалистические накопления в промышленности. ₁Москва₎ Гос. изд-во полит. лит-ры, 1951.

166 p. illus. 20 cm.

At head of title: С. Татур, А. Соколовский, В. Мнацаганова.

1. Labor productivity—Russia. 2. Industrial management—Russia. I. Title *Title transliterated:* Ispol'zovanie lichnykh schetov èkonomii

51–40401

NT 0051544   DLC

Tatur, Sergeĭ Koz'mich.

Как анализировать выполнение плана по выпуску продукции. Москва, Госфиниздат, 1954.

102 p. 17 cm. (В помощь хозяйственному активу предприятий)

1. Industrial management—Russia. I. Title.
Title transliterated: Kak analizirovat' vypolnenie plana po vypusku produktsii.

HD70.R9T3   55–33116

NT 0051545   DLC

Tatur, Sergeĭ Koz'mich.

Хозяйственный расчет на предприятии. Москва, Госпланиздат, 1950.

39 p. 20 cm.

At head of title: Всесоюзный совет научных инженерно-технических обществ. Общественный университет.
Errata slip inserted.

1. Industrial management—Russia.
Title transliterated: Khozĭaĭstvennyĭ raschet na predprĭatii.

HD37.T28   50–35952

NT 0051546   DLC

Tatur, Sergeĭ Koz'mich.

Хозяйственный расчет и повышение рентабельности промышленных предприятий. Москва ₁Правда₎ 1951.

23 p. 22 cm. (Экономика и организация производства социалистического промышленного предприятия)

At head of title: Всесоюзное общество по распространению политических и научных знаний.

1. Industrial management—Russia. I. Title.
Title transliterated: Khozĭaĭstvennyĭ raschet ... promyshlennykh predprĭatiĭ.

HD37.T278   52–34518

NT 0051547   DLC

HD37
.T282

Tatur, Sergeĭ Koz'mich.

Хозяйственный расчет в социалистических государственных предприятиях. Москва, Знание, 1953.

39 p. 22 cm. (Всесоюзное общество по распространению политических и научных знаний. Сер. 2, № 78)

1. Industrial management—Russia. I. Title.
Title transliterated: Khozĭaĭstvennyĭ raschet v sotsialisticheskikh ... predprĭatiĭakh.

54–28354 ‡

NT 0051548   DLC

HD37
.T285

Tatur, Sergeĭ Koz'mich.

Хозрасчет и рентабельность; пути укрепления хозяйственного расчета на промышленном предприятии. Москва, Изд-во Академии наук СССР, 1951.

165 p. 22 cm.

At head of title: Академия наук СССР. Институт экономики.

1. Industrial management—Russia. I. Title.
Title transliterated: Khozraschet i rentabel'nost'.

53–34169

NT 0051549   DLC

Tatur, Sergeĭ Koz'mich.

Организация народно-хозяйственного учета в социалистическом обществе. ₁Москва₎ Изд-во Московского университета, 1955.

35 p. 22 cm.

1. Accounting. I. Title.
Title transliterated: Organizatsiĭa narodno-khozĭaĭstvennogo ucheta.

HF5653.T28   55–59846

NT 0051550   DLC FU

Tatur, Sergeĭ Koz'mich.

Основные вопросы анализа хозяйственной деятельности промышленных предприятий; стенограмма публичной лекции, прочитанной 12 марта 1948 года ... в Москве. Москва ₁Правда₎ 1948.

31 p. 22 cm.

At head of title: Всесоюзное общество по распространению политических и научных знаний.

1. Industrial management.
Title transliterated: Osnovnye voprosy analiza khozĭaĭstvennoĭ deĭatel'nosti.

HD37.T3   50–18914 ‡

NT 0051551   DLC

HF5653
.T3
1948

Tatur, Sergeĭ Koz'mich.

Учет основных средств промышленных предприятий Изд. 2. доп. Москва, Госпланиздат, 1948.

78 p. 22 cm.

At head of title: С. Татур и Л. Краснов.

1. Accounting. I. Krasnov, L., joint author. II. Title.
Title transliterated: Uchet osnovnykh sredstv promyshlennykh predprĭatiĭ.

49–19592*

NT 0051552   DLC

Tatur, Sergeĭ Koz'mich.

Wirtschaftliche Rechnungsführung und Rentabilität des Betriebes; die Wege zur Festigung der wirtschaftlichen Rechnungsführung im Industriebetrieb. Übersetzung aus dem Russischen. Berlin, Verlag Die Wirtschaft, 1953.

191 p. 22 cm.

1. Industrial management—Russia. I. Title.

HD70.R9T354   56–38170 ‡

NT 0051553   DLC

SB23
T38

Tatura, Australia. Horticultural Research Station.
Annual research report.
Victoria, Australia, Victoria Dept. of Agriculture.
v. illus. 26cm.

1. Horticultural   research - Australia
2. Horticulture   - Period.

NT 0051554   NcRS DNAL CU

88
T18

Tatura, Australia. Horticultural Research Station.
Guide book.
₁Melbourne₎ Dept. of Agriculture.

1. Goulburn region, Victoria, Australia.
Pomology. Research.

NT 0051555   DNAL

Tatura, Australia. Horticultural Research Station.
Research report
see its   Annual Research Report.

Taṭwān
see
Tetuán.

Die Tatwelt; Zeitschrift für Erneuerung des Geisteslebens.

Berlin, Junker und Dünnhaupt.

v. in   24 cm. quarterly.

Began publication in 1925. Cf. Union list of serials.
"Begründet von Rudolf Eucken."

1. Philosophy—Period. I. Eucken, Rudolf Christof, 1846–1926.

B3.T35   105   51–39185

NT 0051558   DLC NIC IEN NjP MH PP NN ICRL

Tatwin, abp. of Canterbury, d. 734.
   ÆEnigmata.
     10 p.   (Giles, J.A., Anecdota Bedae, p. 25:
Caxton Soc.)

NT 0051559   MdBP

Tatwin, archbishop of Canterbury, d. 734.
   Tatwini ÆEnigmata. (Wright. The Anglo-Latin
satirical poets. Vol. 2, p. 525-534. London,
1872)

NT 0051560   MB RPB

Tatwin, abp. of Canterbury, d. 734.
   Giles, John Allen, 1808-1884, ed.
     Anecdota Bedæ, Lanfranci, et aliorum. Inedited tracts,
letters, poems, &c., of Venerable Bede, Lanfranc, Tatwin
and others: by the Rev. Dr. Giles. London, D. Nutt,
1851.

Tatwinus
   see   Tatwin, abp. of Canterbury, d. 734.

Tatxer, Antonio Soler
   see   Soler Tatxer, Antonio.

Taty, *pseud.*
   see **Firestein, Tatyana de Rebikoff-Savici,** 1925-

Taty, Théodore.
   *Etude clinique sur les aliénés héréditaires.
Lyon, 1885.
     1 p.l., 110 p., 1 l.   4°.
     No. 288.

NT 0051565   DNLM

WM   TATY, Théodore
T221e   Étude clinique sur les aliénés
1885   héréditaires. Paris, Baillière, 1885.
     114 p.
     Issued also as thesis. Paris.

NT 0051566   DNLM CtY-M

Tatya, Tookaram
   see   Tukārāmā Tātyā.

Tātya, Tukaram
     see
   Tukārāmā Tātyā

Tatya Sastri Patavardhana
   see   Rama Krishna Shastri.

PQ4835   Tatza, Mosnen, tr.
.A27T75
   Papini, Giovanni, 1881-
   ... טרגדיות בכל יום. תרגם. מ. טצה. ורשה, הוצאת
     ישרקליק, תרמ״ג. ₁Warszawa, 1923₁

Tatzel, A   , arr.
   The lancers. Les lanciers. Quadrille original anglais pour pianoforte ...
     see under   Richardson, William, musi-
cian.

Tatzel, Robert Wilhelm, 1861-
   *Beitrag zur Pathologie der Bursa pharyngea.
Freiburg in Baden, H. M. Poppen u. Sohn, 1888.
     24 p., 2 l.   8°.

NT 0051572   DNLM

Tatzel, Robert Wilhelm, 1861-

   ——. Die hypnotische Suggestion und ihre
Heilwirkungen. 64 pp. 12°. *Leipzig, J. A.
Barth,* 1899.

NT 0051573   DNLM

Tatzel, Robert Wilhelm, 1861-
   Die psychotherapie (hypnose). Ihre handhabung und
bedeutung für den praktischen arzt. Mit 8 abbildungen.
Von D⁻ med. Tatzel ... Berlin ₁etc.₁ Heuser's verlag (L.
Heuser) 1894.
     4 p. l., 80 p. illus. 24ᶜᵐ.

   1. Therapeutics, Suggestive.

   Library of Congress   RM921.T2   8-14298

NT 0051574   DLC DHEW OCIW DNLM

Tatzel, Robert Wilhelm, 1861-   tr.

   Tuckey, Charles Lloyd.
     Psychotherapie; oder, Behandlung mittels hypnotismus
und suggestion, von Dr. med. C. Lloyd Tuckey ... Aus
dem englischen, von Dr. med. Tatzel ... Autorisierte
deutsche ausg. mit 13 illustrationen. Berlin ₁etc.₁ Heuser's verlag (L. Heuser) 1895.

Tatzel, Wilhelm Robert
   see   Tatzel, Robert Wilhelm, 1861-

Tau, Herrmann.
   Aktivität, roman von Herrmann Tau. Danzig-Oliva und
Leipzig, Verlag des freimütigen ₁1932₁
     368 p. 18½ᶜᵐ.

   I. Title.

   Library of Congress   PT2642.A7A7 1932   33-17828
   Copyright A—Foreign   20910
                           833.91

NT 0051577   DLC

Tau, Herrmann.
   Die steinerne mauer, roman von Herrmann Tau. 2. aufl.
Danzig-Oliva und Leipzig, Verlag des freimütigen ₁1933₁
     294 p. 21½ᶜᵐ.

   I. Title.

   Library of Congress   PT2642.A788 1933   33-24488
   Copyright A—Foreign   21896
                           833.91

NT 0051578   DLC

Tau Liu Chien, 1905-
   see   Liu, Chien-Tau, 1905-

CT1098   Tau, Max, 1897-   joint ed.
.S45E5
   Engelstad, Carl Fredrik, 1915-   ed.
     Albert Schweitzer erobrer Norge; en liten bok om en stor
opplevelse. Redigert av Carl Fredrik Engelstad og Max
Tau. Oslo, J. G. Tanum, 1954.

Tau, Max, 1897-
   Albert Schweitzer und der Friede. Hamburg, R. Meiner
₁1955₁
     15 p. illus. 24 cm.

   1. Schweitzer, Albert, 1875-

   CT1098.S45T3   56-33260 ‡

NT 0051581   DLC CaBVaU NN MH WU

Tau, Max, 1897-
   Der assoziative faktor in der landschafts- und
ortsdarstellung Theodor Fontanes.   Kiel, 1928.
   Inaug.-diss. - Kiel.
   Bibl.

NT 0051582   ICRL PU

Tau, Max, 1897-
   Der assoziative faktor in der landschafts- und ortsdarstellung
Theodor Fontanes, von dr. Max Tau. ₁bd. 1₁ Oldenburg,
Rudolf Schwartz, 1928.
     2 p. l., 88 p. 24ᶜᵐ. (*Added t.-p.:* Forschungen zur literatur-, theater-
und zeitungswissenschaft ... ₁bd. 3₁)
     The complete work was issued later as the author's inaugural disser-
tation, Kiel, 1928.
     "Literatur-verzeichnis": p. 85-88.

   1. Fontane, Theodor, 1819-1898.

   Title from Univ. of Minn.   Printed by L. C.   A C 33-3558

NT 0051583   MnU ICU

Tau, Max, 1897-
   Denn über uns ist der Himmel; Roman. Hamburg, Hoffmann und Campe ₁1955₁
     315 p. 21 cm.

   I. Title.

   PT2642.A712D4   57-33254 ‡

NT 0051584   DLC WaT CaBVaU CtY NN InU IEN OCl IU MH

PT8950
.T3F6
Tau, Max, 1897–
for over oss er himmelen. ¡På norsk fra forfatterens originalmanuskript av Carl Fredrik Engelstad¡ Oslo, J. G. Tanum, 1954.
343 p. 21 cm.

ɪ. Engelstad, Carl Fredrik, 1915–   tr. ɪɪ. Title.
A 55–6780

Minnesota. Univ. Libr.
for Library of Congress

NT 0051585   MnU CU WU DLC CtY DLC

833.9
T222g
Tau, Max, 1897–
Glaube an den Menschen.   Berlin, F.A. Herbig [1948]
236 p. 22 cm.

NT 0051586   IEN OC1 NN NIC IU

Tau, Max, 1897–   ed.

Görres, Johann Joseph von, 1776–1848.
Joseph Görres, eine auswahl aus seinen schriften; herausgegeben von Max Tau. Mit einer einleitung von p. Friedrich Muckermann, s. ᴊ. Berlin, Deutsche buch-gemeinschaft, g. m. b. h. ¡1931¡

PT1863
Z7T3
Tau, Max, 1897–
Landschafts- und Ortsdarstellung Theodor Fontanes. Oldenburg, R. Schwarts, 1928.
121 p. 20 cm. (His Epische Gestaltung, Bd. 1)

Bibliography: p. 117–121.

1. Fontane, Theodor, 1819–1898. I. Title.

NT 0051588   GU MH NIC

Tau, Max, 1897–
Tro på mennesket, av Max Tau.   ¡Oslo¡ J. Grundt Tanum, 1946. 338 p. 20 cm.

Novel.
"Oversatt av Bjørn Rongen."

409952B. 1. No subject. I. Rongen,   Bjørn, 1906–   , tr. II. Title.
N. Y. P. L.   October 30, 1947

NT 0051589   NN MnU WaU CtY

PT 1324
.T222
TAU, MAX, 1897–   ed.
Vorstoss; Prosa der ungedruckten. Hrsg. von Max Tau und Wolfgang von Einsiedel. Berlin, B. Cassirer, 1930.
314 p.

1. German fiction—20th cent.—Coll. I. Einsiedel, Wolfgang von. II. Tc.

NT 0051590   InU ICU IEN NjP IaU WaU NN MiU MH MdBP

DR
54
T19b
Tau, Theo
Bulgarien; Ferien an der Schwarzmeerküste. Pforzheim, Goldstadtverlag [n.d.]
76 p. illus., map. (Ferien im Ausland, Bd. 19)

1. Bulgaria – Descr. & trav. – Guide-books. I. Title. II. Series.

NT 0051591   CLU

Tau, Vicente.
Geografía física (litósfera, hidrósfera e "hidrobia") por Vicente Tau ... ¡Buenos Aires, Librería y editorial "El Ateneo," 1940¡

3 p. l., ¡9¡–362, ¡4¡ p. illus. (incl. maps) tables, diagrs. 21ᶜᵐ.

"Responde al programa de la materia del Colegio de la Universidad nacional de la Plata."

1. Physical geography—Text-books—1870–   ɪ. Title.
42–27839

Library of Congress   GB55.T26

NT 0051592   DLC

T'au Yüan-Ming
see   T'ao, Ch'ien, 372?–427?

Tau; monatsblätter für verinnerlichung und selbstgestaltung, für erkenntnis und tat ... hft. ¡1¡– mai 1924–

¡Bern, etc., W. Zimmermann, 1924–
v.   illus., plates, ports. 18½ᶜᵐ.
Title varies: May 1924–Dec.? 1926, Tao; monatsblätter für verinnerlichung (later "ferinnerlichung") und selbstgestaltung.
Jan. 1927–Dec. 1932, Tau; monatsblätter für verinnerlichung und selbstgestaltung.
Jan. 1933–Dec. 1935, Tau; monatsblätter für erkenntnis und tat.
Jan. 1936–   Tau; monatsblätter für verinnerlichung und selbstgestaltung und tat.
Editor: May 1924–   Werner Zimmermann.
ɪ. Zimmermann, Werner, 1898–   ed.
40–22859

Library of Congress   AP32.T36
¡2¡   053

NT 0051594   DLC NN

Tau Beta, Detroit.
Annual report.
1926 has title; Social pioneering, the story of the ... Association...

NT 0051595   MiD

Tau beta, Detroit.
History of Tau beta, by Mildred Plumb, historian, 1932–1938. Detroit, Priv. print. by Evans-Winter-Hebb inc., 1938.
181 p. illus. (incl. ports., facsims.) 26½ᶜᵐ.

ɪ. Plumb, Mildred.
38–14793

Library of Congress   HS3353.T33A5
———— Copy 2.
Copyright A 119045   ¡3¡   369.46

NT 0051596   DLC MiD

Tau Beta community house, Hamtramck, Mich.
Tau Beta community house.   [1941?]
28 [1] p. illus.

NT 0051597   MiD

Tau beta pi.
Catalog of the Tau beta pi association, issued by the Executive council, R. C. Matthews, secretary-treasurer ... 3d ed.— April 1916. Cincinnati, O., Press of The Webb-Biddle company ¡1916¡
¡455¡ p. 11 x 17ᶜᵐ.
Various pagings.
Loose-leaf.
To be kept up to date by means of semiannual supplements. cf. Foreword.

ɪ. Matthews, Robert Clayton, 1878–   ed.
34–7841

Library of Congress   LJ75.T223 1916   371.85462

NT 0051598   DLC

Tau Beta Pi.
Catalog of the Tau beta pi association, issued by the Executive council, R. C. Matthews, secretary treasurer... 4th ed. Dec. 1926.   Menasha, Wis. G. Banta pub. co., 1926.
369 p.
Cover-title; The Bent of Tau beta pi, v. 18, no. 1, catalog number. Supplement to Jan, 1927 issu.
I. Matthews, Robert Clayton, 1878–   ed.

NT 0051599   MiD

Tau Beta Pi.
Catalogue...
¡no.¡ 1
Bethlehem, Pa., 1898
no.

1. College societies, Greek letter—   Tau Beta Pi.
N. Y. P. L.   January 27, 1925

NT 0051600   NN

371.85
T191
Tau Beta Pi.
Information about Tau Beta Pi.   Knoxville Tenn., 1949.
24 p. illus. 21 cm.

Cover title.

NT 0051601   IU

Tau Beta Pi.
Membership catalog... Issued by the Executive Council... Menasha, Wis., The Collegiate Press, George Banta Publishing Company [
v. 23 cm.
issue.
Title varies; issue, catalog...
At head of title; Supplement to the Bent of Tau Beta Pi.
Sixth issue has running title: The Bent of Tau Beta Pi.

NT 0051602   NNC

Fifth issue is the Bent of Tau Beta Pi, v. 23, no. 4, pt. 2, Nov. 1932.
Columbia chapter;

NT 0051603   NNC

Tau beta pi.
Membership catalog of the Tau beta pi association (sixth issue), issued by the Executive council. Editors, Charles H. Spencer ¡and¡ R. C. Matthews. Menasha, Wis., The collegiate press, Geo. Banta pub. co., 1939.
x, 754 p.

Running title: The bent of Tau beta pi ¡Its official quarterly magazine¡
Columbia chapter: p. 329–339.
I. Spencer,   Charles H

NT 0051604   NNC

Egleston
D621.3292
T19
Tau beta pi.
"To be or not to be". Prepared by the Civilian protection project, sponsored by the New York alumnus chapter of Tau beta pi. 1950.
61–82 p. tables.

From the Bent of Tau beta pi for April, 1950.
Includes bibliographies.

NT 0051605   NNC

Tau Beta Pi.
What is best in engineering education? Opinions of many alumni from many colleges. [n. p., 1916]
cover title, 107 p.

NT 0051606   MiBC

Tau Beta Pi. Alumni Association of New York. Directory.
ed. 1

[New York, 1924
no.

NT 0051607   NN

Tau Delta
Come listen to my song
see under title

W.C.L. Tau Delta
M780.88
A512VW   There was a time; words from the Lady's
Book. Music composed and arr. for the piano
no.22 forte by Tau Delta. Philad[elphi]a, J. Edgar,
c1833.
[2] l. 34 cm.
Caption title.
For voice and piano.
[No. 22] in a vol. of early American music,
vocal and piano, collected by Miss M. J. Craig.
1. Songs (Medium voice) with piano. I.
Title.   sjw

NT 0051609   NcD ICN

Tau Delta Gamma of Southwestern
see Memphis. Southwestern at Memphis.
Tau Delta Gamma.

Tau delta phi.
The official administrative guide (esoteric) of Tau delta phi fraternity, by Herman Lucius Baskin ... Approved and published by the Executive council. [Menasha, Wis., Printed by the George Banta publishing company] 1933.
4 p. l., 85 p. 23cm.

1. Baskin, Herman Lucius.

Library of Congresss   LJ75.T254 1933   33-25664
——— Copy 2.
Copyright A 66013   371.854296

NT 0051611   DLC

TAU DELTA PHI.
Songs of Tau delta phi. Compiled and edited by Sidney Sugarman. [2d ed.] [n. p.] The executive council of Tau delta phi [c1935] 29 p. 23cm.

Chiefly for piano, with interlinear words.

1. College songs--Tau delta phi.

NT 0051612   NN

Tau epsilon phi.
Geographic and membership roster of the Tau epsilon phi fraternity. New York, The Grand council of Tau epsilon phi, 1934.
x, 134 p. incl. front. 15cm.

On cover: Geographic.
Foreword signed: The Geographic committee, Alfred J. Kleinberger, chairman.

1. Kleinberger, Alfred John.

Library of Congress   LJ75.T273 1934   35-5494
——— Copy 2.
Copyright A 79404   371.854296

NT 0051613   DLC

Tau Kappa Alpha.
Constitution of the Tau Kappa Alpha fraternity... Revised by the fourth annual convention of the fraternity, held at the Hotel Severin, Indianapolis, December 28 and 29; 1914. [Indianapolis: E. J. Hecker, 1914.] 8 l. 16°.

1. College societies, Greek letter—   Tau Kappa Alpha.
N. Y. P. L.   April 14, 1926

NT 0051614   NN

Tau Kappa Alpha.
The Speaker; published in the interest of forensic activities
see under title

Tau Kappa Epsilon.
The golden book of Tau Kappa Epsilon, 1899-1949
see under   Leland, Leland F   ed.

Tau Kappa Epsilon
The Teke
see under title

Tau Kappa Phi bulletin.
v. 1

Auburn, Ala., 1922
v.

1. College societies (Greek letter) :   Tau Kappa Phi.
N. Y. P. L.   September 26, 1924

NT 0051617   NN

Tau Phi Delta
see Sigma Pi.

[Tausphoeus, Franz] Freiherr von, 1908-
[Candelaria./Roman [von] [Franz Taut [pseud.]
Berlin, Holle [1941]
235p. 19cm.

NT 0051619   IEN

Taub, Abraham Haskel, 1911–

Veblen, Oswald, 1880–
Geometry of complex domains; a seminar conducted by Professors Oswald Veblen and John Von Neumann, 1935-36. First term lectures by Professor Veblen, second term lectures by Mr. J. W. Givens, notes by Dr. A. H. Taub and Mr. J. W. Givens. [Princeton] The Institute for advanced study [1937?]

Taub, Abraham Haskel, 1911–
Quantum equations in cosmological spaces ... by Abraham H. Taub ... [Lancaster, Pa.], Lancaster press, inc., 1937]
cover-title, p. 512-525. 28½ x 20cm.

Thesis (PH. D.)—Princeton university, 1935.
Running title: Quantum cosmology.
"Reprinted from the Physical review, vol. 51, no. 6, March 15, 1937."

1. Quantum theory. 2. Relativity (Physics) I. Title: Quantum cosmology.

Library of Congress   QC174.1.T25 1935   38-6073
Princeton Univ. Libr.
——— Copy 2.   530.1

NT 0051621   NjP DLC

Taub, Abraham Haskel, 1911–

Ballantine, John Perry, 1896–
... Six studies in mathematics, by J. P. Ballantine, A. F. Carpenter, L. H. McFarlan [and others] ... Seattle, Wash., University of Washington press, 1940.

Egleston
D629.25
T19   Taub, Alex
Economics of Chevrolet power plant. [1929]
25 l.

"To be presented before meeting of Met-section at Park Central hotel, New York, April 18, 1929."

1. Automobiles - Motors. I. Title: Chevrolet power plant.

NT 0051623   NNC

Taub, Alex.
Some aspects of the industrial potential of the state of Washington. [n.p., 1945?]
32 l.

NT 0051624   Wa

Taub, David.
Perbenzoic acid studies.

Thesis - Harvard, 1950.

NT 0051625   MH-C

Taub, David Rosenmann
see Rosenmann Taub, David.

Taub, Hans, 1880–
Beiträge zur Geschichte und Theorie des sicheren Geleits. Ein rechtshistorischer Versuch ... von Hans Taub ... Borna-Leipzig, R. Noske, 1906.
viii, 51 p. 22cm.

Inaug.-Diss. - Erlangen.
"Literaturverzeichnis": p. [vii]-viii.

NT 0051627   MH-L ICRL NN

Taub, Hans, 1880 –
... Strindberg als traumdichter, von Hans Taub ... Göteborg, Elanders boktryckeri aktiebolag, 1945.
123 p. 25cm. (Göteborgs kungl. vetenskaps- och vitterhets-samhälles Handlingar. 6. följden, ser. A, bd. 2, n:o 3)

"Mitgeteilt am 13 november 1944."
Bibliographical foot-notes.

1. *Strindberg, August, 1849-1912.

Illinois. Univ. Library   A 46-4946
for Library of Congress   AS284.G7 föl. 6, ser. a, bd. 2, no. 3
[3]†   (068.485) 839.726

NT 0051628   IU PU ViU TxU DLC

PT
9812
D72   Taub, Hans, 1880–
T3   Strindbergs "Traumspiel"; eine metaphysische
Studie. München, G. Müller, 1917.
110p. 21cm.

1. Strindberg, August, 1849-1912. Drömspelet

NT 0051629   WU TxU NcU

TAUB, Hans, 1880–
Strindbergs "Traumspiel"; eine metaphysische studie. München, G. Müller, 1918.

NT 0051630   MH

TAUB, HANS, 1880–
Strindbergs "Traumspiel;" eine metaphysische Studie. München, G. Müller, 1917 [cover 1918] 110 p. 21cm.

Film reproduction. Positive.

Strindberg, August, 1849-1912. Ett drömspel.

NT 0051631   NN CLSU

Taub, Harold Jaediker.
Waldorf-in-the-Catskills; the Grossinger legend. Illustrated by John Fischetti. New York, Sterling Pub. Co. [1952]
248 p. illus. 21 cm.

1. The Grossinger, Ferndale, N. Y.   I. Title.

TX941.G75T3   647.94   52–4851 ‡

NT 0051632   DLC WaS MB NN MiD PP PPT NNJ MH

Taub, Herbert.
Führer durch das königreich der Serben, Kroaten und Slowenen (Jugoslawien) herausgegeben im einvernehmen mit den amtlichen stellen zur förderung des reiseverkehrs in Jugoslawien von Herbert Taub; 360 seiten mit 283 illustrationen, 4 stadtpläne, übersichtskarte (1 : 2,500,000) und verkehrskarte. Zürich, Volkswirtschaftlicher verlag a. g., 1928.
325 p. front. (fold. map) illus. 18cm.

On cover: Führer durch Jugoslavien.

1. Yugoslavia—Descr. & trav.—Guide-books.   I. Title.
45–41657

Library of Congress   DR366.T3

NT 0051633   DLC

Taub, Herbert, editor.
Illustrierter Führer durch Jugoslawien (Königreich der Serben, Kroaten und Slowenen)...herausgegeben im Einvernehmen mit den amtlichen Stellen zur Förderung des Reiseverkehrs in Jugoslawien von Herbert Taub. Zürich: Volkswirtschaftlicher Verlag A. G., 1929. 355 p. illus. (incl. plans), maps. 2. ed., rev. and enl. 12°.

Cover-title: Führer durch Jugoslavien.

483370A. 1. Yugoslavia—Guidebooks,   1929.
N. Y. P. L.   July 21, 1930

NT 0051634   NN OC1

DR366   Taub, Herbert
T35   Jugoslawien; illustriertes Touristenhandbuch für Reisen und
1953   Ferien in Jugoslawien ... 3. völlig neu bearb. Aufl.
       Zürich, Stauffacher [1953]
       295 p. plates, maps(1 col. fold.)   (Stauffacher-Reiseführer)

1. Yugoslavia - Descr. & trav. - Guide-books.

NT 0051635   CU NN

DR   Taub, Herbert.
368   Südslawische Tage; vor und nach den Wahlen
.T3   in die Skupschtina des Königreiches der Serben,
      Kroaten und Slowenen, Februar-März, 1925.
      Zürich [1925].

      "Separatabdruck aus der "Neuen Zürcher
      Zeitung", Zürich."

1. Yugoslavia - Pol. & govt. - 1918-1945. I.
Title: Südslawische Tage.

NT 0051636   NNC

Taub, Herbert, 1918–
The magnetic moment of the proton, by Herbert Taub and P. Kusch. [n. p., 1949]
1481-1492 p. diagrs. 27 cm.

Cover title.
H. Taub's thesis—Columbia University.
"Reprinted from the Physical review, vol. 75, no. 10 ... May 15, 1949."
Vita.
Bibliographical footnotes.

1. Protons.   I. Kusch, Polykarp, 1911–   joint author.
II. Title.
QC721.T25   A 55–8567
Columbia Univ.   Libraries
for Library of Congress   [3]†

NT 0051637   NNC DLC

ML3195   Taub, Israel, d. 1920.
.G38
Hebr   Geshuri, Meir Simon, 1897–   ed.
נגינה וחסידות בבית קוזמיר ובנותיה; מאסף ספרותי-מוסיקלי
(לתולדות צדיקי בית מויב ונגינת החסידות של פולין) ירושלים,
[Jerusalem, 1952]. תשי"ב.
החברה להפצת החסידות ונגינתה

BM675   Taub, Israel, d. 1920.
.P4T3
Hebraic   Jews. *Liturgy and ritual. Hagadah.* 1947.
sect.   ... הגדה של פסח בשם אשי ישראל. הכולל שמן פירושם
פירוש האחד, דברי ישראל מאת ... ישראל צוק'ל ...
ממודזיץ ... ו[פירוש השני, ישא ברכה מאת ... שאול
ידידי' אלעזר סאב ... ברוקלין, יוצא לאור מחדש עם
הוספות ע"י ועד אגודת חסידי מודזיץ, תש[.
[Brooklyn, 1947]

AC   Taub, Josef, 1898–
831   Stossartige knickbeanspruchung schlanker
      stäbe im elastischen bereich ... München, n.d.
      23 p.
      Inaug. Diss. -Techn. Hochsch. Berlin, [1932]
      Lebenslauf.

NT 0051640   ICRL

TAUB, JULES.

My heart's desire. Words and music by Jules Taub.
[New York] Duchess music corp. [c1952]

1. Songs. Popular--1890-

NT 0051641   NN

QD402   Taub, Ludwig.
.T32   1-phenyl-4sionitroso-5-triazolon und seine
      spaltungsprodukte.
      Wuerzburg, 1905.
      46p.
      Inaug. diss. Tuebingen.

NT 0051642   ICRL PU MH

Taub, Max, 1910–   ed.
Civil service preparatory course, a study and drill book in preparation for city, State, and Federal examinations. New York, Civil Service Studies [1949]
166 p. 28 cm.

1. Civil service--U. S.--Examinations.   I. Title.

JK716.T3   351.3   49–6720*

NT 0051643   DLC

Taub, Max Largo.
Fundamental facts and simple secrets for proper wind instrument playing. New York, N. Y., M. "L." Taub [1945]
22 p. 14½cm.

1. Wind instruments—Methods.   I. Title.
45–18567
Library of Congress   MT339.T23
             788

NT 0051644   DLC

Taub, Paul, 1915–
The deskbook of Missouri civil procedure. St. Louis, Lawyers Service Co. [1951–
2 v. (loose-leaf) 26 cm.

1. Civil procedure—Missouri.   I. Title.

347.9   52–26293

NT 0051645   DLC

Taub, Samuel James, 1893–
Clinical allergy; a practical guide to diagnosis and treatment. 2d ed., rev. and reset. [New York, P. B. Hoeber [1951]
276 p. 24 cm.

First published in 1945 under title: Essentials of clinical allergy.

1. Allergy.

RC584.T35 1951   615.37   51–12019

NT 0051646   DLC CaBVaU OC1W-H FTaSU DNLM ICJ

Taub, Samuel James, 1893–
Essentials of clinical allergy, by Samuel J. Taub ... Baltimore, The Williams & Wilkins company, 1945.
x, 198 p. incl. illus. xvi pl. on 8 l. 23½cm.

"References" at end of most of the chapters.

1. Allergia.

U. S. Surg.-gen. off. Libr.   S G 45–263
for Library of Congress   RC48.T35
             [5]†   615.3

DLC ViU ICJ
NT 0051647   DNLM OrU-M CU NcGU TxU PPJ PPC CtY CtY-M

[Taub, Szoel, 1886–
... קונטרס מאמרים מכ"ק אדמו"ר ... ממאדזיץ. ברוק
לין, נ. י., אגודת חסידי מודזיץ חובביב, תש"א.
[Brooklyn, 1941–
v. port. 21½ cm.
Vols. 4–   have title: קונטרס תפארת ישראל

1. Hasidism—Songs and music.   I. Title.
Title transliterated: Ḳontres ma'amarim.

M2114.3.T35K6   47–42576

NT 0051648   DLC

BM675   Taub, Szoel, 1886–1947, ed.
.P4T3
Hebraic   Jews. *Liturgy and ritual. Hagadah.* 1947.
sect.   ... הגדה של פסח בשם אשי ישראל. הכולל שמן פירושם
פירוש האחד, דברי ישראל מאת ... ישראל צוק'ל ...
ממודזיץ ... ו[פירוש השני, ישא ברכה מאת ... שאול
ידידי' אלעזר סאב ... ברוקלין, יוצא לאור מחדש עם
הוספות ע"י ועד אגודת חסידי מודזיץ. תש[.

ML3195
.G38 Iaub, Szoel, 1886-1947
Hebr **Geshuri, Meir Simon,** 1897- *ed.*
נגינה והסידות בבית קוזמיר ובנותיה; מאסף ספרותי-מוסיקלי (לתולדות צדיקי בית מויב ונגינת החסידות של פולין) ירושלים, החברה להפצת החסידות ונגינתה. תשי"ב. ‎[Jerusalem, 1952]

Taub, Szymon.
...Dzieje Biura stenograficznego dawnego Sejmu galicyjskiego. Z 2 ilustracjami. Katowice: Nakładem W. Chrapusty, 1925. 47 p. illus. 22½cm. (Bibljoteka stenograficzna. no. 1.)

1. Shorthand—Systems, Polish, 1925.
N. Y. P. L. May 28, 1943

NT 0051651 NN

Taub, Szymon.
Nowoczesny system stenografji polskiej; podręcznik dla szkół i samouków, opracował dr. Szymon Taub... Lwów: Z drukarni J. Willnera w Gródku, 1936. 50, 40 p. 23cm.

1. Shorthand—Systems, Polish, 1936. 2. Shorthand—Exercises, 1936.
N. Y. P. L. December 31, 1940

NT 0051652 NN

AC Taubadel, Hans, 1907-
831 Ueber den mechanismus der polymerisationsvorgänge ... Jena, 1932. 48 p.
Inaug. Diss. Berlin, 1932.
Lebenslauf.

NT 0051653 ICRL

Taubald, Juliane Charlotte.
Die freischaar (1806–1813) Laienspiel ... Berlin, °1933.
70 p. 20cm.
Reproduced from type-written copy.

I. Title.
43-28458
Brief cataloging
Library of Congress PT2642.A713F7

NT 0051654 DLC

Taubate, Modesto de, padre
see Rezende, Modesto, padre.

V24
.T17
1951 **Taube, Aleksandr Mikhaĭlovich.**
Англо-русский морской словарь. Составили А. М. Таубе и В. А. Шмид. Изд. 2., перер. 30 000 слов. Москва, Гос. изд-во иностранных и национальных словарей, 1951.
648 p. 21 cm.
First ed. published in 1943 under title: Морской англо-русский словарь (transliterated: Morskoĭ anglo-russkiĭ slovar')

1. Naval art and science—Dictionaries. 2. English language—Dictionaries—Russian. I. Shmid, V. A., joint author. II. Title.
Title transliterated: Anglo-russkiĭ morskoĭ slovar'.

V24.T17 1951 51-34519

NT 0051656 DLC

Taube, Aleksandr Mikhaĭlovich.
Морской англо-русский словарь; составили А. М Таубе и В. А. Шмид. Москва, Гос. изд-во иностранных и национальных словарей, 1943.
479, [1] p. 16 x 14 cm.
At head of title: Военный институт иностранных языков Красной Армии.
"Использованная литература": p. 4-6.
1. Naval art and science—Dictionaries. 2. English language—Dictionaries—Russian. I. Shmid, V. A., joint author. II. Moscow. Voennyĭ institut inostrannykh ıazykov Krasnoĭ Armii. III. Title.
Title transliterated: Morskoĭ anglo-russkiĭ slovar'
49-34454
V24.T17

NT 0051657 DLC

[Taube, Aleksandr Mikhaĭlovich]
Военный англо-русский словарь; около 25 000 слов и терминов из основных областей военного дела, с приложением словаря военных сокращений. Москва, Изд-во иностранных и национальных словарей, 1938.
470, [2] p. 17½cm.
"Словарь составил А. М. Таубе, под редакцией военинженера I ранга П. В. Васильева."—p. [472]
Errata slip mounted on p. [3]
Bibliography included in preface.
1. Military art and science—Dictionaries. 2. English language—Dictionaries—Russian. I. Vasil'ev, P. V., ed. II. Title. *Title transliterated:* Voennyĭ anglo-russkiĭ slovar'.
42-45926
Library of Congress U25.T3

NT 0051658 DLC

Taube, Aleksandr Mikhaĭlovich.
Военный англо-русский словарь; составил А. М. Таубе. 2. изд. исправленное и дополненное. Москва, Огиз, Государственное издательство иностранных и национальных словарей, 1942.
638, [2] p. 20cm.
Bibliography included in preface.

1. Military art and science—Dictionaries. 2. English language—Dictionaries—Russian. I. Title. *Title transliterated:* Voennyĭ anglo-russkiĭ slovar'.
44-18289
Library of Congress U25.T3 1942

NT 0051659 DLC FMU

Taube, Aleksandr Mikhaĭlovich.
Военный англо-русский словарь. С приложением словаря сокращений. Изд. 3. перер. Москва, Гос. изд-во иностранных и национальных словарей, 1949.
946 p. 21 cm.

1. Military art and science—Dictionaries. 2. English language—Dictionaries—Russian. I. Title.
Title transliterated: Voennyĭ anglo-russkiĭ slovar'.

U25.T3 1949 50-20483

NT 0051660 DLC

Taube, Aleksandr Mikhaĭlovich.
Военный французско-русский словарь; составил А. М. Таубе, под редакцией Л. В. Балабанова. 20 000 слов и терминов из основных областей военного дела. Москва, Огиз РСФСР, Государственное словарно-энциклопедическое изд-во "Советская энциклопедия," 1931.
544 col. 17½cm. (*Added t.-p.:* ... Иностранные словари под общей редакцией О. Ю. Шмидта, при участии К. С. Кузьминского и М. М. Каушанского. Серия военных словарей, вып. II)
Two columns to the page.
Bibliography included in preface.
1. Military art and science—Dictionaries. 2. French language—Dictionaries—Russian. 3. Abbreviations, French. I. Balabanov, L. V., ed.
Title transliterated: Voennyĭ frantsuzsko-russkiĭ slovar'.
42-45925
Library of Congress U25.T33

NT 0051661 DLC

Taube, Aleksandr Mikhaĭlovich.
Военный французско-русский словарь. Под ред. П. В. Васильева. Около 25 000 слов и терминов из основных областей военного дела. С приложением словаря военных сокращений. 2. изд., испр. и доп. Москва, Гос. институт "Советская энциклопедия," 1937.
340 p. 18 cm. (Серия военных словарей)

1. Military art and science—Dictionaries—French. 2. French language—Dictionaries—Russia. 3. Military art and science—Abbreviations. I. Title. (Series: Inostrannye slovari. Serii͡a voennykh slovareĭ) *Title transliterated:* Voennyĭ frantsuzsko-russkiĭ slovar'.

U25.T33 1937 52-23345

NT 0051662 DLC

Taube, Aleksandr Mikhaĭlovich.
Военный французско-русский словарь; составил А. М. Таубе. Около 30000 слов и терминов из основных областей военного дела, с приложением словаря военных сокращений. 3. изд., исправленное и дополненное полковником М. М. Брагинским. Москва, Огиз, Государственное издательство иностранных и национальних словарей, 1942.
384 p. 20cm.
"Словарь сокращений": p. [353]-384.
1. Military art and science—Dictionaries 2. French language—Dictionaries—Russian. I. Braginskiĭ, Mikhail Mikhaĭlovich, 1895-
Title transliterated: Voennyĭ frantsuzsko-russkiĭ slovar'.
44-24934
Library of Congress U25.T33 1942

NT 0051663 DLC

Taube, Aleksandr Mikhaĭlovich, joint author.
U25
.K88 FOR OTHER EDITIONS SEE MAIN ENTRY
1936 **Kuznetsov, Fedor Evgen'evich.**
Военный немецко-русский словарь. Составили Ф. Е. Кузнецов и А. М. Таубе. Около 30 000 слов, около 4 000 сокращений. Изд. 2., испр. и доп. Москва, Сов. энциклопедия, 1936.

U 25
T35
1945 **Taube, Aleksandr Mikhaĭlovich.**
Военный немецко-русский словарь. Около 35000 сло[в] и выражений из основных областей воен. дела, около 600[0] сокращений, применяемых в воен. лит-ре. Изд. 5., перер. и доп. Москва, Гос. изд-во иностранных и национальных словарей, 1945.
612 p. 21 cm.

1. Military art and science—Dictionaries—Russian. 2. German language—Dictionaries—Russian. 3. Military art and science—Abbreviations. *Title transliterated:* Voennyĭ nemetsko-russkiĭ slovar'.

U25.T35 1945 50-21373

NT 0051665 DLC OU

Taube (Alexander). *De membranis serosis in cavis magnis corporis humani obviis. 51 pp., 2 l., 1 pl. 8°. *Dorpati Livonorum, typ. viduæ J. C. Schünmanni et C. Mattieseni,* 1854.

NT 0051666 DNLM

Taube, Alexander von.
Fürst Bismarck zwischen England und Russland; ein beitrag zur politik des reichskanzlers in den jahren von 1871 bis 1890, von Alexander v. Taube. Stuttgart, W. Kohlhammer, 1923.
3 p. l., 156 p. 24cm.
Appeared also as the author's inaugural dissertation, Tübingen, 1923.
"Literaturverzeichnis": p. [154]-156.

1. *Bismarck, Otto, fürst von, 1815-1898. 2. Germany—For. rel.—1871- 3. Europe—Politics—1871-
25-22254
Library of Congress DD221.5.T3

NBuU NN ICU
NT 0051667 DLC NcD NNC-L NNC MiU OKentU IEN IaU IU

Taube, Alfred, 1899-
Lba23 ... Die Frage und ihre Bedeutung für den
933t Unterricht ... Greiffenberg in Schlesien, Greif-Druckerei, G.m.b.H., 1933.
55p. 21cm.
Inaug.-diss. - Breslau.
Lebenslauf.

NT 0051668 CtY PU

GT6 Taube, Arnold, 1869-
T191l Luthers lehre über freiheit und ausrüstung des natürlichen menschen bis zum jahre 1525 auf ihre folgerichtigkeit geprüft. Eine dogmatische kritik. Göttingen, Dieterich, 1901.
55 p. 23 cm.
Inaug.-diss. - Göttingen.
Bibliographical footnotes.

NT 0051669 CtY-D NjPT CtY

Taube, Arnold, 1869-
Die Grösse der Zeit und das Geschlecht, das ihrer wert. Von Pastor Lic. A. Taube... Berlin: Evangelischer Bund, 1915. 16 p. 12°. (Volksschriften zum grossen Krieg. [Nr.] 19.)
Cover-title.
Contents on inside of front cover.

1. European war, 1914- .—Addresses, sermons, etc. 2. Title. 3. Series.
N. Y. P. L. August 25, 1916.

NT 0051670 NN

Taube, Arved, Freiherr von.

DK511
.B3B6
Bosse, Heinrich, *ed.*
Baltische Köpfe; 24 Lebensbilder aus acht Jahrhunderten deutschen Wirkens in den baltischen Landen, mit Beiträgen von Werner Bergengruen ₍et al.₎ Hrsg. von Heinrich Bosse und Arved Freiherr v. Taube. Bovenden bei Göttingen, Baltischer Verlag, 1953.

Taube, Arved, *Freiherr von,* ed.
Deutsche Männer des baltischen Ostens, mit Beiträgen von Max Aschkewitz ₍et al.₎ Berlin, Volk und Reich Verlag, 1943.
178 p. illus., ports. 21 cm. (Kleine Volk und Reich Bücherei)

1. Germans in the Baltic States—Biog.
DK511.B3T29   A 53-1001
Harvard Univ. Library
for Library of Congress   ₍1₎†

NT 0051672   MH CLU NN DLC

Taube, Arved, *Freiherr von.*
Ostland im Machtkampf, 1561–1941. Riga, Verlagsgesellschaft Ostland, 1944.
75, ₍1₎ p. maps. 22 cm. (Ostlandreihe, Schriften zur Kunde des Reichskommissariats Ostland, Heft 2)
"Schrifttum": p. 75–₍76₎

1. Baltic Provinces—Hist. 2. Baltic States—Hist.   I. Title.
(Series)
DK511.B3T3   947.4   50-50504

NT 0051673   DLC CtY MB MH NNC NN RPB

Taube, Bruno.
Die Arbeitstechniken der grafischen Industrie. 2. überarb. Aufl. Berlin, Volk und Wissen, 1955.
159 p. illus. 24 cm. (Lehr- und Fachbücher für die Berufsausbildung)
First ed. published in 1948 under title: Die Arbeitstechniken des graphischen Gewerbes.

1. Printing.   I. Title.
Z116.T25 1955   61-47371 ‡

NT 0051674   DLC

Z245
.K7
Taube, Bruno, joint author.
Kreutzmann, Werner.
Fachrechnen für Setzer, Drucker und verwandte Berufe; eine Anleitung für Setzer, Drucker, Stereotypeure, Galvanoplastiker und Verlagsangestellte, von Werner Kreutzmann und Bruno Taube. Leipzig, Fachbuchverlag, 1955.

Wason
DS775
T22
Taube, Carl.
Från Liao ho till Gula floden; tre år med den mandshuriska armén i fält. Stockholm, A. Bonnier ₍1928₎
164 p. illus., maps. 25cm.

1. China--Hist.--1912-1937. 2. China--Armed Forces. I. Title.

NT 0051676   NIC

Taube, Carl.
Kriget som inte var nagot krig. Som krigskorrespondent i Manchuriet 18 september 1931 - 9 mars 1932. Stockholm, Bonnier [1932]

NT 0051677   MH

Wason
DS795
T22
Taube, Carl.
Peking och Pekingeser. Med 44 illustrationer. Andra upplagan. Stockholm, H. Geber, [1917]
73 p. illus. 24cm.

1. Peking--   Descr.

NT 0051678   NIC

Taube, Carl Eduard
På deras konglige majestäters...
see under   Aurivillius, Kar.

Taube, Carl Evert Bernhard, friherre, 1834-
see   Taube af Odenkat, Carl Evert Bernhard friherre, 1834-1917.

Taube, Carl Gunnar, *friherre,* 1885–
...Kina i världspolitiken, av Carl Taube... Stockholm, 1948.   32 p.   map.   19cm.   (Världspolitikens dagsfrågor. 1948, nr. 1.   Utrikespolitiska institutets broschyrserie)

1. China—For. rel., 1912–   I. Ser.

NT 0051681   NN MH MH-L DLC-P4

Taube, Carl Gunnar, *friherre,* 1885–
Krigstrumma och bambuflöjt; kinesisk kavalkad. Stockholm, Norstedt ₍1952₎
255 p. illus. 22 cm.

1. China—Civilization.   I. Title.
DS721.T37   54-20627 ‡

NT 0051682   DLC NN CU

Taube, Carl Gunnar, *friherre,* 1885–
Den nya regimen i Kina. Stockholm ₍Kooperativa förbundets bokförlag₎ 1950.
32 p.   map.   19 cm.   (Världspolitikens dagsfrågor, 1950, nr. 3)

1. China—Pol. & govt.—1949–   I. Title.   (Series)
DS777.55.T3   51-32988

NT 0051683   DLC NN

Taube, Charlotte.
César Franck—und wir; eine Biographie. Berlin, E. Bote & G. Bock ₍1951₎
158 p. port. 22 cm.
"Verzeichnis der Werke César Franck's": p. 152-158.

1. Franck, César Auguste, 1822-1890.
A 52-1645
Oregon. Univ. Libr.
for Library of Congress

NT 0051684   OrU MH NN IEN

W 4
U92
1694
T.1
TAUBE, Christoph Ernst, fl. 1694, respondent
Dissertatio medica inauguralis de recens natorum sanitate tuenda ... Trajecti ad Rhenum, Ex officina Francisci Halma, 1694.
16 p. 21 cm.
Diss. - Utrecht.

NT 0051685   DNLM

Taube ₍Daniel Joh. 1727-09₎ *De sanguinis ad cerebrum tendentis indole.* 20 pp. 4⁰.
Göttingen, lit. J. F. Hageri, [1747].
For Biography, see Brendel ₍Joh. Gothofred.₎.

NT 0051686   DNLM

Taube,_____Daniel Johann, *1727-1799.*   610.97 FI
Die Geschichte der Kriebel-Krankheit besonders derjenigen welche in den Jahren 1770 und 1771 in den zellischen Gegenden gewütet hat, beschrieben von Johann Taube, ... Göttingen J. C. Dieterich, 1782.
[8], 920 p. 1 fold. pl. 17½ᶜᵐ.

NT 0051687   ICJ DNLM NNNAM

Taube, Edgar.
... Lettlands export und exportfirmen; eine darstellung der wichtigsten exportzweige Lettlands nebst beschreibung der einzelnen exportfirmen. Riga ₍Buchdruckerei der Akt.-ges. Walters und Rapa₎ 1929.
viii, 192 p. incl. map. 22½ᶜᵐ.
At head of title: E. Taube.

1. Latvia—Comm. 2. Latvia—Comm.—Direct.
42-29011
Library of Congress   HF3635.5.T3

NT 0051688   DLC WU CSt-H NN MH-BA

Taube, Edgar.
... Lettlands export und exportfirmen, eine darstellung der wichtigsten exportzweige Lettlands nebst beschreibung der einschlägigen exportfirmen. Riga ₍Gedruckt in der typographie des Lettl. bauernbundes₎ 1930.
176 p. 22½ᶜᵐ.

1. Latvia—Comm. 2. Latvia—Comm.—Direct.
42-29975
Library of Congress   HF3635.5.T3 1930

NT 0051689   DLC NN

Taube, Edgar, tr.
Zalts, Alberts.
... Lettlands wirtschaft und wirtschaftspolitik. Riga ₍Typographie des Lettischen bauernbundes₎ 1930.

Taube, Eduard, 1835-
... Aristoteles de arte physiognomonica ad Alexandrum scriptor, von dem gymnasiallehrer dr. Eduard Taube.
(In Programm des königlichen katholischen gymnasiums zu Gleiwitz, womit zu der am 29. April 1866 stattfindenden fünfzigjährigen stiftungsfeier der anstalt einladet das lehrercollegium. Gleiwitz, Gustav Neumann [1866. no. 2])

NT 0051691   PU NjP NNUT

Taube, Eduard, 1835-
Tractandorum scriptorum Graecorum physiognomonicorum praeparatio... Inest ineditum Aristotelis ad Alexandrum de physiognomonia e lib. ms.   Paris, cum excerptis alibi repertis... Vratislaviae 1862 ?
52 [2] p.   28 cm.
Inaug.-diss. - Breslau.
Vita.

NT 0051692   RPB NjP

F803
TA   Taube, Edward.
     Wild rice. [Washington? Scientific
   Monthly, 1951?]
     [369]-375 p.   illus., map.   27 cm.

     "Reprinted from the Scientific Monthly,
   Vol. LXXIII, No. 6, December, 1951."
   Includes bibliography.
   Cover title.

     1. Indian rice.

NT 0051693   WHi

   Taube, Elise
      see   Taube, Gottliebe Elise, 1861-

   Taube, Emil Heinrich.
     Ein Kirchenjahre in predigten: aus seinem
   nachlass hrsg.   Berlin, Gaertner, 1894.
     404 p.

NT 0051695   PPLT

   Taube, Emil Heinrich.
     Praktische Auslegung der Psalmen zur
   Anregung und Förderung der Schrifter-
   kenntniss den Hirten wie der Heerde
   Christi dargeboten...   4. durchgesehene
   Aufl.   Berlin, R. Gaertner, 1892.
     906 p.   23ᵐ.

NT 0051696   NjPT

   Taube, Emil Heinrich.
     Praktische auslegung der Psalmen zur
   anregung und förderung der schrifterkenntniss den
   hirten wie der heerde Christi.   5. aufl.   Berlin,
   Gaertner, 1897.
     906 p.

NT 0051697   PPLT

W 4   TAUBE, Ernst
G59   De oculorum inflammationibus ... Goettingae, Jo. Christ.
1783   Dieterich [1783]
T.1   22 p.   21 cm.
      Diss. - Göttingen.

NT 0051698   DNLM

   TAUBE, Erwin.
     Beiträge zur Entwicklungsgeschichte der
   Euphausiden.   Leipzig 1909.   42 S.

     München, Phil. Diss.

NT 0051699   MH PU DNLM

   Taube, Evert, 1890-
     Ballader i Bohuslän, diktade, tonsatta och illustrerade av
   Evert Taube.   Stockholm, A. Bonnier [1943]
     65, [1] p.   illus.   27ᵐ.
     For piano, with interlinear words.

     1. Songs (Medium voice) with piano.   I. Title.
              [Full name: Evart Axel Taube]
                         45-20817
   Library of Congress   M1621.T

NT 0051700   DLC MnU

   Taube, Evert, 1890-
     Ballader i Bohuslän, diktade, tonsatta och
   illustrerade av Evert Taube.   Stockholm, Bonnier [1947]

     65 p.   illus.   (His Samlade visor [9])
     Contains music.

NT 0051701   MH

   TAUBE, EVERT, 1890-
     Ballader i det blå; dikter och melodier av Evert
   Taube.   Arrangerade för luta, gitarr och piano av
   Nils B. Söderström.   Illustrerad av Helga Henschen.
   Stockholm, A. Bonnier [1948]   63 p.   illus.   25cm.

     With piano and lute or guitar accompaniment.
   1. Ballads, Swedish.   2. Songs,   Swedish.   3. Songs, with
   guitar.   4. Songs, with lute.   I. Title.   II. Söderstrom, Nils
   B.,   arr.   III. Söderstrom, Nils B.

NT 0051702   NN DLC-P4

M1774
.T3B7   Taube, Evert, 1890-
     Bröllopsballader och rosenrim en Gyldene
   Fredens bok.   Med melodier och akvareller av
   författaren.   Stockholm, P. A. Norstedt [1925]
     99, [1] p.   col. plates.   26 cm.

     For piano, with interlinear words.

     1. Songs, Swedish.   2. Gyldene Freden.
   I. Title.

NT 0051703   NjP

   Taube, Evert, 1880-
     Bröllopsballader och rosenrim, en Gyldene Fredens bok.
   Med melodier och akvareller av författaren.   Stockholm,
   Bonnier [1946]

     99 p.   illus. (part col.)   (His Samlade visor [5])
     Contains music.

NT 0051704   MH

   Taube, Evert, 1890-
     Dikter.   Stockholm, Bonnier [1955]
     198 p.   20 cm.

                  Full name: Evert Axel Taube.

                         A 55-10086
   Minnesota. Univ. Libr.
   for Library of Congress   [2]

NT 0051705   MnU NcD NN

   Taube, Evert, 1890-
     Fritiof Anderssons visbok; nya visor av Evert Taube, med
   författarens teckningar och melodier...   Stockholm: A. Bonnier [, 1929].   84 p.   front., illus.   8°.

     Music for piano with interlinear Swedish words.
     Contents: Företal. Det var "Blue Bird" av Hull. Jag är fri, jag har sonat. Karl-
   Alfred, Fritiof Andersson och jag. Mirrabooka marsch. "När jag var en ung caballeiro."
   Tatuerarevalsen. Havsörnsvals. Stockholmsmelodi. Här är dörren, tryck på knappen.
   Fritiof Anderssons paradmarsch.

   478721A. 1. Songs, Swedish.   2. Poetry, Swedish.   I. Taube, Evert
   Axel, illustrator.   II. Title.   July 2, 1930
   N. Y. P. L.

NT 0051706   NN

   Taube, Evert, 1890-
     Frittiof Anderssons visbok, av Evert Taube.
   Med författerens teckningar och melodier.
   Stockholm, A. Bonnier [1945]
     90 [1] p.,   1 l.   illus.   25 cm.   (Half-title;
   his Samlade visor)
     Cover illustrated in color.
     The musical settings are for piano with inter-
   linear words.

NT 0051707   PU

   Taube, Evert, 1890-
     Fritiof Anderssons visbok. Med författarens
   teckningar och melodier.   Stockholm, Bonnier [1947]

     90 p.   illus.   (His Samlade visor [2])
     Contains music.

NT 0051708   MH

784.49485
T191   Taube, Evert, 1890-
     "Den Gyldene Freden." Ballader och visor
   diktade och tonsatta av Evert Taube.
   Stockholm, Wahlström & Widstrand, 1924.

     47 p.   music.   19 x 25 cm.

     1. Ballads, Swedish.   I. Title.

NT 0051709   MnU

   TAUBE, EVERT, 1890-
     Den gyldene fredens ballader; med författarens
   teckningar och melodier.   Stockholm, A. Bonnier
   [1946]   80 p.   illus.   25cm.   (HIS: Samlade visor. 4)

     For voice and piano.

   1. Songs, Swedish.   2. Ballads,   Drexel Musical Fund
                              Swedish.   I. Title.

NT 0051710   NN MH

   Taube, Evert, 1890-
     Himlajord; dikter, melodier och målningar, av **Evert Taube**
   ... Stockholm, Albert Bonniers förlag [*1938]
     56 p., 1 l. incl. front.   4 col. pl.   27¾ᵐ.
     Cover illustrated in colors.
     The musical settings are for piano with interlinear words.

     I. Title.   [Full name: Evert Axel Taube]

                            A C 40-1118
   New York. Public library
   for Library of Congress

NT 0051711   NN

   Taube, Evert, 1890-
     Himlajord, dikter, melodier och malningar,
   av Evert Taube.   Stockholm, A. Bonnier [1945]
     4 l., 7-56 p., 1 l.   front., illus., col. pl.
   25 cm.   (Half-title; his Samlade visor)
     Cover illustrated in color.
     The musical settings are for piano with
   interlinear words.

NT 0051712   PU

   Taube, Evert, 1890-
     Himlajord, dikter, melodier och målningar.   Stockholm,
   Bonnier [1948]

     56 p.   illus. (part col.)   (His Samlade visor [3])
     Contains music.

NT 0051713   MH

   Taube, Evert, 1890-
      [I dina drömmar; arr.]

     I dina drömmar; nya ballader och visor diktade, tonsatta
   och illustrerade av Evert Taube.   Arrangerade för gitarr
   och piano av Lille Bror Söderlundh och Nils B. Söderström.
   Stockholm, Bonnier [1953]
     65 p.   illus.   26 cm.
     For voice, guitar, and piano.

     1. Songs (Low voice) with instr. ensemble.   2. Ballads, Swedish.
   I. Title.   *Full name: Evert Axel Taube.*
   M1613.3.T24T2   M A 56-2 rev
   Minnesota. Univ. Libr.
   for Library of Congress   [r56b¼]†

NT 0051714   MnU DLC

Taube, Evert, 1890–
I Najadernas gränd. Stockholm, Bonnier [1954]
168 p. illus. 21 cm.

I. Title.

Full name: Evert Axel Taube.

PT9875.T3 I 2   55–17868 ‡

NT 0051715   DLC NN MnU

Taube, Evert, 1890–
Jag kommer av ett brusand' hav; barndomsminnen från
Vinga och Göteborg på Oscar II:s tid. Stockholm, Bonnie
[1953, *1952]
252 p. illus. 19 cm. (Bonniers folkbibliotek)

I. Title.

Full name: Evert Axel Taube.

PT9875.T3J3   53–32249 ‡

NT 0051716   DLC WaU OC1 MnU

PT   Taube, Evert, 1890–
9875   Kärleken och vinden. Ett brev till Otto
T3   G. Carlsund av Evert Taube, med illustra-
K2   tioner av författare. [Stockholm] Konstvärl-
        den, 1943.
        [8] p. illus. 22cm.
        Cover title.
        "Detta särtryck ur Konstvärldens sommarbok
        1943 är tryckt i 200 ex."
        Includes the poem Kärleken och vinden.
        I. Carlsund, Otto Gustaf, 1897–   II. Titl[

NT 0051717   WU

Taube, Evert, 1890–
Kärleksvisor och sjöballader och visorna ur På kryss
med Ellinor. Ill. ur På kryss med Ellinor av Kurt
Jungstedt. Stockholm, Bonnier [1946]

76 p. illus. (His Samlade visor [6])
Contains music.

NT 0051718   MH

Taube, Evert, 1890–
Många hundra gröna mil. Stockholm, Bonnier [1951]
164 p. illus. 23 cm.

I. Title.

Full name: Evert Axel Taube.

PT9875.T3M3   52–24763 ‡

NT 0051719   DLC WaU MH NN OC1

Taube, Evert, 1890–
Pepita dansar, nya ballader; tonsatta och illustrerade av
författaren, musiken arr. av Nils B. Söderström. Stockholm, Bonnier [1950]
64 p. illus. 26 cm.
The musical settings are for piano with interlinear words. Includes
alternative acc. for lute.

1. Music, Swedish.   I. Title.

Full name: Evert Axel Taube.

M1774.T3   50–35365

NT 0051720   DLC NN MnU

Taube, Evert, 1890–
[Visor]
Samlade visor. Stockholm, Bonnier [19
v. illus. (part col.) 25 cm.
Principally for piano, with interlinear words.
CONTENTS.—
v. 4. Den Gyldene fredens ballader.—v. 5. Bröllopsballader och rosen-
rim.—v. 6. Kärleksvisor och sjöballader och visorna ur P kryss med
Ellinor.
1. Songs with piano.

Full name: Evert Axel Taube.

M1620.T22V5   M 53–940

NT 0051721   DLC CLU

Taube, Evert, 1890–
Samlade visor. [Stockholm, Bonnier, 1946–48]
9 v. illus. (part col.)
Contains music.
Each volume has special title-page.
Contents:–1. Sju sjömansvisor och Byssan lull samt
Flickan i Havanna. –2. Fritiof Anderssons visbok. –3.
Himlajord. –4. Den Gyldene Fredens ballader. –5.
Bröllopsballader och rosenrim.–6. Kärleksvisor och
sjöballader och visorna ur På kryss med Ellinor. –7.
Ultra Marin. –8. Sjösalaboken. –9. Ballader i Bohuslän.

NT 0051722   MH

MUSIC
LIBRARY
M
1620   Taube, Evert, 1890–
T29   [Visor]
            Samlade visor. Stockholm, Bonnier [1947]
            9v. illus. 25cm.
            Principally for piano, with interlinear
        words.

        1. Songs with piano.   I. Title: Uniform.

NT 0051723   WU CU

Taube, Evert, 1890–

Sea ballads and other songs; text and music by Evert Taube,
English version by Helen Asbury, illustrated by Georg Lagerstedt. Stockholm, Kings press [*1940]
79 p. incl. illus., plates. 27½ x 20½ᵐ.
"First impression."

I. Asbury, Helen, tr. II. Lagerstedt, Georg, illus. III. Title.
[Full name: Evert Axel Taube]
41–13329
Library of Congress   M1620.T22S3
[2]   784.4

NT 0051724   DLC DAU MWiW

Taube, Evert, 1890–
Sju sjömansvisor och Byssan lull samt Flickan i
Havanna. Med bilder av Kurt Jungstedt. Stockholm,
Bonnier [1947]

114 p. illus. (His Samlade visor [1])
Contains music.

NT 0051725   MH

Taube, Evert, 1890–
Sjösala boken, nya dikter och melodier av Evert Taube; för luta, gitarr
och piano av Lille Bror Söderlundh, illustratör, Roland Svensson. Stockholm, A. Bonnier [1942]

81 p., 1 l. illus. 27cm.

I. Söderlundh, Lille Bror. II. Title.

NT 0051726   MnU

Taube, Evert, 1890–
Sjösalaboken; nya dikter och melodier. För luta,
gitarr och piano av Lille Bror Söderlundh. Illustratör
Roland Svensson. Stockholm, Bonnier [1947]

81 p. illus. (His Samlade visor [8])
Contains music.

NT 0051727   MH

Taube, Evert, 1890–
Sjösalavår och andra visor. Stockholm, Svenska visförlaget [1949]
48 p. 16 cm.

I. Title.

Full name: Evert Axel Taube.

A 50–870

Minnesota. Univ. Libr.
for Library of Congress

NT 0051728   MnU

Taube, Evert, 1890–
Sju sjömansvisor och Byssan lull samt flickan
i Havanna, av Evert Taube. Med bilder av Kurt
Jungstedt. Stockholm, A. Bannier [1945]
14 p. illus. 25 cm. (Half-title; his
Samlade visor)
Cover illustrated in color.
The musical settings are for piano with inter-
linear words.

NT 0051729   PU

Taube, Evert, 1890–
Stora vissamling. Stockholm, Svenska
visförlaget [1947]

110 p. 18cm.

1. Swedish ballads and songs.

NT 0051730   MnU

Taube, Evert, 1890–
Strövtåg i Ranrike. Illustrationer av författaren.
[Stockholm] Rabén & Sjögren [1955]
183 p. illus. 21 cm.

1. Bohuslän, Sweden—Descr. & trav.   I. Title.

Full name: Evert Axel Taube.

A 56–3608

Minnesota. Univ. Libr.
for Library of Congress

NT 0051731   MnU

Taube, Evert, 1890–
Svärmerier, med författarens teckningar och melodier.
Stockholm, Bonnier [1946]
75 p. illus. 25 cm.
For piano, with interlinear words.

1. Songs, Swedish.   I. Title.

Full name: Evert Axel Taube.

M1774.T3S8   M 53–1058

NT 0051732   DLC

---

fPT9595 Taube, Evert, 1890–   comp.
T38   Svenska ballader och visor från medeltiden till
        dagar. För visans vänner samlade av Evert Taube.
        [Stockholm, Lindfors c1948?]
        390 p. illus. music(unacc. melodies) 34cm.

        1. Swedish ballads and songs. I. Title: Svenska
        ballader och visor.

NT 0051733   CU IEN PU NN

Taube, Evert, 1890–
20 [i. e. Tjugu] Taube visor.
Stockholm, Svenska visförlaget
[1954]

3 v. in 1. 16cm.

Cover title.

NT 0051734   MnU

Taube, Evert, 1890–
Trubadurens triumfer, de mest älskade visorna som Evert
Taube diktat och tonsatt. Stockholm, Svenska visförlaget [1950]
32 p. 25cm.

Melodies unaccompanied.
CONTENTS.—Balladen om Gustaf Blom från Borås.—Blondin med de rosende kinder.
—Brevet från Lillian.—Calle Schevens vals.—Den glade bagaren i San Remo.—El-
darevalsen.—Flickan i Havanna.—Flickan i Peru.—Fritiof Anderssons paradmarsch.—
Fritiof i Arkadien.—Fritiof och Carmencita.—Havsörnsvals.—Linnéa.—Maj på Malö.
—Möte i monsunen.—Rosa på bal.—Rönnerdahls polka.—Sjösala vals.—Sommarnatt.
—Vals ombord.

1. Songs, Swedish. I. Title.

NT 0051735   NN DLC–P4 MH

Taube, Evert, 1890-
Ultra Marin. Med teckningar av Bertil Lybeck.
Stockholm, Bonnier [1947]

101 p. illus. (His Samlade visor [7])
Contains music.

NT 0051736   MH PU

4PT   Taube Evert, 1890-
Swed   Visor, ballader, serenader.
277   Stockholm, Svenska visförlaget [1954]
159 p.

NT 0051737   DLC-P4

Taube, Evgeniĭ Petrovich, 1869-
Матеріалы къ клиническому изученію коллатеральнаго
артеріальнаго кровеобращенія въ конечностяхъ. Изъ про-
педевтической хирургической клиники проф. В. А.
Оппель. С.-Петербургъ, Тип. Штаба Отдѣльнаго корпуса
жандармовъ, 1911.
84, 100 p. illus. 24 cm. (Серія докторскихъ диссертацій.
1910/11 учеб. г., № 50)
Diss.—Voenno-meditsinskaia akademiia, Leningrad.
Vita.
Errata slip inserted.
Bibliography: p. [81]-84 (1st group)
1. Blood—Circulation. 2. Extremities (Anatomy)   i. Title.
    Title transliterated: Materialy k klinicheskomu
        izucheniiu kollateral'nago arterial'-
        nago krovoobrashcheniia.
RC691.T35   57-53426

NT 0051738   DLC

Taube (Ewald) [1892-]. *Beitrag zur
Kenntnis der Schädelbasisgeschwülste der
Hypophysengegend beim Hunde. [Leipzig.]
28 pp. 8°. *Rössel, B. Kruttke, 1921.

NT 0051739   DNLM CtY ICRL

Taube, F   A
Conspectus jurisscientiae turcicae;
oder, Uibersicht der türkischen Rechtswissenschaft, Rechtsschriften und
vornehmsten Rechtsgelehrten, nebst
einer Rechts-Tabelle. Hamburg, In
Commission bei .J. S. Heinsius, 1792.
104 p.

4K
10707

NT 0051740   DLC-P4

TAUBE,F. A.
Conspectus jurisscientiae turcicae oder uibersicht der türkischen rechtswissenschaft,
rechtsschriften und vornehmsten rechtsgelehrten, nebst einer rechts-tabelle. Hamburg,Leip-
zig,1792.

NT 0051741   MH-L

4GV-   Taube, Fr   Wilhelm.
193   Meister der Liebesübungen. Leipzig, Quelle &
Meyer, 1930.
178 p. (Bücherei für Leibesübungen und körper-
liche Erziehung)

NT 0051742   DLC-P4

Taube (François). *Ozène des bronches. 72
pp. 8°. *Paris, 1906. No. 128.

NT 0051743   DNLM

Taube, Friedrich, 1904-
... Fruchtfolgen im stadt- und landkreise
Münster und ihre betriebswirtschaftliche
zweckmassigkeit ... Emsdetten (Westf.) 1933.

Münster
diss.
1933

NT 0051744   MiU

Bf3   Taube, Friedrich Wilhelm, 1873-
101   Ludwig der Aeltere als Markgraf von Branden-
18   burg (1323-1351) von Dr. Friedrich Wilhelm
Taube. Berlin,E.Ebering,1900.
2p.ℓ.,146,[2]p. fold.geneal.tab. 23cm.
(Historische Studien, veröffentlicht von E.
Ebering ... Heft XVIII)
Published in part as the author's inaugural
dissertation, Berlin, 1900.
"Ueberblick über die wichtigsten Quellen und
Werke": p.[1]-5.

NT 0051745   CtY CSmH ICRL PU OU MH

Taube, Friedrich Wilhelm von, 1728-1778.
... Abschilderung der engländischen
manufacturen, handlung, schifffahrt und
colonien, nach ihrer jetzigen einrichtung und
beschaffenheit ... 2.stark verm. und verb. aufl.
Wien, J.P.Kraus, 1777-78.
2 v. in 1. front.(plan.) 20.5 cm.

Author's name at head of title.
Volume 2 has title: Abschilderung der
engländischen handlung. schiffahrt und colonien.

First published in 1774 with title:
Historische und politische abschilderung der
engländischen manufacturen.
With this is bound his Geschichte der
engländischen handelschaft ... 1776.

NT 0051747   MH-BA MiU

S.2569 Taube, Friedrich Wilhelm von, 1728-1778.
Geschichte der engländischen handelschaft, manufacturen, colonien und schiffrath in den alten, mittlern
und neuern zeiten, bis auf das laufende jahr 1776. Im
grundrisse entworfen...Mit einer zuverlässigen nach-
richt von den wahren ursachen des jetzigen krieges in
Nordamerika, und andern dergleichen dingen. Leipzig
[etc.] J. P. Kraus, 1776.
8 p.l., 144 p. 20·5 cm.

NT 0051748   MH-BA MiU-C RPJCB CtY MH MnU

Rare bk
D   Taube, Friedrich Wilhelm von, 1728-1778.
147   Historische und geographische Beschreibung
T3.9   des Königreiches Slavonien und des herzogthumes
Syrmien, sowol nach ihrer natürlichen Beschaff-
1777   enheit, als auch nach ihrer itzigen Berfassung und
neuen Einrichtung in Kirchlichen, bürgerlichen
und militarischen Dingen. Mit untermischten
Nachrichten von den angränzenden landern und von
den Illyriern, welch sich in denselben stark aus-
gebreitet haben. Aus eigener Beobachtung und im
Lande selbst gemachten Wahrnehmungen entworfen /

von Friedrich Wilhelm von Taube. - Leipzig :
Kaiserl: Königl Regierungsrathe, 1777.
3 v. in 1 ; 21 cm.
1. Slavs - Hist. I. Title. II. Title:
Beschreibung von Slavonien und Syrmien.

NT 0051750   NcGG MH MnU

Taube, Friedrich Wilhelm, 1728-1778.
Historische und politische Abschilderung der
engländischen Manufacturen, Handlung, Schifffahrt und Colonien, nach ihrer jetzigen Einrichtung und Beschaffenheit ... Wien,J.P.Kraus
1774.
5p.ℓ.,268,[4]p. front.(plan) 20½cm.

774
T1

NT 0051751   CtY MH MH-BA

Taube (Gottliebe Elise) [1861-]. *Rücken-
marksaffektionen in Gefolge von Schwangerschaft und Puerperium mit Einschluss der unter
denselben Verhältnissen auftretenden Neuritis
und Polyneuritis. 65 pp. 8°. *Berlin, Gebr.
*Unger, 1905.

NT 0051752   DNLM ICRL

Taube, Günter.
... Die rolle der natur in Gerhart Hauptmanns gegen-
wartswerken bis zum anfang des 20. jahrhunderts, von dr.
Günter Taube. Berlin, E. Ebering, 1936.
126 p. 24ᶜᵐ. (Germanische studien ... hrsg. von dr. Emil Ebering,
hft. 176)
The author's inaugural dissertation, Berlin.
"Literaturangaben": p. [125]-126.

1. Hauptmann, Gerhart Johann Robert, 1862-   2. Nature in literature.   i. Title.
36-22293
Library of Congress   PT2616.Z9T3
832 91

NjP OU TU TxU CtY MU
NT 0051753   DLC CaBVaU NcU NcD CtY KU NBC CLSU CU

Taube, Guido: Die Eigennamen bei Wolfram von Eschenbach.
Ein Wörterbuch. Breslau 1919: Fleischmann. 2 Bl. 8°
§ Nur Titelbl. u. Lebenslauf. Die Diss. ersch. später.
Breslau, Phil. Diss. v. 15. Nov. 1919, Ref. Siebs
[Geb. 23. Juli 90 Liebau i. Schl.; Wohnort: Liebau; Staatsangeh.: Preußen;
Vorbildung: G. Patschkau Reife 14; Studium: Breslau 3, München 3, Breslau
4 S.; Rig. 22. Okt. 19.]   [U 19. 2217]

NT 0051754   ICRL

Taube, Gurli Elisa (Westgren) friherrinna, 1890-
Ett bildverk om Uppsala

see under

Liljeroth, Erik.

Taube, Gurli Elisa (Westgren) *friherrinna*, 1890-
Från gångna tiders Uppsala. Stockholm, Wahlström &
Widstrand [1950]
197 p. illus., ports. 20 cm.

1. Uppsala—Hist. 2. Uppsala—Civilization.
DL991.U7T36   A 51-3871 rev
Minnesota. Univ. Libr.
for Library of Congress   [r53b⅟]†

NT 0051756   MnU NN DLC

Taube, Gurli Elisa (Westgren) friherrinna,
1890-

Scholander, Fredrik Vilhelm, 1816-1881.
Fredrik Wilhelm Scholanders Uplandsresa 1851. En
resedagbok utg. i faksimil och kommenterad av Gurli Taube.
[Malmö] Allhem [1955]

Taube, Gurli Elisa (Westgren) friherrinna, 1890-
Gluntarne

see under

Wennerberg, Gunnar, 1817-1901.

Taube, Gurli Elisa (Westgren) *friherrinna*, 1890-
Mordet på Cristina, [av] Elise Dufva [pseud.] Stockholm,
Bonnier [1952]
213 p. 21 cm.

i. Title.

PT9875.T33M6   53-18409 ‡

NT 0051759   DLC MnU

Taube, Gurli *Elisa (Westgren) friherrinna, 1890-*
Studenter till häst...
see under   Arsenius, Johan Georg, 1818-
1903.

Taube, Gurli Elisa (Westgren) *friherrinna,* 1890-
Svensk festskriftsbibliografi, åren 1891-1925. Uppsala,
Appelbergs boktr., 1954.

168 p. 25 cm. (Svenska bibliotekariesamfundets skriftserie, 2)

1. Festschriften—Bibl. 2. Swedish literature—Bibl.   I. Title.
(Series: Svenska bibliotekariesamfundet. Skriftserie, 2)
A 54-5793

Minnesota. Univ. Libr.
for Library of Congress

NcU FTaSU TU NIC
NT 0051761   MnU IaU LU DLC ICU MiU TxU ViU NN OU DLC

Taube, Gurli Elisa (Westgren) *friherrinna,* 1890-
Svensk regementshistorisk bibliografi. Uppsala, Almqvist & Wiksells boktr., 1949.

125 p. 25 cm.

1. Sweden. Armén—Bibl.   I. Title.
Z6725.S9T38   A 50-3769 rev
Harvard Univ. Library
for Library of Congress   [r53b⅜]†

NT 0051762   MH DLC

Taube, Gustav Genrychowitch, *baron.*
Countess Janina; an historical novel from Russian
life, by the Baron Gustav Genrychowitch Taube ... New
York, G. W. Dillingham, 1894.

x, 609 p. 19¼ᵐᵐ.

1. Russia—Hist.—Alexander II, 1855-1881—Fiction.
Library of Congress   PZ3.T191C   9-2225†
                           (Copyright 1894: 19794)

NT 0051763   DLC

PZ   Taube, Gustav Genrychowitch, Baron.
3   Glimpses of inner Russia. London, Simpkin,
T191   Marshall, Hamilton, Kent, 1916.
Gl   133 p. 19 cm.

NT 0051764   CU-S NN

Taube, Gustav Genrychowitch, *baron.*
In defence of America, by Baron von Taube. Adelphi,
S. Swift and company limited, 1912.

xii, 297, [1] p. 20ᵐᵐ.

1. National characteristics, American. 2. U. S.—Civilization.   I. Title.
                                              12-17074
Library of Congress   E168.T22

NT 0051765   DLC NIC

Taube, Gustav Genrychowitch, *baron.*
A medicus in love; a novel of student life, by G. von
Taube. New York, W. D. Rowland [1893]

1 p. l., iii, 5-260 p. 20ᵐᵐ. (On cover: The ideal series, no. 4)

                                              9-1480†
Library of Congress   PZ3.T191M
                          (Copyright 1893: 18354)

NT 0051766   DLC

HC337   Taube, Gustaw.
P7P97   ... Komercjalizacja Warszawy. I.Business city.
v.10   II.Metropoliten warszawski. Z przedmową Czesława
          Klarnera ... Warszawa, Przemysł i handel, 1927.
          51 p. fold. plan. 22ᶜᵐ. (On cover:Bibljote-
          ka ekonomiczna tygodnika Przemysł i handel. Rok
          III, tom 10)

          1.Warsaw— Economic conditions. 2.Street rail-
          roads- Warsaw. I.Title. II.Ser.:Przemysł i han-
          del, Warsaw. Bibljoteka ekonomiczna.

NT 0051767   CSt-H

Taube, Gustaw.
Racjonalna organizacja rozwoju Wielkiej Warszawy;
uwagi o planie regulacyjnym. [Warszawa, Druk. M. S.
Wojsk., 1928]

11 p. fold. map. 29 cm.

Cover title.
"Przegląd organizacji, organ Instytutu Naukowej Organizacji;
odbitka z nr. 3-4."

1. Cities and towns—Planning—Warsaw.   I. Title.

NA9212.W3T3   65-59708

NT 0051768   DLC

Taube (Hadovicus Wilhelmus Ludovicus)
[178?-]. *De vera nervi intercostalis origine, 20 pp. 4°. Gottinga, A. Vandenhoeck,
[1743].
For Biography, see Segner (Joan. Andreas).

NT 0051769   DNLM

Taube, Hedwig, afterwards Frau Prohl.
see   Prohl, Frau Hedwig (Taube).
1823-1886.

Taube (Heinrich). *Beitrag zur Percussion des
Magens. 78 pp., 1 l., 1 pl. 8°. Dorpat, Schnakenburg, 1887.*

NT 0051771   DNLM

Taube (Heinrich)* [186?-]. *Ein Beitrag
zur Wirkung der Aqua amygdalarum amararum.
38 pp. 8°. Greifswald, J. Abel, 1888.*

NT 0051772   DNLM

[Taube, Heinrich von]
Gründliche Beschreibung Derer/ Dem
... Herrn Johann Georgen dem Ersten/
Herzogen zu Sachsen ... gehaltener Drey
... Leichbegängnusse. Dresden, pr. Seyf-
fert, 1657.
2°. [engr. t.p., t.p., 6, 98]p. & 5 engr.
pl. (1 large fold., 3 double, 1 single).
(Jantz, German Baroque Lit., No. 2473,
Research Publications, Inc., Reel 510.)
Engravings by Joh. Dürr after Christian
Schiebling & I.H.B. Description of the 3

days of funeral services, 2 & 3 February
at Dresden, 4 February at Freiberg. In
the original black velvet binding (damaged)
together with another work for the occasion
by Jacob Weller.

NT 0051774   NcD CU

Taube, Helene (Keyserling) Freifrau von
see   Taube, Yelena Aleksandrovna
(Keyserling), baronessa von, 1845-

Taube, Henry, 1915-
The interaction of ozone and hydrogen peroxide,
by Henry Taube... [Berkeley, Calif., 1940]
3 p. l., 82 numb. l. incl. tables, mounted
diagrs. 29 cm.
Thesis (Ph. D.) - Univ. of California, May 1940.
Bibliography; p. 82.
1. Ozone. 2. Hydrogen peroxide.

NT 0051776   CU

Taube, Herbert, 1904-
Über gemischte Elektrizitätsleitung fester
Verbindungen... Hamburg, 1930.
Diss. - Hamburg.
Lebenslauf.
"Literaturverzeichnis"; p. 59-60.

NT 0051777   CtY OrU

Taube, Herman.
Remember, by Herman and Suzanne Taube. Translated
from the Yiddish by Helena Frank; foreword by Henry
Turk. Baltimore, N. A. Gossmann Pub. Co. 1951.
182 p. 20 cm.
Six of the stories were published in 1948 as יודישער שריפֿט
by Suzanne Taube.

I. Taube, Suzanne, joint author. II. Title.

PZ3.T1913Re   51-37088 ‡

NT 0051778   DLC ICJS ViU

Taube, Inkeri.
"Kuku", Ambomaan parantaja; lähetyslääkärin elämyksiä Afri-
kassa. Kirjoittanut Inkeri Taube.   Porvoo, Helsinki, W. Söderström [1947] 310 p. illus. 20cm.

435483B. 1. Rainio, Selma, 1873-1939.   2. Missions, Foreign—Africa, Southwest.
N. Y. P. L.   January 28, 1949

NT 0051779   NN DLC

Taube, Johann
see   Taube, Daniel Johann, 1727-1799.

Taube, Juris.
Latgales atseviška eskadrona vēsture (Atbrīvošanas cīņas),
1919. g. - 1921. g.   Jelgavā: Izd. Latgales atseviška eskadrona
bijušo kaŗaviru biedrība [1935] 76 p. illus. (incl. ports.)
23½cm.

1. Army, Lettish—Cav.   I. Latgales atseviška eskadrona
bijušo kaŗaviru biedrība, Jelgavā,   Latvia.
N. Y. P. L.   September 30, 1940

NT 0051781   NN

Taube, Karl Evert Bernhard friherre, 1834-
see   Taube af Odenkat, Carl Evert
Bernhard, friherre, 1834-

Taube, Konrad, 1902-
Der zwischenfrachtfuehrer. Kiel, 1926.
5, 59, (2) p.
Inaug.-diss. - Kiel, 1926.
Bibl.

NT 0051783   ICRL CtY MH-L

Taube, Lotte.
Max Regers meisterjahre (1909–1916) von Lotte Taube.
Berlin, E. Bote & G. Bock ¡*1941¡
87, ¡1¡ p. ports. 21ᶜᵐ.
"Quellenangabe": p. ¡88¡

1. Reger, Max, 1873–1916.

43–44017

Library of Congress   ML410.R25T3

927.8

NT 0051784   DLC MH IEN CU

Taube, Max, 1882–
Erzberger — der Totengräber des Deutschen Reiches. Die
Wahrheit über die angeblichen Enthüllungen Erzbergers in
Weimar, zugleich eine schonungslose Abrechnung mit diesem
Reichsschädling, von Max Taube ... Berlin: Verlagsbuch-
handlung F. Zillessen (H. Beenken) 1919. 32 p. 22cm.

1. Erzberger, Matthias, 1875–1921.   2. Germany—Politics, 1919–.
N. Y. P. L.   April 13, 1938

NT 0051785   NN

J   **TAUBE, MAX,** 1882–
27   Handlungsgehilfen und Sozialdemokratie.
335.0943 Berlin, Verlagsanstalt und Druckerei "Teu-
R 001   tonia", 1911.
          v,104p. 24cm.

NT 0051786   ICN ICJ

Taube, Max, 1882–
Der Kampf um die deutsche Volksseele, von Max Taube...
Berlin: Vaterländischer Volksbund ¡1921¡ 50 p. 22cm.

1. Germany—Politics. 2. Germans.
N. Y. P. L.   July 19, 1943

NT 0051787   NN

Taube, Max, 1882–
Die Preussische Königspartei, Gründung, Ziele, Satzungen,
von Max Taube... Berlin: Verlag Preussische Königspartei,
1921. 20 p. 2. ed. 8°. (Preussische Flugschriften. Nr.
4.)
Aufklärungsschriften der Preussischen Königspartei. Nr. 3.

411733A. 1. Preussische Königspartei.
N. Y. P. L.   May 31, 1929

NT 0051788   NN

Taube, Max, 1882–
"Wenn die Revolution nicht gekommen wäre..." Von Max
Taube... Berlin: Vaterländischer Volksbund, 1920. 15 p.
8°.

1. Germany.—History: Revolution,   1918–.
N. Y. P. L.   December 6, 1922.

NT 0051789   NN

Taube, Max Arthur, 1851–
Die Entstehung der menschlichen Rachendiphtherie
nach Beobachtungen während der letzten Leipziger
Diphtherie-Epidemie 1883–84. Leipzig, C. Reissner,
1884.
67 p.

NT 0051790   ICJ DNLM

Taube, Max Arthur, 1851–   joint ed.
Heller, Theodor, 1869–   ed.
Enzyklopädisches handbuch des kinderschutzes und der
jugendfürsorge, hrsg. unter mitwirkung hervorragender
fachleute von dr. phil. Th. Heller ... dr. jur. Fr. Schiller
... dr. med. M. Taube ... Leipzig, W. Engelmann, 1911.

Taube, Max Arthur, 1851–   362.72 P300
Der Schutz der unehelichen Kinder in Leipzig. Eine Einrichtung zur Fürsorge ohne Findelhäuser. Von Dr. med. Max
Taube. Leipzig, Veit & Co., 1893.
75 p. 23½cm.

NT 0051792   ICJ

Taube, Michel de
    see Taube, Mikhail Aleksandrovich, baron,
1869–

Taube, Mikhail Aleksandrovich, baron 1869–
Аграфа; о незаписанныхъ въ Евангеліи изреченіяхъ
Іисуса Христа. Варшава, Синодальная тип., 1936–49.

2 v. in 1. 24–26 cm. (Библіотека "Братства православныхъ
богослововъ въ Польшѣ," № 11)
At head of title: M. A. Таубе.
Vol. 2, issued without series statement, has imprint: Парижъ, Изд.
Русского православно-вселенскаго (католическаго) журнала "Наш
приходъ."
Bibliographical footnotes.

1. Bible. N. T. Apocryphal books. Logia Iesou—Criticism, interpretation, etc.   I. Title.   *Title romanized:* Agrafa.

BS2970.T3   67–118300

NT 0051794   DLC

Taube, Mikhail Aleksandrovich, baron, 1869–
L'apport de Byzance au développement du droit interna-
tional occidental, par le baron Michel de Taube ...
(*In* Hague. Academy of international law. Recueil des cours,
1939, I. Paris ¡1940¡ 24ᶜᵐ. v. 67, p. ¡233¡–¡339¡ port.)
"Notice biographique. Principales publications": p. ¡235¡–236.
"Bibliographie": p. ¡335¡–337.

1. International law—Hist. 2. Law, Byzantine. 3. ¡International law,
Byzantine¡
[JX74.H3 vol. 67]   A 47–2131
Carnegie endow. int. peace.   Library
for Library of Congress   ¡2¡

NT 0051795   NNCE

4CS   Taube, Mikhail Aleksandrovich, Baron,
113   1869–
          Archiv des uradeligen Geschlechts
          Taube, sonst Tuve genannt. St.
          Petersburg, Buchdr. J. Watsar, 1911–
          v. 1

NT 0051796   DLC-P4 NN

CS858   Taube, Mikhail Aleksandrovich, baron, 1869–
.T28   Les Barons Taube; essai préliminaire.
          Paris, Nicholas Ikonnikov, 1943.
          ¡29¡ l. 27cm.

          On t.p.: La noblesse de Russie; copie des
          livres généalogiques de la Noblesse Russe,
          constitués d'après les actes et les documents
          existants, et complétés par le concours dé-
          voué des nobles Russes.

NT 0051797   NcU

Taube, Mikhail Aleksandrovich, baron, 1869–
L'Empereur Paul Ier de Russie, grand maître de l'Ordre de
Malte et son "grand prieuré russe" de l'Ordre de Saint-Jean-de-
Jérusalem. Paris, 1955. 71 p. port. 21cm.

1. Paul I, emperor of Russia,   1754–1801. 2. Knights of Malta—
Russia.

NT 0051798   NN WU CtY

929.711 Taube, Mikhail Aleksandrovich, baron, 1869–
T19e   L'empereur Paul Iᵉʳ de Russie; grand maître
          de l'Ordre de Malte et son "Grand Prieuré
          russe" de l'Ordre de Saint-Jean-de-Jérusalem.
          Paris ¡H. Aubenas¡ 1955.
          71p. port. 21cm.

          Bibliographical footnotes.

NT 0051799   IU

Taube, Mikhail Aleksandrovich, baron, 1869–
Études sur le développement historique du droit interna-
tional dans l'Europe orientale, par le baron Michel Taube ...
(*In* Hague. Academy of international law. Recueil des cours,
1926, I. Paris, 1927. 24½ᶜᵐ. v. 11, p. 341–535. port.)
"Notice biographique": p. 343.
"Principales publications": p. 344.
"Indications bibliographiques": p. 498–504.

1. International law ¡and relations¡—History. 2. ¡International law,
European¡

Carnegie endow. int. peace.   Library   A 28—61
for Library of Congress   ¡a40r29e1¡

NT 0051800   NNCE NcD

341.09 Taube, Mikhail Aleksandrovich, baron, 1869–
T191e   Études sur le développement historique du
          droit international dans l'Europe orientale,
          par le baron Michel de Taube. Paris, Librairie
          Hachette, 1927.
          189 p.

          "Indications bibliographiques": p. ¡154¡–160.
          At head of title: Academie de droit inter-
          national.

NT 0051801   WaU

Taube, Mikhail Aleksandrovich, baron, 1869–
Ф. Ф. Мартенсъ, 1845–1909; некрологъ. С.-Петербургъ,
Сенатская тип., 1909.
16 p. 25 cm.

"Извлечено изъ Журнала Министерства народнаго просвѣщенія,
за 1909 годъ."
Bibliographical footnotes.

1. Martens, Fedor Fedorovich, 1845–1909.
                                        Title transliterated: F. F. Martens.

JX2952.T3   59–56312

NT 0051802   DLC

Taube, Mikhail Aleksandrovich, baron, 1869–
Der grossen katastrophe entgegen. Die russische politik der
vorkriegszeit und das ende des zarenreiches (1904–1917)
Erinnerungen von dr. Michael freiherrn von Taube ... Berlin
und Leipzig, G. Neuner, 1929.
viii, 376 p. 24ᶜᵐ.

1. Russia—Pol. & govt.—1894–1917. I. Title. II. Title: Die russische
politik der vorkriegszeit.

Library of Congress   DK262.T34   32–5450

947.08

NN
NT 0051803   DLC CaBVaU CU MoSCS NcD ICN WaU MiU MH

Taube, Mikhail Aleksandrovich, baron, 1869–
Der grossen katastrophe entgegen. Die russische politik der
vorkriegszeit und das ende des zarenreiches (1904–1917) Erinnerungen von dr. Michael freiherrn von Taube ... 2. umgearb.
und erweiterte ausg. ... ¡Leipzig¡ K. F. Koehler, 1937.
viii, 415 p. 23ᶜᵐ.

1. Russia—Pol. & govt.—1894–1917.

43–28231

Library of Congress   DK262.T34 1937

947.08

PU
NT 0051804   DLC IU TNJ MeB MH NcU NN CSt-H OCl NNC

Taube, Mikhail Aleksandrovich, *baron*, 1869–
L'inviolabilité des traités, par le baron Michel de Taube ...
(*In* Hague. Academy of international law. Recueil des cours, 1930, II. Paris, 1931. 24½ᶜᵐ. v. 32, p. ₍291₎–389; port.)
"Notice biographique. Principales publications": p. ₍293₎–294.
"Bibliographie": p. ₍384₎–387.
Contents.—L'orient ancien et la religion des traités.—Le droit des traités dans la communauté internationale du monde méditerranéen.—L'inviolabilité des traités au moyen âge.—L'Europe moderne et la clause rebus sic stantibus.—Le xxᵉ siècle, la Société des nations et le droit nouveau.

1. Treaties. 2. League of nations. I. Title.
    A 32–80
Title from Carnegie   Endow. Int. Peace JX1295.A3A24
Library of Congress   vol. 32
   [JX74.H3 vol. 32]

NT   0051805   NNCE NcD

Taube, Mikhail Aleksandrovich, *baron*, 1869–
Исторія зарожденія современнаго международнаго права; средніе вѣка. С.-Петербургъ, 1894–19 0 2
v. 24–27 cm.
Vol. 2 published in Kharkov.
Vol. 2⁻ have also special t. p.
Vol. 3 issued in parts.
Contents.—т. 1. Введеніе: Древній міръ и переходъ къ среднимъ вѣкамъ. Часть общая: Средніе вѣка и зарожденіе идеи международнаго общенія.—т. 2. Часть особенная: Принципы міра и права въ международныхъ столкновеніяхъ среднихъ вѣковъ.—т. 3. Международный строй средневѣковой Европы. Глава 1. Христіанство и организація международнаго міра.
1. International law—Hist.   I. Title. II. Title: Khristianstvo i
organizaṭsiia mezhduna-   rodnago mira.
   Title trans-   *literated:* Istoriia zarozhdeniia so-
    vremennago mezhdunarodnago prava.
JX1308.T3   9–12730 rev 2*

NT   0051806   DLC

Taube, Mikhail Aleksandrovich, *baron*, 1869–
Les origines de l'arbitrage international antiquité et moyen age, par le baron Michel de Taube ...
(*In* Hague. Academy of international law. Recueil des cours, 1932, IV. Paris, 1933. 24½ᶜᵐ. v. 42, p. ₍1₎–115; port.)
"Notice biographique. Principales publications": p. ₍3₎
"Bibliographie": p. ₍112₎–114.

1. Arbitration, International—History.
    A 33–2177
Title from Carnegie   Endow. Int. Peace
Library of Congress   [JX74.H3 vol. 42]

NT   0051807   NNCE NcD

Taube, Mikhail Aleksandrovich, *baron*, 1869–
La politique russe d'avant-guerre et la fin de l'empire des tsars (1904–1917) mémoires du baron M. de Taube ... Paris, E. Leroux, 1928.
2 p. l., ₍vii₎–viii, 412 p. 22½ᶜᵐ.

1. Russia—Pol. & govt.—1894–1917. I. Title.
Library of Congress   DK262.T3
    28–29940

CaBVaU NIC
MH-L NN CSt-L MoU TU KU FU OKentU CLSU InU CU ScU
NT   0051808   DLC PU PBm CtY NcD NcU ViU OCl MiU NjR

Taube, Mikhail Aleksandrovich, *baron*, 1869–
Rome et la Russie avant l'invasion des Tatars (ixᵉ–xiiiᵉ siècle) Paris, Éditions du Cerf, 1947–
v. fold. map. 23 cm. (Russie et chrétienté, 2
Series title on cover also in Russian.
Contents.—1. Le prince Askold, l'origine de l'état de Kiev et la première conversion des Russes (856–882)

1. Russia—Church history. 2. Russia—Hist.—To 1533. I. Title. (Series)
    A 51–7666
New York. Public Libr.
for Library of Congress

GU OKentU MoU OOxM IaU WU   TxU MU
OU OCU IEN PU CU   MH-AH NcU IEG NcD ViU CaBVaU CSt
NT   0051809   NN MH ICU NjP CtY DDO InU NIC MoSU-D PSt

Taube, Mikhail Aleksandrovich, *baron*, 1869–
La Russie et l'Europe occidentale à travers dix siècles, étude d'histoire internationale et de psychologie ethnique. Bruxelles, Lecture au foyer, 1926.
47 p. 23 cm.

1. Russia—For. rel.—Europe. 2. Europe—Politics. I. Title.
DK67.T33   51–48118

NT   0051810   DLC CtY NN IU InU

Taube, Mikhail Aleksandrovich, *baron*, 1869–
... Russland und westeuropa (Russlands historische sonderentwicklung in der europäischen völkergemeinschaft), von prof. dr. Michael freiherr von Taube. Berlin, Georg Stilke, 1928.
63 p. 22½ cm. (Institut für internationales recht an der Universität Kiel. 1. reihe: Vorträge und einzelschriften, hft. 8)

1. Russia—Hist. I. Title.
JX77.K47 hft. 8   A 29–326
Carnegie Endow. for Int.   Peace. Library
for Library of Congress   ₍a56c₎†

NT   0051811   NNCE MH-L DLC

Taube, Mikhail Aleksandrovich, *baron*, 1869–
Le statut juridique de la Mer baltique jusqu'au début du xixᵉ siècle, par le baron Michel de Taube ...
(*In* Hague. Academy of international law. Recueil des cours, 1935, III. Paris, 1936. 24½ᶜᵐ. v. 53, p. ₍437₎–530; port.)
"Notice biographique. Principales publications": p. ₍439₎–440.
"Bibliographie": p. ₍528₎–529.

1. Baltic sea.
    A 36–930
Title from Carnegie   Endow. Int. Peace
Library of Congress   [JX74.H3 vol. 53]

NT   0051812   NNCE WaU

Taube, Mikhail Aleksandrovich, baron, 1869–
Видѣнія и думы; сборникъ стихотвореній. М. Т. ₍Tallinn, Tallinna Eesti Kirjastus-Ühisuse trükikoda₎ 1937.
126 p. illus. 30 cm.
Includes bibliographical references.

I. Title.
    Title romanized: Vidѣniia i dumy.
PG3470.T34V5   71–275199

NT   0051813   DLC

Taube, Mikhail Aleksandrovich, *baron*, 1869–
... Вѣчный миръ или вѣчная война? (Мысли о "Лигѣ націй") ... Берлинъ ₍Русская типографія Е. А. Гутнова₎ 1922.
109, ₍3₎ p. fold. facsim. 22ᶜᵐ.
At head of title: К-во "Дѣтинецъ." Сер. I—№ 4. Проф. бар. М. А. Таубе.
Bibliographical foot-notes.

1. League of nations. I. Title.   *Title transliterated:* Viѣch-
nyĭ mir ili viѣchnaia voĭna?
Library of Congress   JX1975.T34
    43–31589

NT   0051814   DLC OU

Taube, Mikhail Aleksandrovich, baron, 1869–
Die von Uxkull; genealogische Geschichte des uradeligen Geschlechts der Herren, Freiherren und Grafen von Uxkull, 1229–1929. Berlin, [gedr. bei Julius Sittenfeld] 1930.
2, 139 p. illus., facsims, tables.
1. Uexktüll family.

NT   0051815   InU

Taube, Mikhail Aleksandrovich, baron, 1869–
Die von Uxkull; genealogische Geschichte der Gesamtfamilie von Uxkull, 1229–1954. Meine, Kluge & Ströhm, 1955

NT   0051816   MH

025.3
T191
Taube, Mortimer, 1910–
The cataloging of publications of corporate bodies. Preliminary ed. for official use. Washington, 1949.
43 l. 27 cm.

At head of title: The Library of Congress Science and Technology Project.

NT   0051817   KyU NNC

Taube, Mortimer, 1910–1965.
The cataloging of publications of corporate bodies
   see also   U.S. Library of Congress. Descriptive Cataloging Division.
A study of "The cataloging of publications of corporate bodies."

Taube, Mortimer, 1910–1965.
Causation, freedom and determinism; an attempt to solve the causal problem through a study of its origins in seventeenth century philosophy, by Mortimer Taube... [Berkeley, Calif., 1935]
2 p. l., ii, 268 numb. l. 29 cm.
Thesis (Ph. D.) – Univ. of California, May 1935.
Bibliography; p. 265–268.
1. Causation. 2. Free will and determinism.

NT   0051819   CU

Taube, Mortimer, 1910–
Causation, freedom, and determinism; an attempt to solve the causal problem through a study of its origins in seventeenth-century philosophy, by Mortimer Taube ... London, G. Allen & Unwin, ltd. ₍1936₎
262 p. 1 l. 22 cm.
"First published in 1936."
Bibliography: p. ₍257₎–260.

1. Causation. 2. Free will and determinism.
BD541.T3   122   37—196

   OO O OClW WaU
NT   0051820   DLC NIC PPT PP PSC CU CtW CtY NcD OCU

Taube, Mortimer, 1910–
Coordinate indexing without machines. Prepared under contract no. AF18(600)–376 for the Armed Services Technical Information Agency. Washington, Documentation Incorporated, 1952.
4 p. illus. 28 cm. (₍Documentation Incorporated, Washington, D. C.₎ Technical report no. 1)

1. Indexing. I. U. S. Defense Documentation Center. II. Title. (Series)
Z674.D6 no. 1   025.3   53–61611 rev

NT   0051821   DLC

Taube, Mortimer, 1910–
The evaluation of information systems, final report. Prepared under contract no. AF18(600)–376 for the Armed Services Technical Information Agency. Washington, Documentation Incorporated, 1953.
19 p. 28 cm. (Documentation Incorporated, Washington, D. C. Technical report no. 9)

1. Information storage and retrieval systems. I. U. S. Defense Documentation Center. II. Title. (Series)
Z674.D6 no. 9   025.3   53–61619 rev

NT   0051822   DLC

D020.4
T19
Taube, Mortimer, 1910–
Libraries and research, by Mortimer Taube ... ₍1940₎
₍1₎, 22–27 p. 25½ᶜᵐ.

"Reprinted from College and research libraries, December, 1940."

NT   0051823   NNC

Taube, Mortimer, 1910–
The logical structure of coordinate indexing, by Mortimer Taube and Irma S. Wachtel. Prepared under contract no. AF18(600)–376 for the Armed Services Technical Information Agency. Washington, Documentation Incorporated, 1953.
4 p. 28 cm. (₍Documentation Incorporated, Washington, D. C.₎ Technical report no. 4)

1. Indexing. I. Wachtel, Irma S., joint author. II. U. S. Defense Documentation Center. III. Title. (Series)
Z674.D6 no. 4   025.33   53–61614 rev

NT   0051824   DLC

Z1001
.U56

Taube, Mortimer, 1910–   comp.

U. S. *Library of Congress. Committee on Bibliography and Publications.*
Manual for bibliographers in the Library of Congress, by Mortimer Taube and Helen F. Conover. Washington, 1944.

Taube, Mortimer, 1910–
Memorandum for a conference on bibliographical control of government scientific and technical reports. ₁New York? 1948₁
154–160 p. 26 cm.
Caption title.
Reprint from Special libraries, May–June 1948.

1. Bibliography—Theory, methods, etc. 2. Science—Bibl. 3. Technology—Bibl.
Z1001.T27   010.1   51–60096

NT 0051826   DLC

Taube, Mortimer, 1910–
New tools for the control and use of research materials. ₁Philadelphia? 1949₁
248–252 p. 27 cm.
Cover title.
"Preprinted from Proceedings of the American Philosophical Society, vol. 93, no. 3, 1949."

1. Bibliography—Theory, methods, etc. 2. Research. 3. Documentation.   I. Title.
Z1001.T3   010.1   49–5597*

NT 0051827   DLC

Taube, Mortimer, 1910–
The planning and preparation of the Technical information pilot and its cumulative index. ₁n. p., 1948₁
202–206 p. illus. 27 cm.
Caption title.
Reprinted from College and research libraries, July, 1948.

1. Technical information pilot.
Z733.U63S35   016.5   51–61789

NT 0051828   DLC

Taube, Mortimer, 1910–
Specificity in subject headings and coordinate indexing. Prepared under contract no. AF18(600)–376 for the Armed Services Technical Information Agency. Washington, Documentation Incorporated, 1952.
7 p. 28 cm. (₁Documentation Incorporated, Washington, D. C.₁ Technical report no. 2)

1. Subject headings. 2. Indexing.   I. U. S. Defense Documentation Center. II. Title.   (Series)
Z674.D6 no. 2   025.33   53–61612 rev 2

NT 0051829   DLC

Taube, Mortimer, 1910–
Studies in coordinate indexing, by Mortimer Taube and associates. ₁Washington₁ Documentation Incorporated, 1953–
v. 22 cm.
Bibliographical footnotes.

1. Indexing.   I. Title.
Z695.9.T38   029.5   53–4043

NcD IEdS MoU
MB NBuU Or Wa OrU OrU–M PU NN NIC PPSKF OO OClW OU PPAtR MH–P NBuG ICJ ViU Vi WaS DNLM OrP CaBVaU
NT 0051830   DLC DS DSI TU OCl PBL TxU PMarhSO NcRS

Z
695.9
T38

Taube, Mortimer, 1910–
Studies in coordinate indexing. by Mortimer Taube and associates. ₁Washington₁ Documentation Incorporated, 1953–
v. 22 cm.
Bibliographical footnotes.

Microfiche. 11 cards. 12.5x20.5cm.

NT 0051831   NBuC

Taube, Mortimer, 1910–
Surveying the collections of a university library, by Mortimer Taube ... Durham, N. C., 1943.
₁1₁, 602–612 p. 22ᶜᵐ.
"Reprinted from Association of American colleges Bulletin, vol. XXVIII, December 1942, no. 4."

1. Libraries, University and college.   I. Title.
                                    45–13607
Library of Congress   Z675.U5T3
                                    027.7

NT 0051832   DLC NNC

Taube, Mortimer, 1910– *1965.*
Unit terms in coordinate indexing, by Mortimer Taube, C. D. Gull, and Irma S. Wachtel. Prepared under contract no. AF18(600)–376 for the Armed Services Technical Information Agency. Washington, Documentation Incorporated, 1952.
15 p. 28 cm. (₁Documentation Incorporated, Washington, D. C.₁ Technical report no. 3)

1. Indexing.   I. U. S. Defense Documentation Center. II. Title. (Series)
Z674.D6 no. 3   025.33   53–61613 rev

NT 0051833   DLC

PN
2776
U68T22

Taube, Nils Evert, Friherre, 1883-
De Delandska teatersällskapen i Uppsala. En kulturbild från romantikens tid. Uppsala, Almqvist & Wiksell, 1940.
226 p. illus. 25cm. (Skrifter utgivna av Föreningen Drottningholmsteaterns Vänner, 1)

1. Deland family. 2. Theater--Uppsala --History. I. Series: Föreningen Drottninghol   msteaterns Vänner. Skrifter, 1.

NT 0051834   NIC CLSU NjP MH

Taube, Nils Evert, *friherre,* 1883–
Étude sur l'emploi de l'argot des malfaiteurs chez les auteurs romantiques ... par Nils Evert Taube ... Uppsala, Appelbergs boktryckeri a.-b., 1917.
xxix, ₁2₁, 98 p., 1 l. 23ᶜᵐ.
Akademisk afhandling—Uppsala.
"Contributions à la bibliographie de l'argot. (Supplément à la Bibliographie d'Yves-Plessis)": p. ₁xxiii₁–xxiv.
"Bibliographie": p. ₁xxv₁–xxix.

1. French language—Slang. 2. Romanticism—France.
                                    20–8162
Library of Congress   PC3746.T3
                                    ₁a38b1₁

NT 0051835   DLC PU CtY WaU

Taube, Nils Evert, friherre, 1883–
...Molière. ₁Stockholm₁ Lindfors ₁1947₁ 175 p. 21cm.
Bibliographies, p. 171–₁176₁

457437B. 1. Molière, Jean Baptiste   Poquelin, 1622–1673.
N. Y. P. L.   November 9, 1948

NT 0051836   NN CU DLC-P4

Taube, Nils Evert, Friherre, 1883–
Om Gunnar Wennerbergs-porträtt i Uppsala universitets-bibliotek och i andra samlingar. (In: Symbola litteraria. Uppsala, 1927. 4°. p. ₁231–₁262 incl. ports.)

1. Wennerberg, Gunnar, 1817–1901.
N. Y. P. L.   May 21, 1928

NT 0051837   NN

Taube, Nils Evert, friherre, 1883–
Romantikens kavaljer, stockholmsroman från 1830–talet, av Nils E. Taube. ₁Stockholm₁ Lindfors ₁1944₁ 371 p. port. 20cm.

429164B. 1. Dahlqvist, Georg, 18(1873–Fiction. 2. Högqvist, Emilie,
1812–1846—Fiction. I. Title.
N. Y. P. L.   February 19, 1948

NT 0051838   NN

PT9875
T3R6
1944
Scandinavian
Dept.

Taube, Nils Evert, friherre, 1883-
Romantikens kavaljer; Stockholmsroman från 1830-talet.
[2. uppl.] [Stockholm] Lindfors [1944]
371 p. ports.

NT 0051839   CU

Taube, Nils Evert, *friherre,* 1883–
Uppsala i närbild. Sammanställd av Nils E. Taube ₁et al.₁ Stockholm, Wahlström & Widstrand ₁1948₁
220 p. illus., ports. 27 cm.

1. Uppsala—Descr.—Views. 2. Uppsala—Hist. 3. Uppsala—Soc. life & cust.   I. Title.
DL991.U7T38   914.87   A 49–5792*
Minnesota. Univ. Lib.
for Library of Congress   ₁1₁†

NT 0051840   MnU DLC

Taube, Otto, *Freiherr von,* 1879–
Baltischer Adel; drei Novellen. Oldenburg i. O., G. Stalling ₁1932₁
75 p. 20 cm. (Stalling Bücherei. Schriften an die Nation, Nr. 3)
CONTENTS.—König Karls XII. einzige Liebe.—Ungern Sternberg.—Onkel Ottomar.

I. Title.
PT2642.A72B3   52–47139

NT 0051841   DLC MH OCl NN CtY

920
T191b
1955

Taube, Otto, Freiherr von, 1879-
Brüder der oberen Schar. Gestalten aus der Welt der Bibel und der Geschichte der Kirche.   Hamburg, F. Wittig [1955]
295p. 23cm.

1. Saints. Biog. 2. Christian biography. I. Title.

NT 0051842   KU PPLT

Taube, Otto, freiherr von, 1879–

Das **buch** der Keyserlinge. An der grenze zweier welten; lebenserinnerungen aus einem geschlecht. Berlin, S. Fischer verlag ₁1937₁

709.45
T22d   Taube, Otto, freiherr von, 1879-
　　　　Die darstellung des heiligen Georg
　　　　in der italienischen kunst...
　　　　Halle a.S., Kaemmerer, 1910.
　　　　167p. O.

　　　　Inaug.-diss.- Halle.
　　　　Lebenslauf.

NT 0051844   IaU ICN PU MH PPPM NN CtY NjP

Taube, Otto, Freiherr von, 1879-
　　Doktor Alltags phantastische Aufzeichnungen.
　　Hamburg, F. Wittig [195-?]
　　126 p.

NT 0051845   CtY

TAUBE, OTTO, FREIHERR VON, 1879-
　　Doktor Alltags phantastische Aufzeichnungen. Hamburg, F. Wittig [1951] 126 p. 20cm.

NT 0051846   NN NRU

Taube, Otto, Freiherr von, 1879-
　　...Das ende der königsmarcks. Merse-
burg, Friedrich Stollberg, [cl937]
　　122,[1]p. 19cm.
　　At head of title: Otto freiherr von
Taube.
　　Contents.- Das ende der königsmarcks.-
Der sieg Don Alonso Gureas.- Die nonne
und der Capirote.- Der metzgerbub und die
herzögin.

NT 0051847   MWelC

Taube, Otto, freiherr von, 1879-
　　Der fluch über Luhsen. Merseburg, Friedrich
Strollberg [1939]
　　84 [2] p. 20 cm.
　　Contents; Der fluch über Lushen.- Der
postmichel - Der Turmbaumeister. - Die
sturmflut zu Venedig.

NT 0051848   NcD

Taube, Otto, Freiherr von, 1879-
　　Der Fluch über Luhsen. Merseburg, F. Stollberg [1942]
　　84 p. 20 cm.
　　CONTENTS.—Der Fluch über Luhsen.—Der Postmichel—Der Turmbaumeister.—Die Sturmflut zu Venedig.

　　I. Title.

　　PT2642.A72F6

　　　　　　　　　　　　　50-52055

NT 0051849   DLC

Taube, Otto, Freiherr von, 1879-
　　Gab und giebt es eine nachfolge in den besitz...
Inaug. Diss. Leipzig, 1902.

NT 0051850   ICRL

Taube, Otto, Freiherr von, 1879-
　　Gedichte und Szenen. Leipzig, Insel-Verlag, 1908
　　174 p.

NT 0051851   MH InU PPT

Taube, Otto, *Freiherr* von, 1879-
　　Geschichte unseres Volkes. Berlin-Steglitz, Eckart-Ver-
lag, 1938-42 [1938]
　　2 v. 24 cm.
　　L. C. copy incomplete: v. 1 wanting.
　　CONTENTS.—[1] Die Kaiserzeit.—[2] Reformation und Revolution.

　　1. Germany—Hist. I. Title.

　　DD89.T3　　　　　　943　　　　　　49–57426*

NT 0051852   DLC NN MtBC KU IaU MH

TAUBE, OTTO, Freiherr VON, 1879-
　　Geschichte unseres Volkes.   Berlin-Steglitz, Eckart-
Verlag, 1942.   24cm.
　　[Bd. 2]
　　Bibliographical references in "Anmerkungen" v.2, p. 549-576.
　　CONTENTS. —[Bd. 2] Reformation und Revolution.

　　1. Germany — Hist. —Modern period, 1517-

NT 0051853   NN

BR123
.T22   Taube, Otto, Freiherr von, 1879-
　　Gottes Wort und die Geschichte. München,
　　C. Kaiser, 1946.
　　39 p. (Gottes Wort und Geschichte, 1)
　　"Vortrag, gehalten in der Evangelischen Studen-
tengemeinde zu Erlangen am 2. Februar 1946."

　　1. Christianity--Addresses, essays, lectures.
　　2. History--　　　　　　　Philosophy.

NT 0051854   ICU DCU NNUT

PQ6398
.G3 O 74
1946   Taube, Otto, Freiherr von, 1879-   ed.
　　Gracián y Morales, Baltasar, 1601-1658.
　　Hand-Orakel und Kunst der Weltklugheit. Nach der
Übertragung von Arthur Schopenhauer neu hrsg. von Otto
Freiherrn von Taube. [Wiesbaden] Insel-Verlag, 1946.

TAUBE, Otto Freiherr von, 1879-
　　Heiliges Vermaechtnis frueher
Zeugen. Muenchen, Christian Kaiser,
1946.
　　15p. 15.2cm. ("Traktate vom Wirk-
lichen Leben",3)

NT 0051856   MH-AH NNUT DCU

IX
511
K5T22   Taube, Otto, Freiherr von, 1879-
　　Im alten Estland. Kindheitserinnerungen.
Stuttgart, K.F. Köhler [1944]
　　286 p. 22cm.

　　1. Estonia--Soc. life & cust. I. Title.

NT 0051857   NIC CSt FTaSU

Taube, Otto, *Freiherr* von, 1879-
　　Im alten Estland; Kindheitserinnerungen. Stuttgart,
K. F. Köhler [1949]
　　286 p. 22 cm.

　　I. Title.
　　PT2642.A72Z52　　　　　928.3　　　　　A 50-2999
　　Harvard Univ. Library
　　for Library of Congress　　　[1]†

NT 0051858   MH NcU NNC NN LU MnU DLC

DD205
.K8A2
1942   Taube, Otto, freiherr von, 1879-   ed.

　　Kügelgen, Wilhelm Georg Alexander von, 1802–1867.
　　... Jugenderinnerungen eines alten mannes. Mit einer ein-
leitung von Otto freiherrn von Taube. Leipzig, Koehler &
Amelang [1942]

Taube, Otto, *Freiherr* von, 1879-   ed.

　　Klage und Jubel; Briefe um den Tod eines jungen
Christen. München, C. Kaiser, 1946.
　　180 p. 20 cm.

　　1. Taube, Rudolph, Baron von, 1834–1855.
　　DK511.E8T3　　　　　　　　　　A 50-1357
　　Union Theol. Sem. Lib.
　　for Library of Congress　　　[3]†

NT 0051860   NNUT DCU ICRL MH-AH DLC

PT2388
.K67
1942   Taube, Otto, freiherr von, 1879-   ed.

　　Kügelgen, Wilhelm Georg Alexander von, 1802–1867.
　　... Lebenserinnerungen des alten mannes in briefen an
seinen bruder Gerhard. Neu herausgegeben von Otto freiherrn
von Taube. Leipzig, Koehler & Amelang [1942]

Taube, Otto, *Freiherr* von, 1879-   comp.
　　Licht der Welt; eine Gedichtsammlung. München, C.
Kaiser, 1946.
　　271 p. 20 cm.
　　"Biographische und bibliographische Daten": p. 261–[265]

　　I. Title.
　　PT1174.T3　　　　831.91082　　　　A F 48-5205*
　　Yale Univ. Library
　　for Library of Congress　　　[1]†

NT 0051862   CtY OClU CU DLC

Taube, Otto, *freiherr* von, 1879-
　　... Die metzgerpost. Merseburg, F. Stollberg, 1936.
　　222 p. 19cm.
　　Title vignette.

　　I. Title.
　　　　　　　　　　　　　　　　　　38-966
　　Library of Congress　　　PT2642.A72M4 1936
　　Copyright A—Foreign　　　35206
　　　　　　　　　　　　　　　　833.91

NT 0051863   DLC

PT2642
A72N4   Taube, Otto, Freiherr von, 1879-
　　Neue Gedichte.   Leipzig, Insel-Verlag,
1911.
　　162p. 19cm.

NT 0051864   IaU

833.9
T2225o   Taube, Otto, Freiherr von, 1879-
　　Das Opferfest; Roman. Leipzig, Insel, 1926.
　　579p. 18cm.

NT 0051865   IEN OClW OOxM PV RPB

Taube, Otto, Freiherr von, 1879–
Rasputin; von Otto Freiherrn von Taube... München: C. H. Beck [, 1925]. 326 p. incl. port. 16°. (Stern und Unstern. Bd. 1.)

Bibliography, p. 324[–327].

207567A. 1. Rasputin, Grigori Yefi-movich, 1864–1917. 2. Court life
—Russia, 1894–1917. 3. Rasputin, Grigori Yefimovich, 1864–1917.
N. Y. P. L.
—Bibl. 4. Ser.
October 23, 1925

NT 0051866   NN CSt-H

Taube, Otto, *freiherr von*, 1879–
Rasputin, von Otto freiherrn von Taube. Mit Rasputins bildnis. [2. aufl.] München, Beck [*1925].
326, [1] p. incl. port. 17ᶜᵐ. (*Half-title:* Stern und unstern. 1. buch)
Bibliographical notes: p. 322[–327]

1. Rasputin, Grigoriĭ Efimovich, 1871–1916. 2. Russia—Hist.—Nich-olas II, 1894–1917.
28–6829
Library of Congress   DK254.R3T3 1925

NT 0051867   DLC WaSp ICU NIC CLU IaU

Taube, Otto, *Freiherr von*, 1879–   ed. and tr.
Russische Erzählungen. München, F. Ehrenwirth [Nach-wort 1946]
154 p. 21 cm.
Contents.—Melnikow, P. I. Die Fürstin Maria Petrowna.—Grigo-rowitsch, D. W. Eine Christnacht.—Melnikow, P. I. Die Fürstin Warwara Michailowna.—Melnikow, P. I. Das Bildnis des Gouver-neurs.—Ljesskow, N. S. Der Koliwansche Ehemann.

1. Short stories, Russian—Translations into German.   I. Title.
PG3288.T8   55–23383 ‡

NT 0051868   DLC WaU

Taube, Otto, Freiherr von, 1879–   ed. and tr.
Russische Erzählungen. München, F. Ehrenwirth [Nachwort 1946]
154 p. 21 cm.
Film reproduction. Negative. Original discarded.
Contents. - Melnikow, P. I. Die Fürstin Maria Petrowna. - Grigorowitsch, D. W. Eine Christnacht. - Melnikow, P. I. Die Fürstin Warwara Michailowna. - Melnikow, P. I. Das Bildnis des Gouverneurs. - Ljesskow, N. S. Der Koliwansche Ehemann.

1. Fiction, Russian - Translation into German - Collections.

NT 0051870   NN

Taube, Otto,   *freiherr von*, 1814–
Russische märchen, mit sieben steinzeichnungen von Charlotte Christine Engelhorn. viii, 116, [1] p. 7 pl. München, G. Müller, 1919.

NT 0051871   OCl InU IU NjP

Taube, Otto, Freiherr von, 1879–   , tr.
Der Sonnengesang des Heiligen Franziscus von Assisi
see under   Francesco d'Assisi,
Saint, 1182–1226.   (*Cantico de lo frate Sole*)

Taube, Otto, Freiherr von, 1879–
Verse. [Berlin, etc., C. Wigand, 1907]

111 p. 20.5 cm.

NT 0051873   MH

Taube, Otto, *Freiherr von*, 1879–
Vom Ufer, da wir abgestossen. [Leipzig] Insel-Verlag, 1947.
71 p. 19 cm.
Poems.

I. Title.
PT2642.A72V6   831.91   49–25150*

NT 0051874   DLC PU MH OKentU TNJ

Taube, Otto, *Freiherr von*, 1879–
Von den Zeichen der Zeit. München, C. Kaiser, 1947.
18 p. 19 cm. (Gottes Wort und Geschichte, 7)

1. End of the world. 2. Jews—Restoration.   I. Title.   (Series)
BT875.T297   236   48–26568*

NT 0051875   DLC DCU CtY NN

Taube, Otto, *Freiherr von*, 1879–
Wanderjahre; Erinnerungen aus meiner Jugendzeit. Stuttgart, K. F. Koehler [*1950]
343 p. 22 cm.

1. Authors—Correspondence, reminiscences, etc.
PT2642.A72Z54   51–36358

NT 0051876   DLC OrU MiU FTaSU OCl OU MH NN

PT 2642
A72
A6
1937
Taube, Otto, Freiherr von, 1879–
[Works. Selections. 1937]
Wanderlieder und andere Gedichte. Merseburg, F. Stollberg [1937]
77 p.
Author's author's autographed presentation copy.

NT 0051877   CaBVaU

Taube, Otto Freiherr von, 1879–
M1621
.4
.K
Kammeier, Hans, 1902–
Wanderschaft; Liederzyklus nach Gedichten von Otto von Taube für mittlere Stimme und Klavier. Kassel, Bären-reiter-Verlag [1947]

Taube, Otto, Freiherr von, 1879–
...Die Wassermusik; Erzahlungen.   Düsseldorf, A. Bagel [1948] 217 p. 21cm.

NT 0051879   NN

Dlv.S.
270.6
L973ZT
Taube, Otto, Freiherr von, 1879–
Wirkungen Luthers. Berlin, Eckart-Verlag, 1939.
51 p. 21 cm.

1. Luther, Martin. Influence. 2. Refor-mation. Germany.

NT 0051880   NcD MH-AH

Taube, Otto, Freiherr von, 1879–
Zur Frage deutscher Siedlung auf neuerworbenem Gebiete; die Brücke zu den baltischen Provinzen, von Otto Freiherr von Taube... Berlin-Charlottenburg: F. Lehmann Verlag, G.m.b.H. [1916?] 16 p. 8°.

1. Emigration and immigration, Ger-
provinces.
N. Y. P. L.
many. 2. Germans in Baltic
July 23, 1924

NT 0051881   NN

Taube, Paul, Medizinalprakt. a. Rohrsheim (Kr. Halberstadt):
Ein bemerkenswerter Fall von Tetanusinfektion bei der
O   Autopsie einer Tetanusleiche. Leipzig 1914: Peter.   19 S. 8°
Leipzig, Med. Diss. v. 12. März 1914, Ref. v. Strümpell
[Geb. 23. April 87 Nauendorf, Saalkreis; Wohnort: Halberstadt; Staatsangeh.: Preußen; Vorbildung: Latina Halle Reife 07; Studium: Halle Phil. 1, Med. 10 S.; Coll. 12. März 14.]   [U 14. 2371]

NT 0051882   ICRL DNLM CtY

Taube,   Signe Margareta (Wennerberg) 1856–
ed.
Wennerberg, Gunnar, 1817–1901.
... Bref och minnen, samlade och sammanbundna af Signe Taube, född Wennerberg ... Stockholm, H. Geber [1913–

Taube, Signe Margareta (Wennerberg), 1856–   , editor.
Prostinnan; brev och minnen av Gunnar Wennerbergs mo-der, samlade av Signe Taube, f. Wennerberg.   Stockholm: H. Gebers förlag [, 1928]. 206 p. front., illus. (incl. ports.)   8°.

1. Wennerberg, Sara (Klingstedt),   1786–1875. 2. Wennerberg, Gunnar,
N. Y. P. L.
1817–1901.
June 11, 1929

NT 0051884   NN

Taube, Sofiıa Ivanovna (Anichkova) *baronessa.*
... Загадка Ленина. (Изъ воспоминаній редактора) Прага, Изданіе Морского журнала [1935?]
223, [1] p. front. (ports.) illus. (facsims.)   21ᶜᵐ.
At head of title: С. Аничкова (баронесса Таубе)

Title transliterated: Zagadka Lenina.

1. Lenin, Vladimir Il'ich, 1870–1924.
Library of Congress   DK254.L4T3   37–85002

NT 0051885   DLC CaBVaU WU

Taube, Sofiıa Ivanovna (Anichkova), baronessa.
[Zapiski molodiashchełsia starukhı]
Записки молодящейся старухи. Парижъ, 1928.
125 p. 17 cm.
At head of title: С. Аничкова (баронесса Таубе).

I. Title.
PG3467.T3Z2   72–228133

NT 0051886   DLC CSt

PZ3
.T1913
Re
Taube, Suzanne, joint author.

Taube, Herman.
Remember, by Herman and Suzanne Taube. Translated from the Yiddish by Helena Frank; foreword by Henry Turk. Baltimore, N. A. Gossmann Pub. Co. 1951.

Taube, Suzanne.

די אומפֿארגעסלעכע (פֿארציכטנסען) אידיש: הערמאַן
טאָבע. באַלטימאָר, ששה טאובע בוך קאָמיטעט.
₍Baltimore₎ 1948.
142 p. port. 19 cm.
Added t. p.: Die umfargesleche (The unforgotten) Translation:
Herman Taube.
Short stories.

I. Title.   *Title transliterated:* Di umfargeslekhe.

PJ5129.T36U5   52–46059

NT 0051888   DLC MH

Taube, Theodor.
Lyrics of The queen of Brilliants
see under Jakobowski, Edward, 1858–

Taube, Theodor.
Miss Flora Welton. Posse mit Gesang in einem
Aufzuge. Wien, J. Klemm, 1876.
15 p.   8°.   (Wiener Theater-Repertoir.
Lieferung 309)

NT 0051890   NN

TAUBE, THEODOR.
Miss Flora Welton; Posse mit Gesang in einem
Aufzuge. Wien: J. Klemm, 1876. 15 p. 23cm.
(Wiener Theater-Repertoir. Lfg. 309.)

Film reproduction. Negative.
Without music.

I. Drama, German. I Title.

NT 0051891   NN

Taube, Walter: Die Naturphilosophie St. Martins. (Ein Beitr. z.
Religionsphilosophie u. z. Forschung des 'philosophe inconnu'.)
[Maschinenschrift.] 157 S. 4°. — Auszug: Breslau 1922: Schles.
Dr.-Genoss. 2 Bl. 8°
Breslau, Phil. Diss. v. 25. März 1922   [U 22. 1671

NT 0051892   ICRL

Taube (Walther) [1889–]. *Ueber den Einfluss der vollständigen Gaumenmandel-Entfer-
nung (Tonsillektomie) auf den Gelenkrheu-
matismus. 47 pp. 8°. Berlin, Lippert & Co.,
1915

NT 0051893   DNLM CtY

Taube, Werner.
Der lautenschüler; eine anweisung im melodiespiel auf der
laute oder gitarre; unter berücksichtigung des tonalen lehr-
ganges von Carl Eitz nach praktischen unterrichtsgrundsätzen
und -erfahrungen zusammengestellt von Werner Taube. Leipzig, C. Merseburger ₍1927₎
71 p. illus. (incl. music) diagrs. 28ᶜᵐ.
"Bücher, zeitschriften, usw.": p. 70–71.
1. Lute—Instruction and study. 2. Guitar—Instruction and study.
3. Lute music. 4. Guitar music.   I. Eitz, Carl Andreas, 1848–1924.
II. Title.
    31–16125
Library of Congress   MT640.T2
Copyright A—Foreign   11010

NT 0051894   DLC

Taube, Wilhelm, 1890–
... Ueber das Vorkommen von Streptothricheen
bei Lungengangrän und Pleuraempyemen...
Breslau, 1931.
Inaug.–diss. – Breslau.
Lebenslauf.
"Literatur"; p. 19.

NT 0051895   CtY

Taube (Woldemar). *Ueber hypochondrische
Verücktheit. 74 pp., 1l. 8°. *Dorpat, H. Laakmann, 1886.

NT 0051896   DNLM

Taube, Yelena Aleksandrovna (Keyserling), baronessa von,
1845–

...Am russischen Hof in den Jahren der deutscnen Reichs-
gründung; Tagebuch eines Hoffräuleins, hrsg. von Otto Freiherrn
von Taube. Berlin: Der Kentaur-Verlag ₍1921₎. v, 360 p.
front., plates, ports. 16°.

38616A. 1. Court life. Russia,   1870-71. 2. Taube von der Issen,
Otto, Freiherr von, editor.
N. Y. P. L.   May 9, 1922.

NT 0051897   NN MH ICU

BM
165
T3.6
    Taube, Zwi.
    Lebendiges Judentum. Das jüdischg
    Zentrum und seine Erneuerung. Genève,
    Editions Migdal, 1946.
    122 p.   21 cm.   (Collection Migdal,
    Nr.3)

    1. Judaism--History--Ancient period.
    I. Title   II. Series

NT 0051898   OCH

Taube af Odenkat, Carl Evert Bernhard,
friherre, 1834–1917, ed.
Hermelin, Samuel Gustaf, *friherre*, 1744–1820.
Berättelse om Nordamerikas Förenta Stater, 1784; bref till
kanslipresidenten, af friherre Sam. Gust. Hermelin. Stockholm, Kungl. boktryckeriet, P. A. Norstedt & söner, 1894.

4DK
Swed.-
24
    Taube af Odenkat, Carl Evert Bernhard,
    friherre, 1834–1917.
      Svenska beskickningars berättelser om
    främmande makter ar 1793. 1 Preussen - 2 Polen.
    Stockholm, P. A. Norstedt [1893]
    201 p.

NT 0051900   DLC-P4

TAUBE-HAMBURG, Max.

See TAUBE, Max, 1882–

Taube till Odenkat, Karl Evert Bernhard,
friherre, 1834–

see

Taube af Odenkat, Carl Evert Bernhard, friherre,
1834–1917.

Kress
Room
    [Taube von der Issen, Friedrich Wilhelm] 1744–
    1807
    Neuer entwurf eines credit-reglements für
    die güther-besitzer in Liefland ... Riga,
    Gedruckt von J.C.D. Müller, 1802.
    92, [3] p. forms (part fold.) 19 cm.

    1.Agricultural credit - Livonia. 2.Livonia.
    I.Title.

NT 0051903   MH-BA

Taube von der Issen, Otto, freiherr von
see Taube, Otto, freiherr von, 1879–

Die Taube; Ein kleiner bote für der Neuen kirche.
April 1859–1862. Baltimore, 1859–1862.
3 v. in 1.

NT 0051905   PBa

Un taube sur le seizième arrondissement de
Paris
see under [Riviere, Emil] 1835–1922.

Taubeles, Samuel Aron, 1862–
Saadia Goan... Halle a. S., Plötz'sche buch-
druckerei, 1888.
35 [1] p.   24 cm.   [Halle. Universität.
Dissertationen. v. 9, no. 14]
Inaug.-diss. - Halle.
Vita.
"Angabe der literatur über Saadia"; p. [5]-6.

NT 0051907   CU ICRL OCH

Taubeles, Samuel Aron, 1862–
Saadia Gaon, Monographie. Halle a. S., Ploetzsche
Buchdr., 1888.
35 p.   26 cm.
Issued also as dissertation, Halle.
Bibliography: p. ₍5₎–6.

1. Saadiah ben Joseph, gaon, 892?–942.

BM550.S32T3   1888   55–49349 ‡

NT 0051908   DLC PPDrop OCH NNU-W

W 4
M96
1950
    TAUBENBERGER, Alfred, 1901–
    Über Impfschäden im Impfbezirk der
    Bayerischen Landesimpfanstalt München
    von 1939-1948. München, 1950.
    27 ℓ.
    Inaug.-Diss. - Munich.
    1. Vaccination - Germany

NT 0051909   DNLM

Taubenberger, Friedrich, 1911–
Zur Kenntnis der 6-Amino-indoxazene und ihrer
Abkömmlinge... Gelnhausen, 1938.
Inaug.-diss. - Frankfurt am Main.

NT 0051910   CtY

W 4
M96
1953
    TAUBENBERGER, Peter, 1925–
    Beitrag zur quantitativen Bestimmung
    der Phagocytose-Fähigkeit des Blutes,
    insbesondere in Blutkonserven. München,
    1953.
    37 ℓ. illus.
    Inaug.-Diss. - Munich.
    1. Phagocytes & phagocytosis

NT 0051911   DNLM

SF
465
T22
    Das Taubenbuch. Eine Gemeinschaftsarbeit
    deutscher Taubenliebhaber für den Wieder-
    aufbau und zur weiteren Förderung der
    deutschen Taubenzucht. Frankfurt/Main,
    Neue Druck- und Verlags-GmbH. ₍1950₎
    231 p. illus. (part col.), port. 22 cm.

    1. Pigeons.

NT 0051912   NIC

G440
.T22
Taubeneck, George Francis, 1908–
   Around the world with a candid camera,
by George F. Taubeneck ...
[Detroit, Business news publishing co.,
c1937–
   v.   illus.   23½x33cm.

   1. Voyages around the world.   I. Title.

NT 0051913   DLC LU NN IU

Taubeneck, George Francis, 1908–
   Both feet on the ground; the specialty dealer. Detroit,
Conjure House [1950]
   638 p. 24 cm.

   1. Household appliances.   I. Title.

   HF6201.H8T3   658.89643   51–672

NT 0051914   DLC CaBVa NmLcU IU NN

HC
106.4
.T3
1944
Taubeneck, George Francis, 1908–
   Great day coming! Studies in reconversion
for distribution organizations. [2d ed.]
Detroit, Business News Pub. Co., 1944.
   408p. 23cm.

   "Technical bulletins giving data on freezing
preservation of food": p.407–408.

   1. U.S. Economic policy. 2. Home economics
Equipment and   supplies. 3. Reconstruction (1939–1951)   U.S. I. Title.

NT 0051915   OrU MiD LU

Taubeneck, George Francis, 1908–
   Great day coming! Studies in reconversion for distribution
organizations, by George F. Taubeneck. Detroit, Business
news publishing co., 1945.
   3 p. l., [3]–408 p. 23cm.
   "Third edition."
   "Technical bulletins giving data on freezing preservation of food":
p. 407–408.

   1. U. S.—Economic policy. 2. Domestic economy—Equipment and
supplies. 3. Reconstruction (1939–   )—U. S. I. Title.
                                                      45–4908
   Library of Congress   HC106.4.T3
                                                      338

NT 0051916   DLC OC1

Taubeneck, George Francis, 1908–
   It's a great life—(the specialty salesman) by George F.
Taubeneck. Detroit, Business news publishing co. [1946]
   1 p. l., 5–316, [4] p. 22cm.

   1. Salesmen and salesmanship.   I. Title.
                                                      46–5667
   Library of Congress   HF5438.T25
                                                      658.8

NT 0051917   DLC

Taubeneck, George Francis, 1908–
   It's a great life (the specialty salesman) Detroit, Conjure House [1949]
   320 p. 24 cm.

   1. Salesmen and salesmanship.   I. Title.

   HF5438.T25 1949   658.8   49–3662*

NT 0051918   DLC WaT CaBVa

Taubeneck, George Francis, 1908–
   Let's go to Australia! By George F. Taubeneck. [Detroit]
Conjure house [1946]
   5 p. l., [7]–301 p. 24cm.
   Map on lining-papers.

   1. Australia—Descr. & trav.   I. Title.
                                                      46–5058
   Library of Congress   DU104.T3
                                                      919.4

NT 0051919   DLC OC1 TxU CaBVa OrU WaT

Taubeneck, George Francis, 1908–
   The marshal's baton, the specialty sales manager. Detroit,
Conjure House, 1947.
   571 p. 24 cm.

   1. Salesmen and salesmanship. 2. Marketing. I. Title. II. Title:
Specialty sales manager.
   HF5438.T255   658.8   48–27209*

NT 0051920   DLC CaBVa IU

Taubeneck, George Francis, 1908–
   The marshal's baton, the specialty sales manager.
Detroit, Conjure House [1948]
   571 p.
       Rev ed.

NT 0051921   OC1 MiD

Taubeneck, George Francis, 1908–
   One foot in the door; all about specialty merchandising—
including the laughs! By George F. Taubeneck. Detroit,
Mich., Conjure house [1947]
   1 p. l., viii, 386 p. 23½cm.

   1. Advertising.   I. Title.
   HF5823.T19   658.8   47–19039

NT 0051922   DLC CaBVa Or FMU KU

658
.8
T22a
73–3264
1949
Taubeneck, George Francis, 1908–
   One foot in the door (the specialty
selling formula) [5th ed., rev.]
Detroit, Conjure House [1949]
   viii, 386 p. 24 cm.

   1. Advertising. I. Title
   II. Title: The specialty selling
formula.

NT 0051923   N MiDW FTaSU NcC NN ViU

Taubeneck, George Francis, 1908–
   Peace and progress; how to be happy despite the politicians, by George F. Taubeneck plus George Washington [and
others] Illustrated by William A. Bostick. Detroit, Conjure House [1952]
   163 p. illus. 25 cm.

   1. U. S.—Civilization—Addresses, essays, lectures.   I. Title.
   E169.1.T28   917.3   52–2327 ‡

NT 0051924   DLC MB PU PV NN

TP490
.R25
Taubeneck, George Francis, 1908–   ed.
   Refrigerated food news ... v. 2–4, no. 4; Sept. 1, 1941–Dec.
1, 1933. Detroit, Mich. [Business news publishing co.] 1931–
33.

Taubeneck, George Francis, 1908–
   Their heads shall rise again; around the world with a candid
camera just before world war II was unleashed, by George F.
Taubeneck. Detroit, Business news publishing co. [1942?]
   190 p., 1 l. illus. 22 x 33cm.
   Maps on p. [2] and [3] of cover.

   1. Voyages and travels.   I. Title.
                                                      44–50692
   Library of Congress   G463.T28
                                                      910.4

NT 0051926   DLC DNAL NN OC1

Taubeneck, George Francis, 1908–
   They didn't know they wanted it; how John H. Patterson
developed the specialty selling formula, by George F. Taubeneck. Detroit, Mich., Business news publishing co. [1937]
   222 p. 22cm.
   "Limited edition."
   "A large portion of this book was originally published ... in the weekly
issues of Electric refrigeration news, now Air conditioning and refrigeration news, in the issues from July 17, 1935 through October 2, 1935."

   1. Patterson, John Henry, 1844–1922. 2. National cash register com-
pany, Dayton, O. 3. Salesmen and salesmanship.   I. Title.
                                                      37–25326
   Library of Congress   HF5531.N35T3
   ———— Copy 2.
   Copyright A 109909   658.8

NT 0051927   DLC

Taubeneck, George Francis, 1908–
   You'll love this one ... Detroit [c1949]

NT 0051928   WU

4PN–
5010
Taubeneck, George Francis, 1908–
   You'll love this one; anecdotes... Detroit,
Conjure House [1949]
   232 p.

NT 0051929   DLC-P4 MiD

Taubeneck, H   E.
   The condition of the American farmer. By H. E. Taubeneck. Chicago, The Schulte publishing co. [*1896]
   63 p. 20cm. (On cover: Ariel library series, no. 8)

   1. Agriculture—U. S.
                                                      8–1730†
   Library of Congress   HD1765 1896

NT 0051930   DLC GU CtU ICJ NN

Spec.
WJK
2
Taubeneck, H   E
   The philosophy of political parties; [the
conditions and elements required for the success of a new party] by H.E. Taubeneck. Chicago, Schulte Pub. Co. [c1896]
   12 p. 19.4 cm.
   "... the substance of a casual address delivered before the Illinois People's Party
State Central Committee ... early in 1896 ..."
   1. Political parties – United States.
   2. People's Party. I. Title.

NT 0051931   CtU

Taubeneck, Otto Clarke.
   Legal opinions of the non-high school district law of Illinois [by] O. Clarke Taubeneck ... Bloomington, Ill., Public
school publishing company [*1931]
   2 p. l., 84 p. diagrs. 19½cm.

   1. Educational law and legislation—Illinois. 2. High schools—Illi-
nois. 3. Education—Illinois—Finance.   I. Illinois. Laws, statutes.
etc. II. Title.
                                                      31–20900
   Library of Congress   LB2529.I 45T3
   ———— Copy 2.
   Copyright A 40500   [5]   373.773

NT 0051932   DLC NcD DHEW

616.01   Taubeneck, Udo.
T22b   Die Bakterien. 2. Aufl. Wittenberg, A.
1954   Ziemsen, 1954.

    34 p. illus. 22 cm. (Die neue Brehm-
Bücherei, Heft 66)

NT   0051933   KMK MtU

Taubenest, Jakob Ernst, respondent.
... De compensationibus...
    see under   Cosel, Heinrich, d. 1657, praeses

Taubenfliegel, A
    see his later name Avital, A

Taubenfurt, Johann, *freiherr* Tauber von
    see
Tauber von Taubenfurt, Johann, *freiherr*, b. 1736.

Taubenhaus, Ephraim, 1908–   *ed.*
בית הלל; מנש ליובלו השבעים של הרב הגאון הלל פוסק.
תולדותיו. ברכות ומאמרי הערכה. דברי תורה וחכמת ישראל.
,Tel-Aviv, 1951, תשי״א.

    174 p. ports. 25 cm.

    1. Posek, Hillel. 2. Rabbinical literature (Collections)   I. Title.
Title transliterated: Bet Hilel.

BM496.A1T3   58–54116

NT   0051937   DLC

Taubenhaus, Ephraim, 1908–
,Tel-Aviv, 1955, רש״י, חייו ופעלו. תל-אביב, הוצאת ״סיני״.

    106, ,1, p. 24 cm.

    Selected bibliography: p. ,107,

    1. Solomon ben Isaac, called RaSHI, 1040–1105.
Title transliterated: RaSHI.

BM755.S6T3   56–55616

NT   0051938   DLC

PN   Taubenhaus, Ephraim, 1908–
3324   Saharurim niznuzeh machashowoh. Tel
T22   Aviv, Goel, 1949.
    95 p. 18cm.

    Text in Hebrew.
    Translation of title: Sparks of thought.

NT   0051939   NIC

BS1476   Taubenhaus, Ephraim, 1908–
T3   Some chapters and aphorisms from the book
    "Zahrurim". Translated from the Hebrew by
    I.M. Lask. ,n.p.,n.pub.,n.d.,
    24p. 21x16cm.

    Cover title.

    1. Bible. O.T. Ecclesiastes. Commentaries.
I. Lask, Israel Meir, 1905–   tr.

NT   0051940   IaU

PN   Taubenhaus, Ephraim, 1908–
3324   Some chapters and aphorisms from the
T22B5   book "Zaharurim". Translated from the
    Hebrew by I. M. Lask. ,n.p., 1950?,
    24 l. 16 x 21cm.

    Reproduced from typewritten copy.

    I. Lask,.I.M., tr. II. Title.

NT   0051941   NIC

Taubenhaus, Ephraim, 1908–
זהרורים. נצוצי מחשבה. מהדורה ב. תל-אביב. הוצאת ״גויל.״
,Tel-Aviv, 1949/50, תש״י.

    95 p. 17 cm.
    Essays.

    1. Hebrew literature—Addresses, essays, lectures.   I. Title.
Title transliterated: Zaharurim.

PJ5009.T3   1949   55–52694 ‡

NT   0051942   DLC NN IaU UU

Taubenhaus, Godfrey.
    Echoes of wisdom; or, Talmudic sayings with classic, espe-
cially Latin, parallelisms, by G. Taubenhaus ... Brooklyn,
Haedrich & sons' print ,°1900,

    2 p. L, 106 p., 1 l. 17½ᶜᵐ.

    Talmudic sayings in English and Hebrew.
    "The present volume, comprising Talmudic sayings beginning with
'Aleph', is the first of a proposed series to come forth in alphabetical
order, and on the same plan."—Pref.
    No more published?

    I. Talmud. Selections. English. II. Title.
                               9–2781 Revised

    Library of Congress   BM502.T3
                         ,r39b2,   296

NT   0051943   DLC MCE OCH OCU

Taubenhaus, Godfrey, ed.
BM500
.R6   **Talmud.** *English.*
    New edition of the Babylonian Talmud, English translation.
Original text edited, formulated, and punctuated by Michael
L. Rodkinson ... New York, New Amsterdam book company
,°1896–°1903,

Taubenhaus, Godfrey.
    The strength of faith... By G. Taubenhaus... ,New
York, cop. 1918.,   4 p.l., (1)8–90 p., 2 l.   16°.

    Contents: Preface. Poems. Consolatories. Dedication. Rabbinics. Eve-
ning service. Prayer at the grave. A letter to the reader.

    1. Affliction.—Comfort in. 2. Title.
N. Y. P. L.   September 12, 1918.

NT   0051945   NN OCH

Taubenhaus, Haim, 1882–
    Die ammoneen der kreideformation Palästinas und
Syriens ... Breslau, Buchdruckerei H. Fleischmann,
1919.

    cover-title, ,2, 58 p. fold. tables. 22ᶜᵐ.

    Inaug.-diss.—Breslau, 1918.
    Bibliography: p. 55–58.
    Lebenslauf.

    1. Ammonites.   I. Title.
                                 G S 21–138

    Library, U. S. Geological   Survey   659(680) T19

NT   0051946   DI-GS CtY ICRL

Taubennaus, Jacob Joseph, 1885–
    The black rots of the sweet potato. Paper read before the
American Phytopathological Society at the Cleveland meeting,
January 3, 1913. n.t.-p.   n. p., 1913.   159-166 p., 3 pl.   4°.

    Repr.: Phytopathology. v. 3, no. 3.

    1. Potato (Sweet).—Diseases. 2.   Black rot.
N. Y. P. L.   June 6, 1914.

NT   0051947   NN

SB732
.T3   Taubennaus, Jacob Joseph, 1885–
    ,Collected papers, reprints, etc., in plant
pathology.
    v.s. v. p.v.d.v.s.

NT   0051948   DLC

Taubennaus, Jacob Joseph, 1885–
    A contribution to our knowledge of silver scurf (spondylo-
cladium atrovirens Härz) of the white potato, ,by, J. J. Taubenhaus... ,New York, 1916.,   p. 549–560, 3 pl.   4°.

    Caption-title.
    Repr.: New York Botanical Garden. Mem. v. 6.

    1. Potato.—Diseases.
N. Y. P. L.   January 11, 1919.

NT   0051949   NN

Taubennaus, Jacob Joseph, 1885–
    A contribution to our knowledge of the morphology and life
history of Puccinia malvacearum Mont. Presented before the
Boston meeting of the American Phytopathological Society,
December, 1909. n. t.-p.   n. p. ,1911.,   55–62 p.   8°.

    Repr.: Phytopathology. v. 1, no. 2.

    1. Fungi.
N. Y. P. L.   August 19, 1912.

NT   0051950   NN

Taubenhaus, Jacob Joseph, 1885–   joint author.

    Ezekiel, Walter Naphtali, 1901–
    Cotton crop losses from *Phymatotrichum* root rot. By
Walter N. Ezekiel ... and J.J. Taubenhaus ...
    (*In* U. S. Dept. of agriculture. Journal of agricultural research.
v. 49, no. 9, Nov. 1, 1934, p. 843–858. map, diagrs. 23ᶜᵐ. Washington,
1934)

Taubenhaus, Jacob Joseph, 1885–
    The culture and diseases of the onion, by J. J. Tauben-
haus ... and Fred W. Mally ... New York, E. P. Dutton
& company ,°1924,

    xv, 246 p. plates. 21½ᶜᵐ.

    "References" at end of some of the chapters.

    1. Onions. 2. Onions—Diseases and pests.   I. Mally, Frederick Wil-
liam, 1868–   joint author. II. Title.

    Library of Congress   SB341.T3   24–16326

NT   0051952   DLC NcD MBH MtBC CaBVaU OU CU ICJ NN

Taubenhaus, Jacob Joseph, 1885–
    The culture and diseases of the sweet pea, by J. J. Tau-
benhaus ... New York, E. P. Dutton & company ,°1917,

    xx p., 2 l., 232 p. incl. front., illus. plates. 20½ᶜᵐ.

    1. Sweet peas. 2. Sweet peas—Diseases and pests.

    Library of Congress   SB413.S9T2   17–16080

        TxU NcRS ICJ NN MB CaBVaU WaS WaSP MtBC
NT   0051953   DLC CU PU-BZ PPHor MH MBH OCl OU NNBG

Taubenhaus, Jacob Joseph, 1885–
The culture and diseases of the sweet potato, by J. J. Taubenhaus ... New York, E. P. Dutton & company ₁1923₎

xv p., 2 l., 3–286 p. plates. 21ᶜᵐ.
Bibliography: p. 274–281.

1. Sweet potatoes. 2. Sweet potatoes—Diseases and pests.

Library of Congress   SB211.S9T2   23–9658

     ICJ MB
NT 0051954   DLC PU–BZ WaWW CaBVaU OCU OU TU CU NNBG

Taubenhaus, Jacob Joseph, *1885–*   *7995.39.No.261
Diseases of grains, sorghums, and millet, and their control in Texas. [By J. J. Taubenhaus.]
College Station, Texas. 1920. Illus. Plates. Maps. Tables. [Texas. Agricultural and Mechanical College. Agricultural Experiment Station. Bulletin No. 261.] 22½ cm.
Contributed by the Division of Plant Pathology and Physiology.

D6208 — S.r.c. — Texas. Agric — Grain. Diseases.

NT 0051955   MB

Taubenhaus, Jacob Joseph, 1885–
Diseases of greenhouse crops and their control, by J. J. Taubenhaus ... New York, E. P. Dutton & company ₁1920₎

xv, 429 p. plates, diagr. 21ᶜᵐ.

1. Vegetables—Diseases and pests. 2. Botany—Pathology. ɪ. Title.
ɪɪ. Title: Greenhouse crops, Diseases of.

     20—13540
Library of Congress   SB731.T3

     PAmC CU NcU NbU CaBVaU Or IdU MtBC
NT 0051956   DLC ICU MBH OC1 Okak OU NcD PU–BZ PPHor

Taubenhaus, Jacob Joseph, 1885–   VPG
The diseases of the sweet pea. Newark ₁1914₎   1 p.l.,
93 p., 1 table. illus. 8°. (Delaware. Agricultural Experiment Station. Bull. 106.)
————— A second copy.
In: VQE p. v. 13, no. 5.

1. Sweet pea.—Diseases, etc.
N. Y. P. L.   July 5, 1916

NT 0051957   NN

Taubenhaus, Jacob Joseph, 1885–
The diseases of the sweet pea ... ₁by₎ J. J. Taubenhaus. Philadelphia, 1914.

2 p. l., 93 p. illus., tables (1 fold.) 22ᶜᵐ.
Thesis (ᴘʜ. ᴅ.)—University of Pennsylvania, 1913.
Published also as Delaware college agricultural station bulletin no. 106, November, 1914.
"References": p. 88–93.

1. Sweet peas—Diseases and pests.

Library of Congress   SB608.S95T3   15–4132
Univ. of Pennsylvania   Libr.

NT 0051958   PU CtY. Or MiU OU DLC NIC NNBG

Taubenhaus, Jacob Joseph, 1885–
The diseases of the sweet potato and their control, by J. J. Taubenhaus — Thomas F. Manns. Newark, Del., 1915. 55 p., 13 pl. 8°. (Delaware. Agricultural Experiment Station. Bull. no. 109.)
Bibliography, p. 48–51.

1. Potato (Sweet).—Diseases, etc.   2. Manns, Thomas Franklin, 1876–
       ᴊᴛ. ᴀᴜ. 3. Series.
N. Y. P. L.   May 4, 1917

NT 0051959   NN MBH

Taubenhaus, Jacob Joseph, 1885–
Diseases of truck crops and their control, by J. J. Taubenhaus ... New York, E. P. Dutton & company ₁1918₎

xxxi, 396 p. plates. 21ᶜᵐ.

1. Vegetables—Diseases and pests. ɪ. Title.

Library of Congress   SB608.T8T3   18—13011

     MtBC
     MBH OCU OC1W OU OOxM TU NbU ICJ NN MB Or CaBViP
NT 0051960   DLC DNLM IdU WaS CU NcD NcU PU–BZ PP

Taubenhaus, Jacob Joseph, 1885–
A further study of some gloeosporiums and their relation to a sweet pea disease. Newark, Delaware: Delaware College Agricultural Experiment Station, 1912. 153–160 p., 1 pl. 8°.
Repr.: Phytopathology. v. 2, no. 4.

1. Pea.—Diseases, &c.
N. Y. P. L.   January 14, 1913.

NT 0051961   NN

M86:632   Taubenhaus, Jacob Joseph, 1885–
T222in   The influence of moisture and temperature on cotton root rot, by J. J. Taubenhaus and B. F. Dana. College Station, Tex., 1928.
     23. p. tables. 23 cm. (Texas. Agricultural Experiment Station, College Station. Bulletin no. 386)
     1. Cotton root rot. 2. Bioclimatology.
I. t. II. Dana, B. F., joint author. ser.

NT 0051962   DAS

TAUBENHAUS, Jacob Joseph, *1885–*
[Papers reprinted from scientific journals].

NT 0051963   MH

Taubenhaus, Jacob Joseph, 1885–
Pox, or pit (soil rot), of the sweet potato.
(*In* U. S. Dept. of agriculture. Journal of agricultural research. vol. XIII, no. 9, p. 437–450. pl. 51–52 on 1 l. 26ᶜᵐ. Washington, 1918)
Contribution from Texas agricultural experiment station (Tex.—1)
"Literature cited": p. 449–450.

1. ₁Cytospora batata₎ 2. Sweet potatoes—Diseases and pests. ₁2. Sweet potato—Diseases₎ ɪ. Title.

     Agr 18–542
Library, U. S. Dept. of   Agriculture 1Ag84J vol. 13

NT 0051964   DNAL

Taubennaus, Jacob Joseph, 1885–
The problem of plant diseases which confronts the gardener, by J. J. Taubenhaus... ₁Jersey City. 1912.₎   301–304 p. illus. f°.
Caption-title.
Repr.: The gardeners' chronicle of America.
"Read before the convention of the National Association of Gardeners, at Newark, N. J., Nov. 19, 1912."

1. Plants.—Diseases, etc.
N. Y. P. L.   October 16, 1915.

NT 0051965   NN

Taubenhaus, Jacob Joseph, 1885–
A rating of plants with reference to their relative resistance or susceptibility to phymatotrichum root rot ... J.J. Taubenhaus & W.N. Ezekiel.
     52 p. (Texas. Agricultural experiment station (College station) Bul. no. 527)

NT 0051966   PP

Taubenhaus, Jacob Joseph, 1885–
Recent studies of some new or little known diseases of the sweet potato, ₁by₎ J. J. Taubenhaus. Atlanta, 1914. 305–320 p., 3 pl. 8°.
Caption title.
Repr.: Phytopathology, v. 4, no. 4. Aug. 1914.

1. Potato (Sweet).—Diseases.
N. Y. P. L.   September 9, 1915.

NT 0051967   NN

Taubenhaus, Jacob Joseph, 1885–
Recent studies on *Sclerotium rolfsii* Sacc.
(*In* U. S. Dept. of agriculture. Journal of agricultural research. vol. XVIII, no. 3, p. 127–138. illus., pl. 3–6 on 2 l. 26ᶜᵐ. Washington, 1919)
Contribution from Texas agricultural experiment station (Tex.—4)
"Literature cited": p. 137–138.

1. Sclerotium rolfsii.

     Agr 19–1046 Revised
Library, U. S. Dept. of   Agriculture 1Ag84J vol.18

NT 0051968   DNAL

Taubenhaus, Jacob Joseph, 1885–
The relation of parasitic fungi to the contents of the cells of the host plants
see under   Cook, Melville Thurston.

Taubenhaus, Jacob Joseph, 1885–
Role of insects in the distribution of cotton wilt caused by *Fusarium vasinfectum.* By J. J. Taubenhaus ... and L. Dean Christenson ...
(*In* U. S. Dept. of agriculture. Journal of agricultural research. v. 53, no. 9, Nov. 1, 1936, p. 703–712. illus. 23½ᶜᵐ. Washington, 1936)
Contribution from Texas Agricultural experiment station (Tex.—15)
Contribution no. 291, Technical series, Texas Agricultural experiment station.
Published Jan. 21, 1937.
1. Cotton—Diseases and pests. ₁1. Cotton wilt₎ 2. Fusarium vasinfectum. 3. Insects, Injurious and beneficial. ₁3. Insects and plant diseases₎; ɪ. Christenson, Leroy Dean, 1906–   joint author.

     Agr 37–85
U. S. Dept. of agr. Library   1Ag84J vol. 53, no. 9
for Library of Congress   [S21.A75 vol. 53, no. 9]

NT 0051970   DNAL

Taubenhaus, Jacob Joseph, 1885–
Soilstain, or scurf, of the sweet potato.
(*In* U. S. Dept. of agriculture. Journal of agricultural research. vol. V, no. 21, p. 995–1002. pl. LXXVI–LXXVII on 1 l. 26ᶜᵐ. Washington, 1916)
"Literature cited": p. 1001.
Contribution from the Delaware agricultural experiment station.

1. Sweet potatoes—Diseases and pests. ₁1. Sweet potato—Diseases₎ ɪ. Title.

     Agr 16–321
Library, U. S. Dept. of   Agriculture 1Ag84J vol. 5

NT 0051971   DNAL NN

Taubenhaus, Jacob Joseph, 1885–
Sweet pea diseases and their control. By J. J. Taubenhaus... ₁Boston, 1916.₎   p. 131–143. 8°.
Caption-title.
"The John Lewis Russell lecture."
Repr.: Mass. Horticultural Soc. Transac. 1916, part 1.

1. Sweet pea.—Diseases.
N. Y. P. L.   January 11, 1919.

NT 0051972   NN MBH

Taubenhaus, Jacob Joseph, *1885–*   *7995.39.No.260
Wilts of the watermelon and related crops (Fusarium wilts of cucurbits). [By J. J. Taubenhaus.]
College Station, Texas. 1920. 50 pp. Illus. Plates. Charts. Tables. [Texas. Agricultural and Mechanical College. Agricultural Experiment Station. Bulletin no. 260.] 22½ cm.
Bibliography, pp. 49–50.
Contributed by the Division of Plant Pathology and Physiology.

D6201 — S.r.c. — Cucurbitaceae. — Fusarium.

NT 0051973   MB

TAUBENHAUS, JEAN.
Traité du jeu des échecs; enseignement des débuts, étude des fins de parties, méthode claire et facile à l'usage de tous les amateurs. Paris, Société générale d'impression, 1910. 223 p. illus. 25cm.

1. Chess, 1910.

NT 0051974   NN NjP MH OC1

Taubenheim, Bernd, 1906-
Über die Behandlung von Tetanien mit A.T. 10 (Holtz) beobachtet an Füllen im Stadtkrankenhaus Meissen und in der Charité Berlin... Leipzig, 1937.
Inaug.-diss. - Leipzig.
Lebenslauf.

NT 0051975   CtY

JX2323   Taubenheim, Christoph a, respondent.
.L8   Ludewig, Johann Peter von, 1668-1743, *praeses.*
Thema inavgvrale de ivris gentivm laesione, vom verletztem völcker-recht ... Halae Venedorvm, typis Ioan. Henrici Grvnerti ₁1741₎

Taubenheim, Jahn Wilhelm von.
...Dvobvs civilis vitae directoribvs, virtvte et prvdentia
see under Bose, Johann Andreas, 1626-1674, praeses.

Das Taubenpaar. Ein Wahrheits-Gedicht
see under [Schmidt, Wilhelm Gottfried]

Taubenreuther, Artur, 1912-
Die embolektomie als behandlungsmethode der peripheren arteriellen embolie. ... Würzburg, 19-? 29 p.
Inaug. Diss. - Würzburg, n.d.
Lebenslauf.
Literaturverzeichnis.

NT 0051979   DNLM

Taubenschlag, Rafał, 1881-1952.
... Formularze czynności prawno-prywatnych w Polsce XII i XIII wieku, napisał Rafał Taubenschlag. We Lwowie, Nakł. Towarzystwa naukowego, 1930.
2 p. l., ₃3₎-60 p. 23½ᶜᵐ. (Studya nad historyą prawa polskiego wydawane pod redakcyą Oswalda Balzera. t. XII.-zesz. 3)
"Z zasiłkiem Ministerstwa wyz. rel. i ośw. publ."
Bibliographical foot-notes.

1. Forms (Law)—Poland. 2. Civil law—Poland—Hist. 3. Comparative law. I. Towarzystwo naukowe we Lwowie. II. Title.

Library of Congress   37-30052

NT 0052001   DLC NN IU NNC-L ICU

AS
262
.X895
v.68
no.3
Taubenschlag,Rafał,1881-1958.
Geneza pozwu pisemnego w średniowiecznym procesie polskim. W Krakowie, Nakł.Polskiej Akademji Umiejętności; skł.główny w księg.Gebethnera i Wolffa, 1931.
12 p. (Polska Akademja Umiejętności. Rozprawy Wydziału Historyczno-Filozoficznego. Ser. II,t.43 (Ogólnego zbioru t.68) nr.3)
Bibliographical footnotes.

1.Procedure (Law)—Poland. I.Title.

NT 0052002   MiU MH-L

TAUBENSCHLAG, RAFAŁ, 1881-
Geschichte der Rezeption des römischen Privatrechts in Aegypten.
Estr. dagli Studi in onore di P. Bonfante, Pavia, Fusi, 1929, v.1, p.₍368₎-440.

NT 0052003   DDO

Taubenschlag, Rafał, 1881-
Historia i instytucje rzymskiego prawa prywatnego. Wyd. 3. ₍bez żadnych zmian₎ Warszawa, Gebethner i Wolff, 1945.
240 p. 21 cm.
At head of title: Rafał Taubenschlag ₍i₎ Włodzimierz Kozubski.

1. Roman law—Hist. I. Kozubski, Włodzimierz.

51-21555

NT 0052004   DLC NNC MB

Taubenschlag, Rafał, 1881-
... Historia i instytucje rzymskiego prawa prywatnego. Wyd. 4. Warszawa, Gebethner i Wolff, ₍1947₎
366 p. 20½cm.
At head of title: dr Rafał Taubenschlag ... ₍i₎ dr Włodzimierz Kozubski
...
Bibliographical footnotes.

NT 0052005   MH-L InU

Taubenschlag, Rafał, 1881-
The interpreters in the papyri. Varsaviae, 1951.
₍361₎-363 p.
Cover-title.
"Seorsum expressum e libro q. 1. Charisteria Thaddaeo Sinko quinquaginta abhinc annos amplis simis in philosophia honoribus ornato ab amicis collegis discipulis oblata."

NT 0052006   NNC

Taubenschlag, Rafał, 1881-
The law of Greco-Roman Egypt in the light of the papyri, 332 B.C.-640 A.D. New York, Herald Square Press, 1944-48.
2 v. 25 cm.
Vol. 2, issued as Eus supplementa, v. 19, has also special title: Political and administrative law; with imprint: Warsaw, Polish Philological Society.
Bibliographical footnotes.

1. Law—Egypt, Ancient. (Series: Eus supplementa, v. 19)

44-24363 rev*

ICU OrU-L CU-I OrPR OrU CaBVaU MtU OrU-L PPT PSt PHC DDO OCU OO OU OClW ODW GU ICU NIC ICU
NT 0052007   DLC ScU ViU-L ViU CU PU NBuU-L NNR NcD

K342.32
T22l
1948
Taubenschlag, Rafał, 1881-
The law of Greco-Roman Egypt in the light of the papyri, 332 B.C.-640 A.D. Warsaw, Polish Philological Society, 1948-
v. 26cm. (Eus supplementa, v.19)
"Tables of sources": p.₍106₎-117.
Contents:-
v.2. Political and administrative law.

NT 0052008   IaU NNJ

Taubenschlag, Rafał, 1881-
The law of Greco-Roman Egypt in the light of the papyri, 332 B.C.-640 A.D. 2d ed., rev. and enl. Warszawa, Państwowe Wydawnictwo Naukowe, 1955.
xv, 789 p. 25 cm.
"Tables of sources": p. 693-757. Bibliographical footnotes.

1. Law—Egypt, Ancient.

56—22920

MsU CtY-D CU-S
CU CtY-L CU ICU RPB OCU CLU NcU CaQMM NjPT CaBVaU
NT 0052009   DLC DDO FTaSU ViU GU PPiU TxU CtY MH NN

Taubenschlag, Rafał.
... Prawo karne polskiego średniowiecza, napisał Rafał Taubenschlag. We Lwowie, Nakł. Towarzystwa naukowego, 1934.
2 p. l., ₍3₎-95, ₍1₎ p. 23ᶜᵐ. (Studja nad historją prawa polskiego im. Oswalda Balzera. t. XIV-zesz. 3)
Bibliographical foot-notes.

1. Criminal law—Poland—Hist. I. Towarzystwo naukowe we Lwowie. II. Title.

38-35926

NT 0052010   DLC CSt NN

AS
262
.X895
v.68
no.4
Taubenschlag,Rafał,1881-1958.
Odpowiedzialność za wady prawne przy pozbyciu własności w średniowiecznem prawie polskiem. W Krakowie, Nakł.Polskiej Akademji Umiejętności; skł.główny w księg.Gebethnera i Wolffa, 1931.
13 p. (Polska Akademja Umiejętności. Rozprawy Wydziału Historyczno-Filozoficznego. Ser.II, t.43 (Ogólnego zbioru t.68) nr.4)
Bibliographical footnotes.

1.Real property—Poland. 2.Law—Poland—Hist. & crit. I.Title.

NT 0052011   MiU MH-L

Taubenschlag, Rafał, 1881-1958.
... Prawo rzymskie w epoce Dioklecjańskiej. (Das römische recht zur zeit Diokletian's)
(*In* Bulletin international de l'Académie polonaise des sciences et des lettres. Classe de philologie. Classe d'histoire et de philosophie. Cracovie, Imprimerie de l'Université, 1922-1924. 26½ᶜᵐ. p. (141)-281)
Detached copy.
At head of title: Résumés.
Text in German.
Bibliographical foot-notes.

1. Roman law.

NT 0052012   MiU

Taubenschlag, Rafał, 1881-1958.
... Proces polski XIII i XIV wieku do Statutów Kazimierza Wielkiego, napisał Rafał Taubenschlag. We Lwowie, Nakładem Towarzystwa naukowego z zasiłkiem Ministerstwa wyz. rel. i ośw. publ., 1927.
2 p. l., ₍3₎-105 p. 23½ cm. (Studya nad historyą prawa polskiego ... t. x.—zeszyt 3)

1. Civil procedure — Poland. 2. Criminal procedure — Poland. 3. Law—Poland—Hist. & crit. ₍3₎. History of law—Poland₎ I. Title.

30—12899

NT 0052013   DLC CSt WaU ICU CtY OU NN IU

Taubenschlag, Rafał, 1881-
Rzymskie prawo prywatne. ₍Wyd. 1.₎ Warszawa, Państwowe Wydawn. Naukowe, 1955.
327 p. 25 cm.

1. Roman law. I. Title.

56—44374 ‡

NT 0052014   DLC NNC

Taubenschlag, Rafał, 1881–
   Rzymskie prawo prywatne na tle praw antycznych. ₍Wyd. 1.₎ Warszawa, Państwowe Wydawn. Naukowe, 1955.

   363 p. 25 cm.

   Includes bibliographies.

   1. Roman law.   I. Title.

                          56–42372

NT 0052015   DLC MH-L NN MiU CtY-L

AS
262
.Ł895
v.63
no.3

Taubenschlag, Rafał, 1881–1958.
   Spólnoty gminne w zromanizowanych prowincjach rzymskiego Wschodu. Kraków, Nakł.Polskiej Akademji Umiejętności; skł.główny w księg.G.Gebethnera i Ski, 1921.

   15 p.   (Polska Akademja Umiejętności. Wydział Historyczno-Filozoficzny. Rozprawy. Ser.II,t.38 (Ogólnego zbioru t.63) nr.3)
   Bibliographical footnotes.

   1.Community property (Roman law) I.Title.

NT 0052016   MiU

Taubenschlag, Rafał, 1881–1958.
   Das strafrecht im rechte der papyri, von dr. Rafael Taubenschlag ... Leipzig und Berlin. B. G. Teubner, 1916.

   x, 131, ₍1₎ p. 25ᶜᵐ.

   "Diese arbeit wurde in der sitzung der Krakauer akademie der wissenschaften am 17. november 1913 gelesen."
   "Wörterverzeichnis": p. ₍126₎–127.

   1. Criminal law—Greece. 2. Manuscripts, Greek (Papyri)   I. Title.

                          32–12994

NT 0052017   DLC MH-L IU ICU MiU CtY NjP

349.3776 **Taubenschlag, Rafał,** 1881–1958.
T19v   Vormundschaftsrechtliche studien; beiträge zur geschichte des römischen und griechischen vormundschaftsrechts Berlin, 1913.
   88p.

    Bibliographical foot-notes.

NT 0052018   IU MH-L NjP PU

Taubenschlag, Rafał, 1881–1958.
   Vormundschaftrechtliche studien; beiträge zur geschichte des römischen und griechischen vormundschaftsrechts. Von dr. Rafael Taubenschlag. Leipzig ₍etc.₎ B. G. Teubner, 1913.

   1 p. l., 88 p. 24ᶜᵐ.

   "Diese studien wurden in der sitzung der Krakauer akademie der wissenschaften vom 17. juni 1912 gelesen."

   1. Guardian and ward (Roman law) 2. Guardian and ward (Byzantine law)   I. Title.

                          33–13914

NT 0052019   DLC

Taubenschlag, Rafał, 1881–1958.
   ... Wpływy rzymsko-bizantyńskie w drugim Statucie litewskim, napisał Rafał Taubenschlag. We Lwowie, Nakł. Towarzystwa naukowego, 1933.

   2 p. l., ₍3₎–36 p. 23½ᶜᵐ. (Studja nad historją prawa polskiego im. Oswalda Balzera. t. xiv.-zesz. 2)

   "Z zasiłkiem Ministerstwa wyzn. rel. i oświ. publ."

   1. Law—Lithuania—Hist. & crit. 2. Roman law. 3. Law, Byzantine. I. Towarzystwo naukowe we Lwowie. II. Title.

                     40–25634 Revised

NT 0052020   DLC CSt CoU DDO NN

Taubenschlag, Rafał, 1881–1958.
   ... Wybór źródeł do rzymskiego prawa prywatnego dla użytku semnaryjnego. Warszawa, Nakład Gebethnera i Wolffa ₍1947₎

   98 p. 21ᶜᵐ.

   At head of title: Rafał Taubenschlag
   ... Włodzimierz Kozubski ...

NT 0052021   MiU-L MH-L

Ein taubenschlag
    see under   ₍Essig, Hermann₎ 1878–1918.

Taubensperg, Josephus Sabiz de
   see   Sabiz de Taubensperg, Josephus.

447.28
T19   **Die Taubenwelt.**

   Berlin.

   1. Pigeons. Periodicals.

NT 0052024   DNAL

JN6598
.K58
A6845

Tauber, A., ed.
   Kommunisticheskaĭa partiĭa Sovetskogo soĭuza.
   Всесоюзная Коммунистическая партия (большевиков) о социальном страховании; сборник документов. Подготовил к изданию А. Таубер и И. Ахматовский. Москва, Профиздат, 1940.

Tauber, Aaron, d. 1846.
   יד אהרן. ח״י דרשות מיוסדים על אדני המחקר וכבלת חז״ל הטדרים לפי עתותי השנה. המוצא לאור, יהושע בן המחבר הור״א הלוי טויבער. פרעסבורג. תרכ״ם.

   ₍Pressburg, Druck von F. R. Mayer, 1869₎

   59 l. 24 cm.

   —— Microfilm copy (positive)
   Negative film in the New York Public Library.

   1. Sermons, Jewish. 2. Sermons, Hebrew.   I. Tauber, Joshua, ed. II. Title.   *Title transliterated:* Yad Aharon.

BM740.T32   A 56–2135
New York. Public Libr.
for Library of Congress   ₍a56b₁₎†

NT 0052026   NN DLC

Tauber, Aleksandr Semenovich.
   De l'amputation ostéoplastique de la jambe. Paris, A. Delahaye & E. Lecrosnier, 1880
   27 p. 8°.

NT 0052027   DNLM

Tauber, Aleksandr Semenovich, ed.
Seydel, Karl, 1839–
   ... Руководство по военно-полевой хирургіи. Составленное д-ромъ Карломъ Зейделемъ ... Переводъ со 2-го нѣмецкаго изданія 1905г. д-ровъ М. Е. Лiона и Н. Н. Топальскаго, подъ редакцiею А. С. Таубера. 4-ое безплатное приложенiе къ "Военно-медицинскому журналу." С.-Петербургъ, Тип. т-ва "Народная польза," 1905.

Tauber, Aleksandr Semenovich.
   (Sovremennyĭà shkoly khirurgîi v glavnĕĭshikh gosudarstvakh Evropy)
   Современныя школы хирургіи въ главнѣйшихъ государствахъ Европы; очерки клинической и оперативной хирургіи. Составилъ А. С. Таубер. С.-Петербургъ, Изд. Глав. военно-мед. упр., 1889–

   v. illus. 25 cm.

   Includes bibliographical references.
   CONTENTS: кн. 1. Англійскія и шотландскія школы.—кн. 2. Германскія школы.—кн. 3. Французскія и швейцарскія школы.—

   1. Surgery—Study and teaching. 2. Medical education—Europe. I. Title.

RD28.A1T38   75–581631

NT 0052029   DLC DNLM

Tauber, Alfons Friedrich.
   Die fossilen Terediniden der burgenländischen und niederösterreichischen Tertiaerablagerungen. ₍Eisenstadt₎ Burgenländisches Landesmuseum ₍1954₎

   59 p. illus., plates, map. 25 cm. (Wissenschaftliche Arbeiten aus dem Burgenland, Heft 3)

   Bibliography: p. 58–59.

   1. Ship-worms, Fossil. 2. Paleontology—Tertiary. 3. Paleontology—Austria.   (Series)

QE812.T4T3   56–42617

NT 0052030   DLC MH CU

Tauber, Alfons Friedrich.
   Die Talkschieferlagerstätten von Glashütten bei Langeck, Burgenland. Herausgeber und Eigentümer: Burgenländisches Landesmuseum und das Institut für die Wissenschaftliche Erforschung des Neusiedler Sees. Eisenstadt, 1955.

   29 p. illus. 24 cm. (Wissenschaftliche Arbeiten aus dem Burgenland, Heft 8)

   Includes bibliography.

   1. Talc. 2. Schists. 3. Mines and mineral resources—Germany—Burgenland.

TN948.T2T33   553.67   60–45531 ‡

NT 0052031   DLC MH NIC

SD388
M572
vyp. 42,
etc.

Tauber, Boris Abramovich, ed.
   (Issledovanie mashin i mekhanizmov lesnoĭ promyshlennosti)
   Исследование машин и механизмов лесной промышленности. ₍Сборник статей₎. Под общ. ред. д-ра техн. наук, проф. Таубера Б. А. Москва, 19

Tauber, Boris Abramovich.
   Подъемно-транспортные машины в лесной промышленности. Допущено в качестве учебника для лесоинженерных факультетов высших учеб. заведений. Москва, Гослесбумиздат, 1952.

   532 p. illus., diagrs. 23 cm.

   Part of illustrative matter in pocket.
   Bibliography: p. ₍519₎

   1. Hoisting machinery. 2. Conveying machinery. 3. Lumbering—Machinery.   I. Title.   *Title transliterated:* Pod″emno-transportnye mashiny v lesnoĭ promyshlennosti.

TJ1350.T38   54–18974 rev

NT 0052033   DLC

Tauber, Boris Abramovich.
   Сборочно-сварочные приспособления и механизмы. Москва, Гос. научно-техн. изд-во машиностроит. лит-ры, 1951.

   414 p. illus. 23 cm.

   Bibliography: p. ₍413₎

   1. Welding.   I. Title.   *Title transliterated:* Sborochno-svarochnye prisposobleniĭa i mekhanizmy.

TS227.T3   51–37432 rev

NT 0052034   DLC

R708   Tauber, C   G.
.T3   ... Gesundheit und ethik.   München, Drei
masken verlag a. -g. [c1931]
38 [1] p.   17.5 cm.
"Nach einem am 20. oktober 1930 in Bern
gehaltenen vortrag."

NT   0052035   DLC

Tauber, Camilla Burstyn-
see   Burstyn-Tauber, Camilla.

Tauber, Conrad, 1906-
Statement on farm population trends, by Conrad Taeuber, presented before the Senate Committee on education and labor.   Washington,
1940.
[17] l.   maps.

1. Agricultural laborers - U. S.   I. Title:
Farm population trends.   I. U.S. Bureau of
Agricultural Economics.

NT   0052037   NNC

Tauber, Diana (Napier)
Richard Tauber.   With a foreword by Sir Charles B.
Cochran.   Glasgow, Art & Educational Publishers [1949]
237 p.   plates, ports.   22 cm.

1. Tauber, Richard, 1891-1948.

ML420.T126T3   927.8   49-51562*

FTaSU
NT   0052038   DLC WaT WaS CaBVa PP NjR CU-I CU-S IaU

QV   TAUBER, Eduard
T222a   Die Anaesthetica; eine ~~Monographie~~ mit
1881   besonderer Berücksichtigung von zwei
neuen anästhetischen Mitteln, kritisch und
experimentell.   Berlin, Hirschwald, 1881.
vi, 116 p.   illus.

NT   0052039   DNLM PPC

Tauber (Eduard).   *Ueber das Schicksal des
Kodeins im thierischen Organismus.   27 pp.
12°.   Strassburg, J. H. F Heitz, 1892.   C.

NT   0052040   DNLM MBCo

Tauber, Eduard.
Das verhalten der aromatischen verbindungen im thierischen organismus, mit besonderer rücksicht auf die oxy-
dation ...   Jena, Druck von A. Neuenhahn, 1878.
41 p.   21½ cm.
Zur erlangung der venia docendi—Jena.

1. Chemicals, Physiological effect of.
8-21910†

Library of Congress   QP917.A1T2

NT   0052041   DLC DNLM

Tauber, Elmore B
Fusospirillary gangrenous stomatits.   Chicago,
Amer. med. ass'n, 1936.
5 p.   il..   Q.
By Elmore B. Tauber and Leon Goldman.
Reprint, Arch. dermat. & syph. Oct. 1936.

NT   0052042   PU-D

HQ
46   Tauber, Elsa
.T38   Der Mann, ein Buch für Frauen, von Elsa
Tauber und R. Tauber.   Wien, Leipzig, Rhom-
bus [c1925]
314p.   19cm.

1. Men.   2. Marriage.   I. Title.

NT   0052043   TNJ

Tauber, Emil.
Die Weiberfeinde.   Lustspiel in fünf Akten.
Strassburg, J. Singer, 1908.
99 p.   12°.

NT   0052044   NN

AC
831   Tauber, Erich, 1910-
Die teilungsanordnung des erblassers nach
heutigem recht, unter berücksichtigung des
früheren (gemeinen und preussischen) rechts...
1932.   51 p.
Inaug. Diss. -Freiburg i. Br., 1932.
Lebenslauf.
Bibliography.

NT   0052045   ICRL

Tauber, Ernst, 1887-
Steht der kauf in bausch und bogen durchweg unter
der allgemeinen für den kauf geltenden sätzen?
Rostock, 1901.
Inaug. -diss. - Rostock.
Bibl.

NT   0052046   ICRL MH-L

Tauber, Ernst, 1887-
... Ueber luftfahrtrechtliche fragen.   Berlin, Dr. jur. Frens-
dorf [1913]
cover-title, 24 p.   24 cm.
"Vortrag gehalten am 17. oktober 1912 im Berliner anwaltverein von
dr. Ernst Tauber."

1. Aeronautics—Laws and regulations.   2. International law and relations.   I. Title.
31-33160

NT   0052047   DLC CtY NN

Tauber, Ernst, joint author.
1887?-

Heiman, Hanns, 1879-
Wichtige kaufmännische rechtsfragen in kriegszeit
(nebst anhang: Notgesetzliche bestimmungen betr. gläu-
biger- und schuldnerschutz während des krieges)   Von
syndikus dr. Hanns Heimann ... und rechtsanwalt dr.
Ernst Tauber.   6.-8. tausend.   Berlin, Verlag für fachliteratur, g. m. b. h., 1914.

Tauber, Erwin
Der Weg nach Jerusalem; Rede, gehalten im deutsch-
literarischen Kurs der Pressburger Rabbinatshochschule.
Pozsony, Buchdruckerei C.F.Wigand, 1916

23 p.

NT   0052049   MH

Tauber, Esther.
Molding society to man; Israel's new adventure in co-
operation.   Pref. by Horace M. Kallen.   New York, Bloch
Pub. Co., 1955.
151 p.   22 cm.

1. Agriculture, Cooperative—Israel.   2. Cooperation—Israel.
I. Title.
HD1491.P3T3   .34.683   56-617 ‡

InU LNT KU NcD NIC NNC OrSaW CaBVaU
CU NN DS OOxM OCH OrSaW FTaSU WU IEN TNJ IaAS MoU
NT   0052050   DLC PU CU IaU CSt-H NcD NNJ TxU MB NNC

Tauber, Friedrich Adolf, 1894-
Beitrag zur gasanalytischen trennung von azetylen,
aethylen und benzol.
Inaug. diss.   Zurich, techn. hochs., 1919

NT   0052051   ICRL

4QD   **Tauber, Friedrich Adolf,** 1894-
569   Beitrag zur gasanalytischen
Trennung von Azetylen, Aethylen und
Benzol.   Zürich, 1919.
63 p.

NT   0052052   DLC-P4

Tauber, Georg.
Ueber die grundverschiedene dramatische
verwertung des Ishigenienstaffes durch Euripides
und Goethe.   Prag, Rohlicek, 1896-98.
3 v. in 1.

NT   0052053   PU MA

Tauber, Gisela.
... Zur reform des vorverfahrens.   Staatsanwaltschaftliche
ermittlungsverfahren oder gerichtliche voruntersuchung.   Zum
VI. Deutschen juristentag in der Tschechoslowakischen repub-
lik.   Von dr. Gisela Tauber.   Prag, R. Lerche, 1933.
52 p., 1 l.   23 cm.   (Abhandlungen des Kriminologischen institutes an
der deutschen universität Prag.   bd. 1)

1. Public prosecutors—Germany.   2. Informations—Germany.
34-41141

NT   0052054   DLC

Tauber, H., joint author.
Copenhagen natural radiocarbon measurements,
see under   Anderson, Ernest Carl, 1920-

Tauber, H.
De usu parodiae apud Aristophanem.   n. p.,
1849.

NT   0052056   NjP

Tauber (Hans) [1889-   ].   *Ueber 100 Fälle
von Zwillingsschwangerschaft und -geburten.
35 pp. 8°.   Jena, G. Neuenhahn, 1916.

NT   0052057   DNLM CtY

W 4   TAUBER, Hellmut, 1928-
M96   Vergleichende Untersuchungen des
1953   Gasstoffwechsels überlebender Gewebe-
         schnitte aus Herz, Leber und Gehirn
         der Ratte nach Zufuhr von Glukose resp.
         Fruktose. ¡München¡ 1953.
             16 p.
             Inaug.-Diss. - Munich.
             1. Tissues - Respiration

NT 0052058   DNLM

Tauber, Henry, 1897-
    The chemistry and technology of enzymes. New York,
J. Wiley ¡1949¡
    viii, 550 p. illus. 24 cm.
    An expansion of the author's Enzyme technology, 1943.
    Includes "References."

    1. Enzymes. 2. Fermentation. 3. Chemistry, Technical.
    4. Chemistry, Organic.

    TP248.E5T28   661   49-7538*

        OrU-M OrU Wa OrP WaTU MtU IdPI
        OC1U IdU OU MtBC OC1W OrCS Wa OrU OC1W MtBC OU OOxM
        ICU OC1W ViU TxU TU ICJ CU NN WaS OKentU MiU OC1
NT 0052059   DLC PBL PPJ PU-Sc DI MiHM FMU DNLM NNC MB

Tauber, Henry, 1897-
    The chemistry and technology of enzymes. New York,
J. Wiley ¡1950, c1949¡
    viii, 550 p. illus. 24 cm.
    An expansion of the author's Enzyme technology, 1943.
    Includes "References."

NT 0052060   OrPS

Tauber, Henry, 1897-
    Enzyme chemistry, by Henry Tauber ... New York, J
Wiley & sons, inc.; London, Chapman & Hall, limited, 1937.
    xii, 243 p. illus., diagrs. 23½ᶜᵐ. $3.00
    "References" at end of each chapter.

    1. Enzymes. I. Title.

    Library of Congress   QP601.T2   37-2107
    ——— Copy 2.
    Copyright A 101965   ¡5¡   612.0151

        CU MtU WaT WaS OrSaW OrCS OrU-M IdU CaBVaU
        OCU OC1ND OO OU TU ViU OC1W OOxM MH KEmT DNLM CtY-M
NS 0052061   DLC PG1B PV PPJ PPF MoSW NcRS NcD MB ICJ

Tauber, Henry, 1897-
    Enzyme technology ¡by¡ Henry Tauber, PH. D. New York.
J. Wiley and sons, inc.; London, Chapman and Hall, ltd.
¡1943¡
    vii, 275 p. illus., diagrs. 22 cm.
    "References" at end of each chapter.

    1. Enzymes. 2. Fermentation. 3. Chemistry, Technical. 4. Chem-
    istry, Organic. I. Title.

    TP248.E5T3   661   44-22

        OrU-M CaBVa CaBVaU GU NjR
        OC1JC OU OCU TU MiHM ICJ OrPS WaWW OrP WaT MtU IdRR
NT 0052062   DLC NN MH CU PPD PP PHC PSt NcRS NcD ODW

Tauber, Henry, 1897-
    Enzyme technology ¡by¡ Henry Tauber, PH D. New York,
J. Wiley and sons, inc.; London, Chapman and Hall, ltd.
¡1945¡
    vii, 275 p. illus., diagrs. 24 cm.
    "References" at end of each chapter.

NT 0052063   ViU

Tauber, Henry, 1897-
    Experimental enzyme chemistry, by Henry Tauber ... Min-
neapolis, Minn., Burgess publishing company, °1936.
    2 p. l., v, 118 numb. l. incl. illus., tables, diagrs. 27½ᶜᵐ
    Mimeographed.
    "References" at end of each chapter.

    1. Enzymes. I. Title.

                                                A 37-448

    Illinois Univ. Library
    for Library of Congress   ¡5-2¡

NT 0052064   IU PPT PPF PG1B NcRS NNC ViU CU ICJ

Tauber, Herbert, 1912-
    Franz Kafka ... von Herbert Tauber ... Aarau, Druckerei-
genossenschaft, 1941.
    237, ¡3¡ p. 22½ᵐ.
    Abhandlung—Zürich.
    Lebenslauf.
    "Bibliographie": p. 237.

    1. Kafka, Franz, 1883-1924.

    Library of Congress   PT2621.A26Z9   43-32475
                                                    ¡2¡
                                                    833.91

    CLSU ODW OO OCU OC1 NBC AzU TU NN
NT 0052065   DLC PU PSC PBm PHC NcD CtY TxU NjP ICU

Tauber, Herbert.
    Franz Kafka; eine deutung seiner werke, von Herbert
Tauber. Zürich, New York, Verlag Oprecht ¡1941¡
    237, ¡1¡ p., 1 l. 23ᵐ.
    The author's inaugural dissertation, Zürich.
    "Bibliographie": p. 237.

    1. Kafka, Franz, 1883-1924.

                                                A 41-4846

    Harvard univ. Library
    for Library of Congress   ¡3¡

NT 0052066   MH OrPR

Tauber, Herbert, 1912-
    Franz Kafka; an interpretation of his works. ¡Tr. by G.
Humphreys Roberts and Roger Senhouse¡ London, Secker
& Warburg, 1948.
    xv, 252 p. 22 cm.
    Bibliography: p. 251-252.

    1. Kafka, Franz, 1883-1924.

    PT2621.A26Z93   833.91   49-24929*

    CaBVaU
NT 0052067   DLC MH OC1 InU PPLF MiU FU NNC CtY

Tauber, Herbert, 1912-
    Franz Kafka; an interpretation of his works. ¡Tr. by
G. Humphreys Roberts and Roger Senhouse¡ New Haven,
Yale Univ. Press, 1948 °1941¡
    xv, 252 p. 22 cm.
    Bibliography: p. 251-252.

    1. Kafka, Franz, 1883-1924. I. Humphreys-Roberts, G., tr.

    [PT2621.A26Z]   833.91   A 48-6475*
    Yale Univ. Library
    for Library of Congress   ¡5¡

    MiU PBm OrCS WaS CaBVaU OrU OrMonO OrU WaTU
NT 0052068   CtY DAU Or OrP NN CSt TU TxU OU PP PPDrop

Tauber, Ignaz, 1907-
    ... Blasen- und Nierenstein nach 1 Jahr
Sojadiät bei einem 16 Monate alten Knaben und
5 weitere Fälle von kindlichen Harnsteinen...
Zürich, 1936.
    Inaug.-diss. - Zürich.
    Curriculum vitae.
    "Literaturverzeichnis"; p. 27-¡32¡

NT 0052069   CtY

Tauber, Israel, 1823-1904.
אורח רענן, קצת הערות על תולדות הרמב"ם ועל דרכיו
ופסקיו אשר לקטתי מפי ספרים וסופרים ... פרעסבורג,
ח. וויס, תברך. ¡Pressburg, 1862¡
    88 l. 20 cm.

    1. Moses ben Maimon, 1135-1204. I. Title.
                            Title transliterated: Ezrah ra'anan.

    BM755.M6T3   A 51-1245
    New York. Public Libr.
    for Library of Congress   ¡1¡

NT 0052070   NN DLC

Tauber, J   F   d. 1803.
    ¡Variations, flute & orchestra, G major¡
    Variations pour la flute-traversiere, 2 violons, 2 hautbois
2 cors, alto et basso. Composees par J. F. Taubert. ¡180-?¡
    parts. 35 cm.
    Ms., in ink.

    1. Variations (Flute with orchestra)—To 1800—Parts.

    ML30.4c no. 2542 Miller   68-126682/M

NT 0052071   DLC

Tauber, J.S.
    Der Traum ein Leben. Die Raben. Verschollene
Ghettomärchen.   Prague, Jakob B. Brandeis, n.d.
    158 p. 13, 5 cm.
    1. Belles Lettres - German. 2. Legends.
    3. Title. 4. Tauber; Die Raben.

NT 0052072   NNJ

Tauber, J   S
    Der Traum ein Leben. - Die Raben. Verschollene
Ghetto-Märchen.   Prag, J.B.Brandeis,[189-?].
    158 p. 15 cm.

    Bound with: Saphir,M.G., Humoristisches Aller-
lei,189-?.

NT 0052073   OCH

Tauber, Jack.
    Outline of Zionist history, by Jack Tauber.   New York
city: Brith Trumpeldor organization ¡1941¡ iii, 141, ii f. 27½cm.
    Cover-title.
    Reproduced from typewritten copy.

    157399B. 1. Zionism—Hist.   I. Brith Tempeldor of America.
    N. Y. P. L.   March 16, 1942

NT 0052074   NN PPT

IS   Tauber, Jacob.
145   Abraham und die Antisemiten. Wien, Moriz
T38   Weizner, 1894.
1894   8 p.
            "Separat-Abdruck aus Nr.49 und 50 der
        "Neuzeit."

            1.Antisemitism--Hist. 2.Jews in Austria.
        I.Title.

NT 0052075   NSyU

BM   Tauber, Jacob.
740   Religiöse Pflichten. Der Widerstreit
T3.83   des Guten und des Bösen. Zwei
        Predigten. Magdeburg, 1876.
            16 p.   21 cm.
            Cover title.
            Sonderabdruck aus Rahmer's "Isr.
        Predigt-Magazin," Jahrg. II.

NT 0052076   OCH

Tauber, Jacob.
Standpunkt und leistung des r. David Kimchi als grammatiker, mit berücksichtigung seiner vorgänger und nachfolger. (Inaugural-dissertation) von dr. Jacob Tauber. Breslau, Selbstverlag des verfassers, 1867.
46 p. 20½ᶜᵐ.

1. Kimchi, David, 1160?–1235? 2. Hebrew language—Grammar.

Library of Congress   PJ4566.T37
24—13384

NT 0052077   DLC OCH ICRL PP DCU-H

TAUBER, JACOB.
Standpunkt und Leistung des R. David Kimchi als Grammatiker, mit Berücksichtigung seiner Vorgänger und Nachfolger. Breslau, Selbstverlag des Verfassers, 1867. 46 p. 21cm.

Film reproduction. Master negative. Original discarded.
Positive in *ZP-133
Inaug.-Diss. — Breslau?

NT 0052078   NN

Tauber, Jacob.
Trauungs-Rede gehalten im Tempel zu Prerau zur Vermählungsfeier des Theodor Lichtwitz mit Therese Grün am 14. Februar 1892. Prerau, [the author], 1892.
[2] p. 24 cm.

1.Sermons - Marriage. I.ti.

NT 0052079   OCH

Tauber, Jacob.
Das vierzigste Offenbarungsfest unter der Regierung Sr. Majestät Franz Josef I. Rede am 2.Tage des Schebuothfestes. Prerau,1888.
8 p. 22 cm.

1.Shavu'oth. I.ti.

NT 0052080   OCH

W 4
G32
1950
TAUBER, James Isi
Contribution à l'étude de l'anémie de Cooley et de ses formes incomplètes. Ambilly-Annemasse, Impr. franco-suisse, 1950.
32 p. (Geneva. Université. Faculté de médecine. Thèse, M. D., 1950, no. 1975)
1. Anemia - Erythroblastic

NT 0052081   DNLM

[Tauber, Jan] 1906–
...Diogenův žák, komedie o pěti obrazech ze života filosofů chudoby. Praha, Vesmír, 1946. 53 p. 20cm.

Author's pseud., Ivan Holub, at head of title.

1. Drama, Bohemian. 2. Diogenes, the Cynic—Drama.

NT 0052082   NN

Tauber, Jan, ed.
...Zemědělská abeceda, rukověť rostlinné a živočišné výroby. Napsali: prof. dr. František Bilek...[a druzi] S předmluvou ministra zemědělství Julia Ďuriše. Uspořádal ing. Jan. Tauber. Praha, Vesmír, 1947. 801 p. illus. 26cm. (Zemědělská knižnice. sv. 8.)

430651B. 1. Agriculture, 1901–   I. Title.
N. Y. P. L.   April 28, 1948

NT 0052083   NN

33.27
219.
Tauber, Jan, 1906–
Zemědělství Německé Demokratické Republiky. [Vyd. 1.] Praha, Státní zemědělské nakl., 1953.
90 p.

1. Germany. Agriculture. I. Dušek, Josef, joint author.

NT 0052084   DNAL

Tauber, Johan Henrik, 1743–1816.
Blade af rector Joh. Henr. Tauber* dagbøger. Udg. af Julius Clausen og P. Fr. Rist. [København, Gyldendal, Nordisk forlag, 1922]
2 p. l., 224 p. port. 22¾ᶜᵐ. (*Added t.-p.:* Memoirer og breve, udg. af Julius Clausen og P. Fr. Rist. xxxviii)
Illustrated t.-p.
"Trykt i 900 eksemplarer."

ɪ. Clausen, Julius Emil Ferdinand, 1868– ed. ɪɪ. Rist, Peter Frederik, 1844– ed. ɪɪɪ. Title.
24–14385
Library of Congress   DL103.5.M5 xxxviii

NT 0052085   DLC NN MH MnU

Rare
Books
Dept.
[Tauber, Johan Henrik] 1743–1816.
Brøstfaeldighederne i det laerde Skolevaesen uddragne af original-Dokumenter og indstillede til høiere Eftertanke ... Kiøbenhavn, paa G. Poulsens Forlag, 1789.
122 p. 19cm.

NT 0052086   CU

Tauber, Johan Henrik, 1743–1816.
Fortegnelse paa alle de skrifter som trykfriheden har givet anledning til. Hvori findes anført stederne hvor de sælges, hvad de koste, og hvor mange ark de indeholde. Samt en kort erindring om et hvert skrift til efterretning for liebhabere ... [1.–3. aargang, sept. 14 1770–sept. 1773] Kiøbenhavn, Kanneworff, 1771–[73]

TAUBER, Jo[hann] Car[l] Fr[iedrich].
Opuscula cum latini tum germanici sermonis, maximam partem a iuvene elaborata, a seniori iterum collecta. Marienberg, impresserunt Hasperi fratres, 1821.

NT 0052088   MH

Tauber, Johann Daniel, heirs.
Catalogus von alten und neuen chymischen, von berckwercken, kräutern, thieren, von warmen bädern, und von der haushaltungs-kunst handelnden büchern, welche bey Johann Daniel Taubers seel. erben in Nürnberg neben der schuster-gasse, und in Altdorff in der collegen-gasse um billige preisse nebst andern verkaufft werden. Nürnberg und Altdorff, 1722.

v.1.

NT 0052089   NNE

Tauber, Johann Daniel, heirs.
Catalogus von chymischen büchern welche in der Rothscholssischen bibliotheque verhanden seyn. Nürnberg u. Altdorff, bey Johann Daniel Taubers seel.erben, 1725.

v.1.

Bound with his: Catalogus von alten und neuen chymische etc. 1722.

NT 0052090   NNE

Tauber, Johanna.
...Die vollkommene Frau; Leitfaden der intelligenten Frau für Familie, Gesellligkeit, Haushalt und Küche. M.-Ostrau: J. Kittls Nachfolger [1934] 396 p. illus., plates. 21cm.

85061B. 1. Domestic economy, 1926–   2. Woman.
N. Y. P. L.   December 26, 1940

NT 0052091   NN

AC831
K74
1893
Stack
Tauber, Josef.
Ziele und Wege des französischen Unterrichtes auf der Unter- und Mittelstufe der österreichischen Realschulen. Krems, 1893.
22 p.
Programmschrift - Nied.-österr. Landes-Oberrealschule, Krems.
Accompanies Schulnachrichten.

1.French language - Study and teaching.

NT 0052092   CSt

Tauber, Josef, 1873–
... Telefonní ústředny v Plzni. Napsal ing. Josef Tauber ... [Praha, Tiskl E. Beaufort, 1929.
121 p., 1 l. incl. illus., plates. plans (2 fold.) 27ᶜᵐ. ([Czechoslovak republic] Ministerstvo pošt a telegrafů. Technické příručky. čis. 8)
"Vydalo Ministerstvo pošt a telegrafů v Praze."

1. Telephone—Plzeň. 2. Telephone stations.
39–9443
Library of Congress   TK5108.C95 no. 8

NT 0052093   DLC

Tauber, Josef, 1873–
... Telefonní ústředny v systému ústřední baterie. Napsal ing. Josef Tauber ... [V Praze, Vytiskla Státní tiskárna, 1929.
151 p. illus., plates (3 fold.) 27ᶜᵐ. ([Czechoslovak republic] Ministerstvo pošt a telegrafů. Technické příručky. čis. 5)
"Vydalo Ministerstvo pošt a telegrafů v Praze."

1. Telephone stations. 2. Telephone—Current supply.
39–9444
Library of Congress   TK5108.C95 no. 5

NT 0052094   DLC

---

*GB8
V6755R
3.17.48
Tauber, Josef Samuel, 1822–1879.
Alle Brüder! Am Grabe der gefallenen Freiheits-Helden.
[Wien,1848?]
broadside. 21x13.5cm.
Helfert (Wiener Parnass) 411.

NT 0052095   MH

834T191
Og
Tauber, Josef Samuel, 1822–1879.
Gedichte. Leipzig, C. B. Lorck, 1847.
304p. 17cm.

Author's autograph presentation copy.

NT 0052096   IU IEN

Lilly
GR 98
.T222
1853
TAUBER,JOSEF SAMUEL,1822–1879
Die letzten Juden. Verschollene Ghetto-Märchen von J. S. Tauber ... Leipzig, F. A. Brockhaus, 1853.
2v. 18 cm.

Ex libris Fürst Dietrichstein (1813–1871)
In quarter green morocco and green boards; all edges yellow.

NT 0052097   InU NIC

Tauber, Josef Samuel, 1822–1879.
De raven. Eene Joodsche vertelling, naar het Hoogduitsch,
van J. S. Tauber. 's Gravenhage: K. Fuhri, 1854. 127 p.
24°.

1. Fiction, German. 2. Jews in fiction. 3. Title.
N. Y. P. L. September 9, 1926

NT 0052098 NN

PT
2534
T3
Q8
Tauber, Josef Samuel, 1822–1879.
Quinten; kleine Gedichte. Leipzig, F. A.
Brockhaus, 1864.
160p. 18cm.

NT 0052099 WU TNJ

BM740
.T32
Hebr
Tauber, Joshua, ed.

Tauber, Aaron, d. 1846.
יד אהרן. ח"י דרשות מיוסדים על אדני המחקר וקבלת חז"ל
מסודרים לפי עתותי השנה. המוציא לאור. יהושע בן המחבר
מהור"א הלוי טויבער. פרעסבורג. תרנ"ם.
₍Pressburg, Druck von F. R. Mayer, 1869₎

Tauber, Karl.
1 capostipiti dei manoscritti della divina
commedia; ...
Winterthur, 1889.

NT 0052101 NIC

WH
700
qT222u
1952
TAUBER, Karl, 1907–
Untersuchungen über das Verhalten des
Lymphflusses im Milchbrustgang unter nor-
malen und pathophysiologischen Bedingungen. München, 1952.
115ℓ. illus.
Habilitationsschrift - Munich.
1. Lymph

NT 0052102 DNLM

Tauber, Kurt Philip.
The foundations of the doctrine of self-defense; a
critical analysis.

Thesis - Harvard, 1951.

NT 0052103 MH

Tauber, Leonid İÂkovlevich.
... Лига'нация и юридический статут русских бѣжен-
цевъ ... Бѣлградъ ₍Типографија "Светлост"₎ 1933.
cover-title, 32 p. 23ᶜᵐ.
At head of title: Л. Тауберъ.
"Отдѣльный оттискъ изъ Записокъ Русскаго научнаго института,
вып. 9."

1. League of nations. 2. Refugees, Political. 3. Russians. I. Title.
37–36695

NT 0052104 DLC RPB

Tauber, Leonid İÂkovlevich.
Уџбеник трговачког права ... Београд, Издавачко и књи
жарско предузеће Г. Кон, 1935.
xI, 204 p. 24½ᶜᵐ.
At head of title: Л. Тауберъ.
"Литература": p. ₍v₎–vI.

1. Commercial law—Yugoslavia. I. Title.
41–37043

NT 0052105 DLC

Tauber, M.
——. Preisverzeichniss über Brillen, Pince-nez,
Opern- und Reisegläser, Fernrohre, Lupen, Mi-
kroskope, etc. 80 pp., 2 l. 8°. Leipzig, E.
Stephan, ₍1888₎.

NT 0052106 DNLM

Tauber (M.) Preisverzeichniss über physikali-
sche, optische, mathematische Instrumente und
Apparate. 74 pp., 1 l. 8°. Leipzig, ₍A. T.
Engelhardt₎, 1881.

NT 0052107 DNLM

Tauber, M I
Организация автомобильных перевозок на строительстве. Москва, Гос. изд-во лит-ры по строительству и архитектуре, 1952.
128 p. illus., tables. 22 cm.
Bibliography: p. ₍125₎

1. Building machinery. 2. Conveying machinery. 8. Motor-trucks
I. Title. *Title transliterated:* Organizatsiia avtomobil'nykh perevosok

TH900.T3 54–17513

NT 0052108 DLC

780.92
191m
Tauber, Margaretha, comp.
Musikerbriefe aus Wien. Wien, Efi-Ton-
Verlag G. M. B. H. ₍°1947₎
148 p. illus., facsims. 24cm.

1. Musicians - Correspondence, reminiscences,
etc. I. T.

NT 0052109 MiDW IaU NN

Tauber, Márta.
Semleges sók hatása a nádcukor inversiose-
bességére vizes alkoholos közegben ... Budapest, 1929.
Budapest
diss.
1929

NT 0052110 MiU

Tauber, Maurice Falcolm, 1908–
Barnard College Library, a report on facilities and services, prepared at the request of the Barnard College Administration. New York, 1954.
82 l. 20 cm.

1. Barnard College, New York. Library.
Z733.B24T3 56–30826

NT 0052111 DLC NNC MiU CU ICU NcU TxU OClW

LIBRARY SERVICE
D027.7
T19435
Tauber, Maurice Falcolm, 1908–
A brief history of the library of Temple
University. Philadelphia, Pa., 1934.
17 l. illus., port., plan.

Portrait and sketch of building are clippings pasted in.

1. Philadelphia. Temple University. Library.

NT 0052112 NNC PPT

LIBRARY SERVICE
D025.4
T1933
Tauber, Maurice Falcolm, 1908–
Checklist on reclassification and recataloging in college and university libraries, from
libraries adopting the Library of Congress
classification scheme. ₍1939₎
11 l.

1. Classification, Library of Congress.
I. Title: Reclassification and recataloging in
college and univer   sity libraries.

NT 0052113 NNC

Library
School
Z695
.T252
Tauber, Maurice Falcolm, 1908–
Current trends in cataloging and classifica-
tion. n.p., n.p., 1953.
173–355p. (Library trends, v.2, no.2)

1. Cataloging. 2. Classification - Books.
I. Title.

NT 0052114 NcU

025.3
T19c
Tauber, Maurice Falcolm, 1908–   ed.
Current trends in cataloging and
classification. ₍Urbana, University
of Illinois Library School₎ 1953.
173–355 p. 23 cm. (Library trends
vol. 2, no. 2)

Includes bibliographies.

1. Cataloging. 2. Classification.
I. Library tren⌐   ⌐s, vol. 2, no. 2.
II. Title.

NT 0052115 LU OU

LIBRARY SERVICE
D025.22
T19
Tauber, Maurice Falcolm, 1908–
Desiderata files. ₍1950₎
17–19 p.

From Stechert-Hafner book news, vol. 5,
no. 2, Oct. 1950.

1. Books - Want lists. I. Title.

NT 0052116 NNC

Tauber, Maurice Falcolm, 1908–   joint comp.

Philadelphia. Temple university. *Library.*
... Graduate theses and dissertations, 1894–1940, compiled by
J. Periam Danton and Maurice F. Tauber. Philadelphia,
Temple university, 1940.

Tauber, Maurice Falcom, 1908–

Philadelphia. Temple university. *Library.*
Index of theses and dissertations prepared at Temple university, 1908–1935, compiled by Maurice F. Tauber, catalog
librarian. Philadelphia, Pa., Temple university library, 1935.

LIBRARY SERVICE
D027.7
T19433
Tauber, Maurice Falcolm, 1908–
The library of the New York School of Social
Work; a report on physical quarters in rela-
tion to services. Prepared at the request of
the administration of the New York School of
Social Work. 1955.
29 l. plans.

1. New York School of Social Work. Library.
2. Library surveys.

NT 0052119 NNC

Tauber, Maurice Falcolm, 1908–
 A list of theses and dissertations prepared in the School of theology. [Phila., Temple university, 1937]
  p. 17–8. 28 cm.
  Taken from Temple theologian, vol. 2, no. 2, December, 1937.

NT 0052120 PPT

Tauber, Maurice Falcolm, 1908–
 Organization of materials in libraries; outline of a course. Maurice F. Tauber. [New York] Tauber, [1948?]
  [44] p. 28 cm.
  Carbon copy of typescript.
  1. Cataloging – Outlines, syllabi, etc. I. Title.

NT 0052121 NNC

Tauber, Maurice Falcolm, 1908–
 ... Other aspects of union catalogs. [n. p.] 1939.
  p. 411–431. 24 cm.
  "Reprinted for private circulation from The library quarterly, vol. IX, no. 4, Oct., 1939."

NT 0052122 PPT

Tauber, Maurice Falcolm, 1908–
 Outline for the course in Current problems in the technical services in libraries (Library service s279)

  see under Columbia University. School of Library Service.

Tauber, Maurice Falcolm, 1908– joint author.
 Outline for the course in organization

  see under

 Columbia University. School of Library Service.

Tauber, Maurice Falcolm, 1908–
 Reclassification and recataloging in college and university libraries. Chicago, 1941.
  ix, 356 l. illus. 32 cm.
  Typescript (carbon copy)
  Thesis—University of Chicago.
  Bibliography: leaves 355–356.

  1. Classification—Books. 2. Cataloging. 3. Libraries, University and college. I. Title.

 Z696.T22 1941   62–55413

NT 0052125 DLC FTaSU

Micro Z 696 .T22 Govt. Doc. Rm.
 Tauber, Maurice Falcolm, 1908–
 Reclassification and recataloging in college and university libraries. Chicago, 1941.
  Microfilm copy (positive) of typescript by Dept. of Photoduplication, University of Chicago Library.
  Thesis – (Ph.D.) – University of Chicago.

  1. Classification – Books. 2. Cataloging. 3. Libraries, University and college. I. T.

NT 0052126 NBuU CU LU CaBVaU IU

Tauber, Maurice Falcolm, 1908–
 ... Reclassification and recataloging in college and university libraries ... by Maurice F. Tauber ... [n. p., 1942]
  1 p. l., [1], 706–724, 827–845 p. 24ᶜᵐ.
  Part of thesis (PH. D.)—University of Chicago, 1941.
  "Reprinted from the Library quarterly, vol. XII, July and October, 1942."
  Bibliographical foot-notes.

  1. Classification—Books. 2. Libraries, University and college. 3. Cataloging. I. Title.

 Chicago. Univ. Library   A 43–847
 for Library of Congress   Z696.T22
     [5]†   025.4

NT 0052127 ICU PPT OrCS NcU OU DLC

Tauber, Maurice Falcolm, 1908–
 Reclassification and recataloging of materials in college and university libraries [by] Maurice F. Tauber ... [n. p., 1940?]
  cover-title, 187–219 p. 23ᶜᵐ.
  "Reprinted ... from The acquisition and cataloging of books edited by William M. Randall, the University of Chicago press, 1940."

  1. Classification—Books. 2. Cataloging. 3. Libraries, University and college. I. Title.

 Library of Congress   Z696.T22 1940 45–45131
     [2]   025.4

NT 0052128 DLC PPT NcU NNC

D027.7 V59
 Tauber, Maurice Falcolm, 1908–
 Report of a survey of certain aspects of the technical processes of the libraries of the University of Vermont, June 7–9, 1945, by Maurice F. Tauber ... [1945]
  2 p. l., 13 l.

  1. Vermont. University. Library. 2. Library surveys.

NT 0052129 NNC

D025.3 T193
 Tauber, Maurice Falcolm, 1908–
 Report of a survey of the catalogs and cataloging practices of the Augustana college library, May 17, 1944, by Maurice F. Tauber ... 1944.
  2 p. l., 15 l.

  Type-written.
  1. Augustana college and theological seminary, Rock Island, Ill. Denkmann memorial library. 2. Cataloging. 3. Library surveys.

NT 0052130 NNC

Z733 .C81W5
 Tauber, Maurice Falcolm, 1908– joint author.
 Wilson, Louis Round, 1876–
 Report of a survey of the libraries of Cornell University for the Library Board of Cornell University, October 1947–February 1948 [by] Louis R. Wilson, Robert B. Downs [and] Maurice F. Tauber. Ithaca, Cornell Univ., 1948.

Tauber, Maurice Falcolm, 1908–
 Report of a survey of the libraries of the Virginia Polytechnic Institute, for the Virginia Polytechnic Institute, January–May 1949, by Maurice F. Tauber and William H. Jesse. Blacksburg, Virginia Polytechnic Institute, 1949.
  120 p. illus. 23 cm.

  1. Virginia Polytechnic Institute, Blacksburg. Library. 2. Library surveys. I. Jesse, William Herman, 1908– joint author. II. Virginia Polytechnic Institute, Blacksburg.

 Z733.V63T3   026.6   A 49—10504*
 Virginia. State Library
 for Library of Congress   [51g2]†

    PPD MoU NNC-M OrU OrCS CaBVaU IdPI
NT 0052132 Vi DNAL DLC NcD NNC IU ICU MB OC1 OU PU

Tauber, Maurice Falcolm, 1908–
 Report of a survey of the Library of Montana State University for Montana State University, January–May 1951 [by] Maurice F. Tauber and Eugene H. Wilson, on behalf of the American Library Association. Chicago, American Library Association, 1951.
  174 p. diagrs., tables. 28 cm.

  1. Montana. State University, Missoula. Library. 2. Library surveys. I. Wilson, Eugene Holt, 1909– joint author.

 Z733.M765T3 027.7786 52–10544

   CaBVaU CaBViP IdPI IdU MtU MtHi OrCS
NT 0052133 DLC KEmT NN MoU NNC TU CU ICU MH MiD TxU

025.1 T19r
 Tauber, Maurice Falcolm, 1908–
 Report of a survey of the technical services of the Columbia University Libraries December 28, 1943--January 8, 1944, by Maurice F. Tauber and L. Quincy Mumford. Rev. draft, March, 1944. [New York, 1944]
  57 p. diagrs. 29cm.

  Mimeographed.

  1. Library administration. 2. Cataloging. 3. Columbia Univers'·· Library. I. Mumford, Lawrence Quincy, 1903– joint author.

   0
  CU ICU ViU MiU MnU NNC ICJ IU TxU PPD MoU DGW MH NN
NT 0052134 LU DCU NNC PSt NN ScU GU TU NRU NNU-W

Tauber, Maurice Falcolm, 1908–
 Report of a survey of the technical services of the Columbia University Libraries, December 28, 1943--January 8, 1944, by Maurice F. Tauber and L. Quincy Mumford. Revised draft, March, 1944. [New York, 1948]
  57 p. diagrs.

  I. Mumford, Lawrence Quincy, 1903– I. Columbia University. Library. 378.747 974.762(027)

NT 0052135 ICJ WaS OrU CaBVa CaBVaU OrCS

Z733 .S7285 W5
 Tauber, Maurice Falcolm, 1908– joint author.
 Wilson, Louis Round, 1876–
 Report of a survey of the University of South Carolina library for the University of South Carolina, February–May, 1946, by Louis R. Wilson ... and Maurice F. Tauber ... Columbia, S. C., The University of South Carolina, 1946.

LIBRARY SERVICE D027.4 T1944
 Tauber, Maurice Falcolm, 1908–
 Report on certain aspects of the technical services of the New York State Library. New York, 1947.
  19 l.

  1. New York. State Library, Albany. 2. Library surveys.

NT 0052137 NNC

Z733 D251T3 Library School
 Tauber, Maurice Falcolm, 1908–
 A report on the technical services in the Dartmouth College Library, March–May, 1952. [New York?] 1952.
  51 ℓ.

  1. Dartmouth College. Library.

NT 0052138 CU NNC

Tauber, Maurice Falcolm, 1908–
  Russell Herman Conwell, 1843–1925; a bibliography, by Maurice F. Tauber. Philadelphia, Pa., Temple university library, 1935.
    2 p. l., ii, 40 numb. l. 29ᶜᵐ.
    Mimeographed.
    Contents.—Works by R. H. Conwell.—Works about R. H. Conwell.—Articles in encyclopedias, dictionaries, etc.—Sermons.—Index of portraits.—Index.
    1. Conwell, Russell Herman, 1843–1925—Bibl. 2. Philadelphia. Temple university—Bibl.

Library of Congress	Z8190.7.T22	35–3887
—— Copy 2.		
Copyright A 79884	₍2₎	012

NT 0052139   DLC OrU OC1W CtY PPD PU PP PPT NcD OU

Tauber, Maurice Falcom, 1908–
  Should the doctoral program in library science be offered by a southern library school ₑby Mauric₎ F. Tauber, J. W. Gordon Gourlay and Tommie Dora Barker.   n.p., 195–?₎
    12 l.   28cm.

    Mimeographed.
    Reprinted from Virginia Librarian, July, 1956.
    1. Library schools and training. 2. Doctor of philosophy degree. i. Virginia librarian. ii. Title. iii. Title: The doctoral program in library science.

NT 0052140   FMU

Z695
.C718
  Tauber, Maurice Falcolm, 1908–   ed.

  Columbia University. *School of Library Service.*
    The subject analysis of library materials; papers presented at an institute, June 24–28, 1952, under the sponsorship of the School of Library Service, Columbia University, and the A. L. A. Division of Cataloging and Classification. Edited, with an introd., by Maurice F. Tauber. New York ₍1953₎

Z
665
T28
1953
  Tauber, Maurice Falcolm, 1908–   ed.
    Technical services in libraries.

NT 0052142   NBuU

Tauber, Maurice Falcolm, 1908–   *ed.*
  Technical services in libraries. Under the editorial direction of Maurice F. Tauber, with the collaboration of Ralph U. Blasingame ₍and others₎ Prelim. draft. ₍New York₎ School of Library Service, Columbia University, ᵃ1952.
    379 p.   28 cm.

    1. Library science.   i. Title.

Z665.T28	025	53–782 ‡

NT 0052143   DLC Or NNC UU–M

Z
665
.T28
1954
  Tauber, Maurice Falcolm, 1908–   ed.
    Technical services in libraries: acquisitions, cataloging, classification, binding, photographic reproduction, and circulation operations. New York, Columbia University Press ₍c1953₎
    xvi, 487 p. 24 cm. (Columbia University studies in library service, no.7)
    Bibliographical references included in "Notes" (p. ₍414₎–463)

    1. Library science.   I. Title
    II. Series

NT 0052144   MBtS MH–PA OC1W–H

Tauber, Maurice Falcolm, 1908–   *ed.*
  Technical services in libraries: acquisitions, cataloging, classification, binding, photographic reproduction, and circulation operations, by Maurice F. Tauber and associates. New York, Columbia University Press, 1954 ₍ᵃ1953₎
    xvi, 487 p. diagrs. 24 cm. (Columbia University studies in library service, no. 7)
    Bibliographical references included in "Notes" (p. ₍414–463₎)

Continued in next column

Continued from preceding column

    1. Library science.   i. Title.   (Series)

Z665.T28	1954	54—10328

WaTU OrStbM OrU–M
OrPS OrMonO OrLgE OrCS OrAshS CaBViP CaBVa Wa WaT
IdU IdPI MtBC MtU OrP WaS WaSpG WaU–L WaSp OrU OrPR
    OC1 OCU OU PBm OC1W TxU NcC NcRS MiU PRosC IdB
KyU KyU–H NNJ MChB–W DAU NWM KyU–C KyLxCB PSt OCH NN
PSC PBa PHC PPJ IU DI DDO KU MB MH–P KEmT TxU NN
NT 0052145   DLC DNAL OC1W–H MBCo ViU MoU NIC PPLas PBL

Tauber, Maurice Falcolm, 1908–
  Templana classification (including Conwelliana).
    see under   Philadelphia. Temple University. Library.₎

Z675
.U5W745
  Tauber, Maurice Falcolm, 1908–   joint author.

  Wilson, Louis Round, 1876–
    The university library; its organization, administration and functions, by Louis Round Wilson and Maurice F. Tauber. Chicago, University of Chicago press ₍1945₎

DO25.129
T19
  Tauber, Maurice Falcolm, 1908–
    Use of microphotography in university libraries, by Maurice F. Tauber ... ₍1941₎
    cover-title, 150–157 p.

    From the Journal of documentary reproduction, v. 4, September, 1941.

    1. Microphotography.

NT 0052149   NNC PPT

Tauber, Maurice Falcolm, 1908–
  ... What problems do films introduce in cataloging, reference work, storage, etc. ? [n.p.] 1939.
    8 p.   28 cm.
    Typewritten.
    Bibliography, p. 8.

NT 0052150   PPT

DS118
.W4
  Tauber, Meir, joint author.

  Weingarten, Yeraḥmiel.
    ... עמ בעבר ובהוה ... ורשה, ניו־יורק, הוצאת 'קדם,' ₍Warszawa, New York₎ 1937–38.   תרצ״ח

QP
42
T22+
  Tauber, Oscar Ernest, 1908–
    A laboratory guide for elementary physiology, by Oscar E. Tauber, Delma E. Harding ₍and₎ Robert E. Haupt.   ₍Minneapolis, Burgess Publishing Co., c1955₎
    iv, 224 p. illus. 28 cm.

    1. Physiology—Laboratory manuals. I. Harding, Delma E   joint author. II. Haupt, Robert E   joint author. III. Title.

NT 0052152   NIC InU CU IU ICarbS

PG
34
C99
T22
  Tauber, Otakar
    Otázky cyrilo-metodějské.   ₍Přerov, Nákl. Nového národa, 1928.
    2v.   20cm.

    1. Cyrillus, Saint, of Thessalonica, 827 (ca.)–869. 2. Methodius, Saint, Abp. of Moravia, d. 885.

NT 0052153   NIC CtY

Tauber, P. A. M., 1832–
  Om et hidtil ikke bemaerket forhold ved pringabernes tandskifte.   Kjob., 1872.

NT 0052154   NjP

Tauber, P A M 1832–
  —— Om Tanddannelse og Tandskifte hos Hvirveldyrene; Iagttagelser og Bemærkninger. [Formation and change of teeth in vertebrates; observations and remarks.] pp. 450–565, 2 pl. 8°. ₍Kjøbenhavn, 1876.₎
    Cutting from : Naturh. Tidsskr., Kjøbenh., 1876, 3. R., x.

NT 0052155   DNLM

Tauber, Pam., 1832–
  Om Tandsæt og Levemaade hos de danske Flagermuus og Insektædere: prisbelonnet Besvarelse af Universitetets naturhistoriske Opgave for 1869. [On dentition and mode of living of the Danish bat and insectivora: competition for the prize for natural history by the university] [Kjøbenhavn, 1873]
    p. 227–280   2 pl.   8°.
    Cutting from; Naturh. Tidsskr., Kjobenh., 1873, 3. R., viii.

NT 0052156   DNLM

Tauber, P A M 1832–
  ... Pattedyr, ved P. Tauber...   Kjobenhavn, E. Jespersen, 1878–92.
    1 p. l., iv, 306, vii p.   illus., 17 pl. (part. col.)   39 cm.   (Zoologia danica ... Hvirveldyr, 1ste bd.)
    1. Denmark.

NT 0052157   CU

Tauber, P A M 1832–   ed.
  Zoologia danica, afbildninger af danske dyr med populær text; paabegyndte af J. C. Schiødte, udgivne med offentlig understøttelse af H. J. Hansen. Kjøbenhavn, E. Jespersen, ₙ.d.

Tauber, Richard, ed.

  Tauber von Taubenfurt, Johann, *freiherr,* b. 1736.
    ... Über meine violine ... Mit einer einleitung versehen und hrsg. von Richard Tauber. Wien, C. Anfried, 1904.

Tauber, Richard, 1891–1948.
  ₍Old Chelsea. Libretto. English₎

    Old Chelsea, a musical romance in three acts, by Walter Ellis; additional numbers by Bernard Grun; lyrics by Fred S. Tysh and Walter Ellis. London, L. Wright Music Co. ₍1943₎
    68 p. illus. 18 cm.
    ₍1. Musical revues, comedies, etc.—Librettos₎   I. Ellis, Walter W., 1874–   Old Chelsea. II. Grun, Bernard, 1901–   Old Chelsea. III. Title.

ML50.T172O4	1943	44–43864 rev*
	*782.1 782.6	

NT 0052160   DLC

Tauber, Richard, 1891–1948.
  ₍Old Chelsea. Piano-vocal score. English₎

    Old Chelsea, a musical romance in three acts. Book by Walter Ellis, additional numbers by Bernard Grun, lyrics by Fred S. Tysh and Walter Ellis. London, L. Wright Music Co., ᵃ1948.
    141 p. 28 cm.
    1. Musical revues, comedies, etc.—Vocal scores with piano. I. Ellis, Walter W., 1874–   Old Chelsea. II. Tysh, Fred S., 1905– III. Grun, Bernard, 1901–   Old Chelsea.

M1503.T215O4	1948	49–15901 rev*

NT 0052161   DLC MB

Tauber, Richard, 1891–1948.
  ... Richard Tauber ...
    see under   Ludwig, Heinz, ed.

MISSISSIPPI

MsG	William Alexander Percy Memorial Library, Greenville.
MsSC*	Mississippi State University, State College.
MsSM	Mississippi State University, State College.
MsU	University of Mississippi, University.

MONTANA

MtBC	Montana State University, Bozeman.
MtBozC*	Montana State University at Bozeman.
MtU	University of Montana, Missoula.

NEW YORK

N	New York State Library, Albany.
NAlU	State University of New York at Albany.
NAurW	Wells College, Aurora.
NB	Brooklyn Public Library, Brooklyn.
NBB	Brooklyn Museum Libraries, Brooklyn.
NBC	Brooklyn College, Brooklyn.
NBM	Medical Research Library of Brooklyn.
NBPol	Polytechnic Institute of Brooklyn, Brooklyn.
NBSU-M	State University of New York, Downstate Medical Center Library, Brooklyn.
NBiSU-H	State University of New York, Harpur College, Binghamton.
NBronSL	Sarah Lawrence College, Bronxville.
NBu	Buffalo and Erie County Public Library, Buffalo.
NBuC	State University of New York, College at Buffalo.
NBuG	Grosvenor Reference Division, Buffalo and Erie County Public Library, Buffalo.
NBuU	State University of New York at Buffalo.
NCH	Hamilton College, Clinton.
NCaS	St. Lawrence University, Canton.
NCorniC	Corning Glass Works Library, Corning. (Includes Corning Museum of Glass Library)
NCoxHi	Greene County Historical Society, Inc., Coxsackie.
NFQC	Queens College Library, Flushing.
NGrnUN*	United Nations Library.
NHC	Colgate University, Hamilton.
NHi	New York Historical Society, New York.
NIC	Cornell University, Ithaca.
NJQ	Queens Borough Public Library, Jamaica.
NL*	Newberry Library, Chicago.
NLC	Not a library symbol.
NN	New York Public Library.
NNAB	American Bible Society, New York.
NNAHI	Augustinian Historical Institute, New York.
NNAJHi	American Jewish Historical Society, New York.
NNB	Association of the Bar of the City of New York, New York.
NNBG	New York Botanical Garden, Bronx Park, New York.
NNC	Columbia University, New York.
NNC-T	— Teachers College Library.
NNCFR	Council on Foreign Relations, New York.
NNCoCi	City College of New York, New York.
NNE	Engineering Societies Library, New York.
NNF	Fordham University, New York.
NNFI	French Institute in the United States, New York.
NNG	General Theological Seminary of the Protestant Episcopal Church. New York.
NNGr	Grolier Club Library, New York.
NNH	Hispanic Society of America, New York.
NNHeb	Hebrew Union College, Jewish Institute of Religion Library, New York.
NNHi	New York Historical Society.
NNJ	Jewish Theological Seminary of America, New York.
NNJIR*	Jewish Institute of Religion, New York.
NNJef	Jefferson School of Social Science, New York. (Library no longer in existence)
NNM	American Museum of Natural History, New York.
NNMM	Metropolitan Museum of Art Library, New York.
NNMor*	Pierpont Morgan Library.
NNNAM	New York Academy of Medicine, New York.
NNNM	New York Medical College, Flower & Fifth Avenue Hospitals, New York.
NNNPsan	New York Psychoanalytic Institute, New York.
NNPM	Pierpont Morgan Library, New York.
NNQ*	Queens Borough Public Library, New York.
NNQC*	Queens College Library, Flushing.
NNRI	Rockefeller Institute for Medical Research, New York.
NNSU-M*	State University of New York College of Medicine at New York City.

NEW YORK continued

NNU	New York University Libraries, New York.
NNU-W	— Washington Square Library.
NNUN	United Nations Library, New York.
NNUN-W	— Woodrow Wilson Memorial Library.
NNUT	Union Theological Seminary, New York.
NNUT-Mc	— McAlpin Collection.
NNWML	Wagner College Library, Staten Island.
NNYI	Yivo Institute for Jewish Research, New York.
NNZI	Zionist Archives and Library of Palestine Foundation, New York.
NNerC	College of New Rochelle, New Rochelle.
NNiaU	Niagara University, Niagara University.
NPV	Vassar College, Poughkeepsie,
NRAB	Samuel Colgate Baptist Historical Library of the American Baptist Historical Society, Rochester.
NRU	University of Rochester, Rochester.
NSchU	Union College, Schenectady.
NSyU	Syracuse University, Syracuse.
NUt	Utica Public Library.
NWM	U.S. Military Academy, West Point.
NYPL*	New York Public Library.
NYhI	International Business Machines Corporation, Thomas J. Watson Research Center, Yorktown Heights.

NEBRASKA

NbOC	Creighton University, Omaha.
NbU	University of Nebraska, Lincoln.

NORTH CAROLINA

Nc	North Carolina State Library, Raleigh.
Nc-Ar	North Carolina State Department of Archives and History, Raleigh.
NcA	Pack Memorial Public Library, Asheville.
NcA-S	— Sondley Reference Library.
NcAS*	Sondley Reference Library, Asheville.
NcC	Public Library of Charlotte & Mecklenburg County, Charlotte.
NcCC	Charlotte College Library, Charlotte.
NcCJ	Johnson C. Smith University, Charlotte.
NcCU	University of North Carolina at Charlotte.
NcD	Duke University, Durham.
NcDurC	North Carolina College at Durham, Durham.
NcGU*	University of North Carolina at Greensboro.
NcGW	University of North Carolina at Greensboro.
NcGuG	Guilford College, Guilford.
NcR	Olivia Raney Public Library, Raleigh.
NcRR	Richard B. Harrison Public Library, Raleigh.
NcRS	North Carolina State University at Raleigh.
NcU	University of North Carolina, Chapel Hill.
NcWfC*	Wake Forest College, Winston-Salem.
NcWfSB	Southeastern Baptist Theological Seminary Library, Wake Forest.
NcWilA	Atlantic Christian College, Wilson.
NcWilC	Carolina Discipliniana Library, Wilson.
NcWsW	Wake Forest College, Winston-Salem.

NORTH DAKOTA

NdFA	North Dakota State University, Fargo. (Formerly North Dakota Agricultural College)
NdHi	State Historical Society of North Dakota, Bismarck.
NdU	University of North Dakota Library, Grand Forks.

NEW HAMPSHIRE

Nh	New Hampshire State Library, Concord.
NhD	Dartmouth College, Hanover.
NhU	University of New Hampshire, Durham.

NEW JERSEY

NjGbS	Glassboro State College, Glassboro.
NjHi	New Jersey Historical Society, Newark.
NjMD	Drew University, Madison.
NjN	Newark Public Library.
NjNBR*	Rutgers–The State University, New Brunswick.
NjNbS	New Brunswick Theological Seminary, New Brunswick.
NjNbT*	New Brunswick Theological Seminary.
NjP	Princeton University, Princeton.
NjPT	Princeton Theological Seminary, Princeton.
NjR	Rutgers–The State University, New Brunswick.
NjT	Trenton Free Library, Trenton.

NEW MEXICO

NmA	Albuquerque Public Library, New Mexico.
NmU	University of New Mexico, Albuquerque.
NmUpU	New Mexico State University, University Park.

NEVADA

NvU	University of Nevada, Reno.

OHIO

O	Ohio State Library, Columbus.
OAU	Ohio University, Athens.
OAkU	University of Akron, Akron.
OBerB	Baldwin-Wallace College, Berea.
OBlC	Bluffton College, Bluffton.
OC	Public Library of Cincinnati and Hamilton County, Cincinnati.
OCH	Hebrew Union College, Cincinnati.
OCHP	Historical and Philosophical Society of Ohio, Cincinnati.
OCLloyd	Lloyd Library and Museum, Cincinnati.
OCU	University of Cincinnati, Cincinnati.
OCX	Xavier University, Cincinnati.
OCl	Cleveland Public Library.
OClCS	Case Institute of Technology, Cleveland.
OClFC	Cleveland State University, Cleveland. (Formerly Fenn College)
OClJC	John Carroll University, Cleveland.
OClMA	Cleveland Museum of Art, Cleveland.
OClSA	Cleveland Institute of Art, Cleveland.
OClW	Case Western Reserve University, Cleveland.
OClWHi	Western Reserve Historical Society, Cleveland.
ODW	Ohio Wesleyan University, Delaware.
ODa	Dayton and Montgomery County Library, Dayton.
ODaStL	St. Leonard College Library, Dayton.
ODaU	University of Dayton, Dayton.
OEac	East Cleveland Public Library.
OFH	Rutherford B. Hayes Library, Fremont.
OGK	Kenyon College, Gambier.
OHi	Ohio State Historical Society, Columbus.
OKentC	Kent State University, Kent.
OO	Oberlin College, Oberlin.
OOxM	Miami University, Oxford.
OSW	Wittenberg University, Springfield.
OTU	University of Toledo, Toledo.
OU	Ohio State University, Columbus.
OWibfU	Wilberforce University, Carnegie Library, Wilberforce.
OWicB	Borromeo Seminary, Wickliffe.
OWoC	College of Wooster, Wooster.
OWorP	Pontifical College Josephinum, Worthington.
OYesA	Antioch College, Yellow Springs.

OKLAHOMA

Ok	Oklahoma State Library, Oklahoma City.
OkEG	Graduate Seminary Library, Enid.
OkS	Oklahoma State University, Stillwater.
OkT	Tulsa Public Library.
OkU	University of Oklahoma, Norman.

OREGON

Or	Oregon State Library, Salem.
OrCS	Oregon State University Library, Corvallis.
OrHi	Oregon Historical Society, Portland.
OrP	Library Association of Portland, Portland.
OrPR	Reed College, Portland.
OrPS	Portland State College, Portland.
OrSaW	Willamette University, Salem.
OrStbM	Mount Angel College, Mount Angel Abbey, Saint Benedict.
OrU	University of Oregon, Eugene.

PENNSYLVANIA

PBL	Lehigh University, Bethlehem.
PBa	Academy of the New Church, Bryn Athyn.
PBm	Bryn Mawr College, Bryn Mawr.
PCA*	Samuel Colgate Baptist Historical Library of the American Baptist Historical Society, Rochester, N. Y.
PCC	Crozer Theological Seminary, Chester.
PCamA	Alliance College, Cambridge Springs.
PCarlD	Dickinson College, Carlisle.
PHC	Haverford College, Haverford.
PHi	Historical Society of Pennsylvania, Philadelphia.
PJA	Abington Library Society, Jenkintown.
PJAlG	Alverthorpe Gallery, Rosenwald Collection, Jenkintown.
PJB	Beaver College, Jenkintown.